THE HIERATIC PUBLISHING CO.
P.O. Box 133, Medford, Massachusetts 02155
United States of America, Earth

"Publishers of the most exact ephemerides for astrological use."

Hieratic Ephemerides are elegant, professional-level working tools. They are the only ephemerides available that are:

★ Entirely produced by *professional scientists.*

★ Based on the *latest NASA astronomical research.*

★ Photo-typeset by computer for *unparalleled clarity* and *typographical accuracy.*

★ Calculated to *0.1 arc minute precision,* permitting the effect of *nutation* (earth's wobble) to be observed. This enables Hieratic Ephemerides to present retrograde/direct motion changes with added precision *which other ephemerides cannot equal.*

In addition, **The Complete Planetary Ephemeris for 1950 to 2000 A.D.** is the only ephemeris to include *Right Ascension,* a powerful tool for prediction being rediscovered by progressive astrologers. *For more information on the use of Right Ascension, send a self-addressed envelope to the Hieratic Publishing Co.*

MIDNIGHT EPHEMERIDES

THE COMPLETE PLANETARY EPHEMERIS FOR 1950 TO 2000 A.D. AT MIDNIGHT
A most comprehensive ephemeris with clear, accurate listings of daily longitude, latitude, daily right ascension and declination of all the planets plus the moon's node. The only ephemeris with daily right ascensions, which are closely related to the material universe of the earth. Perhaps this potent tool for prediction has been overlooked. For the professional and all who appreciate completeness.
616 pages   *ISBN: 0-915820-00-5, hard $25.00*

THE CONCISE PLANETARY EPHEMERIS FOR 1950 TO 2000 A.D. AT MIDNIGHT
Daily longitude plus declination of all the planets plus the moon's node. Lightweight and portable, an indispensable second ephemeris for the busy professional. Easy to read, it's great for beginners, too. A real bargain at only 18 cents per year!
320 pages   *ISBN: 0-915820-01-3, hard $16.00*
                                               0-915820-02-1, soft $ 9.00

THE CONCISE PLANETARY EPHEMERIS FOR 1900 TO 1950 A.D. AT MIDNIGHT
Companion volume to the above "Concise" for the first half of the century. Same accuracy and convenience.
320 pages   *ISBN: 0-915820-05-6, hard $16.00*
                                               0-915820-06-4, soft $ 9.00

NOON EPHEMERIDES

THE CONCISE PLANETARY EPHEMERIS FOR 1950 TO 2000 A.D. AT NOON
Midnight companion to the above "Concise" for those who prefer working from noon data. Can be used together with its midnight companion for interpolating positions to previously unreachable accuracy.
320 pages   *ISBN: 0-915820-03-X, hard $16.00*
                                               0-915820-04-8, soft $ 9.00

THE CONCISE PLANETARY EPHEMERIS FOR 1900 TO 1950 A.D. AT NOON
First half of the century companion to the above "Concise".
                                               Available Summer 1979

THE CONCISE PLANETARY EPHEMERIS FOR 1900 to 1950 A.D. at MIDNIGHT

**Given at midnight ephemeris time
in the true longitude
and true declination
coordinates of date**

THE HIERATIC PUBLISHING CO.
P.O. BOX 133 MEDFORD, MASSACHUSETTS 02155
UNITED STATES OF AMERICA, EARTH

International Standard Book Numbers: 0-915820-05-6 Hard
0-915820-06-4 Soft

Manufactured in the United States of America.

Distributed exclusively in Continental Europe by *Wolf Metz Import,* Gessnerallee 42, 8011 Zürich, Switzerland.

Distributed exclusively in the British Isles by *L. N. Fowler & Co. Ltd.,* 1201 High Road, Chadwell Heath, Romford Essex RM6 4DH, England.

The indestructable stars are under the throne of His face.

(Egyptian Hymn to Osiris, ca. 1500 B.C.)

**VIDIMUS ENIM STELLUM EJUS IN ORIENTE,
ET VENIMUS ADORARE EUM.**

We saw His star as it rose and have come to do Him homage.

(Matthew 2:2-3)

· τῶν τε πλείστων καὶ ὀλοσχερῶν συμπτωμάτων ἐναργῶς οἴτω
τὴν ἀπὸ τοῦ περιέχοντος αἰτίαν ἐμφανιζόντων.

*It is clearly evident that most events of a widespread nature draw their causes
from the enveloping heavens.*

(Claudius Ptolemy's Tetrabiblos I.1, ca 130 A.D.)

ज्योतिर्गणे शास्त्रपचातिदृक्तो
यद्ब्रह्महत्यां मुनयोवदंति ॥

An error in the calculation of an ephemeris is as sinful as the murder of a Brahmin.

(Varāha Mihira's Brihat Jātaka, ca. 540 A.D.)

Sir, I have studied it, you have not!

(Sir Isaac Newton's reply to comet-discoverer Halley's questioning the basis of Astrology, ca. 1680)

INTRODUCTION

The Concise Planetary Ephemeris for 1900 to 1950 A.D. at Midnight is an economical, durable, and compact listing of planetary longitudes and declinations. It responds to the needs of those who require a convenient, accurate, and sturdy volume at a reasonable price. It maintains the same rigorous, scientific accuracy as the more comprehensive volume, *The Complete Planetary Ephemeris for 1900 to 1950 A.D. at Midnight,* which has been adopted internationally by astronomical and space laboratories of both government and university and is now a standard work. The present volume offers the same excellence to the wider community in a more compact and less expensive form.

Like man's venture into space it is the culmination of centuries of scientific endeavor and introduces a new clarity into the generation of planetary ephemerides. Its mode of calculation explicitly recognizes the fact that each planet flows in harmony with all the other heavenly bodies. At every instant of time each planet's movement is determined by its own momentum together with the sum of the forces of the other celestial orbs. This unifying gravitational theory, known since the time of Isaac Newton, was modelled mathematically to simultaneously generate the planetary positions.

This approach has powerful practical advantages over the traditional, approximate methods which treat each planet separately. Moreover, this unifying vision provides joy for the spirit together with deep philosophical and psychological clarity. It points the way back to the wisdom of the ancient belief in the Great Chain of Being.

The Authors

This work evolved from the studies of two scientists on the Apollo Project, which succeeded in putting a man on the moon in 1969. They bring with them a broad tradition of learning from the Ludwig Maximillian University in Munich, the Massachusetts Institute of Technology, and from the Imperial College of the University of London. Their professional background includes membership in the American Astronomical Society, the American Physical Society, the American Institute of Aeronautics and Astronautics, and the British Institute of Electrical Engineers.

They believe that science and astrology should enrich and sustain each other in the quest for a vision of the truth. Providing scientific ephemerides is one way that science can bring rigor and discipline to the task. Conversely, through the synthesis of man's interaction with the cosmos, astrology can add insights into events that are meaningless when taken in isolation.

Ephemeris Generation

With the advent of large, high speed digital computers it has become feasible to simultaneously integrate the planetary equations of motion (cf. KARL STUMPFF: *Himmelsmechanik,* Berlin 1965). Of the major ephemerides available only this volume and the *Complete Planetary Ephemeris* are generated using such a completely unifying approach. Even the *American Ephemeris and Nautical Almanac* of the United States government does not utilize this completely unified method. This approach clarifies and unites the equations and their solutions and, using reverse integration, provides a self check on the accuracy of the solution.

The integration was performed in a heliocentric, equatorial inertial system referred to the mean equinox and equator of 1950.0. The results are a best fit, in the least-squares sense, to planetary positions observed over many years. The astronomical constants used were those agreed upon at the Twelfth General Assembly of the International Astronomical Union at Hamburg in 1964. For publication the results were first referred to the mean equinox of date at Greenwich midnight using the precessional values of NEWCOMB (cf. M. H. ANDOYER: *Bulletin Astronomique* v. XXVIII). Subsequently they were expressed with respect to the true equinox of date using the nutational values of WOOLARD (cf. the *Astronomical Papers prepared for the use of the American Ephemeris and Nautical Almanac,* v. 15 part 1, 1953).

The calculations were performed on an IBM model 370/168 computer with a core memory of 2 million bytes using 16 significant decimal digits. The results were rounded to the nearest 0ʹ.1 for publication using computer driven phototypesetting equipment. To the precision given the results represent the true geometric positions of the planets and will not need improvement as more precise observational data becomes available. For this reason this volume can be used with confidence as a standard work.

INTRODUCTION

The Concise Planetary Ephemeris for 1900 to 1950 A. D. at Midnight (L'Ephéméride Planétaire Abrégée de 1900 à 1950 A. J. C.) donne d'une façon économique, durable et concise la liste des longitudes et déclinaisons planétaires. Elle répond aux besoins des personnes ayant besoin d'un ouvrage pratique, précis et solide à un prix raisonnable. Celui-ci respecte la même exactitude rigoureuse et scientifique que le volume d'ensemble, *The Complete Planetary Ephemeris for 1900 to 1950 A.D. at Midnight* (L'Ephéméride Planétaire Complète de 1900 à 1950 A. J. C.), qui a été adopté internationalement par les laboratoires d'astronomie et de l'espace aussi bien publics qu'universitaires et qui est maintenant un ouvrage standard. Ce présent volume offre la même perfection à une audience plus vaste sous une forme plus concise et à meilleur marché.

Tout comme l'aventure de l'homme dans l'espace, il représente l'apogée d'une entreprise scientifique de plusieurs siècles et introduit une clarté nouvelle dans la génération des éphémérides planétaires. Ses modes de calcul reflètent explicitement le fait que chaque planète se déplace en harmonie avec les autres corps célestes. A chaque instant la trajectoire de chaque planète est déterminée par la combinaison de sa propre quantité de mouvement et de la somme des forces dues aux autres astres. Cette théorie gravitationnelle unifiée, connue depuis l'époque d'Isaac Newton, a été simulée mathématiquement de façon à produire simultanément les positions planétaires. Cette approche possède des avantages pratiques puissants par rapport aux méthodes d'approximation traditionnelles qui traitent chaque planète séparément.

De plus, cette conception unifiée est une source de joie pour l'esprit ainsi que d'une profonde clarté philosophique et psychologique. Elle montre le chemin remontant à la sagesse de l'ancienne croyance en la Grande Chaîne de l'Existence.

Les Auteurs

Cet ouvrage est né des études de deux savants du projet Apollo qui réussit à poser un homme sur la lune en 1969. Ils apportent avec eux la longue tradition des enseignements venant de l'Université Ludwig Maximillian à Munich, du Massachusetts Institute of Technology et de l'Imperial College de l'Université de Londres. Leur expérience professionnelle est illustrée par leur appartenance à la Société Astronomique Américaine, la Société Physique Américaine, L'Institut Américain d'Aéronautique et d'Astronautique et L'Institut Britannique des Ingénieurs Electriciens.

Ils croient que la science et l'astrologie doivent s'enrichir et se soutenir mutuellement à la recherche d'une vision de la vérité. La réalisation d'éphémérides scientifiques est un des moyens par lesquels la science peut apporter rigueur et discipline à cette tâche. Réciproquement, par la synthèse de l'interaction de l'homme avec le cosmos, l'astrologie peut ajouter à la compréhension de phénomènes qui n'ont pas de sens pris isolément.

Obtention des Ephémérides

Grâce à l'avènement de calculateurs numériques de grande capacité et à vitesse de calcul élevée, il a été possible d'intégrer simultanément les équations planétaires de mouvement (cf. KARL STUMPFF: *Himmelsmechanik,* Berlin 1965). Parmi les éphémérides importantes disponibles, seul ce volume et *The Complete Planetary Ephemeris* sont obtenus en utilisant cette approche totalement unifiée. Même *The American Ephemeris and Nautical Almanac* du gouvernement des Etats-Unis n'utilise pas cette méthode totalement unifiée. Cette approche clarifie et unifie les équations et leurs solutions et, utilisant une intégration inverse, fournit une vérification implicite de la précision de la solution.

L'intégration a été réalisée sur un système inertiel héliocentrique et équatorial prenant comme référence l'équinoxe moyenne et l'équateur de 1950.0. Les résultats représentent une correspondance optimale, au sens des moindres carrés, avec les positions planétaires observées au long de nombreuses années. Les constantes astronomiques utilisées sont celles qui furent convenues lors de la Vingtième Assemblée Générale de l'Union Astronomique Internationale à Hambourg en 1964. En vue de la publication les résultats furent d'abord rapportés à l'équinoxe moyenne de date à minuit Greenwich en utilisant les valeurs de précession de NEWCOMB (cf. M. H. ANDOYER: *Bulletin Astronomique* v. XXVIII). Par la suite ils furent exprimés par rapport à la vraie valeur de l'équinoxe de date en utilisant les valeurs de nutation de WOOLARD (cf. les *Papers Prepared for the use of the American Ephemeris and Nautical Almanac,* v. 15, partie 1, 1953).

Les calculs furent réalisés sur un ordinateur IBM modèle 370/168 possédant une mémoire centrale de 2 millions de mots utilisant 16 décimales. Les résultats furent arrondis à 0,1 près en vue d'une publication par photo-impression commandée par ordinateur. A la précision donnée les résultats représentent les positions géométriques vraies des planètes et ne nécessiteront aucune amélioration au fur et à mesure que des données d'observation plus précises seront disponiblesm Pour cette raison ce volume peut être utilisé avec confiance en tant qu'ouvrage standard.

INTRODUCCIÓN

The Concise Planetary Ephemeris for 1900 to 1950 A.D. at Midnight (El Breviario de Efemérides Planetarias de 1900 a 1950) ofrece en una edición económica, duradera y compacta, una recopilación de datos sobre longiutdes y declinaciones de planetas. Satisface las necesidades de aquéllos que exigen una edición rigurosa a un precio razonable. Mantiene la misma tónica de rigurosidad y precisión científica que el volumen *The Complete Planetary*

Ephemeris for 1900 to 1950 A.D. at Midnight (Tratado Completo de Efemérides Planetarias de 1900 a 1950) que ya ha sido adoptado universalmente por laboratorios de astronomía y de ciencias del espacio dependientes tanto de organismos gubernamentales como de Universidades y que puede ser considerado hoy como una obra clásica. El objeto de la presente edición es pues el de, de una manera mas económica y compacta, hacer asequible la misma calidad de información, a un sector de público más amplio.

Por analogía con la aventura del hombre en el espacio el presente trabajo representa la culminación de siglos de labor científica con vistas a presentar de una manera clara la idea de efemérides planetarias. Su método de cálculo explícito parte del principio de que cada planeta se mueve en el espacio en armonía con el resto de los cuerpos celestes. El movimiento de cada planeta en un instante de tiempo determinado viene establecido por su propio momento y por la resultante de las fuerzas que los demás astros ejercen sobre él. Esta teoría gravitacional, conocida desde los tiempos de Isaac Newton, ha sido utilizada en el contexto de un modelo matemático que permite generar las posiciones de los planetas simultáneamente.

Este método presenta notables ventajas de tipo práctico sobre los métodos clásicos que utilizando procedimientos aproximados tratan a cada planeta como un ente aislado. Más aún, este enfoque unificador proporciona alegría al espíritu y madurez filosófica. Nos recuerda la antigua sabia creencia en la Gran Cadena del Ser.

Sobre los Autores

Este trabajo es fruto de las investigaciones de dos científicos del proyecto Apolo, que consiguió colocar con éxito un hombre en la superficie lunar en 1969. En ellos convergen tradiciones culturales de centros como la Universidad Ludwig Maximillian de Munich, el Instituto Technológico de Massachusetts y el Colegio Imperial de la Universidad de Londres. Son miembros acreditados de la Sociedad Americana de Física, la Sociedad Americana de Astronomía, el Instituto Americano de Aeronáutica y Astronáutica y el Instituto Británico de Ingenieros Eléctricos.

Es creencia de los autores que ciencia y astrología deben enriquecerse y sustentarse mutuamente en la búsqueda de la verdad. Aportar datos sobre efemérides científicas es un modo en que la ciencia puede contribuir a hacer rigurosa y disciplinada esa tarea. Por otra parte es a través de la síntesis de la interacción del hombre con el cosmos que la astrología puede hacer aportaciones valiosas en el estudio de acontecimientos que si aislados no tendrían ningún sentido.

Generación de Efemérides

Con el advenimiento de computadores de alta velocidad digital ha resultado posible integrar simultáneamente el sistema de ecuaciones que describe el movimiento de los planetas (vease KARL STUMPFF: *Himmelsmechanik*, Berlín 1965). Solamente en este Breviario y en el ya citado *Complete Planetary Ephemeris*, se hace un estudio de estas efemérides utilizando el método unificador al que más arriba nos referíamos. Ni siquiera el *American Ephemeris and Nautical Almanac* utiliza un método tan completo como el nuestro. Nuestro procedimiento clasifica y unifica las ecuaciones y sus correspondientes soluciones y utilizando métodos integrales somete a pruebas de autoconsistencia a los resultados obtenidos.

La integración se realiza en un sistema inercial, heliocéntrico y ecuatorial, tomando como referencia la posición del equinoccio y del ecuador en 1950.0. Los resultados se derivan de un ajuste, por métodos de mínimos cuadrados, a las posiciones de los planetas observadas durante varios años. Las constantes astronómicas utilizadas fueron las adoptadas en la XII Reunión General de la Unión Internacional de Astronomía celebrada en Hamburgo en 1964. Los resultados publicados fueron en un principio referidos al equinoccio medio de medianoche en Greenwich utilizando como valores para la precesión los dados por NEWCOMB (vease M. H. ANDOYER: *Bulletin Astroomique,* vol. XXVIII) y posteriormente fueron expresados respecto al verdadero equinoccio utilizando los valores para la nutación calculados por WOOLARD (veanse los *Papers Prepared for the use of the American Ephemeris and Nautical Almanac,* Vol. 15, parte 1, 1953).

Los cálculos fueron realizados en una calculadora IBM modelo 370/168, con una memoria de dos millones de bites o registros y utilizando dieciséis cifras decimales significativas. Posteriormente fueron redondeados con una precisión de 0'.1 utilizando para su publicación final un equipo de fotoimpresión controlado por computador. Los resultados publicados representan, con la precisión señalada, la verdadera posición de los planetas y no necesitarán mejora alguna cuando se disponga de observaciones astronómicas más precisas. Esa es la razón por la que el presente volumen puede ser ya considerado como una referencia clásica.

INTRODUZIONE

The Concise Planetary Ephemeris for 1900 to 1950 A. D. at Midnight (La Concisa Effemeride Planetaria dal 1900 al 1950 dopo Cristo) é un elenco delle longitudini e delle declinazioni planetarie a formato ridotto, di buona durata ed a buon prezzo. Esso risponde al fabbisogno di coloro che desiderano possedere un volume pratico, solido ed a prezzo ragionevole. In esso si é mantenuta la medesima rigorosa precisione scientifica del volume più esteso, *The Complete Planetary Ephemeris for 1900 to 1950 A. D. at Midnight* (La Completa Effemeride Planetaria dal 1900 al 1950 dopo Cristo), adottato su scala internazionale da laboratori astronomici e spaziali universitari nonché governamentali ed attualmente riconosciuto come un classico nel suo campo. Il presente volume offre gli stessi standard di eccellenza ad un pubblico più vasto, a formato ridotto ed a minor costo.

Come l'impresa umana nello spazio, esso rappresenta il culmine dello sforzo scientifico di secoli e getta una luce nuova sulla generazione delle effemeridi planetarie. Il metodo di calcolo sul quale é basato riconosce esplicitamente il fatto che ogni pianeta orbita in armonia con tutti gli altri corpi celesti. Ad ogni istante nel tempo, ciascun movimento del pianeta é determinato dall'impulso che gli é proprio assieme al totale delle forze delle altre sfere celestiali. Questa teoria gravitativa unificatrice, nota dall'epoca di Isacco Newton, é stata modellata matematicamente in modo da dare simultaneamente la posizione dei pianeti.

Questo modo di procedere presenta dei vantaggi enormi dal punto di vista pratico in confronto ai metodi approssimativi tradizionali, che trattano ciascun pianeta separatamente. Per di più, questa visione unificatrice rallegra lo spirito e serba, nel contempo, una profonda chiarezza filosofica e psicologica. Da essa viene indicata la via che riconduce alla saggezza dell'antica credenza nella Grande Catena dell'Essere.

Gli Autori

Questa opera proviene dagli studi di due scienziati che presero parte al Progetto Apollo, mediante il quale fu possibile mandare l'uomo sulla luna nel 1969. Con loro ci perviene la vasta tradizione culturale dell'Uniersità Ludwig Maximillian di Monaco di Baviera, l'Istituto di Tecnologia del Massachusetts ed il Collegio Imperiale di Londra. Il loro curriculum professionale include la partecipazione alla Società Americana di Astronomia, alla Società Americana di Fisica, all'Istituto Americano di Aereonautica ed Astronautica ed all'Istituto Britannico di Ingegneria Elettrica.

E' loro credenza che scienza ed astrologia dovrebbero arricchirsi e sostenersi a vicenda nella ricerca di una visione di verità. Uno dei modi in cui la scienza può aiutare a portare rigore e disciplina a questo compito, consiste nel fornire effemeridi scientifiche. Da parte sua, l'astrologia può meglio discernere, mediante la sintesi delle interazioni tra uomo e cosmo, tra eventi che sarebbero senza significato se fossero presi uno per uno.

La Generazione Dell'Effemeride

Con l'invenzione delle grosse calcolatrici numeriche ad alta velocità, é diventato possibile procedere all'integrazione simultanea delle equazioni di moto planetarie (Rif.: KARL STUMPFF, *Himmelsmechanik*, Berlino 1965). Tra le maggiori effemeridi che si trovano in circolazione, soltanto quelle indicate in questo volume e nella *Complete Planetary Ephemeris*, sono generate tramite un metodo così totalmente unificatore. Neppure l'American Ephemeris and Nautical Almanac del governo statunitense utilizza un metodo così totalmente unficatore. Questo modo di procedere elucida ed unisce le equazioni e le loro soluzioni e fornisce allo stesso tempo, mediante l'integrazione all'inverso, la prova della precisione della soluzione.

L'integrazione é stata compiuta in un sistema inerziale, eliocentrico ed equatoriale, basato sull'equinozio medio e sull'equatore del 1950.0. I risultati sono quelli che, col metodo dei quadrati-minimi, danno il miglior adattamento alle posizioni dei pianeti osservate per un periodo di molti anni. Le costanti astronomiche impiegate sono quelle concordate durante la Dodicesima Assemblea dell'Unione Astronomica Internazionale tenutasi ad Amburgo nel 1964. I risultati destinati a pubblicazione si riferivano in un primo tempo all'equinozio medio di data alla mezzanotte di Greenwich, facendo uso dei valori precessionali di NEWCOMB (Rif. M. H. ANDOYER: *Bulletin Astronomique*, v. XXVIII). In seguito, i risultati furono espressi per rapporto all'equinozio reale di data, facendo uso dei valori nutativi di WOOLARD (Rif. *Astronomical Papers prepared for the use of the American Ephemeris and Nautical Almanac*, v. 15, parte 1, 1953).

I calcoli sono stati eseguiti su di una calcolatrice IBM modello 370/168 con una memoria di 2 milioni di "biti", utilizzando 16 cifre decimali significative. Ai fini della pubblicazione, i risultati sono stati arrotondati allo 0′,1 più vicino, per mezzo dell'apparato fototipografico guidato dalla calcolatrice. Dal punto di vista della precisione sopra-indicata, i risultati rappresentano le vere posizioni geometriche dei pianeti e non occorrerà apportare miglioramenti una volta in possesso di dati di osservazione più esatti. Per tale ragione questo volume può essere adottato con piena fiducia come un classico nel suo campo.

EINLEITUNG

The Concise Planetary Ephemeris for 1900 to 1950 A.D. at Midnight (Kurzer planetarischer Almanach für 1900 bis 1950 A.D.) ist eine preiswerte, haltbare und bündige Zusammenstellung der Längen und Deklinationen der Planeten. Der Almanach ist für all die gedacht, die einen geeigneten, genauen und widerstandsfähigen Band zu einem günstigem Preis benötigen. Er weist dieselbe rigorose wissenschaftliche Genauigkeit wie das umfassendere Werk auf — *The Complete Planetary Ephemeris for 1900 to 1950 A. D. at Midnight* (Vollständiger planetarischer Almanach für 1900 bis 1950 A. D.) — der international von astronomischen wie Weltraumlabors der Regierungen und Universitäten als maßgebendes Werk verwendet wird. Das vorliegende Buch stellt dieselbe hervorragende Leistung einer breiteren Leserschaft in kürzerer und billigerer Form zur Verfügung.

Ähnlich wie das Vordringen der Menschheit in den Weltraum stellt es den Höhepunkt von jahrhundertelanger wissenschaftlicher Untersuchung dar und gibt den planetarischen Almanachs eine bisher unbekannte Klarheit. Die Berechnungsmethode erkennt explizit an, daß jeder Planet sich harmonisch mit all den anderen Himmelskörpern bewegt. Zu jedem Zeitpunkt unterliegt die Bewegung jedes Planeten seinem eigenen Impuls wie auch die Summe der Kräfte, die von den anderen Himmelsbahnen herrühren. Diese, seit der Zeit Isaac Newtons, bekannte vereinigte Theorie der Schwerkraft wurde im mathematischen Modell nachvollzogen, um die Positionen der Planeten simultan zu bestimmen.

Dieser Lösungsweg hat beträchtliche praktische Vorteile gegenüber der üblichen Annäherungsmethode, in der jeder Planet einzeln betrachtet wird. Weiterhin erfreut diese vereinigte Theorie den Geist und zeigt die tiefe philosophische und psychologische Klarheit auf. Hier wird wieder auf den alten Glauben der Großen Kette des Seiens zurückverwiesen.

Die Verfasser

Dieses Werk entstand aus den Studien zweier Wissenschaftler des Apollo Projektes, das im Jahre 1969 zur ersten bemannten Landung auf dem Mond führte. Sie verkörpern eine lange Tradition der Forschung der Ludwig-Maximillian-Universität München, des Massachusetts Institute of Technology und des Imperial College der Universität London. Zu ihren beruflichen Qualifikationen gehört die Mitgliedschaft in der American Astronomical Society, American Physical Society, American Institute of Aeronautics and Astronautics sowie British Institute of Electrical Engineers.

Sie meinen, daß sich Wissenschaft und Astrologie auf der Suche nach der Wahrheit gegenseitig bereichern und stützen sollen. Ein wissenschaftlicher Almanach ist ein Weg, mit dem die Wissenschaft dieser Aufgabe Strenge und Disziplin geben kann. Und umgekehrt kann die Astrologie durch die Synthese der Wechselwirkung von Mensch und Kosmos Einsicht in Geschehen gewinnen, die — wenn einzeln betrachtet — bedeutungslos sind.

Der Almanach

Durch die großen digitalen Schnellrechner ist es jetzt möglich, die Bewegungsgleichungen der Planeten gleichzeitig zu integrieren (vgl. KARL STUMPFF: *Himmelsmechanik*, Berlin, 1965). Unter all den Almanachs wird nur dieses Werk sowie der *Complete Planetary Ephemeris* mit dieser vollständig vereinigten Methoden erstellt. Selbst der *American Ephemeris and Nautical Almanac* der US-Regierung stüzt sich nicht auf diese vollständig vereinigte Methode. Dieser Weg vereinigt und verdeutlicht die Gleichungen und ihre Lösungen und ermöglicht durch umgekehrtes Integrieren eine Selbstprüfung der Lösungsgenauigkeit.

Die Integration wurde in einem heliozentrischen, äquatorialen Trägheitssystem durchgeführt, das als mittlerer Äquator und mittleres Äquinoktium von 1950.0 bezeichnet wird. Die Lösungen sind eine beste Passung — kleinste Fehlerquadrate — an die über lange Jahre beobachteten Planetenpositionen. Die hierbei verwendeten astronomischen Konstanten sind die Werte, die von der 12. Allgemeinversammlung der Internationalen Astronomischen Vereinigung 1964 in Hamburg festgelegt wurden. Für die Veröffentlichung wurden die Ergebnisse erst auf das jewegliche mittlere Äquinoktium — Greenwich Mitternacht — umgesetzt, wobei die Präzessionswerte von NEWCOMB verwendet wurden (vgl. M. H. ANDOYER: *Bulletin Astronomique* v. XXVIII). Danach wurden sie bezügliche des jeweiligen wahren Äquinoktiums ausgedrückt, wobei die Nutationswerte von WOOLARD verwendet wurden (vgl. *Astronomical Papers prepared for the use of the American Ephemeris and Nautical Almanac*, Bd. 15, Teil 1, 1953.).

Die Berechnungen wurden mit einer IBM 370/168 Rechenanlage von 2 M bytes auf 16 Dezimal-Stellen genau bestimmt. Die Ergebnisse wurden auf die nächste Zehntelstelle (0,1) gerundet und im rechnergestützen Lichtdruckerfahren gedruckt. Die Ergebnisse stellen — mit der angegebenen Präzision — die wahren geometrischen Positionen der Planeten dar und müssen nicht verbessert werden, wenn präzisere Beobachtungsdaten zur Verfügung stehen. Aus diesem Grunde kann man den Almanach mit Zuversicht als maßgebendes Werk verwenden.

JANUARY 1900

DAY	EPHEMERIS SIDEREAL TIME	☉	☊	☽	☿	♀	♂	♃	♄	♅	♆	♇
	h m s	° ′	° ′	° ′	° ′	° ′	° ′	° ′	° ′	° ′	° ′	° ′
						LONGITUDE						
1 M	6 40 45.2	10♑ 9.6	19♐ 9.7	2♑25.1	19♐ 0.4	6♒23.1	13♑52.7	1♐ 8.6	27♐43.4	10♐ 8.7	25♊12.8	15♊14.6
2 T	6 44 41.7	11 10.7	19 6.5	16 53.2	20 17.8	7 37.7	14 38.9	1 20.3	27 50.4	10 12.0	25R11.2	15R13.6
3 W	6 48 38.3	12 11.9	19 3.3	1♒34.7	21 36.6	8 52.3	15 25.2	1 31.9	27 57.4	10 15.3	25 9.6	15 12.6
4 T	6 52 34.9	13 13.1	19 0.2	16 22.)	22 56.7	10 6.8	16 11.6	1 43.5	28 4.3	10 18.6	25 8.0	15 11.6
5 F	6 56 31.4	14 14.3	18 57.0	1♓ 8.0	24 18.0	11 21.4	16 57.9	1 54.9	28 11.2	10 21.8	25 6.4	15 10.6
6 S	7 0 28.0	15 15.5	18 53.8	15 45.2	25 40.3	12 35.9	17 44.3	2 6.3	28 18.1	10 25.0	25 4.8	15 9.6
7 S	7 4 24.5	16 16.6	18 50.6	0♈ 8.6	27 3.6	13 50.3	18 30.7	2 17.7	28 25.0	10 28.2	25 3.3	15 8.6
8 M	7 8 21.1	17 17.8	18 47.5	14 14.9	28 27.9	15 4.8	19 17.2	2 28.9	28 31.8	10 31.3	25 1.7	15 7.7
9 T	7 12 17.7	18 19.0	18 44.3	28 2.9	29 52.9	16 19.2	20 3.7	2 40.1	28 38.7	10 34.4	25 0.2	15 6.7
10 W	7 16 14.2	19 20.1	18 41.1	11♉33.0	1♑18.7	17 33.6	20 50.2	2 51.2	28 45.4	10 37.5	24 58.6	15 5.8
11 T	7 20 10.7	20 21.2	18 37.9	24 46.4	2 45.3	18 47.9	21 36.7	3 2.2	28 52.2	10 40.6	24 57.1	15 4.8
12 F	7 24 7.3	21 22.3	18 34.8	7♊44.9	4 12.5	20 2.2	22 23.3	3 13.1	28 59.0	10 43.6	24 55.6	15 3.9
13 S	7 28 3.9	22 23.5	18 31.6	20 30.3	5 40.4	21 16.5	23 9.9	3 24.0	29 5.7	10 46.6	24 54.2	15 3.0
14 S	7 32 0.4	23 24.6	18 28.4	3♋ 4.1	7 8.9	22 30.8	23 56.6	3 34.7	29 12.4	10 49.6	24 52.7	15 2.2
15 M	7 35 57.0	24 25.7	18 25.2	15 27.9	8 38.1	23 45.0	24 43.2	3 45.4	29 19.0	10 52.5	24 51.3	15 1.3
16 T	7 39 53.5	25 26.7	18 22.0	27 42.6	10 7.8	24 59.2	25 29.9	3 55.9	29 25.6	10 55.4	24 49.8	15 0.4
17 W	7 43 50.1	26 27.8	18 18.9	9♌49.4	11 38.1	26 13.3	26 16.7	4 6.4	29 32.2	10 58.3	24 48.4	14 59.6
18 T	7 47 46.7	27 28.9	18 15.7	21 49.5	13 9.1	27 27.4	27 3.4	4 16.8	29 38.8	11 1.1	24 47.1	14 58.8
19 F	7 51 43.2	28 29.9	18 12.5	3♍44.4	14 40.6	28 41.5	27 50.2	4 27.1	29 45.3	11 3.9	24 45.7	14 58.0
20 S	7 55 39.8	29 31.0	18 9.3	15 36.3	16 12.7	29 55.5	28 37.0	4 37.3	29 51.8	11 6.6	24 44.4	14 57.2
21 S	7 59 36.3	0♒32.0	18 6.2	27 27.9	17 45.3	1♓ 9.5	29 23.9	4 47.4	29 58.2	11 9.4	24 43.0	14 56.4
22 M	8 3 32.9	1 33.1	18 3.0	9♎22.7	19 18.6	2 23.5	0♒10.7	4 57.4	0♑ 4.6	11 12.0	24 41.8	14 55.7
23 T	8 7 29.4	2 34.1	17 59.8	21 24.6	20 52.4	3 37.4	0 57.6	5 7.3	0 11.0	11 14.7	24 40.5	14 54.9
24 W	8 11 26.0	3 35.1	17 56.6	3♏38.2	22 26.9	4 51.2	1 44.6	5 17.1	0 17.3	11 17.3	24 39.2	14 54.2
25 T	8 15 22.5	4 36.1	17 53.5	16 8.4	24 2.0	6 5.0	2 31.5	5 26.8	0 23.6	11 19.9	24 38.0	14 53.5
26 F	8 19 19.1	5 37.1	17 50.3	28 59.9	25 37.7	7 18.8	3 18.5	5 36.4	0 29.8	11 22.4	24 36.8	14 52.8
27 S	8 23 15.7	6 38.1	17 47.1	12♐16.7	27 14.0	8 32.6	4 5.5	5 45.9	0 36.0	11 24.9	24 35.6	14 52.2
28 S	8 27 12.2	7 39.1	17 43.9	26 1.5	28 51.0	9 46.3	4 52.5	5 55.2	0 42.2	11 27.3	24 34.5	14 51.5
29 M	8 31 8.8	8 40.1	17 40.7	10♑14.7	0♒28.6	10 59.9	5 39.6	6 4.5	0 48.3	11 29.8	24 33.3	14 50.9
30 T	8 35 5.3	9 41.0	17 37.6	24 53.9	2 6.9	12 13.5	6 26.6	6 13.6	0 54.3	11 32.1	24 32.2	14 50.3
31 W	8 39 1.9	10 41.9	17 34.4	9♒53.2	3 46.0	13 27.1	7 13.7	6 22.6	1 0.4	11 34.4	24 31.1	14 49.7
						DECLINATION						
1 M	6 40 45.2	23S 3.8	23S 0.5	22S19.3	21S52.5	20S19.0	23S38.9	19S36.1	22S25.5	21S55.2	22N 4.0	12N54.8
4 T	6 52 34.9	22 47.7	22 59.8	11 46.7	22 33.6	19 21.3	23 24.3	19 43.1	22 25.9	21 56.6	22 3.9	12 54.9
7 S	7 4 24.5	22 27.5	22 59.0	4N46.9	23 7.3	18 18.7	23 7.2	19 49.8	22 26.3	21 58.0	22 3.8	12 55.0
10 W	7 16 14.2	22 3.4	22 58.2	18 24.2	23 32.2	17 11.6	22 47.9	19 56.3	22 26.6	21 59.4	22 3.7	12 55.2
13 S	7 28 3.9	21 35.4	22 57.4	23 4.4	23 47.3	16 0.2	22 26.1	20 2.5	22 26.9	22 0.7	22 3.6	12 55.4
16 T	7 39 53.5	21 3.7	22 56.5	17 30.9	23 51.6	14 45.0	22 2.1	20 8.4	22 27.1	22 2.0	22 3.5	12 55.7
19 F	7 51 43.2	20 28.3	22 55.7	5 30.8	23 44.5	13 26.3	21 35.9	20 14.1	22 27.2	22 3.2	22 3.5	12 56.0
22 M	8 3 32.9	19 49.5	22 54.8	8S10.2	23 25.5	12 4.4	21 7.4	20 19.4	22 27.3	22 4.3	22 3.4	12 56.3
25 T	8 15 22.5	19 7.3	22 54.0	19 22.7	22 54.1	10 39.8	20 36.9	20 24.5	22 27.3	22 5.4	22 3.4	12 56.7
28 S	8 27 12.2	18 22.0	22 53.1	22 47.3	22 10.0	9 12.6	20 4.3	20 29.4	22 27.3	22 6.5	22 3.3	12 57.1
31 W	8 39 1.9	17 33.7	22 52.2	13 57.7	21 13.0	7 43.4	19 29.6	20 33.9	22 27.2	22 7.5	22 3.3	12 57.6

FEBRUARY 1900

DAY	EPHEMERIS SIDEREAL TIME	☉	☊	☽	☿	♀	♂	♃	♄	♅	♆	♇
						LONGITUDE						
1 T	8 42 58.5	11♒42.9	17♐31.2	25♒ 3.7	5♒25.7	14♓40.6	8♒ 0.8	6♐31.5	1♑ 6.3	11♐36.7	24♊30.1	14♊49.1
2 F	8 46 55.0	12 43.8	17 28.0	10♓15.1	7 6.1	15 54.0	8 47.9	6 40.3	1 12.2	11 39.0	24R29.1	14R48.6
3 S	8 50 51.6	13 44.6	17 24.9	25 16.7	8 47.3	17 7.4	9 35.1	6 48.9	1 18.1	11 41.2	24 28.1	14 48.0
4 S	8 54 48.1	14 45.5	17 21.7	10♈ 0.2	10 29.2	18 20.7	10 22.2	6 57.5	1 23.9	11 43.3	24 27.1	14 47.5
5 M	8 58 44.7	15 46.3	17 18.5	24 19.9	12 11.9	19 34.0	11 9.4	7 5.9	1 29.6	11 45.4	24 26.2	14 47.0
6 T	9 2 41.2	16 47.1	17 15.3	8♉13.8	13 55.3	20 47.2	11 56.6	7 14.2	1 35.3	11 47.5	24 25.3	14 46.6
7 W	9 6 37.8	17 47.9	17 12.2	21 42.3	15 39.5	22 0.3	12 43.8	7 22.3	1 40.9	11 49.5	24 24.4	14 46.1
8 T	9 10 34.3	18 48.7	17 9.0	4♊48.0	17 24.5	23 13.4	13 31.0	7 30.3	1 46.5	11 51.5	24 23.5	14 45.7
9 F	9 14 30.9	19 49.4	17 5.8	17 34.3	19 10.3	24 26.4	14 18.2	7 38.2	1 52.0	11 53.4	24 22.7	14 45.3
10 S	9 18 27.4	20 50.1	17 2.6	0♋ 5.0	20 56.8	25 39.4	15 5.4	7 46.0	1 57.5	11 55.3	24 21.9	14 44.9
11 S	9 22 24.0	21 50.8	16 59.4	12 23.7	22 44.1	26 52.2	15 52.7	7 53.6	2 2.9	11 57.1	24 21.2	14 44.5
12 M	9 26 20.5	22 51.4	16 56.3	24 33.3	24 32.2	28 5.0	16 39.9	8 1.1	2 8.2	11 58.9	24 20.4	14 44.2
13 T	9 30 17.1	23 52.0	16 53.1	6♌36.3	26 21.0	29 17.7	17 27.2	8 8.4	2 13.5	12 0.6	24 19.7	14 43.8
14 W	9 34 13.6	24 52.6	16 49.9	18 34.7	28 10.4	0♈30.4	18 14.4	8 15.6	2 18.7	12 2.3	24 19.1	14 43.5
15 T	9 38 10.2	25 53.2	16 46.7	0♍29.7	0♓ 0.5	1 42.9	19 1.7	8 22.7	2 23.8	12 3.9	24 18.4	14 43.3
16 F	9 42 6.8	26 53.8	16 43.6	12 22.8	1 51.2	2 55.4	19 49.0	8 29.6	2 28.9	12 5.5	24 17.8	14 43.0
17 S	9 46 3.3	27 54.3	16 40.4	24 15.1	3 42.4	4 7.8	20 36.3	8 36.4	2 33.9	12 7.0	24 17.3	14 42.7
18 S	9 49 59.9	28 54.8	16 37.2	6♎ 8.5	5 34.0	5 20.2	21 23.6	8 43.0	2 38.8	12 8.5	24 16.7	14 42.5
19 M	9 53 56.4	29 55.3	16 34.0	18 5.1	7 25.8	6 32.4	22 10.9	8 49.5	2 43.7	12 9.9	24 16.2	14 42.3
20 T	9 57 53.0	0♓55.7	16 30.8	0♏ 7.8	9 17.8	7 44.6	22 58.2	8 55.9	2 48.5	12 11.3	24 15.7	14 42.2
21 W	10 1 49.5	1 56.1	16 27.7	12 20.4	11 9.8	8 56.6	23 45.5	9 2.1	2 53.2	12 12.7	24 15.3	14 42.0
22 T	10 5 46.1	2 56.6	16 24.5	24 47.0	13 1.5	10 8.6	24 32.8	9 8.1	2 57.9	12 14.0	24 14.9	14 41.9
23 F	10 9 42.6	3 56.9	16 21.3	7♐32.3	14 52.7	11 20.5	25 20.1	9 14.0	3 2.5	12 15.2	24 14.5	14 41.8
24 S	10 13 39.2	4 57.3	16 18.1	20 40.8	16 43.1	12 32.4	26 7.4	9 19.7	3 7.0	12 16.4	24 14.2	14 41.7
25 S	10 17 35.8	5 57.6	16 15.0	4♑16.3	18 32.4	13 44.1	26 54.8	9 25.2	3 11.5	12 17.5	24 13.9	14 41.6
26 M	10 21 32.3	6 58.0	16 11.8	18 21.1	20 20.2	14 55.7	27 42.1	9 30.7	3 15.8	12 18.6	24 13.6	14 41.6
27 T	10 25 28.8	7 58.2	16 8.6	2♒54.6	22 6.1	16 7.3	28 29.4	9 35.9	3 20.1	12 19.6	24 13.3	14 41.6
28 W	10 29 25.4	8 58.5	16 5.4	17 53.0	23 49.7	17 18.7	29 16.8	9 41.0	3 24.3	12 20.6	24 13.1	14D41.6
						DECLINATION						
1 T	8 42 58.5	17S16.9	22S51.9	8S46.6	20S51.0	7S13.3	19S17.6	20S35.4	22S27.1	22S 7.8	22N 3.3	12N57.8
4 S	8 54 48.1	16 24.9	22 51.0	8N19.4	19 36.3	5 41.8	18 40.5	20 39.6	22 27.0	22 8.7	22 3.3	12 58.3
7 W	9 6 37.8	15 30.3	22 50.1	20 25.3	18 8.3	4 9.0	18 1.5	20 43.5	22 26.8	22 9.5	22 3.3	12 58.8
10 S	9 18 27.4	14 33.4	22 49.2	22 25.5	16 26.8	2 35.3	17 20.8	20 47.2	22 26.5	22 10.3	22 3.4	12 59.4
13 T	9 30 17.1	13 34.3	22 48.3	14 58.4	14 32.2	1 1.0	16 38.4	20 50.6	22 26.3	22 11.1	22 3.4	12 60.0
16 F	9 42 6.8	12 33.2	22 47.4	2 17.8	12 24.9	0N33.6	15 54.5	20 53.7	22 26.0	22 11.7	22 3.5	13 0.6
19 M	9 53 56.4	11 30.3	22 46.4	11S 4.6	10 6.0	2 8.1	15 9.1	20 56.6	22 25.7	22 12.3	22 3.6	13 1.2
22 T	10 5 46.1	10 25.8	22 45.5	20 48.6	7 37.5	3 42.3	14 22.3	20 59.2	22 25.3	22 12.9	22 3.6	13 1.9
25 S	10 17 35.8	9 19.8	22 44.5	21 51.8	5 2.4	5 15.8	13 34.2	21 1.6	22 25.0	22 13.4	22 3.8	13 2.7
28 W	10 29 25.4	8 12.5	22 43.5	11 17.1	2 25.8	6 48.3	12 44.9	21 3.7	22 24.6	22 13.8	22 3.9	13 3.4

DAY	EPHEMERIS SIDEREAL TIME	☉	☊	☽	☿	♀	♂	♃	♄	♅	♆	♇
	h m s	° ′	° ′	° ′	° ′	° ′	° ′	° ′	° ′	° ′	° ′	° ′
LONGITUDE												
1 T	10 33 22.0	9♓58.7	16♐ 2.2	3♓ 8.5	25♓30.4	18♈30.1	0♓ 4.1	9♐45.9	3♑28.5	12♐21.5	24♊13.0	14♊41.6
2 F	10 37 18.5	10 58.9	15 59.1	18 30.4	27 7.7	19 41.3	0 51.4	9 50.6	3 32.5	12 22.4	24R12.8	14 41.6
3 S	10 41 15.1	11 59.1	15 55.9	3♈46.6	28 41.2	20 52.5	1 38.7	9 55.2	3 36.5	12 23.2	24 12.7	14 41.7
4 S	10 45 11.6	12 59.3	15 52.7	18 46.2	0♈10.1	22 3.5	2 26.0	9 59.6	3 40.4	12 23.9	24 12.6	14 41.8
5 M	10 49 8.2	13 59.4	15 49.5	3♉21.2	1 34.0	23 14.5	3 13.3	10 3.9	3 44.2	12 24.6	24 12.6	14 41.9
6 T	10 53 4.7	14 59.4	15 46.4	17 27.5	2 52.3	24 25.3	4 0.6	10 7.9	3 47.9	12 25.3	24D12.6	14 42.1
7 W	10 57 1.3	15 59.5	15 43.2	1♊ 4.2	4 4.5	25 36.0	4 47.9	10 11.8	3 51.6	12 25.9	24 12.7	14 42.2
8 T	11 0 57.8	16 59.5	15 40.0	14 13.4	5 9.9	26 46.6	5 35.2	10 15.5	3 55.1	12 26.4	24 12.7	14 42.4
9 F	11 4 54.4	17 59.4	15 36.8	26 59.1	6 8.2	27 57.0	6 22.5	10 19.1	3 58.6	12 26.9	24 12.8	14 42.6
10 S	11 8 50.9	18 59.4	15 33.6	9♋25.7	6 58.9	29 7.4	7 9.7	10 22.5	4 2.0	12 27.4	24 13.0	14 42.8
11 S	11 12 47.5	19 59.3	15 30.5	21 38.1	7 41.6	0♉17.6	7 57.0	10 25.7	4 5.3	12 27.7	24 13.1	14 43.1
12 M	11 16 44.1	20 59.1	15 27.3	3♌40.4	8 16.2	1 27.7	8 44.2	10 28.7	4 8.5	12 28.1	24 13.3	14 43.3
13 T	11 20 40.6	21 58.9	15 24.1	15 36.6	8 42.2	2 37.6	9 31.4	10 31.5	4 11.6	12 28.4	24 13.6	14 43.6
14 W	11 24 37.1	22 58.7	15 20.9	27 29.5	8 59.7	3 47.4	10 18.6	10 34.2	4 14.6	12 28.6	24 13.8	14 43.9
15 T	11 28 33.7	23 58.5	15 17.8	9♍21.5	9 8.7	4 57.1	11 5.8	10 36.7	4 17.6	12 28.7	24 14.1	14 44.3
16 F	11 32 30.3	24 58.2	15 14.6	21 14.4	9 9.1	6 6.6	11 53.0	10 39.0	4 20.5	12 28.9	24 14.5	14 44.6
17 S	11 36 26.8	25 57.9	15 11.4	3♎ 9.4	9R 1.3	7 16.0	12 40.2	10 41.1	4 23.2	12 28.9	24 14.9	14 45.0
18 S	11 40 23.4	26 57.5	15 8.2	15 7.7	8 45.6	8 25.2	13 27.3	10 43.0	4 25.9	12 28.9	24 15.3	14 45.4
19 M	11 44 19.9	27 57.1	15 5.0	27 10.9	8 22.4	9 34.3	14 14.5	10 44.8	4 28.5	12R28.9	24 15.7	14 45.8
20 T	11 48 16.5	28 56.7	15 1.9	9♏20.6	7 52.3	10 43.3	15 1.6	10 46.3	4 31.0	12 28.8	24 16.2	14 46.3
21 W	11 52 13.0	29 56.3	14 58.7	21 39.4	7 16.2	11 52.0	15 48.7	10 47.7	4 33.4	12 28.7	24 16.7	14 46.7
22 T	11 56 9.6	0♈55.8	14 55.5	4♐10.0	6 34.8	13 0.7	16 35.8	10 48.9	4 35.7	12 28.5	24 17.2	14 47.2
23 F	12 0 6.1	1 55.3	14 52.3	16 56.2	5 49.1	14 9.1	17 22.8	10 49.9	4 37.9	12 28.2	24 17.8	14 47.7
24 S	12 4 2.7	2 54.7	14 49.2	0♑ 1.6	5 0.2	15 17.4	18 9.9	10 50.7	4 40.1	12 27.9	24 18.4	14 48.3
25 S	12 7 59.2	3 54.2	14 46.0	13 29.9	4 9.1	16 25.5	18 56.9	10 51.4	4 42.1	12 27.6	24 19.1	14 48.8
26 M	12 11 55.8	4 53.6	14 42.8	27 23.5	3 16.9	17 33.5	19 43.9	10 51.8	4 44.0	12 27.2	24 19.7	14 49.4
27 T	12 15 52.3	5 53.0	14 39.6	11♒43.2	2 24.7	18 41.3	20 30.9	10 52.1	4 45.9	12 26.7	24 20.4	14 50.0
28 W	12 19 48.9	6 52.3	14 36.4	26 26.9	1 33.6	19 48.9	21 17.9	10 52.1	4 47.6	12 26.2	24 21.2	14 50.6
29 T	12 23 45.4	7 51.6	14 33.3	11♓29.3	0 44.5	20 56.3	22 4.9	10R52.0	4 49.3	12 25.6	24 22.0	14 51.2
30 F	12 27 42.0	8 50.9	14 30.1	26 41.7	29♓58.2	22 3.6	22 51.8	10 51.7	4 50.8	12 25.0	24 22.8	14 51.8
31 S	12 31 38.6	9 50.2	14 26.9	11♈53.6	29 15.5	23 10.7	23 38.7	10 51.2	4 52.3	12 24.3	24 23.6	14 52.5
DECLINATION												
1 T	10 33 22.0	7S49.9	22S43.2	5S48.5	1S34.4	7N18.8	12S28.3	21S 4.4	22S24.5	22S13.9	22N 3.9	13N 3.6
4 S	10 45 11.6	6 41.2	22 42.2	11N14.6	0N53.4	8 49.5	11 37.5	21 6.2	22 24.1	22 14.2	22 4.1	13 4.4
7 W	10 57 1.3	5 31.7	22 41.2	21 37.1	3 4.7	10 18.5	10 45.8	21 7.7	22 23.7	22 14.5	22 4.2	13 5.2
10 S	11 8 50.9	4 21.6	22 40.1	21 4.6	4 50.8	11 45.3	9 53.1	21 9.0	22 23.3	22 14.7	22 4.4	13 6.0
13 T	11 20 40.6	3 10.9	22 39.1	12 0.1	6 4.1	13 9.8	8 59.7	21 10.1	22 22.9	22 14.9	22 4.6	13 6.8
16 F	11 32 30.3	1 60.0	22 38.1	1S 5.1	6 38.8	14 31.7	8 5.6	21 10.9	22 22.6	22 15.0	22 4.7	13 7.7
19 M	11 44 19.9	0 48.9	22 37.0	13 53.1	6 32.7	15 50.5	7 10.8	21 11.5	22 22.2	22 15.0	22 5.0	13 8.5
22 T	11 56 9.6	0N22.2	22 35.9	21 48.8	5 48.1	17 6.2	6 15.6	21 11.9	22 21.9	22 15.0	22 5.2	13 9.4
25 S	12 7 59.2	1 33.1	22 34.9	20 15.5	4 33.1	18 18.2	5 19.9	21 12.0	22 21.6	22 14.9	22 5.4	13 10.3
28 W	12 19 48.9	2 43.8	22 33.8	8 9.6	3 1.0	19 26.5	4 23.8	21 11.9	22 21.3	22 14.7	22 5.6	13 11.2
31 S	12 31 38.6	3 53.9	22 32.7	8N46.7	1 26.7	20 30.7	3 27.5	21 11.6	22 21.1	22 14.5	22 5.9	13 12.1

APRIL 1900

DAY	EPHEMERIS SIDEREAL TIME	☉	☊	☽	☿	♀	♂	♃	♄	♅	♆	♇
LONGITUDE												
1 S	12 35 35.1	10♈49.4	14♐23.7	26♈54.1	28♓37.0	24♉17.5	24♓25.6	10♐50.5	4♑53.6	12♐23.6	24♊24.5	14♊53.2
2 M	12 39 31.6	11 48.6	14 20.5	11♉34.3	28R 3.1	25 24.2	25 12.4	10R49.7	4 54.9	12R22.9	24 25.4	14 53.9
3 T	12 43 28.2	12 47.7	14 17.4	25 48.3	27 34.4	26 30.7	25 59.2	10 48.6	4 56.0	12 22.1	24 26.3	14 54.6
4 W	12 47 24.8	13 46.8	14 14.2	9♊33.4	27 10.9	27 36.9	26 46.0	10 47.3	4 57.1	12 21.2	24 27.3	14 55.4
5 T	12 51 21.3	14 45.9	14 11.0	22 50.3	26 52.8	28 42.9	27 32.8	10 45.9	4 58.0	12 20.3	24 28.3	14 56.1
6 F	12 55 17.8	15 44.9	14 7.8	5♋41.6	26 40.3	29 48.7	28 19.5	10 44.3	4 58.9	12 19.3	24 29.3	14 56.9
7 S	12 59 14.4	16 43.9	14 4.7	18 11.6	26 33.3	0♊54.3	29 6.2	10 42.5	4 59.7	12 18.3	24 30.3	14 57.7
8 S	13 3 11.0	17 42.9	14 1.5	0♌25.0	26 31.8	1 59.6	29 52.9	10 40.5	5 0.3	12 17.3	24 31.4	14 58.5
9 M	13 7 7.5	18 41.8	13 58.3	12 26.7	26D35.6	3 4.7	0♈39.5	10 38.3	5 0.9	12 16.2	24 32.5	14 59.3
10 T	13 11 4.1	19 40.7	13 55.1	24 21.3	26 44.7	4 9.5	1 26.1	10 36.0	5 1.4	12 15.0	24 33.7	15 0.2
11 W	13 15 0.6	20 39.5	13 51.9	6♍12.9	26 58.7	5 14.1	2 12.7	10 33.4	5 1.7	12 13.8	24 34.8	15 1.1
12 T	13 18 57.2	21 38.3	13 48.8	18 4.7	27 17.7	6 18.4	2 59.2	10 30.7	5 2.0	12 12.6	24 36.0	15 1.9
13 F	13 22 53.7	22 37.1	13 45.6	29 59.4	27 41.3	7 22.4	3 45.8	10 27.8	5 2.2	12 11.3	24 37.3	15 2.8
14 S	13 26 50.3	23 35.8	13 42.4	11♎59.1	28 9.3	8 26.1	4 32.2	10 24.8	5 2.2	12 10.0	24 38.5	15 3.8
15 S	13 30 46.8	24 34.5	13 39.2	24 5.3	28 41.7	9 29.6	5 18.7	10 21.5	5R 2.2	12 8.6	24 39.8	15 4.7
16 M	13 34 43.4	25 33.2	13 36.1	6♏19.1	29 18.0	10 32.7	6 5.1	10 18.1	5 2.1	12 7.2	24 41.1	15 5.6
17 T	13 38 39.9	26 31.8	13 32.9	18 41.7	29 58.3	11 35.6	6 51.4	10 14.5	5 1.9	12 5.8	24 42.5	15 6.6
18 W	13 42 36.5	27 30.4	13 29.7	1♐14.3	0♈42.3	12 38.1	7 37.8	10 10.8	5 1.6	12 4.3	24 43.8	15 7.6
19 T	13 46 33.1	28 29.0	13 26.5	13 58.5	1 29.7	13 40.3	8 24.1	10 6.9	5 1.1	12 2.8	24 45.2	15 8.6
20 F	13 50 29.6	29 27.5	13 23.3	26 55.9	2 20.6	14 42.2	9 10.3	10 2.8	5 0.6	12 1.2	24 46.6	15 9.6
21 S	13 54 26.1	0♉26.1	13 20.2	10♑ 8.8	3 14.6	15 43.7	9 56.6	9 58.6	5 0.0	11 59.6	24 48.1	15 10.6
22 S	13 58 22.7	1 24.6	13 17.0	23 39.1	4 11.8	16 45.0	10 42.7	9 54.2	4 59.3	11 57.9	24 49.6	15 11.7
23 M	14 2 19.3	2 23.0	13 13.8	7♒28.3	5 11.8	17 45.8	11 28.9	9 49.6	4 58.5	11 56.3	24 51.1	15 12.7
24 T	14 6 15.8	3 21.5	13 10.6	21 36.9	6 14.7	18 46.3	12 15.0	9 44.9	4 57.6	11 54.5	24 52.6	15 13.8
25 W	14 10 12.4	4 19.9	13 7.5	6♓ 3.4	7 20.2	19 46.4	13 1.1	9 40.0	4 56.6	11 52.8	24 54.1	15 14.9
26 T	14 14 8.9	5 18.3	13 4.3	20 44.5	8 28.4	20 46.1	13 47.1	9 35.0	4 55.5	11 51.0	24 55.7	15 16.0
27 F	14 18 5.5	6 16.6	13 1.1	5♈34.3	9 39.1	21 45.4	14 33.1	9 29.8	4 54.3	11 49.2	24 57.3	15 17.1
28 S	14 22 2.0	7 15.0	12 57.9	20 25.3	10 52.2	22 44.3	15 19.1	9 24.5	4 53.1	11 47.3	24 58.9	15 18.2
29 S	14 25 58.6	8 13.3	12 54.7	5♉ 9.4	12 7.6	23 42.8	16 5.0	9 19.0	4 51.7	11 45.4	25 0.5	15 19.3
30 M	14 29 55.1	9 11.5	12 51.6	19 38.9	13 25.3	24 40.9	16 50.9	9 13.4	4 50.2	11 43.4	25 2.2	15 20.5
DECLINATION												
1 S	12 35 35.1	4N17.2	22S32.3	13N46.2	0N57.1	20N51.1	3S 8.7	21S11.5	22S21.0	22S14.4	22N 6.0	13N12.4
4 W	12 47 24.8	5 26.4	22 31.2	22 10.3	0S21.1	21 49.4	2 12.1	21 10.8	22 20.8	22 14.1	22 6.2	13 13.2
7 S	12 59 14.4	6 34.7	22 30.1	19 16.3	1 18.9	22 43.2	1 15.6	21 .0.0	22 20.6	22 13.7	22 6.5	13 14.1
10 T	13 11 4.1	7 42.1	22 29.0	8 50.1	1 53.6	23 32.0	0 19.1	21 8.9	22 20.4	22 13.3	22 6.8	13 15.0
13 F	13 22 53.7	8 48.2	22 27.8	4S27.1	2 5.3	24 15.9	0N37.3	21 7.6	22 20.3	22 12.9	22 7.0	13 15.9
16 M	13 34 43.4	9 53.1	22 26.7	16 26.4	1 55.4	24 54.6	1 33.5	21 6.1	22 20.3	22 12.4	22 7.3	13 16.8
19 T	13 46 33.1	10 56.5	22 25.5	22 16.6	1 26.0	25 28.1	2 29.4	21 4.4	22 20.2	22 11.8	22 7.6	13 17.7
22 S	13 58 22.7	11 58.2	22 24.3	17 57.5	0 39.0	25 56.3	3 25.0	21 2.5	22 20.2	22 11.2	22 7.9	13 18.5
25 W	14 10 12.4	12 58.2	22 23.1	4 30.0	0N23.7	26 19.2	4 20.1	21 0.3	22 20.3	22 10.5	22 8.2	13 19.4
28 S	14 22 2.0	13 56.3	22 21.9	11N42.7	1 40.2	26 36.7	5 14.7	20 58.0	22 20.3	22 9.8	22 8.5	13 20.3

MAY 1900

DAY	EPHEMERIS SIDEREAL TIME	⊙	☊	☽	☿	♀	♂	♃	♄	♅	♆	♇
	h m s	° ′	° ′	° ′	° ′	° ′	° ′	° ′	° ′	° ′	° ′	° ′

LONGITUDE

1 T	14 33 51.7	10♉ 9.8	12✠48.4	3✠47.9	14♈45.3	25✠38.5	17♈36.7	9♐ 7.7	4♄48.7	11♐41.5	25✠ 3.9	15✠21.7
2 W	14 37 48.3	11 8.0	12 45.2	17 32.8	16 7.4	26 35.6	18 22.5	9R 1.9	4R47.0	11R39.5	25 5.6	15 22.8
3 T	14 41 44.8	12 6.2	12 42.0	0♋52.6	17 31.7	27 32.2	19 8.3	8 55.9	4 45.3	11 37.5	25 7.3	15 24.0
4 F	14 45 41.4	13 4.3	12 38.9	13 48.3	18 58.1	28 28.4	19 53.9	8 49.8	4 43.4	11 35.4	25 9.1	15 25.2
5 S	14 49 37.9	14 2.4	12 35.7	26 22.9	20 26.5	29 24.0	20 39.6	8 43.6	4 41.5	11 33.3	25 10.8	15 26.4
6 S	14 53 34.5	15 0.5	12 32.5	8♌40.1	21 57.0	0♋19.0	21 25.2	8 37.2	4 39.5	11 31.2	25 12.6	15 27.6
7 M	14 57 31.0	15 58.6	12 29.3	20 44.5	23 29.5	1 13.5	22 10.7	8 30.8	4 37.4	11 29.1	25 14.4	15 28.9
8 T	15 1 27.6	16 56.6	12 26.2	2♍40.7	25 4.1	2 7.4	22 56.2	8 24.3	4 35.3	11 26.9	25 16.3	15 30.1
9 W	15 5 24.1	17 54.6	12 23.0	14 33.3	26 40.6	3 0.7	23 41.7	8 17.6	4 33.0	11 24.8	25 18.1	15 31.3
10 T	15 9 20.7	18 52.6	12 19.8	26 26.4	28 19.2	3 53.4	24 27.1	8 10.9	4 30.7	11 22.5	25 20.0	15 32.6
11 F	15 13 17.2	19 50.5	12 16.6	8≏23.9	29 59.7	4 45.4	25 12.4	8 4.0	4 28.2	11 20.3	25 21.9	15 33.9
12 S	15 17 13.8	20 48.4	12 13.4	20 28.8	1♉42.3	5 36.8	25 57.7	7 57.1	4 25.7	11 18.1	25 23.8	15 35.1
13 S	15 21 10.4	21 46.3	12 10.3	2♏43.4	3 26.8	6 27.4	26 43.0	7 50.1	4 23.1	11 15.8	25 25.7	15 36.4
14 M	15 25 6.9	22 44.1	12 7.1	15 9.5	5 13.4	7 17.4	27 28.2	7 43.0	4 20.5	11 13.5	25 27.6	15 37.7
15 T	15 29 3.5	23 41.9	12 3.9	27 48.1	7 2.0	8 6.5	28 13.4	7 35.9	4 17.7	11 11.2	25 29.6	15 39.0
16 W	15 33 0.0	24 39.7	12 0.7	10♐39.9	8 52.6	8 54.9	28 58.5	7 28.7	4 14.9	11 8.9	25 31.5	15 40.3
17 T	15 36 56.6	25 37.5	11 57.6	23 44.9	10 45.2	9 42.5	29 43.5	7 21.4	4 12.0	11 6.5	25 33.5	15 41.6
18 F	15 40 53.1	26 35.3	11 54.4	7♑ 3.2	12 39.8	10 29.3	0♉28.6	7 14.0	4 9.1	11 4.2	25 35.5	15 43.0
19 S	15 44 49.7	27 33.0	11 51.2	20 34.5	14 36.4	11 15.2	1 13.5	7 6.6	4 6.0	11 1.8	25 37.5	15 44.3
20 S	15 48 46.2	28 30.7	11 48.0	4≈18.4	16 34.9	12 0.2	1 58.4	6 59.2	4 2.9	10 59.4	25 39.6	15 45.6
21 M	15 52 42.8	29 28.4	11 44.9	18 14.3	18 35.2	12 44.3	2 43.3	6 51.7	3 59.7	10 57.0	25 41.6	15 47.0
22 T	15 56 39.4	0♊26.1	11 41.7	2✠21.0	20 37.5	13 27.4	3 28.1	6 44.2	3 56.5	10 54.6	25 43.7	15 48.3
23 W	16 0 35.9	1 23.8	11 38.5	16 36.8	22 41.4	14 9.6	4 12.9	6 36.6	3 53.2	10 52.2	25 45.7	15 49.6
24 T	16 4 32.4	2 21.4	11 35.3	0♈59.0	24 47.0	14 50.7	4 57.6	6 29.0	3 49.8	10 49.7	25 47.8	15 51.0
25 F	16 8 29.0	3 19.0	11 32.1	15 24.1	26 54.1	15 30.7	5 42.3	6 21.4	3 46.4	10 47.3	25 49.9	15 52.4
26 S	16 12 25.6	4 16.7	11 29.0	29 47.7	29 2.6	16 9.6	6 26.9	6 13.8	3 42.9	10 44.8	25 52.0	15 53.7
27 S	16 16 22.1	5 14.3	11 25.8	14♉ 5.1	1✠12.2	16 47.4	7 11.4	6 6.2	3 39.3	10 42.4	25 54.1	15 55.1
28 M	16 20 18.7	6 11.8	11 22.6	28 11.5	3 22.8	17 24.0	7 55.9	5 58.5	3 35.7	10 39.9	25 56.2	15 56.5
29 T	16 24 15.2	7 9.4	11 19.4	12✠ 2.8	5 34.1	17 59.3	8 40.4	5 50.9	3 32.0	10 37.4	25 58.4	15 57.8
30 W	16 28 11.8	8 7.0	11 16.3	25 36.0	7 46.0	18 33.4	9 24.8	5 43.2	3 28.3	10 35.0	26 0.5	15 59.2
31 T	16 32 8.3	9 4.5	11 13.1	8♋49.3	9 58.0	19 6.1	10 9.1	5 35.6	3 24.5	10 32.5	26 2.7	16 0.6

DECLINATION

1 T	14 33 51.7	14N52.4	22S20.7	21N34.9	3N 9.0	26N49.0	6N 8.7	20S55.5	22S20.5	22S 9.0	22N 8.8	13N21.1
4 F	14 45 41.4	15 46.2	22 19.5	19 55.8	4 48.7	26 56.2	7 2.0	20 52.8	20 20.6	22 8.2	22 9.1	13 21.4
7 M	14 57 31.0	16 37.7	22 18.3	9 56.1	6 37.8	26 58.3	7 54.5	20 49.9	22 20.8	22 7.4	22 9.4	13 22.7
10 T	15 9 20.7	17 26.7	22 17.0	3S13.1	8 34.9	26 55.7	8 46.2	20 46.9	22 21.0	22 6.5	22 9.7	13 23.5
13 S	15 21 10.4	18 13.0	22 15.8	15 28.7	10 38.5	26 48.5	9 37.1	20 43.7	22 21.3	22 5.6	22 10.0	13 24.2
16 W	15 33 0.0	18 56.7	22 14.5	22 4.9	12 46.6	26 37.0	10 26.9	20 40.4	22 21.6	22 4.7	22 10.3	13 25.0
19 S	15 44 49.7	19 37.4	22 13.2	18 32.9	14 56.8	26 21.6	11 15.8	20 37.0	22 21.9	22 3.7	22 10.5	13 25.7
22 T	15 56 39.4	20 15.1	22 12.0	5 46.3	17 5.8	26 2.6	12 3.5	20 33.5	22 22.2	22 2.8	22 10.8	13 26.4
25 F	16 8 29.0	20 49.8	22 10.7	10N 4.9	19 9.3	25 40.3	12 50.1	20 29.9	22 22.6	22 1.8	22 11.1	13 27.1
28 M	16 20 18.7	21 21.2	22 9.4	20 54.4	21 2.4	25 15.2	13 35.5	20 26.3	22 22.9	22 0.7	22 11.4	13 27.7
31 T	16 32 8.3	21 49.3	22 8.1	20 41.3	22 39.6	24 47.7	14 19.6	20 22.6	22 23.3	21 59.7	22 11.6	13 28.3

JUNE 1900

LONGITUDE

1 F	16 36 4.9	10✠ 2.0	11✠ 9.9	21♋42.9	12✠10.0	19♋37.4	10♉53.4	5♐28.0	3♄20.7	10♐30.0	26✠ 4.8	16✠ 2.0
2 S	16 40 1.4	10 59.5	11 6.7	4♌17.8	14 21.7	20 7.2	11 37.6	5R20.4	3R16.8	10R27.5	26 7.0	16 3.4
3 S	16 43 58.0	11 56.9	11 3.6	16 36.7	16 32.8	20 35.5	12 21.7	5 12.8	3 12.9	10 25.1	26 9.2	16 4.8
4 M	16 47 54.6	12 54.4	11 0.4	28 42.9	18 43.0	21 2.3	13 5.9	5 5.3	3 8.9	10 22.6	26 11.4	16 6.2
5 T	16 51 51.2	13 51.8	10 57.2	10♍40.6	20 52.2	21 27.4	13 49.9	4 57.8	3 4.9	10 20.1	26 13.6	16 7.6
6 W	16 55 47.7	14 49.2	10 54.0	22 34.2	22 60.0	21 50.8	14 33.9	4 50.3	3 0.8	10 17.6	26 15.8	16 8.9
7 T	16 59 44.2	15 46.6	10 50.8	4≏28.2	25 6.2	22 12.5	15 17.8	4 42.9	2 56.7	10 15.2	26 18.0	16 10.3
8 F	17 3 40.8	16 44.0	10 47.7	16 27.3	27 10.8	22 32.4	16 1.7	4 35.5	2 52.6	10 12.7	26 20.2	16 11.7
9 S	17 7 37.4	17 41.3	10 44.5	28 35.5	29 13.5	22 50.4	16 45.5	4 28.2	2 48.5	10 10.3	26 22.4	16 13.1
10 S	17 11 34.0	18 38.7	10 41.3	10♏56.3	1♋56.2	23 6.5	17 29.2	4 21.0	2 44.3	10 7.8	26 24.6	16 14.5
11 M	17 15 30.5	19 36.0	10 38.1	23 32.5	3 12.8	23 20.5	18 12.9	4 13.8	2 40.0	10 5.4	26 26.8	16 15.9
12 T	17 19 27.0	20 33.3	10 35.0	6♐26.0	5 9.2	23 32.6	18 56.5	4 6.7	2 35.8	10 3.0	26 29.0	16 17.3
13 W	17 23 23.6	21 30.6	10 31.8	19 37.3	7 3.4	23 42.5	19 40.1	3 59.7	2 31.5	10 0.6	26 31.3	16 18.7
14 T	17 27 20.1	22 27.9	10 28.6	3♑ 6.1	8 55.3	23 50.2	20 23.6	3 52.8	2 27.2	9 58.2	26 33.5	16 20.1
15 F	17 31 16.7	23 25.2	10 25.4	16 50.5	10 44.8	23 55.8	21 7.1	3 45.9	2 22.9	9 55.8	26 35.7	16 21.4
16 S	17 35 13.3	24 22.4	10 22.3	0≈47.9	12 32.0	23 59.1	21 50.5	3 39.2	2 18.5	9 53.4	26 38.0	16 22.8
17 S	17 39 9.8	25 19.7	10 19.1	14 55.0	14 16.8	24 0.0	22 33.8	3 32.5	2 14.2	9 51.0	26 40.2	16 24.2
18 M	17 43 6.4	26 16.9	10 15.9	29 8.2	15 59.2	23R58.7	23 17.1	3 25.9	2 9.8	9 48.7	26 42.5	16 25.6
19 T	17 47 2.9	27 14.2	10 12.7	13✠24.1	17 39.2	23 55.0	24 0.3	3 19.5	2 5.4	9 46.4	26 44.7	16 26.9
20 W	17 50 59.5	28 11.4	10 9.5	27 39.4	19 16.7	23 49.0	24 43.5	3 13.1	2 1.0	9 44.1	26 46.9	16 28.3
21 T	17 54 56.1	29 8.7	10 6.4	11♈51.5	20 51.9	23 40.5	25 26.6	3 6.9	1 56.6	9 41.8	26 49.2	16 29.7
22 F	17 58 52.6	0♋ 5.9	10 3.2	25 58.1	22 24.5	23 29.7	26 9.6	3 0.7	1 52.2	9 39.5	26 51.4	16 31.0
23 S	18 2 49.1	1 3.2	10 0.0	9♉57.4	23 54.7	23 16.5	26 52.6	2 54.7	1 47.8	9 37.2	26 53.6	16 32.4
24 S	18 6 45.7	2 0.4	9 56.8	23 47.6	25 22.5	23 0.9	27 35.5	2 48.8	1 43.4	9 35.0	26 55.9	16 33.8
25 M	18 10 42.3	2 57.6	9 53.7	7✠27.1	26 47.6	22 43.0	28 18.4	2 43.0	1 39.0	9 32.8	26 58.1	16 35.1
26 T	18 14 38.8	3 54.9	9 50.5	20 54.2	28 10.3	22 22.9	29 1.2	2 37.4	1 34.5	9 30.6	27 0.3	16 36.4
27 W	18 18 35.4	4 52.1	9 47.3	4♋ 7.6	29 30.4	22 0.5	29 43.9	2 31.9	1 30.1	9 28.4	27 2.5	16 37.8
28 T	18 22 32.0	5 49.3	9 44.1	17 6.4	0♋47.8	21 36.0	0✠26.6	2 26.5	1 25.7	9 26.3	27 4.8	16 39.1
29 F	18 26 28.5	6 46.6	9 41.0	29 50.2	2 2.6	21 9.5	1 9.2	2 21.3	1 21.3	9 24.2	27 7.0	16 40.4
30 S	18 30 25.0	7 43.8	9 37.8	12♌19.4	3 14.7	20 41.1	1 51.7	2 16.2	1 16.9	9 22.1	27 9.2	16 41.7

DECLINATION

1 F	16 36 4.9	21N57.9	22S 7.6	18N17.3	23N 7.5	24N38.1	14N34.0	20S21.4	22S23.5	21S59.4	22N11.7	13N28.5
4 M	16 47 54.6	22 21.5	22 6.3	7 4.9	24 16.1	24 8.0	15 16.3	20 17.8	22 23.9	21 58.3	22 11.9	13 29.1
7 T	16 59 44.2	22 41.5	22 4.9	6S13.4	25 0.1	23 36.7	15 57.2	20 14.2	22 24.3	21 57.3	22 12.2	13 29.6
10 S	17 11 34.0	22 57.9	22 3.6	17 37.9	25 19.4	23 4.4	16 36.6	20 10.6	22 24.7	21 56.3	22 12.4	13 30.1
13 W	17 23 23.6	23 10.8	22 2.2	22 15.4	25 15.6	22 31.6	17 14.4	20 7.2	22 25.1	21 55.2	22 12.6	13 30.6
16 S	17 35 13.3	23 19.9	22 0.9	16 3.4	24 52.0	21 58.7	17 50.8	20 3.8	22 25.5	21 54.2	22 12.8	13 31.1
19 T	17 47 2.9	23 25.4	21 59.5	1 40.4	24 13.2	21 26.0	18 25.0	20 0.6	22 25.9	21 53.2	22 13.0	13 31.5
22 F	17 58 52.6	23 27.1	21 58.1	13N29.8	23 17.1	20 53.8	18 58.6	19 57.6	22 26.4	21 52.2	22 13.2	13 31.9
25 M	18 10 42.3	23 25.1	21 56.7	21 52.9	22 12.5	20 22.3	19 29.9	19 54.7	22 26.8	21 51.2	22 13.3	13 32.2
28 T	18 22 32.0	23 19.4	21 55.3	19 17.2	21 0.5	19 51.7	19 59.6	19 52.1	22 27.2	21 50.3	22 13.5	13 32.5

JULY 1900

LONGITUDE

DAY	EPHEMERIS SIDEREAL TIME h m s	☉ ° ′	☊ ° ′	☽ ° ′	☿ ° ′	♀ ° ′	♂ ° ′	♃ ° ′	♄ ° ′	♅ ° ′	♆ ° ′	♇ ° ′
1 S	18 34 21.6	8♋41.0	9♐34.6	24♌35.3	4♌23.9	20♋10.9	2♊34.2	2♐11.3	1♑12.6	9♐20.1	27♊11.4	16♊43.0
2 M	18 38 18.2	9 38.2	9 31.4	6♍40.2	5 30.3	19R39.1	3 16.6	2R 6.5	1R 8.2	9R18.0	27 13.6	16 44.3
3 T	18 42 14.8	10 35.4	9 28.3	18 37.2	6 33.8	19 5.8	3 59.0	2 1.9	1 3.9	9 16.0	27 15.8	16 45.6
4 W	18 46 11.3	11 32.6	9 25.1	0♎30.2	7 34.2	18 31.3	4 41.2	1 57.4	0 59.6	9 14.1	27 18.0	16 46.9
5 T	18 50 7.8	12 29.8	9 21.9	12 23.4	8 31.4	17 55.7	5 23.5	1 53.1	0 55.3	9 12.1	27 20.1	16 48.2
6 F	18 54 4.4	13 27.0	9 18.7	24 21.7	9 25.4	17 19.2	6 5.6	1 48.9	0 51.0	9 10.2	27 22.3	16 49.5
7 S	18 58 1.0	14 24.2	9 15.5	6♏29.8	10 16.1	16 42.2	6 47.7	1 44.9	0 46.8	9 8.4	27 24.5	16 50.7
8 S	19 1 57.6	15 21.4	9 12.4	18 52.5	11 3.3	16 4.7	7 29.7	1 41.1	0 42.6	9 6.5	27 26.6	16 52.0
9 M	19 5 54.1	16 18.6	9 9.2	1♐33.6	11 46.9	15 27.1	8 11.6	1 37.4	0 38.4	9 4.7	27 28.8	16 53.2
10 T	19 9 50.6	17 15.8	9 6.0	14 36.4	12 26.8	14 49.7	8 53.5	1 33.9	0 34.2	9 2.9	27 30.9	16 54.4
11 W	19 13 47.2	18 12.9	9 2.8	28 2.3	13 2.8	14 12.5	9 35.3	1 30.6	0 30.1	9 1.2	27 33.0	16 55.6
12 T	19 17 43.8	19 10.1	8 59.7	11♑51.1	13 34.7	13 36.0	10 17.1	1 27.4	0 26.1	8 59.5	27 35.1	16 56.9
13 F	19 21 40.3	20 7.3	8 56.5	26 0.3	14 2.5	13 0.3	10 58.8	1 24.4	0 22.1	8 57.9	27 37.2	16 58.1
14 S	19 25 36.9	21 4.5	8 53.3	10♒25.3	14 26.0	12 25.6	11 40.4	1 21.6	0 18.1	8 56.2	27 39.3	16 59.2
15 S	19 29 33.4	22 1.7	8 50.1	25 0.0	14 45.1	11 52.2	12 21.9	1 19.0	0 14.1	8 54.6	27 41.4	17 0.4
16 M	19 33 29.9	22 58.9	8 47.0	9♓37.6	14 59.6	11 20.2	13 3.4	1 16.5	0 10.2	8 53.1	27 43.5	17 1.6
17 T	19 37 26.5	23 56.2	8 43.8	24 11.6	15 9.4	10 49.8	13 44.9	1 14.2	0 6.4	8 51.6	27 45.5	17 2.7
18 W	19 41 23.1	24 53.4	8 40.6	8♈36.6	15 14.5	10 21.3	14 26.2	1 12.1	0 2.6	8 50.1	27 47.6	17 3.9
19 T	19 45 19.7	25 50.7	8 37.4	22 49.3	15 14.6	9 54.6	15 7.5	1 10.2	29♐58.8	8 48.7	27 49.6	17 5.0
20 F	19 49 16.2	26 47.9	8 34.2	6♉47.7	15R 9.9	9 30.0	15 48.8	1 8.4	29 55.1	8 47.3	27 51.6	17 6.1
21 S	19 53 12.7	27 45.2	8 31.1	20 31.6	15 0.2	9 7.6	16 29.9	1 6.8	29 51.4	8 46.0	27 53.6	17 7.2
22 S	19 57 9.3	28 42.5	8 27.9	4♊1.2	14 45.7	8 47.4	17 11.0	1 5.5	29 47.9	8 44.7	27 55.6	17 8.3
23 M	20 1 5.9	29 39.8	8 24.7	17 17.6	14 26.4	8 29.4	17 52.1	1 4.2	29 44.3	8 43.4	27 57.6	17 9.4
24 T	20 5 2.5	0♌37.1	8 21.5	0♋21.6	14 2.5	8 13.8	18 33.0	1 3.2	29 40.8	8 42.2	27 59.5	17 10.5
25 W	20 8 59.0	1 34.4	8 18.4	13 13.8	13 34.3	8 0.6	19 13.9	1 2.4	29 37.4	8 41.0	28 1.5	17 11.5
26 T	20 12 55.6	2 31.8	8 15.2	25 54.6	13 2.0	7 49.7	19 54.8	1 1.7	29 34.1	8 39.9	28 3.4	17 12.5
27 F	20 16 52.1	3 29.2	8 12.0	8♌24.3	12 26.1	7 41.2	20 35.5	1 1.2	29 30.8	8 38.8	28 5.3	17 13.6
28 S	20 20 48.7	4 26.5	8 8.8	20 43.3	11 47.0	7 35.1	21 16.2	1 0.9	29 27.6	8 37.8	28 7.2	17 14.6
29 S	20 24 45.2	5 23.9	8 5.7	2♍52.4	11 5.3	7 31.4	21 56.8	1 0.8	29 24.4	8 36.8	28 9.0	17 15.5
30 M	20 28 41.8	6 21.3	8 2.5	14 53.1	10 21.7	7 30.0	22 37.3	1D 0.9	29 21.3	8 35.8	28 10.9	17 16.5
31 T	20 32 38.4	7 18.7	7 59.3	26 47.4	9 36.9	7D30.9	23 17.8	1 1.2	29 18.3	8 34.9	28 12.7	17 17.5

DECLINATION

DAY	EPHEMERIS SIDEREAL TIME h m s	☉ ° ′	☊ ° ′	☽ ° ′	☿ ° ′	♀ ° ′	♂ ° ′	♃ ° ′	♄ ° ′	♅ ° ′	♆ ° ′	♇ ° ′
1 S	18 34 21.6	23N10.0	21S53.9	8N36.3	19N44.0	19N22.4	20N27.5	19S49.7	22S27.6	21S49.4	22N13.6	13N32.8
4 W	18 46 11.3	22 57.0	21 52.4	4S41.6	18 25.6	18 54.5	20 53.6	19 47.6	22 28.0	21 48.5	22 13.8	13 33.1
7 S	18 58 1.0	22 40.3	21 51.0	16 26.9	17 8.1	18 28.5	21 17.9	19 45.7	22 28.4	21 47.7	22 13.9	13 33.3
10 T	19 9 50.6	22 20.2	21 49.5	22 12.1	15 54.3	18 4.9	21 40.4	19 44.2	22 28.8	21 46.9	22 14.0	13 33.5
13 F	19 21 40.3	21 56.6	21 48.1	17 20.0	14 47.1	17 44.3	22 1.0	19 42.9	22 29.2	21 46.1	22 14.1	13 33.6
16 M	19 33 29.9	21 29.6	21 46.6	3 11.5	13 49.7	17 27.0	22 19.8	19 41.9	22 29.6	21 45.4	22 14.2	13 33.7
19 T	19 45 19.7	20 59.3	21 45.1	12N23.4	13 5.3	17 13.6	22 36.7	19 41.3	22 29.9	21 44.8	22 14.3	13 33.8
22 S	19 57 9.3	20 25.7	21 43.6	21 29.6	12 36.9	17 4.2	22 51.7	19 41.0	22 30.3	21 44.2	22 14.3	13 33.8
25 W	20 8 59.0	19 49.2	21 42.1	19 59.9	12 27.1	16 58.7	23 4.9	19 41.1	22 30.7	21 43.7	22 14.4	13 33.8
28 S	20 20 48.7	19 9.6	21 40.6	10 1.7	12 36.8	16 56.8	23 16.2	19 41.4	22 31.1	21 43.2	22 14.4	13 33.8
31 T	20 32 38.4	18 27.2	21 39.1	3S 9.8	13 4.9	16 58.2	23 25.6	19 42.2	22 31.4	21 42.8	22 14.4	13 33.7

AUGUST 1900

LONGITUDE

DAY	EPHEMERIS SIDEREAL TIME h m s	☉ ° ′	☊ ° ′	☽ ° ′	☿ ° ′	♀ ° ′	♂ ° ′	♃ ° ′	♄ ° ′	♅ ° ′	♆ ° ′	♇ ° ′
1 W	20 36 34.9	8♌16.1	7♐56.1	8♎38.3	8♌51.7	7♋34.1	23♊58.2	1♐1.6	29♐15.4	8♐34.1	28♊14.5	17♊18.4
2 T	20 40 31.4	9 13.5	7 52.9	20 29.5	8R 6.8	7 39.5	24 38.5	1 2.3	29R12.5	8R33.3	28 16.3	17 19.4
3 F	20 44 28.0	10 11.0	7 49.8	2♏25.4	7 23.2	7 47.1	25 18.7	1 3.1	29 9.7	8 32.5	28 18.1	17 20.3
4 S	20 48 24.6	11 8.4	7 46.6	14 31.0	6 41.6	7 56.8	25 58.9	1 4.1	29 7.0	8 31.8	28 19.8	17 21.2
5 S	20 52 21.1	12 5.9	7 43.4	26 51.5	6 3.0	8 8.7	26 39.0	1 5.3	29 4.4	8 31.2	28 21.6	17 22.1
6 M	20 56 17.7	13 3.3	7 40.2	9♐31.7	5 27.9	8 22.5	27 19.0	1 6.6	29 1.8	8 30.6	28 23.3	17 22.9
7 T	21 0 14.2	14 0.8	7 37.1	22 36.0	4 57.2	8 38.3	27 59.0	1 8.2	28 59.4	8 30.0	28 25.0	17 23.8
8 W	21 4 10.8	14 58.3	7 33.9	6♑7.4	4 31.5	8 56.0	28 38.9	1 9.9	28 57.0	8 29.5	28 26.6	17 24.6
9 T	21 8 7.3	15 55.8	7 30.7	20 6.7	4 11.3	9 15.5	29 18.7	1 11.8	28 54.7	8 29.0	28 28.3	17 25.4
10 F	21 12 3.9	16 53.4	7 27.5	4♒31.8	3 57.2	9 36.9	29 58.4	1 13.9	28 52.4	8 28.6	28 29.9	17 26.2
11 S	21 16 0.4	17 50.9	7 24.4	19 17.7	3 49.6	10 0.0	0♋38.0	1 16.2	28 50.3	8 28.2	28 31.5	17 27.0
12 S	21 19 57.0	18 48.5	7 21.2	4♓16.5	3 48.7	10 24.8	1 17.6	1 18.6	28 48.2	8 27.9	28 33.1	17 27.7
13 M	21 23 53.6	19 46.1	7 18.0	19 18.6	3D54.8	10 51.2	1 57.1	1 21.2	28 46.3	8 27.7	28 34.6	17 28.5
14 T	21 27 50.1	20 43.7	7 14.8	4♈14.6	4 8.1	11 19.2	2 36.6	1 24.0	28 44.4	8 27.5	28 36.2	17 29.2
15 W	21 31 46.7	21 41.3	7 11.6	18 56.5	4 28.7	11 48.8	3 15.9	1 27.0	28 42.6	8 27.3	28 37.7	17 29.9
16 T	21 35 43.2	22 39.0	7 8.5	3♉19.2	4 56.6	12 19.8	3 55.2	1 30.1	28 40.9	8 27.2	28 39.1	17 30.6
17 F	21 39 39.7	23 36.7	7 5.3	17 20.2	5 31.7	12 52.2	4 34.4	1 33.4	28 39.2	8 27.1	28 40.6	17 31.2
18 S	21 43 36.3	24 34.4	7 2.1	0♊59.6	6 14.0	13 25.9	5 13.6	1 36.9	28 37.7	8 27.1	28 42.0	17 31.9
19 S	21 47 32.9	25 32.1	6 58.9	14 19.0	7 3.4	14 1.0	5 52.7	1 40.5	28 36.3	8D27.2	28 43.4	17 32.5
20 M	21 51 29.5	26 29.9	6 55.8	27 21.0	7 59.6	14 37.3	6 31.6	1 44.4	28 34.9	8 27.3	28 44.8	17 33.1
21 T	21 55 26.0	27 27.7	6 52.6	10♋8.2	9 2.5	15 14.9	7 10.6	1 48.3	28 33.7	8 27.4	28 46.2	17 33.7
22 W	21 59 22.5	28 25.5	6 49.4	22 43.1	10 11.7	15 53.6	7 49.4	1 52.5	28 32.5	8 27.6	28 47.5	17 34.3
23 T	22 3 19.1	29 23.4	6 46.2	5♌7.7	11 27.1	16 33.4	8 28.1	1 56.8	28 31.4	8 27.8	28 48.8	17 34.8
24 F	22 7 15.7	0♍21.3	6 43.0	17 23.4	12 48.1	17 14.3	9 6.8	2 1.3	28 30.5	8 28.1	28 50.1	17 35.4
25 S	22 11 12.2	1 19.2	6 39.9	29 31.3	14 14.5	17 56.3	9 45.4	2 6.0	28 29.6	8 28.5	28 51.3	17 35.9
26 S	22 15 8.7	2 17.1	6 36.7	11♍32.5	15 45.8	18 39.2	10 23.9	2 10.8	28 28.8	8 28.9	28 52.5	17 36.4
27 M	22 19 5.3	3 15.0	6 33.5	23 28.0	17 21.5	19 23.1	11 2.3	2 15.7	28 28.1	8 29.4	28 53.7	17 36.8
28 T	22 23 1.9	4 13.0	6 30.3	5♎19.4	19 1.3	20 7.9	11 40.7	2 20.9	28 27.5	8 29.9	28 54.9	17 37.3
29 W	22 26 58.4	5 11.0	6 27.2	17 8.8	20 44.6	20 53.6	12 18.9	2 26.2	28 27.0	8 30.4	28 56.0	17 37.7
30 T	22 30 55.0	6 9.1	6 24.0	28 59.0	22 30.9	21 40.2	12 57.1	2 31.6	28 26.6	8 31.0	28 57.1	17 38.1
31 F	22 34 51.5	7 7.1	6 20.8	10♏53.7	24 19.8	22 27.6	13 35.2	2 37.2	28 26.3	8 31.7	28 58.2	17 38.5

DECLINATION

DAY	EPHEMERIS SIDEREAL TIME h m s	☉ ° ′	☊ ° ′	☽ ° ′	☿ ° ′	♀ ° ′	♂ ° ′	♃ ° ′	♄ ° ′	♅ ° ′	♆ ° ′	♇ ° ′
1 W	20 36 34.9	18N12.4	21S38.6	7S29.1	13N17.8	16N59.3	23N28.4	19S42.5	22S31.6	21S42.7	22N14.5	13N33.7
4 S	20 48 24.6	17 26.4	21 37.0	18 12.6	14 4.7	17 4.0	23 35.4	19 43.6	22 31.9	21 42.3	22 14.5	13 33.6
7 T	21 0 14.2	16 37.9	21 35.5	22 2.2	14 58.6	17 10.4	23 40.5	19 45.1	22 32.3	21 42.1	22 14.5	13 33.4
10 F	21 12 3.9	15 46.9	21 33.9	15 4.6	15 52.7	17 17.8	23 43.9	19 47.0	22 32.7	21 41.9	22 14.5	13 33.3
13 M	21 23 53.6	14 53.7	21 32.4	0N18.6	16 40.6	17 25.4	23 45.5	19 49.1	22 33.1	21 41.8	22 14.4	13 33.1
16 T	21 35 43.2	13 58.3	21 30.8	15 19.1	17 16.3	17 32.6	23 45.4	19 51.5	22 33.5	21 41.7	22 14.4	13 32.8
19 S	21 47 32.9	13 0.9	21 29.2	21 57.5	17 34.4	17 38.8	23 43.5	19 54.3	22 34.0	21 41.8	22 14.4	13 32.6
22 W	21 59 22.5	12 1.6	21 27.6	18 1.5	17 30.5	17 43.4	23 40.0	19 57.3	22 34.4	21 41.9	22 14.3	13 32.3
25 S	22 11 12.2	11 0.6	21 26.0	7 0.1	17 1.4	17 45.9	23 34.8	20 0.6	22 34.8	21 42.1	22 14.3	13 32.0
28 T	22 23 1.9	9 58.1	21 24.4	6S 8.3	16 5.9	17 45.8	23 28.1	20 4.1	22 35.3	21 42.3	22 14.2	13 31.6
31 F	22 34 51.5	8 54.1	21 22.7	17 8.4	14 45.2	17 42.8	23 19.9	20 7.9	22 35.7	21 42.6	22 14.2	13 31.3

SEPTEMBER 1900

LONGITUDE

DAY	EPHEMERIS SIDEREAL TIME h m s	☉ ° ′	☊ ° ′	☽ ° ′	☿ ° ′	♀ ° ′	♂ ° ′	♃ ° ′	♄ ° ′	♅ ° ′	♆ ° ′	♇ ° ′
1 S	22 38 48.1	8♍ 5.2	6♐17.6	22♏57.3	26♌10.9	23♋15.8	14♋13.2	2♐43.0	28♐26.1	8♐32.4	28♊59.2	17♊38.8
2 S	22 42 44.6	9 3.3	6 14.4	5♐14.7	28 3.7	24 4.8	14 51.1	2 48.9	28R26.0	8 33.2	29 0.2	17 39.2
3 M	22 46 41.2	10 1.4	6 11.3	17 51.0	29 57.7	24 54.5	15 28.9	2 55.0	28 26.0	8 34.0	29 1.2	17 39.5
4 T	22 50 37.7	10 59.6	6 8.1	0♑51.1	1♍52.7	25 44.9	16 6.6	3 1.2	28D26.1	8 34.9	29 2.1	17 39.8
5 W	22 54 34.3	11 57.7	6 4.9	14 19.1	3 48.3	26 36.0	16 44.3	3 7.6	28 26.3	8 35.8	29 3.1	17 40.1
6 T	22 58 30.8	12 55.9	6 1.7	28 17.2	5 44.3	27 27.8	17 21.8	3 14.1	28 26.5	8 36.8	29 3.9	17 40.3
7 F	23 2 27.4	13 54.1	5 58.6	12♒44.6	7 40.2	28 20.3	17 59.3	3 20.7	28 26.9	8 37.8	29 4.8	17 40.6
8 S	23 6 24.0	14 52.4	5 55.4	27 37.4	9 36.0	29 13.4	18 36.7	3 27.5	28 27.4	8 38.8	29 5.6	17 40.8
9 S	23 10 20.5	15 50.7	5 52.2	12♓47.9	11 31.5	0♌ 7.1	19 14.0	3 34.5	28 28.0	8 40.0	29 6.4	17 41.0
10 M	23 14 17.0	16 49.0	5 49.0	28 5.6	13 26.4	1 1.4	19 51.2	3 41.5	28 28.6	8 41.1	29 7.2	17 41.2
11 T	23 18 13.6	17 47.3	5 45.8	13♈19.1	15 20.8	1 56.3	20 28.3	3 48.8	28 29.4	8 42.3	29 7.9	17 41.3
12 W	23 22 10.2	18 45.7	5 42.7	28 18.4	17 14.4	2 51.8	21 5.3	3 56.1	28 30.3	8 43.6	29 8.6	17 41.5
13 T	23 26 6.7	19 44.1	5 39.5	12♉55.8	19 7.1	3 47.8	21 42.2	4 3.6	28 31.3	8 44.9	29 9.3	17 41.6
14 F	23 30 3.2	20 42.5	5 36.3	27 7.4	20 59.0	4 44.4	22 19.1	4 11.2	28 32.3	8 46.3	29 9.9	17 41.6
15 S	23 33 59.8	21 41.0	5 33.1	10♊52.3	22 50.0	5 41.4	22 55.8	4 19.0	28 33.5	8 47.7	29 10.5	17 41.7
16 S	23 37 56.4	22 39.5	5 29.9	24 12.1	24 40.0	6 38.9	23 32.5	4 26.9	28 34.7	8 49.2	29 11.1	17 41.8
17 M	23 41 52.9	23 38.1	5 26.8	7♋ 9.9	26 29.0	7 37.0	24 9.0	4 34.9	28 36.1	8 50.7	29 11.6	17 41.8
18 T	23 45 49.4	24 36.7	5 23.6	19 49.4	28 17.0	8 35.4	24 45.5	4 43.0	28 37.5	8 52.3	29 12.1	17R41.8
19 W	23 49 46.0	25 35.3	5 20.4	2♌14.2	0♎ 4.0	9 34.4	25 21.9	4 51.3	28 39.1	8 53.9	29 12.6	17 41.8
20 T	23 53 42.6	26 33.9	5 17.2	14 27.9	1 50.0	10 33.7	25 58.1	4 59.7	28 40.7	8 55.5	29 13.1	17 41.7
21 F	23 57 39.1	27 32.6	5 14.1	26 33.1	3 34.9	11 33.5	26 34.3	5 8.2	28 42.4	8 57.2	29 13.5	17 41.6
22 S	0 1 35.7	28 31.4	5 10.9	8♍32.2	5 18.9	12 33.7	27 10.4	5 16.9	28 44.3	8 59.0	29 13.8	17 41.6
23 S	0 5 32.2	29 30.1	5 7.7	20 26.9	7 1.9	13 34.3	27 46.3	5 25.6	28 46.2	9 0.8	29 14.2	17 41.4
24 M	0 9 28.8	0♎28.9	5 4.5	2♎18.7	8 44.0	14 35.2	28 22.1	5 34.5	28 48.2	9 2.6	29 14.5	17 41.3
25 T	0 13 25.3	1 27.8	5 1.3	14 9.1	10 25.1	15 36.5	28 57.9	5 43.5	28 50.3	9 4.5	29 14.8	17 41.2
26 W	0 17 21.9	2 26.6	4 58.2	25 59.7	12 5.2	16 38.2	29 33.5	5 52.7	28 52.5	9 6.4	29 15.0	17 41.0
27 T	0 21 18.5	3 25.5	4 55.0	7♏52.6	13 44.4	17 40.3	0♌ 9.0	6 1.9	28 54.8	9 8.4	29 15.2	17 40.8
28 F	0 25 15.0	4 24.4	4 51.8	19 50.4	15 22.7	18 42.6	0 44.4	6 11.2	28 57.2	9 10.4	29 15.4	17 40.6
29 S	0 29 11.5	5 23.4	4 48.6	1♐56.6	17 0.1	19 45.3	1 19.7	6 20.7	28 59.7	9 12.5	29 15.5	17 40.3
30 S	0 33 8.1	6 22.4	4 45.5	14 14.9	18 36.7	20 48.4	1 54.9	6 30.3	29 2.3	9 14.6	29 15.6	17 40.1

DECLINATION

DAY	SIDEREAL TIME	☉	☊	☽	☿	♀	♂	♃	♄	♅	♆	♇
1 S	22 38 48.1	8N32.5	21S22.2	19S37.6	14N13.3	17N41.1	23N16.8	20S 9.2	22S35.9	21S42.7	22N14.2	13N31.1
4 T	22 50 37.7	7 26.8	21 20.6	21 19.6	12 24.9	17 33.7	23 6.6	20 13.3	22 36.4	21 43.2	22 14.1	13 30.7
7 F	23 2 27.4	6 20.1	21 18.9	12 33.4	10 21.6	17 22.7	22 54.9	20 17.6	22 36.8	21 43.7	22 14.0	13 30.3
10 M	23 14 17.0	5 12.5	21 17.2	3N29.0	8 8.2	17 7.8	22 42.0	20 22.1	22 37.3	21 44.2	22 13.9	13 29.9
13 T	23 26 6.7	4 4.0	21 15.6	17 31.7	5 48.8	16 48.9	22 27.7	20 26.8	22 37.8	21 44.8	22 13.9	13 29.4
16 S	23 37 56.4	2 54.9	21 13.9	21 38.8	3 26.7	16 25.9	22 12.2	20 31.6	22 38.4	21 45.5	22 13.8	13 28.9
19 W	23 49 46.0	1 45.3	21 12.2	15 31.1	1 4.3	15 58.6	21 55.5	20 36.6	22 38.9	21 46.3	22 13.7	13 28.5
22 S	0 1 35.7	0 35.3	21 10.5	3 42.7	1S16.7	15 27.0	21 37.7	20 41.7	22 39.4	21 47.1	22 13.6	13 27.9
25 T	0 13 25.3	0S34.9	21 8.8	9S 7.8	3 35.0	14 51.3	21 18.9	20 46.9	22 39.9	21 48.0	22 13.5	13 27.4
28 F	0 25 15.0	1 45.2	21 7.0	18 51.4	5 49.5	14 11.4	20 59.1	20 52.2	22 40.4	21 48.9	22 13.4	13 26.9

OCTOBER 1900

LONGITUDE

DAY	SIDEREAL TIME	☉	☊	☽	☿	♀	♂	♃	♄	♅	♆	♇
1 M	0 37 4.7	7♎21.4	4♐42.3	26♐49.8	20♎12.4	21♌51.7	2♌30.0	6♐40.0	29♐ 5.0	9♐16.8	29♊15.7	17♊39.8
2 T	0 41 1.2	8 20.5	4 39.1	9♑45.8	21 47.3	22 55.3	3 4.9	6 49.7	29 7.7	9 18.9	29 15.7	17R39.5
3 W	0 44 57.8	9 19.5	4 35.9	23 6.9	23 21.3	23 59.3	3 39.7	6 59.6	29 10.6	9 21.2	29R15.7	17 39.2
4 T	0 48 54.3	10 18.6	4 32.7	6♒55.9	24 54.5	25 3.5	4 14.4	7 9.6	29 13.5	9 23.5	29 15.7	17 38.8
5 F	0 52 50.9	11 17.8	4 29.6	21 13.6	26 26.9	26 8.0	4 49.0	7 19.7	29 16.5	9 25.8	29 15.6	17 38.5
6 S	0 56 47.4	12 16.9	4 26.4	5♓57.7	27 58.5	27 12.8	5 23.5	7 29.9	29 19.6	9 28.1	29 15.5	17 38.1
7 S	1 0 44.0	13 16.1	4 23.2	21 2.4	29 29.3	28 17.9	5 57.8	7 40.2	29 22.8	9 30.5	29 15.4	17 37.7
8 M	1 4 40.5	14 15.4	4 20.0	6♈18.8	0♏59.3	29 23.2	6 32.0	7 50.6	29 26.1	9 33.0	29 15.2	17 37.3
9 T	1 8 37.1	15 14.6	4 16.9	21 36.3	2 28.5	0♍28.8	7 6.1	8 1.1	29 29.5	9 35.5	29 15.0	17 36.8
10 W	1 12 33.6	16 13.9	4 13.7	6♉43.7	3 56.9	1 34.6	7 40.1	8 11.6	29 32.9	9 38.0	29 14.8	17 36.3
11 T	1 16 30.2	17 13.3	4 10.5	21 32.2	5 24.5	2 40.7	8 14.0	8 22.3	29 36.5	9 40.5	29 14.5	17 35.9
12 F	1 20 26.7	18 12.6	4 7.3	5♊55.4	6 51.4	3 47.1	8 47.7	8 33.1	29 40.1	9 43.1	29 14.2	17 35.4
13 S	1 24 23.3	19 12.0	4 4.1	19 50.8	8 17.4	4 53.7	9 21.3	8 43.9	29 43.8	9 45.7	29 13.9	17 34.8
14 S	1 28 19.8	20 11.5	4 1.0	3♋18.5	9 42.5	6 0.5	9 54.7	8 54.9	29 47.6	9 48.4	29 13.5	17 34.3
15 M	1 32 16.4	21 11.0	3 57.8	16 20.7	11 6.8	7 7.5	10 28.1	9 5.9	29 51.4	9 51.1	29 13.1	17 33.7
16 T	1 36 13.0	22 10.5	3 54.6	29 1.1	12 30.2	8 14.8	11 1.2	9 17.0	29 55.4	9 53.9	29 12.7	17 33.1
17 W	1 40 9.5	23 10.1	3 51.4	11♌23.8	13 52.7	9 22.3	11 34.3	9 28.2	29 59.4	9 56.6	29 12.2	17 32.5
18 T	1 44 6.0	24 9.7	3 48.2	23 33.1	15 14.2	10 30.0	12 7.2	9 39.5	0♑ 3.5	9 59.4	29 11.7	17 31.9
19 F	1 48 2.6	25 9.3	3 45.1	5♍33.1	16 34.7	11 37.9	12 39.9	9 50.8	0 7.7	10 2.3	29 11.2	17 31.3
20 S	1 51 59.2	26 9.0	3 41.9	17 27.1	17 54.0	12 46.0	13 12.5	10 2.3	0 11.9	10 5.2	29 10.6	17 30.6
21 S	1 55 55.7	27 8.7	3 38.7	29 18.2	19 12.2	13 54.2	13 45.0	10 13.8	0 16.3	10 8.1	29 10.1	17 30.0
22 M	1 59 52.3	28 8.4	3 35.5	11♎ 8.7	20 29.2	15 2.7	14 17.3	10 25.4	0 20.7	10 11.0	29 9.4	17 29.3
23 T	2 3 48.8	29 8.2	3 32.4	23 0.9	21 44.8	16 11.3	14 49.4	10 37.1	0 25.1	10 14.0	29 8.8	17 28.5
24 W	2 7 45.4	0♏ 8.0	3 29.2	4♏56.3	22 58.9	17 20.2	15 21.4	10 48.8	0 29.7	10 17.0	29 8.1	17 27.8
25 T	2 11 41.9	1 7.9	3 26.0	16 56.8	24 11.5	18 29.2	15 53.2	11 0.6	0 34.3	10 20.0	29 7.4	17 27.1
26 F	2 15 38.5	2 7.8	3 22.8	29 4.1	25 22.3	19 38.3	16 24.8	11 12.5	0 39.0	10 23.1	29 6.6	17 26.3
27 S	2 19 35.0	3 7.7	3 19.7	11♐20.3	26 31.2	20 47.7	16 56.3	11 24.5	0 43.8	10 26.2	29 5.8	17 25.5
28 S	2 23 31.6	4 7.6	3 16.5	23 47.8	27 37.9	21 57.1	17 27.6	11 36.5	0 48.6	10 29.3	29 5.0	17 24.7
29 M	2 27 28.2	5 7.6	3 13.3	6♑29.5	28 42.3	23 6.8	17 58.7	11 48.6	0 53.6	10 32.4	29 4.2	17 23.9
30 T	2 31 24.7	6 7.6	3 10.1	19 28.3	29 44.1	24 16.6	18 29.7	12 0.8	0 58.5	10 35.6	29 3.3	17 23.1
31 W	2 35 21.3	7 7.6	3 6.9	2♒47.0	0♐43.0	25 26.5	19 0.4	12 13.0	1 3.6	10 38.8	29 2.4	17 22.3

DECLINATION

DAY	SIDEREAL TIME	☉	☊	☽	☿	♀	♂	♃	♄	♅	♆	♇
1 M	0 37 4.7	2S55.3	21S 5.3	21S22.0	7S59.4	13N27.4	20N38.5	20S57.6	22S40.9	21S49.9	22N13.3	13N26.4
4 T	0 48 54.3	4 5.1	21 3.6	14 6.2	10 4.2	12 39.5	20 17.0	21 3.0	22 41.4	21 50.9	22 13.2	13 25.8
7 S	1 0 44.0	5 14.4	21 1.8	0N55.3	12 3.2	11 47.7	19 54.7	21 8.5	22 41.9	21 52.0	22 13.1	13 25.3
10 W	1 12 33.6	6 23.2	21 0.1	15 53.7	13 55.9	10 52.3	19 31.8	21 13.9	22 42.3	21 53.2	22 13.0	13 24.7
13 S	1 24 23.3	7 31.2	20 58.3	21 32.0	15 41.7	9 53.3	19 8.3	21 19.4	22 42.8	21 54.4	22 12.9	13 24.2
16 T	1 36 13.0	8 38.3	20 56.5	16 8.5	17 19.9	8 51.1	18 44.3	21 24.9	22 43.2	21 55.6	22 12.8	13 23.6
19 F	1 48 2.6	9 44.4	20 54.7	4 40.2	18 49.7	7 45.9	18 19.8	21 30.4	22 43.6	21 56.9	22 12.7	13 23.1
22 M	1 59 52.3	10 49.1	20 52.9	8S 7.4	20 10.5	6 37.9	17 54.9	21 35.8	22 44.0	21 58.2	22 12.6	13 22.6
25 T	2 11 41.9	11 52.4	20 51.1	18 12.2	21 21.1	5 27.4	17 29.8	21 41.2	22 44.4	21 59.5	22 12.5	13 22.0
28 S	2 23 31.6	12 54.1	20 49.3	21 21.2	22 20.3	4 14.6	17 4.5	21 46.5	22 44.7	22 0.9	22 12.4	13 21.5
31 W	2 35 21.3	13 53.9	20 47.4	15 4.9	23 6.7	2 60.0	16 39.1	21 51.7	22 44.9	22 2.3	22 12.3	13 21.0

NOVEMBER 1900

LONGITUDE

DAY	EPHEMERIS SIDEREAL TIME h m s	☉ ° ′	☊ ° ′	☽ ° ′	☿ ° ′	♀ ° ′	♂ ° ′	♃ ° ′	♄ ° ′	♅ ° ′	♆ ° ′	♇ ° ′
1 T	2 39 17.8	8♏ 7.6	3♐ 3.8	16♒27.9	1♐38.7	26♍36.6	19♌31.0	12♐25.3	1♑ 8.7	10♐42.0	29♊ 1.5	17♊21.4
2 F	2 43 14.4	9 7.7	3 0.6	0♓31.9	2 30.8	27 46.8	20 1.4	12 37.6	1 13.9	10 45.3	29R 0.6	17R20.5
3 S	2 47 10.9	10 7.8	2 57.4	14 58.2	3 18.9	28 57.2	20 31.7	12 50.0	1 19.1	10 48.6	28 59.6	17 19.7
4 S	2 51 7.5	11 8.0	2 54.2	29 43.2	4 2.4	0♎ 7.7	21 1.7	13 2.5	1 24.4	10 51.9	28 58.6	17 18.8
5 M	2 55 4.0	12 8.1	2 51.1	14♈41.2	4 41.0	1 18.3	21 31.5	13 15.0	1 29.8	10 55.2	28 57.6	17 17.8
6 T	2 59 0.6	13 8.3	2 47.9	29 44.2	5 14.0	2 29.1	22 1.1	13 27.6	1 35.2	10 58.5	28 56.5	17 16.9
7 W	3 2 57.1	14 8.5	2 44.7	14♉43.2	5 40.7	3 40.0	22 30.6	13 40.2	1 40.7	11 1.9	28 55.4	17 16.0
8 T	3 6 53.7	15 8.7	2 41.5	29 29.4	6 0.7	4 51.0	22 59.8	13 52.9	1 46.2	11 5.3	28 54.3	17 15.0
9 F	3 10 50.3	16 9.0	2 38.4	13♊56.0	6 13.1	6 2.1	23 28.9	14 5.6	1 51.8	11 8.7	28 53.2	17 14.1
10 S	3 14 46.8	17 9.3	2 35.2	27 58.2	6 17.2	7 13.4	23 57.7	14 18.4	1 57.4	11 12.1	28 52.0	17 13.1
11 S	3 18 43.4	18 9.6	2 32.0	11♋34.0	6R12.5	8 24.8	24 26.3	14 31.2	2 3.1	11 15.6	28 50.8	17 12.1
12 M	3 22 39.9	19 10.0	2 28.8	24 44.0	5 58.2	9 36.3	24 54.7	14 44.1	2 8.9	11 19.0	28 49.6	17 11.1
13 T	3 26 36.5	20 10.4	2 25.6	7♌30.3	5 34.0	10 47.9	25 22.8	14 57.0	2 14.7	11 22.5	28 48.4	17 10.1
14 W	3 30 33.0	21 10.8	2 22.5	19 56.6	4 59.6	11 59.7	25 50.8	15 10.0	2 20.6	11 26.0	28 47.1	17 9.1
15 T	3 34 29.6	22 11.3	2 19.3	2♍ 7.1	4 14.9	13 11.5	26 18.5	15 23.0	2 26.5	11 29.5	28 45.8	17 8.0
16 F	3 38 26.1	23 11.8	2 16.1	14 6.4	3 20.4	14 23.5	26 45.9	15 36.0	2 32.5	11 33.0	28 44.5	17 7.0
17 S	3 42 22.7	24 12.3	2 12.9	25 58.9	2 16.9	15 35.5	27 13.2	15 49.1	2 38.5	11 36.6	28 43.2	17 5.9
18 S	3 46 19.3	25 12.9	2 9.8	7♎48.9	1 5.7	16 47.7	27 40.1	16 2.3	2 44.6	11 40.1	28 41.9	17 4.9
19 M	3 50 15.8	26 13.4	2 6.6	19 40.1	29♏48.6	17 59.9	28 6.8	16 15.4	2 50.7	11 43.7	28 40.5	17 3.8
20 T	3 54 12.3	27 14.1	2 3.4	1♏35.6	28 28.0	19 12.2	28 33.3	16 28.6	2 56.9	11 47.3	28 39.1	17 2.7
21 W	3 58 8.9	28 14.7	2 0.2	13 38.0	27 6.4	20 24.6	28 59.5	16 41.9	3 3.1	11 50.9	28 37.7	17 1.6
22 T	4 2 5.5	29 15.4	1 57.0	25 49.4	25 46.5	21 37.2	29 25.4	16 55.2	3 9.3	11 54.5	28 36.3	17 0.6
23 F	4 6 2.1	0♐16.0	1 53.9	8♐11.3	24 31.0	22 49.7	29 51.0	17 8.5	3 15.6	11 58.1	28 34.8	16 59.5
24 S	4 9 58.6	1 16.8	1 50.7	20 44.8	23 22.3	24 2.4	0♍16.3	17 21.8	3 22.0	12 1.7	28 33.3	16 58.3
25 S	4 13 55.1	2 17.5	1 47.5	3♑30.9	22 22.3	25 15.1	0 41.4	17 35.2	3 28.3	12 5.4	28 31.9	16 57.2
26 M	4 17 51.7	3 18.2	1 44.3	16 30.2	21 32.6	26 28.0	1 6.1	17 48.6	3 34.8	12 9.0	28 30.4	16 56.1
27 T	4 21 48.3	4 19.0	1 41.2	29 43.3	20 54.0	27 40.9	1 30.6	18 2.0	3 41.2	12 12.7	28 28.9	16 55.0
28 W	4 25 44.8	5 19.8	1 38.0	13♒10.9	20 27.0	28 53.8	1 54.8	18 15.4	3 47.7	12 16.3	28 27.3	16 53.8
29 T	4 29 41.4	6 20.6	1 34.8	26 53.1	20 11.5	0♏ 6.9	2 18.6	18 28.9	3 54.3	12 20.0	28 25.8	16 52.7
30 F	4 33 37.9	7 21.4	1 31.6	10♓50.0	20 7.2	1 19.9	2 42.1	18 42.4	4 0.8	12 23.6	28 24.2	16 51.6

DECLINATION

DAY	EPHEMERIS SIDEREAL TIME h m s	☉ ° ′	☊ ° ′	☽ ° ′	☿ ° ′	♀ ° ′	♂ ° ′	♃ ° ′	♄ ° ′	♅ ° ′	♆ ° ′	♇ ° ′
1 T	2 39 17.8	14S13.4	20S46.8	11S 4.7	23S19.0	2N34.7	16N30.6	21S53.5	22S45.0	22S 2.7	22N12.2	13N20.8
4 S	2 51 7.5	15 10.5	20 45.0	4N 9.1	23 45.2	1 17.9	16 5.2	21 58.6	22 45.2	22 4.1	22 12.1	13 20.3
7 W	3 2 57.1	16 5.4	20 43.1	17 44.6	23 52.9	0S 0.1	15 39.8	22 3.6	22 45.4	22 5.6	22 12.0	13 19.8
10 S	3 14 46.8	16 57.9	20 41.3	21 6.2	23 38.4	1 19.1	15 14.6	22 8.4	22 45.5	22 7.0	22 11.9	13 19.4
13 T	3 26 36.5	17 47.8	20 39.4	13 44.6	22 56.7	2 38.7	14 49.6	22 13.2	22 45.6	22 8.5	22 11.9	13 18.9
16 F	3 38 26.1	18 34.9	20 37.5	1 29.2	21 44.0	3 58.6	14 25.1	22 17.8	22 45.6	22 9.9	22 11.8	13 18.5
19 M	3 50 15.8	19 19.0	20 35.6	10S59.0	20 3.0	5 18.5	14 1.0	22 22.2	22 45.5	22 11.4	22 11.7	13 18.1
22 T	4 2 5.5	20 0.1	20 33.7	19 45.5	18 10.0	6 38.0	13 37.4	22 26.5	22 45.4	22 12.9	22 11.6	13 17.7
25 S	4 13 55.1	20 37.8	20 31.8	20 37.0	16 32.5	7 56.7	13 14.5	22 30.6	22 45.3	22 14.4	22 11.5	13 17.4
28 W	4 25 44.8	21 12.0	20 29.9	12 3.4	15 33.0	9 14.4	12 52.4	22 34.6	22 45.0	22 15.8	22 11.4	13 17.1

DECEMBER 1900

LONGITUDE

DAY	EPHEMERIS SIDEREAL TIME h m s	☉ ° ′	☊ ° ′	☽ ° ′	☿ ° ′	♀ ° ′	♂ ° ′	♃ ° ′	♄ ° ′	♅ ° ′	♆ ° ′	♇ ° ′
1 S	4 37 34.5	8♐22.2	1♐28.5	25♓ 0.6	20♏13.6	2♏33.1	3♍ 5.3	18♐55.9	4♑ 7.4	12♐27.3	28♊22.7	16♊50.4
2 S	4 41 31.1	9 23.1	1 25.3	9♈23.2	20D29.7	3 46.3	3 28.1	19 9.4	4 14.0	12 31.0	28R21.1	16R49.3
3 M	4 45 27.6	10 23.9	1 22.1	23 54.6	20 54.8	4 59.6	3 50.7	19 23.0	4 20.7	12 34.7	28 19.5	16 48.1
4 T	4 49 24.1	11 24.8	1 18.9	8♉30.4	21 28.0	6 13.0	4 12.8	19 36.6	4 27.4	12 38.3	28 17.9	16 47.0
5 W	4 53 20.7	12 25.7	1 15.7	23 5.1	22 8.5	7 26.4	4 34.7	19 50.1	4 34.1	12 42.0	28 16.3	16 45.8
6 T	4 57 17.3	13 26.6	1 12.6	7♊32.7	22 55.5	8 39.8	4 56.2	20 3.7	4 40.9	12 45.7	28 14.6	16 44.7
7 F	5 1 13.8	14 27.5	1 9.4	21 47.4	23 48.0	9 53.4	5 17.3	20 17.3	4 47.7	12 49.4	28 13.0	16 43.5
8 S	5 5 10.4	15 28.5	1 6.2	5♋44.3	24 45.6	11 6.9	5 38.0	20 31.0	4 54.5	12 53.0	28 11.3	16 42.3
9 S	5 9 6.9	16 29.4	1 3.0	19 20.1	25 47.5	12 20.6	5 58.4	20 44.6	5 1.3	12 56.7	28 9.7	16 41.2
10 M	5 13 3.5	17 30.4	0 59.9	2♌33.3	26 53.2	13 34.3	6 18.3	20 58.2	5 8.1	13 0.4	28 8.0	16 40.0
11 T	5 17 0.1	18 31.4	0 56.7	15 24.2	28 2.2	14 48.0	6 37.9	21 11.9	5 15.0	13 4.1	28 6.4	16 38.9
12 W	5 20 56.6	19 32.4	0 53.5	27 54.9	29 14.1	16 1.8	6 57.1	21 25.5	5 21.9	13 7.7	28 4.7	16 37.7
13 T	5 24 53.2	20 33.4	0 50.3	10♍ 8.6	0♐28.5	17 15.6	7 15.8	21 39.2	5 28.8	13 11.4	28 3.0	16 36.5
14 F	5 28 49.7	21 34.4	0 47.2	22 9.6	1 45.0	18 29.5	7 34.1	21 52.9	5 35.7	13 15.0	28 1.3	16 35.4
15 S	5 32 46.3	22 35.5	0 44.0	4♎ 2.6	3 3.4	19 43.5	7 52.0	22 6.5	5 42.7	13 18.7	27 59.6	16 34.2
16 S	5 36 42.9	23 36.6	0 40.8	15 52.5	4 23.5	20 57.5	8 9.4	22 20.2	5 49.7	13 22.3	27 57.9	16 33.1
17 M	5 40 39.4	24 37.7	0 37.6	27 44.3	5 45.0	22 11.5	8 26.4	22 33.9	5 56.7	13 25.9	27 56.2	16 31.9
18 T	5 44 36.0	25 38.8	0 34.4	9♏42.3	7 7.7	23 25.6	8 42.9	22 47.5	6 3.7	13 29.6	27 54.5	16 30.8
19 W	5 48 32.5	26 39.9	0 31.3	21 50.4	8 31.6	24 39.7	8 58.9	23 1.2	6 10.7	13 33.2	27 52.8	16 29.6
20 T	5 52 29.1	27 41.0	0 28.1	4♐11.9	9 56.3	25 53.8	9 14.4	23 14.9	6 17.7	13 36.8	27 51.1	16 28.5
21 F	5 56 25.6	28 42.2	0 24.9	16 48.9	11 22.0	27 8.0	9 29.4	23 28.5	6 24.8	13 40.4	27 49.4	16 27.4
22 S	6 0 22.2	29 43.3	0 21.7	29 42.4	12 48.4	28 22.2	9 44.0	23 42.2	6 31.8	13 43.9	27 47.7	16 26.2
23 S	6 4 18.7	0♑44.5	0 18.6	12♑52.2	14 15.4	29 36.4	9 57.9	23 55.8	6 38.9	13 47.5	27 46.0	16 25.1
24 M	6 8 15.3	1 45.6	0 15.4	26 17.4	15 43.1	0♐50.7	10 11.4	24 9.5	6 45.9	13 51.0	27 44.3	16 24.0
25 T	6 12 11.9	2 46.8	0 12.2	9♒55.8	17 11.4	2 5.0	10 24.3	24 23.1	6 53.0	13 54.6	27 42.6	16 22.9
26 W	6 16 8.4	3 47.9	0 9.0	23 44.9	18 40.1	3 19.3	10 36.7	24 36.7	7 0.1	13 58.1	27 40.9	16 21.8
27 T	6 20 5.0	4 49.1	0 5.9	7♓42.2	20 9.3	4 33.7	10 48.5	24 50.3	7 7.2	14 1.6	27 39.2	16 20.7
28 F	6 24 1.5	5 50.3	0 2.7	21 45.3	21 38.9	5 48.0	10 59.7	25 3.9	7 14.3	14 5.1	27 37.5	16 19.6
29 S	6 27 58.1	6 51.4	29♏59.5	5♈52.2	23 9.0	7 2.4	11 10.3	25 17.4	7 21.3	14 8.6	27 35.9	16 18.5
30 S	6 31 54.7	7 52.6	29 56.3	20 1.2	24 39.4	8 16.8	11 20.4	25 31.0	7 28.4	14 12.0	27 34.2	16 17.4
31 M	6 35 51.2	8 53.8	29 53.2	4♉10.7	26 10.3	9 31.3	11 29.9	25 44.5	7 35.5	14 15.5	27 32.5	16 16.4

DECLINATION

DAY	EPHEMERIS SIDEREAL TIME h m s	☉ ° ′	☊ ° ′	☽ ° ′	☿ ° ′	♀ ° ′	♂ ° ′	♃ ° ′	♄ ° ′	♅ ° ′	♆ ° ′	♇ ° ′
1 S	4 37 34.5	21S42.7	20S28.0	2N28.9	15S17.2	10S30.6	12N31.1	22S38.3	22S44.7	22S17.3	22N11.3	13N16.8
4 T	4 49 24.1	22 9.6	20 26.0	16 19.8	15 37.8	11 45.0	12 10.9	22 41.8	22 44.4	22 18.7	22 11.3	13 16.5
7 F	5 1 13.8	22 32.7	20 24.1	21 23.5	16 23.4	12 57.3	11 51.6	22 45.2	22 43.9	22 20.2	22 11.2	13 16.3
10 M	5 13 3.5	22 51.8	20 22.1	15 6.8	17 23.5	14 7.0	11 33.6	22 48.4	22 43.4	22 21.6	22 11.1	13 16.1
13 T	5 24 53.2	23 6.9	20 20.1	2 56.6	18 30.2	15 13.9	11 16.9	22 51.3	22 42.8	22 23.0	22 11.1	13 15.9
16 S	5 36 42.9	23 17.8	20 18.2	9S44.0	19 37.9	16 17.6	11 1.7	22 54.0	22 42.2	22 24.4	22 11.0	13 15.8
19 W	5 48 32.5	23 24.5	20 16.2	19 6.5	20 42.8	17 17.7	10 48.0	22 56.5	22 41.5	22 25.7	22 10.9	13 15.7
22 S	6 0 22.2	23 27.0	20 14.2	20 59.5	21 42.1	18 13.9	10 36.0	22 58.8	22 40.7	22 27.1	22 10.9	13 15.6
25 T	6 12 11.9	23 25.3	20 12.2	13 6.0	22 34.1	19 5.8	10 25.9	23 0.9	22 39.9	22 28.4	22 10.8	13 15.6
28 F	6 24 1.5	23 19.3	20 10.2	1N12.4	23 17.4	19 53.1	10 17.7	23 2.8	22 39.0	22 29.6	22 10.8	13 15.6
31 M	6 35 51.2	23 9.1	20 8.2	15 9.0	23 50.9	20 35.5	10 11.6	23 4.4	22 38.0	22 30.9	22 10.7	13 15.6

JANUARY 1901

DAY	EPHEMERIS SIDEREAL TIME	☉	☊	☽	☿	♀	♂	♃	♄	♅	♆	♇
	h m s	° ′	° ′	° ′	° ′	° ′	° ′	° ′	° ′	° ′	° ′	° ′
						LONGITUDE						
1 T	6 39 47.8	9♑54.9	29♏50.0	18♉19.0	27♐41.5	10♐45.7	11♍38.7	25♐58.0	7♑42.6	14♐18.9	27♊30.9	16♊15.3
2 W	6 43 44.3	10 56.1	29 46.8	2♊24.2	29 13.1	12 0.2	11 46.9	26 11.5	7 49.7	14 22.3	27R29.2	16R14.3
3 T	6 47 40.9	11 57.2	29 43.6	16 23.5	0♑45.0	13 14.7	11 54.5	26 24.9	7 56.8	14 25.6	27 27.6	16 13.2
4 F	6 51 37.4	12 58.3	29 40.4	0♋13.9	2 17.4	14 29.2	12 1.4	26 38.3	8 3.8	14 29.0	27 25.9	16 12.2
5 S	6 55 34.0	13 59.5	29 37.3	13 52.3	3 50.1	15 43.8	12 7.7	26 51.7	8 10.9	14 32.3	27 24.3	16 11.2
6 S	6 59 30.6	15 0.6	29 34.1	27 15.5	5 23.2	16 58.3	12 13.3	27 5.1	8 18.0	14 35.6	27 22.7	16 10.2
7 M	7 3 27.1	16 1.8	29 30.9	10♌21.6	6 56.6	18 12.9	12 18.2	27 18.5	8 25.0	14 38.9	27 21.1	16 9.2
8 T	7 7 23.7	17 2.9	29 27.7	23 9.6	8 30.5	19 27.5	12 22.4	27 31.8	8 32.0	14 42.1	27 19.5	16 8.2
9 W	7 11 20.2	18 4.0	29 24.6	5♍40.0	10 4.8	20 42.1	12 26.0	27 45.1	8 39.1	14 45.4	27 18.0	16 7.3
10 T	7 15 16.8	19 5.2	29 21.4	17 54.5	11 39.5	21 56.8	12 28.8	27 58.3	8 46.1	14 48.6	27 16.4	16 6.3
11 F	7 19 13.3	20 6.3	29 18.2	29 56.4	13 14.7	23 11.4	12 30.9	28 11.5	8 53.1	14 51.8	27 14.8	16 5.4
12 S	7 23 9.9	21 7.4	29 15.0	11♎49.7	14 50.3	24 26.1	12 32.2	28 24.7	9 0.1	14 54.9	27 13.3	16 4.4
13 S	7 27 6.5	22 8.6	29 11.9	23 39.2	16 26.4	25 40.8	12 32.8	28 37.9	9 7.1	14 58.0	27 11.8	16 3.5
14 M	7 31 3.0	23 9.7	29 8.7	5♏30.2	18 2.9	26 55.5	12R32.6	28 51.0	9 14.0	15 1.1	27 10.3	16 2.6
15 T	7 34 59.6	24 10.8	29 5.5	17 28.1	19 40.0	28 10.2	12 31.7	29 4.0	9 21.0	15 4.2	27 8.8	16 1.7
16 W	7 38 56.1	25 11.9	29 2.3	29 38.0	21 17.6	29 24.9	12 30.0	29 17.1	9 27.9	15 7.2	27 7.4	16 0.9
17 T	7 42 52.7	26 13.1	28 59.1	12♐4.4	22 55.7	0♑39.6	12 27.5	29 30.0	9 34.8	15 10.2	27 5.9	16 0.0
18 F	7 46 49.2	27 14.2	28 56.0	24 50.8	24 34.3	1 54.4	12 24.3	29 43.0	9 41.7	15 13.2	27 4.5	15 59.2
19 S	7 50 45.8	28 15.3	28 52.8	7♑59.3	26 13.5	3 9.1	12 20.2	29 55.9	9 48.5	15 16.2	27 3.1	15 58.4
20 S	7 54 42.4	29 16.4	28 49.6	21 30.1	27 53.2	4 23.9	12 15.3	0♑8.7	9 55.4	15 19.1	27 1.7	15 57.5
21 M	7 58 38.9	0♒17.5	28 46.4	5♒21.0	29 33.5	5 38.7	12 9.6	0 21.5	10 2.2	15 21.9	27 0.3	15 56.7
22 T	8 2 35.5	1 18.5	28 43.3	19 28.4	1♒14.4	6 53.4	12 3.1	0 34.2	10 9.0	15 24.8	26 59.0	15 56.0
23 W	8 6 32.0	2 19.6	28 40.1	3♓46.7	2 55.9	8 8.2	11 55.9	0 46.9	10 15.7	15 27.6	26 57.6	15 55.2
24 T	8 10 28.6	3 20.6	28 36.9	18 10.0	4 38.0	9 23.0	11 47.8	0 59.6	10 22.4	15 30.3	26 56.3	15 54.5
25 F	8 14 25.1	4 21.7	28 33.7	2♈32.9	6 20.7	10 37.8	11 38.9	1 12.2	10 29.1	15 33.1	26 55.0	15 53.7
26 S	8 18 21.7	5 22.7	28 30.6	16 51.0	8 4.0	11 52.6	11 29.2	1 24.7	10 35.8	15 35.8	26 53.8	15 53.0
27 S	8 22 18.2	6 23.7	28 27.4	1♉1.3	9 47.8	13 7.4	11 18.7	1 37.1	10 42.4	15 38.4	26 52.5	15 52.3
28 M	8 26 14.8	7 24.6	28 24.2	15 2.6	11 32.2	14 22.2	11 7.5	1 49.5	10 49.0	15 41.1	26 51.3	15 51.7
29 T	8 30 11.3	8 25.6	28 21.0	28 54.5	13 17.1	15 37.0	10 55.4	2 1.9	10 55.6	15 43.6	26 50.1	15 51.0
30 W	8 34 7.9	9 26.5	28 17.8	12♊37.0	15 2.5	16 51.8	10 42.6	2 14.2	11 2.1	15 46.2	26 49.0	15 50.4
31 T	8 38 4.5	10 27.4	28 14.7	26 10.4	16 48.3	18 6.6	10 29.1	2 26.4	11 8.6	15 48.7	26 47.8	15 49.8
						DECLINATION						
2 W	6 43 44.3	23 0.1	20 6.8	20N33.3	24 7.3	21 0.9	10 8.7	23 5.4	22 37.3	22 31.7	22 10.7	13 15.7
5 S	6 55 34.0	22 42.9	20 4.8	19 14.9	24 22.7	21 34.5	10 6.3	23 6.7	22 36.2	22 32.9	22 10.7	13 15.8
8 T	7 7 23.7	22 21.8	20 2.7	8 59.6	24 26.3	22 2.6	10 6.2	23 7.8	22 35.1	22 34.0	22 10.6	13 15.9
11 F	7 19 13.3	21 56.7	20 0.7	4S 4.8	24 17.6	22 24.8	10 8.6	23 8.7	22 33.9	22 35.1	22 10.6	13 16.1
14 M	7 31 3.0	21 27.7	19 58.6	15 24.4	23 56.2	22 41.0	10 13.5	23 9.3	22 32.6	22 36.2	22 10.6	13 16.4
17 T	7 42 52.7	20 55.0	19 56.5	21 13.4	23 21.6	22 51.0	10 21.0	23 9.8	22 31.3	22 37.3	22 10.6	13 16.6
20 S	7 54 42.4	20 18.7	19 54.4	17 48.8	22 33.6	22 54.9	10 31.2	23 10.0	22 30.0	22 38.3	22 10.6	13 16.9
23 W	8 6 32.0	19 39.0	19 52.3	5 25.2	21 31.7	22 52.5	10 43.9	23 10.1	22 28.6	22 39.2	22 10.6	13 17.3
26 S	8 18 21.7	18 56.0	19 50.2	9N47.4	20 16.0	22 43.9	10 59.2	23 10.0	22 27.2	22 40.1	22 10.6	13 17.7
29 T	8 30 11.3	18 9.9	19 48.1	19 57.6	18 46.3	22 29.0	11 16.8	23 9.8	22 25.7	22 41.0	22 10.7	13 18.1

FEBRUARY 1901

DAY	EPHEMERIS SIDEREAL TIME	☉	☊	☽	☿	♀	♂	♃	♄	♅	♆	♇
						LONGITUDE						
1 F	8 42 1.0	11♒28.3	28♏11.5	9♋34.3	18♒34.5	19♑21.4	10♍14.8	2♑38.5	11♑15.1	15♐51.1	26♊46.7	15♊49.2
2 S	8 45 57.6	12 29.1	28 8.3	22 48.0	20 21.1	20 36.2	9R59.8	2 50.6	11 21.5	15 53.6	26R45.6	15R48.6
3 S	8 49 54.1	13 30.0	28 5.1	5♌50.4	22 7.8	21 51.0	9 44.0	3 2.6	11 27.9	15 55.9	26 44.6	15 48.0
4 M	8 53 50.7	14 30.8	28 2.0	18 40.3	23 54.6	23 5.8	9 27.6	3 14.5	11 34.2	15 58.3	26 43.5	15 47.5
5 T	8 57 47.2	15 31.6	27 58.8	1♍16.8	25 41.4	24 20.6	9 10.5	3 26.4	11 40.5	16 0.6	26 42.5	15 47.0
6 W	9 1 43.8	16 32.4	27 55.6	13 39.9	27 28.0	25 35.4	8 52.8	3 38.2	11 46.8	16 2.8	26 41.5	15 46.5
7 T	9 5 40.4	17 33.1	27 52.4	25 50.3	29 14.2	26 50.2	8 34.4	3 50.0	11 53.0	16 5.1	26 40.6	15 46.0
8 F	9 9 36.9	18 33.9	27 49.3	7♎49.9	0♓59.7	28 5.0	8 15.3	4 1.6	11 59.2	16 7.2	26 39.7	15 45.6
9 S	9 13 33.4	19 34.6	27 46.1	19 41.9	2 44.3	29 19.8	7 55.7	4 13.2	12 5.3	16 9.3	26 38.8	15 45.1
10 S	9 17 30.0	20 35.3	27 42.9	1♏30.3	4 27.6	0♒34.6	7 35.6	4 24.7	12 11.4	16 11.4	26 37.9	15 44.7
11 M	9 21 26.6	21 36.0	27 39.7	13 19.7	6 9.3	1 49.5	7 14.9	4 36.1	12 17.4	16 13.5	26 37.1	15 44.3
12 T	9 25 23.1	22 36.7	27 36.5	25 15.7	7 48.9	3 4.3	6 53.7	4 47.4	12 23.4	16 15.5	26 36.3	15 43.9
13 W	9 29 19.7	23 37.3	27 33.4	7♐23.6	9 26.0	4 19.1	6 32.1	4 58.6	12 29.3	16 17.4	26 35.5	15 43.6
14 T	9 33 16.2	24 38.0	27 30.2	19 49.1	11 0.1	5 33.9	6 10.1	5 9.8	12 35.2	16 19.3	26 34.8	15 43.3
15 F	9 37 12.8	25 38.6	27 27.0	2♑36.9	12 30.5	6 48.7	5 47.6	5 20.9	12 41.0	16 21.2	26 34.0	15 42.9
16 S	9 41 9.3	26 39.2	27 23.8	15 50.4	13 56.7	8 3.6	5 24.9	5 31.9	12 46.8	16 23.0	26 33.4	15 42.7
17 S	9 45 5.9	27 39.7	27 20.7	29 31.1	15 18.1	9 18.4	5 1.8	5 42.8	12 52.5	16 24.7	26 32.7	15 42.4
18 M	9 49 2.4	28 40.3	27 17.5	13♒37.9	16 33.8	10 33.2	4 38.5	5 53.5	12 58.2	16 26.4	26 32.1	15 42.1
19 T	9 52 59.0	29 40.8	27 14.3	28 6.7	17 43.4	11 48.0	4 14.9	6 4.3	13 3.8	16 28.1	26 31.5	15 41.9
20 W	9 56 55.6	0♓41.3	27 11.1	12♓50.7	18 46.0	13 2.8	3 51.2	6 14.9	13 9.3	16 29.7	26 30.9	15 41.7
21 T	10 0 52.1	1 41.8	27 7.9	27 41.5	19 41.1	14 17.6	3 27.4	6 25.4	13 14.8	16 31.3	26 30.4	15 41.5
22 F	10 4 48.7	2 42.2	27 4.8	12♈30.4	20 28.1	15 32.4	3 3.5	6 35.8	13 20.2	16 32.8	26 29.9	15 41.4
23 S	10 8 45.2	3 42.6	27 1.6	27 10.1	21 6.3	16 47.2	2 39.6	6 46.1	13 25.6	16 34.2	26 29.5	15 41.2
24 S	10 12 41.8	4 43.0	26 58.4	11♉35.4	21 35.3	18 1.9	2 15.7	6 56.3	13 30.9	16 35.6	26 29.0	15 41.1
25 M	10 16 38.3	5 43.3	26 55.2	25 43.6	21 54.9	19 16.7	1 51.9	7 6.4	13 36.2	16 37.0	26 28.7	15 41.0
26 T	10 20 34.9	6 43.6	26 52.1	9♊34.1	22 4.7	20 31.5	1 28.3	7 16.4	13 41.3	16 38.3	26 28.3	15 41.0
27 W	10 24 31.4	7 43.9	26 48.9	23 7.7	22 4.8	21 46.2	1 4.7	7 26.3	13 46.4	16 39.6	26 28.0	15 40.9
28 T	10 28 28.0	8 44.2	26 45.7	6♋26.1	21R55.2	23 0.9	0 41.4	7 36.1	13 51.5	16 40.8	26 27.7	15 40.9
						DECLINATION						
1 F	8 42 1.0	17S20.9	19S46.0	19N50.6	17S 3.1	22S 7.9	11N36.7	23S 9.3	22S24.3	22S41.8	22N10.7	13N18.5
4 M	8 53 50.7	16 29.2	19 43.9	10 32.3	15 6.9	21 40.9	11 58.5	23 8.7	22 22.8	22 42.6	22 10.7	13 19.0
7 T	9 5 40.4	15 34.8	19 41.7	2S25.2	12 59.3	21 7.9	12 21.9	23 8.0	22 21.2	22 43.3	22 10.8	13 19.6
10 S	9 17 30.0	14 38.1	19 39.6	14 5.5	10 43.0	20 29.3	12 46.7	23 7.1	22 19.7	22 44.0	22 10.8	13 20.1
13 W	9 29 19.7	13 39.2	19 37.4	20 42.5	8 22.4	19 45.2	13 12.4	23 6.1	22 18.2	22 44.7	22 10.9	13 20.7
16 S	9 41 9.3	12 38.2	19 35.3	18 46.6	6 3.8	18 55.9	13 38.6	23 5.0	22 16.6	22 45.3	22 11.0	13 21.3
19 T	9 52 59.0	11 35.4	19 33.1	7 26.1	3 56.2	18 1.7	14 4.6	23 3.8	22 15.1	22 45.8	22 11.1	13 21.9
22 F	10 4 48.7	10 30.9	19 30.9	8N 9.2	2 9.9	17 2.9	14 30.2	23 2.5	22 13.6	22 46.3	22 11.2	13 22.6
25 M	10 16 38.3	9 25.0	19 28.7	19 14.8	0 55.2	15 59.7	14 54.6	23 1.1	22 12.1	22 46.8	22 11.3	13 23.3
28 T	10 28 28.0	8 17.9	19 26.5	20 2.4	0 20.5	14 52.5	15 17.6	22 59.6	22 10.6	22 47.2	22 11.4	13 24.0

MARCH 1901

DAY	EPHEMERIS SIDEREAL TIME	☉	☊	☾	☿	♀	♂	♃	♄	♅	♆	♇
	h m s	° ′	° ′	° ′	° ′	° ′	° ′	° ′	° ′	° ′	° ′	° ′
						LONGITUDE						
1 F	10 32 24.5	9♓44.4	26♏42.5	19♋31.0	21♓36.4	24♒15.7	0♍18.4	7♑45.7	13♑56.5	16♐41.9	26♊27.4	15♊40.9
2 S	10 36 21.1	10 44.5	26 39.3	2♌23.9	21R 8.7	25 30.4	29♌55.6	7 55.3	14 1.4	16 43.0	26R27.2	15D40.9
3 S	10 40 17.6	11 44.7	26 36.2	15 5.5	20 32.9	26 45.1	29R33.2	8 4.7	14 6.2	16 44.1	26 27.0	15 41.0
4 M	10 44 14.2	12 44.8	26 33.0	27 36.7	19 49.9	27 59.8	29 11.1	8 14.0	14 11.0	16 45.1	26 26.9	15 41.0
5 T	10 48 10.7	13 44.8	26 29.8	9♍57.8	19 0.9	29 14.5	28 49.5	8 23.3	14 15.7	16 46.0	26 26.7	15 41.1
6 W	10 52 7.3	14 44.9	26 26.6	22 9.2	18 7.0	0♓29.2	28 28.3	8 32.4	14 20.3	16 46.9	26 26.7	15 41.2
7 T	10 56 3.9	15 44.9	26 23.5	4♎11.7	17 9.6	1 43.9	28 7.6	8 41.3	14 24.9	16 47.8	26 26.6	15 41.4
8 F	11 0 0.4	16 44.9	26 20.3	16 6.7	16 10.1	2 58.5	27 47.3	8 50.2	14 29.3	16 48.5	26 26.6	15 41.5
9 S	11 3 56.9	17 44.8	26 17.1	27 56.4	15 10.0	4 13.2	27 27.6	8 58.9	14 33.7	16 49.3	26D26.6	15 41.7
10 S	11 7 53.5	18 44.8	26 13.9	9♏43.8	14 10.5	5 27.9	27 8.5	9 7.5	14 38.1	16 50.0	26 26.6	15 41.9
11 M	11 11 50.1	19 44.7	26 10.7	21 32.7	13 12.9	6 42.5	26 50.0	9 16.0	14 42.3	16 50.6	26 26.7	15 42.1
12 T	11 15 46.6	20 44.5	26 7.6	3♐27.6	12 18.4	7 57.2	26 32.1	9 24.3	14 46.5	16 51.2	26 26.9	15 42.4
13 W	11 19 43.2	21 44.3	26 4.4	15 33.7	11 27.9	9 11.8	26 14.8	9 32.6	14 50.6	16 51.7	26 27.0	15 42.6
14 T	11 23 39.7	22 44.2	26 1.2	27 56.2	10 42.1	10 26.4	25 58.2	9 40.6	14 54.6	16 52.2	26 27.2	15 42.9
15 F	11 27 36.3	23 43.9	25 58.0	10♑40.3	10 1.8	11 41.1	25 42.3	9 48.6	14 58.6	16 52.6	26 27.4	15 43.2
16 S	11 31 32.8	24 43.7	25 54.9	23 50.5	9 27.3	12 55.7	25 27.0	9 56.4	15 2.5	16 53.0	26 27.7	15 43.6
17 S	11 35 29.4	25 43.4	25 51.7	7♒29.4	8 58.8	14 10.3	25 12.5	10 4.1	15 6.2	16 53.3	26 28.0	15 43.9
18 M	11 39 25.9	26 43.1	25 48.5	21 37.6	8 36.7	15 24.9	24 58.8	10 11.6	15 9.9	16 53.5	26 28.3	15 44.3
19 T	11 43 22.5	27 42.8	25 45.3	6♓12.5	8 20.8	16 39.5	24 45.8	10 19.0	15 13.6	16 53.7	26 28.6	15 44.7
20 W	11 47 19.0	28 42.4	25 42.1	21 8.0	8 11.1	17 54.1	24 33.5	10 26.3	15 17.1	16 53.9	26 29.0	15 45.1
21 T	11 51 15.6	29 42.0	25 39.0	6♈15.4	8 7.5	19 8.7	24 22.0	10 33.4	15 20.5	16 54.0	26 29.4	15 45.5
22 F	11 55 12.1	0♈41.6	25 35.8	21 24.5	8D 9.9	20 23.2	24 11.3	10 40.4	15 23.9	16 54.1	26 29.9	15 46.0
23 S	11 59 8.7	1 41.1	25 32.6	6♉25.7	8 17.9	21 37.8	24 1.4	10 47.2	15 27.2	16 54.0	26 30.4	15 46.5
24 S	12 3 .2	2 40.6	25 29.4	21 11.0	8 31.3	22 52.3	23 52.3	10 53.9	15 30.4	16R54.0	26 30.9	15 47.0
25 M	12 7 1.8	3 40.0	25 26.2	5♊35.3	8 50.0	24 6.8	23 44.0	11 0.4	15 33.5	16 53.9	26 31.5	15 47.5
26 T	12 10 58.3	4 39.4	25 23.1	19 36.4	9 13.5	25 21.3	23 36.4	11 6.8	15 36.5	16 53.7	26 32.1	15 48.0
27 W	12 14 54.9	5 38.8	25 19.9	3♋14.2	9 41.7	26 35.8	23 29.7	11 13.0	15 39.4	16 53.5	26 32.7	15 48.6
28 T	12 18 51.4	6 38.2	25 16.7	16 30.6	10 14.3	27 50.3	23 23.8	11 19.0	15 42.2	16 53.2	26 33.4	15 49.2
29 F	12 22 48.0	7 37.5	25 13.5	29 27.9	10 51.1	29 4.7	23 18.6	11 24.9	15 45.0	16 52.9	26 34.0	15 49.8
30 S	12 26 44.6	8 36.7	25 10.4	12♌ 9.1	11 31.8	0♈19.2	23 14.2	11 30.7	15 47.6	16 52.5	26 34.8	15 50.4
31 S	12 30 41.1	9 35.9	25 7.2	24 36.8	12 16.3	1 33.6	23 10.6	11 36.3	15 50.2	16 52.1	26 35.5	15 51.1
						DECLINATION						
1 F	10 32 24.5	7S55.3	19S25.8	18N 1.7	0S18.6	14S29.3	15N24.8	22S59.1	22S10.1	22S47.3	22N11.5	13N24.3
4 M	10 44 14.2	6 46.7	19 23.6	7 35.6	0 41.7	13 17.2	15 45.2	22 57.6	22 8.7	22 47.6	22 11.6	13 25.0
7 T	10 56 3.9	5 37.3	19 21.4	5S15.2	1 41.9	12 1.9	16 3.4	22 56.1	22 7.3	22 47.9	22 11.7	13 25.8
10 S	11 7 53.5	4 27.3	19 19.1	15 58.8	3 5.6	10 43.7	16 19.1	22 54.5	22 6.0	22 48.2	22 11.9	13 26.6
13 W	11 19 43.2	3 16.7	19 16.9	20 51.2	4 36.2	9 22.9	16 32.2	22 53.0	22 4.7	22 48.4	22 12.0	13 27.4
16 S	11 31 32.8	2 5.7	19 14.6	17 1.6	5 59.2	7 59.9	16 42.5	22 51.5	22 3.4	22 48.5	22 12.2	13 28.2
19 T	11 43 22.5	0 54.6	19 12.4	4 36.3	7 5.4	6 34.9	16 50.2	22 50.0	22 2.3	22 48.6	22 12.4	13 29.0
22 F	11 55 12.1	0N16.5	19 10.1	10N53.8	7 50.7	5 8.3	16 55.2	22 48.5	22 1.2	22 48.7	22 12.6	13 29.9
25 M	12 7 1.8	1 27.5	19 7.8	20 12.3	8 14.3	3 40.4	16 57.5	22 47.1	22 0.1	22 48.7	22 12.8	13 30.7
28 T	12 18 51.4	2 38.1	19 5.6	18 21.5	8 17.1	2 11.6	16 57.2	22 45.7	21 59.2	22 48.7	22 13.0	13 31.6
31 S	12 30 41.1	3 48.3	19 3.3	8 28.1	8 0.9	0 42.2	16 54.5	22 44.5	21 58.3	22 48.6	22 13.2	13 32.5

APRIL 1901

DAY	EPHEMERIS SIDEREAL TIME	☉	☊	☾	☿	♀	♂	♃	♄	♅	♆	♇
						LONGITUDE						
1 M	12 34 37.7	10♈35.1	25♏ 4.0	6♍53.5	13♓ 4.2	2♈48.0	23♌ 7.8	11♑41.7	15♑52.7	16♐51.6	26♊36.3	15♊51.7
2 T	12 38 34.2	11 34.3	25 0.8	19 1.0	13 55.4	4 2.4	23R 5.7	11 46.9	15 55.1	16R51.1	26 37.1	15 52.4
3 W	12 42 30.7	12 33.4	24 57.6	1♎ 1.3	14 49.8	5 16.8	23 4.4	11 52.0	15 57.3	16 50.5	26 38.0	15 53.1
4 T	12 46 27.3	13 32.4	24 54.5	12 55.8	15 47.2	6 31.2	23 3.8	11 57.0	15 59.5	16 49.9	26 38.9	15 53.8
5 F	12 50 23.9	14 31.5	24 51.3	24 46.3	16 47.4	7 45.6	23D 4.0	12 1.7	16 1.6	16 49.2	26 39.8	15 54.6
6 S	12 54 20.4	15 30.5	24 48.1	6♏34.6	17 50.3	8 59.9	23 4.9	12 6.3	16 3.6	16 48.5	26 40.7	15 55.3
7 S	12 58 17.0	16 29.5	24 44.9	18 23.1	18 55.7	10 14.2	23 6.5	12 10.8	16 5.6	16 47.7	26 41.7	15 56.1
8 M	13 2 13.5	17 28.4	24 41.8	0♐14.6	20 3.6	11 28.6	23 8.8	12 15.0	16 7.4	16 46.9	26 42.7	15 56.9
9 T	13 6 10.1	18 27.3	24 38.6	12 12.5	21 13.9	12 42.9	23 11.8	12 19.1	16 9.1	16 46.1	26 43.8	15 57.7
10 W	13 10 6.6	19 26.2	24 35.4	24 20.7	22 26.4	13 57.2	23 15.5	12 23.1	16 10.7	16 45.1	26 44.8	15 58.5
11 T	13 14 3.2	20 25.1	24 32.2	6♑43.6	23 41.1	15 11.5	23 19.9	12 26.8	16 12.3	16 44.2	26 45.9	15 59.4
12 F	13 17 59.7	21 23.9	24 29.0	19 25.7	24 57.8	16 25.8	23 24.9	12 30.4	16 13.7	16 43.2	26 47.0	16 0.2
13 S	13 21 56.3	22 22.7	24 25.9	2♒30.9	26 16.7	17 40.0	23 30.6	12 33.8	16 15.0	16 42.1	26 48.2	16 1.1
14 S	13 25 52.8	23 21.5	24 22.7	16 2.6	27 37.5	18 54.3	23 36.9	12 37.0	16 16.3	16 41.0	26 49.4	16 2.0
15 M	13 29 49.4	24 20.2	24 19.5	0♓ 2.2	29 0.2	20 8.5	23 43.9	12 40.0	16 17.4	16 39.8	26 50.6	16 2.9
16 T	13 33 45.9	25 18.9	24 16.3	14 29.0	0♈24.8	21 22.8	23 51.5	12 42.9	16 18.5	16 38.6	26 51.8	16 3.9
17 W	13 37 42.5	26 17.6	24 13.1	29 19.0	1 51.2	22 37.0	23 59.8	12 45.6	16 19.4	16 37.4	26 53.1	16 4.8
18 T	13 41 39.1	27 16.2	24 10.0	14♈25.5	3 19.5	23 51.2	24 8.6	12 48.1	16 20.3	16 36.1	26 54.4	16 5.8
19 F	13 45 35.6	28 14.9	24 6.8	29 39.3	4 49.6	25 5.4	24 18.1	12 50.4	16 21.0	16 34.8	26 55.7	16 6.8
20 S	13 49 32.2	29 13.4	24 3.6	14♉50.3	6 21.4	26 19.6	24 28.1	12 52.5	16 21.7	16 33.4	26 57.1	16 7.8
21 S	13 53 28.7	0♉12.0	24 0.4	29 49.2	7 54.9	27 33.8	24 38.7	12 54.4	16 22.2	16 32.0	26 58.4	16 8.8
22 M	13 57 25.3	1 10.5	23 57.3	14♊28.4	9 30.2	28 47.9	24 49.9	12 56.2	16 22.7	16 30.6	26 59.9	16 9.8
23 T	14 1 21.8	2 9.0	23 54.1	28 43.4	11 7.3	0♉ 2.1	25 1.6	12 57.7	16 23.0	16 29.1	27 1.3	16 10.8
24 W	14 5 18.4	3 7.5	23 50.9	12♋32.1	12 46.1	1 16.2	25 13.9	12 59.1	16 23.3	16 27.5	27 2.8	16 11.9
25 T	14 9 14.9	4 5.9	23 47.7	25 55.1	14 26.5	2 30.3	25 26.7	13 0.3	16 23.5	16 25.9	27 4.2	16 13.0
26 F	14 13 11.5	5 4.2	23 44.5	8♌54.5	16 8.8	3 44.4	25 40.0	13 1.3	16 23.5	16 24.3	27 5.7	16 14.0
27 S	14 17 8.0	6 2.6	23 41.4	21 33.4	17 52.8	4 58.5	25 53.8	13 2.1	16R23.5	16 22.7	27 7.3	16 15.1
28 S	14 21 4.6	7 0.9	23 38.2	3♍55.5	19 38.5	6 12.6	26 8.2	13 2.7	16 23.4	16 21.0	27 8.8	16 16.3
29 M	14 25 1.1	7 59.2	23 35.0	16 4.5	21 25.9	7 26.6	26 23.0	13 3.2	16 23.1	16 19.3	27 10.4	16 17.4
30 T	14 28 57.7	8 57.4	23 31.8	28 3.9	23 15.2	8 40.7	26 38.3	13 3.4	16 22.8	16 17.5	27 12.0	16 18.5
						DECLINATION						
1 M	12 34 37.7	4N11.5	19S 2.5	4N20.0	7S51.5	0S12.4	16N53.1	22S44.1	21S58.1	22S48.5	22N13.2	13N32.7
4 T	12 46 27.3	5 20.8	19 0.2	8S10.8	7 12.3	1N17.3	16 47.4	22 43.0	21 57.3	22 48.4	22 13.4	13 33.6
7 S	12 58 17.0	6 29.2	18 57.9	17 42.1	6 17.8	2 46.9	16 39.6	22 41.9	21 56.7	22 48.2	22 13.6	13 34.5
10 W	13 10 6.6	7 36.6	18 55.6	20 36.2	5 9.2	4 16.1	16 29.7	22 41.1	21 56.1	22 48.0	22 13.8	13 35.3
13 S	13 21 56.3	8 42.9	18 53.2	14 49.8	3 47.7	5 44.5	16 17.9	22 40.3	21 55.7	22 47.7	22 14.1	13 36.2
16 T	13 33 45.9	9 47.9	18 50.9	1 37.3	2 14.5	7 11.7	16 4.3	22 39.7	21 55.3	22 47.4	22 14.3	13 37.1
19 F	13 45 35.6	10 51.4	18 48.6	13N16.7	0 30.3	8 37.6	15 49.0	22 39.2	21 55.1	22 47.1	22 14.5	13 37.9
22 M	13 57 25.3	11 53.3	18 46.2	20 36.0	1N23.7	10 1.7	15 32.0	22 38.9	21 55.0	22 46.7	22 14.7	13 38.8
25 T	14 9 14.9	12 53.5	18 43.8	16 20.8	3 26.8	11 23.7	15 13.5	22 38.8	21 55.0	22 46.2	22 14.9	13 39.6
28 S	14 21 4.6	13 51.7	18 41.5	5 15.2	5 37.9	12 43.3	14 53.4	22 38.8	21 55.0	22 45.8	22 15.1	13 40.4

MAY 1901

DAY	EPHEMERIS SIDEREAL TIME h m s	☉ ° ′	☊ ° ′	☽ ° ′	☿ ° ′	♀ ° ′	♂ ° ′	♃ ° ′	♄ ° ′	♅ ° ′	♆ ° ′	♇ ° ′
						LONGITUDE						
1 W	14 32 54.2	9♉55.6	23♏28.7	9♎56.9	25♈ 6.2	9♉54.7	26♌54.0	13♑ 3.5	16♑22.4	16♐15.7	27♊13.6	16♊19.7
2 T	14 36 50.8	10 53.8	23 25.5	21 46.4	26 58.9	11 8.7	27 10.2	13R 3.4	16R21.9	16R13.9	27 15.3	16 20.8
3 F	14 40 47.4	11 52.0	23 22.3	3♏34.8	28 53.4	12 22.7	27 26.9	13 3.1	16 21.2	16 12.0	27 17.0	16 22.0
4 S	14 44 43.9	12 50.1	23 19.1	15 24.4	0♉49.7	13 36.7	27 44.0	13 2.6	16 20.5	16 10.1	27 18.6	16 23.2
5 S	14 48 40.4	13 48.2	23 15.9	27 17.4	2 47.7	14 50.6	28 1.5	13 1.9	16 19.7	16 8.2	27 20.4	16 24.4
6 M	14 52 37.0	14 46.2	23 12.8	9♐16.0	4 47.4	16 4.6	28 19.4	13 1.0	16 18.8	16 6.2	27 22.1	16 25.6
7 T	14 56 33.6	15 44.3	23 9.6	21 22.5	6 48.8	17 18.5	28 37.8	12 59.9	16 17.8	16 4.2	27 23.9	16 26.8
8 W	15 0 30.1	16 42.3	23 6.4	3♑39.5	8 51.8	18 32.5	28 56.5	12 58.7	16 16.7	16 2.2	27 25.6	16 28.0
9 T	15 4 26.7	17 40.3	23 3.2	16 9.8	10 56.3	19 46.4	29 15.6	12 57.3	16 15.5	16 0.2	27 27.4	16 29.3
10 F	15 8 23.2	18 38.2	23 0.1	28 56.3	13 2.3	21 0.3	29 35.1	12 55.6	16 14.3	15 58.1	27 29.2	16 30.5
11 S	15 12 19.8	19 36.2	22 56.9	12♒ 1.8	15 9.6	22 14.2	29 55.0	12 53.8	16 12.9	15 56.0	27 31.1	16 31.8
12 S	15 16 16.4	20 34.1	22 53.7	25 28.8	17 18.0	23 28.1	0♍15.3	12 51.8	16 11.4	15 53.9	27 32.9	16 33.0
13 M	15 20 12.9	21 32.0	22 50.5	9♓18.8	19 27.5	24 42.0	0 35.9	12 49.7	16 9.9	15 51.7	27 34.8	16 34.3
14 T	15 24 9.5	22 29.9	22 47.4	23 31.8	21 37.7	25 55.9	0 56.9	12 47.3	16 8.2	15 49.5	27 36.7	16 35.6
15 W	15 28 6.0	23 27.7	22 44.2	8♈ 6.0	23 48.6	27 9.8	1 18.2	12 44.7	16 6.5	15 47.3	27 38.6	16 36.9
16 T	15 32 2.6	24 25.6	22 41.0	22 57.3	25 59.7	28 23.6	1 39.9	12 42.0	16 4.7	15 45.1	27 40.5	16 38.2
17 F	15 35 59.1	25 23.4	22 37.8	7♉59.0	28 11.0	29 37.5	2 1.9	12 39.1	16 2.8	15 42.8	27 42.5	16 39.5
18 S	15 39 55.7	26 21.2	22 34.6	23 3.1	0♊22.1	0♊51.3	2 24.3	12 36.0	16 0.8	15 40.6	27 44.4	16 40.8
19 S	15 43 52.2	27 19.0	22 31.5	8♊ 0.9	2 32.7	2 5.2	2 46.9	12 32.8	15 58.7	15 38.3	27 46.4	16 42.1
20 M	15 47 48.8	28 16.7	22 28.3	22 44.2	4 42.5	3 19.0	3 9.9	12 29.3	15 56.5	15 36.0	27 48.4	16 43.4
21 T	15 51 45.4	29 14.5	22 25.1	7♋ 6.5	6 51.3	4 32.8	3 33.3	12 25.7	15 54.2	15 33.6	27 50.4	16 44.8
22 W	15 55 41.9	0♊12.2	22 21.9	21 3.8	8 58.8	5 46.6	3 56.9	12 21.9	15 51.9	15 31.3	27 52.4	16 46.1
23 T	15 59 38.5	1 9.8	22 18.8	4♌34.7	11 4.7	7 0.4	4 20.8	12 18.0	15 49.5	15 28.9	27 54.5	16 47.5
24 F	16 3 34.9	2 7.5	22 15.6	17 39.8	13 8.9	8 14.1	4 45.0	12 13.9	15 47.0	15 26.6	27 56.5	16 48.8
25 S	16 7 31.5	3 5.1	22 12.4	0♍21.8	15 11.2	9 27.9	5 9.5	12 9.6	15 44.4	15 24.2	27 58.6	16 50.2
26 S	16 11 28.1	4 2.7	22 9.2	12 44.2	17 11.3	10 41.7	5 34.3	12 5.2	15 41.7	15 21.8	28 0.6	16 51.5
27 M	16 15 24.7	5 0.3	22 6.1	24 51.4	19 9.1	11 55.4	5 59.3	12 0.6	15 39.0	15 19.4	28 2.7	16 52.9
28 T	16 19 21.2	5 57.9	22 2.9	6♎47.8	21 4.5	13 9.1	6 24.6	11 55.8	15 36.2	15 17.0	28 4.8	16 54.3
29 W	16 23 17.7	6 55.4	21 59.7	18 38.0	22 57.4	14 22.8	6 50.2	11 50.9	15 33.3	15 14.5	28 6.9	16 55.6
30 T	16 27 14.3	7 52.9	21 56.5	0♏25.8	24 47.7	15 36.5	7 16.0	11 45.8	15 30.3	15 12.1	28 9.0	16 57.0
31 F	16 31 10.9	8 50.4	21 53.3	12 15.1	26 35.3	16 50.2	7 42.1	11 40.6	15 27.3	15 9.7	28 11.2	16 58.4
						DECLINATION						
1 W	14 32 54.2	14N47.9	18S39.1	7S14.0	7N55.6	14N 0.2	14N32.0	22S39.0	21S55.3	22S45.2	22N15.4	13N41.2
4 S	14 44 43.9	15 41.9	18 36.7	17 5.5	10 18.4	15 14.0	14 9.2	22 39.4	21 55.6	22 44.7	22 15.6	13 42.0
7 T	14 56 33.6	16 33.5	18 34.3	20 37.0	12 43.8	16 24.3	13 45.1	22 40.0	21 56.0	22 44.1	22 15.8	13 42.8
10 F	15 8 23.2	17 22.7	18 31.9	15 37.6	15 8.7	17 31.0	13 19.8	22 40.7	21 56.5	22 43.5	22 16.0	13 43.6
13 M	15 20 12.9	18 9.3	18 29.5	3 22.6	17 28.8	18 33.5	12 53.2	22 41.6	21 57.1	22 42.9	22 16.2	13 44.3
16 T	15 32 2.6	18 53.2	18 27.1	11N21.8	19 39.0	19 31.7	12 25.5	22 42.6	21 57.9	22 42.2	22 16.4	13 45.0
19 S	15 43 52.2	19 34.2	18 24.6	20 15.6	21 33.8	20 25.1	11 56.7	22 43.8	21 58.7	22 41.5	22 16.6	13 45.7
22 W	15 55 41.9	20 12.2	18 22.2	17 20.2	23 8.4	21 13.6	11 26.7	22 45.2	21 59.6	22 40.8	22 16.7	13 46.4
25 S	16 7 31.5	20 47.1	18 19.7	6 26.4	24 19.8	21 56.7	10 55.7	22 46.7	22 0.6	22 40.0	22 16.9	13 47.1
28 T	16 19 21.2	21 18.7	18 17.3	6S10.9	25 7.3	22 34.4	10 23.7	22 48.3	22 1.7	22 39.3	22 17.1	13 47.7
31 F	16 31 10.9	21 47.1	18 14.8	16 25.6	25 31.8	23 6.2	9 50.7	22 50.0	22 2.9	22 38.5	22 17.2	13 48.3

JUNE 1901

DAY	SIDEREAL TIME	☉	☊	☽	☿	♀	♂	♃	♄	♅	♆	♇
						LONGITUDE						
1 S	16 35 7.5	9♊47.9	21♏50.2	24♏ 8.8	28♊20.2	18♊ 3.9	8♍ 8.4	11♑35.3	15♑24.2	15♐ 7.2	28♊13.3	16♊59.8
2 S	16 39 4.0	10 45.3	21 47.0	6♐ 9.5	0♋ 2.4	19 17.6	8 35.0	11R29.8	15R21.0	15R 4.8	28 15.4	17 1.2
3 M	16 43 0.5	11 42.8	21 43.8	18 19.2	1 41.8	20 31.3	9 1.8	11 24.2	15 17.8	15 2.3	28 17.6	17 2.6
4 T	16 46 57.1	12 40.2	21 40.6	0♑39.7	3 18.4	21 44.9	9 28.9	11 18.4	15 14.5	14 59.8	28 19.8	17 4.0
5 W	16 50 53.6	13 37.6	21 37.5	13 12.3	4 52.1	22 58.6	9 56.1	11 12.6	15 11.1	14 57.4	28 21.9	17 5.4
6 T	16 54 50.2	14 35.0	21 34.3	25 57.9	6 22.9	24 12.2	10 23.6	11 6.6	15 7.7	14 54.9	28 24.1	17 6.7
7 F	16 58 46.8	15 32.4	21 31.1	8♒57.6	7 50.9	25 25.8	10 51.3	11 0.4	15 4.2	14 52.4	28 26.3	17 8.1
8 S	17 2 43.3	16 29.7	21 27.9	22 12.2	9 15.9	26 39.4	11 19.3	10 54.2	15 0.6	14 50.0	28 28.5	17 9.5
9 S	17 6 39.9	17 27.1	21 24.8	5♓42.5	10 38.0	27 53.1	11 47.4	10 47.8	14 57.0	14 47.5	28 30.7	17 10.9
10 M	17 10 36.5	18 24.5	21 21.6	19 28.9	11 57.1	29 6.7	12 15.8	10 41.3	14 53.3	14 45.0	28 32.9	17 12.3
11 T	17 14 33.0	19 21.8	21 18.4	3♈31.5	13 13.1	0♋20.3	12 44.3	10 34.7	14 49.6	14 42.6	28 35.1	17 13.7
12 W	17 18 29.6	20 19.1	21 15.2	17 49.2	14 26.1	1 33.9	13 13.1	10 28.0	14 45.8	14 40.1	28 37.3	17 15.1
13 T	17 22 26.1	21 16.5	21 12.0	2♉20.0	15 35.9	2 47.5	13 42.1	10 21.2	14 42.0	14 37.7	28 39.5	17 16.5
14 F	17 26 22.7	22 13.8	21 8.9	17 0.1	16 42.6	4 1.1	14 11.3	10 14.4	14 38.2	14 35.2	28 41.8	17 17.9
15 S	17 30 19.3	23 11.1	21 5.7	1♊44.4	17 45.9	5 14.7	14 40.7	10 7.4	14 34.2	14 32.8	28 44.0	17 19.3
16 S	17 34 15.8	24 8.4	21 2.5	16 26.3	18 45.9	6 28.2	15 10.2	10 0.3	14 30.3	14 30.4	28 46.2	17 20.7
17 M	17 38 12.4	25 5.7	20 59.3	0♋59.0	19 42.5	7 41.8	15 40.0	9 53.2	14 26.2	14 28.0	28 48.5	17 22.1
18 T	17 42 8.9	26 3.0	20 56.2	15 16.1	20 35.6	8 55.3	16 9.9	9 46.0	14 22.2	14 25.5	28 50.7	17 23.4
19 W	17 46 5.5	27 0.3	20 53.0	29 12.5	21 25.0	10 8.9	16 40.1	9 38.7	14 18.1	14 23.2	28 52.9	17 24.8
20 T	17 50 2.0	27 57.6	20 49.8	12♌45.1	22 10.8	11 22.5	17 10.4	9 31.3	14 14.0	14 20.8	28 55.2	17 26.2
21 F	17 53 58.6	28 54.8	20 46.6	25 53.1	22 52.7	12 36.0	17 40.9	9 23.9	14 9.8	14 18.4	28 57.4	17 27.6
22 S	17 57 55.1	29 52.1	20 43.5	8♍37.7	23 30.6	13 49.5	18 11.6	9 16.5	14 5.6	14 16.1	28 59.6	17 28.9
23 S	18 1 51.7	0♋49.3	20 40.3	21 2.0	24 4.5	15 3.0	18 42.5	9 9.0	14 1.4	14 13.7	29 1.9	17 30.3
24 M	18 5 48.3	1 46.5	20 37.1	3♎ 9.8	24 34.3	16 16.5	19 13.5	9 1.4	13 57.2	14 11.4	29 4.1	17 31.7
25 T	18 9 44.8	2 43.8	20 33.9	15 6.2	24 59.7	17 30.0	19 44.7	8 53.8	13 52.9	14 9.1	29 6.3	17 33.0
26 W	18 13 41.3	3 41.0	20 30.7	26 56.1	25 20.8	18 43.5	20 16.1	8 46.2	13 48.6	14 6.8	29 8.6	17 34.4
27 T	18 17 37.9	4 38.2	20 27.6	8♏44.5	25 37.5	19 56.9	20 47.6	8 38.6	13 44.3	14 4.6	29 10.8	17 35.7
28 F	18 21 34.5	5 35.4	20 24.4	20 36.1	25 49.6	21 10.4	21 19.3	8 30.9	13 39.9	14 2.3	29 13.0	17 37.1
29 S	18 25 31.1	6 32.6	20 21.2	2♐35.0	25 57.1	22 23.8	21 51.1	8 23.3	13 35.6	14 0.1	29 15.3	17 38.4
30 S	18 29 27.6	7 29.7	20 18.0	14 44.6	25 59.9	23 37.3	22 23.1	8 15.6	13 31.2	13 57.9	29 17.5	17 39.7
						DECLINATION						
1 S	16 35 7.5	21N55.8	18S14.0	18S40.8	25N35.3	23N15.5	9N39.5	22S50.5	22S 3.3	22S38.3	22N17.3	13N48.5
4 T	16 46 57.1	22 19.6	18 11.5	20 12.0	25 33.0	23 39.3	9 5.3	22 52.4	22 4.6	22 37.5	22 17.4	13 49.0
7 F	16 58 46.8	22 39.9	18 9.1	13 6.0	25 13.9	23 56.9	8 30.3	22 54.2	22 5.9	22 36.7	22 17.5	13 49.6
10 M	17 10 36.5	22 56.7	18 6.6	0N 7.8	24 41.1	24 8.2	7 54.3	22 56.2	22 7.3	22 35.9	22 17.7	13 50.1
13 T	17 22 26.1	23 9.8	18 4.1	13 58.6	23 57.7	24 13.1	7 17.5	22 58.2	22 8.7	22 35.0	22 17.8	13 50.5
16 S	17 34 15.8	23 19.2	18 1.6	20 38.2	23 6.5	24 11.5	6 40.0	23 0.2	22 10.2	22 34.2	22 17.9	13 51.0
19 W	17 46 5.5	23 25.0	17 59.1	15 38.3	22 10.4	24 3.5	6 1.6	23 2.2	22 11.7	22 33.4	22 18.0	13 51.4
22 S	17 57 55.1	23 27.0	17 56.5	3 43.3	21 12.2	23 49.0	5 22.5	23 4.2	22 13.2	22 32.6	22 18.0	13 51.8
25 T	18 9 44.8	23 25.3	17 54.0	8S49.4	20 14.6	23 28.3	4 42.8	23 6.1	22 14.7	22 31.9	22 18.1	13 52.1
28 F	18 21 34.5	23 19.9	17 51.5	18 1.6	19 20.4	23 1.3	4 2.4	23 8.0	22 16.3	22 31.1	22 18.2	13 52.4

JULY 1901

LONGITUDE

DAY	EPHEMERIS SIDEREAL TIME	☉	☊	☽	☿	♀	♂	♃	♄	♅	♆	♇
	h m s	° ′	° ′	° ′	° ′	° ′	° ′	° ′	° ′	° ′	° ′	° ′
1 M	18 33 24.1	8♋26.9	20♏14.9	27♐ 7.3	25♋58.1	24♋50.7	22♍55.2	8♑ 7.9	13♑26.8	13♐55.7	29♊19.7	17♊41.0
2 T	18 37 20.7	9 24.1	20 11.7	9♑44.6	25R51.8	26 4.1	23 27.5	8R 0.2	13R22.4	13R53.6	29 21.9	17 42.3
3 W	18 41 17.3	10 21.3	20 8.5	22 37.0	25 40.9	27 17.5	23 59.9	7 52.5	13 18.0	13 51.5	29 24.1	17 43.7
4 T	18 45 13.8	11 18.5	20 5.3	5♒44.1	25 25.6	28 30.9	24 32.5	7 44.8	13 13.6	13 49.4	29 26.3	17 45.0
5 F	18 49 10.4	12 15.6	20 2.2	19 4.8	25 6.0	29 44.3	25 5.2	7 37.2	13 9.2	13 47.3	29 28.5	17 46.2
6 S	18 53 6.9	13 12.8	19 59.0	2♓37.6	24 42.5	0♌57.6	25 38.1	7 29.5	13 4.8	13 45.2	29 30.7	17 47.5
7 S	18 57 3.5	14 !0.0	19 55.8	16 21.1	24 15.4	2 11.0	26 11.1	7 21.9	13 0.3	13 43.2	29 32.9	17 48.8
8 M	19 1 0.0	15 7.2	19 52.6	0♈13.8	23 45.0	3 24.4	26 44.2	7 14.3	12 55.9	13 41.2	29 35.0	17 50.1
9 T	19 4 56.6	16 4.4	19 49.5	14 14.7	23 11.7	4 37.7	27 17.5	7 6.8	12 51.5	13 39.3	29 37.2	17 51.3
10 W	19 8 53.2	17 1.6	19 46.3	28 22.7	22 36.0	5 51.0	27 50.9	6 59.3	12 47.1	13 37.4	29 39.4	17 52.6
11 T	19 12 49.7	17 58.8	19 43.1	12♉36.7	21 58.6	7 4.4	28 24.5	6 51.8	12 42.7	13 35.5	29 41.5	17 53.8
12 F	19 16 46.3	18 56.0	19 39.9	26 55.0	21 20.0	8 17.7	28 58.2	6 44.4	12 38.3	13 33.6	29 43.6	17 55.0
13 S	19 20 42.8	19 53.3	19 36.7	11♊14.9	20 40.8	9 31.0	29 32.0	6 37.1	12 33.9	13 31.8	29 45.8	17 56.2
14 S	19 24 39.4	20 50.5	19 33.6	25 32.7	20 1.8	10 44.3	0♎ 6.0	6 29.8	12 29.6	13 30.0	29 47.9	17 57.4
15 M	19 28 36.0	21 47.8	19 30.4	9♋43.9	19 23.6	11 57.6	0 40.1	6 22.6	12 25.2	13 28.2	29 50.0	17 58.6
16 T	19 32 32.5	22 45.0	19 27.2	23 43.7	18 46.9	13 10.9	1 14.4	6 15.5	12 20.9	13 26.5	29 52.1	17 59.8
17 W	19 36 29.1	23 42.3	19 24.0	7♌27.6	18 12.3	14 24.1	1 48.7	6 8.4	12 16.6	13 24.8	29 54.2	18 1.0
18 T	19 40 25.6	24 39.6	19 20.9	20 52.1	17 40.5	15 37.4	2 23.2	6 1.5	12 12.4	13 23.2	29 56.3	18 2.1
19 F	19 44 22.2	25 36.8	19 17.7	3♍55.6	17 12.1	16 50.6	2 57.8	5 54.6	12 8.1	13 21.5	29 58.3	18 3.3
20 S	19 48 18.7	26 34.1	19 14.5	16 38.2	16 47.6	18 3.9	3 32.6	5 47.8	12 3.9	13 20.0	0♋ 0.4	18 4.4
21 S	19 52 15.3	27 31.4	19 11.3	29 1.6	16 27.4	19 17.1	4 7.5	5 41.1	11 59.7	13 18.4	0 2.4	18 5.5
22 M	19 56 11.9	28 28.7	19 8.2	11♎ 9.2	16 12.1	20 30.3	4 42.5	5 34.5	11 55.6	13 16.9	0 4.4	18 6.7
23 T	20 0 8.4	29 26.0	19 5.0	23 5.4	16 1.8	21 43.5	5 17.6	5 28.1	11 51.4	13 15.5	0 6.4	18 7.8
24 W	20 4 4.9	0♌23.3	19 1.8	4♏55.3	15 57.1	22 56.6	5 52.8	5 21.7	11 47.4	13 14.0	0 8.4	18 8.8
25 T	20 8 1.5	1 20.6	18 58.6	16 44.2	15D58.0	24 9.8	6 28.1	5 15.5	11 43.3	13 12.7	0 10.4	18 9.9
26 F	20 11 58.1	2 17.9	18 55.4	28 37.6	16 4.8	25 22.9	7 3.6	5 9.3	11 39.3	13 11.3	0 12.4	18 10.9
27 S	20 15 54.7	3 15.2	18 52.3	10♐40.3	16 17.6	26 36.0	7 39.2	5 3.3	11 35.4	13 10.0	0 14.3	18 12.0
28 S	20 19 51.2	4 12.6	18 49.1	22 56.8	16 36.5	27 49.1	8 14.9	4 57.5	11 31.5	13 8.8	0 16.2	18 13.0
29 M	20 23 47.7	5 9.9	18 45.9	5♑30.4	17 1.5	29 2.2	8 50.7	4 51.7	11 27.6	13 7.6	0 18.1	18 14.0
30 T	20 27 44.3	6 7.2	18 42.7	18 23.0	17 32.7	0♍15.2	9 26.6	4 46.1	11 23.8	13 6.4	0 20.0	18 15.0
31 W	20 31 40.9	7 4.6	18 39.6	1♒35.1	18 10.1	1 28.3	10 2.6	4 40.7	11 20.0	13 5.3	0 21.9	18 16.0

DECLINATION

DAY	EPHEMERIS SIDEREAL TIME	☉	☊	☽	☿	♀	♂	♃	♄	♅	♆	♇
1 M	18 33 24.1	23N10.9	17S48.9	20S26.6	18N32.4	22N28.4	3N21.4	23S 9.9	22S17.8	22S30.3	22N18.2	13N52.7
4 T	18 45 13.8	22 58.1	17 46.4	14 4.0	17 53.0	21 49.6	2 39.8	23 11.7	22 19.4	22 29.6	22 18.2	13 52.9
7 S	18 57 3.5	22 41.8	17 43.8	1 7.1	17 24.6	21 5.2	1 57.7	23 13.4	22 21.0	22 28.9	22 18.3	13 53.1
10 W	19 8 53.2	22 21.9	17 41.3	12N45.0	17 8.6	20 15.4	1 15.1	23 15.1	22 22.5	22 28.2	22 18.3	13 53.3
13 S	19 20 42.8	21 58.6	17 38.7	20 23.2	17 5.7	19 20.6	0 32.1	23 16.6	22 24.0	22 27.5	22 18.3	13 53.5
16 T	19 32 32.5	21 31.8	17 36.1	16 54.7	17 15.4	18 21.0	0S11.4	23 18.1	22 25.5	22 26.9	22 18.3	13 53.6
19 F	19 44 22.2	21 1.8	17 33.5	5 29.1	17 36.1	17 16.8	0 55.2	23 19.5	22 27.0	22 26.3	22 18.3	13 53.7
22 M	19 56 11.9	20 28.5	17 30.9	7S20.7	18 5.4	16 8.6	1 39.4	23 20.8	22 28.4	22 25.8	22 18.2	13 53.7
25 T	20 8 1.5	19 52.2	17 28.3	17 6.9	18 39.9	14 56.4	2 23.9	23 22.0	22 29.8	22 25.3	22 18.2	13 53.7
28 S	20 19 51.2	19 12.9	17 25.7	20 30.0	19 15.9	13 40.8	3 8.6	23 23.1	22 31.1	22 24.8	22 18.1	13 53.7
31 W	20 31 40.9	18 30.7	17 23.1	15 8.9	19 49.1	12 22.0	3 53.5	23 24.1	22 32.4	22 24.4	22 18.1	13 53.6

AUGUST 1901

LONGITUDE

DAY	EPHEMERIS SIDEREAL TIME	☉	☊	☽	☿	♀	♂	♃	♄	♅	♆	♇
1 T	20 35 37.4	8♌ 2.0	18♏36.4	15♒ 5.3	18♋53.5	2♍41.3	10♎38.7	4♑35.3	11♑16.3	13♐ 4.2	0♋23.8	18♊17.0
2 F	20 39 34.0	8 59.4	18 33.2	28 51.1	19 43.1	3 54.3	11 14.9	4R30.2	11R12.7	13R 3.2	0 25.6	18 17.9
3 S	20 43 30.5	9 56.8	18 30.0	12♓48.6	20 38.5	5 7.2	11 51.3	4 25.1	11 9.1	13 2.2	0 27.4	18 18.9
4 S	20 47 27.1	10 54.2	18 26.9	26 53.8	21 39.9	6 20.2	12 27.7	4 20.2	11 5.5	13 1.3	0 29.2	18 19.8
5 M	20 51 23.6	11 51.7	18 23.7	11♈ 2.9	22 47.0	7 33.1	13 4.3	4 15.5	11 2.1	13 0.4	0 31.0	18 20.7
6 T	20 55 20.2	12 49.1	18 20.5	25 12.9	23 59.6	8 46.1	13 41.0	4 10.9	10 58.6	12 59.6	0 32.8	18 21.6
7 W	20 59 16.7	13 46.6	18 17.3	9♉21.9	25 17.6	9 59.0	14 17.7	4 6.5	10 55.3	12 58.8	0 34.5	18 22.4
8 T	21 3 13.2	14 44.1	18 14.1	23 28.5	26 40.8	11 11.8	14 54.6	4 2.3	10 52.0	12 58.0	0 36.2	18 23.3
9 F	21 7 9.8	15 41.7	18 11.0	7♊31.9	28 8.9	12 24.7	15 31.6	3 58.2	10 48.8	12 57.3	0 37.9	18 24.1
10 S	21 11 6.4	16 39.2	18 7.8	21 31.2	29 41.7	13 37.6	16 8.7	3 54.3	10 45.6	12 56.7	0 39.6	18 24.9
11 S	21 15 3.0	17 36.8	18 4.6	5♋24.9	1♌18.9	14 50.4	16 45.9	3 50.5	10 42.5	12 56.1	0 41.3	18 25.8
12 M	21 18 59.5	18 34.4	18 1.4	19 11.1	3 0.0	16 3.2	17 23.2	3 46.9	10 39.5	12 55.5	0 42.9	18 26.5
13 T	21 22 56.0	19 32.0	17 58.3	2♌47.1	4 44.9	17 16.0	18 0.6	3 43.5	10 36.5	12 55.0	0 44.5	18 27.3
14 W	21 26 52.6	20 29.7	17 55.1	16 10.2	6 33.0	18 28.8	18 38.1	3 40.3	10 33.7	12 54.5	0 46.1	18 28.0
15 T	21 30 49.2	21 27.4	17 51.9	29 18.2	8 24.1	19 41.5	19 15.7	3 37.2	10 30.9	12 54.1	0 47.7	18 28.8
16 F	21 34 45.8	22 25.0	17 48.7	12♍ 9.4	10 17.6	20 54.3	19 53.4	3 34.3	10 28.2	12 53.8	0 49.2	18 29.5
17 S	21 38 42.3	23 22.8	17 45.5	24 43.5	12 13.2	22 7.0	20 31.2	3 31.6	10 25.5	12 53.5	0 50.8	18 30.2
18 S	21 42 38.8	24 20.5	17 42.4	7♎ 1.6	14 10.5	23 19.7	21 9.1	3 29.1	10 22.9	12 53.2	0 52.2	18 30.8
19 M	21 46 35.4	25 18.2	17 39.2	19 6.0	16 9.1	24 32.3	21 47.2	3 26.8	10 20.5	12 53.0	0 53.7	18 31.5
20 T	21 50 32.0	26 16.0	17 36.0	1♏ 0.4	18 8.6	25 45.0	22 25.3	3 24.7	10 18.1	12 52.9	0 55.2	18 32.1
21 W	21 54 28.5	27 13.8	17 32.8	12 49.1	20 8.7	26 57.6	23 3.5	3 22.7	10 15.7	12 52.8	0 56.6	18 32.7
22 T	21 58 25.0	28 11.6	17 29.7	24 37.3	22 9.1	28 10.1	23 41.8	3 20.9	10 13.5	12 52.7	0 58.0	18 33.3
23 F	22 2 21.6	29 9.4	17 26.5	6♐30.5	24 9.6	29 22.7	24 20.2	3 19.3	10 11.4	12D52.7	0 59.3	18 33.9
24 S	22 6 18.1	0♍ 7.3	17 23.3	18 34.0	26 9.8	0♎35.2	24 58.7	3 18.0	10 9.3	12 52.8	1 0.7	18 34.5
25 S	22 10 14.7	1 5.2	17 20.1	0♑53.0	28 9.7	1 47.7	25 37.3	3 16.7	10 7.3	12 52.9	1 2.0	18 35.0
26 M	22 14 11.3	2 3.0	17 16.9	13 31.9	0♍ 8.9	3 0.1	26 15.9	3 15.7	10 5.4	12 53.0	1 3.3	18 35.5
27 T	22 18 7.8	3 0.9	17 13.8	26 33.5	2 7.3	4 12.6	26 54.7	3 14.9	10 3.6	12 53.2	1 4.5	18 36.0
28 W	22 22 4.3	3 58.9	17 10.6	9♒59.1	4 5.0	5 25.0	27 33.6	3 14.3	10 1.9	12 53.5	1 5.7	18 36.5
29 T	22 26 0.9	4 56.8	17 7.4	23 47.6	6 1.6	6 37.3	28 12.5	3 13.8	10 0.3	12 53.8	1 6.9	18 36.9
30 F	22 29 57.5	5 54.8	17 4.2	7♓55.8	7 57.2	7 49.7	28 51.6	3 13.6	9 58.8	12 54.2	1 8.1	18 37.4
31 S	22 33 54.0	6 52.8	17 1.1	22 18.6	9 51.8	9 2.0	29 30.7	3 13.5	9 57.3	12 54.6	1 9.3	18 37.8

DECLINATION

DAY	EPHEMERIS SIDEREAL TIME	☉	☊	☽	☿	♀	♂	♃	♄	♅	♆	♇
1 T	20 35 37.4	18N16.1	17S22.2	11S31.7	19N58.7	11N55.0	4S 8.5	23S24.4	22S32.8	22S24.3	22N18.1	13N53.6
4 S	20 47 27.1	17 30.3	17 19.6	2N23.7	20 20.7	10 32.5	4 53.6	23 25.3	22 34.0	22 24.0	22 18.0	13 53.5
7 W	20 59 16.7	16 41.9	17 16.9	15 23.0	20 28.5	9 7.4	5 38.7	23 26.2	22 35.2	22 23.7	22 17.9	13 53.4
10 S	21 11 6.4	15 51.1	17 14.3	20 26.1	20 17.3	7 40.3	6 23.9	23 26.9	22 36.3	22 23.4	22 17.9	13 53.2
13 T	21 22 56.0	14 58.0	17 11.6	14 50.2	19 43.6	6 11.4	7 9.1	23 27.6	22 37.4	22 23.2	22 17.8	13 53.0
16 F	21 34 45.8	14 2.8	17 9.0	2 47.3	18 45.6	4 41.0	7 54.2	23 28.2	22 38.4	22 23.1	22 17.7	13 52.8
19 M	21 46 35.4	13 5.6	17 6.3	9S40.6	17 24.5	3 9.4	8 39.1	23 28.8	22 39.3	22 23.0	22 17.6	13 52.5
22 T	21 58 25.0	12 6.4	17 3.6	18 16.9	15 43.3	1 37.0	9 23.9	23 29.3	22 40.2	22 23.0	22 17.5	13 52.3
25 S	22 10 14.7	11 5.6	17 0.9	19 56.1	13 46.4	0 4.1	10 8.4	23 29.7	22 41.0	22 23.1	22 17.4	13 52.0
28 W	22 22 4.3	10 3.2	16 58.2	12 55.6	11 38.4	1S29.0	10 52.6	23 30.1	22 41.7	22 23.2	22 17.3	13 51.6
31 S	22 33 54.0	8 59.4	16 55.5	0N41.5	9 23.1	3 2.1	11 36.4	23 30.5	22 42.4	22 23.3	22 17.2	13 51.3

SEPTEMBER 1901

LONGITUDE

DAY	EPHEMERIS SIDEREAL TIME h m s	☉ ° ′	☊ ° ′	☽ ° ′	☿ ° ′	♀ ° ′	♂ ° ′	♃ ° ′	♄ ° ′	♅ ° ′	♆ ° ′	♇ ° ′
1 S	22 37 50.5	7♍50.9	16♏57.9	6♈49.5	11♍45.2	10♎14.2	0♏ 9.9	3♑13.6	9♑56.0	12♐55.0	1♋10.4	18♊38.2
2 M	22 41 47.1	8 48.9	16 54.7	21 22.2	13 37.4	11 26.5	0 49.2	3D13.9	9R54.7	12 55.5	1 11.5	18 38.6
3 T	22 45 43.7	9 47.1	16 51.5	5♉51.3	15 28.4	12 38.7	1 28.6	3 14.4	9 53.6	12 56.1	1 12.5	18 38.9
4 W	22 49 40.3	10 45.2	16 48.3	20 12.5	17 18.3	13 50.8	2 8.1	3 15.1	9 52.5	12 56.7	1 13.5	18 39.2
5 T	22 53 36.8	11 43.4	16 45.2	4♊23.6	19 6.9	15 3.0	2 47.7	3 16.0	9 51.5	12 57.4	1 14.5	18 39.5
6 F	22 57 33.3	12 41.6	16 42.0	18 23.2	20 54.4	16 15.1	3 27.3	3 17.0	9 50.7	12 58.1	1 15.5	18 39.8
7 S	23 1 29.9	13 39.8	16 38.8	2♋11.2	22 40.6	17 27.2	4 7.1	3 18.3	9 49.9	12 58.9	1 16.4	18 40.1
8 S	23 5 26.5	14 38.1	16 35.6	15 47.5	24 25.7	18 39.2	4 47.0	3 19.7	9 49.2	12 59.7	1 17.4	18 40.3
9 M	23 9 23.0	15 36.4	16 32.5	29 12.1	26 9.7	19 51.2	5 26.9	3 21.4	9 48.6	13 0.6	1 18.2	18 40.6
10 T	23 13 19.5	16 34.7	16 29.3	12♌24.9	27 52.5	21 3.2	6 6.9	3 23.2	9 48.1	13 1.5	1 19.1	18 40.8
11 W	23 17 16.1	17 33.1	16 26.1	25 25.3	29 34.1	22 15.2	6 47.1	3 25.2	9 47.7	13 2.5	1 19.9	18 40.9
12 T	23 21 12.7	18 31.5	16 22.9	8♍12.7	1♎14.7	23 27.1	7 27.3	3 27.4	9 47.4	13 3.5	1 20.7	18 41.1
13 F	23 25 9.2	19 29.9	16 19.7	20 47.0	2 54.1	24 39.0	8 7.6	3 29.8	9 47.2	13 4.6	1 21.4	18 41.2
14 S	23 29 5.8	20 28.4	16 16.6	3♎ 8.2	4 32.4	25 50.9	8 48.0	3 32.3	9 47.1	13 5.7	1 22.1	18 41.4
15 S	23 33 2.3	21 26.9	16 13.4	15 17.3	6 9.7	27 2.7	9 28.4	3 35.1	9 47.1	13 6.9	1 22.8	18 41.4
16 M	23 36 58.9	22 25.4	16 10.2	27 15.9	7 45.9	28 14.5	10 9.0	3 38.0	9D47.2	13 8.1	1 23.5	18 41.5
17 T	23 40 55.4	23 24.0	16 7.0	9♏ 6.9	9 21.1	29 26.2	10 49.7	3 41.1	9 47.4	13 9.4	1 24.1	18 41.6
18 W	23 44 52.0	24 22.6	16 3.9	20 53.8	10 55.3	0♏37.9	11 30.4	3 44.4	9 47.7	13 10.7	1 24.7	18 41.6
19 T	23 48 48.5	25 21.2	16 0.7	2♐40.7	12 28.4	1 49.6	12 11.2	3 47.9	9 48.1	13 12.1	1 25.2	18 41.6
20 F	23 52 45.1	26 19.8	15 57.5	14 32.7	14 0.5	3 1.2	12 52.1	3 51.5	9 48.6	13 13.5	1 25.7	18R41.6
21 S	23 56 41.6	27 18.5	15 54.3	26 34.7	15 31.6	4 12.7	13 33.1	3 55.4	9 49.2	13 15.0	1 26.2	18 41.5
22 S	0 0 38.2	28 17.2	15 51.1	8♑52.2	17 1.7	5 24.3	14 14.2	3 59.4	9 49.9	13 16.5	1 26.7	18 41.5
23 M	0 4 34.8	29 15.9	15 48.0	21 29.9	18 30.7	6 35.8	14 55.3	4 3.6	9 50.7	13 18.0	1 27.1	18 41.4
24 T	0 8 31.3	0♎14.7	15 44.8	4♒31.8	19 58.8	7 47.2	15 36.5	4 7.9	9 51.6	13 19.7	1 27.5	18 41.3
25 W	0 12 27.9	1 13.5	15 41.6	18 0.4	21 25.8	8 58.6	16 17.8	4 12.5	9 52.5	13 21.3	1 27.9	18 41.2
26 T	0 16 24.4	2 12.3	15 38.4	1♓56.0	22 51.8	10 9.9	16 59.2	4 17.2	9 53.6	13 23.0	1 28.2	18 41.0
27 F	0 20 21.0	3 11.1	15 35.2	16 16.3	24 16.7	11 21.2	17 40.7	4 22.1	9 54.8	13 24.8	1 28.5	18 40.9
28 S	0 24 17.5	4 10.0	15 32.1	0♈56.2	25 40.5	12 32.4	18 22.2	4 27.1	9 56.1	13 26.6	1 28.7	18 40.7
29 S	0 28 14.1	5 8.9	15 28.9	15 48.6	27 3.3	13 43.6	19 3.8	4 32.3	9 57.4	13 28.4	1 28.9	18 40.4
30 M	0 32 10.6	6 7.9	15 25.7	0♉45.3	28 24.9	14 54.7	19 45.5	4 37.7	9 58.9	13 30.3	1 29.1	18 40.2

DECLINATION

DAY	EPHEMERIS SIDEREAL TIME	☉	☊	☽	☿	♀	♂	♃	♄	♅	♆	♇
1 S	22 37 50.5	8N37.8	16S54.6	5N38.6	8N36.9	3S33.0	11S50.9	23S30.6	22S42.7	22S23.4	22N17.1	13N51.2
4 W	22 49 40.3	7 32.3	16 51.9	17 25.5	6 16.8	5 5.4	12 34.1	23 30.9	22 43.3	22 23.6	22 17.0	13 50.8
7 S	23 1 29.9	6 25.6	16 49.2	19 44.4	3 55.7	6 37.0	13 16.8	23 31.1	22 43.8	22 23.9	22 16.9	13 50.4
10 T	23 13 19.5	5 18.0	16 46.5	12 12.7	1 35.5	8 7.5	13 58.9	23 31.3	22 44.3	22 24.3	22 16.8	13 50.0
13 F	23 25 9.2	4 9.5	16 43.8	0S 8.8	0S42.7	9 36.6	14 40.3	23 31.4	22 44.7	22 24.7	22 16.7	13 49.5
16 M	23 36 58.9	3 0.5	16 41.0	11 56.2	2 57.9	11 3.8	15 20.9	23 31.5	22 45.0	22 25.2	22 16.6	13 49.1
19 T	23 48 48.5	1 50.9	16 38.3	19 7.9	5 9.1	12 29.0	16 0.8	23 31.5	22 45.3	22 25.7	22 16.4	13 48.6
22 S	0 0 38.2	0 40.9	16 35.5	18 58.0	7 15.7	13 51.8	16 39.7	23 31.5	22 45.5	22 26.3	22 16.3	13 48.1
25 W	0 12 27.9	0S29.2	16 32.7	10 31.8	9 16.9	15 11.8	17 17.7	23 31.3	22 45.6	22 26.9	22 16.2	13 47.6
28 S	0 24 17.5	1 39.4	16 30.0	3N37.7	11 12.1	16 28.8	17 54.6	23 31.1	22 45.7	22 27.5	22 16.1	13 47.1

OCTOBER 1901

LONGITUDE

DAY	EPHEMERIS SIDEREAL TIME h m s	☉ ° ′	☊ ° ′	☽ ° ′	☿ ° ′	♀ ° ′	♂ ° ′	♃ ° ′	♄ ° ′	♅ ° ′	♆ ° ′	♇ ° ′
1 T	0 36 7.2	7♎ 6.8	15♏22.5	15♉37.9	29♎45.3	16♏ 5.8	20♏27.3	4♑43.2	10♑ 0.5	13♐32.3	1♋29.3	18♊40.0
2 W	0 40 3.7	8 5.9	15 19.4	0♊19.7	1♏ 4.5	17 16.8	21 9.2	4 48.9	10 2.2	13 34.2	1 29.4	18R39.7
3 T	0 44 0.3	9 4.9	15 16.2	14 45.9	2 22.5	18 27.8	21 51.1	4 54.8	10 3.9	13 36.3	1 29.5	18 39.4
4 F	0 47 56.8	10 4.0	15 13.0	28 53.6	3 39.1	19 38.7	22 33.1	5 0.8	10 5.8	13 38.3	1 29.5	18 39.1
5 S	0 51 53.4	11 3.1	15 9.8	12♋42.1	4 54.2	20 49.5	23 15.2	5 7.0	10 7.7	13 40.4	1 29.6	18 38.7
6 S	0 55 49.9	12 2.3	15 6.6	26 11.6	6 7.9	22 0.3	23 57.4	5 13.3	10 9.7	13 42.6	1R29.6	18 38.4
7 M	0 59 46.5	13 1.5	15 3.5	9♌23.5	7 20.0	23 11.1	24 39.7	5 19.8	10 11.9	13 44.8	1 29.5	18 38.0
8 T	1 3 43.0	14 0.8	15 0.3	22 19.4	8 30.4	24 21.8	25 22.0	5 26.4	10 14.1	13 47.0	1 29.4	18 37.6
9 W	1 7 39.6	15 0.1	14 57.1	5♍ 0.9	9 38.9	25 32.4	26 4.4	5 33.2	10 16.4	13 49.3	1 29.3	18 37.2
10 T	1 11 36.1	15 59.4	14 53.9	17 29.6	10 45.5	26 43.0	26 46.9	5 40.2	10 18.9	13 51.6	1 29.2	18 36.7
11 F	1 15 32.7	16 58.8	14 50.8	29 47.0	11 49.9	27 53.5	27 29.5	5 47.3	10 21.4	13 54.0	1 29.0	18 36.3
12 S	1 19 29.3	17 58.2	14 47.6	11♎54.5	12 51.9	29 4.0	28 12.1	5 54.5	10 24.0	13 56.4	1 28.8	18 35.8
13 S	1 23 25.8	18 57.6	14 44.4	23 53.6	13 51.4	0♐14.4	28 54.9	6 1.9	10 26.7	13 58.8	1 28.5	18 35.3
14 M	1 27 22.3	19 57.1	14 41.2	5♏46.0	14 48.1	1 24.7	29 37.7	6 9.5	10 29.5	14 1.3	1 28.2	18 34.8
15 T	1 31 18.9	20 56.6	14 38.0	17 33.9	15 41.7	2 35.0	0♐20.6	6 17.1	10 32.3	14 3.8	1 27.9	18 34.2
16 W	1 35 15.5	21 56.1	14 34.9	29 20.0	16 32.0	3 45.2	1 3.5	6 25.0	10 35.3	14 6.4	1 27.6	18 33.7
17 T	1 39 12.0	22 55.7	14 31.7	11♐ 7.4	17 18.5	4 55.3	1 46.5	6 32.9	10 38.4	14 9.0	1 27.2	18 33.1
18 F	1 43 8.5	23 55.3	14 28.5	22 59.8	18 0.9	6 5.3	2 29.6	6 41.0	10 41.5	14 11.6	1 26.8	18 32.5
19 S	1 47 5.1	24 54.9	14 25.3	5♑ 1.5	18 38.8	7 15.3	3 12.8	6 49.3	10 44.7	14 14.3	1 26.3	18 31.9
20 S	1 51 1.7	25 54.5	14 22.2	17 16.8	19 11.7	8 25.2	3 56.1	6 57.7	10 48.1	14 17.0	1 25.8	18 31.2
21 M	1 54 58.2	26 54.2	14 19.0	29 50.5	19 39.2	9 34.9	4 39.4	7 6.2	10 51.5	14 19.7	1 25.3	18 30.6
22 T	1 58 54.8	27 53.9	14 15.8	12♒46.8	20 0.6	10 44.6	5 22.8	7 14.8	10 54.9	14 22.5	1 24.8	18 29.9
23 W	2 2 51.3	28 53.7	14 12.6	26 8.9	20 15.5	11 54.2	6 6.2	7 23.6	10 58.5	14 25.3	1 24.2	18 29.2
24 T	2 6 47.9	29 53.4	14 9.4	9♓58.9	20 23.2	13 3.8	6 49.7	7 32.5	11 2.2	14 28.2	1 23.6	18 28.5
25 F	2 10 44.4	0♏53.2	14 6.3	24 16.2	20 23.2	14 13.2	7 33.3	7 41.5	11 5.9	14 31.0	1 23.0	18 27.8
26 S	2 14 41.0	1 53.1	14 3.1	8♈57.9	20R15.0	15 22.5	8 17.0	7 50.6	11 9.7	14 34.0	1 22.3	18 27.1
27 S	2 18 37.5	2 52.9	13 59.9	23 58.0	19 57.9	16 31.7	9 0.7	7 59.9	11 13.6	14 36.9	1 21.6	18 26.3
28 M	2 22 34.1	3 52.8	13 56.7	9♉ 8.4	19 31.8	17 40.8	9 44.5	8 9.3	11 17.6	14 39.9	1 20.8	18 25.5
29 T	2 26 30.6	4 52.7	13 53.6	24 19.4	18 56.3	18 49.8	10 28.4	8 18.8	11 21.7	14 42.9	1 20.1	18 24.7
30 W	2 30 27.2	5 52.7	13 50.4	9♊21.9	18 11.6	19 58.7	11 12.3	8 28.4	11 25.8	14 45.9	1 19.3	18 23.9
31 T	2 34 23.8	6 52.7	13 47.2	24 7.9	17 17.9	21 7.5	11 56.3	8 38.2	11 30.0	14 48.9	1 18.5	18 23.1

DECLINATION

DAY	EPHEMERIS SIDEREAL TIME	☉	☊	☽	☿	♀	♂	♃	♄	♅	♆	♇
1 T	0 36 7.2	2S49.5	16S27.2	16N23.2	13S 0.6	17S42.3	18S30.3	23S30.8	22S45.7	22S28.3	22N16.0	13N46.6
4 F	0 47 56.8	3 59.3	16 24.4	19 45.7	14 41.5	18 52.1	19 4.9	23 30.5	22 45.6	22 29.0	22 15.9	13 46.1
7 M	0 59 46.5	5 8.8	16 21.6	12 53.5	16 13.8	19 57.9	19 38.2	23 30.0	22 45.5	22 29.8	22 15.8	13 45.6
10 T	1 11 36.1	6 17.6	16 18.8	0 56.1	17 36.3	20 59.4	20 10.0	23 29.4	22 45.3	22 30.7	22 15.7	13 45.1
13 S	1 23 25.8	7 25.8	16 16.0	10S55.5	18 47.3	21 56.1	20 40.5	23 28.7	22 45.0	22 31.6	22 15.7	13 44.5
16 W	1 35 15.5	8 33.0	16 13.2	18 37.0	19 44.6	22 48.0	21 9.3	23 27.8	22 44.6	22 32.5	22 15.6	13 44.0
19 S	1 47 5.1	9 39.1	16 10.4	19 13.6	20 25.4	23 34.6	21 36.6	23 26.8	22 44.2	22 33.4	22 15.5	13 43.5
22 T	1 58 54.8	10 43.9	16 7.6	11 54.6	20 45.6	24 15.7	22 2.1	23 25.7	22 43.7	22 34.4	22 15.4	13 43.0
25 F	2 10 44.4	11 47.3	16 4.7	1N24.6	20 39.8	24 51.1	22 25.9	23 24.5	22 43.1	22 35.4	22 15.4	13 42.5
28 M	2 22 34.1	12 49.0	16 1.9	14 56.1	20 1.3	25 20.7	22 47.7	23 23.0	22 42.4	22 36.4	22 15.3	13 42.0
31 T	2 34 23.8	13 49.0	15 59.1	19 52.3	18 45.0	25 44.2	23 7.7	23 21.4	22 41.6	22 37.5	22 15.2	13 41.5

NOVEMBER 1901

LONGITUDE

DAY	EPHEMERIS SIDEREAL TIME h m s	☉ ° ′	☊ ° ′	☽ ° ′	☿ ° ′	♀ ° ′	♂ ° ′	♃ ° ′	♄ ° ′	♅ ° ′	♆ ° ′	♇ ° ′
1 F	2 38 20.3	7♏52.7	13♏44.0	8♋31.9	16♏16.1	22♐16.1	12♐40.4	8♑48.0	11♑34.3	14♐52.0	1♋17.6	18♊22.3
2 S	2 42 16.9	8 52.8	13 40.8	22 31.0	15R 7.3	23 24.7	13 24.5	8 58.0	11 38.7	14 55.2	1R16.7	18R21.4
3 S	2 46 13.4	9 52.9	13 37.7	6♌ 4.9	13 53.1	24 33.1	14 8.7	9 8.1	11 43.2	14 58.3	1 15.8	18 20.6
4 M	2 50 10.0	10 53.0	13 34.5	19 14.9	12 35.5	25 41.4	14 53.0	9 18.2	11 47.7	15 1.5	1 14.9	18 19.7
5 T	2 54 6.5	11 53.2	13 31.3	2♍ 3.6	11 16.7	26 49.6	15 37.3	9 28.5	11 52.3	15 4.7	1 13.9	18 18.8
6 W	2 58 3.1	12 53.4	13 28.1	14 34.2	9 59.3	27 57.6	16 21.7	9 38.9	11 56.9	15 7.9	1 12.9	18 17.9
7 T	3 1 59.6	13 53.6	13 25.0	26 50.3	8 45.8	29 5.5	17 6.2	9 49.5	12 1.7	15 11.1	1 11.9	18 16.9
8 F	3 5 56.2	14 53.9	13 21.8	8♎55.1	7 38.5	0♑13.3	17 50.7	10 0.1	12 6.5	15 14.4	1 10.9	18 16.0
9 S	3 9 52.8	15 54.2	13 18.6	20 51.7	6 39.4	1 20.9	18 35.3	10 10.8	12 11.4	15 17.7	1 9.8	18 15.1
10 S	3 13 49.3	16 54.5	13 15.4	2♏42.7	5 50.2	2 28.4	19 20.0	10 21.6	12 16.3	15 21.0	1 8.7	18 14.1
11 M	3 17 45.8	17 54.9	13 12.2	14 30.6	5 11.8	3 35.7	20 4.7	10 32.5	12 21.3	15 24.4	1 7.6	18 13.1
12 T	3 21 42.4	18 55.3	13 9.1	26 17.7	4 45.0	4 42.9	20 49.5	10 43.6	12 26.4	15 27.7	1 6.4	18 12.1
13 W	3 25 39.0	19 55.7	13 5.9	8♐ 6.0	4 29.9	5 49.9	21 34.4	10 54.7	12 31.6	15 31.1	1 5.2	18 11.1
14 T	3 29 35.5	20 56.1	13 2.7	19 57.8	4 26.3	6 56.7	22 19.3	11 5.9	12 36.8	15 34.5	1 4.0	18 10.1
15 F	3 33 32.1	21 56.6	12 59.5	1♑55.6	4D33.8	8 3.3	23 4.3	11 17.2	12 42.1	15 37.9	1 2.8	18 9.1
16 S	3 37 28.6	22 57.1	12 56.4	14 2.0	4 51.6	9 9.8	23 49.3	11 28.6	12 47.4	15 41.4	1 1.6	18 8.0
17 S	3 41 25.2	23 57.6	12 53.2	26 20.1	5 18.9	10 16.1	24 34.4	11 40.1	12 52.8	15 44.8	1 0.3	18 7.0
18 M	3 45 21.7	24 58.2	12 50.0	8♒53.2	5 54.8	11 22.1	25 19.6	11 51.6	12 58.3	15 48.3	0 59.0	18 6.0
19 T	3 49 18.3	25 58.7	12 46.8	21 44.9	6 38.5	12 28.0	26 4.8	12 3.3	13 3.8	15 51.8	0 57.7	18 4.9
20 W	3 53 14.9	26 59.3	12 43.6	4♓58.2	7 29.1	13 33.6	26 50.0	12 15.0	13 9.4	15 55.3	0 56.3	18 3.8
21 T	3 57 11.4	27 59.9	12 40.5	18 35.9	8 25.7	14 39.0	27 35.3	12 26.8	13 15.0	15 58.8	0 55.0	18 2.7
22 F	4 1 8.0	29 0.5	12 37.3	2♈39.2	9 27.5	15 44.2	28 20.7	12 38.7	13 20.7	16 2.4	0 53.6	18 1.7
23 S	4 5 4.5	0♐ 1.2	12 34.1	17 7.5	10 34.0	16 49.2	29 6.1	12 50.7	13 26.5	16 5.9	0 52.2	18 0.6
24 S	4 9 1.1	1 1.8	12 30.9	1♉57.5	11 44.4	17 53.8	29 51.6	13 2.8	13 32.3	16 9.5	0 50.8	17 59.5
25 M	4 12 57.6	2 2.5	12 27.8	17 3.4	12 58.1	18 58.2	0♑37.1	13 14.9	13 38.1	16 13.1	0 49.4	17 58.3
26 T	4 16 54.2	3 3.2	12 24.6	2♊16.9	14 14.8	20 2.4	1 22.7	13 27.1	13 44.1	16 16.6	0 47.9	17 57.2
27 W	4 20 50.8	4 3.9	12 21.4	17 28.2	15 34.0	21 6.2	2 8.4	13 39.4	13 50.0	16 20.2	0 46.4	17 56.1
28 T	4 24 47.3	5 4.7	12 18.2	2♋27.5	16 55.3	22 9.8	2 54.0	13 51.7	13 56.0	16 23.8	0 45.0	17 55.0
29 F	4 28 43.9	6 5.4	12 15.1	17 6.5	18 18.4	23 13.1	3 39.8	14 4.1	14 2.1	16 27.5	0 43.4	17 53.9
30 S	4 32 40.4	7 6.2	12 11.9	1♌19.7	19 43.0	24 16.0	4 25.6	14 16.6	14 8.2	16 31.1	0 41.9	17 52.7

DECLINATION

DAY	EPHEMERIS SIDEREAL TIME h m s	☉	☊	☽	☿	♀	♂	♃	♄	♅	♆	♇
1 F	2 38 20.3	14S 8.6	15S58.1	18N50.4	18S11.2	25S50.6	23S13.9	23S20.9	22S41.3	22S37.9	22N15.2	13N41.3
4 M	2 50 10.0	15 5.9	15 55.3	10 2.3	16 10.2	26 5.9	23 31.1	23 19.0	22 40.5	22 38.9	22 15.2	13 40.9
7 T	3 1 59.6	16 1.0	15 52.4	2S17.5	14 0.1	26 14.9	23 46.2	23 17.0	22 39.5	22 40.0	22 15.1	13 40.4
10 S	3 13 49.3	16 53.7	15 49.5	13 21.7	12 12.6	26 17.6	23 59.2	23 14.8	22 38.5	22 41.1	22 15.1	13 40.0
13 W	3 25 39.0	17 43.8	15 46.6	19 29.6	11 10.4	26 14.1	24 9.9	23 12.4	22 37.3	22 42.3	22 15.1	13 39.5
16 S	3 37 28.6	18 31.1	15 43.8	18 7.7	10 58.3	26 4.5	24 18.4	23 9.8	22 36.1	22 43.4	22 15.0	13 39.1
19 T	3 49 18.3	19 15.5	15 40.9	9 18.2	11 27.6	25 48.8	24 24.5	23 6.9	22 34.8	22 44.5	22 15.0	13 38.7
22 F	4 1 8.0	19 56.8	15 38.0	4N14.1	12 25.8	25 27.3	24 28.2	23 3.9	22 33.4	22 45.6	22 15.0	13 38.4
25 M	4 12 57.6	20 34.8	15 35.1	16 37.6	13 41.4	25 0.2	24 29.6	23 0.6	22 31.9	22 46.8	22 15.0	13 38.0
28 T	4 24 47.3	21 9.3	15 32.2	19 27.3	15 5.9	24 27.7	24 28.5	22 57.1	22 30.3	22 47.9	22 15.0	13 37.7

DECEMBER 1901

LONGITUDE

DAY	EPHEMERIS SIDEREAL TIME h m s	☉ ° ′	☊ ° ′	☽ ° ′	☿ ° ′	♀ ° ′	♂ ° ′	♃ ° ′	♄ ° ′	♅ ° ′	♆ ° ′	♇ ° ′
1 S	4 36 37.0	8♐ 7.0	12♏ 8.7	15♌ 4.5	21♏ 8.9	25♑18.7	5♑11.4	14♑29.2	14♑14.4	16♐34.7	0♋40.4	17♊51.6
2 M	4 40 33.5	9 7.9	12 5.5	28 21.0	22 35.9	26 21.0	5 57.3	14 41.8	14 20.6	16 38.3	0R38.8	17R50.4
3 T	4 44 30.1	10 8.7	12 2.4	11♍11.8	24 3.8	27 23.0	6 43.2	14 54.5	14 26.8	16 42.0	0 37.3	17 49.3
4 W	4 48 26.6	11 9.6	11 59.2	23 40.5	25 32.5	28 24.6	7 29.2	15 7.2	14 33.1	16 45.6	0 35.7	17 48.1
5 T	4 52 23.2	12 10.5	11 56.0	5♎51.9	27 1.8	29 25.9	8 15.3	15 20.1	14 39.4	16 49.3	0 34.1	17 47.0
6 F	4 56 19.8	13 11.5	11 52.8	17 50.6	28 31.7	0♒26.7	9 1.3	15 32.9	14 45.8	16 52.9	0 32.5	17 45.8
7 S	5 0 16.3	14 12.4	11 49.6	29 41.2	0♐ 2.1	1 27.2	9 47.5	15 45.9	14 52.2	16 56.6	0 30.9	17 44.7
8 S	5 4 12.9	15 13.4	11 46.5	11♏27.9	1 32.8	2 27.3	10 33.7	15 58.9	14 58.7	17 0.3	0 29.3	17 43.5
9 M	5 8 9.4	16 14.4	11 43.3	23 14.3	3 3.9	3 27.0	11 19.9	16 11.9	15 5.2	17 3.9	0 27.6	17 42.3
10 T	5 12 6.0	17 15.4	11 40.1	5♐ 3.3	4 35.3	4 26.2	12 6.2	16 25.0	15 11.7	17 7.6	0 26.0	17 41.2
11 W	5 16 2.6	18 16.4	11 36.9	16 57.2	6 6.9	5 25.0	12 52.5	16 38.2	15 18.3	17 11.3	0 24.3	17 40.0
12 T	5 19 59.1	19 17.4	11 33.8	28 57.8	7 38.8	6 23.3	13 38.9	16 51.4	15 24.9	17 14.9	0 22.7	17 38.8
13 F	5 23 55.7	20 18.5	11 30.6	11♑ 6.7	9 10.9	7 21.1	14 25.3	17 4.6	15 31.5	17 18.6	0 21.0	17 37.7
14 S	5 27 52.2	21 19.5	11 27.4	23 25.1	10 43.1	8 18.4	15 11.7	17 17.9	15 38.2	17 22.2	0 19.3	17 36.5
15 S	5 31 48.8	22 20.6	11 24.2	5♒54.3	12 15.5	9 15.2	15 58.2	17 31.3	15 44.9	17 25.9	0 17.6	17 35.3
16 M	5 35 45.3	23 21.7	11 21.1	18 35.9	13 48.1	10 11.4	16 44.7	17 44.7	15 51.6	17 29.6	0 16.0	17 34.2
17 T	5 39 41.9	24 22.8	11 17.9	1♓31.4	15 20.8	11 7.0	17 31.3	17 58.1	15 58.4	17 33.2	0 14.3	17 33.0
18 W	5 43 38.4	25 23.8	11 14.7	14 42.8	16 53.7	12 2.1	18 17.9	18 11.6	16 5.2	17 36.9	0 12.6	17 31.9
19 T	5 47 35.0	26 24.9	11 11.5	28 12.3	18 26.7	12 56.4	19 4.5	18 25.1	16 12.0	17 40.5	0 10.9	17 30.7
20 F	5 51 31.5	27 26.0	11 8.3	12♈ 1.3	19 59.9	13 50.2	19 51.2	18 38.7	16 18.8	17 44.1	0 9.2	17 29.6
21 S	5 55 28.1	28 27.1	11 5.2	26 10.8	21 33.3	14 43.2	20 37.9	18 52.3	16 25.7	17 47.7	0 7.5	17 28.5
22 S	5 59 24.7	29 28.3	11 2.0	10♉39.9	23 6.9	15 35.6	21 24.7	19 5.9	16 32.6	17 51.3	0 5.8	17 27.3
23 M	6 3 21.2	0♑29.4	10 58.8	25 25.7	24 40.7	16 27.1	22 11.4	19 19.6	16 39.5	17 54.9	0 4.1	17 26.2
24 T	6 7 17.8	1 30.5	10 55.6	10♊22.9	26 14.6	17 18.0	22 58.2	19 33.3	16 46.4	17 58.5	0 2.4	17 25.1
25 W	6 11 14.3	2 31.6	10 52.5	25 23.7	27 48.8	18 8.0	23 45.1	19 47.0	16 53.3	18 2.1	0 0.7	17 23.9
26 T	6 15 10.9	3 32.7	10 49.3	10♋19.2	29 23.3	18 57.1	24 31.9	20 0.8	17 0.3	18 5.7	29♊59.0	17 22.8
27 F	6 19 7.5	4 33.8	10 46.1	25 0.3	0♑57.9	19 45.4	25 18.8	20 14.6	17 7.3	18 9.2	29 57.3	17 21.7
28 S	6 23 4.0	5 35.0	10 42.9	9♌19.5	2 32.9	20 32.8	26 5.8	20 28.4	17 14.3	18 12.8	29 55.6	17 20.6
29 S	6 27 0.6	6 36.1	10 39.8	23 12.2	4 8.1	21 19.3	26 52.7	20 42.3	17 21.3	18 16.3	29 53.9	17 19.5
30 M	6 30 57.1	7 37.3	10 36.6	6♍36.5	5 43.6	22 4.7	27 39.7	20 56.1	17 28.3	18 19.8	29 52.2	17 18.4
31 T	6 34 53.7	8 38.4	10 33.4	19 33.3	7 19.5	22 49.2	28 26.7	21 10.0	17 35.3	18 23.3	29 50.5	17 17.4

DECLINATION

DAY	EPHEMERIS SIDEREAL TIME h m s	☉	☊	☽	☿	♀	♂	♃	♄	♅	♆	♇
1 S	4 36 37.0	21S40.3	15S29.2	11N17.8	16S33.2	23S50.1	24S24.9	22S53.4	22S28.6	22S49.0	22N15.0	13N37.5
4 W	4 48 26.6	22 7.5	15 26.3	1S10.1	17 58.9	23 7.8	24 18.9	22 49.4	22 26.9	22 50.1	22 15.0	13 37.2
7 S	5 0 16.3	22 30.9	15 23.4	12 31.8	19 20.4	22 21.0	24 10.3	22 45.2	22 25.0	22 51.2	22 15.0	13 37.0
10 T	5 12 6.0	22 50.4	15 20.5	19 15.1	20 35.6	21 30.3	23 59.4	22 40.7	22 23.1	22 52.3	22 15.0	13 36.8
13 F	5 23 55.7	23 5.7	15 17.5	18 36.2	21 43.1	20 35.9	23 45.9	22 36.1	22 21.1	22 53.4	22 15.0	13 36.6
16 M	5 35 45.3	23 17.0	15 14.6	10 21.8	22 41.6	19 38.3	23 30.0	22 31.1	22 19.0	22 54.5	22 15.0	13 36.5
19 T	5 47 35.0	23 24.1	15 11.6	2N36.6	23 30.4	18 38.0	23 11.7	22 26.0	22 16.8	22 55.5	22 15.1	13 36.4
22 S	5 59 24.7	23 26.9	15 8.7	15 12.0	24 8.6	17 35.5	22 51.0	22 20.6	22 14.5	22 56.5	22 15.1	13 36.4
25 W	6 11 14.3	23 25.6	15 5.7	19 52.7	24 35.6	16 31.3	22 27.9	22 14.9	22 12.2	22 57.5	22 15.1	13 36.3
28 S	6 23 4.0	23 19.9	15 2.7	13 0.2	24 50.7	15 25.8	22 2.5	22 9.1	22 9.8	22 58.5	22 15.2	13 36.4
31 T	6 34 53.7	23 10.1	14 59.7	0 24.7	24 53.5	14 19.7	21 34.9	22 2.9	22 7.3	22 59.5	22 15.2	13 36.4

JANUARY 1902

DAY	EPHEMERIS SIDEREAL TIME	☉	☊	☽	☿	♀	♂	♃	♄	♅	♆	♇
	h m s	° ′	° ′	° ′	° ′	° ′	° ′	° ′	° ′	° ′	° ′	° ′
LONGITUDE												
1 W	6 38 50.2	9♑39.6	10♏30.2	2♎ 5.9	8♑55.6	23♒32.6	29♑13.8	21♑24.0	17♑42.4	18♐26.8	29♊48.8	17♊16.3
2 T	6 42 46.8	10 40.7	10 27.0	14 18.9	10 32.1	24 14.9	0♒ 0.8	21 37.9	17 49.4	18 30.3	29R47.2	17R15.2
3 F	6 46 43.4	11 41.9	10 23.9	26 17.4	12 9.0	24 56.1	0 47.9	21 51.9	17 56.5	18 33.7	29 45.5	17 14.2
4 S	6 50 39.9	12 43.1	10 20.7	8♏ 7.0	13 46.2	25 36.1	1 35.1	22 5.9	18 3.6	18 37.2	29 43.9	17 13.1
5 S	6 54 36.5	13 44.2	10 17.5	19 53.1	15 23.8	26 14.9	2 22.2	22 19.9	18 10.7	18 40.6	29 42.2	17 12.1
6 M	6 58 33.0	14 45.4	10 14.3	1♐40.3	17 1.7	26 52.4	3 9.4	22 33.9	18 17.8	18 44.0	29 40.6	17 11.1
7 T	7 2 29.6	15 46.6	10 11.2	13 32.8	18 40.1	27 28.5	3 56.6	22 47.9	18 24.9	18 47.3	29 39.0	17 10.1
8 W	7 6 26.1	16 47.8	10 8.0	25 33.7	20 18.9	28 3.3	4 43.8	23 2.0	18 32.0	18 50.7	29 37.3	17 9.1
9 T	7 10 22.7	17 49.0	10 4.8	7♑45.3	21 58.0	28 36.6	5 31.1	23 16.1	18 39.1	18 54.0	29 35.7	17 8.1
10 F	7 14 19.3	18 50.1	10 1.6	20 8.8	23 37.6	29 8.4	6 18.3	23 30.1	18 46.2	18 57.3	29 34.1	17 7.1
11 S	7 18 15.8	19 51.3	9 58.5	2♒44.7	25 17.5	29 38.7	7 5.6	23 44.2	18 53.3	19 0.6	29 32.6	17 6.2
12 S	7 22 12.4	20 52.5	9 55.3	15 32.8	26 57.8	0♓ 7.3	7 52.9	23 58.3	19 0.4	19 3.9	29 31.0	17 5.2
13 M	7 26 8.9	21 53.6	9 52.1	28 32.5	28 38.4	0 34.3	8 40.2	24 12.4	19 7.5	19 7.1	29 29.4	17 4.3
14 T	7 30 5.5	22 54.8	9 48.9	11♓43.5	0♒19.4	0 59.5	9 27.6	24 26.5	19 14.6	19 10.3	29 27.9	17 3.4
15 W	7 34 2.0	23 55.9	9 45.7	25 5.5	2 0.6	1 22.8	10 14.9	24 40.6	19 21.7	19 13.5	29 26.4	17 2.5
16 T	7 37 58.6	24 57.0	9 42.6	8♈38.9	3 42.1	1 44.3	11 2.3	24 54.7	19 28.8	19 16.7	29 24.9	17 1.6
17 F	7 41 55.2	25 58.1	9 39.4	22 24.2	5 23.7	2 3.8	11 49.6	25 8.9	19 35.9	19 19.8	29 23.4	17 0.7
18 S	7 45 51.7	26 59.2	9 36.2	6♉22.2	7 5.4	2 21.3	12 37.0	25 23.0	19 42.9	19 22.9	29 21.9	16 59.9
19 S	7 49 48.3	28 0.3	9 33.0	20 32.8	8 47.2	2 36.7	13 24.4	25 37.1	19 50.0	19 26.0	29 20.5	16 59.0
20 M	7 53 44.8	29 1.3	9 29.9	4♊55.2	10 28.8	2 49.9	14 11.8	25 51.2	19 57.0	19 29.0	29 19.0	16 58.2
21 T	7 57 41.4	0♒ 2.4	9 26.7	19 26.6	12 10.1	3 0.9	14 59.2	26 5.3	20 4.1	19 32.0	29 17.6	16 57.4
22 W	8 1 37.9	1 3.4	9 23.5	4♋ 2.5	13 51.0	3 9.6	15 46.6	26 19.4	20 11.1	19 35.0	29 16.2	16 56.6
23 T	8 5 34.5	2 4.4	9 20.3	18 36.6	15 31.3	3 16.0	16 34.1	26 33.5	20 18.1	19 37.9	29 14.8	16 55.8
24 F	8 9 31.1	3 5.4	9 17.2	3♌ 1.8	17 10.7	3 19.9	17 21.5	26 47.5	20 25.1	19 40.8	29 13.5	16 55.0
25 S	8 13 27.6	4 6.4	9 14.0	17 11.1	18 49.0	3 21.5	18 8.9	27 1.6	20 32.1	19 43.7	29 12.1	16 54.3
26 S	8 17 24.1	5 7.4	9 10.8	0♍59.3	20 25.8	3R20.5	18 56.4	27 15.7	20 39.1	19 46.6	29 10.8	16 53.5
27 M	8 21 20.7	6 8.4	9 7.6	14 23.1	22 0.8	3 17.1	19 43.8	27 29.7	20 46.0	19 49.4	29 9.5	16 52.8
28 T	8 25 17.3	7 9.3	9 4.4	27 22.1	23 33.5	3 11.2	20 31.3	27 43.7	20 52.9	19 52.2	29 8.3	16 52.1
29 W	8 29 13.8	8 10.3	9 1.3	9♎57.8	25 3.5	3 2.7	21 18.7	27 57.8	20 59.8	19 54.9	29 7.0	16 51.5
30 T	8 33 10.4	9 11.2	8 58.1	22 13.8	26 30.2	2 51.7	22 6.2	28 11.8	21 6.7	19 57.6	29 5.8	16 50.8
31 F	8 37 6.9	10 12.1	8 54.9	4♏14.8	27 53.0	2 38.2	22 53.7	28 25.7	21 13.6	20 0.3	29 4.6	16 50.2
DECLINATION												
1 W	6 38 50.2	23S 5.9	14S58.7	3S50.3	24S51.5	13S57.5	21S25.2	22S 0.9	22S 6.4	22S59.8	22N15.2	13N36.4
4 S	6 50 39.9	22 50.5	14 55.8	14 31.8	24 36.9	12 51.4	20 54.7	21 54.5	22 3.9	23 0.7	22 15.3	13 36.5
7 T	7 2 29.6	22 31.0	14 52.8	19 46.2	24 8.7	11 46.0	20 22.0	21 47.8	22 1.2	23 1.6	22 15.3	13 36.7
10 F	7 14 19.3	22 7.5	14 49.8	17 17.0	23 26.6	10 42.0	19 47.3	21 41.0	21 58.5	23 2.5	22 15.4	13 36.8
13 M	7 26 8.9	21 40.2	14 46.8	7 29.4	22 30.4	9 40.2	19 10.6	21 33.9	21 55.7	23 3.3	22 15.4	13 37.1
16 T	7 37 58.6	21 9.0	14 43.7	5N52.0	21 20.0	8 41.5	18 32.1	21 26.7	21 52.9	23 4.1	22 15.5	13 37.3
19 S	7 49 48.3	20 34.2	14 40.7	17 1.2	19 55.7	7 46.8	17 51.8	21 19.3	21 50.1	23 4.9	22 15.5	13 37.6
22 W	8 1 37.9	19 55.9	14 37.7	19 19.3	18 18.4	6 57.1	17 9.7	21 11.6	21 47.2	23 5.6	22 15.6	13 37.9
25 S	8 13 27.6	19 14.3	14 34.7	10 57.4	16 29.8	6 13.6	16 26.0	21 3.8	21 44.3	23 6.3	22 15.7	13 38.3
28 T	8 25 17.3	18 29.5	14 31.6	2S 1.2	14 33.0	5 37.2	15 40.8	20 55.9	21 41.3	23 7.0	22 15.8	13 38.7
31 F	8 37 6.9	17 41.7	14 28.6	13 19.1	12 33.2	5 9.1	14 54.2	20 47.8	21 38.4	23 7.7	22 15.8	13 39.1

FEBRUARY 1902

DAY	EPHEMERIS SIDEREAL TIME	☉	☊	☽	☿	♀	♂	♃	♄	♅	♆	♇
LONGITUDE												
1 S	8 41 3.5	11♒13.0	8♏51.7	16♏ 6.2	29♒11.2	2♓22.3	23♒41.1	28♑39.7	21♑20.4	20♐ 2.9	29♊ 3.4	16♊49.5
2 S	8 45 0.1	12 13.9	8 48.6	27 53.6	0♓24.2	2R 3.9	24 28.6	28 53.7	21 27.2	20 5.5	29R 2.2	16R48.9
3 M	8 48 56.6	13 14.8	8 45.4	9♐42.6	1 31.2	1 43.2	25 16.1	29 7.6	21 34.0	20 8.1	29 1.1	16 48.4
4 T	8 52 53.1	14 15.6	8 42.2	21 38.2	2 31.3	1 20.2	26 3.5	29 21.5	21 40.8	20 10.6	29 0.0	16 47.8
5 W	8 56 49.7	15 16.5	8 39.0	3♑44.6	3 23.9	0 55.0	26 51.0	29 35.4	21 47.5	20 13.1	28 58.9	16 47.2
6 T	9 0 46.3	16 17.3	8 35.9	16 5.1	4 8.1	0 27.8	27 38.5	29 49.2	21 54.2	20 15.5	28 57.9	16 46.7
7 F	9 4 42.8	17 18.1	8 32.7	28 41.7	4 43.2	29♒58.6	28 25.9	0♒ 3.1	22 0.9	20 17.9	28 56.9	16 46.2
8 S	9 8 39.4	18 18.9	8 29.5	11♒35.0	5 8.6	29 27.7	29 13.4	0 16.9	22 7.5	20 20.2	28 55.9	16 45.7
9 S	9 12 35.9	19 19.7	8 26.3	24 44.3	5 23.7	28 55.2	0♓ 0.9	0 30.6	22 14.1	20 22.6	28 54.9	16 45.3
10 M	9 16 32.5	20 20.4	8 23.1	8♓ 7.6	5 28.3	28 21.4	0 48.3	0 44.4	22 20.7	20 24.8	28 54.0	16 44.8
11 T	9 20 29.0	21 21.2	8 20.0	21 42.7	5R22.1	27 46.3	1 35.8	0 58.1	22 27.2	20 27.1	28 53.1	16 44.4
12 W	9 24 25.6	22 21.9	8 16.8	5♈27.0	5 5.2	27 10.4	2 23.2	1 11.8	22 33.7	20 29.3	28 52.2	16 44.0
13 T	9 28 22.1	23 22.5	8 13.6	19 18.1	4 38.0	26 33.6	3 10.6	1 25.4	22 40.2	20 31.4	28 51.3	16 43.6
14 F	9 32 18.7	24 23.2	8 10.4	3♉14.7	4 1.1	25 56.5	3 58.0	1 39.0	22 46.6	20 33.5	28 50.5	16 43.3
15 S	9 36 15.2	25 23.8	8 7.2	17 15.7	3 15.5	25 19.1	4 45.4	1 52.6	22 53.0	20 35.5	28 49.7	16 42.9
16 S	9 40 11.8	26 24.4	8 4.1	1♊20.5	2 22.4	24 41.7	5 32.8	2 6.1	22 59.3	20 37.5	28 49.0	16 42.6
17 M	9 44 8.4	27 24.9	8 0.9	15 28.5	1 23.1	24 4.7	6 20.2	2 19.6	23 5.6	20 39.5	28 48.3	16 42.3
18 T	9 48 4.9	28 25.4	7 57.7	29 38.3	0 19.3	23 28.2	7 7.5	2 33.0	23 11.8	20 41.4	28 47.6	16 42.1
19 W	9 52 1.5	29 25.9	7 54.5	13♋47.6	29♒12.9	22 52.5	7 54.9	2 46.4	23 18.0	20 43.3	28 46.9	16 41.8
20 T	9 55 58.0	0♓26.4	7 51.4	27 53.3	28 5.5	22 17.8	8 42.2	2 59.7	23 24.2	20 45.1	28 46.3	16 41.6
21 F	9 59 54.6	1 26.8	7 48.2	11♌51.2	26 58.8	21 44.4	9 29.5	3 13.0	23 30.3	20 46.9	28 45.7	16 41.4
22 S	10 3 51.1	2 27.2	7 45.0	25 37.0	25 54.4	21 12.5	10 16.8	3 26.3	23 36.4	20 48.6	28 45.1	16 41.2
23 S	10 7 47.7	3 27.6	7 41.8	9♍ 6.9	24 53.7	20 42.2	11 4.0	3 39.5	23 42.4	20 50.3	28 44.6	16 41.0
24 M	10 11 44.2	4 27.9	7 38.7	22 18.2	23 57.9	20 13.8	11 51.3	3 52.6	23 48.4	20 51.9	28 44.1	16 40.9
25 T	10 15 40.8	5 28.3	7 35.5	5♎ 9.7	23 7.8	19 47.4	12 38.5	4 5.7	23 54.3	20 53.5	28 43.6	16 40.8
26 W	10 19 37.4	6 28.6	7 32.3	17 42.1	22 24.1	19 23.1	13 25.8	4 18.8	24 0.2	20 55.0	28 43.1	16 40.7
27 T	10 23 33.9	7 28.8	7 29.1	29 57.5	21 47.3	19 1.0	14 12.9	4 31.8	24 6.0	20 56.5	28 42.7	16 40.6
28 F	10 27 30.4	8 29.1	7 25.9	11♏59.4	21 17.6	18 41.3	15 0.1	4 44.7	24 11.7	20 58.0	28 42.4	16 40.5
DECLINATION												
1 S	8 41 3.5	17S25.1	14S27.6	16S 2.8	11S53.8	5S 1.7	14S38.3	20S45.0	21S37.4	23S 7.9	22N15.9	13N39.3
4 T	8 52 53.1	16 33.5	14 24.5	19 45.4	10 2.3	4 45.8	13 49.8	20 36.7	21 34.4	23 8.5	22 16.0	13 39.7
7 F	9 4 42.8	15 39.4	14 21.5	15 35.4	8 29.5	4 39.8	13 0.2	20 28.3	21 31.4	23 9.0	22 16.0	13 40.2
10 M	9 16 32.5	14 42.8	14 18.4	4 30.8	7 26.8	4 43.7	12 9.4	20 19.7	21 28.4	23 9.6	22 16.1	13 40.8
13 T	9 28 22.1	13 44.0	14 15.3	8N59.8	7 3.5	4 56.9	11 17.5	20 11.1	21 25.4	23 10.1	22 16.3	13 41.4
16 S	9 40 11.8	12 43.2	14 12.2	18 24.1	7 22.0	5 18.3	10 24.7	20 2.3	21 22.4	23 10.6	22 16.4	13 41.9
19 W	9 52 1.5	11 40.6	14 9.2	18 6.7	8 15.4	5 46.2	9 31.1	19 53.5	21 19.5	23 11.0	22 16.5	13 42.6
22 S	10 3 51.1	10 36.3	14 6.1	8 29.3	9 29.1	6 18.5	8 36.8	19 44.7	21 16.5	23 11.4	22 16.6	13 43.2
25 T	10 15 40.8	9 30.6	14 3.0	4S27.0	10 46.5	6 53.2	7 41.7	19 35.7	21 13.6	23 11.8	22 16.7	13 43.9
28 F	10 27 30.4	8 23.5	13 59.9	14 55.4	11 55.0	7 28.2	6 46.2	19 26.8	21 10.8	23 12.1	22 16.8	13 44.6

MARCH 1902

DAY	EPHEMERIS SIDEREAL TIME h m s	☉ ° ′	☊ ° ′	☽ ° ′	☿ ° ′	♀ ° ′	♂ ° ′	♃ ° ′	♄ ° ′	♅ ° ′	♆ ° ′	♇ ° ′
LONGITUDE												
1 S	10 31 27.0	9♓29.3	7♏22.8	23♏52.2	20♒55.1	18♒24.0	15♓47.3	4♒57.6	24♑17.4	20♐59.3	28♊42.0	16♊40.5
2 S	10 35 23.6	10 29.5	7 19.6	5♐41.0	20R39.6	18R 9.1	16 34.4	5 10.5	24 23.1	21 0.7	28R41.7	16R40.5
3 M	10 39 20.1	11 29.7	7 16.4	17 31.2	20 31.1	17 56.6	17 21.5	5 23.2	24 28.7	21 2.0	28 41.4	16D40.5
4 T	10 43 16.7	12 29.8	7 13.2	29 28.1	20 29.3	17 46.7	18 8.6	5 35.9	24 34.2	21 3.2	28 41.2	16 40.6
5 W	10 47 13.2	13 29.9	7 10.0	11♑36.6	20D33.8	17 39.3	18 55.7	5 48.6	24 39.7	21 4.4	28 41.0	16 40.6
6 T	10 51 9.7	14 30.0	7 6.9	24 1.1	20 44.4	17 34.3	19 42.8	6 1.1	24 45.1	21 5.5	28 40.8	16 40.7
7 F	10 55 6.3	15 30.1	7 3.7	6♒44.7	21 0.8	17 31.8	20 29.8	6 13.7	24 50.5	21 6.6	28 40.7	16 40.8
8 S	10 59 2.9	16 30.1	7 0.5	19 49.1	21 22.5	17 31.7	21 16.8	6 26.1	24 55.8	21 7.6	28 40.6	16 40.9
9 S	11 2 59.4	17 30.1	6 57.3	3♓14.2	21 49.3	17D34.0	22 3.8	6 38.5	25 1.0	21 8.6	28 40.5	16 41.1
10 M	11 6 56.0	18 30.1	6 54.2	16 58.4	22 20.8	17 38.7	22 50.7	6 50.8	25 6.2	21 9.5	28 40.5	16 41.3
11 T	11 10 52.5	19 30.0	6 51.0	0♈58.2	22 56.7	17 45.6	23 37.6	7 3.0	25 11.3	21 10.4	28 40.5	16 41.5
12 W	11 14 49.1	20 29.9	6 47.8	15 9.3	23 36.8	17 54.8	24 24.5	7 15.2	25 16.3	21 11.2	28D40.5	16 41.7
13 T	11 18 45.6	21 29.8	6 44.6	29 27.0	24 20.7	18 6.1	25 11.4	7 27.3	25 21.3	21 12.0	28 40.6	16 41.9
14 F	11 22 42.2	22 29.6	6 41.4	13♉46.8	25 8.2	18 19.6	25 58.2	7 39.3	25 26.2	21 12.7	28 40.7	16 42.2
15 S	11 26 38.7	23 29.4	6 38.3	28 5.1	25 59.0	18 35.1	26 45.0	7 51.2	25 31.0	21 13.4	28 40.8	16 42.5
16 S	11 30 35.3	24 29.2	6 35.1	12♊19.2	26 53.1	18 52.6	27 31.8	8 3.0	25 35.8	21 14.0	28 41.0	16 42.8
17 M	11 34 31.8	25 28.9	6 31.9	26 27.1	27 50.0	19 12.0	28 18.5	8 14.8	25 40.5	21 14.5	28 41.2	16 43.1
18 T	11 38 28.4	26 28.6	6 28.7	10♋27.6	28 49.8	19 33.2	29 5.2	8 26.5	25 45.1	21 15.0	28 41.4	16 43.4
19 W	11 42 24.9	27 28.2	6 25.6	24 19.4	29 52.2	19 56.3	29 51.9	8 38.1	25 49.6	21 15.5	28 41.7	16 43.8
20 T	11 46 21.5	28 27.8	6 22.4	8♌ 1.6	0♓57.0	20 21.1	0♈38.5	8 49.6	25 54.1	21 15.9	28 42.0	16 44.2
21 F	11 50 18.1	29 27.4	6 19.2	21 32.7	2 4.3	20 47.6	1 25.1	9 1.0	25 58.5	21 16.2	28 42.3	16 44.6
22 S	11 54 14.6	0♈26.9	6 16.0	4♍51.5	3 13.7	21 15.7	2 11.6	9 12.4	26 2.8	21 16.5	28 42.7	16 45.1
23 S	11 58 11.1	1 26.4	6 12.8	17 56.6	4 25.3	21 45.3	2 58.1	9 23.6	26 7.0	21 16.7	28 43.1	16 45.5
24 M	12 2 7.7	2 25.9	6 9.7	0♎47.4	5 39.0	22 16.5	3 44.6	9 34.8	26 11.2	21 16.9	28 43.6	16 46.0
25 T	12 6 4.2	3 25.3	6 6.5	13 23.4	6 54.5	22 49.1	4 31.1	9 45.8	26 15.3	21 17.1	28 44.0	16 46.5
26 W	12 10 0.8	4 24.7	6 3.3	25 45.5	8 12.0	23 23.1	5 17.5	9 56.8	26 19.3	21 17.2	28 44.5	16 47.0
27 T	12 13 57.4	5 24.1	6 0.1	7♏54.9	9 31.3	23 58.4	6 3.8	10 7.7	26 23.2	21 17.2	28 45.1	16 47.5
28 F	12 17 53.9	6 23.4	5 57.0	19 54.1	10 52.4	24 35.0	6 50.2	10 18.4	26 27.1	21R17.2	28 45.7	16 48.1
29 S	12 21 50.5	7 22.7	5 53.8	1♐46.4	12 15.1	25 12.9	7 36.5	10 29.1	26 30.9	21 17.1	28 46.3	16 48.7
30 S	12 25 47.0	8 22.0	5 50.6	13 35.6	13 39.5	25 52.0	8 22.7	10 39.7	26 34.6	21 17.0	28 46.9	16 49.3
31 M	12 29 43.6	9 21.2	5 47.4	25 26.3	15 5.6	26 32.2	9 8.9	10 50.2	26 38.2	21 16.8	28 47.6	16 49.9
DECLINATION												
1 S	10 31 27.0	8S 0.9	13S58.8	17S12.9	12S14.6	7S39.6	6S27.5	19S23.8	21S 9.9	23S12.2	22N16.9	13N44.8
4 T	10 43 16.7	6 52.4	13 55.7	19 19.3	13 1.6	8 12.3	5 31.3	19 14.9	21 7.1	23 12.5	22 17.0	13 45.6
7 F	10 55 6.3	5 43.1	13 52.6	13 38.2	13 30.5	8 41.9	4 34.8	19 5.9	21 4.4	23 12.8	22 17.2	13 46.3
10 M	11 6 56.0	4 33.0	13 49.5	1 36.8	13 41.5	9 7.4	3 38.0	18 57.0	21 1.8	23 13.0	22 17.3	13 47.1
13 T	11 18 45.6	3 22.4	13 46.4	11N45.2	13 35.6	9 28.3	2 41.0	18 48.2	20 59.2	23 13.2	22 17.4	13 47.9
16 S	11 30 35.3	2 11.5	13 43.2	19 9.8	13 13.9	9 44.0	1 43.9	18 39.4	20 56.8	23 13.4	22 17.6	13 48.7
19 W	11 42 24.9	1 0.4	13 40.1	16 14.6	12 37.5	9 54.4	0 46.9	18 30.7	20 54.4	23 13.5	22 17.7	13 49.5
22 S	11 54 14.6	0N10.7	13 36.9	5 32.9	11 47.1	9 59.3	0N10.0	18 22.1	20 52.2	23 13.6	22 17.9	13 50.3
25 T	12 6 4.2	1 21.7	13 33.8	7S 1.4	10 43.8	9 58.6	1 6.8	18 13.6	20 50.0	23 13.7	22 18.1	13 51.1
28 F	12 17 53.9	2 32.3	13 30.6	16 22.7	9 28.0	9 52.3	2 3.3	18 5.3	20 48.0	23 13.8	22 18.2	13 51.9
31 M	12 29 43.6	3 42.5	13 27.5	19 17.7	8 0.5	9 40.5	2 59.5	17 57.1	20 46.1	23 13.8	22 18.4	13 52.8

APRIL 1902

DAY	EPHEMERIS SIDEREAL TIME h m s	☉ ° ′	☊ ° ′	☽ ° ′	☿ ° ′	♀ ° ′	♂ ° ′	♃ ° ′	♄ ° ′	♅ ° ′	♆ ° ′	♇ ° ′
LONGITUDE												
1 T	12 33 40.1	10♈20.4	5♏44.2	7♑23.1	16♓33.2	27♒13.4	9♈55.1	11♒ 0.5	26♑41.7	21♐16.5	28♊48.3	16♊50.5
2 W	12 37 36.6	11 19.6	5 41.1	19 31.0	18 2.4	27 55.8	10 41.2	11 10.8	26 45.1	21R16.3	28 49.0	16 51.2
3 T	12 41 33.2	12 18.8	5 37.9	1♒54.7	19 33.2	28 39.1	11 27.3	11 21.0	26 48.5	21 15.9	28 49.8	16 51.9
4 F	12 45 29.8	13 17.9	5 34.7	14 38.3	21 5.5	29 23.4	12 13.4	11 31.0	26 51.8	21 15.5	28 50.6	16 52.6
5 S	12 49 26.3	14 17.0	5 31.5	27 44.8	22 39.3	0♓ 8.7	12 59.4	11 41.0	26 55.0	21 15.1	28 51.4	16 53.3
6 S	12 53 22.9	15 16.0	5 28.3	11♓15.6	24 14.7	0 54.8	13 45.4	11 50.8	26 58.1	21 14.6	28 52.3	16 54.0
7 M	12 57 19.4	16 15.1	5 25.2	25 10.3	25 51.5	1 41.7	14 31.4	12 0.5	27 1.1	21 14.1	28 53.2	16 54.8
8 T	13 1 16.0	17 14.1	5 22.0	9♈26.4	27 29.9	2 29.5	15 17.3	12 10.1	27 4.0	21 13.5	28 54.1	16 55.5
9 W	13 5 12.5	18 13.0	5 18.8	23 59.1	29 9.7	3 18.1	16 3.1	12 19.6	27 6.8	21 12.8	28 55.1	16 56.3
10 T	13 9 9.1	19 12.0	5 15.6	8♉42.2	0♈51.1	4 7.4	16 48.9	12 29.0	27 9.6	21 12.2	28 56.1	16 57.2
11 F	13 13 5.6	20 10.8	5 12.5	23 28.7	2 34.0	4 57.5	17 34.7	12 38.2	27 12.2	21 11.4	28 57.1	16 58.0
12 S	13 17 2.2	21 9.7	5 9.3	8♊11.8	4 18.4	5 48.2	18 20.4	12 47.3	27 14.8	21 10.6	28 58.1	16 58.8
13 S	13 20 58.7	22 8.5	5 6.1	22 45.8	6 4.3	6 39.6	19 6.1	12 56.3	27 17.2	21 9.8	28 59.2	16 59.7
14 M	13 24 55.3	23 7.3	5 2.9	7♋ 6.3	7 51.8	7 31.6	19 51.7	13 5.2	27 19.6	21 8.9	29 0.3	17 0.6
15 T	13 28 51.8	24 6.1	4 59.7	21 10.6	9 40.8	8 24.2	20 37.3	13 13.9	27 21.9	21 8.0	29 1.5	17 1.5
16 W	13 32 48.4	25 4.8	4 56.6	4♌57.5	11 31.3	9 17.5	21 22.8	13 22.5	27 24.1	21 7.0	29 2.7	17 2.4
17 T	13 36 44.9	26 3.4	4 53.4	18 27.1	13 23.5	10 11.3	22 8.3	13 31.0	27 26.2	21 6.0	29 3.9	17 3.3
18 F	13 40 41.5	27 2.1	4 50.2	1♍39.9	15 17.2	11 5.7	22 53.7	13 39.3	27 28.2	21 4.9	29 5.1	17 4.3
19 S	13 44 38.1	28 0.7	4 47.0	14 37.2	17 12.5	12 0.5	23 39.1	13 47.6	27 30.1	21 3.8	29 6.3	17 5.2
20 S	13 48 34.6	28 59.2	4 43.9	27 20.3	19 9.3	12 56.0	24 24.4	13 55.6	27 31.9	21 2.6	29 7.6	17 6.2
21 M	13 52 31.1	29 57.7	4 40.7	9♎50.5	21 7.6	13 51.9	25 9.7	14 3.6	27 33.6	21 1.4	29 8.9	17 7.2
22 T	13 56 27.7	0♉56.2	4 37.5	22 9.3	23 7.5	14 48.3	25 54.9	14 11.4	27 35.3	21 0.2	29 10.3	17 8.2
23 W	14 0 24.3	1 54.7	4 34.3	4♏18.2	25 8.9	15 45.1	26 40.1	14 19.1	27 36.8	20 58.9	29 11.6	17 9.2
24 T	14 4 20.8	2 53.1	4 31.2	16 18.9	27 11.6	16 42.4	27 25.3	14 26.6	27 38.2	20 57.6	29 13.0	17 10.3
25 F	14 8 17.4	3 51.5	4 28.0	28 13.3	29 15.7	17 40.2	28 10.3	14 34.0	27 39.6	20 56.2	29 14.4	17 11.3
26 S	14 12 13.9	4 49.9	4 24.8	10♐ 3.8	1♉21.1	18 38.3	28 55.4	14 41.2	27 40.8	20 54.8	29 15.9	17 12.4
27 S	14 16 10.5	5 48.2	4 21.6	21 53.2	3 27.6	19 36.9	29 40.4	14 48.3	27 41.9	20 53.3	29 17.3	17 13.5
28 M	14 20 7.0	6 46.6	4 18.4	3♑44.7	5 35.1	20 35.9	0♉25.3	14 55.3	27 43.0	20 51.8	29 18.8	17 14.6
29 T	14 24 3.6	7 44.8	4 15.3	15 42.1	7 43.4	21 35.2	1 10.2	15 2.1	27 44.0	20 50.3	29 20.4	17 15.7
30 W	14 28 0.1	8 43.1	4 12.1	27 49.3	9 52.4	22 34.9	1 55.1	15 8.7	27 44.8	20 48.7	29 21.9	17 16.8
DECLINATION												
1 T	12 33 40.1	4N 5.8	13S26.4	18S34.5	7S28.8	9S35.4	3N18.1	17S54.5	20S45.5	23S13.8	22N18.4	13N53.1
4 F	12 45 29.8	5 15.1	13 23.2	11 29.7	5 46.4	9 16.5	4 13.8	17 46.5	20 43.8	23 13.7	22 18.6	13 53.9
7 M	12 57 19.4	6 23.6	13 20.1	1N 8.5	3 53.6	8 52.5	5 8.9	17 38.8	20 42.2	23 13.7	22 18.7	13 54.7
10 T	13 9 9.1	7 31.2	13 16.9	14 1.7	1 50.8	8 23.7	6 3.4	17 31.3	20 40.8	23 13.6	22 18.9	13 55.6
13 S	13 20 58.7	8 37.6	13 13.7	19 18.1	0N21.2	7 50.2	6 57.2	17 24.1	20 39.5	23 13.5	22 19.1	13 56.4
16 W	13 32 48.4	9 42.7	13 10.5	13 54.1	2 41.6	7 12.3	7 50.3	17 17.2	20 38.4	23 13.3	22 19.2	13 57.3
19 S	13 44 38.1	10 46.3	13 7.3	2 19.7	5 9.5	6 30.2	8 42.5	17 10.5	20 37.4	23 13.2	22 19.4	13 58.1
22 T	13 56 27.7	11 48.3	13 4.1	9S40.2	7 43.2	5 44.3	9 33.9	17 4.2	20 36.6	23 13.0	22 19.5	13 58.9
25 F	14 8 17.4	12 48.6	13 0.9	17 40.7	10 20.4	4 54.7	10 24.3	16 58.2	20 36.0	23 12.7	22 19.7	13 59.7
28 M	14 20 7.0	13 47.0	12 57.7	18 50.3	12 57.8	4 1.8	11 13.7	16 52.5	20 35.5	23 12.5	22 19.8	14 0.5

MAY 1902

DAY	EPHEMERIS SIDEREAL TIME	☉	☊	☽	☿	♀	♂	♃	♄	♅	♆	♇
	h m s	° ′	° ′	° ′	° ′	° ′	° ′	° ′	° ′	° ′	° ′	° ′
						LONGITUDE						
1 T	14 31 56.7	9♉41.3	4♏ 8.9	10♒10.8	12♉ 1.7	23♓35.0	2♉39.9	15♒15.2	27♑45.6	20♐47.1	29♊23.5	17♊17.9
2 F	14 35 53.2	10 39.5	4 5.7	22 50.7	14 11.3	24 35.4	3 24.6	15 21.5	27 46.2	20R45.4	29 25.0	17 19.1
3 S	14 39 49.8	11 37.7	4 2.5	5♓52.9	16 20.8	25 36.1	4 9.3	15 27.7	27 46.8	20 43.7	29 26.7	17 20.2
4 S	14 43 46.4	12 35.9	3 59.4	19 20.1	18 29.8	26 37.1	4 54.0	15 33.8	27 47.2	20 42.0	29 28.3	17 21.4
5 M	14 47 42.9	13 34.0	3 56.2	3♈13.6	20 38.3	27 38.4	5 38.6	15 39.6	27 47.6	20 40.2	29 29.9	17 22.6
6 T	14 51 39.5	14 32.2	3 53.0	17 32.8	22 45.7	28 40.1	6 23.1	15 45.3	27 47.9	20 38.4	29 31.6	17 23.8
7 W	14 55 36.0	15 30.2	3 49.8	2♉14.2	24 51.9	29 42.0	7 7.6	15 50.9	27 48.0	20 36.6	29 33.3	17 25.0
8 T	14 59 32.6	16 28.3	3 46.7	17 12.0	26 56.6	0♈44.2	7 52.1	15 56.3	27 48.1	20 34.7	29 35.1	17 26.2
9 F	15 3 29.1	17 26.3	3 43.5	2♊18.0	28 59.5	1 46.6	8 36.5	16 1.5	27R48.1	20 32.8	29 36.8	17 27.4
10 S	15 7 25.7	18 24.4	3 40.3	17 23.3	1♊ 0.2	2 49.3	9 20.8	16 6.5	27 47.9	20 30.9	29 38.6	17 28.7
11 S	15 11 22.2	19 22.3	3 37.1	2♋18.8	2 58.7	3 52.2	10 5.1	16 11.4	27 47.7	20 28.9	29 40.4	17 29.9
12 M	15 15 18.8	20 20.3	3 34.0	16 57.3	4 54.7	4 55.4	10 49.3	16 16.1	27 47.4	20 26.9	29 42.2	17 31.2
13 T	15 19 15.4	21 18.2	3 30.8	1♌13.8	6 48.0	5 58.8	11 33.5	16 20.6	27 47.0	20 24.9	29 44.0	17 32.5
14 W	15 23 11.9	22 16.1	3 27.6	15 6.0	8 38.5	7 2.4	12 17.6	16 25.0	27 46.5	20 22.8	29 45.8	17 33.7
15 T	15 27 8.4	23 13.9	3 24.4	28 33.9	10 26.0	8 6.2	13 1.7	16 29.2	27 45.8	20 20.8	29 47.7	17 35.0
16 F	15 31 5.0	24 11.8	3 21.2	11♍39.1	12 10.5	9 10.2	13 45.7	16 33.2	27 45.1	20 18.7	29 49.6	17 36.3
17 S	15 35 1.6	25 9.6	3 18.1	24 24.4	13 51.8	10 14.5	14 29.7	16 37.0	27 44.3	20 16.5	29 51.5	17 37.6
18 S	15 38 58.1	26 7.4	3 14.9	6♎53.1	15 29.9	11 18.9	15 13.6	16 40.7	27 43.4	20 14.4	29 53.4	17 38.9
19 M	15 42 54.7	27 5.1	3 11.7	19 8.5	17 4.7	12 23.5	15 57.4	16 44.2	27 42.4	20 12.2	29 55.3	17 40.2
20 T	15 46 51.2	28 2.8	3 8.5	1♏13.8	18 36.1	13 28.4	16 41.2	16 47.5	27 41.4	20 10.0	29 57.3	17 41.5
21 W	15 50 47.8	29 0.5	3 5.4	13 11.8	20 4.1	14 33.4	17 24.9	16 50.6	27 40.2	20 7.8	29 59.2	17 42.9
22 T	15 54 44.4	29 58.2	3 2.2	25 4.8	21 28.7	15 38.5	18 8.6	16 53.6	27 38.9	20 5.5	0♋ 1.2	17 44.2
23 F	15 58 40.9	0♊55.9	2 59.0	6♐55.3	22 49.8	16 43.9	18 52.3	16 56.3	27 37.5	20 3.3	0 3.2	17 45.6
24 S	16 2 37.4	1 53.5	2 55.8	18 45.0	24 7.4	17 49.4	19 35.8	16 58.9	27 36.1	20 1.0	0 5.2	17 46.9
25 S	16 6 34.0	2 51.1	2 52.6	0♑36.2	25 21.3	18 55.1	20 19.4	17 1.3	27 34.5	19 58.7	0 7.2	17 48.3
26 M	16 10 30.6	3 48.7	2 49.5	12 30.9	26 31.7	20 1.0	21 2.8	17 3.5	27 32.9	19 56.4	0 9.3	17 49.6
27 T	16 14 27.1	4 46.3	2 46.3	24 31.8	27 38.4	21 7.0	21 46.3	17 5.6	27 31.2	19 54.0	0 11.3	17 51.0
28 W	16 18 23.6	5 43.8	2 43.1	6♒41.6	28 41.3	22 13.2	22 29.6	17 7.4	27 29.4	19 51.7	0 13.4	17 52.4
29 T	16 22 20.2	6 41.4	2 39.9	19 3.5	29 40.4	23 19.5	23 12.9	17 9.1	27 27.5	19 49.3	0 15.5	17 53.7
30 F	16 26 16.8	7 38.9	2 36.8	1♓41.2	0♋35.6	24 26.0	23 56.2	17 10.5	27 25.5	19 46.9	0 17.5	17 55.1
31 S	16 30 13.3	8 36.4	2 33.6	14 38.4	1 26.9	25 32.6	24 39.4	17 11.8	27 23.4	19 44.6	0 19.7	17 56.5
						DECLINATION						
1 T	14 31 56.7	14N43.4	12S54.5	12S37.5	15N31.1	3S 5.8	12N 2.0	16S47.2	20S35.2	23S12.2	22N19.9	14N 1.3
4 S	14 43 46.4	15 37.6	12 51.2	0 46.5	17 55.0	2 7.1	12 49.2	16 42.3	20 35.1	23 11.9	22 20.1	14 2.1
7 W	14 55 36.0	16 29.4	12 48.0	12N26.5	20 3.9	1 6.0	13 35.1	16 37.9	20 35.2	23 11.5	22 20.2	14 2.8
10 S	15 7 25.7	17 18.8	12 44.8	19 15.7	21 53.4	0 2.9	14 19.8	16 33.8	20 35.5	23 11.1	22 20.3	14 3.6
13 T	15 19 15.4	18 5.7	12 41.5	14 45.3	23 20.7	1N 2.1	15 3.2	16 30.2	20 35.9	23 10.7	22 20.4	14 4.3
16 F	15 31 5.0	18 49.7	12 38.3	3 19.1	24 25.1	2 8.5	15 45.1	16 27.1	20 36.5	23 10.3	22 20.5	14 5.0
19 M	15 42 54.7	19 30.9	12 35.0	8S46.5	25 7.4	3 16.1	16 25.6	16 24.4	20 37.3	23 9.9	22 20.6	14 5.7
22 T	15 54 44.4	20 9.2	12 31.8	17 14.2	25 29.7	4 24.5	17 4.7	16 22.2	20 38.2	23 9.4	22 20.7	14 6.3
25 S	16 6 34.0	20 44.3	12 28.5	19 5.8	25 34.5	5 33.5	17 42.1	16 20.5	20 39.3	23 8.9	22 20.8	14 7.0
28 W	16 18 23.6	21 16.3	12 25.3	13 34.1	25 24.2	6 42.8	18 18.0	16 19.3	20 40.6	23 8.5	22 20.8	14 7.6
31 S	16 30 13.3	21 44.9	12 22.0	2 24.5	25 1.5	7 51.9	18 52.2	16 18.7	20 42.0	23 7.9	22 20.9	14 8.2

JUNE 1902

DAY	EPHEMERIS SIDEREAL TIME	☉	☊	☽	☿	♀	♂	♃	♄	♅	♆	♇
						LONGITUDE						
1 S	16 34 9.9	9♊33.9	2♏30.4	27♓58.3	2♋14.1	26♈39.4	25♉22.6	17♒12.9	27♑21.2	19♐42.1	0♋21.8	17♊57.9
2 M	16 38 6.4	10 31.4	2 27.2	11♈43.6	2 57.2	27 46.3	26 5.7	17 13.8	27R19.0	19R39.7	0 23.9	17 59.3
3 T	16 42 3.0	11 28.9	2 24.0	25 55.1	3 36.1	28 53.3	26 48.7	17 14.5	27 16.6	19 37.3	0 26.0	18 0.6
4 W	16 45 59.5	12 26.4	2 20.9	10♉31.6	4 10.8	0♉ 0.4	27 31.7	17 15.0	27 14.2	19 34.9	0 28.2	18 2.0
5 T	16 49 56.1	13 23.8	2 17.7	25 29.0	4 41.1	1 7.7	28 14.7	17 15.3	27 11.7	19 32.4	0 30.3	18 3.4
6 F	16 53 52.7	14 21.3	2 14.5	10♊40.0	5 7.0	2 15.1	28 57.6	17 15.5	27 9.2	19 30.0	0 32.5	18 4.8
7 S	16 57 49.2	15 18.7	2 11.3	25 55.2	5 28.4	3 22.6	29 40.4	17R15.4	27 6.5	19 27.5	0 34.6	18 6.2
8 S	17 1 45.8	16 16.1	2 8.2	11♋ 3.9	5 45.3	4 30.2	0♊23.2	17 15.1	27 3.8	19 25.1	0 36.8	18 7.6
9 M	17 5 42.3	17 13.5	2 5.0	25 56.5	5 57.6	5 37.9	1 5.9	17 14.7	27 0.9	19 22.6	0 39.0	18 9.0
10 T	17 9 38.9	18 10.9	2 1.8	10♌25.7	6 5.3	6 45.7	1 48.6	17 14.0	26 58.1	19 20.2	0 41.2	18 10.4
11 W	17 13 35.5	19 8.2	1 58.6	24 27.2	6 8.5	7 53.6	2 31.2	17 13.2	26 55.1	19 17.7	0 43.4	18 11.8
12 T	17 17 32.0	20 5.6	1 55.5	8♍ 0.0	6R 7.1	9 1.7	3 13.7	17 12.2	26 52.1	19 15.2	0 45.6	18 13.2
13 F	17 21 28.6	21 2.9	1 52.3	21 5.8	6 1.2	10 9.8	3 56.2	17 10.9	26 49.0	19 12.8	0 47.8	18 14.6
14 S	17 25 25.1	22 0.2	1 49.1	3♎47.9	5 51.1	11 18.0	4 38.7	17 9.5	26 45.8	19 10.3	0 50.0	18 16.0
15 S	17 29 21.7	22 57.5	1 45.9	16 10.6	5 36.8	12 26.3	5 21.1	17 7.9	26 42.6	19 7.9	0 52.2	18 17.4
16 M	17 33 18.2	23 54.8	1 42.8	28 18.6	5 18.6	13 34.7	6 3.4	17 6.2	26 39.3	19 5.4	0 54.4	18 18.8
17 T	17 37 14.8	24 52.1	1 39.6	10♏16.5	4 56.8	14 43.2	6 45.7	17 4.2	26 35.9	19 3.0	0 56.7	18 20.2
18 W	17 41 11.3	25 49.3	1 36.4	22 8.3	4 31.7	15 51.8	7 27.9	17 2.0	26 32.5	19 0.5	0 58.9	18 21.6
19 T	17 45 7.9	26 46.6	1 33.2	3♐57.4	4 3.7	17 0.5	8 10.1	16 59.7	26 29.0	18 58.1	1 1.1	18 23.0
20 F	17 49 4.5	27 43.8	1 30.1	15 46.7	3 33.2	18 9.3	8 52.2	16 57.2	26 25.4	18 55.7	1 3.3	18 24.4
21 S	17 53 1.0	28 41.1	1 26.9	27 38.4	3 0.7	19 18.1	9 34.2	16 54.4	26 21.8	18 53.3	1 5.6	18 25.7
22 S	17 56 57.6	29 38.3	1 23.7	9♑34.3	2 26.9	20 27.1	10 16.2	16 51.5	26 18.1	18 50.9	1 7.8	18 27.1
23 M	18 0 54.1	0♋35.5	1 20.5	21 36.0	1 52.1	21 36.1	10 58.2	16 48.5	26 14.4	18 48.5	1 10.0	18 28.5
24 T	18 4 50.7	1 32.7	1 17.3	3♒44.8	1 17.1	22 45.2	11 40.1	16 45.2	26 10.6	18 46.1	1 12.3	18 29.8
25 W	18 8 47.3	2 29.9	1 14.2	16 2.5	0 42.5	23 54.4	12 21.9	16 41.8	26 6.8	18 43.7	1 14.5	18 31.2
26 T	18 12 43.8	3 27.1	1 11.0	28 30.8	0 8.7	25 3.7	13 3.7	16 38.2	26 2.9	18 41.4	1 16.7	18 32.6
27 F	18 16 40.4	4 24.3	1 7.8	11♓12.1	29♊36.5	26 13.1	13 45.4	16 34.4	25 59.0	18 39.0	1 19.0	18 33.9
28 S	18 20 36.9	5 21.5	1 4.6	24 9.2	29 6.4	27 22.5	14 27.1	16 30.5	25 55.1	18 36.7	1 21.2	18 35.3
29 S	18 24 33.5	6 18.8	1 1.5	7♈25.0	28 38.8	28 32.1	15 8.8	16 26.3	25 51.1	18 34.4	1 23.4	18 36.6
30 M	18 28 30.0	7 16.0	0 58.3	21 2.1	28 14.3	29 41.7	15 50.3	16 22.0	25 47.0	18 32.1	1 25.7	18 38.0
						DECLINATION						
1 S	16 34 9.9	21N53.7	12S20.9	1N59.8	24N51.7	8N14.9	19N 3.3	16S18.6	20S42.5	23S 7.8	22N20.9	14N 8.4
4 W	16 45 59.5	22 17.8	12 17.6	14 24.8	24 16.3	9 23.4	19 35.3	16 18.6	20 44.1	23 7.2	22 20.9	14 8.9
7 S	16 57 49.2	22 38.4	12 14.3	19 18.2	23 34.1	10 31.1	20 5.6	16 19.2	20 45.9	23 6.7	22 21.0	14 9.4
10 T	17 9 38.9	22 55.4	12 11.1	12 42.2	22 47.4	11 37.6	20 34.1	16 20.3	20 47.8	23 6.1	22 21.0	14 9.9
13 F	17 21 28.6	23 8.8	12 7.8	0 20.5	21 58.4	12 42.6	21 0.8	16 21.9	20 49.8	23 5.6	22 21.0	14 10.4
16 M	17 33 18.2	23 18.6	12 4.5	11S18.0	21 9.7	13 45.9	21 25.7	16 24.1	20 51.9	23 5.0	22 21.0	14 10.8
19 T	17 45 7.9	23 24.6	12 1.2	18 22.7	20 23.7	14 47.0	21 48.7	16 26.7	20 54.1	23 4.4	22 21.0	14 11.2
22 S	17 56 57.6	23 27.0	11 57.9	18 26.8	19 43.5	15 45.6	22 9.9	16 29.9	20 56.4	23 3.8	22 21.0	14 11.6
25 W	18 8 47.3	23 25.6	11 54.5	11 19.5	19 12.0	16 41.5	22 29.1	16 33.5	20 58.8	23 3.3	22 20.9	14 11.9
28 S	18 20 36.9	23 20.5	11 51.2	0N33.0	18 51.6	17 34.4	22 46.5	16 37.6	21 1.3	23 2.7	22 20.9	14 12.2

JULY 1902

DAY	EPHEMERIS SIDEREAL TIME	☉	☊	☽	☿	♀	♂	♃	♄	♅	♆	♇
	h m s	° ′	° ′	° ′	° ′	° ′	° ′	° ′	° ′	° ′	° ′	° ′
						LONGITUDE						
1 T	18 32 26.6	8♋13.2	0♏55.1	5♉ 2.5	27♊53.3	0♊51.4	16♊31.9	16♒17.6	25♑42.9	18♐29.8	1♋27.9	18♊39.3
2 W	18 36 23.1	9 10.4	0 51.9	19 26.2	27R36.2	2 1.2	17 13.4	16R12.9	25R38.8	18R27.6	1 30.1	18 40.6
3 T	18 40 19.7	10 7.6	0 48.8	4♊11.2	27 23.3	3 11.0	17 54.8	16 8.2	25 34.6	18 25.3	1 32.3	18 41.9
4 F	18 44 16.3	11 4.8	0 45.6	19 12.1	27 14.9	4 20.9	18 36.2	16 3.2	25 30.4	18 23.1	1 34.6	18 43.2
5 S	18 48 12.8	12 2.1	0 42.4	4♋21.1	27 11.2	5 30.9	19 17.5	15 58.1	25 26.2	18 20.9	1 36.8	18 44.5
6 S	18 52 9.3	12 59.3	0 39.2	19 28.1	27D12.4	6 41.0	19 58.7	15 52.9	25 21.9	18 18.8	1 39.0	18 45.8
7 M	18 56 5.9	13 56.5	0 36.0	4♌22.8	27 18.6	7 51.1	20 39.9	15 47.4	25 17.6	18 16.6	1 41.2	18 47.1
8 T	19 0 2.5	14 53.7	0 32.9	18 56.7	27 29.8	9 1.3	21 21.1	15 41.9	25 13.3	18 14.5	1 43.4	18 48.4
9 W	19 3 59.1	15 51.0	0 29.7	3♍ 3.8	27 46.3	10 11.5	22 2.2	15 36.2	25 9.0	18 12.4	1 45.5	18 49.7
10 T	19 7 55.6	16 48.2	0 26.5	16 41.8	28 7.9	11 21.8	22 43.3	15 30.4	25 4.6	18 10.4	1 47.7	18 50.9
11 F	19 11 52.1	17 45.4	0 23.3	29 51.2	28 34.7	12 32.2	23 24.2	15 24.4	25 0.3	18 8.3	1 49.9	18 52.2
12 S	19 15 48.7	18 42.6	0 20.2	12♎35.1	29 6.8	13 42.7	24 5.2	15 18.3	24 55.9	18 6.3	1 52.0	18 53.4
13 S	19 19 45.3	19 39.8	0 17.0	24 57.8	29 44.0	14 53.2	24 46.1	15 12.1	24 51.5	18 4.4	1 54.2	18 54.7
14 M	19 23 41.9	20 37.1	0 13.8	7♏ 4.5	0♋26.4	16 3.7	25 26.9	15 5.8	24 47.1	18 2.4	1 56.3	18 55.9
15 T	19 27 38.4	21 34.3	0 10.6	19 0.5	1 13.8	17 14.4	26 7.6	14 59.3	24 42.7	18 0.5	1 58.5	18 57.1
16 W	19 31 34.9	22 31.5	0 7.4	0♐50.6	2 6.3	18 25.1	26 48.4	14 52.7	24 38.2	17 58.6	2 0.6	18 58.3
17 T	19 35 31.5	23 28.7	0 4.3	12 39.4	3 3.9	19 35.8	27 29.0	14 46.1	24 33.8	17 56.8	2 2.7	18 59.5
18 F	19 39 28.0	24 26.0	0 1.1	24 30.5	4 6.3	20 46.6	28 9.6	14 39.3	24 29.4	17 54.9	2 4.8	19 0.7
19 S	19 43 24.6	25 23.2	29♎57.9	6♑26.7	5 13.6	21 57.5	28 50.2	14 32.4	24 24.9	17 53.2	2 6.9	19 1.8
20 S	19 47 21.2	26 20.4	29 54.7	18 30.1	6 25.7	23 8.5	29 30.7	14 25.4	24 20.5	17 51.4	2 9.0	19 3.0
21 M	19 51 17.7	27 17.7	29 51.6	0♒42.1	7 42.4	24 19.5	0♋11.1	14 18.4	24 16.1	17 49.7	2 11.0	19 4.1
22 T	19 55 14.3	28 15.0	29 48.4	13 3.4	9 3.8	25 30.5	0 51.5	14 11.2	24 11.7	17 48.0	2 13.1	19 5.2
23 W	19 59 10.8	29 12.2	29 45.2	25 34.7	10 29.6	26 41.7	1 31.9	14 4.0	24 7.3	17 46.4	2 15.1	19 6.4
24 T	20 3 7.4	0♌ 9.5	29 42.0	8♓16.4	11 59.8	27 52.9	2 12.2	13 56.6	24 2.9	17 44.8	2 17.2	19 7.5
25 F	20 7 3.9	1 6.8	29 38.9	21 9.4	13 34.2	29 4.1	2 52.4	13 49.3	23 58.5	17 43.2	2 19.2	19 8.5
26 S	20 11 0.5	2 4.1	29 35.7	4♈15.0	15 12.6	0♋15.5	3 32.6	13 41.8	23 54.1	17 41.7	2 21.2	19 9.6
27 S	20 14 57.1	3 1.4	29 32.5	17 34.8	16 54.8	1 26.9	4 12.7	13 34.3	23 49.8	17 40.2	2 23.2	19 10.7
28 M	20 18 53.6	3 58.8	29 29.3	1♉10.5	18 40.6	2 38.3	4 52.8	13 26.7	23 45.4	17 38.7	2 25.1	19 11.7
29 T	20 22 50.2	4 56.1	29 26.1	15 3.7	20 29.7	3 49.8	5 32.9	13 19.1	23 41.1	17 37.3	2 27.1	19 12.8
30 W	20 26 46.7	5 53.5	29 23.0	29 14.9	22 21.8	5 1.4	6 12.9	13 11.4	23 36.8	17 36.0	2 29.0	19 13.8
31 T	20 30 43.3	6 50.9	29 19.8	13♊43.1	24 16.7	6 13.0	6 52.8	13 3.7	23 32.6	17 34.6	2 30.9	19 14.8
						DECLINATION						
1 T	18 32 26.6	23N11.7	11S47.9	12N57.5	18N44.0	18N23.8	23N 2.0	16S42.2	21S 3.8	23S 2.1	22N20.8	14N12.5
4 F	18 44 16.3	22 59.2	11 44.6	19 18.3	18 49.6	19 9.6	23 15.5	16 47.1	21 6.4	23 1.6	22 20.8	14 12.7
7 M	18 56 5.9	22 43.2	11 41.2	14 17.0	19 7.4	19 51.4	23 27.1	16 52.5	21 9.0	23 1.0	22 20.7	14 12.9
10 T	19 7 55.6	22 23.6	11 37.9	1 59.7	19 35.2	20 28.9	23 36.8	16 58.2	21 11.6	23 0.5	22 20.6	14 13.1
13 S	19 19 45.3	22 0.5	11 34.6	10S 9.8	20 9.9	21 1.9	23 44.6	17 4.2	21 14.2	22 60.0	22 20.5	14 13.2
16 W	19 31 34.9	21 34.0	11 31.2	17 52.2	20 47.6	21 30.1	23 50.4	17 10.4	21 16.9	22 59.5	22 20.4	14 13.4
19 S	19 43 24.6	21 4.2	11♎27.9	18 43.4	21 24.0	21 53.3	23 54.4	17 17.0	21 19.5	22 59.0	22 20.3	14 13.4
22 T	19 55 14.3	20 31.3	11 24.5	12 13.8	21 54.0	22 11.3	23 56.5	17 23.7	21 22.1	22 58.6	22 20.2	14 13.5
25 F	20 7 3.9	19 55.2	11 21.2	0 38.6	22 12.4	22 23.9	23 56.7	17 30.5	21 24.6	22 58.2	22 20.0	14 13.5
28 M	20 18 53.6	19 16.1	11 17.8	11N43.9	22 14.0	22 31.1	23 55.1	17 37.5	21 27.1	22 57.8	22 19.9	14 13.5
31 T	20 30 43.3	18 34.1	11 14.4	18 57.0	21 54.5	22 32.5	23 51.6	17 44.5	21 29.6	22 57.4	22 19.8	14 13.4

AUGUST 1902

DAY	EPHEMERIS SIDEREAL TIME	☉	☊	☽	☿	♀	♂	♃	♄	♅	♆	♇
						LONGITUDE						
1 F	20 34 39.8	7♌48.3	29♎16.6	28♊25.1	26♋14.0	7♋24.8	7♋32.7	12♒56.0	23♑28.3	17♐33.4	2♋32.9	19♊15.8
2 S	20 38 36.4	8 45.8	29 13.4	13♋15.0	28 13.3	8 36.5	8 12.5	12R48.2	23R24.1	17R32.1	2 34.7	19 16.8
3 S	20 42 32.9	9 43.2	29 10.3	28 5.3	0♌14.3	9 48.3	8 52.3	12 40.4	23 19.9	17 30.9	2 36.6	19 17.7
4 M	20 46 29.5	10 40.7	29 7.1	12♌47.1	2 16.6	11 0.2	9 32.0	12 32.6	23 15.8	17 29.8	2 38.5	19 18.7
5 T	20 50 26.1	11 38.2	29 3.9	27 12.6	4 19.9	12 12.1	10 11.7	12 24.8	23 11.7	17 28.7	2 40.3	19 19.6
6 W	20 54 22.6	12 35.7	29 0.7	11♍15.6	6 23.9	13 24.1	10 51.3	12 17.0	23 7.7	17 27.6	2 42.1	19 20.5
7 T	20 58 19.1	13 33.2	28 57.6	24 52.6	8 28.2	14 36.1	11 30.9	12 9.2	23 3.6	17 26.6	2 43.9	19 21.4
8 F	21 2 15.7	14 30.7	28 54.4	8♎ 3.0	10 32.6	15 48.2	12 10.4	12 1.3	22 59.7	17 25.6	2 45.7	19 22.3
9 S	21 6 12.3	15 28.2	28 51.2	20 48.7	12 36.7	17 0.4	12 49.9	11 53.5	22 55.7	17 24.7	2 47.4	19 23.1
10 S	21 10 8.9	16 25.8	28 48.0	3♏13.3	14 40.5	18 12.6	13 29.3	11 45.8	22 51.9	17 23.8	2 49.2	19 24.0
11 M	21 14 5.4	17 23.4	28 44.8	15 21.5	16 43.6	19 24.8	14 8.6	11 38.0	22 48.0	17 23.0	2 50.9	19 24.8
12 T	21 18 1.9	18 20.9	28 41.7	27 18.5	18 45.9	20 37.1	14 47.9	11 30.3	22 44.2	17 22.2	2 52.6	19 25.6
13 W	21 21 58.5	19 18.5	28 38.5	9♐ 9.8	20 47.2	21 49.5	15 27.1	11 22.6	22 40.5	17 21.4	2 54.2	19 26.4
14 T	21 25 55.1	20 16.1	28 35.3	21 0.1	22 47.5	23 1.9	16 6.3	11 14.9	22 36.8	17 20.8	2 55.9	19 27.2
15 F	21 29 51.6	21 13.8	28 32.1	2♑54.2	24 46.6	24 14.3	16 45.5	11 7.3	22 33.2	17 20.1	2 57.5	19 27.9
16 S	21 33 48.2	22 11.4	28 29.0	14 55.5	26 44.6	25 26.8	17 24.5	10 59.8	22 29.7	17 19.5	2 59.1	19 28.7
17 S	21 37 44.7	23 9.1	28 25.8	27 6.8	28 41.2	26 39.4	18 3.6	10 52.3	22 26.2	17 19.0	3 0.7	19 29.4
18 M	21 41 41.3	24 6.8	28 22.6	9♒30.1	0♍36.5	27 52.0	18 42.5	10 44.9	22 22.7	17 18.5	3 2.2	19 30.1
19 T	21 45 37.8	25 4.5	28 19.4	22 6.0	2 30.4	29 4.7	19 21.4	10 37.5	22 19.4	17 18.0	3 3.8	19 30.7
20 W	21 49 34.4	26 2.2	28 16.2	4♓54.7	4 23.0	0♌17.4	20 0.3	10 30.2	22 16.1	17 17.7	3 5.3	19 31.4
21 T	21 53 30.9	26 60.0	28 13.1	17 55.7	6 14.2	1 30.2	20 39.1	10 23.0	22 12.8	17 17.3	3 6.8	19 32.0
22 F	21 57 27.5	27 57.8	28 9.9	1♈ 8.3	8 4.0	2 43.0	21 17.9	10 15.9	22 9.7	17 17.0	3 8.2	19 32.7
23 S	22 1 24.0	28 55.6	28 6.7	14 31.9	9 52.5	3 55.9	21 56.6	10 8.9	22 6.6	17 16.8	3 9.6	19 33.3
24 S	22 5 20.6	29 53.4	28 3.5	28 6.2	11 39.5	5 8.9	22 35.3	10 1.9	22 3.5	17 16.6	3 11.0	19 33.9
25 M	22 9 17.1	0♍51.3	28 0.4	11♉51.0	13 25.3	6 21.9	23 13.9	9 55.1	22 0.6	17 16.4	3 12.4	19 34.4
26 T	22 13 13.7	1 49.2	27 57.2	25 46.5	15 9.7	7 34.9	23 52.4	9 48.3	21 57.7	17 16.3	3 13.8	19 35.0
27 W	22 17 10.2	2 47.1	27 54.0	9♊52.4	16 52.7	8 48.0	24 30.9	9 41.7	21 54.9	17 16.3	3 15.1	19 35.5
28 T	22 21 6.8	3 45.0	27 50.8	24 7.6	18 34.5	10 1.2	25 9.4	9 35.2	21 52.1	17 16.3	3 16.4	19 36.0
29 F	22 25 3.4	4 43.0	27 47.6	8♋30.0	20 14.9	11 14.4	25 47.8	9 28.8	21 49.5	17D16.4	3 17.7	19 36.5
30 S	22 28 59.9	5 41.0	27 44.5	22 56.0	21 54.1	12 27.7	26 26.1	9 22.5	21 46.9	17 16.5	3 18.9	19 36.9
31 S	22 32 56.4	6 39.1	27 41.3	7♌20.6	23 32.0	13 41.0	27 4.4	9 16.3	21 44.4	17 16.6	3 20.1	19 37.4
						DECLINATION						
1 F	20 34 39.8	18N19.5	11S13.3	19N 7.0	21N42.8	22N31.8	23N50.1	17S46.8	21S30.4	22S57.3	22N19.7	14N13.4
4 M	20 46 29.5	17 33.9	11 9.9	12 18.5	20 51.8	22 25.7	23 44.3	17 53.9	21 32.8	22 57.0	22 19.6	14 13.3
7 T	20 58 19.1	16 45.8	11 6.6	0S30.7	19 37.9	22 13.8	23 36.8	18 0.8	21 35.1	22 56.7	22 19.4	14 13.2
10 S	21 10 8.9	15 55.2	11 3.2	12 9.9	18 4.1	21 56.3	23 27.6	18 7.7	21 37.3	22 56.5	22 19.3	14 13.0
13 W	21 21 58.5	15 2.3	10 59.8	18 32.1	16 14.6	21 33.1	23 16.7	18 14.4	21 39.4	22 56.2	22 19.1	14 12.8
16 S	21 33 48.2	14 7.2	10 56.4	17 43.0	14 13.4	21 4.3	23 4.2	18 21.0	21 41.4	22 56.1	22 18.9	14 12.6
19 T	21 45 37.8	13 10.2	10 53.0	9 48.2	12 4.3	20 30.0	22 50.2	18 27.3	21 43.4	22 56.0	22 18.8	14 12.4
22 F	21 57 27.5	12 11.2	10 49.6	2N28.8	9 50.4	19 50.5	22 34.6	18 33.4	21 45.2	22 55.9	22 18.6	14 12.1
25 M	22 9 17.1	11 10.5	10 46.2	14 7.6	7 34.0	19 5.7	22 17.6	18 39.2	21 46.9	22 55.8	22 18.4	14 11.8
28 T	22 21 6.8	10 8.2	10 42.8	19 0.6	5 17.0	18 16.1	21 59.1	18 44.6	21 48.4	22 55.8	22 18.3	14 11.5
31 S	22 32 56.4	9 4.5	10 39.3	13 34.9	3 1.0	17 21.7	21 39.3	18 49.7	21 49.9	22 55.9	22 18.1	14 11.2

SEPTEMBER 1902

DAY	EPHEMERIS SIDEREAL TIME	☉	☊	☽	☿	♀	♂	♃	♄	♅	♆	♇
	h m s	° ′	° ′	° ′	° ′	° ′	° ′	° ′	° ′	° ′	° ′	° ′
						LONGITUDE						
1 M	22 36 53.0	7♍37.2	27♎38.1	21♌38.1	25♍ 8.6	14♌54.4	27♋42.7	9♒10.3	21♑42.0	17♐16.8	3♋21.3	19♊37.8
2 T	22 40 49.6	8 35.3	27 34.9	5♍42.8	26 44.0	16 7.8	28 20.9	9R 4.4	21R39.7	17 17.1	3 22.5	19 38.2
3 W	22 44 46.1	9 33.4	27 31.8	19 30.0	28 18.2	17 21.2	28 59.0	8 58.7	21 37.4	17 17.4	3 23.6	19 38.6
4 T	22 48 42.7	10 31.6	27 28.6	2♎56.4	29 51.1	18 34.7	29 37.1	8 53.1	21 35.3	17 17.8	3 24.7	19 38.9
5 F	22 52 39.2	11 29.8	27 25.4	16 0.8	1♎22.7	19 48.3	0♌15.1	8 47.6	21 33.2	17 18.2	3 25.8	19 39.3
6 S	22 56 35.8	12 28.0	27 22.2	28 44.0	2 53.2	21 1.9	0 53.0	8 42.3	21 31.2	17 18.7	3 26.8	19 39.6
7 S	23 0 32.3	13 26.2	27 19.0	11♏ 8.4	4 22.4	22 15.5	1 30.9	8 37.1	21 29.3	17 19.2	3 27.8	19 39.9
8 M	23 4 28.9	14 24.5	27 15.9	23 17.6	5 50.4	23 29.2	2 8.8	8 32.1	21 27.5	17 19.8	3 28.8	19 40.1
9 T	23 8 25.4	15 22.8	27 12.7	5♐15.9	7 17.1	24 42.9	2 46.5	8 27.3	21 25.8	17 20.4	3 29.8	19 40.4
10 W	23 12 22.0	16 21.1	27 9.5	17 8.4	8 42.5	25 56.7	3 24.3	8 22.6	21 24.2	17 21.1	3 30.7	19 40.6
11 T	23 16 18.5	17 19.4	27 6.3	29 0.1	10 6.6	27 10.5	4 1.9	8 18.1	21 22.6	17 21.8	3 31.6	19 40.8
12 F	23 20 15.1	18 17.8	27 3.1	10♑55.9	11 29.4	28 24.3	4 39.5	8 13.8	21 21.2	17 22.6	3 32.4	19 41.0
13 S	23 24 11.6	19 16.2	26 60.0	23 0.1	12 50.9	29 38.2	5 17.1	8 9.6	21 19.9	17 23.4	3 33.3	19 41.2
14 S	23 28 8.2	20 14.6	26 56.8	5♒16.6	14 11.0	0♍52.1	5 54.6	8 5.6	21 18.6	17 24.3	3 34.1	19 41.3
15 M	23 32 4.7	21 13.1	26 53.6	17 48.1	15 29.6	2 6.1	6 32.0	8 1.8	21 17.5	17 25.2	3 34.8	19 41.4
16 T	23 36 1.3	22 11.5	26 50.4	0♓36.3	16 46.8	3 20.1	7 9.4	7 58.1	21 16.4	17 26.2	3 35.6	19 41.5
17 W	23 39 57.8	23 10.0	26 47.3	13 41.6	18 2.5	4 34.1	7 46.7	7 54.7	21 15.4	17 27.3	3 36.3	19 41.6
18 T	23 43 54.4	24 8.6	26 44.1	27 3.4	19 16.5	5 48.2	8 23.9	7 51.4	21 14.6	17 28.3	3 36.9	19 41.7
19 F	23 47 50.9	25 7.2	26 40.9	10♈39.8	20 28.9	7 2.4	9 1.1	7 48.3	21 13.8	17 29.5	3 37.6	19 41.7
20 S	23 51 47.5	26 5.8	26 37.7	24 28.7	21 39.4	8 16.5	9 38.3	7 45.4	21 13.1	17 30.6	3 38.2	19 41.7
21 S	23 55 44.0	27 4.4	26 34.5	8♉27.1	22 48.2	9 30.7	10 15.3	7 42.7	21 12.5	17 31.9	3 38.7	19R41.7
22 M	23 59 40.6	28 3.1	26 31.4	22 32.4	23 54.9	10 45.0	10 52.4	7 40.1	21 12.0	17 33.2	3 39.3	19 41.7
23 T	0 3 37.2	29 1.8	26 28.2	6♊42.1	24 59.5	11 59.3	11 29.3	7 37.8	21 11.7	17 34.5	3 39.8	19 41.6
24 W	0 7 33.7	0♎ 0.5	26 25.0	20 54.0	26 1.9	13 13.6	12 6.2	7 35.6	21 11.4	17 35.9	3 40.3	19 41.5
25 T	0 11 30.3	0 59.3	26 21.8	5♋ 5.9	27 1.8	14 28.0	12 43.1	7 33.7	21 11.2	17 37.3	3 40.7	19 41.4
26 F	0 15 26.8	1 58.2	26 18.7	19 15.8	27 59.1	15 42.4	13 19.9	7 31.9	21 11.1	17 38.8	3 41.1	19 41.3
27 S	0 19 23.4	2 57.0	26 15.5	3♌21.4	28 53.6	16 56.8	13 56.6	7 30.3	21D11.1	17 40.3	3 41.5	19 41.2
28 S	0 23 19.9	3 55.9	26 12.3	17 20.2	29 45.1	18 11.3	14 33.3	7 28.9	21 11.2	17 41.9	3 41.8	19 41.0
29 M	0 27 16.5	4 54.9	26 9.1	1♍ 9.7	0♏33.3	19 25.8	15 9.9	7 27.8	21 11.4	17 43.5	3 42.1	19 40.8
30 T	0 31 13.0	5 53.8	26 5.9	14 47.1	1 17.9	20 40.4	15 46.4	7 26.8	21 11.7	17 45.1	3 42.4	19 40.6
						DECLINATION						
1 M	22 36 53.0	8N42.9	10S38.2	9N54.8	2N16.1	17N 2.6	21N32.4	18S51.4	21S50.3	22S55.9	22N18.1	14N11.1
4 T	22 48 42.7	7 37.4	10 34.8	3S 1.5	0 3.1	16 2.4	21 10.8	18 56.0	21 51.6	22 56.0	22 17.9	14 10.7
7 S	23 0 32.3	6 30.8	10 31.4	13 53.3	2S 6.5	14 58.1	20 47.9	19 0.2	21 52.8	22 56.2	22 17.7	14 10.3
10 W	23 12 22.0	5 23.3	10 27.9	18 48.4	4 11.8	13 50.0	20 23.9	19 4.0	21 53.8	22 56.4	22 17.6	14 9.9
13 S	23 24 11.6	4 15.0	10 24.5	16 22.9	6 11.8	12 38.3	19 58.8	19 7.3	21 54.7	22 56.6	22 17.4	14 9.5
16 T	23 36 1.3	3 5.9	10 21.1	7 16.6	8 5.7	11 23.5	19 32.6	19 10.2	21 55.4	22 56.9	22 17.3	14 9.1
19 F	23 47 50.9	1 56.4	10 17.6	5N27.1	9 52.5	10 5.7	19 5.3	19 12.7	21 56.0	22 57.2	22 17.1	14 8.7
22 M	23 59 40.6	0 46.5	10 14.2	16 6.3	11 30.7	8 45.3	18 37.1	19 14.7	21 56.5	22 57.5	22 17.0	14 8.2
25 T	0 11 30.3	0S23.6	10 10.7	18 26.5	12 59.0	7 22.7	18 8.0	19 16.2	21 56.8	22 57.9	22 16.9	14 7.7
28 S	0 23 19.9	1 33.8	10 7.3	11 0.3	14 15.0	5 58.1	17 38.1	19 17.3	21 57.0	22 58.4	22 16.8	14 7.3

OCTOBER 1902

						LONGITUDE						
1 W	0 35 9.6	6♎52.9	26♎ 2.8	28♍10.4	1♏58.6	21♍54.9	16♌22.9	7♒26.0	21♑12.1	17♐46.9	3♋42.6	19♊40.4
2 T	0 39 6.1	7 51.9	25 59.6	11♎17.8	2 35.1	23 9.5	16 59.3	7R25.4	21 12.6	17 48.6	3 42.9	19R40.2
3 F	0 43 2.7	8 51.0	25 56.4	24 8.6	3 7.0	24 24.2	17 35.6	7 25.0	21 13.3	17 50.4	3 43.0	19 39.9
4 S	0 46 59.2	9 50.1	25 53.2	6♏43.3	3 33.8	25 38.8	18 11.9	7 24.8	21 14.0	17 52.3	3 43.2	19 39.6
5 S	0 50 55.8	10 49.2	25 50.0	19 3.0	3 55.2	26 53.5	18 48.1	7D24.8	21 14.8	17 54.2	3 43.3	19 39.3
6 M	0 54 52.4	11 48.4	25 46.9	1♐10.3	4 10.8	28 8.3	19 24.2	7 25.1	21 15.7	17 56.1	3 43.3	19 39.0
7 T	0 58 48.9	12 47.6	25 43.7	13 8.2	4 19.9	29 23.0	20 0.2	7 25.5	21 16.7	17 58.1	3 43.4	19 38.6
8 W	1 2 45.5	13 46.9	25 40.5	25 0.8	4 22.3	0♎37.8	20 36.2	7 26.1	21 17.8	18 0.1	3R43.4	19 38.2
9 T	1 6 42.0	14 46.1	25 37.3	6♑52.3	4R17.3	1 52.6	21 12.1	7 26.9	21 19.0	18 2.2	3 43.3	19 37.8
10 F	1 10 38.5	15 45.4	25 34.2	18 47.5	4 4.6	3 7.4	21 48.0	7 27.9	21 20.3	18 4.3	3 43.3	19 37.4
11 S	1 14 35.1	16 44.8	25 31.0	0♒51.1	3 44.0	4 22.2	22 23.7	7 29.1	21 21.7	18 6.5	3 43.2	19 37.0
12 S	1 18 31.7	17 44.1	25 27.8	13 7.6	3 15.0	5 37.1	22 59.4	7 30.5	21 23.2	18 8.7	3 43.0	19 36.5
13 M	1 22 28.2	18 43.5	25 24.6	25 41.0	2 37.7	6 52.0	23 35.1	7 32.1	21 24.8	18 10.9	3 42.9	19 36.0
14 T	1 26 24.8	19 42.9	25 21.4	8♓34.2	1 52.3	8 6.9	24 10.6	7 33.9	21 26.5	18 13.2	3 42.7	19 35.5
15 W	1 30 21.3	20 42.4	25 18.3	21 49.1	0 59.1	9 21.8	24 46.1	7 35.9	21 28.3	18 15.5	3 42.4	19 35.0
16 T	1 34 17.9	21 41.9	25 15.1	5♈25.9	29♎58.8	10 36.8	25 21.5	7 38.1	21 30.2	18 17.9	3 42.2	19 34.5
17 F	1 38 14.4	22 41.4	25 11.9	19 23.2	28 52.5	11 51.8	25 56.8	7 40.5	21 32.2	18 20.3	3 41.9	19 33.9
18 S	1 42 11.0	23 40.9	25 8.7	3♉37.6	27 41.6	13 6.8	26 32.1	7 43.0	21 34.3	18 22.8	3 41.5	19 33.4
19 S	1 46 7.5	24 40.5	25 5.6	18 4.4	26 27.9	14 21.8	27 7.2	7 45.8	21 36.4	18 25.3	3 41.2	19 32.8
20 M	1 50 4.1	25 40.1	25 2.4	2♊38.0	25 13.4	15 36.8	27 42.3	7 48.8	21 38.7	18 27.8	3 40.8	19 32.2
21 T	1 54 0.6	26 39.8	24 59.2	17 12.4	24 0.3	16 51.9	28 17.4	7 51.9	21 41.1	18 30.3	3 40.3	19 31.5
22 W	1 57 57.2	27 39.4	24 56.0	1♋42.3	22 50.7	18 7.0	28 52.3	7 55.2	21 43.5	18 32.9	3 39.9	19 30.9
23 T	2 1 53.7	28 39.2	24 52.8	16 3.3	21 46.8	19 22.1	29 27.2	7 58.8	21 46.1	18 35.6	3 39.4	19 30.2
24 F	2 5 50.3	29 38.9	24 49.7	0♌12.4	20 50.5	20 37.2	0♍ 2.0	8 2.5	21 48.7	18 38.2	3 38.8	19 29.5
25 S	2 9 46.9	0♏38.7	24 46.5	14 7.7	20 3.3	21 52.4	0 36.7	8 6.4	21 51.4	18 40.9	3 38.3	19 28.8
26 S	2 13 43.4	1 38.6	24 43.3	27 48.5	19 26.5	23 7.5	1 11.3	8 10.4	21 54.3	18 43.7	3 37.7	19 28.1
27 M	2 17 40.0	2 38.5	24 40.1	11♍14.7	19 0.7	24 22.7	1 45.8	8 14.7	21 57.2	18 46.5	3 37.1	19 27.4
28 T	2 21 36.5	3 38.4	24 37.0	24 26.7	18 46.4	25 37.9	2 20.3	8 19.1	22 0.2	18 49.3	3 36.4	19 26.6
29 W	2 25 33.0	4 38.3	24 33.8	7♎24.9	18 43.6	26 53.1	2 54.6	8 23.8	22 3.3	18 52.1	3 35.7	19 25.8
30 T	2 29 29.6	5 38.3	24 30.6	20 10.2	18D51.9	28 8.3	3 28.9	8 28.6	22 6.5	18 55.0	3 35.0	19 25.0
31 F	2 33 26.2	6 38.3	24 27.4	2♏43.2	19 10.8	29 23.6	4 3.1	8 33.6	22 9.7	18 57.9	3 34.3	19 24.2
						DECLINATION						
1 W	0 35 9.6	2S44.0	10S 3.8	1S28.5	15S16.0	4N31.8	17N 7.3	19S17.9	21S57.1	22S58.8	22N16.6	14N 6.8
4 S	0 46 59.2	3 53.9	10 0.3	12 46.4	15 58.2	3 4.2	16 35.9	19 18.0	21 57.0	22 59.4	22 16.5	14 6.3
7 T	0 58 48.9	5 3.3	9 56.9	18 29.8	16 16.3	1 35.6	16 3.7	19 17.7	21 56.7	22 59.9	22 16.4	14 5.8
10 F	1 10 38.5	6 12.2	9 53.4	16 55.9	16 3.9	0 6.4	15 31.0	19 16.8	21 56.3	23 0.5	22 16.4	14 5.3
13 M	1 22 28.2	7 20.4	9 49.9	8 39.9	15 14.1	1S23.1	14 57.7	19 15.6	21 55.8	23 1.1	22 16.3	14 4.8
16 T	1 34 17.9	8 27.6	9 46.4	3N48.7	13 43.5	2 52.6	14 24.0	19 13.8	21 55.2	23 1.7	22 16.2	14 4.3
19 S	1 46 7.5	9 33.8	9 42.9	15 15.0	11 39.1	4 21.8	13 49.8	19 11.6	21 54.4	23 2.4	22 16.2	14 3.8
22 W	1 57 57.2	10 38.7	9 39.5	18 35.4	9 22.4	5 50.3	13 15.2	19 9.0	21 53.4	23 3.0	22 16.1	14 3.3
25 S	2 9 46.9	11 42.2	9 36.0	11 47.9	7 24.7	7 17.7	12 40.2	19 5.9	21 52.3	23 3.7	22 16.1	14 2.8
28 T	2 21 36.5	12 44.1	9 32.5	0S17.3	6 10.8	8 43.8	12 5.0	19 2.3	21 51.1	23 4.5	22 16.0	14 2.3
31 F	2 33 26.2	13 44.3	9 29.0	11 47.0	5 49.4	10 8.2	11 29.7	18 58.3	21 49.7	23 5.2	22 16.0	14 1.9

NOVEMBER 1902

LONGITUDE

DAY	EPHEMERIS SIDEREAL TIME	☉	☊	☽	☿	♀	♂	♃	♄	♅	♆	♇
	h m s	° ′	° ′	° ′	° ′	° ′	° ′	° ′	° ′	° ′	° ′	° ′
1 S	2 37 22.7	7♏38.4	24♎24.2	15♏ 4.7	19♎39.7	0♏38.9	4♍37.2	8♒38.7	22♑13.1	19♐ 0.8	3♋33.5	19♊23.4
2 S	2 41 19.3	8 38.5	24 21.1	27 15.9	20 17.6	1 54.1	5 11.1	8 44.1	22 16.6	19 3.8	3R32.7	19R22.6
3 M	2 45 15.8	9 38.6	24 17.9	9♐18.4	21 3.7	3 9.4	5 45.0	8 49.6	22 20.1	19 6.8	3 31.8	19 21.7
4 T	2 49 12.4	10 38.7	24 14.7	21 14.0	21 57.2	4 24.7	6 18.8	8 55.3	22 23.7	19 9.9	3 31.0	19 20.9
5 W	2 53 8.9	11 38.9	24 11.5	3♑ 5.6	22 57.1	5 40.0	6 52.5	9 1.1	22 27.4	19 12.9	3 30.1	19 20.0
6 T	2 57 5.5	12 39.1	24 8.4	14 56.3	24 2.8	6 55.3	7 26.1	9 7.1	22 31.2	19 16.0	3 29.2	19 19.1
7 F	3 1 2.0	13 39.3	24 5.2	26 49.8	25 13.3	8 10.6	7 59.6	9 13.3	22 35.1	19 19.1	3 28.2	19 18.2
8 S	3 4 58.6	14 39.5	24 2.0	8♒50.6	26 28.1	9 26.0	8 33.0	9 19.7	22 39.0	19 22.3	3 27.2	19 17.3
9 S	3 8 55.2	15 39.8	23 58.8	21 3.2	27 46.5	10 41.3	9 6.3	9 26.2	22 43.1	19 25.4	3 26.2	19 16.3
10 M	3 12 51.7	16 40.1	23 55.6	3♓32.1	29 7.9	11 56.6	9 39.4	9 32.9	22 47.2	19 28.6	3 25.2	19 15.4
11 T	3 16 48.3	17 40.4	23 52.5	16 21.7	0♏31.9	13 12.0	10 12.5	9 39.8	22 51.4	19 31.8	3 24.1	19 14.4
12 W	3 20 44.8	18 40.7	23 49.3	29 35.5	1 58.1	14 27.3	10 45.4	9 46.8	22 55.7	19 35.1	3 23.0	19 13.4
13 T	3 24 41.4	19 41.1	23 46.1	13♈15.6	3 26.0	15 42.7	11 18.3	9 53.9	23 0.0	19 38.4	3 21.9	19 12.4
14 F	3 28 37.9	20 41.5	23 42.9	27 22.1	4 55.4	16 58.1	11 51.0	10 1.2	23 4.4	19 41.7	3 20.8	19 11.4
15 S	3 32 34.5	21 41.9	23 39.8	11♉52.4	6 26.0	18 13.5	12 23.7	10 8.7	23 8.9	19 45.0	3 19.6	19 10.4
16 S	3 36 31.0	22 42.3	23 36.6	26 41.5	7 57.6	19 28.8	12 56.2	10 16.3	23 13.5	19 48.3	3 18.4	19 9.4
17 M	3 40 27.6	23 42.8	23 33.4	11♊41.7	9 30.0	20 44.2	13 28.6	10 24.1	23 18.1	19 51.7	3 17.2	19 8.4
18 T	3 44 24.2	24 43.3	23 30.2	26 43.9	11 3.0	21 59.6	14 0.9	10 32.0	23 22.9	19 55.0	3 16.0	19 7.3
19 W	3 48 20.7	25 43.8	23 27.1	11♋39.1	12 36.5	23 15.0	14 33.0	10 40.1	23 27.7	19 58.4	3 14.7	19 6.3
20 T	3 52 17.3	26 44.4	23 23.9	26 19.6	14 10.3	24 30.4	15 5.1	10 48.3	23 32.5	20 1.9	3 13.4	19 5.2
21 F	3 56 13.8	27 45.0	23 20.7	10♌40.2	15 44.5	25 45.8	15 37.0	10 56.6	23 37.5	20 5.3	3 12.1	19 4.2
22 S	4 0 10.4	28 45.6	23 17.5	24 38.2	17 18.8	27 1.3	16 8.8	11 5.1	23 42.5	20 8.7	3 10.8	19 3.1
23 S	4 4 6.9	29 46.2	23 14.3	8♍13.4	18 53.2	28 16.7	16 40.5	11 13.7	23 47.5	20 12.2	3 9.5	19 2.0
24 M	4 8 3.5	0♐46.9	23 11.2	21 27.4	20 27.7	29 32.2	17 12.0	11 22.5	23 52.7	20 15.7	3 8.1	19 0.9
25 T	4 12 0.0	1 47.6	23 8.0	4♎22.6	22 2.3	0♐47.6	17 43.4	11 31.4	23 57.9	20 19.2	3 6.7	18 59.8
26 W	4 15 56.6	2 48.3	23 4.8	17 2.0	23 36.9	2 3.1	18 14.7	11 40.5	24 3.1	20 22.7	3 5.3	18 58.7
27 T	4 19 53.2	3 49.1	23 1.6	29 28.6	25 11.5	3 18.5	18 45.8	11 49.6	24 8.5	20 26.2	3 3.9	18 57.6
28 F	4 23 49.7	4 49.8	22 58.5	11♏44.8	26 46.0	4 34.0	19 16.8	11 58.9	24 13.9	20 29.8	3 2.4	18 56.5
29 S	4 27 46.3	5 50.6	22 55.3	23 52.8	28 20.5	5 49.4	19 47.6	12 8.4	24 19.3	20 33.3	3 0.9	18 55.3
30 S	4 31 42.8	6 51.4	22 52.1	5♐54.3	29 54.9	7 4.9	20 18.3	12 17.9	24 24.9	20 36.9	2 59.5	18 54.2

DECLINATION

DAY	EPHEMERIS SIDEREAL TIME	☉	☊	☽	☿	♀	♂	♃	♄	♅	♆	♇
1 S	2 37 22.7	14S 3.9	9S27.8	14S39.5	5S53.2	10S35.9	11N17.8	18S56.9	21S49.2	23S 5.4	22N16.0	14N 1.7
4 T	2 49 12.4	15 1.4	9 24.3	18 48.2	6 31.8	11 57.4	10 42.3	18 52.3	21 47.7	23 6.2	22 16.0	14 1.3
7 F	3 1 2.0	15 56.7	9 20.8	15 38.4	7 41.6	13 16.3	10 6.7	18 47.3	21 46.0	23 7.0	22 16.0	14 0.8
10 M	3 12 51.7	16 49.5	9 17.3	6 22.1	9 11.0	14 32.3	9 31.0	18 41.9	21 44.2	23 7.7	22 16.0	14 0.4
13 T	3 24 41.4	17 39.8	9 13.8	6N14.3	10 51.1	15 45.0	8 55.4	18 36.1	21 42.2	23 8.5	22 16.1	14 0.0
16 S	3 36 31.0	18 27.4	9 10.2	16 45.6	12 35.6	16 54.0	8 19.9	18 29.8	21 40.1	23 9.3	22 16.1	13 59.6
19 W	3 48 20.7	19 12.0	9 6.7	17 53.2	14 20.0	17 59.1	7 44.6	18 23.2	21 37.8	23 10.1	22 16.1	13 59.3
22 S	4 0 10.4	19 53.5	9 3.2	9 2.9	16 1.3	18 59.7	7 9.5	18 16.1	21 35.5	23 10.9	22 16.2	13 58.9
25 T	4 12 0.0	20 31.8	8 59.7	3S24.9	17 37.5	19 55.7	6 34.6	18 8.7	21 33.0	23 11.7	22 16.2	13 58.6
28 F	4 23 49.7	21 6.6	8 56.1	13 55.9	19 7.0	20 46.6	6 0.1	18 0.9	21 30.4	23 12.5	22 16.3	13 58.3

DECEMBER 1902

LONGITUDE

DAY	EPHEMERIS SIDEREAL TIME	☉	☊	☽	☿	♀	♂	♃	♄	♅	♆	♇
1 M	4 35 39.4	7♐52.3	22♎48.9	17♐50.8	1♐29.3	8♐20.4	20♍48.8	12♒27.6	24♑30.4	20♐40.5	2♋58.0	18♊53.0
2 T	4 39 35.9	8 53.2	22 45.8	29 43.8	3 3.6	9 35.9	21 19.2	12 37.5	24 36.1	20 44.1	2R56.5	18R51.9
3 W	4 43 32.5	9 54.0	22 42.6	11♑34.9	4 37.9	10 51.3	21 49.4	12 47.4	24 41.8	20 47.7	2 54.9	18 50.8
4 T	4 47 29.0	10 54.9	22 39.4	23 26.0	6 12.1	12 6.8	22 19.5	12 57.4	24 47.5	20 51.3	2 53.4	18 49.6
5 F	4 51 25.6	11 55.8	22 36.2	5♒19.8	7 46.3	13 22.3	22 49.4	13 7.6	24 53.3	20 54.9	2 51.8	18 48.4
6 S	4 55 22.1	12 56.7	22 33.0	17 19.4	9 20.5	14 37.8	23 19.1	13 17.9	24 59.2	20 58.5	2 50.2	18 47.3
7 S	4 59 18.7	13 57.7	22 29.9	29 28.7	10 54.7	15 53.3	23 48.7	13 28.3	25 5.1	21 2.1	2 48.7	18 46.1
8 M	5 3 15.3	14 58.6	22 26.7	11♓52.1	12 28.9	17 8.7	24 18.1	13 38.8	25 11.1	21 5.8	2 47.1	18 45.0
9 T	5 7 11.8	15 59.6	22 23.5	24 34.1	14 3.0	18 24.2	24 47.3	13 49.5	25 17.1	21 9.4	2 45.5	18 43.8
10 W	5 11 8.4	17 0.5	22 20.3	7♈39.3	15 37.2	19 39.7	25 16.3	14 0.2	25 23.2	21 13.1	2 43.8	18 42.6
11 T	5 15 4.9	18 1.5	22 17.2	21 11.3	17 11.5	20 55.1	25 45.2	14 11.1	25 29.3	21 16.7	2 42.2	18 41.5
12 F	5 19 1.5	19 2.5	22 14.0	5♉12.4	18 45.8	22 10.6	26 13.8	14 22.0	25 35.5	21 20.3	2 40.6	18 40.3
13 S	5 22 58.1	20 3.5	22 10.8	19 42.2	20 20.2	23 26.1	26 42.3	14 33.1	25 41.7	21 24.0	2 38.9	18 39.1
14 S	5 26 54.6	21 4.5	22 7.6	4♊37.0	21 54.6	24 41.5	27 10.6	14 44.2	25 47.9	21 27.6	2 37.3	18 38.0
15 M	5 30 51.2	22 5.5	22 4.5	19 49.7	23 29.2	25 57.0	27 38.7	14 55.5	25 54.2	21 31.3	2 35.6	18 36.8
16 T	5 34 47.7	23 6.6	22 1.3	5♋10.0	25 3.9	27 12.4	28 6.6	15 6.8	26 0.6	21 34.9	2 33.9	18 35.7
17 W	5 38 44.3	24 7.6	21 58.1	20 26.4	26 38.7	28 27.9	28 34.3	15 18.3	26 7.0	21 38.6	2 32.3	18 34.5
18 T	5 42 40.8	25 8.7	21 54.9	5♌27.9	28 13.7	29 43.3	29 1.8	15 29.8	26 13.4	21 42.2	2 30.6	18 33.3
19 F	5 46 37.4	26 9.7	21 51.7	20 6.4	29 48.9	0♑58.8	29 29.1	15 41.5	26 19.8	21 45.9	2 28.9	18 32.2
20 S	5 50 34.0	27 10.8	21 48.6	4♍17.0	1♑24.2	2 14.3	29 56.2	15 53.2	26 26.3	21 49.5	2 27.2	18 31.0
21 S	5 54 30.5	28 11.9	21 45.4	17 58.7	2 59.7	3 29.7	0♎23.1	16 5.0	26 32.9	21 53.2	2 25.5	18 29.9
22 M	5 58 27.1	29 13.0	21 42.2	1♎13.1	4 35.3	4 45.2	0 49.7	16 16.9	26 39.5	21 56.8	2 23.8	18 28.7
23 T	6 2 23.6	0♑14.1	21 39.0	14 3.6	6 11.2	6 0.6	1 16.1	16 28.9	26 46.1	22 0.4	2 22.1	18 27.6
24 W	6 6 20.2	1 15.3	21 35.9	26 34.7	7 47.3	7 16.1	1 42.3	16 41.0	26 52.7	22 4.0	2 20.4	18 26.4
25 T	6 10 16.7	2 16.4	21 32.7	8♏50.8	9 23.5	8 31.5	2 8.2	16 53.2	26 59.4	22 7.6	2 18.7	18 25.3
26 F	6 14 13.3	3 17.6	21 29.5	20 56.2	10 60.0	9 47.0	2 33.9	17 5.4	27 6.1	22 11.2	2 17.0	18 24.2
27 S	6 18 9.9	4 18.7	21 26.3	2♐54.5	12 36.6	11 2.4	2 59.4	17 17.8	27 12.9	22 14.8	2 15.3	18 23.1
28 S	6 22 6.4	5 19.9	21 23.2	14 48.5	14 13.3	12 17.9	3 24.5	17 30.2	27 19.7	22 18.4	2 13.6	18 22.0
29 M	6 26 3.0	6 21.1	21 20.0	26 40.5	15 50.2	13 33.3	3 49.4	17 42.7	27 26.5	22 22.0	2 11.9	18 20.9
30 T	6 29 59.5	7 22.2	21 16.8	8♑32.1	17 27.2	14 48.8	4 14.1	17 55.3	27 33.3	22 25.6	2 10.2	18 19.8
31 W	6 33 56.1	8 23.4	21 13.6	20 24.6	19 4.2	16 4.2	4 38.4	18 7.9	27 40.2	22 29.1	2 8.5	18 18.7

DECLINATION

DAY	EPHEMERIS SIDEREAL TIME	☉	☊	☽	☿	♀	♂	♃	♄	♅	♆	♇
1 M	4 35 39.4	21S37.9	8S52.6	18S47.4	20S28.7	21S32.2	5N26.0	17S52.6	21S27.6	23S13.2	22N16.4	13N58.0
4 T	4 47 29.0	22 5.4	8 49.1	16 21.9	21 41.7	22 12.1	4 52.3	17 44.0	21 24.7	23 14.0	22 16.5	13 57.8
7 S	4 59 18.7	22 29.1	8 45.5	7 44.9	22 45.2	22 46.1	4 19.2	17 35.1	21 21.7	23 14.8	22 16.5	13 57.6
10 W	5 11 8.4	22 48.9	8 42.0	4N21.3	23 38.5	23 14.0	3 46.7	17 25.8	21 18.6	23 15.5	22 16.6	13 57.4
13 S	5 22 58.1	23 4.6	8 38.4	15 31.2	24 20.9	23 35.5	3 14.7	17 16.1	21 15.4	23 16.3	22 16.7	13 57.3
16 T	5 34 47.7	23 16.2	8 34.9	18 32.3	24 51.8	23 50.5	2 43.5	17 6.1	21 12.0	23 17.0	22 16.8	13 57.2
19 F	5 46 37.4	23 23.6	8 31.3	10 29.8	25 10.6	23 58.9	2 13.0	16 55.7	21 8.6	23 17.7	22 16.9	13 57.1
22 M	5 58 27.1	23 26.8	8 27.7	2S12.7	25 16.8	24 0.6	1 43.3	16 45.0	21 5.0	23 18.4	22 17.1	13 57.0
25 T	6 10 16.7	23 25.8	8 24.2	13 8.0	25 9.7	23 55.6	1 14.5	16 34.0	21 1.4	23 19.1	22 17.2	13 57.0
28 S	6 22 6.4	23 20.5	8 20.6	18 38.1	24 48.9	23 44.0	0 46.7	16 22.7	20 57.6	23 19.8	22 17.3	13 57.0
31 W	6 33 56.1	23 11.0	8 17.0	16 57.3	24 14.1	23 25.7	0 19.9	16 11.1	20 53.8	23 20.4	22 17.4	13 57.1

JANUARY 1903

DAY	EPHEMERIS SIDEREAL TIME	☉	☊	☽	☿	♀	♂	♃	♄	♅	♆	♇
	h m s	° ′	° ′	° ′	° ′	° ′	° ′	° ′	° ′	° ′	° ′	° ′
						LONGITUDE						
1 T	6 37 52.6	9♑24.6	21≏10.4	2♒19.3	20♑41.2	17♑19.6	5≏ 2.5	18♒20.6	27♑47.0	22♐32.7	2♋ 6.8	18♊17.6
2 F	6 41 49.2	10 25.8	21 7.3	14 17.6	22 18.2	18 35.1	5 26.3	18 33.4	27 53.9	22 36.2	2R 5.1	18R16.5
3 S	6 45 45.8	11 27.0	21 4.1	26 21.5	23 55.0	19 50.5	5 49.8	18 46.3	28 0.9	22 39.7	2 3.5	18 15.5
4 S	6 49 42.3	12 28.1	21 0.9	8♓33.5	25 31.5	21 5.9	6 13.0	18 59.2	28 7.8	22 43.2	2 1.8	18 14.4
5 M	6 53 38.9	13 29.3	20 57.7	20 56.9	27 7.7	22 21.3	6 35.9	19 12.2	28 14.8	22 46.7	2 0.1	18 13.4
6 T	6 57 35.4	14 30.5	20 54.6	3♈35.5	28 43.4	23 36.7	6 58.5	19 25.2	28 21.8	22 50.1	1 58.5	18 12.3
7 W	7 1 32.0	15 31.6	20 51.4	16 33.5	0♒18.4	24 52.1	7 20.8	19 38.3	28 28.8	22 53.6	1 56.8	18 11.3
8 T	7 5 28.5	16 32.8	20 48.2	29 55.0	1 52.5	26 7.5	7 42.7	19 51.5	28 35.8	22 57.0	1 55.2	18 10.3
9 F	7 9 25.1	17 33.9	20 45.0	13♉43.3	3 25.5	27 22.8	8 4.3	20 4.8	28 42.9	23 0.4	1 53.6	18 9.3
10 S	7 13 21.7	18 35.1	20 41.9	27 59.6	4 57.2	28 38.2	8 25.6	20 18.1	28 49.9	23 3.8	1 51.9	18 8.3
11 S	7 17 18.2	19 36.2	20 38.7	12♊42.8	6 27.0	29 53.5	8 46.6	20 31.4	28 57.0	23 7.2	1 50.3	18 7.3
12 M	7 21 14.8	20 37.3	20 35.5	27 47.8	7 54.9	1♒ 8.8	9 7.1	20 44.8	29 4.0	23 10.5	1 48.7	18 6.4
13 T	7 25 11.3	21 38.4	20 32.3	13♋ 6.1	9 20.1	2 24.2	9 27.4	20 58.3	29 11.1	23 13.8	1 47.1	18 5.4
14 W	7 29 7.9	22 39.5	20 29.2	28 26.4	10 42.4	3 39.5	9 47.3	21 11.8	29 18.2	23 17.2	1 45.6	18 4.5
15 T	7 33 4.5	23 40.6	20 26.0	13♌36.9	12 1.1	4 54.8	10 6.8	21 25.3	29 25.3	23 20.4	1 44.0	18 3.6
16 F	7 37 1.0	24 41.7	20 22.8	28 27.4	13 15.6	6 10.1	10 25.9	21 38.9	29 32.5	23 23.7	1 42.5	18 2.7
17 S	7 40 57.5	25 42.8	20 19.6	12♍50.8	14 25.2	7 25.3	10 44.6	21 52.6	29 39.6	23 26.9	1 40.9	18 1.8
18 S	7 44 54.1	26 43.9	20 16.4	26 43.8	15 29.1	8 40.6	11 2.9	22 6.3	29 46.7	23 30.1	1 39.4	18 0.9
19 M	7 48 50.7	27 44.9	20 13.3	10≏ 6.7	16 26.6	9 55.9	11 20.9	22 20.0	29 53.8	23 33.3	1 37.9	18 0.0
20 T	7 52 47.2	28 46.0	20 10.1	23 2.4	17 16.7	11 11.1	11 38.4	22 33.8	0♒ 1.0	23 36.5	1 36.5	17 59.2
21 W	7 56 43.8	29 47.1	20 6.9	5♏35.3	17 58.7	12 26.3	11 55.4	22 47.7	0 8.1	23 39.6	1 35.0	17 58.3
22 T	8 0 40.3	0♒48.1	20 3.7	17 50.3	18 31.6	13 41.6	12 12.1	23 1.5	0 15.2	23 42.7	1 33.5	17 57.5
23 F	8 4 36.9	1 49.2	20 0.6	29 52.8	18 54.7	14 56.8	12 28.2	23 15.5	0 22.4	23 45.8	1 32.1	17 56.7
24 S	8 8 33.5	2 50.2	19 57.4	11♐47.3	19 7.3	16 12.0	12 44.0	23 29.4	0 29.5	23 48.8	1 30.7	17 55.9
25 S	8 12 30.0	3 51.2	19 54.2	23 38.0	19 8.7	17 27.2	12 59.2	23 43.4	0 36.6	23 51.8	1 29.3	17 55.1
26 M	8 16 26.5	4 52.3	19 51.0	5♑28.2	18R58.8	18 42.4	13 14.0	23 57.4	0 43.8	23 54.8	1 27.9	17 54.4
27 T	8 20 23.1	5 53.3	19 47.8	17 20.5	18 37.4	19 57.5	13 28.3	24 11.5	0 50.9	23 57.8	1 26.6	17 53.6
28 W	8 24 19.7	6 54.3	19 44.7	29 16.7	18 4.8	21 12.7	13 42.0	24 25.6	0 58.0	24 0.7	1 25.3	17 52.9
29 T	8 28 16.2	7 55.2	19 41.5	11♒18.0	17 21.8	22 27.8	13 55.3	24 39.7	1 5.1	24 3.6	1 24.0	17 52.2
30 F	8 32 12.8	8 56.2	19 38.3	23 25.4	16 29.3	23 43.0	14 8.0	24 53.9	1 12.2	24 6.4	1 22.7	17 51.6
31 S	8 36 9.3	9 57.1	19 35.1	5♓40.0	15 28.7	24 58.1	14 20.2	25 8.0	1 19.3	24 9.3	1 21.4	17 50.9
						DECLINATION						
1 T	6 37 52.6	23S 6.9	8S15.8	14S51.6	23S59.4	23S18.1	0N11.2	16S 7.1	20S52.5	23S20.6	22N17.5	13N57.1
4 S	6 49 42.3	22 51.9	8 12.3	5 12.4	23 5.9	22 51.2	0S14.1	15 55.1	20 48.5	23 21.2	22 17.6	13 57.2
7 W	7 1 32.0	22 32.7	8 8.7	6N52.6	21 58.9	22 18.0	0 38.3	15 42.8	20 44.5	23 21.8	22 17.7	13 57.4
10 S	7 13 21.7	22 9.6	8 5.1	16 46.1	20 39.7	21 38.8	1 1.1	15 30.3	20 40.4	23 22.4	22 17.8	13 57.5
13 T	7 25 11.3	21 42.5	8 1.5	17 52.1	19 10.5	20 53.7	1 22.7	15 17.4	20 36.2	23 22.9	22 18.0	13 57.7
16 F	7 37 1.0	21 11.7	7 57.9	8 19.7	17 35.8	20 3.1	1 42.9	15 4.4	20 32.0	23 23.5	22 18.1	13 58.0
19 M	7 48 50.7	20 37.2	7 54.3	4S47.2	16 2.1	19 7.2	2 1.6	14 51.1	20 27.7	23 24.0	22 18.2	13 58.3
22 T	8 0 40.3	19 59.2	7 50.8	14 52.3	14 38.9	18 6.4	2 18.7	14 37.5	20 23.3	23 24.5	22 18.4	13 58.6
25 S	8 12 30.0	19 17.8	7 47.2	18 46.9	13 37.1	17 1.0	2 34.2	14 23.8	20 18.9	23 25.0	22 18.5	13 59.0
28 W	8 24 19.7	18 33.3	7 43.6	15 29.2	13 6.7	15 51.3	2 47.9	14 9.8	20 14.5	23 25.4	22 18.6	13 59.3
31 S	8 36 9.3	17 45.7	7 39.9	6 15.8	13 11.6	14 37.7	2 59.8	13 55.7	20 10.1	23 25.8	22 18.8	13 59.8

FEBRUARY 1903

DAY	EPHEMERIS SIDEREAL TIME	☉	☊	☽	☿	♀	♂	♃	♄	♅	♆	♇
						LONGITUDE						
1 S	8 40 5.9	10♒58.1	19≏32.0	18♓ 2.9	14♒21.9	26♒13.1	14≏31.9	25♒22.3	1♒26.4	24♐12.0	1♋20.2	17♊50.2
2 M	8 44 2.4	11 59.0	19 28.8	0♈36.0	13R10.8	27 28.2	14 43.0	25 36.5	1 33.5	24 14.8	1R19.0	17R49.6
3 T	8 47 59.0	12 59.9	19 25.6	13 21.5	11 57.5	28 43.3	14 53.5	25 50.8	1 40.5	24 17.5	1 17.8	17 49.0
4 W	8 51 55.6	14 0.7	19 22.4	26 22.3	10 44.1	29 58.3	15 3.5	26 5.0	1 47.6	24 20.2	1 16.6	17 48.4
5 T	8 55 52.1	15 1.6	19 19.2	9♉41.1	9 32.7	1♓13.3	15 12.9	26 19.3	1 54.6	24 22.8	1 15.5	17 47.9
6 F	8 59 48.7	16 2.4	19 16.1	23 20.9	8 24.9	2 28.3	15 21.7	26 33.6	2 1.6	24 25.4	1 14.4	17 47.3
7 S	9 3 45.2	17 3.2	19 12.9	7♊23.2	7 22.3	3 43.2	15 29.8	26 48.0	2 8.6	24 28.0	1 13.3	17 46.8
8 S	9 7 41.8	18 3.9	19 9.7	21 47.8	6 26.1	4 58.2	15 37.4	27 2.3	2 15.5	24 30.5	1 12.2	17 46.3
9 M	9 11 38.3	19 4.7	19 6.5	6♋32.0	5 37.2	6 13.1	15 44.4	27 16.7	2 22.5	24 33.0	1 11.2	17 45.8
10 T	9 15 34.9	20 5.4	19 3.4	21 30.1	4 56.0	7 27.9	15 50.7	27 31.1	2 29.4	24 35.5	1 10.2	17 45.3
11 W	9 19 31.4	21 6.1	19 0.2	6♌33.7	4 22.9	8 42.8	15 56.3	27 45.5	2 36.3	24 37.9	1 9.2	17 44.9
12 T	9 23 28.0	22 6.7	18 57.0	21 33.0	3 57.9	9 57.6	16 1.4	27 59.9	2 43.2	24 40.2	1 8.3	17 44.4
13 F	9 27 24.5	23 7.4	18 53.8	6♍18.6	3 40.9	11 12.4	16 5.7	28 14.3	2 50.0	24 42.6	1 7.4	17 44.0
14 S	9 31 21.1	24 8.0	18 50.6	20 42.7	3 31.6	12 27.2	16 9.4	28 28.7	2 56.9	24 44.8	1 6.5	17 43.6
15 S	9 35 17.6	25 8.6	18 47.5	4≏40.5	3 29.7	13 41.9	16 12.3	28 43.1	3 3.7	24 47.1	1 5.6	17 43.3
16 M	9 39 14.2	26 9.2	18 44.3	18 10.4	3D34.9	14 56.7	16 14.6	28 57.6	3 10.4	24 49.3	1 4.8	17 42.9
17 T	9 43 10.8	27 9.7	18 41.1	1♏13.5	3 46.6	16 11.4	16 16.2	29 12.0	3 17.2	24 51.5	1 4.0	17 42.6
18 W	9 47 7.3	28 10.2	18 37.9	13 52.7	4 4.4	17 26.0	16 17.0	29 26.4	3 23.9	24 53.6	1 3.2	17 42.3
19 T	9 51 3.8	29 10.7	18 34.8	26 12.6	4 28.0	18 40.7	16 17.1	29 40.9	3 30.6	24 55.6	1 2.5	17 42.0
20 F	9 55 0.4	0♓11.2	18 31.6	8♐17.9	4 56.8	19 55.3	16R16.5	29 55.3	3 37.2	24 57.7	1 1.8	17 41.8
21 S	9 58 57.0	1 11.7	18 28.4	20 13.8	5 30.6	21 9.9	16 15.1	0♓ 9.8	3 43.9	24 59.6	1 1.1	17 41.6
22 S	10 2 53.5	2 12.2	18 25.2	2♑ 5.1	6 8.8	22 24.5	16 13.0	0 24.2	3 50.5	25 1.6	1 0.4	17 41.3
23 M	10 6 50.1	3 12.6	18 22.1	13 56.2	6 51.3	23 39.0	16 10.0	0 38.7	3 57.0	25 3.5	0 59.8	17 41.2
24 T	10 10 46.6	4 13.0	18 18.9	25 50.5	7 37.5	24 53.5	16 6.3	0 53.1	4 3.5	25 5.3	0 59.2	17 41.0
25 W	10 14 43.2	5 13.3	18 15.7	7♒51.1	8 27.4	26 8.0	16 1.9	1 7.6	4 10.0	25 7.1	0 58.7	17 40.8
26 T	10 18 39.7	6 13.7	18 12.5	20 0.0	9 20.5	27 22.4	15 56.6	1 22.0	4 16.4	25 8.8	0 58.2	17 40.7
27 F	10 22 36.3	7 14.0	18 9.3	2♓18.7	10 16.7	28 36.8	15 50.6	1 36.4	4 22.8	25 10.5	0 57.7	17 40.6
28 S	10 26 32.8	8 14.3	18 6.2	14 47.8	11 15.8	29 51.2	15 43.8	1 50.8	4 29.2	25 12.2	0 57.2	17 40.5
						DECLINATION						
1 S	8 40 5.9	17S29.2	7S38.7	2S23.7	13S20.4	14S12.4	3S 3.3	13S50.9	20S 8.6	23S26.0	22N18.8	13N59.9
4 W	8 51 55.6	16 37.8	7 35.1	9N29.3	14 2.5	12 54.1	3 12.7	13 36.5	20 4.1	23 26.3	22 19.0	14 0.4
7 S	9 3 45.2	15 43.9	7 31.5	17 44.2	14 57.4	11 32.8	3 20.0	13 22.0	19 59.6	23 26.7	22 19.1	14 0.9
10 T	9 15 34.9	14 47.5	7 27.9	16 43.6	15 52.6	10 8.7	3 25.2	13 7.3	19 55.1	23 27.1	22 19.3	14 1.4
13 F	9 27 24.5	13 49.0	7 24.3	6 5.5	16 40.4	8 42.2	3 28.3	12 52.5	19 50.7	23 27.4	22 19.4	14 1.9
16 M	9 39 14.2	12 48.3	7 20.7	7S 2.3	17 17.1	7 13.7	3 29.2	12 37.6	19 46.2	23 27.7	22 19.5	14 2.5
19 T	9 51 3.8	11 45.9	7 17.1	16 9.1	17 41.1	5 43.5	3 27.7	12 22.6	19 41.8	23 28.0	22 19.7	14 3.1
22 S	10 2 53.5	10 41.7	7 13.4	18 27.9	17 52.1	4 11.9	3 23.9	12 7.5	19 37.4	23 28.3	22 19.8	14 3.8
25 W	10 14 43.2	9 36.0	7 9.8	13 40.4	17 50.2	2 39.3	3 17.6	11 52.3	19 33.0	23 28.5	22 20.0	14 4.4
28 S	10 26 32.8	8 29.1	7 6.2	3 29.5	17 35.3	1 6.1	3 9.0	11 37.1	19 28.7	23 28.8	22 20.1	14 5.1

MARCH 1903

LONGITUDE

DAY	EPHEMERIS SIDEREAL TIME	☉	☊	☽	☿	♀	♂	♃	♄	♅	♆	♇
	h m s	° '	° '	° '	° '	° '	° '	° '	° '	° '	° '	° '
1 S	10 30 29.4	9♓14.5	18♎ 3.0	27♓28.1	12♒17.5	1♈ 5.6	15♎36.2	2♓ 5.2	4♒35.5	25♐13.8	0♋56.8	17♊40.5
2 M	10 34 25.9	10 14.8	17 59.8	10♈19.8	13 21.6	2 19.9	15R27.8	2 19.6	4 41.8	25 15.4	0R56.4	17R40.4
3 T	10 38 22.5	11 15.0	17 56.6	23 23.4	14 28.1	3 34.2	15 18.6	2 34.0	4 48.0	25 16.9	0 56.0	17 40.4
4 W	10 42 19.0	12 15.1	17 53.5	6♉39.6	15 36.7	4 48.4	15 8.7	2 48.4	4 54.1	25 18.3	0 55.7	17D40.4
5 T	10 46 15.6	13 15.3	17 50.3	20 9.1	16 47.4	6 2.6	14 58.0	3 2.7	5 0.3	25 19.7	0 55.4	17 40.5
6 F	10 50 12.1	14 15.4	17 47.1	3♊52.8	18 0.1	7 16.8	14 46.5	3 17.0	5 6.4	25 21.1	0 55.2	17 40.5
7 S	10 54 8.7	15 15.4	17 43.9	17 50.9	19 14.6	8 30.9	14 34.3	3 31.4	5 12.4	25 22.4	0 55.0	17 40.6
8 S	10 58 5.3	16 15.4	17 40.7	2♋ 2.8	20 30.8	9 45.0	14 21.4	3 45.6	5 18.4	25 23.7	0 54.8	17 40.7
9 M	11 2 1.8	17 15.4	17 37.6	16 26.7	21 48.7	10 59.0	14 7.7	3 59.9	5 24.3	25 24.9	0 54.6	17 40.8
10 T	11 5 58.3	18 15.4	17 34.4	0♌59.1	23 8.3	12 13.0	13 53.3	4 14.1	5 30.2	25 26.0	0 54.5	17 41.0
11 W	11 9 54.9	19 15.3	17 31.2	15 34.8	24 29.3	13 27.0	13 38.2	4 28.4	5 36.0	25 27.1	0 54.4	17 41.2
12 T	11 13 51.5	20 15.1	17 28.0	0♍ 7.7	25 51.9	14 40.9	13 22.4	4 42.6	5 41.8	25 28.2	0 54.4	17 41.3
13 F	11 17 48.0	21 15.0	17 24.9	14 31.2	27 16.0	15 54.8	13 6.0	4 56.7	5 47.5	25 29.2	0 54.3	17 41.6
14 S	11 21 44.6	22 14.8	17 21.7	28 39.5	28 41.5	17 8.6	12 48.9	5 10.9	5 53.2	25 30.1	0D54.4	17 41.8
15 S	11 25 41.1	23 14.6	17 18.5	12♎28.2	0♓ 8.3	18 22.3	12 31.2	5 25.0	5 58.8	25 31.0	0 54.4	17 42.0
16 M	11 29 37.7	24 14.3	17 15.3	25 54.8	1 36.6	19 36.1	12 12.9	5 39.1	6 4.3	25 31.9	0 54.5	17 42.3
17 T	11 33 34.2	25 14.0	17 12.1	8♏58.8	3 6.2	20 49.8	11 54.0	5 53.1	6 9.8	25 32.7	0 54.6	17 42.6
18 W	11 37 30.8	26 13.7	17 9.0	21 41.4	4 37.1	22 3.4	11 34.5	6 7.1	6 15.2	25 33.4	0 54.8	17 42.9
19 T	11 41 27.3	27 13.4	17 5.8	4♐ 5.6	6 9.3	23 17.0	11 14.5	6 21.1	6 20.6	25 34.1	0 54.9	17 43.3
20 F	11 45 23.9	28 13.0	17 2.6	16 15.0	7 42.9	24 30.5	10 54.1	6 35.1	6 25.9	25 34.7	0 55.2	17 43.7
21 S	11 49 20.4	29 12.6	16 59.4	28 14.1	9 17.7	25 44.1	10 33.1	6 49.0	6 31.1	25 35.3	0 55.4	17 44.0
22 S	11 53 17.0	0♈12.1	16 56.2	10♑ 7.6	10 53.9	26 57.5	10 11.8	7 2.9	6 36.3	25 35.9	0 55.7	17 44.5
23 M	11 57 13.5	1 11.7	16 53.1	22 0.2	12 31.3	28 10.9	9 50.0	7 16.7	6 41.4	25 36.3	0 56.0	17 44.9
24 T	12 1 10.1	2 11.2	16 49.9	3♒56.4	14 10.1	29 24.3	9 27.9	7 30.5	6 46.5	25 36.8	0 56.4	17 45.3
25 W	12 5 6.6	3 10.7	16 46.7	16 0.1	15 50.2	0♉37.6	9 5.5	7 44.3	6 51.5	25 37.1	0 56.8	17 45.8
26 T	12 9 3.2	4 10.1	16 43.5	28 14.8	17 31.6	1 50.9	8 42.8	7 58.0	6 56.4	25 37.5	0 57.2	17 46.3
27 F	12 12 59.8	5 9.5	16 40.4	10♓42.8	19 14.3	3 4.1	8 20.0	8 11.7	7 1.2	25 37.7	0 57.7	17 46.8
28 S	12 16 56.3	6 8.9	16 37.2	23 25.8	20 58.3	4 17.3	7 56.9	8 25.3	7 6.0	25 38.0	0 58.2	17 47.3
29 S	12 20 52.8	7 8.3	16 34.0	6♈24.5	22 43.7	5 30.4	7 33.7	8 38.9	7 10.7	25 38.1	0 58.7	17 47.9
30 M	12 24 49.4	8 7.6	16 30.8	19 38.6	24 30.4	6 43.5	7 10.4	8 52.5	7 15.3	25 38.2	0 59.2	17 48.5
31 T	12 28 45.9	9 6.9	16 27.6	3♉ 7.1	26 18.6	7 56.5	6 47.0	9 6.0	7 19.9	25 38.3	0 59.8	17 49.1

DECLINATION

DAY	EPHEMERIS SIDEREAL TIME	☉	☊	☽	☿	♀	♂	♃	♄	♅	♆	♇
1 S	10 30 29.4	8S 6.5	7S 5.0	0N31.6	17S27.6	0S34.9	3S 5.6	11S32.0	19S27.3	23S28.8	22N20.2	14N 5.3
4 W	10 42 19.0	6 58.0	7 1.3	12 1.4	16 56.0	0N58.7	2 53.8	11 16.7	19 23.0	23 29.0	22 20.3	14 6.0
7 S	10 54 8.7	5 48.8	6 57.7	18 19.4	16 12.0	2 32.2	2 39.7	11 1.4	19 18.9	23 29.2	22 20.5	14 6.8
10 T	11 5 58.3	4 38.8	6 54.0	15 1.3	15 16.0	4 5.3	2 23.5	10 46.1	19 14.8	23 29.4	22 20.6	14 7.5
13 F	11 17 48.0	3 28.3	6 50.4	3 34.3	14 8.2	5 37.6	2 5.4	10 30.8	19 10.9	23 29.6	22 20.7	14 8.3
16 M	11 29 37.7	2 17.4	6 46.7	9S10.0	12 48.7	7 8.8	1 45.6	10 15.5	19 7.0	23 29.7	22 20.9	14 9.0
19 T	11 41 27.3	1 6.3	6 43.1	17 7.3	11 17.8	8 38.6	1 24.2	10 0.2	19 3.2	23 29.8	22 21.0	14 9.8
22 S	11 53 17.0	0N 4.8	6 39.4	17 50.5	9 35.8	10 6.6	1 1.7	9 45.1	18 59.6	23 29.9	22 21.2	14 10.6
25 W	12 5 6.6	1 15.8	6 35.8	11 41.3	7 43.0	11 32.6	0 38.5	9 30.0	18 56.1	23 30.0	22 21.3	14 11.4
28 S	12 16 56.3	2 26.6	6 32.1	0 45.3	5 39.6	12 56.1	0 14.9	9 15.0	18 52.7	23 30.1	22 21.4	14 12.2
31 T	12 28 45.9	3 36.8	6 28.5	11N 5.0	3 26.1	14 16.8	0N 8.5	9 0.1	18 49.5	23 30.1	22 21.5	14 13.0

APRIL 1903

LONGITUDE

DAY	EPHEMERIS SIDEREAL TIME	☉	☊	☽	☿	♀	♂	♃	♄	♅	♆	♇
1 W	12 32 42.5	10♈ 6.1	16♎24.5	16♉48.5	28♓ 8.1	9♉ 9.5	6♎23.7	9♓19.4	7♒24.4	25♐38.3	1♋ 0.5	17♊49.7
2 T	12 36 39.1	11 5.3	16 21.3	0♊40.8	29 58.9	10 22.4	6R 0.4	9 32.8	7 28.8	25R38.2	1 1.1	17 50.3
3 F	12 40 35.6	12 4.5	16 18.1	14 41.8	1♈51.2	11 35.3	5 37.3	9 46.1	7 33.1	25 38.1	1 1.8	17 51.0
4 S	12 44 32.2	13 3.6	16 14.9	28 49.3	3 44.8	12 48.1	5 14.2	9 59.4	7 37.4	25 38.0	1 2.5	17 51.7
5 S	12 48 28.7	14 2.7	16 11.8	13♋ 1.0	5 39.9	14 0.8	4 51.4	10 12.6	7 41.6	25 37.8	1 3.3	17 52.4
6 M	12 52 25.3	15 1.7	16 8.6	27 14.6	7 36.3	15 13.5	4 28.8	10 25.8	7 45.7	25 37.5	1 4.1	17 53.1
7 T	12 56 21.8	16 0.8	16 5.4	11♌27.7	9 34.1	16 26.1	4 6.5	10 38.9	7 49.7	25 37.2	1 4.9	17 53.8
8 W	13 0 18.4	16 59.7	16 2.2	25 37.4	11 33.2	17 38.6	3 44.5	10 51.9	7 53.7	25 36.9	1 5.7	17 54.6
9 T	13 4 14.9	17 58.7	15 59.0	9♍40.9	13 33.6	18 51.1	3 22.9	11 4.9	7 57.5	25 36.5	1 6.6	17 55.3
10 F	13 8 11.5	18 57.6	15 55.9	23 35.2	15 35.3	20 3.5	3 1.6	11 17.8	8 1.3	25 36.0	1 7.5	17 56.1
11 S	13 12 8.0	19 56.4	15 52.7	7♎17.6	17 38.1	21 15.9	2 40.8	11 30.6	8 5.0	25 35.5	1 8.5	17 56.9
12 S	13 16 4.6	20 55.3	15 49.5	20 45.6	19 41.9	22 28.2	2 20.5	11 43.4	8 8.6	25 35.0	1 9.4	17 57.8
13 M	13 20 1.1	21 54.0	15 46.3	3♏57.4	21 46.7	23 40.4	2 0.6	11 56.1	8 12.2	25 34.4	1 10.5	17 58.6
14 T	13 23 57.7	22 52.8	15 43.1	16 52.4	23 52.4	24 52.6	1 41.3	12 8.8	8 15.6	25 33.7	1 11.5	17 59.5
15 W	13 27 54.2	23 51.6	15 40.0	29 30.8	25 58.7	26 4.7	1 22.5	12 21.4	8 19.0	25 33.0	1 12.6	18 0.3
16 T	13 31 50.8	24 50.2	15 36.8	11♐54.0	28 5.4	27 16.7	1 4.3	12 33.9	8 22.3	25 32.3	1 13.6	18 1.2
17 F	13 35 47.3	25 48.9	15 33.6	24 4.2	0♉12.3	28 28.6	0 46.7	12 46.3	8 25.5	25 31.5	1 14.8	18 2.1
18 S	13 39 43.9	26 47.6	15 30.4	6♑ 4.7	2 19.3	29 40.5	0 29.8	12 58.7	8 28.6	25 30.6	1 15.9	18 3.1
19 S	13 43 40.4	27 46.2	15 27.3	17 59.3	4 25.9	0♊52.4	0 13.5	13 11.0	8 31.6	25 29.7	1 17.1	18 4.0
20 M	13 47 37.0	28 44.8	15 24.1	29 52.6	6 31.9	2 4.1	29♍57.9	13 23.2	8 34.6	25 28.8	1 18.3	18 5.0
21 T	13 51 33.5	29 43.3	15 20.9	11♒49.0	8 37.1	3 15.8	29 43.0	13 35.4	8 37.4	25 27.8	1 19.6	18 6.0
22 W	13 55 30.1	0♉41.9	15 17.7	23 53.2	10 41.0	4 27.4	29 28.7	13 47.4	8 40.2	25 26.8	1 20.8	18 6.9
23 T	13 59 26.6	1 40.4	15 14.5	6♓ 9.7	12 43.3	5 39.0	29 15.3	13 59.4	8 42.9	25 25.7	1 22.1	18 8.0
24 F	14 3 23.2	2 38.8	15 11.4	18 42.2	14 43.8	6 50.5	29 2.6	14 11.3	8 45.5	25 24.5	1 23.4	18 9.0
25 S	14 7 19.8	3 37.3	15 8.2	1♈33.8	16 42.1	8 1.9	28 50.6	14 23.1	8 47.9	25 23.4	1 24.8	18 10.0
26 S	14 11 16.3	4 35.7	15 5.0	14 46.2	18 37.9	9 13.2	28 39.4	14 34.8	8 50.3	25 22.2	1 26.2	18 11.1
27 M	14 15 12.9	5 34.1	15 1.8	28 19.6	20 31.0	10 24.4	28 29.0	14 46.5	8 52.6	25 20.9	1 27.6	18 12.1
28 T	14 19 9.4	6 32.5	14 58.7	12♉12.5	22 21.2	11 35.6	28 19.4	14 58.0	8 54.9	25 19.6	1 29.0	18 13.2
29 W	14 23 6.0	7 30.8	14 55.5	26 21.6	24 8.1	12 46.7	28 10.5	15 9.5	8 57.0	25 18.3	1 30.4	18 14.3
30 T	14 27 2.5	8 29.1	14 52.3	10♊42.4	25 51.6	13 57.8	28 2.5	15 20.9	8 59.0	25 16.9	1 31.9	18 15.4

DECLINATION

DAY	EPHEMERIS SIDEREAL TIME	☉	☊	☽	☿	♀	♂	♃	♄	♅	♆	♇
1 W	12 32 42.5	4N 0.1	6S27.2	14N15.4	2S39.5	14N43.1	0N16.2	8S55.1	18S48.4	23S30.2	22N21.6	14N13.3
4 S	12 44 32.2	5 9.5	6 23.6	18 23.5	0 13.4	15 59.7	0 38.7	8 40.4	18 45.4	23 30.2	22 21.7	14 14.1
7 T	12 56 21.8	6 18.1	6 19.9	12 45.6	2N20.9	17 12.7	1 0.0	8 25.9	18 42.6	23 30.2	22 21.8	14 15.0
10 F	13 8 11.5	7 25.7	6 16.2	0 41.9	5 1.9	18 21.9	1 19.8	8 11.5	18 39.9	23 30.2	22 21.9	14 15.8
13 M	13 20 1.1	8 32.2	6 12.6	11S18.1	7 47.2	19 26.9	1 37.6	7 57.3	18 37.4	23 30.2	22 22.0	14 16.6
16 T	13 31 50.8	9 37.3	6 8.9	17 53.1	10 33.3	20 27.5	1 53.2	7 43.3	18 35.1	23 30.2	22 22.1	14 17.4
19 S	13 43 40.4	10 41.1	6 5.2	17 1.0	13 15.7	21 23.2	2 6.4	7 29.5	18 33.0	23 30.2	22 22.2	14 18.2
22 W	13 55 30.1	11 43.3	6 1.5	9 38.3	15 48.7	22 13.9	2 17.0	7 16.0	18 31.1	23 30.1	22 22.3	14 19.0
25 S	14 7 19.8	12 43.7	5 57.9	1N49.3	18 7.0	22 59.3	2 24.8	7 2.7	18 29.5	23 30.0	22 22.4	14 19.8
28 T	14 19 9.4	13 42.3	5 54.2	13 17.2	20 6.0	23 39.2	2 29.9	6 49.7	18 28.0	23 29.9	22 22.5	14 20.6

MAY 1903

DAY	EPHEMERIS SIDEREAL TIME h m s	☉ ° ′	☊ ° ′	☽ ° ′	☿ ° ′	♀ ° ′	♂ ° ′	♃ ° ′	♄ ° ′	♅ ° ′	♆ ° ′	♇ ° ′
							LONGITUDE					
1 F	14 30 59.1	9♉27.4	14♎49.1	25♊ 9.5	27♉31.5	15♊ 8.7	27♍55.3	15♓32.1	9♒ 0.9	25♐15.4	1♋33.4	18♊16.5
2 S	14 34 55.6	10 25.6	14 45.9	9♋37.3	29 7.7	16 19.6	27R48.9	15 43.3	9 2.8	25R14.0	1 35.0	18 17.7
3 S	14 38 52.2	11 23.8	14 42.8	24 1.0	0♊40.1	17 30.3	27 43.3	15 54.4	9 4.5	25 12.5	1 36.5	18 18.8
4 M	14 42 48.8	12 22.0	14 39.6	8♌16.8	2 8.6	18 41.0	27 38.5	16 5.4	9 6.2	25 10.9	1 38.1	18 20.0
5 T	14 46 45.3	13 20.1	14 36.4	22 22.2	3 33.0	19 51.6	27 34.5	16 16.3	9 7.7	25 9.3	1 39.7	18 21.2
6 W	14 50 41.8	14 18.2	14 33.2	6♍15.7	4 53.3	21 2.1	27 31.3	16 27.1	9 9.2	25 7.7	1 41.3	18 22.3
7 T	14 54 38.4	15 16.3	14 30.1	19 56.9	6 9.3	22 12.5	27 28.9	16 37.8	9 10.5	25 6.0	1 43.0	18 23.5
8 F	14 58 35.0	16 14.3	14 26.9	3♎25.6	7 21.1	23 22.8	27 27.2	16 48.3	9 11.8	25 4.3	1 44.6	18 24.7
9 S	15 2 31.5	17 12.3	14 23.7	16 41.9	8 28.6	24 33.0	27 26.4	16 58.8	9 12.9	25 2.6	1 46.3	18 26.0
10 S	15 6 28.1	18 10.3	14 20.5	29 45.9	9 31.6	25 43.1	27 26.3	17 9.2	9 14.0	25 0.8	1 48.0	18 27.2
11 M	15 10 24.6	19 8.2	14 17.3	12♏37.7	10 30.2	26 53.2	27D26.9	17 19.5	9 15.0	24 59.0	1 49.8	18 28.4
12 T	15 14 21.2	20 6.1	14 14.2	25 17.2	11 24.2	28 3.1	27 28.3	17 29.6	9 15.9	24 57.2	1 51.5	18 29.7
13 W	15 18 17.7	21 4.0	14 11.0	7♐44.8	12 13.7	29 12.9	27 30.4	17 39.7	9 16.6	24 55.3	1 53.3	18 30.9
14 T	15 22 14.3	22 1.9	14 7.8	20 1.2	12 58.5	0♋22.6	27 33.3	17 49.6	9 17.3	24 53.4	1 55.1	18 32.2
15 F	15 26 10.8	22 59.7	14 4.6	2♑ 7.8	13 38.6	1 32.2	27 36.9	17 59.4	9 17.9	24 51.5	1 56.9	18 33.5
16 S	15 30 7.4	23 57.6	14 1.5	14 6.6	14 13.9	2 41.7	27 41.2	18 9.1	9 18.4	24 49.5	1 58.7	18 34.8
17 S	15 34 4.0	24 55.4	13 58.3	26 0.4	14 44.4	3 51.1	27 46.1	18 18.7	9 18.8	24 47.5	2 0.6	18 36.1
18 M	15 38 0.5	25 53.2	13 55.1	7♒52.8	15 10.0	5 0.3	27 51.8	18 28.2	9 19.1	24 45.5	2 2.4	18 37.4
19 T	15 41 57.1	26 50.9	13 51.9	19 47.9	15 30.8	6 9.5	27 58.2	18 37.5	9 19.3	24 43.5	2 4.3	18 38.7
20 W	15 45 53.6	27 48.7	13 48.7	1♓50.4	15 46.7	7 18.5	28 5.2	18 46.7	9 19.3	24 41.4	2 6.2	18 40.0
21 T	15 49 50.2	28 46.4	13 45.6	14 5.3	15 57.7	8 27.5	28 12.9	18 55.8	9 19.3	24 39.3	2 8.2	18 41.3
22 F	15 53 46.7	29 44.1	13 42.4	26 37.2	16 4.0	9 36.3	28 21.2	19 4.8	9R19.2	24 37.1	2 10.1	18 42.6
23 S	15 57 43.3	0♊41.8	13 39.2	9♈30.6	16 5.5	10 45.0	28 30.2	19 13.7	9 19.0	24 35.0	2 12.1	18 44.0
24 S	16 1 39.8	1 39.5	13 36.0	22 48.4	16R 2.3	11 53.6	28 39.8	19 22.4	9 18.7	24 32.8	2 14.0	18 45.3
25 M	16 5 36.3	2 37.1	13 32.9	6♉32.4	15 54.7	13 2.0	28 50.0	19 31.0	9 18.3	24 30.6	2 16.0	18 46.7
26 T	16 9 32.9	3 34.8	13 29.7	20 41.5	15 42.7	14 10.4	29 0.9	19 39.4	9 17.9	24 28.4	2 18.0	18 48.0
27 W	16 13 29.5	4 32.4	13 26.5	5♊12.3	15 26.8	15 18.6	29 12.3	19 47.7	9 17.3	24 26.1	2 20.0	18 49.4
28 T	16 17 26.1	5 30.0	13 23.3	19 58.6	15 7.1	16 26.7	29 24.4	19 55.9	9 16.6	24 23.9	2 22.1	18 50.8
29 F	16 21 22.6	6 27.6	13 20.2	4♋52.2	14 44.0	17 34.6	29 37.0	20 4.0	9 15.8	24 21.6	2 24.1	18 52.1
30 S	16 25 19.1	7 25.1	13 17.0	19 44.4	14 17.9	18 42.4	29 50.2	20 11.9	9 14.9	24 19.3	2 26.2	18 53.5
31 S	16 29 15.7	8 22.7	13 13.8	4♌27.4	13 49.3	19 50.1	0♎ 3.9	20 19.6	9 13.9	24 17.0	2 28.2	18 54.9
							DECLINATION					
1 F	14 30 59.1	14N38.9	5S50.5	18N27.9	21N43.3	24N13.3	2N32.1	6S37.0	18S26.7	23S29.8	22N22.5	14N21.3
4 M	14 42 48.8	15 33.3	5 46.8	13 32.0	22 58.1	24 41.5	2 31.5	6 24.6	18 25.7	23 29.7	22 22.6	14 22.1
7 T	14 54 38.4	16 25.3	5 43.1	1 53.4	23 51.0	25 3.5	2 28.2	6 12.6	18 24.9	23 29.6	22 22.6	14 22.8
10 S	15 6 28.1	17 14.9	5 39.4	10S12.5	24 23.4	25 19.4	2 22.3	6 1.0	18 24.4	23 29.4	22 22.6	14 23.5
13 W	15 18 17.7	18 1.9	5 35.7	17 34.0	24 36.9	25 29.1	2 13.8	5 49.7	18 24.0	23 29.3	22 22.7	14 24.2
16 S	15 30 7.4	18 46.2	5 32.0	17 33.9	24 33.3	25 32.5	2 2.9	5 38.8	18 23.9	23 29.1	22 22.7	14 24.9
19 T	15 41 57.1	19 27.7	5 28.3	10 50.8	24 14.1	25 29.6	1 49.8	5 28.3	18 24.1	23 28.9	22 22.7	14 25.6
22 F	15 53 46.7	20 6.2	5 24.6	0N 9.5	23 41.0	25 20.6	1 34.4	5 18.2	18 24.5	23 28.7	22 22.7	14 26.2
25 M	16 5 36.3	20 41.6	5 20.9	11 55.4	22 55.7	25 5.5	1 16.9	5 8.6	18 25.1	23 28.4	22 22.7	14 26.8
28 T	16 17 26.1	21 13.8	5 17.2	18 26.6	22 0.9	24 44.5	0 57.5	4 59.5	18 25.9	23 28.2	22 22.6	14 27.4
31 S	16 29 15.7	21 42.7	5 13.5	14 29.5	20 60.0	24 17.7	0 36.2	4 50.9	18 27.0	23 27.9	22 22.6	14 28.0

JUNE 1903

DAY	EPHEMERIS SIDEREAL TIME h m s	☉ ° ′	☊ ° ′	☽ ° ′	☿ ° ′	♀ ° ′	♂ ° ′	♃ ° ′	♄ ° ′	♅ ° ′	♆ ° ′	♇ ° ′
							LONGITUDE					
1 M	16 33 12.3	9♊20.2	13♎10.6	18♌55.1	13♊18.6	20♋57.6	0♎18.3	20♓27.2	9♒12.9	24♐14.6	2♋30.3	18♊56.3
2 T	16 37 8.8	10 17.7	13 7.4	3♍ 4.1	12R46.4	22 4.9	0 33.1	20 34.7	9R11.7	24R12.3	2 32.4	18 57.7
3 W	16 41 5.3	11 15.2	13 4.3	16 53.2	12 13.2	23 12.1	0 48.5	20 42.0	9 10.5	24 9.9	2 34.5	18 59.0
4 T	16 45 1.9	12 12.6	13 1.1	0♎23.1	11 39.6	24 19.2	1 4.3	20 49.2	9 9.1	24 7.5	2 36.6	19 0.4
5 F	16 48 58.5	13 10.0	12 57.9	13 35.7	11 6.2	25 26.0	1 20.7	20 56.2	9 7.7	24 5.2	2 38.7	19 1.8
6 S	16 52 55.0	14 7.5	12 54.7	26 33.0	10 33.6	26 32.7	1 37.6	21 3.1	9 6.1	24 2.8	2 40.9	19 3.2
7 S	16 56 51.6	15 4.8	12 51.6	9♏17.3	10 2.2	27 39.3	1 55.0	21 9.9	9 4.5	24 0.4	2 43.0	19 4.6
8 M	17 0 48.1	16 2.2	12 48.4	21 50.5	9 32.7	28 45.6	2 12.8	21 16.4	9 2.8	23 57.9	2 45.2	19 6.0
9 T	17 4 44.7	16 59.6	12 45.2	4♐13.9	9 5.6	29 51.8	2 31.1	21 22.8	9 1.0	23 55.5	2 47.3	19 7.4
10 W	17 8 41.3	17 56.9	12 42.0	16 28.8	8 41.3	0♌57.8	2 49.9	21 29.1	8 59.1	23 53.1	2 49.5	19 8.8
11 T	17 12 37.8	18 54.3	12 38.9	28 35.9	8 20.1	2 3.6	3 9.1	21 35.2	8 57.1	23 50.7	2 51.7	19 10.2
12 F	17 16 34.4	19 51.6	12 35.7	10♑36.5	8 2.5	3 9.2	3 28.7	21 41.2	8 55.1	23 48.2	2 53.9	19 11.6
13 S	17 20 30.9	20 48.9	12 32.5	22 31.8	7 48.7	4 14.6	3 48.7	21 47.0	8 52.9	23 45.8	2 56.0	19 13.0
14 S	17 24 27.5	21 46.2	12 29.3	4♒23.9	7 39.0	5 19.8	4 9.2	21 52.6	8 50.7	23 43.3	2 58.2	19 14.4
15 M	17 28 24.0	22 43.5	12 26.2	16 15.3	7 33.6	6 24.8	4 30.1	21 58.0	8 48.4	23 40.9	3 0.4	19 15.8
16 T	17 32 20.6	23 40.8	12 23.0	28 9.4	7 32.6	7 29.6	4 51.4	22 3.3	8 46.0	23 38.4	3 2.7	19 17.2
17 W	17 36 17.2	24 38.0	12 19.8	10♓10.4	7D36.2	8 34.1	5 13.1	22 8.5	8 43.5	23 36.0	3 4.9	19 18.6
18 T	17 40 13.7	25 35.3	12 16.6	22 22.8	7 44.3	9 38.5	5 35.1	22 13.4	8 40.9	23 33.5	3 7.1	19 20.0
19 F	17 44 10.3	26 32.6	12 13.4	4♈51.8	7 57.1	10 42.6	5 57.6	22 18.2	8 38.3	23 31.1	3 9.3	19 21.4
20 S	17 48 6.8	27 29.8	12 10.3	17 42.1	8 14.5	11 46.5	6 20.4	22 22.8	8 35.6	23 28.6	3 11.5	19 22.8
21 S	17 52 3.4	28 27.1	12 7.1	0♉58.1	8 36.5	12 50.2	6 43.6	22 27.3	8 32.8	23 26.2	3 13.8	19 24.2
22 M	17 55 59.9	29 24.4	12 3.9	14 42.7	9 3.2	13 53.6	7 7.1	22 31.5	8 29.9	23 23.7	3 16.0	19 25.6
23 T	17 59 56.5	0♋21.6	12 0.7	28 56.2	9 34.3	14 56.8	7 31.1	22 35.6	8 27.0	23 21.3	3 18.2	19 27.0
24 W	18 3 53.1	1 18.9	11 57.6	13♊36.2	10 10.0	15 59.7	7 55.3	22 39.5	8 23.9	23 18.9	3 20.5	19 28.4
25 T	18 7 49.7	2 16.1	11 54.4	28 36.6	10 50.2	17 2.3	8 19.9	22 43.2	8 20.8	23 16.5	3 22.7	19 29.7
26 F	18 11 46.2	3 13.4	11 51.2	13♋48.1	11 34.7	18 4.7	8 44.9	22 46.8	8 17.7	23 14.0	3 24.9	19 31.1
27 S	18 15 42.7	4 10.6	11 48.0	28 59.9	12 23.5	19 6.8	9 10.2	22 50.1	8 14.4	23 11.6	3 27.2	19 32.5
28 S	18 19 39.3	5 7.8	11 44.8	14♌ 1.7	13 16.6	20 8.6	9 35.8	22 53.3	8 11.1	23 9.2	3 29.4	19 33.8
29 M	18 23 35.9	6 5.1	11 41.7	28 45.1	14 13.8	21 10.2	10 1.8	22 56.3	8 7.8	23 6.9	3 31.6	19 35.2
30 T	18 27 32.4	7 2.3	11 38.5	13♍ 4.8	15 15.2	22 11.4	10 28.0	22 59.1	8 4.3	23 4.5	3 33.9	19 36.5
							DECLINATION					
1 M	16 33 12.3	21N51.6	5S12.3	11N 9.2	20N39.2	24N 7.6	0N28.7	4S48.1	18S27.4	23S27.8	22N22.6	14N28.2
4 T	16 45 1.9	22 16.0	5 8.6	1S17.1	19 37.8	23 33.5	0 5.1	4 40.2	18 28.8	23 27.6	22 22.5	14 28.7
7 S	16 56 51.6	22 36.9	5 4.9	12 33.2	18 42.6	22 54.2	0S20.0	4 32.7	18 30.4	23 27.3	22 22.4	14 29.2
10 W	17 8 41.3	22 54.2	5 1.1	18 18.1	17 58.9	22 10.0	0 46.7	4 25.9	18 32.2	23 27.0	22 22.4	14 29.7
13 S	17 20 30.9	23 7.9	4 57.4	16 39.5	17 30.6	21 21.3	1 14.8	4 19.6	18 34.2	23 26.7	22 22.3	14 30.1
16 T	17 32 20.6	23 17.9	4 53.7	8 46.4	17 19.5	20 28.1	1 44.1	4 13.9	18 36.4	23 26.3	22 22.2	14 30.5
19 F	17 44 10.3	23 24.2	4 50.0	2N34.9	17 25.6	19 31.0	2 14.7	4 8.8	18 38.7	23 26.0	22 22.1	14 30.9
22 M	17 55 59.9	23 26.9	4 46.3	13 42.3	17 47.5	18 30.3	2 46.3	4 4.4	18 41.3	23 25.7	22 21.9	14 31.3
25 T	18 7 49.7	23 25.8	4 42.6	18 34.3	18 22.5	17 26.2	3 19.1	4 0.6	18 44.0	23 25.3	22 21.8	14 31.6
28 S	18 19 39.3	23 21.0	4 38.8	12 32.9	19 7.7	16 19.1	3 52.8	3 57.4	18 46.9	23 25.0	22 21.6	14 31.9

JULY 1903

LONGITUDE

DAY	EPHEMERIS SIDEREAL TIME h m s	☉ ° ′	☊ ° ′	☽ ° ′	☿ ° ′	♀ ° ′	♂ ° ′	♃ ° ′	♄ ° ′	♅ ° ′	♆ ° ′	♇ ° ′
1 W	18 31 29.0	7♋59.5	11♎35.3	26♍58.9	16♊20.7	23♌12.2	10♎54.6	23♓ 1.7	8♒ 0.8	23♐ 2.2	3♋36.1	19♊37.9
2 T	18 35 25.5	8 56.7	11 32.1	10♎28.1	17 30.2	24 12.8	11 21.4	23 4.2	7R57.3	22R59.8	3 38.3	19 39.2
3 F	18 39 22.1	9 53.9	11 29.0	23 35.0	18 43.7	25 13.0	11 48.6	23 6.4	7 53.7	22 57.5	3 40.5	19 40.5
4 S	18 43 18.7	10 51.1	11 25.8	6♏22.9	20 1.1	26 12.9	12 16.0	23 8.5	7 50.0	22 55.2	3 42.8	19 41.9
5 S	18 47 15.2	11 48.3	11 22.6	18 55.5	21 22.3	27 12.3	12 43.8	23 10.3	7 46.3	22 52.9	3 45.0	19 43.2
6 M	18 51 11.7	12 45.5	11 19.4	1♐16.0	22 47.4	28 11.5	13 11.8	23 12.0	7 42.5	22 50.7	3 47.2	19 44.5
7 T	18 55 8.3	13 42.6	11 16.3	13 27.3	24 16.2	29 10.2	13 40.0	23 13.5	7 38.7	22 48.4	3 49.4	19 45.8
8 W	18 59 4.8	14 39.8	11 13.1	25 31.6	25 48.8	0♍ 8.5	14 8.6	23 14.8	7 34.8	22 46.2	3 51.6	19 47.1
9 T	19 3 1.4	15 37.0	11 9.9	7♑30.6	27 25.0	1 6.4	14 37.4	23 15.9	7 30.9	22 44.0	3 53.8	19 48.4
10 F	19 6 58.0	16 34.2	11 6.7	19 25.8	29 4.7	2 3.9	15 6.5	23 16.8	7 26.9	22 41.9	3 56.0	19 49.6
11 S	19 10 54.5	17 31.4	11 3.5	1♒18.4	0♋47.8	3 0.9	15 35.8	23 17.5	7 22.9	22 39.7	3 58.2	19 50.9
12 S	19 14 51.1	18 28.6	11 0.4	13 10.0	2 34.2	3 57.5	16 5.3	23 18.0	7 18.8	22 37.6	4 0.4	19 52.2
13 M	19 18 47.6	19 25.8	10 57.2	25 2.6	4 23.8	4 53.6	16 35.2	23 18.3	7 14.7	22 35.5	4 2.5	19 53.4
14 T	19 22 44.2	20 23.0	10 54.0	6♓58.5	6 16.3	5 49.2	17 5.2	23 18.5	7 10.6	22 33.4	4 4.7	19 54.7
15 W	19 26 40.8	21 20.2	10 50.8	19 1.0	8 11.7	6 44.4	17 35.5	23R18.4	7 6.4	22 31.3	4 6.9	19 55.9
16 T	19 30 37.3	22 17.4	10 47.7	1♈14.0	10 9.5	7 39.0	18 6.0	23 18.1	7 2.2	22 29.3	4 9.0	19 57.1
17 F	19 34 33.8	23 14.6	10 44.5	13 41.9	12 9.6	8 33.1	18 36.8	23 17.7	6 58.0	22 27.3	4 11.1	19 58.3
18 S	19 38 30.4	24 11.9	10 41.3	26 29.4	14 11.7	9 26.6	19 7.8	23 17.0	6 53.7	22 25.4	4 13.3	19 59.5
19 S	19 42 27.0	25 9.1	10 38.1	9♉40.8	16 15.5	10 19.6	19 39.0	23 16.2	6 49.4	22 23.4	4 15.4	20 0.7
20 M	19 46 23.6	26 6.4	10 35.0	23 19.7	18 20.7	11 12.0	20 10.4	23 15.1	6 45.1	22 21.5	4 17.5	20 1.9
21 T	19 50 20.1	27 3.7	10 31.8	7♊27.7	20 27.0	12 3.8	20 42.1	23 13.9	6 40.7	22 19.6	4 19.6	20 3.0
22 W	19 54 16.6	28 1.0	10 28.6	22 3.6	22 34.0	12 54.9	21 13.9	23 12.4	6 36.4	22 17.8	4 21.7	20 4.2
23 T	19 58 13.2	28 58.3	10 25.4	7♋ 2.8	24 41.4	13 45.4	21 46.0	23 10.8	6 32.0	22 16.0	4 23.8	20 5.3
24 F	20 2 9.7	29 55.6	10 22.3	22 17.0	26 49.0	14 35.3	22 18.3	23 9.0	6 27.6	22 14.2	4 25.8	20 6.4
25 S	20 6 6.3	0♌52.9	10 19.1	7♌35.5	28 56.4	15 24.4	22 50.9	23 6.9	6 23.1	22 12.5	4 27.9	20 7.5
26 S	20 10 2.9	1 50.3	10 15.9	22 47.2	1♌ 3.4	16 12.8	23 23.6	23 4.7	6 18.7	22 10.8	4 29.9	20 8.6
27 M	20 13 59.4	2 47.6	10 12.7	7♍41.8	3 9.9	17 0.5	23 56.5	23 2.3	6 14.3	22 9.1	4 31.9	20 9.7
28 T	20 17 56.0	3 45.0	10 9.5	22 12.5	5 15.5	17 47.4	24 29.7	22 59.7	6 9.8	22 7.5	4 33.9	20 10.8
29 W	20 21 52.5	4 42.4	10 6.4	6♎15.7	7 20.1	18 33.4	25 3.0	22 56.9	6 5.4	22 5.9	4 35.9	20 11.8
30 T	20 25 49.1	5 39.7	10 3.2	19 51.0	9 23.7	19 18.6	25 36.5	22 53.9	6 0.9	22 4.3	4 37.9	20 12.9
31 F	20 29 45.7	6 37.1	10 0.0	3♏ 0.5	11 25.9	20 2.9	26 10.2	22 50.8	5 56.4	22 2.8	4 39.9	20 13.9

DECLINATION

DAY	EPHEMERIS SIDEREAL TIME h m s	☉	☊	☽	☿	♀	♂	♃	♄	♅	♆	♇
1 W	18 31 29.0	23N12.5	4S35.1	0N 1.2	19N59.4	15N 9.4	4S27.4	3S54.9	18S49.9	23S24.6	22N21.5	14N32.2
4 S	18 43 18.7	23 0.3	4 31.4	11S39.8	20 53.7	13 57.4	5 2.8	3 53.1	18 53.0	23 24.3	22 21.3	14 32.4
7 T	18 55 8.3	22 44.6	4 27.6	18 1.9	21 46.1	12 43.5	5 38.9	3 51.9	18 56.3	23 24.0	22 21.1	14 32.6
10 F	19 6 58.0	22 25.3	4 23.9	17 9.1	22 31.7	11 28.1	6 15.7	3 51.4	18 59.6	23 23.6	22 21.0	14 32.8
13 M	19 18 47.6	22 2.5	4 20.2	9 49.2	23 5.2	10 11.4	6 53.1	3 51.7	19 3.1	23 23.3	22 20.8	14 32.9
16 T	19 30 37.3	21 36.3	4 16.4	1N11.8	23 21.3	8 53.9	7 30.9	3 52.6	19 6.5	23 23.0	22 20.6	14 33.0
19 S	19 42 27.0	21 6.8	4 12.7	12 20.2	23 15.6	7 35.9	8 9.2	3 54.2	19 10.1	23 22.6	22 20.4	14 33.1
22 W	19 54 16.6	20 34.0	4 9.0	18 25.0	22 45.9	6 17.8	8 47.8	3 56.5	19 13.6	23 22.3	22 20.1	14 33.2
25 S	20 6 6.3	19 58.2	4 5.2	14 4.9	21 52.2	4 59.9	9 26.8	3 59.5	19 17.2	23 22.0	22 19.9	14 33.2
28 T	20 17 56.0	19 19.3	4 1.5	1 44.7	20 37.0	3 42.6	10 5.9	4 3.2	19 20.8	23 21.8	22 19.7	14 33.2
31 F	20 29 45.7	18 37.6	3 57.7	10S33.9	19 4.0	2 26.6	10 45.3	4 7.5	19 24.4	23 21.5	22 19.5	14 33.1

AUGUST 1903

LONGITUDE

DAY	EPHEMERIS SIDEREAL TIME h m s	☉ ° ′	☊ ° ′	☽ ° ′	☿ ° ′	♀ ° ′	♂ ° ′	♃ ° ′	♄ ° ′	♅ ° ′	♆ ° ′	♇ ° ′
1 S	20 33 42.2	7♌34.5	9♎56.8	15♏47.6	13♌26.9	20♍46.3	26♎44.1	22♓47.4	5♒52.0	22♐ 1.3	4♋41.8	20♊14.9
2 S	20 37 38.8	8 31.9	9 53.7	28 16.5	15 26.5	21 28.8	27 18.2	22R43.9	5R47.5	21R59.9	4 43.8	20 15.9
3 M	20 41 35.3	9 29.3	9 50.5	10♐31.4	17 24.5	22 10.2	27 52.5	22 40.2	5 43.1	21 58.5	4 45.7	20 16.9
4 T	20 45 31.9	10 26.7	9 47.3	22 36.1	19 21.1	22 50.6	28 26.9	22 36.3	5 38.7	21 57.1	4 47.6	20 17.8
5 W	20 49 28.4	11 24.2	9 44.1	4♑34.2	21 16.2	23 29.9	29 1.5	22 32.2	5 34.2	21 55.8	4 49.4	20 18.8
6 T	20 53 25.0	12 21.6	9 40.9	16 28.2	23 9.7	24 8.1	29 36.3	22 28.0	5 29.8	21 54.6	4 51.3	20 19.7
7 F	20 57 21.5	13 19.1	9 37.8	28 20.6	25 1.6	24 45.1	0♏11.3	22 23.6	5 25.4	21 53.3	4 53.1	20 20.7
8 S	21 1 18.1	14 16.6	9 34.6	10♒12.9	26 52.0	25 20.9	0 46.4	22 19.0	5 21.0	21 52.2	4 55.0	20 21.6
9 S	21 5 14.6	15 14.1	9 31.4	22 7.0	28 40.9	25 55.5	1 21.7	22 14.3	5 16.7	21 51.0	4 56.8	20 22.4
10 M	21 9 11.2	16 11.6	9 28.2	4♓ 4.4	0♍28.1	26 28.7	1 57.2	22 9.4	5 12.3	21 49.9	4 58.5	20 23.3
11 T	21 13 7.8	17 9.1	9 25.1	16 6.8	2 13.9	27 0.7	2 32.8	22 4.3	5 8.0	21 48.9	5 0.3	20 24.2
12 W	21 17 4.3	18 6.7	9 21.9	28 16.6	3 58.1	27 31.2	3 8.6	21 59.1	5 3.7	21 47.9	5 2.1	20 25.0
13 T	21 21 0.8	19 4.3	9 18.7	10♈36.5	5 40.8	28 0.2	3 44.5	21 53.7	4 59.5	21 46.9	5 3.8	20 25.8
14 F	21 24 57.4	20 1.9	9 15.5	23 9.6	7 22.0	28 27.8	4 20.6	21 48.1	4 55.3	21 46.0	5 5.5	20 26.6
15 S	21 28 54.0	20 59.5	9 12.4	5♉59.4	9 1.8	28 53.8	4 56.8	21 42.4	4 51.1	21 45.1	5 7.2	20 27.4
16 S	21 32 50.5	21 57.2	9 9.2	19 9.6	10 40.0	29 18.2	5 33.3	21 36.6	4 46.9	21 44.3	5 8.8	20 28.1
17 M	21 36 47.1	22 54.9	9 6.0	2♊43.2	12 16.8	29 40.9	6 9.8	21 30.6	4 42.8	21 43.5	5 10.5	20 28.9
18 T	21 40 43.6	23 52.6	9 2.8	16 41.8	13 52.1	0♎ 1.9	6 46.5	21 24.5	4 38.7	21 42.8	5 12.1	20 29.6
19 W	21 44 40.2	24 50.3	8 59.6	1♋ 5.4	15 25.9	0 21.1	7 23.4	21 18.3	4 34.6	21 42.1	5 13.7	20 30.3
20 T	21 48 36.8	25 48.1	8 56.5	15 50.9	16 58.3	0 38.5	8 0.4	21 11.9	4 30.6	21 41.5	5 15.2	20 31.0
21 F	21 52 33.3	26 45.9	8 53.3	0♌52.3	18 29.3	0 53.9	8 37.6	21 5.4	4 26.7	21 40.9	5 16.8	20 31.7
22 S	21 56 29.8	27 43.7	8 50.1	16 1.1	19 58.7	1 7.4	9 14.9	20 58.7	4 22.7	21 40.4	5 18.3	20 32.3
23 S	22 0 26.4	28 41.5	8 46.9	1♍ 7.4	21 26.7	1 18.9	9 52.4	20 52.0	4 18.9	21 39.9	5 19.8	20 32.9
24 M	22 4 23.0	29 39.4	8 43.7	16 1.5	22 53.2	1 28.3	10 30.0	20 45.1	4 15.1	21 39.4	5 21.3	20 33.6
25 T	22 8 19.5	0♍37.3	8 40.6	0♎35.7	24 18.2	1 35.6	11 7.8	20 38.2	4 11.3	21 39.1	5 22.7	20 34.2
26 W	22 12 16.1	1 35.2	8 37.4	14 44.8	25 41.6	1 40.7	11 45.7	20 31.1	4 7.6	21 38.7	5 24.1	20 34.7
27 T	22 16 12.6	2 33.1	8 34.2	28 26.8	27 3.5	1 43.5	12 23.7	20 23.9	4 3.9	21 38.4	5 25.5	20 35.3
28 F	22 20 9.2	3 31.1	8 31.0	11♏42.3	28 23.7	1 44.0	13 1.9	20 16.6	4 0.4	21 38.2	5 26.9	20 35.8
29 S	22 24 5.7	4 29.0	8 27.9	24 33.7	29 42.4	1R42.2	13 40.2	20 9.3	3 56.8	21 38.0	5 28.2	20 36.3
30 S	22 28 2.3	5 27.0	8 24.7	7♐ 4.7	0♎59.3	1 38.1	14 18.6	20 1.9	3 53.4	21 37.9	5 29.5	20 36.8
31 M	22 31 58.8	6 25.1	8 21.5	19 19.6	2 14.5	1 31.5	14 57.2	19 54.4	3 50.0	21 37.8	5 30.8	20 37.3

DECLINATION

DAY	EPHEMERIS SIDEREAL TIME h m s	☉	☊	☽	☿	♀	♂	♃	♄	♅	♆	♇
1 S	20 33 42.2	18N23.1	3S56.5	13S38.8	18N29.7	2N 1.5	10S58.4	4S 9.1	19S25.6	23S21.4	22N19.4	14N33.1
4 T	20 45 31.9	17 37.7	3 52.7	18 22.2	16 39.2	0 47.7	11 37.8	4 14.2	19 29.1	23 21.2	22 19.2	14 33.0
7 F	20 57 21.5	16 49.8	3 49.0	15 49.4	14 39.7	0S23.8	12 17.1	4 20.0	19 32.6	23 20.9	22 18.9	14 32.9
10 M	21 9 11.2	15 59.4	3 45.3	7 22.0	12 34.4	1 32.4	12 56.3	4 26.3	19 36.0	23 20.7	22 18.7	14 32.7
13 T	21 21 0.8	15 6.7	3 41.5	3N57.7	10 25.6	2 37.5	13 35.4	4 33.2	19 39.3	23 20.6	22 18.4	14 32.6
16 S	21 32 50.5	14 11.8	3 37.8	14 13.8	8 15.4	3 38.2	14 14.1	4 40.5	19 42.6	23 20.4	22 18.2	14 32.4
19 W	21 44 40.2	13 14.9	3 34.0	18 19.2	6 5.3	4 33.8	14 52.5	4 48.4	19 45.7	23 20.3	22 18.0	14 32.1
22 S	21 56 29.8	12 16.0	3 30.2	12 11.0	3 56.8	5 23.4	15 30.5	4 56.6	19 48.7	23 20.2	22 17.7	14 31.9
25 T	22 8 19.5	11 15.5	3 26.5	0S47.2	1 51.1	6 5.8	16 8.0	5 5.3	19 51.6	23 20.1	22 17.5	14 31.6
28 F	22 20 9.2	10 13.3	3 22.7	12 32.4	0S10.7	6 39.9	16 44.9	5 14.2	19 54.3	23 20.1	22 17.2	14 31.3
31 M	22 31 58.8	9 9.7	3 19.0	18 4.4	2 7.3	7 4.4	17 21.2	5 23.3	19 56.9	23 20.0	22 17.0	14 31.0

SEPTEMBER 1903

DAY	EPHEMERIS SIDEREAL TIME	☉	☊	☽	☿	♀	♂	♃	♄	♅	♆	♇
	h m s	° ′	° ′	° ′	° ′	° ′	° ′	° ′	° ′	° ′	° ′	° ′
						LONGITUDE						
1 T	22 35 55.4	7♍23.1	8♎18.3	1♑22.8	3♎27.9	1♎22.6	15♏35.9	19♓46.8	3♒46.6	21♐37.8	5♋32.1	20♊37.7
2 W	22 39 51.9	8 21.2	8 15.1	13 18.7	4 39.4	1R11.2	16 14.8	19R39.2	3R43.4	21D37.8	5 33.3	20 38.1
3 T	22 43 48.5	9 19.2	8 12.0	25 10.9	5 48.9	0 57.5	16 53.7	19 31.5	3 40.2	21 37.9	5 34.5	20 38.6
4 F	22 47 45.0	10 17.4	8 8.8	7♒ 2.9	6 56.4	0 41.4	17 32.8	19 23.7	3 37.1	21 38.0	5 35.7	20 38.9
5 S	22 51 41.6	11 15.5	8 5.6	18 57.4	8 1.7	0 22.9	18 12.0	19 15.9	3 34.0	21 38.2	5 36.8	20 39.3
6 S	22 55 38.1	12 13.7	8 2.4	0♓56.5	9 4.7	0 2.2	18 51.3	19 8.1	3 31.0	21 38.4	5 37.9	20 39.6
7 M	22 59 34.7	13 11.9	7 59.3	13 2.3	10 5.3	29♍39.4	19 30.8	19 0.2	3 28.1	21 38.7	5 39.0	20 40.0
8 T	23 3 31.3	14 10.1	7 56.1	25 16.2	11 3.4	29 14.4	20 10.4	18 52.3	3 25.3	21 39.0	5 40.1	20 40.3
9 W	23 7 27.8	15 8.4	7 52.9	7♈39.6	11 58.7	28 47.4	20 50.1	18 44.3	3 22.5	21 39.4	5 41.1	20 40.6
10 T	23 11 24.3	16 6.6	7 49.7	20 14.1	12 51.1	28 18.6	21 29.9	18 36.4	3 19.9	21 39.8	5 42.1	20 40.8
11 F	23 15 20.9	17 4.9	7 46.5	3♉ 1.2	13 40.4	27 48.0	22 9.8	18 28.4	3 17.3	21 40.3	5 43.1	20 41.0
12 S	23 19 17.4	18 3.3	7 43.4	16 2.7	14 26.4	27 16.0	22 49.8	18 20.4	3 14.7	21 40.8	5 44.0	20 41.3
13 S	23 23 14.0	19 1.7	7 40.2	29 20.2	15 8.8	26 42.5	23 30.0	18 12.5	3 12.3	21 41.4	5 44.9	20 41.4
14 M	23 27 10.5	20 0.1	7 37.0	12♊55.1	15 47.4	26 8.0	24 10.2	18 4.5	3 10.0	21 42.0	5 45.8	20 41.6
15 T	23 31 7.1	20 58.6	7 33.8	26 48.3	16 21.8	25 32.5	24 50.6	17 56.5	3 7.7	21 42.7	5 46.7	20 41.8
16 W	23 35 3.7	21 57.1	7 30.7	10♋59.4	16 51.9	24 56.3	25 31.1	17 48.6	3 5.5	21 43.5	5 47.5	20 41.9
17 T	23 39 0.2	22 55.6	7 27.5	25 26.5	17 17.2	24 19.6	26 11.8	17 40.6	3 3.4	21 44.3	5 48.3	20 42.0
18 F	23 42 56.7	23 54.2	7 24.3	10♌ 5.9	17 37.4	23 42.6	26 52.5	17 32.7	3 1.4	21 45.1	5 49.0	20 42.1
19 S	23 46 53.3	24 52.8	7 21.1	24 52.1	17 52.1	23 5.7	27 33.3	17 24.9	2 59.5	21 46.0	5 49.7	20 42.2
20 S	23 50 49.9	25 51.4	7 17.9	9♍38.3	18 1.1	22 29.0	28 14.3	17 17.1	2 57.7	21 46.9	5 50.4	20 42.2
21 M	23 54 46.4	26 50.1	7 14.8	24 17.1	18 3.8	21 52.7	28 55.4	17 9.3	2 56.0	21 47.9	5 51.1	20 42.2
22 T	23 58 43.0	27 48.8	7 11.6	8♎41.8	18R 0.0	21 17.2	29 36.5	17 1.6	2 54.3	21 49.0	5 51.7	20 42.2
23 W	0 2 39.6	28 47.6	7 8.4	22 47.0	17 49.4	20 42.6	0♐17.8	16 53.9	2 52.8	21 50.1	5 52.3	20R42.2
24 T	0 6 36.1	29 46.3	7 5.2	6♏29.5	17 31.6	20 9.1	0 59.2	16 46.3	2 51.4	21 51.2	5 52.8	20 42.1
25 F	0 10 32.6	0♎45.1	7 2.0	19 48.1	17 6.5	19 36.9	1 40.7	16 38.8	2 50.0	21 52.4	5 53.4	20 42.1
26 S	0 14 29.2	1 43.9	6 58.9	2♐43.5	16 34.1	19 6.3	2 22.3	16 31.3	2 48.7	21 53.6	5 53.8	20 42.0
27 S	0 18 25.8	2 42.8	6 55.7	15 18.2	15 54.4	18 37.3	3 4.1	16 23.9	2 47.6	21 54.9	5 54.3	20 41.9
28 M	0 22 22.3	3 41.7	6 52.5	27 35.7	15 7.7	18 10.2	3 45.9	16 16.7	2 46.5	21 56.3	5 54.7	20 41.7
29 T	0 26 18.9	4 40.6	6 49.3	9♑40.1	14 14.6	17 45.0	4 27.8	16 9.5	2 45.6	21 57.7	5 55.1	20 41.6
30 W	0 30 15.4	5 39.6	6 46.2	21 36.1	13 15.7	17 21.9	5 9.8	16 2.4	2 44.7	21 59.1	5 55.5	20 41.4
						DECLINATION						
1 T	22 35 55.4	8N48.1	3S17.7	18S15.4	2S44.8	7S10.2	17S33.1	5S26.4	19S57.8	23S20.0	22N17.0	14N30.9
4 F	22 47 45.0	7 42.8	3 14.0	14 8.4	4 32.4	7 20.2	18 8.2	5 35.9	20 0.1	23 20.1	22 16.7	14 30.6
7 M	22 59 34.7	6 36.3	3 10.2	4 42.6	6 11.4	7 18.0	18 42.5	5 45.4	20 2.3	23 20.1	22 16.5	14 30.2
10 T	23 11 24.3	5 28.9	3 6.4	6N46.6	7 39.8	7 3.4	19 15.8	5 54.9	20 4.4	23 20.2	22 16.3	14 29.8
13 S	23 23 14.0	4 20.6	3 2.7	15 55.9	8 54.8	6 36.6	19 48.1	6 4.4	20 6.2	23 20.3	22 16.1	14 29.4
16 W	23 35 3.7	3 11.6	2 58.9	17 45.3	9 53.0	5 58.6	20 19.1	6 13.9	20 7.9	23 20.4	22 15.9	14 29.0
19 S	23 46 53.3	2 2.1	2 55.1	9 54.5	10 29.8	5 11.4	20 49.0	6 23.2	20 9.3	23 20.6	22 15.8	14 28.6
22 T	23 58 43.0	0 52.2	2 51.4	3S17.1	10 39.5	4 17.6	21 17.5	6 32.3	20 10.6	23 20.8	22 15.6	14 28.2
25 F	0 10 32.6	0S17.9	2 47.6	14 12.9	10 15.7	3 20.0	21 44.6	6 41.1	20 11.7	23 21.0	22 15.4	14 27.7
28 M	0 22 22.3	1 28.2	2 43.8	18 12.4	9 13.5	2 21.9	22 10.2	6 49.5	20 12.5	23 21.2	22 15.3	14 27.3

OCTOBER 1903

DAY	EPHEMERIS SIDEREAL TIME	☉	☊	☽	☿	♀	♂	♃	♄	♅	♆	♇
						LONGITUDE						
1 T	0 34 11.9	6♎38.5	6♎43.0	3♒28.2	12♎12.1	17♍ 1.0	5♐51.9	15♓55.4	2♒43.9	22♐ 0.6	5♋55.8	20♊41.2
2 F	0 38 8.5	7 37.5	6 39.8	15 20.8	11R 5.1	16R42.4	6 34.1	15R48.5	2R43.2	22 2.1	5 56.1	20R41.0
3 S	0 42 5.1	8 36.6	6 36.6	27 17.7	9 56.3	16 26.2	7 16.4	15 41.8	2 42.7	22 3.7	5 56.3	20 40.7
4 S	0 46 1.6	9 35.6	6 33.4	9♓22.3	8 47.3	16 12.3	7 58.8	15 35.1	2 42.2	22 5.3	5 56.6	20 40.5
5 M	0 49 58.2	10 34.7	6 30.3	21 37.4	7 40.1	16 0.9	8 41.2	15 28.6	2 41.8	22 7.0	5 56.7	20 40.2
6 T	0 53 54.7	11 33.9	6 27.1	4♈ 4.9	6 36.4	15 51.9	9 23.8	15 22.2	2 41.5	22 8.7	5 56.9	20 39.9
7 W	0 57 51.3	12 33.0	6 23.9	16 46.1	5 38.2	15 45.3	10 6.5	15 15.9	2 41.4	22 10.5	5 57.0	20 39.5
8 T	1 1 47.8	13 32.2	6 20.7	29 41.5	4 46.9	15 41.2	10 49.2	15 9.8	2 41.3	22 12.3	5 57.1	20 39.2
9 F	1 5 44.4	14 31.5	6 17.6	12♉51.0	4 4.1	15 39.5	11 32.0	15 3.8	2D41.3	22 14.2	5 57.2	20 38.8
10 S	1 9 40.9	15 30.7	6 14.4	26 14.2	3 30.9	15D40.3	12 15.0	14 58.0	2 41.4	22 16.1	5 57.2	20 38.4
11 S	1 13 37.5	16 30.1	6 11.2	9♊50.0	3 8.0	15 43.4	12 58.0	14 52.3	2 41.6	22 18.0	5R57.2	20 38.0
12 M	1 17 34.0	17 29.4	6 8.0	23 37.4	2 55.9	15 48.9	13 41.1	14 46.8	2 42.0	22 20.0	5 57.1	20 37.6
13 T	1 21 30.6	18 28.8	6 4.8	7♋35.0	2 54.7	15 56.6	14 24.3	14 41.4	2 42.4	22 22.0	5 57.0	20 37.1
14 W	1 25 27.1	19 28.2	6 1.7	21 41.4	3D 4.3	16 6.6	15 7.5	14 36.1	2 42.9	22 24.1	5 56.9	20 36.7
15 T	1 29 23.7	20 27.7	5 58.5	5♌54.7	3 24.5	16 18.7	15 50.9	14 31.1	2 43.5	22 26.2	5 56.8	20 36.2
16 F	1 33 20.2	21 27.2	5 55.3	20 12.8	3 54.6	16 33.0	16 34.4	14 26.2	2 44.3	22 28.4	5 56.6	20 35.7
17 S	1 37 16.8	22 26.7	5 52.1	4♍32.6	4 34.0	16 49.4	17 17.9	14 21.4	2 45.1	22 30.6	5 56.4	20 35.1
18 S	1 41 13.3	23 26.3	5 49.0	18 50.8	5 22.0	17 7.7	18 1.5	14 16.9	2 46.0	22 32.9	5 56.1	20 34.6
19 M	1 45 9.9	24 25.9	5 45.8	3♎ 3.4	6 17.7	17 28.0	18 45.2	14 12.5	2 47.0	22 35.1	5 55.8	20 34.0
20 T	1 49 6.4	25 25.6	5 42.6	17 6.3	7 20.3	17 50.1	19 29.0	14 8.3	2 48.2	22 37.5	5 55.5	20 33.4
21 W	1 53 3.0	26 25.3	5 39.4	0♏55.6	8 29.0	18 14.1	20 12.9	14 4.3	2 49.4	22 39.9	5 55.2	20 32.8
22 T	1 56 59.6	27 25.0	5 36.2	14 28.0	9 43.0	18 39.7	20 56.9	14 0.4	2 50.7	22 42.3	5 54.8	20 32.2
23 F	2 0 56.1	28 24.7	5 33.1	27 41.6	11 1.7	19 7.1	21 40.9	13 56.8	2 52.2	22 44.7	5 54.4	20 31.5
24 S	2 4 52.6	29 24.5	5 29.9	10♐35.6	12 24.2	19 36.1	22 25.0	13 53.3	2 53.7	22 47.2	5 53.9	20 30.9
25 S	2 8 49.2	0♏24.3	5 26.7	23 11.0	13 50.2	20 6.6	23 9.2	13 50.1	2 55.3	22 49.7	5 53.4	20 30.2
26 M	2 12 45.8	1 24.2	5 23.5	5♑29.7	15 18.9	20 38.7	23 53.5	13 47.0	2 57.1	22 52.3	5 52.9	20 29.5
27 T	2 16 42.3	2 24.0	5 20.4	17 35.1	16 49.9	21 12.2	24 37.8	13 44.1	2 58.9	22 54.9	5 52.4	20 28.8
28 W	2 20 38.9	3 23.9	5 17.2	29 31.3	18 22.7	21 47.1	25 22.2	13 41.4	3 0.8	22 57.5	5 51.8	20 28.0
29 T	2 24 35.4	4 23.9	5 14.0	11♒23.0	19 57.1	22 23.4	26 6.7	13 39.0	3 2.8	23 0.2	5 51.2	20 27.3
30 F	2 28 32.0	5 23.8	5 10.8	23 15.1	21 32.7	23 1.0	26 51.3	13 36.7	3 5.0	23 2.9	5 50.6	20 26.5
31 S	2 32 28.5	6 23.8	5 7.6	5♓12.5	23 9.3	23 39.8	27 35.9	13 34.6	3 7.2	23 5.7	5 49.9	20 25.7
						DECLINATION						
1 T	0 34 11.9	2S38.3	2S40.1	14S47.0	7S33.3	1S25.9	22S34.2	6S57.6	20S13.2	23S21.5	22N15.2	14N26.8
4 S	0 46 1.6	3 48.2	2 36.3	5 47.7	5 26.7	0 34.5	22 56.5	7 5.3	20 13.6	23 21.8	22 15.0	14 26.3
7 W	0 57 51.3	4 57.6	2 32.5	5N44.8	3 16.9	0N10.7	23 17.0	7 12.4	20 13.8	23 22.1	22 14.9	14 25.8
10 S	1 9 40.9	6 6.6	2 28.7	15 24.8	1 31.1	0 48.4	23 35.7	7 19.0	20 13.9	23 22.4	22 14.9	14 25.4
13 T	1 21 30.6	7 14.8	2 25.0	17 57.9	0 28.9	1 17.9	23 52.4	7 25.1	20 13.7	23 22.8	22 14.8	14 24.9
16 F	1 33 20.2	8 22.1	2 21.2	11 6.8	0 16.7	1 39.0	24 7.2	7 30.5	20 13.3	23 23.1	22 14.7	14 24.4
19 M	1 45 9.9	9 28.4	2 17.4	1S31.9	0 50.1	1 51.8	24 19.8	7 35.3	20 12.7	23 23.5	22 14.7	14 24.0
22 T	1 56 59.6	10 33.5	2 13.6	13 6.7	1 59.1	1 56.5	24 30.3	7 39.5	20 11.8	23 23.9	22 14.6	14 23.5
25 S	2 8 49.2	11 37.1	2 9.8	18 11.1	3 32.7	1 53.5	24 38.6	7 42.9	20 10.8	23 24.3	22 14.6	14 23.0
28 W	2 20 38.9	12 39.2	2 6.1	15 32.6	5 21.6	1 43.2	24 44.7	7 45.7	20 9.6	23 24.8	22 14.6	14 22.6
31 S	2 32 28.5	13 39.5	2 2.3	7 4.2	7 18.5	1 26.0	24 48.4	7 47.7	20 8.1	23 25.2	22 14.6	14 22.1

NOVEMBER 1903

LONGITUDE

DAY	EPHEMERIS SIDEREAL TIME h m s	☉ ° ′	☊ ° ′	☽ ° ′	☿ ° ′	♀ ° ′	♂ ° ′	♃ ° ′	♄ ° ′	♅ ° ′	♆ ° ′	♇ ° ′
1 S	2 36 25.1	7♏23.8	5♎ 4.5	17♓19.8	24♎46.5	24♍19.8	28♐20.6	13♓32.7	3♒ 9.5	23♐ 8.5	5♋49.2	20♊24.9
2 M	2 40 21.6	8 23.8	5 1.3	29 41.0	26 24.2	25 1.0	29 5.3	13R31.0	3 11.9	23 11.3	5R48.4	20R24.1
3 T	2 44 18.2	9 23.9	4 58.1	12♈19.4	28 2.3	25 43.4	29 50.2	13 29.6	3 14.4	23 14.1	5 47.7	20 23.3
4 W	2 48 14.7	10 24.0	4 54.9	25 16.7	29 40.6	26 26.8	0♑35.1	13 28.3	3 17.0	23 17.0	5 46.9	20 22.4
5 T	2 52 11.3	11 24.1	4 51.8	8♉33.6	1♏18.9	27 11.3	1 20.0	13 27.2	3 19.7	23 19.9	5 46.1	20 21.6
6 F	2 56 7.9	12 24.3	4 48.6	22 9.0	2 57.3	27 56.8	2 5.0	13 26.4	3 22.4	23 22.9	5 45.2	20 20.7
7 S	3 0 4.4	13 24.4	4 45.4	6♊ 0.2	4 35.7	28 43.2	2 50.1	13 25.7	3 25.3	23 25.8	5 44.3	20 19.8
8 S	3 4 0.9	14 24.7	4 42.2	20 3.6	6 13.9	29 30.6	3 35.2	13 25.3	3 28.3	23 28.8	5 43.4	20 18.9
9 M	3 7 57.5	15 24.9	4 39.0	4♋14.7	7 51.9	0♎18.9	4 20.4	13 25.0	3 31.3	23 31.9	5 42.5	20 18.0
10 T	3 11 54.1	16 25.2	4 35.9	18 29.3	9 29.8	1 8.1	5 5.7	13 25.0	3 34.5	23 34.9	5 41.5	20 17.0
11 W	3 15 50.6	17 25.5	4 32.7	2♌43.6	11 7.4	1 58.2	5 51.0	13D25.1	3 37.7	23 38.0	5 40.5	20 16.1
12 T	3 19 47.2	18 25.8	4 29.5	16 54.8	12 44.7	2 49.0	6 36.4	13 25.5	3 41.0	23 41.1	5 39.5	20 15.1
13 F	3 23 43.7	19 26.2	4 26.3	1♍ 0.9	14 21.9	3 40.6	7 21.9	13 26.1	3 44.4	23 44.3	5 38.5	20 14.1
14 S	3 27 40.3	20 26.6	4 23.2	15 0.8	15 58.7	4 33.0	8 7.4	13 26.8	3 47.9	23 47.4	5 37.4	20 13.2
15 S	3 31 36.8	21 27.1	4 20.0	28 53.6	17 35.3	5 26.1	8 52.9	13 27.8	3 51.5	23 50.6	5 36.3	20 12.2
16 M	3 35 33.4	22 27.6	4 16.8	12♎38.5	19 11.6	6 19.9	9 38.6	13 29.0	3 55.2	23 53.8	5 35.2	20 11.1
17 T	3 39 29.9	23 28.1	4 13.6	26 14.4	20 47.7	7 14.3	10 24.2	13 30.4	3 59.0	23 57.1	5 34.0	20 10.1
18 W	3 43 26.5	24 28.6	4 10.4	9♏39.7	22 23.5	8 9.4	11 10.0	13 32.0	4 2.8	24 0.4	5 32.8	20 9.1
19 T	3 47 23.1	25 29.2	4 7.3	22 52.8	23 59.0	9 5.1	11 55.8	13 33.8	4 6.7	24 3.7	5 31.6	20 8.1
20 F	3 51 19.6	26 29.7	4 4.1	5♐52.3	25 34.4	10 1.4	12 41.6	13 35.8	4 10.7	24 7.0	5 30.4	20 7.0
21 S	3 55 16.2	27 30.4	4 0.9	18 37.1	27 9.5	10 58.3	13 27.5	13 38.0	4 14.8	24 10.3	5 29.1	20 5.9
22 S	3 59 12.7	28 31.0	3 57.7	1♑ 7.0	28 44.4	11 55.7	14 13.5	13 40.5	4 19.0	24 13.7	5 27.9	20 4.9
23 M	4 3 9.3	29 31.6	3 54.6	13 22.9	0♐19.1	12 53.6	14 59.5	13 43.1	4 23.2	24 17.0	5 26.6	20 3.8
24 T	4 7 5.9	0♐32.3	3 51.4	25 26.8	1 53.6	13 52.1	15 45.5	13 45.9	4 27.6	24 20.4	5 25.3	20 2.7
25 W	4 11 2.4	1 33.0	3 48.2	7♒21.7	3 28.0	14 51.1	16 31.6	13 48.9	4 32.0	24 23.8	5 23.9	20 1.6
26 T	4 14 58.9	2 33.7	3 45.0	19 11.8	5 2.2	15 50.5	17 17.7	13 52.1	4 36.5	24 27.3	5 22.6	20 0.5
27 F	4 18 55.5	3 34.5	3 41.8	1♓ 1.8	6 36.3	16 50.4	18 3.9	13 55.5	4 41.0	24 30.7	5 21.2	19 59.4
28 S	4 22 52.1	4 35.2	3 38.7	12 57.0	8 10.2	17 50.8	18 50.2	13 59.1	4 45.7	24 34.2	5 19.8	19 58.3
29 S	4 26 48.6	5 36.0	3 35.5	25 2.6	9 44.1	18 51.6	19 36.4	14 2.9	4 50.4	24 37.7	5 18.4	19 57.2
30 M	4 30 45.2	6 36.8	3 32.3	7♈24.0	11 17.9	19 52.8	20 22.7	14 6.9	4 55.2	24 41.2	5 16.9	19 56.0

DECLINATION

DAY	EPHEMERIS SIDEREAL TIME h m s	☉	☊	☽	☿	♀	♂	♃	♄	♅	♆	♇
1 S	2 36 25.1	13S59.1	2S 1.0	3S25.1	7S58.3	1N18.9	24S49.2	7S48.3	20S 7.6	23S25.4	22N14.6	14N22.0
4 W	2 48 14.7	14 56.8	1 57.2	8N13.5	9 58.0	0 53.4	24 49.8	7 49.4	20 5.9	23 25.8	22 14.7	14 21.6
7 S	3 0 4.4	15 52.2	1 53.5	16 55.0	11 55.9	0 22.2	24 48.0	7 49.7	20 4.0	23 26.3	22 14.7	14 21.2
10 T	3 11 54.1	16 45.3	1 49.7	17 10.3	13 49.9	0S14.2	24 43.8	7 49.4	20 1.8	23 26.7	22 14.8	14 20.8
13 F	3 23 43.7	17 35.8	1 45.9	8 20.5	15 38.4	0 55.3	24 37.1	7 48.3	19 59.5	23 27.2	22 14.8	14 20.4
16 M	3 35 33.4	18 23.6	1 42.1	4S26.9	17 20.2	1 40.5	24 28.0	7 46.5	19 57.0	23 27.6	22 14.9	14 20.0
19 T	3 47 23.1	19 8.4	1 38.3	14 52.3	18 54.5	2 29.5	24 16.5	7 44.0	19 54.3	23 28.1	22 15.0	14 19.7
22 S	3 59 12.7	19 50.2	1 34.5	18 21.8	20 20.5	3 21.7	24 2.5	7 40.8	19 51.4	23 28.6	22 15.1	14 19.4
25 W	4 11 2.4	20 28.8	1 30.8	14 16.0	21 37.6	4 16.7	23 46.1	7 36.9	19 48.4	23 29.0	22 15.3	14 19.1
28 S	4 22 52.1	21 3.9	1 27.0	4 56.0	22 44.9	5 14.0	23 27.3	7 32.3	19 45.1	23 29.5	22 15.4	14 18.8

DECEMBER 1903

LONGITUDE

DAY	EPHEMERIS SIDEREAL TIME h m s	☉ ° ′	☊ ° ′	☽ ° ′	☿ ° ′	♀ ° ′	♂ ° ′	♃ ° ′	♄ ° ′	♅ ° ′	♆ ° ′	♇ ° ′
1 T	4 34 41.7	7♐37.6	3♎29.1	20♈ 5.8	12♐51.6	20♎54.4	21♑ 9.1	14♓11.1	5♒ 0.0	24♐44.7	5♋15.5	19♊54.9
2 W	4 38 38.3	8 38.4	3 26.0	3♉11.2	14 25.2	21 56.4	21 55.5	14 15.4	5 5.0	24 48.2	5R14.0	19R53.8
3 T	4 42 34.9	9 39.2	3 22.8	16 42.1	15 58.8	22 58.8	22 41.9	14 20.0	5 10.0	24 51.7	5 12.5	19 52.6
4 F	4 46 31.4	10 40.1	3 19.6	0♊37.5	17 32.4	24 1.6	23 28.3	14 24.7	5 15.0	24 55.3	5 11.0	19 51.5
5 S	4 50 27.9	11 40.9	3 16.4	14 54.2	19 5.9	25 4.7	24 14.8	14 29.6	5 20.1	24 58.8	5 9.5	19 50.3
6 S	4 54 24.5	12 41.8	3 13.3	29 26.6	20 39.4	26 8.2	25 1.3	14 34.7	5 25.3	25 2.4	5 8.0	19 49.1
7 M	4 58 21.1	13 42.7	3 10.1	14♋ 7.0	22 12.9	27 12.0	25 47.9	14 40.0	5 30.6	25 6.0	5 6.4	19 48.0
8 T	5 2 17.6	14 43.6	3 6.9	28 48.0	23 46.3	28 16.2	26 34.5	14 45.5	5 35.9	25 9.6	5 4.8	19 46.8
9 W	5 6 14.2	15 44.6	3 3.7	13♌22.4	25 19.8	29 20.6	27 21.1	14 51.1	5 41.3	25 13.2	5 3.3	19 45.7
10 T	5 10 10.7	16 45.5	3 0.5	27 45.4	26 53.2	0♏25.4	28 7.8	14 56.9	5 46.8	25 16.8	5 1.7	19 44.5
11 F	5 14 7.3	17 46.5	2 57.4	11♍54.1	28 26.5	1 30.5	28 54.5	15 2.9	5 52.3	25 20.4	5 0.1	19 43.3
12 S	5 18 3.9	18 47.5	2 54.2	25 47.5	29 59.9	2 35.9	29 41.2	15 9.1	5 57.9	25 24.0	4 58.5	19 42.2
13 S	5 22 0.4	19 48.5	2 51.0	9♎26.3	1♑33.1	3 41.5	0♒27.9	15 15.4	6 3.5	25 27.6	4 56.8	19 41.0
14 M	5 25 57.0	20 49.6	2 47.8	22 51.5	3 6.2	4 47.4	1 14.7	15 21.9	6 9.2	25 31.2	4 55.2	19 39.8
15 T	5 29 53.5	21 50.6	2 44.7	6♏ 4.5	4 39.2	5 53.6	2 1.5	15 28.6	6 15.0	25 34.9	4 53.6	19 38.7
16 W	5 33 50.1	22 51.7	2 41.5	19 6.4	6 12.0	7 0.0	2 48.4	15 35.4	6 20.8	25 38.5	4 51.9	19 37.5
17 T	5 37 46.6	23 52.8	2 38.3	1♐57.5	7 44.6	8 6.7	3 35.3	15 42.4	6 26.7	25 42.1	4 50.2	19 36.3
18 F	5 41 43.2	24 53.9	2 35.1	14 38.1	9 16.8	9 13.6	4 22.1	15 49.6	6 32.6	25 45.8	4 48.6	19 35.2
19 S	5 45 39.8	25 55.0	2 32.0	27 7.9	10 48.6	10 20.7	5 9.1	15 56.9	6 38.6	25 49.4	4 46.9	19 34.0
20 S	5 49 36.3	26 56.1	2 28.8	9♑26.9	12 19.9	11 28.0	5 56.0	16 4.4	6 44.6	25 53.0	4 45.2	19 32.8
21 M	5 53 32.9	27 57.2	2 25.6	21 35.6	13 50.5	12 35.6	6 43.0	16 12.0	6 50.7	25 56.7	4 43.5	19 31.7
22 T	5 57 29.4	28 58.4	2 22.4	3♒35.0	15 20.4	13 43.3	7 30.0	16 19.8	6 56.8	26 0.3	4 41.8	19 30.5
23 W	6 1 26.0	29 59.5	2 19.3	15 27.3	16 49.3	14 51.2	8 17.0	16 27.8	7 3.0	26 4.0	4 40.2	19 29.4
24 T	6 5 22.5	1♑ 0.6	2 16.1	27 15.4	18 17.0	15 59.4	9 4.0	16 35.9	7 9.2	26 7.6	4 38.5	19 28.2
25 F	6 9 19.1	2 1.8	2 12.9	9♓ 3.3	19 43.3	17 7.7	9 51.0	16 44.1	7 15.5	26 11.2	4 36.8	19 27.1
26 S	6 13 15.7	3 2.9	2 9.7	20 55.6	21 8.0	18 16.1	10 38.1	16 52.5	7 21.8	26 14.8	4 35.1	19 26.0
27 S	6 17 12.2	4 4.1	2 6.6	2♈57.6	22 30.6	19 24.8	11 25.2	17 1.1	7 28.2	26 18.5	4 33.4	19 24.8
28 M	6 21 8.8	5 5.2	2 3.4	15 14.9	23 50.8	20 33.6	12 12.2	17 9.8	7 34.6	26 22.1	4 31.7	19 23.7
29 T	6 25 5.3	6 6.3	2 0.2	27 52.9	25 8.2	21 42.6	12 59.3	17 18.6	7 41.1	26 25.6	4 29.9	19 22.6
30 W	6 29 1.9	7 7.5	1 57.0	10♉56.4	26 22.2	22 51.7	13 46.4	17 27.6	7 47.6	26 29.2	4 28.2	19 21.5
31 T	6 32 58.4	8 8.6	1 53.8	24 28.5	27 32.4	24 1.0	14 33.5	17 36.7	7 54.1	26 32.8	4 26.6	19 20.4

DECLINATION

DAY	EPHEMERIS SIDEREAL TIME h m s	☉	☊	☽	☿	♀	♂	♃	♄	♅	♆	♇
1 T	4 34 41.7	21S35.5	1S23.2	6N37.2	23S42.1	6S13.2	23S 6.1	7S27.0	19S41.7	23S29.9	22N15.5	14N18.5
4 F	4 46 31.4	22 3.3	1 19.4	16 11.4	24 28.3	7 13.8	22 42.6	7 21.1	19 38.1	23 30.3	22 15.7	14 18.3
7 M	4 58 21.1	22 27.3	1 15.6	17 46.1	25 3.0	8 15.4	22 16.8	7 14.6	19 34.3	23 30.8	22 15.9	14 18.1
10 T	5 10 10.7	22 47.4	1 11.8	9 27.9	25 25.5	9 17.6	21 48.8	7 7.4	19 30.4	23 31.2	22 16.0	14 18.0
13 S	5 22 0.4	23 3.4	1 8.0	3S16.6	25 35.3	10 19.9	21 18.6	6 59.6	19 26.3	23 31.6	22 16.2	14 17.8
16 W	5 33 50.1	23 15.4	1 4.2	14 3.0	25 31.9	11 22.0	20 46.2	6 51.3	19 22.1	23 32.0	22 16.4	14 17.7
19 S	5 45 39.8	23 23.1	1 0.5	18 26.9	25 14.9	12 23.4	20 11.9	6 42.4	19 17.7	23 32.3	22 16.6	14 17.6
22 T	5 57 29.4	23 26.7	0 56.7	15 11.8	24 44.3	13 23.6	19 35.5	6 32.9	19 13.2	23 32.7	22 16.8	14 17.6
25 F	6 9 19.1	23 26.0	0 52.9	6 21.6	24 0.7	14 22.4	18 57.3	6 22.9	19 8.6	23 33.1	22 17.0	14 17.6
28 M	6 21 8.8	23 21.1	0 49.1	4N55.7	23 5.2	15 19.2	18 17.2	6 12.3	19 3.8	23 33.4	22 17.2	14 17.6
31 T	6 32 58.4	23 11.9	0 45.3	15 0.6	22 0.4	16 13.7	17 35.4	6 1.3	18 58.9	23 33.7	22 17.4	14 17.7

JANUARY 1904

DAY	EPHEMERIS SIDEREAL TIME	☉	☊	☽	☿	♀	♂	♃	♄	♅	♆	♇
	h m s	° ′	° ′	° ′	° ′	° ′	° ′	° ′	° ′	° ′	° ′	° ′
						LONGITUDE						
1 F	6 36 55.0	9♑ 9.8	1♎50.7	8♊30.0	28♑37.9	25♏10.4	15♒20.7	17♓45.9	8♒ 0.7	26♐36.4	4♋24.9	19♊19.3
2 S	6 40 51.6	10 10.9	1 47.5	22 58.9	29 38.3	26 20.0	16 7.8	17 55.3	8 7.3	26 40.0	4R23.2	19R18.2
3 S	6 44 48.1	11 12.1	1 44.3	7♋49.4	0♒32.6	27 29.7	16 54.9	18 4.8	8 13.9	26 43.5	4 21.5	19 17.1
4 M	6 48 44.7	12 13.2	1 41.1	22 52.9	1 20.0	28 39.6	17 42.1	18 14.4	8 20.6	26 47.1	4 19.8	19 16.1
5 T	6 52 41.2	13 14.3	1 38.0	7♌59.3	1 59.6	29 49.6	18 29.2	18 24.1	8 27.3	26 50.6	4 18.1	19 15.0
6 W	6 56 37.8	14 15.5	1 34.8	22 58.7	2 30.6	0♐59.7	19 16.3	18 34.0	8 34.0	26 54.1	4 16.4	19 14.0
7 T	7 0 34.3	15 16.6	1 31.6	7♍42.9	2 51.9	2 9.9	20 3.5	18 44.0	8 40.8	26 57.6	4 14.8	19 12.9
8 F	7 4 30.9	16 17.8	1 28.4	22 7.0	3 2.9	3 20.3	20 50.7	18 54.1	8 47.6	27 1.1	4 13.1	19 11.9
9 S	7 8 27.5	17 18.9	1 25.2	6♎ 8.6	3R 2.8	4 30.8	21 37.8	19 4.4	8 54.4	27 4.6	4 11.5	19 10.9
10 S	7 12 24.0	18 20.0	1 22.1	19 48.1	2 51.1	5 41.4	22 25.0	19 14.7	9 1.3	27 8.0	4 9.8	19 9.9
11 M	7 16 20.6	19 21.2	1 18.9	3♏ 7.3	2 27.6	6 52.1	23 12.1	19 25.2	9 8.2	27 11.5	4 8.2	19 8.9
12 T	7 20 17.1	20 22.3	1 15.7	16 8.8	1 52.3	8 2.9	23 59.3	19 35.8	9 15.1	27 14.9	4 6.6	19 7.9
13 W	7 24 13.7	21 23.5	1 12.5	28 55.3	1 6.0	9 13.9	24 46.5	19 46.5	9 22.0	27 18.3	4 5.0	19 6.9
14 T	7 28 10.2	22 24.6	1 9.4	11♐29.4	0 9.5	10 24.9	25 33.7	19 57.3	9 29.0	27 21.7	4 3.4	19 6.0
15 F	7 32 6.8	23 25.8	1 6.2	23 53.0	29♑ 4.4	11 36.0	26 20.8	20 8.3	9 36.0	27 25.1	4 1.8	19 5.1
16 S	7 36 3.3	24 26.9	1 3.0	6♑ 7.5	27 52.6	12 47.2	27 8.0	20 19.3	9 43.0	27 28.4	4 0.2	19 4.1
17 S	7 39 59.9	25 28.0	0 59.8	18 14.1	26 36.4	13 58.5	27 55.2	20 30.4	9 50.0	27 31.7	3 58.6	19 3.2
18 M	7 43 56.4	26 29.1	0 56.6	0♒13.8	25 18.1	15 9.9	28 42.3	20 41.7	9 57.0	27 35.0	3 57.1	19 2.3
19 T	7 47 53.0	27 30.3	0 53.5	12 7.6	24 0.3	16 21.4	29 29.5	20 53.0	10 4.1	27 38.3	3 55.5	19 1.4
20 W	7 51 49.6	28 31.4	0 50.3	23 57.2	22 45.1	17 32.9	0♓16.6	21 4.5	10 11.2	27 41.6	3 54.0	19 0.5
21 T	7 55 46.1	29 32.5	0 47.1	5♓44.7	21 34.7	18 44.5	1 3.8	21 16.0	10 18.3	27 44.8	3 52.5	18 59.7
22 F	7 59 42.7	0♒33.5	0 43.9	17 32.9	20 30.6	19 56.2	1 50.9	21 27.7	10 25.4	27 48.0	3 51.0	18 58.8
23 S	8 3 39.2	1 34.6	0 40.8	29 25.4	19 34.2	21 8.0	2 38.0	21 39.4	10 32.5	27 51.2	3 49.6	18 58.0
24 S	8 7 35.8	2 35.6	0 37.6	11♈26.5	18 46.3	22 19.8	3 25.1	21 51.3	10 39.6	27 54.4	3 48.1	18 57.2
25 M	8 11 32.4	3 36.6	0 34.4	23 41.1	18 7.3	23 31.7	4 12.2	22 3.2	10 46.8	27 57.5	3 46.7	18 56.4
26 T	8 15 28.9	4 37.7	0 31.2	6♉14.4	17 37.4	24 43.6	4 59.3	22 15.2	10 53.9	28 0.6	3 45.3	18 55.6
27 W	8 19 25.5	5 38.6	0 28.1	19 11.2	17 16.5	25 55.6	5 46.4	22 27.3	11 1.1	28 3.7	3 43.9	18 54.9
28 T	8 23 22.0	6 39.6	0 24.9	2♊35.6	17 4.3	27 7.7	6 33.4	22 39.5	11 8.2	28 6.7	3 42.5	18 54.1
29 F	8 27 18.6	7 40.6	0 21.7	16 29.9	17 0.4	28 19.8	7 20.4	22 51.7	11 15.4	28 9.7	3 41.1	18 53.4
30 S	8 31 15.1	8 41.5	0 18.5	0♋53.8	17D 4.3	29 32.0	8 7.4	23 4.1	11 22.6	28 12.7	3 39.8	18 52.7
31 S	8 35 11.7	9 42.4	0 15.3	15 43.7	17 15.5	0♑44.2	8 54.4	23 16.5	11 29.8	28 15.7	3 38.5	18 52.0
						DECLINATION						
1 F	6 36 55.0	23S 7.9	0S44.0	17N10.1	21S37.4	16S31.2	17S21.1	5S57.5	18S57.2	23S33.8	22N17.4	14N17.7
4 M	6 48 44.7	22 53.2	0 40.2	16 54.9	20 27.4	17 22.1	16 37.2	5 45.9	18 52.1	23 34.1	22 17.6	14 17.8
7 T	7 0 34.3	22 34.4	0 36.4	6 51.1	19 21.7	18 9.7	15 51.7	5 33.8	18 47.0	23 34.4	22 17.9	14 18.0
10 S	7 12 24.0	22 11.6	0 32.7	6S12.1	18 29.2	18 53.7	15 4.9	5 21.3	18 41.7	23 34.7	22 18.1	14 18.1
13 W	7 24 13.7	21 44.9	0 28.9	15 43.3	17 57.4	19 33.9	14 16.6	5 8.3	18 36.3	23 34.9	22 18.3	14 18.4
16 S	7 36 3.3	21 14.3	0 25.1	18 18.2	17 49.2	20 9.8	13 27.1	4 55.0	18 30.9	23 35.2	22 18.5	14 18.6
19 T	7 47 53.0	20 40.1	0 21.3	13 35.6	18 0.8	20 41.2	12 36.5	4 41.3	18 25.3	23 35.4	22 18.7	14 18.9
22 F	7 59 42.7	20 2.4	0 17.5	3 59.1	18 24.9	21 7.8	11 44.8	4 27.3	18 19.7	23 35.6	22 18.9	14 19.2
25 M	8 11 32.4	19 21.3	0 13.7	7N12.2	18 55.0	21 29.4	10 52.2	4 12.9	18 14.1	23 35.8	22 19.1	14 19.5
28 T	8 23 22.0	18 37.0	0 9.9	16 10.6	19 26.2	21 45.7	9 58.7	3 58.2	18 8.4	23 36.0	22 19.3	14 19.9
31 S	8 35 11.7	17 49.6	0 6.1	17 39.2	19 55.0	21 56.6	9 4.5	3 43.2	18 2.6	23 36.1	22 19.5	14 20.3

FEBRUARY 1904

DAY	EPHEMERIS SIDEREAL TIME	☉	☊	☽	☿	♀	♂	♃	♄	♅	♆	♇
						LONGITUDE						
1 M	8 39 8.2	10♒43.3	0♎12.2	0♌52.4	17♑33.4	1♑56.5	9♓41.4	23♓29.0	11♒36.9	28♐18.6	3♋37.2	18♊51.4
2 T	8 43 4.8	11 44.2	0 9.0	16 10.1	17 57.6	3 8.8	10 28.4	23 41.6	11 44.1	28 21.5	3R35.9	18R50.7
3 W	8 47 1.4	12 45.0	0 5.8	1♍25.6	18 27.5	4 21.2	11 15.3	23 54.2	11 51.3	28 24.4	3 34.7	18 50.1
4 T	8 50 57.9	13 45.8	0 2.6	16 28.9	19 2.5	5 33.7	12 2.2	24 7.0	11 58.5	28 27.2	3 33.5	18 49.5
5 F	8 54 54.4	14 46.7	29♍59.5	1♎11.9	19 42.4	6 46.2	12 49.1	24 19.7	12 5.7	28 30.0	3 32.3	18 48.9
6 S	8 58 51.0	15 47.5	29 56.3	15 29.9	20 26.5	7 58.7	13 36.0	24 32.6	12 12.8	28 32.7	3 31.1	18 48.3
7 S	9 2 47.6	16 48.3	29 53.1	29 21.5	21 14.7	9 11.3	14 22.8	24 45.6	12 20.0	28 35.4	3 29.9	18 47.7
8 M	9 6 44.1	17 49.0	29 49.9	12♏47.2	22 6.4	10 24.0	15 9.7	24 58.6	12 27.2	28 38.1	3 28.8	18 47.2
9 T	9 10 40.7	18 49.8	29 46.8	25 49.7	23 1.5	11 36.7	15 56.5	25 11.6	12 34.3	28 40.8	3 27.7	18 46.7
10 W	9 14 37.2	19 50.5	29 43.6	8♐32.3	23 59.6	12 49.4	16 43.3	25 24.8	12 41.5	28 43.4	3 26.6	18 46.2
11 T	9 18 33.8	20 51.3	29 40.4	20 58.7	25 0.4	14 2.2	17 30.0	25 38.0	12 48.6	28 46.0	3 25.6	18 45.7
12 F	9 22 30.3	21 52.0	29 37.2	3♑12.3	26 3.9	15 15.0	18 16.8	25 51.2	12 55.8	28 48.5	3 24.6	18 45.3
13 S	9 26 26.9	22 52.6	29 34.0	15 16.2	27 9.7	16 27.8	19 3.5	26 4.6	13 2.9	28 51.0	3 23.6	18 44.8
14 S	9 30 23.4	23 53.3	29 30.9	27 13.2	28 17.7	17 40.7	19 50.2	26 17.9	13 10.0	28 53.5	3 22.6	18 44.4
15 M	9 34 20.0	24 53.9	29 27.7	9♒ 5.5	29 27.7	18 53.6	20 36.8	26 31.4	13 17.1	28 55.9	3 21.7	18 44.0
16 T	9 38 16.6	25 54.6	29 24.5	20 55.1	0♒39.7	20 6.6	21 23.5	26 44.9	13 24.2	28 58.3	3 20.8	18 43.7
17 W	9 42 13.1	26 55.2	29 21.3	2♓43.8	1 53.4	21 19.5	22 10.1	26 58.4	13 31.2	29 0.6	3 19.9	18 43.3
18 T	9 46 9.7	27 55.7	29 18.2	14 33.4	3 8.8	22 32.5	22 56.7	27 12.0	13 38.3	29 2.9	3 19.1	18 43.0
19 F	9 50 6.2	28 56.3	29 15.0	26 26.2	4 25.8	23 45.6	23 43.2	27 25.7	13 45.3	29 5.2	3 18.3	18 42.7
20 S	9 54 2.7	29 56.8	29 11.8	8♈24.5	5 44.2	24 58.6	24 29.7	27 39.4	13 52.3	29 7.4	3 17.5	18 42.4
21 S	9 57 59.3	0♓57.3	29 8.6	20 31.4	7 4.1	26 11.7	25 16.2	27 53.1	13 59.3	29 9.5	3 16.7	18 42.2
22 M	10 1 55.9	1 57.7	29 5.4	2♉50.2	8 25.4	27 24.8	26 2.7	28 6.9	14 6.3	29 11.7	3 16.0	18 41.9
23 T	10 5 52.4	2 58.2	29 2.3	15 24.9	9 48.0	28 37.9	26 49.1	28 20.8	14 13.2	29 13.8	3 15.3	18 41.7
24 W	10 9 49.0	3 58.5	28 59.1	28 19.2	11 11.8	29 51.0	27 35.5	28 34.6	14 20.1	29 15.8	3 14.6	18 41.5
25 T	10 13 45.5	4 58.9	28 55.9	11♊36.6	12 36.8	1♒ 4.2	28 21.8	28 48.5	14 27.0	29 17.8	3 14.0	18 41.3
26 F	10 17 42.1	5 59.2	28 52.7	25 19.7	14 3.1	2 17.4	29 8.2	29 2.5	14 33.9	29 19.7	3 13.4	18 41.2
27 S	10 21 38.6	6 59.5	28 49.6	9♋29.3	15 30.5	3 30.6	29 54.4	29 16.5	14 40.8	29 21.6	3 12.9	18 41.1
28 S	10 25 35.2	7 59.8	28 46.4	24 3.9	16 59.1	4 43.8	0♈40.7	29 30.5	14 47.6	29 23.5	3 12.3	18 40.9
29 M	10 29 31.7	8 60.0	28 43.2	8♌59.1	18 28.8	5 57.0	1 26.9	29 44.6	14 54.3	29 25.3	3 11.8	18 40.9
						DECLINATION						
1 M	8 39 8.2	17S33.2	0S 4.8	15N44.1	20S 3.5	21S59.0	8S46.2	3S38.1	18S 0.7	23S36.2	22N19.6	14N20.5
4 T	8 50 57.9	16 42.1	0 1.1	4 21.8	20 24.8	22 2.4	7 51.1	3 22.8	17 54.9	23 36.3	22 19.8	14 20.9
7 S	9 2 47.6	15 48.4	0N 2.7	8S44.5	20 38.4	22 0.1	6 55.4	3 7.2	17 49.0	23 36.5	22 20.0	14 21.4
10 W	9 14 37.2	14 52.2	0 6.5	16 54.9	20 42.8	21 52.1	5 59.3	2 51.3	17 43.2	23 36.6	22 20.2	14 21.9
13 S	9 26 26.9	13 53.8	0 10.3	17 39.2	20 37.2	21 38.4	5 2.8	2 35.3	17 37.3	23 36.7	22 20.4	14 22.5
16 T	9 38 16.6	12 53.3	0 14.1	11 34.0	20 20.9	21 18.9	4 6.0	2 19.0	17 31.5	23 36.8	22 20.6	14 23.0
19 F	9 50 6.2	11 50.9	0 17.9	1 19.2	19 53.5	20 53.9	3 9.0	2 2.5	17 25.7	23 36.9	22 20.7	14 23.6
22 M	10 1 55.9	10 46.9	0 21.7	9N36.5	19 14.7	20 23.3	2 11.9	1 45.9	17 19.8	23 37.0	22 20.9	14 24.2
25 T	10 13 45.5	9 41.3	0 25.5	17 10.5	18 24.4	19 47.4	1 14.8	1 29.2	17 14.1	23 37.1	22 21.1	14 24.9
28 S	10 25 35.2	8 34.5	0 29.3	16 39.8	17 22.5	19 6.3	0 17.8	1 12.3	17 8.3	23 37.2	22 21.3	14 25.5

MARCH 1904

LONGITUDE

DAY	EPHEMERIS SIDEREAL TIME h m s	☉ ° ′	☊ ° ′	☽ ° ′	☿ ° ′	♀ ° ′	♂ ° ′	♃ ° ′	♄ ° ′	♅ ° ′	♆ ° ′	♇ ° ′
1 T	10 33 28.3	10♓ 0.2	28♍40.0	24♌ 7.8	19♒59.6	7♒10.2	2♈13.0	29♓58.7	15♒ 1.1	29♐27.1	3♋11.3	18♊40.8
2 W	10 37 24.8	11 0.4	28 36.8	9♍20.6	21 31.5	8 23.5	2 59.2	0♈12.8	15 7.8	29 28.8	3R 10.9	18R 40.8
3 T	10 41 21.4	12 0.5	28 33.7	24 27.7	23 4.6	9 36.8	3 45.2	0R 27.0	15 14.5	29 30.5	3 10.5	18 40.7
4 F	10 45 17.9	13 0.6	28 30.5	9♎20.1	24 38.7	10 50.1	4 31.3	0D 41.2	15 21.1	29 32.1	3 10.1	18D 40.8
5 S	10 49 14.5	14 0.7	28 27.3	23 50.7	26 13.9	12 3.4	5 17.3	0 55.4	15 27.8	29 33.6	3 9.8	18 40.8
6 S	10 53 11.1	15 0.7	28 24.1	7♏55.4	27 50.3	13 16.8	6 3.3	1 9.7	15 34.4	29 35.2	3 9.5	18 40.8
7 M	10 57 7.6	16 0.7	28 21.0	21 32.8	29 27.7	14 30.1	6 49.2	1 23.9	15 40.9	29 36.7	3 9.2	18 40.9
8 T	11 1 4.2	17 0.7	28 17.8	4♐43.8	1♓ 6.3	15 43.5	7 35.1	1 38.2	15 47.4	29 38.1	3 9.0	18 41.0
9 W	11 5 0.7	18 0.7	28 14.6	17 31.1	2 46.0	16 56.9	8 20.9	1 52.6	15 53.9	29 39.5	3 8.8	18 41.1
10 T	11 8 57.2	19 0.6	28 11.4	29 58.3	4 26.8	18 10.3	9 6.7	2 6.9	16 0.3	29 40.8	3 8.6	18 41.3
11 F	11 12 53.8	20 0.5	28 8.2	12♑ 9.8	6 8.7	19 23.8	9 52.5	2 21.3	16 6.7	29 42.1	3 8.5	18 41.4
12 S	11 16 50.4	21 0.4	28 5.1	24 9.7	7 51.9	20 37.2	10 38.3	2 35.7	16 13.1	29 43.3	3 8.4	18 41.6
13 S	11 20 46.9	22 0.3	28 1.9	6♒ 2.1	9 36.2	21 50.6	11 24.0	2 50.1	16 19.4	29 44.5	3 8.3	18 41.8
14 M	11 24 43.4	23 0.1	27 58.7	17 50.7	11 21.6	23 4.1	12 9.6	3 4.5	16 25.6	29 45.6	3 8.3	18 42.0
15 T	11 28 40.0	23 59.9	27 55.5	29 38.7	13 8.3	24 17.6	12 55.2	3 19.0	16 31.8	29 46.7	3 8.3	18 42.3
16 W	11 32 36.6	24 59.6	27 52.3	11♓29.0	14 56.2	25 31.1	13 40.8	3 33.4	16 38.0	29 47.7	3D 8.3	18 42.6
17 T	11 36 33.1	25 59.4	27 49.2	23 23.8	16 45.3	26 44.6	14 26.3	3 47.9	16 44.1	29 48.7	3 8.4	18 42.9
18 F	11 40 29.7	26 59.1	27 46.0	5♈25.3	18 35.6	27 58.0	15 11.8	4 2.4	16 50.2	29 49.6	3 8.5	18 43.2
19 S	11 44 26.2	27 58.7	27 42.8	17 35.1	20 27.2	29 11.5	15 57.2	4 16.9	16 56.2	29 50.5	3 8.6	18 43.5
20 S	11 48 22.8	28 58.3	27 39.6	29 55.2	22 20.0	0♓25.0	16 42.6	4 31.4	17 2.2	29 51.3	3 8.8	18 43.9
21 M	11 52 19.3	29 57.9	27 36.5	12♉27.2	24 14.0	1 38.6	17 28.0	4 45.9	17 8.1	29 52.1	3 9.0	18 44.3
22 T	11 56 15.9	0♈57.5	27 33.3	25 13.1	26 9.2	2 52.1	18 13.3	5 0.4	17 14.0	29 52.8	3 9.2	18 44.7
23 W	12 0 12.4	1 57.0	27 30.1	8♊14.8	28 5.6	4 5.6	18 58.6	5 14.9	17 19.8	29 53.5	3 9.5	18 45.1
24 T	12 4 9.0	2 56.5	27 26.9	21 33.9	0♈ 3.1	5 19.1	19 43.8	5 29.5	17 25.5	29 54.1	3 9.8	18 45.5
25 F	12 8 5.5	3 55.9	27 23.7	5♋12.1	2 1.8	6 32.6	20 28.9	5 44.0	17 31.2	29 54.6	3 10.1	18 46.0
26 S	12 12 2.1	4 55.3	27 20.6	19 9.8	4 1.5	7 46.2	21 14.0	5 58.5	17 36.9	29 55.1	3 10.5	18 46.5
27 S	12 15 58.6	5 54.7	27 17.4	3♌26.5	6 2.1	8 59.7	21 59.1	6 13.1	17 42.4	29 55.6	3 10.9	18 47.0
28 M	12 19 55.2	6 54.0	27 14.2	18 0.1	8 3.7	10 13.2	22 44.1	6 27.6	17 48.0	29 56.0	3 11.4	18 47.5
29 T	12 23 51.7	7 53.3	27 11.0	2♍46.3	10 6.0	11 26.7	23 29.1	6 42.1	17 53.4	29 56.3	3 11.8	18 48.1
30 W	12 27 48.3	8 52.5	27 7.9	17 39.4	12 8.9	12 40.3	24 14.0	6 56.6	17 58.8	29 56.6	3 12.3	18 48.7
31 T	12 31 44.9	9 51.7	27 4.7	2♎32.0	14 12.2	13 53.8	24 58.9	7 11.2	18 4.2	29 56.9	3 12.9	18 49.3

DECLINATION

DAY	EPHEMERIS SIDEREAL TIME h m s	☉ ° ′	☊ ° ′	☽ ° ′	☿ ° ′	♀ ° ′	♂ ° ′	♃ ° ′	♄ ° ′	♅ ° ′	♆ ° ′	♇ ° ′
1 T	10 33 28.3	7S 49.3	0N 31.8	10N 44.5	16S 34.7	18S 36.1	0N 20.2	1S 1.0	17S 4.6	23S 37.2	22N 21.4	14N 26.0
4 F	10 45 17.9	6 40.7	0 35.6	2S 42.1	15 13.4	17 46.9	1 16.9	0 44.0	16 58.9	23 37.3	22 21.5	14 26.7
7 M	10 57 7.6	5 31.2	0 39.4	14 1.1	13 40.5	16 53.1	2 13.4	0 26.8	16 53.4	23 37.4	22 21.7	14 27.4
10 T	11 8 57.2	4 21.0	0 43.2	18 9.8	11 56.0	15 55.0	3 9.5	0 9.6	16 47.9	23 37.4	22 21.8	14 28.1
13 S	11 20 46.9	3 10.4	0 47.0	14 45.1	10 0.2	14 52.8	4 5.1	0N 7.6	16 42.5	23 37.5	22 22.0	14 28.9
16 W	11 32 36.6	1 59.4	0 50.8	5 54.3	7 53.2	13 47.0	5 0.3	0 24.9	16 37.2	23 37.6	22 22.1	14 29.6
19 S	11 44 26.2	0 48.3	0 54.6	5N 13.1	5 35.4	12 37.6	5 54.9	0 42.2	16 32.0	23 37.6	22 22.2	14 30.4
22 T	11 56 15.9	0N 22.9	0 58.4	14 43.4	3 7.4	11 25.2	6 48.8	0 59.5	16 27.0	23 37.7	22 22.4	14 31.1
25 F	12 8 5.5	1 33.8	1 2.2	18 6.2	0 30.3	10 9.9	7 42.0	1 16.8	16 22.1	23 37.7	22 22.5	14 31.9
28 M	12 19 55.2	2 44.4	1 6.0	12 13.8	2N 14.4	8 52.2	8 34.4	1 34.0	16 17.3	23 37.8	22 22.6	14 32.7
31 T	12 31 44.9	3 54.5	1 9.7	0S 34.9	5 3.8	7 32.2	9 25.9	1 51.2	16 12.7	23 37.9	22 22.7	14 33.5

APRIL 1904

LONGITUDE

DAY	EPHEMERIS SIDEREAL TIME h m s	☉ ° ′	☊ ° ′	☽ ° ′	☿ ° ′	♀ ° ′	♂ ° ′	♃ ° ′	♄ ° ′	♅ ° ′	♆ ° ′	♇ ° ′
1 F	12 35 41.4	10♈50.9	27♍ 1.5	17♎16.3	16♈15.8	15♓ 7.3	25♈43.7	7♈25.7	18♒ 9.5	29♐57.1	3♋13.5	18♊49.9
2 S	12 39 37.9	11 50.0	26 58.3	1♏45.4	18 19.3	16 20.9	26 28.4	7 40.2	18 14.7	29 57.2	3 14.1	18 50.5
3 S	12 43 34.5	12 49.2	26 55.1	15 53.4	20 22.6	17 34.4	27 13.2	7 54.7	18 19.8	29 57.3	3 14.7	18 51.2
4 M	12 47 31.1	13 48.2	26 52.0	29 37.1	22 25.4	18 48.0	27 57.8	8 9.2	18 24.9	29 57.3	3 15.4	18 51.8
5 T	12 51 27.6	14 47.3	26 48.8	12♐55.2	24 27.2	20 1.5	28 42.5	8 23.6	18 29.9	29 57.3	3 16.1	18 52.5
6 W	12 55 24.2	15 46.3	26 45.6	25 48.8	26 27.8	21 15.1	29 27.1	8 38.1	18 34.9	29R 57.3	3 16.8	18 53.2
7 T	12 59 20.7	16 45.3	26 42.4	8♑20.5	28 26.9	22 28.6	0♉11.6	8 52.6	18 39.8	29 57.2	3 17.6	18 54.0
8 F	13 3 17.3	17 44.2	26 39.2	20 34.3	0♉24.0	23 42.2	0 56.1	9 7.0	18 44.6	29 57.0	3 18.4	18 54.7
9 S	13 7 13.8	18 43.2	26 36.1	2♒34.8	2 18.8	24 55.8	1 40.5	9 21.4	18 49.3	29 56.8	3 19.2	18 55.5
10 S	13 11 10.4	19 42.1	26 32.9	14 26.7	4 11.0	26 9.4	2 24.9	9 35.8	18 54.0	29 56.5	3 20.1	18 56.3
11 M	13 15 6.9	20 40.9	26 29.7	26 14.9	6 0.2	27 22.9	3 9.2	9 50.2	18 58.6	29 56.2	3 21.0	18 57.1
12 T	13 19 3.5	21 39.8	26 26.5	8♓ 3.7	7 46.0	28 36.5	3 53.5	10 4.6	19 3.1	29 55.8	3 21.9	18 57.9
13 W	13 23 0.0	22 38.6	26 23.4	19 57.3	9 28.2	29 50.1	4 37.8	10 19.0	19 7.6	29 55.4	3 22.9	18 58.8
14 T	13 26 56.6	23 37.4	26 20.2	1♈58.8	11 6.5	1♈ 3.7	5 22.0	10 33.3	19 12.0	29 54.9	3 23.9	18 59.6
15 F	13 30 53.1	24 36.1	26 17.0	14 11.0	12 40.6	2 17.2	6 6.1	10 47.6	19 16.3	29 54.4	3 24.9	19 0.5
16 S	13 34 49.7	25 34.8	26 13.8	26 35.6	14 10.3	3 30.8	6 50.2	11 1.9	19 20.5	29 53.8	3 25.9	19 1.4
17 S	13 38 46.2	26 33.5	26 10.6	9♉13.8	15 35.4	4 44.4	7 34.2	11 16.2	19 24.6	29 53.2	3 27.0	19 2.3
18 M	13 42 42.8	27 32.2	26 7.5	22 6.0	16 55.8	5 58.0	8 18.2	11 30.4	19 28.7	29 52.5	3 28.1	19 3.2
19 T	13 46 39.4	28 30.8	26 4.3	5♊12.1	18 11.3	7 11.5	9 2.2	11 44.6	19 32.7	29 51.8	3 29.3	19 4.2
20 W	13 50 35.9	29 29.4	26 1.1	18 31.6	19 21.7	8 25.1	9 46.1	11 58.8	19 36.6	29 51.0	3 30.4	19 5.1
21 T	13 54 32.4	0♉27.9	25 57.9	2♋ 3.9	20 26.9	9 38.6	10 29.9	12 13.0	19 40.4	29 50.2	3 31.6	19 6.1
22 F	13 58 29.0	1 26.4	25 54.8	15 48.4	21 26.9	10 52.2	11 13.7	12 27.1	19 44.2	29 49.3	3 32.8	19 7.1
23 S	14 2 25.6	2 24.9	25 51.6	29 44.2	22 21.5	12 5.7	11 57.4	12 41.2	19 47.9	29 48.4	3 34.1	19 8.1
24 S	14 6 22.1	3 23.3	25 48.4	13♌50.6	23 10.7	13 19.3	12 41.1	12 55.2	19 51.4	29 47.5	3 35.4	19 9.1
25 M	14 10 18.7	4 21.7	25 45.2	28 6.3	23 54.4	14 32.8	13 24.8	13 9.2	19 54.9	29 46.5	3 36.7	19 10.2
26 T	14 14 15.2	5 20.1	25 42.0	12♍29.2	24 32.5	15 46.3	14 8.3	13 23.2	19 58.4	29 45.4	3 38.0	19 11.2
27 W	14 18 11.8	6 18.4	25 38.9	26 56.3	25 5.0	16 59.9	14 51.9	13 37.2	20 1.7	29 44.3	3 39.4	19 12.3
28 T	14 22 8.3	7 16.7	25 35.7	11♎23.7	25 31.9	18 13.4	15 35.3	13 51.1	20 4.9	29 43.2	3 40.8	19 13.4
29 F	14 26 4.9	8 15.0	25 32.5	25 46.3	25 53.2	19 26.9	16 18.8	14 4.9	20 8.1	29 42.0	3 42.2	19 14.5
30 S	14 30 1.4	9 13.2	25 29.3	9♏58.7	26 8.9	20 40.5	17 2.1	14 18.7	20 11.2	29 40.8	3 43.6	19 15.6

DECLINATION

DAY	EPHEMERIS SIDEREAL TIME h m s	☉ ° ′	☊ ° ′	☽ ° ′	☿ ° ′	♀ ° ′	♂ ° ′	♃ ° ′	♄ ° ′	♅ ° ′	♆ ° ′	♇ ° ′
1 F	12 35 41.4	4N 17.7	1N 11.0	5S 7.9	6N 0.8	7S 5.1	9N 42.9	1N 56.9	16S 11.2	23S 37.9	22N 22.7	14N 33.8
4 M	12 47 31.1	5 26.9	1 14.8	15 31.0	8 50.4	5 42.7	10 33.2	2 14.0	16 6.8	23 37.9	22 22.8	14 34.6
7 T	12 59 20.7	6 35.2	1 18.6	18 1.4	11 34.0	4 18.8	11 22.4	2 31.1	16 2.6	23 38.0	22 22.9	14 35.4
10 S	13 11 10.4	7 42.6	1 22.4	13 3.9	14 5.7	2 53.7	12 10.6	2 48.0	15 58.5	23 38.1	22 22.9	14 36.2
13 W	13 23 0.0	8 48.7	1 26.2	3 21.0	16 20.0	1 27.8	12 57.6	3 4.8	15 54.7	23 38.1	22 23.0	14 36.9
16 S	13 34 49.7	9 53.6	1 30.0	7N 52.6	18 13.0	0 1.3	13 43.4	3 21.5	15 51.1	23 38.2	22 23.0	14 37.7
19 T	13 46 39.4	10 57.0	1 33.7	16 25.3	19 42.6	1N 25.4	14 28.0	3 38.1	15 47.7	23 38.2	22 23.1	14 38.5
22 F	13 58 29.0	11 58.8	1 37.5	17 37.1	20 48.0	2 52.0	15 11.2	3 54.5	15 44.5	23 38.3	22 23.1	14 39.3
25 M	14 10 18.7	12 58.8	1 41.3	9 46.4	21 29.2	4 18.2	15 53.1	4 10.8	15 41.5	23 38.3	22 23.1	14 40.0
28 T	14 22 8.3	13 56.8	1 45.1	3S 19.2	21 46.4	5 43.8	16 33.6	4 26.8	15 38.8	23 38.4	22 23.1	14 40.8

MAY 1904

DAY	EPHEMERIS SIDEREAL TIME	☉	☊	☽	☿	♀	♂	♃	♄	♅	♆	♇
	h m s	° ′	° ′	° ′	° ′	° ′	° ′	° ′	° ′	° ′	° ′	° ′
						LONGITUDE						
1 S	14 33 58.0	10♉11.4	25♍26.2	23♏56.0	26♉19.1	21♈54.0	17♉45.4	14♈32.5	20♒14.1	29♐39.5	3♋45.1	19♊16.7
2 M	14 37 54.5	11 9.6	25 23.0	7♐34.1	26 23.9	23 7.5	18 28.7	14 46.3	20 17.0	29R38.2	3 46.6	19 17.8
3 T	14 41 51.1	12 7.7	25 19.8	20 50.5	26R23.4	24 21.0	19 11.9	14 60.0	20 19.8	29 36.8	3 48.1	19 19.0
4 W	14 45 47.6	13 5.8	25 16.6	3♑44.9	26 17.7	25 34.6	19 55.1	15 13.6	20 22.6	29 35.5	3 49.6	19 20.1
5 T	14 49 44.2	14 3.9	25 13.4	16 18.5	26 7.1	26 48.1	20 38.2	15 27.2	20 25.2	29 34.0	3 51.2	19 21.3
6 F	14 53 40.7	15 2.0	25 10.3	28 34.2	25 51.9	28 1.6	21 21.3	15 40.8	20 27.7	29 32.5	3 52.8	19 22.5
7 S	14 57 37.3	16 0.1	25 7.1	10♒36.0	25 32.5	29 15.1	22 4.3	15 54.3	20 30.2	29 31.0	3 54.4	19 23.7
8 S	15 1 33.9	16 58.1	25 3.9	22 28.7	25 9.2	0♉28.7	22 47.3	16 7.8	20 32.5	29 29.5	3 56.0	19 24.9
9 M	15 5 30.4	17 56.1	25 0.7	4♓17.6	24 42.4	1 42.2	23 30.2	16 21.2	20 34.8	29 27.9	3 57.7	19 26.1
10 T	15 9 26.9	18 54.1	24 57.6	16 7.8	24 12.8	2 55.7	24 13.1	16 34.5	20 37.0	29 26.2	3 59.3	19 27.3
11 W	15 13 23.5	19 52.0	24 54.4	28 4.4	23 40.7	4 9.3	24 55.9	16 47.8	20 39.0	29 24.6	4 1.0	19 28.6
12 T	15 17 20.1	20 50.0	24 51.2	10♈11.7	23 6.9	5 22.8	25 38.7	17 1.1	20 41.0	29 22.9	4 2.8	19 29.8
13 F	15 21 16.6	21 47.9	24 48.0	22 33.5	22 31.8	6 36.3	26 21.4	17 14.3	20 42.9	29 21.1	4 4.5	19 31.1
14 S	15 25 13.2	22 45.8	24 44.8	5♉12.1	21 56.2	7 49.9	27 4.1	17 27.4	20 44.7	29 19.3	4 6.3	19 32.3
15 S	15 29 9.7	23 43.6	24 41.7	18 8.9	21 20.7	9 3.4	27 46.7	17 40.5	20 46.4	29 17.5	4 8.0	19 33.6
16 M	15 33 6.3	24 41.5	24 38.5	1♊23.4	20 45.9	10 16.9	28 29.3	17 53.5	20 48.0	29 15.7	4 9.9	19 34.9
17 T	15 37 2.9	25 39.3	24 35.3	14 54.2	20 12.3	11 30.4	29 11.8	18 6.5	20 49.5	29 13.8	4 11.7	19 36.2
18 W	15 40 59.4	26 37.1	24 32.1	28 38.5	19 40.6	12 44.0	29 54.3	18 19.3	20 50.9	29 11.9	4 13.5	19 37.5
19 T	15 44 55.9	27 34.9	24 29.0	12♋33.1	19 11.2	13 57.5	0♊36.7	18 32.2	20 52.2	29 10.0	4 15.4	19 38.8
20 F	15 48 52.5	28 32.6	24 25.8	26 34.7	18 44.6	15 11.0	1 19.1	18 44.9	20 53.4	29 8.0	4 17.3	19 40.1
21 S	15 52 49.1	29 30.3	24 22.6	10♌40.4	18 21.2	16 24.5	2 1.4	18 57.6	20 54.5	29 6.0	4 19.2	19 41.5
22 S	15 56 45.6	0♊28.0	24 19.4	24 48.2	18 1.4	17 38.1	2 43.7	19 10.2	20 55.5	29 4.0	4 21.1	19 42.8
23 M	16 0 42.1	1 25.7	24 16.3	8♍56.4	17 45.4	18 51.6	3 25.9	19 22.8	20 56.5	29 1.9	4 23.0	19 44.1
24 T	16 4 38.7	2 23.3	24 13.1	23 3.9	17 33.5	20 5.1	4 8.1	19 35.2	20 57.3	28 59.8	4 24.9	19 45.5
25 W	16 8 35.3	3 20.9	24 9.9	7♎9.5	17 25.8	21 18.6	4 50.2	19 47.6	20 58.0	28 57.7	4 26.9	19 46.8
26 T	16 12 31.8	4 18.5	24 6.7	21 11.7	17 22.5	22 32.1	5 32.3	19 60.0	20 58.6	28 55.6	4 28.9	19 48.2
27 F	16 16 28.4	5 16.1	24 3.5	5♏8.3	17D23.6	23 45.6	6 14.3	20 12.2	20 59.2	28 53.5	4 30.9	19 49.6
28 S	16 20 24.9	6 13.6	24 0.4	18 56.3	17 29.3	24 59.1	6 56.3	20 24.4	20 59.6	28 51.3	4 32.9	19 50.9
29 S	16 24 21.5	7 11.1	23 57.2	2♐32.7	17 39.4	26 12.6	7 38.2	20 36.5	20 59.9	28 49.1	4 34.9	19 52.3
30 M	16 28 18.0	8 8.6	23 54.0	15 54.4	17 54.0	27 26.1	8 20.1	20 48.5	21 0.2	28 46.8	4 36.9	19 53.7
31 T	16 32 14.6	9 6.1	23 50.8	28 59.2	18 13.1	28 39.7	9 1.9	21 0.4	21 0.3	28 44.6	4 39.0	19 55.1
						DECLINATION						
1 S	14 33 58.0	14N52.8	1N48.9	14S33.7	21N40.3	7N 8.3	17N12.5	4N42.7	15S36.4	23S38.4	22N23.1	14N41.5
4 W	14 45 47.6	15 46.6	1 52.7	18 17.7	21 12.0	8 31.4	17 50.0	4 58.3	15 34.1	23 38.4	22 23.1	14 42.2
7 S	14 57 37.3	16 38.0	1 56.4	14 2.1	20 23.3	9 53.0	18 25.8	5 13.7	15 32.2	23 38.5	22 23.0	14 42.9
10 T	15 9 26.9	17 27.0	2 0.2	4 38.3	19 18.3	11 12.6	19 0.1	5 28.9	15 30.5	23 38.5	22 23.0	14 43.6
13 F	15 21 16.6	18 13.4	2 4.0	6N40.2	18 3.0	12 29.9	19 32.7	5 43.9	15 29.1	23 38.5	22 22.9	14 44.3
16 M	15 33 6.3	18 57.0	2 7.8	15 55.0	16 45.2	13 44.6	20 3.6	5 58.5	15 27.9	23 38.5	22 22.9	14 45.0
19 T	15 44 55.9	19 37.7	2 11.6	18 1.7	15 33.5	14 56.3	20 32.8	6 12.9	15 27.1	23 38.6	22 22.8	14 45.6
22 S	15 56 45.6	20 15.4	2 15.3	10 49.8	14 35.0	16 4.8	21 0.2	6 27.0	15 26.5	23 38.6	22 22.7	14 46.2
25 W	16 8 35.3	20 50.0	2 19.1	1S52.4	13 54.6	17 9.7	21 25.8	6 40.8	15 26.2	23 38.6	22 22.6	14 46.8
28 S	16 20 24.9	21 21.4	2 22.9	13 31.8	13 34.8	18 10.7	21 49.6	6 54.3	15 26.2	23 38.6	22 22.4	14 47.4
31 T	16 32 14.6	21 49.4	2 26.7	18 26.0	13 35.5	19 7.4	22 11.5	7 7.4	15 26.5	23 38.5	22 22.3	14 47.9

JUNE 1904

DAY	EPHEMERIS SIDEREAL TIME	☉	☊	☽	☿	♀	♂	♃	♄	♅	♆	♇
						LONGITUDE						
1 W	16 36 11.2	10♊3.6	23♍47.7	11♑46.0	18♉36.5	29♉53.2	9♊43.7	21♈12.3	21♒0.3	28♐42.3	4♋41.0	19♊56.4
2 T	16 40 7.7	11 1.0	23 44.5	24 15.3	19 4.3	1♊6.7	10 25.4	21 24.0	21R0.3	28R40.1	4 43.1	19 57.8
3 F	16 44 4.2	11 58.5	23 41.3	6♒28.8	19 36.2	2 20.2	11 7.1	21 35.7	21 0.1	28 37.8	4 45.2	19 59.2
4 S	16 48 0.8	12 55.9	23 38.1	18 29.6	20 12.3	3 33.8	11 48.7	21 47.3	20 59.9	28 35.5	4 47.3	20 0.6
5 S	16 51 57.4	13 53.3	23 35.0	0♓22.0	20 52.4	4 47.3	12 30.3	21 58.8	20 59.5	28 33.1	4 49.4	20 2.0
6 M	16 55 54.0	14 50.7	23 31.8	12 10.8	21 36.5	6 0.9	13 11.9	22 10.2	20 59.1	28 30.8	4 51.5	20 3.4
7 T	16 59 50.5	15 48.1	23 28.6	24 1.4	22 24.4	7 14.4	13 53.4	22 21.6	20 58.5	28 28.4	4 53.6	20 4.8
8 W	17 3 47.0	16 45.5	23 25.4	5♈59.2	23 16.0	8 28.0	14 34.8	22 32.8	20 57.9	28 26.0	4 55.8	20 6.2
9 T	17 7 43.6	17 42.9	23 22.2	18 9.6	24 11.4	9 41.6	15 16.2	22 44.0	20 57.1	28 23.7	4 57.9	20 7.6
10 F	17 11 40.2	18 40.3	23 19.1	0♉36.9	25 10.3	10 55.1	15 57.6	22 55.0	20 56.3	28 21.3	5 0.1	20 9.0
11 S	17 15 36.7	19 37.6	23 15.9	13 24.9	26 12.7	12 8.7	16 38.9	23 6.0	20 55.4	28 18.9	5 2.2	20 10.4
12 S	17 19 33.3	20 35.0	23 12.7	26 35.3	27 18.6	13 22.3	17 20.2	23 16.8	20 54.3	28 16.4	5 4.4	20 11.8
13 M	17 23 29.8	21 32.3	23 9.5	10♊8.4	28 27.9	14 35.9	18 1.4	23 27.6	20 53.2	28 14.0	5 6.6	20 13.2
14 T	17 27 26.4	22 29.6	23 6.4	24 1.8	29 40.5	15 49.5	18 42.6	23 38.2	20 52.0	28 11.6	5 8.8	20 14.7
15 W	17 31 22.9	23 27.0	23 3.2	8♋11.5	0♊56.5	17 3.1	19 23.8	23 48.7	20 50.7	28 9.2	5 11.0	20 16.1
16 T	17 35 19.5	24 24.3	23 0.0	22 32.0	2 15.6	18 16.7	20 4.9	23 59.2	20 49.3	28 6.7	5 13.2	20 17.5
17 F	17 39 16.1	25 21.6	22 56.8	6♌57.4	3 38.0	19 30.3	20 45.9	24 9.5	20 47.8	28 4.3	5 15.4	20 18.9
18 S	17 43 12.6	26 18.8	22 53.6	21 22.2	5 3.6	20 43.9	21 26.9	24 19.7	20 46.2	28 1.8	5 17.6	20 20.3
19 S	17 47 9.2	27 16.1	22 50.5	5♍42.3	6 32.3	21 57.6	22 7.9	24 29.8	20 44.5	27 59.4	5 19.8	20 21.7
20 M	17 51 5.7	28 13.4	22 47.3	19 54.9	8 4.2	23 11.2	22 48.8	24 39.8	20 42.8	27 56.9	5 22.0	20 23.1
21 T	17 55 2.3	29 10.6	22 44.1	3♎58.5	9 39.1	24 24.8	23 29.7	24 49.7	20 40.9	27 54.5	5 24.2	20 24.5
22 W	17 58 58.9	0♋7.8	22 40.9	17 52.6	11 17.1	25 38.5	24 10.5	24 59.5	20 38.9	27 52.1	5 26.5	20 25.9
23 T	18 2 55.4	1 5.1	22 37.8	1♏37.2	12 58.1	26 52.1	24 51.3	25 9.1	20 36.9	27 49.6	5 28.7	20 27.2
24 F	18 6 52.0	2 2.3	22 34.6	15 11.9	14 42.1	28 5.7	25 32.0	25 18.6	20 34.8	27 47.2	5 30.9	20 28.6
25 S	18 10 48.5	2 59.5	22 31.4	28 36.2	16 29.0	29 19.4	26 12.7	25 28.1	20 32.6	27 44.7	5 33.2	20 30.0
26 S	18 14 45.1	3 56.7	22 28.2	11♐49.1	18 18.7	0♋33.0	26 53.3	25 37.3	20 30.3	27 42.3	5 35.4	20 31.4
27 M	18 18 41.6	4 53.9	22 25.1	24 49.7	20 11.3	1 46.7	27 33.9	25 46.5	20 27.9	27 39.9	5 37.6	20 32.7
28 T	18 22 38.2	5 51.0	22 21.9	7♑36.7	22 6.4	3 0.4	28 14.5	25 55.6	20 25.4	27 37.5	5 39.9	20 34.1
29 W	18 26 34.8	6 48.2	22 18.7	20 9.8	24 4.0	4 14.1	28 55.0	26 4.5	20 22.9	27 35.1	5 42.1	20 35.5
30 T	18 30 31.3	7 45.4	22 15.5	2♒29.3	26 4.0	5 27.8	29 35.4	26 13.3	20 20.3	27 32.7	5 44.3	20 36.8
						DECLINATION						
1 W	16 36 11.2	21N58.0	2N27.9	18S 8.9	13N40.1	19N25.3	22N18.4	7N11.7	15S26.6	23S38.5	22N22.2	14N48.1
4 S	16 48 0.8	22 21.5	2 31.7	12 30.2	14 5.8	20 16.0	22 37.8	7 24.4	15 27.3	23 38.5	22 22.1	14 48.6
7 T	16 59 50.5	22 41.5	2 35.5	2 23.6	14 47.5	21 1.7	22 55.4	7 36.7	15 28.2	23 38.4	22 21.9	14 49.1
10 F	17 11 40.2	22 57.9	2 39.2	8N51.0	15 42.4	21 42.2	23 11.0	7 48.7	15 29.4	23 38.4	22 21.7	14 49.5
13 M	17 23 29.8	23 10.7	2 43.0	17 8.8	16 47.5	22 17.3	23 24.7	8 0.3	15 30.9	23 38.3	22 21.5	14 49.9
16 T	17 35 19.5	23 19.8	2 46.8	17 16.0	17 59.8	22 46.7	23 36.5	8 11.4	15 32.6	23 38.3	22 21.3	14 50.3
19 S	17 47 9.2	23 25.2	2 50.5	8 4.1	19 15.9	23 10.3	23 46.4	8 22.2	15 34.6	23 38.2	22 21.1	14 50.7
22 W	17 58 58.9	23 26.9	2 54.3	5S 0.4	20 32.0	23 27.8	23 54.3	8 32.5	15 36.9	23 38.1	22 20.9	14 51.0
25 S	18 10 48.5	23 24.9	2 58.1	15 21.5	21 43.7	23 39.1	24 0.4	8 42.4	15 39.4	23 38.0	22 20.6	14 51.3
28 T	18 22 38.2	23 19.2	3 1.8	18 24.6	22 46.0	23 44.2	24 4.5	8 51.9	15 42.1	23 37.9	22 20.4	14 51.6

JULY 1904

LONGITUDE

DAY	EPHEMERIS SIDEREAL TIME h m s	☉ ° ′	☊ ° ′	☽ ° ′	☿ ° ′	♀ ° ′	♂ ° ′	♃ ° ′	♄ ° ′	♅ ° ′	♆ ° ′	♇ ° ′
1 F	18 34 27.8	8♋42.6	22♍12.3	14♒36.4	28♊ 6.1	6♋41.4	0♋15.9	26♈21.9	20♒17.6	27♐30.3	5♋46.6	20♊38.2
2 S	18 38 24.4	9 39.8	22 9.2	26 33.4	0♋10.1	7 55.2	0 56.3	26 30.4	20R14.8	27R27.9	5 48.8	20 39.5
3 S	18 42 21.0	10 36.9	22 6.0	8♓23.7	2 15.9	9 8.9	1 36.6	26 38.9	20 11.9	27 25.5	5 51.0	20 40.9
4 M	18 46 17.6	11 34.1	22 2.8	20 11.3	4 23.0	10 22.6	2 16.9	26 47.1	20 9.0	27 23.2	5 53.2	20 42.2
5 T	18 50 14.1	12 31.3	21 59.6	2♈ 1.3	6 31.3	11 36.4	2 57.2	26 55.2	20 6.0	27 20.9	5 55.5	20 43.5
6 W	18 54 10.6	13 28.5	21 56.5	13 58.7	8 40.4	12 50.1	3 37.4	27 3.2	20 2.9	27 18.5	5 57.7	20 44.8
7 T	18 58 7.2	14 25.7	21 53.3	26 8.9	10 50.0	14 3.9	4 17.6	27 11.1	19 59.8	27 16.2	5 59.9	20 46.1
8 F	19 2 3.8	15 22.9	21 50.1	8♉37.3	12 60.0	15 17.7	4 57.8	27 18.8	19 56.6	27 13.9	6 2.1	20 47.4
9 S	19 6 0.4	16 20.1	21 46.9	21 28.0	15 9.9	16 31.4	5 37.9	27 26.4	19 53.3	27 11.7	6 4.3	20 48.7
10 S	19 9 56.9	17 17.4	21 43.8	4♊44.1	17 19.5	17 45.2	6 17.9	27 33.8	19 49.9	27 9.4	6 6.5	20 50.0
11 M	19 13 53.4	18 14.6	21 40.6	18 26.6	19 28.5	18 59.1	6 58.0	27 41.0	19 46.5	27 7.2	6 8.7	20 51.3
12 T	19 17 50.0	19 11.8	21 37.4	2♋34.0	21 36.8	20 12.9	7 38.0	27 48.2	19 43.0	27 5.0	6 10.9	20 52.5
13 W	19 21 46.5	20 9.1	21 34.2	17 2.2	23 44.1	21 26.7	8 17.9	27 55.1	19 39.4	27 2.8	6 13.1	20 53.8
14 T	19 25 43.1	21 6.3	21 31.1	1♌44.7	25 50.3	22 40.6	8 57.8	28 1.9	19 35.8	27 0.6	6 15.3	20 55.0
15 F	19 29 39.6	22 3.6	21 27.9	16 33.7	27 55.2	23 54.4	9 37.7	28 8.6	19 32.2	26 58.5	6 17.4	20 56.3
16 S	19 33 36.2	23 0.8	21 24.7	1♍21.3	29 58.7	25 8.3	10 17.5	28 15.1	19 28.4	26 56.3	6 19.6	20 57.5
17 S	19 37 32.8	23 58.1	21 21.5	16 0.8	2♌ 0.7	26 22.1	10 57.3	28 21.5	19 24.7	26 54.3	6 21.8	20 58.7
18 M	19 41 29.3	24 55.3	21 18.4	0♎27.3	4 1.2	27 36.0	11 37.1	28 27.6	19 20.8	26 52.2	6 23.9	20 59.9
19 T	19 45 25.9	25 52.6	21 15.2	14 38.0	5 60.0	28 49.9	12 16.8	28 33.7	19 16.9	26 50.1	6 26.0	21 1.1
20 W	19 49 22.4	26 49.8	21 12.0	28 31.9	7 57.1	0♌ 3.8	12 56.5	28 39.5	19 13.0	26 48.1	6 28.2	21 2.3
21 T	19 53 19.0	27 47.1	21 8.8	12♏ 9.1	9 52.5	1 17.7	13 36.1	28 45.2	19 9.0	26 46.1	6 30.3	21 3.4
22 F	19 57 15.5	28 44.4	21 5.6	25 30.7	11 46.2	2 31.6	14 15.7	28 50.8	19 5.0	26 44.2	6 32.4	21 4.6
23 S	20 1 12.1	29 41.7	21 2.5	8♐37.7	13 38.1	3 45.5	14 55.3	28 56.1	19 0.9	26 42.3	6 34.5	21 5.7
24 S	20 5 8.7	0♌39.0	20 59.3	21 31.1	15 28.3	4 59.4	15 34.8	29 1.3	18 56.8	26 40.4	6 36.6	21 6.9
25 M	20 9 5.2	1 36.2	20 56.1	4♑11.9	17 16.7	6 13.3	16 14.2	29 6.4	18 52.6	26 38.5	6 38.6	21 8.0
26 T	20 13 1.8	2 33.5	20 52.9	16 40.8	19 3.4	7 27.3	16 53.7	29 11.2	18 48.5	26 36.7	6 40.7	21 9.1
27 W	20 16 58.3	3 30.9	20 49.8	28 58.5	20 48.4	8 41.2	17 33.1	29 15.9	18 44.2	26 34.9	6 42.7	21 10.2
28 T	20 20 54.9	4 28.2	20 46.6	11♒ 6.2	22 31.6	9 55.1	18 12.4	29 20.4	18 40.0	26 33.1	6 44.7	21 11.3
29 F	20 24 51.4	5 25.5	20 43.4	23 5.0	24 13.2	11 9.1	18 51.8	29 24.7	18 35.7	26 31.4	6 46.8	21 12.3
30 S	20 28 48.0	6 22.9	20 40.2	4♓57.1	25 53.0	12 23.1	19 31.1	29 28.9	18 31.4	26 29.7	6 48.8	21 13.4
31 S	20 32 44.6	7 20.2	20 37.0	16 44.9	27 31.1	13 37.0	20 10.3	29 32.9	18 27.0	26 28.1	6 50.7	21 14.4

DECLINATION

DAY	EPHEMERIS SIDEREAL TIME h m s	☉	☊	☽	☿	♀	♂	♃	♄	♅	♆	♇
1 F	18 34 27.8	23N 9.8	3N 5.6	13S34.7	23N33.7	23N42.9	24N 6.7	9N 0.8	15S45.1	23S37.8	22N20.1	14N51.9
4 M	18 46 17.6	22 56.7	3 9.4	3 49.5	24 1.5	23 35.3	24 7.0	9 9.4	15 48.3	23 37.7	22 19.9	14 52.1
7 T	18 58 7.2	22 40.0	3 13.1	7N21.6	24 5.9	23 21.4	24 5.5	9 17.4	15 51.6	23 37.6	22 19.6	14 52.3
10 S	19 9 56.9	22 19.8	3 16.9	16 17.4	23 45.3	23 1.3	24 2.1	9 24.9	15 55.2	23 37.4	22 19.3	14 52.4
13 W	19 21 46.5	21 56.2	3 20.7	17 51.6	23 0.7	22 35.1	23 56.9	9 31.9	15 58.9	23 37.3	22 19.0	14 52.5
16 S	19 33 36.2	21 29.1	3 24.4	9 28.1	21 55.0	22 2.8	23 49.9	9 38.4	16 2.8	23 37.2	22 18.7	14 52.6
19 T	19 45 25.9	20 58.8	3 28.2	3S47.4	20 32.0	21 24.8	23 41.2	9 44.4	16 6.7	23 37.0	22 18.4	14 52.7
22 F	19 57 15.5	20 25.3	3 31.9	14 36.4	18 55.4	20 41.2	23 30.7	9 49.8	16 10.9	23 36.9	22 18.1	14 52.7
25 M	20 9 5.2	19 48.7	3 35.7	18 25.4	17 8.8	19 52.3	23 18.6	9 54.6	16 15.1	23 36.8	22 17.7	14 52.7
28 T	20 20 54.9	19 9.1	3 39.4	14 23.3	15 15.2	18 58.3	23 4.7	9 58.9	16 19.3	23 36.6	22 17.4	14 52.7
31 S	20 32 44.6	18 26.7	3 43.2	5 2.5	13 17.2	17 59.5	22 49.3	10 2.6	16 23.7	23 36.5	22 17.1	14 52.7

AUGUST 1904

LONGITUDE

DAY	EPHEMERIS SIDEREAL TIME h m s	☉ ° ′	☊ ° ′	☽ ° ′	☿ ° ′	♀ ° ′	♂ ° ′	♃ ° ′	♄ ° ′	♅ ° ′	♆ ° ′	♇ ° ′
1 M	20 36 41.1	8♌17.6	20♍33.9	28♓31.8	29♌ 7.5	14♌51.0	20♋49.6	29♈36.7	18♒22.7	26♐26.5	6♋52.7	21♊15.4
2 T	20 40 37.6	9 15.0	20 30.7	10♈21.7	0♍42.2	16 5.0	21 28.7	29 40.3	18R18.3	26R24.9	6 54.7	21 16.4
3 W	20 44 34.2	10 12.4	20 27.5	22 19.0	2 15.2	17 19.0	22 7.9	29 43.7	18 13.9	26 23.3	6 56.6	21 17.4
4 T	20 48 30.8	11 9.9	20 24.3	4♉28.5	3 46.5	18 33.0	22 47.0	29 47.0	18 9.4	26 21.8	6 58.5	21 18.4
5 F	20 52 27.3	12 7.4	20 21.2	16 55.3	5 16.1	19 47.0	23 26.1	29 50.0	18 5.0	26 20.4	7 0.4	21 19.3
6 S	20 56 23.9	13 4.8	20 18.0	29 43.8	6 44.0	21 1.1	24 5.2	29 52.9	18 0.5	26 18.9	7 2.3	21 20.3
7 S	21 0 20.4	14 2.3	20 14.8	12♊57.8	8 10.1	22 15.1	24 44.2	29 55.6	17 56.1	26 17.6	7 4.2	21 21.2
8 M	21 4 17.0	14 59.9	20 11.6	26 39.5	9 34.5	23 29.1	25 23.2	29 58.1	17 51.6	26 16.2	7 6.0	21 22.1
9 T	21 8 13.5	15 57.4	20 8.4	10♋48.7	10 57.0	24 43.2	26 2.1	0♉ 0.4	17 47.1	26 14.9	7 7.9	21 23.0
10 W	21 12 10.1	16 55.0	20 5.3	25 22.7	12 17.8	25 57.3	26 41.1	0 2.5	17 42.6	26 13.7	7 9.7	21 23.9
11 T	21 16 6.7	17 52.6	20 2.1	10♌15.7	13 36.7	27 11.3	27 19.9	0 4.4	17 38.1	26 12.4	7 11.5	21 24.8
12 F	21 20 3.2	18 50.2	19 58.9	25 19.8	14 53.6	28 25.4	27 58.8	0 6.2	17 33.6	26 11.3	7 13.3	21 25.6
13 S	21 23 59.8	19 47.8	19 55.7	10♍25.8	16 8.6	29 39.5	28 37.6	0 7.7	17 29.1	26 10.1	7 15.0	21 26.4
14 S	21 27 56.3	20 45.5	19 52.6	25 24.8	17 21.6	0♍53.6	29 16.4	0 9.0	17 24.6	26 9.0	7 16.8	21 27.2
15 M	21 31 52.9	21 43.2	19 49.4	10♎ 9.4	18 32.4	2 7.7	29 55.1	0 10.1	17 20.2	26 8.0	7 18.5	21 28.0
16 T	21 35 49.4	22 40.8	19 46.2	24 34.4	19 41.1	3 21.8	0♌33.8	0 11.1	17 15.7	26 7.0	7 20.2	21 28.8
17 W	21 39 46.0	23 38.5	19 43.0	8♏37.1	20 47.5	4 35.9	1 12.5	0 11.8	17 11.2	26 6.1	7 21.8	21 29.5
18 T	21 43 42.5	24 36.3	19 39.8	22 17.1	21 51.5	5 49.9	1 51.2	0 12.3	17 6.8	26 5.2	7 23.5	21 30.3
19 F	21 47 39.1	25 34.0	19 36.7	5♐35.3	22 53.1	7 4.0	2 29.8	0 12.7	17 2.4	26 4.3	7 25.1	21 31.0
20 S	21 51 35.6	26 31.8	19 33.5	18 33.8	23 52.0	8 18.1	3 8.3	0 12.8	16 58.0	26 3.5	7 26.7	21 31.7
21 S	21 55 32.2	27 29.5	19 30.3	1♑15.1	24 48.2	9 32.2	3 46.9	0R12.7	16 53.6	26 2.8	7 28.3	21 32.3
22 M	21 59 28.7	28 27.3	19 27.1	13 41.7	25 41.4	10 46.3	4 25.3	0 12.5	16 49.2	26 2.0	7 29.8	21 33.0
23 T	22 3 25.3	29 25.1	19 24.0	25 56.3	26 31.7	12 0.4	5 3.8	0 12.0	16 44.9	26 1.4	7 31.4	21 33.6
24 W	22 7 21.9	0♍23.0	19 20.8	8♒ 1.2	27 18.7	13 14.5	5 42.3	0 11.4	16 40.6	26 0.8	7 32.9	21 34.3
25 T	22 11 18.4	1 20.9	19 17.6	19 58.5	28 2.2	14 28.7	6 20.7	0 10.5	16 36.3	26 0.2	7 34.4	21 34.9
26 F	22 15 14.9	2 18.7	19 14.4	1♓50.3	28 42.1	15 42.7	6 59.0	0 9.5	16 32.1	25 59.7	7 35.8	21 35.4
27 S	22 19 11.5	3 16.6	19 11.2	13 38.8	29 18.2	16 56.8	7 37.3	0 8.2	16 27.9	25 59.2	7 37.3	21 36.0
28 S	22 23 8.0	4 14.6	19 8.1	25 26.1	29 50.1	18 10.9	8 15.6	0 6.8	16 23.7	25 58.8	7 38.7	21 36.5
29 M	22 27 4.6	5 12.6	19 4.9	7♈14.9	0♎17.7	19 25.1	8 53.9	0 5.1	16 19.6	25 58.4	7 40.1	21 37.0
30 T	22 31 1.2	6 10.5	19 1.7	19 7.9	0 40.6	20 39.2	9 32.2	0 3.3	16 15.5	25 58.1	7 41.4	21 37.5
31 W	22 34 57.7	7 8.6	18 58.5	1♉ 8.5	0 58.6	21 53.3	10 10.4	0 1.2	16 11.4	25 57.8	7 42.7	21 38.0

DECLINATION

DAY	EPHEMERIS SIDEREAL TIME h m s	☉	☊	☽	☿	♀	♂	♃	♄	♅	♆	♇
1 M	20 36 41.1	18N11.9	3N44.4	1S22.3	12N37.3	17N38.9	22N43.8	10N 3.7	16S25.1	23S36.5	22N17.0	14N52.6
4 T	20 48 30.8	17 25.9	3 48.2	9N31.2	10 36.7	16 34.1	22 26.3	10 6.6	16 29.5	23 36.4	22 16.7	14 52.6
7 S	21 0 20.4	16 37.3	3 51.9	17 13.5	8 36.2	15 25.3	22 7.3	10 9.0	16 33.9	23 36.2	22 16.3	14 52.4
10 W	21 12 10.1	15 46.3	3 55.7	16 56.9	6 37.5	14 12.7	21 46.8	10 10.7	16 38.3	23 36.1	22 16.0	14 52.3
13 S	21 23 59.8	14 53.0	3 59.4	6 57.7	4 42.1	12 56.6	21 24.8	10 11.8	16 42.7	23 36.0	22 15.7	14 52.1
16 T	21 35 49.4	13 57.6	4 3.2	6S39.4	2 51.7	11 37.4	21 1.5	10 12.3	16 47.0	23 36.0	22 15.4	14 51.9
19 F	21 47 39.1	13 0.2	4 6.9	16 12.4	1 8.1	10 15.4	20 36.9	10 12.1	16 51.2	23 35.9	22 15.0	14 51.7
22 M	21 59 28.7	12 1.0	4 10.6	18 0.3	0S26.6	8 50.9	20 11.0	10 11.4	16 55.4	23 35.8	22 14.7	14 51.5
25 T	22 11 18.4	11 0.0	4 14.4	12 26.1	1 50.0	7 24.3	19 43.9	10 10.0	16 59.4	23 35.7	22 14.4	14 51.2
28 S	22 23 8.0	9 57.5	4 18.1	2 24.3	2 58.7	5 55.9	19 15.6	10 8.1	17 3.4	23 35.7	22 14.1	14 50.9
31 W	22 34 57.7	8 53.5	4 21.9	8N30.4	3 48.9	4 26.0	18 46.2	10 5.5	17 7.2	23 35.7	22 13.8	14 50.6

SEPTEMBER 1904

DAY	EPHEMERIS SIDEREAL TIME h m s	☉ ° ′	☊ ° ′	☽ ° ′	☿ ° ′	♀ ° ′	♂ ° ′	♃ ° ′	♄ ° ′	♅ ° ′	♆ ° ′	♇ ° ′
					LONGITUDE							
1 T	22 38 54.3	8♍ 6.6	18♍55.4	13♉20.3	1♎11.4	23♍ 7.4	10♌48.6	29♈59.0	16♒ 7.4	25♐57.6	7♋44.0	21♊38.5
2 F	22 42 50.8	9 4.7	18 52.2	25 47.3	1 18.8	24 21.5	11 26.7	29R56.5	16R 3.5	25R57.4	7 45.3	21 38.9
3 S	22 46 47.4	10 2.8	18 49.0	8♊33.3	1 20.4	25 35.6	12 4.8	29 53.9	15 59.6	25 57.3	7 46.6	21 39.3
4 S	22 50 43.9	11 1.0	18 45.8	21 42.0	1R16.0	26 49.7	12 42.9	29 51.1	15 55.7	25 57.2	7 47.8	21 39.7
5 M	22 54 40.5	11 59.2	18 42.6	5♋16.0	1 5.3	28 3.8	13 21.0	29 48.1	15 51.9	25 57.2	7 49.0	21 40.1
6 T	22 58 37.0	12 57.4	18 39.5	19 16.7	0 48.4	29 18.0	13 59.0	29 44.8	15 48.1	25D57.2	7 50.1	21 40.4
7 W	23 2 33.6	13 55.7	18 36.3	3♌43.0	0 24.9	0♎32.1	14 37.0	29 41.4	15 44.5	25 57.3	7 51.3	21 40.8
8 T	23 6 30.1	14 54.0	18 33.1	18 31.4	29♍55.0	1 46.2	15 15.0	29 37.8	15 40.8	25 57.5	7 52.4	21 41.1
9 F	23 10 26.7	15 52.3	18 29.9	3♍35.6	29 18.8	3 0.3	15 52.9	29 34.1	15 37.2	25 57.6	7 53.4	21 41.4
10 S	23 14 23.2	16 50.6	18 26.7	18 47.3	28 36.5	4 14.4	16 30.8	29 30.1	15 33.7	25 57.9	7 54.5	21 41.6
11 S	23 18 19.8	17 49.0	18 23.6	3♎56.9	27 48.5	5 28.6	17 8.7	29 25.9	15 30.3	25 58.2	7 55.5	21 41.9
12 M	23 22 16.3	18 47.4	18 20.4	18 55.3	26 55.6	6 42.7	17 46.5	29 21.6	15 26.9	25 58.5	7 56.5	21 42.1
13 T	23 26 12.9	19 45.9	18 17.2	3♏34.8	25 58.5	7 56.8	18 24.3	29 17.1	15 23.6	25 58.9	7 57.4	21 42.3
14 W	23 30 9.4	20 44.3	18 14.0	17 50.3	24 58.2	9 10.9	19 2.1	29 12.4	15 20.4	25 59.3	7 58.4	21 42.5
15 T	23 34 6.0	21 42.8	18 10.9	1♐39.4	23 55.9	10 25.0	19 39.8	29 7.6	15 17.2	25 59.8	7 59.2	21 42.6
16 F	23 38 2.5	22 41.3	18 7.7	15 2.2	22 53.1	11 39.1	20 17.5	29 2.6	15 14.1	26 0.4	8 0.1	21 42.8
17 S	23 41 59.1	23 39.9	18 4.5	28 0.5	21 51.1	12 53.2	20 55.2	28 57.4	15 11.1	26 1.0	8 0.9	21 42.9
18 S	23 45 55.6	24 38.5	18 1.3	10♑37.6	20 51.6	14 7.3	21 32.8	28 52.0	15 8.1	26 1.6	8 1.7	21 43.0
19 M	23 49 52.2	25 37.1	17 58.2	22 57.3	19 55.9	15 21.4	22 10.4	28 46.5	15 5.3	26 2.3	8 2.5	21 43.0
20 T	23 53 48.7	26 35.7	17 55.0	5♒ 3.5	19 5.6	16 35.4	22 47.9	28 40.9	15 2.5	26 3.1	8 3.2	21 43.1
21 W	23 57 45.3	27 34.4	17 51.8	17 0.2	18 21.9	17 49.5	23 25.5	28 35.0	14 59.8	26 3.9	8 3.9	21 43.1
22 T	0 1 41.9	28 33.1	17 48.6	28 50.9	17 46.1	19 3.5	24 3.0	28 29.1	14 57.1	26 4.7	8 4.6	21 43.1
23 F	0 5 38.4	29 31.8	17 45.4	10♓38.8	17 19.0	20 17.6	24 40.4	28 23.0	14 54.6	26 5.6	8 5.3	21R43.1
24 S	0 9 35.0	0♎30.5	17 42.3	22 26.6	17 1.2	21 31.6	25 17.9	28 16.7	14 52.1	26 6.6	8 5.9	21 43.1
25 S	0 13 31.5	1 29.3	17 39.1	4♈16.8	16 53.4	22 45.6	25 55.3	28 10.3	14 49.8	26 7.6	8 6.4	21 43.0
26 M	0 17 28.1	2 28.1	17 35.9	16 11.5	16D55.7	23 59.7	26 32.6	28 3.8	14 47.5	26 8.7	8 7.0	21 42.9
27 T	0 21 24.7	3 27.0	17 32.7	28 12.7	17 8.0	25 13.7	27 10.0	27 57.2	14 45.3	26 9.8	8 7.5	21 42.8
28 W	0 25 21.2	4 25.9	17 29.5	10♉22.4	17 30.3	26 27.7	27 47.3	27 50.4	14 43.2	26 10.9	8 8.0	21 42.7
29 T	0 29 17.7	5 24.8	17 26.4	22 42.8	18 2.2	27 41.7	28 24.6	27 43.5	14 41.1	26 12.1	8 8.4	21 42.5
30 F	0 33 14.3	6 23.8	17 23.2	5♊16.2	18 43.2	28 55.7	29 1.8	27 36.5	14 39.2	26 13.4	8 8.8	21 42.3
					DECLINATION							
1 T	22 38 54.3	8N31.9	4N23.1	11N42.8	4S 0.7	3N55.8	18N36.1	10N 4.5	17S 8.4	23S35.7	22N13.7	14N50.5
4 S	22 50 43.9	7 26.3	4 26.8	17 54.6	4 18.4	2 24.4	18 5.2	10 1.1	17 12.0	23 35.6	22 13.5	14 50.2
7 W	23 2 33.6	6 19.5	4 30.6	15 41.6	4 5.5	0 52.3	17 33.4	9 57.1	17 15.4	23 35.6	22 13.2	14 49.8
10 S	23 14 23.2	5 11.8	4 34.3	4 27.7	3 18.0	0S40.2	17 0.6	9 52.6	17 18.6	23 35.7	22 12.9	14 49.4
13 T	23 26 12.9	4 3.3	4 38.0	9S10.6	1 56.2	2 12.7	16 26.8	9 47.5	17 21.7	23 35.7	22 12.7	14 49.1
16 F	23 38 2.5	2 54.2	4 41.8	17 21.0	0 8.0	3 45.1	15 52.3	9 41.9	17 24.5	23 35.7	22 12.5	14 48.7
19 M	23 49 52.2	1 44.6	4 45.5	17 10.8	1N49.5	5 16.8	15 16.9	9 35.8	17 27.1	23 35.8	22 12.2	14 48.3
22 T	0 1 41.9	0 34.6	4 49.2	10 12.1	3 34.9	6 47.6	14 40.8	9 29.2	17 29.5	23 35.8	22 12.0	14 47.8
25 S	0 13 31.5	0S35.5	4 52.9	0N23.0	4 49.3	8 17.2	14 4.0	9 22.2	17 31.6	23 35.9	22 11.9	14 47.4
28 W	0 25 21.2	1 45.7	4 56.6	10 59.5	5 21.9	9 45.2	13 26.5	9 14.8	17 33.5	23 36.0	22 11.7	14 47.0

OCTOBER 1904

DAY	EPHEMERIS SIDEREAL TIME h m s	☉ ° ′	☊ ° ′	☽ ° ′	☿ ° ′	♀ ° ′	♂ ° ′	♃ ° ′	♄ ° ′	♅ ° ′	♆ ° ′	♇ ° ′
					LONGITUDE							
1 S	0 37 10.9	7♎22.8	17♍20.0	18♊ 5.1	19♍32.8	0♏ 9.7	29♌39.0	27♈29.4	14♒37.4	26♐14.7	8♋ 9.2	21♊42.2
2 S	0 41 7.4	8 21.8	17 16.8	1♋11.9	20 30.2	1 23.7	0♍16.2	27R22.2	14R35.6	26 16.0	8 9.5	21R41.9
3 M	0 45 4.0	9 20.9	17 13.7	14 38.9	21 34.8	2 37.7	0 53.4	27 14.9	14 33.9	26 17.4	8 9.8	21 41.7
4 T	0 49 0.5	10 20.0	17 10.5	28 27.7	22 45.9	3 51.7	1 30.5	27 7.5	14 32.4	26 18.9	8 10.1	21 41.4
5 W	0 52 57.0	11 19.2	17 7.3	12♌38.8	24 2.7	5 5.6	2 7.6	26 60.0	14 30.9	26 20.4	8 10.3	21 41.2
6 T	0 56 53.6	12 18.4	17 4.1	27 10.8	25 24.5	6 19.6	2 44.6	26 52.4	14 29.5	26 21.9	8 10.5	21 40.9
7 F	1 0 50.2	13 17.6	17 0.9	12♍ 0.2	26 50.6	7 33.6	3 21.6	26 44.7	14 28.3	26 23.5	8 10.7	21 40.5
8 S	1 4 46.7	14 16.9	16 57.8	27 1.1	28 20.5	8 47.6	3 58.6	26 37.0	14 27.1	26 25.1	8 10.9	21 40.2
9 S	1 8 43.3	15 16.2	16 54.6	12♎ 5.6	29 53.4	10 1.5	4 35.6	26 29.2	14 26.0	26 26.8	8 11.0	21 39.8
10 M	1 12 39.8	16 15.5	16 51.4	27 4.7	1♎28.9	11 15.5	5 12.5	26 21.3	14 25.0	26 28.5	8 11.0	21 39.5
11 T	1 16 36.4	17 14.9	16 48.2	11♏49.7	3 6.5	12 29.4	5 49.3	26 13.4	14 24.1	26 30.3	8 11.1	21 39.0
12 W	1 20 32.9	18 14.3	16 45.1	26 13.4	4 45.8	13 43.3	6 26.2	26 5.4	14 23.3	26 32.1	8 11.1	21 38.6
13 T	1 24 29.5	19 13.7	16 41.9	10♐11.1	6 26.4	14 57.3	7 3.0	25 57.4	14 22.7	26 34.0	8R11.0	21 38.2
14 F	1 28 26.0	20 13.2	16 38.7	23 41.1	8 8.0	16 11.2	7 39.7	25 49.4	14 22.1	26 35.9	8 11.0	21 37.7
15 S	1 32 22.6	21 12.7	16 35.5	6♑44.2	9 50.3	17 25.1	8 16.5	25 41.3	14 21.6	26 37.9	8 10.9	21 37.2
16 S	1 36 19.1	22 12.2	16 32.3	19 23.2	11 33.0	18 39.0	8 53.1	25 33.2	14 21.2	26 39.9	8 10.7	21 36.7
17 M	1 40 15.7	23 11.8	16 29.2	1♒42.0	13 16.0	19 52.8	9 29.8	25 25.1	14 20.9	26 41.9	8 10.6	21 36.2
18 T	1 44 12.2	24 11.4	16 26.0	13 45.7	14 59.2	21 6.7	10 6.4	25 17.0	14 20.8	26 44.0	8 10.4	21 35.6
19 W	1 48 8.8	25 11.0	16 22.8	25 39.1	16 42.3	22 20.5	10 43.0	25 8.8	14 20.7	26 46.2	8 10.1	21 35.1
20 T	1 52 5.3	26 10.6	16 19.6	7♓27.1	18 25.2	23 34.4	11 19.5	25 0.7	14D20.7	26 48.3	8 9.9	21 34.5
21 F	1 56 1.9	27 10.3	16 16.5	19 14.1	20 8.0	24 48.2	11 56.0	24 52.6	14 20.9	26 50.6	8 9.6	21 33.9
22 S	1 59 58.5	28 10.0	16 13.3	1♈ 3.8	21 50.4	26 2.0	12 32.4	24 44.5	14 21.1	26 52.8	8 9.2	21 33.3
23 S	2 3 55.0	29 9.8	16 10.1	12 59.5	23 32.5	27 15.8	13 8.8	24 36.4	14 21.4	26 55.1	8 8.9	21 32.6
24 M	2 7 51.5	0♏ 9.5	16 6.9	25 3.5	25 14.1	28 29.6	13 45.2	24 28.4	14 21.8	26 57.4	8 8.5	21 31.9
25 T	2 11 48.1	1 9.3	16 3.7	7♉17.3	26 55.4	29 43.4	14 21.6	24 20.4	14 22.4	26 59.8	8 8.0	21 31.3
26 W	2 15 44.7	2 9.2	16 0.6	19 42.2	28 36.1	0♐57.1	14 57.9	24 12.4	14 23.0	27 2.3	8 7.6	21 30.6
27 T	2 19 41.2	3 9.0	15 57.4	2♊18.8	0♏16.4	2 10.9	15 34.1	24 4.5	14 23.8	27 4.7	8 7.1	21 29.9
28 F	2 23 37.8	4 8.9	15 54.2	15 7.4	1 56.3	3 24.6	16 10.3	23 56.6	14 24.6	27 7.2	8 6.5	21 29.1
29 S	2 27 34.3	5 8.9	15 51.0	28 8.6	3 35.6	4 38.3	16 46.5	23 48.7	14 25.6	27 9.7	8 6.0	21 28.4
30 S	2 31 30.9	6 8.8	15 47.9	11♋22.8	5 14.5	5 52.0	17 22.7	23 41.0	14 26.6	27 12.3	8 5.4	21 27.6
31 M	2 35 27.4	7 8.9	15 44.7	24 50.8	6 52.9	7 5.7	17 58.8	23 33.3	14 27.8	27 14.9	8 4.8	21 26.8
					DECLINATION							
1 S	0 37 10.9	2S55.8	5N 0.4	17N40.2	5N10.7	11S11.2	12N48.4	9N 7.0	17S35.1	23S36.1	22N11.5	14N46.5
4 T	0 49 0.5	4 5.6	5 4.1	16 31.7	4 19.9	12 35.0	12 9.8	8 59.0	17 36.5	23 36.2	22 11.4	14 46.1
7 F	1 0 50.2	5 15.0	5 7.8	6 31.2	2 57.5	13 56.2	11 30.6	8 50.7	17 37.6	23 36.4	22 11.3	14 45.6
10 M	1 12 39.8	6 23.8	5 11.5	7S22.5	1 12.5	15 14.4	10 51.0	8 42.1	17 38.5	23 36.5	22 11.2	14 45.2
13 T	1 24 29.5	7 31.8	5 15.2	16 52.1	0S47.0	16 29.3	10 11.0	8 33.5	17 39.0	23 36.6	22 11.1	14 44.7
16 S	1 36 19.1	8 38.9	5 18.9	17 37.9	2 54.5	17 40.5	9 30.6	8 24.8	17 39.3	23 36.8	22 11.1	14 44.3
19 W	1 48 8.8	9 44.9	5 22.6	11 6.0	5 5.2	18 47.6	8 49.9	8 16.0	17 39.4	23 36.9	22 11.0	14 43.9
22 S	1 59 58.5	10 49.6	5 26.3	0 38.9	7 15.8	19 50.4	8 8.9	8 7.3	17 39.1	23 37.1	22 11.0	14 43.4
25 T	2 11 48.1	11 52.9	5 30.0	10N14.7	9 23.7	20 48.5	7 27.7	7 58.7	17 38.6	23 37.2	22 11.0	14 43.0
28 F	2 23 37.8	12 54.5	5 33.7	17 31.2	11 27.5	21 41.5	6 46.4	7 50.3	17 37.9	23 37.4	22 11.0	14 42.6
31 M	2 35 27.4	13 54.3	5 37.4	17 9.6	13 25.8	22 29.2	6 4.8	7 42.1	17 36.8	23 37.6	22 11.1	14 42.1

NOVEMBER 1904

LONGITUDE

DAY	EPHEMERIS SIDEREAL TIME h m s	☉ ° ′	☊ ° ′	☽ ° ′	☿ ° ′	♀ ° ′	♂ ° ′	♃ ° ′	♄ ° ′	♅ ° ′	♆ ° ′	♇ ° ′
1 T	2 39 24.0	8♏ 8.9	15♍41.5	8♌33.6	8♏30.8	8♐19.4	18♍34.8	23♈25.7	14♒29.0	27♐17.6	8♋ 4.1	21♊26.0
2 W	2 43 20.5	9 9.0	15 38.3	22 31.7	10 8.3	9 33.1	19 10.9	23R18.1	14 30.3	27 20.2	8R 3.4	21R25.2
3 T	2 47 17.1	10 9.1	15 35.1	6♍45.1	11 45.3	10 46.7	19 46.8	23 10.7	14 31.8	27 22.9	8 2.7	21 24.4
4 F	2 51 13.7	11 9.3	15 32.0	21 12.5	13 21.9	12 0.4	20 22.8	23 3.3	14 33.4	27 25.7	8 2.0	21 23.5
5 S	2 55 10.2	12 9.4	15 28.8	5♎50.8	14 58.0	13 14.0	20 58.7	22 56.1	14 35.0	27 28.5	8 1.2	21 22.7
6 S	2 59 6.7	13 9.7	15 25.6	20 34.9	16 33.8	14 27.6	21 34.5	22 48.9	14 36.8	27 31.3	8 0.4	21 21.8
7 M	3 3 3.3	14 9.9	15 22.4	5♏18.3	18 9.2	15 41.2	22 10.3	22 41.9	14 38.6	27 34.1	7 59.5	21 20.9
8 T	3 6 59.9	15 10.2	15 19.3	19 53.2	19 44.2	16 54.8	22 46.1	22 34.9	14 40.6	27 37.0	7 58.7	21 20.0
9 W	3 10 56.4	16 10.5	15 16.1	4♐12.3	21 18.9	18 8.4	23 21.8	22 28.1	14 42.6	27 40.0	7 57.8	21 19.1
10 T	3 14 53.0	17 10.9	15 12.9	18 9.9	22 53.2	19 22.0	23 57.4	22 21.4	14 44.8	27 42.9	7 56.8	21 18.2
11 F	3 18 49.5	18 11.2	15 9.7	1♑42.3	24 27.2	20 35.5	24 33.0	22 14.9	14 47.0	27 45.9	7 55.9	21 17.2
12 S	3 22 46.1	19 11.6	15 6.5	14 48.9	26 0.9	21 49.0	25 8.6	22 8.4	14 49.4	27 48.9	7 54.9	21 16.2
13 S	3 26 42.6	20 12.0	15 3.4	27 30.9	27 34.3	23 2.5	25 44.1	22 2.2	14 51.8	27 51.9	7 53.9	21 15.3
14 M	3 30 39.2	21 12.5	15 0.2	9♒51.9	29 7.4	24 16.0	26 19.5	21 56.0	14 54.3	27 55.0	7 52.9	21 14.3
15 T	3 34 35.7	22 12.9	14 57.0	21 56.4	0♐40.3	25 29.4	26 54.9	21 50.1	14 57.0	27 58.1	7 51.8	21 13.3
16 W	3 38 32.3	23 13.4	14 53.8	3♓49.8	2 12.8	26 42.9	27 30.2	21 44.2	14 59.7	28 1.2	7 50.7	21 12.3
17 T	3 42 28.9	24 13.9	14 50.7	15 37.7	3 45.2	27 56.3	28 5.5	21 38.5	15 2.5	28 4.3	7 49.6	21 11.3
18 F	3 46 25.4	25 14.4	14 47.5	27 25.3	5 17.3	29 9.6	28 40.8	21 33.0	15 5.5	28 7.5	7 48.5	21 10.2
19 S	3 50 22.0	26 15.0	14 44.3	9♈17.6	6 49.1	0♑23.0	29 15.9	21 27.7	15 8.5	28 10.7	7 47.3	21 9.2
20 S	3 54 18.5	27 15.5	14 41.1	21 18.9	8 20.8	1 36.3	29 51.1	21 22.5	15 11.6	28 13.9	7 46.1	21 8.1
21 M	3 58 15.1	28 16.1	14 37.9	3♉32.2	9 52.2	2 49.6	0♎26.1	21 17.5	15 14.8	28 17.2	7 44.9	21 7.1
22 T	4 2 11.6	29 16.7	14 34.8	15 59.7	11 23.3	4 2.8	1 1.1	21 12.6	15 18.0	28 20.4	7 43.7	21 6.0
23 W	4 6 8.2	0♐17.4	14 31.6	28 42.3	12 54.2	5 16.0	1 36.1	21 8.0	15 21.4	28 23.7	7 42.4	21 4.9
24 T	4 10 4.7	1 18.0	14 28.4	11♊39.7	14 24.9	6 29.2	2 11.0	21 3.5	15 24.9	28 27.0	7 41.1	21 3.8
25 F	4 14 1.3	2 18.7	14 25.2	24 50.7	15 55.2	7 42.4	2 45.8	20 59.2	15 28.4	28 30.4	7 39.8	21 2.7
26 S	4 17 57.8	3 19.4	14 22.1	8♋13.7	17 25.3	8 55.5	3 20.6	20 55.1	15 32.1	28 33.7	7 38.5	21 1.6
27 S	4 21 54.4	4 20.2	14 18.9	21 46.8	18 55.1	10 8.6	3 55.4	20 51.1	15 35.8	28 37.1	7 37.1	21 0.5
28 M	4 25 51.0	5 20.9	14 15.7	5♌28.5	20 24.5	11 21.7	4 30.0	20 47.4	15 39.6	28 40.5	7 35.8	20 59.4
29 T	4 29 47.5	6 21.7	14 12.5	19 17.7	21 53.5	12 34.7	5 4.7	20 43.8	15 43.5	28 43.9	7 34.4	20 58.3
30 W	4 33 44.1	7 22.5	14 9.4	3♍14.0	23 22.0	13 47.7	5 39.2	20 40.5	15 47.5	28 47.3	7 33.0	20 57.2

DECLINATION

DAY	SID. TIME	☉	☊	☽	☿	♀	♂	♃	♄	♅	♆	♇
1 T	2 39 24.0	14S13.8	5N38.6	15N 1.6	14S 3.9	22S43.9	5N51.0	7N39.4	17S36.4	23S37.6	22N11.1	14N42.0
4 F	2 51 13.7	15 10.9	5 42.3	3 49.0	15 53.6	23 24.0	5 9.3	7 31.6	17 35.0	23 37.8	22 11.2	14 41.6
7 M	3 3 3.3	16 5.8	5 46.0	9S42.2	17 36.1	23 58.1	4 27.7	7 24.2	17 33.3	23 38.0	22 11.2	14 41.2
10 T	3 14 53.0	16 58.2	5 49.7	17 52.0	19 10.7	24 25.9	3 46.0	7 17.2	17 31.4	23 38.1	22 11.4	14 40.9
13 S	3 26 42.6	17 48.1	5 53.4	16 54.9	20 36.7	24 47.4	3 4.5	7 10.6	17 29.2	23 38.3	22 11.5	14 40.5
16 W	3 38 32.3	18 35.2	5 57.1	9 5.7	21 53.6	25 2.3	2 23.0	7 4.5	17 26.7	23 38.4	22 11.6	14 40.2
19 S	3 50 22.0	19 19.3	6 0.8	1N50.6	23 0.8	25 10.5	1 41.6	6 59.1	17 24.0	23 38.6	22 11.8	14 39.9
22 T	4 2 11.6	20 0.3	6 4.4	12 26.6	23 57.6	25 12.0	1 0.5	6 54.1	17 21.0	23 38.7	22 11.9	14 39.6
25 F	4 14 1.3	20 37.9	6 8.1	18 24.5	24 43.5	25 6.7	0 19.5	6 49.9	17 17.9	23 38.8	22 12.1	14 39.3
28 M	4 25 51.0	21 12.2	6 11.8	15 49.2	25 17.6	24 54.8	0S21.1	6 46.2	17 14.4	23 39.0	22 12.3	14 39.1

DECEMBER 1904

LONGITUDE

DAY	SID. TIME h m s	☉ ° ′	☊ ° ′	☽ ° ′	☿ ° ′	♀ ° ′	♂ ° ′	♃ ° ′	♄ ° ′	♅ ° ′	♆ ° ′	♇ ° ′
1 T	4 37 40.6	8♐23.3	14♍ 6.2	17♍17.2	24♐50.0	15♑ 0.6	6♎13.7	20♈37.3	15♒51.5	28♐50.7	7♋31.5	20♊56.0
2 F	4 41 37.2	9 24.2	14 3.0	1♎26.9	26 17.5	16 13.6	6 48.1	20R34.4	15 55.7	28 54.2	7R30.1	20R54.9
3 S	4 45 33.8	10 25.1	13 59.8	15 41.7	27 44.2	17 26.5	7 22.5	20 31.6	15 59.9	28 57.7	7 28.6	20 53.7
4 S	4 49 30.3	11 26.0	13 56.6	29 59.5	29 10.1	18 39.3	7 56.8	20 29.0	16 4.2	29 1.2	7 27.1	20 52.6
5 M	4 53 26.9	12 26.9	13 53.5	14♏16.3	0♑35.1	19 52.1	8 31.0	20 26.7	16 8.6	29 4.7	7 25.6	20 51.4
6 T	4 57 23.4	13 27.8	13 50.3	28 27.4	1 59.0	21 4.9	9 5.1	20 24.5	16 13.0	29 8.2	7 24.1	20 50.3
7 W	5 1 20.0	14 28.8	13 47.1	12♐27.4	3 21.6	22 17.6	9 39.2	20 22.6	16 17.6	29 11.7	7 22.6	20 49.1
8 T	5 5 16.5	15 29.8	13 43.9	26 11.2	4 42.7	23 30.3	10 13.2	20 20.8	16 22.2	29 15.3	7 21.1	20 48.0
9 F	5 9 13.1	16 30.8	13 40.8	9♑35.1	6 2.0	24 42.9	10 47.1	20 19.3	16 26.9	29 18.8	7 19.5	20 46.8
10 S	5 13 9.6	17 31.8	13 37.6	22 37.4	7 19.4	25 55.5	11 21.0	20 18.0	16 31.7	29 22.4	7 17.9	20 45.6
11 S	5 17 6.2	18 32.8	13 34.4	5♒18.2	8 34.3	27 8.1	11 54.7	20 16.9	16 36.5	29 25.9	7 16.3	20 44.4
12 M	5 21 2.8	19 33.8	13 31.2	17 39.5	9 46.5	28 20.5	12 28.4	20 16.0	16 41.5	29 29.5	7 14.8	20 43.3
13 T	5 24 59.3	20 34.9	13 28.1	29 44.9	10 55.5	29 32.9	13 2.0	20 15.3	16 46.4	29 33.1	7 13.1	20 42.1
14 W	5 28 55.9	21 35.9	13 24.9	11♓39.1	12 0.8	0♒45.3	13 35.6	20 14.8	16 51.5	29 36.7	7 11.5	20 40.9
15 T	5 32 52.4	22 36.9	13 21.7	23 27.4	13 1.8	1 57.6	14 9.0	20 14.5	16 56.6	29 40.3	7 9.9	20 39.8
16 F	5 36 49.0	23 38.0	13 18.5	5♈15.5	13 57.9	3 9.8	14 42.4	20 14.4	17 1.8	29 43.9	7 8.3	20 38.6
17 S	5 40 45.6	24 39.1	13 15.4	17 9.0	14 48.4	4 22.0	15 15.6	20D14.6	17 7.1	29 47.5	7 6.6	20 37.4
18 S	5 44 42.1	25 40.1	13 12.2	29 12.8	15 32.4	5 34.1	15 48.8	20 14.9	17 12.4	29 51.1	7 5.0	20 36.3
19 M	5 48 38.6	26 41.2	13 9.0	11♉31.5	16 9.2	6 46.1	16 21.9	20 15.5	17 17.8	29 54.8	7 3.3	20 35.1
20 T	5 52 35.2	27 42.3	13 5.8	24 8.1	16 37.8	7 58.0	16 54.9	20 16.3	17 23.3	29 58.4	7 1.6	20 33.9
21 W	5 56 31.8	28 43.4	13 2.6	7♊ 4.4	16 57.4	9 9.9	17 27.8	20 17.3	17 28.8	0♑ 2.0	6 59.9	20 32.8
22 T	6 0 28.3	29 44.5	12 59.5	20 20.5	17 7.1	10 21.7	18 0.7	20 18.5	17 34.4	0 5.6	6 58.3	20 31.6
23 F	6 4 24.9	0♑45.6	12 56.3	3♋54.5	17R 6.0	11 33.4	18 33.4	20 19.8	17 40.1	0 9.2	6 56.6	20 30.5
24 S	6 8 21.4	1 46.7	12 53.1	17 43.5	16 53.5	12 45.0	19 6.0	20 21.4	17 45.8	0 12.9	6 54.9	20 29.3
25 S	6 12 18.0	2 47.8	12 49.9	1♌43.3	16 29.4	13 56.5	19 38.6	20 23.2	17 51.5	0 16.5	6 53.2	20 28.2
26 M	6 16 14.6	3 48.9	12 46.8	15 49.8	15 53.4	15 8.0	20 11.0	20 25.3	17 57.3	0 20.1	6 51.5	20 27.0
27 T	6 20 11.1	4 50.1	12 43.6	29 59.3	15 6.0	16 19.3	20 43.4	20 27.5	18 3.2	0 23.7	6 49.8	20 25.9
28 W	6 24 7.7	5 51.2	12 40.4	14♍ 8.8	14 8.1	17 30.6	21 15.7	20 29.9	18 9.2	0 27.3	6 48.1	20 24.8
29 T	6 28 4.2	6 52.4	12 37.2	28 16.7	13 1.0	18 41.8	21 47.8	20 32.5	18 15.1	0 30.9	6 46.4	20 23.7
30 F	6 32 0.8	7 53.5	12 34.1	12♎21.8	11 46.7	19 52.8	22 19.9	20 35.3	18 21.2	0 34.5	6 44.7	20 22.6
31 S	6 35 57.4	8 54.7	12 30.9	26 23.2	10 27.5	21 3.8	22 51.8	20 38.3	18 27.3	0 38.1	6 43.0	20 21.5

DECLINATION

DAY	SID. TIME	☉	☊	☽	☿	♀	♂	♃	♄	♅	♆	♇
1 T	4 37 40.6	21S42.8	6N15.5	5N14.8	25S39.6	24S36.2	1S 1.5	6N43.2	17S10.8	23S39.1	22N12.5	14N38.8
4 S	4 49 30.3	22 9.7	6 19.1	8S 6.5	25 48.8	24 11.1	1 41.6	6 41.0	17 6.9	23 39.2	22 12.8	14 38.6
7 W	5 1 20.0	22 32.7	6 22.8	17 20.2	25 45.0	23 39.6	2 21.2	6 39.4	17 2.7	23 39.3	22 13.0	14 38.5
10 S	5 13 9.6	22 51.8	6 26.5	17 42.9	25 28.3	23 2.1	3 0.4	6 38.5	16 58.4	23 39.3	22 13.2	14 38.3
13 T	5 24 59.3	23 6.9	6 30.1	10 28.5	24 59.4	22 18.7	3 39.2	6 38.3	16 53.9	23 39.4	22 13.5	14 38.2
16 F	5 36 49.0	23 17.8	6 33.8	0N19.7	24 20.0	21 29.6	4 17.4	6 38.9	16 49.1	23 39.4	22 13.8	14 38.1
19 M	5 48 38.6	23 24.5	6 37.4	11 11.6	23 32.9	20 35.3	4 55.1	6 40.2	16 44.2	23 39.5	22 14.0	14 38.1
22 T	6 0 28.3	23 26.9	6 41.1	18 8.0	22 42.6	19 36.0	5 32.2	6 42.1	16 39.1	23 39.5	22 14.3	14 38.1
25 S	6 12 18.0	23 25.2	6 44.7	16 36.8	21 53.9	18 32.1	6 8.7	6 44.8	16 33.8	23 39.5	22 14.6	14 38.1
28 W	6 24 7.7	23 19.2	6 48.4	6 27.2	21 11.5	17 23.9	6 44.6	6 48.2	16 28.3	23 39.5	22 14.9	14 38.1
31 S	6 35 57.4	23 9.0	6 52.0	6S50.2	20 38.1	16 11.7	7 19.8	6 52.2	16 22.7	23 39.5	22 15.2	14 38.2

JANUARY 1905

LONGITUDE

DAY	EPHEMERIS SIDEREAL TIME h m s	☉ ° ′	☊ ° ′	☽ ° ′	☿ ° ′	♀ ° ′	♂ ° ′	♃ ° ′	♄ ° ′	♅ ° ′	♆ ° ′	♇ ° ′
1 S	6 39 53.9	9♑55.8	12♍27.7	10♏20.2	9♑ 6.1	22♒14.7	23♎23.6	20♈41.5	18♒33.4	0♑41.7	6♋41.3	20♊20.4
2 M	6 43 50.4	10 57.0	12 24.5	24 11.3	7R45.1	23 25.5	23 55.3	20 44.9	18 39.6	0 45.3	6R39.6	20R19.3
3 T	6 47 47.0	11 58.2	12 21.3	7♐54.5	6 27.1	24 36.1	24 26.9	20 48.5	18 45.9	0 48.9	6 37.9	20 18.2
4 W	6 51 43.6	12 59.4	12 18.2	21 27.3	5 14.4	25 46.7	24 58.4	20 52.3	18 52.2	0 52.5	6 36.2	20 17.1
5 T	6 55 40.1	14 0.6	12 15.0	4♑47.3	4 8.9	26 57.1	25 29.8	20 56.3	18 58.5	0 56.0	6 34.5	20 16.1
6 F	6 59 36.7	15 1.8	12 11.8	17 52.2	3 11.9	28 7.4	26 1.0	21 0.5	19 4.9	0 59.6	6 32.9	20 15.0
7 S	7 3 33.2	16 2.9	12 8.6	0♒40.7	2 24.4	29 17.6	26 32.1	21 4.9	19 11.3	1 3.1	6 31.2	20 14.0
8 S	7 7 29.8	17 4.1	12 5.5	13 12.7	1 46.8	0♓27.7	27 3.0	21 9.4	19 17.8	1 6.6	6 29.5	20 12.9
9 M	7 11 26.4	18 5.3	12 2.3	25 29.1	1 19.2	1 37.6	27 33.9	21 14.2	19 24.3	1 10.1	6 27.8	20 11.9
10 T	7 15 22.9	19 6.4	11 59.1	7♓32.4	1 1.5	2 47.4	28 4.6	21 19.1	19 30.9	1 13.6	6 26.2	20 10.9
11 W	7 19 19.5	20 7.6	11 55.9	19 26.0	0 53.2	3 57.1	28 35.1	21 24.2	19 37.5	1 17.1	6 24.5	20 9.9
12 T	7 23 16.0	21 8.7	11 52.7	1♈14.3	0D53.8	5 6.6	29 5.6	21 29.5	19 44.1	1 20.6	6 22.9	20 8.9
13 F	7 27 12.6	22 9.9	11 49.6	13 2.1	1 2.6	6 16.0	29 35.8	21 35.0	19 50.8	1 24.0	6 21.3	20 7.9
14 S	7 31 9.1	23 11.0	11 46.4	24 55.0	1 19.1	7 25.2	0♏ 6.0	21 40.7	19 57.5	1 27.5	6 19.7	20 7.0
15 S	7 35 5.7	24 12.1	11 43.2	6♉58.0	1 42.5	8 34.2	0 36.0	21 46.5	20 4.2	1 30.9	6 18.1	20 6.0
16 M	7 39 2.2	25 13.2	11 40.0	19 16.4	2 12.3	9 43.1	1 5.8	21 52.5	20 11.0	1 34.3	6 16.5	20 5.1
17 T	7 42 58.8	26 14.3	11 36.9	1♊54.5	2 47.8	10 51.8	1 35.5	21 58.7	20 17.8	1 37.7	6 14.9	20 4.2
18 W	7 46 55.4	27 15.4	11 33.7	14 55.2	3 28.5	12 0.3	2 5.0	22 5.0	20 24.7	1 41.0	6 13.3	20 3.3
19 T	7 50 51.9	28 16.4	11 30.5	28 20.1	4 13.9	13 8.6	2 34.4	22 11.5	20 31.5	1 44.4	6 11.8	20 2.4
20 F	7 54 48.5	29 17.5	11 27.3	12♋ 8.4	5 3.4	14 16.7	3 3.6	22 18.2	20 38.4	1 47.7	6 10.2	20 1.5
21 S	7 58 45.0	0♒18.5	11 24.2	26 17.3	5 56.8	15 24.6	3 32.6	22 25.0	20 45.3	1 51.0	6 8.7	20 0.6
22 S	8 2 41.6	1 19.5	11 21.0	10♌42.0	6 53.6	16 32.4	4 1.5	22 32.0	20 52.3	1 54.3	6 7.2	19 59.8
23 M	8 6 38.1	2 20.5	11 17.8	25 16.3	7 53.5	17 39.9	4 30.3	22 39.2	20 59.3	1 57.5	6 5.7	19 59.0
24 T	8 10 34.7	3 21.5	11 14.6	9♍53.7	8 56.2	18 47.2	4 58.8	22 46.5	21 6.3	2 0.8	6 4.2	19 58.2
25 W	8 14 31.3	4 22.5	11 11.5	24 28.3	10 1.5	19 54.3	5 27.2	22 54.0	21 13.3	2 4.0	6 2.8	19 57.4
26 T	8 18 27.8	5 23.5	11 8.3	8♎55.2	11 9.1	21 1.2	5 55.4	23 1.6	21 20.3	2 7.1	6 1.3	19 56.6
27 F	8 22 24.4	6 24.5	11 5.1	23 11.2	12 18.7	22 7.8	6 23.4	23 9.4	21 27.4	2 10.3	5 59.9	19 55.8
28 S	8 26 20.9	7 25.4	11 1.9	7♏14.4	13 30.4	23 14.2	6 51.2	23 17.3	21 34.5	2 13.4	5 58.5	19 55.1
29 S	8 30 17.5	8 26.4	10 58.7	21 3.9	14 43.8	24 20.4	7 18.8	23 25.4	21 41.6	2 16.5	5 57.1	19 54.3
30 M	8 34 14.0	9 27.3	10 55.6	4♐39.5	15 58.9	25 26.3	7 46.2	23 33.6	21 48.7	2 19.6	5 55.7	19 53.6
31 T	8 38 10.6	10 28.2	10 52.4	18 1.5	17 15.5	26 31.9	8 13.4	23 42.0	21 55.8	2 22.7	5 54.4	19 52.9

DECLINATION

DAY	EPHEMERIS SIDEREAL TIME	☉	☊	☽	☿	♀	♂	♃	♄	♅	♆	♇
1 S	6 39 53.9	23S 4.6	6N53.2	10S47.4	20S29.4	15S46.8	7S31.3	6N53.7	16S20.8	23S39.5	22N15.3	14N38.2
4 W	6 51 43.6	22 48.9	6 56.9	18 11.4	20 11.8	14 29.9	8 5.6	6 58.6	16 15.0	23 39.5	22 15.5	14 38.4
7 S	7 3 33.2	22 29.0	7 0.5	16 48.8	20 8.6	13 9.9	8 39.0	7 4.1	16 9.0	23 39.4	22 15.8	14 38.5
10 T	7 15 22.9	22 5.2	7 4.1	8 30.4	20 19.2	11 47.1	9 11.7	7 10.3	16 2.9	23 39.4	22 16.1	14 38.7
13 F	7 27 12.6	21 37.5	7 7.8	2N34.8	20 40.0	10 22.0	9 43.5	7 17.0	15 56.6	23 39.3	22 16.4	14 38.9
16 M	7 39 2.2	21 6.0	7 11.4	12 54.7	21 5.9	8 54.8	10 14.5	7 24.3	15 50.3	23 39.2	22 16.7	14 39.2
19 T	7 50 51.9	20 30.9	7 15.0	18 32.2	21 32.3	7 25.9	10 44.6	7 32.2	15 43.8	23 39.1	22 17.0	14 39.5
22 S	8 2 41.6	19 52.4	7 18.7	15 7.8	21 55.6	5 55.8	11 13.8	7 40.6	15 37.2	23 39.0	22 17.3	14 39.8
25 W	8 14 31.3	19 10.4	7 22.3	3 25.1	22 13.1	4 24.6	11 42.1	7 49.5	15 30.6	23 38.9	22 17.6	14 40.1
28 S	8 26 20.9	18 25.4	7 25.9	9S46.0	22 22.7	2 52.8	12 9.5	7 58.8	15 23.8	23 38.8	22 17.8	14 40.5
31 T	8 38 10.6	17 37.3	7 29.5	17 45.9	22 23.3	1 20.6	12 35.9	8 8.6	15 17.0	23 38.7	22 18.1	14 40.9

FEBRUARY 1905

LONGITUDE

DAY	EPHEMERIS SIDEREAL TIME	☉	☊	☽	☿	♀	♂	♃	♄	♅	♆	♇
1 W	8 42 7.1	11♒29.1	10♍49.2	1♑10.0	18♑33.5	27♓37.3	8♏40.4	23♈50.5	22♒ 3.0	2♑25.7	5♋53.1	19♊52.3
2 T	8 46 3.7	12 30.0	10 46.0	14 5.2	19 52.8	28 42.5	9 7.2	23 59.2	22 10.2	2 28.7	5R51.8	19R51.6
3 F	8 50 0.2	13 30.9	10 42.9	26 47.4	21 13.4	29 47.3	9 33.8	24 8.0	22 17.3	2 31.6	5 50.5	19 51.0
4 S	8 53 56.8	14 31.8	10 39.7	9♒17.0	22 35.2	0♈51.9	10 0.1	24 16.9	22 24.5	2 34.6	5 49.2	19 50.3
5 S	8 57 53.3	15 32.6	10 36.5	21 34.7	23 58.2	1 56.1	10 26.2	24 26.0	22 31.7	2 37.5	5 48.0	19 49.7
6 M	9 1 49.9	16 33.5	10 33.3	3♓41.6	25 22.2	3 0.1	10 52.1	24 35.2	22 39.0	2 40.3	5 46.8	19 49.2
7 T	9 5 46.5	17 34.3	10 30.1	15 39.5	26 47.2	4 3.7	11 17.7	24 44.5	22 46.2	2 43.2	5 45.6	19 48.6
8 W	9 9 43.0	18 35.0	10 27.0	27 30.8	28 13.3	5 7.0	11 43.1	24 54.0	22 53.4	2 45.9	5 44.5	19 48.1
9 T	9 13 39.6	19 35.8	10 23.8	9♈18.5	29 40.3	6 10.0	12 8.2	25 3.5	23 0.6	2 48.7	5 43.3	19 47.5
10 F	9 17 36.1	20 36.5	10 20.6	21 6.4	1♒ 8.3	7 12.6	12 33.1	25 13.3	23 7.9	2 51.4	5 42.2	19 47.0
11 S	9 21 32.7	21 37.2	10 17.4	2♉58.8	2 37.2	8 14.8	12 57.7	25 23.1	23 15.1	2 54.1	5 41.1	19 46.6
12 S	9 25 29.3	22 37.9	10 14.3	15 0.2	4 7.0	9 16.7	13 22.0	25 33.1	23 22.4	2 56.8	5 40.1	19 46.1
13 M	9 29 25.8	23 38.6	10 11.1	27 15.6	5 37.7	10 18.1	13 46.1	25 43.1	23 29.6	2 59.4	5 39.1	19 45.7
14 T	9 33 22.3	24 39.2	10 7.9	9♊49.5	7 9.3	11 19.2	14 9.9	25 53.3	23 36.8	3 2.0	5 38.0	19 45.2
15 W	9 37 18.9	25 39.8	10 4.7	22 46.1	8 41.9	12 19.8	14 33.4	26 3.6	23 44.1	3 4.5	5 37.1	19 44.9
16 T	9 41 15.5	26 40.3	10 1.5	6♋ 8.1	10 15.3	13 20.0	14 56.6	26 14.0	23 51.3	3 7.0	5 36.1	19 44.5
17 F	9 45 12.0	27 40.9	9 58.4	19 57.0	11 49.6	14 19.7	15 19.5	26 24.6	23 58.5	3 9.5	5 35.2	19 44.1
18 S	9 49 8.6	28 41.4	9 55.2	4♌11.5	13 24.8	15 19.0	15 42.1	26 35.2	24 5.8	3 11.9	5 34.3	19 43.8
19 S	9 53 5.1	29 41.8	9 52.0	18 48.2	15 1.0	16 17.8	16 4.5	26 45.9	24 13.0	3 14.3	5 33.5	19 43.5
20 M	9 57 1.7	0♓42.3	9 48.8	3♍41.0	16 38.0	17 16.0	16 26.5	26 56.8	24 20.2	3 16.7	5 32.6	19 43.2
21 T	10 0 58.2	1 42.7	9 45.7	18 42.1	18 16.0	18 13.8	16 48.2	27 7.7	24 27.4	3 19.0	5 31.9	19 42.9
22 W	10 4 54.8	2 43.1	9 42.5	3♎42.8	19 54.9	19 11.0	17 9.5	27 18.8	24 34.6	3 21.2	5 31.1	19 42.7
23 T	10 8 51.3	3 43.5	9 39.3	18 35.0	21 34.8	20 7.7	17 30.6	27 29.9	24 41.8	3 23.5	5 30.3	19 42.5
24 F	10 12 47.9	4 43.8	9 36.1	3♏12.2	23 15.7	21 3.8	17 51.2	27 41.2	24 49.0	3 25.6	5 29.6	19 42.3
25 S	10 16 44.4	5 44.1	9 32.9	17 29.8	24 57.5	21 59.3	18 11.6	27 52.5	24 56.1	3 27.8	5 29.0	19 42.1
26 S	10 20 41.0	6 44.5	9 29.8	1♐25.6	26 40.4	22 54.3	18 31.5	28 4.0	25 3.3	3 29.9	5 28.3	19 41.9
27 M	10 24 37.5	7 44.7	9 26.6	14 59.3	28 24.2	23 48.6	18 51.1	28 15.5	25 10.4	3 31.9	5 27.7	19 41.8
28 T	10 28 34.1	8 45.0	9 23.4	28 12.2	0♓ 9.1	24 42.2	19 10.3	28 27.1	25 17.5	3 33.9	5 27.1	19 41.7

DECLINATION

DAY	EPHEMERIS SIDEREAL TIME	☉	☊	☽	☿	♀	♂	♃	♄	♅	♆	♇
1 W	8 42 7.1	17S20.6	7N30.7	18S35.2	22S21.2	0S49.8	12S44.4	8N12.0	15S14.7	23S38.7	22N18.2	14N41.1
4 S	8 53 56.8	16 28.8	7 34.3	15 24.0	22 8.1	0N42.3	13 9.5	8 22.4	15 7.9	23 38.6	22 18.5	14 41.5
7 T	9 5 46.5	15 34.4	7 37.9	6 11.7	21 44.1	2 14.0	13 33.6	8 33.2	15 0.9	23 38.4	22 18.7	14 42.0
10 F	9 17 36.1	14 37.7	7 41.6	4N58.4	21 8.7	3 45.0	13 56.6	8 44.3	14 54.0	23 38.3	22 19.0	14 42.5
13 M	9 29 25.8	13 38.7	7 45.2	14 31.3	20 21.5	5 15.0	14 18.5	8 55.8	14 47.0	23 38.2	22 19.2	14 43.1
16 T	9 41 15.5	12 37.8	7 48.8	18 35.5	19 22.5	6 43.5	14 39.5	9 7.6	14 39.9	23 38.1	22 19.4	14 43.6
19 S	9 53 5.1	11 35.0	7 52.4	13 25.6	18 11.4	8 10.4	14 59.3	9 19.7	14 32.9	23 37.9	22 19.7	14 44.2
22 W	10 4 54.8	10 30.6	7 56.0	0 32.2	16 48.1	9 35.3	15 18.1	9 32.1	14 25.9	23 37.8	22 19.9	14 44.8
25 S	10 16 44.4	9 24.7	7 59.5	12S19.9	15 12.6	10 57.8	15 35.9	9 44.7	14 18.9	23 37.7	22 20.1	14 45.4
28 T	10 28 34.1	8 17.6	8 3.1	18 25.3	13 25.0	12 17.8	15 52.6	9 57.6	14 12.0	23 37.6	22 20.3	14 46.1

MARCH 1905

DAY	EPHEMERIS SIDEREAL TIME	☉	☊	☽	☿	♀	♂	♃	♄	♅	♆	♇
	h m s	° ′	° ′	° ′	° ′	° ′	° ′	° ′	° ′	° ′	° ′	° ′
						LONGITUDE						
1 W	10 32 30.6	9♓45.2	9♍20.2	11♑ 6.2	1♓55.0	25♈35.2	19♏29.2	28♈38.9	25♒24.6	3♑35.9	5♋26.6	19♊41.6
2 T	10 36 27.2	10 45.4	9 17.1	23 44.0	3 42.0	26 27.5	19 47.6	28 50.7	25 31.7	3 37.8	5R26.0	19R41.5
3 F	10 40 23.8	11 45.6	9 13.9	6♒ 7.9	5 30.0	27 19.0	20 5.6	29 2.6	25 38.8	3 39.7	5 25.6	19 41.5
4 S	10 44 20.3	12 45.7	9 10.7	18 20.5	7 19.0	28 9.9	20 23.2	29 14.5	25 45.9	3 41.5	5 25.1	19 41.5
5 S	10 48 16.8	13 45.8	9 7.5	0♓24.1	9 9.2	28 59.9	20 40.3	29 26.6	25 52.9	3 43.3	5 24.7	19 41.5
6 M	10 52 13.4	14 45.9	9 4.3	12 20.8	11 0.4	29 49.1	20 57.1	29 38.7	25 59.9	3 45.0	5 24.3	19D41.5
7 T	10 56 10.0	15 46.0	9 1.2	24 12.4	12 52.6	0♉37.5	21 13.3	29 50.9	26 6.9	3 46.7	5 23.9	19 41.5
8 W	11 0 6.5	16 46.0	8 58.0	6♈ 1.2	14 45.9	1 25.1	21 29.1	0♉ 3.2	26 13.8	3 48.4	5 23.6	19 41.6
9 T	11 4 3.1	17 46.0	8 54.8	17 49.2	16 40.2	2 11.7	21 44.5	0 15.6	26 20.7	3 50.0	5 23.3	19 41.7
10 F	11 7 59.6	18 46.0	8 51.6	29 39.1	18 35.4	2 57.4	21 59.3	0 28.1	26 27.6	3 51.5	5 23.1	19 41.8
11 S	11 11 56.2	19 45.9	8 48.5	11♉33.8	20 31.6	3 42.1	22 13.7	0 40.6	26 34.5	3 53.0	5 22.9	19 41.9
12 S	11 15 52.7	20 45.8	8 45.3	23 36.5	22 28.6	4 25.8	22 27.6	0 53.2	26 41.3	3 54.5	5 22.7	19 42.1
13 M	11 19 49.3	21 45.6	8 42.1	5♊51.1	24 26.4	5 8.4	22 41.0	1 5.8	26 48.2	3 55.9	5 22.5	19 42.3
14 T	11 23 45.8	22 45.4	8 38.9	18 21.5	26 24.8	5 50.0	22 53.8	1 18.6	26 54.9	3 57.2	5 22.4	19 42.5
15 W	11 27 42.4	23 45.2	8 35.7	1♋11.7	28 23.8	6 30.3	23 6.2	1 31.3	27 1.7	3 58.5	5 22.3	19 42.7
16 T	11 31 38.9	24 45.0	8 32.6	14 25.3	0♈23.1	7 9.5	23 18.0	1 44.2	27 8.4	3 59.7	5 22.3	19 43.0
17 F	11 35 35.5	25 44.7	8 29.4	28 4.9	2 22.6	7 47.5	23 29.3	1 57.1	27 15.1	4 1.0	5 22.3	19 43.2
18 S	11 39 32.0	26 44.3	8 26.2	12♌11.5	4 22.0	8 24.1	23 40.0	2 10.1	27 21.7	4 2.1	5D22.3	19 43.5
19 S	11 43 28.6	27 43.9	8 23.0	26 43.9	6 21.2	8 59.4	23 50.1	2 23.1	27 28.3	4 3.2	5 22.3	19 43.8
20 M	11 47 25.1	28 43.5	8 19.8	11♍38.1	8 19.8	9 33.3	23 59.7	2 36.2	27 34.9	4 4.2	5 22.4	19 44.2
21 T	11 51 21.7	29 43.1	8 16.7	26 47.3	10 17.5	10 5.8	24 8.6	2 49.4	27 41.4	4 5.2	5 22.5	19 44.5
22 W	11 55 18.2	0♈42.6	8 13.5	12♎ 2.4	12 14.0	10 36.8	24 17.0	3 2.6	27 47.9	4 6.2	5 22.7	19 44.9
23 T	11 59 14.8	1 42.1	8 10.3	27 13.2	14 8.8	11 6.2	24 24.8	3 15.8	27 54.3	4 7.1	5 22.9	19 45.3
24 F	12 3 11.3	2 41.6	8 7.1	12♏10.1	16 1.6	11 34.0	24 31.9	3 29.1	28 0.7	4 7.9	5 23.1	19 45.7
25 S	12 7 7.9	3 41.0	8 4.0	26 45.6	17 52.0	12 0.1	24 38.5	3 42.5	28 7.1	4 8.7	5 23.4	19 46.2
26 S	12 11 4.4	4 40.4	8 0.8	10♐55.1	19 39.5	12 24.5	24 44.3	3 55.9	28 13.4	4 9.5	5 23.6	19 46.6
27 M	12 15 1.0	5 39.7	7 57.6	24 36.8	21 23.7	12 47.1	24 49.5	4 9.4	28 19.7	4 10.2	5 24.0	19 47.1
28 T	12 18 57.5	6 39.1	7 54.4	7♑51.6	23 4.3	13 7.9	24 54.1	4 22.9	28 25.9	4 10.8	5 24.3	19 47.6
29 W	12 22 54.1	7 38.4	7 51.2	20 42.3	24 40.7	13 26.8	24 57.9	4 36.4	28 32.1	4 11.4	5 24.7	19 48.2
30 T	12 26 50.7	8 37.7	7 48.1	3♒12.6	26 12.6	13 43.8	25 1.1	4 50.0	28 38.2	4 11.9	5 25.1	19 48.7
31 F	12 30 47.2	9 36.9	7 44.9	15 26.8	27 39.7	13 58.7	25 3.5	5 3.7	28 44.3	4 12.4	5 25.6	19 49.3
						DECLINATION						
1 W	10 32 30.6	7S54.9	8N 4.3	18S29.4	12S46.4	12N43.8	15S57.9	10N 1.9	14S 9.6	23S37.6	22N20.4	14N46.3
4 S	10 44 20.3	6 46.3	8 7.9	13 31.6	10 42.6	13 59.9	16 13.1	10 15.0	14 2.7	23 37.5	22 20.5	14 47.0
7 T	10 56 10.0	5 36.9	8 11.5	3 33.1	8 27.2	15 12.6	16 27.2	10 28.3	13 55.9	23 37.4	22 20.7	14 47.7
10 F	11 7 59.6	4 26.8	8 15.1	7N32.2	6 0.7	16 21.6	16 40.3	10 41.8	13 49.1	23 37.3	22 20.9	14 48.4
13 M	11 19 49.3	3 16.2	8 18.6	16 5.7	3 24.3	17 26.6	16 52.2	10 55.4	13 42.4	23 37.3	22 21.0	14 49.1
16 T	11 31 38.9	2 5.2	8 22.2	18 22.3	0 40.0	18 27.1	17 3.0	11 9.1	13 35.7	23 37.2	22 21.2	14 49.8
19 S	11 43 28.6	0 54.1	8 25.8	11 31.7	2N 9.0	19 22.8	17 12.8	11 22.9	13 29.2	23 37.2	22 21.3	14 50.6
22 W	11 55 18.2	0N17.0	8 29.3	2S 8.1	4 58.3	20 13.1	17 21.4	11 36.8	13 22.8	23 37.1	22 21.4	14 51.3
25 S	12 7 7.9	1 27.9	8 32.9	14 26.9	7 42.0	20 57.5	17 28.9	11 50.7	13 16.5	23 37.1	22 21.5	14 52.1
28 T	12 18 57.5	2 38.5	8 36.5	18 37.5	10 13.4	21 35.4	17 35.3	12 4.7	13 10.3	23 37.1	22 21.6	14 52.8
31 F	12 30 47.2	3 48.7	8 40.0	14 11.9	12 26.4	22 6.0	17 40.6	12 18.7	13 4.3	23 37.1	22 21.7	14 53.6

APRIL 1905

DAY	EPHEMERIS SIDEREAL TIME	☉	☊	☽	☿	♀	♂	♃	♄	♅	♆	♇
						LONGITUDE						
1 S	12 34 43.7	10♈36.1	7♍41.7	27♒29.1	29♈ 1.6	14♉11.5	25♏ 5.2	5♉17.3	28♒50.3	4♑12.8	5♋26.1	19♊49.9
2 S	12 38 40.3	11 35.3	7 38.5	9♓23.3	0♉18.0	14 22.2	25 6.2	5 31.0	28 56.3	4 13.2	5 26.6	19 50.5
3 M	12 42 36.8	12 34.5	7 35.3	21 12.9	1 28.7	14 30.7	25 6.5	5 44.8	29 2.2	4 13.5	5 27.2	19 51.1
4 T	12 46 33.4	13 33.6	7 32.2	3♈ 0.6	2 33.5	14 36.9	25R 6.0	5 58.6	29 8.1	4 13.8	5 27.8	19 51.8
5 W	12 50 30.0	14 32.7	7 29.0	14 48.9	3 32.1	14 40.8	25 4.8	6 12.4	29 14.0	4 14.0	5 28.4	19 52.4
6 T	12 54 26.5	15 31.7	7 25.8	26 39.7	4 24.4	14 42.4	25 2.8	6 26.3	29 19.7	4 14.2	5 29.0	19 53.1
7 F	12 58 23.0	16 30.8	7 22.6	8♉34.9	5 10.2	14R41.6	25 0.1	6 40.2	29 25.4	4 14.3	5 29.7	19 53.8
8 S	13 2 19.6	17 29.7	7 19.5	20 36.2	5 49.4	14 38.3	24 56.6	6 54.1	29 31.1	4 14.4	5 30.4	19 54.5
9 S	13 6 16.2	18 28.7	7 16.3	2♊45.7	6 22.1	14 32.6	24 52.3	7 8.1	29 36.7	4 14.4	5 31.2	19 55.3
10 M	13 10 12.7	19 27.6	7 13.1	15 5.5	6 48.0	14 24.5	24 47.3	7 22.1	29 42.2	4R14.4	5 32.0	19 56.1
11 T	13 14 9.3	20 26.5	7 9.9	27 38.3	7 7.4	14 13.8	24 41.5	7 36.1	29 47.7	4 14.3	5 32.8	19 56.8
12 W	13 18 5.8	21 25.3	7 6.7	10♋27.1	7 20.1	14 0.7	24 35.0	7 50.1	29 53.1	4 14.1	5 33.7	19 57.6
13 T	13 22 2.4	22 24.1	7 3.6	23 35.0	7 26.3	13 45.1	24 27.6	8 4.2	29 58.4	4 13.9	5 34.5	19 58.5
14 F	13 25 58.9	23 22.9	7 0.4	7♌ 4.8	7R26.2	13 27.1	24 19.6	8 18.3	0♓ 3.7	4 13.7	5 35.4	19 59.3
15 S	13 29 55.5	24 21.6	6 57.2	20 58.6	7 19.9	13 6.7	24 10.7	8 32.4	0 8.9	4 13.4	5 36.4	20 0.2
16 S	13 33 52.0	25 20.3	6 54.0	5♍17.2	7 7.8	12 44.0	24 1.2	8 46.5	0 14.0	4 13.1	5 37.4	20 1.0
17 M	13 37 48.6	26 18.9	6 50.9	19 58.7	6 50.2	12 19.1	23 50.8	9 0.7	0 19.1	4 12.7	5 38.4	20 1.9
18 T	13 41 45.1	27 17.6	6 47.7	4♎58.9	6 27.6	11 52.1	23 39.8	9 14.8	0 24.2	4 12.2	5 39.4	20 2.8
19 W	13 45 41.7	28 16.1	6 44.5	20 10.2	6 0.4	11 23.2	23 28.0	9 29.0	0 29.1	4 11.7	5 40.5	20 3.8
20 T	13 49 38.2	29 14.7	6 41.3	5♏23.0	5 29.2	10 52.4	23 15.5	9 43.2	0 34.0	4 11.2	5 41.6	20 4.7
21 F	13 53 34.8	0♉13.2	6 38.1	20 26.7	4 54.6	10 20.0	23 2.3	9 57.4	0 38.8	4 10.6	5 42.7	20 5.7
22 S	13 57 31.3	1 11.7	6 35.0	5♐12.1	4 17.4	9 46.1	22 48.4	10 11.6	0 43.5	4 10.0	5 43.8	20 6.6
23 S	14 1 27.9	2 10.1	6 31.8	19 32.0	3 38.2	9 11.0	22 33.8	10 25.9	0 48.2	4 9.3	5 45.0	20 7.6
24 M	14 5 24.5	3 8.6	6 28.6	3♑22.9	2 57.8	8 34.9	22 18.6	10 40.1	0 52.8	4 8.5	5 46.2	20 8.6
25 T	14 9 21.0	4 7.0	6 25.4	16 44.4	2 17.0	7 58.0	22 2.7	10 54.4	0 57.3	4 7.8	5 47.4	20 9.7
26 W	14 13 17.5	5 5.3	6 22.3	29 38.5	1 36.4	7 20.5	21 46.1	11 8.7	1 1.8	4 6.9	5 48.7	20 10.7
27 T	14 17 14.1	6 3.7	6 19.1	12♒ 9.4	0 56.9	6 42.7	21 29.0	11 22.9	1 6.1	4 6.0	5 50.0	20 11.7
28 F	14 21 10.7	7 2.0	6 15.9	24 21.7	0 19.0	6 44.9	21 11.3	11 37.2	1 10.5	4 5.1	5 51.3	20 12.8
29 S	14 25 7.2	8 0.3	6 12.7	6♓20.8	29♈43.5	5 27.3	20 53.1	11 51.5	1 14.7	4 4.1	5 52.7	20 13.9
30 S	14 29 3.8	8 58.6	6 9.5	18 11.6	29 10.8	4 50.0	20 34.3	12 5.8	1 18.8	4 3.1	5 54.0	20 15.0
						DECLINATION						
1 S	12 34 43.7	4N11.9	8N41.2	11S21.5	13N 5.7	22N14.5	17S42.0	12N23.4	13S 2.3	23S37.1	22N21.7	14N53.9
4 T	12 46 33.4	5 21.2	8 44.8	0 44.7	14 46.6	22 34.1	17 45.7	12 37.4	12 56.5	23 37.2	22 21.8	14 54.6
7 F	12 58 23.0	6 29.6	8 48.3	10N 7.7	15 59.5	22 44.2	17 48.1	12 51.4	12 50.8	23 37.2	22 21.8	14 55.4
10 M	13 10 12.7	7 37.1	8 51.8	17 30.9	16 42.6	22 44.0	17 49.3	13 5.3	12 45.4	23 37.3	22 21.8	14 56.2
13 T	13 22 2.4	8 43.4	8 55.4	17 47.9	16 54.7	22 32.2	17 49.2	13 19.2	12 40.1	23 37.4	22 21.8	14 56.9
16 S	13 33 52.0	9 48.3	8 58.9	9 19.1	16 36.1	22 8.1	17 47.8	13 33.0	12 35.0	23 37.4	22 21.9	14 57.7
19 W	13 45 41.7	10 51.8	9 2.4	4S42.4	15 49.0	21 31.4	17 45.1	13 46.8	12 30.1	23 37.5	22 21.8	14 58.4
22 S	13 57 31.3	11 53.7	9 6.0	16 9.0	14 38.7	20 42.6	17 41.2	14 0.4	12 25.5	23 37.7	22 21.8	14 59.2
25 T	14 9 21.0	12 53.8	9 9.5	18 27.4	13 13.7	19 43.1	17 36.0	14 14.0	12 21.1	23 37.8	22 21.8	14 59.9
28 F	14 21 10.7	13 52.0	9 13.0	12 18.0	11 44.8	18 35.4	17 29.5	14 27.4	12 16.9	23 37.9	22 21.7	15 0.6

MAY 1905

DAY	EPHEMERIS SIDEREAL TIME	☉	☊	☽	☿	♀	♂	♃	♄	♅	♆	♇
	h m s	° ′	° ′	° ′	° ′	° ′	° ′	° ′	° ′	° ′	° ′	° ′
						LONGITUDE						
1 M	14 33 0.3	9♉56.8	6♍ 6.4	29♓58.8	28♈41.4	4♉13.5	20♏15.1	12♉20.1	1♓22.9	4♑ 2.1	5♋55.4	20♊16.1
2 T	14 36 56.9	10 55.1	6 3.2	11♈46.1	28R15.8	3R37.9	19R55.4	12 34.4	1 26.9	4R 1.0	5 56.9	20 17.2
3 W	14 40 53.4	11 53.3	6 0.0	23 36.7	27 54.2	3 3.4	19 35.3	12 48.7	1 30.8	3 59.8	5 58.3	20 18.3
4 T	14 44 50.0	12 51.4	5 56.8	5♉33.0	27 37.0	2 30.2	19 14.9	13 3.0	1 34.6	3 58.6	5 59.8	20 19.5
5 F	14 48 46.5	13 49.6	5 53.7	17 36.7	27 24.2	1 58.5	18 54.1	13 17.4	1 38.3	3 57.4	6 1.3	20 20.6
6 S	14 52 43.1	14 47.7	5 50.5	29 49.1	27 16.1	1 28.5	18 33.0	13 31.7	1 42.0	3 56.1	6 2.8	20 21.8
7 S	14 56 39.7	15 45.8	5 47.3	12♊10.9	27 12.6	1 0.3	18 11.7	13 46.0	1 45.6	3 54.8	6 4.4	20 23.0
8 M	15 0 36.2	16 43.8	5 44.1	24 43.0	27D13.9	0 34.1	17 50.2	14 0.2	1 49.1	3 53.4	6 5.9	20 24.2
9 T	15 4 32.8	17 41.8	5 40.9	7♋26.5	27 19.9	0 10.0	17 28.5	14 14.5	1 52.5	3 52.0	6 7.5	20 25.4
10 W	15 8 29.3	18 39.8	5 37.8	20 22.7	27 30.5	29♈48.0	17 6.7	14 28.8	1 55.8	3 50.5	6 9.2	20 26.6
11 T	15 12 25.9	19 37.8	5 34.6	3♌33.4	27 45.7	29 28.3	16 44.9	14 43.1	1 59.0	3 49.0	6 10.8	20 27.9
12 F	15 16 22.4	20 35.7	5 31.4	17 0.7	28 5.3	29 10.9	16 23.1	14 57.3	2 2.2	3 47.5	6 12.5	20 29.1
13 S	15 20 19.0	21 33.6	5 28.2	0♍46.5	28 29.4	28 55.9	16 1.3	15 11.6	2 5.2	3 46.0	6 14.2	20 30.4
14 S	15 24 15.5	22 31.5	5 25.1	14 51.8	28 57.6	28 43.3	15 39.6	15 25.8	2 8.2	3 44.3	6 15.9	20 31.6
15 M	15 28 12.1	23 29.3	5 21.9	29 16.5	29 30.0	28 33.1	15 18.0	15 40.0	2 11.1	3 42.7	6 17.6	20 32.9
16 T	15 32 8.6	24 27.1	5 18.7	13♎58.1	0♉ 6.3	28 25.3	14 56.6	15 54.2	2 13.9	3 41.0	6 19.3	20 34.2
17 W	15 36 5.2	25 24.9	5 15.5	28 51.6	0 46.6	28 19.9	14 35.4	16 8.4	2 16.6	3 39.3	6 21.1	20 35.4
18 T	15 40 1.8	26 22.7	5 12.4	13♏49.6	1 30.5	28 17.0	14 14.5	16 22.6	2 19.2	3 37.6	6 22.9	20 36.7
19 F	15 43 58.3	27 20.4	5 9.2	28 43.1	2 18.1	28 16.4	13 53.8	16 36.7	2 21.7	3 35.8	6 24.7	20 38.0
20 S	15 47 54.9	28 18.1	5 6.0	13♐22.9	3 9.2	28D18.1	13 33.5	16 50.8	2 24.1	3 34.0	6 26.5	20 39.4
21 S	15 51 51.4	29 15.8	5 2.8	27 41.6	4 3.6	28 22.2	13 13.6	17 5.0	2 26.5	3 32.1	6 28.4	20 40.7
22 M	15 55 48.0	0♊13.5	4 59.6	11♑34.3	5 1.3	28 28.5	12 54.1	17 19.1	2 28.7	3 30.2	6 30.3	20 42.0
23 T	15 59 44.5	1 11.2	4 56.5	24 59.0	6 2.3	28 37.0	12 35.0	17 33.1	2 30.9	3 28.3	6 32.1	20 43.3
24 W	16 3 41.0	2 8.8	4 53.3	7♒56.7	7 6.3	28 47.7	12 16.4	17 47.2	2 32.9	3 26.4	6 34.0	20 44.7
25 T	16 7 37.6	3 6.4	4 50.1	20 30.5	8 13.3	29 0.4	11 58.3	18 1.2	2 34.9	3 24.4	6 36.0	20 46.0
26 F	16 11 34.2	4 4.0	4 46.9	2♓44.9	9 23.3	29 15.2	11 40.8	18 15.2	2 36.8	3 22.4	6 37.9	20 47.4
27 S	16 15 30.8	5 1.6	4 43.8	14 45.2	10 36.1	29 32.0	11 23.8	18 29.2	2 38.5	3 20.4	6 39.8	20 48.7
28 S	16 19 27.3	5 59.2	4 40.6	26 36.9	11 51.8	29 50.6	11 7.5	18 43.1	2 40.2	3 18.3	6 41.8	20 50.1
29 M	16 23 23.8	6 56.7	4 37.4	8♈25.0	13 10.2	0♉11.1	10 51.8	18 57.0	2 41.8	3 16.2	6 43.8	20 51.5
30 T	16 27 20.4	7 54.3	4 34.2	20 14.5	14 31.4	0 33.4	10 36.8	19 10.9	2 43.3	3 14.1	6 45.8	20 52.9
31 W	16 31 17.0	8 51.8	4 31.1	2♉ 9.3	15 55.3	0 57.4	10 22.5	19 24.8	2 44.7	3 12.0	6 47.8	20 54.2
						DECLINATION						
1 M	14 33 0.3	14N48.2	9N16.5	1S47.6	10N22.9	17N22.9	17S21.9	14N40.7	12S13.0	23S38.1	22N21.6	15N 1.4
4 T	14 44 50.0	15 42.2	9 20.0	9N19.0	9 16.4	16 9.0	17 13.2	14 53.9	12 9.3	23 38.3	22 21.6	15 2.1
7 S	14 56 39.7	16 33.9	9 23.5	17 17.5	8 30.5	14 57.6	17 3.6	15 6.9	12 5.9	23 38.4	22 21.4	15 2.7
10 W	15 8 29.3	17 23.1	9 27.1	18 19.1	8 7.1	13 51.5	16 53.4	15 19.7	12 2.8	23 38.6	22 21.3	15 3.4
13 S	15 20 19.0	18 9.7	9 30.6	10 45.8	8 6.1	12 53.3	16 42.7	15 32.4	11 60.0	23 38.8	22 21.2	15 4.1
16 T	15 32 8.6	18 53.5	9 34.1	2S39.0	8 25.8	12 4.4	16 32.0	15 44.8	11 57.4	23 39.0	22 21.0	15 4.7
19 F	15 43 58.3	19 34.4	9 37.5	15 1.2	9 4.1	11 25.7	16 21.4	15 57.1	11 55.2	23 39.2	22 20.9	15 5.3
22 M	15 55 48.0	20 12.4	9 41.0	18 55.0	9 58.5	10 57.2	16 11.4	16 9.1	11 53.2	23 39.4	22 20.7	15 5.9
25 T	16 7 37.6	20 47.2	9 44.5	13 28.1	11 6.7	10 38.7	16 2.1	16 21.0	11 51.6	23 39.6	22 20.5	15 6.4
28 S	16 19 27.3	21 18.9	9 48.0	3 4.0	12 26.2	10 29.6	15 53.9	16 32.6	11 50.2	23 39.8	22 20.3	15 7.0
31 W	16 31 17.0	21 47.2	9 51.5	8N14.7	13 54.6	10 29.0	15 47.0	16 44.0	11 49.2	23 40.0	22 20.0	15 7.5

JUNE 1905

DAY	EPHEMERIS SIDEREAL TIME	☉	☊	☽	☿	♀	♂	♃	♄	♅	♆	♇
						LONGITUDE						
1 T	16 35 13.5	9♊49.3	4♍27.9	14♉12.5	17♉21.8	1♉23.0	10♏ 8.9	19♉38.6	2♓46.0	3♑ 9.9	6♋49.8	20♊55.6
2 F	16 39 10.1	10 46.8	4 24.7	26 26.2	18 51.0	1 50.2	9R56.0	19 52.4	2 47.2	3R 7.7	6 51.9	20 57.0
3 S	16 43 6.6	11 44.3	4 21.5	8♊51.8	20 22.8	2 18.9	9 43.9	20 6.1	2 48.2	3 5.5	6 53.9	20 58.4
4 S	16 47 3.2	12 41.8	4 18.3	21 29.6	21 57.2	2 49.1	9 32.5	20 19.8	2 49.2	3 3.2	6 56.0	20 59.8
5 M	16 50 59.7	13 39.2	4 15.2	4♋19.4	23 34.2	3 20.7	9 22.0	20 33.5	2 50.1	3 1.0	6 58.1	21 1.2
6 T	16 54 56.3	14 36.7	4 12.0	17 20.9	25 13.7	3 53.6	9 12.2	20 47.2	2 50.9	2 58.7	7 0.2	21 2.6
7 W	16 58 52.9	15 34.1	4 8.8	0♌33.7	26 55.9	4 27.9	9 3.3	21 0.8	2 51.6	2 56.5	7 2.3	21 4.0
8 T	17 2 49.4	16 31.5	4 5.6	13 57.7	28 40.5	5 3.4	8 55.2	21 14.3	2 52.2	2 54.2	7 4.4	21 5.4
9 F	17 6 45.9	17 28.9	4 2.5	27 33.3	0♊27.8	5 40.1	8 47.9	21 27.8	2 52.7	2 51.8	7 6.5	21 6.8
10 S	17 10 42.5	18 26.2	3 59.3	11♍21.0	2 17.5	6 18.0	8 41.4	21 41.3	2 53.1	2 49.5	7 8.6	21 8.2
11 S	17 14 39.1	19 23.6	3 56.1	25 21.3	4 9.6	6 56.9	8 35.8	21 54.7	2 53.4	2 47.2	7 10.8	21 9.6
12 M	17 18 35.7	20 20.9	3 52.9	9♎33.9	6 4.2	7 37.0	8 31.0	22 8.1	2 53.6	2 44.8	7 12.9	21 11.1
13 T	17 22 32.2	21 18.2	3 49.7	23 57.4	8 1.1	8 18.1	8 27.1	22 21.4	2 53.7	2 42.4	7 15.1	21 12.5
14 W	17 26 28.8	22 15.5	3 46.6	8♏28.6	10 0.2	9 0.1	8 24.0	22 34.7	2 53.8	2 40.1	7 17.2	21 13.9
15 T	17 30 25.3	23 12.8	3 43.4	23 2.6	12 1.5	9 43.2	8 21.7	22 47.9	2R53.7	2 37.7	7 19.4	21 15.3
16 F	17 34 21.9	24 10.1	3 40.2	7♐33.1	14 4.7	10 27.1	8 20.2	23 1.1	2 53.5	2 35.3	7 21.6	21 16.7
17 S	17 38 18.4	25 7.3	3 37.0	21 53.4	16 9.8	11 12.0	8 19.6	23 14.2	2 53.2	2 32.9	7 23.8	21 18.1
18 S	17 42 15.0	26 4.6	3 33.9	5♑57.2	18 16.6	11 57.7	8D19.7	23 27.3	2 52.8	2 30.4	7 26.0	21 19.5
19 M	17 46 11.5	27 1.8	3 30.7	19 39.9	20 24.8	12 44.3	8 20.7	23 40.3	2 52.3	2 28.0	7 28.2	21 20.9
20 T	17 50 8.1	27 59.1	3 27.5	2♒59.2	22 34.1	13 31.6	8 22.4	23 53.3	2 51.8	2 25.6	7 30.4	21 22.3
21 W	17 54 4.6	28 56.3	3 24.3	15 54.8	24 44.4	14 19.7	8 25.0	24 6.2	2 51.1	2 23.2	7 32.6	21 23.7
22 T	17 58 1.2	29 53.5	3 21.2	28 28.8	26 55.4	15 8.6	8 28.3	24 19.1	2 50.3	2 20.7	7 34.8	21 25.1
23 F	18 1 57.8	0♋50.8	3 18.0	10♓44.6	29 6.8	15 58.1	8 32.4	24 31.9	2 49.4	2 18.3	7 37.0	21 26.5
24 S	18 5 54.3	1 48.0	3 14.8	22 46.8	1♋18.2	16 48.4	8 37.2	24 44.6	2 48.5	2 15.9	7 39.3	21 27.9
25 S	18 9 50.9	2 45.2	3 11.6	4♈40.3	3 29.5	17 39.3	8 42.9	24 57.3	2 47.4	2 13.4	7 41.5	21 29.3
26 M	18 13 47.4	3 42.4	3 8.5	16 30.6	5 40.4	18 30.9	8 49.2	25 9.9	2 46.3	2 11.0	7 43.7	21 30.7
27 T	18 17 44.0	4 39.6	3 5.3	28 22.6	7 50.5	19 23.0	8 56.3	25 22.4	2 45.0	2 8.5	7 45.9	21 32.1
28 W	18 21 40.6	5 36.9	3 2.1	10♉21.1	9 59.8	20 15.8	9 4.2	25 34.9	2 43.7	2 6.1	7 48.2	21 33.4
29 T	18 25 37.1	6 34.1	2 58.9	22 29.9	12 8.0	21 9.1	9 12.7	25 47.3	2 42.2	2 3.7	7 50.4	21 34.8
30 F	18 29 33.7	7 31.3	2 55.7	4♊52.1	14 14.8	22 3.0	9 22.0	25 59.6	2 40.7	2 1.2	7 52.6	21 36.2
						DECLINATION						
1 T	16 35 13.5	21N55.9	9N52.6	11N36.8	14N25.6	10N30.6	15S45.0	16N47.7	11S49.0	23S40.1	22N20.0	15N 7.7
4 S	16 47 3.2	22 19.7	9 56.1	18 24.8	16 2.0	10 40.0	15 40.2	16 58.8	11 48.4	23 40.3	22 19.7	15 8.2
7 W	16 58 52.9	22 40.0	9 59.6	17 22.3	17 41.1	10 55.8	15 37.2	17 9.6	11 48.1	23 40.5	22 19.5	15 8.6
10 S	17 10 42.5	22 56.7	10 3.0	7 58.4	19 19.5	11 17.2	15 36.2	17 20.2	11 48.2	23 40.6	22 19.2	15 9.1
13 T	17 22 32.2	23 9.8	10 6.5	5S39.2	20 53.0	11 43.2	15 37.1	17 30.5	11 48.5	23 40.8	22 18.9	15 9.5
16 F	17 34 21.9	23 19.2	10 10.0	16 37.3	22 16.8	12 13.2	15 40.1	17 40.5	11 49.2	23 41.0	22 18.6	15 9.9
19 M	17 46 11.5	23 24.9	10 13.4	18 36.6	23 25.4	12 46.4	15 45.1	17 50.2	11 50.3	23 41.2	22 18.3	15 10.2
22 T	17 58 1.2	23 26.9	10 16.9	11 42.2	24 13.7	13 22.1	15 52.0	17 59.7	11 51.6	23 41.4	22 17.9	15 10.5
25 S	18 9 50.9	23 25.2	10 20.3	0 40.1	24 38.2	13 59.6	16 0.9	18 8.9	11 53.2	23 41.5	22 17.6	15 10.8
28 W	18 21 40.6	23 19.8	10 23.7	10N25.5	24 37.3	14 38.4	16 11.6	18 17.8	11 55.2	23 41.7	22 17.2	15 11.1

JULY 1905

LONGITUDE

DAY	EPHEMERIS SIDEREAL TIME h m s	☉ ° ′	☊ ° ′	☽ ° ′	☿ ° ′	♀ ° ′	♂ ° ′	♃ ° ′	♄ ° ′	♅ ° ′	♆ ° ′	♇ ° ′
1 S	18 33 30.2	8♋28.5	2♍52.6	17♊29.7	16♋20.2	22♉57.4	9♏32.0	26♉11.9	2♓39.0	1♑58.8	7♋54.9	21♊37.5
2 S	18 37 26.8	9 25.8	2 49.4	0♋23.1	18 24.1	23 52.3	9 42.7	26 24.1	2R37.3	1R56.4	7 57.1	21 38.9
3 M	18 41 23.3	10 23.0	2 46.2	13 32.2	20 26.2	24 47.7	9 54.0	26 36.2	2 35.5	1 54.0	7 59.3	21 40.2
4 T	18 45 19.9	11 20.2	2 43.0	26 55.6	22 26.6	25 43.5	10 6.1	26 48.3	2 33.6	1 51.6	8 1.6	21 41.6
5 W	18 49 16.5	12 17.4	2 39.9	10♌31.3	24 25.2	26 39.8	10 18.8	27 0.2	2 31.6	1 49.2	8 3.8	21 42.9
6 T	18 53 13.0	13 14.6	2 36.7	24 17.2	26 21.9	27 36.6	10 32.1	27 12.1	2 29.5	1 46.8	8 6.0	21 44.2
7 F	18 57 9.5	14 11.9	2 33.5	8♍11.6	28 16.8	28 33.7	10 46.1	27 23.9	2 27.4	1 44.4	8 8.3	21 45.6
8 S	19 1 6.1	15 9.1	2 30.3	22 12.7	0♌ 9.6	29 31.3	11 0.7	27 35.7	2 25.1	1 42.1	8 10.5	21 46.9
9 S	19 5 2.7	16 6.3	2 27.2	6♎19.0	2 0.6	0♊29.3	11 16.0	27 47.3	2 22.8	1 39.8	8 12.7	21 48.2
10 M	19 8 59.3	17 3.5	2 24.0	20 29.4	3 49.6	1 27.7	11 31.8	27 58.9	2 20.3	1 37.4	8 14.9	21 49.5
11 T	19 12 55.8	18 0.7	2 20.8	4♏42.1	5 36.6	2 26.4	11 48.2	28 10.4	2 17.8	1 35.1	8 17.1	21 50.8
12 W	19 16 52.3	18 57.9	2 17.6	18 54.9	7 21.6	3 25.5	12 5.3	28 21.8	2 15.2	1 32.8	8 19.3	21 52.0
13 T	19 20 48.9	19 55.1	2 14.4	3♐ 4.9	9 4.7	4 25.0	12 22.8	28 33.1	2 12.6	1 30.5	8 21.5	21 53.3
14 F	19 24 45.5	20 52.3	2 11.3	17 8.5	10 45.9	5 24.8	12 41.0	28 44.3	2 9.8	1 28.3	8 23.7	21 54.6
15 S	19 28 42.1	21 49.5	2 8.1	1♑ 2.1	12 25.1	6 24.9	12 59.7	28 55.4	2 7.0	1 26.0	8 25.9	21 55.8
16 S	19 32 38.6	22 46.8	2 4.9	14 41.8	14 2.3	7 25.4	13 18.9	29 6.4	2 4.1	1 23.8	8 28.1	21 57.1
17 M	19 36 35.1	23 44.0	2 1.7	28 5.0	15 37.6	8 26.2	13 38.6	29 17.4	2 1.1	1 21.6	8 30.3	21 58.3
18 T	19 40 31.7	24 41.2	1 58.6	11♒ 9.8	17 10.9	9 27.3	13 58.8	29 28.2	1 58.1	1 19.4	8 32.4	21 59.5
19 W	19 44 28.2	25 38.4	1 55.4	23 56.1	18 42.2	10 28.7	14 19.6	29 39.0	1 54.9	1 17.3	8 34.6	22 0.7
20 T	19 48 24.8	26 35.7	1 52.2	6♓24.8	20 11.6	11 30.4	14 40.8	29 49.6	1 51.7	1 15.2	8 36.7	22 1.9
21 F	19 52 21.4	27 32.9	1 49.0	18 38.4	21 39.0	12 32.4	15 2.5	0♊ 0.2	1 48.5	1 13.1	8 38.9	22 3.1
22 S	19 56 17.9	28 30.2	1 45.9	0♈40.3	23 4.3	13 34.7	15 24.7	0 10.6	1 45.1	1 11.0	8 41.0	22 4.3
23 S	20 0 14.5	29 27.5	1 42.7	12 34.6	24 27.6	14 37.2	15 47.4	0 21.0	1 41.7	1 8.9	8 43.1	22 5.5
24 M	20 4 11.0	0♌24.8	1 39.5	24 25.8	25 48.8	15 40.0	16 10.5	0 31.2	1 38.2	1 6.9	8 45.2	22 6.6
25 T	20 8 7.6	1 22.1	1 36.3	6♉19.0	27 7.9	16 43.1	16 34.0	0 41.3	1 34.7	1 4.9	8 47.3	22 7.7
26 W	20 12 4.1	2 19.4	1 33.1	18 18.9	28 24.8	17 46.4	16 58.0	0 51.4	1 31.1	1 2.9	8 49.4	22 8.9
27 T	20 16 0.7	3 16.8	1 30.0	0♊30.1	29 39.5	18 50.0	17 22.4	1 1.3	1 27.4	1 1.0	8 51.5	22 10.0
28 F	20 19 57.3	4 14.1	1 26.8	12 56.4	0♍52.0	19 53.8	17 47.3	1 11.1	1 23.7	0 59.1	8 53.5	22 11.1
29 S	20 23 53.8	5 11.5	1 23.6	25 40.8	2 2.1	20 57.8	18 12.6	1 20.8	1 19.9	0 57.2	8 55.6	22 12.2
30 S	20 27 50.4	6 8.9	1 20.4	8♋45.0	3 9.7	22 2.1	18 38.2	1 30.4	1 16.1	0 55.3	8 57.6	22 13.2
31 M	20 31 46.9	7 6.3	1 17.3	22 9.4	4 14.9	23 6.6	19 4.3	1 39.8	1 12.2	0 53.5	8 59.6	22 14.3

DECLINATION

DAY	EPHEMERIS SIDEREAL TIME h m s	☉ ° ′	☊ ° ′	☽ ° ′	☿ ° ′	♀ ° ′	♂ ° ′	♃ ° ′	♄ ° ′	♅ ° ′	♆ ° ′	♇ ° ′
1 S	18 33 30.2	23N10.7	10N27.2	17N58.7	24N12.1	15N17.9	16S24.0	18N26.5	11S57.4	23S41.8	22N16.9	15N11.3
4 T	18 45 19.9	22 57.9	10 30.6	17 56.7	23 25.2	15 57.4	16 38.0	18 34.8	11 59.9	23 41.9	22 16.5	15 11.6
7 F	18 57 9.5	22 41.5	10 34.0	9 5.6	22 20.1	16 36.6	16 53.6	18 42.8	12 2.7	23 42.0	22 16.1	15 11.7
10 M	19 8 59.3	22 21.6	10 37.4	4S22.3	21 0.5	17 14.9	17 10.5	18 50.6	12 5.8	23 42.1	22 15.7	15 11.9
13 T	19 20 48.9	21 58.2	10 40.9	15 43.2	19 29.9	17 51.8	17 28.8	18 58.0	12 9.2	23 42.2	22 15.3	15 12.0
16 S	19 32 38.6	21 31.5	10 44.3	18 56.2	17 51.4	18 27.0	17 48.1	19 5.1	12 12.7	23 42.3	22 14.9	15 12.1
19 W	19 44 28.2	21 1.4	10 47.7	12 59.0	16 7.6	18 59.9	18 8.4	19 11.9	12 16.5	23 42.4	22 14.5	15 12.2
22 S	19 56 17.9	20 28.1	10 51.1	2 8.4	14 20.9	19 30.4	18 29.5	19 18.5	12 20.5	23 42.5	22 14.1	15 12.2
25 T	20 8 7.6	19 51.8	10 54.5	9N 7.6	12 33.4	19 57.9	18 51.3	19 24.7	12 24.7	23 42.5	22 13.7	15 12.2
28 F	20 19 57.3	19 12.4	10 57.9	17 17.6	10 47.3	20 22.1	19 13.6	19 30.6	12 29.1	23 42.6	22 13.2	15 12.2
31 M	20 31 46.9	18 30.2	11 1.3	18 25.5	9 4.5	20 42.7	19 36.4	19 36.2	12 33.6	23 42.6	22 12.8	15 12.1

AUGUST 1905

LONGITUDE

DAY	EPHEMERIS SIDEREAL TIME h m s	☉ ° ′	☊ ° ′	☽ ° ′	☿ ° ′	♀ ° ′	♂ ° ′	♃ ° ′	♄ ° ′	♅ ° ′	♆ ° ′	♇ ° ′
1 T	20 35 43.5	8♌ 3.7	1♍14.1	5♌52.7	5♍17.4	24♊11.2	19♏30.8	1♊49.2	1♓ 8.3	0♑51.7	9♋ 1.7	22♊15.3
2 W	20 39 40.0	9 1.2	1 10.9	19 52.3	6 17.2	25 16.1	19 57.7	1 58.4	1R 4.3	0R50.0	9 3.7	22 16.4
3 T	20 43 36.6	9 58.6	1 7.7	4♍ 4.3	7 14.2	26 21.2	20 25.0	2 7.5	1 0.2	0 48.3	9 5.6	22 17.4
4 F	20 47 33.1	10 56.1	1 4.5	18 24.4	8 8.2	27 26.5	20 52.6	2 16.5	0 56.1	0 46.6	9 7.6	22 18.4
5 S	20 51 29.7	11 53.6	1 1.4	2♎48.1	8 59.1	28 32.0	21 20.6	2 25.3	0 52.0	0 45.0	9 9.5	22 19.3
6 S	20 55 26.3	12 51.1	0 58.2	17 11.3	9 46.8	29 37.6	21 49.0	2 34.0	0 47.8	0 43.3	9 11.5	22 20.3
7 M	20 59 22.8	13 48.6	0 55.0	1♏30.4	10 31.1	0♋43.5	22 17.8	2 42.6	0 43.6	0 41.8	9 13.4	22 21.3
8 T	21 3 19.3	14 46.1	0 51.8	15 42.7	11 11.7	1 49.5	22 46.8	2 51.1	0 39.4	0 40.3	9 15.3	22 22.2
9 W	21 7 15.9	15 43.6	0 48.7	29 45.9	11 48.6	2 55.7	23 16.3	2 59.4	0 35.1	0 38.8	9 17.2	22 23.1
10 T	21 11 12.5	16 41.2	0 45.5	13♐38.5	12 21.5	4 2.1	23 46.0	3 7.6	0 30.8	0 37.3	9 19.0	22 24.0
11 F	21 15 9.0	17 38.7	0 42.3	27 19.1	12 50.2	5 8.6	24 16.1	3 15.7	0 26.5	0 35.9	9 20.9	22 24.9
12 S	21 19 5.6	18 36.3	0 39.1	10♑46.8	13 14.4	6 15.3	24 46.5	3 23.6	0 22.1	0 34.5	9 22.7	22 25.8
13 S	21 23 2.1	19 33.9	0 35.9	24 0.8	13 34.1	7 22.2	25 17.1	3 31.4	0 7.7	0 33.2	9 24.5	22 26.6
14 M	21 26 58.7	20 31.5	0 32.8	7♒ 0.5	13 49.0	8 29.3	25 48.1	3 39.0	0 13.3	0 31.9	9 26.3	22 27.4
15 T	21 30 55.3	21 29.1	0 29.6	19 46.0	13 58.8	9 36.5	26 19.4	3 46.5	0 8.8	0 30.7	9 28.1	22 28.2
16 W	21 34 51.8	22 26.8	0 26.4	2♓17.7	14 3.4	10 43.9	26 51.0	3 53.9	0 4.4	0 29.5	9 29.8	22 29.0
17 T	21 38 48.3	23 24.4	0 23.2	14 36.6	14R 2.5	11 51.4	27 22.9	4 1.1	29♒59.9	0 28.3	9 31.5	22 29.8
18 F	21 42 44.9	24 22.1	0 20.1	26 44.3	13 56.1	12 59.1	27 55.0	4 8.1	29 55.4	0 27.2	9 33.2	22 30.6
19 S	21 46 41.5	25 19.8	0 16.9	8♈43.2	13 43.9	14 6.9	28 27.5	4 15.0	29 50.9	0 26.1	9 34.9	22 31.3
20 S	21 50 38.0	26 17.6	0 13.7	20 36.4	13 26.1	15 14.9	29 0.2	4 21.8	29 46.4	0 25.1	9 36.6	22 32.0
21 M	21 54 34.6	27 15.4	0 10.5	2♉27.3	13 2.5	16 23.0	29 33.1	4 28.4	29 41.9	0 24.1	9 38.2	22 32.7
22 T	21 58 31.1	28 13.2	0 7.4	14 20.2	12 33.3	17 31.3	0♐ 6.4	4 34.9	29 37.3	0 23.2	9 39.8	22 33.4
23 W	22 2 27.7	29 11.0	0 4.2	26 19.3	11 58.6	18 39.8	0 39.9	4 41.2	29 32.8	0 22.3	9 41.4	22 34.1
24 T	22 6 24.2	0♍ 8.8	0 1.0	8♊29.2	11 18.9	19 48.3	1 13.6	4 47.3	29 28.2	0 21.5	9 43.0	22 34.7
25 F	22 10 20.8	1 6.7	29 57.8	20 54.5	10 34.5	20 57.0	1 47.6	4 53.3	29 23.7	0 20.7	9 44.5	22 35.4
26 S	22 14 17.3	2 4.6	29 54.6	3♋38.9	9 46.0	22 5.9	2 21.9	4 59.1	29 19.2	0 19.9	9 46.1	22 36.0
27 S	22 18 13.9	3 2.6	29 51.5	16 45.7	8 54.2	23 14.8	2 56.4	5 4.8	29 14.7	0 19.2	9 47.6	22 36.6
28 M	22 22 10.4	4 0.6	29 48.3	0♌16.5	8 0.0	24 24.0	3 31.1	5 10.3	29 10.1	0 18.6	9 49.0	22 37.1
29 T	22 26 7.0	4 58.6	29 45.1	14 11.5	7 4.4	25 33.2	4 6.1	5 15.6	29 5.6	0 18.0	9 50.5	22 37.7
30 W	22 30 3.6	5 56.6	29 41.9	28 28.3	6 8.3	26 42.5	4 41.3	5 20.7	29 1.1	0 17.4	9 51.9	22 38.2
31 T	22 34 0.1	6 54.7	29 38.8	13♍ 2.8	5 13.2	27 52.0	5 16.8	5 25.7	28 56.7	0 16.9	9 53.3	22 38.7

DECLINATION

DAY	EPHEMERIS SIDEREAL TIME h m s	☉ ° ′	☊ ° ′	☽ ° ′	☿ ° ′	♀ ° ′	♂ ° ′	♃ ° ′	♄ ° ′	♅ ° ′	♆ ° ′	♇ ° ′
1 T	20 35 43.5	18N15.5	11N 2.4	16N42.2	8N31.4	20N48.7	19S44.0	19N38.0	12S35.2	23S42.6	22N12.7	15N12.1
4 F	20 47 33.1	17 29.7	11 5.8	6 5.9	6 56.6	21 4.1	20 7.2	19 43.2	12 39.9	23 42.7	22 12.3	15 12.0
7 M	20 59 22.8	16 41.3	11 9.2	7S40.0	5 30.7	21 15.3	20 30.4	19 48.1	12 44.7	23 42.7	22 11.8	15 11.9
10 T	21 11 12.5	15 50.5	11 12.6	17 21.4	4 16.7	21 21.9	20 53.7	19 52.7	12 49.6	23 42.7	22 11.4	15 11.8
13 S	21 23 2.1	14 57.4	11 15.9	18 14.4	3 18.1	21 24.0	21 16.8	19 57.0	12 54.6	23 42.7	22 11.0	15 11.6
16 W	21 34 51.8	14 2.2	11 19.3	10 50.5	2 39.2	21 21.2	21 39.6	20 0.9	12 59.6	23 42.8	22 10.6	15 11.4
19 S	21 46 41.5	13 5.0	11 22.7	0N25.7	2 24.2	21 13.6	22 2.0	20 4.6	13 4.6	23 42.8	22 10.2	15 11.2
22 T	21 58 31.1	12 5.9	11 26.0	11 17.0	2 37.2	21 0.9	22 23.9	20 8.0	13 9.6	23 42.8	22 9.8	15 11.0
25 F	22 10 20.8	11 5.0	11 29.4	18 11.9	3 19.9	20 43.2	22 45.1	20 11.0	13 14.6	23 42.8	22 9.4	15 10.7
28 M	22 22 10.4	10 2.6	11 32.7	17 30.7	4 30.3	20 20.4	23 5.6	20 13.8	13 19.5	23 42.8	22 9.1	15 10.5
31 T	22 34 0.1	8 58.7	11 36.1	7 44.8	6 0.2	19 52.6	23 25.1	20 16.3	13 24.4	23 42.7	22 8.7	15 10.2

SEPTEMBER 1905

DAY	EPHEMERIS SIDEREAL TIME	☉	☊	☽	☿	♀	♂	♃	♄	♅	♆	♇
	h m s	° ′	° ′	° ′	° ′	° ′	° ′	° ′	° ′	° ′	° ′	° ′
						LONGITUDE						
1 F	22 37 56.6	7♍52.7	29♌35.6	27♍48.7	4♍20.0	29♋ 1.6	5♐52.4	5♊30.5	28♒52.2	0♑16.5	9♋54.7	22♊39.2
2 S	22 41 53.2	8 50.9	29 32.4	12♎38.8	3R30.1	0♌11.3	6 28.4	5 35.1	28R47.7	0R16.1	9 56.0	22 39.7
3 S	22 45 49.8	9 49.0	29 29.2	27 25.7	2 44.6	1 21.2	7 4.5	5 39.6	28 43.3	0 15.7	9 57.3	22 40.1
4 M	22 49 46.3	10 47.2	29 26.0	12♏ 2.7	2 4.5	2 31.1	7 40.8	5 43.9	28 38.9	0 15.4	9 58.6	22 40.5
5 T	22 53 42.8	11 45.3	29 22.9	26 25.0	1 30.9	3 41.1	8 17.4	5 47.9	28 34.6	0 15.1	9 59.9	22 40.9
6 W	22 57 39.4	12 43.5	29 19.7	10♐29.4	1 4.6	4 51.3	8 54.1	5 51.9	28 30.2	0 14.9	10 1.1	22 41.3
7 T	23 1 35.9	13 41.8	29 16.5	24 14.6	0 46.2	6 1.6	9 31.1	5 55.6	28 25.9	0 14.8	10 2.3	22 41.7
8 F	23 5 32.5	14 40.0	29 13.3	7♑41.1	0 36.3	7 11.9	10 8.3	5 59.1	28 21.7	0 14.7	10 3.5	22 42.0
9 S	23 9 29.0	15 38.3	29 10.2	20 49.8	0 35.2	8 22.4	10 45.6	6 2.5	28 17.4	0 14.6	10 4.6	22 42.3
10 S	23 13 25.6	16 36.6	29 7.0	3♒42.7	0D43.1	9 33.0	11 23.1	6 5.7	28 13.3	0 14.6	10 5.8	22 42.6
11 M	23 17 22.2	17 35.0	29 3.8	16 21.4	1 0.2	10 43.7	12 0.9	6 8.7	28 9.1	0D14.7	10 6.8	22 42.9
12 T	23 21 18.7	18 33.3	29 0.6	28 48.1	1 26.3	11 54.5	12 38.8	6 11.5	28 5.0	0 14.8	10 7.9	22 43.1
13 W	23 25 15.3	19 31.7	28 57.4	11♓ 4.3	2 1.2	13 5.4	13 16.9	6 14.1	28 0.9	0 14.9	10 8.9	22 43.4
14 T	23 29 11.8	20 30.2	28 54.3	23 11.7	2 44.6	14 16.4	13 55.1	6 16.5	27 56.9	0 15.1	10 9.9	22 43.6
15 F	23 33 8.4	21 28.6	28 51.1	5♈12.0	3 36.1	15 27.5	14 33.5	6 18.7	27 53.0	0 15.4	10 10.9	22 43.8
16 S	23 37 4.9	22 27.1	28 47.9	17 6.9	4 35.4	16 38.7	15 12.1	6 20.8	27 49.0	0 15.7	10 11.8	22 43.9
17 S	23 41 1.5	23 25.6	28 44.7	28 58.5	5 41.7	17 50.1	15 50.9	6 22.6	27 45.2	0 16.0	10 12.8	22 44.1
18 M	23 44 58.0	24 24.2	28 41.6	10♉49.2	6 54.6	19 1.5	16 29.9	6 24.3	27 41.4	0 16.5	10 13.6	22 44.2
19 T	23 48 54.6	25 22.8	28 38.4	22 41.9	8 13.5	20 13.0	17 8.9	6 25.7	27 37.6	0 16.9	10 14.5	22 44.3
20 W	23 52 51.1	26 21.4	28 35.2	4♊40.2	9 37.7	21 24.6	17 48.2	6 27.0	27 33.9	0 17.4	10 15.3	22 44.4
21 T	23 56 47.7	27 20.1	28 32.0	16 48.0	11 6.5	22 36.3	18 27.6	6 28.0	27 30.3	0 18.0	10 16.1	22 44.4
22 F	0 0 44.3	28 18.8	28 28.8	29 9.5	12 39.5	23 48.1	19 7.2	6 28.9	27 26.7	0 18.6	10 16.8	22 44.4
23 S	0 4 40.8	29 17.5	28 25.7	11♋49.1	14 15.9	24 60.0	19 46.9	6 29.6	27 23.2	0 19.2	10 17.6	22 44.5
24 S	0 8 37.4	0♎16.3	28 22.5	24 50.9	15 55.3	26 11.9	20 26.8	6 30.0	27 19.8	0 20.0	10 18.2	22R44.4
25 M	0 12 33.9	1 15.1	28 19.3	8♌18.1	17 37.1	27 24.0	21 6.8	6 30.3	27 16.4	0 20.7	10 18.9	22 44.4
26 T	0 16 30.5	2 13.9	28 16.1	22 12.7	19 20.9	28 36.1	21 47.0	6 30.3	27 13.1	0 21.5	10 19.5	22 44.4
27 W	0 20 27.0	3 12.8	28 12.9	6♍34.1	21 6.2	29 48.4	22 27.4	6R30.2	27 9.9	0 22.4	10 20.1	22 44.3
28 T	0 24 23.6	4 11.8	28 9.8	21 19.1	22 52.7	1♍ 0.7	23 7.8	6 29.9	27 6.7	0 23.3	10 20.7	22 44.2
29 F	0 28 20.1	5 10.7	28 6.6	6♎21.5	24 39.9	2 13.1	23 48.5	6 29.3	27 3.7	0 24.3	10 21.2	22 44.1
30 S	0 32 16.7	6 9.7	28 3.4	21 32.4	26 27.8	3 25.6	24 29.2	6 28.5	27 0.7	0 25.3	10 21.7	22 43.9

DAY	EPHEMERIS SIDEREAL TIME	☉	☊	☽	☿	♀	♂	♃	♄	♅	♆	♇
						DECLINATION						
1 F	22 37 56.6	8N37.1	11N37.2	3N 7.0	6N32.2	19N42.3	23S31.4	20N17.0	13S26.0	23S42.7	22N 8.6	15N10.1
4 M	22 49 46.3	7 31.5	11 40.5	10S40.6	8 6.9	19 7.8	23 49.6	20 19.1	13 30.8	23 42.7	22 8.2	15 9.7
7 T	23 1 35.9	6 24.9	11 43.9	18 30.4	9 27.6	18 28.6	24 6.6	20 20.8	13 35.4	23 42.7	22 7.9	15 9.4
10 S	23 13 25.6	5 17.2	11 47.2	17 2.1	10 22.1	17 44.6	24 22.4	20 22.3	13 39.8	23 42.7	22 7.6	15 9.1
13 W	23 25 15.3	4 8.8	11 50.5	8 19.9	10 43.0	16 56.1	24 36.8	20 23.4	13 44.1	23 42.7	22 7.3	15 8.7
16 S	23 37 4.9	2 59.8	11 53.8	3N11.0	10 27.8	16 3.3	24 49.8	20 24.3	13 48.3	23 42.7	22 7.0	15 8.3
19 T	23 48 54.6	1 50.2	11 57.1	13 26.1	9 37.8	15 6.2	25 1.1	20 24.9	13 52.2	23 42.7	22 6.7	15 7.9
22 F	0 0 44.3	0 40.3	12 0.4	18 53.1	8 17.6	14 5.2	25 10.8	20 25.1	13 55.9	23 42.6	22 6.5	15 7.5
25 M	0 12 33.9	0S29.9	12 3.8	16 20.0	6 33.8	13 0.5	25 18.8	20 25.1	13 59.4	23 42.6	22 6.3	15 7.1
28 T	0 24 23.6	1 40.1	12 7.1	5 11.4	4 33.2	11 52.4	25 24.9	20 24.8	14 2.6	23 42.6	22 6.1	15 6.7

OCTOBER 1905

DAY	EPHEMERIS SIDEREAL TIME	☉	☊	☽	☿	♀	♂	♃	♄	♅	♆	♇
						LONGITUDE						
1 S	0 36 13.2	7♎ 8.7	28♌ 0.2	6♏41.9	28♍15.9	4♍38.1	25♐10.1	6♊27.6	26♒57.7	0♑26.4	10♋22.1	22♊43.7
2 M	0 40 9.8	8 7.8	27 57.1	21 40.0	0♎ 4.1	5 50.8	25 51.2	6R26.4	26R54.9	0 27.5	10 22.6	22R43.6
3 T	0 44 6.3	9 6.9	27 53.9	6♐18.8	1 52.2	7 3.5	26 32.4	6 25.1	26 52.1	0 28.7	10 23.0	22 43.3
4 W	0 48 2.9	10 6.0	27 50.7	20 33.4	3 40.1	8 16.2	27 13.7	6 23.5	26 49.4	0 29.9	10 23.3	22 43.1
5 T	0 51 59.4	11 5.1	27 47.5	4♑21.9	5 27.6	9 29.1	27 55.1	6 21.7	26 46.8	0 31.1	10 23.6	22 42.9
6 F	0 55 56.0	12 4.3	27 44.3	17 44.9	7 14.7	10 42.0	28 36.7	6 19.8	26 44.3	0 32.5	10 23.9	22 42.6
7 S	0 59 52.6	13 3.5	27 41.2	0♒45.0	9 1.3	11 55.0	29 18.3	6 17.6	26 41.9	0 33.8	10 24.2	22 42.3
8 S	1 3 49.1	14 2.7	27 38.0	13 25.4	10 47.3	13 8.0	0♑ 0.1	6 15.3	26 39.6	0 35.2	10 24.4	22 42.0
9 M	1 7 45.6	15 2.0	27 34.8	25 50.2	12 32.7	14 21.1	0 42.0	6 12.7	26 37.3	0 36.7	10 24.6	22 41.6
10 T	1 11 42.2	16 1.3	27 31.6	8♓ 2.9	14 17.4	15 34.3	1 24.0	6 9.9	26 35.2	0 38.2	10 24.7	22 41.3
11 W	1 15 38.7	17 0.6	27 28.4	20 6.8	16 1.4	16 47.6	2 6.2	6 7.0	26 33.1	0 39.8	10 24.9	22 40.9
12 T	1 19 35.3	17 60.0	27 25.3	2♈ 4.6	17 44.8	18 0.9	2 48.4	6 3.9	26 31.1	0 41.4	10 25.0	22 40.5
13 F	1 23 31.9	18 59.4	27 22.1	13 58.6	19 27.5	19 14.3	3 30.8	6 0.5	26 29.3	0 43.0	10 25.0	22 40.1
14 S	1 27 28.4	19 58.8	27 18.9	25 50.6	21 9.4	20 27.7	4 13.2	5 57.0	26 27.5	0 44.7	10 25.0	22 39.6
15 S	1 31 24.9	20 58.3	27 15.7	7♉42.1	22 50.7	21 41.2	4 55.7	5 53.3	26 25.8	0 46.5	10R25.0	22 39.2
16 M	1 35 21.5	21 57.8	27 12.6	19 34.7	24 31.3	22 54.8	5 38.4	5 49.4	26 24.2	0 48.2	10 25.0	22 38.7
17 T	1 39 18.1	22 57.3	27 9.4	1♊30.3	26 11.2	24 8.4	6 21.1	5 45.3	26 22.7	0 50.1	10 24.9	22 38.2
18 W	1 43 14.6	23 56.9	27 6.2	13 31.1	27 50.5	25 22.1	7 4.0	5 41.1	26 21.3	0 52.0	10 24.8	22 37.7
19 T	1 47 11.2	24 56.5	27 3.0	25 39.9	29 29.1	26 35.9	7 46.9	5 36.6	26 20.0	0 53.9	10 24.6	22 37.1
20 F	1 51 7.7	25 56.1	26 59.8	8♋ 0.0	1♏ 7.1	27 49.7	8 30.0	5 32.0	26 18.8	0 55.9	10 24.4	22 36.6
21 S	1 55 . 4.3	26 55.8	26 56.7	20 35.5	2 44.5	29 3.6	9 13.1	5 27.2	26 17.7	0 57.9	10 24.2	22 36.0
22 S	1 59 0.8	27 55.5	26 53.5	3♌30.3	4 21.2	0♎17.5	9 56.3	5 22.2	26 16.6	0 59.9	10 24.0	22 35.4
23 M	2 2 57.4	28 55.2	26 50.3	16 48.0	5 57.4	1 31.5	10 39.6	5 17.1	26 15.7	1 2.0	10 23.7	22 34.8
24 T	2 6 53.9	29 55.0	26 47.1	0♍33.5	7 33.1	2 45.5	11 23.1	5 11.8	26 14.9	1 4.2	10 23.4	22 34.1
25 W	2 10 50.5	0♏54.9	26 44.0	14 46.3	9 8.1	3 59.6	12 6.6	5 6.3	26 14.2	1 6.3	10 23.0	22 33.5
26 T	2 14 47.1	1 54.7	26 40.8	29 26.1	10 42.7	5 13.7	12 50.1	5 0.7	26 13.6	1 8.6	10 22.7	22 32.8
27 F	2 18 43.6	2 54.6	26 37.6	14♎28.2	12 16.7	6 27.9	13 33.8	4 54.9	26 13.1	1 10.8	10 22.2	22 32.1
28 S	2 22 40.1	3 54.6	26 34.4	29 44.6	13 50.3	7 42.2	14 17.6	4 48.9	26 12.7	1 13.1	10 21.8	22 31.4
29 S	2 26 36.7	4 54.5	26 31.2	15♏ 4.6	15 23.3	8 56.4	15 1.4	4 42.8	26 12.4	1 15.5	10 21.3	22 30.7
30 M	2 30 33.3	5 54.5	26 28.1	0♐16.7	16 55.9	10 10.8	15 45.3	4 36.6	26 12.2	1 17.9	10 20.8	22 29.9
31 T	2 34 29.8	6 54.6	26 24.9	15 10.3	18 28.0	11 25.1	16 29.3	4 30.2	26 12.1	1 20.3	10 20.2	22 29.2

DAY	EPHEMERIS SIDEREAL TIME	☉	☊	☽	☿	♀	♂	♃	♄	♅	♆	♇
						DECLINATION						
1 S	0 36 13.2	2S50.2	12N10.3	9S15.0	2N22.1	10N41.0	25S29.1	20N24.2	14S 5.5	23S42.6	22N 5.9	15N 6.3
4 W	0 48 2.9	4 0.1	12 13.6	18 17.7	0 5.5	9 26.8	25 31.4	20 23.2	14 8.2	23 42.6	22 5.7	15 5.9
7 S	0 59 52.6	5 9.5	12 16.9	17 34.0	2S12.9	8 10.0	25 31.6	20 22.0	14 10.7	23 42.5	22 5.6	15 5.5
10 T	1 11 42.2	6 18.3	12 20.2	9 16.1	4 30.4	6 51.0	25 29.8	20 20.5	14 12.8	23 42.5	22 5.5	15 5.0
13 F	1 23 31.9	7 26.4	12 23.5	2N11.8	6 45.2	5 29.9	25 25.8	20 18.7	14 14.6	23 42.5	22 5.4	15 4.6
16 M	1 35 21.5	8 33.6	12 26.7	12 47.7	8 56.0	4 7.1	25 19.6	20 16.6	14 16.1	23 42.4	22 5.3	15 4.2
19 T	1 47 11.2	9 39.6	12 30.0	18 51.2	11 1.7	2 42.9	25 11.2	20 14.3	14 17.3	23 42.4	22 5.3	15 3.8
22 S	1 59 0.8	10 44.4	12 33.3	17 17.8	13 1.6	1 17.6	25 0.7	20 11.7	14 18.2	23 42.3	22 5.3	15 3.3
25 W	2 10 50.5	11 47.8	12 36.5	7 20.0	14 55.1	0S 8.4	24 47.8	20 8.8	14 18.8	23 42.2	22 5.3	15 2.9
28 S	2 22 40.1	12 49.6	12 39.8	7S13.0	16 41.5	1 34.8	24 32.8	20 5.6	14 19.0	23 42.2	22 5.3	15 2.5
31 T	2 34 29.8	13 49.6	12 43.0	17 50.8	18 20.4	3 1.4	24 15.5	20 2.2	14 19.0	23 42.1	22 5.4	15 2.1

NOVEMBER 1905

DAY	EPHEMERIS SIDEREAL TIME h m s	☉ ° ′	☊ ° ′	☽ ° ′	☿ ° ′	♀ ° ′	♂ ° ′	♃ ° ′	♄ ° ′	♅ ° ′	♆ ° ′	♇ ° ′
LONGITUDE												
1 W	2 38 26.4	7♏54.6	26♌21.7	29♐38.1	19♏59.6	12♎39.5	17♑13.4	4♊23.7	26♒12.2	1♑22.8	10♋19.7	22♊28.4
2 T	2 42 22.9	8 54.7	26 18.5	13♑36.3	21 30.8	13 54.0	17 57.6	4R17.0	26D12.3	1 25.3	10R19.0	22R27.6
3 F	2 46 19.5	9 54.8	26 15.4	27 4.8	23 1.6	15 8.4	18 41.8	4 10.3	26 12.5	1 27.8	10 18.4	22 26.8
4 S	2 50 16.0	10 55.0	26 12.2	10♒6.0	24 31.9	16 23.0	19 26.1	4 3.4	26 12.8	1 30.4	10 17.7	22 25.9
5 S	2 54 12.6	11 55.1	26 9.0	22 43.9	26 1.7	17 37.5	20 10.5	3 56.4	26 13.3	1 33.0	10 17.0	22 25.1
6 M	2 58 9.1	12 55.3	26 5.8	5♓3.4	27 31.1	18 52.1	20 54.9	3 49.2	26 13.8	1 35.7	10 16.3	22 24.2
7 T	3 2 5.7	13 55.5	26 2.6	17 9.5	29 0.0	20 6.7	21 39.4	3 42.0	26 14.4	1 38.4	10 15.5	22 23.3
8 W	3 6 2.2	14 55.8	25 59.5	29 6.7	0♐28.5	21 21.4	22 23.9	3 34.7	26 15.2	1 41.1	10 14.7	22 22.5
9 T	3 9 58.8	15 56.0	25 56.3	10♈59.0	1 56.4	22 36.1	23 8.5	3 27.2	26 16.0	1 43.9	10 13.9	22 21.6
10 F	3 13 55.3	16 56.3	25 53.1	22 49.6	3 23.9	23 50.8	23 53.2	3 19.7	26 17.0	1 46.6	10 13.1	22 20.6
11 S	3 17 51.9	17 56.6	25 49.9	4♉41.0	4 50.8	25 5.5	24 37.9	3 12.1	26 18.0	1 49.5	10 12.2	22 19.7
12 S	3 21 48.4	18 57.0	25 46.8	16 34.9	6 17.1	26 20.3	25 22.7	3 4.4	26 19.2	1 52.3	10 11.3	22 18.8
13 M	3 25 45.0	19 57.4	25 43.6	28 32.7	7 42.8	27 35.1	26 7.5	2 56.7	26 20.5	1 55.2	10 10.3	22 17.8
14 T	3 29 41.6	20 57.8	25 40.4	10♊35.5	9 7.8	28 50.0	26 52.4	2 48.8	26 21.8	1 58.1	10 9.4	22 16.8
15 W	3 33 38.1	21 58.2	25 37.2	22 44.4	10 32.0	0♏4.8	27 37.3	2 40.9	26 23.3	2 1.1	10 8.4	22 15.9
16 T	3 37 34.7	22 58.6	25 34.0	5♋1.0	11 55.5	1 19.7	28 22.3	2 33.0	26 24.9	2 4.0	10 7.3	22 14.9
17 F	3 41 31.2	23 59.1	25 30.9	17 27.1	13 18.0	2 34.7	29 7.3	2 25.0	26 26.5	2 7.0	10 6.3	22 13.8
18 S	3 45 27.8	24 59.6	25 27.7	0♌5.5	14 39.6	3 49.6	29 52.4	2 16.9	26 28.3	2 10.1	10 5.2	22 12.8
19 S	3 49 24.4	26 0.2	25 24.5	12 59.3	16 0.0	5 4.6	0♒37.5	2 8.9	26 30.2	2 13.2	10 4.1	22 11.8
20 M	3 53 20.9	27 0.8	25 21.3	26 12.0	17 19.1	6 19.6	1 22.7	2 0.7	26 32.2	2 16.2	10 3.0	22 10.8
21 T	3 57 17.4	28 1.4	25 18.2	9♍46.7	18 36.8	7 34.7	2 7.9	1 52.6	26 34.2	2 19.4	10 1.8	22 9.7
22 W	4 1 14.0	29 2.0	25 15.0	23 45.8	19 52.9	8 49.7	2 53.2	1 44.4	26 36.4	2 22.5	10 0.7	22 8.6
23 T	4 5 10.6	0♐2.7	25 11.8	8♎9.7	21 7.1	10 4.8	3 38.5	1 36.2	26 38.7	2 25.7	9 59.5	22 7.6
24 F	4 9 7.1	1 3.4	25 8.6	22 56.0	22 19.2	11 20.0	4 23.8	1 28.0	26 41.0	2 28.9	9 58.2	22 6.5
25 S	4 13 3.7	2 4.1	25 5.5	7♏59.2	23 28.8	12 35.1	5 9.2	1 19.8	26 43.5	2 32.1	9 57.0	22 5.4
26 S	4 17 0.2	3 4.8	25 2.3	23 10.6	24 35.7	13 50.2	5 54.6	1 11.7	26 46.1	2 35.3	9 55.7	22 4.3
27 M	4 20 56.8	4 5.6	24 59.1	8♐19.4	25 39.5	15 5.4	6 40.1	1 3.5	26 48.7	2 38.6	9 54.4	22 3.2
28 T	4 24 53.4	5 6.4	24 55.9	23 14.9	26 39.6	16 20.6	7 25.6	0 55.3	26 51.5	2 41.9	9 53.1	22 2.1
29 W	4 28 49.9	6 7.2	24 52.8	7♑48.4	27 35.7	17 35.8	8 11.1	0 47.2	26 54.4	2 45.2	9 51.8	22 1.0
30 T	4 32 46.4	7 8.0	24 49.6	21 54.3	28 27.0	18 51.0	8 56.7	0 39.1	26 57.3	2 48.5	9 50.4	21 59.9
DECLINATION												
1 W	2 38 26.4	14S 9.2	12N44.1	19S10.7	18S51.6	3S30.2	24S 9.2	20N 1.1	14S18.9	23S42.1	22N 5.4	15N 2.0
4 S	2 50 16.0	15 6.4	12 47.3	16 17.0	20 19.4	4 56.3	23 49.0	19 57.4	14 18.3	23 42.0	22 5.5	15 1.6
7 T	3 2 5.7	16 1.5	12 50.5	6 39.9	21 38.3	6 21.7	23 26.5	19 53.5	14 17.5	23 41.9	22 5.6	15 1.3
10 F	3 13 55.3	16 54.2	12 53.8	5N 1.3	22 47.6	7 46.0	23 1.9	19 49.4	14 16.4	23 41.8	22 5.7	15 0.9
13 M	3 25 45.0	17 44.2	12 57.0	14 58.6	23 46.6	9 9.0	22 35.1	19 45.2	14 14.9	23 41.6	22 5.9	15 0.6
16 T	3 37 34.7	18 31.5	13 0.2	19 29.2	24 34.6	10 30.2	22 6.3	19 40.8	14 13.1	23 41.5	22 6.1	15 0.3
19 S	3 49 24.4	19 15.8	13 3.4	15 53.3	25 11.0	11 49.3	21 35.4	19 36.4	14 11.0	23 41.4	22 6.3	15 0.0
22 W	4 1 14.0	19 57.1	13 6.6	4 41.0	25 35.1	13 6.0	21 2.6	19 31.8	14 8.6	23 41.2	22 6.5	14 59.7
25 S	4 13 3.7	20 35.0	13 9.8	9S38.4	25 46.3	14 19.8	20 27.8	19 27.2	14 5.9	23 41.0	22 6.7	14 59.5
28 T	4 24 53.4	21 9.6	13 13.0	18 53.3	25 44.3	15 30.5	19 51.2	19 22.6	14 2.8	23 40.8	22 7.0	14 59.3

DECEMBER 1905

DAY	EPHEMERIS SIDEREAL TIME h m s	☉ ° ′	☊ ° ′	☽ ° ′	☿ ° ′	♀ ° ′	♂ ° ′	♃ ° ′	♄ ° ′	♅ ° ′	♆ ° ′	♇ ° ′
LONGITUDE												
1 F	4 36 43.0	8♐8.9	24♌46.4	5♒30.5	29♐13.0	20♏6.3	9♒42.3	0♊31.0	27♒0.3	2♑51.9	9♋49.0	21♊58.7
2 S	4 40 39.6	9 9.7	24 43.2	18 38.1	29 53.0	21 21.5	10 27.9	0R23.0	27 3.5	2 55.3	9R47.6	21R57.6
3 S	4 44 36.2	10 10.6	24 40.0	1♓20.4	0♑26.2	22 36.8	11 13.6	0 15.1	27 6.7	2 58.7	9 46.2	21 56.4
4 M	4 48 32.7	11 11.5	24 36.9	13 42.1	0 51.8	23 52.0	11 59.3	0 7.2	27 10.0	3 2.1	9 44.8	21 55.3
5 T	4 52 29.2	12 12.4	24 33.7	25 48.4	1 8.9	25 7.3	12 45.0	29♉59.3	27 13.5	3 5.5	9 43.3	21 54.1
6 W	4 56 25.8	13 13.3	24 30.5	7♈44.7	1 16.8	26 22.6	13 30.7	29 51.5	27 17.0	3 8.9	9 41.8	21 53.0
7 T	5 0 22.4	14 14.2	24 27.3	19 35.8	1R14.5	27 37.9	14 16.4	29 43.9	27 20.6	3 12.4	9 40.3	21 51.8
8 F	5 4 18.9	15 15.1	24 24.2	1♉25.9	1 1.5	28 53.2	15 2.2	29 36.2	27 24.3	3 15.9	9 38.8	21 50.7
9 S	5 8 15.5	16 16.1	24 21.0	13 18.7	0 37.2	0♐8.5	15 48.0	29 28.7	27 28.0	3 19.3	9 37.3	21 49.5
10 S	5 12 12.0	17 17.0	24 17.8	25 16.7	0 1.5	1 23.8	16 33.8	29 21.3	27 31.9	3 22.8	9 35.8	21 48.3
11 M	5 16 8.6	18 18.0	24 14.6	7♊21.7	29♐14.5	2 39.2	17 19.6	29 13.9	27 35.8	3 26.3	9 34.2	21 47.2
12 T	5 20 5.1	19 19.0	24 11.5	19 35.0	28 16.9	3 54.5	18 5.4	29 6.7	27 39.8	3 29.9	9 32.7	21 46.0
13 W	5 24 1.7	20 20.0	24 8.3	1♋57.0	27 10.0	5 9.9	18 51.3	28 59.6	27 44.0	3 33.4	9 31.1	21 44.8
14 T	5 27 58.3	21 21.0	24 5.1	14 28.5	25 55.4	6 25.2	19 37.1	28 52.6	27 48.1	3 36.9	9 29.5	21 43.6
15 F	5 31 54.8	22 22.0	24 1.9	27 9.8	24 35.4	7 40.6	20 23.0	28 45.7	27 52.4	3 40.5	9 27.9	21 42.5
16 S	5 35 51.4	23 23.1	23 58.7	10♌2.0	23 12.7	8 56.0	21 8.9	28 38.9	27 56.8	3 44.0	9 26.3	21 41.3
17 S	5 39 47.9	24 24.1	23 55.6	23 6.3	21 50.0	10 11.4	21 54.7	28 32.3	28 1.2	3 47.6	9 24.7	21 40.1
18 M	5 43 44.5	25 25.2	23 52.4	6♍24.5	20 30.2	11 26.8	22 40.6	28 25.8	28 5.7	3 51.2	9 23.0	21 39.0
19 T	5 47 41.0	26 26.3	23 49.2	19 58.5	19 15.8	12 42.2	23 26.5	28 19.4	28 10.3	3 54.8	9 21.4	21 37.8
20 W	5 51 37.6	27 27.4	23 46.0	3♎49.8	18 8.8	13 57.6	24 12.4	28 13.1	28 15.0	3 58.4	9 19.7	21 36.6
21 T	5 55 34.2	28 28.5	23 42.9	17 58.9	17 10.9	15 13.0	24 58.3	28 7.1	28 19.8	4 2.0	9 18.1	21 35.5
22 F	5 59 30.7	29 29.6	23 39.7	2♏24.7	16 23.1	16 28.4	25 44.3	28 1.1	28 24.6	4 5.6	9 16.4	21 34.3
23 S	6 3 27.3	0♑30.8	23 36.5	17 3.9	15 46.1	17 43.9	26 30.2	27 55.3	28 29.5	4 9.2	9 14.7	21 33.1
24 S	6 7 23.8	1 31.9	23 33.3	1♐50.8	15 19.8	18 59.3	27 16.1	27 49.7	28 34.4	4 12.8	9 13.1	21 32.0
25 M	6 11 20.4	2 33.1	23 30.2	16 37.9	15 4.2	20 14.8	28 2.1	27 44.2	28 39.5	4 16.4	9 11.4	21 30.8
26 T	6 15 16.9	3 34.2	23 27.0	1♑16.9	14 58.8	21 30.2	28 48.0	27 38.9	28 44.6	4 20.0	9 9.7	21 29.7
27 W	6 19 13.5	4 35.4	23 23.8	15 40.2	15D 2.8	22 45.7	29 34.0	27 33.8	28 49.8	4 23.6	9 8.0	21 28.5
28 T	6 23 10.1	5 36.6	23 20.6	29 41.9	15 15.7	24 1.1	0♓19.9	27 28.9	28 55.1	4 27.2	9 6.3	21 27.4
29 F	6 27 6.6	6 37.8	23 17.4	13♒18.6	15 36.6	25 16.6	1 5.9	27 24.1	29 0.4	4 30.8	9 4.6	21 26.3
30 S	6 31 3.2	7 38.9	23 14.3	26 29.8	16 4.8	26 32.0	1 51.8	27 19.5	29 5.8	4 34.4	9 2.9	21 25.1
31 S	6 34 59.7	8 40.1	23 11.1	9♓16.9	16 39.6	27 47.5	2 37.8	27 15.1	29 11.3	4 38.0	9 1.2	21 24.0
DECLINATION												
1 F	4 36 43.0	21S40.5	13N16.2	17S20.3	25S29.3	16S37.6	19S12.7	19N18.0	13S59.5	23S40.6	22N 7.2	14N59.1
4 M	4 48 32.7	22 7.7	13 19.4	7 59.1	25 1.4	17 40.8	18 32.6	19 13.5	13 55.9	23 40.4	22 7.5	14 58.9
7 T	5 0 22.4	22 31.1	13 22.5	3N48.4	24 21.3	18 39.7	17 50.9	19 9.1	13 52.1	23 40.2	22 7.8	14 58.7
10 S	5 12 12.0	22 50.5	13 25.7	14 12.3	23 29.7	19 34.1	17 7.6	19 4.8	13 47.9	23 39.9	22 8.1	14 58.6
13 W	5 24 1.7	23 5.8	13 28.9	19 30.8	22 28.2	20 23.5	16 22.8	19 0.7	13 43.5	23 39.7	22 8.5	14 58.5
16 S	5 35 51.4	23 17.0	13 32.0	16 40.7	21 22.6	21 7.8	15 36.6	18 56.8	13 38.8	23 39.4	22 8.8	14 58.5
19 T	5 47 41.0	23 24.1	13 35.2	6 8.7	20 24.7	21 46.5	14 49.2	18 53.2	13 33.9	23 39.1	22 9.2	14 58.4
22 F	5 59 30.7	23 26.9	13 38.3	7S48.2	19 47.7	22 19.4	14 0.5	18 49.8	13 28.7	23 38.8	22 9.5	14 58.4
25 M	6 11 20.4	23 25.5	13 41.5	18 9.1	19 37.0	22 46.3	13 10.8	18 46.7	13 23.3	23 38.5	22 9.9	14 58.4
28 T	6 23 10.1	23 19.8	13 44.6	18 20.0	19 49.5	23 7.1	12 19.9	18 44.0	13 17.7	23 38.1	22 10.2	14 58.5
31 S	6 34 59.7	23 9.9	13 47.7	9 32.6	20 17.6	23 21.4	11 28.2	18 41.6	13 11.9	23 37.8	22 10.6	14 58.6

JANUARY 1906

DAY	EPHEMERIS SIDEREAL TIME	☉	☊	☽	☿	♀	♂	♃	♄	♅	♆	♇
	h m s	° ′	° ′	° ′	° ′	° ′	° ′	° ′	° ′	° ′	° ′	° ′
						LONGITUDE						
1 M	6 38 56.3	9♑41.3	23♌ 7.9	21♓43.4	17♐20.2	29♐ 2.9	3♓23.7	27♉10.8	29♒16.8	4♑41.6	8♋59.5	21♊22.9
2 T	6 42 52.8	10 42.4	23 4.7	3♈53.6	18 6.1	0♑18.4	4 9.6	27R 6.8	29 22.4	4 45.2	8R57.8	21R21.8
3 W	6 46 49.4	11 43.6	23 1.6	15 52.5	18 56.6	1 33.8	4 55.5	27 3.0	29 28.0	4 48.8	8 56.1	21 20.7
4 T	6 50 46.0	12 44.8	22 58.4	27 45.1	19 51.3	2 49.3	5 41.4	26 59.3	29 33.7	4 52.4	8 54.4	21 19.6
5 F	6 54 42.5	13 45.9	22 55.2	9♉36.4	20 49.8	4 4.7	6 27.3	26 55.8	29 39.5	4 56.0	8 52.7	21 18.6
6 S	6 58 39.1	14 47.1	22 52.0	21 30.9	21 51.5	5 20.1	7 13.2	26 52.6	29 45.3	4 59.6	8 51.0	21 17.5
7 S	7 2 35.6	15 48.2	22 48.9	3♊32.2	22 56.1	6 35.6	7 59.1	26 49.5	29 51.2	5 3.1	8 49.3	21 16.4
8 M	7 6 32.2	16 49.3	22 45.7	15 43.4	24 3.4	7 51.0	8 44.9	26 46.6	29 57.2	5 6.7	8 47.7	21 15.4
9 T	7 10 28.8	17 50.5	22 42.5	28 6.4	25 13.0	9 6.4	9 30.8	26 43.9	0♓ 3.2	5 10.2	8 46.0	21 14.4
10 W	7 14 25.3	18 51.6	22 39.3	10♋42.5	26 24.7	10 21.9	10 16.6	26 41.5	0 9.2	5 13.8	8 44.3	21 13.3
11 T	7 18 21.9	19 52.7	22 36.2	23 32.0	27 38.3	11 37.3	11 2.4	26 39.2	0 15.3	5 17.3	8 42.7	21 12.3
12 F	7 22 18.4	20 53.8	22 33.0	6♌34.7	28 53.6	12 52.7	11 48.2	26 37.1	0 21.5	5 20.8	8 41.0	21 11.3
13 S	7 26 15.0	21 54.9	22 29.8	19 49.7	0♑10.4	14 8.1	12 34.0	26 35.2	0 27.7	5 24.3	8 39.3	21 10.3
14 S	7 30 11.5	22 56.0	22 26.6	3♍16.5	1 28.7	15 23.5	13 19.8	26 33.6	0 34.0	5 27.8	8 37.7	21 9.4
15 M	7 34 8.1	23 57.1	22 23.4	16 54.1	2 48.3	16 38.9	14 5.5	26 32.1	0 40.3	5 31.3	8 36.1	21 8.4
16 T	7 38 4.6	24 58.2	22 20.3	0♎41.8	4 9.0	17 54.4	14 51.2	26 30.9	0 46.6	5 34.7	8 34.5	21 7.4
17 W	7 42 1.2	25 59.3	22 17.1	14 39.0	5 30.9	19 9.8	15 36.9	26 29.8	0 53.0	5 38.2	8 32.8	21 6.5
18 T	7 45 57.7	27 0.4	22 13.9	28 44.8	6 53.7	20 25.2	16 22.6	26 29.0	0 59.5	5 41.6	8 31.3	21 5.6
19 F	7 49 54.3	28 1.5	22 10.7	12♏57.6	8 17.6	21 40.6	17 8.3	26 28.3	1 6.0	5 45.0	8 29.7	21 4.7
20 S	7 53 50.9	29 2.5	22 7.6	27 15.3	9 42.3	22 56.0	17 53.9	26 27.9	1 12.5	5 48.4	8 28.1	21 3.8
21 S	7 57 47.4	0♒ 3.6	22 4.4	11♐34.6	11 7.9	24 11.4	18 39.5	26 27.7	1 19.1	5 51.8	8 26.5	21 2.9
22 M	8 1 44.0	1 4.7	22 1.2	25 51.6	12 34.3	25 26.8	19 25.1	26 27.7	1 25.7	5 55.2	8 25.0	21 2.0
23 T	8 5 40.5	2 5.7	21 58.0	10♑ 1.6	14 1.5	26 42.2	20 10.7	26D27.9	1 32.4	5 58.5	8 23.5	21 1.2
24 W	8 9 37.1	3 6.8	21 54.9	24 0.0	15 29.5	27 57.6	20 56.3	26 28.3	1 39.1	6 1.8	8 21.9	21 0.3
25 T	8 13 33.6	4 7.8	21 51.7	7♒43.0	16 58.2	29 13.0	21 41.8	26 28.9	1 45.8	6 5.1	8 20.4	20 59.5
26 F	8 17 30.2	5 8.8	21 48.5	21 7.7	18 27.6	0♒28.4	22 27.4	26 29.7	1 52.6	6 8.4	8 18.9	20 58.7
27 S	8 21 26.7	6 9.8	21 45.3	4♓12.7	19 57.7	1 43.8	23 12.8	26 30.7	1 59.4	6 11.6	8 17.5	20 57.9
28 S	8 25 23.3	7 10.8	21 42.1	16 58.2	21 28.5	2 59.1	23 58.3	26 31.9	2 6.3	6 14.9	8 16.0	20 57.1
29 M	8 29 19.9	8 11.8	21 39.0	29 25.9	23 0.0	4 14.5	24 43.8	26 33.3	2 13.1	6 18.1	8 14.6	20 56.4
30 T	8 33 16.4	9 12.7	21 35.8	11♈38.7	24 32.3	5 29.8	25 29.2	26 35.0	2 20.0	6 21.3	8 13.2	20 55.7
31 W	8 37 13.0	10 13.6	21 32.6	23 40.1	26 5.2	6 45.2	26 14.5	26 36.8	2 27.0	6 24.4	8 11.8	20 54.9
						DECLINATION						
1 M	6 38 56.3	23S 5.7	13N48.8	5S40.0	20S29.1	23S24.8	11S10.7	18N40.8	13S 9.9	23S37.7	22N10.7	14N58.6
4 T	6 50 46.0	22 50.3	13 51.9	6N15.3	21 6.8	23 30.5	10 17.8	18 38.9	13 3.8	23 37.3	22 11.1	14 58.7
7 S	7 2 35.6	22 30.8	13 55.0	15 53.7	21 45.2	23 29.8	9 24.2	18 37.4	12 57.5	23 37.0	22 11.5	14 58.9
10 W	7 14 25.3	22 7.3	13 58.1	19 39.1	22 20.3	23 22.4	8 29.9	18 36.4	12 51.0	23 36.6	22 11.9	14 59.1
13 S	7 26 15.0	21 39.9	14 1.2	14 46.0	22 49.6	23 8.5	7 35.1	18 35.7	12 44.3	23 36.2	22 12.2	14 59.3
16 T	7 38 4.6	21 8.7	14 4.3	2 47.4	23 10.9	22 48.3	6 39.8	18 35.4	12 37.5	23 35.8	22 12.6	14 59.6
19 F	7 49 54.3	20 33.9	14 7.4	10S47.1	23 23.1	22 21.7	5 44.1	18 35.6	12 30.6	23 35.4	22 13.0	14 59.9
22 M	8 1 44.0	19 55.6	14 10.5	19 4.7	23 25.1	21 49.0	4 48.1	18 36.2	12 23.4	23 35.0	22 13.3	15 0.2
25 T	8 13 33.6	19 13.9	14 13.6	17 11.1	23 16.1	21 10.3	3 51.9	18 37.3	12 16.2	23 34.6	22 13.7	15 0.5
28 S	8 25 23.3	18 29.1	14 16.7	7 17.1	22 55.7	20 26.0	2 55.5	18 38.7	12 8.8	23 34.2	22 14.1	15 0.9
31 W	8 37 13.0	17 41.2	14 19.7	4N49.5	22 23.3	19 36.2	1 59.0	18 40.6	12 1.4	23 33.8	22 14.4	15 1.3

FEBRUARY 1906

DAY	EPHEMERIS SIDEREAL TIME	☉	☊	☽	☿	♀	♂	♃	♄	♅	♆	♇
						LONGITUDE						
1 T	8 41 9.5	11♒14.5	21♌29.4	5♉34.6	27♑38.8	8♒ 0.5	26♓59.9	26♉38.8	2♓33.9	6♑27.5	8♋10.4	20♊54.2
2 F	8 45 6.1	12 15.4	21 26.3	17 26.9	29 13.1	9 15.8	27 45.2	26 41.1	2 40.9	6 30.6	8R 9.1	20R53.6
3 S	8 49 2.7	13 16.3	21 23.1	29 21.8	0♒48.1	10 31.1	28 30.5	26 43.5	2 48.0	6 33.7	8 7.7	20 52.9
4 S	8 52 59.2	14 17.1	21 19.9	11♊23.7	2 23.9	11 46.4	29 15.8	26 46.1	2 55.0	6 36.8	8 6.4	20 52.3
5 M	8 56 55.7	15 17.9	21 16.7	23 37.0	4 0.3	13 1.7	0♈ 1.0	26 48.9	3 2.1	6 39.8	8 5.1	20 51.6
6 T	9 0 52.3	16 18.7	21 13.5	6♋ 5.1	5 37.6	14 17.0	0 46.2	26 51.9	3 9.2	6 42.8	8 3.9	20 51.0
7 W	9 4 48.9	17 19.5	21 10.4	18 50.4	7 15.5	15 32.2	1 31.3	26 55.2	3 16.3	6 45.7	8 2.6	20 50.4
8 T	9 8 45.4	18 20.2	21 7.2	1♌54.3	8 54.3	16 47.5	2 16.4	26 58.5	3 23.4	6 48.7	8 1.4	20 49.9
9 F	9 12 42.0	19 20.9	21 4.0	15 16.9	10 33.8	18 2.7	3 1.5	27 2.1	3 30.6	6 51.6	8 0.2	20 49.3
10 S	9 16 38.5	20 21.6	21 0.8	28 56.9	12 14.2	19 17.9	3 46.6	27 5.9	3 37.7	6 54.4	7 59.1	20 48.8
11 S	9 20 35.1	21 22.3	20 57.7	12♍51.8	13 55.4	20 33.2	4 31.6	27 9.9	3 44.9	6 57.3	7 57.9	20 48.3
12 M	9 24 31.6	22 23.0	20 54.5	26 58.2	15 37.4	21 48.4	5 16.6	27 14.0	3 52.1	7 0.1	7 56.8	20 47.8
13 T	9 28 28.2	23 23.6	20 51.3	11♎12.1	17 20.2	23 3.6	6 1.5	27 18.3	3 59.3	7 2.8	7 55.7	20 47.3
14 W	9 32 24.7	24 24.2	20 48.1	25 29.6	19 4.0	24 18.7	6 46.4	27 22.8	4 6.6	7 5.5	7 54.6	20 46.9
15 T	9 36 21.3	25 24.8	20 44.9	9♏46.9	20 48.5	25 33.9	7 31.2	27 27.5	4 13.8	7 8.2	7 53.6	20 46.5
16 F	9 40 17.9	26 25.4	20 41.8	24 1.0	22 34.0	26 49.1	8 16.1	27 32.4	4 21.1	7 10.9	7 52.6	20 46.1
17 S	9 44 14.4	27 25.9	20 38.6	8♐ 9.3	24 20.4	28 4.2	9 0.9	27 37.4	4 28.3	7 13.5	7 51.6	20 45.7
18 S	9 48 11.0	28 26.5	20 35.4	22 9.9	26 7.6	29 19.4	9 45.6	27 42.7	4 35.6	7 16.1	7 50.6	20 45.3
19 M	9 52 7.5	29 27.0	20 32.2	6♑ 1.4	27 55.8	0♓34.5	10 30.4	27 48.1	4 42.9	7 18.7	7 49.7	20 45.0
20 T	9 56 4.0	0♓27.5	20 29.1	19 42.4	29 44.8	1 49.6	11 15.0	27 53.6	4 50.2	7 21.2	7 48.8	20 44.7
21 W	10 0 0.6	1 27.9	20 25.9	3♒11.8	1♓34.7	3 4.8	11 59.7	27 59.4	4 57.5	7 23.7	7 47.9	20 44.4
22 T	10 3 57.2	2 28.4	20 22.7	16 28.6	3 25.4	4 19.9	12 44.3	28 5.3	5 4.8	7 26.1	7 47.1	20 44.1
23 F	10 7 53.7	3 28.8	20 19.5	29 31.9	5 16.9	5 34.9	13 28.9	28 11.3	5 12.1	7 28.5	7 46.3	20 43.9
24 S	10 11 50.3	4 29.2	20 16.3	12♓21.3	7 9.2	6 50.0	14 13.4	28 17.6	5 19.4	7 30.9	7 45.5	20 43.6
25 S	10 15 46.8	5 29.5	20 13.2	24 56.8	9 2.1	8 5.1	14 57.9	28 24.0	5 26.7	7 33.2	7 44.8	20 43.4
26 M	10 19 43.4	6 29.9	20 10.0	7♈19.1	10 55.7	9 20.1	15 42.4	28 30.5	5 34.1	7 35.5	7 44.0	20 43.2
27 T	10 23 39.9	7 30.2	20 6.8	19 29.6	12 49.9	10 35.1	16 26.8	28 37.2	5 41.4	7 37.7	7 43.3	20 43.1
28 W	10 27 36.5	8 30.4	20 3.6	1♉30.7	14 44.4	11 50.1	17 11.2	28 44.1	5 48.7	7 39.9	7 42.7	20 42.9
						DECLINATION						
1 T	8 41 9.5	17S24.7	14N20.8	8N34.7	22S 9.8	19S18.5	1S40.2	18N41.3	11S58.9	23S33.6	22N14.5	15N 1.4
4 S	8 52 59.2	16 33.1	14 23.8	17 15.0	21 21.0	18 21.9	0 43.8	18 43.8	11 51.3	23 33.2	22 14.8	15 1.9
7 W	9 4 48.9	15 38.9	14 26.9	19 20.3	20 19.5	17 20.6	0N12.5	18 46.6	11 43.6	23 32.8	22 15.2	15 2.4
10 S	9 16 38.5	14 42.4	14 29.9	12 32.3	19 5.3	16 15.0	1 8.6	18 49.8	11 35.9	23 32.4	22 15.5	15 2.9
13 T	9 28 28.2	13 43.6	14 33.0	0S41.3	17 38.1	15 5.2	2 4.4	18 53.3	11 28.1	23 32.0	22 15.8	15 3.4
16 F	9 40 17.9	12 42.8	14 36.0	13 40.0	15 58.0	13 51.8	2 59.9	18 57.2	11 20.2	23 31.6	22 16.1	15 3.9
19 M	9 52 7.5	11 40.2	14 39.0	19 34.9	14 4.9	12 34.9	3 55.0	19 1.4	11 12.3	23 31.3	22 16.3	15 4.5
22 T	10 3 57.2	10 35.9	14 42.1	15 30.6	11 59.2	11 15.0	4 49.6	19 5.9	11 4.4	23 30.9	22 16.6	15 5.1
25 S	10 15 46.8	9 30.1	14 45.1	4 42.9	9 41.6	9 52.4	5 43.6	19 10.8	10 56.5	23 30.6	22 16.8	15 5.7
28 W	10 27 36.5	8 23.0	14 48.1	7N20.9	7 13.1	8 27.4	6 37.0	19 15.8	10 48.5	23 30.3	22 17.1	15 6.3

MARCH 1906

LONGITUDE

DAY	EPHEMERIS SIDEREAL TIME h m s	☉ ° ′	☊ ° ′	☽ ° ′	☿ ° ′	♀ ° ′	♂ ° ′	♃ ° ′	♄ ° ′	♅ ° ′	♆ ° ′	♇ ° ′
1 T	10 31 33.0	9♓30.7	20♌ 0.5	13♉25.4	16♓39.2	13♓ 5.1	17♈55.5	28♉51.1	5♓56.0	7♑42.0	7♋42.1	20♊42.8
2 F	10 35 29.6	10 30.9	19 57.3	25 17.5	18 34.0	14 20.1	18 39.8	28 58.3	6 3.3	7 44.1	7R41.5	20R42.7
3 S	10 39 26.2	11 31.0	19 54.1	7♊11.3	20 28.8	15 35.0	19 24.1	29 5.7	6 10.6	7 46.2	7 40.9	20 42.7
4 S	10 43 22.7	12 31.2	19 50.9	19 11.4	22 23.2	16 50.0	20 8.3	29 13.1	6 17.9	7 48.2	7 40.4	20 42.6
5 M	10 47 19.2	13 31.3	19 47.7	1♋22.6	24 16.9	18 4.9	20 52.5	29 20.8	6 25.1	7 50.2	7 39.9	20 42.6
6 T	10 51 15.8	14 31.3	19 44.6	13 49.6	26 9.7	19 19.8	21 36.6	29 28.5	6 32.4	7 52.1	7 39.4	20 42.6
7 W	10 55 12.4	15 31.4	19 41.4	26 36.3	28 1.2	20 34.6	22 20.7	29 36.5	6 39.7	7 54.0	7 39.0	20D42.6
8 T	10 59 8.9	16 31.4	19 38.2	9♌45.7	29 51.0	21 49.5	23 4.7	29 44.5	6 46.9	7 55.9	7 38.6	20 42.6
9 F	11 3 5.5	17 31.3	19 35.0	23 19.4	1♈38.6	23 4.3	23 48.7	29 52.7	6 54.1	7 57.7	7 38.2	20 42.7
10 S	11 7 2.0	18 31.2	19 31.9	7♍16.9	3 23.7	24 19.1	24 32.6	0♊ 1.0	7 1.4	7 59.4	7 37.9	20 42.8
11 S	11 10 58.5	19 31.1	19 28.7	21 35.5	5 5.7	25 33.9	25 16.5	0 9.5	7 8.6	8 1.1	7 37.6	20 42.9
12 M	11 14 55.1	20 31.0	19 25.5	6♎10.1	6 44.1	26 48.6	26 0.3	0 18.1	7 15.8	8 2.8	7 37.3	20 43.0
13 T	11 18 51.7	21 30.8	19 22.3	20 53.9	8 18.4	28 3.4	26 44.2	0 26.8	7 22.9	8 4.4	7 37.1	20 43.2
14 W	11 22 48.2	22 30.6	19 19.1	5♏39.4	9 48.1	29 18.1	27 27.9	0 35.6	7 30.1	8 5.9	7 36.8	20 43.4
15 T	11 26 44.8	23 30.4	19 16.0	20 19.2	11 12.7	0♈32.8	28 11.6	0 44.6	7 37.2	8 7.4	7 36.7	20 43.6
16 F	11 30 41.3	24 30.1	19 12.8	4♐47.6	12 31.7	1 47.5	28 55.3	0 53.7	7 44.3	8 8.9	7 36.5	20 43.8
17 S	11 34 37.9	25 29.8	19 9.6	19 0.6	13 44.7	3 2.2	29 38.9	1 2.9	7 51.4	8 10.3	7 36.4	20 44.0
18 S	11 38 34.4	26 29.5	19 6.4	2♑56.4	14 51.3	4 16.8	0♉22.5	1 12.3	7 58.5	8 11.7	7 36.4	20 44.3
19 M	11 42 31.0	27 29.2	19 3.2	16 34.7	15 51.1	5 31.5	1 6.1	1 21.7	8 5.6	8 13.0	7 36.3	20 44.6
20 T	11 46 27.5	28 28.8	19 0.1	29 56.4	16 43.7	6 46.1	1 49.6	1 31.3	8 12.6	8 14.3	7D36.3	20 44.9
21 W	11 50 24.1	29 28.4	18 56.9	13♒ 3.2	17 29.0	8 0.7	2 33.0	1 41.0	8 19.6	8 15.5	7 36.4	20 45.2
22 T	11 54 20.7	0♈27.9	18 53.7	25 56.6	18 6.6	9 15.2	3 16.4	1 50.9	8 26.6	8 16.7	7 36.4	20 45.6
23 F	11 58 17.2	1 27.5	18 50.5	8♓38.1	18 36.4	10 29.8	3 59.8	2 0.8	8 33.5	8 17.8	7 36.5	20 45.9
24 S	12 2 13.7	2 27.0	18 47.4	21 8.9	18 58.5	11 44.3	4 43.1	2 10.8	8 40.4	8 18.9	7 36.7	20 46.3
25 S	12 6 10.3	3 26.4	18 44.2	3♈29.9	19 12.6	12 58.8	5 26.4	2 21.0	8 47.3	8 19.9	7 36.8	20 46.7
26 M	12 10 6.8	4 25.9	18 41.0	15 42.1	19 19.0	14 13.3	6 9.7	2 31.2	8 54.2	8 20.9	7 37.1	20 47.2
27 T	12 14 3.4	5 25.3	18 37.8	27 46.3	19R17.7	15 27.8	6 52.9	2 41.6	9 1.0	8 21.8	7 37.3	20 47.7
28 W	12 17 60.0	6 24.7	18 34.6	9♉44.1	19 9.1	16 42.2	7 36.0	2 52.0	9 7.8	8 22.6	7 37.6	20 48.1
29 T	12 21 56.5	7 24.0	18 31.5	21 37.3	18 53.4	17 56.6	8 19.1	3 2.6	9 14.5	8 23.4	7 37.9	20 48.6
30 F	12 25 53.0	8 23.3	18 28.3	3♊28.5	18 31.2	19 11.0	9 2.2	3 13.3	9 21.3	8 24.2	7 38.2	20 49.2
31 S	12 29 49.6	9 22.5	18 25.1	15 21.1	18 2.9	20 25.4	9 45.2	3 24.0	9 28.0	8 24.9	7 38.6	20 49.7

DECLINATION

DAY	EPHEMERIS SIDEREAL TIME h m s	☉	☊	☽	☿	♀	♂	♃	♄	♅	♆	♇
1 T	10 31 33.0	8S 0.4	14N49.1	10N54.1	6S21.6	7S58.7	6N54.7	19N17.6	10S45.9	23S30.2	22N17.2	15N 6.5
4 S	10 43 22.7	6 51.9	14 52.1	18 24.2	3 42.2	6 31.1	7 47.2	19 23.0	10 38.0	23 29.9	22 17.4	15 7.2
7 W	10 55 12.4	5 42.6	14 55.1	18 43.7	0 59.1	5 2.0	8 38.9	19 28.6	10 30.1	23 29.6	22 17.6	15 7.9
10 S	11 7 2.0	4 32.5	14 58.1	10 13.1	1N42.2	3 31.7	9 29.8	19 34.4	10 22.2	23 29.3	22 17.8	15 8.5
13 T	11 18 51.7	3 22.0	15 1.1	3S58.1	4 14.6	2 0.6	10 19.7	19 40.4	10 14.4	23 29.1	22 17.9	15 9.2
16 F	11 30 41.3	2 11.1	15 4.0	16 8.8	6 30.4	0 28.9	11 8.7	19 46.6	10 6.7	23 28.9	22 18.1	15 9.9
19 M	11 42 31.0	1 0.0	15 7.0	19 32.5	8 21.9	1N 3.1	11 56.7	19 52.9	9 59.0	23 28.7	22 18.2	15 10.7
22 T	11 54 20.7	0N11.1	15 10.0	13 20.5	9 43.1	2 34.9	12 43.6	19 59.3	9 51.4	23 28.5	22 18.3	15 11.4
25 S	12 6 10.3	1 22.1	15 12.9	1 50.6	10 29.2	4 6.3	13 29.4	20 5.8	9 43.9	23 28.4	22 18.4	15 12.1
28 W	12 17 60.0	2 32.8	15 15.9	9N57.0	10 37.8	5 37.0	14 14.0	20 12.4	9 36.6	23 28.3	22 18.5	15 12.9
31 S	12 29 49.6	3 43.0	15 18.8	18 3.4	10 9.3	7 6.5	14 57.4	20 19.0	9 29.3	23 28.2	22 18.6	15 13.6

APRIL 1906

LONGITUDE

DAY	EPHEMERIS SIDEREAL TIME h m s	☉ ° ′	☊ ° ′	☽ ° ′	☿ ° ′	♀ ° ′	♂ ° ′	♃ ° ′	♄ ° ′	♅ ° ′	♆ ° ′	♇ ° ′
1 S	12 33 46.2	10♈21.8	18♌21.9	27♊19.1	17♈29.3	21♈39.7	10♉28.2	3♊34.9	9♓34.6	8♑25.6	7♋39.0	20♊50.3
2 M	12 37 42.7	11 20.9	18 18.8	9♋27.0	16R51.1	22 54.0	11 11.1	3 45.8	9 41.2	8 26.2	7 39.4	20 50.9
3 T	12 41 39.3	12 20.1	18 15.6	21 49.7	16 9.1	24 8.3	11 54.0	3 56.9	9 47.8	8 26.8	7 39.9	20 51.5
4 W	12 45 35.8	13 19.2	18 12.4	4♌32.2	15 24.3	25 22.6	12 36.8	4 8.0	9 54.3	8 27.3	7 40.4	20 52.1
5 T	12 49 32.4	14 18.2	18 9.2	17 38.8	14 37.5	26 36.8	13 19.6	4 19.2	10 0.8	8 27.7	7 41.0	20 52.7
6 F	12 53 28.9	15 17.3	18 6.0	1♍12.6	13 49.7	27 51.0	14 2.3	4 30.5	10 7.2	8 28.1	7 41.5	20 53.4
7 S	12 57 25.5	16 16.2	18 2.9	15 15.0	13 1.9	29 5.1	14 45.0	4 41.9	10 13.6	8 28.5	7 42.1	20 54.1
8 S	13 1 22.0	17 15.2	17 59.7	29 44.3	12 15.0	0♉19.3	15 27.6	4 53.4	10 20.0	8 28.8	7 42.8	20 54.8
9 M	13 5 18.6	18 14.1	17 56.5	14♎35.8	11 29.7	1 33.4	16 10.2	5 4.9	10 26.3	8 29.0	7 43.5	20 55.5
10 T	13 9 15.1	19 13.0	17 53.3	29 41.5	10 47.0	2 47.5	16 52.7	5 16.5	10 32.6	8 29.2	7 44.2	20 56.3
11 W	13 13 11.7	20 11.8	17 50.2	14♏51.4	10 7.4	4 1.5	17 35.2	5 28.2	10 38.8	8 29.4	7 44.9	20 57.0
12 T	13 17 8.2	21 10.7	17 47.0	29 55.0	9 31.5	5 15.6	18 17.7	5 40.0	10 44.9	8 29.4	7 45.7	20 57.8
13 F	13 21 4.8	22 9.5	17 43.8	14♐43.5	8 59.9	6 29.6	19 0.1	5 51.9	10 51.0	8 29.5	7 46.5	20 58.6
14 S	13 25 1.3	23 8.2	17 40.6	29 10.5	8 32.8	7 43.6	19 42.5	6 3.8	10 57.1	8R29.5	7 47.3	20 59.4
15 S	13 28 57.9	24 7.0	17 37.4	13♑13.2	8 10.7	8 57.5	20 24.8	6 15.8	11 3.1	8 29.4	7 48.2	21 0.3
16 M	13 32 54.4	25 5.7	17 34.3	26 51.1	7 53.5	10 11.5	21 7.1	6 27.9	11 9.1	8 29.3	7 49.1	21 1.1
17 T	13 36 51.0	26 4.3	17 31.1	10♒ 6.3	7 41.6	11 25.4	21 49.3	6 40.0	11 15.0	8 29.2	7 50.0	21 2.0
18 W	13 40 47.5	27 3.0	17 27.9	23 1.7	7 34.8	12 39.3	22 31.5	6 52.3	11 20.8	8 28.9	7 50.9	21 2.9
19 T	13 44 44.1	28 1.6	17 24.7	5♓40.8	7 33.2	13 53.1	23 13.6	7 4.5	11 26.7	8 28.7	7 51.9	21 3.8
20 F	13 48 40.7	29 0.2	17 21.6	18 6.9	7D36.7	15 7.0	23 55.7	7 16.9	11 32.4	8 28.4	7 52.9	21 4.7
21 S	13 52 37.2	29 58.8	17 18.4	0♈22.8	7 45.2	16 20.8	24 37.8	7 29.3	11 38.1	8 28.0	7 54.0	21 5.6
22 S	13 56 33.8	0♉57.3	17 15.2	12 30.9	7 58.6	17 34.5	25 19.8	7 41.8	11 43.7	8 27.6	7 55.1	21 6.6
23 M	14 0 30.3	1 55.8	17 12.0	24 32.8	8 16.8	18 48.3	26 1.8	7 54.3	11 49.3	8 27.1	7 56.2	21 7.6
24 T	14 4 26.9	2 54.3	17 8.8	6♉30.1	8 39.5	20 2.0	26 43.7	8 6.9	11 54.8	8 26.6	7 57.3	21 8.6
25 W	14 8 23.4	3 52.7	17 5.7	18 23.9	9 6.6	21 15.7	27 25.6	8 19.6	12 0.2	8 26.1	7 58.5	21 9.6
26 T	14 12 20.0	4 51.1	17 2.5	0♊15.7	9 37.9	22 29.4	28 7.5	8 32.3	12 5.6	8 25.4	7 59.7	21 10.6
27 F	14 16 16.5	5 49.5	16 59.3	12 7.1	10 13.3	23 43.0	28 49.3	8 45.0	12 10.9	8 24.8	8 0.9	21 11.6
28 S	14 20 13.1	6 47.8	16 56.1	24 0.5	10 52.5	24 56.7	29 31.0	8 57.8	12 16.1	8 24.1	8 2.1	21 12.7
29 S	14 24 9.7	7 46.2	16 53.0	5♋58.9	11 35.5	26 10.3	0♊12.8	9 10.7	12 21.3	8 23.3	8 3.4	21 13.7
30 M	14 28 6.2	8 44.4	16 49.8	18 6.2	12 22.1	27 23.8	0 54.4	9 23.6	12 26.4	8 22.5	8 4.7	21 14.8

DECLINATION

DAY	EPHEMERIS SIDEREAL TIME h m s	☉	☊	☽	☿	♀	♂	♃	♄	♅	♆	♇
1 S	12 33 46.2	4N 6.3	15N19.8	19N22.3	9N52.1	7N36.1	15N11.5	20N21.2	9S26.9	23S28.2	22N18.6	15N13.8
4 W	12 45 35.8	5 15.6	15 22.8	17 51.0	8 42.1	9 3.6	15 53.1	20 27.9	9 19.8	23 28.2	22 18.6	15 14.6
7 S	12 57 25.5	6 24.1	15 25.7	7 51.9	7 13.0	10 29.3	16 33.4	20 34.6	9 12.9	23 28.2	22 18.7	15 15.3
10 T	13 9 15.1	7 31.6	15 28.6	6S53.4	5 38.4	11 52.8	17 12.2	20 41.3	9 6.1	23 28.2	22 18.7	15 16.1
13 F	13 21 4.8	8 37.9	15 31.5	18 2.9	4 11.0	13 13.7	17 49.5	20 48.0	8 59.5	23 28.3	22 18.7	15 16.8
16 M	13 32 54.4	9 43.0	15 34.4	18 56.9	3 0.3	14 31.7	18 25.4	20 54.6	8 53.1	23 28.3	22 18.6	15 17.5
19 T	13 44 44.1	10 46.6	15 37.3	10 49.3	2 11.3	15 46.5	18 59.7	21 1.2	8 46.8	23 28.5	22 18.6	15 18.3
22 S	13 56 33.8	11 48.7	15 40.2	1N11.2	1 45.8	16 57.8	19 32.4	21 7.8	8 40.8	23 28.6	22 18.5	15 19.0
25 W	14 8 23.4	12 49.0	15 43.1	12 29.9	1 43.2	18 5.1	20 3.5	21 14.2	8 35.0	23 28.8	22 18.4	15 19.7
28 S	14 20 13.1	13 47.4	15 46.0	19 18.3	2 1.7	19 8.3	20 32.9	21 20.6	8 29.4	23 29.0	22 18.3	15 20.4

MAY 1906

DAY	EPHEMERIS SIDEREAL TIME	☉	☊	☽	☿	♀	♂	♃	♄	♅	♆	♇
	h m s	° ′	° ′	° ′	° ′	° ′	° ′	° ′	° ′	° ′	° ′	° ′
						LONGITUDE						
1 T	14 32 2.7	9♉42.7	16♌46.6	0♌26.5	13♈12.0	28♉37.3	1♊36.0	9♊36.6	12♓31.5	8♑21.7	8♋6.0	21♊15.9
2 W	14 35 59.3	10 40.9	16 43.4	13 4.8	14 5.3	29 50.8	2 17.6	9 49.6	12 36.5	8R20.8	8 7.4	21 17.0
3 T	14 39 55.8	11 39.1	16 40.2	26 5.8	15 1.7	1♊4.3	2 59.2	10 2.7	12 41.4	8 19.8	8 8.8	21 18.1
4 F	14 43 52.4	12 37.2	16 37.1	9♍33.5	16 1.1	2 17.7	3 40.7	10 15.8	12 46.2	8 18.8	8 10.2	21 19.3
5 S	14 47 49.0	13 35.3	16 33.9	23 30.4	17 3.4	3 31.1	4 22.1	10 28.9	12 51.0	8 17.8	8 11.6	21 20.4
6 S	14 51 45.5	14 33.4	16 30.7	7♎56.8	18 8.5	4 44.5	5 3.5	10 42.1	12 55.7	8 16.7	8 13.1	21 21.6
7 M	14 55 42.1	15 31.4	16 27.5	22 49.2	19 16.4	5 57.8	5 44.9	10 55.3	13 0.3	8 15.6	8 14.6	21 22.8
8 T	14 59 38.6	16 29.5	16 24.4	8♏0.7	20 26.9	7 11.1	6 26.2	11 8.6	13 4.9	8 14.4	8 16.1	21 23.9
9 W	15 3 35.2	17 27.5	16 21.2	23 21.0	21 39.9	8 24.4	7 7.5	11 21.9	13 9.3	8 13.2	8 17.6	21 25.1
10 T	15 7 31.7	18 25.4	16 18.0	8♐38.6	22 55.5	9 37.6	7 48.7	11 35.2	13 13.7	8 12.0	8 19.2	21 26.3
11 F	15 11 28.3	19 23.4	16 14.8	23 42.3	24 13.4	10 50.8	8 29.9	11 48.6	13 18.0	8 10.7	8 20.8	21 27.6
12 S	15 15 24.8	20 21.3	16 11.6	8♑23.7	25 33.8	12 4.0	9 11.0	12 2.0	13 22.3	8 9.3	8 22.4	21 28.8
13 S	15 19 21.4	21 19.2	16 8.5	22 37.9	26 56.5	13 17.1	9 52.1	12 15.4	13 26.5	8 8.0	8 24.0	21 30.0
14 M	15 23 18.0	22 17.1	16 5.3	6♒23.5	28 21.5	14 30.2	10 33.2	12 28.9	13 30.6	8 6.5	8 25.7	21 31.3
15 T	15 27 14.5	23 14.9	16 2.1	19 41.9	29 48.8	15 43.3	11 14.2	12 42.4	13 34.6	8 5.1	8 27.3	21 32.5
16 W	15 31 11.0	24 12.7	15 58.9	2♓36.4	1♉18.4	16 56.3	11 55.2	12 55.9	13 38.5	8 3.6	8 29.0	21 33.8
17 T	15 35 7.6	25 10.6	15 55.8	15 11.1	2 50.1	18 9.4	12 36.2	13 9.5	13 42.4	8 2.1	8 30.7	21 35.1
18 F	15 39 4.2	26 8.4	15 52.6	27 30.5	4 24.1	19 22.4	13 17.1	13 23.0	13 46.1	8 0.5	8 32.5	21 36.4
19 S	15 43 0.7	27 6.1	15 49.4	9♈38.5	6 0.3	20 35.3	13 58.0	13 36.7	13 49.8	7 58.9	8 34.2	21 37.7
20 S	15 46 57.3	28 3.9	15 46.2	21 38.7	7 38.6	21 48.3	14 38.8	13 50.3	13 53.4	7 57.2	8 36.0	21 39.0
21 M	15 50 53.8	29 1.6	15 43.0	3♉33.9	9 19.2	23 1.2	15 19.6	14 3.9	13 56.9	7 55.5	8 37.8	21 40.3
22 T	15 54 50.4	29 59.4	15 39.9	15 26.6	11 2.0	24 14.1	16 0.4	14 17.6	14 0.4	7 53.8	8 39.6	21 41.6
23 W	15 58 47.0	0♊57.1	15 36.7	27 18.3	12 46.9	25 26.9	16 41.2	14 31.3	14 3.7	7 52.1	8 41.5	21 43.0
24 T	16 2 43.5	1 54.7	15 33.5	9♊10.6	14 34.0	26 39.7	17 21.8	14 45.1	14 7.0	7 50.3	8 43.3	21 44.3
25 F	16 6 40.0	2 52.4	15 30.3	21 4.9	16 23.3	27 52.5	18 2.5	14 58.8	14 10.1	7 48.4	8 45.2	21 45.6
26 S	16 10 36.6	3 50.0	15 27.2	3♋2.9	18 14.8	29 5.2	18 43.1	15 12.6	14 13.2	7 46.6	8 47.1	21 47.0
27 S	16 14 33.1	4 47.6	15 24.0	15 6.7	20 8.4	0♋17.9	19 23.7	15 26.3	14 16.2	7 44.7	8 49.0	21 48.3
28 M	16 18 29.7	5 45.2	15 20.8	27 18.9	22 4.1	1 30.6	20 4.2	15 40.1	14 19.1	7 42.8	8 50.9	21 49.7
29 T	16 22 26.3	6 42.8	15 17.6	9♌42.9	24 1.9	2 43.2	20 44.7	15 53.9	14 21.9	7 40.8	8 52.9	21 51.1
30 W	16 26 22.8	7 40.3	15 14.5	22 22.4	26 1.7	3 55.8	21 25.2	16 7.8	14 24.6	7 38.8	8 54.8	21 52.4
31 T	16 30 19.4	8 37.9	15 11.3	5♍21.6	28 3.4	5 8.4	22 5.6	16 21.6	14 27.3	7 36.8	8 56.8	21 53.8
						DECLINATION						
1 T	14 32 2.7	14N43.8	15N48.9	18N40.3	2N39.3	20N 6.9	21N 0.6	21N26.8	8S24.0	23S29.2	22N18.2	15N21.1
4 F	14 43 52.4	15 37.9	15 51.8	9 47.8	3 33.7	21 0.7	21 26.6	21 32.9	8 18.9	23 29.4	22 18.0	15 21.8
7 M	14 55 42.1	16 29.8	15 54.6	4S36.9	4 42.9	21 49.3	21 50.8	21 38.9	8 14.0	23 29.7	22 17.8	15 22.4
10 T	15 7 31.7	17 19.1	15 57.5	17 11.1	6 4.9	22 32.5	22 13.3	21 44.8	8 9.4	23 30.0	22 17.7	15 23.1
13 S	15 19 21.4	18 5.9	16 0.3	19 36.1	7 38.1	23 10.0	22 33.9	21 50.5	8 5.1	23 30.3	22 17.5	15 23.7
16 W	15 31 11.0	18 50.0	16 3.2	11 55.4	9 20.7	23 41.6	22 52.6	21 56.0	8 1.1	23 30.6	22 17.2	15 24.3
19 S	15 43 0.7	19 31.2	16 6.0	0N 4.4	11 10.8	24 7.2	23 9.6	22 1.4	7 57.3	23 31.0	22 17.0	15 24.9
22 T	15 54 50.4	20 9.4	16 8.8	11 40.6	13 6.6	24 26.5	23 24.7	22 6.6	7 53.9	23 31.3	22 16.7	15 25.4
25 F	16 6 40.0	20 44.5	16 11.6	19 7.7	15 5.8	24 39.5	23 37.9	22 11.6	7 50.7	23 31.7	22 16.4	15 26.0
28 M	16 18 29.7	21 16.5	16 14.5	19 16.7	17 5.3	24 46.0	23 49.2	22 16.4	7 47.9	23 32.1	22 16.1	15 26.5
31 T	16 30 19.4	21 45.1	16 17.3	11 16.6	19 1.4	24 46.0	23 58.6	22 21.0	7 45.4	23 32.5	22 15.8	15 27.0

JUNE 1906

DAY	EPHEMERIS SIDEREAL TIME	☉	☊	☽	☿	♀	♂	♃	♄	♅	♆	♇
						LONGITUDE						
1 F	16 34 15.9	9♊35.4	15♌8.1	18♍44.1	0♊7.0	6♋20.9	22♊46.0	16♊35.4	14♓29.8	7♑34.8	8♋58.8	21♊55.2
2 S	16 38 12.5	10 32.8	15 4.9	2♎32.7	2 12.4	7 33.4	23 26.4	16 49.3	14 32.2	7R32.7	9 0.8	21 56.6
3 S	16 42 9.1	11 30.3	15 1.7	16 48.6	4 19.3	8 45.8	24 6.7	17 3.1	14 34.6	7 30.6	9 2.8	21 58.0
4 M	16 46 5.6	12 27.7	14 58.6	1♏29.8	6 27.6	9 58.2	24 46.9	17 17.0	14 36.8	7 28.5	9 4.8	21 59.4
5 T	16 50 2.2	13 25.1	14 55.4	16 31.3	8 37.2	11 10.6	25 27.2	17 30.8	14 39.0	7 26.4	9 6.9	22 0.8
6 W	16 53 58.7	14 22.5	14 52.2	1♐44.7	10 47.7	12 22.9	26 7.4	17 44.7	14 41.1	7 24.3	9 9.0	22 2.2
7 T	16 57 55.3	15 19.9	14 49.0	16 59.6	12 59.0	13 35.2	26 47.5	17 58.5	14 43.1	7 22.1	9 11.0	22 3.6
8 F	17 1 51.8	16 17.3	14 45.9	2♑5.0	15 10.9	14 47.4	27 27.7	18 12.4	14 44.9	7 19.9	9 13.1	22 5.0
9 S	17 5 48.4	17 14.6	14 42.7	16 51.8	17 22.9	15 59.6	28 7.8	18 26.3	14 46.7	7 17.6	9 15.2	22 6.4
10 S	17 9 45.0	18 12.0	14 39.5	1♒13.4	19 35.0	17 11.8	28 47.8	18 40.2	14 48.4	7 15.4	9 17.3	22 7.8
11 M	17 13 41.5	19 9.3	14 36.3	15 6.8	21 46.7	18 23.9	29 27.8	18 54.0	14 50.0	7 13.1	9 19.4	22 9.2
12 T	17 17 38.1	20 6.7	14 33.2	28 32.1	23 57.9	19 35.9	0♋7.8	19 7.9	14 51.5	7 10.9	9 21.5	22 10.6
13 W	17 21 34.6	21 4.0	14 30.0	11♓31.4	26 8.2	20 48.0	0 47.8	19 21.8	14 52.9	7 8.6	9 23.7	22 12.1
14 T	17 25 31.2	22 1.3	14 26.8	24 8.6	28 17.5	21 59.9	1 27.7	19 35.6	14 54.2	7 6.3	9 25.8	22 13.5
15 F	17 29 27.8	22 58.6	14 23.6	6♈28.2	0♋25.4	23 11.9	2 7.6	19 49.5	14 55.4	7 3.9	9 28.0	22 14.9
16 S	17 33 24.3	23 55.9	14 20.5	18 34.6	2 32.0	24 23.8	2 47.5	20 3.3	14 56.5	7 1.6	9 30.1	22 16.3
17 S	17 37 20.8	24 53.2	14 17.3	0♉32.3	4 36.9	25 35.7	3 27.3	20 17.2	14 57.5	6 59.2	9 32.3	22 17.7
18 M	17 41 17.4	25 50.5	14 14.1	12 25.2	6 40.0	26 47.5	4 7.2	20 31.0	14 58.4	6 56.9	9 34.5	22 19.1
19 T	17 45 14.0	26 47.8	14 10.9	24 16.4	8 41.3	27 59.3	4 46.9	20 44.8	14 59.2	6 54.5	9 36.7	22 20.5
20 W	17 49 10.5	27 45.1	14 7.7	6♊8.7	10 40.6	29 11.0	5 26.7	20 58.6	14 59.9	6 52.1	9 38.9	22 22.0
21 T	17 53 7.1	28 42.3	14 4.6	18 4.1	12 37.8	0♌22.7	6 6.4	21 12.4	15 0.5	6 49.7	9 41.0	22 23.4
22 F	17 57 3.6	29 39.6	14 1.4	0♋4.4	14 32.9	1 34.3	6 46.1	21 26.2	15 1.0	6 47.3	9 43.2	22 24.8
23 S	18 1 0.2	0♋36.9	13 58.2	12 11.1	16 26.0	2 45.9	7 25.8	21 40.0	15 1.5	6 44.9	9 45.5	22 26.2
24 S	18 4 56.7	1 34.1	13 55.0	24 25.7	18 16.8	3 57.5	8 5.4	21 53.8	15 1.8	6 42.5	9 47.7	22 27.6
25 M	18 8 53.3	2 31.4	13 51.9	6♌49.8	20 5.4	5 9.0	8 45.0	22 7.5	15 2.0	6 40.0	9 49.9	22 29.0
26 T	18 12 49.9	3 28.6	13 48.7	19 25.4	21 51.9	6 20.4	9 24.5	22 21.2	15 2.1	6 37.6	9 52.1	22 30.4
27 W	18 16 46.4	4 25.8	13 45.5	2♍14.8	23 36.1	7 31.8	10 4.1	22 34.9	15 2.1	6 35.2	9 54.3	22 31.8
28 T	18 20 42.9	5 23.0	13 42.3	15 20.4	25 18.1	8 43.2	10 43.6	22 48.6	15R 2.0	6 32.7	9 56.6	22 33.1
29 F	18 24 39.5	6 20.3	13 39.2	28 44.7	26 57.8	9 54.4	11 23.1	23 2.2	15 1.8	6 30.3	9 58.8	22 34.5
30 S	18 28 36.1	7 17.5	13 36.0	12♎29.6	28 35.3	11 5.7	12 2.5	23 15.9	15 1.5	6 27.9	10 1.0	22 35.9
						DECLINATION						
1 F	16 34 15.9	21N53.9	16N18.2	7N 7.7	19N38.6	24N44.6	24N 1.4	22N22.5	7S44.6	23S32.6	22N15.7	15N27.2
4 M	16 46 5.6	22 18.0	16 21.0	7S20.8	21 23.0	24 36.0	24 8.3	22 26.8	7 42.5	23 33.0	22 15.4	15 27.7
7 T	16 57 55.3	22 38.5	16 23.8	18 36.1	22 52.2	24 21.0	24 13.3	22 31.0	7 40.8	23 33.4	22 15.0	15 28.1
10 S	17 9 45.0	22 55.5	16 26.6	18 51.9	24 1.3	23 59.8	24 16.5	22 34.9	7 39.4	23 33.8	22 14.6	15 28.5
13 W	17 21 34.6	23 8.9	16 29.3	9 30.2	24 46.5	23 32.4	24 17.8	22 38.6	7 38.3	23 34.3	22 14.3	15 28.9
16 S	17 33 24.3	23 18.6	16 32.1	2N57.9	25 6.5	22 59.0	24 17.2	22 42.0	7 37.6	23 34.7	22 13.9	15 29.3
19 T	17 45 14.0	23 24.6	16 34.9	13 58.6	25 2.2	22 19.9	24 14.8	22 45.3	7 37.2	23 35.1	22 13.4	15 29.6
22 F	17 57 3.6	23 26.9	16 37.6	19 59.1	24 36.1	21 35.3	24 10.6	22 48.3	7 37.2	23 35.5	22 13.0	15 29.9
25 M	18 8 53.3	23 25.5	16 40.4	18 6.4	23 51.3	20 45.5	24 4.6	22 51.1	7 37.6	23 35.9	22 12.6	15 30.2
28 T	18 20 42.9	23 20.4	16 43.1	8 24.2	22 51.4	19 50.7	23 56.8	22 53.7	7 38.2	23 36.3	22 12.1	15 30.5

JULY 1906

LONGITUDE

DAY	EPHEMERIS SIDEREAL TIME h m s	☉ ° ′	☊ ° ′	☽ ° ′	☿ ° ′	♀ ° ′	♂ ° ′	♃ ° ′	♄ ° ′	♅ ° ′	♆ ° ′	♇ ° ′
1 S	18 32 32.7	8♋14.7	13♌32.8	26♎35.6	0♌10.6	12♌16.8	12♋41.9	23♊29.5	15♓ 1.1	6♑25.4	10♋ 3.3	22♊37.3
2 M	18 36 29.2	9 11.9	13 29.6	11♏ 1.7	1 43.6	13 27.9	13 21.3	23 43.1	15R 0.6	6R23.0	10 5.5	22 38.6
3 T	18 40 25.8	10 9.1	13 26.4	25 44.5	3 14.3	14 39.0	14 0.7	23 56.6	15 0.0	6 20.6	10 7.7	22 40.0
4 W	18 44 22.3	11 6.2	13 23.3	10♐38.2	4 42.7	15 50.0	14 40.0	24 10.2	14 59.3	6 18.2	10 10.0	22 41.4
5 T	18 48 18.9	12 3.4	13 20.1	25 35.1	6 8.8	17 0.9	15 19.3	24 23.7	14 58.6	6 15.7	10 12.2	22 42.7
6 F	18 52 15.4	13 0.6	13 16.9	10♑26.6	7 32.6	18 11.7	15 58.5	24 37.1	14 57.7	6 13.3	10 14.4	22 44.0
7 S	18 56 12.0	13 57.8	13 13.7	25 4.6	8 54.0	19 22.5	16 37.8	24 50.6	14 56.7	6 10.9	10 16.6	22 45.4
8 S	19 0 8.6	14 55.0	13 10.6	9♒22.7	10 13.0	20 33.3	17 17.0	25 4.0	14 55.6	6 8.5	10 18.9	22 46.7
9 M	19 4 5.1	15 52.2	13 7.4	23 16.9	11 29.5	21 43.9	17 56.2	25 17.3	14 54.5	6 6.1	10 21.1	22 48.0
10 T	19 8 1.6	16 49.4	13 4.2	6♓45.5	12 43.5	22 54.5	18 35.4	25 30.7	14 53.2	6 3.7	10 23.3	22 49.3
11 W	19 11 58.2	17 46.5	13 1.0	19 49.3	13 54.9	24 5.0	19 14.5	25 44.0	14 51.8	6 1.4	10 25.5	22 50.6
12 T	19 15 54.8	18 43.8	12 57.9	2♈30.7	15 3.7	25 15.5	19 53.6	25 57.3	14 50.4	5 59.0	10 27.7	22 51.9
13 F	19 19 51.4	19 41.0	12 54.7	14 53.5	16 9.8	26 25.9	20 32.7	26 10.5	14 48.8	5 56.7	10 30.0	22 53.2
14 S	19 23 47.9	20 38.2	12 51.5	27 2.0	17 13.1	27 36.2	21 11.8	26 23.7	14 47.2	5 54.3	10 32.2	22 54.5
15 S	19 27 44.4	21 35.4	12 48.3	9♉ 0.5	18 13.5	28 46.5	21 50.8	26 36.9	14 45.4	5 52.0	10 34.4	22 55.8
16 M	19 31 41.0	22 32.7	12 45.1	20 53.7	19 10.9	29 56.7	22 29.8	26 50.0	14 43.6	5 49.7	10 36.6	22 57.0
17 T	19 35 37.6	23 29.9	12 42.0	2♊45.7	20 5.2	1♍ 6.8	23 8.8	27 3.0	14 41.7	5 47.4	10 38.8	22 58.3
18 W	19 39 34.1	24 27.2	12 38.8	14 40.1	20 56.2	2 16.8	23 47.8	27 16.1	14 39.7	5 45.2	10 40.9	22 59.5
19 T	19 43 30.7	25 24.5	12 35.6	26 40.0	21 43.9	3 26.8	24 26.8	27 29.1	14 37.6	5 42.9	10 43.1	23 0.7
20 F	19 47 27.2	26 21.8	12 32.4	8♋47.9	22 28.1	4 36.7	25 5.7	27 42.0	14 35.4	5 40.7	10 45.3	23 2.0
21 S	19 51 23.8	27 19.1	12 29.3	21 5.8	23 8.7	5 46.5	25 44.6	27 54.9	14 33.1	5 38.5	10 47.5	23 3.2
22 S	19 55 20.3	28 16.4	12 26.1	3♌35.2	23 45.4	6 56.3	26 23.5	28 7.7	14 30.7	5 36.3	10 49.6	23 4.4
23 M	19 59 16.9	29 13.7	12 22.9	16 16.8	24 18.3	8 5.9	27 2.4	28 20.5	14 28.3	5 34.1	10 51.8	23 5.5
24 T	20 3 13.5	0♌11.0	12 19.7	29 11.5	24 46.9	9 15.5	27 41.2	28 33.2	14 25.7	5 32.0	10 53.9	23 6.7
25 W	20 7 10.0	1 8.3	12 16.6	12♍19.8	25 11.3	10 25.0	28 20.1	28 45.9	14 23.1	5 29.9	10 56.0	23 7.9
26 T	20 11 6.5	2 5.7	12 13.4	25 41.9	25 31.2	11 34.4	28 58.9	28 58.6	14 20.4	5 27.8	10 58.1	23 9.0
27 F	20 15 3.1	3 3.0	12 10.2	9♎18.1	25 46.5	12 43.7	29 37.6	29 11.1	14 17.6	5 25.7	11 0.2	23 10.1
28 S	20 18 59.7	4 0.4	12 7.0	23 8.1	25 57.0	13 53.0	0♌16.4	29 23.6	14 14.7	5 23.7	11 2.3	23 11.3
29 S	20 22 56.3	4 57.7	12 3.8	7♏11.3	26 2.6	15 2.1	0 55.1	29 36.1	14 11.8	5 21.6	11 4.4	23 12.4
30 M	20 26 52.8	5 55.1	12 0.7	21 26.3	26 3.1	16 11.1	1 33.8	29 48.5	14 8.8	5 19.6	11 6.5	23 13.5
31 T	20 30 49.3	6 52.5	11 57.5	5♐50.5	25R58.5	17 20.0	2 12.5	0♋ 0.8	14 5.7	5 17.7	11 8.5	23 14.5

DECLINATION

DAY	EPHEMERIS SIDEREAL TIME h m s	☉	☊	☽	☿	♀	♂	♃	♄	♅	♆	♇
1 S	18 32 32.7	23N11.6	16N45.9	5S35.2	21N39.8	18N51.2	23N47.3	22N56.0	7S39.3	23S36.7	22N11.7	15N30.7
4 W	18 44 22.3	22 59.1	16 48.6	17 31.6	20 19.5	17 47.4	23 36.0	22 58.2	7 40.6	23 37.0	22 11.2	15 30.9
7 S	18 56 12.0	22 43.0	16 51.3	19 38.3	18 53.4	16 39.6	23 23.1	23 0.1	7 42.3	23 37.4	22 10.7	15 31.1
10 T	19 8 1.6	22 23.4	16 54.0	11 5.2	17 24.1	15 28.1	23 8.6	23 1.8	7 44.3	23 37.8	22 10.2	15 31.2
13 F	19 19 51.4	22 0.3	16 56.7	1N33.3	15 54.1	14 13.1	22 52.4	23 3.2	7 46.7	23 38.1	22 9.7	15 31.3
16 M	19 31 41.0	21 33.8	16 59.4	12 59.0	14 25.9	12 55.1	22 34.6	23 4.5	7 49.3	23 38.4	22 9.2	15 31.4
19 T	19 43 30.7	21 4.0	17 2.1	19 40.9	13 2.2	11 34.3	22 15.3	23 5.6	7 52.3	23 38.7	22 8.7	15 31.5
22 S	19 55 20.3	20 31.0	17 4.8	18 38.1	11 45.8	10 11.1	21 54.5	23 6.4	7 55.6	23 39.0	22 8.2	15 31.5
25 W	20 7 10.0	19 54.8	17 7.5	9 25.5	10 39.7	8 45.8	21 32.3	23 7.1	7 59.1	23 39.3	22 7.6	15 31.5
28 S	20 18 59.7	19 15.7	17 10.1	4S20.5	9 47.5	7 18.6	21 8.6	23 7.5	8 2.9	23 39.6	22 7.1	15 31.5
31 T	20 30 49.3	18 33.7	17 12.8	16 32.4	9 12.8	5 50.0	20 43.6	23 7.8	8 7.0	23 39.8	22 6.6	15 31.4

AUGUST 1906

LONGITUDE

DAY	EPHEMERIS SIDEREAL TIME h m s	☉ ° ′	☊ ° ′	☽ ° ′	☿ ° ′	♀ ° ′	♂ ° ′	♃ ° ′	♄ ° ′	♅ ° ′	♆ ° ′	♇ ° ′
1 W	20 34 45.9	7♌49.8	11♌54.3	20♐20.4	25♌48.7	18♍28.9	2♌51.2	0♋13.1	14♓ 2.5	5♑15.8	11♋10.6	23♊15.6
2 T	20 38 42.5	8 47.2	11 51.1	4♑51.2	25R33.8	19 37.6	3 29.8	0 25.3	13R59.3	5R13.9	11 12.6	23 16.7
3 F	20 42 39.0	9 44.7	11 48.0	19 17.8	25 13.7	20 46.2	4 8.4	0 37.4	13 55.9	5 12.0	11 14.6	23 17.7
4 S	20 46 35.5	10 42.1	11 44.8	3♒34.7	24 48.7	21 54.7	4 47.0	0 49.5	13 52.6	5 10.2	11 16.6	23 18.7
5 S	20 50 32.1	11 39.5	11 41.6	17 37.1	24 18.8	23 3.1	5 25.6	1 1.5	13 49.1	5 8.4	11 18.6	23 19.7
6 M	20 54 28.7	12 37.0	11 38.4	1♓21.3	23 44.6	24 11.4	6 4.2	1 13.5	13 45.6	5 6.6	11 20.6	23 20.7
7 T	20 58 25.2	13 34.4	11 35.3	14 45.0	23 6.2	25 19.5	6 42.7	1 25.3	13 42.0	5 4.9	11 22.5	23 21.7
8 W	21 2 21.8	14 31.9	11 32.1	27 47.7	22 24.3	26 27.6	7 21.3	1 37.1	13 38.4	5 3.2	11 24.5	23 22.6
9 T	21 6 18.3	15 29.4	11 28.9	10♈30.2	21 39.4	27 35.5	7 59.8	1 48.9	13 34.7	5 1.5	11 26.4	23 23.6
10 F	21 10 14.9	16 27.0	11 25.7	22 55.0	20 52.3	28 43.3	8 38.3	2 0.5	13 30.9	4 59.9	11 28.3	23 24.5
11 S	21 14 11.4	17 24.5	11 22.5	5♉ 5.3	20 3.8	29 51.0	9 16.8	2 12.1	13 27.1	4 58.3	11 30.2	23 25.4
12 S	21 18 8.0	18 22.1	11 19.4	17 5.2	19 14.7	0♎58.5	9 55.2	2 23.6	13 23.2	4 56.7	11 32.1	23 26.3
13 M	21 22 4.6	19 19.7	11 16.2	28 59.2	18 25.9	2 6.0	10 33.7	2 35.0	13 19.2	4 55.2	11 33.9	23 27.2
14 T	21 26 1.1	20 17.4	11 13.0	10♊51.8	17 38.4	3 13.3	11 12.1	2 46.4	13 15.3	4 53.8	11 35.8	23 28.0
15 W	21 29 57.7	21 15.0	11 9.8	22 47.7	16 53.2	4 20.5	11 50.5	2 57.6	13 11.2	4 52.3	11 37.6	23 28.9
16 T	21 33 54.2	22 12.7	11 6.7	4♋51.0	16 11.1	5 27.5	12 28.9	3 8.8	13 7.1	4 50.9	11 39.4	23 29.7
17 F	21 37 50.8	23 10.4	11 3.5	17 5.3	15 33.1	6 34.4	13 7.3	3 19.9	13 3.0	4 49.6	11 41.2	23 30.5
18 S	21 41 47.3	24 8.1	11 0.3	29 33.5	14 59.9	7 41.2	13 45.7	3 30.9	12 58.8	4 48.3	11 42.9	23 31.3
19 S	21 45 43.8	25 5.9	10 57.1	12♌17.7	14 32.4	8 47.8	14 24.1	3 41.8	12 54.6	4 47.0	11 44.6	23 32.0
20 M	21 49 40.4	26 3.7	10 53.9	25 18.9	14 11.1	9 54.3	15 2.4	3 52.6	12 50.3	4 45.8	11 46.4	23 32.8
21 T	21 53 37.0	27 1.5	10 50.8	8♍36.8	13 56.7	11 0.6	15 40.7	4 3.4	12 46.0	4 44.6	11 48.1	23 33.5
22 W	21 57 33.6	27 59.3	10 47.6	22 10.4	13 49.4	12 6.8	16 19.0	4 14.0	12 41.7	4 43.4	11 49.7	23 34.2
23 T	22 1 30.1	28 57.1	10 44.4	5♎57.5	13D49.7	13 12.8	16 57.3	4 24.5	12 37.3	4 42.3	11 51.4	23 34.9
24 F	22 5 26.6	29 55.0	10 41.2	19 55.4	13 57.7	14 18.6	17 35.6	4 35.0	12 32.9	4 41.3	11 53.0	23 35.6
25 S	22 9 23.2	0♍52.9	10 38.1	4♏ 1.2	14 13.7	15 24.3	18 13.9	4 45.3	12 28.5	4 40.3	11 54.6	23 36.3
26 S	22 13 19.7	1 50.8	10 34.9	18 12.0	14 37.6	16 29.8	18 52.1	4 55.6	12 24.0	4 39.3	11 56.2	23 36.9
27 M	22 17 16.3	2 48.7	10 31.7	2♐25.0	15 9.4	17 35.1	19 30.3	5 5.7	12 19.6	4 38.4	11 57.8	23 37.5
28 T	22 21 12.9	3 46.7	10 28.5	16 37.7	15 49.0	18 40.2	20 8.6	5 15.7	12 15.1	4 37.5	11 59.3	23 38.1
29 W	22 25 9.4	4 44.6	10 25.3	0♑48.0	16 36.3	19 45.1	20 46.8	5 25.7	12 10.5	4 36.7	12 0.8	23 38.7
30 T	22 29 5.9	5 42.6	10 22.2	14 53.8	17 30.9	20 49.9	21 24.9	5 35.5	12 6.0	4 35.9	12 2.3	23 39.2
31 F	22 33 2.5	6 40.6	10 19.0	28 52.7	18 32.6	21 54.4	22 3.1	5 45.2	12 1.5	4 35.2	12 3.7	23 39.8

DECLINATION

DAY	EPHEMERIS SIDEREAL TIME h m s	☉	☊	☽	☿	♀	♂	♃	♄	♅	♆	♇
1 W	20 34 45.9	18N19.1	17N13.7	18S58.6	9N 5.7	5N20.1	20N35.0	23N 7.9	8S 8.4	23S39.9	22N 6.4	15N31.4
4 S	20 46 35.5	17 33.5	17 16.3	18 38.0	8 59.2	3 49.9	20 8.2	23 7.9	8 12.7	23 40.1	22 5.9	15 31.3
7 T	20 58 25.2	16 45.4	17 19.0	8 40.1	9 16.3	2 18.9	19 40.2	23 7.8	8 17.3	23 40.3	22 5.4	15 31.2
10 F	21 10 14.9	15 54.8	17 21.6	4N16.0	9 55.8	0 47.4	19 10.9	23 7.6	8 22.1	23 40.5	22 4.9	15 31.1
13 M	21 22 4.6	15 1.9	17 24.2	15 0.9	10 53.6	0S44.4	18 40.5	23 7.2	8 27.0	23 40.7	22 4.4	15 30.9
16 T	21 33 54.2	14 6.8	17 26.8	20 11.3	12 1.9	2 16.1	18 9.0	23 6.6	8 32.1	23 40.8	22 3.9	15 30.8
19 S	21 45 43.8	13 9.7	17 29.4	17 9.9	13 11.3	3 47.6	17 36.4	23 6.0	8 37.3	23 40.9	22 3.4	15 30.6
22 W	21 57 33.6	12 10.7	17 32.1	6 14.6	14 12.4	5 18.4	17 2.7	23 5.2	8 42.6	23 41.1	22 2.9	15 30.3
25 S	22 9 23.2	11 10.0	17 34.6	7S57.8	14 57.4	6 48.4	16 28.1	23 4.3	8 47.9	23 41.1	22 2.5	15 30.1
28 T	22 21 12.9	10 7.6	17 37.2	18 29.9	15 19.9	8 17.3	15 52.6	23 3.4	8 53.4	23 41.2	22 2.0	15 29.8
31 F	22 33 2.5	9 3.9	17 39.8	19 15.5	15 15.8	9 44.7	15 16.1	23 2.3	8 58.8	23 41.3	22 1.6	15 29.6

SEPTEMBER 1906

DAY	EPHEMERIS SIDEREAL TIME	☉	☊	☽	☿	♀	♂	♃	♄	♅	♆	♇
	h m s	° ′	° ′	° ′	° ′	° ′	° ′	° ′	° ′	° ′	° ′	° ′
						LONGITUDE						
1 S	22 36 59.1	7♍38.7	10♌15.8	12♒42.7	19♌41.0	22♎58.7	22♌41.3	5♋54.8	11♓56.9	4♑34.5	12♋ 5.2	23♊40.3
2 S	22 40 55.6	8 36.7	10 12.6	26 21.4	20 55.7	24 2.8	23 19.4	6 4.3	11R52.3	4R33.9	12 6.6	23 40.8
3 M	22 44 52.2	9 34.8	10 9.5	9♓46.6	22 16.3	25 6.6	23 57.5	6 13.7	11 47.8	4 33.3	12 8.0	23 41.2
4 T	22 48 48.7	10 32.9	10 6.3	22 56.7	23 42.3	26 10.3	24 35.6	6 23.0	11 43.2	4 32.8	12 9.3	23 41.7
5 W	22 52 45.3	11 31.1	10 3.1	5♈50.6	25 13.2	27 13.6	25 13.7	6 32.1	11 38.6	4 32.3	12 10.7	23 42.1
6 T	22 56 41.8	12 29.3	9 59.9	18 28.3	26 48.4	28 16.8	25 51.8	6 41.2	11 34.0	4 31.8	12 12.0	23 42.5
7 F	23 0 38.3	13 27.5	9 56.7	0♉50.8	28 27.4	29 19.7	26 29.9	6 50.1	11 29.4	4 31.5	12 13.2	23 42.9
8 S	23 4 34.9	14 25.7	9 53.6	13 0.3	0♍ 9.8	0♏22.3	27 8.0	6 58.9	11 24.8	4 31.1	12 14.5	23 43.3
9 S	23 8 31.5	15 24.0	9 50.4	24 59.8	1 55.0	1 24.7	27 46.0	7 7.5	11 20.3	4 30.8	12 15.7	23 43.6
10 M	23 12 28.1	16 22.3	9 47.2	6♊53.2	3 42.5	2 26.9	28 24.1	7 16.1	11 15.7	4 30.6	12 16.9	23 44.0
11 T	23 16 24.6	17 20.6	9 44.0	18 45.0	5 31.8	3 28.7	29 2.1	7 24.5	11 11.1	4 30.4	12 18.1	23 44.3
12 W	23 20 21.1	18 19.0	9 40.8	0♋40.1	7 22.6	4 30.3	29 40.1	7 32.8	11 6.6	4 30.3	12 19.2	23 44.5
13 T	23 24 17.7	19 17.4	9 37.7	12 43.6	9 14.5	5 31.6	0♍18.2	7 41.0	11 2.1	4 30.2	12 20.3	23 44.8
14 F	23 28 14.3	20 15.9	9 34.5	25 0.1	11 7.1	6 32.5	0 56.2	7 49.0	10 57.6	4 30.1	12 21.4	23 45.0
15 S	23 32 10.8	21 14.4	9 31.3	7♌33.9	13 0.2	7 33.2	1 34.2	7 56.9	10 53.1	4 30.1	12 22.4	23 45.3
16 S	23 36 7.3	22 12.9	9 28.1	20 28.1	14 53.4	8 33.5	2 12.2	8 4.6	10 48.6	4D30.2	12 23.4	23 45.5
17 M	23 40 3.9	23 11.4	9 25.0	3♍44.7	16 46.6	9 33.6	2 50.1	8 12.3	10 44.2	4 30.3	12 24.4	23 45.6
18 T	23 44 0.5	24 10.0	9 21.8	17 23.6	18 39.5	10 33.2	3 28.1	8 19.7	10 39.8	4 30.5	12 25.4	23 45.8
19 W	23 47 57.0	25 8.6	9 18.6	1♎22.7	20 32.1	11 32.6	4 6.1	8 27.1	10 35.4	4 30.7	12 26.3	23 45.9
20 T	23 51 53.6	26 7.3	9 15.4	15 38.1	22 24.1	12 31.5	4 44.0	8 34.2	10 31.1	4 31.0	12 27.2	23 46.0
21 F	23 55 50.1	27 6.0	9 12.2	0♏ 4.0	24 15.6	13 30.1	5 22.0	8 41.3	10 26.8	4 31.3	12 28.1	23 46.1
22 S	23 59 46.7	28 4.7	9 9.1	14 34.3	26 6.3	14 28.3	5 59.9	8 48.2	10 22.5	4 31.7	12 28.9	23 46.2
23 S	0 3 43.3	29 3.4	9 5.9	29 3.1	27 56.2	15 26.0	6 37.8	8 54.9	10 18.3	4 32.1	12 29.7	23 46.2
24 M	0 7 39.8	0♎ 2.2	9 2.7	13♐25.3	29 45.4	16 23.4	7 15.7	9 1.5	10 14.1	4 32.6	12 30.5	23 46.2
25 T	0 11 36.3	1 1.0	8 59.5	27 37.8	1♎33.6	17 20.3	7 53.6	9 7.9	10 9.9	4 33.1	12 31.2	23R46.2
26 W	0 15 32.9	1 59.8	8 56.4	11♑38.7	3 21.0	18 16.7	8 31.4	9 14.2	10 5.8	4 33.7	12 31.9	23 46.2
27 T	0 19 29.5	2 58.7	8 53.2	25 27.6	5 7.5	19 12.6	9 9.3	9 20.3	10 1.8	4 34.3	12 32.6	23 46.1
28 F	0 23 26.0	3 57.6	8 50.0	9♒ 4.4	6 53.1	20 8.1	9 47.2	9 26.3	9 57.8	4 35.0	12 33.2	23 46.1
29 S	0 27 22.6	4 56.5	8 46.8	22 29.8	8 37.8	21 3.0	10 25.0	9 32.1	9 53.9	4 35.7	12 33.8	23 46.0
30 S	0 31 19.1	5 55.4	8 43.6	5♓43.8	10 21.6	21 57.4	11 2.8	9 37.8	9 50.0	4 36.5	12 34.4	23 45.8
						DECLINATION						
1 S	22 36 59.1	8N42.3	17N40.7	17S 5.7	15N 8.1	10S13.5	15N 3.8	23N 2.0	9S 0.7	23S41.3	22N 1.4	15N29.5
4 T	22 48 48.7	7 36.9	17 43.2	5 58.1	14 25.4	11 38.6	14 26.2	23 0.9	9 6.1	23 41.4	22 1.0	15 29.2
7 F	23 0 38.3	6 30.3	17 45.8	6N58.8	13 14.7	13 1.7	13 47.9	22 59.7	9 11.5	23 41.4	22 0.6	15 28.8
10 M	23 12 28.1	5 22.8	17 48.4	16 51.1	11 39.6	14 22.5	13 8.8	22 58.5	9 16.9	23 41.4	22 0.2	15 28.5
13 T	23 24 17.7	4 14.4	17 50.9	20 22.4	9 45.4	15 40.7	12 29.1	22 57.3	9 22.2	23 41.4	21 59.9	15 28.2
16 S	23 36 7.3	3 5.4	17 53.4	15 27.9	7 37.7	16 56.1	11 48.7	22 56.1	9 27.3	23 41.4	21 59.5	15 27.8
19 W	23 47 57.0	1 55.8	17 56.0	3 5.1	5 21.5	18 8.5	11 7.6	22 54.9	9 32.4	23 41.3	21 59.2	15 27.4
22 S	23 59 46.7	0 45.9	17 58.5	11S19.6	3 0.9	19 17.6	10 26.1	22 53.7	9 37.3	23 41.3	21 58.9	15 27.1
25 T	0 11 36.3	0S24.3	18 1.0	19 56.0	0 38.8	20 23.1	9 44.0	22 52.6	9 42.0	23 41.2	21 58.6	15 26.7
28 F	0 23 26.0	1 34.5	18 3.5	17 52.3	1S42.4	21 24.9	9 1.4	22 51.5	9 46.5	23 41.1	21 58.4	15 26.3

OCTOBER 1906

DAY	EPHEMERIS SIDEREAL TIME	☉	☊	☽	☿	♀	♂	♃	♄	♅	♆	♇
						LONGITUDE						
1 M	0 35 15.6	6♎54.4	8♌40.5	18♓46.6	12♎ 4.5	22♏51.2	11♍40.6	9♋43.2	9♓46.2	4♑37.3	12♋34.9	23♊45.7
2 T	0 39 12.2	7 53.4	8 37.3	1♈37.8	13 46.6	23 44.5	12 18.4	9 48.6	9R42.4	4 38.2	12 35.5	23R45.5
3 W	0 43 8.8	8 52.4	8 34.1	14 17.2	15 27.8	24 37.2	12 56.2	9 53.7	9 38.7	4 39.2	12 35.9	23 45.4
4 T	0 47 5.3	9 51.5	8 30.9	26 44.5	17 8.1	25 29.2	13 34.0	9 58.7	9 35.1	4 40.1	12 36.4	23 45.2
5 F	0 51 1.9	10 50.6	8 27.8	9♉ 0.2	18 47.6	26 20.6	14 11.8	10 3.5	9 31.5	4 41.2	12 36.8	23 44.9
6 S	0 54 58.4	11 49.7	8 24.6	21 5.5	20 26.3	27 11.3	14 49.6	10 8.2	9 28.0	4 42.3	12 37.2	23 44.7
7 S	0 58 55.0	12 48.9	8 21.4	3♊ 2.3	22 4.2	28 1.3	15 27.4	10 12.6	9 24.5	4 43.4	12 37.5	23 44.4
8 M	1 2 51.5	13 48.1	8 18.2	14 53.7	23 41.3	28 50.6	16 5.1	10 16.9	9 21.2	4 44.6	12 37.8	23 44.1
9 T	1 6 48.1	14 47.4	8 15.0	26 43.4	25 17.6	29 39.1	16 42.9	10 21.0	9 17.9	4 45.8	12 38.1	23 43.8
10 W	1 10 44.6	15 46.7	8 11.9	8♋36.1	26 53.2	0♐26.9	17 20.6	10 25.0	9 14.6	4 47.1	12 38.3	23 43.5
11 T	1 14 41.2	16 46.0	8 8.7	20 36.9	28 28.1	1 13.9	17 58.4	10 28.7	9 11.5	4 48.4	12 38.5	23 43.1
12 F	1 18 37.8	17 45.4	8 5.5	2♌51.1	0♏ 2.3	1 60.0	18 36.1	10 32.3	9 8.4	4 49.8	12 38.7	23 42.8
13 S	1 22 34.3	18 44.8	8 2.3	15 23.9	1 35.7	2 45.2	19 13.8	10 35.7	9 5.4	4 51.2	12 38.8	23 42.4
14 S	1 26 30.8	19 44.2	7 59.1	28 19.9	3 8.5	3 29.6	19 51.5	10 38.9	9 2.5	4 52.7	12 38.9	23 42.0
15 M	1 30 27.4	20 43.7	7 56.0	11♍42.4	4 40.6	4 13.0	20 29.2	10 41.9	8 59.6	4 54.2	12 39.0	23 41.5
16 T	1 34 24.0	21 43.3	7 52.8	25 32.5	6 12.0	4 55.4	21 6.9	10 44.8	8 56.9	4 55.8	12 39.1	23 41.1
17 W	1 38 20.5	22 42.8	7 49.6	9♎48.7	7 42.8	5 36.8	21 44.6	10 47.4	8 54.2	4 57.4	12 39.1	23 40.6
18 T	1 42 17.1	23 42.4	7 46.4	24 26.5	9 12.9	6 17.1	22 22.3	10 49.9	8 51.7	4 59.1	12R39.0	23 40.1
19 F	1 46 13.6	24 42.0	7 43.3	9♏18.4	10 42.4	6 56.4	22 60.0	10 52.1	8 49.2	5 0.8	12 39.0	23 39.6
20 S	1 50 10.1	25 41.7	7 40.1	24 15.3	12 11.1	7 34.4	23 37.6	10 54.2	8 46.7	5 2.5	12 38.9	23 39.0
21 S	1 54 6.7	26 41.4	7 36.9	9♐ 8.2	13 39.2	8 11.3	24 15.3	10 56.1	8 44.4	5 4.3	12 38.7	23 38.5
22 M	1 58 3.3	27 41.1	7 33.7	23 49.2	15 6.7	8 46.9	24 52.9	10 57.8	8 42.2	5 6.2	12 38.6	23 37.9
23 T	2 1 59.8	28 40.9	7 30.6	8♑13.1	16 33.4	9 21.1	25 30.5	10 59.2	8 40.1	5 8.1	12 38.4	23 37.3
24 W	2 5 56.4	29 40.6	7 27.4	22 17.4	17 59.4	9 54.0	26 8.1	11 0.5	8 38.1	5 10.0	12 38.1	23 36.7
25 T	2 9 52.9	0♏40.4	7 24.2	6♒ 1.8	19 24.7	10 25.5	26 45.7	11 1.6	8 36.1	5 12.0	12 37.9	23 36.0
26 F	2 13 49.5	1 40.3	7 21.0	19 27.6	20 49.2	10 55.5	27 23.3	11 2.5	8 34.3	5 14.0	12 37.6	23 35.4
27 S	2 17 46.0	2 40.1	7 17.8	2♓37.1	22 12.9	11 23.9	28 0.9	11 3.2	8 32.5	5 16.1	12 37.2	23 34.7
28 S	2 21 42.6	3 40.0	7 14.7	15 32.5	23 35.7	11 50.7	28 38.5	11 3.7	8 30.9	5 18.2	12 36.9	23 34.0
29 M	2 25 39.1	4 39.9	7 11.5	28 15.9	24 57.6	12 15.8	29 16.0	11 4.0	8 29.3	5 20.4	12 36.5	23 33.3
30 T	2 29 35.7	5 39.9	7 8.3	10♈48.7	26 18.6	12 39.2	29 53.6	11 4.1	8 27.9	5 22.6	12 36.0	23 32.6
31 W	2 33 32.3	6 39.9	7 5.1	23 12.0	27 38.5	13 0.8	0♎31.1	11R 4.0	8 26.5	5 24.8	12 35.6	23 31.9
						DECLINATION						
1 M	0 35 15.6	2S44.6	18N 6.0	7S21.2	4S 1.1	22S22.7	8N18.5	22N50.5	9S50.8	23S41.0	21N58.2	15N25.9
4 T	0 47 5.3	3 54.4	18 8.5	5N43.0	6 16.3	23 16.4	7 35.1	22 49.6	9 54.8	23 40.9	21 58.0	15 25.5
7 S	0 58 55.0	5 3.9	18 11.0	16 13.3	8 26.9	24 5.7	6 51.4	22 48.7	9 58.6	23 40.7	21 57.8	15 25.1
10 W	1 10 44.6	6 12.7	18 13.5	20 35.3	10 32.4	24 50.5	6 7.5	22 48.0	10 2.1	23 40.6	21 57.7	15 24.7
13 S	1 22 34.3	7 20.9	18 15.9	16 45.1	12 32.1	25 30.7	5 23.2	22 47.4	10 5.4	23 40.4	21 57.5	15 24.3
16 T	1 34 24.0	8 28.1	18 18.4	5 7.9	14 25.4	26 6.2	4 38.7	22 46.9	10 8.3	23 40.2	21 57.5	15 23.9
19 F	1 46 13.6	9 34.3	18 20.8	9S50.5	16 11.7	26 36.8	3 54.1	22 46.5	10 10.9	23 40.0	21 57.4	15 23.5
22 M	1 58 3.3	10 39.3	18 23.3	19 47.8	17 50.6	27 2.4	3 9.3	22 46.3	10 13.2	23 39.8	21 57.4	15 23.1
25 T	2 9 52.9	11 42.8	18 25.7	18 36.5	19 21.3	27 22.8	2 24.5	22 46.2	10 15.2	23 39.5	21 57.4	15 22.7
28 S	2 21 42.6	12 44.7	18 28.1	8 32.1	20 43.3	27 37.9	1 39.6	22 46.3	10 16.8	23 39.3	21 57.4	15 22.4
31 W	2 33 32.3	13 44.8	18 30.6	4N31.1	21 55.6	27 47.5	0 54.7	22 46.6	10 18.1	23 39.0	21 57.5	15 22.0

DAY	EPHEMERIS SIDEREAL TIME	☉	☊	☽	☿	♀	♂	♃	♄	♅	♆	♇
	h m s	° ′	° ′	° ′	° ′	° ′	° ′	° ′	° ′	° ′	° ′	° ′
						LONGITUDE						
1 T	2 37 28.8	7♏39.9	7♌ 2.0	5♉26.6	28♏57.3	13♐20.5	1♎ 8.6	11♋ 3.7	8♓25.3	5♑27.1	12♋35.1	23♊31.1
2 F	2 41 25.3	8 39.9	6 58.8	17 33.1	0♐14.8	13 38.3	1 46.2	11R 3.2	8R 24.1	5 29.4	12R 34.5	23R 30.3
3 S	2 45 21.9	9 40.0	6 55.6	29 32.2	1 31.0	13 54.2	2 23.7	11 2.5	8 23.0	5 31.8	12 34.0	23 29.5
4 S	2 49 18.5	10 40.1	6 52.4	11♊25.5	2 45.8	14 7.9	3 1.2	11 1.6	8 22.1	5 34.2	12 33.4	23 28.7
5 M	2 53 15.0	11 40.2	6 49.2	23 15.0	3 58.8	14 19.6	3 38.7	11 0.5	8 21.3	5 36.6	12 32.8	23 27.9
6 T	2 57 11.6	12 40.4	6 46.1	5♋ 3.4	5 10.1	14 29.1	4 16.2	10 59.2	8 20.5	5 39.1	12 32.1	23 27.1
7 W	3 1 8.1	13 40.6	6 42.9	16 54.6	6 19.3	14 36.4	4 53.6	10 57.7	8 19.9	5 41.6	12 31.4	23 26.2
8 T	3 5 4.7	14 40.8	6 39.7	28 53.1	7 26.3	14 41.4	5 31.1	10 56.0	8 19.3	5 44.1	12 30.7	23 25.3
9 F	3 9 1.2	15 41.1	6 36.5	11♌ 3.7	8 30.7	14 44.1	6 8.6	10 54.1	8 18.9	5 46.7	12 29.9	23 24.4
10 S	3 12 57.8	16 41.4	6 33.4	23 32.1	9 32.3	14 44.5	6 46.0	10 52.0	8 18.6	5 49.4	12 29.2	23 23.5
11 S	3 16 54.4	17 41.7	6 30.2	6♍23.2	10 30.6	14R 42.4	7 23.4	10 49.7	8 18.3	5 52.0	12 28.4	23 22.6
12 M	3 20 50.9	18 42.1	6 27.0	19 41.5	11 25.4	14 38.0	8 0.9	10 47.2	8 18.2	5 54.7	12 27.5	23 21.7
13 T	3 24 47.5	19 42.5	6 23.8	3♎29.8	12 16.1	14 31.1	8 38.3	10 44.5	8 18.2	5 57.4	12 26.6	23 20.7
14 W	3 28 44.0	20 42.9	6 20.6	17 48.1	13 2.3	14 21.8	9 15.7	10 41.6	8D 18.3	6 0.2	12 25.8	23 19.8
15 T	3 32 40.6	21 43.4	6 17.5	2♏33.1	13 43.3	14 10.1	9 53.1	10 38.5	8 18.5	6 3.0	12 24.8	23 18.8
16 F	3 36 37.1	22 43.9	6 14.3	17 37.8	14 18.6	13 55.9	10 30.5	10 35.2	8 18.8	6 5.8	12 23.9	23 17.8
17 S	3 40 33.7	23 44.4	6 11.1	2♐52.4	14 47.5	13 39.4	11 7.8	10 31.8	8 19.2	6 8.7	12 22.9	23 16.8
18 S	3 44 30.3	24 44.9	6 7.9	18 5.8	15 9.2	13 20.5	11 45.2	10 28.1	8 19.7	6 11.6	12 21.9	23 15.8
19 M	3 48 26.8	25 45.5	6 4.8	3♑ 7.6	15 23.0	12 59.4	12 22.5	10 24.3	8 20.3	6 14.5	12 20.8	23 14.8
20 T	3 52 23.4	26 46.1	6 1.6	17 49.7	15 28.2	12 36.1	12 59.9	10 20.2	8 21.1	6 17.5	12 19.8	23 13.8
21 W	3 56 19.9	27 46.7	5 58.4	2♒ 7.6	15R 24.0	12 10.6	13 37.2	10 16.0	8 21.9	6 20.4	12 18.7	23 12.7
22 T	4 0 16.4	28 47.3	5 55.2	15 59.8	15 9.8	11 43.2	14 14.5	10 11.6	8 22.8	6 23.5	12 17.6	23 11.7
23 F	4 4 13.0	29 48.0	5 52.1	29 27.5	14 45.1	11 14.0	14 51.7	10 7.1	8 23.9	6 26.5	12 16.4	23 10.6
24 S	4 8 9.6	0♐48.6	5 48.9	12♓33.2	14 9.6	10 43.1	15 29.0	10 2.3	8 25.0	6 29.6	12 15.3	23 9.6
25 S	4 12 6.1	1 49.3	5 45.7	25 20.3	13 23.4	10 10.7	16 6.3	9 57.4	8 26.3	6 32.7	12 14.1	23 8.5
26 M	4 16 2.7	2 50.0	5 42.5	7♈52.2	12 27.1	9 37.1	16 43.5	9 52.3	8 27.6	6 35.8	12 12.9	23 7.4
27 T	4 19 59.2	3 50.7	5 39.3	20 12.1	11 21.5	9 2.3	17 20.7	9 47.1	8 29.1	6 38.9	12 11.6	23 6.3
28 W	4 23 55.8	4 51.5	5 36.2	2♉22.7	10 8.3	8 26.8	17 57.9	9 41.7	8 30.7	6 42.1	12 10.4	23 5.2
29 T	4 27 52.4	5 52.2	5 33.0	14 26.0	8 49.4	7 50.6	18 35.1	9 36.1	8 32.4	6 45.3	12 9.1	23 4.1
30 F	4 31 48.9	6 53.0	5 29.8	26 23.8	7 27.4	7 14.2	19 12.3	9 30.4	8 34.1	6 48.5	12 7.8	23 3.0
						DECLINATION						
1 T	2 37 28.8	14S 4.4	18N31.4	8N38.1	22S17.5	27S49.4	0N39.7	22N46.7	10S18.4	23S38.9	21N57.5	15N21.9
4 S	2 49 18.5	15 1.8	18 33.8	18 5.6	23 15.7	27 51.0	0S 5.2	22 47.1	10 19.2	23 38.6	21 57.6	15 21.5
7 W	3 1 8.1	15 57.1	18 36.2	20 43.7	24 2.1	27 46.3	0 49.9	22 47.7	10 19.7	23 38.2	21 57.7	15 21.2
10 S	3 12 57.8	16 49.9	18 38.5	15 6.7	24 35.6	27 34.7	1 34.6	22 48.5	10 19.7	23 37.9	21 57.9	15 20.9
13 T	3 24 47.5	17 40.2	18 40.9	2 30.7	24 54.7	27 15.8	2 19.0	22 49.4	10 19.5	23 37.5	21 58.1	15 20.6
16 F	3 36 37.1	18 27.8	18 43.3	12S22.6	24 57.7	26 48.8	3 3.3	22 50.4	10 18.8	23 37.1	21 58.3	15 20.3
19 M	3 48 26.8	19 12.4	18 45.7	20 44.4	24 42.2	26 13.6	3 47.3	22 51.6	10 17.8	23 36.7	21 58.5	15 20.0
22 T	4 0 16.4	19 53.9	18 48.0	16 58.8	24 5.3	25 29.9	4 31.1	22 52.9	10 16.4	23 36.3	21 58.8	15 19.8
25 S	4 12 6.1	20 32.1	18 50.4	5 26.9	23 3.9	24 38.2	5 14.4	22 54.3	10 14.7	23 35.8	21 59.1	15 19.5
28 W	4 23 55.8	21 6.9	18 52.7	7N32.9	21 39.0	23 39.7	5 57.4	22 55.8	10 12.6	23 35.3	21 59.4	15 19.3

DECEMBER 1906

DAY	EPHEMERIS SIDEREAL TIME	☉	☊	☽	☿	♀	♂	♃	♄	♅	♆	♇
						LONGITUDE						
1 S	4 35 45.5	7♐53.8	5♌26.6	8♊17.4	6♐ 4.8	6♐37.6	19♎49.4	9♋24.5	8♓36.0	6♑51.8	12♋ 6.4	23♊ 1.8
2 S	4 39 42.0	8 54.6	5 23.5	20 8.2	4R 44.6	6R 1.3	20 26.6	9R 18.5	8 38.0	6 55.0	12R 5.1	23R 0.7
3 M	4 43 38.6	9 55.5	5 20.3	1♋57.8	3 29.5	5 25.4	21 3.7	9 12.4	8 40.1	6 58.3	12 3.7	22 59.6
4 T	4 47 35.1	10 56.3	5 17.1	13 48.3	2 21.6	4 50.1	21 40.8	9 6.1	8 42.2	7 1.6	12 2.3	22 58.4
5 W	4 51 31.7	11 57.2	5 13.9	25 42.3	1 22.8	4 15.9	22 17.9	8 59.6	8 44.5	7 5.0	12 0.9	22 57.3
6 T	4 55 28.2	12 58.1	5 10.8	7♌43.1	0 34.5	3 42.7	22 55.0	8 53.0	8 46.9	7 8.3	11 59.5	22 56.1
7 F	4 59 24.8	13 59.0	5 7.6	19 54.7	29♏57.3	3 11.0	23 32.1	8 46.3	8 49.4	7 11.7	11 58.1	22 55.0
8 S	5 3 21.4	14 60.0	5 4.4	2♍21.5	29 31.6	2 40.9	24 9.1	8 39.5	8 52.0	7 15.1	11 56.6	22 53.8
9 S	5 7 17.9	16 0.9	5 1.2	15 8.2	29 17.1	2 12.5	24 46.2	8 32.6	8 54.6	7 18.5	11 55.1	22 52.6
10 M	5 11 14.5	17 1.9	4 58.0	28 19.0	29 13.4	1 46.0	25 23.2	8 25.5	8 57.4	7 21.9	11 53.6	22 51.5
11 T	5 15 11.0	18 2.9	4 54.9	11♎57.4	29D 19.9	1 21.6	26 0.2	8 18.3	9 0.3	7 25.3	11 52.1	22 50.3
12 W	5 19 7.6	19 3.9	4 51.7	26 4.8	29 35.9	0 59.4	26 37.2	8 11.1	9 3.3	7 28.8	11 50.6	22 49.1
13 T	5 23 4.2	20 5.0	4 48.5	10♏39.9	0♐ 0.4	0 39.4	27 14.2	8 3.7	9 6.3	7 32.3	11 49.0	22 48.0
14 F	5 27 0.7	21 6.0	4 45.3	25 38.1	0 32.6	0 21.8	27 51.1	7 56.3	9 9.5	7 35.7	11 47.5	22 46.8
15 S	5 30 57.3	22 7.1	4 42.2	10♐51.4	1 11.7	0 6.6	28 28.0	7 48.7	9 12.7	7 39.2	11 45.9	22 45.6
16 S	5 34 53.8	23 8.1	4 39.0	26 9.6	1 57.0	29♏53.8	29 4.9	7 41.1	9 16.1	7 42.7	11 44.3	22 44.4
17 M	5 38 50.4	24 9.2	4 35.8	11♑21.6	2 47.6	29 43.5	29 41.8	7 33.4	9 19.5	7 46.2	11 42.7	22 43.2
18 T	5 42 47.0	25 10.3	4 32.6	26 17.6	3 43.1	29 35.7	0♏18.7	7 25.6	9 23.1	7 49.8	11 41.1	22 42.1
19 W	5 46 43.5	26 11.4	4 29.5	10♒50.7	4 42.8	29 30.3	0 55.5	7 17.7	9 26.7	7 53.3	11 39.5	22 40.9
20 T	5 50 40.1	27 12.6	4 26.3	24 56.8	5 46.1	29 27.4	1 32.3	7 9.8	9 30.4	7 56.9	11 37.9	22 39.7
21 F	5 54 36.6	28 13.7	4 23.1	8♓35.3	6 52.7	29 27.0	2 9.1	7 1.9	9 34.2	8 0.4	11 36.2	22 38.5
22 S	5 58 33.2	29 14.8	4 19.9	21 47.6	8 2.1	29D 28.9	2 45.9	6 53.9	9 38.1	8 4.0	11 34.6	22 37.4
23 S	6 2 29.7	0♑15.9	4 16.8	4♈36.9	9 14.0	29 33.3	3 22.6	6 45.9	9 42.1	8 7.5	11 32.9	22 36.2
24 M	6 6 26.3	1 17.0	4 13.6	17 7.0	10 28.1	29 40.0	3 59.3	6 37.8	9 46.1	8 11.1	11 31.2	22 35.0
25 T	6 10 22.8	2 18.2	4 10.4	29 22.0	11 44.1	29 48.9	4 36.0	6 29.7	9 50.3	8 14.7	11 29.6	22 33.9
26 W	6 14 19.4	3 19.3	4 7.2	11♉26.0	13 1.8	0♐ 0.2	5 12.6	6 21.6	9 54.5	8 18.3	11 27.9	22 32.7
27 T	6 18 16.0	4 20.4	4 4.0	23 22.5	14 21.1	0 13.6	5 49.3	6 13.5	9 58.8	8 21.9	11 26.2	22 31.6
28 F	6 22 12.5	5 21.6	4 0.9	5♊14.5	15 41.6	0 29.1	6 25.9	6 5.3	10 3.2	8 25.5	11 24.5	22 30.4
29 S	6 26 9.1	6 22.7	3 57.7	17 4.7	17 3.4	0 46.7	7 2.4	5 57.2	10 7.7	8 29.0	11 22.8	22 29.3
30 S	6 30 5.6	7 23.8	3 54.5	28 55.3	18 26.2	1 6.2	7 39.0	5 49.1	10 12.3	8 32.6	11 21.2	22 28.2
31 M	6 34 2.2	8 25.0	3 51.3	10♋48.0	19 50.0	1 27.8	8 15.5	5 41.0	10 16.9	8 36.2	11 19.5	22 27.0
						DECLINATION						
1 S	4 35 45.5	21S38.1	18N55.0	17N33.2	20S 1.4	22S36.6	6S40.0	22N57.4	10S10.2	23S34.8	21N59.7	15N19.1
4 T	4 47 35.1	22 5.6	18 57.3	21 0.5	18 33.4	21 31.6	7 22.2	22 59.1	10 7.4	23 34.3	22 0.1	15 19.0
7 F	4 59 24.8	22 29.3	18 59.7	16 13.8	17 36.2	20 27.8	8 3.9	23 0.8	10 4.3	23 33.8	22 0.4	15 18.9
10 M	5 11 14.5	22 49.0	19 2.0	4 32.2	17 17.2	19 28.2	8 45.0	23 2.5	10 0.9	23 33.2	22 0.8	15 18.8
13 T	5 23 4.2	23 4.7	19 4.3	10S10.1	17 31.3	18 35.1	9 25.6	23 4.2	9 57.1	23 32.7	22 1.2	15 18.7
16 S	5 34 53.8	23 16.3	19 6.5	20 17.2	18 8.2	17 50.2	10 5.6	23 6.0	9 53.0	23 32.1	22 1.6	15 18.6
19 W	5 46 43.5	23 23.7	19 8.8	18 12.6	18 58.4	17 14.4	10 44.9	23 7.7	9 48.6	23 31.5	22 2.0	15 18.6
22 S	5 58 33.2	23 26.9	19 11.1	6 51.7	19 54.2	16 47.9	11 23.5	23 9.4	9 43.9	23 30.8	22 2.5	15 18.6
25 T	6 10 22.8	23 25.8	19 13.4	6N23.0	20 50.3	16 30.4	12 1.4	23 11.0	9 38.9	23 30.2	22 2.9	15 18.6
28 F	6 22 12.5	23 20.5	19 15.6	16 51.0	21 43.0	16 21.1	12 38.6	23 12.6	9 33.7	23 29.5	22 3.4	15 18.7
31 M	6 34 2.2	23 10.9	19 17.8	21 4.4	22 29.7	16 19.2	13 14.9	23 14.1	9 28.2	23 28.9	22 3.8	15 18.8

JANUARY 1907

DAY	EPHEMERIS SIDEREAL TIME	☉	☊	☽	☿	♀	♂	♃	♄	♅	♆	♇
	h m s	° ′	° ′	° ′	° ′	° ′	° ′	° ′	° ′	° ′	° ′	° ′
						LONGITUDE						
1 T	6 37 58.8	9♑26.1	3♌48.2	22♋44.8	21♐14.6	1♐51.2	8♏52.0	5♋32.9	10♓21.6	8♑39.8	11♋17.8	22♊25.9
2 W	6 41 55.3	10 27.3	3 45.0	4♌47.5	22 40.1	2 16.4	9 28.5	5R24.8	10 26.4	8 43.4	11R16.1	22R24.8
3 T	6 45 51.9	11 28.4	3 41.8	16 58.2	24 6.2	2 43.4	10 4.9	5 16.7	10 31.3	8 47.0	11 14.4	22 23.7
4 F	6 49 48.4	12 29.5	3 38.6	29 19.2	25 33.1	3 12.1	10 41.3	5 8.7	10 36.2	8 50.6	11 12.7	22 22.6
5 S	6 53 45.0	13 30.7	3 35.5	11♍53.5	27 0.6	3 42.4	11 17.7	5 0.7	10 41.3	8 54.2	11 11.0	22 21.5
6 S	6 57 41.5	14 31.8	3 32.3	24 43.8	28 28.7	4 14.2	11 54.1	4 52.8	10 46.4	8 57.8	11 9.3	22 20.4
7 M	7 1 38.1	15 33.0	3 29.1	7♎53.2	29 57.3	4 47.6	12 30.4	4 44.9	10 51.5	9 1.4	11 7.6	22 19.4
8 T	7 5 34.6	16 34.2	3 25.9	21 24.3	1♑26.5	5 22.4	13 6.7	4 37.1	10 56.7	9 4.9	11 5.9	22 18.3
9 W	7 9 31.2	17 35.3	3 22.7	5♏18.5	2 56.2	5 58.6	13 43.0	4 29.3	11 2.1	9 8.5	11 4.2	22 17.2
10 T	7 13 27.8	18 36.5	3 19.6	19 35.7	4 26.5	6 36.1	14 19.2	4 21.6	11 7.4	9 12.1	11 2.5	22 16.2
11 F	7 17 24.3	19 37.6	3 16.4	4♐13.7	5 57.2	7 14.9	14 55.4	4 14.0	11 12.9	9 15.6	11 0.8	22 15.2
12 S	7 21 20.9	20 38.8	3 13.2	19 7.6	7 28.5	7 55.0	15 31.6	4 6.5	11 18.4	9 19.2	10 59.2	22 14.1
13 S	7 25 17.4	21 39.9	3 10.0	4♑10.4	9 0.2	8 36.2	16 7.7	3 59.0	11 24.0	9 22.7	10 57.5	22 13.1
14 M	7 29 14.0	22 41.1	3 6.9	19 13.2	10 32.4	9 18.5	16 43.8	3 51.7	11 29.6	9 26.3	10 55.8	22 12.1
15 T	7 33 10.6	23 42.3	3 3.7	4♒ 7.1	12 5.1	10 2.0	17 19.9	3 44.4	11 35.3	9 29.8	10 54.2	22 11.2
16 W	7 37 7.1	24 43.4	3 0.5	18 44.3	13 38.3	10 46.4	17 55.9	3 37.3	11 41.1	9 33.3	10 52.5	22 10.2
17 T	7 41 3.6	25 44.5	2 57.3	2♓58.9	15 12.1	11 31.8	18 31.8	3 30.2	11 46.9	9 36.8	10 50.9	22 9.2
18 F	7 45 0.2	26 45.6	2 54.2	16 47.5	16 46.3	12 18.2	19 7.7	3 23.3	11 52.8	9 40.2	10 49.3	22 8.3
19 S	7 48 56.8	27 46.7	2 51.0	0♈ 9.7	18 21.1	13 5.5	19 43.6	3 16.5	11 58.7	9 43.7	10 47.7	22 7.4
20 S	7 52 53.3	28 47.8	2 47.8	13 6.7	19 56.4	13 53.7	20 19.4	3 9.8	12 4.7	9 47.2	10 46.1	22 6.4
21 M	7 56 49.9	29 48.9	2 44.6	25 41.7	21 32.2	14 42.7	20 55.2	3 3.3	12 10.8	9 50.6	10 44.5	22 5.5
22 T	8 0 46.4	0♒49.9	2 41.4	7♉58.6	23 8.6	15 32.6	21 31.0	2 56.9	12 16.9	9 54.0	10 42.9	22 4.6
23 W	8 4 43.0	1 51.0	2 38.3	20 2.0	24 45.6	16 23.2	22 6.7	2 50.6	12 23.1	9 57.4	10 41.3	22 3.8
24 T	8 8 39.6	2 52.0	2 35.1	1♊56.5	26 23.2	17 14.5	22 42.3	2 44.5	12 29.3	10 0.8	10 39.8	22 2.9
25 F	8 12 36.1	3 53.0	2 31.9	13 46.3	28 1.3	18 6.6	23 17.9	2 38.5	12 35.6	10 4.2	10 38.2	22 2.1
26 S	8 16 32.7	4 54.0	2 28.7	25 35.6	29 40.1	18 59.4	23 53.5	2 32.6	12 41.9	10 7.6	10 36.7	22 1.3
27 S	8 20 29.2	5 54.9	2 25.6	7♋27.6	1♒19.6	19 52.9	24 29.0	2 26.9	12 48.3	10 10.9	10 35.2	22 0.4
28 M	8 24 25.8	6 55.9	2 22.4	19 25.4	2 59.7	20 47.0	25 4.5	2 21.4	12 54.7	10 14.2	10 33.7	21 59.7
29 T	8 28 22.3	7 56.8	2 19.2	1♌31.2	4 40.4	21 41.7	25 39.9	2 16.1	13 1.2	10 17.5	10 32.3	21 58.9
30 W	8 32 18.9	8 57.8	2 16.0	13 46.9	6 21.9	22 37.1	26 15.3	2 10.8	13 7.7	10 20.8	10 30.8	21 58.1
31 T	8 36 15.4	9 58.7	2 12.8	26 13.8	8 4.0	23 33.0	26 50.6	2 5.8	13 14.2	10 24.0	10 29.4	21 57.4
						DECLINATION						
1 T	6 37 58.8	23S 6.8	19N18.6	20N39.1	22S43.7	16S20.1	13S26.9	23N14.6	9S26.3	23S28.6	22N 4.0	15N18.8
4 F	6 49 48.4	22 51.8	19 20.8	13 56.8	23 19.7	16 26.5	14 2.1	23 16.0	9 20.4	23 28.0	22 4.4	15 19.0
7 M	7 1 38.1	22 32.6	19 23.0	1 16.7	23 46.2	16 37.8	14 36.5	23 17.3	9 14.3	23 27.3	22 4.9	15 19.1
10 T	7 13 27.8	22 9.4	19 25.3	12S46.6	24 2.3	16 53.1	15 10.0	23 18.6	9 7.9	23 26.6	22 5.3	15 19.3
13 S	7 25 17.4	21 42.3	19 27.5	20 52.5	24 7.2	17 11.2	15 42.6	23 19.7	9 1.4	23 25.8	22 5.8	15 19.6
16 W	7 37 7.1	21 11.4	19 29.7	16 37.8	24 0.5	17 31.4	16 14.2	23 20.8	8 54.6	23 25.1	22 6.3	15 19.8
19 S	7 48 56.8	20 36.9	19 31.9	4 2.6	23 41.4	17 52.6	16 44.8	23 21.8	8 47.6	23 24.4	22 6.7	15 20.1
22 T	8 0 46.4	19 58.9	19 34.0	9N10.8	23 9.7	18 14.2	17 14.4	23 22.7	8 40.4	23 23.7	22 7.2	15 20.4
25 F	8 12 36.1	19 17.5	19 36.2	18 30.4	22 25.0	18 35.5	17 42.9	23 23.5	8 33.1	23 23.0	22 7.6	15 20.8
28 M	8 24 25.8	18 32.9	19 38.4	20 51.2	21 27.0	18 55.7	18 10.3	23 24.2	8 25.5	23 22.2	22 8.0	15 21.1
31 T	8 36 15.4	17 45.3	19 40.5	14 47.1	20 15.5	19 14.4	18 36.7	23 24.9	8 17.9	23 21.5	22 8.4	15 21.5

FEBRUARY 1907

DAY	EPHEMERIS SIDEREAL TIME	☉	☊	☽	☿	♀	♂	♃	♄	♅	♆	♇
						LONGITUDE						
1 F	8 40 12.0	10♒59.5	2♌ 9.7	8♍52.9	9♒46.8	24♐29.5	27♏25.9	2♋ 0.9	13♓20.8	10♑27.2	10♋27.9	21♊56.7
2 S	8 44 8.6	12 0.4	2 6.5	21 45.0	11 30.3	25 26.5	28 1.1	1R56.2	13 27.5	10 30.4	10R26.5	21R56.0
3 S	8 48 5.1	13 1.3	2 3.3	4♎50.8	13 14.6	26 24.0	28 36.3	1 51.7	13 34.2	10 33.6	10 25.2	21 55.3
4 M	8 52 1.7	14 2.1	2 0.1	18 10.9	14 59.5	27 22.0	29 11.4	1 47.3	13 40.9	10 36.8	10 23.8	21 54.6
5 T	8 55 58.2	15 2.9	1 57.0	1♏45.7	16 45.1	28 20.6	29 46.5	1 43.2	13 47.6	10 39.9	10 22.5	21 53.9
6 W	8 59 54.8	16 3.8	1 53.8	15 35.5	18 31.4	29 19.5	0♐21.5	1 39.2	13 54.4	10 43.0	10 21.1	21 53.3
7 T	9 3 51.3	17 4.6	1 50.6	29 39.8	20 18.4	0♑18.9	0 56.4	1 35.4	14 1.3	10 46.1	10 19.8	21 52.7
8 F	9 7 47.9	18 5.3	1 47.4	13♐57.5	22 5.9	1 18.8	1 31.3	1 31.7	14 8.1	10 49.1	10 18.6	21 52.1
9 S	9 11 44.5	19 6.1	1 44.3	28 26.0	23 54.1	2 19.0	2 6.1	1 28.3	14 15.1	10 52.1	10 17.3	21 51.5
10 S	9 15 41.0	20 6.8	1 41.1	13♑ 1.8	25 42.8	3 19.7	2 40.9	1 25.1	14 22.0	10 55.1	10 16.1	21 51.0
11 M	9 19 37.5	21 7.6	1 37.9	27 39.7	27 31.9	4 20.7	3 15.6	1 22.0	14 29.0	10 58.1	10 14.9	21 50.4
12 T	9 23 34.1	22 8.3	1 34.7	12♒13.7	29 21.4	5 22.1	3 50.2	1 19.1	14 36.0	11 1.0	10 13.7	21 49.9
13 W	9 27 30.7	23 9.0	1 31.5	26 37.7	1♓11.1	6 23.8	4 24.8	1 16.5	14 43.0	11 3.9	10 12.5	21 49.4
14 T	9 31 27.2	24 9.6	1 28.4	10♓45.8	3 1.0	7 25.9	4 59.3	1 14.0	14 50.1	11 6.8	10 11.4	21 49.0
15 F	9 35 23.8	25 10.3	1 25.2	24 33.7	4 50.8	8 28.3	5 33.7	1 11.7	14 57.1	11 9.6	10 10.3	21 48.5
16 S	9 39 20.3	26 10.9	1 22.0	7♈58.9	6 40.3	9 31.0	6 8.0	1 9.7	15 4.3	11 12.4	10 9.2	21 48.1
17 S	9 43 16.9	27 11.5	1 18.8	21 0.8	8 29.4	10 34.0	6 42.3	1 7.8	15 11.4	11 15.2	10 8.2	21 47.7
18 M	9 47 13.4	28 12.0	1 15.7	3♉40.6	10 17.6	11 37.2	7 16.4	1 6.1	15 18.6	11 17.9	10 7.2	21 47.3
19 T	9 51 10.0	29 12.5	1 12.5	16 1.4	12 4.9	12 40.8	7 50.5	1 4.6	15 25.7	11 20.6	10 6.2	21 46.9
20 W	9 55 6.5	0♓13.0	1 9.3	28 7.1	13 50.7	13 44.6	8 24.6	1 3.4	15 33.0	11 23.3	10 5.2	21 46.6
21 T	9 59 3.1	1 13.5	1 6.1	10♊ 2.4	15 34.7	14 48.7	8 58.5	1 2.3	15 40.2	11 25.9	10 4.2	21 46.3
22 F	10 2 59.7	2 13.9	1 3.0	21 52.2	17 16.4	15 53.1	9 32.4	1 1.4	15 47.4	11 28.5	10 3.3	21 46.0
23 S	10 6 56.2	3 14.3	0 59.8	3♋41.7	18 55.3	16 57.6	10 6.2	1 0.7	15 54.7	11 31.1	10 2.5	21 45.7
24 S	10 10 52.7	4 14.7	0 56.6	15 35.5	20 30.9	18 2.5	10 39.9	1 0.3	16 2.0	11 33.6	10 1.6	21 45.4
25 M	10 14 49.3	5 15.0	0 53.4	27 37.7	22 2.7	19 7.5	11 13.5	0 60.0	16 9.2	11 36.1	10 0.8	21 45.2
26 T	10 18 45.9	6 15.3	0 50.2	9♌52.0	23 30.0	20 12.8	11 47.0	0 59.9	16 16.6	11 38.5	9 60.0	21 45.0
27 W	10 22 42.4	7 15.6	0 47.1	22 20.7	24 52.2	21 18.3	12 20.4	1D 0.0	16 23.9	11 40.9	9 59.2	21 44.8
28 T	10 26 39.0	8 15.8	0 43.9	5♍ 5.5	26 8.7	22 24.0	12 53.8	1 0.4	16 31.2	11 43.3	9 58.5	21 44.6
						DECLINATION						
1 F	8 40 12.0	17S28.8	19N41.2	11N 9.2	19S48.6	19S20.1	18S45.3	23N25.1	8S15.3	23S21.3	22N 8.6	15N21.7
4 M	8 52 1.7	16 37.4	19 43.4	2S23.8	18 18.9	19 35.8	19 10.2	23 25.7	8 7.4	23 20.6	22 9.0	15 22.1
7 T	9 3 51.3	15 43.5	19 45.5	15 29.9	16 35.6	19 48.7	19 33.9	23 26.3	7 59.4	23 19.9	22 9.4	15 22.6
10 S	9 15 41.0	14 47.1	19 47.6	21 3.7	14 39.2	19 58.4	19 56.6	23 26.8	7 51.4	23 19.2	22 9.7	15 23.0
13 W	9 27 30.7	13 48.5	19 49.7	14 40.3	12 30.4	20 4.5	20 18.1	23 27.3	7 43.2	23 18.5	22 10.1	15 23.6
16 S	9 39 20.3	12 47.8	19 51.8	1 13.4	10 10.9	20 6.8	20 38.4	23 27.7	7 34.9	23 17.9	22 10.5	15 24.1
19 T	9 51 10.0	11 45.3	19 53.9	11N45.9	7 43.6	20 5.0	20 57.6	23 28.2	7 26.5	23 17.3	22 10.8	15 24.6
22 F	10 2 59.7	10 41.1	19 56.0	19 48.9	5 12.9	19 58.8	21 15.6	23 28.6	7 18.1	23 16.6	22 11.1	15 25.2
25 M	10 14 49.3	9 35.4	19 58.1	20 14.0	2 45.3	19 48.2	21 32.5	23 28.9	7 9.6	23 16.1	22 11.4	15 25.8
28 T	10 26 39.0	8 28.5	20 0.2	12 16.6	0 29.3	19 33.0	21 48.2	23 29.3	7 1.1	23 15.5	22 11.7	15 26.4

MARCH 1907

DAY	EPHEMERIS SIDEREAL TIME	☉	☊	☽	☿	♀	♂	♃	♄	♅	♆	♇
	h m s	° '	° '	° '	° '	° '	° '	° '	° '	° '	° '	° '
						LONGITUDE						
1 F	10 30 35.5	9♓16.0	0♌40.7	18♍ 6.6	27♓18.9	23♑29.9	13♐27.0	1♋ 0.9	16♓38.5	11♑45.6	9♋57.8	21♊44.5
2 S	10 34 32.1	10 16.2	0 37.5	1♎23.3	28 22.2	24 36.1	14 0.2	1 1.6	16 45.9	11 47.9	9R57.1	21R44.4
3 S	10 38 28.6	11 16.4	0 34.3	14 53.9	29 18.1	25 42.4	14 33.3	1 2.5	16 53.3	11 50.2	9 56.5	21 44.3
4 M	10 42 25.2	12 16.5	0 31.2	28 36.4	0♈ 6.0	26 48.9	15 6.3	1 3.6	17 0.6	11 52.4	9 55.8	21 44.2
5 T	10 46 21.7	13 16.6	0 28.0	12♏28.2	0 45.6	27 55.6	15 39.1	1 4.9	17 8.0	11 54.5	9 55.3	21 44.1
6 W	10 50 18.3	14 16.7	0 24.8	26 27.1	1 16.6	29 2.4	16 11.9	1 6.4	17 15.4	11 56.6	9 54.7	21 44.1
7 T	10 54 14.8	15 16.7	0 21.6	10♐31.3	1 38.5	0♒ 9.5	16 44.6	1 8.1	17 22.8	11 58.7	9 54.2	21 44.1
8 F	10 58 11.4	16 16.8	0 18.5	24 39.3	1 51.5	1 16.7	17 17.1	1 10.0	17 30.1	12 0.7	9 53.7	21D44.1
9 S	11 2 7.9	17 16.8	0 15.3	8♑49.6	1 55.3	2 24.0	17 49.6	1 12.1	17 37.5	12 2.7	9 53.3	21 44.1
10 S	11 6 4.5	18 16.7	0 12.1	23 0.7	1R50.2	3 31.5	18 21.9	1 14.3	17 44.9	12 4.7	9 52.8	21 44.2
11 M	11 10 1.0	19 16.7	0 8.9	7♒10.7	1 36.4	4 39.2	18 54.1	1 16.8	17 52.3	12 6.6	9 52.5	21 44.3
12 T	11 13 57.6	20 16.6	0 5.7	21 16.7	1 14.4	5 47.0	19 26.2	1 19.4	17 59.7	12 8.4	9 52.1	21 44.4
13 W	11 17 54.2	21 16.5	0 2.6	5♓15.6	0 44.8	6 54.9	19 58.2	1 22.3	18 7.1	12 10.3	9 51.8	21 44.5
14 T	11 21 50.7	22 16.3	29♋59.4	19 3.6	0 8.2	8 3.0	20 30.0	1 25.3	18 14.5	12 12.0	9 51.5	21 44.6
15 F	11 25 47.2	23 16.1	29 56.2	2♈37.0	29♓25.7	9 11.2	21 1.7	1 28.5	18 21.8	12 13.7	9 51.2	21 44.8
16 S	11 29 43.8	24 15.9	29 53.0	15 53.2	28 38.2	10 19.5	21 33.3	1 31.9	18 29.2	12 15.4	9 51.0	21 45.0
17 S	11 33 40.4	25 15.7	29 49.9	28 50.6	27 46.9	11 27.9	22 4.7	1 35.4	18 36.6	12 17.0	9 50.8	21 45.2
18 M	11 37 36.9	26 15.4	29 46.7	11♉29.0	26 53.0	12 36.5	22 36.0	1 39.2	18 43.9	12 18.6	9 50.7	21 45.5
19 T	11 41 33.5	27 15.1	29 43.5	23 50.0	25 57.6	13 45.1	23 7.2	1 43.1	18 51.3	12 20.1	9 50.6	21 45.7
20 W	11 45 30.0	28 14.7	29 40.3	5♊56.4	25 2.0	14 53.9	23 38.2	1 47.2	18 58.6	12 21.6	9 50.5	21 46.0
21 T	11 49 26.6	29 14.3	29 37.1	17 52.2	24 7.4	16 2.7	24 9.0	1 51.5	19 5.9	12 23.0	9 50.4	21 46.3
22 F	11 53 23.1	0♈13.9	29 34.0	29 42.1	23 14.7	17 11.7	24 39.7	1 55.9	19 13.2	12 24.4	9 50.4	21 46.6
23 S	11 57 19.7	1 13.4	29 30.8	11♋31.5	22 25.0	18 20.7	25 10.3	2 0.6	19 20.5	12 25.8	9D50.5	21 47.0
24 S	12 1 16.2	2 12.9	29 27.6	23 25.7	21 39.1	19 29.9	25 40.7	2 5.4	19 27.8	12 27.0	9 50.5	21 47.4
25 M	12 5 12.8	3 12.3	29 24.4	5♌29.9	20 57.7	20 39.1	26 10.9	2 10.3	19 35.0	12 28.3	9 50.6	21 47.7
26 T	12 9 9.3	4 11.8	29 21.3	17 48.9	20 21.2	21 48.4	26 41.0	2 15.5	19 42.3	12 29.5	9 50.7	21 48.2
27 W	12 13 5.9	5 11.1	29 18.1	0♍26.4	19 50.1	22 57.9	27 10.9	2 20.8	19 49.5	12 30.6	9 50.9	21 48.6
28 T	12 17 2.4	6 10.5	29 14.9	13 24.7	19 24.6	24 7.4	27 40.6	2 26.2	19 56.7	12 31.7	9 51.1	21 49.1
29 F	12 20 59.0	7 9.8	29 11.7	26 44.8	19 5.0	25 17.0	28 10.2	2 31.8	20 3.9	12 32.7	9 51.3	21 49.5
30 S	12 24 55.5	8 9.0	29 8.5	10♎25.2	18 51.1	26 26.6	28 39.6	2 37.6	20 11.0	12 33.7	9 51.5	21 50.0
31 S	12 28 52.1	9 8.3	29 5.4	24 22.8	18 43.1	27 36.4	29 8.8	2 43.5	20 18.2	12 34.7	9 51.8	21 50.6
						DECLINATION						
1 F	10 30 35.5	8S 5.9	20N 0.9	8N 8.2	0N11.8	19S26.9	21S53.2	23N29.4	6S58.2	23S15.3	22N11.8	15N26.6
4 M	10 42 25.2	6 57.5	20 2.9	6S 9.7	1 57.6	19 5.4	22 7.4	23 29.7	6 49.7	23 14.8	22 12.0	15 27.3
7 T	10 54 14.8	5 48.2	20 5.0	18 3.2	3 10.2	18 39.3	22 20.5	23 30.0	6 41.1	23 14.3	22 12.3	15 27.9
10 S	11 6 4.5	4 38.2	20 7.0	20 43.5	3 43.1	18 8.5	22 32.6	23 30.3	6 32.6	23 13.8	22 12.5	15 28.6
13 W	11 17 54.2	3 27.7	20 9.0	12 14.3	3 33.5	17 33.1	22 43.5	23 30.6	6 24.0	23 13.4	22 12.7	15 29.3
16 S	11 29 43.8	2 16.7	20 11.1	1N42.6	2 44.7	16 53.3	22 53.5	23 30.8	6 15.5	23 13.0	22 12.8	15 29.9
19 T	11 41 33.5	1 5.6	20 13.1	14 11.4	1 26.4	16 9.1	23 2.4	23 31.0	6 7.0	23 12.6	22 13.0	15 30.6
22 F	11 53 23.1	0N 5.5	20 15.1	20 49.5	0S 6.5	15 20.7	23 10.4	23 31.1	5 58.6	23 12.3	22 13.1	15 31.3
25 M	12 5 12.8	1 16.5	20 17.1	19 19.8	1 38.4	14 28.3	23 17.5	23 31.2	5 50.3	23 12.0	22 13.2	15 32.0
28 T	12 17 2.4	2 27.2	20 19.0	9 42.9	2 57.3	13 32.2	23 23.8	23 31.2	5 42.0	23 11.8	22 13.3	15 32.8
31 S	12 28 52.1	3 37.4	20 21.0	4S47.3	3 56.2	12 32.5	23 29.2	23 31.1	5 33.8	23 11.6	22 13.4	15 33.5

APRIL 1907

DAY	EPHEMERIS SIDEREAL TIME	☉	☊	☽	☿	♀	♂	♃	♄	♅	♆	♇
						LONGITUDE						
1 M	12 32 48.7	10♈ 7.5	29♋ 2.2	8♏33.1	18♓40.8	28♒46.3	29♐37.9	2♋49.6	20♓25.3	12♑35.6	9♋52.1	21♊51.1
2 T	12 36 45.2	11 6.6	28 59.0	22 50.7	18D44.1	29 56.2	0♑ 6.7	2 55.9	20 32.4	12 36.4	9 52.5	21 51.7
3 W	12 40 41.7	12 5.8	28 55.8	7♐10.3	18 52.8	1♓ 6.2	0 35.4	3 2.3	20 39.5	12 37.2	9 52.9	21 52.2
4 T	12 44 38.3	13 4.9	28 52.6	21 27.8	19 6.7	2 16.3	1 3.8	3 8.8	20 46.5	12 37.9	9 53.3	21 52.8
5 F	12 48 34.9	14 4.0	28 49.5	5♑40.1	19 25.6	3 26.4	1 32.1	3 15.5	20 53.5	12 38.6	9 53.8	21 53.5
6 S	12 52 31.4	15 3.0	28 46.3	19 45.6	19 49.3	4 36.6	2 0.1	3 22.3	21 0.5	12 39.2	9 54.3	21 54.1
7 S	12 56 28.0	16 2.0	28 43.1	3♒43.4	20 17.5	5 46.9	2 27.9	3 29.3	21 7.4	12 39.8	9 54.8	21 54.8
8 M	13 0 24.5	17 1.0	28 39.9	17 33.4	20 50.1	6 57.3	2 55.5	3 36.4	21 14.4	12 40.3	9 55.3	21 55.4
9 T	13 4 21.1	18 0.0	28 36.8	1♓15.3	21 26.7	8 7.7	3 22.9	3 43.7	21 21.3	12 40.8	9 55.9	21 56.1
10 W	13 8 17.6	18 58.9	28 33.6	14 48.4	22 7.3	9 18.2	3 50.0	3 51.1	21 28.1	12 41.2	9 56.5	21 56.9
11 T	13 12 14.2	19 57.8	28 30.4	28 11.4	22 51.5	10 28.7	4 16.9	3 58.7	21 34.9	12 41.6	9 57.2	21 57.6
12 F	13 16 10.7	20 56.7	28 27.2	11♈22.8	23 39.3	11 39.3	4 43.5	4 6.3	21 41.7	12 41.9	9 57.9	21 58.4
13 S	13 20 7.3	21 55.6	28 24.0	24 21.0	24 30.3	12 49.9	5 9.9	4 14.2	21 48.5	12 42.2	9 58.6	21 59.2
14 S	13 24 3.8	22 54.4	28 20.9	7♉ 5.0	25 24.6	14 0.6	5 36.0	4 22.1	21 55.2	12 42.4	9 59.4	21 60.0
15 M	13 28 0.4	23 53.1	28 17.7	19 34.3	26 21.8	15 11.3	6 1.9	4 30.2	22 1.9	12 42.6	10 0.1	22 0.8
16 T	13 31 56.9	24 51.9	28 14.5	1♊49.6	27 22.0	16 22.1	6 27.4	4 38.4	22 8.5	12 42.7	10 1.0	22 1.6
17 W	13 35 53.5	25 50.6	28 11.3	13 52.7	28 24.8	17 32.9	6 52.7	4 46.7	22 15.1	12 42.8	10 1.8	22 2.4
18 T	13 39 50.0	26 49.2	28 8.2	25 46.7	29 30.4	18 43.8	7 17.7	4 55.2	22 21.6	12 42.8	10 2.7	22 3.3
19 F	13 43 46.6	27 47.9	28 5.0	7♋35.5	0♈38.4	19 54.7	7 42.5	5 3.8	22 28.1	12R42.8	10 3.6	22 4.2
20 S	13 47 43.2	28 46.5	28 1.8	19 23.8	1 48.9	21 5.7	8 6.9	5 12.5	22 34.6	12 42.7	10 4.5	22 5.1
21 S	13 51 39.7	29 45.0	27 58.6	1♌17.1	3 1.7	22 16.7	8 31.0	5 21.3	22 41.0	12 42.6	10 5.5	22 6.0
22 M	13 55 36.2	0♉43.5	27 55.4	13 20.7	4 16.7	23 27.7	8 54.8	5 30.2	22 47.4	12 42.4	10 6.5	22 7.0
23 T	13 59 32.8	1 42.0	27 52.3	25 40.1	5 34.0	24 38.8	9 18.3	5 39.3	22 53.7	12 42.1	10 7.5	22 7.9
24 W	14 3 29.4	2 40.5	27 49.1	8♍20.1	6 53.4	25 49.9	9 41.5	5 48.5	22 60.0	12 41.8	10 8.6	22 8.9
25 T	14 7 25.9	3 38.9	27 45.9	21 24.4	8 14.9	27 1.1	10 4.3	5 57.8	23 6.2	12 41.5	10 9.7	22 9.9
26 F	14 11 22.5	4 37.3	27 42.7	4♎54.6	9 38.4	28 12.2	10 26.8	6 7.1	23 12.4	12 41.1	10 10.8	22 10.9
27 S	14 15 19.0	5 35.6	27 39.6	18 50.3	11 4.0	29 23.5	10 49.0	6 16.6	23 18.5	12 40.7	10 12.0	22 11.9
28 S	14 19 15.6	6 33.9	27 36.4	3♏ 8.2	12 31.5	0♈34.7	11 10.8	6 26.2	23 24.6	12 40.2	10 13.1	22 12.9
29 M	14 23 12.1	7 32.2	27 33.2	17 42.7	14 0.9	1 46.0	11 32.2	6 35.9	23 30.6	12 39.7	10 14.3	22 14.0
30 T	14 27 8.7	8 30.5	27 30.0	2♐26.2	15 32.3	2 57.4	11 53.3	6 45.8	23 36.6	12 39.1	10 15.6	22 15.1
						DECLINATION						
1 M	12 32 48.7	4N 0.7	20N21.7	9S38.5	4S10.9	12S11.9	23S30.9	23N31.1	5S31.1	23S11.5	22N13.4	15N33.7
4 T	12 44 38.3	5 10.1	20 23.6	20 4.4	4 39.6	11 7.8	23 35.4	23 31.0	5 23.0	23 11.4	22 13.4	15 34.4
7 S	12 56 28.0	6 18.6	20 25.6	19 42.4	4 46.0	10 0.7	23 39.3	23 30.7	5 15.0	23 11.3	22 13.4	15 35.1
10 W	13 8 17.6	7 26.2	20 27.5	9 18.2	4 31.9	8 50.9	23 42.6	23 30.4	5 7.2	23 11.2	22 13.4	15 35.9
13 S	13 20 7.3	8 32.7	20 29.4	4N47.9	3 59.1	7 38.7	23 45.4	23 30.0	4 59.5	23 11.2	22 13.4	15 36.6
16 T	13 31 56.9	9 38.0	20 31.4	16 26.9	3 9.6	6 24.3	23 47.9	23 29.4	4 52.0	23 11.2	22 13.3	15 37.3
19 F	13 43 46.6	10 41.7	20 33.3	21 29.7	2 5.0	5 8.0	23 50.0	23 28.7	4 44.6	23 11.3	22 13.2	15 38.0
22 M	13 55 36.2	11 43.9	20 35.2	18 7.8	0 46.9	3 50.1	23 52.0	23 27.9	4 37.4	23 11.4	22 13.1	15 38.7
25 T	14 7 25.9	12 44.3	20 37.1	7 8.7	0N43.3	2 30.9	23 53.9	23 27.0	4 30.4	23 11.6	22 13.0	15 39.4
28 S	14 19 15.6	13 42.9	20 39.0	7S52.3	2 24.5	1 10.7	23 55.8	23 25.9	4 23.6	23 11.8	22 12.8	15 40.0

MAY 1907

LONGITUDE

DAY	EPHEMERIS SIDEREAL TIME h m s	☉ ° ′	☊ ° ′	☽ ° ′	☿ ° ′	♀ ° ′	♂ ° ′	♃ ° ′	♄ ° ′	♅ ° ′	♆ ° ′	♇ ° ′
1 W	14 31 5.2	9♉28.7	27♋26.8	17♐11.0	17♈ 5.6	4♈ 8.8	12♑14.0	6♋55.7	23♓42.5	12♑38.5	10♋16.8	22♊16.1
2 T	14 35 1.8	10 26.9	27 23.7	1♑49.8	18 40.8	5 20.2	12 34.3	7 5.7	23 48.3	12R37.8	10 18.1	22 17.2
3 F	14 38 58.4	11 25.1	27 20.5	16 17.6	20 17.8	6 31.6	12 54.2	7 15.8	23 54.1	12 37.1	10 19.4	22 18.3
4 S	14 42 54.9	12 23.2	27 17.3	0♒31.1	21 56.8	7 43.1	13 13.7	7 26.0	23 59.9	12 36.3	10 20.8	22 19.5
5 S	14 46 51.5	13 21.4	27 14.1	14 29.0	23 37.6	8 54.7	13 32.8	7 36.3	24 5.6	12 35.5	10 22.1	22 20.6
6 M	14 50 48.0	14 19.5	27 11.0	28 11.5	25 20.4	10 6.2	13 51.4	7 46.7	24 11.2	12 34.6	10 23.5	22 21.7
7 T	14 54 44.5	15 17.5	27 7.8	11♓39.5	27 5.0	11 17.8	14 9.6	7 57.2	24 16.7	12 33.7	10 25.0	22 22.9
8 W	14 58 41.1	16 15.6	27 4.6	24 54.2	28 51.5	12 29.4	14 27.3	8 7.7	24 22.3	12 32.7	10 26.4	22 24.1
9 T	15 2 37.7	17 13.6	27 1.4	7♈56.3	0♉40.0	13 41.1	14 44.6	8 18.4	24 27.7	12 31.7	10 27.9	22 25.3
10 F	15 6 34.2	18 11.7	26 58.3	20 46.5	2 30.3	14 52.7	15 1.3	8 29.1	24 33.1	12 30.7	10 29.4	22 26.4
11 S	15 10 30.8	19 9.6	26 55.1	3♉25.0	4 22.5	16 4.4	15 17.6	8 40.0	24 38.4	12 29.6	10 30.9	22 27.6
12 S	15 14 27.3	20 7.6	26 51.9	15 52.1	6 16.6	17 16.2	15 33.4	8 50.9	24 43.6	12 28.4	10 32.4	22 28.9
13 M	15 18 23.9	21 5.5	26 48.7	28 8.1	8 12.6	18 27.9	15 48.6	9 1.9	24 48.8	12 27.2	10 34.0	22 30.1
14 T	15 22 20.5	22 3.5	26 45.5	10♊13.9	10 10.4	19 39.7	16 3.3	9 13.0	24 53.9	12 26.0	10 35.6	22 31.3
15 W	15 26 17.0	23 1.3	26 42.4	22 10.8	12 10.1	20 51.5	16 17.5	9 24.2	24 59.0	12 24.8	10 37.2	22 32.6
16 T	15 30 13.6	23 59.2	26 39.2	4♋ 1.3	14 11.5	22 3.3	16 31.2	9 35.4	25 3.9	12 23.4	10 38.9	22 33.9
17 F	15 34 10.1	24 57.0	26 36.0	15 48.3	16 14.6	23 15.2	16 44.2	9 46.7	25 8.8	12 22.1	10 40.5	22 35.1
18 S	15 38 6.7	25 54.8	26 32.8	27 35.9	18 19.4	24 27.0	16 56.8	9 58.1	25 13.7	12 20.7	10 42.2	22 36.4
19 S	15 42 3.2	26 52.6	26 29.7	9♌28.4	20 25.6	25 38.9	17 8.7	10 9.6	25 18.4	12 19.3	10 43.9	22 37.7
20 M	15 45 59.8	27 50.4	26 26.5	21 30.9	22 33.3	26 50.8	17 20.1	10 21.1	25 23.1	12 17.8	10 45.6	22 39.0
21 T	15 49 56.3	28 48.1	26 23.3	3♍48.8	24 42.2	28 2.7	17 30.8	10 32.7	25 27.7	12 16.3	10 47.4	22 40.3
22 W	15 53 52.9	29 45.8	26 20.1	16 27.1	26 52.1	29 14.7	17 41.0	10 44.4	25 32.2	12 14.7	10 49.2	22 41.6
23 T	15 57 49.5	0♊43.5	26 17.0	29 30.2	29 2.8	0♉26.7	17 50.5	10 56.1	25 36.7	12 13.2	10 51.0	22 43.0
24 F	16 1 46.0	1 41.1	26 13.8	13♎ 1.0	1♊14.2	1 38.6	17 59.4	11 7.9	25 41.1	12 11.5	10 52.8	22 44.3
25 S	16 5 42.5	2 38.7	26 10.6	27 0.1	3 25.9	2 50.6	18 7.7	11 19.8	25 45.4	12 9.9	10 54.6	22 45.6
26 S	16 9 39.1	3 36.3	26 7.4	11♏25.7	5 37.7	4 2.7	18 15.4	11 31.7	25 49.6	12 8.2	10 56.4	22 47.0
27 M	16 13 35.7	4 33.9	26 4.2	26 12.6	7 49.3	5 14.7	18 22.4	11 43.7	25 53.7	12 6.4	10 58.3	22 48.3
28 T	16 17 32.2	5 31.5	26 1.1	11♐13.1	10 0.5	6 26.8	18 28.7	11 55.7	25 57.8	12 4.7	11 0.2	22 49.7
29 W	16 21 28.8	6 29.0	25 57.9	26 17.8	12 11.0	7 38.9	18 34.3	12 7.8	26 1.8	12 2.9	11 2.1	22 51.0
30 T	16 25 25.3	7 26.5	25 54.7	11♑17.7	14 20.4	8 51.0	18 39.3	12 20.0	26 5.7	12 1.0	11 4.0	22 52.4
31 F	16 29 21.9	8 24.0	25 51.5	26 4.9	16 28.6	10 3.2	18 43.5	12 32.2	26 9.5	11 59.2	11 5.9	22 53.8

DECLINATION

DAY	h m s	☉	☊	☽	☿	♀	♂	♃	♄	♅	♆	♇
1 W	14 31 5.2	14N39.4	20N40.8	19S38.9	4N15.5	0N10.2	23S57.8	23N24.7	4S16.9	23S12.0	22N12.7	15N40.7
4 S	14 42 54.9	15 33.7	20 42.7	20 24.2	6 15.1	1 31.6	24 0.1	23 23.3	4 10.5	23 12.3	22 12.5	15 41.3
7 T	14 54 44.5	16 25.7	20 44.5	10 31.1	8 22.0	2 53.2	24 2.8	23 21.7	4 4.3	23 12.6	22 12.2	15 42.0
10 F	15 6 34.2	17 15.3	20 46.4	3N27.5	10 34.5	4 14.6	24 6.0	23 20.0	3 58.4	23 13.0	22 12.0	15 42.6
13 M	15 18 23.9	18 2.4	20 48.2	15 36.2	12 50.7	5 35.6	24 9.9	23 18.1	3 52.7	23 13.3	22 11.7	15 43.2
16 T	15 30 13.6	18 46.7	20 50.1	21 33.6	15 7.6	6 55.8	24 14.5	23 16.0	3 47.3	23 13.8	22 11.4	15 43.8
19 S	15 42 3.2	19 28.1	20 51.9	19 7.6	17 21.8	8 14.9	24 20.0	23 13.7	3 42.1	23 14.2	22 11.1	15 44.3
22 W	15 53 52.9	20 6.6	20 53.7	9 2.5	19 28.4	9 32.7	24 26.4	23 11.2	3 37.2	23 14.7	22 10.8	15 44.9
25 S	16 5 42.5	20 41.9	20 55.5	5S38.2	21 22.2	10 48.8	24 34.0	23 8.5	3 32.6	23 15.2	22 10.4	15 45.4
28 T	16 17 32.2	21 14.1	20 57.3	18 39.1	22 57.7	12 3.0	24 42.6	23 5.6	3 28.3	23 15.8	22 10.0	15 45.9
31 F	16 29 21.9	21 43.0	20 59.0	21 6.4	24 11.0	13 14.8	24 52.6	23 2.5	3 24.3	23 16.3	22 9.6	15 46.4

JUNE 1907

LONGITUDE

DAY	h m s	☉	☊	☽	☿	♀	♂	♃	♄	♅	♆	♇
1 S	16 33 18.4	9♊21.5	25♋48.4	10♒34.0	18♊35.4	11♉15.3	18♑47.0	12♋44.5	26♓13.3	11♑57.3	11♋ 7.9	22♊55.2
2 S	16 37 15.0	10 19.0	25 45.2	24 42.0	20 40.4	12 27.5	18 49.9	12 56.8	26 16.9	11R55.4	11 9.8	22 56.6
3 M	16 41 11.5	11 16.5	25 42.0	8♓28.3	22 43.7	13 39.8	18 51.9	13 9.2	26 20.5	11 53.4	11 11.8	22 57.9
4 T	16 45 8.1	12 13.9	25 38.8	21 53.8	24 44.9	14 52.0	18 53.3	13 21.6	26 24.0	11 51.4	11 13.8	22 59.3
5 W	16 49 4.7	13 11.4	25 35.7	5♈ 0.2	26 44.0	16 4.3	18 53.9	13 34.1	26 27.4	11 49.4	11 15.8	23 0.7
6 T	16 53 1.2	14 8.8	25 32.5	17 49.9	28 40.8	17 16.6	18R53.7	13 46.6	26 30.7	11 47.4	11 17.8	23 2.1
7 F	16 56 57.8	15 6.2	25 29.3	0♉25.1	0♋35.3	18 28.9	18 52.8	13 59.2	26 33.9	11 45.3	11 19.9	23 3.5
8 S	17 0 54.3	16 3.6	25 26.1	12 47.9	2 27.5	19 41.2	18 51.1	14 11.8	26 37.1	11 43.2	11 21.9	23 5.0
9 S	17 4 50.9	17 1.0	25 22.9	25 0.2	4 17.2	20 53.6	18 48.6	14 24.4	26 40.1	11 41.1	11 24.0	23 6.4
10 M	17 8 47.5	17 58.4	25 19.8	7♊ 3.7	6 4.4	22 6.0	18 45.4	14 37.1	26 43.1	11 39.0	11 26.1	23 7.8
11 T	17 12 44.0	18 55.8	25 16.6	19 0.1	7 49.1	23 18.4	18 41.4	14 49.9	26 45.9	11 36.8	11 28.1	23 9.2
12 W	17 16 40.6	19 53.1	25 13.4	0♋51.0	9 31.2	24 30.8	18 36.7	15 2.7	26 48.7	11 34.6	11 30.2	23 10.6
13 T	17 20 37.1	20 50.5	25 10.2	12 38.5	11 10.8	25 43.2	18 31.2	15 15.5	26 51.4	11 32.4	11 32.3	23 12.0
14 F	17 24 33.7	21 47.8	25 7.1	24 25.2	12 47.7	26 55.7	18 25.0	15 28.3	26 54.0	11 30.2	11 34.5	23 13.4
15 S	17 28 30.2	22 45.2	25 3.9	6♌14.1	14 22.1	28 8.1	18 18.0	15 41.2	26 56.5	11 28.0	11 36.6	23 14.9
16 S	17 32 26.8	23 42.5	25 0.7	18 8.6	15 53.9	29 20.6	18 10.3	15 54.2	26 58.9	11 25.7	11 38.7	23 16.3
17 M	17 36 23.4	24 39.8	24 57.5	0♍12.7	17 23.0	0♊33.2	18 1.9	16 7.1	27 1.2	11 23.4	11 40.9	23 17.7
18 T	17 40 19.9	25 37.0	24 54.4	12 30.9	18 49.5	1 45.7	17 52.8	16 20.1	27 3.4	11 21.1	11 43.0	23 19.1
19 W	17 44 16.4	26 34.3	24 51.2	25 7.6	20 13.2	2 58.2	17 43.0	16 33.2	27 5.5	11 18.8	11 45.2	23 20.5
20 T	17 48 13.0	27 31.6	24 48.0	8♎ 7.1	21 34.2	4 10.8	17 32.6	16 46.2	27 7.5	11 16.5	11 47.4	23 22.0
21 F	17 52 9.6	28 28.8	24 44.8	21 32.6	22 52.5	5 23.4	17 21.5	16 59.3	27 9.5	11 14.1	11 49.6	23 23.4
22 S	17 56 6.2	29 26.1	24 41.6	5♏25.9	24 7.9	6 36.0	17 9.7	17 12.4	27 11.3	11 11.8	11 51.7	23 24.8
23 S	18 0 2.7	0♋23.3	24 38.5	19 46.5	25 20.5	7 48.6	16 57.4	17 25.5	27 13.0	11 9.4	11 53.9	23 26.2
24 M	18 3 59.3	1 20.5	24 35.3	4♐31.2	26 30.1	9 1.3	16 44.5	17 38.7	27 14.7	11 7.0	11 56.1	23 27.6
25 T	18 7 55.8	2 17.7	24 32.1	19 33.7	27 36.7	10 14.0	16 31.1	17 51.9	27 16.2	11 4.7	11 58.3	23 29.0
26 W	18 11 52.4	3 14.9	24 28.9	4♑45.6	28 40.3	11 26.7	16 17.1	18 5.1	27 17.6	11 2.3	12 0.5	23 30.4
27 T	18 15 48.9	4 12.1	24 25.8	19 57.0	29 40.7	12 39.4	16 2.6	18 18.3	27 19.0	10 59.9	12 2.8	23 31.8
28 F	18 19 45.5	5 9.3	24 22.6	4♒58.8	0♌37.8	13 52.1	15 47.6	18 31.6	27 20.2	10 57.5	12 5.0	23 33.2
29 S	18 23 42.1	6 6.5	24 19.4	19 43.1	1 31.6	15 4.9	15 32.2	18 44.8	27 21.4	10 55.0	12 7.2	23 34.6
30 S	18 27 38.6	7 3.7	24 16.2	4♓ 4.8	2 22.0	16 17.7	15 16.3	18 58.1	27 22.4	10 52.6	12 9.4	23 36.0

DECLINATION

DAY	h m s	☉	☊	☽	☿	♀	♂	♃	♄	♅	♆	♇
1 S	16 33 18.4	21N51.8	20N59.6	18S59.8	24N30.0	13N38.2	24S56.1	23N 1.4	3S23.0	23S16.5	22N 9.5	15N46.5
4 T	16 45 8.1	22 16.2	21 1.4	7 13.8	25 10.7	14 46.5	25 7.7	22 58.0	3 19.4	23 17.1	22 9.1	15 47.0
7 F	16 56 57.8	22 37.0	21 3.1	6N48.4	25 27.7	15 51.8	25 20.6	22 54.4	3 16.2	23 17.7	22 8.6	15 47.4
10 M	17 8 47.5	22 54.3	21 4.9	17 46.4	25 23.1	16 53.7	25 34.6	22 50.6	3 13.2	23 18.3	22 8.2	15 47.8
13 T	17 20 37.1	23 8.0	21 6.6	21 51.7	24 60.0	17 52.0	25 49.7	22 46.6	3 10.6	23 18.9	22 7.7	15 48.2
16 S	17 32 26.8	23 18.0	21 8.3	17 28.4	24 21.5	18 46.4	26 5.7	22 42.4	3 8.3	23 19.5	22 7.2	15 48.5
19 W	17 44 16.4	23 24.3	21 10.1	6 10.2	23 31.0	19 36.4	26 22.4	22 37.9	3 6.4	23 20.2	22 6.7	15 48.9
22 S	17 56 6.2	23 26.9	21 11.8	8S29.4	22 31.4	20 21.9	26 39.6	22 33.2	3 4.9	23 20.8	22 6.2	15 49.2
25 T	18 7 55.8	23 25.8	21 13.4	20 6.7	21 25.7	21 2.6	26 56.9	22 28.4	3 3.6	23 21.4	22 5.6	15 49.4
28 F	18 19 45.5	23 21.0	21 15.1	20 3.5	20 16.7	21 38.2	27 14.1	22 23.3	3 2.8	23 22.1	22 5.1	15 49.7

LONGITUDE

DAY	EPHEMERIS SIDEREAL TIME h m s	☉ ° ′	☊ ° ′	☽ ° ′	☿ ° ′	♀ ° ′	♂ ° ′	♃ ° ′	♄ ° ′	♅ ° ′	♆ ° ′	♇ ° ′
1 M	18 31 35.1	8♋ 0.9	24♋13.1	18♓ 1.2	3♌ 8.8	17♊30.6	15♑ 0.1	19♋11.4	27♓23.4	10♑50.2	12♋11.6	23♊37.4
2 T	18 35 31.7	8 58.0	24 9.9	1♈32.1	3 52.0	18 43.4	14R43.6	19 24.7	27 24.2	10R47.8	12 13.9	23 38.7
3 W	18 39 28.3	9 55.2	24 6.7	14 39.1	4 31.3	19 56.3	14 26.7	19 38.1	27 24.9	10 45.3	12 16.1	23 40.1
4 T	18 43 24.9	10 52.5	24 3.5	27 24.9	5 6.7	21 9.2	14 9.6	19 51.4	27 25.6	10 42.9	12 18.3	23 41.5
5 F	18 47 21.4	11 49.7	24 0.4	9♉52.9	5 38.1	22 22.1	13 52.2	20 4.8	27 26.1	10 40.5	12 20.6	23 42.9
6 S	18 51 17.9	12 46.9	23 57.2	22 6.6	6 5.3	23 35.1	13 34.7	20 18.2	27 26.6	10 38.1	12 22.8	23 44.2
7 S	18 55 14.5	13 44.1	23 54.0	4♊ 9.3	6 28.2	24 48.1	13 17.1	20 31.6	27 26.9	10 35.6	12 25.0	23 45.6
8 M	18 59 11.1	14 41.3	23 50.8	16 4.2	6 46.6	26 1.1	12 59.3	20 45.0	27 27.2	10 33.2	12 27.3	23 46.9
9 T	19 3 7.6	15 38.5	23 47.6	27 54.1	7 0.6	27 14.1	12 41.6	20 58.4	27 27.3	10 30.8	12 29.5	23 48.2
10 W	19 7 4.2	16 35.8	23 44.5	9♋41.5	7 9.9	28 27.2	12 23.8	21 11.8	27 27.3	10 28.4	12 31.7	23 49.6
11 T	19 11 0.7	17 33.0	23 41.3	21 28.9	7 14.5	29 40.3	12 6.2	21 25.2	27R27.3	10 26.0	12 34.0	23 50.9
12 F	19 14 57.3	18 30.2	23 38.1	3♌18.5	7R14.3	0♋53.4	11 48.6	21 38.6	27 27.1	10 23.6	12 36.2	23 52.2
13 S	19 18 53.8	19 27.5	23 34.9	15 12.7	7 9.4	2 6.5	11 31.2	21 52.1	27 26.8	10 21.2	12 38.4	23 53.5
14 S	19 22 50.4	20 24.7	23 31.8	27 14.0	6 59.7	3 19.7	11 14.1	22 5.5	27 26.5	10 18.8	12 40.6	23 54.8
15 M	19 26 47.0	21 21.9	23 28.6	9♍25.0	6 45.3	4 32.9	10 57.2	22 18.9	27 26.0	10 16.4	12 42.8	23 56.1
16 T	19 30 43.5	22 19.2	23 25.4	21 48.9	6 26.4	5 46.1	10 40.6	22 32.4	27 25.4	10 14.1	12 45.0	23 57.3
17 W	19 34 40.0	23 16.4	23 22.2	4♎28.7	6 3.1	6 59.3	10 24.3	22 45.8	27 24.8	10 11.7	12 47.2	23 58.6
18 T	19 38 36.6	24 13.7	23 19.1	17 27.6	5 35.8	8 12.6	10 8.5	22 59.2	27 24.0	10 9.4	12 49.4	23 59.9
19 F	19 42 33.2	25 10.9	23 15.9	0♏48.3	5 4.7	9 25.9	9 53.0	23 12.6	27 23.1	10 7.1	12 51.6	24 1.1
20 S	19 46 29.8	26 8.2	23 12.7	14 32.7	4 30.2	10 39.2	9 38.1	23 26.1	27 22.2	10 4.8	12 53.8	24 2.3
21 S	19 50 26.3	27 5.4	23 9.5	28 41.4	3 52.8	11 52.5	9 23.7	23 39.5	27 21.1	10 2.5	12 56.0	24 3.6
22 M	19 54 22.8	28 2.7	23 6.3	13♐13.0	3 13.2	13 5.8	9 9.8	23 52.9	27 19.9	10 0.2	12 58.2	24 4.8
23 T	19 58 19.4	28 60.0	23 3.2	28 3.6	2 31.8	14 19.2	8 56.5	24 6.3	27 18.7	9 57.9	13 0.3	24 6.0
24 W	20 2 16.0	29 57.3	22 60.0	13♑ 7.1	1 49.5	15 32.6	8 43.8	24 19.6	27 17.3	9 55.7	13 2.5	24 7.2
25 T	20 6 12.5	0♌54.5	22 56.8	28 15.2	1 7.0	16 46.1	8 31.7	24 33.0	27 15.9	9 53.5	13 4.6	24 8.3
26 F	20 10 9.1	1 51.8	22 53.6	13♒19.0	0 24.9	17 59.5	8 20.2	24 46.4	27 14.3	9 51.3	13 6.8	24 9.5
27 S	20 14 5.6	2 49.1	22 50.5	28 9.8	29♋44.1	19 13.0	8 9.5	24 59.7	27 12.7	9 49.1	13 8.9	24 10.7
28 S	20 18 2.2	3 46.4	22 47.3	12♓40.5	29 5.3	20 26.5	7 59.4	25 13.1	27 11.0	9 47.0	13 11.0	24 11.8
29 M	20 21 58.7	4 43.8	22 44.1	26 46.2	28 29.2	21 40.1	7 50.1	25 26.4	27 9.1	9 44.8	13 13.1	24 12.9
30 T	20 25 55.3	5 41.1	22 40.9	10♈25.0	27 56.7	22 53.6	7 41.4	25 39.7	27 7.2	9 42.7	13 15.2	24 14.0
31 W	20 29 51.9	6 38.5	22 37.8	23 37.1	27 28.2	24 7.2	7 33.6	25 53.0	27 5.2	9 40.7	13 17.3	24 15.1

DECLINATION

DAY	EPHEMERIS SIDEREAL TIME h m s	☉	☊	☽	☿	♀	♂	♃	♄	♅	♆	♇
1 M	18 31 35.1	23N12.5	21N16.8	8S41.9	19N 7.2	22N 8.4	27S30.7	22N18.0	3S 2.3	23S22.7	22N 4.5	15N49.9
4 T	18 43 24.9	23 0.3	21 18.5	5N38.3	17 60.0	22 33.2	27 46.5	22 12.5	3 2.1	23 23.3	22 3.9	15 50.1
7 S	18 55 14.5	22 44.5	21 20.1	17 2.8	16 58.0	22 52.2	28 1.1	22 6.8	3 2.3	23 23.9	22 3.3	15 50.3
10 W	19 7 4.2	22 25.1	21 21.8	21 50.7	16 4.3	23 5.3	28 14.1	22 0.9	3 2.9	23 24.5	22 2.7	15 50.4
13 S	19 18 53.8	22 2.3	21 23.4	18 10.1	15 21.8	23 12.5	28 25.5	21 54.9	3 3.9	23 25.1	22 2.1	15 50.5
16 T	19 30 43.5	21 36.1	21 25.0	7 23.8	14 53.3	23 13.6	28 35.0	21 48.6	3 5.1	23 25.7	22 1.5	15 50.6
19 F	19 42 33.2	21 6.5	21 26.7	6S49.9	14 40.7	23 8.6	28 42.5	21 42.2	3 6.8	23 26.2	22 0.9	15 50.6
22 M	19 54 22.8	20 33.7	21 28.3	18 60.0	14 44.7	22 57.4	28 48.1	21 35.6	3 8.8	23 26.7	22 0.3	15 50.7
25 T	20 6 12.5	19 57.9	21 29.9	20 57.6	15 4.4	22 40.2	28 51.8	21 28.8	3 11.1	23 27.2	21 59.7	15 50.7
28 S	20 18 2.2	19 19.0	21 31.4	10 30.6	15 37.0	22 17.0	28 53.6	21 21.9	3 13.7	23 27.7	21 59.1	15 50.6
31 W	20 29 51.9	18 37.3	21 33.0	4N15.6	16 18.1	21 47.9	28 53.8	21 14.8	3 16.7	23 28.2	21 58.4	15 50.6

AUGUST 1907

LONGITUDE

DAY	EPHEMERIS SIDEREAL TIME h m s	☉ ° ′	☊ ° ′	☽ ° ′	☿ ° ′	♀ ° ′	♂ ° ′	♃ ° ′	♄ ° ′	♅ ° ′	♆ ° ′	♇ ° ′
1 T	20 33 48.4	7♌35.9	22♋34.6	6♉25.0	27♋ 4.3	25♋20.9	7♑26.5	26♋ 6.3	27♓ 3.1	9♑38.6	13♋19.4	24♊16.2
2 F	20 37 45.0	8 33.3	22 31.4	18 52.0	26R45.7	26 34.5	7R20.2	26 19.5	27R 0.9	9R36.6	13 21.5	24 17.3
3 S	20 41 41.5	9 30.7	22 28.2	1♊ 2.5	26 32.6	27 48.2	7 14.6	26 32.8	26 58.6	9 34.6	13 23.5	24 18.4
4 S	20 45 38.1	10 28.2	22 25.0	13 1.0	26 25.5	29 1.9	7 9.9	26 46.0	26 56.2	9 32.6	13 25.6	24 19.4
5 M	20 49 34.6	11 25.6	22 21.9	24 51.8	26 24.7	0♌15.7	7 6.0	26 59.2	26 53.8	9 30.7	13 27.6	24 20.4
6 T	20 53 31.2	12 23.1	22 18.7	6♋39.1	26D30.3	1 29.5	7 3.0	27 12.4	26 51.2	9 28.7	13 29.6	24 21.4
7 W	20 57 27.8	13 20.6	22 15.5	18 26.3	26 42.6	2 43.3	7 0.8	27 25.5	26 48.6	9 26.9	13 31.6	24 22.4
8 T	21 1 24.3	14 18.2	22 12.3	0♌16.7	27 1.6	3 57.1	6 59.4	27 38.6	26 45.9	9 25.0	13 33.6	24 23.4
9 F	21 5 20.9	15 15.7	22 9.2	12 12.8	27 27.3	5 10.9	6 58.8	27 51.7	26 43.1	9 23.2	13 35.5	24 24.4
10 S	21 9 17.4	16 13.2	22 6.0	24 16.7	27 59.9	6 24.8	6D59.1	28 4.8	26 40.2	9 21.4	13 37.5	24 25.3
11 S	21 13 14.0	17 10.8	22 2.8	6♍30.2	28 39.2	7 38.7	7 0.3	28 17.8	26 37.2	9 19.6	13 39.4	24 26.3
12 M	21 17 10.5	18 8.4	21 59.6	18 54.7	29 25.2	8 52.7	7 2.3	28 30.8	26 34.2	9 17.9	13 41.3	24 27.2
13 T	21 21 7.1	19 6.0	21 56.4	1♎31.6	0♌17.8	10 6.6	7 5.1	28 43.8	26 31.0	9 16.3	13 43.2	24 28.1
14 W	21 25 3.6	20 3.7	21 53.3	14 22.3	1 16.8	11 20.6	7 8.8	28 56.7	26 27.8	9 14.6	13 45.1	24 29.0
15 T	21 29 0.2	21 1.3	21 50.1	27 28.0	2 22.0	12 34.6	7 13.3	29 9.6	26 24.6	9 13.0	13 47.0	24 29.8
16 F	21 32 56.8	21 59.0	21 46.9	10♏50.1	3 33.2	13 48.6	7 18.7	29 22.5	26 21.2	9 11.4	13 48.8	24 30.7
17 S	21 36 53.3	22 56.7	21 43.7	24 29.7	4 50.2	15 2.7	7 24.8	29 35.3	26 17.8	9 9.9	13 50.7	24 31.5
18 S	21 40 49.8	23 54.4	21 40.6	8♐27.4	6 12.7	16 16.8	7 31.8	29 48.1	26 14.3	9 8.4	13 52.5	24 32.3
19 M	21 44 46.4	24 52.1	21 37.4	22 42.9	7 40.3	17 30.8	7 39.6	0♌ 0.9	26 10.8	9 6.9	13 54.2	24 33.1
20 T	21 48 43.0	25 49.8	21 34.2	7♑14.3	9 12.7	18 45.0	7 48.1	0 13.6	26 7.1	9 5.5	13 56.0	24 33.9
21 W	21 52 39.5	26 47.6	21 31.0	21 58.1	10 49.6	19 59.1	7 57.4	0 26.2	26 3.5	9 4.1	13 57.8	24 34.7
22 T	21 56 36.1	27 45.3	21 27.8	6♒49.0	12 30.4	21 13.3	8 7.5	0 38.8	25 59.7	9 2.8	13 59.5	24 35.4
23 F	22 0 32.6	28 43.1	21 24.7	21 39.9	14 14.8	22 27.4	8 18.4	0 51.4	25 55.9	9 1.5	14 1.2	24 36.1
24 S	22 4 29.2	29 40.9	21 21.5	6♓23.2	16 2.3	23 41.6	8 29.9	1 3.9	25 52.0	9 0.3	14 2.9	24 36.8
25 S	22 8 25.8	0♍38.8	21 18.3	20 51.4	17 52.5	24 55.9	8 42.2	1 16.4	25 48.1	8 59.1	14 4.5	24 37.5
26 M	22 12 22.3	1 36.6	21 15.1	4♈58.5	19 45.0	26 10.1	8 55.2	1 28.8	25 44.2	8 57.9	14 6.2	24 38.2
27 T	22 16 18.8	2 34.5	21 12.0	18 40.8	21 39.2	27 24.4	9 8.9	1 41.2	25 40.1	8 56.8	14 7.8	24 38.8
28 W	22 20 15.4	3 32.5	21 8.8	1♉56.9	23 34.9	28 38.7	9 23.3	1 53.6	25 36.0	8 55.7	14 9.4	24 39.4
29 T	22 24 11.9	4 30.4	21 5.6	14 48.0	25 31.7	29 53.0	9 38.3	2 5.8	25 31.9	8 54.7	14 11.0	24 40.0
30 F	22 28 8.5	5 28.4	21 2.4	27 16.9	27 29.1	1♍ 7.4	9 54.0	2 18.1	25 27.7	8 53.7	14 12.5	24 40.6
31 S	22 32 5.1	6 26.4	20 59.3	9♊27.8	29 27.0	2 21.7	10 10.4	2 30.2	25 23.5	8 52.7	14 14.0	24 41.2

DECLINATION

DAY	EPHEMERIS SIDEREAL TIME h m s	☉	☊	☽	☿	♀	♂	♃	♄	♅	♆	♇
1 T	20 33 48.4	18N22.7	21N33.5	8N48.1	16N32.9	21N37.0	28S53.5	21N12.4	3S17.8	23S28.3	21N58.2	15N50.6
4 S	20 45 38.1	17 37.3	21 35.1	18 58.5	17 17.8	21 0.3	28 51.7	21 5.2	3 21.2	23 28.8	21 57.6	15 50.5
7 W	20 57 27.8	16 49.4	21 36.6	21 43.7	17 59.6	20 18.1	28 48.4	20 57.8	3 24.8	23 29.2	21 57.0	15 50.4
10 S	21 9 17.4	15 58.9	21 38.2	15 58.9	18 33.0	19 30.6	28 44.0	20 50.3	3 28.8	23 29.6	21 56.4	15 50.3
13 T	21 21 7.1	15 6.2	21 39.7	3 51.2	18 53.3	18 38.1	28 38.5	20 42.8	3 33.0	23 29.9	21 55.8	15 50.1
16 F	21 32 56.8	14 11.3	21 41.2	10S20.9	18 55.4	17 40.8	28 31.9	20 35.1	3 37.4	23 30.2	21 55.2	15 49.9
19 M	21 44 46.4	13 14.3	21 42.8	20 36.6	18 35.4	16 39.1	28 24.5	20 27.3	3 42.1	23 30.5	21 54.6	15 49.7
22 T	21 56 36.1	12 15.5	21 44.3	19 46.7	17 50.7	15 33.1	28 16.2	20 19.5	3 47.0	23 30.8	21 54.1	15 49.5
25 S	22 8 25.8	11 14.9	21 45.7	7 39.9	16 41.0	14 23.3	28 7.0	20 11.7	3 52.1	23 31.0	21 53.5	15 49.3
28 W	22 20 15.4	10 12.8	21 47.2	7N21.5	15 8.6	13 9.9	27 56.9	20 3.8	3 57.3	23 31.2	21 53.0	15 49.0
31 S	22 32 5.1	9 9.1	21 48.7	18 22.8	13 17.6	11 53.2	27 46.0	19 55.8	4 2.7	23 31.4	21 52.5	15 48.8

SEPTEMBER 1907

LONGITUDE

DAY	EPHEMERIS SIDEREAL TIME	☉	☊	☽	☿	♀	♂	♃	♄	♅	♆	♇
	h m s	° ′	° ′	° ′	° ′	° ′	° ′	° ′	° ′	° ′	° ′	° ′
1 S	22 36 1.6	7♍24.5	20♋56.1	21♊25.7	1♍24.9	3♍36.1	10♑27.4	2♌42.3	25♓19.2	8♑51.8	14♋15.5	24♊41.7
2 M	22 39 58.2	8 22.5	20 52.9	3♋15.6	3 22.8	4 50.5	10 45.1	2 54.4	25R14.9	8R51.0	14 17.0	24 42.2
3 T	22 43 54.7	9 20.7	20 49.7	15 2.8	5 20.3	6 5.0	11 3.3	3 6.4	25 10.6	8 50.2	14 18.5	24 42.7
4 W	22 47 51.3	10 18.8	20 46.5	26 51.9	7 17.3	7 19.4	11 22.2	3 18.3	25 6.2	8 49.4	14 19.9	24 43.2
5 T	22 51 47.8	11 17.0	20 43.4	8♌46.9	9 13.7	8 33.9	11 41.7	3 30.2	25 1.8	8 48.7	14 21.3	24 43.7
6 F	22 55 44.3	12 15.2	20 40.2	20 51.3	11 9.3	9 48.4	12 1.8	3 42.0	24 57.3	8 48.0	14 22.6	24 44.1
7 S	22 59 40.9	13 13.4	20 37.0	3♍ 7.3	13 4.1	11 2.9	12 22.4	3 53.8	24 52.8	8 47.4	14 24.0	24 44.5
8 S	23 3 37.5	14 11.7	20 33.8	15 36.7	14 57.9	12 17.5	12 43.6	4 5.4	24 48.3	8 46.9	14 25.3	24 44.9
9 M	23 7 34.0	15 10.0	20 30.7	28 19.8	16 50.7	13 32.0	13 5.4	4 17.0	24 43.8	8 46.3	14 26.6	24 45.3
10 T	23 11 30.6	16 8.3	20 27.5	11♎16.6	18 42.5	14 46.6	13 27.7	4 28.6	24 39.2	8 45.9	14 27.9	24 45.7
11 W	23 15 27.1	17 6.7	20 24.3	24 26.5	20 33.3	16 1.2	13 50.6	4 40.0	24 34.6	8 45.4	14 29.1	24 46.0
12 T	23 19 23.7	18 5.0	20 21.1	7♏48.6	22 22.9	17 15.8	14 13.9	4 51.4	24 30.1	8 45.1	14 30.3	24 46.3
13 F	23 23 20.3	19 3.5	20 17.9	21 21.9	24 11.5	18 30.4	14 37.8	5 2.7	24 25.4	8 44.8	14 31.5	24 46.6
14 S	23 27 16.8	20 1.9	20 14.8	5♐ 6.1	25 59.0	19 45.0	15 2.2	5 14.0	24 20.8	8 44.5	14 32.6	24 46.9
15 S	23 31 13.3	21 0.4	20 11.6	19 0.6	27 45.3	20 59.7	15 27.1	5 25.1	24 16.2	8 44.3	14 33.8	24 47.1
16 M	23 35 9.9	21 58.8	20 8.4	3♑ 5.1	29 30.6	22 14.3	15 52.4	5 36.2	24 11.6	8 44.1	14 34.8	24 47.3
17 T	23 39 6.4	22 57.3	20 5.2	17 19.0	1♎14.8	23 29.0	16 18.3	5 47.2	24 6.9	8 44.0	14 35.9	24 47.5
18 W	23 43 3.0	23 55.9	20 2.0	1♒40.6	2 58.0	24 43.7	16 44.5	5 58.1	24 2.3	8 43.9	14 36.9	24 47.7
19 T	23 46 59.6	24 54.5	19 58.9	16 7.3	4 40.1	25 58.4	17 11.2	6 9.0	23 57.6	8 43.9	14 37.9	24 47.9
20 F	23 50 56.1	25 53.1	19 55.7	0♓34.7	6 21.2	27 13.1	17 38.3	6 19.7	23 53.0	8D43.9	14 38.9	24 48.0
21 S	23 54 52.7	26 51.7	19 52.5	14 57.6	8 1.3	28 27.8	18 5.9	6 30.4	23 48.4	8 44.0	14 39.9	24 48.1
22 S	23 58 49.2	27 50.3	19 49.3	29 10.0	9 40.3	29 42.5	18 33.8	6 40.9	23 43.7	8 44.2	14 40.8	24 48.2
23 M	0 2 45.8	28 49.0	19 46.2	13♈ 6.4	11 18.4	0♎57.2	19 2.1	6 51.4	23 39.1	8 44.3	14 41.6	24 48.3
24 T	0 6 42.3	29 47.8	19 43.0	26 42.5	12 55.5	2 12.0	19 30.8	7 1.8	23 34.5	8 44.6	14 42.5	24 48.3
25 W	0 10 38.9	0♎46.5	19 39.8	9♉55.9	14 31.7	3 26.7	19 59.9	7 12.1	23 29.9	8 44.9	14 43.3	24 48.3
26 T	0 14 35.4	1 45.3	19 36.6	22 46.4	16 7.0	4 41.5	20 29.4	7 22.3	23 25.3	8 45.2	14 44.1	24 48.3
27 F	0 18 32.0	2 44.1	19 33.4	5♊15.8	17 41.3	5 56.3	20 59.2	7 32.4	23 20.8	8 45.6	14 44.8	24R48.3
28 S	0 22 28.6	3 43.0	19 30.3	17 27.3	19 14.8	7 11.1	21 29.3	7 42.4	23 16.2	8 46.0	14 45.6	24 48.3
29 S	0 26 25.1	4 41.9	19 27.1	29 25.6	20 47.3	8 25.9	21 59.8	7 52.3	23 11.7	8 46.5	14 46.3	24 48.2
30 M	0 30 21.6	5 40.9	19 23.9	11♋15.9	22 19.0	9 40.7	22 30.7	8 2.1	23 7.2	8 47.1	14 46.9	24 48.1

DECLINATION

DAY	EPHEMERIS SIDEREAL TIME	☉	☊	☽	☿	♀	♂	♃	♄	♅	♆	♇
1 S	22 36 1.6	8N47.6	21N49.2	20N30.0	12N37.3	11N26.9	27S42.2	19N53.2	4S 4.5	23S31.5	21N52.3	15N48.7
4 W	22 47 51.3	7 42.3	21 50.6	21 10.5	10 29.0	10 6.4	27 30.0	19 45.3	4 10.0	23 31.6	21 51.8	15 48.4
7 S	22 59 40.9	6 35.8	21 52.1	13 28.9	8 12.7	8 43.3	27 16.9	19 37.4	4 15.6	23 31.7	21 51.3	15 48.1
10 T	23 11 30.6	5 28.3	21 53.5	0 8.7	5 52.2	7 18.1	27 2.7	19 29.5	4 21.3	23 31.8	21 50.9	15 47.8
13 F	23 23 20.3	4 19.9	21 54.9	13S50.1	3 30.0	5 51.0	26 47.5	19 21.6	4 26.9	23 31.8	21 50.4	15 47.5
16 M	23 35 9.9	3 11.0	21 56.4	21 48.0	1 8.1	4 22.3	26 31.2	19 13.9	4 32.6	23 31.8	21 50.0	15 47.1
19 T	23 46 59.6	2 1.5	21 57.8	18 2.3	1S11.8	2 52.5	26 13.7	19 6.2	4 38.3	23 31.8	21 49.6	15 46.8
22 S	23 58 49.2	0 51.6	21 59.2	4 37.8	3 28.8	1 21.9	25 54.9	18 58.6	4 43.9	23 31.8	21 49.3	15 46.4
25 W	0 10 38.9	0S18.5	22 0.5	10N16.5	5 41.9	0S 9.3	25 34.9	18 51.2	4 49.4	23 31.7	21 48.9	15 46.0
28 S	0 22 28.6	1 28.7	22 1.9	20 7.1	7 50.4	1 40.7	25 13.6	18 43.8	4 54.8	23 31.6	21 48.6	15 45.7

OCTOBER 1907

LONGITUDE

DAY	EPHEMERIS SIDEREAL TIME	☉	☊	☽	☿	♀	♂	♃	♄	♅	♆	♇
1 T	0 34 18.2	6♎39.8	19♋20.7	23♋ 3.6	23♎49.7	10♎55.6	23♑ 1.8	8♌11.8	23♓ 2.8	8♑47.7	14♋47.5	24♊48.0
2 W	0 38 14.8	7 38.9	19 17.6	4♌54.3	25 19.6	12 10.4	23 33.3	8 21.4	22R58.4	8 48.3	14 48.1	24R47.9
3 T	0 42 11.3	8 37.9	19 14.4	16 53.0	26 48.7	13 25.3	24 5.1	8 30.9	22 54.0	8 49.0	14 48.7	24 47.7
4 F	0 46 7.9	9 37.0	19 11.2	29 3.9	28 16.8	14 40.2	24 37.2	8 40.3	22 49.6	8 49.8	14 49.2	24 47.6
5 S	0 50 4.4	10 36.2	19 8.0	11♍30.5	29 44.0	15 55.0	25 9.6	8 49.6	22 45.3	8 50.6	14 49.7	24 47.4
6 S	0 54 0.9	11 35.3	19 4.8	24 14.7	1♏10.4	17 9.9	25 42.4	8 58.7	22 41.0	8 51.4	14 50.2	24 47.1
7 M	0 57 57.5	12 34.6	19 1.7	7♎17.1	2 35.8	18 24.8	26 15.4	9 7.8	22 36.8	8 52.3	14 50.6	24 46.9
8 T	1 1 54.1	13 33.8	18 58.5	20 36.7	4 0.3	19 39.7	26 48.7	9 16.7	22 32.6	8 53.3	14 51.0	24 46.6
9 W	1 5 50.6	14 33.1	18 55.3	4♏11.2	5 23.8	20 54.7	27 22.2	9 25.5	22 28.5	8 54.3	14 51.3	24 46.4
10 T	1 9 47.2	15 32.4	18 52.1	17 57.6	6 46.3	22 9.6	27 56.1	9 34.2	22 24.4	8 55.3	14 51.7	24 46.1
11 F	1 13 43.7	16 31.7	18 48.9	1♐52.3	8 7.8	23 24.5	28 30.2	9 42.7	22 20.3	8 56.4	14 52.0	24 45.7
12 S	1 17 40.3	17 31.1	18 45.8	15 52.6	9 28.2	24 39.4	29 4.5	9 51.2	22 16.4	8 57.6	14 52.2	24 45.4
13 S	1 21 36.8	18 30.5	18 42.6	29 55.9	10 47.4	25 54.3	29 39.2	9 59.5	22 12.4	8 58.8	14 52.4	24 45.0
14 M	1 25 33.4	19 29.9	18 39.4	14♑ 1.0	12 5.4	27 9.3	0♒14.0	10 7.7	22 8.6	9 0.0	14 52.6	24 44.6
15 T	1 29 29.9	20 29.4	18 36.2	28 6.8	13 22.2	28 24.2	0 49.1	10 15.7	22 4.8	9 1.3	14 52.8	24 44.2
16 W	1 33 26.5	21 28.9	18 33.1	12♒12.6	14 37.5	29 39.1	1 24.4	10 23.6	22 1.0	9 2.7	14 52.9	24 43.8
17 T	1 37 23.1	22 28.4	18 29.9	26 17.3	15 51.4	0♏54.1	1 60.0	10 31.4	21 57.4	9 4.1	14 53.0	24 43.3
18 F	1 41 19.6	23 27.9	18 26.7	10♓19.2	17 3.7	2 9.0	2 35.7	10 39.1	21 53.8	9 5.5	14 53.0	24 42.9
19 S	1 45 16.1	24 27.5	18 23.5	24 15.7	18 14.3	3 24.0	3 11.7	10 46.6	21 50.2	9 7.0	14 53.1	24 42.4
20 S	1 49 12.7	25 27.1	18 20.3	8♈ 3.2	19 23.0	4 38.9	3 47.8	10 54.0	21 46.8	9 8.6	14R53.0	24 41.8
21 M	1 53 9.3	26 26.7	18 17.2	21 38.4	20 29.7	5 53.9	4 24.2	11 1.2	21 43.4	9 10.2	14 53.0	24 41.3
22 T	1 57 5.8	27 26.4	18 14.0	4♉57.9	21 34.2	7 8.8	5 0.7	11 8.3	21 40.1	9 11.8	14 52.9	24 40.8
23 W	2 1 2.4	28 26.1	18 10.8	17 59.6	22 36.1	8 23.8	5 37.5	11 15.3	21 36.8	9 13.5	14 52.8	24 40.2
24 T	2 4 58.9	29 25.8	18 7.6	0♊42.7	23 35.4	9 38.7	6 14.4	11 22.1	21 33.6	9 15.2	14 52.6	24 39.6
25 F	2 8 55.5	0♏25.6	18 4.5	13 7.8	24 31.7	10 53.7	6 51.4	11 28.8	21 30.6	9 17.0	14 52.5	24 39.0
26 S	2 12 52.0	1 25.4	18 1.3	25 17.4	25 24.6	12 8.6	7 28.7	11 35.3	21 27.5	9 18.8	14 52.3	24 38.4
27 S	2 16 48.6	2 25.3	17 58.1	7♋14.9	26 13.9	13 23.6	8 6.1	11 41.7	21 24.6	9 20.7	14 52.0	24 37.7
28 M	2 20 45.1	3 25.2	17 54.9	19 4.8	26 59.0	14 38.6	8 43.7	11 47.9	21 21.8	9 22.6	14 51.7	24 37.0
29 T	2 24 41.7	4 25.1	17 51.8	0♌52.3	27 39.6	15 53.5	9 21.4	11 54.0	21 19.0	9 24.5	14 51.4	24 36.4
30 W	2 28 38.2	5 25.0	17 48.6	12 43.0	28 15.2	17 8.5	9 59.3	11 59.9	21 16.4	9 26.5	14 51.1	24 35.6
31 T	2 32 34.8	6 25.0	17 45.4	24 42.3	28 45.3	18 23.5	10 37.4	12 5.6	21 13.8	9 28.6	14 50.7	24 34.9

DECLINATION

DAY	EPHEMERIS SIDEREAL TIME	☉	☊	☽	☿	♀	♂	♃	♄	♅	♆	♇
1 T	0 34 18.2	2S38.8	22N 3.3	21N43.4	9S53.7	3S12.0	24S51.0	18N36.7	5S 0.1	23S31.4	21N48.4	15N45.3
4 F	0 46 7.9	3 48.7	22 4.6	14 46.4	11 51.2	4 42.9	24 26.9	18 29.7	5 5.2	23 31.3	21 48.1	15 44.9
7 M	0 57 57.5	4 58.2	22 6.0	1 36.2	13 42.2	6 12.9	24 1.4	18 22.9	5 10.2	23 31.1	21 47.9	15 44.5
10 T	1 9 47.2	6 7.2	22 7.3	12S58.2	15 26.1	7 41.8	23 34.5	18 16.4	5 14.9	23 30.8	21 47.8	15 44.2
13 S	1 21 36.8	7 15.4	22 8.6	21 49.3	17 2.1	9 9.2	23 6.1	18 10.1	5 19.4	23 30.6	21 47.6	15 43.8
16 W	1 33 26.5	8 22.8	22 9.9	19 4.5	18 29.3	10 34.8	22 36.3	18 4.0	5 23.7	23 30.3	21 47.5	15 43.4
19 S	1 45 16.1	9 29.0	22 11.2	6 28.9	19 46.7	11 58.1	22 5.0	17 58.3	5 27.7	23 29.9	21 47.4	15 43.1
22 T	1 57 5.8	10 34.0	22 12.5	8N39.9	20 52.9	13 18.9	21 32.3	17 52.8	5 31.4	23 29.6	21 47.4	15 42.7
25 F	2 8 55.5	11 37.6	22 13.8	19 34.0	21 46.2	14 36.8	20 58.2	17 47.7	5 34.8	23 29.2	21 47.4	15 42.3
28 M	2 20 45.1	12 39.7	22 15.0	22 15.3	22 24.4	15 51.4	20 22.7	17 42.9	5 37.9	23 28.8	21 47.4	15 42.0
31 T	2 32 34.8	13 39.9	22 16.3	16 12.3	22 44.3	17 2.4	19 45.8	17 38.5	5 40.6	23 28.3	21 47.5	15 41.6

NOVEMBER 1907

LONGITUDE

DAY	EPHEMERIS SIDEREAL TIME	☉	☊	☽	☿	♀	♂	♃	♄	♅	♆	♇
	h m s	° ′	° ′	° ′	° ′	° ′	° ′	° ′	° ′	° ′	° ′	° ′
1 F	2 36 31.4	7♏25.1	17♋42.2	6♍55.4	29♏ 9.1	19♏38.5	11♒15.6	12♌11.2	21♓11.3	9♑30.6	14♋50.3	24♊34.2
2 S	2 40 27.9	8 25.1	17 39.0	19 26.7	29 26.2	20 53.5	11 54.0	12 16.6	21R 8.9	9 32.8	14R49.8	24R33.4
3 S	2 44 24.5	9 25.2	17 35.9	2♎19.3	29 35.8	22 8.4	12 32.5	12 21.9	21 6.6	9 34.9	14 49.3	24 32.7
4 M	2 48 21.0	10 25.4	17 32.7	15 34.7	29 37.4	23 23.4	13 11.1	12 27.0	21 4.4	9 37.1	14 48.8	24 31.9
5 T	2 52 17.6	11 25.5	17 29.5	29 12.4	29R30.3	24 38.4	13 49.9	12 31.9	21 2.2	9 39.4	14 48.3	24 31.1
6 W	2 56 14.1	12 25.7	17 26.3	13♏ 9.6	29 14.0	25 53.4	14 28.8	12 36.7	21 0.2	9 41.7	14 47.7	24 30.2
7 T	3 0 10.7	13 25.9	17 23.2	27 21.9	28 48.0	27 8.4	15 7.9	12 41.3	20 58.3	9 44.0	14 47.1	24 29.4
8 F	3 4 7.2	14 26.2	17 20.0	11♐43.8	28 12.1	28 23.4	15 47.0	12 45.7	20 56.4	9 46.4	14 46.4	24 28.5
9 S	3 8 3.8	15 26.5	17 16.8	26 9.3	27 26.5	29 38.4	16 26.3	12 49.9	20 54.7	9 48.8	14 45.8	24 27.7
10 S	3 12 0.4	16 26.8	17 13.6	10♑33.6	26 31.4	0♐53.4	17 5.8	12 54.0	20 53.1	9 51.3	14 45.1	24 26.8
11 M	3 15 56.9	17 27.1	17 10.4	24 52.7	25 27.8	2 8.4	17 45.3	12 57.9	20 51.6	9 53.7	14 44.3	24 25.9
12 T	3 19 53.5	18 27.5	17 7.3	9♒ 4.2	24 16.8	3 23.4	18 25.0	13 1.6	20 50.1	9 56.3	14 43.5	24 25.0
13 W	3 23 50.0	19 27.8	17 4.1	23 6.8	23 0.4	4 38.4	19 4.7	13 5.1	20 48.8	9 58.8	14 42.8	24 24.0
14 T	3 27 46.6	20 28.2	17 0.9	6♓60.0	21 40.6	5 53.4	19 44.6	13 8.5	20 47.6	10 1.4	14 41.9	24 23.1
15 F	3 31 43.1	21 28.7	16 57.7	20 43.3	20 20.0	7 8.4	20 24.5	13 11.6	20 46.5	10 4.1	14 41.1	24 22.1
16 S	3 35 39.7	22 29.1	16 54.6	4♈16.3	19 1.3	8 23.3	21 4.6	13 14.6	20 45.4	10 6.7	14 40.2	24 21.2
17 S	3 39 36.2	23 29.6	16 51.4	17 38.3	17 46.9	9 38.3	21 44.7	13 17.4	20 44.5	10 9.4	14 39.3	24 20.2
18 M	3 43 32.8	24 30.1	16 48.2	0♉48.4	16 39.4	10 53.3	22 25.0	13 20.0	20 43.7	10 12.2	14 38.3	24 19.2
19 T	3 47 29.4	25 30.6	16 45.0	13 45.4	15 40.6	12 8.2	23 5.3	13 22.5	20 43.0	10 14.9	14 37.4	24 18.2
20 W	3 51 25.9	26 31.1	16 41.9	26 28.7	14 52.1	13 23.2	23 45.7	13 24.7	20 42.4	10 17.8	14 36.4	24 17.2
21 T	3 55 22.5	27 31.7	16 38.7	8♊58.0	14 14.8	14 38.2	24 26.2	13 26.7	20 41.9	10 20.6	14 35.3	24 16.1
22 F	3 59 19.0	28 32.3	16 35.5	21 13.9	13 49.1	15 53.1	25 6.7	13 28.6	20 41.5	10 23.5	14 34.3	24 15.1
23 S	4 3 15.6	29 32.9	16 32.3	3♋17.9	13 35.1	17 8.1	25 47.4	13 30.3	20 41.3	10 26.4	14 33.2	24 14.1
24 S	4 7 12.2	0♐33.5	16 29.1	15 12.5	13 32.4	18 23.0	26 28.1	13 31.8	20 41.1	10 29.3	14 32.1	24 13.0
25 M	4 11 8.7	1 34.2	16 26.0	27 1.2	13D40.4	19 38.0	27 8.8	13 33.0	20 41.0	10 32.2	14 31.0	24 11.9
26 T	4 15 5.2	2 34.9	16 22.8	8♌48.0	13 58.4	20 52.9	27 49.7	13 34.1	20D41.0	10 35.2	14 29.8	24 10.8
27 W	4 19 1.8	3 35.6	16 19.6	20 37.8	14 25.6	22 7.9	28 30.6	13 35.0	20 41.2	10 38.2	14 28.7	24 9.7
28 T	4 22 58.4	4 36.4	16 16.4	2♍35.6	15 1.0	23 22.8	29 11.5	13 35.7	20 41.5	10 41.3	14 27.5	24 8.7
29 F	4 26 54.9	5 37.2	16 13.3	14 46.8	15 43.8	24 37.7	29 52.6	13 36.2	20 41.8	10 44.4	14 26.2	24 7.6
30 S	4 30 51.5	6 38.0	16 10.1	27 16.2	16 33.1	25 52.7	0♓33.7	13 36.5	20 42.3	10 47.5	14 25.0	24 6.4

DECLINATION

DAY	EPHEMERIS SIDEREAL TIME	☉	☽	☿	♀	♂	♃	♄	♅	♆	♇
1 F	2 36 31.4	13S59.6	22N16.7	12N34.0	22S46.1	17S25.2	19S33.2	17N37.2	5S41.5	23S28.1	21N47.5	15N41.5
4 M	2 48 21.0	14 57.2	22 18.0	1S28.3	22 34.7	18 30.8	18 54.5	17 33.3	5 43.8	23 27.7	21 47.6	15 41.2
7 T	3 0 10.7	15 52.7	22 19.2	15 51.6	21 53.4	19 32.0	18 14.6	17 29.8	5 45.7	23 27.1	21 47.8	15 40.9
10 S	3 12 0.4	16 45.8	22 20.4	22 32.9	20 37.5	20 28.3	17 33.3	17 26.8	5 47.3	23 26.6	21 47.9	15 40.6
13 W	3 23 50.0	17 36.3	22 21.6	16 44.3	18 49.8	21 19.6	16 50.9	17 24.2	5 48.5	23 26.0	21 48.2	15 40.3
16 S	3 35 39.7	18 24.0	22 22.8	2 53.7	16 47.9	22 5.3	16 7.3	17 22.1	5 49.3	23 25.4	21 48.4	15 40.1
19 T	3 47 29.4	19 8.9	22 24.0	11N40.5	15 1.4	22 45.3	15 22.6	17 20.4	5 49.7	23 24.7	21 48.7	15 39.8
22 F	3 59 19.0	19 50.6	22 25.2	21 5.0	13 54.7	23 19.3	14 36.9	17 19.3	5 49.7	23 24.0	21 49.0	15 39.6
25 M	4 11 8.7	20 29.1	22 26.3	21 49.7	13 35.2	23 47.1	13 50.2	17 18.6	5 49.4	23 23.3	21 49.3	15 39.4
28 T	4 22 58.4	21 4.2	22 27.5	14 8.1	13 55.7	24 8.4	13 2.6	17 18.5	5 48.7	23 22.6	21 49.6	15 39.2

DECEMBER 1907

LONGITUDE

DAY	EPHEMERIS SIDEREAL TIME	☉	☊	☽	☿	♀	♂	♃	♄	♅	♆	♇
1 S	4 34 48.0	7♐38.8	16♋ 6.9	10♎ 8.2	17♏28.1	27♐ 7.6	1♓14.8	13♌36.6	20♓42.9	10♑50.6	14♋23.7	24♊ 5.3
2 M	4 38 44.6	8 39.6	16 3.7	23 25.5	18 28.1	28 22.5	1 56.0	13R36.5	20 43.5	10 53.7	14R22.4	24R 4.2
3 T	4 42 41.1	9 40.5	16 0.6	7♏ 9.1	19 32.5	29 37.5	2 37.3	13 36.2	20 44.3	10 56.9	14 21.1	24 3.1
4 W	4 46 37.7	10 41.4	15 57.4	21 17.8	20 40.7	0♑52.4	3 18.7	13 35.8	20 45.2	11 0.1	14 19.8	24 1.9
5 T	4 50 34.3	11 42.3	15 54.2	5♐47.4	21 52.1	2 7.3	4 0.1	13 35.1	20 46.3	11 3.4	14 18.4	24 0.8
6 F	4 54 30.8	12 43.2	15 51.0	20 31.8	23 6.3	3 22.3	4 41.5	13 34.2	20 47.4	11 6.6	14 17.0	23 59.6
7 S	4 58 27.4	13 44.2	15 47.8	5♑23.4	24 23.0	4 37.2	5 23.0	13 33.1	20 48.6	11 9.9	14 15.6	23 58.5
8 S	5 2 23.9	14 45.1	15 44.7	20 14.3	25 41.8	5 52.1	6 4.5	13 31.8	20 49.9	11 13.2	14 14.2	23 57.3
9 M	5 6 20.5	15 46.1	15 41.5	4♒57.4	27 2.4	7 7.0	6 46.1	13 30.3	20 51.4	11 16.5	14 12.8	23 56.1
10 T	5 10 17.0	16 47.1	15 38.3	19 27.5	28 24.5	8 21.9	7 27.8	13 28.6	20 52.9	11 19.8	14 11.3	23 55.0
11 W	5 14 13.6	17 48.1	15 35.1	3♓41.0	29 47.9	9 36.7	8 9.4	13 26.8	20 54.5	11 23.2	14 9.8	23 53.8
12 T	5 18 10.2	18 49.1	15 32.0	17 36.6	1♐12.6	10 51.6	8 51.2	13 24.7	20 56.3	11 26.5	14 8.3	23 52.6
13 F	5 22 6.7	19 50.1	15 28.8	1♈13.9	2 38.2	12 6.5	9 32.9	13 22.4	20 58.2	11 29.9	14 6.8	23 51.5
14 S	5 26 3.3	20 51.1	15 25.6	14 33.9	4 4.6	13 21.3	10 14.7	13 20.0	21 0.1	11 33.3	14 5.3	23 50.3
15 S	5 29 59.8	21 52.2	15 22.4	27 37.7	5 31.8	14 36.1	10 56.5	13 17.3	21 2.2	11 36.7	14 3.8	23 49.1
16 M	5 33 56.4	22 53.2	15 19.3	10♉26.9	6 59.7	15 51.0	11 38.3	13 14.5	21 4.4	11 40.2	14 2.2	23 47.9
17 T	5 37 53.0	23 54.2	15 16.1	23 2.8	8 28.1	17 5.8	12 20.2	13 11.5	21 6.6	11 43.6	14 0.7	23 46.7
18 W	5 41 49.5	24 55.3	15 12.9	5♊26.8	9 57.1	18 20.6	13 2.1	13 8.2	21 9.0	11 47.1	13 59.1	23 45.6
19 T	5 45 46.1	25 56.4	15 9.7	17 40.2	11 26.5	19 35.3	13 44.0	13 4.8	21 11.5	11 50.5	13 57.5	23 44.4
20 F	5 49 42.6	26 57.4	15 6.5	29 44.3	12 56.3	20 50.1	14 25.9	13 1.3	21 14.0	11 54.0	13 55.9	23 43.2
21 S	5 53 39.2	27 58.5	15 3.4	11♋40.9	14 26.5	22 4.8	15 7.9	12 57.5	21 16.7	11 57.5	13 54.3	23 42.0
22 S	5 57 35.7	28 59.6	15 0.2	23 31.8	15 57.0	23 19.6	15 49.9	12 53.5	21 19.5	12 1.0	13 52.6	23 40.9
23 M	6 1 32.3	0♑ 0.7	14 57.0	5♌19.5	17 27.9	24 34.3	16 31.9	12 49.4	21 22.4	12 4.5	13 51.0	23 39.7
24 T	6 5 28.9	1 1.8	14 53.8	17 6.9	18 59.1	25 49.0	17 13.9	12 45.1	21 25.3	12 8.1	13 49.4	23 38.5
25 W	6 9 25.4	2 2.9	14 50.7	28 57.5	20 30.5	27 3.7	17 55.9	12 40.6	21 28.4	12 11.6	13 47.7	23 37.3
26 T	6 13 22.0	3 4.1	14 47.5	10♍55.2	22 2.3	28 18.4	18 37.9	12 36.0	21 31.5	12 15.2	13 46.1	23 36.2
27 F	6 17 18.5	4 5.2	14 44.3	23 4.5	23 34.3	29 33.0	19 20.0	12 31.2	21 34.8	12 18.7	13 44.4	23 35.0
28 S	6 21 15.1	5 6.4	14 41.1	5♎29.9	25 6.7	0♒47.7	20 2.1	12 26.2	21 38.2	12 22.3	13 42.7	23 33.9
29 S	6 25 11.6	6 7.5	14 38.0	18 15.8	26 39.3	2 2.3	20 44.1	12 21.0	21 41.6	12 25.8	13 41.0	23 32.7
30 M	6 29 8.2	7 8.7	14 34.8	1♏25.9	28 12.2	3 16.9	21 26.2	12 15.7	21 45.1	12 29.4	13 39.4	23 31.6
31 T	6 33 4.8	8 9.9	14 31.6	15 2.9	29 45.4	4 31.5	22 8.4	12 10.3	21 48.8	12 33.0	13 37.7	23 30.4

DECLINATION

DAY	EPHEMERIS SIDEREAL TIME	☉	☽	☿	♀	♂	♃	♄	♅	♆	♇
1 S	4 34 48.0	21S35.7	22N28.6	0N44.7	14S44.4	24S23.2	12S14.2	17N18.9	5S47.5	23S21.9	21N50.0	15N39.1
4 W	4 46 37.7	22 3.6	22 29.8	14S 3.5	15 50.0	24 31.2	11 24.9	17 19.7	5 46.0	23 21.1	21 50.4	15 38.9
7 S	4 58 27.4	22 27.6	22 30.9	22 30.8	17 3.9	24 32.5	10 34.9	17 21.1	5 44.2	23 20.2	21 50.8	15 38.8
10 T	5 10 17.0	22 47.6	22 32.0	17 50.8	18 20.0	24 27.0	9 44.2	17 23.0	5 41.9	23 19.4	21 51.3	15 38.7
13 F	5 22 6.7	23 3.7	22 33.1	4 11.7	19 34.2	24 14.7	8 52.9	17 25.4	5 39.2	23 18.5	21 51.7	15 38.6
16 M	5 33 56.4	23 15.6	22 34.2	10N28.5	20 43.6	23 55.7	8 1.1	17 28.4	5 36.2	23 17.7	21 52.2	15 38.6
19 T	5 45 46.1	23 23.3	22 35.3	20 31.5	21 46.3	23 30.2	7 8.8	17 31.7	5 32.9	23 16.7	21 52.7	15 38.6
22 S	5 57 35.7	23 26.8	22 36.4	22 14.5	22 40.7	22 58.3	6 16.2	17 35.6	5 29.2	23 15.8	21 53.2	15 38.6
25 W	6 9 25.4	23 26.1	22 37.4	15 20.0	23 25.9	22 20.2	5 23.2	17 39.8	5 25.1	23 14.9	21 53.7	15 38.7
28 S	6 21 15.1	23 21.1	22 38.5	2 37.2	24 0.8	21 36.1	4 29.9	17 44.5	5 20.8	23 13.9	21 54.2	15 38.7
31 T	6 33 4.8	23 11.9	22 39.5	11S59.8	24 24.7	20 46.4	3 36.5	17 49.6	5 16.1	23 12.9	21 54.8	15 38.9

JANUARY 1908

LONGITUDE

DAY	EPHEMERIS SIDEREAL TIME h m s	☉ ° ′	☊ ° ′	☽ ° ′	☿ ° ′	♀ ° ′	♂ ° ′	♃ ° ′	♄ ° ′	♅ ° ′	♆ ° ′	♇ ° ′
1 W	6 37 1.3	9♑11.0	14♋28.4	29♏ 7.4	1♑18.9	5♒46.1	22♓50.5	12♌ 4.6	21♓52.5	12♑36.6	13♋36.0	23♊29.3
2 T	6 40 57.9	10 12.2	14 25.3	13♐37.6	2 52.8	7 0.7	23 32.6	11R58.9	21 56.3	12 40.1	13R34.3	23R28.2
3 F	6 44 54.4	11 13.4	14 22.1	28 29.2	4 26.9	8 15.2	24 14.8	11 52.9	22 0.2	12 43.7	13 32.6	23 27.1
4 S	6 48 51.0	12 14.6	14 18.9	13♑34.7	6 1.4	9 29.7	24 56.9	11 46.9	22 4.2	12 47.3	13 30.9	23 25.9
5 S	6 52 47.6	13 15.8	14 15.7	28 45.3	7 36.3	10 44.2	25 39.1	11 40.7	22 8.3	12 50.9	13 29.2	23 24.8
6 M	6 56 44.1	14 17.0	14 12.6	13♒51.5	9 11.5	11 58.7	26 21.3	11 34.4	22 12.4	12 54.5	13 27.5	23 23.8
7 T	7 0 40.7	15 18.2	14 9.4	28 44.5	10 47.1	13 13.1	27 3.4	11 27.9	22 16.7	12 58.1	13 25.8	23 22.7
8 W	7 4 37.2	16 19.3	14 6.2	13♓17.7	12 23.1	14 27.6	27 45.6	11 21.3	22 21.0	13 1.6	13 24.1	23 21.6
9 T	7 8 33.8	17 20.5	14 3.0	27 27.2	13 59.5	15 42.0	28 27.8	11 14.6	22 25.4	13 5.2	13 22.4	23 20.5
10 F	7 12 30.3	18 21.6	13 59.8	11♈11.3	15 36.3	16 56.3	29 10.0	11 7.8	22 29.9	13 8.8	13 20.7	23 19.5
11 S	7 16 26.9	19 22.8	13 56.7	24 30.9	17 13.6	18 10.6	29 52.2	11 0.8	22 34.5	13 12.4	13 19.0	23 18.4
12 S	7 20 23.5	20 23.9	13 53.5	7♉28.2	18 51.3	19 24.9	0♈34.4	10 53.8	22 39.2	13 15.9	13 17.3	23 17.4
13 M	7 24 20.0	21 25.1	13 50.3	20 6.3	20 29.5	20 39.2	1 16.5	10 46.7	22 43.9	13 19.5	13 15.7	23 16.3
14 T	7 28 16.6	22 26.2	13 47.1	2♊28.5	22 8.1	21 53.4	1 58.7	10 39.4	22 48.8	13 23.0	13 14.0	23 15.3
15 W	7 32 13.1	23 27.3	13 44.0	14 38.3	23 47.3	23 7.6	2 40.9	10 32.1	22 53.7	13 26.6	13 12.3	23 14.3
16 T	7 36 9.7	24 28.4	13 40.8	26 38.8	25 26.9	24 21.8	3 23.0	10 24.7	22 58.6	13 30.1	13 10.7	23 13.3
17 F	7 40 6.2	25 29.5	13 37.6	8♋32.9	27 7.0	25 35.9	4 5.2	10 17.2	23 3.7	13 33.6	13 9.0	23 12.4
18 S	7 44 2.8	26 30.6	13 34.4	20 23.0	28 47.7	26 49.9	4 47.3	10 9.6	23 8.8	13 37.2	13 7.3	23 11.4
19 S	7 47 59.4	27 31.6	13 31.3	2♌11.3	0♒28.9	28 4.0	5 29.4	10 2.0	23 14.0	13 40.7	13 5.7	23 10.5
20 M	7 51 55.9	28 32.7	13 28.1	13 59.9	2 10.5	29 18.0	6 11.6	9 54.3	23 19.3	13 44.2	13 4.1	23 9.5
21 T	7 55 52.5	29 33.7	13 24.9	25 50.8	3 52.7	0♓31.9	6 53.7	9 46.6	23 24.6	13 47.7	13 2.5	23 8.6
22 W	7 59 49.0	0♒34.8	13 21.7	7♍46.3	5 35.3	1 45.8	7 35.8	9 38.8	23 30.0	13 51.1	13 0.9	23 7.7
23 T	8 3 45.6	1 35.8	13 18.5	19 48.9	7 18.4	2 59.7	8 17.8	9 30.9	23 35.5	13 54.6	12 59.3	23 6.8
24 F	8 7 42.1	2 36.8	13 15.4	2♎ 1.4	9 1.9	4 13.5	8 59.9	9 23.0	23 41.0	13 58.0	12 57.7	23 5.9
25 S	8 11 38.7	3 37.8	13 12.2	14 27.2	10 45.7	5 27.3	9 42.0	9 15.1	23 46.6	14 1.5	12 56.1	23 5.1
26 S	8 15 35.3	4 38.8	13 9.0	27 9.5	12 29.9	6 41.0	10 24.0	9 7.1	23 52.3	14 4.9	12 54.6	23 4.2
27 M	8 19 31.8	5 39.8	13 5.8	10♏12.0	14 14.4	7 54.7	11 6.0	8 59.2	23 58.1	14 8.3	12 53.0	23 3.4
28 T	8 23 28.3	6 40.8	13 2.7	23 37.7	15 59.0	9 8.4	11 48.1	8 51.2	24 3.9	14 11.7	12 51.5	23 2.5
29 W	8 27 24.9	7 41.8	12 59.5	7♐28.7	17 43.6	10 22.0	12 30.1	8 43.1	24 9.7	14 15.0	12 50.0	23 1.8
30 T	8 31 21.5	8 42.8	12 56.3	21 45.5	19 28.2	11 35.5	13 12.1	8 35.1	24 15.7	14 18.4	12 48.5	23 1.0
31 F	8 35 18.0	9 43.7	12 53.1	6♑26.4	21 12.6	12 49.0	13 54.1	8 27.1	24 21.6	14 21.7	12 47.0	23 0.2

DECLINATION

DAY	EPHEMERIS SIDEREAL TIME h m s	☉ ° ′	☊ ° ′	☽ ° ′	☿ ° ′	♀ ° ′	♂ ° ′	♃ ° ′	♄ ° ′	♅ ° ′	♆ ° ′	♇ ° ′
1 W	6 37 1.3	23S 7.9	22N39.8	16S17.8	24S30.1	20S28.6	3S18.6	17N51.3	5S14.4	23S12.6	21N55.0	15N38.9
4 S	6 48 51.0	22 53.2	22 40.9	22 41.6	24 38.5	19 31.8	2 25.0	17 56.9	5 9.3	23 11.6	21 55.5	15 39.0
7 T	7 0 40.7	22 34.3	22 41.9	15 24.1	24 34.4	18 29.9	1 31.3	18 2.7	5 3.9	23 10.6	21 56.0	15 39.2
10 F	7 12 30.3	22 11.5	22 42.9	0 26.6	24 17.5	17 23.5	0 37.6	18 8.8	4 58.2	23 9.6	21 56.6	15 39.4
13 M	7 24 20.0	21 44.7	22 43.9	13N37.8	23 47.3	16 12.8	0N16.0	18 15.1	4 52.2	23 8.5	21 57.1	15 39.6
16 T	7 36 9.7	21 14.1	22 44.8	21 47.8	23 3.5	14 58.2	1 9.5	18 21.6	4 45.9	23 7.5	21 57.7	15 39.9
19 S	7 47 59.4	20 39.9	22 45.8	21 15.8	22 5.7	13 40.0	2 2.7	18 28.2	4 39.4	23 6.4	21 58.2	15 40.2
22 W	7 59 49.0	20 2.2	22 46.8	12 35.5	20 53.9	12 18.6	2 55.7	18 34.9	4 32.7	23 5.4	21 58.7	15 40.5
25 S	8 11 38.7	19 21.0	22 47.7	0S50.7	19 28.0	10 54.3	3 48.3	18 41.6	4 25.7	23 4.4	21 59.2	15 40.8
28 T	8 23 28.3	18 36.7	22 48.6	14 45.1	17 48.6	9 27.6	4 40.5	18 48.3	4 18.6	23 3.3	21 59.7	15 41.2
31 F	8 35 18.0	17 49.3	22 49.6	22 35.3	15 56.5	7 58.7	5 32.3	18 55.0	4 11.2	23 2.3	22 0.2	15 41.6

FEBRUARY 1908

LONGITUDE

DAY	EPHEMERIS SIDEREAL TIME h m s	☉ ° ′	☊ ° ′	☽ ° ′	☿ ° ′	♀ ° ′	♂ ° ′	♃ ° ′	♄ ° ′	♅ ° ′	♆ ° ′	♇ ° ′
1 S	8 39 14.6	10♒44.6	12♋49.9	21♑26.6	22♒56.5	14♓ 2.5	14♈36.0	8♌19.1	24♓27.7	14♑25.0	12♋45.5	22♊59.5
2 S	8 43 11.1	11 45.6	12 46.8	6♒38.8	24 39.7	15 15.9	15 18.0	8R11.1	24 33.8	14 28.3	12R44.1	22R58.7
3 M	8 47 7.7	12 46.5	12 43.6	21 53.4	26 22.1	16 29.2	15 60.0	8 3.1	24 40.0	14 31.6	12 42.7	22 58.0
4 T	8 51 4.2	13 47.4	12 40.4	7♓ 0.0	28 3.1	17 42.5	16 41.9	7 55.2	24 46.2	14 34.8	12 41.2	22 57.3
5 W	8 55 0.8	14 48.2	12 37.2	21 49.4	29 42.6	18 55.7	17 23.8	7 47.2	24 52.4	14 38.0	12 39.8	22 56.6
6 T	8 58 57.3	15 49.1	12 34.1	6♈14.4	1♓20.2	20 8.9	18 5.7	7 39.4	24 58.8	14 41.2	12 38.5	22 56.0
7 F	9 2 53.9	16 49.9	12 30.9	20 11.3	2 55.2	21 22.0	18 47.6	7 31.5	25 5.1	14 44.4	12 37.1	22 55.4
8 S	9 6 50.5	17 50.7	12 27.7	3♉39.3	4 27.3	22 35.0	19 29.4	7 23.7	25 11.6	14 47.6	12 35.8	22 54.7
9 S	9 10 47.0	18 51.4	12 24.5	16 40.1	5 55.8	23 48.0	20 11.3	7 16.0	25 18.0	14 50.7	12 34.5	22 54.1
10 M	9 14 43.6	19 52.2	12 21.4	29 17.2	7 20.1	25 0.9	20 53.1	7 8.3	25 24.5	14 53.8	12 33.2	22 53.6
11 T	9 18 40.1	20 52.9	12 18.2	11♊35.0	8 39.6	26 13.7	21 34.9	7 0.7	25 31.1	14 56.9	12 31.9	22 53.0
12 W	9 22 36.7	21 53.6	12 15.0	23 38.6	9 53.6	27 26.5	22 16.7	6 53.2	25 37.7	14 59.9	12 30.7	22 52.5
13 T	9 26 33.3	22 54.2	12 11.8	5♋32.4	11 1.3	28 39.1	22 58.4	6 45.7	25 44.4	15 2.9	12 29.5	22 51.9
14 F	9 30 29.8	23 54.9	12 8.6	17 20.9	12 2.0	29 51.7	23 40.1	6 38.4	25 51.1	15 5.9	12 28.3	22 51.4
15 S	9 34 26.3	24 55.5	12 5.5	29 7.7	12 55.0	1♈ 4.2	24 21.8	6 31.1	25 57.8	15 8.9	12 27.1	22 51.0
16 S	9 38 22.9	25 56.0	12 2.3	10♌56.0	13 39.6	2 16.7	25 3.5	6 23.9	26 4.6	15 11.8	12 26.0	22 50.5
17 M	9 42 19.5	26 56.6	11 59.1	22 48.1	14 15.3	3 29.0	25 45.2	6 16.8	26 11.4	15 14.7	12 24.9	22 50.1
18 T	9 46 16.0	27 57.1	11 55.9	4♍45.9	14 41.4	4 41.3	26 26.8	6 9.8	26 18.3	15 17.6	12 23.8	22 49.7
19 W	9 50 12.6	28 57.6	11 52.8	16 51.0	14 57.6	5 53.5	27 8.4	6 2.9	26 25.1	15 20.4	12 22.7	22 49.3
20 T	9 54 9.1	29 58.1	11 49.6	29 4.6	15 3.7	7 5.5	27 50.0	5 56.1	26 32.1	15 23.2	12 21.7	22 48.9
21 F	9 58 5.7	0♓58.5	11 46.4	11♎28.0	14R59.5	8 17.6	28 31.5	5 49.5	26 39.0	15 26.0	12 20.7	22 48.5
22 S	10 2 2.2	1 59.0	11 43.2	24 2.6	14 45.3	9 29.5	29 13.0	5 42.9	26 46.0	15 28.7	12 19.7	22 48.2
23 S	10 5 58.8	2 59.4	11 40.0	6♏50.2	14 21.4	10 41.3	29 54.5	5 36.5	26 53.1	15 31.4	12 18.7	22 47.9
24 M	10 9 55.3	3 59.8	11 36.9	19 53.0	13 48.4	11 53.0	0♉36.0	5 30.2	27 0.1	15 34.1	12 17.8	22 47.6
25 T	10 13 51.9	5 0.1	11 33.7	3♐13.3	13 7.2	13 4.7	1 17.4	5 24.1	27 7.2	15 36.7	12 16.9	22 47.4
26 W	10 17 48.4	6 0.5	11 30.5	16 53.1	12 18.8	14 16.2	1 58.9	5 18.0	27 14.3	15 39.3	12 16.1	22 47.1
27 T	10 21 45.0	7 0.8	11 27.3	0♑54.1	11 24.5	15 27.7	2 40.3	5 12.2	27 21.5	15 41.9	12 15.2	22 46.9
28 F	10 25 41.6	8 1.1	11 24.2	15 16.2	10 25.7	16 39.0	3 21.6	5 6.4	27 28.7	15 44.4	12 14.4	22 46.7
29 S	10 29 38.1	9 1.3	11 21.0	29 57.5	9 23.9	17 50.3	4 3.0	5 0.8	27 35.9	15 46.9	12 13.6	22 46.5

DECLINATION

DAY	EPHEMERIS SIDEREAL TIME h m s	☉ ° ′	☊ ° ′	☽ ° ′	☿ ° ′	♀ ° ′	♂ ° ′	♃ ° ′	♄ ° ′	♅ ° ′	♆ ° ′	♇ ° ′
1 S	8 39 14.6	17S32.9	22N49.9	22S24.0	15S16.6	7S28.6	5N49.5	18N57.2	4S 8.7	23S 2.0	22N 0.4	15N41.7
4 T	8 51 4.2	16 41.7	22 50.8	12 49.1	13 10.8	5 57.4	6 40.6	19 3.7	4 1.0	23 1.0	22 0.9	15 42.2
7 F	9 2 53.9	15 48.0	22 51.7	3N 5.4	10 59.1	4 24.8	7 31.2	19 10.1	3 53.2	22 60.0	22 1.4	15 42.6
10 M	9 14 43.6	14 51.8	22 52.6	16 26.0	8 47.6	2 51.2	8 21.1	19 16.2	3 45.3	22 59.0	22 1.8	15 43.1
13 T	9 26 33.3	13 53.3	22 53.5	22 35.1	6 44.7	1 17.0	9 10.3	19 22.2	3 37.2	22 58.0	22 2.2	15 43.6
16 S	9 38 22.9	12 52.8	22 54.3	19 46.2	5 1.1	0N17.6	9 58.7	19 27.8	3 28.9	22 57.1	22 2.6	15 44.1
19 W	9 50 12.6	11 50.5	22 55.2	9 25.4	3 47.8	1 52.2	10 46.3	19 33.2	3 20.6	22 56.2	22 3.0	15 44.7
22 S	10 2 2.2	10 46.4	22 56.0	4S39.0	3 14.1	3 26.4	11 33.0	19 38.3	3 12.1	22 55.3	22 3.4	15 45.2
25 T	10 13 51.9	9 40.9	22 56.9	17 35.7	3 24.0	5 0.1	12 18.8	19 43.0	3 3.5	22 54.4	22 3.8	15 45.8
28 F	10 25 41.6	8 34.0	22 57.7	22 47.6	4 13.2	6 32.7	13 3.7	19 47.4	2 54.9	22 53.6	22 4.1	15 46.4

MARCH 1908

LONGITUDE

DAY	EPHEMERIS SIDEREAL TIME h m s	☉ ° ′	☊ ° ′	☽ ° ′	☿ ° ′	♀ ° ′	♂ ° ′	♃ ° ′	♄ ° ′	♅ ° ′	♆ ° ′	♇ ° ′
1 S	10 33 34.6	10♓ 1.5	11♋17.8	14♒53.4	8♓20.8	19♈ 1.4	4♉44.3	4♌55.4	27♓43.1	15♑49.4	12♋12.9	22♊46.4
2 M	10 37 31.2	11 1.8	11 14.6	29 56.6	7R17.7	20 12.5	5 25.6	4R50.1	27 50.3	15 51.8	12R12.2	22R46.2
3 T	10 41 27.8	12 1.9	11 11.5	14♓58.0	6 16.3	21 23.4	6 6.9	4 45.0	27 57.6	15 54.2	12 11.5	22 46.1
4 W	10 45 24.3	13 2.1	11 8.3	29 48.0	5 17.6	22 34.3	6 48.2	4 40.0	28 4.9	15 56.5	12 10.8	22 46.1
5 T	10 49 20.9	14 2.2	11 5.1	14♈18.0	4 22.9	23 45.0	7 29.4	4 35.2	28 12.2	15 58.8	12 10.2	22 46.0
6 F	10 53 17.4	15 2.3	11 1.9	28 22.2	3 33.1	24 55.6	8 10.6	4 30.6	28 19.5	16 1.0	12 9.6	22 46.0
7 S	10 57 14.0	16 2.3	10 58.7	11♉57.7	2 48.8	26 6.1	8 51.8	4 26.1	28 26.9	16 3.3	12 9.0	22 45.9
8 S	11 1 10.5	17 2.4	10 55.6	25 4.9	2 10.6	27 16.5	9 32.9	4 21.8	28 34.3	16 5.4	12 8.5	22D45.9
9 M	11 5 7.1	18 2.3	10 52.4	7♊46.3	1 38.9	28 26.7	10 14.0	4 17.7	28 41.6	16 7.5	12 8.0	22 46.0
10 T	11 9 3.6	19 2.3	10 49.2	20 6.3	1 13.7	29 36.8	10 55.1	4 13.8	28 49.0	16 9.6	12 7.5	22 46.0
11 W	11 13 0.2	20 2.2	10 46.0	2♋10.1	0 55.1	0♉46.8	11 36.2	4 10.0	28 56.4	16 11.7	12 7.1	22 46.1
12 T	11 16 56.7	21 2.0	10 42.8	14 3.1	0 43.2	1 56.6	12 17.2	4 6.4	29 3.9	16 13.7	12 6.7	22 46.2
13 F	11 20 53.3	22 1.9	10 39.7	25 50.7	0 37.6	3 6.3	12 58.2	4 3.0	29 11.3	16 15.6	12 6.3	22 46.3
14 S	11 24 49.8	23 1.7	10 36.5	7♌37.7	0D38.2	4 15.9	13 39.2	3 59.8	29 18.7	16 17.5	12 6.0	22 46.5
15 S	11 28 46.4	24 1.4	10 33.3	19 28.2	0 44.8	5 25.3	14 20.1	3 56.8	29 26.1	16 19.4	12 5.7	22 46.6
16 M	11 32 43.0	25 1.1	10 30.1	1♍25.6	0 57.1	6 34.5	15 1.0	3 53.9	29 33.6	16 21.2	12 5.4	22 46.8
17 T	11 36 39.5	26 0.8	10 27.0	13 32.3	1 14.8	7 43.6	15 41.9	3 51.3	29 41.1	16 23.0	12 5.2	22 47.0
18 W	11 40 36.1	27 0.5	10 23.8	25 49.7	1 37.6	8 52.6	16 22.8	3 48.8	29 48.5	16 24.7	12 5.0	22 47.3
19 T	11 44 32.6	28 0.1	10 20.6	8♎18.5	2 5.2	10 1.4	17 3.6	3 46.5	29 56.0	16 26.4	12 4.8	22 47.5
20 F	11 48 29.1	28 59.7	10 17.4	20 58.9	2 37.4	11 10.0	17 44.3	3 44.4	0♈ 3.4	16 28.0	12 4.7	22 47.8
21 S	11 52 25.7	29 59.2	10 14.2	3♏50.7	3 13.8	12 18.4	18 25.1	3 42.5	0 10.9	16 29.6	12 4.6	22 48.1
22 S	11 56 22.3	0♈58.8	10 11.1	16 53.8	3 54.3	13 26.7	19 5.8	3 40.8	0 18.4	16 31.2	12 4.5	22 48.4
23 M	12 0 18.8	1 58.2	10 7.9	0♐ 8.3	4 38.5	14 34.9	19 46.5	3 39.2	0 25.8	16 32.7	12 4.5	22 48.8
24 T	12 4 15.4	2 57.7	10 4.7	13 34.9	5 26.2	15 42.8	20 27.2	3 37.9	0 33.3	16 34.1	12 4.5	22 49.1
25 W	12 8 11.9	3 57.1	10 1.5	27 14.5	6 17.3	16 50.6	21 7.8	3 36.7	0 40.8	16 35.5	12D 4.5	22 49.5
26 T	12 12 8.5	4 56.5	9 58.4	11♑ 8.1	7 11.6	17 58.2	21 48.4	3 35.8	0 48.2	16 36.9	12 4.6	22 49.9
27 F	12 16 5.0	5 55.9	9 55.2	25 16.0	8 8.8	19 5.6	22 29.0	3 35.0	0 55.7	16 38.2	12 4.7	22 50.3
28 S	12 20 1.6	6 55.3	9 52.0	9♒37.6	9 8.8	20 12.8	23 9.6	3 34.4	1 3.1	16 39.5	12 4.8	22 50.8
29 S	12 23 58.1	7 54.6	9 48.8	24 10.4	10 11.5	21 19.9	23 50.1	3 34.0	1 10.6	16 40.7	12 5.0	22 51.3
30 M	12 27 54.7	8 53.9	9 45.6	8♓50.0	11 16.7	22 26.7	24 30.6	3 33.8	1 18.0	16 41.8	12 5.2	22 51.8
31 T	12 31 51.3	9 53.1	9 42.5	23 30.0	12 24.3	23 33.3	25 11.1	3 33.8	1 25.4	16 42.9	12 5.4	22 52.3

DECLINATION

DAY	EPHEMERIS SIDEREAL TIME h m s	☉	☊	☽	☿	♀	♂	♃	♄	♅	♆	♇
1 S	10 33 34.6	7S48.8	22N58.2	18S58.3	5S 2.0	7N33.8	13N33.0	19N50.1	2S49.1	22S53.0	22N 4.3	15N46.8
4 W	10 45 24.3	6 40.1	22 59.0	4 37.3	6 26.7	9 4.3	14 16.1	19 53.8	2 40.3	22 52.3	22 4.6	15 47.4
7 S	10 57 14.0	5 30.6	22 59.8	11N14.5	7 50.8	10 32.9	14 58.2	19 57.2	2 31.5	22 51.5	22 4.9	15 48.0
10 T	11 9 3.6	4 20.4	23 0.6	21 12.1	9 2.6	11 59.4	15 39.0	20 0.1	2 22.7	22 50.9	22 5.1	15 48.7
13 F	11 20 53.3	3 9.8	23 1.4	22 12.0	9 55.9	13 23.6	16 18.7	20 2.6	2 13.8	22 50.2	22 5.3	15 49.3
16 M	11 32 43.0	1 58.8	23 2.1	14 34.2	10 28.8	14 45.0	16 57.1	20 4.7	2 4.9	22 49.6	22 5.5	15 50.0
19 T	11 44 32.6	0 47.7	23 2.9	1 18.2	10 41.6	16 3.4	17 34.1	20 6.4	1 56.1	22 49.0	22 5.7	15 50.7
22 S	11 56 22.3	0N23.4	23 3.6	13S 1.0	10 35.5	17 18.4	18 9.9	20 7.6	1 47.2	22 48.5	22 5.8	15 51.4
25 W	12 8 11.9	1 34.3	23 4.3	22 17.5	10 12.0	18 29.9	18 44.2	20 8.5	1 38.4	22 48.1	22 5.9	15 52.1
28 S	12 20 1.6	2 44.9	23 5.0	20 14.5	9 32.5	19 37.6	19 17.1	20 8.9	1 29.6	22 47.7	22 6.0	15 52.7
31 T	12 31 51.3	3 55.1	23 5.7	6 59.7	8 38.3	20 41.1	19 48.6	20 8.9	1 20.9	22 47.3	22 6.1	15 53.4

APRIL 1908

LONGITUDE

DAY	EPHEMERIS SIDEREAL TIME h m s	☉ ° ′	☊ ° ′	☽ ° ′	☿ ° ′	♀ ° ′	♂ ° ′	♃ ° ′	♄ ° ′	♅ ° ′	♆ ° ′	♇ ° ′
1 W	12 35 47.8	10♈52.3	9♋39.3	8♈ 2.9	13♓34.2	24♉39.8	25♉51.5	3♌34.0	1♈32.9	16♑44.0	12♋ 5.7	22♊52.8
2 T	12 39 44.3	11 51.5	9 36.1	22 21.2	14 46.3	25 46.0	26 31.9	3D34.4	1 40.2	16 45.0	12 6.0	22 53.4
3 F	12 43 40.9	12 50.7	9 32.9	6♉19.0	16 0.5	26 52.0	27 12.3	3 35.0	1 47.6	16 45.9	12 6.4	22 53.9
4 S	12 47 37.5	13 49.8	9 29.8	19 52.4	17 16.8	27 57.8	27 52.7	3 35.7	1 55.0	16 46.9	12 6.7	22 54.6
5 S	12 51 34.0	14 48.9	9 26.6	3♊ 0.3	18 35.0	29 3.3	28 33.0	3 36.7	2 2.4	16 47.7	12 7.1	22 55.2
6 M	12 55 30.6	15 47.9	9 23.4	15 44.1	19 55.1	0♊ 8.6	29 13.3	3 37.8	2 9.7	16 48.5	12 7.6	22 55.8
7 T	12 59 27.1	16 46.9	9 20.2	28 6.8	21 17.0	1 13.7	29 53.6	3 39.1	2 17.0	16 49.3	12 8.0	22 56.5
8 W	13 3 23.6	17 45.9	9 17.0	10♋13.0	22 40.7	2 18.5	0♊33.9	3 40.7	2 24.3	16 50.0	12 8.6	22 57.1
9 T	13 7 20.2	18 44.8	9 13.9	22 8.0	24 6.2	3 23.1	1 14.1	3 42.4	2 31.6	16 50.6	12 9.1	22 57.8
10 F	13 11 16.8	19 43.7	9 10.7	3♌57.2	25 33.5	4 27.4	1 54.3	3 44.3	2 38.9	16 51.2	12 9.7	22 58.6
11 S	13 15 13.3	20 42.6	9 7.5	15 46.1	27 2.4	5 31.4	2 34.4	3 46.3	2 46.1	16 51.8	12 10.3	22 59.3
12 S	13 19 9.9	21 41.4	9 4.3	27 39.6	28 33.0	6 35.1	3 14.5	3 48.6	2 53.4	16 52.3	12 10.9	23 0.1
13 M	13 23 6.4	22 40.2	9 1.1	9♍42.0	0♈ 5.3	7 38.5	3 54.6	3 51.0	3 0.5	16 52.7	12 11.6	23 0.8
14 T	13 27 3.0	23 38.9	8 58.0	21 56.5	1 39.2	8 41.6	4 34.7	3 53.6	3 7.7	16 53.1	12 12.3	23 1.6
15 W	13 30 59.5	24 37.6	8 54.8	4♎25.3	3 14.8	9 44.4	5 14.7	3 56.4	3 14.9	16 53.5	12 13.0	23 2.4
16 T	13 34 56.1	25 36.3	8 51.6	17 9.5	4 51.9	10 46.9	5 54.7	3 59.4	3 22.0	16 53.8	12 13.8	23 3.3
17 F	13 38 52.6	26 34.9	8 48.4	0♏ 8.7	6 30.8	11 49.1	6 34.7	4 2.5	3 29.1	16 54.0	12 14.6	23 4.1
18 S	13 42 49.2	27 33.5	8 45.3	13 21.9	8 11.2	12 50.9	7 14.7	4 5.8	3 36.1	16 54.2	12 15.4	23 5.0
19 S	13 46 45.8	28 32.1	8 42.1	26 47.5	9 53.3	13 52.4	7 54.6	4 9.3	3 43.2	16 54.4	12 16.3	23 5.9
20 M	13 50 42.3	29 30.6	8 38.9	10♐23.4	11 37.1	14 53.6	8 34.5	4 13.0	3 50.2	16 54.5	12 17.2	23 6.8
21 T	13 54 38.8	0♉29.1	8 35.7	24 8.2	13 22.5	15 54.3	9 14.3	4 16.8	3 57.1	16 54.5	12 18.1	23 7.7
22 W	13 58 35.4	1 27.6	8 32.5	8♑ 0.5	15 9.5	16 54.7	9 54.1	4 20.8	4 4.1	16R54.5	12 19.0	23 8.6
23 T	14 2 32.0	2 26.1	8 29.4	21 59.6	16 58.3	17 54.7	10 34.0	4 24.9	4 11.0	16 54.4	12 20.0	23 9.6
24 F	14 6 28.5	3 24.5	8 26.2	6♒ 4.9	18 48.7	18 54.4	11 13.7	4 29.3	4 17.8	16 54.3	12 21.0	23 10.6
25 S	14 10 25.1	4 23.0	8 23.0	20 15.6	20 40.8	19 53.6	11 53.5	4 33.8	4 24.7	16 54.2	12 22.1	23 11.5
26 S	14 14 21.6	5 21.3	8 19.8	4♓30.1	22 34.5	20 52.4	12 33.2	4 38.4	4 31.5	16 54.0	12 23.2	23 12.5
27 M	14 18 18.2	6 19.7	8 16.7	18 45.8	24 30.0	21 50.7	13 12.9	4 43.2	4 38.2	16 53.7	12 24.3	23 13.6
28 T	14 22 14.7	7 18.0	8 13.5	2♈59.0	26 27.1	22 48.7	13 52.6	4 48.2	4 44.9	16 53.4	12 25.4	23 14.6
29 W	14 26 11.3	8 16.3	8 10.3	17 5.2	28 25.8	23 46.1	14 32.3	4 53.3	4 51.6	16 53.0	12 26.6	23 15.6
30 T	14 30 7.8	9 14.6	8 7.1	0♉59.6	0♉26.2	24 43.1	15 11.9	4 58.6	4 58.3	16 52.6	12 27.7	23 16.7

DECLINATION

DAY	EPHEMERIS SIDEREAL TIME h m s	☉	☊	☽	☿	♀	♂	♃	♄	♅	♆	♇
1 W	12 35 47.8	4N18.3	23N 6.0	1S24.3	8S17.2	21N 1.3	19N58.7	20N 8.8	1S18.0	22S47.2	22N 6.1	15N53.7
4 S	12 47 37.5	5 27.5	23 6.6	14N 3.1	7 5.2	21 59.1	20 28.2	20 8.3	1 9.4	22 47.0	22 6.1	15 54.4
7 T	12 59 27.1	6 35.9	23 7.3	22 29.9	5 40.9	22 52.1	20 56.0	20 7.3	1 0.8	22 46.7	22 6.1	15 55.1
10 F	13 11 16.8	7 43.2	23 8.0	21 22.0	4 5.1	23 40.4	21 22.3	20 6.0	0 52.4	22 46.6	22 6.1	15 55.7
13 M	13 23 6.4	8 49.4	23 8.6	12 1.0	2 18.6	24 23.6	21 47.0	20 4.3	0 44.0	22 46.5	22 6.0	15 56.4
16 T	13 34 56.1	9 54.2	23 9.3	2S 9.5	0 22.1	25 1.8	22 10.0	20 2.1	0 35.8	22 46.4	22 5.9	15 57.1
19 S	13 46 45.8	10 57.5	23 9.9	16 14.5	1N43.6	25 34.6	22 31.3	19 59.6	0 27.6	22 46.4	22 5.8	15 57.8
22 W	13 58 35.4	11 59.3	23 10.5	23 16.2	3 57.7	26 2.3	22 50.9	19 56.7	0 19.7	22 46.5	22 5.7	15 58.4
25 S	14 10 25.1	12 59.2	23 11.1	18 1.6	6 18.9	26 24.6	23 8.8	19 53.5	0 11.8	22 46.6	22 5.5	15 59.1
28 T	14 22 14.7	13 57.3	23 11.7	3 27.3	8 45.8	26 41.7	23 25.0	19 49.8	0 4.2	22 46.8	22 5.3	15 59.7

MAY 1908

DAY	EPHEMERIS SIDEREAL TIME	☉	☊	☽	☿	♀	♂	♃	♄	♅	♆	♇
	h m s	° ′	° ′	° ′	° ′	° ′	° ′	° ′	° ′	° ′	° ′	° ′
						LONGITUDE						
1 F	14 34 4.4	10♉12.9	8♋ 4.0	14♉38.1	2♉28.1	25♊39.6	15♊51.5	5♌ 4.1	5♈ 4.8	16♑52.2	12♋29.0	23♊17.8
2 S	14 38 0.9	11 11.1	8 0.8	27 57.5	4 31.5	26 35.7	16 31.1	5 9.7	5 11.4	16R51.7	12 30.2	23 18.9
3 S	14 41 57.5	12 9.3	7 57.6	10♊56.6	6 36.4	27 31.1	17 10.7	5 15.4	5 17.9	16 51.1	12 31.5	23 20.0
4 M	14 45 54.1	13 7.4	7 54.4	23 35.7	8 42.6	28 26.1	17 50.2	5 21.3	5 24.3	16 50.5	12 32.8	23 21.1
5 T	14 49 50.6	14 5.5	7 51.2	5♋56.8	10 49.9	29 20.4	18 29.7	5 27.4	5 30.8	16 49.8	12 34.1	23 22.2
6 W	14 53 47.2	15 3.6	7 48.1	18 3.3	12 58.4	0♋14.2	19 9.2	5 33.6	5 37.1	16 49.1	12 35.5	23 23.4
7 T	14 57 43.7	16 1.7	7 44.9	29 59.4	15 7.7	1 7.4	19 48.6	5 39.9	5 43.4	16 48.4	12 36.8	23 24.5
8 F	15 1 40.3	16 59.7	7 41.7	11♌50.1	17 17.6	1 59.9	20 28.1	5 46.4	5 49.7	16 47.6	12 38.3	23 25.7
9 S	15 5 36.8	17 57.7	7 38.5	23 40.6	19 28.1	2 51.8	21 7.5	5 53.1	5 55.9	16 46.8	12 39.7	23 26.9
10 S	15 9 33.4	18 55.7	7 35.4	5♍35.9	21 38.7	3 43.0	21 46.8	5 59.8	6 2.1	16 45.9	12 41.1	23 28.1
11 M	15 13 29.9	19 53.6	7 32.2	17 41.0	23 49.3	4 33.5	22 26.2	6 6.7	6 8.2	16 44.9	12 42.6	23 29.3
12 T	15 17 26.5	20 51.6	7 29.0	29 59.9	25 59.5	5 23.2	23 5.5	6 13.8	6 14.2	16 44.0	12 44.1	23 30.5
13 W	15 21 23.1	21 49.4	7 25.8	12♎35.8	28 9.1	6 12.2	23 44.8	6 21.0	6 20.2	16 42.9	12 45.7	23 31.8
14 T	15 25 19.6	22 47.3	7 22.7	25 30.8	0♊17.7	7 0.5	24 24.1	6 28.3	6 26.2	16 41.9	12 47.2	23 33.0
15 F	15 29 16.2	23 45.1	7 19.5	8♏45.1	2 25.2	7 47.8	25 3.3	6 35.7	6 32.0	16 40.8	12 48.8	23 34.2
16 S	15 33 12.7	24 42.9	7 16.3	22 17.9	4 31.2	8 34.4	25 42.5	6 43.2	6 37.9	16 39.6	12 50.4	23 35.5
17 S	15 37 9.3	25 40.7	7 13.1	6♐ 6.7	6 35.5	9 20.1	26 21.7	6 50.9	6 43.6	16 38.4	12 52.0	23 36.8
18 M	15 41 5.9	26 38.4	7 9.9	20 8.0	8 37.9	10 4.8	27 0.9	6 58.8	6 49.4	16 37.2	12 53.7	23 38.1
19 T	15 45 2.4	27 36.2	7 6.8	4♑18.2	10 38.1	10 48.6	27 40.1	7 6.7	6 55.0	16 35.9	12 55.4	23 39.4
20 W	15 48 58.9	28 33.9	7 3.6	18 33.2	12 36.0	11 31.5	28 19.2	7 14.7	7 0.6	16 34.6	12 57.0	23 40.6
21 T	15 52 55.5	29 31.6	7 0.4	2♒49.8	14 31.4	12 13.3	28 58.3	7 22.9	7 6.1	16 33.2	12 58.8	23 42.0
22 F	15 56 52.1	0♊29.3	6 57.2	17 5.2	16 24.2	12 54.1	29 37.4	7 31.2	7 11.6	16 31.8	13 0.5	23 43.3
23 S	16 0 48.6	1 26.9	6 54.1	1♓17.1	18 14.4	13 33.8	0♋16.4	7 39.6	7 17.0	16 30.4	13 2.2	23 44.6
24 S	16 4 45.2	2 24.6	6 50.9	15 23.7	20 1.7	14 12.3	0 55.5	7 48.2	7 22.3	16 28.9	13 4.0	23 45.9
25 M	16 8 41.7	3 22.2	6 47.7	29 23.2	21 46.2	14 49.7	1 34.5	7 56.8	7 27.6	16 27.4	13 5.8	23 47.3
26 T	16 12 38.3	4 19.8	6 44.5	13♈13.9	23 27.7	15 25.9	2 13.5	8 5.6	7 32.8	16 25.8	13 7.6	23 48.6
27 W	16 16 34.8	5 17.4	6 41.4	26 54.0	25 6.3	16 0.9	2 52.5	8 14.4	7 37.9	16 24.2	13 9.5	23 50.0
28 T	16 20 31.4	6 15.0	6 38.2	10♉21.6	26 41.9	16 34.5	3 31.5	8 23.4	7 43.0	16 22.6	13 11.3	23 51.3
29 F	16 24 27.9	7 12.5	6 35.0	23 35.2	28 14.4	17 6.7	4 10.4	8 32.5	7 48.0	16 20.9	13 13.2	23 52.7
30 S	16 28 24.5	8 10.1	6 31.8	6♊33.6	29 43.9	17 37.6	4 49.3	8 41.7	7 52.9	16 19.2	13 15.1	23 54.1
31 S	16 32 21.1	9 7.6	6 28.6	19 16.4	1♋10.2	18 6.9	5 28.3	8 51.0	7 57.7	16 17.4	13 17.0	23 55.5
						DECLINATION						
1 F	14 34 4.4	14N53.3	23N12.3	12N24.3	11N16.3	26N53.6	23N39.4	19N45.9	0N 3.3	22S47.1	22N 5.0	16N 0.4
4 M	14 45 54.1	15 47.1	23 12.9	22 10.1	13 47.2	27 0.5	23 52.0	19 41.5	0 10.7	22 47.3	22 4.8	16 1.0
7 T	14 57 43.7	16 38.6	23 13.4	22 11.1	16 14.5	27 2.5	24 2.9	19 36.8	0 17.8	22 47.7	22 4.5	16 1.6
10 S	15 9 33.4	17 27.5	23 14.0	13 34.6	18 33.2	26 59.8	24 11.9	19 31.8	0 24.7	22 48.1	22 4.2	16 2.2
13 W	15 21 23.1	18 13.9	23 14.5	0S16.3	20 37.6	26 52.6	24 19.2	19 26.4	0 31.4	22 48.5	22 3.9	16 2.7
16 S	15 33 12.7	18 57.4	23 15.1	14 55.2	22 23.0	26 41.3	24 24.6	19 20.6	0 37.9	22 49.0	22 3.5	16 3.3
19 T	15 45 2.4	19 38.1	23 15.6	23 15.9	23 46.1	26 26.2	24 28.3	19 14.6	0 44.1	22 49.5	22 3.1	16 3.8
22 F	15 56 52.1	20 15.8	23 16.1	19 0.5	24 45.6	26 7.6	24 30.2	19 8.2	0 50.1	22 50.1	22 2.7	16 4.3
25 M	16 8 41.7	20 50.3	23 16.6	4 59.3	25 22.3	25 45.9	24 30.2	19 1.5	0 55.9	22 50.7	22 2.3	16 4.8
28 T	16 20 31.4	21 21.7	23 17.1	10N52.5	25 38.2	25 21.5	24 28.5	18 54.5	1 1.4	22 51.4	22 1.8	16 5.3
31 S	16 32 21.1	21 49.8	23 17.5	21 34.9	25 35.9	24 54.8	24 25.1	18 47.2	1 6.6	22 52.1	22 1.3	16 5.8

JUNE 1908

DAY	EPHEMERIS SIDEREAL TIME	☉	☊	☽	☿	♀	♂	♃	♄	♅	♆	♇
						LONGITUDE						
1 M	16 36 17.6	10♊ 5.1	6♋25.5	1♋44.3	2♋33.4	18♋34.8	6♋ 7.2	9♌ 0.4	8♈ 2.5	16♑15.7	13♋18.9	23♊56.9
2 T	16 40 14.2	11 2.6	6 22.3	13 58.5	3 53.4	19 1.1	6 46.0	9 9.9	8 7.2	16R13.9	13 20.8	23 58.2
3 W	16 44 10.7	12 0.1	6 19.1	26 1.5	5 10.2	19 25.7	7 24.9	9 19.5	8 11.8	16 12.0	13 22.8	23 59.6
4 T	16 48 7.3	12 57.6	6 15.9	7♌56.4	6 23.7	19 48.6	8 3.7	9 29.2	8 16.4	16 10.1	13 24.8	24 1.0
5 F	16 52 3.9	13 55.0	6 12.8	19 47.0	7 33.8	20 9.8	8 42.5	9 39.0	8 20.9	16 8.2	13 26.7	24 2.4
6 S	16 56 0.4	14 52.4	6 9.6	1♍37.7	8 40.6	20 29.1	9 21.3	9 48.9	8 25.3	16 6.3	13 28.8	24 3.8
7 S	16 59 57.0	15 49.8	6 6.4	13 33.2	9 43.9	20 46.6	10 0.1	9 58.9	8 29.6	16 4.4	13 30.8	24 5.2
8 M	17 3 53.5	16 47.2	6 3.2	25 38.2	10 43.7	21 2.1	10 38.9	10 8.9	8 33.8	16 2.4	13 32.8	24 6.7
9 T	17 7 50.1	17 44.5	6 0.1	7♎57.4	11 39.9	21 15.6	11 17.6	10 19.1	8 38.0	16 0.3	13 34.8	24 8.1
10 W	17 11 46.6	18 41.9	5 56.9	20 34.7	12 32.4	21 27.0	11 56.3	10 29.3	8 42.0	15 58.3	13 36.9	24 9.5
11 T	17 15 43.2	19 39.2	5 53.7	3♏33.2	13 21.1	21 36.3	12 35.0	10 39.7	8 46.0	15 56.2	13 39.0	24 10.9
12 F	17 19 39.7	20 36.5	5 50.5	16 54.7	14 5.9	21 43.4	13 13.7	10 50.1	8 49.9	15 54.1	13 41.0	24 12.3
13 S	17 23 36.3	21 33.8	5 47.3	0♐39.3	14 46.8	21 48.3	13 52.3	11 0.6	8 53.8	15 52.0	13 43.1	24 13.7
14 S	17 27 32.8	22 31.1	5 44.2	14 45.1	15 23.6	21 50.9	14 31.0	11 11.2	8 57.5	15 49.9	13 45.2	24 15.2
15 M	17 31 29.4	23 28.4	5 41.0	29 8.4	15 56.3	21 51.1	15 9.6	11 21.8	9 1.2	15 47.7	13 47.3	24 16.6
16 T	17 35 26.0	24 25.7	5 37.8	13♑43.8	16 24.6	21R49.1	15 48.2	11 32.6	9 4.8	15 45.5	13 49.5	24 18.0
17 W	17 39 22.5	25 22.9	5 34.6	28 25.1	16 48.7	21 44.6	16 26.8	11 43.4	9 8.2	15 43.3	13 51.6	24 19.4
18 T	17 43 19.1	26 20.2	5 31.5	13♒ 6.0	17 8.3	21 37.7	17 5.4	11 54.3	9 11.6	15 41.1	13 53.7	24 20.9
19 F	17 47 15.6	27 17.4	5 28.3	27 40.7	17 23.4	21 28.5	17 43.9	12 5.2	9 15.0	15 38.9	13 55.9	24 22.3
20 S	17 51 12.2	28 14.7	5 25.1	12♓ 4.5	17 34.0	21 16.9	18 22.5	12 16.3	9 18.2	15 36.6	13 58.0	24 23.7
21 S	17 55 8.8	29 11.9	5 21.9	26 14.2	17 40.0	21 2.8	19 1.0	12 27.4	9 21.3	15 34.3	14 0.2	24 25.1
22 M	17 59 5.3	0♋ 9.1	5 18.8	10♈ 8.2	17 41.5	20 46.5	19 39.6	12 38.6	9 24.4	15 32.0	14 2.4	24 26.5
23 T	18 3 1.9	1 6.4	5 15.6	23 45.6	17R38.4	20 27.8	20 18.1	12 49.8	9 27.3	15 29.7	14 4.6	24 28.0
24 W	18 6 58.4	2 3.6	5 12.4	7♉ 6.7	17 30.9	20 6.9	20 56.6	13 1.1	9 30.2	15 27.4	14 6.7	24 29.4
25 T	18 10 55.0	3 0.8	5 9.2	20 12.2	17 19.0	19 43.8	21 35.1	13 12.5	9 33.0	15 25.0	14 8.9	24 30.8
26 F	18 14 51.5	3 58.1	5 6.1	3♊ 3.0	17 2.9	19 18.6	22 13.5	13 24.0	9 35.7	15 22.7	14 11.1	24 32.2
27 S	18 18 48.1	4 55.3	5 2.9	15 40.2	16 42.9	18 51.4	22 52.0	13 35.5	9 38.2	15 20.3	14 13.3	24 33.6
28 S	18 22 44.7	5 52.5	4 59.7	28 5.1	16 19.1	18 22.4	23 30.5	13 47.1	9 40.7	15 18.0	14 15.6	24 35.0
29 M	18 26 41.3	6 49.8	4 56.5	10♋19.2	15 52.0	17 51.6	24 8.9	13 58.7	9 43.1	15 15.6	14 17.8	24 36.4
30 T	18 30 37.8	7 47.0	4 53.3	22 23.8	15 22.0	17 19.3	24 47.3	14 10.4	9 45.4	15 13.2	14 20.0	24 37.8
						DECLINATION						
1 M	16 36 17.6	21N58.4	23N17.7	23N 7.4	25N31.6	24N45.5	24N23.5	18N44.7	1N 8.3	22S52.3	22N 1.1	16N 5.9
4 T	16 48 7.3	22 21.9	23 18.1	21 2.4	25 9.7	24 16.5	24 17.8	18 36.9	1 13.1	22 53.0	22 0.6	16 6.3
7 S	16 59 57.0	22 41.8	23 18.6	10 58.8	24 36.3	23 46.2	24 10.3	18 28.9	1 17.6	22 53.8	22 0.1	16 6.7
10 W	17 11 46.6	22 58.2	23 19.0	3S20.0	23 54.3	23 15.0	24 1.0	18 20.6	1 21.9	22 54.6	21 59.5	16 7.1
13 S	17 23 36.3	23 10.9	23 19.4	17 22.3	23 6.4	22 43.2	23 50.2	18 12.0	1 25.8	22 55.4	21 59.0	16 7.4
16 T	17 35 26.0	23 20.0	23 19.9	23 31.8	22 15.3	22 11.2	23 37.6	18 3.1	1 29.4	22 56.2	21 58.4	16 7.8
19 F	17 47 15.6	23 25.4	23 20.3	16 13.4	21 23.5	21 39.2	23 23.5	17 54.0	1 32.8	22 57.0	21 57.8	16 8.1
22 M	17 59 5.3	23 27.0	23 20.6	0 49.7	20 33.6	21 7.5	23 7.7	17 44.6	1 35.7	22 57.9	21 57.1	16 8.3
25 T	18 10 55.0	23 25.0	23 21.0	14N11.9	19 48.0	20 36.1	22 50.4	17 34.9	1 38.4	22 58.7	21 56.5	16 8.6
28 S	18 22 44.7	23 19.2	23 21.4	22 47.1	19 9.2	20 5.4	22 31.6	17 25.0	1 40.7	22 59.5	21 55.9	16 8.8

JULY 1908

DAY	EPHEMERIS SIDEREAL TIME h m s	☉ ° ′	☊ ° ′	☽ ° ′	☿ ° ′	♀ ° ′	♂ ° ′	♃ ° ′	♄ ° ′	♅ ° ′	♆ ° ′	♇ ° ′
						LONGITUDE						
1 W	18 34 34.3	8♋44.2	4♋50.2	4♌21.0	14♋49.4	16♋45.7	25♋25.7	14♌22.2	9♈47.6	15♑10.8	14♋22.2	24♊39.2
2 T	18 38 30.9	9 41.4	4 47.0	16 13.1	14R14.8	16R10.8	26 4.2	14 34.0	9 49.7	15R 8.4	14 24.4	24 40.6
3 F	18 42 27.5	10 38.6	4 43.8	28 2.8	13 38.8	15 34.9	26 42.6	14 45.9	9 51.7	15 6.0	14 26.7	24 42.0
4 S	18 46 24.0	11 35.9	4 40.6	9♍53.5	13 1.9	14 58.3	27 20.9	14 57.8	9 53.7	15 3.6	14 28.9	24 43.3
5 S	18 50 20.6	12 33.1	4 37.5	21 48.7	12 24.8	14 21.2	27 59.3	15 9.8	9 55.5	15 1.1	14 31.1	24 44.7
6 M	18 54 17.1	13 30.3	4 34.3	3♎52.7	11 48.1	13 43.7	28 37.7	15 21.8	9 57.2	14 58.7	14 33.4	24 46.0
7 T	18 58 13.7	14 27.5	4 31.1	16 9.7	11 12.5	13 6.2	29 16.0	15 33.9	9 58.8	14 56.3	14 35.6	24 47.4
8 W	19 2 10.2	15 24.7	4 27.9	28 44.1	10 38.5	12 28.9	29 54.4	15 46.1	10 0.3	14 53.9	14 37.8	24 48.8
9 T	19 6 6.8	16 21.9	4 24.8	11♏39.7	10 6.8	11 51.9	0♌32.7	15 58.2	10 1.7	14 51.5	14 40.1	24 50.1
10 F	19 10 3.4	17 19.1	4 21.6	24 59.7	9 38.0	11 15.7	1 11.0	16 10.5	10 3.0	14 49.0	14 42.3	24 51.4
11 S	19 13 59.9	18 16.2	4 18.4	8♐45.7	9 12.5	10 40.2	1 49.3	16 22.7	10 4.2	14 46.6	14 44.5	24 52.7
12 S	19 17 56.4	19 13.4	4 15.2	22 57.5	8 50.8	10 5.9	2 27.6	16 35.0	10 5.4	14 44.2	14 46.7	24 54.1
13 M	19 21 53.0	20 10.6	4 12.0	7♑32.2	8 33.4	9 32.9	3 5.9	16 47.4	10 6.4	14 41.8	14 49.0	24 55.4
14 T	19 25 49.6	21 7.8	4 8.9	22 24.7	8 20.6	9 1.4	3 44.1	16 59.8	10 7.3	14 39.4	14 51.2	24 56.7
15 W	19 29 46.2	22 5.0	4 5.7	7♒27.4	8 12.7	8 31.5	4 22.4	17 12.2	10 8.1	14 37.0	14 53.4	24 58.0
16 T	19 33 42.7	23 2.3	4 2.5	22 31.4	8 10.0	8 3.5	5 0.7	17 24.7	10 8.8	14 34.6	14 55.6	24 59.2
17 F	19 37 39.3	23 59.5	3 59.3	7♓28.0	8D12.6	7 37.4	5 38.9	17 37.2	10 9.4	14 32.2	14 57.8	25 0.5
18 S	19 41 35.8	24 56.7	3 56.2	22 9.6	8 20.8	7 13.5	6 17.2	17 49.7	10 9.9	14 29.9	15 0.0	25 1.8
19 S	19 45 32.4	25 54.0	3 53.0	6♈30.7	8 34.6	6 51.6	6 55.4	18 2.3	10 10.4	14 27.5	15 2.2	25 3.0
20 M	19 49 28.9	26 51.2	3 49.8	20 28.6	8 54.0	6 32.1	7 33.6	18 14.9	10 10.7	14 25.1	15 4.4	25 4.3
21 T	19 53 25.5	27 48.5	3 46.6	4♉ 2.8	9 19.2	6 14.8	8 11.9	18 27.6	10 10.9	14 22.8	15 6.6	25 5.5
22 W	19 57 22.1	28 45.8	3 43.5	17 14.6	9 50.1	5 59.9	8 50.1	18 40.3	10 11.0	14 20.5	15 8.8	25 6.7
23 T	20 1 18.6	29 43.1	3 40.3	0♊ 6.5	10 26.8	5 47.4	9 28.3	18 53.0	10 11.0	14 18.2	15 11.0	25 7.9
24 F	20 5 15.1	0♌40.4	3 37.1	12 41.4	11 9.1	5 37.3	10 6.5	19 5.8	10R10.9	14 15.9	15 13.2	25 9.1
25 S	20 9 11.7	1 37.7	3 33.9	25 2.4	11 57.1	5 29.6	10 44.7	19 18.5	10 10.6	14 13.6	15 15.3	25 10.3
26 S	20 13 8.3	2 35.1	3 30.7	7♋12.7	12 50.6	5 24.3	11 22.9	19 31.3	10 10.3	14 11.3	15 17.5	25 11.5
27 M	20 17 4.8	3 32.4	3 27.6	19 14.6	13 49.7	5 21.3	12 1.1	19 44.2	10 9.9	14 9.1	15 19.6	25 12.7
28 T	20 21 1.4	4 29.8	3 24.4	1♌10.6	14 54.1	5 20.7	12 39.4	19 57.0	10 9.4	14 6.9	15 21.8	25 13.8
29 W	20 24 57.9	5 27.2	3 21.2	13 2.6	16 3.9	5D22.4	13 17.6	20 9.9	10 8.8	14 4.7	15 23.9	25 14.9
30 T	20 28 54.5	6 24.6	3 18.0	24 52.6	17 18.8	5 26.4	13 55.7	20 22.8	10 8.1	14 2.5	15 26.0	25 16.1
31 F	20 32 51.1	7 22.0	3 14.9	6♍42.6	18 38.8	5 32.5	14 33.9	20 35.7	10 7.2	14 0.3	15 28.1	25 17.2
						DECLINATION						
1 W	18 34 34.3	23N 9.8	23N21.7	21N41.4	18N39.2	19N35.6	22N11.2	17N14.8	1N42.6	23S 0.4	21N55.2	16N 9.0
4 S	18 46 24.0	22 56.7	23 22.1	12 17.2	18 19.9	19 7.0	21 49.5	17 4.4	1 44.2	23 1.2	21 54.5	16 9.2
7 T	18 58 13.7	22 40.0	23 22.4	1S34.3	18 12.1	18 40.4	21 26.3	16 53.8	1 45.5	23 2.1	21 53.8	16 9.3
10 F	19 10 3.4	22 19.7	23 22.7	15 42.9	18 16.3	18 16.3	21 1.7	16 42.9	1 46.4	23 2.9	21 53.1	16 9.4
13 M	19 21 53.0	21 56.1	23 23.0	23 27.3	18 31.5	17 55.3	20 35.8	16 31.8	1 46.9	23 3.7	21 52.4	16 9.5
16 T	19 33 42.7	21 29.0	23 23.3	17 40.4	18 56.0	17 38.2	20 8.6	16 20.5	1 47.1	23 4.5	21 51.7	16 9.6
19 S	19 45 32.4	20 58.6	23 23.6	2 14.2	19 27.0	17 25.3	19 40.1	16 9.1	1 46.9	23 5.3	21 51.0	16 9.6
22 W	19 57 22.1	20 25.1	23 23.9	13N15.2	20 1.1	17 16.6	19 10.4	15 57.4	1 46.4	23 6.1	21 50.3	16 9.6
25 S	20 9 11.7	19 48.4	23 24.2	22 26.7	20 34.1	17 12.0	18 39.5	15 45.6	1 45.5	23 6.8	21 49.6	16 9.6
28 T	20 21 1.4	19 8.8	23 24.4	22 9.2	21 1.3	17 11.0	18 7.6	15 33.5	1 44.2	23 7.5	21 48.8	16 9.6
31 F	20 32 51.1	18 26.3	23 24.7	13 18.3	21 17.6	17 13.2	17 34.5	15 21.4	1 42.6	23 8.2	21 48.1	16 9.5

AUGUST 1908

DAY	EPHEMERIS SIDEREAL TIME h m s	☉ ° ′	☊ ° ′	☽ ° ′	☿ ° ′	♀ ° ′	♂ ° ′	♃ ° ′	♄ ° ′	♅ ° ′	♆ ° ′	♇ ° ′
						LONGITUDE						
1 S	20 36 47.6	8♌19.4	3♋11.7	18♍34.9	20♋ 3.6	5♋40.8	15♌12.1	20♌48.7	10♈ 6.3	13♑58.2	15♋30.2	25♊18.3
2 S	20 40 44.2	9 16.8	3 8.5	0♎31.9	21 33.1	5 51.3	15 50.3	21 1.6	10R 5.3	13R56.1	15 32.3	25 19.3
3 M	20 44 40.7	10 14.3	3 5.3	12 36.7	23 7.0	6 3.8	16 28.5	21 14.6	10 4.2	13 54.0	15 34.3	25 20.4
4 T	20 48 37.3	11 11.7	3 2.2	24 52.9	24 45.1	6 18.3	17 6.7	21 27.6	10 3.0	13 51.9	15 36.4	25 21.5
5 W	20 52 33.8	12 9.2	2 59.0	7♏24.2	26 27.2	6 34.7	17 44.8	21 40.6	10 1.6	13 49.9	15 38.4	25 22.5
6 T	20 56 30.4	13 6.7	2 55.8	20 14.6	28 12.9	6 53.0	18 23.0	21 53.7	10 0.2	13 47.8	15 40.5	25 23.5
7 F	21 0 27.0	14 4.2	2 52.6	3♐27.9	0♌ 1.8	7 13.1	19 1.2	22 6.7	9 58.7	13 45.9	15 42.5	25 24.5
8 S	21 4 23.5	15 1.7	2 49.4	17 7.1	1 53.7	7 35.0	19 39.3	22 19.7	9 57.1	13 43.9	15 44.5	25 25.5
9 S	21 8 20.0	15 59.2	2 46.3	1♑13.6	3 48.2	7 58.7	20 17.5	22 32.8	9 55.4	13 42.0	15 46.5	25 26.5
10 M	21 12 16.6	16 56.7	2 43.1	15 46.6	5 44.8	8 24.0	20 55.6	22 45.9	9 53.6	13 40.1	15 48.4	25 27.4
11 T	21 16 13.2	17 54.3	2 39.9	0♒42.1	7 43.3	8 50.8	21 33.8	22 59.0	9 51.7	13 38.2	15 50.4	25 28.4
12 W	21 20 9.7	18 51.9	2 36.7	15 53.3	9 43.1	9 19.3	22 11.9	23 12.0	9 49.7	13 36.4	15 52.3	25 29.3
13 T	21 24 6.2	19 49.4	2 33.6	1♓10.5	11 44.1	9 49.2	22 50.1	23 25.1	9 47.6	13 34.6	15 54.3	25 30.2
14 F	21 28 2.8	20 47.0	2 30.4	16 23.0	13 45.7	10 20.6	23 28.2	23 38.2	9 45.4	13 32.8	15 56.2	25 31.1
15 S	21 31 59.4	21 44.7	2 27.2	1♈20.5	15 47.8	10 53.4	24 6.4	23 51.3	9 43.2	13 31.1	15 58.1	25 32.0
16 S	21 35 56.0	22 42.4	2 24.0	15 55.3	17 50.0	11 27.5	24 44.5	24 4.4	9 40.8	13 29.4	15 59.9	25 32.8
17 M	21 39 52.5	23 40.0	2 20.9	0♉ 2.6	19 52.1	12 2.9	25 22.7	24 17.5	9 38.4	13 27.7	16 1.8	25 33.7
18 T	21 43 49.0	24 37.7	2 17.7	13 41.3	21 53.8	12 39.6	26 0.9	24 30.6	9 35.8	13 26.1	16 3.6	25 34.5
19 W	21 47 45.6	25 35.5	2 14.5	26 52.7	23 54.9	13 17.5	26 39.0	24 43.7	9 33.2	13 24.5	16 5.4	25 35.3
20 T	21 51 42.2	26 33.2	2 11.3	9♊40.0	25 55.4	13 56.5	27 17.2	24 56.9	9 30.5	13 22.9	16 7.3	25 36.1
21 F	21 55 38.7	27 31.0	2 8.1	22 7.5	27 54.9	14 36.6	27 55.4	25 !0.0	9 27.7	13 21.4	16 9.0	25 36.9
22 S	21 59 35.3	28 28.9	2 5.0	4♋19.7	29 53.5	15 17.8	28 33.5	25 23.1	9 24.8	13 19.9	16 10.8	25 37.6
23 S	22 3 31.8	29 26.7	2 1.8	16 21.0	1♍51.0	16 0.1	29 11.7	25 36.2	9 21.8	13 18.5	16 12.5	25 38.3
24 M	22 7 28.4	0♍24.6	1 58.6	28 15.3	3 47.4	16 43.3	29 49.9	25 49.3	9 18.8	13 17.1	16 14.2	25 39.0
25 T	22 11 24.9	1 22.5	1 55.4	10♌ 5.9	5 42.6	17 27.5	0♍28.1	26 2.3	9 15.7	13 15.7	16 15.9	25 39.7
26 W	22 15 21.5	2 20.4	1 52.3	21 55.4	7 36.6	18 12.6	1 6.3	26 15.4	9 12.5	13 14.4	16 17.6	25 40.4
27 T	22 19 18.0	3 18.4	1 49.1	3♍45.8	9 29.3	18 58.5	1 44.4	26 28.5	9 9.2	13 13.1	16 19.3	25 41.1
28 F	22 23 14.5	4 16.4	1 45.9	15 39.0	11 20.8	19 45.4	2 22.6	26 41.5	9 5.8	13 11.9	16 20.9	25 41.7
29 S	22 27 11.1	5 14.4	1 42.7	27 36.4	13 11.0	20 33.0	3 0.8	26 54.6	9 2.4	13 10.7	16 22.5	25 42.3
30 S	22 31 7.7	6 12.4	1 39.5	9♎39.4	14 59.9	21 21.4	3 39.0	27 7.6	8 58.9	13 9.6	16 24.1	25 42.9
31 M	22 35 4.3	7 10.5	1 36.4	21 50.0	16 47.5	22 10.6	4 17.2	27 20.6	8 55.3	13 8.5	16 25.7	25 43.5
						DECLINATION						
1 S	20 36 47.6	18N11.6	23N24.7	9N 6.1	21N19.7	17N14.5	17N23.2	15N17.3	1N42.0	23S 8.5	21N47.9	16N 9.5
4 T	20 48 37.3	17 25.5	23 25.0	5S 6.7	21 13.7	17 19.8	16 48.7	15 4.9	1 40.0	23 9.1	21 47.2	16 9.4
7 F	21 0 27.0	16 36.9	23 25.2	18 13.8	20 46.0	17 26.5	16 13.3	14 52.4	1 37.6	23 9.7	21 46.5	16 9.3
10 M	21 12 16.6	15 45.9	23 25.4	23 31.5	19 54.6	17 34.0	15 36.9	14 39.7	1 34.9	23 10.3	21 45.7	16 9.2
13 T	21 24 6.2	14 52.6	23 25.6	15 5.0	18 39.8	17 41.6	14 59.6	14 27.0	1 31.8	23 10.8	21 45.1	16 9.0
16 S	21 35 56.0	13 57.2	23 25.8	1N37.9	17 4.6	17 48.6	14 21.4	14 14.2	1 28.5	23 11.4	21 44.4	16 8.9
19 W	21 47 45.6	12 59.8	23 25.9	16 27.5	15 12.8	17 54.4	13 42.4	14 1.2	1 24.9	23 11.8	21 43.7	16 8.7
22 S	21 59 35.3	12 0.5	23 26.1	23 25.2	13 8.9	17 58.5	13 2.7	13 48.2	1 21.0	23 12.3	21 43.1	16 8.5
25 T	22 11 24.9	10 59.5	23 26.2	20 37.8	10 56.9	18 0.3	12 22.2	13 35.1	1 16.8	23 12.7	21 42.4	16 8.2
28 F	22 23 14.5	9 56.9	23 26.4	10 5.9	8 40.0	17 59.4	11 41.0	13 22.0	1 12.4	23 13.0	21 41.8	16 8.0
31 M	22 35 4.3	8 52.9	23 26.5	4S 4.7	6 20.7	17 55.5	10 59.2	13 8.8	1 7.7	23 13.3	21 41.2	16 7.7

SEPTEMBER 1908

DAY	EPHEMERIS SIDEREAL TIME	☉	☊	☽	☿	♀	♂	♃	♄	♅	♆	♇
	h m s	° ′	° ′	° ′	° ′	° ′	° ′	° ′	° ′	° ′	° ′	° ′
						LONGITUDE						
1 T	22 39 0.8	8♍ 8.5	1♋33.2	4♏10.3	18♍33.9	23♋ 0.5	4♍55.4	27♌33.6	8♈51.7	13♑ 7.4	16♋27.2	25♊44.0
2 W	22 42 57.3	9 6.7	1 30.0	16 43.2	20 19.0	23 51.2	5 33.6	27 46.6	8R48.0	13R 6.4	16 28.7	25 44.5
3 T	22 46 53.9	10 4.8	1 26.8	29 31.9	22 2.9	24 42.5	6 11.9	27 59.6	8 44.2	13 5.4	16 30.2	25 45.1
4 F	22 50 50.5	11 2.9	1 23.7	12♐39.8	23 45.5	25 34.5	6 50.1	28 12.5	8 40.4	13 4.5	16 31.7	25 45.5
5 S	22 54 47.0	12 1.1	1 20.5	26 10.2	25 27.0	26 27.1	7 28.3	28 25.4	8 36.5	13 3.6	16 33.1	25 46.0
6 S	22 58 43.5	12 59.3	1 17.3	10♑ 5.7	27 7.2	27 20.3	8 6.5	28 38.3	8 32.5	13 2.8	16 34.5	25 46.5
7 M	23 2 40.1	13 57.5	1 14.1	24 26.8	28 46.3	28 14.2	8 44.7	28 51.2	8 28.5	13 2.0	16 35.9	25 46.9
8 T	23 6 36.7	14 55.8	1 10.9	9♒11.7	0♎24.2	29 8.6	9 23.0	29 4.0	8 24.4	13 1.3	16 37.2	25 47.3
9 W	23 10 33.3	15 54.1	1 7.8	24 15.4	2 0.9	0♌ 3.6	10 1.2	29 16.9	8 20.3	13 0.6	16 38.6	25 47.7
10 T	23 14 29.8	16 52.4	1 4.6	9♓29.6	3 36.6	0 59.2	10 39.5	29 29.7	8 16.1	12 60.0	16 39.9	25 48.0
11 F	23 18 26.3	17 50.7	1 1.4	24 43.7	5 11.0	1 55.2	11 17.7	29 42.4	8 11.9	12 59.4	16 41.2	25 48.4
12 S	23 22 22.9	18 49.1	0 58.2	9♈46.7	6 44.4	2 51.9	11 56.0	29 55.2	8 7.7	12 58.8	16 42.4	25 48.7
13 S	23 26 19.4	19 47.5	0 55.1	24 29.2	8 16.7	3 49.0	12 34.2	0♍ 7.9	8 3.4	12 58.3	16 43.6	25 49.0
14 M	23 30 16.0	20 45.9	0 51.9	8♉44.6	9 47.8	4 46.6	13 12.5	0 20.5	7 59.0	12 57.9	16 44.8	25 49.3
15 T	23 34 12.5	21 44.4	0 48.7	22 30.2	11 17.9	5 44.6	13 50.8	0 33.2	7 54.6	12 57.5	16 46.0	25 49.5
16 W	23 38 9.1	22 42.9	0 45.5	5♊46.2	12 46.9	6 43.2	14 29.1	0 45.8	7 50.2	12 57.1	16 47.1	25 49.7
17 T	23 42 5.6	23 41.5	0 42.3	18 35.7	14 14.7	7 42.2	15 7.4	0 58.4	7 45.7	12 56.8	16 48.2	25 50.0
18 F	23 46 2.2	24 40.0	0 39.2	1♋ 3.0	15 41.4	8 41.6	15 45.7	1 10.9	7 41.2	12 56.6	16 49.3	25 50.1
19 S	23 49 58.8	25 38.7	0 36.0	13 13.3	17 7.0	9 41.4	16 24.0	1 23.4	7 36.7	12 56.4	16 50.4	25 50.3
20 S	23 53 55.3	26 37.3	0 32.8	25 11.8	18 31.5	10 41.7	17 2.3	1 35.9	7 32.1	12 56.2	16 51.4	25 50.4
21 M	23 57 51.8	27 36.0	0 29.6	7♌ 3.3	19 54.7	11 42.3	17 40.7	1 48.3	7 27.5	12 56.1	16 52.4	25 50.6
22 T	0 1 48.4	28 34.7	0 26.4	18 52.3	21 16.8	12 43.3	18 19.0	2 0.7	7 22.9	12 56.1	16 53.3	25 50.7
23 W	0 5 45.0	29 33.5	0 23.3	0♍42.2	22 37.6	13 44.7	18 57.4	2 13.0	7 18.3	12D56.1	16 54.2	25 50.7
24 T	0 9 41.6	0♎32.3	0 20.1	12 35.8	23 57.1	14 46.4	19 35.7	2 25.3	7 13.7	12 56.1	16 55.1	25 50.8
25 F	0 13 38.1	1 31.1	0 16.9	24 34.9	25 15.4	15 48.5	20 14.1	2 37.5	7 9.0	12 56.2	16 56.0	25 50.8
26 S	0 17 34.6	2 30.0	0 13.7	6♎41.0	26 32.2	16 51.0	20 52.5	2 49.7	7 4.3	12 56.4	16 56.8	25 50.8
27 S	0 21 31.2	3 28.9	0 10.6	18 55.0	27 47.5	17 53.7	21 30.9	3 1.9	6 59.6	12 56.6	16 57.6	25R50.8
28 M	0 25 27.8	4 27.8	0 7.4	1♏17.5	29 1.4	18 56.8	22 9.3	3 14.0	6 54.9	12 56.9	16 58.4	25 50.8
29 T	0 29 24.3	5 26.8	0 4.2	13 49.5	0♏13.6	20 0.2	22 47.7	3 26.0	6 50.2	12 57.2	16 59.1	25 50.7
30 W	0 33 20.9	6 25.8	0 1.0	26 32.3	1 24.1	21 3.8	23 26.1	3 38.0	6 45.5	12 57.5	16 59.8	25 50.6
						DECLINATION						
1 T	22 39 0.8	8N31.2	23N26.5	8S51.3	5N34.2	17N53.4	10N45.1	13N 4.4	1N 6.1	23S13.4	21N41.0	16N 7.6
4 F	22 50 50.5	7 25.6	23 26.6	20 37.3	3 14.8	17 44.9	10 2.4	12 51.2	1 1.2	23 13.7	21 40.4	16 7.4
7 M	23 2 40.1	6 18.8	23 26.7	23 6.5	0 56.9	17 32.8	9 19.2	12 38.0	0 56.1	23 13.9	21 39.9	16 7.1
10 T	23 14 29.8	5 11.1	23 26.8	12 18.5	1S18.2	17 16.7	8 35.6	12 24.8	0 50.8	23 14.0	21 39.4	16 6.8
13 S	23 26 19.4	4 2.7	23 26.9	5N11.1	3 29.9	16 56.6	7 51.4	12 11.7	0 45.4	23 14.2	21 38.9	16 6.4
16 W	23 38 9.1	2 53.6	23 26.9	19 7.9	5 37.2	16 32.2	7 6.8	11 58.6	0 39.9	23 14.2	21 38.4	16 6.1
19 S	23 49 58.8	1 43.9	23 27.0	23 49.9	7 39.4	16 3.7	6 21.8	11 45.5	0 34.4	23 14.3	21 37.9	16 5.8
22 T	0 1 48.4	0 33.9	23 27.0	18 42.2	9 35.9	15 30.9	5 36.5	11 32.5	0 28.7	23 14.3	21 37.5	16 5.4
25 F	0 13 38.1	0S36.2	23 27.1	6 42.5	11 25.6	14 53.9	4 50.8	11 19.6	0 23.1	23 14.2	21 37.2	16 5.1
28 M	0 25 27.8	1 46.5	23 27.1	7S55.3	13 7.8	14 12.7	4 4.9	11 6.8	0 17.4	23 14.1	21 36.8	16 4.8

OCTOBER 1908

DAY	EPHEMERIS SIDEREAL TIME	☉	☊	☽	☿	♀	♂	♃	♄	♅	♆	♇
						LONGITUDE						
1 T	0 37 17.4	7♎24.8	29♊57.8	9♐27.7	2♏32.7	22♌ 7.8	24♍ 4.6	3♍49.9	6♈40.8	12♑58.0	17♋ 0.5	25♊50.5
2 F	0 41 14.0	8 23.8	29 54.7	22 37.9	3 39.4	23 12.1	24 43.0	4 1.8	6R36.1	12 58.4	17 1.2	25R50.4
3 S	0 45 10.5	9 22.9	29 51.5	6♑ 5.4	4 43.9	24 16.6	25 21.4	4 13.6	6 31.4	12 58.9	17 1.8	25 50.3
4 S	0 49 7.1	10 22.0	29 48.3	19 52.3	5 46.1	25 21.4	25 59.9	4 25.3	6 26.7	12 59.5	17 2.3	25 50.1
5 M	0 53 3.6	11 21.2	29 45.1	3♒59.8	6 45.9	26 26.5	26 38.4	4 37.0	6 22.0	13 0.1	17 2.9	25 49.9
6 T	0 57 0.2	12 20.3	29 42.0	18 27.3	7 43.0	27 31.8	27 16.8	4 48.7	6 17.3	13 0.8	17 3.4	25 49.7
7 W	1 0 56.7	13 19.5	29 38.8	3♓11.9	8 37.1	28 37.4	27 55.3	5 0.2	6 12.7	13 1.5	17 3.9	25 49.5
8 T	1 4 53.3	14 18.8	29 35.6	18 7.6	9 28.0	29 43.3	28 33.8	5 11.7	6 8.0	13 2.3	17 4.3	25 49.2
9 F	1 8 49.8	15 18.0	29 32.4	3♈ 6.3	10 15.5	0♍49.3	29 12.3	5 23.1	6 3.4	13 3.1	17 4.7	25 48.9
10 S	1 12 46.4	16 17.3	29 29.2	17 58.5	10 59.1	1 55.7	29 50.8	5 34.5	5 58.8	13 4.0	17 5.1	25 48.6
11 S	1 16 42.9	17 16.6	29 26.1	2♉35.3	11 38.5	3 2.2	0♎29.4	5 45.8	5 54.3	13 4.9	17 5.4	25 48.3
12 M	1 20 39.5	18 16.0	29 22.9	16 49.5	12 13.3	4 9.0	1 7.9	5 57.0	5 49.7	13 5.9	17 5.7	25 48.0
13 T	1 24 36.1	19 15.4	29 19.7	0♊37.0	12 43.0	5 16.0	1 46.5	6 8.2	5 45.2	13 6.9	17 6.0	25 47.6
14 W	1 28 32.6	20 14.8	29 16.5	13 56.7	13 7.3	6 23.3	2 25.0	6 19.2	5 40.7	13 8.0	17 6.3	25 47.2
15 T	1 32 29.1	21 14.3	29 13.4	26 50.2	13 25.5	7 30.7	3 3.6	6 30.2	5 36.3	13 9.1	17 6.5	25 46.8
16 F	1 36 25.7	22 13.8	29 10.2	9♋20.9	13 37.3	8 38.4	3 42.2	6 41.2	5 31.8	13 10.3	17 6.6	25 46.4
17 S	1 40 22.3	23 13.4	29 7.0	21 33.7	13 42.0	9 46.3	4 20.8	6 52.0	5 27.5	13 11.5	17 6.8	25 45.9
18 S	1 44 18.8	24 13.0	29 3.8	3♌33.6	13R39.0	10 54.4	4 59.4	7 2.8	5 23.1	13 12.8	17 6.9	25 45.5
19 M	1 48 15.4	25 12.6	29 0.6	15 26.0	13 28.1	12 2.6	5 38.1	7 13.4	5 18.9	13 14.1	17 6.9	25 45.0
20 T	1 52 11.9	26 12.3	28 57.5	27 15.9	13 8.6	13 11.1	6 16.7	7 24.0	5 14.6	13 15.4	17 7.0	25 44.5
21 W	1 56 8.5	27 12.0	28 54.3	9♍ 7.8	12 40.4	14 19.7	6 55.4	7 34.6	5 10.4	13 16.9	17 7.0	25 44.0
22 T	2 0 5.0	28 11.7	28 51.1	21 5.2	12 3.3	15 28.5	7 34.1	7 45.0	5 6.3	13 18.3	17R 7.0	25 43.4
23 F	2 4 1.6	29 11.5	28 47.9	3♎11.1	11 17.5	16 37.5	8 12.8	7 55.3	5 2.2	13 19.8	17 6.9	25 42.8
24 S	2 7 58.1	0♏11.3	28 44.8	15 27.2	10 23.2	17 46.7	8 51.5	8 5.5	4 58.1	13 21.4	17 6.8	25 42.2
25 S	2 11 54.7	1 11.1	28 41.6	27 54.6	9 21.3	18 56.0	9 30.2	8 15.7	4 54.2	13 23.0	17 6.7	25 41.6
26 M	2 15 51.3	2 11.0	28 38.4	10♏33.6	8 13.0	20 5.5	10 8.9	8 25.8	4 50.3	13 24.7	17 6.5	25 41.0
27 T	2 19 47.8	3 10.9	28 35.2	23 24.1	6 59.8	21 15.1	10 47.7	8 35.7	4 46.4	13 26.4	17 6.3	25 40.4
28 W	2 23 44.3	4 10.9	28 32.0	6♐25.8	5 43.5	22 24.9	11 26.4	8 45.6	4 42.6	13 28.1	17 6.1	25 39.7
29 T	2 27 40.9	5 10.8	28 28.9	19 38.7	4 26.5	23 34.8	12 5.2	8 55.3	4 38.9	13 29.9	17 5.8	25 39.0
30 F	2 31 37.5	6 10.8	28 25.7	3♑ 3.0	3 11.0	24 44.9	12 44.0	9 5.0	4 35.2	13 31.7	17 5.5	25 38.3
31 S	2 35 34.0	7 10.9	28 22.5	16 39.1	1 59.5	25 55.1	13 22.8	9 14.5	4 31.7	13 33.6	17 5.2	25 37.6
						DECLINATION						
1 T	0 37 17.4	2S56.6	23N27.1	20S10.2	14S41.1	13N27.5	3N18.7	10N54.1	0N11.7	23S14.0	21N36.5	16N 4.4
4 S	0 49 7.1	4 6.4	23 27.1	23 43.2	16 4.2	12 38.3	2 32.4	10 41.6	0 6.1	23 13.8	21 36.2	16 4.0
7 W	1 0 56.7	5 15.8	23 27.1	14 32.6	17 15.1	11 45.3	1 46.0	10 29.2	0 0.6	23 13.5	21 36.0	16 3.7
10 S	1 12 46.4	6 24.5	23 27.0	2N39.8	18 11.1	10 48.8	0 59.4	10 17.0	0S 4.8	23 13.2	21 35.8	16 3.3
13 T	1 24 36.1	7 32.5	23 27.0	17 58.9	18 48.7	9 48.8	0 12.8	10 5.0	0 10.1	23 12.9	21 35.6	16 3.0
16 F	1 36 25.7	8 39.6	23 26.9	24 5.5	19 3.0	8 45.6	0S33.8	9 53.3	0 15.2	23 12.5	21 35.5	16 2.6
19 M	1 48 15.4	9 45.6	23 26.9	19 46.4	18 47.6	7 39.4	1 20.5	9 41.7	0 20.1	23 12.1	21 35.4	16 2.3
22 T	2 0 5.0	10 50.3	23 26.8	8 9.2	17 55.9	6 30.5	2 7.0	9 30.5	0 24.8	23 11.7	21 35.4	16 2.0
25 S	2 11 54.7	11 53.5	23 26.7	6S38.8	16 24.4	5 19.1	2 53.5	9 19.5	0 29.3	23 11.2	21 35.3	16 1.6
28 W	2 23 44.3	12 55.2	23 26.6	19 36.9	14 20.1	4 5.6	3 39.8	9 8.8	0 33.6	23 10.6	21 35.4	16 1.3
31 S	2 35 34.0	13 55.0	23 26.5	24 7.7	12 6.0	2 50.2	4 25.9	8 58.4	0 37.5	23 10.0	21 35.4	16 1.0

NOVEMBER 1908

DAY	EPHEMERIS SIDEREAL TIME	☉	☊	☽	☿	♀	♂	♃	♄	♅	♆	♇
	h m s	° ′	° ′	° ′	° ′	° ′	° ′	° ′	° ′	° ′	° ′	° ′
						LONGITUDE						
1 S	2 39 30.6	8 ♏ 10.9	28 ♊ 19.3	0 ♒ 27.6	0 ♏ 54.2	27 ♍ 5.5	14 ♎ 1.6	9 ♍ 24.0	4 ♈ 28.2	13 ♑ 35.5	17 ♋ 4.8	25 ♊ 36.9
2 M	2 43 27.1	9 11.0	28 16.2	14 28.8	29 ♎ 57.0	28 16.0	14 40.4	9 33.3	4 R 24.7	13 37.5	17 R 4.4	25 R 36.1
3 T	2 47 23.7	10 11.1	28 13.0	28 42.2	29 R 9.5	29 26.6	15 19.2	9 42.5	4 21.4	13 39.5	17 3.9	25 35.3
4 W	2 51 20.2	11 11.2	28 9.8	13 ♓ 5.8	28 32.8	0 ♎ 37.4	15 58.1	9 51.6	4 18.1	13 41.6	17 3.5	25 34.5
5 T	2 55 16.8	12 11.4	28 6.6	27 36.1	28 7.5	1 48.2	16 36.9	10 0.6	4 14.9	13 43.7	17 3.0	25 33.7
6 F	2 59 13.3	13 11.5	28 3.5	12 ♈ 7.9	27 53.9	2 59.2	17 15.8	10 9.5	4 11.8	13 45.8	17 2.4	25 32.9
7 S	3 3 9.9	14 11.8	28 0.3	26 35.0	27 51.8	4 10.3	17 54.7	10 18.3	4 8.7	13 48.0	17 1.9	25 32.1
8 S	3 7 6.5	15 12.0	27 57.1	10 ♉ 51.0	28 D 0.8	5 21.6	18 33.6	10 27.0	4 5.8	13 50.2	17 1.3	25 31.2
9 M	3 11 3.0	16 12.3	27 53.9	24 50.2	28 20.2	6 33.0	19 12.5	10 35.5	4 2.9	13 52.5	17 0.7	25 30.4
10 T	3 14 59.6	17 12.5	27 50.7	8 ♊ 28.8	28 49.2	7 44.4	19 51.4	10 43.9	4 0.1	13 54.8	17 0.0	25 29.5
11 W	3 18 56.1	18 12.9	27 47.6	21 44.6	29 27.0	8 56.0	20 30.3	10 52.2	3 57.4	13 57.1	16 59.3	25 28.6
12 T	3 22 52.7	19 13.2	27 44.4	4 ♋ 37.9	0 ♏ 12.6	10 7.7	21 9.3	11 0.4	3 54.8	13 59.5	16 58.6	25 27.7
13 F	3 26 49.2	20 13.6	27 41.2	17 10.6	1 5.2	11 19.5	21 48.3	11 8.4	3 52.3	14 2.0	16 57.8	25 26.7
14 S	3 30 45.8	21 14.0	27 38.0	29 26.1	2 4.0	12 31.5	22 27.3	11 16.3	3 49.9	14 4.4	16 57.1	25 25.8
15 S	3 34 42.4	22 14.5	27 34.9	11 ♌ 28.7	3 8.1	13 43.5	23 6.3	11 24.1	3 47.6	14 6.9	16 56.3	25 24.8
16 M	3 38 38.9	23 15.0	27 31.7	23 23.2	4 16.9	14 55.6	23 45.3	11 31.8	3 45.3	14 9.5	16 55.4	25 23.9
17 T	3 42 35.5	24 15.5	27 28.5	5 ♍ 14.6	5 29.6	16 7.8	24 24.3	11 39.3	3 43.2	14 12.0	16 54.5	25 22.9
18 W	3 46 32.0	25 16.0	27 25.3	17 7.9	6 45.8	17 20.2	25 3.4	11 46.7	3 41.2	14 14.6	16 53.6	25 21.9
19 T	3 50 28.6	26 16.6	27 22.2	29 7.6	8 4.9	18 32.6	25 42.5	11 53.9	3 39.2	14 17.3	16 52.7	25 20.9
20 F	3 54 25.1	27 17.2	27 19.0	11 ♎ 17.5	9 26.4	19 45.1	26 21.6	12 1.0	3 37.4	14 20.0	16 51.8	25 19.9
21 S	3 58 21.7	28 17.8	27 15.8	23 40.7	10 50.0	20 57.6	27 0.7	12 8.0	3 35.7	14 22.7	16 50.8	25 18.8
22 S	4 2 18.2	29 18.5	27 12.6	6 ♏ 19.2	12 15.3	22 10.3	27 39.8	12 14.8	3 34.0	14 25.4	16 49.8	25 17.8
23 M	4 6 14.8	0 ♐ 19.1	27 9.4	19 13.8	13 42.2	23 23.1	28 18.9	12 21.5	3 32.5	14 28.2	16 48.7	25 16.8
24 T	4 10 11.4	1 19.8	27 6.3	2 ♐ 24.5	15 10.2	24 35.9	28 58.1	12 28.0	3 31.1	14 31.0	16 47.7	25 15.7
25 W	4 14 7.9	2 20.6	27 3.1	15 50.1	16 39.2	25 48.8	29 37.2	12 34.4	3 29.7	14 33.9	16 46.6	25 14.6
26 T	4 18 4.5	3 21.3	26 59.9	29 28.7	18 9.1	27 1.7	0 ♏ 16.4	12 40.6	3 28.5	14 36.8	16 45.5	25 13.5
27 F	4 22 1.0	4 22.1	26 56.7	13 ♑ 18.2	19 39.6	28 14.8	0 55.6	12 46.7	3 27.4	14 39.7	16 44.3	25 12.5
28 S	4 25 57.6	5 22.9	26 53.6	27 16.1	21 10.7	29 27.9	1 34.8	12 52.6	3 26.4	14 42.6	16 43.1	25 11.4
29 S	4 29 54.2	6 23.7	26 50.4	11 ♒ 20.3	22 42.3	0 ♏ 41.0	2 14.0	12 58.4	3 25.5	14 45.6	16 41.9	25 10.3
30 M	4 33 50.7	7 24.5	26 47.2	25 28.8	24 14.2	1 54.3	2 53.2	13 4.0	3 24.7	14 48.6	16 40.7	25 9.1
						DECLINATION						
1 S	2 39 30.6	14 S 14.5	23 N 26.4	22 S 49.9	11 S 24.7	2 N 24.7	4 S 41.2	8 N 55.1	0 S 38.8	23 S 9.8	21 N 35.5	16 N 0.9
4 W	2 51 20.2	15 11.6	23 26.3	11 14.9	9 46.3	1 7.3	5 26.9	8 45.2	0 42.4	23 9.2	21 35.6	16 0.6
7 S	3 3 9.9	16 6.4	23 26.2	6 N 5.8	8 57.7	0 S 11.3	6 12.4	8 35.6	0 45.6	23 8.5	21 35.7	16 0.3
10 T	3 14 59.6	16 58.8	23 26.0	20 9.2	8 59.1	1 30.7	6 57.5	8 26.5	0 48.5	23 7.7	21 35.9	16 0.1
13 F	3 26 49.2	17 48.6	23 25.9	24 10.9	9 40.4	2 50.7	7 42.2	8 17.8	0 51.1	23 7.0	21 36.2	15 59.8
16 M	3 38 38.9	18 35.7	23 25.7	17 51.1	10 48.9	4 10.9	8 26.5	8 9.5	0 53.3	23 6.1	21 36.4	15 59.6
19 T	3 50 28.6	19 19.8	23 25.5	5 7.1	12 13.6	5 31.0	9 10.3	8 1.7	0 55.2	23 5.3	21 36.7	15 59.4
22 S	4 2 18.2	20 0.7	23 25.3	9 S 51.9	13 46.3	6 50.7	9 53.6	7 54.3	0 56.6	23 4.4	21 37.1	15 59.2
25 W	4 14 7.9	20 38.4	23 25.1	21 46.7	15 21.3	8 9.5	10 36.3	7 47.5	0 57.7	23 3.5	21 37.4	15 59.0
28 S	4 25 57.6	21 12.6	23 24.9	23 23.8	16 54.6	9 27.2	11 18.4	7 41.2	0 58.4	23 2.5	21 37.8	15 58.9

DECEMBER 1908

DAY	EPHEMERIS SIDEREAL TIME	☉	☊	☽	☿	♀	♂	♃	♄	♅	♆	♇
						LONGITUDE						
1 T	4 37 47.2	8 ♐ 25.3	26 ♊ 44.0	9 ♓ 39.5	25 ♏ 46.5	3 ♏ 7.5	3 ♏ 32.5	13 ♍ 9.4	3 ♈ 24.0	14 ♑ 51.6	16 ♋ 39.5	25 ♊ 8.0
2 W	4 41 43.8	9 26.2	26 40.9	23 50.5	27 18.9	4 20.9	4 11.7	13 14.7	3 R 23.4	14 54.7	16 R 38.2	25 R 6.9
3 T	4 45 40.4	10 27.0	26 37.7	7 ♈ 59.5	28 51.6	5 34.3	4 51.0	13 19.8	3 23.0	14 57.7	16 36.9	25 5.8
4 F	4 49 36.9	11 27.9	26 34.5	22 3.9	0 ♐ 24.4	6 47.8	5 30.3	13 24.8	3 22.6	15 0.8	16 35.6	25 4.6
5 S	4 53 33.5	12 28.8	26 31.3	6 ♉ 1.0	1 57.3	8 1.3	6 9.5	13 29.6	3 22.3	15 4.0	16 34.3	25 3.5
6 S	4 57 30.0	13 29.7	26 28.1	19 47.8	3 30.3	9 14.9	6 48.8	13 34.2	3 22.2	15 7.1	16 32.9	25 2.3
7 M	5 1 26.6	14 30.6	26 25.0	3 ♊ 21.6	5 3.5	10 28.5	7 28.2	13 38.6	3 22.2	15 10.3	16 31.6	25 1.2
8 T	5 5 23.2	15 31.5	26 21.8	16 40.1	6 36.7	11 42.2	8 7.5	13 42.9	3 D 22.2	15 13.5	16 30.2	24 60.0
9 W	5 9 19.7	16 32.5	26 18.6	29 42.1	8 10.0	12 55.9	8 46.9	13 47.0	3 22.4	15 16.7	16 28.8	24 58.8
10 T	5 13 16.3	17 33.4	26 15.4	12 ♋ 27.2	9 43.3	14 9.7	9 26.2	13 51.0	3 22.7	15 20.0	16 27.3	24 57.7
11 F	5 17 12.8	18 34.4	26 12.3	24 56.2	11 16.7	15 23.5	10 5.6	13 54.8	3 23.1	15 23.3	16 25.9	24 56.5
12 S	5 21 9.4	19 35.4	26 9.1	7 ♌ 11.0	12 50.2	16 37.4	10 45.0	13 58.3	3 23.6	15 26.5	16 24.4	24 55.3
13 S	5 25 6.0	20 36.4	26 5.9	19 14.4	14 23.8	17 51.4	11 24.4	14 1.8	3 24.2	15 29.9	16 23.0	24 54.1
14 M	5 29 2.5	21 37.4	26 2.7	1 ♍ 10.1	15 57.5	19 5.3	12 3.9	14 5.0	3 25.0	15 33.2	16 21.5	24 53.0
15 T	5 32 59.1	22 38.5	25 59.6	13 2.2	17 31.3	20 19.4	12 43.3	14 8.0	3 25.8	15 36.5	16 19.9	24 51.8
16 W	5 36 55.6	23 39.6	25 56.4	24 55.3	19 5.2	21 33.4	13 22.8	14 10.9	3 26.7	15 39.9	16 18.4	24 50.6
17 T	5 40 52.2	24 40.6	25 53.2	6 ♎ 54.2	20 39.2	22 47.5	14 2.3	14 13.6	3 27.8	15 43.3	16 16.9	24 49.4
18 F	5 44 48.8	25 41.7	25 50.0	19 3.6	22 13.4	24 1.7	14 41.8	14 16.1	3 28.9	15 46.7	16 15.3	24 48.2
19 S	5 48 45.3	26 42.8	25 46.8	1 ♏ 27.6	23 47.7	25 15.9	15 21.3	14 18.4	3 30.2	15 50.1	16 13.7	24 47.0
20 S	5 52 41.8	27 43.9	25 43.7	14 9.9	25 22.1	26 30.1	16 0.8	14 20.5	3 31.6	15 53.5	16 12.2	24 45.9
21 M	5 56 38.4	28 45.1	25 40.5	27 12.9	26 56.8	27 44.3	16 40.4	14 22.5	3 33.1	15 57.0	16 10.6	24 44.7
22 T	6 0 35.0	29 46.2	25 37.3	10 ♐ 37.5	28 31.6	28 58.6	17 20.0	14 24.2	3 34.7	16 0.4	16 9.0	24 43.5
23 W	6 4 31.6	0 ♑ 47.4	25 34.2	24 23.1	0 ♑ 6.7	0 ♐ 12.9	17 59.5	14 25.8	3 36.4	16 3.9	16 7.3	24 42.3
24 T	6 8 28.1	1 48.5	25 31.0	8 ♑ 27.4	1 42.0	1 27.3	18 39.1	14 27.2	3 38.2	16 7.4	16 5.7	24 41.1
25 F	6 12 24.6	2 49.7	25 27.8	22 46.1	3 17.5	2 41.6	19 18.7	14 28.3	3 40.1	16 10.9	16 4.1	24 40.0
26 S	6 16 21.2	3 50.8	25 24.6	7 ♒ 14.1	4 53.3	3 56.0	19 58.3	14 29.3	3 42.1	16 14.4	16 2.4	24 38.8
27 S	6 20 17.8	4 52.0	25 21.4	21 45.5	6 29.3	5 10.5	20 37.9	14 30.1	3 44.2	16 17.9	16 0.8	24 37.6
28 M	6 24 14.3	5 53.2	25 18.3	6 ♓ 14.9	8 5.7	6 24.9	21 17.6	14 30.7	3 46.5	16 21.4	15 59.1	24 36.5
29 T	6 28 10.9	6 54.3	25 15.1	20 37.6	9 42.3	7 39.4	21 57.2	14 31.1	3 48.8	16 24.9	15 57.4	24 35.3
30 W	6 32 7.4	7 55.5	25 11.9	4 ♈ 50.1	11 19.1	8 53.8	22 36.9	14 31.3	3 51.2	16 28.5	15 55.7	24 34.2
31 T	6 36 4.0	8 56.7	25 8.7	18 50.4	12 56.3	10 8.3	23 16.5	14 31.3	3 53.8	16 32.0	15 54.1	24 33.0
						DECLINATION						
1 T	4 37 47.2	21 S 43.2	23 N 24.6	12 S 37.4	18 S 23.6	10 S 43.3	11 S 59.8	7 N 35.4	0 S 58.7	23 S 1.5	21 N 38.3	15 N 58.7
4 F	4 49 36.9	22 10.1	23 24.4	4 N 12.4	19 46.3	11 57.6	12 40.5	7 30.2	0 58.6	23 0.4	21 38.7	15 58.6
7 M	5 1 26.6	22 33.1	23 24.2	18 50.9	21 1.4	13 9.7	13 20.4	7 25.6	0 58.1	22 59.4	21 39.2	15 58.5
10 T	5 13 16.3	22 52.1	23 23.9	24 22.2	22 7.9	14 19.1	13 59.5	7 21.6	0 57.2	22 58.2	21 39.7	15 58.5
13 S	5 25 6.0	23 7.1	23 23.6	19 5.2	23 4.8	15 25.7	14 37.7	7 18.2	0 55.9	22 57.1	21 40.2	15 58.4
16 W	5 36 55.6	23 17.9	23 23.3	6 52.1	23 51.4	16 28.9	15 15.1	7 15.4	0 54.3	22 55.9	21 40.8	15 58.4
19 S	5 48 45.3	23 24.6	23 23.0	7 S 56.7	24 27.0	17 28.5	15 51.4	7 13.3	0 52.2	22 54.7	21 41.3	15 58.4
22 T	6 0 35.0	23 27.1	23 22.7	20 39.8	24 51.1	18 24.1	16 26.8	7 11.8	0 49.8	22 53.5	21 41.9	15 58.5
25 F	6 12 24.6	23 25.3	23 22.4	23 52.9	25 2.9	19 15.3	17 1.1	7 10.9	0 46.9	22 52.3	21 42.5	15 58.6
28 M	6 24 14.3	23 19.2	23 22.1	13 50.2	25 1.9	20 1.9	17 34.2	7 10.8	0 43.7	22 51.0	21 43.1	15 58.7
31 T	6 36 4.0	23 9.0	23 21.7	2 N 53.1	24 47.6	20 43.5	18 6.2	7 11.3	0 40.2	22 49.7	21 43.7	15 58.8

JANUARY 1909

DAY	EPHEMERIS SIDEREAL TIME h m s	☉ ° ′	☊ ° ′	☽ ° ′	☿ ° ′	♀ ° ′	♂ ° ′	♃ ° ′	♄ ° ′	♅ ° ′	♆ ° ′	♇ ° ′
						LONGITUDE						
1 F	6 40 0.6	9♑57.8	25♓ 5.6	2♉37.2	14♑33.8	11♐22.9	23♏56.2	14♍31.2	3♈56.4	16♑35.6	15♋52.4	24♊31.9
2 S	6 43 57.1	10 59.0	25 2.4	16 10.5	16 11.6	12 37.4	24 35.9	14R30.8	3 59.1	16 39.1	15R50.7	24R30.8
3 S	6 47 53.7	12 0.1	24 59.2	29 30.4	17 49.7	13 52.0	25 15.6	14 30.2	4 2.0	16 42.7	15 49.0	24 29.6
4 M	6 51 50.2	13 1.3	24 56.0	12♊37.3	19 28.1	15 6.5	25 55.3	14 29.5	4 4.9	16 46.3	15 47.3	24 28.5
5 T	6 55 46.8	14 2.4	24 52.9	25 31.6	21 6.8	16 21.1	26 35.1	14 28.5	4 8.0	16 49.8	15 45.6	24 27.4
6 W	6 59 43.4	15 3.5	24 49.7	8♋13.7	22 45.7	17 35.7	27 14.8	14 27.4	4 11.1	16 53.4	15 43.9	24 26.3
7 T	7 3 39.9	16 4.7	24 46.5	20 44.1	24 24.9	18 50.4	27 54.6	14 26.0	4 14.3	16 57.0	15 42.2	24 25.2
8 F	7 7 36.4	17 5.8	24 43.3	3♌ 3.4	26 4.3	20 5.0	28 34.4	14 24.5	4 17.6	17 0.5	15 40.5	24 24.1
9 S	7 11 33.0	18 6.9	24 40.1	15 12.8	27 43.8	21 19.7	29 14.2	14 22.8	4 21.1	17 4.1	15 38.8	24 23.1
10 S	7 15 29.6	19 8.1	24 37.0	27 13.9	29 23.4	22 34.4	29 54.0	14 20.9	4 24.6	17 7.7	15 37.1	24 22.0
11 M	7 19 26.2	20 9.2	24 33.8	9♍ 8.9	1♒ 3.0	23 49.1	0♐33.8	14 18.8	4 28.2	17 11.2	15 35.4	24 21.0
12 T	7 23 22.7	21 10.3	24 30.6	21 0.6	2 42.6	25 3.8	1 13.6	14 16.5	4 31.9	17 14.8	15 33.7	24 19.9
13 W	7 27 19.2	22 11.4	24 27.4	2♎52.8	4 22.0	26 18.5	1 53.5	14 14.0	4 35.7	17 18.4	15 32.1	24 18.9
14 T	7 31 15.8	23 12.5	24 24.3	14 49.6	6 1.1	27 33.2	2 33.3	14 11.3	4 39.6	17 21.9	15 30.4	24 17.9
15 F	7 35 12.4	24 13.7	24 21.1	26 55.5	7 39.7	28 48.0	3 13.2	14 8.5	4 43.5	17 25.5	15 28.7	24 16.9
16 S	7 39 8.9	25 14.8	24 17.9	9♏15.4	9 17.6	0♑ 2.7	3 53.1	14 5.4	4 47.6	17 29.0	15 27.0	24 15.9
17 S	7 43 5.5	26 15.9	24 14.7	21 53.8	10 54.7	1 17.5	4 33.0	14 2.2	4 51.8	17 32.6	15 25.4	24 14.9
18 M	7 47 2.0	27 17.0	24 11.6	4♐55.0	12 30.6	2 32.3	5 12.9	13 58.8	4 56.0	17 36.1	15 23.7	24 13.9
19 T	7 50 58.6	28 18.1	24 8.4	18 21.7	14 5.1	3 47.1	5 52.9	13 55.2	5 0.3	17 39.6	15 22.1	24 13.0
20 W	7 54 55.2	29 19.2	24 5.2	2♑15.2	15 37.8	5 1.9	6 32.8	13 51.4	5 4.7	17 43.1	15 20.4	24 12.0
21 T	7 58 51.7	0♒20.3	24 2.0	16 34.1	17 8.2	6 16.7	7 12.8	13 47.5	5 9.2	17 46.7	15 18.8	24 11.1
22 F	8 2 48.3	1 21.3	23 58.8	1♒14.2	18 35.9	7 31.5	7 52.7	13 43.4	5 13.8	17 50.2	15 17.2	24 10.2
23 S	8 6 44.8	2 22.4	23 55.7	16 8.8	20 0.5	8 46.4	8 32.7	13 39.1	5 18.5	17 53.7	15 15.5	24 9.3
24 S	8 10 41.4	3 23.4	23 52.5	1♓ 9.2	21 21.2	10 1.2	9 12.7	13 34.6	5 23.2	17 57.1	15 13.9	24 8.4
25 M	8 14 37.9	4 24.5	23 49.3	16 6.0	22 37.4	11 16.0	9 52.7	13 30.0	5 28.0	18 0.6	15 12.4	24 7.5
26 T	8 18 34.5	5 25.5	23 46.1	0♈51.0	23 48.4	12 30.9	10 32.7	13 25.2	5 32.9	18 4.0	15 10.8	24 6.6
27 W	8 22 31.0	6 26.5	23 43.0	15 18.1	24 53.5	13 45.7	11 12.7	13 20.2	5 37.9	18 7.5	15 9.2	24 5.8
28 T	8 26 27.6	7 27.4	23 39.8	29 24.0	25 51.7	15 0.5	11 52.7	13 15.1	5 43.0	18 10.9	15 7.7	24 5.0
29 F	8 30 24.2	8 28.4	23 36.6	13♉ 7.7	26 42.4	16 15.4	12 32.7	13 9.9	5 48.1	18 14.3	15 6.1	24 4.2
30 S	8 34 20.7	9 29.3	23 33.4	26 30.2	27 24.6	17 30.2	13 12.8	13 4.5	5 53.3	18 17.7	15 4.6	24 3.4
31 S	8 38 17.3	10 30.2	23 30.3	9♊34.0	27 57.7	18 45.0	13 52.8	12 58.9	5 58.6	18 21.1	15 3.1	24 2.6
						DECLINATION						
1 F	6 40 0.6	23S 4.6	23N21.6	8N24.6	24S39.9	20S56.2	18S16.6	7N11.7	0S38.9	22S49.3	21N43.9	15N58.8
4 M	6 51 50.2	22 48.8	23 21.2	21 6.8	24 7.3	21 30.7	18 47.0	7 13.1	0 34.9	22 48.0	21 44.5	15 59.0
7 T	7 3 39.9	22 29.0	23 20.9	24 1.8	23 20.6	21 59.7	19 16.1	7 15.2	0 30.5	22 46.7	21 45.2	15 59.2
10 S	7 15 29.6	22 5.1	23 20.5	16 45.1	22 19.7	22 22.8	19 43.9	7 17.9	0 25.8	22 45.3	21 45.8	15 59.4
13 W	7 27 19.2	21 37.4	23 20.1	3 36.6	21 4.9	22 40.0	20 10.3	7 21.3	0 20.8	22 44.0	21 46.4	15 59.6
16 S	7 39 8.9	21 5.9	23 19.7	10S59.8	19 37.1	22 51.1	20 35.3	7 25.4	0 15.5	22 42.7	21 47.0	15 59.9
19 T	7 50 58.6	20 30.7	23 19.3	22 16.9	17 58.1	22 56.0	20 58.9	7 30.0	0 9.9	22 41.3	21 47.7	16 0.2
22 F	8 2 48.3	19 52.1	23 18.9	22 50.7	16 11.0	22 54.6	21 21.0	7 35.3	0 4.0	22 40.0	21 48.3	16 0.5
25 M	8 14 37.9	19 10.1	23 18.4	10 10.9	14 21.2	22 46.9	21 41.6	7 41.1	0N 2.2	22 38.6	21 48.9	16 0.9
28 T	8 26 27.6	18 25.0	23 18.0	7N16.0	12 36.7	22 32.9	22 0.6	7 47.5	0 8.6	22 37.3	21 49.4	16 1.2
31 S	8 38 17.3	17 36.8	23 17.5	20 31.4	11 8.0	22 12.8	22 18.0	7 54.3	0 15.3	22 35.9	21 50.0	16 1.6

FEBRUARY 1909

DAY	SIDEREAL TIME	☉	☊	☽	☿	♀	♂	♃	♄	♅	♆	♇
						LONGITUDE						
1 M	8 42 13.8	11♒31.1	23♓27.1	22♊21.7	28♒20.8	19♑59.9	14♐32.8	12♍53.2	6♈ 4.0	18♑24.4	15♋ 1.6	24♊ 1.9
2 T	8 46 10.4	12 32.0	23 23.9	4♋56.1	28 33.4	21 14.7	15 12.9	12R47.3	6 9.4	18 27.8	15R 0.1	24R 1.1
3 W	8 50 7.0	13 32.8	23 20.7	17 19.6	28 35.1	22 29.5	15 53.0	12 41.4	6 14.9	18 31.1	14 58.7	24 0.4
4 T	8 54 3.5	14 33.6	23 17.5	29 34.4	28R25.7	23 44.4	16 33.1	12 35.3	6 20.4	18 34.4	14 57.3	23 59.7
5 F	8 58 0.0	15 34.4	23 14.4	11♌41.9	28 5.3	24 59.2	17 13.1	12 29.0	6 26.1	18 37.7	14 55.8	23 59.0
6 S	9 1 56.6	16 35.2	23 11.2	23 43.4	27 34.2	26 14.1	17 53.2	12 22.7	6 31.7	18 41.0	14 54.4	23 58.4
7 S	9 5 53.2	17 36.0	23 8.0	5♍40.2	26 53.2	27 28.9	18 33.4	12 16.2	6 37.5	18 44.2	14 53.1	23 57.7
8 M	9 9 49.7	18 36.7	23 4.8	17 33.6	26 3.3	28 43.7	19 13.5	12 9.6	6 43.3	18 47.4	14 51.7	23 57.1
9 T	9 13 46.3	19 37.5	23 1.7	29 25.3	25 5.8	29 58.6	19 53.6	12 2.9	6 49.2	18 50.6	14 50.4	23 56.5
10 W	9 17 42.8	20 38.2	22 58.5	11♎17.8	24 2.3	1♒13.4	20 33.8	11 56.0	6 55.1	18 53.8	14 49.1	23 55.9
11 T	9 21 39.4	21 38.8	22 55.3	23 14.1	22 54.8	2 28.3	21 13.9	11 49.1	7 1.2	18 56.9	14 47.8	23 55.3
12 F	9 25 36.0	22 39.5	22 52.1	5♏18.0	21 45.0	3 43.1	21 54.1	11 42.1	7 7.2	19 0.1	14 46.5	23 54.8
13 S	9 29 32.5	23 40.2	22 49.0	17 33.8	20 34.9	4 57.9	22 34.3	11 35.0	7 13.3	19 3.2	14 45.2	23 54.3
14 S	9 33 29.0	24 40.8	22 45.8	0♐ 6.3	19 26.3	6 12.8	23 14.5	11 27.8	7 19.5	19 6.2	14 44.0	23 53.8
15 M	9 37 25.6	25 41.4	22 42.6	13 0.2	18 20.8	7 27.6	23 54.7	11 20.5	7 25.8	19 9.3	14 42.8	23 53.3
16 T	9 41 22.2	26 42.0	22 39.4	26 19.9	17 19.9	8 42.5	24 34.9	11 13.1	7 32.1	19 12.3	14 41.6	23 52.8
17 W	9 45 18.7	27 42.6	22 36.2	10♑ 8.3	16 24.6	9 57.3	25 15.1	11 5.7	7 38.4	19 15.3	14 40.5	23 52.4
18 T	9 49 15.3	28 43.1	22 33.1	24 26.1	15 35.8	11 12.2	25 55.3	10 58.2	7 44.8	19 18.2	14 39.4	23 52.0
19 F	9 53 11.8	29 43.6	22 29.9	9♒10.9	14 54.1	12 27.0	26 35.5	10 50.6	7 51.3	19 21.2	14 38.2	23 51.6
20 S	9 57 8.4	0♓44.1	22 26.7	24 16.6	14 19.8	13 41.8	27 15.7	10 43.0	7 57.8	19 24.1	14 37.2	23 51.2
21 S	10 1 4.9	1 44.6	22 23.5	9♓33.8	13 53.1	14 56.7	27 56.0	10 35.3	8 4.3	19 26.9	14 36.1	23 50.8
22 M	10 5 1.5	2 45.0	22 20.4	24 51.2	13 33.9	16 11.5	28 36.2	10 27.6	8 10.9	19 29.8	14 35.1	23 50.5
23 T	10 8 58.0	3 45.4	22 17.2	9♈57.5	13 22.0	17 26.3	29 16.4	10 19.9	8 17.6	19 32.6	14 34.1	23 50.2
24 W	10 12 54.6	4 45.8	22 14.0	24 43.6	13 17.2	18 41.1	29 56.7	10 12.1	8 24.3	19 35.4	14 33.1	23 49.9
25 T	10 16 51.1	5 46.2	22 10.8	9♉ 3.8	13D19.2	19 55.9	0♑36.9	10 4.3	8 31.0	19 38.1	14 32.2	23 49.6
26 F	10 20 47.7	6 46.5	22 7.6	22 55.9	13 27.6	21 10.7	1 17.2	9 56.4	8 37.8	19 40.8	14 31.3	23 49.4
27 S	10 24 44.3	7 46.8	22 4.5	6♊20.7	13 42.0	22 25.4	1 57.4	9 48.6	8 44.6	19 43.5	14 30.4	23 49.1
28 S	10 28 40.8	8 47.0	22 1.3	19 21.3	14 2.2	23 40.2	2 37.6	9 40.7	8 51.4	19 46.1	14 29.5	23 48.9
						DECLINATION						
1 M	8 42 13.8	17S20.2	23N17.4	22N58.8	10S44.0	22S 4.8	22S23.4	7N56.7	0N17.6	22S35.5	21N50.2	16N 1.8
4 T	8 54 3.5	16 28.4	23 16.9	23 5.5	9 54.2	21 36.6	22 38.6	8 4.2	0 24.5	22 34.2	21 50.8	16 2.2
7 S	9 5 53.2	15 34.0	23 16.4	13 54.3	9 43.2	21 2.6	22 52.2	8 12.0	0 31.7	22 32.9	21 51.3	16 2.7
10 W	9 17 42.8	14 37.2	23 15.9	0S 0.2	10 10.7	20 22.9	23 4.1	8 20.2	0 39.1	22 31.6	21 51.8	16 3.1
13 S	9 29 32.5	13 38.2	23 15.4	14 10.9	11 6.7	19 37.9	23 14.3	8 28.8	0 46.7	22 30.3	21 52.3	16 3.6
16 T	9 41 22.2	12 37.3	23 14.9	23 37.2	12 15.6	18 47.6	23 22.7	8 37.5	0 54.5	22 29.1	21 52.8	16 4.1
19 F	9 53 11.8	11 34.4	23 14.3	21 26.6	13 22.9	17 52.5	23 29.4	8 46.4	1 2.4	22 27.9	21 53.3	16 4.7
22 M	10 5 1.5	10 30.0	23 13.8	6 39.7	14 19.5	16 52.7	23 34.4	8 55.5	1 10.5	22 26.7	21 53.7	16 5.2
25 T	10 16 51.1	9 24.0	23 13.2	11N12.6	15 1.2	15 48.7	23 37.6	9 4.6	1 18.7	22 25.6	21 54.1	16 5.8
28 S	10 28 40.8	8 16.8	23 12.7	22 43.4	15 26.9	14 40.8	23 39.1	9 13.8	1 27.0	22 24.5	21 54.5	16 6.4

MARCH 1909

LONGITUDE

DAY	EPHEMERIS SIDEREAL TIME	☉	☊	☽	☿	♀	♂	♃	♄	♅	♆	♇
	h m s	° ′	° ′	° ′	° ′	° ′	° ′	° ′	° ′	° ′	° ′	° ′
1 M	10 32 37.3	9♓47.2	21♓58.1	2♋ 1.5	14♒27.6	24♒55.0	3♑17.9	9♍32.9	8♈58.3	19♑48.7	14♋28.7	23♊48.7
2 T	10 36 33.9	10 47.4	21 54.9	14 25.6	14 57.9	26 9.7	3 58.1	9R25.0	9 5.3	19 51.3	14R27.9	23R48.6
3 W	10 40 30.5	11 47.6	21 51.8	26 37.8	15 32.9	27 24.5	4 38.4	9 17.2	9 12.3	19 53.8	14 27.2	23 48.5
4 T	10 44 27.0	12 47.7	21 48.6	8♌41.6	16 12.1	28 39.2	5 18.6	9 9.3	9 19.3	19 56.3	14 26.4	23 48.3
5 F	10 48 23.6	13 47.8	21 45.4	20 39.9	16 55.3	29 53.9	5 58.9	9 1.5	9 26.3	19 58.8	14 25.7	23 48.3
6 S	10 52 20.1	14 47.8	21 42.2	2♍34.7	17 42.2	1♓ 8.6	6 39.2	8 53.7	9 33.4	20 1.2	14 25.1	23 48.2
7 S	10 56 16.7	15 47.8	21 39.0	14 27.9	18 32.6	2 23.3	7 19.4	8 45.9	9 40.5	20 3.6	14 24.4	23 48.1
8 M	11 0 13.3	16 47.8	21 35.9	26 20.6	19 26.1	3 38.0	7 59.7	8 38.2	9 47.6	20 5.9	14 23.8	23 48.1
9 T	11 4 9.8	17 47.8	21 32.7	8♎14.1	20 22.7	4 52.7	8 40.0	8 30.5	9 54.8	20 8.2	14 23.2	23 48.1
10 W	11 8 6.3	18 47.7	21 29.5	20 10.0	21 22.1	6 7.4	9 20.2	8 22.9	10 2.0	20 10.5	14 22.7	23D48.1
11 T	11 12 2.9	19 47.6	21 26.3	2♏10.2	22 24.1	7 22.1	10 0.5	8 15.3	10 9.2	20 12.7	14 22.2	23 48.2
12 F	11 15 59.4	20 47.4	21 23.2	14 17.3	23 28.6	8 36.7	10 40.8	8 7.7	10 16.5	20 14.9	14 21.7	23 48.3
13 S	11 19 56.0	21 47.3	21 20.0	26 34.5	24 35.4	9 51.4	11 21.1	8 0.2	10 23.8	20 17.0	14 21.2	23 48.4
14 S	11 23 52.6	22 47.1	21 16.8	9♐ 5.8	25 44.5	11 6.0	12 1.4	7 52.8	10 31.1	20 19.1	14 20.8	23 48.5
15 M	11 27 49.1	23 46.9	21 13.6	21 55.4	26 55.6	12 20.7	12 41.6	7 45.5	10 38.4	20 21.1	14 20.4	23 48.6
16 T	11 31 45.7	24 46.6	21 10.4	5♑ 7.7	28 8.7	13 35.3	13 21.9	7 38.2	10 45.7	20 23.2	14 20.1	23 48.8
17 W	11 35 42.2	25 46.3	21 7.3	18 46.3	29 23.8	14 49.9	14 2.2	7 31.0	10 53.1	20 25.1	14 19.8	23 48.9
18 T	11 39 38.8	26 46.0	21 4.1	2♒53.2	0♓40.7	16 4.6	14 42.5	7 23.9	11 0.5	20 27.0	14 19.5	23 49.1
19 F	11 43 35.3	27 45.7	21 0.9	17 27.8	1 59.3	17 19.2	15 22.8	7 16.9	11 7.9	20 28.9	14 19.2	23 49.4
20 S	11 47 31.9	28 45.3	20 57.7	2♓26.3	3 19.7	18 33.8	16 3.0	7 10.0	11 15.3	20 30.8	14 19.0	23 49.6
21 S	11 51 28.4	29 44.9	20 54.6	17 40.8	4 41.7	19 48.4	16 43.3	7 3.2	11 22.8	20 32.6	14 18.8	23 49.9
22 M	11 55 25.0	0♈44.5	20 51.4	3♈ 0.8	6 5.2	21 2.9	17 23.5	6 56.5	11 30.2	20 34.3	14 18.7	23 50.2
23 T	11 59 21.5	1 44.0	20 48.2	18 14.5	7 30.4	22 17.5	18 3.8	6 49.9	11 37.7	20 36.0	14 18.6	23 50.5
24 W	12 3 18.1	2 43.5	20 45.0	3♉11.3	8 57.0	23 32.0	18 44.0	6 43.4	11 45.2	20 37.6	14 18.5	23 50.8
25 T	12 7 14.6	3 43.0	20 41.8	17 43.4	10 25.1	24 46.6	19 24.2	6 37.1	11 52.7	20 39.2	14 18.4	23 51.2
26 F	12 11 11.2	4 42.4	20 38.7	1♊46.5	11 54.7	26 1.1	20 4.4	6 30.9	12 0.2	20 40.8	14 18.4	23 51.6
27 S	12 15 7.8	5 41.8	20 35.5	15 20.1	13 25.8	27 15.6	20 44.6	6 24.8	12 7.7	20 42.3	14D18.4	23 52.0
28 S	12 19 4.3	6 41.2	20 32.3	28 26.1	14 58.3	28 30.1	21 24.8	6 18.8	12 15.3	20 43.8	14 18.5	23 52.4
29 M	12 23 0.8	7 40.5	20 29.1	11♋ 8.5	16 32.2	29 44.6	22 5.0	6 12.9	12 22.8	20 45.2	14 18.6	23 52.9
30 T	12 26 57.4	8 39.7	20 26.0	23 31.9	18 7.5	0♈59.1	22 45.1	6 7.3	12 30.3	20 46.6	14 18.7	23 53.3
31 W	12 30 54.0	9 39.0	20 22.8	5♌41.1	19 44.2	2 13.5	23 25.3	6 1.7	12 37.9	20 47.9	14 18.9	23 53.8

DECLINATION

DAY	EPHEMERIS SIDEREAL TIME	☉	☊	☽	☿	♀	♂	♃	♄	♅	♆	♇
1 M	10 32 37.3	7S54.2	23N12.5	24N15.0	15S31.9	14S17.3	23S39.2	9N16.8	1N29.8	22S24.2	21N54.6	16N 6.6
4 T	10 44 27.0	6 45.6	23 11.9	21 35.2	15 36.4	13 4.6	23 38.3	9 25.9	1 38.3	22 23.1	21 54.9	16 7.2
7 S	10 56 16.7	5 36.2	23 11.3	10 40.6	15 25.9	11 48.7	23 35.6	9 34.8	1 46.8	22 22.1	21 55.2	16 7.8
10 W	11 8 6.3	4 26.1	23 10.7	3S49.8	15 1.1	10 29.9	23 31.2	9 43.5	1 55.5	22 21.2	21 55.5	16 8.4
13 S	11 19 56.0	3 15.5	23 10.1	17 22.8	14 22.7	9 8.6	23 25.1	9 52.0	2 4.2	22 20.3	21 55.8	16 9.1
16 T	11 31 45.7	2 4.6	23 9.5	24 35.6	13 31.2	7 45.1	23 17.3	10 0.2	2 12.9	22 19.4	21 56.0	16 9.7
19 F	11 43 35.3	0 53.5	23 8.8	19 36.2	12 27.3	6 19.7	23 7.8	10 8.1	2 21.7	22 18.7	21 56.2	16 10.4
22 M	11 55 25.0	0N17.7	23 8.2	3 16.9	11 11.3	4 52.7	22 56.6	10 15.5	2 30.5	22 17.9	21 56.4	16 11.0
25 T	12 7 14.6	1 28.7	23 7.5	14N33.4	9 43.8	3 24.6	22 43.8	10 22.6	2 39.3	22 17.3	21 56.5	16 11.7
28 S	12 19 4.3	2 39.3	23 6.8	24 12.8	8 5.1	1 55.6	22 29.4	10 29.1	2 48.1	22 16.7	21 56.6	16 12.3
31 W	12 30 54.0	3 49.5	23 6.2	22 23.1	6 15.7	0 26.0	22 13.5	10 35.2	2 56.9	22 16.1	21 56.7	16 13.0

APRIL 1909

LONGITUDE

DAY	EPHEMERIS SIDEREAL TIME	☉	☊	☽	☿	♀	♂	♃	♄	♅	♆	♇
1 T	12 34 50.5	10♈38.2	20♓19.6	17♌40.7	21♓22.3	3♈27.9	24♑ 5.4	5♍56.3	12♈45.4	20♑49.2	14♋19.0	23♊54.3
2 F	12 38 47.1	11 37.3	20 16.4	29 34.7	23 1.9	4 42.4	24 45.5	5R51.0	12 53.0	20 50.4	14 19.3	23 54.9
3 S	12 42 43.6	12 36.4	20 13.2	11♍26.4	24 42.9	5 56.8	25 25.6	5 45.9	13 0.5	20 51.5	14 19.5	23 55.4
4 S	12 46 40.2	13 35.5	20 10.1	23 18.3	26 25.3	7 11.1	26 5.7	5 41.0	13 8.1	20 52.7	14 19.8	23 56.0
5 M	12 50 36.7	14 34.6	20 6.9	5♎12.5	28 9.1	8 25.5	26 45.8	5 36.1	13 15.6	20 53.8	14 20.1	23 56.6
6 T	12 54 33.3	15 33.6	20 3.7	17 10.4	29 54.4	9 39.9	27 25.9	5 31.5	13 23.2	20 54.8	14 20.5	23 57.2
7 W	12 58 29.8	16 32.5	20 0.5	29 13.3	1♈41.2	10 54.2	28 5.9	5 27.0	13 30.7	20 55.7	14 20.9	23 57.8
8 T	13 2 26.4	17 31.5	19 57.3	11♏22.4	3 29.4	12 8.6	28 46.0	5 22.7	13 38.2	20 56.7	14 21.3	23 58.5
9 F	13 6 22.9	18 30.4	19 54.2	23 39.4	5 19.1	13 22.9	29 26.0	5 18.5	13 45.8	20 57.6	14 21.8	23 59.2
10 S	13 10 19.5	19 29.3	19 51.0	6♐ 6.1	7 10.3	14 37.2	0♒ 6.0	5 14.5	13 53.3	20 58.4	14 22.2	23 59.9
11 S	13 14 16.1	20 28.1	19 47.8	18 45.1	9 3.0	15 51.5	0 46.0	5 10.7	14 0.8	20 59.2	14 22.8	24 0.6
12 M	13 18 12.6	21 27.0	19 44.6	1♑39.4	10 57.2	17 5.8	1 26.0	5 7.1	14 8.3	20 59.9	14 23.3	24 1.3
13 T	13 22 9.1	22 25.8	19 41.5	14 51.9	12 52.9	18 20.1	2 6.0	5 3.6	14 15.8	21 0.6	14 23.9	24 2.1
14 W	13 26 5.7	23 24.5	19 38.3	28 25.6	14 50.0	19 34.3	2 45.9	5 0.3	14 23.3	21 1.2	14 24.5	24 2.8
15 T	13 30 2.3	24 23.3	19 35.1	12♒22.4	16 48.6	20 48.6	3 25.8	4 57.1	14 30.8	21 1.8	14 25.2	24 3.6
16 F	13 33 58.8	25 22.0	19 31.9	26 42.5	18 48.7	22 2.8	4 5.7	4 54.2	14 38.3	21 2.3	14 25.9	24 4.4
17 S	13 37 55.4	26 20.7	19 28.8	11♓23.4	20 50.1	23 17.1	4 45.5	4 51.4	14 45.8	21 2.8	14 26.6	24 5.3
18 S	13 41 51.9	27 19.3	19 25.6	26 19.9	22 52.9	24 31.3	5 25.4	4 48.8	14 53.2	21 3.2	14 27.3	24 6.1
19 M	13 45 48.5	28 17.9	19 22.4	11♈24.2	24 56.9	25 45.5	6 5.2	4 46.4	15 0.6	21 3.6	14 28.1	24 7.0
20 T	13 49 45.0	29 16.5	19 19.2	26 26.6	27 2.0	26 59.7	6 44.9	4 44.1	15 8.1	21 3.9	14 28.9	24 7.9
21 W	13 53 41.6	0♉15.1	19 16.0	11♉17.5	29 8.2	28 13.9	7 24.6	4 42.1	15 15.5	21 4.1	14 29.8	24 8.8
22 T	13 57 38.1	1 13.6	19 12.9	25 48.9	1♉15.2	29 28.1	8 4.3	4 40.2	15 22.8	21 4.4	14 30.6	24 9.7
23 F	14 1 34.7	2 12.1	19 9.7	9♊55.4	3 23.0	0♉42.2	8 44.0	4 38.5	15 30.2	21 4.5	14 31.5	24 10.6
24 S	14 5 31.3	3 10.6	19 6.5	23 34.6	5 31.2	1 56.3	9 23.6	4 37.0	15 37.5	21 4.7	14 32.5	24 11.6
25 S	14 9 27.8	4 9.0	19 3.3	6♋47.0	7 39.8	3 10.5	10 3.1	4 35.7	15 44.8	21 4.7	14 33.4	24 12.5
26 M	14 13 24.3	5 7.4	19 0.2	19 35.0	9 48.3	4 24.6	10 42.6	4 34.6	15 52.1	21 4.7	14 34.4	24 13.5
27 T	14 17 20.9	6 5.7	18 57.0	2♌ 2.5	11 56.6	5 38.7	11 22.1	4 33.7	15 59.4	21R 4.7	14 35.5	24 14.5
28 W	14 21 17.5	7 4.1	18 53.8	14 14.1	14 4.3	6 52.7	12 1.6	4 32.9	16 6.6	21 4.6	14 36.5	24 15.5
29 T	14 25 14.0	8 2.3	18 50.6	26 14.7	16 11.3	8 6.8	12 41.0	4 32.3	16 13.8	21 4.5	14 37.6	24 16.6
30 F	14 29 10.6	9 0.6	18 47.4	8♍ 8.7	18 17.0	9 20.8	13 20.3	4 32.0	16 21.0	21 4.3	14 38.7	24 17.6

DECLINATION

DAY	EPHEMERIS SIDEREAL TIME	☉	☊	☽	☿	♀	♂	♃	♄	♅	♆	♇
1 T	12 34 50.5	4N12.8	23N 5.9	19N37.1	5S36.9	0N 3.9	22S 7.8	10N37.1	2N59.9	22S16.0	21N56.7	16N13.2
4 S	12 46 40.2	5 22.0	23 5.2	7 15.9	3 33.8	1 33.7	21 49.9	10 42.5	3 8.6	22 15.5	21 56.7	16 13.9
7 W	12 58 29.8	6 30.4	23 4.5	7S37.1	1 21.2	3 3.3	21 30.5	10 47.3	3 17.4	22 15.1	21 56.7	16 14.6
10 S	13 10 19.5	7 37.8	23 3.8	20 17.2	1N 0.5	4 32.4	21 9.6	10 51.5	3 26.1	22 14.8	21 56.7	16 15.2
13 T	13 22 9.1	8 44.0	23 3.1	24 54.6	3 30.1	6 0.7	20 47.5	10 55.2	3 34.7	22 14.6	21 56.6	16 15.9
16 F	13 33 58.8	9 49.0	23 2.3	17 5.2	6 6.2	7 27.8	20 24.0	10 58.2	3 43.2	22 14.4	21 56.5	16 16.5
19 M	13 45 48.5	10 52.5	23 1.6	0N12.1	8 46.8	8 53.4	19 59.3	11 0.6	3 51.7	22 14.3	21 56.4	16 17.2
22 T	13 57 38.1	11 54.4	23 0.8	17 22.5	11 28.6	10 17.3	19 33.4	11 2.4	4 0.0	22 14.2	21 56.2	16 17.8
25 S	14 9 27.8	12 54.6	23 0.0	24 59.4	14 7.4	11 38.9	19 6.4	11 3.6	4 8.3	22 14.3	21 56.0	16 18.4
28 W	14 21 17.5	13 52.8	22 59.2	20 42.2	16 37.9	12 58.1	18 38.3	11 4.2	4 16.4	22 14.4	21 55.7	16 19.1

MAY 1909

LONGITUDE

DAY	EPHEMERIS SIDEREAL TIME	☉	☊	☽	☿	♀	♂	♃	♄	♅	♆	♇
	h m s	° ′	° ′	° ′	° ′	° ′	° ′	° ′	° ′	° ′	° ′	° ′
1 S	14 33 7.1	9♉58.8	18♊44.3	20♍ 0.5	20♉21.3	10♉34.9	13♒59.6	4♍31.8	16♈28.2	21♑ 4.0	14♋39.9	24♊18.7
2 S	14 37 3.7	10 57.0	18 41.1	1♎53.5	22 23.8	11 48.9	14 38.9	4R31.7	16 35.3	21R 3.8	14 41.1	24 19.8
3 M	14 41 0.2	11 55.2	18 37.9	13 50.8	24 24.3	13 2.9	15 18.1	4D31.9	16 42.4	21 3.4	14 42.3	24 20.8
4 T	14 44 56.8	12 53.3	18 34.7	25 54.7	26 22.6	14 16.9	15 57.2	4 32.3	16 49.5	21 3.1	14 43.5	24 22.0
5 W	14 48 53.4	13 51.4	18 31.6	8♏ 6.8	28 18.2	15 30.8	16 36.4	4 32.8	16 56.5	21 2.6	14 44.7	24 23.1
6 T	14 52 49.9	14 49.4	18 28.4	20 28.6	0♊11.2	16 44.8	17 15.4	4 33.5	17 3.5	21 2.1	14 46.0	24 24.2
7 F	14 56 46.4	15 47.5	18 25.2	3♐ 0.8	2 1.2	17 58.7	17 54.4	4 34.4	17 10.4	21 1.6	14 47.3	24 25.3
8 S	15 0 43.0	16 45.5	18 22.0	15 44.5	3 48.1	19 12.7	18 33.4	4 35.5	17 17.4	21 1.0	14 48.7	24 26.5
9 S	15 4 39.6	17 43.5	18 18.9	28 40.5	5 31.8	20 26.6	19 12.3	4 36.8	17 24.3	21 0.4	14 50.0	24 27.7
10 M	15 8 36.1	18 41.4	18 15.7	11♑49.9	7 12.2	21 40.5	19 51.1	4 38.2	17 31.1	20 59.7	14 51.4	24 28.9
11 T	15 12 32.7	19 39.4	18 12.5	25 13.8	8 49.1	22 54.4	20 29.9	4 39.8	17 37.9	20 59.0	14 52.9	24 30.1
12 W	15 16 29.2	20 37.3	18 9.3	8♒53.1	10 22.5	24 8.3	21 8.6	4 41.6	17 44.7	20 58.3	14 54.3	24 31.3
13 T	15 20 25.8	21 35.2	18 6.1	22 48.2	11 52.3	25 22.2	21 47.3	4 43.6	17 51.4	20 57.4	14 55.8	24 32.5
14 F	15 24 22.3	22 33.1	18 3.0	6♓58.8	13 18.4	26 36.0	22 25.8	4 45.7	17 58.1	20 56.6	14 57.3	24 33.7
15 S	15 28 18.9	23 30.9	17 59.8	21 22.8	14 40.8	27 49.9	23 4.3	4 48.0	18 4.8	20 55.7	14 58.8	24 35.0
16 S	15 32 15.4	24 28.8	17 56.6	5♈57.0	15 59.5	29 3.8	23 42.8	4 50.5	18 11.4	20 54.7	15 0.3	24 36.2
17 M	15 36 12.0	25 26.6	17 53.4	20 36.2	17 14.3	0♊17.6	24 21.1	4 53.2	18 18.0	20 53.7	15 1.9	24 37.5
18 T	15 40 8.6	26 24.4	17 50.3	5♉14.2	18 25.2	1 31.5	24 59.3	4 56.1	18 24.5	20 52.7	15 3.5	24 38.8
19 W	15 44 5.1	27 22.2	17 47.1	19 44.2	19 32.2	2 45.3	25 37.5	4 59.1	18 30.9	20 51.6	15 5.1	24 40.0
20 T	15 48 1.7	28 19.9	17 43.9	4♊ 0.1	20 35.2	3 59.1	26 15.6	5 2.2	18 37.4	20 50.5	15 6.7	24 41.3
21 F	15 51 58.2	29 17.7	17 40.7	17 57.0	21 34.2	5 12.9	26 53.5	5 5.6	18 43.7	20 49.3	15 8.4	24 42.6
22 S	15 55 54.8	0♊15.4	17 37.5	1♋32.1	22 29.0	6 26.7	27 31.4	5 9.1	18 50.0	20 48.1	15 10.1	24 43.9
23 S	15 59 51.4	1 13.1	17 34.4	14 44.3	23 19.6	7 40.5	28 9.2	5 12.8	18 56.3	20 46.8	15 11.8	24 45.3
24 M	16 3 47.9	2 10.7	17 31.2	27 34.5	24 5.9	8 54.3	28 46.9	5 16.7	19 2.5	20 45.5	15 13.5	24 46.6
25 T	16 7 44.4	3 8.4	17 28.0	10♌ 5.3	24 47.9	10 8.0	29 24.5	5 20.7	19 8.7	20 44.2	15 15.2	24 47.9
26 W	16 11 41.0	4 6.0	17 24.8	22 20.1	25 25.5	11 21.8	0♓ 1.9	5 24.9	19 14.8	20 42.8	15 17.0	24 49.3
27 T	16 15 37.6	5 3.6	17 21.7	4♍23.0	25 58.6	12 35.5	0 39.3	5 29.2	19 20.9	20 41.4	15 18.8	24 50.6
28 F	16 19 34.1	6 1.1	17 18.5	16 18.7	26 27.2	13 49.2	1 16.5	5 33.7	19 26.9	20 39.9	15 20.6	24 52.0
29 S	16 23 30.6	6 58.7	17 15.3	28 11.6	26 51.2	15 2.9	1 53.7	5 38.4	19 32.8	20 38.4	15 22.4	24 53.3
30 S	16 27 27.2	7 56.2	17 12.1	10♎ 6.2	27 10.5	16 16.6	2 30.7	5 43.2	19 38.7	20 36.9	15 24.2	24 54.7
31 M	16 31 23.8	8 53.7	17 9.0	22 6.5	27 25.1	17 30.3	3 7.6	5 48.2	19 44.5	20 35.3	15 26.1	24 56.1

DECLINATION

DAY	EPHEMERIS SIDEREAL TIME	☉	☊	☽	☿	♀	♂	♃	♄	♅	♆	♇
1 S	14 33 7.1	14N48.9	22N58.4	8N42.1	18N54.6	14N14.5	18S 9.3	11N 4.1	4N24.4	22S14.6	21N55.5	16N19.7
4 T	14 44 56.8	15 42.9	22 57.6	6S15.3	20 52.8	15 27.7	17 39.4	11 3.4	4 32.3	22 14.8	21 55.2	16 20.2
7 F	14 56 46.4	16 34.5	22 56.8	19 33.0	22 29.4	16 37.5	17 8.7	11 2.1	4 40.0	22 15.1	21 54.9	16 20.8
10 M	15 8 36.1	17 23.6	22 56.0	25 7.8	23 43.5	17 43.4	16 37.1	11 0.2	4 47.5	22 15.5	21 54.5	16 21.4
13 T	15 20 25.8	18 10.2	22 55.1	18 26.1	24 35.5	18 45.2	16 4.9	10 57.8	4 54.9	22 15.9	21 54.1	16 21.9
16 S	15 32 15.4	18 54.0	22 54.3	2 10.6	25 7.1	19 42.6	15 32.1	10 54.7	5 2.1	22 16.4	21 53.7	16 22.5
19 W	15 44 5.1	19 34.9	22 53.4	15N23.1	25 20.5	20 35.2	14 58.8	10 51.1	5 9.1	22 17.0	21 53.2	16 23.0
22 S	15 55 54.8	20 12.9	22 52.5	24 47.9	25 17.9	21 22.7	14 25.1	10 46.9	5 15.9	22 17.6	21 52.8	16 23.5
25 T	16 7 44.4	20 47.8	22 51.6	21 48.0	25 1.6	22 4.9	13 51.0	10 42.1	5 22.5	22 18.3	21 52.3	16 23.9
28 F	16 19 34.1	21 19.4	22 50.7	10 15.3	24 33.7	22 41.5	13 16.7	10 36.8	5 28.9	22 19.0	21 51.7	16 24.4
31 M	16 31 23.8	21 47.7	22 49.8	4S37.3	23 56.2	23 12.3	12 42.2	10 31.0	5 35.0	22 19.8	21 51.2	16 24.8

JUNE 1909

LONGITUDE

DAY	EPHEMERIS SIDEREAL TIME	☉	☊	☽	☿	♀	♂	♃	♄	♅	♆	♇
1 T	16 35 20.4	9♊51.2	17♊ 5.8	4♏15.7	27♊35.1	18♊44.0	3♓44.4	5♍53.3	19♈50.3	20♑33.7	15♋28.0	24♊57.5
2 W	16 39 16.9	10 48.6	17 2.6	16 36.7	27 40.5	19 57.6	4 21.0	5 58.6	19 56.0	20R32.1	15 29.9	24 58.9
3 T	16 43 13.4	11 46.1	16 59.4	29 11.4	27 41.2	21 11.3	4 57.5	6 4.0	20 1.6	20 30.4	15 31.8	25 0.2
4 F	16 47 10.0	12 43.5	16 56.2	12♐ 0.8	27R37.5	22 24.9	5 33.9	6 9.5	20 7.2	20 28.7	15 33.7	25 1.6
5 S	16 51 6.6	13 40.9	16 53.1	25 5.4	27 29.4	23 38.6	6 10.2	6 15.3	20 12.7	20 26.9	15 35.7	25 3.0
6 S	16 55 3.1	14 38.3	16 49.9	8♑24.8	27 17.0	24 52.2	6 46.4	6 21.1	20 18.1	20 25.2	15 37.6	25 4.4
7 M	16 58 59.7	15 35.7	16 46.7	21 57.8	27 0.7	26 5.8	7 22.3	6 27.1	20 23.5	20 23.3	15 39.6	25 5.9
8 T	17 2 56.2	16 33.0	16 43.5	5♒43.2	26 40.8	27 19.4	7 58.2	6 33.2	20 28.8	20 21.5	15 41.6	25 7.3
9 W	17 6 52.8	17 30.4	16 40.4	19 39.2	26 17.4	28 33.0	8 33.9	6 39.5	20 34.1	20 19.6	15 43.6	25 8.7
10 T	17 10 49.3	18 27.7	16 37.2	3♓43.8	25 51.1	29 46.6	9 9.4	6 45.9	20 39.3	20 17.7	15 45.6	25 10.1
11 F	17 14 45.9	19 25.1	16 34.0	17 54.8	25 22.2	1♋ 0.2	9 44.8	6 52.5	20 44.4	20 15.8	15 47.6	25 11.5
12 S	17 18 42.5	20 22.4	16 30.8	2♈ 9.9	24 51.3	2 13.7	10 19.9	6 59.2	20 49.4	20 13.8	15 49.7	25 12.9
13 S	17 22 39.0	21 19.7	16 27.7	16 26.5	24 18.8	3 27.3	10 55.0	7 6.0	20 54.4	20 11.8	15 51.7	25 14.4
14 M	17 26 35.6	22 17.1	16 24.5	0♉41.6	23 45.3	4 40.9	11 29.8	7 13.0	20 59.3	20 9.8	15 53.8	25 15.8
15 T	17 30 32.1	23 14.4	16 21.3	14 52.0	23 11.4	5 54.4	12 4.4	7 20.1	21 4.1	20 7.7	15 55.9	25 17.2
16 W	17 34 28.7	24 11.7	16 18.1	28 54.4	22 37.6	7 8.0	12 38.9	7 27.3	21 8.8	20 5.7	15 58.0	25 18.6
17 T	17 38 25.3	25 9.0	16 15.0	12♊45.5	22 4.6	8 21.5	13 13.1	7 34.6	21 13.5	20 3.6	16 0.1	25 20.1
18 F	17 42 21.8	26 6.3	16 11.8	26 22.5	21 32.8	9 35.1	13 47.2	7 42.1	21 18.1	20 1.4	16 2.2	25 21.5
19 S	17 46 18.4	27 3.6	16 8.6	9♋43.1	21 2.9	10 48.6	14 21.0	7 49.7	21 22.6	19 59.3	16 4.3	25 22.9
20 S	17 50 15.0	28 0.8	16 5.4	22 46.3	20 35.3	12 2.1	14 54.6	7 57.4	21 27.1	19 57.1	16 6.5	25 24.4
21 M	17 54 11.5	28 58.1	16 2.3	5♌31.8	20 10.5	13 15.6	15 28.0	8 5.3	21 31.4	19 54.9	16 8.6	25 25.8
22 T	17 58 8.0	29 55.3	15 59.1	18 0.8	19 49.0	14 29.1	16 1.1	8 13.2	21 35.7	19 52.7	16 10.8	25 27.2
23 W	18 2 4.6	0♋52.6	15 55.9	0♍15.6	19 31.0	15 42.6	16 34.0	8 21.3	21 39.9	19 50.5	16 12.9	25 28.6
24 T	18 6 1.2	1 49.8	15 52.7	12 19.1	19 17.0	16 56.1	17 6.7	8 29.5	21 44.0	19 48.2	16 15.1	25 30.1
25 F	18 9 57.8	2 47.1	15 49.6	24 15.3	19 7.2	18 9.5	17 39.1	8 37.8	21 48.1	19 46.0	16 17.3	25 31.5
26 S	18 13 54.3	3 44.3	15 46.4	6♎ 8.4	19 1.8	19 23.0	18 11.3	8 46.3	21 52.0	19 43.7	16 19.5	25 32.9
27 S	18 17 50.8	4 41.5	15 43.2	18 3.2	19 0.9	20 36.4	18 43.2	8 54.8	21 55.9	19 41.4	16 21.7	25 34.3
28 M	18 21 47.4	5 38.7	15 40.0	0♏ 4.2	19D 4.8	21 49.9	19 14.9	9 3.4	21 59.6	19 39.1	16 23.8	25 35.7
29 T	18 25 44.0	6 35.9	15 36.8	12 16.0	19 13.5	23 3.3	19 46.3	9 12.2	22 3.3	19 36.8	16 26.1	25 37.1
30 W	18 29 40.6	7 33.1	15 33.7	24 42.3	19 27.1	24 16.7	20 17.4	9 21.1	22 7.0	19 34.4	16 28.3	25 38.5

DECLINATION

DAY	EPHEMERIS SIDEREAL TIME	☉	☊	☽	☿	♀	♂	♃	♄	♅	♆	♇
1 T	16 35 20.4	21N56.4	22N49.5	9S35.6	23N41.9	23N21.2	12S30.7	10N29.0	5N37.0	22S20.0	21N51.0	16N24.9
4 F	16 47 10.0	22 20.1	22 48.6	21 49.2	22 54.9	23 43.9	11 56.1	10 22.5	5 42.9	22 20.9	21 50.4	16 25.3
7 M	16 58 59.7	22 40.3	22 47.7	24 40.6	22 3.3	24 0.4	11 21.6	10 15.6	5 48.4	22 21.7	21 49.8	16 25.7
10 T	17 10 49.3	22 57.0	22 46.7	14 56.1	21 10.1	24 10.5	10 47.2	10 8.1	5 53.8	22 22.6	21 49.1	16 26.1
13 S	17 22 39.0	23 10.1	22 45.8	2N13.9	20 18.9	24 14.2	10 13.0	10 0.2	5 58.8	22 23.6	21 48.5	16 26.4
16 W	17 34 28.7	23 19.5	22 44.8	18 21.0	19 33.6	24 11.5	9 39.2	9 51.9	6 3.6	22 24.6	21 47.8	16 26.7
19 S	17 46 18.4	23 25.1	22 43.8	25 9.5	18 58.3	24 2.3	9 5.8	9 43.1	6 8.1	22 25.5	21 47.1	16 27.0
22 T	17 58 8.0	23 27.1	22 42.8	19 50.0	18 35.9	23 46.7	8 33.1	9 33.9	6 12.4	22 26.6	21 46.4	16 27.2
25 F	18 9 57.8	23 25.3	22 41.8	7 3.9	18 28.2	23 24.8	8 0.9	9 24.3	6 16.3	22 27.6	21 45.7	16 27.5
28 M	18 21 47.4	23 19.9	22 40.8	7S55.6	18 35.4	22 56.7	7 29.6	9 14.3	6 19.9	22 28.6	21 44.9	16 27.7

JULY 1909

LONGITUDE

DAY	EPHEMERIS SIDEREAL TIME	☉	☊	☽	☿	♀	♂	♃	♄	♅	♆	♇
	h m s	° ′	° ′	° ′	° ′	° ′	° ′	° ′	° ′	° ′	° ′	° ′
1 T	18 33 37.1	8♋30.3	15♊30.5	7♐26.3	19♊45.5	25♋30.1	20♓48.2	9♍30.0	22♈10.5	19♑32.1	16♋30.5	25♊39.9
2 F	18 37 33.6	9 27.4	15 27.3	20 30.1	20 8.9	26 43.5	21 18.8	9 39.1	22 13.9	19R29.7	16 32.7	25 41.3
3 S	18 41 30.2	10 24.6	15 24.1	3♑54.2	20 37.2	27 56.8	21 49.0	9 48.3	22 17.2	19 27.3	16 34.9	25 42.7
4 S	18 45 26.8	11 21.8	15 21.0	17 37.7	21 10.4	29 10.2	22 19.0	9 57.5	22 20.5	19 25.0	16 37.1	25 44.1
5 M	18 49 23.3	12 19.0	15 17.8	1♒37.8	21 48.4	0♌23.5	22 48.6	10 6.9	22 23.7	19 22.6	16 39.3	25 45.5
6 T	18 53 19.9	13 16.1	15 14.6	15 50.7	22 31.2	1 36.8	23 17.9	10 16.4	22 26.7	19 20.2	16 41.6	25 46.8
7 W	18 57 16.4	14 13.3	15 11.4	0♓11.5	23 18.8	2 50.2	23 46.9	10 25.9	22 29.7	19 17.8	16 43.8	25 48.2
8 T	19 1 13.0	15 10.5	15 8.3	14 35.2	24 11.0	4 3.5	24 15.6	10 35.6	22 32.6	19 15.4	16 46.0	25 49.6
9 F	19 5 9.5	16 7.7	15 5.1	28 57.2	25 7.9	5 16.8	24 43.9	10 45.3	22 35.4	19 13.0	16 48.3	25 50.9
10 S	19 9 6.1	17 4.9	15 1.9	13♈13.8	26 9.4	6 30.1	25 11.8	10 55.2	22 38.1	19 10.6	16 50.5	25 52.3
11 S	19 13 2.7	18 2.1	14 58.7	27 22.4	27 15.5	7 43.4	25 39.4	11 5.1	22 40.7	19 8.1	16 52.7	25 53.6
12 M	19 16 59.2	18 59.3	14 55.5	11♉21.2	28 25.9	8 56.6	26 6.6	11 15.1	22 43.2	19 5.7	16 54.9	25 54.9
13 T	19 20 55.8	19 56.6	14 52.4	25 9.4	29 40.8	10 9.9	26 33.3	11 25.2	22 45.7	19 3.3	16 57.2	25 56.3
14 W	19 24 52.4	20 53.8	14 49.2	8♊46.3	1♋0.0	11 23.2	26 59.7	11 35.4	22 48.0	19 0.9	16 59.4	25 57.6
15 T	19 28 48.9	21 51.1	14 46.0	22 11.7	2 23.5	12 36.4	27 25.6	11 45.7	22 50.2	18 58.5	17 1.6	25 58.9
16 F	19 32 45.5	22 48.3	14 42.8	5♋24.9	3 51.1	13 49.6	27 51.2	11 56.1	22 52.3	18 56.1	17 3.9	26 0.2
17 S	19 36 42.0	23 45.6	14 39.7	18 25.6	5 22.7	15 2.8	28 16.2	12 6.5	22 54.4	18 53.6	17 6.1	26 1.5
18 S	19 40 38.6	24 42.8	14 36.5	1♌13.2	6 58.3	16 16.1	28 40.8	12 17.1	22 56.3	18 51.2	17 8.3	26 2.8
19 M	19 44 35.1	25 40.1	14 33.3	13 47.8	8 37.7	17 29.2	29 5.0	12 27.7	22 58.1	18 48.9	17 10.5	26 4.0
20 T	19 48 31.7	26 37.4	14 30.1	26 9.7	10 20.8	18 42.4	29 28.7	12 38.4	22 59.9	18 46.5	17 12.7	26 5.3
21 W	19 52 28.2	27 34.7	14 27.0	8♍20.2	12 7.3	19 55.6	29 51.9	12 49.1	23 1.5	18 44.1	17 14.9	26 6.6
22 T	19 56 24.8	28 32.0	14 23.8	20 21.2	13 57.0	21 8.7	0♈14.6	12 60.0	23 3.0	18 41.7	17 17.1	26 7.8
23 F	20 0 21.4	29 29.3	14 20.6	2♎15.8	15 49.7	22 21.9	0 36.8	13 10.9	23 4.4	18 39.3	17 19.3	26 9.0
24 S	20 4 17.9	0♌26.6	14 17.4	14 7.4	17 45.1	23 35.0	0 58.4	13 21.8	23 5.8	18 37.0	17 21.5	26 10.2
25 S	20 8 14.4	1 23.9	14 14.2	26 0.5	19 43.0	24 48.1	1 19.6	13 32.9	23 7.0	18 34.7	17 23.7	26 11.4
26 M	20 12 11.0	2 21.2	14 11.1	7♏59.8	21 43.0	26 1.2	1 40.2	13 44.0	23 8.1	18 32.3	17 25.9	26 12.6
27 T	20 16 7.6	3 18.6	14 7.9	20 10.4	23 44.8	27 14.2	2 0.3	13 55.2	23 9.1	18 30.0	17 28.0	26 13.8
28 W	20 20 4.2	4 15.9	14 4.7	2♐37.1	25 48.1	28 27.3	2 19.8	14 6.5	23 10.0	18 27.7	17 30.2	26 15.0
29 T	20 24 0.7	5 13.3	14 1.5	15 24.2	27 52.4	29 40.3	2 38.7	14 17.8	23 10.8	18 25.4	17 32.3	26 16.1
30 F	20 27 57.2	6 10.6	13 58.4	28 35.2	29 57.6	0♍53.3	2 57.1	14 29.1	23 11.5	18 23.2	17 34.5	26 17.3
31 S	20 31 53.8	7 8.0	13 55.2	12♑11.7	2♌3.2	2 6.2	3 14.8	14 40.6	23 12.1	18 20.9	17 36.6	26 18.4

DECLINATION

DAY	EPHEMERIS SIDEREAL TIME	☉	☊	☽	☿	♀	♂	♃	♄	♅	♆	♇
1 T	18 33 37.1	23N10.7	22N39.8	20S44.2	18N56.0	22N22.6	6S59.1	9N 3.9	6N23.2	22S29.7	21N44.2	16N27.9
4 S	18 45 26.8	22 57.9	22 38.8	24 58.0	19 27.6	21 42.8	6 29.5	8 53.2	6 26.3	22 30.8	21 43.4	16 28.0
7 W	18 57 16.4	22 41.5	22 37.7	16 5.3	20 7.0	20 57.4	6 1.1	8 42.1	6 28.9	22 31.8	21 42.6	16 28.1
10 S	19 9 6.1	22 21.6	22 36.7	0N56.5	20 50.1	20 6.7	5 33.8	8 30.7	6 31.3	22 32.9	21 41.8	16 28.3
13 T	19 20 55.8	21 58.2	22 35.6	17 14.1	21 32.8	19 10.9	5 7.8	8 18.9	6 33.4	22 33.9	21 41.0	16 28.3
16 F	19 32 45.5	21 31.4	22 34.5	25 2.3	22 10.1	18 10.5	4 43.2	8 6.9	6 35.1	22 34.9	21 40.2	16 28.4
19 M	19 44 35.1	21 1.2	22 33.4	20 51.9	22 36.6	17 5.6	4 20.2	7 54.5	6 36.4	22 36.0	21 39.4	16 28.4
22 T	19 56 24.8	20 27.9	22 32.3	8 32.1	22 47.1	15 56.6	3 58.9	7 41.9	6 37.5	22 37.0	21 38.6	16 28.4
25 S	20 8 14.4	19 51.5	22 31.2	6S23.5	22 37.0	14 43.8	3 39.4	7 29.0	6 38.2	22 38.0	21 37.7	16 28.4
28 W	20 20 4.2	19 12.1	22 30.1	19 33.5	22 3.5	13 27.5	3 21.7	7 15.9	6 38.5	22 38.9	21 36.9	16 28.4
31 S	20 31 53.8	18 29.9	22 29.0	25 10.8	21 6.1	12 8.1	3 6.0	7 2.5	6 38.5	22 39.8	21 36.1	16 28.3

AUGUST 1909

LONGITUDE

DAY	EPHEMERIS SIDEREAL TIME	☉	☊	☽	☿	♀	♂	♃	♄	♅	♆	♇
1 S	20 35 50.4	8♌5.4	13♊52.0	26♑13.1	4♌9.0	3♍19.2	3♈32.0	14♍52.1	23♈12.7	18♑18.7	17♋38.7	26♊19.5
2 M	20 39 46.9	9 2.7	13 48.8	10♒36.3	6 14.7	4 32.1	3 48.5	15 3.7	23 13.1	18R16.5	17 40.8	26 20.6
3 T	20 43 43.5	10 0.2	13 45.7	25 15.6	8 20.1	5 45.0	4 4.4	15 15.3	23 13.4	18 14.3	17 42.9	26 21.7
4 W	20 47 40.0	10 57.6	13 42.5	10♓3.5	10 24.8	6 57.9	4 19.7	15 26.9	23 13.5	18 12.1	17 45.0	26 22.8
5 T	20 51 36.6	11 55.0	13 39.3	24 51.6	12 28.9	8 10.8	4 34.3	15 38.7	23 13.6	18 10.0	17 47.1	26 23.8
6 F	20 55 33.1	12 52.5	13 36.1	9♈32.5	14 32.0	9 23.6	4 48.2	15 50.5	23R13.6	18 7.9	17 49.1	26 24.9
7 S	20 59 29.7	13 50.0	13 32.9	24 0.3	16 34.1	10 36.5	5 1.4	16 2.3	23 13.5	18 5.8	17 51.2	26 25.9
8 S	21 3 26.3	14 47.5	13 29.8	8♉11.6	18 35.0	11 49.3	5 13.9	16 14.2	23 13.3	18 3.7	17 53.2	26 26.9
9 M	21 7 22.8	15 45.0	13 26.6	22 4.9	20 34.6	13 2.1	5 25.7	16 26.1	23 13.0	18 1.6	17 55.3	26 27.9
10 T	21 11 19.3	16 42.6	13 23.4	5♊40.7	22 33.0	14 14.8	5 36.7	16 38.1	23 12.5	17 59.6	17 57.3	26 28.9
11 W	21 15 15.9	17 40.1	13 20.2	19 0.3	24 30.0	15 27.6	5 47.0	16 50.2	23 12.0	17 57.6	17 59.3	26 29.9
12 T	21 19 12.5	18 37.7	13 17.1	2♋5.5	26 25.5	16 40.3	5 56.5	17 2.3	23 11.4	17 55.6	18 1.3	26 30.8
13 F	21 23 9.0	19 35.4	13 13.9	14 57.9	28 19.7	17 53.0	6 5.2	17 14.4	23 10.6	17 53.7	18 3.2	26 31.8
14 S	21 27 5.6	20 33.0	13 10.7	27 39.0	0♍12.4	19 5.7	6 13.1	17 26.6	23 9.8	17 51.8	18 5.2	26 32.7
15 S	21 31 2.1	21 30.7	13 7.5	10♌9.6	2 3.6	20 18.4	6 20.3	17 38.8	23 8.8	17 49.9	18 7.1	26 33.6
16 M	21 34 58.7	22 28.4	13 4.4	22 30.6	3 53.4	21 31.1	6 26.6	17 51.1	23 7.8	17 48.0	18 9.0	26 34.5
17 T	21 38 55.3	23 26.1	13 1.2	4♍42.4	5 41.8	22 43.7	6 32.1	18 3.4	23 6.6	17 46.2	18 10.9	26 35.3
18 W	21 42 51.8	24 23.8	12 58.0	16 46.0	7 28.7	23 56.3	6 36.8	18 15.7	23 5.4	17 44.4	18 12.8	26 36.2
19 T	21 46 48.3	25 21.6	12 54.8	28 42.6	9 14.2	25 8.8	6 40.6	18 28.1	23 4.0	17 42.7	18 14.7	26 37.0
20 F	21 50 44.9	26 19.4	12 51.6	10♎34.4	10 58.2	26 21.4	6 43.7	18 40.6	23 2.6	17 41.0	18 16.5	26 37.8
21 S	21 54 41.5	27 17.2	12 48.5	22 24.0	12 40.9	27 33.9	6 45.8	18 53.0	23 1.0	17 39.3	18 18.3	26 38.6
22 S	21 58 38.0	28 15.0	12 45.3	4♏15.1	14 22.2	28 46.4	6 47.2	19 5.5	22 59.3	17 37.6	18 20.2	26 39.4
23 M	22 2 34.6	29 12.8	12 42.1	16 12.0	16 2.0	29 58.9	6 47.7	19 18.0	22 57.6	17 36.0	18 21.9	26 40.2
24 T	22 6 31.1	0♍10.7	12 38.9	28 19.5	17 40.6	1♎11.3	6R47.3	19 30.6	22 55.7	17 34.5	18 23.7	26 40.9
25 W	22 10 27.7	1 8.5	12 35.8	10♐43.0	19 17.7	2 23.7	6 46.2	19 43.2	22 53.8	17 32.9	18 25.5	26 41.6
26 T	22 14 24.2	2 6.4	12 32.6	23 27.6	20 53.5	3 36.1	6 44.1	19 55.8	22 51.8	17 31.4	18 27.2	26 42.3
27 F	22 18 20.8	3 4.4	12 29.4	6♑37.6	22 28.0	4 48.4	6 41.3	20 8.5	22 49.6	17 30.0	18 28.9	26 43.0
28 S	22 22 17.4	4 2.3	12 26.2	20 16.2	24 1.1	6 0.7	6 37.6	20 21.1	22 47.4	17 28.6	18 30.6	26 43.6
29 S	22 26 13.9	5 0.3	12 23.0	4♒24.0	25 32.9	7 13.0	6 33.1	20 33.8	22 45.1	17 27.2	18 32.2	26 44.3
30 M	22 30 10.4	5 58.3	12 19.9	18 58.9	27 3.4	8 25.2	6 27.8	20 46.6	22 42.7	17 25.8	18 33.9	26 44.9
31 T	22 34 7.0	6 56.3	12 16.7	3♓54.8	28 32.5	9 37.4	6 21.7	20 59.3	22 40.2	17 24.5	18 35.5	26 45.5

DECLINATION

DAY	EPHEMERIS SIDEREAL TIME	☉	☊	☽	☿	♀	♂	♃	♄	♅	♆	♇
1 S	20 35 50.4	18N15.2	22N28.6	24S11.5	20N42.0	11N41.0	3S 1.2	6N58.0	6N38.5	22S40.1	21N35.8	16N28.3
4 W	20 47 40.0	17 29.4	22 27.4	12 29.1	19 16.3	10 18.0	2 48.1	6 44.3	6 38.0	22 41.0	21 35.0	16 28.2
7 S	20 59 29.7	16 41.0	22 26.3	5N38.7	17 33.8	8 52.6	2 37.3	6 30.4	6 37.2	22 41.9	21 34.2	16 28.1
10 T	21 11 19.3	15 50.2	22 25.1	20 28.2	15 38.6	7 25.1	2 28.7	6 16.3	6 36.1	22 42.7	21 33.4	16 28.0
13 F	21 23 9.0	14 57.1	22 23.9	25 9.0	13 34.4	5 55.9	2 22.4	6 2.0	6 34.7	22 43.5	21 32.6	16 27.8
16 M	21 34 58.7	14 1.8	22 22.8	18 25.7	11 24.5	4 25.3	2 18.6	5 47.6	6 32.9	22 44.2	21 31.8	16 27.7
19 T	21 46 48.3	13 4.5	22 21.6	4 57.8	9 11.2	2 53.5	2 17.1	5 33.0	6 30.8	22 44.9	21 31.1	16 27.5
22 S	21 58 38.0	12 5.3	22 20.3	9S56.9	6 56.7	1 21.0	2 18.0	5 18.2	6 28.3	22 45.5	21 30.3	16 27.3
25 W	22 10 27.7	11 4.5	22 19.1	21 50.7	4 42.6	0S12.0	2 21.2	5 3.4	6 25.6	22 46.1	21 29.6	16 27.0
28 S	22 22 17.4	10 2.0	22 17.9	24 55.6	2 30.1	1 45.2	2 26.5	4 48.4	6 22.6	22 46.6	21 28.9	16 26.8
31 T	22 34 7.0	8 58.1	22 16.7	14 40.9	0 20.3	3 18.1	2 33.9	4 33.3	6 19.3	22 47.1	21 28.2	16 26.6

SEPTEMBER 1909

DAY	EPHEMERIS SIDEREAL TIME	☉	☊	☽	☿	♀	♂	♃	♄	♅	♆	♇
	h m s	° ′	° ′	° ′	° ′	° ′	° ′	° ′	° ′	° ′	° ′	° ′
						LONGITUDE						
1 W	22 38 3.6	7♍54.3	12♊13.5	19♓ 3.1	0♎ 0.3	10♎49.5	6♈14.8	21♍12.1	22♈37.6	17♑23.3	18♋37.1	26♊46.1
2 T	22 42 0.1	8 52.4	12 10.3	4♈13.2	1 26.7	12 1.7	6R 7.1	21 24.9	22R34.9	17R22.1	18 38.7	26 46.6
3 F	22 45 56.7	9 50.5	12 7.2	19 14.9	2 51.8	13 13.8	5 58.6	21 37.7	22 32.1	17 20.9	18 40.2	26 47.2
4 S	22 49 53.2	10 48.6	12 4.0	3♉59.7	4 15.4	14 25.8	5 49.4	21 50.5	22 29.3	17 19.8	18 41.7	26 47.7
5 S	22 53 49.8	11 46.8	12 0.8	18 22.4	5 37.7	15 37.8	5 39.4	22 3.4	22 26.3	17 18.7	18 43.2	26 48.2
6 M	22 57 46.3	12 45.0	11 57.6	2♊20.8	6 58.5	16 49.8	5 28.7	22 16.2	22 23.3	17 17.7	18 44.7	26 48.7
7 T	23 1 42.9	13 43.2	11 54.4	15 55.4	8 17.7	18 1.8	5 17.2	22 29.1	22 20.2	17 16.7	18 46.2	26 49.1
8 W	23 5 39.4	14 41.5	11 51.3	29 8.3	9 35.5	19 13.7	5 5.1	22 42.0	22 17.0	17 15.7	18 47.6	26 49.6
9 T	23 9 36.0	15 39.8	11 48.1	12♋ 2.7	10 51.7	20 25.6	4 52.4	22 54.9	22 13.7	17 14.8	18 49.0	26 50.0
10 F	23 13 32.5	16 38.1	11 44.9	24 41.6	12 6.2	21 37.5	4 39.0	23 7.9	22 10.4	17 14.0	18 50.4	26 50.4
11 S	23 17 29.1	17 36.5	11 41.7	7♌ 8.2	13 19.0	22 49.3	4 25.1	23 20.8	22 7.0	17 13.1	18 51.7	26 50.7
12 S	23 21 25.6	18 34.9	11 38.6	19 24.8	14 30.0	24 1.1	4 10.5	23 33.8	22 3.5	17 12.4	18 53.0	26 51.1
13 M	23 25 22.2	19 33.3	11 35.4	1♍33.5	15 39.1	25 12.8	3 55.5	23 46.7	21 59.9	17 11.7	18 54.3	26 51.4
14 T	23 29 18.7	20 31.8	11 32.2	13 35.6	16 46.1	26 24.6	3 40.1	23 59.7	21 56.3	17 11.0	18 55.6	26 51.7
15 W	23 33 15.3	21 30.3	11 29.0	25 32.3	17 51.1	27 36.2	3 24.1	24 12.7	21 52.5	17 10.4	18 56.8	26 52.0
16 T	23 37 11.9	22 28.8	11 25.8	7♎24.9	18 53.8	28 47.9	3 7.9	24 25.6	21 48.8	17 9.8	18 58.0	26 52.3
17 F	23 41 8.4	23 27.4	11 22.7	19 14.9	19 54.2	29 59.5	2 51.3	24 38.6	21 44.9	17 9.3	18 59.2	26 52.5
18 S	23 45 5.0	24 26.0	11 19.5	1♏ 4.3	20 51.9	1♏11.0	2 34.4	24 51.6	21 41.0	17 8.8	19 0.4	26 52.7
19 S	23 49 1.5	25 24.6	11 16.3	12 55.9	21 46.9	2 22.6	2 17.2	25 4.6	21 37.0	17 8.4	19 1.5	26 52.9
20 M	23 52 58.1	26 23.2	11 13.1	24 52.9	22 39.0	3 34.0	1 59.9	25 17.6	21 33.0	17 8.0	19 2.6	26 53.1
21 T	23 56 54.6	27 21.9	11 10.0	6♐59.6	23 27.8	4 45.5	1 42.5	25 30.6	21 28.9	17 7.7	19 3.6	26 53.2
22 W	0 0 51.2	28 20.6	11 6.8	19 20.7	24 13.2	5 56.8	1 25.0	25 43.5	21 24.8	17 7.4	19 4.7	26 53.4
23 T	0 4 47.8	29 19.4	11 3.6	2♑ 1.1	24 54.9	7 8.2	1 7.5	25 56.5	21 20.6	17 7.2	19 5.7	26 53.5
24 F	0 8 44.3	0♎18.1	11 0.4	15 5.7	25 32.6	8 19.4	0 49.9	26 9.5	21 16.3	17 7.0	19 6.7	26 53.6
25 S	0 12 40.9	1 16.9	10 57.2	28 38.1	26 5.9	9 30.7	0 32.5	26 22.4	21 12.0	17 6.9	19 7.6	26 53.6
26 S	0 16 37.4	2 15.7	10 54.1	12♒40.6	26 34.4	10 41.8	0 15.2	26 35.4	21 7.7	17 6.8	19 8.5	26 53.7
27 M	0 20 34.0	3 14.6	10 50.9	27 12.2	26 57.9	11 53.0	29♓58.0	26 48.3	21 3.3	17 6.8	19 9.4	26 53.7
28 T	0 24 30.5	4 13.5	10 47.7	12♓ 8.8	27 15.9	13 4.0	29 41.1	27 1.3	20 58.9	17D 6.8	19 10.2	26R53.7
29 W	0 28 27.1	5 12.4	10 44.5	27 22.4	27 28.0	14 15.0	29 24.4	27 14.2	20 54.4	17 6.9	19 11.0	26 53.6
30 T	0 32 23.6	6 11.3	10 41.4	12♈42.5	27 33.7	15 26.0	29 8.0	27 27.1	20 49.9	17 7.0	19 11.8	26 53.6
						DECLINATION						
1 W	22 38 3.6	8N36.6	22N16.2	8S54.3	0S22.2	3S49.1	2S36.7	4N28.3	6N18.1	22S47.3	21N28.0	16N26.5
4 S	22 49 53.2	7 31.0	22 15.0	9N56.0	2 26.7	5 21.4	2 46.4	4 13.1	6 14.4	22 47.7	21 27.3	16 26.2
7 T	23 1 42.9	6 24.3	22 13.7	23 2.9	4 26.1	6 52.8	2 57.6	3 57.8	6 10.5	22 48.0	21 26.7	16 25.9
10 F	23 13 32.5	5 16.7	22 12.4	24 33.3	6 19.3	8 23.0	3 10.1	3 42.5	6 6.3	22 48.3	21 26.1	16 25.6
13 M	23 25 22.2	4 8.3	22 11.1	15 31.2	8 5.2	9 51.8	3 23.3	3 27.2	6 1.9	22 48.6	21 25.5	16 25.3
16 T	23 37 11.9	2 59.1	22 9.9	1 10.1	9 42.3	11 18.8	3 37.0	3 11.8	5 57.4	22 48.8	21 24.9	16 25.0
19 S	23 49 1.5	1 49.5	22 8.5	13S30.7	11 8.6	12 43.6	3 50.5	2 56.4	5 52.6	22 48.9	21 24.4	16 24.7
22 W	0 0 51.2	0 39.5	22 7.2	23 49.4	12 21.6	14 6.0	4 3.4	2 41.0	5 47.6	22 49.0	21 23.9	16 24.4
25 S	0 12 40.9	0S30.6	22 5.9	24 9.3	13 18.0	15 25.5	4 15.3	2 25.6	5 42.5	22 49.0	21 23.5	16 24.1
28 T	0 24 30.5	1 40.8	22 4.5	11 40.0	13 53.3	16 42.0	4 25.7	2 10.3	5 37.4	22 49.0	21 23.1	16 23.7

OCTOBER 1909

DAY	EPHEMERIS SIDEREAL TIME	☉	☊	☽	☿	♀	♂	♃	♄	♅	♆	♇
						LONGITUDE						
1 F	0 36 20.2	7♎10.3	10♊38.2	27♈57.6	27♎32.7	16♏36.9	28♓51.9	27♍40.0	20♈45.4	17♑ 7.2	19♋12.6	26♊53.5
2 S	0 40 16.7	8 9.3	10 35.0	12♉57.3	27R24.5	17 47.7	28R36.2	27 52.9	20R40.8	17 7.4	19 13.3	26R53.4
3 S	0 44 13.3	9 8.4	10 31.8	27 34.2	27 8.8	18 58.5	28 21.0	28 5.8	20 36.2	17 7.7	19 14.0	26 53.3
4 M	0 48 9.8	10 7.5	10 28.6	11♊44.2	26 45.4	20 9.2	28 6.1	28 18.6	20 31.6	17 8.1	19 14.7	26 53.2
5 T	0 52 6.4	11 6.6	10 25.5	25 26.5	26 14.1	21 19.8	27 51.8	28 31.5	20 26.9	17 8.4	19 15.3	26 53.0
6 W	0 56 3.0	12 5.8	10 22.3	8♋42.8	25 35.0	22 30.5	27 37.9	28 44.3	20 22.3	17 8.9	19 15.9	26 52.8
7 T	0 59 59.5	13 5.0	10 19.1	21 36.3	24 48.2	23 41.0	27 24.7	28 57.1	20 17.6	17 9.4	19 16.4	26 52.6
8 F	1 3 56.1	14 4.2	10 15.9	4♌10.8	23 54.3	24 51.5	27 12.0	29 9.9	20 12.8	17 9.9	19 17.0	26 52.4
9 S	1 7 52.6	15 3.5	10 12.8	16 30.3	22 53.9	26 1.9	26 59.9	29 22.6	20 8.1	17 10.5	19 17.4	26 52.1
10 S	1 11 49.2	16 2.8	10 9.6	28 38.7	21 48.3	27 12.3	26 48.5	29 35.3	20 3.3	17 11.1	19 17.9	26 51.9
11 M	1 15 45.7	17 2.2	10 6.4	10♍39.2	20 38.7	28 22.5	26 37.7	29 48.0	19 58.6	17 11.8	19 18.3	26 51.6
12 T	1 19 42.3	18 1.6	10 3.2	22 34.3	19 26.9	29 32.8	26 27.6	0♎ 0.7	19 53.8	17 12.6	19 18.7	26 51.3
13 W	1 23 38.8	19 1.0	10 0.0	4♎26.4	18 14.7	0♐42.9	26 18.3	0 13.4	19 49.1	17 13.4	19 19.1	26 50.9
14 T	1 27 35.4	20 0.5	9 56.9	16 17.1	17 4.2	1 53.0	26 9.7	0 26.0	19 44.3	17 14.2	19 19.4	26 50.6
15 F	1 31 31.9	20 60.0	9 53.7	28 8.0	15 57.5	3 3.0	26 1.8	0 38.5	19 39.5	17 15.1	19 19.7	26 50.2
16 S	1 35 28.5	21 59.5	9 50.5	10♏ 0.9	14 56.5	4 13.0	25 54.7	0 51.1	19 34.7	17 16.0	19 20.0	26 49.8
17 S	1 39 25.1	22 59.1	9 47.3	21 57.7	14 3.0	5 22.8	25 48.4	1 3.6	19 30.0	17 17.0	19 20.2	26 49.4
18 M	1 43 21.6	23 58.7	9 44.2	4♐ 0.8	13 18.5	6 32.6	25 42.9	1 16.1	19 25.2	17 18.1	19 20.4	26 48.9
19 T	1 47 18.1	24 58.3	9 41.0	16 12.9	12 44.1	7 42.3	25 38.2	1 28.5	19 20.5	17 19.2	19 20.5	26 48.4
20 W	1 51 14.7	25 58.0	9 37.8	28 37.7	12 20.6	8 51.9	25 34.3	1 40.9	19 15.8	17 20.3	19 20.6	26 48.0
21 T	1 55 11.3	26 57.7	9 34.6	11♑18.9	12 8.2	10 1.4	25 31.3	1 53.3	19 11.1	17 21.5	19 20.7	26 47.5
22 F	1 59 7.8	27 57.4	9 31.4	24 20.4	12 7.2	11 10.9	25 29.0	2 5.6	19 6.4	17 22.8	19 20.8	26 46.9
23 S	2 3 4.4	28 57.2	9 28.3	7♒45.7	12D17.2	12 20.2	25 27.5	2 17.9	19 1.7	17 24.1	19 20.8	26 46.4
24 S	2 7 0.9	29 56.9	9 25.1	21 37.2	12 37.7	13 29.4	25 26.9	2 30.1	18 57.1	17 25.4	19R20.8	26 45.8
25 M	2 10 57.5	0♏56.7	9 21.9	5♓55.2	13 8.1	14 38.5	25D27.0	2 42.3	18 52.4	17 26.8	19 20.7	26 45.2
26 T	2 14 54.0	1 56.6	9 18.7	20 37.5	13 47.6	15 47.5	25 28.0	2 54.4	18 47.9	17 28.2	19 20.6	26 44.6
27 W	2 18 50.6	2 56.4	9 15.6	5♈38.6	14 35.4	16 56.4	25 29.8	3 6.5	18 43.3	17 29.7	19 20.5	26 44.0
28 T	2 22 47.1	3 56.3	9 12.4	20 50.3	15 30.6	18 5.2	25 32.3	3 18.6	18 38.8	17 31.3	19 20.4	26 43.4
29 F	2 26 43.7	4 56.2	9 9.2	6♉ 2.5	16 32.5	19 13.9	25 35.6	3 30.5	18 34.3	17 32.8	19 20.2	26 42.7
30 S	2 30 40.3	5 56.2	9 6.0	21 5.1	17 40.1	20 22.4	25 39.7	3 42.5	18 29.9	17 34.5	19 20.0	26 42.0
31 S	2 34 36.8	6 56.2	9 2.9	5♊49.3	18 52.7	21 30.9	25 44.5	3 54.4	18 25.5	17 36.1	19 19.7	26 41.3
						DECLINATION						
1 F	0 36 20.2	2S50.9	22N 3.2	7N36.9	14S 1.6	17S55.0	4S34.3	1N55.0	5N32.1	22S48.9	21N22.7	16N23.4
4 M	0 48 9.8	4 0.7	22 1.8	22 25.5	13 36.4	19 4.2	4 40.9	1 39.8	5 26.7	22 48.7	21 22.4	16 23.1
7 T	0 59 59.5	5 10.1	22 0.5	25 7.0	12 31.7	20 9.3	4 45.1	1 24.7	5 21.3	22 48.5	21 22.1	16 22.7
10 S	1 11 49.2	6 19.0	21 59.1	16 38.8	10 47.9	21 10.1	4 46.7	1 9.6	5 15.9	22 48.2	21 21.9	16 22.4
13 W	1 23 38.8	7 27.1	21 57.7	2 27.1	8 36.7	22 6.2	4 45.8	0 54.7	5 10.5	22 47.9	21 21.6	16 22.1
16 S	1 35 28.5	8 34.3	21 56.3	12S31.1	6 23.9	22 57.3	4 42.1	0 39.9	5 5.1	22 47.5	21 21.5	16 21.8
19 T	1 47 18.1	9 40.4	21 54.9	23 27.9	4 38.7	23 43.1	4 35.6	0 25.2	4 59.8	22 47.1	21 21.4	16 21.5
22 F	1 59 7.8	10 45.2	21 53.4	24 56.8	3 40.9	24 23.5	4 26.4	0 10.7	4 54.6	22 46.5	21 21.3	16 21.1
25 M	2 10 57.5	11 48.6	21 52.0	14 9.3	3 34.7	24 58.2	4 14.6	0S 3.6	4 49.5	22 46.0	21 21.2	16 20.8
28 T	2 22 47.1	12 50.3	21 50.6	4N36.8	4 13.0	25 26.9	4 0.2	0 17.7	4 44.6	22 45.4	21 21.3	16 20.5
31 S	2 34 36.8	13 50.2	21 49.1	21 7.3	5 24.1	25 49.6	3 43.5	0 31.6	4 39.8	22 44.7	21 21.3	16 20.3

NOVEMBER 1909

DAY	EPHEMERIS SIDEREAL TIME	☉	☊	☽	☿	♀	♂	♃	♄	♅	♆	♇
	h m s	° ′	° ′	° ′	° ′	° ′	° ′	° ′	° ′	° ′	° ′	° ′
						LONGITUDE						
1 M	2 38 33.4	7♏56.2	8♓59.7	20♊ 9.2	20♎ 9.7	22♐39.2	25♓50.1	4♎ 6.2	18♈21.1	17♑37.9	19♋19.4	26♊40.6
2 T	2 42 29.9	8 56.2	8 56.5	4♋ 1.8	21 30.3	23 47.3	25 56.4	4 18.0	18R16.8	17 39.6	19R19.1	26R39.9
3 W	2 46 26.5	9 56.3	8 53.3	17 26.9	22 54.0	24 55.4	26 3.4	4 29.7	18 12.5	17 41.4	19 18.8	26 39.1
4 T	2 50 23.0	10 56.5	8 50.1	0♌26.6	24 20.3	26 3.3	26 11.2	4 41.3	18 8.3	17 43.3	19 18.4	26 38.4
5 F	2 54 19.6	11 56.6	8 47.0	13 4.3	25 48.8	27 11.0	26 19.7	4 52.9	18 4.2	17 45.2	19 18.0	26 37.6
6 S	2 58 16.1	12 56.8	8 43.8	25 24.1	27 19.1	28 18.7	26 28.8	5 4.4	18 0.1	17 47.1	19 17.5	26 36.8
7 S	3 2 12.7	13 57.0	8 40.6	7♍30.4	28 50.8	29 26.1	26 38.6	5 15.9	17 56.0	17 49.1	19 17.0	26 36.0
8 M	3 6 9.2	14 57.3	8 37.4	19 27.6	0♏23.6	0♑33.5	26 49.2	5 27.3	17 52.1	17 51.1	19 16.5	26 35.1
9 T	3 10 5.8	15 57.6	8 34.3	1♎19.5	1 57.4	1 40.6	27 0.4	5 38.6	17 48.1	17 53.2	19 16.0	26 34.3
10 W	3 14 2.4	16 57.9	8 31.1	13 9.5	3 31.9	2 47.6	27 12.2	5 49.9	17 44.3	17 55.3	19 15.4	26 33.4
11 T	3 17 58.9	17 58.3	8 27.9	25 0.6	5 7.0	3 54.5	27 24.7	6 1.1	17 40.5	17 57.5	19 14.8	26 32.5
12 F	3 21 55.5	18 58.7	8 24.7	6♏55.1	6 42.4	5 1.2	27 37.8	6 12.2	17 36.8	17 59.7	19 14.1	26 31.6
13 S	3 25 52.0	19 59.1	8 21.5	18 55.1	8 18.2	6 7.6	27 51.6	6 23.2	17 33.1	18 1.9	19 13.5	26 30.7
14 S	3 29 48.6	20 59.5	8 18.4	1♐ 2.2	9 54.1	7 14.0	28 5.9	6 34.2	17 29.6	18 4.2	19 12.7	26 29.8
15 M	3 33 45.1	21 60.0	8 15.2	13 17.9	11 30.1	8 20.1	28 20.9	6 45.1	17 26.1	18 6.5	19 12.0	26 28.9
16 T	3 37 41.7	23 0.5	8 12.0	25 43.9	13 6.2	9 26.0	28 36.4	6 55.9	17 22.7	18 8.9	19 11.2	26 27.9
17 W	3 41 38.2	24 1.0	8 8.8	8♑22.0	14 42.2	10 31.7	28 52.5	7 6.6	17 19.3	18 11.3	19 10.4	26 26.9
18 T	3 45 34.8	25 1.6	8 5.7	21 14.0	16 18.2	11 37.2	29 9.2	7 17.2	17 16.1	18 13.7	19 9.6	26 26.0
19 F	3 49 31.4	26 2.1	8 2.5	4♒22.0	17 54.1	12 42.4	29 26.5	7 27.8	17 12.9	18 16.2	19 8.8	26 25.0
20 S	3 53 27.9	27 2.7	7 59.3	17 47.6	19 29.9	13 47.5	29 44.2	7 38.2	17 9.8	18 18.7	19 7.9	26 24.0
21 S	3 57 24.5	28 3.3	7 56.1	1♓32.3	21 5.5	14 52.2	0♈ 2.5	7 48.6	17 6.8	18 21.3	19 7.0	26 22.9
22 M	4 1 21.0	29 3.9	7 52.9	15 36.5	22 41.0	15 56.8	0 21.3	7 58.9	17 3.9	18 23.9	19 6.0	26 21.9
23 T	4 5 17.6	0♐ 4.6	7 49.8	29 58.9	24 16.4	17 1.0	0 40.6	8 9.1	17 1.1	18 26.5	19 5.0	26 20.9
24 W	4 9 14.2	1 5.2	7 46.6	14♈36.6	25 51.6	18 5.0	1 0.4	8 19.2	16 58.3	18 29.2	19 4.0	26 19.8
25 T	4 13 10.7	2 5.9	7 43.4	29 24.7	27 26.7	19 8.7	1 20.7	8 29.2	16 55.7	18 31.9	19 3.0	26 18.8
26 F	4 17 7.3	3 6.6	7 40.2	14♉16.4	29 1.6	20 12.1	1 41.3	8 39.1	16 53.1	18 34.6	19 2.0	26 17.7
27 S	4 21 3.8	4 7.3	7 37.1	29 4.1	0♐36.4	21 15.2	2 2.5	8 48.9	16 50.7	18 37.3	19 0.9	26 16.6
28 S	4 25 0.4	5 8.1	7 33.9	13♊40.4	2 11.1	22 18.0	2 24.1	8 58.6	16 48.3	18 40.1	18 59.8	26 15.5
29 M	4 28 56.9	6 8.8	7 30.7	27 58.7	3 45.6	23 20.5	2 46.0	9 8.2	16 46.0	18 43.0	18 58.6	26 14.4
30 T	4 32 53.5	7 9.6	7 27.5	11♋54.7	5 20.1	24 22.6	3 8.4	9 17.8	16 43.9	18 45.8	18 57.5	26 13.3
						DECLINATION						
1 M	2 38 33.4	14S 9.8	21N48.6	24N12.8	5S53.0	25S55.8	3S37.4	0S36.2	4N38.3	22S44.4	21N21.3	16N20.2
4 T	2 50 23.0	15 7.0	21 47.1	24 8.1	7 30.7	26 10.3	3 17.7	0 49.8	4 33.8	22 43.7	21 21.4	16 19.9
7 S	3 2 12.7	16 2.1	21 45.7	13 36.8	9 18.1	26 18.6	2 56.0	1 3.2	4 29.5	22 42.9	21 21.6	16 19.7
10 W	3 14 2.4	16 54.7	21 44.2	1S15.9	11 9.3	26 20.7	2 32.4	1 16.3	4 25.5	22 42.0	21 21.8	16 19.4
13 S	3 25 52.0	17 44.8	21 42.7	15 50.7	13 0.3	26 16.5	2 6.9	1 29.1	4 21.7	22 41.1	21 22.0	16 19.2
16 T	3 37 41.7	18 32.1	21 41.2	25 2.6	14 48.2	26 6.3	1 39.8	1 41.6	4 18.2	22 40.1	21 22.3	16 19.0
19 F	3 49 31.4	19 16.4	21 39.6	23 28.6	16 31.0	25 50.1	1 11.0	1 53.8	4 15.0	22 39.1	21 22.6	16 18.8
22 M	4 1 21.0	19 57.6	21 38.1	10 29.8	18 7.2	25 28.2	0 40.9	2 5.6	4 12.1	22 38.0	21 23.0	16 18.6
25 T	4 13 10.7	20 35.5	21 36.6	8N12.9	19 36.0	25 0.7	0 9.4	2 17.1	4 9.6	22 36.9	21 23.4	16 18.5
28 S	4 25 0.4	21 10.0	21 35.0	23 1.5	20 56.2	24 28.0	0N23.3	2 28.2	4 7.4	22 35.7	21 23.8	16 18.3

DECEMBER 1909

DAY	EPHEMERIS SIDEREAL TIME	☉	☊	☽	☿	♀	♂	♃	♄	♅	♆	♇
						LONGITUDE						
1 W	4 36 50.1	8♐10.4	7♓24.4	25♋25.9	6♐54.5	25♑24.4	3♈31.2	9♎27.2	16♈41.8	18♑48.7	18♋56.3	26♊12.2
2 T	4 40 46.6	9 11.2	7 21.2	8♌32.5	8 28.8	26 25.8	3 54.4	9 36.5	16R39.8	18 51.6	18R55.1	26R11.1
3 F	4 44 43.2	10 12.1	7 18.0	21 16.2	10 3.1	27 26.8	4 18.0	9 45.7	16 38.0	18 54.6	18 53.9	26 9.9
4 S	4 48 39.7	11 13.0	7 14.8	3♍40.3	11 37.3	28 27.5	4 41.9	9 54.7	16 36.2	18 57.5	18 52.6	26 8.8
5 S	4 52 36.3	12 13.8	7 11.7	15 48.8	13 11.5	29 27.7	5 6.2	10 3.7	16 34.5	19 0.5	18 51.3	26 7.7
6 M	4 56 32.8	13 14.8	7 8.5	27 46.4	14 45.7	0♒27.6	5 30.9	10 12.5	16 33.0	19 3.6	18 50.0	26 6.5
7 T	5 0 29.4	14 15.7	7 5.3	9♎37.8	16 19.9	1 27.0	5 55.9	10 21.3	16 31.5	19 6.6	18 48.7	26 5.4
8 W	5 4 26.0	15 16.7	7 2.1	21 27.6	17 54.1	2 26.0	6 21.2	10 29.9	16 30.2	19 9.7	18 47.4	26 4.2
9 T	5 8 22.5	16 17.7	6 59.0	3♏20.0	19 28.4	3 24.5	6 46.9	10 38.4	16 28.9	19 12.8	18 46.0	26 3.0
10 F	5 12 19.1	17 18.6	6 55.8	15 18.6	21 2.7	4 22.5	7 12.9	10 46.8	16 27.8	19 16.0	18 44.6	26 1.9
11 S	5 16 15.6	18 19.7	6 52.6	27 26.4	22 37.1	5 20.1	7 39.2	10 55.0	16 26.7	19 19.1	18 43.2	26 0.7
12 S	5 20 12.2	19 20.7	6 49.4	9♐45.8	24 11.5	6 17.1	8 5.8	11 3.2	16 25.8	19 22.3	18 41.8	25 59.5
13 M	5 24 8.8	20 21.7	6 46.2	22 18.2	25 46.1	7 13.6	8 32.7	11 11.2	16 25.0	19 25.5	18 40.4	25 58.3
14 T	5 28 5.3	21 22.8	6 43.1	5♑ 4.4	27 20.7	8 9.5	8 59.9	11 19.1	16 24.3	19 28.8	18 38.9	25 57.2
15 W	5 32 1.9	22 23.9	6 39.9	18 4.6	28 55.4	9 4.8	9 27.4	11 26.8	16 23.7	19 32.0	18 37.4	25 56.0
16 T	5 35 58.4	23 24.9	6 36.7	1♒18.3	0♑30.3	9 59.6	9 55.2	11 34.4	16 23.2	19 35.3	18 36.0	25 54.8
17 F	5 39 55.0	24 26.0	6 33.5	14 45.1	2 5.2	10 53.6	10 23.3	11 41.9	16 22.9	19 38.6	18 34.4	25 53.6
18 S	5 43 51.6	25 27.1	6 30.4	28 23.9	3 40.2	11 47.1	10 51.6	11 49.2	16 22.6	19 41.9	18 32.9	25 52.4
19 S	5 47 48.1	26 28.2	6 27.2	12♓13.9	5 15.3	12 39.8	11 20.2	11 56.4	16 22.4	19 45.2	18 31.4	25 51.2
20 M	5 51 44.7	27 29.3	6 24.0	26 14.0	6 50.5	13 31.8	11 49.0	12 3.5	16 22.4	19 48.6	18 29.8	25 50.0
21 T	5 55 41.2	28 30.4	6 20.8	10♈23.0	8 25.7	14 23.1	12 18.1	12 10.4	16D22.5	19 51.9	18 28.3	25 48.9
22 W	5 59 37.8	29 31.5	6 17.7	24 39.1	10 1.0	15 13.6	12 47.4	12 17.2	16 22.7	19 55.3	18 26.7	25 47.7
23 T	6 3 34.3	0♑32.6	6 14.5	9♉ 0.0	11 36.2	16 3.3	13 17.0	12 23.8	16 23.0	19 58.7	18 25.1	25 46.5
24 F	6 7 30.9	1 33.7	6 11.3	23 22.5	13 11.5	16 52.1	13 46.7	12 30.3	16 23.4	20 2.1	18 23.5	25 45.3
25 S	6 11 27.4	2 34.8	6 8.1	7♊42.6	14 46.6	17 40.0	14 16.7	12 36.6	16 23.9	20 5.5	18 21.9	25 44.1
26 S	6 15 24.0	3 36.0	6 5.0	21 55.8	16 21.6	18 27.0	14 46.9	12 42.8	16 24.5	20 9.0	18 20.3	25 43.0
27 M	6 19 20.6	4 37.1	6 1.8	5♋57.4	17 56.3	19 13.1	15 17.2	12 48.8	16 25.3	20 12.4	18 18.6	25 41.8
28 T	6 23 17.1	5 38.2	5 58.6	19 43.3	19 30.7	19 58.1	15 47.8	12 54.7	16 26.1	20 15.9	18 17.0	25 40.6
29 W	6 27 13.7	6 39.3	5 55.4	3♌10.2	21 4.7	20 42.1	16 18.5	13 0.4	16 27.1	20 19.4	18 15.3	25 39.5
30 T	6 31 10.2	7 40.5	5 52.2	16 16.6	22 38.1	21 25.1	16 49.5	13 6.0	16 28.1	20 22.9	18 13.7	25 38.3
31 F	6 35 6.8	8 41.6	5 49.1	29 2.5	24 10.8	22 6.9	17 20.6	13 11.4	16 29.3	20 26.4	18 12.0	25 37.1
						DECLINATION						
1 W	4 36 50.1	21S40.9	21N33.4	24N55.9	22S 7.4	23S50.2	0N57.1	2S38.9	4N 5.6	22S34.5	21N24.3	16N18.2
4 S	4 48 39.7	22 8.1	21 31.9	15 4.8	23 8.6	23 7.9	1 31.8	2 49.2	4 4.2	22 33.3	21 24.8	16 18.2
7 T	5 0 29.4	22 31.4	21 30.3	0 18.3	23 59.4	22 21.3	2 7.3	2 59.1	4 3.1	22 32.0	21 25.3	16 18.1
10 F	5 12 19.1	22 50.8	21 28.7	14S31.3	24 39.0	21 30.8	2 43.7	3 8.5	4 2.4	22 30.6	21 25.8	16 18.0
13 M	5 24 8.8	23 6.1	21 27.1	24 34.6	25 6.8	20 36.8	3 20.7	3 17.5	4 2.1	22 29.3	21 26.4	16 18.0
16 T	5 35 58.4	23 17.3	21 25.5	24 1.6	25 22.2	19 39.8	3 58.4	3 26.0	4 2.1	22 27.8	21 27.0	16 18.0
19 S	5 47 48.1	23 24.3	21 23.9	11 48.7	25 24.7	18 40.2	4 36.7	3 34.0	4 2.6	22 26.4	21 27.7	16 18.1
22 W	5 59 37.8	23 27.1	21 22.2	6N14.1	25 13.7	17 38.6	5 15.4	3 41.5	4 3.4	22 24.9	21 28.3	16 18.1
25 S	6 11 27.4	23 25.6	21 20.6	21 38.2	24 49.0	16 35.4	5 54.4	3 48.4	4 4.7	22 23.4	21 29.0	16 18.2
28 T	6 23 17.1	23 19.9	21 18.9	25 29.4	24 10.3	15 31.3	6 33.8	3 54.8	4 6.3	22 21.9	21 29.6	16 18.3
31 F	6 35 6.8	23 10.0	21 17.3	16 38.2	23 18.0	14 26.7	7 13.3	4 0.6	4 8.3	22 20.3	21 30.3	16 18.5

JANUARY 1910

DAY	EPHEMERIS SIDEREAL TIME	☉	☊	☽	☿	♀	♂	♃	♄	♅	♆	♇
	h m s	° ′	° ′	° ′	° ′	° ′	° ′	° ′	° ′	° ′	° ′	° ′
						LONGITUDE						
1 S	6 39 3.4	9♑42.8	5♊45.9	11♍29.5	25♑42.5	22♒47.6	17♈51.9	13♎16.7	16♈30.6	20♑29.9	18♋10.3	25♊36.0
2 S	6 42 59.9	10 43.9	5 42.7	23 40.6	27 13.1	23 27.0	18 23.4	13 21.8	16 32.0	20 33.4	18R 8.7	25R34.9
3 M	6 46 56.5	11 45.1	5 39.5	5♎39.6	28 42.3	24 5.2	18 55.0	13 26.7	16 33.5	20 36.9	18 7.0	25 33.7
4 T	6 50 53.0	12 46.2	5 36.4	17 31.5	0♒ 9.8	24 42.1	19 26.8	13 31.5	16 35.1	20 40.4	18 5.3	25 32.6
5 W	6 54 49.6	13 47.4	5 33.2	29 21.1	1 35.1	25 17.6	19 58.7	13 36.1	16 36.8	20 44.0	18 3.6	25 31.5
6 T	6 58 46.2	14 48.6	5 30.0	11♏13.8	2 58.0	25 51.7	20 30.9	13 40.5	16 38.6	20 47.5	18 1.9	25 30.4
7 F	7 2 42.7	15 49.7	5 26.8	23 14.4	4 17.9	26 24.4	21 3.1	13 44.7	16 40.6	20 51.1	18 0.2	25 29.2
8 S	7 6 39.3	16 50.9	5 23.7	5♐27.3	5 34.2	26 55.5	21 35.5	13 48.8	16 42.6	20 54.6	17 58.5	25 28.1
9 S	7 10 35.8	17 52.1	5 20.5	17 56.0	6 46.5	27 25.0	22 8.1	13 52.7	16 44.8	20 58.2	17 56.8	25 27.1
10 M	7 14 32.4	18 53.2	5 17.3	0♑42.9	7 53.9	27 52.9	22 40.8	13 56.5	16 47.0	21 1.7	17 55.1	25 26.0
11 T	7 18 29.0	19 54.4	5 14.1	13 49.1	8 55.7	28 19.1	23 13.7	14 0.0	16 49.4	21 5.3	17 53.4	25 24.9
12 W	7 22 25.5	20 55.5	5 10.9	13.9	9 51.2	28 43.5	23 46.7	14 3.4	16 51.8	21 8.8	17 51.7	25 23.8
13 T	7 26 22.0	21 56.7	5 7.8	10♒55.3	10 39.4	29 6.1	24 19.8	14 6.6	16 54.4	21 12.4	17 50.0	25 22.8
14 F	7 30 18.6	22 57.8	5 4.6	24 50.0	11 19.5	29 26.8	24 53.0	14 9.7	16 57.1	21 16.0	17 48.3	25 21.8
15 S	7 34 15.2	23 59.0	5 1.4	8♓53.9	11 50.6	29 45.4	25 26.4	14 12.5	16 59.8	21 19.5	17 46.6	25 20.7
16 S	7 38 11.7	25 0.1	4 58.2	23 2.9	12 11.9	0♓ 2.1	25 59.9	14 15.2	17 2.7	21 23.1	17 45.0	25 19.7
17 M	7 42 8.3	26 1.2	4 55.1	7♈13.5	12 22.5	0 16.6	26 33.5	14 17.6	17 5.7	21 26.6	17 43.3	25 18.7
18 T	7 46 4.8	27 2.3	4 51.9	21 23.1	12R21.9	0 28.9	27 7.3	14 19.9	17 8.7	21 30.2	17 41.6	25 17.7
19 W	7 50 1.4	28 3.4	4 48.7	5♉29.7	12 9.7	0 39.0	27 41.1	14 22.1	17 11.9	21 33.7	17 39.9	25 16.8
20 T	7 53 58.0	29 4.4	4 45.5	19 32.4	11 45.8	0 46.8	28 15.1	14 24.0	17 15.2	21 37.2	17 38.3	25 15.8
21 F	7 57 54.5	0♒ 5.5	4 42.4	3♊30.2	11 10.5	0 52.2	28 49.1	14 25.7	17 18.6	21 40.8	17 36.6	25 14.8
22 S	8 1 51.1	1 6.5	4 39.2	17 22.1	10 24.5	0 55.3	29 23.3	14 27.3	17 22.0	21 44.3	17 35.0	25 13.9
23 S	8 5 47.6	2 7.5	4 36.0	1♋ 6.9	9 28.9	0 55.8	29 57.5	14 28.6	17 25.6	21 47.8	17 33.3	25 13.0
24 M	8 9 44.2	3 8.5	4 32.8	14 42.7	8 25.2	0R53.9	0♉31.9	14 29.8	17 29.2	21 51.3	17 31.7	25 12.1
25 T	8 13 40.8	4 9.5	4 29.7	28 7.1	7 15.3	0 49.4	1 6.3	14 30.8	17 33.0	21 54.8	17 30.1	25 11.2
26 W	8 17 37.3	5 10.5	4 26.5	11♌18.1	6 1.3	0 42.4	1 40.8	14 31.6	17 36.8	21 58.3	17 28.5	25 10.3
27 T	8 21 33.9	6 11.5	4 23.3	24 13.9	4 45.5	0 32.9	2 15.4	14 32.2	17 40.7	22 1.8	17 26.9	25 9.4
28 F	8 25 30.4	7 12.4	4 20.1	6♍53.7	3 30.2	0 20.8	2 50.1	14 32.7	17 44.8	22 5.3	17 25.3	25 8.6
29 S	8 29 27.0	8 13.3	4 17.0	19 17.8	2 17.4	0 6.3	3 24.8	14 32.9	17 48.9	22 8.7	17 23.8	25 7.8
30 S	8 33 23.5	9 14.3	4 13.8	1♎27.8	1 8.9	29♒49.2	3 59.7	14 33.0	17 53.1	22 12.2	17 22.2	25 7.0
31 M	8 37 20.1	10 15.2	4 10.6	13 26.6	0 6.5	29 29.8	4 34.6	14R32.8	17 57.4	22 15.6	17 20.7	25 6.2
						DECLINATION						
1 S	6 39 3.4	23S 5.8	21N16.7	12N 3.0	22S57.7	14S 5.2	7N26.5	4S 2.4	4N 9.0	22S19.8	21N30.5	16N18.5
4 T	6 50 53.0	22 50.3	21 15.0	3S13.6	21 48.9	13 1.1	8 6.1	4 7.5	4 11.5	22 18.2	21 31.2	16 18.7
7 F	7 2 42.7	22 30.8	21 13.4	17 23.9	20 30.3	11 58.0	8 45.8	4 11.9	4 14.4	22 16.6	21 31.9	16 18.9
10 M	7 14 32.4	22 7.2	21 11.7	25 32.2	19 6.3	10 56.7	9 25.5	4 15.8	4 17.6	22 15.0	21 32.6	16 19.1
13 T	7 26 22.0	21 39.8	21 10.0	21 56.7	17 43.4	9 58.1	10 5.1	4 19.0	4 21.2	22 13.3	21 33.3	16 19.4
16 S	7 38 11.7	21 8.6	21 8.3	7 16.0	16 31.0	9 3.0	10 44.6	4 21.5	4 25.1	22 11.7	21 34.0	16 19.6
19 W	7 50 1.4	20 33.7	21 6.5	10N53.3	15 39.3	8 12.3	11 23.8	4 23.5	4 29.3	22 10.1	21 34.7	16 19.9
22 S	8 1 51.1	19 55.3	21 4.8	23 50.6	15 16.6	7 27.3	12 2.8	4 24.8	4 33.9	22 8.4	21 35.4	16 20.3
25 T	8 13 40.8	19 13.7	21 3.0	24 28.8	15 24.3	6 48.9	12 41.3	4 25.4	4 38.7	22 6.8	21 36.1	16 20.6
28 F	8 25 30.4	18 28.8	21 1.3	13 40.5	15 55.5	6 18.2	13 19.5	4 25.4	4 43.9	22 5.1	21 36.8	16 21.0
31 M	8 37 20.1	17 40.9	20 59.5	1S38.9	16 38.7	5 56.1	13 57.1	4 24.7	4 49.3	22 3.5	21 37.4	16 21.4

FEBRUARY 1910

DAY	EPHEMERIS SIDEREAL TIME	☉	☊	☽	☿	♀	♂	♃	♄	♅	♆	♇
						LONGITUDE						
1 T	8 41 16.6	11♒16.0	4♊ 7.4	25♎18.0	29♑11.0	29♒ 8.0	5♉ 9.6	14♎32.5	18♈ 1.7	22♑19.0	17♋19.1	25♊ 5.4
2 W	8 45 13.2	12 16.9	4 4.2	7♏ 6.8	28R23.5	28R44.1	5 44.6	14R31.9	18 6.2	22 22.4	17R17.6	25R 4.6
3 T	8 49 9.8	13 17.8	4 1.1	18 58.3	27 44.3	28 17.9	6 19.8	14 31.2	18 10.7	22 25.8	17 16.1	25 3.9
4 F	8 53 6.3	14 18.6	3 57.9	0♐57.9	27 13.7	27 49.8	6 55.0	14 30.3	18 15.3	22 29.2	17 14.6	25 3.2
5 S	8 57 2.9	15 19.5	3 54.7	13 11.1	26 51.5	27 19.9	7 30.2	14 29.2	18 20.1	22 32.5	17 13.2	25 2.4
6 S	9 0 59.4	16 20.3	3 51.5	25 42.7	26 37.6	26 48.2	8 5.6	14 27.9	18 24.8	22 35.9	17 11.7	25 1.8
7 M	9 4 56.0	17 21.1	3 48.4	8♑36.6	26 31.7	26 15.1	8 41.0	14 26.4	18 29.7	22 39.2	17 10.3	25 1.1
8 T	9 8 52.5	18 21.9	3 45.2	21 54.9	26D33.3	25 40.8	9 16.5	14 24.8	18 34.7	22 42.5	17 8.9	25 0.4
9 W	9 12 49.1	19 22.7	3 42.0	5♒37.8	26 41.9	25 5.3	9 52.0	14 22.9	18 39.7	22 45.8	17 7.5	24 59.8
10 T	9 16 45.6	20 23.4	3 38.8	19 42.8	26 57.2	24 29.0	10 27.6	14 20.9	18 44.8	22 49.0	17 6.1	24 59.2
11 F	9 20 42.2	21 24.1	3 35.6	4♓ 5.1	27 18.5	23 52.2	11 3.2	14 18.6	18 50.0	22 52.3	17 4.8	24 58.6
12 S	9 24 38.8	22 24.8	3 32.5	18 38.0	27 45.5	23 15.0	11 39.0	14 16.2	18 55.2	22 55.5	17 3.5	24 58.0
13 S	9 28 35.3	23 25.5	3 29.3	3♈14.3	28 17.6	22 37.7	12 14.7	14 13.6	19 0.6	22 58.7	17 2.2	24 57.5
14 M	9 32 31.9	24 26.1	3 26.1	17 47.2	28 54.5	22 0.5	12 50.6	14 10.8	19 6.0	23 1.8	17 0.9	24 56.9
15 T	9 36 28.4	25 26.8	3 22.9	2♉11.6	29 35.9	21 23.8	13 26.5	14 7.8	19 11.4	23 5.0	16 59.6	24 56.4
16 W	9 40 25.0	26 27.4	3 19.8	16 24.2	0♒21.2	20 47.7	14 2.4	14 4.7	19 17.0	23 8.1	16 58.4	24 55.9
17 T	9 44 21.5	27 27.9	3 16.6	0♊23.6	1 10.3	20 12.6	14 38.4	14 1.3	19 22.6	23 11.2	16 57.2	24 55.5
18 F	9 48 18.1	28 28.4	3 13.4	14 9.9	2 2.7	19 38.5	15 14.4	13 57.8	19 28.3	23 14.3	16 56.0	24 55.0
19 S	9 52 14.6	29 28.9	3 10.2	27 43.8	2 58.3	19 5.9	15 50.5	13 54.2	19 34.0	23 17.3	16 54.8	24 54.6
20 S	9 56 11.2	0♓29.4	3 7.0	11♋ 6.2	3 56.8	18 34.7	16 26.6	13 50.3	19 39.8	23 20.3	16 53.7	24 54.2
21 M	10 0 7.7	1 29.8	3 3.9	24 17.8	4 58.0	18 5.3	17 2.7	13 46.3	19 45.7	23 23.3	16 52.6	24 53.8
22 T	10 4 4.3	2 30.3	3 0.7	7♌18.7	6 1.8	17 37.8	17 38.9	13 42.1	19 51.7	23 26.3	16 51.5	24 53.4
23 W	10 8 0.9	3 30.6	2 57.5	20 8.6	7 7.8	17 12.3	18 15.1	13 37.8	19 57.7	23 29.2	16 50.4	24 53.1
24 T	10 11 57.4	4 31.0	2 54.3	2♍47.0	8 16.0	16 49.0	18 51.4	13 33.2	20 3.7	23 32.1	16 49.4	24 52.8
25 F	10 15 54.0	5 31.3	2 51.2	15 13.8	9 26.3	16 27.9	19 27.6	13 28.6	20 9.9	23 35.0	16 48.4	24 52.5
26 S	10 19 50.5	6 31.6	2 48.0	27 28.9	10 38.5	16 9.2	20 4.0	13 23.8	20 16.0	23 37.8	16 47.4	24 52.2
27 S	10 23 47.1	7 31.9	2 44.8	9♎33.4	11 52.6	15 52.9	20 40.3	13 18.8	20 22.3	23 40.6	16 46.5	24 51.9
28 M	10 27 43.6	8 32.1	2 41.6	21 29.1	13 8.3	15 39.1	21 16.7	13 13.6	20 28.6	23 43.4	16 45.5	24 51.7
						DECLINATION						
1 T	8 41 16.6	17S24.4	20N58.9	6S46.6	16S53.9	5S50.8	14N 9.5	4S24.3	4N51.2	22S 2.9	21N37.7	16N21.5
4 F	8 53 6.3	16 32.8	20 57.2	20 1.6	17 38.0	5 41.2	14 46.4	4 22.8	4 57.0	22 1.3	21 38.3	16 21.9
7 M	9 4 56.0	15 38.6	20 55.4	25 58.9	18 16.2	5 41.0	15 22.7	4 20.6	5 3.1	21 59.7	21 38.9	16 22.4
10 T	9 16 45.6	14 41.9	20 53.6	19 30.9	18 45.7	5 50.0	15 58.3	4 17.7	5 9.4	21 58.1	21 39.5	16 22.8
13 S	9 28 35.3	13 43.1	20 51.8	2 43.3	19 5.1	6 7.1	16 33.2	4 14.2	5 15.9	21 56.6	21 40.1	16 23.3
16 W	9 40 25.0	12 42.3	20 50.0	15N19.7	19 13.6	6 30.9	17 7.3	4 10.1	5 22.7	21 55.1	21 40.6	16 23.8
19 S	9 52 14.6	11 39.6	20 48.1	25 30.2	19 10.7	6 59.6	17 40.5	4 5.4	5 29.6	21 53.6	21 41.2	16 24.4
22 T	10 4 4.3	10 35.3	20 46.3	22 48.3	18 56.2	7 31.2	18 12.8	4 0.1	5 36.8	21 52.1	21 41.7	16 24.9
25 F	10 15 54.0	9 29.5	20 44.4	10 18.7	18 29.9	8 3.8	18 44.2	3 54.3	5 44.1	21 50.7	21 42.1	16 25.5
28 M	10 27 43.6	8 22.5	20 42.6	5S21.4	17 51.8	8 35.7	19 14.6	3 47.9	5 51.5	21 49.3	21 42.6	16 26.0

DAY	EPHEMERIS SIDEREAL TIME	☉	☊	☽	☿	♀	♂	♃	♄	♅	♆	♇
	h m s	° ′	° ′	° ′	° ′	° ′	° ′	° ′	° ′	° ′	° ′	° ′
						LONGITUDE						
1 T	10 31 40.2	9♓32.3	2♊38.5	3♏18.9	14♒25.7	15♒27.7	21♉53.1	13♎ 8.4	20♈34.9	23♑46.1	16♋44.6	24♊51.5
2 W	10 35 36.7	10 32.5	2 35.3	15 6.5	15 44.7	15R18.9	22 29.6	13R 2.9	20 41.3	23 48.8	16R43.8	24R51.3
3 T	10 39 33.3	11 32.6	2 32.1	26 56.6	17 5.1	15 12.5	23 6.1	12 57.4	20 47.8	23 51.5	16 42.9	24 51.1
4 F	10 43 29.8	12 32.8	2 28.9	8♐54.2	18 27.0	15 8.7	23 42.6	12 51.7	20 54.3	23 54.2	16 42.1	24 51.0
5 S	10 47 26.4	13 32.9	2 25.7	21 5.1	19 50.4	15 7.2	24 19.1	12 45.8	21 0.8	23 56.8	16 41.3	24 50.9
6 S	10 51 22.9	14 33.0	2 22.6	3♑34.5	21 15.0	15D 8.3	24 55.7	12 39.8	21 7.4	23 59.3	16 40.6	24 50.8
7 M	10 55 19.5	15 33.0	2 19.4	16 27.3	22 41.0	15 11.7	25 32.3	12 33.7	21 14.1	24 1.9	16 39.9	24 50.7
8 T	10 59 16.1	16 33.1	2 16.2	29 47.1	24 8.3	15 17.4	26 8.9	12 27.5	21 20.8	24 4.4	16 39.2	24 50.7
9 W	11 3 12.6	17 33.1	2 13.0	13♒35.5	25 36.9	15 25.4	26 45.5	12 21.2	21 27.6	24 6.8	16 38.5	24 50.6
10 T	11 7 9.2	18 33.0	2 9.8	27 51.2	27 6.7	15 35.6	27 22.2	12 14.7	21 34.3	24 9.3	16 37.9	24 50.6
11 F	11 11 5.7	19 33.0	2 6.7	12♓29.8	28 37.8	15 48.0	27 58.9	12 8.1	21 41.2	24 11.6	16 37.3	24D50.6
12 S	11 15 2.3	20 32.9	2 3.5	27 23.9	0♓10.1	16 2.5	28 35.7	12 1.5	21 48.1	24 14.0	16 36.8	24 50.7
13 S	11 18 58.8	21 32.8	2 0.3	12♈24.5	1 43.6	16 19.0	29 12.4	11 54.7	21 55.0	24 16.3	16 36.2	24 50.8
14 M	11 22 55.4	22 32.6	1 57.1	27 22.0	3 18.3	16 37.4	29 49.2	11 47.8	22 2.0	24 18.6	16 35.7	24 50.8
15 T	11 26 51.9	23 32.4	1 54.0	12♉ 8.4	4 54.2	16 57.7	0♊26.0	11 40.8	22 9.0	24 20.8	16 35.3	24 50.9
16 W	11 30 48.5	24 32.2	1 50.8	26 38.0	6 31.3	17 19.9	1 2.8	11 33.8	22 16.0	24 23.0	16 34.8	24 51.1
17 T	11 34 45.0	25 31.9	1 47.6	10♊47.7	8 9.7	17 43.8	1 39.6	11 26.6	22 23.1	24 25.1	16 34.4	24 51.2
18 F	11 38 41.6	26 31.6	1 44.4	24 36.9	9 49.2	18 9.5	2 16.5	11 19.4	22 30.2	24 27.2	16 34.1	24 51.4
19 S	11 42 38.2	27 31.3	1 41.3	8♋ 6.6	11 30.0	18 36.7	2 53.4	11 12.1	22 37.3	24 29.3	16 33.7	24 51.6
20 S	11 46 34.7	28 30.9	1 38.1	21 18.7	13 12.1	19 5.6	3 30.3	11 4.8	22 44.5	24 31.3	16 33.4	24 51.8
21 M	11 50 31.3	29 30.5	1 34.9	4♌15.4	14 55.4	19 36.0	4 7.2	10 57.4	22 51.7	24 33.3	16 33.2	24 52.1
22 T	11 54 27.8	0♈30.0	1 31.7	16 58.8	16 39.9	20 7.8	4 44.1	10 49.9	22 58.9	24 35.2	16 32.9	24 52.3
23 W	11 58 24.4	1 29.5	1 28.5	29 30.5	18 25.7	20 41.1	5 21.0	10 42.4	23 6.2	24 37.1	16 32.7	24 52.6
24 T	12 2 20.9	2 29.0	1 25.4	11♍52.0	20 12.8	21 15.7	5 58.0	10 34.8	23 13.5	24 38.9	16 32.6	24 52.9
25 F	12 6 17.5	3 28.4	1 22.2	24 4.2	22 1.3	21 51.7	6 34.9	10 27.2	23 20.8	24 40.7	16 32.4	24 53.3
26 S	12 10 14.0	4 27.8	1 19.0	6♎ 8.2	23 51.0	22 28.9	7 11.9	10 19.6	23 28.1	24 42.5	16 32.3	24 53.6
27 S	12 14 10.6	5 27.2	1 15.8	18 5.2	25 42.1	23 7.3	7 48.8	10 11.9	23 35.5	24 44.2	16 32.3	24 54.0
28 M	12 18 7.1	6 26.5	1 12.7	29 56.6	27 34.4	23 46.9	8 25.8	10 4.3	23 42.9	24 45.9	16 32.2	24 54.4
29 T	12 22 3.7	7 25.8	1 9.5	11♏44.8	29 28.1	24 27.6	9 2.8	9 56.5	23 50.3	24 47.5	16 32.2	24 54.8
30 W	12 26 0.2	8 25.1	1 6.3	23 32.5	1♈23.1	25 9.4	9 39.8	9 48.8	23 57.8	24 49.1	16D32.3	24 55.3
31 T	12 29 56.8	9 24.3	1 3.1	5♐23.3	3 19.5	25 52.2	10 16.8	9 41.1	24 5.2	24 50.6	16 32.3	24 55.7
						DECLINATION						
1 T	10 31 40.2	7S59.8	20N42.0	10S21.8	17S36.5	8S45.9	19N24.4	3S45.7	5N54.1	21S48.8	21N42.7	16N26.2
4 F	10 43 29.8	6 51.3	20 40.1	22 25.3	16 42.6	9 14.7	19 53.4	3 38.7	6 1.7	21 47.5	21 43.1	16 26.8
7 M	10 55 19.5	5 42.0	20 38.2	25 58.2	15 37.1	9 39.9	20 21.2	3 31.3	6 9.5	21 46.3	21 43.5	16 27.4
10 T	11 7 9.2	4 31.9	20 36.3	16 56.0	14 20.0	10 0.9	20 47.8	3 23.5	6 17.4	21 45.0	21 43.8	16 28.0
13 S	11 18 58.8	3 21.3	20 34.4	1N25.9	12 51.5	10 17.2	21 13.3	3 15.3	6 25.5	21 43.9	21 44.1	16 28.6
16 W	11 30 48.5	2 10.3	20 32.5	19 4.6	11 11.7	10 28.4	21 37.5	3 6.8	6 33.6	21 42.8	21 44.4	16 29.2
19 S	11 42 38.2	0 59.2	20 30.6	26 18.2	9 20.8	10 34.5	22 0.4	2 58.1	6 41.8	21 41.7	21 44.6	16 29.9
22 T	11 54 27.8	0N11.9	20 28.7	20 27.2	7 19.0	10 35.3	22 22.0	2 49.2	6 50.0	21 40.8	21 44.8	16 30.5
25 F	12 6 17.5	1 22.9	20 26.8	6 36.3	5 6.8	10 30.8	22 42.2	2 40.2	6 58.3	21 39.9	21 45.0	16 31.1
28 M	12 18 7.1	2 33.5	20 24.8	9S 6.2	2 44.5	10 20.9	23 1.0	2 31.0	7 6.6	21 39.0	21 45.1	16 31.8
31 T	12 29 56.8	3 43.7	20 22.9	21 45.4	0 13.0	10 5.7	23 18.4	2 21.9	7 15.0	21 38.3	21 45.2	16 32.4

APRIL 1910

DAY	EPHEMERIS SIDEREAL TIME	☉	☊	☽	☿	♀	♂	♃	♄	♅	♆	♇
						LONGITUDE						
1 F	12 33 53.4	10♈23.5	0♊59.9	17♐21.3	5♈17.1	26♒36.0	10♊53.9	9♎33.4	24♈12.7	24♑52.1	16♋32.4	24♊56.2
2 S	12 37 49.9	11 22.7	0 56.8	29 31.4	7 16.0	27 20.8	11 30.9	9R25.6	24 20.2	24 53.5	16 32.6	24 56.7
3 S	12 41 46.4	12 21.8	0 53.6	11♑58.4	9 16.0	28 6.4	12 7.9	9 17.9	24 27.7	24 54.9	16 32.7	24 57.2
4 M	12 45 43.0	13 20.9	0 50.4	24 47.3	11 17.2	28 53.0	12 45.0	9 10.2	24 35.2	24 56.2	16 32.9	24 57.8
5 T	12 49 39.5	14 20.0	0 47.2	8♒ 2.2	13 19.5	29 40.4	13 22.1	9 2.5	24 42.8	24 57.5	16 33.2	24 58.4
6 W	12 53 36.1	15 19.1	0 44.1	21 45.6	15 22.8	0♓28.6	13 59.1	8 54.8	24 50.3	24 58.7	16 33.5	24 59.0
7 T	12 57 32.7	16 18.1	0 40.9	5♓58.0	17 26.8	1 17.6	14 36.2	8 47.2	24 57.9	24 59.9	16 33.8	24 59.6
8 F	13 1 29.2	17 17.1	0 37.7	20 36.7	19 31.6	2 7.3	15 13.3	8 39.6	25 5.5	25 1.1	16 34.1	25 0.2
9 S	13 5 25.8	18 16.1	0 34.5	5♈35.8	21 36.9	2 57.8	15 50.4	8 32.0	25 13.1	25 2.2	16 34.5	25 0.9
10 S	13 9 22.3	19 15.0	0 31.3	20 46.7	23 42.5	3 48.9	16 27.6	8 24.5	25 20.7	25 3.2	16 34.9	25 1.5
11 M	13 13 18.9	20 13.9	0 28.2	5♉59.2	25 48.1	4 40.7	17 4.7	8 17.0	25 28.3	25 4.2	16 35.3	25 2.2
12 T	13 17 15.4	21 12.8	0 25.0	21 3.4	27 53.6	5 33.1	17 41.8	8 9.6	25 35.9	25 5.2	16 35.8	25 2.9
13 W	13 21 12.0	22 11.6	0 21.8	5♊51.1	29 58.5	6 26.1	18 19.0	8 2.3	25 43.5	25 6.0	16 36.3	25 3.7
14 T	13 25 8.5	23 10.4	0 18.6	20 16.9	2♉ 2.7	7 19.6	18 56.1	7 55.0	25 51.1	25 6.9	16 36.8	25 4.4
15 F	13 29 5.1	24 9.2	0 15.5	4♋18.1	4 5.8	8 13.8	19 33.3	7 47.8	25 58.8	25 7.7	16 37.4	25 5.2
16 S	13 33 1.7	25 7.9	0 12.3	17 54.5	6 7.4	9 8.5	20 10.4	7 40.7	26 6.4	25 8.4	16 38.0	25 6.0
17 S	13 36 58.2	26 6.6	0 9.1	1♌ 7.6	8 7.2	10 3.6	20 47.6	7 33.6	26 14.0	25 9.1	16 38.6	25 6.8
18 M	13 40 54.7	27 5.2	0 5.9	14 0.3	10 4.9	10 59.3	21 24.8	7 26.7	26 21.6	25 9.8	16 39.3	25 7.6
19 T	13 44 51.3	28 3.8	0 2.7	26 35.5	12 0.1	11 55.5	22 1.9	7 19.8	26 29.3	25 10.4	16 40.0	25 8.4
20 W	13 48 47.9	29 2.4	29♉59.6	8♍56.6	13 52.5	12 52.2	22 39.1	7 13.0	26 36.9	25 10.9	16 40.7	25 9.3
21 T	13 52 44.4	0♉ 0.9	29 56.4	21 6.4	15 41.9	13 49.3	23 16.3	7 6.4	26 44.5	25 11.4	16 41.5	25 10.2
22 F	13 56 41.0	0 59.4	29 53.2	3♎ 7.6	17 28.0	14 46.9	23 53.5	6 59.8	26 52.1	25 11.8	16 42.3	25 11.1
23 S	14 0 37.5	1 57.9	29 50.0	15 2.6	19 10.6	15 44.8	24 30.7	6 53.3	26 59.8	25 12.2	16 43.1	25 12.0
24 S	14 4 34.1	2 56.3	29 46.9	26 53.4	20 49.3	16 43.2	25 7.8	6 47.0	27 7.4	25 12.6	16 44.0	25 12.9
25 M	14 8 30.6	3 54.7	29 43.7	8♏42.1	22 24.2	17 42.0	25 45.0	6 40.8	27 15.0	25 12.9	16 44.9	25 13.9
26 T	14 12 27.2	4 53.1	29 40.5	20 30.8	23 55.0	18 41.2	26 22.2	6 34.6	27 22.6	25 13.1	16 45.8	25 14.9
27 W	14 16 23.7	5 51.5	29 37.3	2♐21.6	25 21.5	19 40.7	26 59.4	6 28.7	27 30.1	25 13.3	16 46.7	25 15.8
28 T	14 20 20.3	6 49.8	29 34.1	14 17.3	26 43.6	20 40.6	27 36.6	6 22.8	27 37.7	25 13.4	16 47.7	25 16.8
29 F	14 24 16.9	7 48.1	29 31.0	26 20.7	28 1.3	21 40.8	28 13.8	6 17.1	27 45.3	25 13.5	16 48.7	25 17.8
30 S	14 28 13.4	8 46.3	29 27.8	8♑35.4	29 14.5	22 41.4	28 51.0	6 11.5	27 52.8	25 13.6	16 49.8	25 18.9
						DECLINATION						
1 F	12 33 53.4	4N 7.0	20N22.2	24S26.9	0N39.4	9S59.5	23N23.8	2S18.9	7N17.8	21S38.0	21N45.2	16N32.6
4 M	12 45 43.0	5 16.3	20 20.2	25 22.0	3 21.1	9 37.5	23 39.2	2 9.8	7 26.2	21 37.4	21 45.2	16 33.3
7 T	12 57 32.7	6 24.8	20 18.3	14 4.9	6 8.1	9 10.6	23 53.1	2 0.8	7 34.6	21 36.8	21 45.2	16 33.9
10 S	13 9 22.3	7 32.4	20 16.3	5N 9.5	8 56.8	8 39.0	24 5.5	1 52.0	7 42.9	21 36.3	21 45.2	16 34.6
13 W	13 21 12.0	8 38.8	20 14.3	21 56.1	11 42.6	8 2.9	24 16.3	1 43.5	7 51.3	21 35.9	21 45.1	16 35.2
16 S	13 33 1.7	9 43.9	20 12.3	26 9.9	14 20.1	7 22.6	24 25.6	1 35.2	7 59.6	21 35.5	21 45.0	16 35.8
19 T	13 44 51.3	10 47.5	20 10.3	17 32.8	16 43.6	6 38.4	24 33.2	1 27.3	8 7.9	21 35.3	21 44.9	16 36.4
22 F	13 56 41.0	11 49.5	20 8.2	2 41.9	18 48.4	5 50.4	24 39.3	1 19.7	8 16.1	21 35.1	21 44.7	16 37.0
25 M	14 8 30.6	12 49.7	20 6.2	12S44.5	20 31.5	4 58.9	24 43.8	1 12.6	8 24.2	21 35.0	21 44.5	16 37.6
28 T	14 20 20.3	13 48.1	20 4.2	23 58.4	21 51.9	4 4.2	24 46.6	1 5.9	8 32.3	21 35.0	21 44.2	16 38.2

MAY 1910

LONGITUDE

DAY	EPHEMERIS SIDEREAL TIME h m s	☉ ° ′	☊ ° ′	☽ ° ′	☿ ° ′	♀ ° ′	♂ ° ′	♃ ° ′	♄ ° ′	♅ ° ′	♆ ° ′	♇ ° ′
1 S	14 32 10.0	9♉44.5	29♉24.6	21♑ 5.1	0♊23.0	23♓42.3	29♊28.2	6♎ 6.0	28♈ 0.3	25♑13.6	16♋50.8	25♊19.9
2 M	14 36 6.5	10 42.8	29 21.4	3♒53.6	1 26.8	24 43.5	0♋ 5.4	6R 0.7	28 7.9	25R13.5	16 51.9	25 21.0
3 T	14 40 3.1	11 40.9	29 18.3	17 4.3	2 25.8	25 45.0	0 42.6	5 55.5	28 15.4	25 13.4	16 53.1	25 22.1
4 W	14 43 59.6	12 39.1	29 15.1	0♓39.9	3 19.9	26 46.8	1 19.8	5 50.5	28 22.9	25 13.2	16 54.2	25 23.1
5 T	14 47 56.2	13 37.3	29 11.9	14 41.7	4 9.1	27 48.9	1 57.0	5 45.6	28 30.3	25 13.0	16 55.4	25 24.2
6 F	14 51 52.7	14 35.4	29 8.7	29 8.7	4 53.4	28 51.3	2 34.2	5 40.8	28 37.8	25 12.8	16 56.6	25 25.4
7 S	14 55 49.3	15 33.5	29 5.5	13♈57.4	5 32.6	29 53.9	3 11.5	5 36.2	28 45.2	25 12.5	16 57.9	25 26.5
8 S	14 59 45.8	16 31.5	29 2.4	29 1.4	6 6.7	0♈56.8	3 48.7	5 31.8	28 52.6	25 12.1	16 59.1	25 27.6
9 M	15 3 42.4	17 29.6	28 59.2	14♉12.2	6 35.8	1 59.9	4 26.0	5 27.5	29 0.0	25 11.7	17 0.4	25 28.8
10 T	15 7 39.0	18 27.6	28 56.0	29 20.3	6 59.7	3 3.2	5 3.2	5 23.4	29 7.4	25 11.2	17 1.8	25 30.0
11 W	15 11 35.5	19 25.6	28 52.8	14♊16.7	7 18.4	4 6.8	5 40.4	5 19.5	29 14.7	25 10.7	17 3.1	25 31.2
12 T	15 15 32.1	20 23.5	28 49.7	28 53.9	7 32.1	5 10.6	6 17.7	5 15.7	29 22.0	25 10.2	17 4.5	25 32.4
13 F	15 19 28.6	21 21.5	28 46.5	13♋ 6.8	7 40.6	6 14.6	6 55.0	5 12.1	29 29.3	25 9.6	17 5.9	25 33.6
14 S	15 23 25.2	22 19.4	28 43.3	26 53.4	7 44.2	7 18.7	7 32.2	5 8.7	29 36.6	25 8.9	17 7.3	25 34.8
15 S	15 27 21.7	23 17.2	28 40.1	10♌13.6	7R42.9	8 23.1	8 9.5	5 5.4	29 43.8	25 8.2	17 8.8	25 36.0
16 M	15 31 18.3	24 15.1	28 37.0	23 9.6	7 36.8	9 27.7	8 46.7	5 2.3	29 51.0	25 7.5	17 10.3	25 37.3
17 T	15 35 14.9	25 12.9	28 33.8	5♍44.5	7 26.2	10 32.5	9 24.0	4 59.4	29 58.2	25 6.7	17 11.8	25 38.5
18 W	15 39 11.4	26 10.7	28 30.6	18 2.2	7 11.3	11 37.4	10 1.2	4 56.6	0♉ 5.3	25 5.9	17 13.3	25 39.8
19 T	15 43 8.0	27 8.4	28 27.4	0♎ 6.9	6 52.5	12 42.6	10 38.5	4 54.1	0 12.4	25 5.0	17 14.8	25 41.1
20 F	15 47 4.5	28 6.2	28 24.2	12 2.4	6 30.0	13 47.9	11 15.8	4 51.7	0 19.5	25 4.1	17 16.4	25 42.3
21 S	15 51 1.1	29 3.9	28 21.1	23 52.5	6 4.3	14 53.4	11 53.0	4 49.5	0 26.5	25 3.1	17 18.0	25 43.6
22 S	15 54 57.6	0♊ 1.5	28 17.9	5♏40.6	5 35.9	15 59.0	12 30.3	4 47.4	0 33.5	25 2.1	17 19.6	25 44.9
23 M	15 58 54.2	0 59.2	28 14.7	17 29.5	5 5.2	17 4.8	13 7.6	4 45.6	0 40.5	25 1.0	17 21.3	25 46.3
24 T	16 2 50.7	1 56.8	28 11.5	29 21.7	4 32.9	18 10.8	13 44.8	4 43.9	0 47.4	24 59.9	17 23.0	25 47.6
25 W	16 6 47.3	2 54.5	28 8.4	11♐19.5	3 59.3	19 16.9	14 22.1	4 42.4	0 54.3	24 58.8	17 24.6	25 48.9
26 T	16 10 43.8	3 52.0	28 5.2	23 24.8	3 25.3	20 23.2	14 59.3	4 41.1	1 1.1	24 57.6	17 26.3	25 50.2
27 F	16 14 40.4	4 49.6	28 2.0	5♑39.8	2 51.3	21 29.6	15 36.6	4 39.9	1 8.0	24 56.3	17 28.1	25 51.6
28 S	16 18 37.0	5 47.2	27 58.8	18 6.3	2 18.0	22 36.1	16 13.9	4 39.0	1 14.7	24 55.1	17 29.8	25 52.9
29 S	16 22 33.5	6 44.7	27 55.7	0♒46.3	1 45.8	23 42.9	16 51.2	4 38.2	1 21.4	24 53.8	17 31.6	25 54.3
30 M	16 26 30.1	7 42.3	27 52.5	13 41.9	1 15.4	24 49.7	17 28.4	4 37.6	1 28.1	24 52.4	17 33.4	25 55.7
31 T	16 30 26.6	8 39.8	27 49.3	26 55.2	0 47.3	25 56.7	18 5.7	4 37.1	1 34.7	24 51.0	17 35.2	25 57.0

DECLINATION

DAY	EPHEMERIS SIDEREAL TIME h m s	☉ ° ′	☊ ° ′	☽ ° ′	☿ ° ′	♀ ° ′	♂ ° ′	♃ ° ′	♄ ° ′	♅ ° ′	♆ ° ′	♇ ° ′
1 S	14 32 10.0	14N44.4	20N 2.1	25S56.9	22N49.6	3S 6.7	24N47.8	0S59.7	8N40.2	21S35.1	21N43.9	16N38.8
4 W	14 43 59.6	15 38.6	20 0.1	16 9.9	23 25.6	2 6.5	24 47.4	0 54.1	8 48.1	21 35.2	21 43.6	16 39.4
7 S	14 55 49.3	16 30.4	19 58.0	2N 6.3	23 41.1	1 4.0	24 45.4	0 49.0	8 55.9	21 35.5	21 43.2	16 39.9
10 T	15 7 39.0	17 19.8	19 55.9	20 7.3	23 37.3	0N 0.5	24 41.8	0 44.5	9 3.5	21 35.8	21 42.8	16 40.4
13 F	15 19 28.6	18 6.6	19 53.8	26 31.5	23 15.3	1 6.6	24 36.5	0 40.6	9 11.0	21 36.2	21 42.4	16 41.0
16 M	15 31 18.3	18 50.7	19 51.7	18 46.7	22 36.7	2 14.0	24 29.7	0 37.4	9 18.4	21 36.7	21 41.9	16 41.5
19 T	15 43 8.0	19 31.8	19 49.6	4 4.9	21 43.7	3 22.5	24 21.2	0 34.8	9 25.6	21 37.2	21 41.4	16 41.9
22 S	15 54 57.6	20 10.0	19 47.5	11S29.9	20 40.0	4 31.8	24 11.2	0 32.8	9 32.7	21 37.8	21 40.9	16 42.4
25 W	16 6 47.3	20 45.1	19 45.4	23 20.2	19 31.0	5 41.4	23 59.6	0 31.5	9 39.6	21 38.5	21 40.3	16 42.9
28 S	16 18 37.0	21 17.0	19 43.3	26 14.1	18 23.1	6 51.3	23 46.5	0 30.8	9 46.4	21 39.2	21 39.7	16 43.3
31 T	16 30 26.6	21 45.5	19 41.1	17 30.1	17 23.3	8 0.9	23 31.8	0 30.8	9 52.9	21 40.1	21 39.1	16 43.7

JUNE 1910

LONGITUDE

DAY	EPHEMERIS SIDEREAL TIME h m s	☉ ° ′	☊ ° ′	☽ ° ′	☿ ° ′	♀ ° ′	♂ ° ′	♃ ° ′	♄ ° ′	♅ ° ′	♆ ° ′	♇ ° ′
1 W	16 34 23.2	9♊37.3	27♉46.1	10♓27.7	0♊21.9	27♈ 3.8	18♋43.0	4♎36.9	1♉41.3	24♑49.6	17♋37.0	25♊58.4
2 T	16 38 19.8	10 34.8	27 43.0	24 20.3	29♉59.6	28 11.0	19 20.3	4R36.8	1 47.9	24R48.1	17 38.9	25 59.8
3 F	16 42 16.3	11 32.2	27 39.8	8♈33.0	29R40.8	29 18.4	19 57.6	4D37.0	1 54.4	24 46.6	17 40.7	26 1.2
4 S	16 46 12.8	12 29.7	27 36.6	23 4.0	29 25.8	0♉25.8	20 34.9	4 37.2	2 0.8	24 45.1	17 42.6	26 2.6
5 S	16 50 9.4	13 27.2	27 33.4	7♉49.4	29 14.7	1 33.4	21 12.2	4 37.7	2 7.2	24 43.5	17 44.5	26 4.0
6 M	16 54 6.0	14 24.6	27 30.2	22 43.8	29 7.8	2 41.1	21 49.5	4 38.4	2 13.6	24 41.8	17 46.5	26 5.4
7 T	16 58 2.6	15 22.0	27 27.1	7♊40.0	29 5.3	3 48.9	22 26.9	4 39.2	2 19.9	24 40.2	17 48.4	26 6.8
8 W	17 1 59.1	16 19.4	27 23.9	22 29.9	29D 7.2	4 56.8	23 4.2	4 40.2	2 26.1	24 38.5	17 50.3	26 8.2
9 T	17 5 55.6	17 16.8	27 20.7	7♋ 6.0	29 13.6	6 4.8	23 41.5	4 41.4	2 32.3	24 36.8	17 52.3	26 9.6
10 F	17 9 52.2	18 14.2	27 17.5	21 22.0	29 24.5	7 13.0	24 18.9	4 42.8	2 38.4	24 35.0	17 54.3	26 11.0
11 S	17 13 48.8	19 11.6	27 14.4	5♌13.8	29 40.0	8 21.2	24 56.2	4 44.4	2 44.5	24 33.2	17 56.3	26 12.5
12 S	17 17 45.3	20 9.0	27 11.2	18 39.7	29 59.9	9 29.5	25 33.5	4 46.1	2 50.5	24 31.4	17 58.3	26 13.9
13 M	17 21 41.9	21 6.3	27 8.0	1♍40.4	0♊24.2	10 37.9	26 10.9	4 48.0	2 56.4	24 29.5	18 0.3	26 15.3
14 T	17 25 38.4	22 3.6	27 4.8	14 18.1	0 53.0	11 46.3	26 48.2	4 50.1	3 2.3	24 27.6	18 2.4	26 16.7
15 W	17 29 35.0	23 0.9	27 1.7	26 36.8	1 26.1	12 54.9	27 25.6	4 52.4	3 8.2	24 25.7	18 4.4	26 18.2
16 T	17 33 31.6	23 58.2	26 58.5	8♎40.7	2 3.5	14 3.6	28 3.0	4 54.8	3 13.9	24 23.8	18 6.5	26 19.6
17 F	17 37 28.1	24 55.5	26 55.3	20 34.8	2 45.1	15 12.3	28 40.3	4 57.4	3 19.7	24 21.8	18 8.6	26 21.0
18 S	17 41 24.7	25 52.8	26 52.1	2♏23.6	3 30.8	16 21.1	29 17.7	5 0.2	3 25.3	24 19.8	18 10.6	26 22.5
19 S	17 45 21.2	26 50.0	26 49.0	14 11.8	4 20.6	17 30.0	29 55.1	5 3.1	3 30.9	24 17.8	18 12.7	26 23.9
20 M	17 49 17.8	27 47.3	26 45.8	26 3.3	5 14.3	18 39.0	0♌32.4	5 6.2	3 36.4	24 15.7	18 14.8	26 25.3
21 T	17 53 14.4	28 44.5	26 42.6	8♐ 1.3	6 12.0	19 48.1	1 9.8	5 9.5	3 41.9	24 13.6	18 17.0	26 26.8
22 W	17 57 10.9	29 41.7	26 39.4	20 8.7	7 13.5	20 57.3	1 47.2	5 12.9	3 47.2	24 11.5	18 19.1	26 28.2
23 T	18 1 7.5	0♋38.9	26 36.2	2♑27.4	8 18.8	22 6.5	2 24.6	5 16.5	3 52.6	24 9.4	18 21.2	26 29.6
24 F	18 5 4.0	1 36.2	26 33.1	14 58.7	9 27.9	23 15.9	3 2.0	5 20.3	3 57.8	24 7.2	18 23.4	26 31.1
25 S	18 9 0.6	2 33.4	26 29.9	27 43.4	10 40.6	24 25.3	3 39.4	5 24.2	4 3.0	24 5.1	18 25.5	26 32.5
26 S	18 12 57.2	3 30.6	26 26.7	10♒41.5	11 57.0	25 34.8	4 16.8	5 28.3	4 8.1	24 2.9	18 27.7	26 33.9
27 M	18 16 53.7	4 27.8	26 23.5	23 53.2	13 17.0	26 44.3	4 54.2	5 32.5	4 13.1	24 0.7	18 29.9	26 35.3
28 T	18 20 50.2	5 25.0	26 20.4	7♓18.3	14 40.6	27 54.0	5 31.6	5 36.9	4 18.1	23 58.4	18 32.0	26 36.7
29 W	18 24 46.8	6 22.2	26 17.2	20 56.5	16 7.7	29 3.7	6 9.1	5 41.5	4 23.0	23 56.2	18 34.2	26 38.2
30 T	18 28 43.4	7 19.4	26 14.0	4♈47.7	17 38.3	0♊13.5	6 46.5	5 46.2	4 27.8	23 53.9	18 36.4	26 39.6

DECLINATION

DAY	EPHEMERIS SIDEREAL TIME h m s	☉ ° ′	☊ ° ′	☽ ° ′	☿ ° ′	♀ ° ′	♂ ° ′	♃ ° ′	♄ ° ′	♅ ° ′	♆ ° ′	♇ ° ′
1 W	16 34 23.2	21N54.3	19N40.4	12S25.3	17N 6.2	8N24.0	23N26.6	0S30.9	9N55.1	21S40.3	21N38.9	16N43.8
4 S	16 46 12.8	22 18.4	19 38.2	6N 8.4	16 25.8	9 33.0	23 10.0	0 31.7	10 1.4	21 41.2	21 38.2	16 44.2
7 T	16 58 2.6	22 38.9	19 36.1	22 27.3	16 3.6	10 41.0	22 51.9	0 33.2	10 7.5	21 42.2	21 37.5	16 44.5
10 F	17 9 52.2	22 55.9	19 33.9	25 54.8	16 0.4	11 47.7	22 32.3	0 35.4	10 13.4	21 43.2	21 36.8	16 44.9
13 M	17 21 41.9	23 9.2	19 31.7	15 46.4	16 15.2	12 52.9	22 11.3	0 38.1	10 19.1	21 44.2	21 36.1	16 45.2
16 T	17 33 31.6	23 18.9	19 29.5	0 13.4	16 45.9	13 56.1	21 49.0	0 41.5	10 24.5	21 45.3	21 35.3	16 45.5
19 S	17 45 21.2	23 24.9	19 27.3	14S54.2	17 29.7	14 57.1	21 25.3	0 45.5	10 29.8	21 46.4	21 34.6	16 45.7
22 W	17 57 10.9	23 27.1	19 25.1	25 2.6	18 23.5	15 55.6	21 0.2	0 50.1	10 34.8	21 47.6	21 33.8	16 46.0
25 S	18 9 0.6	23 25.6	19 22.9	25 1.6	19 24.0	16 51.3	20 33.9	0 55.3	10 39.5	21 48.8	21 32.9	16 46.2
28 T	18 20 50.2	23 20.5	19 20.7	13 34.1	20 27.2	17 43.8	20 6.4	1 1.0	10 44.0	21 50.0	21 32.1	16 46.4

JULY 1910

LONGITUDE

DAY	EPHEMERIS SIDEREAL TIME h m s	☉ ° ′	☊ ° ′	☽ ° ′	☿ ° ′	♀ ° ′	♂ ° ′	♃ ° ′	♄ ° ′	♅ ° ′	♆ ° ′	♇ ° ′
1 F	18 32 40.0	8♋16.6	26♉10.8	18♈51.2	19♊12.3	1♊23.4	7♌23.9	5♎51.0	4♉32.5	23♑51.6	18♋38.6	26♊41.0
2 S	18 36 36.5	9 13.8	26 7.7	3♉ 6.3	20 49.6	2 33.3	8 1.4	5 56.1	4 37.2	23R49.3	18 40.8	26 42.4
3 S	18 40 33.0	10 11.0	26 4.5	17 31.1	22 30.3	3 43.3	8 38.9	6 1.2	4 41.8	23 47.0	18 43.0	26 43.8
4 M	18 44 29.6	11 8.2	26 1.3	2♊ 2.5	24 14.2	4 53.4	9 16.3	6 6.5	4 46.3	23 44.7	18 45.2	26 45.2
5 T	18 48 26.2	12 5.5	25 58.1	16 36.3	26 1.3	6 3.6	9 53.8	6 12.0	4 50.7	23 42.4	18 47.5	26 46.6
6 W	18 52 22.7	13 2.7	25 55.0	1♋ 6.8	27 51.3	7 13.8	10 31.3	6 17.6	4 55.1	23 40.0	18 49.7	26 48.0
7 T	18 56 19.3	13 59.9	25 51.8	15 28.2	29 44.3	8 24.1	11 8.8	6 23.4	4 59.3	23 37.7	18 51.9	26 49.4
8 F	19 0 15.8	14 57.1	25 48.6	29 34.7	1♋39.9	9 34.5	11 46.4	6 29.3	5 3.5	23 35.3	18 54.1	26 50.7
9 S	19 4 12.4	15 54.4	25 45.4	13♌21.4	3 38.0	10 44.9	12 23.9	6 35.3	5 7.6	23 32.9	18 56.4	26 52.1
10 S	19 8 8.9	16 51.6	25 42.3	26 45.6	5 38.5	11 55.3	13 1.4	6 41.5	5 11.6	23 30.5	18 58.6	26 53.5
11 M	19 12 5.5	17 48.8	25 39.1	9♍46.5	7 40.9	13 5.9	13 39.0	6 47.9	5 15.6	23 28.1	19 0.8	26 54.8
12 T	19 16 2.1	18 46.0	25 35.9	22 25.3	9 45.2	14 16.5	14 16.5	6 54.3	5 19.4	23 25.7	19 3.0	26 56.2
13 W	19 19 58.7	19 43.3	25 32.7	4♎44.8	11 50.9	15 27.1	14 54.1	7 0.9	5 23.2	23 23.3	19 5.3	26 57.5
14 T	19 23 55.2	20 40.5	25 29.5	16 49.2	13 57.8	16 37.8	15 31.7	7 7.7	5 26.8	23 20.9	19 7.5	26 58.8
15 F	19 27 51.8	21 37.7	25 26.4	28 43.3	16 5.6	17 48.6	16 9.3	7 14.6	5 30.4	23 18.5	19 9.7	27 0.2
16 S	19 31 48.3	22 34.9	25 23.2	10♏32.4	18 14.0	18 59.5	16 46.9	7 21.6	5 33.9	23 16.1	19 12.0	27 1.5
17 S	19 35 44.9	23 32.2	25 20.0	22 21.7	20 22.6	20 10.3	17 24.5	7 28.7	5 37.3	23 13.7	19 14.2	27 2.8
18 M	19 39 41.5	24 29.4	25 16.8	4♐16.1	22 31.2	21 21.3	18 2.1	7 36.0	5 40.6	23 11.3	19 16.4	27 4.1
19 T	19 43 38.0	25 26.7	25 13.7	16 20.0	24 39.6	22 32.3	18 39.7	7 43.3	5 43.9	23 8.9	19 18.6	27 5.4
20 W	19 47 34.6	26 23.9	25 10.5	28 36.9	26 47.4	23 43.4	19 17.3	7 50.9	5 47.0	23 6.5	19 20.9	27 6.6
21 T	19 51 31.1	27 21.2	25 7.3	11♑ 9.3	28 54.5	24 54.5	19 55.0	7 58.5	5 50.0	23 4.1	19 23.1	27 7.9
22 F	19 55 27.6	28 18.4	25 4.1	23 58.4	1♌ 0.7	26 5.7	20 32.6	8 6.2	5 53.0	23 1.7	19 25.3	27 9.2
23 S	19 59 24.2	29 15.7	25 1.0	7♒ 4.3	3 5.7	27 17.0	21 10.3	8 14.1	5 55.8	22 59.3	19 27.5	27 10.4
24 S	20 3 20.8	0♌13.0	24 57.8	20 25.7	5 9.6	28 28.3	21 47.9	8 22.1	5 58.6	22 56.9	19 29.7	27 11.6
25 M	20 7 17.4	1 10.3	24 54.6	4♓ 0.5	7 12.1	29 39.7	22 25.6	8 30.2	6 1.2	22 54.5	19 31.9	27 12.9
26 T	20 11 13.9	2 7.6	24 51.4	17 46.2	9 13.2	0♋51.1	23 3.3	8 38.5	6 3.8	22 52.1	19 34.1	27 14.1
27 W	20 15 10.4	3 4.9	24 48.2	1♈40.0	11 12.8	2 2.6	23 41.0	8 46.8	6 6.3	22 49.8	19 36.2	27 15.3
28 T	20 19 7.0	4 2.2	24 45.1	15 40.0	13 10.9	3 14.2	24 18.8	8 55.3	6 8.6	22 47.4	19 38.4	27 16.5
29 F	20 23 3.6	4 59.6	24 41.9	29 44.3	15 7.4	4 25.8	24 56.5	9 3.8	6 10.9	22 45.1	19 40.6	27 17.7
30 S	20 27 0.1	5 56.9	24 38.7	13♉51.9	17 2.3	5 37.5	25 34.3	9 12.5	6 13.1	22 42.8	19 42.7	27 18.8
31 S	20 30 56.7	6 54.3	24 35.5	28 1.6	18 55.5	6 49.2	26 12.0	9 21.3	6 15.1	22 40.4	19 44.9	27 20.0

DECLINATION

DAY	EPHEMERIS SIDEREAL TIME h m s	☉ ° ′	☊ ° ′	☽ ° ′	☿ ° ′	♀ ° ′	♂ ° ′	♃ ° ′	♄ ° ′	♅ ° ′	♆ ° ′	♇ ° ′
1 F	18 32 40.0	23N11.6	19N18.5	4N23.2	21N29.0	18N32.9	19N37.6	1S 7.2	10N48.3	21S51.2	21N31.2	16N46.5
4 M	18 44 29.6	22 59.1	19 16.2	20 58.6	22 24.7	19 18.2	19 7.6	1 14.0	10 52.3	21 52.4	21 30.4	16 46.7
7 T	18 56 19.3	22 43.0	19 14.0	26 21.3	23 8.8	19 59.4	18 36.5	1 21.3	10 56.0	21 53.7	21 29.5	16 46.8
10 S	19 8 8.9	22 23.3	19 11.7	17 24.6	23 36.2	20 36.3	18 4.3	1 29.1	10 59.5	21 54.9	21 28.6	16 46.9
13 W	19 19 58.7	22 0.1	19 9.5	1 49.7	23 42.2	21 8.6	17 31.0	1 37.4	11 2.6	21 56.2	21 27.7	16 47.0
16 S	19 31 48.3	21 33.6	19 7.2	13S37.6	23 24.0	21 36.0	16 56.7	1 46.2	11 5.5	21 57.5	21 26.8	16 47.0
19 T	19 43 38.0	21 3.7	19 4.9	24 27.3	22 41.5	21 58.4	16 21.4	1 55.4	11 8.1	21 58.7	21 25.9	16 47.0
22 F	19 55 27.6	20 30.7	19 2.6	25 32.1	21 36.5	22 15.5	15 45.1	2 5.0	11 10.4	21 59.9	21 25.0	16 47.0
25 M	20 7 17.4	19 54.5	19 0.3	14 42.0	20 12.6	22 27.2	15 7.9	2 15.0	11 12.4	22 1.1	21 24.0	16 47.0
28 T	20 19 7.0	19 15.4	18 58.0	3N 9.7	18 33.8	22 33.3	14 29.9	2 25.3	11 14.2	22 2.3	21 23.1	16 47.0
31 S	20 30 56.7	18 33.4	18 55.7	19 56.4	16 43.8	22 33.8	13 51.0	2 36.1	11 15.6	22 3.5	21 22.2	16 46.9

AUGUST 1910

LONGITUDE

DAY	EPHEMERIS SIDEREAL TIME h m s	☉ ° ′	☊ ° ′	☽ ° ′	☿ ° ′	♀ ° ′	♂ ° ′	♃ ° ′	♄ ° ′	♅ ° ′	♆ ° ′	♇ ° ′
1 M	20 34 53.2	7♌51.7	24♉32.4	12♊12.2	20♌47.2	8♋ 1.0	26♌49.8	9♎30.2	6♉17.1	22♑38.1	19♋47.0	27♊21.1
2 T	20 38 49.8	8 49.2	24 29.2	26 21.8	22 37.2	9 12.9	27 27.7	9 39.2	6 19.0	22R35.8	19 49.2	27 22.2
3 W	20 42 46.4	9 46.6	24 26.0	10♋27.3	24 25.6	10 24.8	28 5.5	9 48.3	6 20.8	22 33.6	19 51.3	27 23.3
4 T	20 46 42.9	10 44.1	24 22.8	24 25.3	26 12.3	11 36.8	28 43.3	9 57.5	6 22.4	22 31.3	19 53.4	27 24.4
5 F	20 50 39.4	11 41.5	24 19.6	8♌11.8	27 57.5	12 48.8	29 21.2	10 6.8	6 24.0	22 29.1	19 55.5	27 25.5
6 S	20 54 36.0	12 39.0	24 16.5	21 43.0	29 41.0	14 0.9	29 59.0	10 16.2	6 25.5	22 26.9	19 57.6	27 26.6
7 S	20 58 32.6	13 36.6	24 13.3	4♍56.2	1♍23.0	15 13.0	0♍36.9	10 25.8	6 26.8	22 24.7	19 59.7	27 27.6
8 M	21 2 29.1	14 34.1	24 10.1	17 49.9	3 3.3	16 25.2	1 14.8	10 35.4	6 28.1	22 22.5	20 1.8	27 28.7
9 T	21 6 25.7	15 31.6	24 6.9	0♎24.5	4 42.1	17 37.4	1 52.8	10 45.1	6 29.2	22 20.3	20 3.8	27 29.7
10 W	21 10 22.2	16 29.2	24 3.8	12 41.7	6 19.3	18 49.7	2 30.7	10 54.9	6 30.3	22 18.2	20 5.9	27 30.7
11 T	21 14 18.8	17 26.8	24 0.6	24 44.9	7 55.0	20 2.1	3 8.6	11 4.8	6 31.2	22 16.1	20 7.9	27 31.7
12 F	21 18 15.3	18 24.4	23 57.4	6♏38.3	9 29.0	21 14.5	3 46.6	11 14.8	6 32.1	22 14.0	20 9.9	27 32.7
13 S	21 22 11.9	19 22.0	23 54.2	18 27.0	11 1.5	22 26.9	4 24.6	11 24.8	6 32.8	22 11.9	20 11.9	27 33.6
14 S	21 26 8.5	20 19.6	23 51.1	0♐16.5	12 32.5	23 39.4	5 2.6	11 35.0	6 33.4	22 9.9	20 13.9	27 34.6
15 M	21 30 5.0	21 17.2	23 47.9	12 12.1	14 1.9	24 51.9	5 40.6	11 45.2	6 33.9	22 7.9	20 15.9	27 35.5
16 T	21 34 1.6	22 14.9	23 44.7	24 19.2	15 29.6	26 4.5	6 18.6	11 55.6	6 34.4	22 5.9	20 17.8	27 36.4
17 W	21 37 58.1	23 12.6	23 41.5	6♑42.1	16 55.8	27 17.2	6 56.7	12 6.0	6 34.7	22 4.0	20 19.8	27 37.3
18 T	21 41 54.7	24 10.2	23 38.4	19 24.3	18 20.3	28 29.9	7 34.7	12 16.5	6 34.9	22 2.0	20 21.7	27 38.2
19 F	21 45 51.2	25 8.0	23 35.2	2♒27.7	19 43.2	29 42.6	8 12.8	12 27.0	6 35.0	22 0.1	20 23.6	27 39.0
20 S	21 49 47.8	26 5.7	23 32.0	15 52.5	21 4.4	0♌55.4	8 50.9	12 37.7	6 35.0	21 58.3	20 25.5	27 39.9
21 S	21 53 44.4	27 3.4	23 28.8	29 36.8	22 23.9	2 8.3	9 29.0	12 48.4	6R34.9	21 56.5	20 27.4	27 40.7
22 M	21 57 40.9	28 1.2	23 25.6	13♓36.9	23 41.7	3 21.2	10 7.2	12 59.2	6 34.7	21 54.7	20 29.2	27 41.5
23 T	22 1 37.4	28 59.0	23 22.5	27 48.2	24 57.6	4 34.2	10 45.3	13 10.1	6 34.3	21 52.9	20 31.1	27 42.3
24 W	22 5 34.0	29 56.8	23 19.3	12♈ 5.6	26 11.6	5 47.2	11 23.5	13 21.1	6 33.9	21 51.2	20 32.9	27 43.0
25 T	22 9 30.6	0♍54.7	23 16.1	26 24.2	27 23.7	7 0.2	12 1.7	13 32.1	6 33.4	21 49.5	20 34.7	27 43.8
26 F	22 13 27.1	1 52.6	23 12.9	10♉40.5	28 33.8	8 13.4	12 39.9	13 43.2	6 32.8	21 47.8	20 36.5	27 44.5
27 S	22 17 23.7	2 50.5	23 9.8	24 51.9	29 41.8	9 26.5	13 18.1	13 54.4	6 32.0	21 46.2	20 38.2	27 45.2
28 S	22 21 20.2	3 48.5	23 6.6	8♊57.2	0♎47.6	10 39.7	13 56.4	14 5.6	6 31.2	21 44.6	20 40.0	27 45.9
29 M	22 25 16.8	4 46.4	23 3.4	22 55.6	1 51.1	11 53.0	14 34.7	14 16.9	6 30.2	21 43.0	20 41.7	27 46.6
30 T	22 29 13.3	5 44.4	23 0.2	6♋46.5	2 52.2	13 6.3	15 13.0	14 28.3	6 29.2	21 41.5	20 43.4	27 47.2
31 W	22 33 9.9	6 42.5	22 57.0	20 29.3	3 50.7	14 19.7	15 51.3	14 39.8	6 28.0	21 40.0	20 45.1	27 47.9

DECLINATION

DAY	EPHEMERIS SIDEREAL TIME h m s	☉ ° ′	☊ ° ′	☽ ° ′	☿ ° ′	♀ ° ′	♂ ° ′	♃ ° ′	♄ ° ′	♅ ° ′	♆ ° ′	♇ ° ′
1 M	20 34 53.2	18N18.8	18N54.9	23N42.3	16N 5.2	22N32.7	13N37.8	2S39.8	11N16.0	22S 3.9	21N21.9	16N46.9
4 T	20 46 42.9	17 33.1	18 52.6	25 29.6	14 5.4	22 25.6	12 57.9	2 51.0	11 17.0	22 5.0	21 21.0	16 46.8
7 S	20 58 32.6	16 44.9	18 50.2	14 17.8	12 1.2	22 12.7	12 17.1	3 2.6	11 17.7	22 6.1	21 20.1	16 46.7
10 W	21 10 22.2	15 54.2	18 47.9	1S55.9	9 54.9	21 54.1	11 35.7	3 14.4	11 18.1	22 7.1	21 19.2	16 46.6
13 S	21 22 11.9	15 1.3	18 45.5	16 50.5	7 48.2	21 29.8	10 53.5	3 26.6	11 18.2	22 8.1	21 18.3	16 46.4
16 T	21 34 1.6	14 6.2	18 43.2	25 52.0	5 42.6	20 59.9	10 10.8	3 39.0	11 18.0	22 9.1	21 17.4	16 46.2
19 F	21 45 51.2	13 9.1	18 40.8	24 10.0	3 39.5	20 24.7	9 27.5	3 51.7	11 17.4	22 10.0	21 16.5	16 46.1
22 M	21 57 40.9	12 10.1	18 38.4	10 46.7	1 40.3	19 44.1	8 43.6	4 4.6	11 16.6	22 10.9	21 15.7	16 45.9
25 T	22 9 30.6	11 9.4	18 36.0	8N 6.0	0S13.7	18 58.4	7 59.2	4 17.8	11 15.5	22 11.7	21 14.9	16 45.7
28 S	22 21 20.2	10 7.1	18 33.6	23 11.8	2 1.0	18 7.8	7 14.3	4 31.1	11 14.1	22 12.4	21 14.1	16 45.4
31 W	22 33 9.9	9 3.3	18 31.2	26 6.3	3 39.8	17 12.5	6 28.9	4 44.7	11 12.4	22 13.1	21 13.3	16 45.2

SEPTEMBER 1910

DAY	EPHEMERIS SIDEREAL TIME	☉	☊	☽	☿	♀	♂	♃	♄	♅	♆	♇
	h m s	° ′	° ′	° ′	° ′	° ′	° ′	° ′	° ′	° ′	° ′	° ′
						LONGITUDE						
1 T	22 37 6.4	7♍40.6	22♉53.9	4♌ 2.6	4♎46.5	15♌33.1	16♍29.7	14♎51.3	6♉26.8	21♑38.6	20♋46.7	27♊48.5
2 F	22 41 3.0	8 38.7	22 50.7	17 24.9	5 39.5	16 46.6	17 8.0	15 2.8	6R25.4	21R37.2	20 48.4	27 49.1
3 S	22 44 59.6	9 36.8	22 47.5	0♍34.5	6 29.3	18 0.1	17 46.4	15 14.5	6 23.9	21 35.8	20 50.0	27 49.6
4 S	22 48 56.1	10 35.0	22 44.3	13 29.6	7 16.0	19 13.7	18 24.8	15 26.2	6 22.4	21 34.5	20 51.6	27 50.2
5 M	22 52 52.6	11 33.2	22 41.2	26 9.6	7 59.1	20 27.3	19 3.3	15 37.9	6 20.7	21 33.2	20 53.1	27 50.7
6 T	22 56 49.2	12 31.4	22 38.0	8♎34.4	8 38.5	21 41.0	19 41.7	15 49.7	6 18.9	21 32.0	20 54.7	27 51.2
7 W	23 0 45.8	13 29.6	22 34.8	20 45.3	9 14.0	22 54.6	20 20.2	16 1.6	6 17.1	21 30.8	20 56.2	27 51.7
8 T	23 4 42.3	14 27.9	22 31.6	2♏44.6	9 45.1	24 8.4	20 58.7	16 13.5	6 15.1	21 29.7	20 57.7	27 52.2
9 F	23 8 38.9	15 26.2	22 28.4	14 35.7	10 11.8	25 22.2	21 37.3	16 25.5	6 13.0	21 28.6	20 59.1	27 52.6
10 S	23 12 35.4	16 24.5	22 25.3	26 23.0	10 33.6	26 36.0	22 15.8	16 37.5	6 10.9	21 27.5	21 0.6	27 53.0
11 S	23 16 32.0	17 22.9	22 22.1	8♐11.4	10 50.2	27 49.8	22 54.4	16 49.6	6 8.6	21 26.5	21 2.0	27 53.4
12 M	23 20 28.5	18 21.2	22 18.9	20 6.2	11 1.2	29 3.7	23 33.0	17 1.7	6 6.3	21 25.5	21 3.3	27 53.8
13 T	23 24 25.1	19 19.6	22 15.7	2♑12.9	11 6.5	0♍17.7	24 11.6	17 13.8	6 3.8	21 24.6	21 4.7	27 54.2
14 W	23 28 21.7	20 18.1	22 12.6	14 36.5	11R 5.5	1 31.7	24 50.2	17 26.1	6 1.3	21 23.7	21 6.0	27 54.5
15 T	23 32 18.2	21 16.5	22 9.4	27 21.6	10 58.2	2 45.7	25 28.9	17 38.3	5 58.7	21 22.9	21 7.3	27 54.8
16 F	23 36 14.7	22 15.0	22 6.2	10♒31.0	10 44.1	3 59.7	26 7.6	17 50.6	5 55.9	21 22.1	21 8.6	27 55.1
17 S	23 40 11.3	23 13.5	22 3.0	24 6.0	10 23.1	5 13.8	26 46.3	18 3.0	5 53.1	21 21.4	21 9.9	27 55.4
18 S	23 44 7.9	24 12.1	21 59.8	8♓ 5.4	9 55.2	6 27.9	27 25.0	18 15.3	5 50.2	21 20.7	21 11.1	27 55.6
19 M	23 48 4.4	25 10.6	21 56.7	22 25.6	9 20.3	7 42.1	28 3.8	18 27.8	5 47.3	21 20.0	21 12.3	27 55.8
20 T	23 52 0.9	26 9.2	21 53.5	7♈ 0.6	8 38.6	8 56.3	28 42.6	18 40.2	5 44.2	21 19.4	21 13.5	27 56.0
21 W	23 55 57.5	27 7.9	21 50.3	21 43.4	7 50.6	10 10.5	29 21.4	18 52.7	5 41.0	21 18.9	21 14.6	27 56.2
22 T	23 59 54.1	28 6.5	21 47.1	6♉26.6	6 56.8	11 24.8	0♎ 0.2	19 5.3	5 37.8	21 18.4	21 15.7	27 56.4
23 F	0 3 50.6	29 5.3	21 44.0	21 3.8	5 58.0	12 39.2	0 39.1	19 17.8	5 34.5	21 18.0	21 16.8	27 56.5
24 S	0 7 47.2	0♎ 4.0	21 40.8	5♊30.3	4 55.3	13 53.5	1 18.0	19 30.5	5 31.1	21 17.6	21 17.8	27 56.6
25 S	0 11 43.7	1 2.8	21 37.6	19 43.2	3 50.0	15 7.9	1 56.9	19 43.1	5 27.6	21 17.2	21 18.8	27 56.7
26 M	0 15 40.3	2 1.6	21 34.4	3♋41.2	2 43.5	16 22.3	2 35.8	19 55.8	5 24.1	21 16.9	21 19.8	27 56.8
27 T	0 19 36.9	3 0.5	21 31.2	17 24.0	1 37.5	17 36.8	3 14.8	20 8.5	5 20.5	21 16.6	21 20.8	27 56.8
28 W	0 23 33.4	3 59.4	21 28.1	0♌52.2	0 33.7	18 51.3	3 53.8	20 21.2	5 16.8	21 16.4	21 21.7	27 56.9
29 T	0 27 30.0	4 58.3	21 24.9	14 6.3	29♍33.7	20 5.9	4 32.8	20 34.0	5 13.0	21 16.3	21 22.6	27 56.9
30 F	0 31 26.5	5 57.3	21 21.7	27 7.1	28 39.3	21 20.4	5 11.9	20 46.8	5 9.2	21 16.2	21 23.5	27R56.8
						DECLINATION						
1 T	22 37 6.4	8N41.7	18N30.4	23N53.3	4S10.5	16N53.1	6N13.7	4S49.2	11N11.7	22S13.3	21N13.0	16N45.1
4 S	22 48 56.1	7 36.2	18 28.0	10 48.5	5 34.5	15 52.0	5 27.9	5 3.0	11 9.6	22 13.9	21 12.3	16 44.9
7 W	23 0 45.8	6 29.6	18 25.6	5S42.4	6 43.8	14 46.9	4 41.6	5 16.9	11 7.2	22 14.5	21 11.6	16 44.6
10 S	23 12 35.4	5 22.0	18 23.1	19 47.4	7 34.5	13 38.0	3 55.1	5 31.0	11 4.6	22 14.9	21 10.9	16 44.3
13 T	23 24 25.1	4 13.6	18 20.7	26 46.5	8 1.6	12 25.7	3 8.3	5 45.2	11 1.7	22 15.3	21 10.2	16 44.0
16 F	23 36 14.7	3 4.6	18 18.3	22 25.3	7 59.1	11 10.2	2 21.3	5 59.4	10 58.5	22 15.7	21 9.6	16 43.7
19 M	23 48 4.4	1 55.0	18 15.8	6 59.3	7 21.6	9 51.8	1 34.1	6 13.8	10 55.1	22 16.0	21 9.0	16 43.4
22 T	23 59 54.1	0 45.2	18 13.3	12N30.3	6 6.2	8 30.9	0 46.8	6 28.2	10 51.5	22 16.2	21 8.4	16 43.1
25 S	0 11 43.7	0S25.0	18 10.9	25 34.3	4 17.7	7 7.8	0S 0.7	6 42.7	10 47.7	22 16.3	21 7.9	16 42.8
28 W	0 23 33.4	1 35.2	18 8.4	24 42.4	2 11.7	5 42.8	0 48.2	6 57.3	10 43.7	22 16.4	21 7.5	16 42.5

OCTOBER 1910

DAY	EPHEMERIS SIDEREAL TIME	☉	☊	☽	☿	♀	♂	♃	♄	♅	♆	♇
						LONGITUDE						
1 S	0 35 23.1	6♎56.3	21♉18.5	9♍54.9	27♍51.9	22♍35.0	5♎51.0	20♎59.6	5♉ 5.3	21♑16.1	21♋24.3	27♊56.8
2 S	0 39 19.6	7 55.3	21 15.4	22 30.3	27R12.8	23 49.7	6 30.1	21 12.4	5R 1.3	21 16.1	21 25.1	27R56.7
3 M	0 43 16.2	8 54.4	21 12.2	4♎53.6	26 43.0	25 4.4	7 9.3	21 25.3	4 57.3	21D16.2	21 25.9	27 56.7
4 T	0 47 12.7	9 53.5	21 9.0	17 5.7	26 23.2	26 19.1	7 48.4	21 38.2	4 53.2	21 16.3	21 26.6	27 56.5
5 W	0 51 9.3	10 52.7	21 5.8	29 7.7	26 13.8	27 33.8	8 27.6	21 51.1	4 49.1	21 16.5	21 27.3	27 56.4
6 T	0 55 5.8	11 51.9	21 2.6	11♏ 1.6	26D15.1	28 48.5	9 6.9	22 4.0	4 44.8	21 16.7	21 28.0	27 56.2
7 F	0 59 2.4	12 51.1	20 59.5	22 49.9	26 26.9	0♎ 3.3	9 46.1	22 16.9	4 40.6	21 16.9	21 28.6	27 56.1
8 S	1 2 59.0	13 50.3	20 56.3	4♐35.9	26 49.0	1 18.1	10 25.4	22 29.9	4 36.3	21 17.2	21 29.2	27 55.9
9 S	1 6 55.5	14 49.6	20 53.1	16 23.6	27 20.8	2 32.9	11 4.7	22 42.9	4 31.9	21 17.6	21 29.8	27 55.6
10 M	1 10 52.0	15 48.9	20 49.9	28 17.3	28 1.8	3 47.8	11 44.1	22 55.9	4 27.5	21 18.0	21 30.4	27 55.4
11 T	1 14 48.6	16 48.3	20 46.8	10♑22.1	28 51.3	5 2.6	12 23.4	23 8.9	4 23.1	21 18.5	21 30.9	27 55.1
12 W	1 18 45.2	17 47.6	20 43.6	22 43.0	29 48.6	6 17.5	13 2.8	23 21.9	4 18.6	21 19.0	21 31.3	27 54.8
13 T	1 22 41.7	18 47.0	20 40.4	5♒24.7	0♎52.8	7 32.4	13 42.2	23 34.9	4 14.0	21 19.5	21 31.8	27 54.5
14 F	1 26 38.3	19 46.4	20 37.2	18 31.1	2 3.2	8 47.4	14 21.7	23 47.9	4 9.5	21 20.2	21 32.2	27 54.2
15 S	1 30 34.8	20 45.9	20 34.0	2♓ 4.7	3 19.1	10 2.3	15 1.2	24 1.0	4 4.9	21 20.8	21 32.6	27 53.8
16 S	1 34 31.4	21 45.4	20 30.9	16 6.0	4 39.6	11 17.3	15 40.7	24 14.0	4 0.2	21 21.5	21 32.9	27 53.5
17 M	1 38 27.9	22 44.9	20 27.7	0♈32.9	6 4.2	12 32.3	16 20.2	24 27.1	3 55.6	21 22.3	21 33.2	27 53.1
18 T	1 42 24.5	23 44.4	20 24.5	15 20.3	7 32.2	13 47.3	16 59.8	24 40.1	3 50.9	21 23.1	21 33.5	27 52.7
19 W	1 46 21.0	24 44.0	20 21.3	0♉20.9	9 3.0	15 2.3	17 39.4	24 53.2	3 46.1	21 24.0	21 33.7	27 52.2
20 T	1 50 17.6	25 43.6	20 18.2	15 25.8	10 36.2	16 17.4	18 19.0	25 6.2	3 41.4	21 24.9	21 33.9	27 51.8
21 F	1 54 14.1	26 43.3	20 15.0	0♊26.1	12 11.3	17 32.5	18 58.7	25 19.3	3 36.6	21 25.9	21 34.1	27 51.3
22 S	1 58 10.7	27 43.0	20 11.8	15 14.3	13 48.0	18 47.6	19 38.4	25 32.3	3 31.9	21 26.9	21 34.2	27 50.8
23 S	2 2 7.3	28 42.7	20 8.6	29 44.4	15 25.8	20 2.7	20 18.1	25 45.4	3 27.1	21 28.0	21 34.3	27 50.3
24 M	2 6 3.8	29 42.5	20 5.4	13♋53.4	17 4.6	21 17.8	20 57.9	25 58.5	3 22.3	21 29.1	21 34.4	27 49.7
25 T	2 10 0.4	0♏42.3	20 2.3	27 40.0	18 44.0	22 32.9	21 37.6	26 11.5	3 17.5	21 30.2	21 34.4	27 49.2
26 W	2 13 56.9	1 42.1	19 59.1	11♌ 4.8	20 23.9	23 48.1	22 17.5	26 24.5	3 12.6	21 31.5	21 34.4	27 48.6
27 T	2 17 53.5	2 42.0	19 55.9	24 9.6	22 4.1	25 3.3	22 57.3	26 37.6	3 7.8	21 32.7	21R34.4	27 48.0
28 F	2 21 50.0	3 41.9	19 52.7	6♍56.6	23 44.4	26 18.5	23 37.2	26 50.6	3 3.0	21 34.0	21 34.3	27 47.4
29 S	2 25 46.6	4 41.8	19 49.6	19 28.3	25 24.8	27 33.7	24 17.1	27 3.6	2 58.1	21 35.4	21 34.2	27 46.7
30 S	2 29 43.1	5 41.8	19 46.4	1♎47.2	27 5.1	28 49.0	24 57.1	27 16.6	2 53.3	21 36.8	21 34.1	27 46.1
31 M	2 33 39.7	6 41.8	19 43.2	13 55.6	28 45.2	0♏ 4.2	25 37.1	27 29.7	2 48.5	21 38.3	21 33.9	27 45.4
						DECLINATION						
1 S	0 35 23.1	2S45.3	18N 5.9	12N20.0	0S12.2	4N16.2	1S35.7	7S11.8	10N39.5	22S16.4	21N 7.0	16N42.2
4 T	0 47 12.7	3 55.2	18 3.4	4S 8.3	1N17.4	2 48.3	2 23.2	7 26.4	10 35.1	22 16.3	21 6.6	16 41.9
7 F	0 59 2.4	5 4.7	18 0.9	18 46.6	2 2.5	1 19.5	3 10.7	7 41.0	10 30.6	22 16.1	21 6.3	16 41.6
10 M	1 10 52.0	6 13.6	17 58.4	26 42.6	1 59.9	0S 9.9	3 58.0	7 55.5	10 26.0	22 15.9	21 6.0	16 41.3
13 T	1 22 41.7	7 21.8	17 55.8	23 50.3	1 15.0	1 39.5	4 45.2	8 10.0	10 21.3	22 15.6	21 5.7	16 41.0
16 S	1 34 31.4	8 29.0	17 53.3	9 47.7	0S 2.8	3 9.1	5 32.1	8 24.5	10 16.5	22 15.2	21 5.5	16 40.7
19 W	1 46 21.0	9 35.1	17 50.8	9N59.9	1 43.6	4 38.2	6 18.8	8 38.9	10 11.7	22 14.8	21 5.3	16 40.4
22 S	1 58 10.7	10 40.0	17 48.2	24 55.6	3 38.5	6 6.6	7 5.2	8 53.2	10 6.8	22 14.3	21 5.2	16 40.1
25 T	2 10 0.4	11 43.5	17 45.7	25 26.3	5 40.8	7 33.9	7 51.2	9 7.4	10 2.0	22 13.7	21 5.2	16 39.8
28 F	2 21 50.0	12 45.4	17 43.1	13 37.7	7 45.7	8 59.8	8 36.9	9 21.6	9 57.1	22 13.0	21 5.1	16 39.6
31 M	2 33 39.7	13 45.5	17 40.5	2S40.8	9 49.7	10 23.8	9 22.1	9 35.6	9 52.3	22 12.3	21 5.2	16 39.3

NOVEMBER 1910

DAY	EPHEMERIS SIDEREAL TIME	☉	☊	☽	☿	♀	♂	♃	♄	♅	♆	♇
	h m s	° ′	° ′	° ′	° ′	° ′	° ′	° ′	° ′	° ′	° ′	° ′
						LONGITUDE						
1 T	2 37 36.3	7♏41.9	19♉40.0	25♎55.6	0♏25.2	1♏19.5	26♎17.1	27♎42.6	2♉43.7	21♑39.8	21♋33.7	27♊44.7
2 W	2 41 32.8	8 42.0	19 36.9	7♏49.2	2 4.9	2 34.8	26 57.2	27 55.6	2R38.9	21 41.3	21R33.5	27R44.0
3 T	2 45 29.3	9 42.1	19 33.7	19 38.3	3 44.3	3 50.1	27 37.3	28 8.6	2 34.1	21 42.9	21 33.2	27 43.3
4 F	2 49 25.9	10 42.2	19 30.5	1♐25.2	5 23.3	5 5.4	28 17.4	28 21.5	2 29.4	21 44.6	21 32.9	27 42.5
5 S	2 53 22.5	11 42.4	19 27.3	13 12.2	7 2.1	6 20.7	28 57.5	28 34.4	2 24.6	21 46.3	21 32.6	27 41.8
6 S	2 57 19.0	12 42.6	19 24.1	25 2.1	8 40.5	7 36.0	29 37.7	28 47.3	2 19.9	21 48.0	21 32.2	27 41.0
7 M	3 1 15.6	13 42.8	19 21.0	6♑58.1	10 18.5	8 51.3	0♏17.9	29 0.2	2 15.2	21 49.8	21 31.8	27 40.2
8 T	3 5 12.1	14 43.1	19 17.8	19 4.0	11 56.1	10 6.7	0 58.2	29 13.0	2 10.6	21 51.6	21 31.4	27 39.4
9 W	3 9 8.7	15 43.3	19 14.6	1♒23.5	13 33.4	11 22.0	1 38.5	29 25.8	2 5.9	21 53.5	21 30.9	27 38.5
10 T	3 13 5.3	16 43.6	19 11.4	14 1.0	15 10.4	12 37.4	2 18.8	29 38.6	2 1.3	21 55.5	21 30.4	27 37.7
11 F	3 17 1.8	17 44.0	19 8.3	27 0.2	16 46.9	13 52.7	2 59.1	29 51.4	1 56.8	21 57.4	21 29.9	27 36.8
12 S	3 20 58.4	18 44.3	19 5.1	10♓24.5	18 23.2	15 8.1	3 39.5	0♏ 4.1	1 52.3	21 59.4	21 29.3	27 35.9
13 S	3 24 54.9	19 44.7	19 1.9	24 15.8	19 59.1	16 23.4	4 19.9	0 16.9	1 47.8	22 1.5	21 28.7	27 35.0
14 M	3 28 51.5	20 45.1	18 58.7	8♈34.1	21 34.7	17 38.8	5 0.3	0 29.5	1 43.4	22 3.6	21 28.1	27 34.1
15 T	3 32 48.0	21 45.5	18 55.6	23 16.8	23 10.0	18 54.2	5 40.8	0 42.2	1 39.0	22 5.7	21 27.4	27 33.2
16 W	3 36 44.6	22 45.9	18 52.4	8♉18.5	24 45.1	20 9.6	6 21.3	0 54.8	1 34.6	22 7.9	21 26.7	27 32.3
17 T	3 40 41.1	23 46.4	18 49.2	23 31.2	26 19.8	21 25.0	7 1.8	1 7.4	1 30.4	22 10.1	21 26.0	27 31.3
18 F	3 44 37.7	24 46.9	18 46.0	8♊45.4	27 54.3	22 40.4	7 42.4	1 19.9	1 26.1	22 12.4	21 25.2	27 30.3
19 S	3 48 34.3	25 47.4	18 42.8	23 51.3	29 28.6	23 55.8	8 23.0	1 32.4	1 22.0	22 14.7	21 24.5	27 29.4
20 S	3 52 30.8	26 48.0	18 39.7	8♋40.2	1♐ 2.7	25 11.2	9 3.7	1 44.8	1 17.8	22 17.0	21 23.6	27 28.4
21 M	3 56 27.4	27 48.5	18 36.5	23 5.8	2 36.6	26 26.6	9 44.3	1 57.3	1 13.8	22 19.4	21 22.8	27 27.4
22 T	4 0 23.9	28 49.2	18 33.3	7♌ 4.8	4 10.3	27 42.0	10 25.1	2 9.6	1 9.8	22 21.8	21 21.9	27 26.3
23 W	4 4 20.5	29 49.8	18 30.1	20 36.5	5 43.8	28 57.4	11 5.8	2 22.0	1 5.9	22 24.2	21 21.0	27 25.3
24 T	4 8 17.1	0♐50.5	18 27.0	3♍42.4	7 17.2	0♐12.9	11 46.6	2 34.3	1 2.0	22 26.7	21 20.1	27 24.3
25 F	4 12 13.6	1 51.1	18 23.8	16 25.6	8 50.4	1 28.3	12 27.4	2 46.5	0 58.2	22 29.3	21 19.1	27 23.2
26 S	4 16 10.2	2 51.9	18 20.6	28 49.9	10 23.5	2 43.7	13 8.3	2 58.7	0 54.5	22 31.8	21 18.2	27 22.2
27 S	4 20 6.7	3 52.6	18 17.4	10♎59.3	11 56.5	3 59.2	13 49.2	3 10.8	0 50.8	22 34.4	21 17.1	27 21.1
28 M	4 24 3.3	4 53.4	18 14.3	22 58.0	13 29.3	5 14.7	14 30.1	3 22.9	0 47.3	22 37.1	21 16.1	27 20.0
29 T	4 27 59.9	5 54.2	18 11.1	4♏49.7	15 2.1	6 30.1	15 11.1	3 35.0	0 43.8	22 39.7	21 15.0	27 18.9
30 W	4 31 56.4	6 55.0	18 7.9	16 37.5	16 34.7	7 45.6	15 52.1	3 47.0	0 40.4	22 42.4	21 13.9	27 17.8
						DECLINATION						
1 T	2 37 36.3	14S 5.1	17N39.7	8S 4.3	10S30.5	10S51.4	9S37.0	9S40.2	9N50.8	22S12.0	21N 5.2	16N39.2
4 F	2 49 25.9	15 2.6	17 37.1	21 33.5	12 29.8	12 12.5	10 21.6	9 54.0	9 46.1	22 11.2	21 5.3	16 39.0
7 M	3 1 15.6	15 57.8	17 34.5	27 11.5	14 23.9	13 31.0	11 5.5	10 7.7	9 41.5	22 10.3	21 5.4	16 38.8
10 T	3 13 5.3	16 50.7	17 31.9	21 40.7	16 11.6	14 46.5	11 48.8	10 21.2	9 37.0	22 9.4	21 5.6	16 38.5
13 S	3 24 54.9	17 40.9	17 29.3	6 16.0	17 52.0	15 58.6	12 31.4	10 34.5	9 32.7	22 8.4	21 5.9	16 38.3
16 W	3 36 44.6	18 28.4	17 26.7	13N19.7	19 24.5	17 7.0	13 13.3	10 47.7	9 28.6	22 7.3	21 6.1	16 38.2
19 S	3 48 34.3	19 13.0	17 24.1	26 19.3	20 48.4	18 11.3	13 54.3	11 0.6	9 24.6	22 6.2	21 6.5	16 38.0
22 T	4 0 23.9	19 54.4	17 21.4	23 30.8	22 3.1	19 11.1	14 34.5	11 13.3	9 20.9	22 5.0	21 6.8	16 37.9
25 F	4 12 13.6	20 32.6	17 18.8	9 41.6	23 8.0	20 6.2	15 13.8	11 25.8	9 17.4	22 3.7	21 7.2	16 37.7
28 M	4 24 3.3	21 7.4	17 16.2	6S45.3	24 2.3	20 56.2	15 52.2	11 38.0	9 14.2	22 2.4	21 7.7	16 37.6

DECEMBER 1910

DAY	EPHEMERIS SIDEREAL TIME	☉	☊	☽	☿	♀	♂	♃	♄	♅	♆	♇
						LONGITUDE						
1 T	4 35 53.0	7♐55.8	18♉ 4.7	28♏24.4	18♐ 7.2	9♐ 1.1	16♏33.1	3♏58.9	0♉37.0	22♑45.2	21♋12.8	27♊16.7
2 F	4 39 49.5	8 56.7	18 1.5	10♐12.6	19 39.6	10 16.5	17 14.2	4 10.7	0R33.8	22 48.0	21R11.7	27R15.6
3 S	4 43 46.1	9 57.6	17 58.4	22 4.2	21 11.9	11 32.0	17 55.3	4 22.6	0 30.6	22 50.8	21 10.5	27 14.5
4 S	4 47 42.6	10 58.5	17 55.2	4♑ 1.2	22 44.1	12 47.5	18 36.4	4 34.3	0 27.5	22 53.6	21 9.3	27 13.3
5 M	4 51 39.2	11 59.4	17 52.0	16 5.4	24 16.1	14 2.9	19 17.6	4 46.0	0 24.5	22 56.5	21 8.1	27 12.2
6 T	4 55 35.7	13 0.3	17 48.8	28 19.0	25 47.9	15 18.4	19 58.8	4 57.6	0 21.6	22 59.4	21 6.8	27 11.1
7 W	4 59 32.3	14 1.2	17 45.7	10♒44.1	27 19.6	16 33.9	20 40.0	5 9.2	0 18.8	23 2.3	21 5.6	27 9.9
8 T	5 3 28.9	15 2.2	17 42.5	23 23.5	28 50.9	17 49.4	21 21.3	5 20.6	0 16.1	23 5.3	21 4.3	27 8.8
9 F	5 7 25.4	16 3.1	17 39.3	6♓19.9	0♑22.0	19 4.8	22 2.6	5 32.1	0 13.5	23 8.2	21 3.0	27 7.6
10 S	5 11 22.0	17 4.1	17 36.1	19 36.0	1 52.8	20 20.3	22 44.0	5 43.4	0 11.0	23 11.3	21 1.6	27 6.4
11 S	5 15 18.5	18 5.1	17 33.0	3♈14.3	3 23.1	21 35.8	23 25.3	5 54.7	0 8.5	23 14.3	21 0.3	27 5.2
12 M	5 19 15.1	19 6.1	17 29.8	17 16.1	4 52.9	22 51.2	24 6.7	6 5.9	0 6.2	23 17.4	20 58.9	27 4.1
13 T	5 23 11.7	20 7.1	17 26.6	1♉41.2	6 22.1	24 6.7	24 48.2	6 17.0	0 4.0	23 20.5	20 57.5	27 2.9
14 W	5 27 8.2	21 8.1	17 23.4	16 27.0	7 50.6	25 22.1	25 29.7	6 28.0	0 1.9	23 23.6	20 56.1	27 1.7
15 T	5 31 4.8	22 9.1	17 20.3	1♊28.5	9 18.2	26 37.6	26 11.2	6 39.0	29♈59.8	23 26.7	20 54.7	27 0.5
16 F	5 35 1.3	23 10.2	17 17.1	16 37.9	10 44.8	27 53.0	26 52.7	6 49.9	29 57.9	23 29.9	20 53.2	26 59.3
17 S	5 38 57.9	24 11.2	17 13.9	1♋45.8	12 10.1	29 8.5	27 34.3	7 0.7	29 56.1	23 33.1	20 51.8	26 58.2
18 S	5 42 54.5	25 12.3	17 10.7	16 42.4	13 34.0	0♑23.9	28 15.9	7 11.4	29 54.4	23 36.3	20 50.3	26 57.0
19 M	5 46 51.0	26 13.3	17 7.6	1♌19.3	14 56.1	1 39.4	28 57.6	7 22.0	29 52.8	23 39.5	20 48.8	26 55.8
20 T	5 50 47.6	27 14.4	17 4.4	15 30.2	16 16.2	2 54.8	29 39.2	7 32.6	29 51.2	23 42.8	20 47.3	26 54.6
21 W	5 54 44.1	28 15.5	17 1.2	29 12.4	17 33.9	4 10.3	0♐21.0	7 43.0	29 49.8	23 46.0	20 45.7	26 53.4
22 T	5 58 40.7	29 16.6	16 58.0	12♍25.9	18 48.7	5 25.7	1 2.7	7 53.4	29 48.6	23 49.3	20 44.2	26 52.2
23 F	6 2 37.2	0♑17.7	16 54.8	25 13.0	20 0.2	6 41.1	1 44.5	8 3.7	29 47.4	23 52.6	20 42.6	26 51.0
24 S	6 6 33.8	1 18.8	16 51.7	7♎37.9	21 7.9	7 56.6	2 26.4	8 13.9	29 46.3	23 56.0	20 41.1	26 49.8
25 S	6 10 30.4	2 19.9	16 48.5	19 45.5	22 11.0	9 12.0	3 8.2	8 24.0	29 45.3	23 59.3	20 39.5	26 48.7
26 M	6 14 26.9	3 21.1	16 45.3	1♏40.8	23 9.0	10 27.5	3 50.2	8 34.0	29 44.5	24 2.7	20 37.9	26 47.5
27 T	6 18 23.5	4 22.2	16 42.1	13 29.1	24 1.1	11 42.9	4 32.1	8 43.9	29 43.7	24 6.1	20 36.3	26 46.3
28 W	6 22 20.0	5 23.4	16 39.0	25 14.9	24 46.3	12 58.3	5 14.1	8 53.7	29 43.1	24 9.5	20 34.6	26 45.1
29 T	6 26 16.6	6 24.6	16 35.8	7♐ 2.2	25 24.0	14 13.8	5 56.1	9 3.4	29 42.5	24 12.9	20 33.0	26 43.9
30 F	6 30 13.1	7 25.7	16 32.6	18 54.1	25 53.0	15 29.2	6 38.2	9 12.9	29 42.1	24 16.3	20 31.4	26 42.8
31 S	6 34 9.7	8 26.9	16 29.4	0♑53.3	26 12.6	16 44.6	7 20.3	9 22.4	29 41.8	24 19.7	20 29.7	26 41.6
						DECLINATION						
1 T	4 35 53.0	21S38.6	17N13.5	20S38.0	24S45.6	21S40.8	16S29.5	11S50.0	9N11.2	22S 1.0	21N 8.2	16N37.5
4 S	4 47 42.6	22 6.1	17 10.9	27 5.8	25 17.1	22 19.7	17 5.7	12 1.7	9 8.6	21 59.6	21 8.7	16 37.5
7 W	4 59 32.3	22 29.7	17 8.2	22 32.0	25 36.2	22 52.7	17 40.7	12 13.1	9 6.2	21 58.1	21 9.3	16 37.4
10 S	5 11 22.0	22 49.4	17 5.5	8 15.6	25 42.5	23 19.4	18 14.5	12 24.3	9 4.1	21 56.5	21 9.9	16 37.4
13 T	5 23 11.7	23 5.1	17 2.8	10N36.5	25 35.5	23 39.8	18 47.0	12 35.1	9 2.4	21 55.0	21 10.5	16 37.4
16 F	5 35 1.3	23 16.6	17 0.2	25 11.7	25 15.2	23 53.6	19 18.2	12 45.6	9 1.0	21 53.3	21 11.2	16 37.5
19 M	5 46 51.0	23 23.9	16 57.5	24 42.0	24 41.9	24 0.8	19 48.0	12 55.8	9 0.0	21 51.7	21 11.8	16 37.5
22 T	5 58 40.7	23 27.0	16 54.8	11 16.4	23 56.9	24 1.3	20 16.3	13 5.6	8 59.3	21 50.0	21 12.5	16 37.6
25 S	6 10 30.4	23 25.9	16 52.1	5S25.5	23 2.4	23 55.1	20 43.1	13 15.1	8 59.0	21 48.2	21 13.3	16 37.7
28 W	6 22 20.0	23 20.6	16 49.3	19 40.8	22 2.6	23 42.2	21 8.4	13 24.3	8 59.0	21 46.4	21 14.0	16 37.8
31 S	6 34 9.7	23 11.0	16 46.6	26 55.2	21 3.3	23 22.7	21 32.0	13 33.1	8 59.4	21 44.6	21 14.7	16 38.0

JANUARY 1911

LONGITUDE

DAY	EPHEMERIS SIDEREAL TIME	☉	☊	☽	☿	♀	♂	♃	♄	♅	♆	♇
	h m s	° ′	° ′	° ′	° ′	° ′	° ′	° ′	° ′	° ′	° ′	° ′
1 S	6 38 6.3	9♑28.1	16♉26.3	13♑ 1.3	26♑21.9	18♑ 0.0	8♐ 2.4	9♏31.8	29♈41.6	24♑23.2	20♋28.1	26♊40.5
2 M	6 42 2.8	10 29.3	16 23.1	25 19.3	26R20.2	19 15.5	8 44.5	9 41.1	29R41.6	24 26.7	20R26.4	26R39.3
3 T	6 45 59.4	11 30.5	16 19.9	7♒47.9	26 6.8	20 30.9	9 26.7	9 50.2	29D41.6	24 30.1	20 24.7	26 38.1
4 W	6 49 55.9	12 31.6	16 16.7	20 27.8	25 41.6	21 46.3	10 9.0	9 59.2	29 41.7	24 33.6	20 23.1	26 37.0
5 T	6 53 52.5	13 32.8	16 13.6	3♓19.4	25 4.6	23 1.7	10 51.2	10 8.2	29 42.0	24 37.1	20 21.4	26 35.9
6 F	6 57 49.1	14 34.0	16 10.4	16 23.6	24 16.4	24 17.0	11 33.5	10 17.0	29 42.4	24 40.6	20 19.7	26 34.7
7 S	7 1 45.6	15 35.2	16 7.2	29 41.5	23 17.9	25 32.4	12 15.8	10 25.7	29 42.9	24 44.1	20 18.0	26 33.6
8 S	7 5 42.2	16 36.3	16 4.0	13♈14.7	22 10.8	26 47.8	12 58.2	10 34.2	29 43.5	24 47.6	20 16.3	26 32.5
9 M	7 9 38.7	17 37.4	16 0.8	27 4.4	20 57.0	28 3.1	13 40.6	10 42.7	29 44.2	24 51.2	20 14.6	26 31.4
10 T	7 13 35.3	18 38.6	15 57.7	11♉11.3	19 38.9	29 18.5	14 23.0	10 51.0	29 45.0	24 54.7	20 12.9	26 30.3
11 W	7 17 31.9	19 39.7	15 54.5	25 35.0	18 18.9	0♒33.8	15 5.4	10 59.2	29 46.0	24 58.2	20 11.2	26 29.2
12 T	7 21 28.4	20 40.8	15 51.3	10♊13.0	16 59.7	1 49.1	15 47.9	11 7.2	29 47.0	25 1.8	20 9.5	26 28.2
13 F	7 25 25.0	21 41.9	15 48.1	25 0.9	15 43.6	3 4.4	16 30.4	11 15.2	29 48.2	25 5.3	20 7.8	26 27.1
14 S	7 29 21.5	22 43.0	15 45.0	9♋51.7	14 32.8	4 19.7	17 13.0	11 23.0	29 49.4	25 8.8	20 6.1	26 26.0
15 S	7 33 18.1	23 44.1	15 41.8	24 37.3	13 28.9	5 35.0	17 55.6	11 30.7	29 50.8	25 12.4	20 4.4	26 25.0
16 M	7 37 14.6	24 45.2	15 38.6	9♌ 9.3	12 33.2	6 50.3	18 38.2	11 38.2	29 52.3	25 15.9	20 2.7	26 24.0
17 T	7 41 11.2	25 46.3	15 35.4	23 20.6	11 46.5	8 5.5	19 20.9	11 45.6	29 53.9	25 19.5	20 1.1	26 22.9
18 W	7 45 7.7	26 47.4	15 32.3	7♍ 6.5	11 9.2	9 20.8	20 3.6	11 52.9	29 55.6	25 23.0	19 59.4	26 21.9
19 T	7 49 4.3	27 48.4	15 29.1	20 25.2	10 41.5	10 36.0	20 46.3	12 0.0	29 57.4	25 26.6	19 57.7	26 20.9
20 F	7 53 0.9	28 49.5	15 25.9	3♎17.6	10 23.1	11 51.2	21 29.1	12 7.0	29 59.3	25 30.1	19 56.0	26 20.0
21 S	7 56 57.4	29 50.6	15 22.7	15 46.6	10 13.7	13 6.5	22 11.9	12 13.9	0♉ 1.4	25 33.6	19 54.3	26 19.0
22 S	8 0 54.0	0♒51.6	15 19.5	27 56.8	10 12.7	14 21.7	22 54.7	12 20.6	0 3.5	25 37.2	19 52.7	26 18.0
23 M	8 4 50.5	1 52.6	15 16.4	9♏53.5	10D19.8	15 36.9	23 37.6	12 27.1	0 5.7	25 40.7	19 51.0	26 17.1
24 T	8 8 47.1	2 53.7	15 13.2	21 42.4	10 34.2	16 52.0	24 20.5	12 33.5	0 8.1	25 44.2	19 49.4	26 16.2
25 W	8 12 43.7	3 54.7	15 10.0	3♐28.9	10 55.3	18 7.2	25 3.5	12 39.8	0 10.5	25 47.8	19 47.7	26 15.2
26 T	8 16 40.2	4 55.7	15 6.8	15 18.1	11 22.7	19 22.4	25 46.5	12 45.9	0 13.1	25 51.3	19 46.1	26 14.3
27 F	8 20 36.8	5 56.7	15 3.7	27 14.4	11 55.7	20 37.5	26 29.5	12 51.9	0 15.7	25 54.8	19 44.5	26 13.5
28 S	8 24 33.3	6 57.7	15 0.5	9♑21.1	12 33.8	21 52.6	27 12.5	12 57.7	0 18.5	25 58.3	19 42.9	26 12.6
29 S	8 28 29.9	7 58.7	14 57.3	21 40.6	13 16.6	23 7.7	27 55.6	13 3.3	0 21.4	26 1.8	19 41.3	26 11.7
30 M	8 32 26.5	8 59.6	14 54.1	4♒14.1	14 3.6	24 22.8	28 38.7	13 8.8	0 24.3	26 5.3	19 39.7	26 10.9
31 T	8 36 23.0	10 0.6	14 51.0	17 1.7	14 54.4	25 37.9	29 21.9	13 14.1	0 27.4	26 8.7	19 38.1	26 10.1

DECLINATION

DAY	EPHEMERIS SIDEREAL TIME	☉	☊	☽	☿	♀	♂	♃	♄	♅	♆	♇
1 S	6 38 6.3	23S 6.9	16N45.7	26S58.5	20S44.9	23S14.7	21S39.5	13S35.9	8N59.6	21S44.0	21N15.0	16N38.0
4 W	6 49 55.9	22 51.7	16 43.0	19 29.3	19 57.8	22 46.6	22 0.8	13 44.2	9 0.5	21 42.2	21 15.8	16 38.2
7 S	7 1 45.6	22 32.5	16 40.2	3 34.7	19 26.8	22 12.3	22 20.4	13 52.1	9 1.7	21 40.3	21 16.5	16 38.4
10 T	7 13 35.3	22 9.3	16 37.5	14N40.8	19 13.2	21 31.9	22 38.1	13 59.5	9 3.3	21 38.4	21 17.3	16 38.6
13 F	7 25 25.0	21 42.1	16 34.7	26 28.2	19 14.7	20 45.8	22 54.0	14 6.6	9 5.2	21 36.5	21 18.1	16 38.9
16 M	7 37 14.6	21 11.2	16 32.0	22 47.5	19 27.7	19 54.2	23 8.0	14 13.2	9 7.5	21 34.6	21 18.9	16 39.2
19 T	7 49 4.3	20 36.7	16 29.2	7 38.3	19 48.7	18 57.4	23 20.0	14 19.5	9 10.1	21 32.7	21 19.7	16 39.5
22 S	8 0 54.0	19 58.6	16 26.4	9S16.6	20 14.0	17 55.7	23 30.1	14 25.3	9 13.0	21 30.7	21 20.4	16 39.8
25 W	8 12 43.7	19 17.2	16 23.6	22 21.2	20 39.8	16 49.5	23 38.1	14 30.6	9 16.3	21 28.8	21 21.2	16 40.2
28 S	8 24 33.3	18 32.6	16 20.8	27 9.3	21 2.9	15 39.0	23 44.2	14 35.5	9 19.9	21 26.9	21 22.0	16 40.5
31 T	8 36 23.0	17 44.9	16 18.1	20 29.6	21 20.3	14 24.7	23 48.1	14 40.0	9 23.8	21 24.9	21 22.7	16 40.9

FEBRUARY 1911

LONGITUDE

DAY	EPHEMERIS SIDEREAL TIME	☉	☊	☽	☿	♀	♂	♃	♄	♅	♆	♇
1 W	8 40 19.6	11♒ 1.5	14♉47.8	0♓ 2.6	15♑48.7	26♒53.0	0♑ 5.0	13♏19.3	0♉30.6	26♑12.2	19♋36.5	26♊ 9.3
2 T	8 44 16.1	12 2.4	14 44.6	13 15.5	16 46.2	28 8.0	0 48.2	13 24.3	0 33.9	26 15.6	19R35.0	26R 8.5
3 F	8 48 12.7	13 3.3	14 41.4	26 39.0	17 46.6	29 23.1	1 31.5	13 29.1	0 37.2	26 19.1	19 33.5	26 7.7
4 S	8 52 9.2	14 4.2	14 38.3	10♈12.1	18 49.7	0♓38.1	2 14.7	13 33.8	0 40.7	26 22.5	19 32.0	26 7.0
5 S	8 56 5.8	15 5.0	14 35.1	23 54.0	19 55.1	1 53.0	2 58.0	13 38.3	0 44.2	26 25.9	19 30.4	26 6.2
6 M	9 0 2.3	16 5.8	14 31.9	7♉44.8	21 2.8	3 8.0	3 41.3	13 42.6	0 47.9	26 29.3	19 29.0	26 5.5
7 T	9 3 58.9	17 6.6	14 28.7	21 44.5	22 12.6	4 22.9	4 24.7	13 46.8	0 51.7	26 32.7	19 27.5	26 4.8
8 W	9 7 55.5	18 7.4	14 25.5	5♊52.9	23 24.3	5 37.8	5 8.1	13 50.8	0 55.5	26 36.1	19 26.0	26 4.2
9 T	9 11 52.0	19 8.1	14 22.4	20 9.1	24 37.7	6 52.7	5 51.5	13 54.6	0 59.4	26 39.4	19 24.6	26 3.5
10 F	9 15 48.6	20 8.8	14 19.2	4♋31.0	25 52.8	8 7.6	6 34.9	13 58.2	1 3.5	26 42.7	19 23.2	26 2.8
11 S	9 19 45.1	21 9.5	14 16.0	18 54.5	27 9.4	9 22.4	7 18.4	14 1.7	1 7.6	26 46.0	19 21.8	26 2.2
12 S	9 23 41.7	22 10.2	14 12.8	3♌14.6	28 27.5	10 37.2	8 1.9	14 5.0	1 11.8	26 49.3	19 20.4	26 1.6
13 M	9 27 38.2	23 10.8	14 9.7	17 25.2	29 47.0	11 52.0	8 45.4	14 8.1	1 16.1	26 52.6	19 19.1	26 1.1
14 T	9 31 34.8	24 11.4	14 6.5	1♍20.8	1♒ 7.8	13 6.7	9 29.0	14 11.0	1 20.5	26 55.9	19 17.7	26 0.5
15 W	9 35 31.3	25 12.0	14 3.3	14 56.8	2 29.9	14 21.4	10 12.6	14 13.8	1 24.9	26 59.1	19 16.4	25 60.0
16 T	9 39 27.9	26 12.6	14 0.1	28 10.6	3 53.2	15 36.1	10 56.2	14 16.4	1 29.5	27 2.3	19 15.1	25 59.4
17 F	9 43 24.4	27 13.1	13 56.9	11♎ 1.8	5 17.6	16 50.8	11 39.9	14 18.8	1 34.1	27 5.5	19 13.9	25 58.9
18 S	9 47 21.0	28 13.6	13 53.8	23 31.9	6 43.2	18 5.4	12 23.6	14 21.0	1 38.8	27 8.6	19 12.6	25 58.5
19 S	9 51 17.6	29 14.1	13 50.6	5♏44.2	8 9.9	19 20.0	13 7.3	14 23.0	1 43.6	27 11.8	19 11.4	25 58.0
20 M	9 55 14.1	0♓14.6	13 47.4	17 43.1	9 37.7	20 34.6	13 51.0	14 24.9	1 48.5	27 14.9	19 10.2	25 57.6
21 T	9 59 10.7	1 15.1	13 44.2	29 33.9	11 6.5	21 49.1	14 34.8	14 26.6	1 53.5	27 18.0	19 9.0	25 57.2
22 W	10 3 7.2	2 15.5	13 41.1	11♐22.1	12 36.4	23 3.7	15 18.7	14 28.0	1 58.5	27 21.1	19 7.9	25 56.8
23 T	10 7 3.8	3 15.9	13 37.9	23 13.1	14 7.3	24 18.1	16 2.5	14 29.3	2 3.7	27 24.1	19 6.7	25 56.4
24 F	10 11 0.3	4 16.3	13 34.7	5♑12.0	15 39.2	25 32.6	16 46.4	14 30.4	2 8.8	27 27.1	19 5.6	25 56.0
25 S	10 14 56.9	5 16.7	13 31.5	17 23.5	17 12.1	26 47.0	17 30.3	14 31.4	2 14.1	27 30.1	19 4.6	25 55.7
26 S	10 18 53.4	6 17.0	13 28.4	29 50.8	18 46.1	28 1.4	18 14.2	14 32.1	2 19.5	27 33.1	19 3.5	25 55.4
27 M	10 22 50.0	7 17.3	13 25.2	12♒36.0	20 21.1	29 15.8	18 58.2	14 32.6	2 24.9	27 36.0	19 2.5	25 55.1
28 T	10 26 46.6	8 17.6	13 22.0	25 39.8	21 57.1	0♈30.2	19 42.1	14 33.0	2 30.4	27 38.9	19 1.5	25 54.9

DECLINATION

DAY	EPHEMERIS SIDEREAL TIME	☉	☊	☽	☿	♀	♂	♃	♄	♅	♆	♇
1 W	8 40 19.6	17S28.4	16N17.1	15S58.4	21S24.6	13S59.1	23S48.9	14S41.4	9N25.1	21S24.3	21N22.9	16N41.1
4 S	8 52 9.2	16 37.0	16 14.3	1N26.4	21 31.8	12 40.2	23 50.1	14 45.2	9 29.4	21 22.4	21 23.7	16 41.5
7 T	9 3 58.9	15 43.0	16 11.5	18 50.5	21 29.6	11 18.3	23 49.1	14 48.5	9 34.0	21 20.5	21 24.4	16 41.9
10 F	9 15 48.6	14 46.6	16 8.7	27 14.5	21 17.3	9 53.7	23 46.0	14 51.4	9 38.8	21 18.6	21 25.0	16 42.4
13 M	9 27 38.2	13 47.9	16 5.8	20 22.4	20 54.3	8 26.8	23 40.8	14 53.8	9 43.9	21 16.7	21 25.7	16 42.9
16 T	9 39 27.9	12 47.3	16 3.0	3 59.2	20 20.0	6 57.9	23 33.5	14 55.7	9 49.2	21 14.9	21 26.3	16 43.4
19 S	9 51 17.6	11 44.8	16 0.2	12S50.7	19 34.3	5 27.4	23 24.0	14 57.1	9 54.7	21 13.1	21 26.9	16 43.9
22 W	10 3 7.2	10 40.6	15 57.3	24 33.3	18 37.0	3 55.6	23 12.4	14 58.1	10 0.5	21 11.4	21 27.5	16 44.4
25 S	10 14 56.9	9 34.9	15 54.5	26 51.2	17 27.9	2 22.8	22 58.8	14 58.5	10 6.5	21 9.7	21 28.0	16 44.9
28 T	10 26 46.6	8 27.9	15 51.6	17 35.3	16 6.9	0 49.4	22 43.1	14 58.5	10 12.6	21 8.0	21 28.5	16 45.5

MARCH 1911

LONGITUDE

DAY	EPHEMERIS SIDEREAL TIME h m s	☉ ° ′	☊ ° ′	☽ ° ′	☿ ° ′	♀ ° ′	♂ ° ′	♃ ° ′	♄ ° ′	♅ ° ′	♆ ° ′	♇ ° ′
1 W	10 30 43.1	9 ♓ 17.9	13 ♉ 18.8	9 ♓ 1.4	23 ♒ 34.1	1 ♈ 44.5	20 ♑ 26.1	14 ♏ 33.1	2 ♉ 35.9	27 ♑ 41.8	19 ♋ 0.5	25 ♊ 54.6
2 T	10 34 39.6	10 18.1	13 15.6	22 38.3	25 12.1	2 58.7	21 10.2	14 R 33.1	2 41.6	27 44.6	18 R 59.6	25 R 54.4
3 F	10 38 36.2	11 18.3	13 12.5	6 ♈ 27.5	26 51.2	4 13.0	21 54.2	14 32.9	2 47.3	27 47.4	18 58.7	25 54.2
4 S	10 42 32.8	12 18.5	13 9.3	20 25.5	28 31.4	5 27.2	22 38.3	14 32.5	2 53.1	27 50.2	18 57.8	25 54.0
5 S	10 46 29.3	13 18.6	13 6.1	4 ♉ 29.1	0 ♓ 12.6	6 41.3	23 22.4	14 31.9	2 58.9	27 53.0	18 57.0	25 53.9
6 M	10 50 25.9	14 18.7	13 2.9	18 35.6	1 54.8	7 55.4	24 6.5	14 31.1	3 4.8	27 55.7	18 56.1	25 53.8
7 T	10 54 22.4	15 18.8	12 59.8	2 ♊ 43.2	3 38.2	9 9.5	24 50.6	14 30.1	3 10.8	27 58.3	18 55.3	25 53.7
8 W	10 58 19.0	16 18.8	12 56.6	16 50.5	5 22.7	10 23.6	25 34.8	14 29.0	3 16.8	28 1.0	18 54.6	25 53.6
9 T	11 2 15.5	17 18.8	12 53.4	0 ♋ 56.6	7 8.2	11 37.5	26 19.0	14 27.6	3 22.9	28 3.6	18 53.9	25 53.5
10 F	11 6 12.1	18 18.7	12 50.2	14 60.0	8 54.9	12 51.5	27 3.2	14 26.1	3 29.0	28 6.2	18 53.2	25 53.5
11 S	11 10 8.6	19 18.6	12 47.0	28 58.9	10 42.8	14 5.4	27 47.4	14 24.4	3 35.2	28 8.7	18 52.5	25 53.5
12 S	11 14 5.2	20 18.5	12 43.9	12 ♌ 51.1	12 31.8	15 19.2	28 31.7	14 22.5	3 41.5	28 11.2	18 51.8	25 D 53.5
13 M	11 18 1.8	21 18.4	12 40.7	26 33.7	14 21.9	16 33.1	29 16.0	14 20.4	3 47.8	28 13.7	18 51.2	25 53.5
14 T	11 21 58.3	22 18.2	12 37.5	10 ♍ 3.6	16 13.2	17 46.8	0 ♒ 0.3	14 18.1	3 54.2	28 16.1	18 50.7	25 53.6
15 W	11 25 54.9	23 17.9	12 34.3	23 18.5	18 5.7	19 0.5	0 44.6	14 15.7	4 0.6	28 18.5	18 50.1	25 53.7
16 T	11 29 51.4	24 17.7	12 31.2	6 ♎ 16.5	19 59.3	20 14.2	1 28.9	14 13.0	4 7.1	28 20.8	18 49.6	25 53.8
17 F	11 33 48.0	25 17.4	12 28.0	18 57.3	21 54.0	21 27.8	2 13.3	14 10.2	4 13.7	28 23.1	18 49.1	25 53.9
18 S	11 37 44.5	26 17.1	12 24.8	1 ♏ 21.6	23 49.8	22 41.4	2 57.7	14 7.2	4 20.3	28 25.4	18 48.7	25 54.0
19 S	11 41 41.1	27 16.7	12 21.6	13 31.5	25 46.7	23 54.9	3 42.1	14 4.1	4 26.9	28 27.7	18 48.3	25 54.2
20 M	11 45 37.6	28 16.3	12 18.4	25 30.2	27 44.7	25 8.4	4 26.5	14 0.7	4 33.6	28 29.8	18 47.9	25 54.4
21 T	11 49 34.2	29 15.9	12 15.3	7 ♐ 21.8	29 43.5	26 21.8	5 11.0	13 57.2	4 40.3	28 32.0	18 47.5	25 54.6
22 W	11 53 30.7	0 ♈ 15.5	12 12.1	19 10.9	1 ♈ 43.3	27 35.2	5 55.4	13 53.5	4 47.1	28 34.1	18 47.2	25 54.8
23 T	11 57 27.3	1 15.0	12 8.9	1 ♑ 2.7	3 43.8	28 48.6	6 39.9	13 49.7	4 53.9	28 36.2	18 46.9	25 55.1
24 F	12 1 23.8	2 14.5	12 5.7	13 2.3	5 44.9	0 ♉ 1.9	7 24.4	13 45.7	5 0.8	28 38.2	18 46.7	25 55.4
25 S	12 5 20.4	3 14.0	12 2.6	25 14.6	7 46.5	1 15.1	8 9.0	13 41.5	5 7.7	28 40.2	18 46.5	25 55.7
26 S	12 9 16.9	4 13.4	11 59.4	7 ♒ 43.9	9 48.4	2 28.3	8 53.5	13 37.1	5 14.6	28 42.1	18 46.3	25 56.0
27 M	12 13 13.5	5 12.8	11 56.2	20 33.6	11 50.4	3 41.4	9 38.1	13 32.6	5 21.6	28 44.0	18 46.1	25 56.4
28 T	12 17 10.1	6 12.2	11 53.0	3 ♓ 45.6	13 52.1	4 54.5	10 22.7	13 28.0	5 28.7	28 45.9	18 46.0	25 56.7
29 W	12 21 6.6	7 11.6	11 49.8	17 20.0	15 53.4	6 7.6	11 7.3	13 23.2	5 35.8	28 47.7	18 45.9	25 57.1
30 T	12 25 3.2	8 10.9	11 46.7	1 ♈ 15.1	17 54.0	7 20.6	11 51.9	13 18.2	5 42.9	28 49.5	18 45.9	25 57.6
31 F	12 28 59.7	9 10.2	11 43.5	15 27.3	19 53.4	8 33.5	12 36.5	13 13.1	5 50.0	28 51.2	18 45.9	25 58.0

DECLINATION

DAY	EPHEMERIS SIDEREAL TIME h m s	☉	☊	☽	☿	♀	♂	♃	♄	♅	♆	♇
1 W	10 30 43.1	8 S 5.3	15 N 50.6	12 S 21.7	15 S 37.3	0 S 18.2	22 S 37.4	14 S 58.3	10 N 14.7	21 S 7.4	21 N 28.7	16 N 45.7
4 S	10 42 32.8	6 56.8	15 47.8	6 N 16.6	14 0.6	1 N 15.5	22 18.9	14 57.6	10 21.1	21 5.8	21 29.2	16 46.2
7 T	10 54 22.4	5 47.5	15 44.9	22 31.7	12 12.2	2 49.0	21 58.5	14 56.4	10 27.7	21 4.3	21 29.6	16 46.8
10 F	11 6 12.1	4 37.5	15 42.0	27 9.3	10 12.2	4 22.1	21 36.1	14 54.7	10 34.4	21 2.8	21 30.0	16 47.4
13 M	11 18 1.8	3 26.9	15 39.1	17 17.7	8 0.8	5 54.3	21 11.8	14 52.6	10 41.3	21 1.4	21 30.3	16 48.0
16 T	11 29 51.4	2 16.1	15 36.2	0 11.0	5 38.5	7 25.3	20 45.6	14 50.0	10 48.2	20 60.0	21 30.7	16 48.6
19 S	11 41 41.1	1 5.0	15 33.3	16 S 9.3	3 6.0	8 54.8	20 17.6	14 46.9	10 55.3	20 58.7	21 30.9	16 49.2
22 W	11 53 30.7	0 N 6.2	15 30.4	26 14.0	0 24.8	10 22.5	19 47.8	14 43.3	11 2.5	20 57.5	21 31.2	16 49.8
25 S	12 5 20.4	1 17.2	15 27.5	26 0.9	2 N 22.9	11 48.1	19 16.3	14 39.4	11 9.7	20 56.3	21 31.4	16 50.4
28 T	12 17 10.1	2 27.9	15 24.5	14 34.4	5 13.8	13 11.2	18 43.1	14 35.0	11 17.1	20 55.2	21 31.5	16 51.1
31 F	12 28 59.7	3 38.2	15 21.6	4 N 4.2	8 3.0	14 31.5	18 8.4	14 30.2	11 24.5	20 54.2	21 31.6	16 51.7

APRIL 1911

LONGITUDE

DAY	EPHEMERIS SIDEREAL TIME h m s	☉ ° ′	☊ ° ′	☽ ° ′	☿ ° ′	♀ ° ′	♂ ° ′	♃ ° ′	♄ ° ′	♅ ° ′	♆ ° ′	♇ ° ′
1 S	12 32 56.3	10 ♈ 9.4	11 ♉ 40.3	29 ♈ 51.6	21 ♈ 51.3	9 ♉ 46.4	13 ♒ 21.1	13 ♏ 7.8	5 ♉ 57.2	28 ♑ 52.9	18 ♋ 45.9	25 ♊ 58.5
2 S	12 36 52.8	11 8.6	11 37.1	14 ♉ 22.3	23 47.4	10 59.2	14 5.7	13 R 2.4	6 4.4	28 54.5	18 D 45.9	25 58.9
3 M	12 40 49.4	12 7.8	11 34.0	28 54.0	25 41.3	12 12.0	14 50.4	12 56.8	6 11.7	28 56.1	18 46.0	25 59.4
4 T	12 44 45.9	13 6.9	11 30.8	13 ♊ 21.8	27 32.5	13 24.7	15 35.0	12 51.1	6 19.0	28 57.6	18 46.1	25 60.0
5 W	12 48 42.5	14 6.0	11 27.6	27 41.9	29 20.7	14 37.3	16 19.7	12 45.3	6 26.3	28 59.1	18 46.3	26 0.5
6 T	12 52 39.1	15 5.1	11 24.4	11 ♋ 51.7	1 ♉ 5.5	15 49.9	17 4.4	12 39.4	6 33.6	29 0.6	18 46.5	26 1.1
7 F	12 56 35.6	16 4.1	11 21.2	25 49.6	2 46.6	17 2.5	17 49.0	12 33.3	6 41.0	29 2.0	18 46.7	26 1.7
8 S	13 0 32.1	17 3.1	11 18.1	9 ♌ 34.7	4 23.6	18 14.9	18 33.7	12 27.1	6 48.4	29 3.3	18 46.9	26 2.3
9 S	13 4 28.7	18 2.0	11 14.9	23 6.5	5 56.3	19 27.3	19 18.4	12 20.8	6 55.8	29 4.6	18 47.2	26 2.9
10 M	13 8 25.2	19 0.9	11 11.7	6 ♍ 24.7	7 24.3	20 39.6	20 3.1	12 14.4	7 3.2	29 5.9	18 47.6	26 3.5
11 T	13 12 21.8	19 59.8	11 8.5	19 29.4	8 47.5	21 51.9	20 47.8	12 7.9	7 10.7	29 7.1	18 47.9	26 4.2
12 W	13 16 18.4	20 58.6	11 5.4	2 ♎ 20.4	10 5.5	23 4.1	21 32.5	12 1.3	7 18.2	29 8.2	18 48.3	26 4.9
13 T	13 20 14.9	21 57.4	11 2.2	14 58.0	11 18.2	24 16.2	22 17.2	11 54.6	7 25.7	29 9.3	18 48.7	26 5.6
14 F	13 24 11.5	22 56.2	10 59.0	27 23.0	12 25.5	25 28.2	23 1.9	11 47.8	7 33.2	29 10.4	18 49.2	26 6.3
15 S	13 28 8.0	23 54.9	10 55.8	9 ♏ 36.2	13 27.2	26 40.2	23 46.7	11 40.9	7 40.8	29 11.4	18 49.7	26 7.1
16 S	13 32 4.6	24 53.6	10 52.6	21 39.5	14 23.2	27 52.1	24 31.4	11 33.9	7 48.3	29 12.4	18 50.2	26 7.9
17 M	13 36 1.1	25 52.3	10 49.5	3 ♐ 35.0	15 13.3	29 3.9	25 16.1	11 26.8	7 55.9	29 13.3	18 50.7	26 8.6
18 T	13 39 57.7	26 50.9	10 46.3	15 25.7	15 57.6	0 ♊ 15.7	26 0.9	11 19.7	8 3.5	29 14.1	18 51.3	26 9.4
19 W	13 43 54.2	27 49.6	10 43.1	27 15.1	16 35.8	1 27.4	26 45.6	11 12.5	8 11.1	29 15.0	18 51.9	26 10.3
20 T	13 47 50.8	28 48.1	10 39.9	9 ♑ 7.3	17 8.1	2 39.0	27 30.4	11 5.2	8 18.7	29 15.7	18 52.6	26 11.1
21 F	13 51 47.4	29 46.7	10 36.8	21 6.6	17 34.3	3 50.6	28 15.1	10 57.9	8 26.4	29 16.4	18 53.3	26 12.0
22 S	13 55 43.9	0 ♉ 45.2	10 33.6	3 ♒ 17.7	17 54.6	5 2.1	28 59.9	10 50.5	8 34.0	29 17.1	18 54.0	26 12.8
23 S	13 59 40.4	1 43.7	10 30.4	15 45.0	18 8.8	6 13.5	29 44.6	10 43.0	8 41.7	29 17.7	18 54.7	26 13.7
24 M	14 3 37.0	2 42.2	10 27.2	28 32.7	18 17.2	7 24.8	0 ♓ 29.4	10 35.6	8 49.3	29 18.3	18 55.5	26 14.7
25 T	14 7 33.6	3 40.6	10 24.1	11 ♓ 43.9	18 19.8	8 36.1	1 14.1	10 28.0	8 57.0	29 18.8	18 56.3	26 15.6
26 W	14 11 30.1	4 39.1	10 20.9	25 20.5	18 R 16.8	9 47.3	1 58.9	10 20.5	9 4.7	29 19.3	18 57.2	26 16.5
27 T	14 15 26.7	5 37.5	10 17.7	9 ♈ 22.1	18 8.5	10 58.4	2 43.6	10 12.9	9 12.4	29 19.7	18 58.0	26 17.5
28 F	14 19 23.2	6 35.8	10 14.5	23 46.4	17 55.0	12 9.4	3 28.3	10 5.2	9 20.1	29 20.0	18 58.9	26 18.5
29 S	14 23 19.8	7 34.2	10 11.3	8 ♉ 28.6	17 36.8	13 20.3	4 13.0	9 57.6	9 27.8	29 20.4	18 59.9	26 19.5
30 S	14 27 16.4	8 32.5	10 8.2	23 22.0	17 14.2	14 31.2	4 57.7	9 49.9	9 35.5	29 20.6	19 0.8	26 20.5

DECLINATION

DAY	EPHEMERIS SIDEREAL TIME h m s	☉	☊	☽	☿	♀	♂	♃	♄	♅	♆	♇
1 S	12 32 56.3	4 N 1.5	15 N 20.6	10 N 33.0	8 N 58.1	14 N 57.6	17 S 56.5	14 S 28.5	11 N 26.9	20 S 53.9	21 N 31.7	16 N 51.9
4 T	12 44 45.9	5 10.9	15 17.7	25 15.8	11 36.0	16 13.6	17 19.7	14 23.3	11 34.4	20 53.0	21 31.7	16 52.5
7 F	12 56 35.6	6 19.5	15 14.7	25 58.7	13 58.4	17 26.1	16 41.5	14 17.6	11 41.9	20 52.2	21 31.7	16 53.1
10 M	13 8 25.2	7 27.1	15 11.8	13 31.8	16 0.3	18 34.6	16 2.0	14 11.7	11 49.4	20 51.5	21 31.7	16 53.7
13 T	13 20 14.9	8 33.5	15 8.8	3 S 50.6	17 38.5	19 38.9	15 21.1	14 5.5	11 56.9	20 50.9	21 31.6	16 54.3
16 S	13 32 4.6	9 38.7	15 5.9	19 13.4	18 51.1	20 38.7	14 39.1	13 59.1	12 4.4	20 50.4	21 31.5	16 54.9
19 W	13 43 54.2	10 42.4	15 2.9	27 18.4	19 37.3	21 33.7	13 55.9	13 52.4	12 11.9	20 49.9	21 31.4	16 55.5
22 S	13 55 43.9	11 44.5	14 59.9	24 31.9	19 56.8	22 23.5	13 11.6	13 45.6	12 19.4	20 49.6	21 31.2	16 56.1
25 T	14 7 33.6	12 45.0	14 56.9	11 19.4	19 49.8	23 8.0	12 26.3	13 38.7	12 26.9	20 49.3	21 31.0	16 56.7
28 F	14 19 23.2	13 43.5	14 53.9	7 N 51.2	19 17.3	23 47.0	11 40.1	13 31.7	12 34.3	20 49.2	21 30.7	16 57.2

MAY 1911

DAY	EPHEMERIS SIDEREAL TIME	☉	☊	☽	☿	♀	♂	♃	♄	♅	♆	♇
	h m s	° ′	° ′	° ′	° ′	° ′	° ′	° ′	° ′	° ′	° ′	° ′
						LONGITUDE						
1 M	14 31 12.9	9♉30.7	10♉ 5.0	8♊18.7	16♉47.7	15♊42.0	5♓42.4	9♏42.3	9♉43.2	29♑20.8	19♋ 1.8	26♊21.5
2 T	14 35 9.5	10 29.0	10 1.8	23 10.7	16R17.9	16 52.7	6 27.1	9R34.6	9 50.9	29 21.0	19 2.9	26 22.6
3 W	14 39 6.0	11 27.2	9 58.6	7♋51.2	15 45.2	18 3.3	7 11.7	9 27.0	9 58.6	29 21.1	19 3.9	26 23.6
4 T	14 43 2.6	12 25.4	9 55.5	22 15.0	15 10.3	19 13.8	7 56.4	9 19.3	10 6.3	29 21.2	19 5.0	26 24.7
5 F	14 46 59.1	13 23.5	9 52.3	6♌19.0	14 33.9	20 24.2	8 41.0	9 11.7	10 14.0	29 21.2	19 6.1	26 25.8
6 S	14 50 55.7	14 21.6	9 49.1	20 2.0	13 56.5	21 34.5	9 25.6	9 4.1	10 21.7	29R21.1	19 7.2	26 26.9
7 S	14 54 52.2	15 19.7	9 45.9	3♍24.5	13 19.0	22 44.8	10 10.2	8 56.5	10 29.4	29 21.0	19 8.4	26 28.0
8 M	14 58 48.8	16 17.7	9 42.7	16 28.0	12 41.9	23 54.9	10 54.8	8 48.9	10 37.1	29 20.9	19 9.6	26 29.1
9 T	15 2 45.4	17 15.8	9 39.6	29 14.7	12 5.9	25 4.9	11 39.3	8 41.4	10 44.7	29 20.7	19 10.9	26 30.3
10 W	15 6 41.9	18 13.7	9 36.4	11♎46.7	11 31.6	26 14.8	12 23.8	8 33.9	10 52.4	29 20.5	19 12.1	26 31.4
11 T	15 10 38.4	19 11.7	9 33.2	24 6.4	10 59.5	27 24.6	13 8.4	8 26.5	11 0.0	29 20.2	19 13.4	26 32.6
12 F	15 14 35.0	20 9.6	9 30.0	6♏16.1	10 30.2	28 34.3	13 52.9	8 19.1	11 7.7	29 19.9	19 14.7	26 33.8
13 S	15 18 31.6	21 7.5	9 26.9	18 17.8	10 4.1	29 43.9	14 37.3	8 11.8	11 15.3	29 19.5	19 16.0	26 35.0
14 S	15 22 28.1	22 5.4	9 23.7	0♐13.5	9 41.5	0♋53.4	15 21.8	8 4.5	11 22.9	29 19.0	19 17.4	26 36.2
15 M	15 26 24.7	23 3.2	9 20.5	12 5.1	9 22.9	2 2.8	16 6.2	7 57.3	11 30.5	29 18.6	19 18.8	26 37.4
16 T	15 30 21.2	24 1.1	9 17.3	23 54.9	9 8.3	3 12.1	16 50.6	7 50.1	11 38.1	29 18.0	19 20.2	26 38.6
17 W	15 34 17.8	24 58.9	9 14.1	5♑45.3	8 58.1	4 21.2	17 35.0	7 43.1	11 45.7	29 17.5	19 21.6	26 39.9
18 T	15 38 14.3	25 56.6	9 11.0	17 39.2	8 52.4	5 30.2	18 19.4	7 36.1	11 53.3	29 16.8	19 23.1	26 41.1
19 F	15 42 10.9	26 54.4	9 7.8	29 39.8	8 51.1	6 39.2	19 3.7	7 29.2	12 0.8	29 16.2	19 24.6	26 42.4
20 S	15 46 7.5	27 52.2	9 4.6	11♒50.8	8D54.5	7 47.9	19 48.0	7 22.4	12 8.3	29 15.5	19 26.1	26 43.7
21 S	15 50 4.0	28 49.9	9 1.4	24 16.1	9 2.4	8 56.6	20 32.3	7 15.7	12 15.8	29 14.7	19 27.6	26 45.0
22 M	15 54 0.6	29 47.6	8 58.3	6♓59.7	9 14.8	10 5.2	21 16.6	7 9.0	12 23.3	29 13.9	19 29.2	26 46.3
23 T	15 57 57.1	0♊45.3	8 55.1	20 5.4	9 31.7	11 13.6	22 0.8	7 2.5	12 30.8	29 13.0	19 30.8	26 47.6
24 W	16 1 53.7	1 43.0	8 51.9	3♈36.0	9 53.0	12 21.9	22 45.0	6 56.1	12 38.2	29 12.1	19 32.4	26 48.9
25 T	16 5 50.2	2 40.6	8 48.7	17 33.2	10 18.6	13 30.1	23 29.1	6 49.8	12 45.6	29 11.2	19 34.0	26 50.2
26 F	16 9 46.8	3 38.2	8 45.6	1♉56.5	10 48.4	14 38.1	24 13.2	6 43.6	12 53.0	29 10.2	19 35.7	26 51.5
27 S	16 13 43.4	4 35.9	8 42.4	16 42.7	11 22.3	15 46.0	24 57.3	6 37.5	13 0.4	29 9.2	19 37.4	26 52.9
28 S	16 17 39.9	5 33.5	8 39.2	1♊45.8	12 0.2	16 53.8	25 41.3	6 31.6	13 7.7	29 8.1	19 39.1	26 54.2
29 M	16 21 36.5	6 31.1	8 36.0	16 57.4	12 42.0	18 1.4	26 25.2	6 25.7	13 15.0	29 7.0	19 40.8	26 55.6
30 T	16 25 33.0	7 28.6	8 32.9	2♋ 7.6	13 27.6	19 8.9	27 9.2	6 20.0	13 22.3	29 5.8	19 42.5	26 56.9
31 W	16 29 29.6	8 26.2	8 29.7	17 6.8	14 16.8	20 16.2	27 53.0	6 14.4	13 29.6	29 4.6	19 44.3	26 58.3
						DECLINATION						
1 M	14 31 12.9	14N40.1	14N50.9	24N11.1	18N22.2	24N20.2	10S53.1	13S24.6	12N41.6	20S49.1	21N30.4	16N57.8
4 T	14 43 2.6	15 34.5	14 47.9	26 35.1	17 9.7	24 47.4	10 5.4	13 17.5	12 48.9	20 49.1	21 30.0	16 58.3
7 S	14 54 52.2	16 26.5	14 44.9	14 47.1	15 47.7	25 8.5	9 17.0	13 10.5	12 56.2	20 49.2	21 29.6	16 58.8
10 W	15 6 41.9	17 16.0	14 41.9	2S21.0	14 25.6	25 23.4	8 28.0	13 3.6	13 3.3	20 49.5	21 29.2	16 59.3
13 S	15 18 31.6	18 3.0	14 38.9	18 0.9	13 12.6	25 32.1	7 38.5	12 56.9	13 10.3	20 49.8	21 28.7	16 59.8
16 T	15 30 21.2	18 47.2	14 35.8	26 58.0	12 15.8	25 34.5	6 48.6	12 50.3	13 17.3	20 50.2	21 28.2	17 0.3
19 F	15 42 10.9	19 28.6	14 32.8	25 17.4	11 39.4	25 30.8	5 58.3	12 44.0	13 24.1	20 50.6	21 27.7	17 0.7
22 M	15 54 0.6	20 7.1	14 29.7	13 17.5	11 24.7	25 20.8	5 7.8	12 37.9	13 30.9	20 51.2	21 27.1	17 1.2
25 T	16 5 50.2	20 42.4	14 26.7	5N 2.6	11 31.1	25 4.9	4 17.1	12 32.1	13 37.5	20 51.9	21 26.5	17 1.6
28 S	16 17 39.9	21 14.6	14 23.6	22 26.4	11 56.9	24 43.1	3 26.2	12 26.7	13 44.0	20 52.6	21 25.8	17 2.0
31 W	16 29 29.6	21 43.4	14 20.6	27 8.1	12 39.6	24 15.6	2 35.4	12 21.7	13 50.3	20 53.4	21 25.1	17 2.4

JUNE 1911

DAY	EPHEMERIS SIDEREAL TIME	☉	☊	☽	☿	♀	♂	♃	♄	♅	♆	♇
						LONGITUDE						
1 T	16 33 26.1	9♊23.7	8♉26.5	1♌47.1	15♉ 9.6	21♋23.4	28♓36.9	6♏ 9.0	13♉36.8	29♑ 3.3	19♋46.0	26♊59.7
2 F	16 37 22.7	10 21.2	8 23.3	16 2.9	16 5.9	22 30.4	29 20.6	6R 3.7	13 44.0	29R 2.0	19 47.9	27 1.1
3 S	16 41 19.3	11 18.7	8 20.2	29 52.1	17 5.6	23 37.2	0♈ 4.4	5 58.6	13 51.1	29 0.7	19 49.7	27 2.5
4 S	16 45 15.8	12 16.1	8 17.0	13♍14.8	18 8.5	24 43.9	0 48.0	5 53.6	13 58.2	28 59.3	19 51.5	27 3.9
5 M	16 49 12.4	13 13.6	8 13.8	26 13.4	19 14.8	25 50.4	1 31.6	5 48.7	14 5.3	28 57.9	19 53.4	27 5.2
6 T	16 53 8.9	14 11.0	8 10.6	8♎51.3	20 24.2	26 56.7	2 15.2	5 44.0	14 12.4	28 56.5	19 55.2	27 6.7
7 W	16 57 5.5	15 8.4	8 7.4	21 12.4	21 36.7	28 2.9	2 58.7	5 39.4	14 19.4	28 55.0	19 57.1	27 8.1
8 T	17 1 2.1	16 5.8	8 4.3	3♏20.7	22 52.3	29 8.8	3 42.1	5 35.0	14 26.3	28 53.5	19 59.0	27 9.5
9 F	17 4 58.6	17 3.2	8 1.1	15 20.0	24 10.9	0♌14.6	4 25.5	5 30.8	14 33.3	28 51.9	20 1.0	27 10.9
10 S	17 8 55.1	18 0.5	7 57.9	27 13.4	25 32.5	1 20.1	5 8.8	5 26.7	14 40.1	28 50.3	20 2.9	27 12.3
11 S	17 12 51.7	18 57.8	7 54.7	9♐ 3.8	26 57.1	2 25.5	5 52.1	5 22.8	14 47.0	28 48.7	20 4.9	27 13.7
12 M	17 16 48.3	19 55.2	7 51.6	20 53.4	28 24.6	3 30.7	6 35.3	5 19.0	14 53.8	28 47.0	20 6.8	27 15.2
13 T	17 20 44.8	20 52.5	7 48.4	2♑44.3	29 55.1	4 35.6	7 18.5	5 15.4	15 0.6	28 45.3	20 8.8	27 16.6
14 W	17 24 41.4	21 49.8	7 45.2	14 38.3	1♊28.4	5 40.3	8 1.6	5 12.0	15 7.3	28 43.5	20 10.8	27 18.0
15 T	17 28 37.9	22 47.1	7 42.0	26 37.1	3 4.6	6 44.8	8 44.6	5 8.7	15 13.9	28 41.8	20 12.8	27 19.5
16 F	17 32 34.5	23 44.3	7 38.9	8♒43.0	4 43.6	7 49.1	9 27.5	5 5.6	15 20.6	28 40.0	20 14.9	27 20.9
17 S	17 36 31.1	24 41.6	7 35.7	20 58.1	6 25.5	8 53.2	10 10.4	5 2.7	15 27.1	28 38.1	20 16.9	27 22.3
18 S	17 40 27.6	25 38.9	7 32.5	3♓25.4	8 10.1	9 57.0	10 53.2	4 60.0	15 33.7	28 36.3	20 19.0	27 23.8
19 M	17 44 24.2	26 36.1	7 29.3	16 8.1	9 57.5	11 0.5	11 36.0	4 57.4	15 40.1	28 34.4	20 21.0	27 25.2
20 T	17 48 20.7	27 33.4	7 26.2	29 9.5	11 47.6	12 3.9	12 18.6	4 55.0	15 46.6	28 32.5	20 23.1	27 26.6
21 W	17 52 17.3	28 30.7	7 23.0	12♈32.8	13 40.3	13 6.9	13 1.2	4 52.7	15 53.0	28 30.5	20 25.2	27 28.1
22 T	17 56 13.9	29 27.9	7 19.8	26 20.6	15 35.6	14 9.7	13 43.7	4 50.7	15 59.3	28 28.5	20 27.3	27 29.5
23 F	18 0 10.4	0♋25.2	7 16.6	10♉33.9	17 33.3	15 12.3	14 26.1	4 48.8	16 5.5	28 26.5	20 29.4	27 30.9
24 S	18 4 7.0	1 22.4	7 13.4	25 11.5	19 33.2	16 14.5	15 8.5	4 47.1	16 11.8	28 24.5	20 31.5	27 32.4
25 S	18 8 3.5	2 19.7	7 10.3	10♊ 9.4	21 35.4	17 16.5	15 50.7	4 45.6	16 17.9	28 22.4	20 33.7	27 33.8
26 M	18 12 0.1	3 16.9	7 7.1	25 20.4	23 39.4	18 18.2	16 32.9	4 44.3	16 24.0	28 20.3	20 35.8	27 35.3
27 T	18 15 56.6	4 14.2	7 3.9	10♋34.8	25 45.2	19 19.6	17 14.9	4 43.1	16 30.1	28 18.2	20 38.0	27 36.7
28 W	18 19 53.2	5 11.4	7 0.7	25 41.9	27 52.5	20 20.7	17 56.9	4 42.1	16 36.0	28 16.1	20 40.1	27 38.1
29 T	18 23 49.8	6 8.6	6 57.6	10♌32.0	0♋ 1.1	21 21.5	18 38.8	4 41.3	16 42.0	28 13.9	20 42.3	27 39.5
30 F	18 27 46.4	7 5.9	6 54.4	24 57.5	2 10.6	22 21.9	19 20.5	4 40.7	16 47.8	28 11.7	20 44.5	27 41.0
						DECLINATION						
1 T	16 33 26.1	21N52.3	14N19.6	24N48.5	12N57.1	24N 5.2	2S18.5	12S20.1	13N52.4	20S53.7	21N24.9	17N 2.5
4 S	16 45 15.8	22 16.6	14 16.5	10 35.9	13 58.2	23 30.4	1 27.7	12 15.6	13 58.6	20 54.6	21 24.2	17 2.9
7 W	16 57 5.5	22 37.4	14 13.4	6S44.8	15 10.0	22 50.6	0 37.2	12 11.6	14 4.6	20 55.6	21 23.4	17 3.2
10 S	17 8 55.1	22 54.7	14 10.3	21 4.6	16 29.7	22 5.9	0N13.2	12 8.1	14 10.4	20 56.6	21 22.6	17 3.5
13 T	17 20 44.8	23 8.3	14 7.2	27 33.5	17 54.4	21 16.6	1 3.2	12 5.0	14 16.1	20 57.7	21 21.8	17 3.8
16 F	17 32 34.5	23 18.3	14 4.2	23 2.6	19 20.6	20 23.2	1 52.9	12 2.5	14 21.6	20 58.9	21 21.0	17 4.0
19 M	17 44 24.2	23 24.5	14 1.1	9 14.5	20 44.5	19 25.8	2 42.1	12 0.5	14 26.9	21 0.1	21 20.1	17 4.3
22 T	17 56 13.9	23 27.1	13 58.0	9N 8.2	22 1.5	18 24.9	3 30.8	11 59.0	14 32.0	21 1.4	21 19.2	17 4.5
25 S	18 8 3.5	23 25.9	13 54.8	24 37.4	23 6.3	17 20.7	4 18.9	11 58.0	14 37.0	21 2.7	21 18.3	17 4.7
28 W	18 19 53.2	23 21.1	13 51.7	25 53.4	23 53.7	16 13.7	5 6.3	11 57.6	14 41.7	21 4.0	21 17.4	17 4.9

JULY 1911

LONGITUDE

DAY	EPHEMERIS SIDEREAL TIME h m s	☉ ° '	☊ ° '	☽ ° '	☿ ° '	♀ ° '	♂ ° '	♃ ° '	♄ ° '	♅ ° '	♆ ° '	♇ ° '
1 S	18 31 42.9	8♋ 3.1	6♉51.2	8♍54.5	4♋20.8	23♌22.0	20♈ 2.2	4♏40.3	16♉53.6	28♑ 9.5	20♋46.6	27♊42.4
2 S	18 35 39.4	9 0.3	6 48.0	22 22.2	6 31.4	24 21.8	20 43.7	4R40.0	16 59.4	28R 7.3	20 48.8	27 43.8
3 M	18 39 36.0	9 57.5	6 44.9	5♎22.5	8 42.1	25 21.1	21 25.1	4 40.0	17 5.0	28 5.1	20 51.0	27 45.2
4 T	18 43 32.5	10 54.7	6 41.7	17 59.1	10 52.6	26 20.1	22 6.5	4D40.1	17 10.6	28 2.8	20 53.2	27 46.6
5 W	18 47 29.1	11 51.9	6 38.5	0♏16.7	13 2.7	27 18.7	22 47.7	4 40.4	17 16.2	28 0.6	20 55.4	27 48.0
6 T	18 51 25.7	12 49.1	6 35.3	12 20.4	15 12.2	28 16.9	23 28.8	4 40.9	17 21.6	27 58.3	20 57.6	27 49.4
7 F	18 55 22.2	13 46.3	6 32.2	24 15.0	17 20.7	29 14.7	24 9.8	4 41.5	17 27.0	27 56.0	20 59.9	27 50.8
8 S	18 59 18.8	14 43.5	6 29.0	6♐ 4.8	19 28.2	0♍12.0	24 50.7	4 42.4	17 32.4	27 53.7	21 2.1	27 52.2
9 S	19 3 15.3	15 40.7	6 25.8	17 53.6	21 34.4	1 8.9	25 31.5	4 43.4	17 37.6	27 51.3	21 4.3	27 53.6
10 M	19 7 11.9	16 37.9	6 22.6	29 44.3	23 39.2	2 5.3	26 12.2	4 44.6	17 42.8	27 49.0	21 6.5	27 55.0
11 T	19 11 8.5	17 35.0	6 19.5	11♑39.2	25 42.6	3 1.3	26 52.7	4 46.0	17 48.0	27 46.7	21 8.7	27 56.3
12 W	19 15 5.1	18 32.2	6 16.3	23 39.9	27 44.3	3 56.7	27 33.1	4 47.5	17 53.0	27 44.3	21 11.0	27 57.7
13 T	19 19 1.6	19 29.4	6 13.1	5♒47.8	29 44.4	4 51.6	28 13.4	4 49.2	17 58.0	27 41.9	21 13.2	27 59.0
14 F	19 22 58.1	20 26.6	6 9.9	18 3.9	1♌42.7	5 46.1	28 53.6	4 51.1	18 2.9	27 39.6	21 15.4	28 0.4
15 S	19 26 54.7	21 23.8	6 6.7	0♓29.3	3 39.3	6 39.9	29 33.6	4 53.2	18 7.7	27 37.2	21 17.6	28 1.7
16 S	19 30 51.3	22 21.1	6 3.6	13 5.5	5 34.1	7 33.2	0♉13.5	4 55.4	18 12.5	27 34.8	21 19.9	28 3.1
17 M	19 34 47.8	23 18.3	6 0.4	25 54.2	7 27.1	8 26.0	0 53.3	4 57.9	18 17.1	27 32.4	21 22.1	28 4.4
18 T	19 38 44.4	24 15.5	5 57.2	8♈57.8	9 18.2	9 18.1	1 32.9	5 0.5	18 21.7	27 30.0	21 24.3	28 5.7
19 W	19 42 41.0	25 12.8	5 54.0	22 18.8	11 7.5	10 9.6	2 12.4	5 3.2	18 26.2	27 27.6	21 26.6	28 7.0
20 T	19 46 37.5	26 10.0	5 50.9	5♉59.5	12 55.1	11 0.5	2 51.8	5 6.1	18 30.7	27 25.2	21 28.8	28 8.3
21 F	19 50 34.0	27 7.3	5 47.7	20 1.6	14 40.7	11 50.7	3 30.9	5 9.2	18 35.0	27 22.8	21 31.0	28 9.6
22 S	19 54 30.6	28 4.6	5 44.5	4♊25.0	16 24.6	12 40.2	4 10.0	5 12.5	18 39.3	27 20.4	21 33.2	28 10.8
23 S	19 58 27.2	29 1.9	5 41.3	19 7.4	18 6.7	13 29.1	4 48.9	5 16.0	18 43.5	27 18.0	21 35.4	28 12.1
24 M	20 2 23.8	29 59.2	5 38.2	4♋ 3.9	19 46.9	14 17.1	5 27.6	5 19.6	18 47.6	27 15.6	21 37.7	28 13.4
25 T	20 6 20.3	0♌56.5	5 35.0	19 6.7	21 25.3	15 4.5	6 6.1	5 23.3	18 51.6	27 13.2	21 39.9	28 14.6
26 W	20 10 16.8	1 53.9	5 31.8	4♌ 6.2	23 2.0	15 51.0	6 44.5	5 27.3	18 55.5	27 10.8	21 42.1	28 15.8
27 T	20 14 13.4	2 51.2	5 28.6	18 52.8	24 36.8	16 36.7	7 22.7	5 31.4	18 59.4	27 8.4	21 44.3	28 17.1
28 F	20 18 10.0	3 48.6	5 25.4	3♍18.5	26 9.9	17 21.5	8 0.7	5 35.6	19 3.1	27 6.0	21 46.5	28 18.3
29 S	20 22 6.5	4 46.0	5 22.3	17 17.9	27 41.1	18 5.5	8 38.6	5 40.1	19 6.8	27 3.6	21 48.6	28 19.5
30 S	20 26 3.1	5 43.3	5 19.1	0♎48.8	29 10.5	18 48.5	9 16.2	5 44.7	19 10.4	27 1.2	21 50.8	28 20.7
31 M	20 29 59.6	6 40.7	5 15.9	13 52.1	0♍38.0	19 30.5	9 53.7	5 49.4	19 13.8	26 58.9	21 53.0	28 21.8

DECLINATION

DAY	EPHEMERIS SIDEREAL TIME h m s	☉	☊	☽	☿	♀	♂	♃	♄	♅	♆	♇
1 S	18 31 42.9	23N12.5	13N48.6	12N17.0	24N19.0	15N 4.1	5N53.0	11S57.8	14N46.3	21S 5.4	21N16.5	17N 5.0
4 T	18 43 32.5	23 0.2	13 45.5	5S26.6	24 19.6	13 52.4	6 38.8	11 58.5	14 50.6	21 6.8	21 15.5	17 5.1
7 F	18 55 22.2	22 44.4	13 42.3	20 13.6	23 55.3	12 38.8	7 23.8	11 59.7	14 54.8	21 8.2	21 14.6	17 5.3
10 M	19 7 11.9	22 25.0	13 39.2	27 25.8	23 7.9	11 23.8	8 7.9	12 1.5	14 58.7	21 9.6	21 13.6	17 5.3
13 T	19 19 1.6	22 2.1	13 36.1	23 41.5	22 0.8	10 7.7	8 51.0	12 3.8	15 2.4	21 11.1	21 12.6	17 5.4
16 S	19 30 51.3	21 35.9	13 32.9	10 22.9	20 37.8	8 51.0	9 33.1	12 6.6	15 5.9	21 12.5	21 11.6	17 5.4
19 W	19 42 41.0	21 6.3	13 29.8	7N32.8	19 2.6	7 33.9	10 14.2	12 .0.0	15 9.2	21 13.9	21 10.6	17 5.4
22 S	19 54 30.6	20 33.5	13 26.6	23 21.9	17 18.4	6 16.8	10 54.1	12 13.8	15 12.2	21 15.4	21 9.5	17 5.4
25 T	20 6 20.3	19 57.6	13 23.4	26 50.0	15 28.1	5 0.2	11 32.9	12 18.1	15 15.0	21 16.8	21 8.5	17 5.4
28 F	20 18 10.0	19 18.6	13 20.2	14 25.8	13 34.0	3 44.4	12 10.5	12 22.9	15 17.5	21 18.2	21 7.5	17 5.4
31 M	20 29 59.6	18 36.8	13 17.1	3S46.7	11 38.4	2 30.0	12 46.8	12 28.2	15 19.8	21 19.6	21 6.5	17 5.3

AUGUST 1911

LONGITUDE

DAY	EPHEMERIS SIDEREAL TIME h m s	☉ ° '	☊ ° '	☽ ° '	☿ ° '	♀ ° '	♂ ° '	♃ ° '	♄ ° '	♅ ° '	♆ ° '	♇ ° '
1 T	20 33 56.2	7♌38.1	5♉12.7	26♎30.9	2♍ 3.7	20♍11.6	10♉31.0	5♏54.3	19♉17.2	26♑56.5	21♋55.2	28♊23.0
2 W	20 37 52.7	8 35.5	5 9.6	8♏49.6	3 27.4	20 51.6	11 8.1	5 59.4	19 20.5	26R54.2	21 57.3	28 24.1
3 T	20 41 49.3	9 33.0	5 6.4	20 53.4	4 49.3	21 30.5	11 45.0	6 4.6	19 23.7	26 51.8	21 59.5	28 25.3
4 F	20 45 45.9	10 30.4	5 3.2	2♐47.7	6 9.2	22 8.2	12 21.7	6 9.9	19 26.9	26 49.5	22 1.6	28 26.4
5 S	20 49 42.4	11 27.8	5 0.0	14 37.6	7 27.1	22 44.8	12 58.2	6 15.4	19 29.9	26 47.2	22 3.7	28 27.5
6 S	20 53 39.0	12 25.3	4 56.9	26 27.5	8 43.0	23 20.1	13 34.5	6 21.1	19 32.8	26 44.9	22 5.8	28 28.6
7 M	20 57 35.5	13 22.8	4 53.7	8♑21.4	9 56.7	23 54.2	14 10.5	6 26.9	19 35.6	26 42.7	22 8.0	28 29.7
8 T	21 1 32.1	14 20.2	4 50.5	20 22.1	11 8.2	24 26.9	14 46.4	6 32.9	19 38.4	26 40.4	22 10.1	28 30.7
9 W	21 5 28.6	15 17.7	4 47.3	2♒31.7	12 17.6	24 58.3	15 22.1	6 39.0	19 41.0	26 38.1	22 12.1	28 31.8
10 T	21 9 25.2	16 15.3	4 44.1	14 51.4	13 24.5	25 28.2	15 57.5	6 45.2	19 43.5	26 35.9	22 14.2	28 32.8
11 F	21 13 21.7	17 12.8	4 41.0	27 21.9	14 29.1	25 56.7	16 32.7	6 51.6	19 46.0	26 33.7	22 16.3	28 33.8
12 S	21 17 18.3	18 10.4	4 37.8	10♓ 3.4	15 31.1	26 23.6	17 7.7	6 58.1	19 48.3	26 31.5	22 18.3	28 34.8
13 S	21 21 14.9	19 7.9	4 34.6	22 55.7	16 30.5	26 49.0	17 42.5	7 4.8	19 50.5	26 29.4	22 20.4	28 35.8
14 M	21 25 11.4	20 5.5	4 31.4	5♈59.3	17 27.1	27 12.7	18 17.0	7 11.5	19 52.7	26 27.2	22 22.4	28 36.8
15 T	21 29 8.0	21 3.1	4 28.3	19 14.7	18 20.8	27 34.6	18 51.2	7 18.5	19 54.7	26 25.1	22 24.4	28 37.7
16 W	21 33 4.5	22 0.8	4 25.1	2♉42.8	19 11.4	27 54.9	19 25.2	7 25.5	19 56.7	26 23.0	22 26.4	28 38.7
17 T	21 37 1.1	22 58.5	4 21.9	16 24.7	19 58.9	28 13.3	19 59.0	7 32.8	19 58.5	26 21.0	22 28.4	28 39.6
18 F	21 40 57.6	23 56.2	4 18.7	0♊21.4	20 42.9	28 29.9	20 32.5	7 40.1	20 0.2	26 18.9	22 30.4	28 40.5
19 S	21 44 54.2	24 53.9	4 15.6	14 32.9	21 23.3	28 44.5	21 5.7	7 47.5	20 1.9	26 16.9	22 32.3	28 41.4
20 S	21 48 50.7	25 51.7	4 12.4	28 58.0	21 60.0	28 57.1	21 38.7	7 55.1	20 3.4	26 14.9	22 34.2	28 42.2
21 M	21 52 47.3	26 49.4	4 9.2	13♋33.3	22 32.6	29 7.7	22 11.3	8 2.9	20 4.8	26 12.9	22 36.2	28 43.1
22 T	21 56 43.8	27 47.2	4 6.0	28 13.6	23 0.9	29 16.2	22 43.7	8 10.7	20 6.1	26 11.0	22 38.1	28 43.9
23 W	22 0 40.4	28 45.1	4 2.8	12♌51.9	23 24.8	29 22.5	23 15.8	8 18.7	20 7.3	26 9.1	22 39.9	28 44.7
24 T	22 4 37.0	29 42.9	3 59.7	27 20.9	23 43.9	29 26.7	23 47.5	8 26.8	20 8.4	26 7.2	22 41.8	28 45.5
25 F	22 8 33.5	0♍40.8	3 56.5	11♍33.6	23 58.1	29 28.6	24 19.0	8 35.0	20 9.4	26 5.4	22 43.7	28 46.3
26 S	22 12 30.1	1 38.7	3 53.3	25 24.9	24 6.9	29R28.2	24 50.1	8 43.3	20 10.3	26 3.5	22 45.5	28 47.1
27 S	22 16 26.6	2 36.7	3 50.1	8♎51.9	24 10.3	29 25.5	25 21.0	8 51.8	20 11.1	26 1.8	22 47.3	28 47.8
28 M	22 20 23.2	3 34.6	3 47.0	21 54.3	24R 8.0	29 20.4	25 51.4	9 0.3	20 11.8	26 0.0	22 49.1	28 48.5
29 T	22 24 19.7	4 32.6	3 43.8	4♏33.9	23 59.7	29 12.9	26 21.6	9 9.0	20 12.4	25 58.3	22 50.9	28 49.2
30 W	22 28 16.3	5 30.6	3 40.6	16 54.2	23 45.4	29 3.0	26 51.4	9 17.8	20 12.8	25 56.6	22 52.6	28 49.9
31 T	22 32 12.9	6 28.6	3 37.4	28 59.7	23 25.0	28 50.8	27 20.9	9 26.7	20 13.2	25 55.0	22 54.3	28 50.5

DECLINATION

DAY	EPHEMERIS SIDEREAL TIME h m s	☉	☊	☽	☿	♀	♂	♃	♄	♅	♆	♇
1 T	20 33 56.2	18N22.3	13N16.0	9S31.3	10N59.8	2N 5.5	12N58.6	12S30.1	15N20.6	21S20.1	21N 6.1	17N 5.3
4 F	20 45 45.9	17 36.9	13 12.8	23 1.5	9 5.0	0 53.7	13 33.2	12 35.9	15 22.5	21 21.4	21 5.1	17 5.2
7 M	20 57 35.5	16 48.9	13 9.6	27 40.0	7 12.8	0S15.4	14 6.5	12 42.2	15 24.3	21 22.7	21 4.1	17 5.1
10 T	21 9 25.2	15 58.4	13 6.4	21 5.2	5 25.2	1 21.2	14 38.6	12 48.9	15 25.8	21 24.0	21 3.1	17 4.9
13 S	21 21 14.9	15 5.7	13 3.2	5 49.9	3 43.9	2 23.0	15 9.3	12 55.9	15 27.0	21 25.3	21 2.1	17 4.8
16 W	21 33 4.5	14 10.8	13 0.0	12N20.9	2 11.4	3 19.9	15 38.7	13 3.3	15 28.0	21 26.5	21 1.2	17 4.6
19 S	21 44 54.2	13 13.8	12 56.8	25 51.5	0 50.2	4 11.1	16 6.7	13 11.1	15 28.7	21 27.6	21 0.2	17 4.5
22 T	21 56 43.8	12 14.9	12 53.6	25 27.0	0S16.3	4 55.5	16 33.4	13 19.1	15 29.2	21 28.7	20 59.3	17 4.3
25 F	22 8 33.5	11 14.3	12 50.4	10 52.9	1 4.2	5 32.0	16 58.8	13 27.5	15 29.5	21 29.7	20 58.3	17 4.0
28 M	22 20 23.2	10 12.1	12 47.1	7S39.8	1 28.7	5 59.5	17 22.9	13 36.2	15 29.4	21 30.7	20 57.4	17 3.8
31 T	22 32 12.9	9 8.4	12 43.9	22 10.3	1 24.8	6 16.6	17 45.6	13 45.2	15 29.2	21 31.6	20 56.6	17 3.6

SEPTEMBER 1911

DAY	EPHEMERIS SIDEREAL TIME	☉	☊	☽	☿	♀	♂	♃	♄	♅	♆	♇
	h m s	° ′	° ′	° ′	° ′	° ′	° ′	° ′	° ′	° ′	° ′	° ′
						LONGITUDE						
1 F	22 36 9.4	7♍26.7	3♉34.3	10♐55.5	22♍58.3	28♍36.1	27♉50.0	9♏35.8	20♉13.4	25♑53.4	22♋56.0	28♊51.2
2 S	22 40 6.0	8 24.8	3 31.1	22 46.7	22R25.7	28R19.1	28 18.7	9 44.9	20 13.6	25R51.8	22 57.7	28 51.8
3 S	22 44 2.5	9 22.8	3 27.9	4♑38.5	21 47.2	27 59.8	28 47.1	9 54.1	20 13.6	25 50.3	22 59.4	28 52.4
4 M	22 47 59.1	10 21.0	3 24.7	16 35.4	21 3.2	27 38.3	29 15.1	10 3.5	20R13.5	25 48.8	23 1.0	28 53.0
5 T	22 51 55.6	11 19.1	3 21.5	28 41.1	20 14.4	27 14.6	29 42.7	10 12.9	20 13.3	25 47.3	23 2.7	28 53.5
6 W	22 55 52.2	12 17.3	3 18.4	10♒58.6	19 21.2	26 48.8	0♊9.9	10 22.5	20 13.1	25 45.9	23 4.3	28 54.1
7 T	22 59 48.7	13 15.5	3 15.2	23 29.7	18 24.7	26 21.1	0 36.7	10 32.1	20 12.7	25 44.5	23 5.8	28 54.6
8 F	23 3 45.3	14 13.7	3 12.0	6♓15.4	17 25.9	25 51.5	1 3.1	10 41.9	20 12.2	25 43.2	23 7.4	28 55.1
9 S	23 7 41.8	15 12.0	3 8.8	19 15.5	16 25.9	25 20.3	1 29.1	10 51.7	20 11.6	25 41.9	23 8.9	28 55.5
10 S	23 11 38.4	16 10.2	3 5.6	2♈29.2	15 26.1	24 47.7	1 54.7	11 1.7	20 10.8	25 40.7	23 10.4	28 56.0
11 M	23 15 34.9	17 8.6	3 2.5	15 55.1	14 27.9	24 13.7	2 19.9	11 11.7	20 10.0	25 39.5	23 11.9	28 56.4
12 T	23 19 31.5	18 6.9	2 59.3	29 31.9	13 32.5	23 38.7	2 44.6	11 21.8	20 9.1	25 38.3	23 13.3	28 56.8
13 W	23 23 28.1	19 5.3	2 56.1	13♉18.1	12 41.4	23 2.8	3 8.8	11 32.1	20 8.1	25 37.2	23 14.7	28 57.2
14 T	23 27 24.6	20 3.7	2 52.9	27 12.7	11 55.8	22 26.2	3 32.6	11 42.4	20 6.9	25 36.1	23 16.1	28 57.6
15 F	23 31 21.2	21 2.1	2 49.8	11♊14.8	11 17.0	21 49.3	3 55.9	11 52.8	20 5.7	25 35.0	23 17.5	28 57.9
16 S	23 35 17.7	22 0.6	2 46.6	25 23.3	10 45.8	21 12.2	4 18.7	12 3.3	20 4.3	25 34.0	23 18.9	28 58.3
17 S	23 39 14.3	22 59.2	2 43.4	9♋36.7	10 23.2	20 35.3	4 41.0	12 13.9	20 2.9	25 33.1	23 20.2	28 58.6
18 M	23 43 10.8	23 57.7	2 40.2	23 52.8	10 9.6	19 58.6	5 2.8	12 24.5	20 1.3	25 32.2	23 21.5	28 58.8
19 T	23 47 7.4	24 56.3	2 37.1	8♌8.3	10 5.4	19 22.6	5 24.1	12 35.3	19 59.7	25 31.4	23 22.7	28 59.1
20 W	23 51 3.9	25 55.0	2 33.9	22 19.3	10D11.0	18 47.3	5 44.8	12 46.1	19 57.9	25 30.5	23 24.0	28 59.3
21 T	23 55 0.5	26 53.6	2 30.7	6♍21.5	10 26.2	18 13.1	6 5.0	12 57.0	19 56.0	25 29.8	23 25.2	28 59.5
22 F	23 58 57.0	27 52.3	2 27.5	20 10.6	10 51.0	17 40.1	6 24.6	13 8.0	19 54.1	25 29.1	23 26.4	28 59.7
23 S	0 2 53.6	28 51.1	2 24.3	3♎43.1	11 25.1	17 8.5	6 43.6	13 19.1	19 52.0	25 28.4	23 27.5	28 59.9
24 S	0 6 50.2	29 49.8	2 21.2	16 56.9	12 8.0	16 38.5	7 2.0	13 30.3	19 49.9	25 27.8	23 28.6	29 0.0
25 M	0 10 46.7	0♎48.6	2 18.0	29 51.1	12 59.3	16 10.2	7 19.9	13 41.5	19 47.6	25 27.2	23 29.7	29 0.2
26 T	0 14 43.3	1 47.5	2 14.8	12♏26.7	13 58.3	15 43.9	7 37.1	13 52.8	19 45.2	25 26.7	23 30.8	29 0.3
27 W	0 18 39.8	2 46.3	2 11.6	24 45.7	15 4.4	15 19.5	7 53.7	14 4.2	19 42.8	25 26.2	23 31.8	29 0.3
28 T	0 22 36.4	3 45.2	2 8.4	6♐51.4	16 17.0	14 57.3	8 9.7	14 15.6	19 40.2	25 25.8	23 32.8	29 0.4
29 F	0 26 32.9	4 44.2	2 5.3	18 48.0	17 35.3	14 37.3	8 25.0	14 27.2	19 37.6	25 25.4	23 33.8	29 0.4
30 S	0 30 29.5	5 43.1	2 2.1	0♑40.1	18 58.8	14 19.6	8 39.7	14 38.7	19 34.8	25 25.1	23 34.7	29 0.4
						DECLINATION						
1 F	22 36 9.4	8N46.9	12N42.8	25S14.6	1S16.4	6S19.8	17N52.9	13S48.2	15N29.0	21S31.9	20N56.3	17N 3.5
4 M	22 47 59.1	7 41.5	12 39.6	27 18.0	0 29.1	6 21.5	18 14.0	13 57.5	15 28.4	21 32.7	20 55.4	17 3.3
7 T	22 59 48.7	6 35.0	12 36.3	18 10.9	0N49.8	6 10.9	18 33.8	14 7.0	15 27.6	21 33.5	20 54.6	17 3.0
10 S	23 11 38.4	5 27.5	12 33.1	1 18.7	2 31.7	5 48.1	18 52.5	14 16.7	15 26.5	21 34.1	20 53.8	17 2.8
13 W	23 23 28.1	4 19.3	12 29.8	16N50.6	4 20.9	5 13.9	19 10.1	14 26.6	15 25.1	21 34.7	20 53.1	17 2.5
16 S	23 35 17.7	3 10.3	12 26.6	27 33.0	5 58.4	4 30.2	19 26.6	14 36.6	15 23.5	21 35.3	20 52.4	17 2.2
19 T	23 47 7.4	2 0.7	12 23.3	23 12.1	7 7.7	3 39.2	19 42.0	14 46.8	15 21.7	21 35.7	20 51.7	17 1.9
22 F	23 58 57.0	0 50.8	12 20.0	7 1.8	7 39.2	2 44.0	19 56.4	14 57.2	15 19.7	21 36.1	20 51.1	17 1.6
25 M	0 10 46.7	0S19.4	12 16.7	11S19.1	7 29.8	1 47.4	20 9.9	15 7.6	15 17.4	21 36.3	20 50.5	17 1.4
28 T	0 22 36.4	1 29.6	12 13.4	24 29.0	6 42.2	0 52.3	20 22.4	15 18.2	15 15.0	21 36.5	20 49.9	17 1.1

OCTOBER 1911

DAY	EPHEMERIS SIDEREAL TIME	☉	☊	☽	☿	♀	♂	♃	♄	♅	♆	♇
						LONGITUDE						
1 S	0 34 26.0	6♎42.1	1♉58.9	12♑32.5	20♍26.6	14♍4.3	8♊53.7	14♏50.4	19♉32.0	25♑24.8	23♋35.7	29♊0.4
2 M	0 38 22.6	7 41.1	1 55.7	24 30.1	21 58.3	13R51.3	9 7.0	15 2.1	19R29.1	25R24.6	23 36.5	29R 0.4
3 T	0 42 19.2	8 40.2	1 52.6	6♒37.4	23 33.1	13 40.8	9 19.6	15 13.9	19 26.1	25 24.4	23 37.4	29 0.3
4 W	0 46 15.7	9 39.2	1 49.4	18 58.3	25 10.6	13 32.7	9 31.6	15 25.8	19 23.0	25 24.3	23 38.2	29 0.2
5 T	0 50 12.2	10 38.3	1 46.2	1♓35.9	26 50.3	13 27.0	9 42.8	15 37.7	19 19.8	25 24.2	23 39.0	29 0.1
6 F	0 54 8.8	11 37.5	1 43.0	14 32.2	28 31.7	13 23.7	9 53.3	15 49.6	19 16.6	25 24.2	23 39.7	28 60.0
7 S	0 58 5.4	12 36.6	1 39.8	27 47.9	0♎14.5	13 22.9	10 3.0	16 1.7	19 13.2	25D24.2	23 40.5	28 59.9
8 S	1 2 1.9	13 35.8	1 36.7	11♈22.0	1 58.2	13D24.5	10 12.0	16 13.7	19 9.8	25 24.3	23 41.1	28 59.7
9 M	1 5 58.5	14 35.1	1 33.5	25 12.6	3 42.7	13 28.4	10 20.2	16 25.9	19 6.3	25 24.5	23 41.8	28 59.5
10 T	1 9 55.0	15 34.3	1 30.3	9♉16.5	5 27.6	13 34.6	10 27.7	16 38.1	19 2.7	25 24.6	23 42.4	28 59.3
11 W	1 13 51.6	16 33.6	1 27.1	23 29.6	7 12.8	13 43.1	10 34.3	16 50.3	18 59.1	25 24.9	23 43.0	28 59.0
12 T	1 17 48.1	17 33.0	1 24.0	7♊48.0	8 58.1	13 53.8	10 40.2	17 2.6	18 55.4	25 25.1	23 43.6	28 58.8
13 F	1 21 44.7	18 32.4	1 20.8	22 7.8	10 43.3	14 6.6	10 45.2	17 15.0	18 51.6	25 25.5	23 44.1	28 58.5
14 S	1 25 41.3	19 31.8	1 17.6	6♋25.6	12 28.3	14 21.6	10 49.4	17 27.4	18 47.7	25 25.9	23 44.6	28 58.2
15 S	1 29 37.8	20 31.2	1 14.4	20 38.5	14 13.0	14 38.6	10 52.8	17 39.8	18 43.8	25 26.3	23 45.0	28 57.9
16 M	1 33 34.3	21 30.7	1 11.2	4♌44.3	15 57.3	14 57.6	10 55.3	17 52.3	18 39.8	25 26.8	23 45.5	28 57.5
17 T	1 37 30.9	22 30.3	1 8.1	18 41.1	17 41.2	15 18.5	10 56.9	18 4.9	18 35.7	25 27.3	23 45.9	28 57.2
18 W	1 41 27.5	23 29.8	1 4.9	2♍27.5	19 24.6	15 41.3	10 57.7	18 17.5	18 31.6	25 27.9	23 46.2	28 56.8
19 T	1 45 24.0	24 29.4	1 1.7	16 2.2	21 7.5	16 5.9	10R57.6	18 30.1	18 27.4	25 28.5	23 46.5	28 56.4
20 F	1 49 20.6	25 29.1	0 58.5	29 24.0	22 49.9	16 32.1	10 56.5	18 42.8	18 23.1	25 29.2	23 46.8	28 55.9
21 S	1 53 17.1	26 28.8	0 55.4	12♎32.1	24 31.7	17 0.1	10 54.6	18 55.5	18 18.8	25 30.0	23 47.1	28 55.5
22 S	1 57 13.7	27 28.5	0 52.2	25 26.0	26 12.9	17 29.6	10 51.8	19 8.2	18 14.5	25 30.8	23 47.3	28 55.0
23 M	2 1 10.2	28 28.3	0 49.0	8♏5.5	27 53.5	18 0.7	10 48.1	19 21.0	18 10.1	25 31.6	23 47.5	28 54.5
24 T	2 5 6.8	29 28.0	0 45.8	20 31.4	29 33.6	18 33.3	10 43.5	19 33.9	18 5.6	25 32.5	23 47.6	28 54.0
25 W	2 9 3.3	0♏27.9	0 42.6	2♐44.9	1♏13.1	19 7.3	10 38.0	19 46.7	18 1.1	25 33.5	23 47.8	28 53.4
26 T	2 12 59.9	1 27.7	0 39.5	14 48.0	2 52.1	19 42.7	10 31.6	19 59.6	17 56.6	25 34.5	23 47.8	28 52.9
27 F	2 16 56.5	2 27.6	0 36.3	26 43.7	4 30.5	20 19.5	10 24.3	20 12.6	17 52.0	25 35.5	23 47.9	28 52.3
28 S	2 20 53.0	3 27.5	0 33.1	8♑35.2	6 8.3	20 57.5	10 16.1	20 25.6	17 47.3	25 36.6	23 47.9	28 51.7
29 S	2 24 49.6	4 27.4	0 29.9	20 26.8	7 45.7	21 36.7	10 7.0	20 38.5	17 42.7	25 37.7	23R47.9	28 51.1
30 M	2 28 46.1	5 27.4	0 26.8	2♒22.8	9 22.5	22 17.1	9 57.1	20 51.6	17 38.0	25 38.9	23 47.8	28 50.5
31 T	2 32 42.7	6 27.4	0 23.6	14 27.8	10 58.8	22 58.7	9 46.3	21 4.6	17 33.3	25 40.2	23 47.8	28 49.8
						DECLINATION						
1 S	0 34 26.0	2S39.7	12N10.2	27S48.2	5N22.7	0S 1.1	20N34.2	15S28.8	15N12.3	21S36.7	20N49.4	17N 0.8
4 W	0 46 15.7	3 49.6	12 6.9	19 52.8	3 39.4	0N44.5	20 45.1	15 39.6	15 9.5	21 36.7	20 49.0	17 0.5
7 S	0 58 5.4	4 59.1	12 3.6	3 31.0	1 39.9	1 23.2	20 55.3	15 50.3	15 6.4	21 36.6	20 48.6	17 0.2
10 T	1 9 55.0	6 8.0	12 0.3	15N19.2	0S29.2	1 54.2	21 4.9	16 1.1	15 3.2	21 36.5	20 48.2	16 59.9
13 F	1 21 44.7	7 16.2	11 56.9	27 19.5	2 42.9	2 17.0	21 13.7	16 11.9	14 59.9	21 36.3	20 47.9	16 59.6
16 M	1 33 34.3	8 23.5	11 53.6	24 11.7	4 57.4	2 31.5	21 21.9	16 22.7	14 56.4	21 36.0	20 47.6	16 59.4
19 T	1 45 24.0	9 29.8	11 50.3	8 56.8	7 10.3	2 38.1	21 29.3	16 33.4	14 52.7	21 35.6	20 47.4	16 59.1
22 S	1 57 13.7	10 34.8	11 47.0	9S22.2	9 19.7	2 36.9	21 36.0	16 44.2	14 49.0	21 35.1	20 47.2	16 58.8
25 W	2 9 3.3	11 38.5	11 43.7	23 27.5	11 24.4	2 28.5	21 41.9	16 54.9	14 45.2	21 34.5	20 47.1	16 58.6
28 S	2 20 53.0	12 40.5	11 40.3	28 3.2	13 23.3	2 13.2	21 47.0	17 5.5	14 41.3	21 33.9	20 47.1	16 58.3
31 T	2 32 42.7	13 40.8	11 37.0	21 24.6	15 15.7	1 51.5	21 51.2	17 16.1	14 37.3	21 33.2	20 47.1	16 58.1

NOVEMBER 1911

DAY	EPHEMERIS SIDEREAL TIME h m s	☉ ° ′	☊ ° ′	☽ ° ′	☿ ° ′	♀ ° ′	♂ ° ′	♃ ° ′	♄ ° ′	♅ ° ′	♆ ° ′	♇ ° ′
						LONGITUDE						
1 W	2 36 39.2	7♏27.4	0♉20.4	26♒46.5	12♏34.6	23♍41.4	9♊34.7	21♏17.7	17♉28.5	25♑41.5	23♋47.6	28♊49.2
2 T	2 40 35.8	8 27.4	0 17.2	9♓23.1	14 10.0	24 25.2	9R22.2	21 30.8	17R23.7	25 42.8	23R47.5	28R48.5
3 F	2 44 32.3	9 27.5	0 14.1	22 21.2	15 45.0	25 9.9	9 9.0	21 43.9	17 18.9	25 44.2	23 47.3	28 47.7
4 S	2 48 28.9	10 27.6	0 10.9	5♈42.8	17 19.5	25 55.7	8 54.9	21 57.1	17 14.1	25 45.6	23 47.1	28 47.0
5 S	2 52 25.5	11 27.7	0 7.7	19 28.8	18 53.6	26 42.4	8 40.1	22 10.2	17 9.3	25 47.1	23 46.8	28 46.3
6 M	2 56 22.0	12 27.9	0 4.5	3♉37.6	20 27.3	27 30.1	8 24.6	22 23.4	17 4.5	25 48.7	23 46.5	28 45.5
7 T	3 0 18.6	13 28.1	0 1.3	18 5.4	22 0.6	28 18.6	8 8.3	22 36.6	16 59.6	25 50.2	23 46.2	28 44.7
8 W	3 4 15.1	14 28.3	29♈58.2	2♊46.7	23 33.6	29 8.0	7 51.3	22 49.8	16 54.7	25 51.9	23 45.9	28 43.9
9 T	3 8 11.7	15 28.5	29 55.0	17 34.3	25 6.2	29 58.3	7 33.7	23 3.1	16 49.9	25 53.5	23 45.5	28 43.1
10 F	3 12 8.2	16 28.8	29 51.8	2♋20.7	26 38.4	0♎49.3	7 15.5	23 16.3	16 45.0	25 55.3	23 45.0	28 42.3
11 S	3 16 4.8	17 29.1	29 48.6	16 59.1	28 10.4	1 41.1	6 56.6	23 29.6	16 40.1	25 57.0	23 44.6	28 41.5
12 S	3 20 1.3	18 29.5	29 45.5	1♌24.2	29 42.0	2 33.7	6 37.2	23 42.9	16 35.2	25 58.8	23 44.1	28 40.6
13 M	3 23 57.9	19 29.8	29 42.3	15 32.6	1♐13.2	3 26.9	6 17.2	23 56.1	16 30.4	26 0.7	23 43.6	28 39.7
14 T	3 27 54.5	20 30.2	29 39.1	29 22.6	2 44.2	4 20.9	5 56.8	24 9.5	16 25.5	26 2.6	23 43.0	28 38.8
15 W	3 31 51.0	21 30.7	29 35.9	12♍54.5	4 14.8	5 15.5	5 35.9	24 22.8	16 20.6	26 4.5	23 42.5	28 37.9
16 T	3 35 47.6	22 31.2	29 32.8	26 9.1	5 45.1	6 10.8	5 14.6	24 36.1	16 15.8	26 6.5	23 41.8	28 37.0
17 F	3 39 44.1	23 31.7	29 29.6	9♎ 8.2	7 15.1	7 6.7	4 53.0	24 49.4	16 11.0	26 8.5	23 41.2	28 36.0
18 S	3 43 40.7	24 32.2	29 26.4	21 53.4	8 44.8	8 3.2	4 31.0	25 2.7	16 6.2	26 10.6	23 40.5	28 35.1
19 S	3 47 37.2	25 32.7	29 23.2	4♏26.6	10 14.0	9 0.2	4 8.8	25 16.1	16 1.4	26 12.7	23 39.8	28 34.1
20 M	3 51 33.8	26 33.3	29 20.1	16 49.0	11 42.9	9 57.8	3 46.5	25 29.4	15 56.6	26 14.9	23 39.1	28 33.1
21 T	3 55 30.4	27 34.0	29 16.9	29 2.2	13 11.4	10 55.9	3 23.9	25 42.7	15 51.9	26 17.1	23 38.3	28 32.2
22 W	3 59 26.9	28 34.6	29 13.7	11♐ 7.2	14 39.4	11 54.5	3 1.3	25 56.0	15 47.2	26 19.3	23 37.5	28 31.1
23 T	4 3 23.5	29 35.3	29 10.5	23 5.6	16 6.9	12 53.7	2 38.6	26 9.4	15 42.5	26 21.6	23 36.7	28 30.1
24 F	4 7 20.0	0♐35.9	29 7.3	4♑59.2	17 33.8	13 53.3	2 16.0	26 22.7	15 37.9	26 23.9	23 35.8	28 29.1
25 S	4 11 16.6	1 36.6	29 4.2	16 50.0	19 0.2	14 53.3	1 53.5	26 36.0	15 33.3	26 26.3	23 34.9	28 28.1
26 S	4 15 13.1	2 37.4	29 1.0	28 40.9	20 25.8	15 53.8	1 31.0	26 49.3	15 28.7	26 28.6	23 34.0	28 27.0
27 M	4 19 9.7	3 38.1	28 57.8	10♒35.3	21 50.6	16 54.7	1 8.8	27 2.6	15 24.2	26 31.1	23 33.0	28 25.9
28 T	4 23 6.3	4 38.9	28 54.6	22 37.3	23 14.5	17 56.1	0 46.7	27 15.9	15 19.7	26 33.6	23 32.1	28 24.9
29 W	4 27 2.8	5 39.7	28 51.5	4♓51.1	24 37.4	18 57.8	0 25.0	27 29.2	15 15.3	26 36.1	23 31.1	28 23.8
30 T	4 30 59.4	6 40.4	28 48.3	17 21.7	25 59.1	19 59.9	0 3.6	27 42.5	15 10.9	26 38.6	23 30.0	28 22.7
						DECLINATION						
1 W	2 36 39.2	14S 0.4	11N35.9	17S 3.7	15S51.7	1N43.0	21N52.4	17S19.6	14N36.0	21S32.9	20N47.1	16N58.0
4 S	2 48 28.9	14 58.0	11 32.5	0N12.0	17 34.5	1 13.5	21 55.3	17 30.0	14 32.0	21 32.1	20 47.2	16 57.8
7 T	3 0 18.6	15 53.4	11 29.2	18 43.4	19 9.4	0 38.8	21 57.2	17 40.4	14 28.0	21 31.2	20 47.3	16 57.6
10 F	3 12 8.2	16 46.4	11 25.8	28 3.3	20 35.7	0S 0.9	21 57.8	17 50.6	14 24.0	21 30.2	20 47.5	16 57.4
13 M	3 23 57.9	17 36.9	11 22.5	21 2.3	21 53.1	0 44.9	21 57.3	18 0.7	14 20.0	21 29.1	20 47.7	16 57.3
16 T	3 35 47.6	18 24.7	11 19.1	4 16.8	23 0.7	1 32.9	21 55.5	18 10.7	14 16.1	21 27.9	20 48.0	16 57.1
19 S	3 47 37.2	19 9.5	11 15.7	13S18.8	23 58.0	2 24.4	21 52.5	18 20.5	14 12.2	21 26.7	20 48.3	16 57.0
22 W	3 59 26.9	19 51.2	11 12.4	25 28.0	24 44.3	3 18.8	21 48.4	18 30.1	14 8.5	21 25.4	20 48.7	16 56.9
25 S	4 11 16.6	20 29.7	11 9.0	27 23.9	25 19.0	4 15.7	21 43.4	18 39.6	14 4.9	21 24.1	20 49.1	16 56.8
28 T	4 23 6.3	21 4.8	11 5.6	18 31.3	25 41.4	5 14.7	21 37.7	18 48.9	14 1.4	21 22.6	20 49.6	16 56.7

DECEMBER 1911

DAY	EPHEMERIS SIDEREAL TIME h m s	☉ ° ′	☊ ° ′	☽ ° ′	☿ ° ′	♀ ° ′	♂ ° ′	♃ ° ′	♄ ° ′	♅ ° ′	♆ ° ′	♇ ° ′
						LONGITUDE						
1 F	4 34 55.9	7♐41.2	28♈45.1	0♈13.3	27♐19.4	21♎ 2.4	29♉42.5	27♏55.7	15♉ 6.6	26♑41.2	23♋29.0	28♊21.6
2 S	4 38 52.5	8 42.1	28 41.9	13 30.1	28 38.1	22 5.3	29R21.8	28 9.0	15R 2.3	26 43.8	23R27.9	28R20.5
3 S	4 42 49.0	9 42.9	28 38.8	27 14.5	29 55.0	23 8.5	29 1.7	28 22.2	14 58.1	26 46.5	23 26.8	28 19.4
4 M	4 46 45.6	10 43.8	28 35.6	11♉27.1	1♑ 9.9	24 12.1	28 42.0	28 35.4	14 54.0	26 49.2	23 25.7	28 18.3
5 T	4 50 42.2	11 44.6	28 32.4	26 5.5	2 22.2	25 16.0	28 22.8	28 48.6	14 49.9	26 51.9	23 24.5	28 17.1
6 W	4 54 38.7	12 45.5	28 29.2	11♊ 4.2	3 31.8	26 20.2	28 4.2	29 1.7	14 45.9	26 54.6	23 23.3	28 16.0
7 T	4 58 35.3	13 46.4	28 26.0	26 14.7	4 38.2	27 24.8	27 46.2	29 14.9	14 42.0	26 57.4	23 22.1	28 14.8
8 F	5 2 31.8	14 47.3	28 22.9	11♋26.7	5 40.8	28 29.6	27 28.8	29 28.0	14 38.1	27 0.2	23 20.9	28 13.7
9 S	5 6 28.4	15 48.3	28 19.7	26 29.9	6 39.2	29 34.8	27 12.0	29 41.1	14 34.3	27 3.1	23 19.6	28 12.5
10 S	5 10 25.0	16 49.2	28 16.5	11♌15.5	7 32.7	0♏40.2	26 56.0	29 54.2	14 30.5	27 5.9	23 18.3	28 11.4
11 M	5 14 21.5	17 50.2	28 13.3	25 37.7	8 20.7	1 45.9	26 40.6	0♐ 7.2	14 26.9	27 8.9	23 17.0	28 10.2
12 T	5 18 18.1	18 51.2	28 10.2	9♍33.9	9 2.3	2 51.9	26 25.9	0 20.2	14 23.3	27 11.8	23 15.7	28 9.0
13 W	5 22 14.6	19 52.2	28 7.0	23 4.3	9 36.8	3 58.1	26 12.0	0 33.2	14 19.8	27 14.8	23 14.4	28 7.8
14 T	5 26 11.2	20 53.3	28 3.8	6♎11.3	10 3.3	5 4.6	25 58.8	0 46.2	14 16.4	27 17.8	23 13.0	28 6.7
15 F	5 30 7.8	21 54.3	28 0.6	18 58.1	10 20.8	6 11.4	25 46.4	0 59.1	14 13.0	27 20.8	23 11.6	28 5.5
16 S	5 34 4.3	22 55.4	27 57.5	1♏28.6	10 28.7	7 18.3	25 34.8	1 12.0	14 9.8	27 23.8	23 10.2	28 4.3
17 S	5 38 0.9	23 56.5	27 54.3	13 46.4	10R26.0	8 25.5	25 23.9	1 24.9	14 6.6	27 26.9	23 8.8	28 3.1
18 M	5 41 57.5	24 57.6	27 51.1	25 54.7	10 12.1	9 32.9	25 13.9	1 37.7	14 3.5	27 30.0	23 7.4	28 1.9
19 T	5 45 54.0	25 58.7	27 47.9	7♐56.3	9 46.6	10 40.6	25 4.7	1 50.5	14 0.5	27 33.1	23 5.9	28 0.7
20 W	5 49 50.5	26 59.8	27 44.8	19 53.1	9 9.4	11 48.4	24 56.4	2 3.2	13 57.6	27 36.3	23 4.4	27 59.5
21 T	5 53 47.1	28 0.9	27 41.6	1♑46.8	8 20.9	12 56.4	24 48.8	2 15.9	13 54.8	27 39.4	23 2.9	27 58.3
22 F	5 57 43.7	29 2.1	27 38.4	13 38.7	7 21.9	14 4.6	24 42.1	2 28.6	13 52.1	27 42.6	23 1.4	27 57.1
23 S	6 1 40.2	0♑ 3.2	27 35.2	25 30.2	6 13.8	15 13.0	24 36.3	2 41.2	13 49.5	27 45.9	22 59.9	27 55.9
24 S	6 5 36.8	1 4.3	27 32.1	7♒23.0	4 58.5	16 21.6	24 31.2	2 53.7	13 47.0	27 49.1	22 58.4	27 54.7
25 M	6 9 33.3	2 5.5	27 28.9	19 19.3	3 38.3	17 30.3	24 27.0	3 6.3	13 44.6	27 52.4	22 56.8	27 53.5
26 T	6 13 29.9	3 6.6	27 25.7	1♓21.7	2 16.0	18 39.2	24 23.6	3 18.7	13 42.3	27 55.6	22 55.2	27 52.4
27 W	6 17 26.5	4 7.8	27 22.5	13 33.9	0 54.3	19 48.2	24 21.1	3 31.1	13 40.0	27 58.9	22 53.6	27 51.2
28 T	6 21 23.0	5 9.0	27 19.4	25 59.9	29♐35.9	20 57.4	24 19.3	3 43.5	13 37.9	28 2.3	22 52.1	27 50.0
29 F	6 25 19.6	6 10.1	27 16.2	8♈44.2	28 23.1	22 6.8	24 18.4	3 55.8	13 35.9	28 5.6	22 50.5	27 48.8
30 S	6 29 16.1	7 11.3	27 13.0	21 51.3	27 17.8	23 16.3	24 18.2	4 8.1	13 34.0	28 8.9	22 48.8	27 47.6
31 S	6 33 12.7	8 12.4	27 9.8	5♉25.1	26 21.5	24 25.9	24D18.9	4 20.3	13 32.2	28 12.3	22 47.2	27 46.5
						DECLINATION						
1 F	4 34 55.9	21S36.3	11N 2.2	2S18.4	25S51.2	6S15.4	21N31.6	18S58.0	13N58.0	21S21.1	20N50.1	16N56.6
4 M	4 46 45.6	22 4.0	10 58.8	16N13.4	25 48.0	7 17.3	21 25.3	19 6.9	13 54.9	21 19.5	20 50.6	16 56.6
7 T	4 58 35.3	22 28.0	10 55.4	27 40.0	25 32.3	8 20.1	21 19.0	19 15.6	13 51.9	21 17.9	20 51.2	16 56.6
10 S	5 10 25.0	22 48.0	10 52.0	22 14.4	25 4.8	9 23.3	21 13.2	19 24.1	13 49.2	21 16.2	20 51.9	16 56.6
13 W	5 22 14.6	23 3.9	10 48.6	5 34.3	24 27.3	10 26.5	21 7.9	19 32.4	13 46.6	21 14.5	20 52.5	16 56.6
16 S	5 34 4.3	23 15.8	10 45.2	12S 8.3	23 42.6	11 29.3	21 3.5	19 40.5	13 44.3	21 12.7	20 53.2	16 56.6
19 T	5 45 54.0	23 23.5	10 41.8	24 45.6	22 53.9	12 31.3	21 0.1	19 48.3	13 42.3	21 10.8	20 53.9	16 56.7
22 F	5 57 43.7	23 27.0	10 38.4	27 35.7	22 4.2	13 32.0	20 57.9	19 55.9	13 40.5	21 8.9	20 54.7	16 56.8
25 M	6 9 33.3	23 26.2	10 35.0	19 30.8	21 17.2	14 31.0	20 57.0	20 3.2	13 39.0	21 7.0	20 55.5	16 56.9
28 T	6 21 23.0	23 21.2	10 31.6	4 4.5	20 38.6	15 28.0	20 57.4	20 10.3	13 37.8	21 5.0	20 56.3	16 57.1
31 S	6 33 12.7	23 11.9	10 28.1	13N56.0	20 15.7	16 22.5	20 59.2	20 17.1	13 36.9	21 2.9	20 57.1	16 57.2

JANUARY 1912

LONGITUDE

DAY	EPHEMERIS SIDEREAL TIME h m s	☉ ° ′	☊ ° ′	☽ ° ′	☿ ° ′	♀ ° ′	♂ ° ′	♃ ° ′	♄ ° ′	♅ ° ′	♆ ° ′	♇ ° ′
1 M	6 37 9.3	9♑13.6	27♈ 6.6	19♉27.9	25♐35.0	25♏35.7	24♉20.3	4♐32.4	13♉30.5	28♑15.7	22♋45.6	27♊45.3
2 T	6 41 5.8	10 14.7	27 3.5	3♊59.7	24R58.8	26 45.6	24 22.5	4 44.5	13R28.9	28 19.1	22R43.9	27R44.1
3 W	6 45 2.4	11 15.9	27 0.3	18 56.9	24 33.1	27 55.7	24 25.4	4 56.5	13 27.5	28 22.5	22 42.3	27 43.0
4 T	6 48 58.9	12 17.0	26 57.1	4♋12.3	24 17.4	29 5.8	24 29.1	5 8.5	13 26.1	28 25.9	22 40.6	27 41.8
5 F	6 52 55.5	13 18.1	26 53.9	19 35.3	24 11.5	0♐16.1	24 33.5	5 20.3	13 24.8	28 29.3	22 39.0	27 40.7
6 S	6 56 52.1	14 19.3	26 50.8	4♌54.0	24D14.6	1 26.6	24 38.6	5 32.2	13 23.7	28 32.8	22 37.3	27 39.5
7 S	7 0 48.6	15 20.4	26 47.6	19 57.0	24 26.2	2 37.1	24 44.4	5 43.9	13 22.6	28 36.2	22 35.6	27 38.4
8 M	7 4 45.2	16 21.6	26 44.4	4♍35.7	24 45.5	3 47.7	24 50.9	5 55.6	13 21.7	28 39.7	22 33.9	27 37.3
9 T	7 8 41.7	17 22.7	26 41.2	18 45.3	25 11.8	4 58.5	24 58.1	6 7.2	13 20.9	28 43.2	22 32.2	27 36.1
10 W	7 12 38.3	18 23.8	26 38.1	2♎24.6	25 44.5	6 9.4	25 5.9	6 18.8	13 20.2	28 46.7	22 30.5	27 35.0
11 T	7 16 34.9	19 25.0	26 34.9	15 35.6	26 22.8	7 20.4	25 14.4	6 30.3	13 19.6	28 50.2	22 28.9	27 33.9
12 F	7 20 31.4	20 26.1	26 31.7	28 21.9	27 6.4	8 31.5	25 23.5	6 41.7	13 19.1	28 53.7	22 27.2	27 32.9
13 S	7 24 28.0	21 27.3	26 28.5	10♏48.3	27 54.5	9 42.6	25 33.2	6 53.0	13 18.7	28 57.2	22 25.5	27 31.8
14 S	7 28 24.5	22 28.4	26 25.3	22 59.7	28 46.8	10 53.9	25 43.6	7 4.3	13 18.4	29 0.7	22 23.8	27 30.7
15 M	7 32 21.1	23 29.5	26 22.2	5♐ 0.7	29 42.8	12 5.3	25 54.6	7 15.4	13 18.3	29 4.2	22 22.1	27 29.6
16 T	7 36 17.6	24 30.7	26 19.0	16 55.4	0♑42.1	13 16.7	26 6.1	7 26.5	13 18.3	29 7.7	22 20.4	27 28.6
17 W	7 40 14.2	25 31.8	26 15.8	28 47.0	1 44.4	14 28.2	26 18.2	7 37.5	13D18.3	29 11.3	22 18.7	27 27.5
18 T	7 44 10.7	26 32.9	26 12.6	10♑37.9	2 49.3	15 39.9	26 31.0	7 48.4	13 18.5	29 14.8	22 17.0	27 26.5
19 F	7 48 7.3	27 34.0	26 9.5	22 30.0	3 56.7	16 51.5	26 44.2	7 59.3	13 18.8	29 18.3	22 15.3	27 25.5
20 S	7 52 3.9	28 35.1	26 6.3	4♒24.7	5 6.3	18 3.3	26 58.0	8 10.0	13 19.3	29 21.9	22 13.6	27 24.5
21 S	7 56 0.4	29 36.2	26 3.1	16 23.1	6 17.9	19 15.1	27 12.4	8 20.7	13 19.8	29 25.4	22 11.9	27 23.5
22 M	7 59 57.0	0♒37.3	25 59.9	28 26.3	7 31.3	20 27.0	27 27.2	8 31.2	13 20.4	29 28.9	22 10.2	27 22.5
23 T	8 3 53.5	1 38.4	25 56.8	10♓35.9	8 46.3	21 39.0	27 42.6	8 41.7	13 21.2	29 32.5	22 8.6	27 21.6
24 W	8 7 50.1	2 39.4	25 53.6	22 54.1	10 2.9	22 51.0	27 58.5	8 52.1	13 22.1	29 36.0	22 6.9	27 20.6
25 T	8 11 46.7	3 40.4	25 50.4	5♈23.6	11 20.9	24 3.1	28 14.8	9 2.3	13 23.1	29 39.5	22 5.2	27 19.7
26 F	8 15 43.2	4 41.5	25 47.2	18 7.9	12 40.2	25 15.2	28 31.6	9 12.5	13 24.2	29 43.1	22 3.6	27 18.8
27 S	8 19 39.8	5 42.4	25 44.1	1♉10.5	14 0.7	26 27.4	28 48.9	9 22.6	13 25.4	29 46.6	22 1.9	27 17.9
28 S	8 23 36.3	6 43.4	25 40.9	14 35.3	15 22.3	27 39.6	29 6.7	9 32.6	13 26.7	29 50.1	22 0.3	27 17.0
29 M	8 27 32.9	7 44.4	25 37.7	28 25.1	16 45.1	28 51.9	29 24.8	9 42.4	13 28.1	29 53.6	21 58.7	27 16.1
30 T	8 31 29.5	8 45.3	25 34.5	12♊41.1	18 8.8	0♑ 4.3	29 43.5	9 52.2	13 29.7	29 57.1	21 57.1	27 15.2
31 W	8 35 26.0	9 46.2	25 31.4	27 21.9	19 33.6	1 16.7	0♊ 2.5	10 1.8	13 31.3	0♒ 0.6	21 55.5	27 14.4

DECLINATION

DAY	EPHEMERIS SIDEREAL TIME h m s	☉ ° ′	☊ ° ′	☽ ° ′	☿ ° ′	♀ ° ′	♂ ° ′	♃ ° ′	♄ ° ′	♅ ° ′	♆ ° ′	♇ ° ′
1 M	6 37 9.3	23S 7.9	10N27.0	19N22.3	20S12.3	16S40.1	21N 0.1	20S19.4	13N36.7	21S 2.2	20N57.4	16N57.3
4 T	6 48 58.9	22 53.1	10 23.5	27 58.9	20 14.6	17 30.8	21 3.7	20 25.9	13 36.2	21 0.2	20 58.2	16 57.5
7 S	7 0 48.6	22 34.2	10 20.1	19 13.7	20 32.3	18 18.2	21 8.6	20 32.1	13 36.0	20 58.1	20 59.0	16 57.7
10 W	7 12 38.3	22 11.3	10 16.7	0 58.3	20 59.2	19 1.9	21 14.7	20 38.1	13 36.1	20 55.9	20 59.9	16 58.0
13 S	7 24 28.0	21 44.5	10 13.2	16S13.0	21 29.6	19 41.7	21 21.8	20 43.9	13 36.5	20 53.8	21 0.8	16 58.2
16 T	7 36 17.6	21 13.9	10 9.8	26 38.1	21 59.0	20 17.1	21 30.0	20 49.4	13 37.2	20 51.6	21 1.6	16 58.5
19 F	7 48 7.3	20 39.6	10 6.3	26 28.5	22 24.0	20 47.9	21 39.1	20 54.6	13 38.2	20 49.4	21 2.5	16 58.8
22 M	7 59 57.0	20 1.7	10 2.8	15 57.1	22 42.2	21 13.9	21 49.0	20 59.6	13 39.6	20 47.2	21 3.3	16 59.2
25 T	8 11 46.7	19 20.5	9 59.4	0N35.1	22 52.0	21 34.7	21 59.6	21 4.4	13 41.2	20 45.0	21 4.2	16 59.5
28 S	8 23 36.3	18 36.2	9 55.9	17 50.2	22 52.2	21 50.2	22 10.8	21 8.8	13 43.1	20 42.8	21 5.0	16 59.9
31 W	8 35 26.0	17 48.7	9 52.4	27 53.0	22 41.9	22 0.1	22 22.5	21 13.1	13 45.4	20 40.6	21 5.8	17 0.3

FEBRUARY 1912

LONGITUDE

DAY	EPHEMERIS SIDEREAL TIME h m s	☉ ° ′	☊ ° ′	☽ ° ′	☿ ° ′	♀ ° ′	♂ ° ′	♃ ° ′	♄ ° ′	♅ ° ′	♆ ° ′	♇ ° ′
1 T	8 39 22.5	10♒47.1	25♈28.2	12♋22.8	20♑59.2	2♑29.1	0♊21.9	10♐11.4	13♉33.1	0♒ 4.1	21♋53.9	27♊13.6
2 F	8 43 19.1	11 48.0	25 25.0	27 35.6	22 25.8	3 41.6	0 41.7	10 20.8	13 35.0	0 7.6	21R52.3	27R12.8
3 S	8 47 15.7	12 48.8	25 21.8	12♌49.7	23 53.3	4 54.2	1 1.9	10 30.2	13 36.9	0 11.1	21 50.7	27 12.0
4 S	8 51 12.2	13 49.7	25 18.6	27 54.1	25 21.6	6 6.8	1 22.4	10 39.4	13 39.0	0 14.5	21 49.2	27 11.2
5 M	8 55 8.8	14 50.5	25 15.5	12♍38.9	26 50.7	7 19.4	1 43.4	10 48.5	13 41.2	0 18.0	21 47.6	27 10.4
6 T	8 59 5.3	15 51.3	25 12.3	26 57.5	28 20.7	8 32.1	2 4.6	10 57.4	13 43.5	0 21.4	21 46.1	27 9.7
7 W	9 3 1.9	16 52.1	25 9.1	10♎46.6	29 51.6	9 44.8	2 26.2	11 6.3	13 45.9	0 24.8	21 44.6	27 9.0
8 T	9 6 58.5	17 52.8	25 5.9	24 6.4	1♒23.2	10 57.6	2 48.2	11 15.1	13 48.4	0 28.3	21 43.1	27 8.3
9 F	9 10 55.0	18 53.6	25 2.8	6♏59.5	2 55.7	12 10.4	3 10.5	11 23.7	13 51.1	0 31.7	21 41.6	27 7.6
10 S	9 14 51.6	19 54.3	24 59.6	19 30.1	4 28.9	13 23.3	3 33.1	11 32.2	13 53.8	0 35.0	21 40.2	27 6.9
11 S	9 18 48.1	20 55.0	24 56.4	1♐43.2	6 3.0	14 36.2	3 56.0	11 40.5	13 56.6	0 38.4	21 38.7	27 6.3
12 M	9 22 44.7	21 55.7	24 53.2	13 44.1	7 37.9	15 49.1	4 19.2	11 48.8	13 59.5	0 41.8	21 37.3	27 5.6
13 T	9 26 41.2	22 56.4	24 50.1	25 37.5	9 13.7	17 2.1	4 42.7	11 56.9	14 2.5	0 45.1	21 35.9	27 5.0
14 W	9 30 37.8	23 57.1	24 46.9	7♑27.8	10 50.3	18 15.1	5 6.6	12 4.9	14 5.7	0 48.4	21 34.5	27 4.4
15 T	9 34 34.3	24 57.7	24 43.7	19 18.7	12 27.7	19 28.1	5 30.7	12 12.8	14 8.9	0 51.7	21 33.2	27 3.9
16 F	9 38 30.9	25 58.3	24 40.5	1♒12.8	14 6.0	20 41.2	5 55.1	12 20.5	14 12.2	0 55.0	21 31.8	27 3.3
17 S	9 42 27.4	26 58.9	24 37.3	13 12.4	15 45.2	21 54.3	6 19.7	12 28.1	14 15.6	0 58.3	21 30.5	27 2.8
18 S	9 46 24.0	27 59.5	24 34.2	25 18.9	17 25.3	23 7.4	6 44.7	12 35.5	14 19.2	1 1.6	21 29.2	27 2.3
19 M	9 50 20.6	29 0.0	24 31.0	7♓33.2	19 6.2	24 20.5	7 9.9	12 42.8	14 22.8	1 4.8	21 27.9	27 1.8
20 T	9 54 17.1	0♓ 0.5	24 27.8	19 56.2	20 48.1	25 33.7	7 35.3	12 50.0	14 26.5	1 8.0	21 26.6	27 1.3
21 W	9 58 13.7	1 1.0	24 24.6	2♈28.8	22 30.9	26 46.9	8 1.0	12 57.0	14 30.3	1 11.2	21 25.4	27 0.9
22 T	10 2 10.2	2 1.5	24 21.5	15 12.2	24 14.7	28 0.1	8 27.0	13 3.9	14 34.2	1 14.3	21 24.2	27 0.5
23 F	10 6 6.8	3 1.9	24 18.3	28 7.9	25 59.4	29 13.3	8 53.2	13 10.6	14 38.2	1 17.5	21 23.0	27 0.1
24 S	10 10 3.3	4 2.3	24 15.1	11♉18.0	27 45.1	0♒26.5	9 19.6	13 17.2	14 42.3	1 20.6	21 21.9	26 59.7
25 S	10 13 59.9	5 2.7	24 11.9	24 44.5	29 31.7	1 39.8	9 46.2	13 23.6	14 46.5	1 23.7	21 20.7	26 59.3
26 M	10 17 56.4	6 3.0	24 8.7	8♊29.2	1♓19.3	2 53.1	10 13.1	13 29.9	14 50.7	1 26.7	21 19.6	26 59.0
27 T	10 21 53.0	7 3.3	24 5.6	22 33.1	3 7.9	4 6.4	10 40.1	13 36.0	14 55.1	1 29.8	21 18.5	26 58.7
28 W	10 25 49.6	8 3.6	24 2.4	6♋55.5	4 57.5	5 19.7	11 7.4	13 42.0	14 59.5	1 32.8	21 17.5	26 58.4
29 T	10 29 46.1	9 3.8	23 59.2	21 33.4	6 48.1	6 33.0	11 34.9	13 47.8	15 4.1	1 35.8	21 16.4	26 58.1

DECLINATION

DAY	EPHEMERIS SIDEREAL TIME h m s	☉ ° ′	☊ ° ′	☽ ° ′	☿ ° ′	♀ ° ′	♂ ° ′	♃ ° ′	♄ ° ′	♅ ° ′	♆ ° ′	♇ ° ′
1 T	8 39 22.5	17S32.3	9N51.3	27N45.5	22S36.0	22S 2.2	22N26.4	21S14.4	13N46.2	20S39.9	21N 6.1	17N 0.4
4 S	8 51 12.2	16 41.1	9 47.8	16 8.0	22 10.9	22 4.7	22 38.5	21 18.3	13 48.8	20 37.7	21 6.9	17 0.8
7 W	9 3 1.9	15 47.4	9 44.3	3S12.4	21 34.0	22 1.5	22 50.7	21 22.0	13 51.6	20 35.5	21 7.7	17 1.3
10 S	9 14 51.6	14 51.2	9 40.8	19 43.9	20 45.2	21 52.5	23 3.0	21 25.4	13 54.8	20 33.3	21 8.5	17 1.7
13 T	9 26 41.2	13 52.7	9 37.4	27 50.9	19 44.2	21 37.7	23 15.3	21 28.6	13 58.2	20 31.2	21 9.2	17 2.2
16 F	9 38 30.9	12 52.1	9 33.9	24 47.2	18 30.8	21 17.2	23 27.4	21 31.6	14 1.8	20 29.1	21 9.9	17 2.7
19 M	9 50 20.6	11 49.7	9 30.4	12 5.5	17 5.0	20 51.1	23 39.4	21 34.3	14 5.7	20 27.0	21 10.6	17 3.2
22 T	10 2 10.2	10 45.6	9 26.9	5N23.2	15 26.6	20 19.5	23 51.0	21 36.8	14 9.8	20 25.0	21 11.2	17 3.7
25 S	10 13 59.9	9 40.0	9 23.4	21 37.6	13 35.7	19 42.6	24 2.3	21 39.1	14 14.1	20 23.0	21 11.8	17 4.2
28 W	10 25 49.6	8 33.1	9 19.8	28 13.2	11 32.5	19 0.5	24 13.0	21 41.2	14 18.7	20 21.0	21 12.4	17 4.8

MARCH 1912

DAY	EPHEMERIS SIDEREAL TIME h m s	☉ ° ′	☊ ° ′	☽ ° ′	☿ ° ′	♀ ° ′	♂ ° ′	♃ ° ′	♄ ° ′	♅ ° ′	♆ ° ′	♇ ° ′
LONGITUDE												
1 F	10 33 42.6	10♓ 4.0	23♈56.0	6♌21.8	8♓39.6	7♒46.3	12♊ 2.6	13♐53.4	15♉ 8.7	1♒38.7	21♋15.4	26♊57.9
2 S	10 37 39.2	11 4.2	23 52.9	21 13.2	10 32.1	8 59.7	12 30.4	13 58.9	15 13.4	1 41.7	21 R 14.5	26 R 57.7
3 S	10 41 35.8	12 4.3	23 49.7	5♍59.5	12 25.5	10 13.1	12 58.5	14 4.3	15 18.2	1 44.6	21 13.5	26 57.5
4 M	10 45 32.3	13 4.4	23 46.5	20 32.5	14 19.8	11 26.5	13 26.7	14 9.5	15 23.0	1 47.4	21 12.6	26 57.3
5 T	10 49 28.9	14 4.4	23 43.3	4♎45.7	16 14.8	12 39.8	13 55.1	14 14.5	15 28.0	1 50.3	21 11.7	26 57.1
6 W	10 53 25.4	15 4.5	23 40.1	18 34.8	18 10.6	13 53.3	14 23.6	14 19.3	15 33.0	1 53.1	21 10.8	26 57.0
7 T	10 57 22.0	16 4.5	23 37.0	1♏58.2	20 7.1	15 6.7	14 52.4	14 24.0	15 38.1	1 55.9	21 10.0	26 56.9
8 F	11 1 18.6	17 4.5	23 33.8	14 56.9	22 4.1	16 20.2	15 21.3	14 28.5	15 43.2	1 58.6	21 9.2	26 56.8
9 S	11 5 15.1	18 4.4	23 30.6	27 33.3	24 1.4	17 33.6	15 50.3	14 32.9	15 48.5	2 1.3	21 8.4	26 56.8
10 S	11 9 11.6	19 4.4	23 27.4	9♐51.5	25 59.0	18 47.1	16 19.5	14 37.1	15 53.8	2 4.0	21 7.7	26 56.7
11 M	11 13 8.2	20 4.3	23 24.3	21 56.1	27 56.5	20 0.6	16 48.9	14 41.1	15 59.2	2 6.6	21 6.9	26 56.7
12 T	11 17 4.7	21 4.1	23 21.1	3♑51.9	29 53.9	21 14.1	17 18.4	14 44.9	16 4.7	2 9.3	21 6.3	26 D 56.7
13 W	11 21 1.3	22 4.0	23 17.9	15 43.7	1♈50.7	22 27.6	17 48.1	14 48.6	16 10.2	2 11.8	21 5.6	26 56.7
14 T	11 24 57.9	23 3.8	23 14.7	27 36.1	3 46.8	23 41.2	18 17.9	14 52.1	16 15.9	2 14.4	21 5.0	26 56.8
15 F	11 28 54.4	24 3.6	23 11.5	9♒32.8	5 41.7	24 54.7	18 47.9	14 55.4	16 21.5	2 16.9	21 4.4	26 56.8
16 S	11 32 51.0	25 3.3	23 8.4	21 37.2	7 35.1	26 8.3	19 18.0	14 58.5	16 27.3	2 19.4	21 3.8	26 56.9
17 S	11 36 47.5	26 3.1	23 5.2	3♓51.6	9 26.5	27 21.8	19 48.2	15 1.5	16 33.1	2 21.8	21 3.3	26 57.1
18 M	11 40 44.1	27 2.8	23 2.0	16 17.8	11 15.6	28 35.4	20 18.6	15 4.3	16 39.0	2 24.2	21 2.8	26 57.2
19 T	11 44 40.6	28 2.4	22 58.8	28 56.6	13 1.9	29 48.9	20 49.1	15 6.9	16 45.0	2 26.5	21 2.3	26 57.4
20 W	11 48 37.2	29 2.0	22 55.7	11♈48.5	14 44.9	1♓ 2.5	21 19.7	15 9.3	16 51.0	2 28.9	21 1.9	26 57.5
21 T	11 52 33.7	0♈ 1.6	22 52.5	24 53.3	16 24.2	2 16.1	21 50.4	15 11.5	16 57.1	2 31.1	21 1.5	26 57.8
22 F	11 56 30.3	1 1.2	22 49.3	8♉10.9	17 59.3	3 29.7	22 21.3	15 13.6	17 3.2	2 33.4	21 1.1	26 58.0
23 S	12 0 26.9	2 0.7	22 46.1	21 40.7	19 29.7	4 43.3	22 52.3	15 15.4	17 9.4	2 35.6	21 0.8	26 58.3
24 S	12 4 23.4	3 0.2	22 42.9	5♊22.4	20 55.2	5 56.8	23 23.4	15 17.1	17 15.7	2 37.7	21 0.5	26 58.5
25 M	12 8 19.9	3 59.6	22 39.8	19 15.5	22 15.2	7 10.4	23 54.7	15 18.6	17 22.0	2 39.9	21 0.2	26 58.8
26 T	12 12 16.5	4 59.0	22 36.6	3♋19.0	23 29.5	8 24.0	24 26.0	15 19.9	17 28.4	2 41.9	21 0.0	26 59.1
27 W	12 16 13.1	5 58.4	22 33.4	17 31.6	24 37.6	9 37.6	24 57.5	15 21.0	17 34.8	2 44.0	20 59.8	26 59.5
28 T	12 20 9.6	6 57.7	22 30.2	1♌51.1	25 39.4	10 51.2	25 29.0	15 21.9	17 41.3	2 46.0	20 59.7	26 59.9
29 F	12 24 6.2	7 57.0	22 27.1	16 14.2	26 34.6	12 4.8	26 0.6	15 22.7	17 47.8	2 47.9	20 59.5	27 0.3
30 S	12 28 2.7	8 56.3	22 23.9	0♍36.8	27 22.9	13 18.3	26 32.4	15 23.2	17 54.4	2 49.8	20 59.4	27 0.7
31 S	12 31 59.3	9 55.5	22 20.7	14 54.2	28 4.3	14 31.9	27 4.2	15 23.6	18 1.0	2 51.7	20 59.3	27 1.1
DECLINATION												
1 F	10 33 42.6	7S47.9	9N17.5	23N31.2	10S 3.7	18S29.7	24N19.9	21S42.5	14N21.8	20S19.7	21N12.8	17N 5.1
4 M	10 45 32.3	6 39.3	9 14.0	6 14.0	7 41.0	17 39.6	24 29.6	21 44.2	14 26.6	20 17.9	21 13.3	17 5.7
7 T	10 57 22.0	5 29.8	9 10.5	13S 0.9	5 7.9	16 44.9	24 38.7	21 45.7	14 31.6	20 16.0	21 13.8	17 6.2
10 S	11 9 11.6	4 19.6	9 6.9	25 45.7	2 26.4	15 45.9	24 47.0	21 47.1	14 36.8	20 14.3	21 14.2	17 6.8
13 W	11 21 1.3	3 9.0	9 3.4	27 39.8	0N20.3	14 42.9	24 54.4	21 48.2	14 42.1	20 12.6	21 14.6	17 7.4
16 S	11 32 51.0	1 58.0	8 59.9	18 35.0	3 7.7	13 36.3	25 1.0	21 49.1	14 47.6	20 11.0	21 15.0	17 8.0
19 T	11 44 40.6	0 46.8	8 56.4	2 16.3	5 49.7	12 26.2	25 6.7	21 49.9	14 53.2	20 9.4	21 15.3	17 8.6
22 F	11 56 30.3	0N24.4	8 52.8	15N39.9	8 19.2	11 13.1	25 11.4	21 50.5	14 58.9	20 7.9	21 15.6	17 9.2
25 M	12 8 19.9	1 35.3	8 49.3	27 26.9	10 29.6	9 57.2	25 15.1	21 50.9	15 4.7	20 6.6	21 15.8	17 9.8
28 T	12 20 9.6	2 45.9	8 45.7	24 48.0	12 14.9	8 38.9	25 17.6	21 51.1	15 10.6	20 5.2	21 16.0	17 10.4
31 S	12 31 59.3	3 56.0	8 42.2	8 51.1	13 30.8	7 18.4	25 19.1	21 51.1	15 16.6	20 4.0	21 16.1	17 10.9

APRIL 1912

DAY	EPHEMERIS SIDEREAL TIME h m s	☉ ° ′	☊ ° ′	☽ ° ′	☿ ° ′	♀ ° ′	♂ ° ′	♃ ° ′	♄ ° ′	♅ ° ′	♆ ° ′	♇ ° ′
LONGITUDE												
1 M	12 35 55.8	10♈54.6	22♈17.5	29♍ 1.7	28♈38.6	15♓45.5	27♊36.2	15♐23.8	18♉ 7.7	2♒53.5	20♋59.3	27♊ 1.6
2 T	12 39 52.4	11 53.8	22 14.3	12♎54.9	29 5.7	16 59.1	28 8.2	15 R 23.8	18 14.5	2 55.3	20 59.3	27 2.0
3 W	12 43 48.9	12 52.9	22 11.2	26 30.5	29 25.7	18 12.7	28 40.3	15 23.6	18 21.2	2 57.0	20 D 59.4	27 2.5
4 T	12 47 45.5	13 52.0	22 8.0	9♏46.6	29 38.6	19 26.3	29 12.5	15 23.2	18 28.1	2 58.7	20 59.4	27 3.0
5 F	12 51 42.1	14 51.0	22 4.8	22 42.7	29 44.4	20 39.9	29 44.8	15 22.7	18 35.0	3 0.3	20 59.5	27 3.6
6 S	12 55 38.6	15 50.0	22 1.6	5♐19.9	29 R 43.4	21 53.5	0♋17.2	15 21.9	18 41.9	3 1.9	20 59.7	27 4.1
7 S	12 59 35.1	16 49.0	21 58.5	17 40.5	29 35.7	23 7.1	0 49.6	15 21.0	18 48.8	3 3.5	20 59.8	27 4.7
8 M	13 3 31.7	17 47.9	21 55.3	29 48.0	29 21.8	24 20.7	1 22.1	15 19.8	18 55.8	3 5.0	21 0.0	27 5.3
9 T	13 7 28.3	18 46.9	21 52.1	11♑46.3	29 2.0	25 34.3	1 54.8	15 18.5	19 2.9	3 6.5	21 0.3	27 6.0
10 W	13 11 24.8	19 45.8	21 48.9	23 39.9	28 36.8	26 47.9	2 27.5	15 17.0	19 10.0	3 7.9	21 0.5	27 6.6
11 T	13 15 21.4	20 44.6	21 45.8	5♒33.5	28 6.8	28 1.6	3 0.2	15 15.4	19 17.1	3 9.2	21 0.8	27 7.3
12 F	13 19 17.9	21 43.4	21 42.6	17 31.5	27 32.6	29 15.2	3 33.1	15 13.5	19 24.2	3 10.6	21 1.2	27 7.9
13 S	13 23 14.5	22 42.2	21 39.4	29 38.4	26 55.0	0♈28.8	4 6.0	15 11.4	19 31.4	3 11.8	21 1.5	27 8.6
14 S	13 27 11.0	23 41.0	21 36.2	11♓57.7	26 14.6	1 42.4	4 39.0	15 9.2	19 38.7	3 13.0	21 1.9	27 9.4
15 M	13 31 7.6	24 39.8	21 33.0	24 32.5	25 32.3	2 56.0	5 12.1	15 6.8	19 45.9	3 14.2	21 2.4	27 10.1
16 T	13 35 4.1	25 38.5	21 29.9	7♈24.5	24 49.0	4 9.6	5 45.3	15 4.2	19 53.2	3 15.3	21 2.9	27 10.9
17 W	13 39 0.7	26 37.2	21 26.7	20 34.7	24 5.4	5 23.3	6 18.5	15 1.4	20 0.6	3 16.4	21 3.4	27 11.7
18 T	13 42 57.2	27 35.8	21 23.5	4♉ 2.5	23 22.3	6 36.9	6 51.8	14 58.4	20 7.9	3 17.4	21 3.9	27 12.5
19 F	13 46 53.8	28 34.4	21 20.3	17 46.4	22 40.6	7 50.5	7 25.2	14 55.3	20 15.3	3 18.4	21 4.5	27 13.3
20 S	13 50 50.4	29 33.0	21 17.2	1♊43.5	22 0.8	9 4.1	7 58.6	14 52.0	20 22.7	3 19.4	21 5.1	27 14.1
21 S	13 54 46.9	0♉31.6	21 14.0	15 50.6	21 23.8	10 17.7	8 32.1	14 48.5	20 30.2	3 20.2	21 5.7	27 15.0
22 M	13 58 43.5	1 30.1	21 10.8	0♋ 4.0	20 49.9	11 31.3	9 5.7	14 44.9	20 37.6	3 21.1	21 6.4	27 15.9
23 T	14 2 40.0	2 28.6	21 7.6	14 20.1	20 19.7	12 44.9	9 39.3	14 41.0	20 45.1	3 21.9	21 7.1	27 16.8
24 W	14 6 36.6	3 27.0	21 4.4	28 35.6	19 53.6	13 58.5	10 13.0	14 37.1	20 52.7	3 22.6	21 7.8	27 17.7
25 T	14 10 33.1	4 25.4	21 1.3	12♌47.7	19 31.9	15 12.0	10 46.8	14 32.9	21 0.2	3 23.3	21 8.6	27 18.6
26 F	14 14 29.7	5 23.8	20 58.1	26 54.2	19 14.8	16 25.6	11 20.6	14 28.6	21 7.7	3 23.9	21 9.4	27 19.5
27 S	14 18 26.2	6 22.1	20 54.9	10♍53.2	19 2.4	17 39.2	11 54.4	14 24.1	21 15.3	3 24.5	21 10.2	27 20.5
28 S	14 22 22.8	7 20.4	20 51.7	24 43.0	18 54.9	18 52.7	12 28.3	14 19.5	21 22.9	3 25.0	21 11.0	27 21.5
29 M	14 26 19.4	8 18.7	20 48.6	8♎22.1	18 52.3	20 6.3	13 2.3	14 14.7	21 30.5	3 25.5	21 11.9	27 22.5
30 T	14 30 15.9	9 16.9	20 45.4	21 49.1	18 D 54.6	21 19.9	13 36.3	14 9.8	21 38.2	3 25.9	21 12.8	27 23.5
DECLINATION												
1 M	12 35 55.8	4N19.2	8N41.0	2N14.4	13N49.0	6S51.2	25N19.3	21S51.1	15N18.6	20S 3.6	21N16.1	17N11.1
4 T	12 47 45.5	5 28.4	8 37.4	16S19.4	14 21.4	5 28.4	25 19.2	21 50.9	15 24.6	20 2.5	21 16.2	17 11.7
7 S	12 59 35.1	6 36.7	8 33.9	27 15.0	14 19.8	4 4.1	25 17.9	21 50.5	15 30.7	20 1.5	21 16.2	17 12.3
10 W	13 11 24.8	7 44.0	8 30.3	26 34.4	13 45.2	2 38.7	25 15.4	21 50.0	15 36.9	20 0.6	21 16.2	17 12.9
13 S	13 23 14.5	8 50.2	8 26.8	15 29.8	12 42.2	1 12.5	25 11.6	21 49.3	15 43.1	19 59.8	21 16.1	17 13.5
16 T	13 35 4.1	9 55.0	8 23.2	1N45.2	11 19.1	0N14.1	25 6.5	21 48.4	15 49.3	19 59.1	21 16.0	17 14.0
19 F	13 46 53.8	10 58.4	8 19.6	19 22.8	9 47.4	1 41.0	25 0.2	21 47.4	15 55.5	19 58.5	21 15.8	17 14.6
22 M	13 58 43.5	12 0.2	8 16.1	28 21.5	8 19.0	3 7.7	24 52.6	21 46.2	16 1.7	19 57.9	21 15.6	17 15.1
25 T	14 10 33.1	13 0.1	8 12.5	21 41.1	7 4.1	4 33.9	24 43.6	21 44.8	16 7.9	19 57.5	21 15.4	17 15.7
28 S	14 22 22.8	13 58.2	8 8.9	4 17.1	6 8.9	5 59.4	24 33.4	21 43.2	16 14.1	19 57.2	21 15.1	17 16.2

MAY 1912

LONGITUDE

DAY	EPHEMERIS SIDEREAL TIME h m s	☉ ° ′	☊ ° ′	☽ ° ′	☿ ° ′	♀ ° ′	♂ ° ′	♃ ° ′	♄ ° ′	♅ ° ′	♆ ° ′	♇ ° ′
1 W	14 34 12.5	10♉15.1	20♈42.2	5♏ 2.8	19♈ 1.7	22♈33.4	14♋10.4	14♐ 4.7	21♉45.8	3♒26.3	21♋13.8	27♊24.5
2 T	14 38 9.0	11 13.3	20 39.0	18 2.3	19 13.5	23 47.0	14 44.5	13R59.5	21 53.5	3 26.6	21 14.8	27 25.6
3 F	14 42 5.6	12 11.4	20 35.8	0♐47.2	19 30.0	25 0.5	15 18.7	13 54.1	22 1.2	3 26.9	21 15.8	27 26.6
4 S	14 46 2.1	13 9.6	20 32.7	13 17.8	19 51.1	26 14.1	15 52.9	13 48.7	22 8.9	3 27.2	21 16.8	27 27.7
5 S	14 49 58.7	14 7.6	20 29.5	25 35.4	20 16.5	27 27.6	16 27.2	13 43.0	22 16.6	3 27.3	21 17.9	27 28.8
6 M	14 53 55.2	15 5.7	20 26.3	7♑42.0	20 46.1	28 41.2	17 1.5	13 37.3	22 24.3	3 27.5	21 19.0	27 29.9
7 T	14 57 51.8	16 3.8	20 23.1	19 40.3	21 19.8	29 54.7	17 35.9	13 31.4	22 32.0	3 27.6	21 20.1	27 31.0
8 W	15 1 48.4	17 1.8	20 20.0	1♒34.0	21 57.5	1♉ 8.3	18 10.3	13 25.3	22 39.7	3 27.6	21 21.3	27 32.1
9 T	15 5 44.9	17 59.8	20 16.8	13 27.3	22 39.0	2 21.9	18 44.8	13 19.2	22 47.4	3R27.6	21 22.4	27 33.3
10 F	15 9 41.5	18 57.7	20 13.6	25 24.7	23 24.1	3 35.4	19 19.3	13 12.9	22 55.2	3 27.5	21 23.6	27 34.4
11 S	15 13 38.0	19 55.7	20 10.4	7♓31.1	24 12.8	4 49.0	19 53.9	13 6.6	23 2.9	3 27.4	21 24.9	27 35.6
12 S	15 17 34.6	20 53.6	20 7.3	19 51.0	25 4.8	6 2.5	20 28.5	13 0.1	23 10.7	3 27.2	21 26.2	27 36.8
13 M	15 21 31.2	21 51.5	20 4.1	2♈28.7	26 0.2	7 16.1	21 3.1	12 53.5	23 18.5	3 27.0	21 27.5	27 38.0
14 T	15 25 27.7	22 49.4	20 0.9	15 27.6	26 58.7	8 29.6	21 37.8	12 46.8	23 26.2	3 26.8	21 28.8	27 39.2
15 W	15 29 24.2	23 47.3	19 57.7	28 49.6	28 0.2	9 43.2	22 12.6	12 40.0	23 34.0	3 26.4	21 30.1	27 40.4
16 T	15 33 20.8	24 45.1	19 54.5	12♉34.9	29 4.7	10 56.8	22 47.4	12 33.2	23 41.7	3 26.1	21 31.5	27 41.6
17 F	15 37 17.4	25 43.0	19 51.4	26 41.6	0♉12.1	12 10.3	23 22.2	12 26.2	23 49.5	3 25.7	21 32.9	27 42.9
18 S	15 41 13.9	26 40.8	19 48.2	11♊ 5.6	1 22.3	13 23.9	23 57.1	12 19.2	23 57.2	3 25.2	21 34.3	27 44.2
19 S	15 45 10.5	27 38.5	19 45.0	25 41.0	2 35.2	14 37.4	24 32.1	12 12.1	24 5.0	3 24.7	21 35.8	27 45.4
20 M	15 49 7.0	28 36.3	19 41.8	10♋20.8	3 50.7	15 51.0	25 7.0	12 4.9	24 12.7	3 24.2	21 37.2	27 46.7
21 T	15 53 3.6	29 34.0	19 38.7	24 58.1	5 8.9	17 4.5	25 42.1	11 57.6	24 20.5	3 23.6	21 38.7	27 48.0
22 W	15 57 0.1	0♊31.7	19 35.5	9♌27.2	6 29.6	18 18.1	26 17.1	11 50.3	24 28.2	3 22.9	21 40.3	27 49.3
23 T	16 0 56.7	1 29.4	19 32.3	23 43.7	7 52.9	19 31.6	26 52.2	11 42.9	24 35.9	3 22.2	21 41.8	27 50.6
24 F	16 4 53.2	2 27.0	19 29.1	7♍45.4	9 18.6	20 45.2	27 27.4	11 35.5	24 43.7	3 21.5	21 43.4	27 51.9
25 S	16 8 49.8	3 24.6	19 26.0	21 31.5	10 46.8	21 58.7	28 2.5	11 28.0	24 51.4	3 20.7	21 45.0	27 53.2
26 S	16 12 46.4	4 22.2	19 22.8	5♎ 2.4	12 17.4	23 12.2	28 37.7	11 20.5	24 59.1	3 19.9	21 46.6	27 54.6
27 M	16 16 42.9	5 19.8	19 19.6	18 19.1	13 50.5	24 25.8	29 13.0	11 13.0	25 6.7	3 19.0	21 48.2	27 55.9
28 T	16 20 39.5	6 17.4	19 16.4	1♏22.7	15 26.0	25 39.3	29 48.3	11 5.4	25 14.4	3 18.1	21 49.9	27 57.2
29 W	16 24 36.0	7 14.9	19 13.2	14 14.3	17 3.9	26 52.9	0♌23.6	10 57.8	25 22.1	3 17.1	21 51.6	27 58.6
30 T	16 28 32.6	8 12.4	19 10.1	26 54.6	18 44.2	28 6.4	0 58.9	10 50.2	25 29.7	3 16.1	21 53.3	27 60.0
31 F	16 32 29.1	9 9.9	19 6.9	9♐24.1	20 26.9	29 19.9	1 34.3	10 42.6	25 37.3	3 15.0	21 55.0	28 1.3

DECLINATION

DAY	EPHEMERIS SIDEREAL TIME	☉	☊	☽	☿	♀	♂	♃	♄	♅	♆	♇
1 W	14 34 12.5	14N54.1	8N 5.3	14S22.1	5N36.6	7N23.8	24N21.8	21S41.5	16N20.2	19S57.0	21N14.7	17N16.7
4 S	14 46 2.1	15 47.9	8 1.7	26 29.7	5 27.3	8 46.8	24 8.9	21 39.7	16 26.3	19 56.9	21 14.4	17 17.2
7 T	14 57 51.8	16 39.2	7 58.1	27 10.6	5 39.7	10 8.1	23 54.7	21 37.7	16 32.4	19 56.9	21 13.9	17 17.7
10 F	15 9 41.5	17 28.2	7 54.5	17 7.6	6 11.9	11 27.4	23 39.1	21 35.5	16 38.4	19 57.1	21 13.5	17 18.2
13 M	15 21 31.2	18 14.5	7 51.0	0 33.6	7 1.4	12 44.3	23 22.3	21 33.2	16 44.4	19 57.3	21 12.9	17 18.6
16 T	15 33 20.8	18 58.0	7 47.4	17N25.4	8 6.0	13 58.6	23 4.1	21 30.8	16 50.3	19 57.6	21 12.4	17 19.1
19 S	15 45 10.5	19 38.7	7 43.8	28 3.2	9 23.4	15 9.9	22 44.7	21 28.2	16 56.1	19 58.0	21 11.8	17 19.5
22 W	15 57 0.1	20 16.4	7 40.1	22 36.9	10 51.5	16 17.8	22 23.9	21 25.6	17 1.8	19 58.5	21 11.1	17 19.9
25 S	16 8 49.8	20 50.9	7 36.5	5 41.4	12 28.3	17 22.1	22 2.0	21 22.8	17 7.4	19 59.1	21 10.5	17 20.3
28 T	16 20 39.5	21 22.2	7 32.9	12S50.6	14 11.4	18 22.3	21 38.7	21 20.0	17 13.0	19 59.8	21 9.8	17 20.7
31 F	16 32 29.1	21 50.2	7 29.3	25 40.6	15 58.5	19 18.3	21 14.3	21 17.1	17 18.4	20 0.6	21 9.0	17 21.0

JUNE 1912

LONGITUDE

DAY	EPHEMERIS SIDEREAL TIME h m s	☉ ° ′	☊ ° ′	☽ ° ′	☿ ° ′	♀ ° ′	♂ ° ′	♃ ° ′	♄ ° ′	♅ ° ′	♆ ° ′	♇ ° ′
1 S	16 36 25.7	10♊ 7.3	19♈ 3.7	21♐43.6	22♉12.0	0♊33.5	2♌ 9.8	10♐34.9	25♉44.9	3♒13.9	21♋56.8	28♊ 2.7
2 S	16 40 22.3	11 4.8	19 0.5	3♑53.8	23 59.5	1 47.0	2 45.2	10R27.3	25 52.5	3R12.8	21 58.5	28 4.1
3 M	16 44 18.8	12 2.2	18 57.4	15 55.9	25 49.3	3 0.6	3 20.7	10 19.6	26 0.1	3 11.6	22 0.3	28 5.5
4 T	16 48 15.3	12 59.7	18 54.2	27 51.8	27 41.4	4 14.1	3 56.2	10 12.0	26 7.6	3 10.4	22 2.1	28 6.9
5 W	16 52 11.9	13 57.1	18 51.0	9♒44.1	29 35.9	5 27.7	4 31.8	10 4.4	26 15.2	3 9.1	22 4.0	28 8.3
6 T	16 56 8.5	14 54.5	18 47.8	21 36.1	1♊32.6	6 41.3	5 7.4	9 56.8	26 22.7	3 7.8	22 5.8	28 9.7
7 F	17 0 5.1	15 51.9	18 44.7	3♓31.9	3 31.5	7 54.8	5 43.0	9 49.2	26 30.2	3 6.5	22 7.7	28 11.1
8 S	17 4 1.6	16 49.2	18 41.5	15 36.2	5 32.4	9 8.4	6 18.7	9 41.6	26 37.6	3 5.1	22 9.5	28 12.5
9 S	17 7 58.2	17 46.6	18 38.3	27 53.8	7 35.3	10 22.0	6 54.4	9 34.1	26 45.1	3 3.6	22 11.4	28 13.9
10 M	17 11 54.7	18 44.0	18 35.1	10♈29.7	9 40.1	11 35.6	7 30.2	9 26.6	26 52.5	3 2.2	22 13.4	28 15.4
11 T	17 15 51.3	19 41.3	18 32.0	23 28.4	11 46.6	12 49.2	8 5.9	9 19.2	26 59.9	3 0.7	22 15.3	28 16.8
12 W	17 19 47.8	20 38.7	18 28.8	6♉53.4	13 54.5	14 2.8	8 41.8	9 11.8	27 7.2	2 59.1	22 17.2	28 18.2
13 T	17 23 44.4	21 36.0	18 25.6	20 46.1	16 3.8	15 16.4	9 17.6	9 4.4	27 14.5	2 57.6	22 19.2	28 19.7
14 F	17 27 41.0	22 33.3	18 22.4	5♊ 5.6	18 14.0	16 30.0	9 53.5	8 57.2	27 21.8	2 55.9	22 21.2	28 21.1
15 S	17 31 37.5	23 30.7	18 19.3	19 47.7	20 25.1	17 43.6	10 29.4	8 49.9	27 29.1	2 54.3	22 23.2	28 22.5
16 S	17 35 34.1	24 28.0	18 16.1	4♋45.2	22 36.7	18 57.3	11 5.4	8 42.8	27 36.3	2 52.6	22 25.2	28 24.0
17 M	17 39 30.6	25 25.3	18 12.9	19 48.9	24 48.6	20 10.9	11 41.4	8 35.7	27 43.5	2 50.9	22 27.2	28 25.4
18 T	17 43 27.2	26 22.6	18 9.7	4♌49.0	27 0.4	21 24.5	12 17.4	8 28.7	27 50.7	2 49.1	22 29.2	28 26.9
19 W	17 47 23.8	27 19.8	18 6.5	19 36.6	29 11.9	22 38.2	12 53.5	8 21.8	27 57.8	2 47.3	22 31.3	28 28.3
20 T	17 51 20.3	28 17.1	18 3.4	4♍ 5.7	1♋22.8	23 51.8	13 29.6	8 15.0	28 4.9	2 45.5	22 33.3	28 29.7
21 F	17 55 16.9	29 14.4	18 0.2	18 12.8	3 32.9	25 5.5	14 5.7	8 8.2	28 12.0	2 43.7	22 35.4	28 31.2
22 S	17 59 13.4	0♋11.6	17 57.0	1♎57.2	5 42.0	26 19.1	14 41.9	8 1.6	28 19.0	2 41.8	22 37.5	28 32.6
23 S	18 3 10.0	1 8.8	17 53.8	15 20.2	7 49.9	27 32.8	15 18.1	7 55.1	28 25.9	2 39.9	22 39.6	28 34.1
24 M	18 7 6.5	2 6.1	17 50.7	28 24.4	9 56.3	28 46.5	15 54.3	7 48.6	28 32.9	2 37.9	22 41.7	28 35.5
25 T	18 11 3.1	3 3.3	17 47.5	11♏12.6	12 1.2	0♋ 0.1	16 30.6	7 42.3	28 39.8	2 36.0	22 43.8	28 37.0
26 W	18 14 59.7	4 0.5	17 44.3	23 47.7	14 4.4	1 13.8	17 6.9	7 36.1	28 46.6	2 34.0	22 46.0	28 38.4
27 T	18 18 56.2	4 57.7	17 41.1	6♐12.0	16 5.8	2 27.5	17 43.2	7 30.0	28 53.4	2 32.0	22 48.1	28 39.8
28 F	18 22 52.8	5 54.8	17 38.0	18 27.4	18 5.4	3 41.2	18 19.5	7 24.1	29 0.1	2 29.9	22 50.2	28 41.3
29 S	18 26 49.3	6 52.0	17 34.8	0♑35.4	20 3.0	4 54.9	18 55.9	7 18.2	29 6.8	2 27.9	22 52.4	28 42.7
30 S	18 30 45.9	7 49.2	17 31.6	12 37.3	21 58.7	6 8.6	19 32.3	7 12.5	29 13.5	2 25.8	22 54.5	28 44.1

DECLINATION

DAY	EPHEMERIS SIDEREAL TIME	☉	☊	☽	☿	♀	♂	♃	♄	♅	♆	♇
1 S	16 36 25.7	21N58.8	7N28.1	27S39.7	16N34.6	19N36.0	21N 5.9	21S16.2	17N20.2	20S 0.9	21N 8.8	17N21.1
4 T	16 48 15.3	22 22.2	7 24.5	25 32.6	18 22.2	20 25.8	20 39.8	21 13.2	17 25.5	20 1.8	21 8.0	17 21.4
7 F	17 0 5.1	22 42.1	7 20.9	13 39.3	20 5.8	21 10.6	20 12.6	21 10.3	17 30.7	20 2.8	21 7.1	17 21.7
10 M	17 11 54.7	22 58.5	7 17.3	3N23.9	21 40.7	21 50.2	19 44.3	21 7.3	17 35.7	20 3.9	21 6.3	17 22.0
13 T	17 23 44.4	23 11.2	7 13.6	20 28.9	23 1.3	22 24.3	19 14.8	21 4.4	17 40.7	20 5.1	21 5.4	17 22.3
16 S	17 35 34.1	23 20.2	7 10.0	28 14.9	24 2.6	22 52.6	18 44.3	21 1.6	17 45.5	20 6.3	21 4.5	17 22.5
19 W	17 47 23.8	23 25.6	7 6.4	19 3.9	24 40.4	23 15.1	18 12.6	20 58.8	17 50.1	20 7.6	21 3.5	17 22.7
22 S	17 59 13.4	23 27.2	7 2.7	0 34.3	24 53.0	23 31.4	17 39.9	20 56.1	17 54.6	20 8.9	21 2.6	17 22.9
25 T	18 11 3.1	23 25.0	6 59.1	17S 2.0	24 40.9	23 41.6	17 6.3	20 53.5	17 59.0	20 10.3	21 1.6	17 23.1
28 F	18 22 52.8	23 19.2	6 55.5	27 16.6	24 6.3	23 45.5	16 31.6	20 51.1	18 3.2	20 11.7	21 0.6	17 23.2

JULY 1912

DAY	EPHEMERIS SIDEREAL TIME	☉	☊	☽	☿	♀	♂	♃	♄	♅	♆	♇
	h m s	° ′	° ′	° ′	° ′	° ′	° ′	° ′	° ′	° ′	° ′	° ′
						LONGITUDE						
1 M	18 34 42.5	8♋46.4	17♈28.4	24♑34.0	23♋52.3	7♋22.3	20♌ 8.7	7♐ 7.0	29♉20.1	2♒23.7	22♋56.7	28♊45.5
2 T	18 38 39.0	9 43.6	17 25.3	6♒27.0	25 43.9	8 36.0	20 45.2	7R 1.5	29 26.7	2R21.5	22 58.9	28 47.0
3 W	18 42 35.6	10 40.7	17 22.1	18 18.2	27 33.5	9 49.7	21 21.7	6 56.2	29 33.2	2 19.3	23 1.1	28 48.4
4 T	18 46 32.1	11 37.9	17 18.9	0♓10.0	29 21.0	11 3.5	21 58.3	6 51.1	29 39.7	2 17.2	23 3.3	28 49.8
5 F	18 50 28.7	12 35.1	17 15.7	12 5.7	1♌ 6.4	12 17.2	22 34.8	6 46.0	29 46.1	2 15.0	23 5.5	28 51.2
6 S	18 54 25.2	13 32.3	17 12.5	24 9.1	2 49.8	13 31.0	23 11.4	6 41.2	29 52.4	2 12.7	23 7.7	28 52.6
7 S	18 58 21.8	14 29.5	17 9.4	6♈24.8	4 31.1	14 44.7	23 48.1	6 36.4	29 58.7	2 10.5	23 9.9	28 54.0
8 M	19 2 18.4	15 26.7	17 6.2	18 57.8	6 10.4	15 58.5	24 24.7	6 31.9	0♊ 5.0	2 8.3	23 12.1	28 55.4
9 T	19 6 15.0	16 23.9	17 3.0	1♉52.8	7 47.6	17 12.3	25 1.4	6 27.4	0 11.2	2 6.0	23 14.3	28 56.8
10 W	19 10 11.5	17 21.1	16 59.8	15 14.2	9 22.7	18 26.1	25 38.2	6 23.2	0 17.3	2 3.7	23 16.5	28 58.2
11 T	19 14 8.0	18 18.3	16 56.7	29 4.7	10 55.8	19 39.9	26 15.0	6 19.1	0 23.4	2 1.4	23 18.7	28 59.6
12 F	19 18 4.6	19 15.6	16 53.5	13♊24.5	12 26.7	20 53.7	26 51.8	6 15.1	0 29.4	1 59.1	23 20.9	29 0.9
13 S	19 22 1.2	20 12.8	16 50.3	28 10.9	13 55.6	22 7.6	27 28.6	6 11.4	0 35.4	1 56.7	23 23.2	29 2.3
14 S	19 25 57.8	21 10.1	16 47.1	13♋17.1	15 22.3	23 21.4	28 5.5	6 7.8	0 41.3	1 54.4	23 25.4	29 3.6
15 M	19 29 54.3	22 7.3	16 44.0	28 33.4	16 46.9	24 35.3	28 42.4	6 4.3	0 47.1	1 52.1	23 27.6	29 5.0
16 T	19 33 50.8	23 4.6	16 40.8	13♌48.8	18 9.3	25 49.2	29 19.3	6 1.1	0 52.8	1 49.7	23 29.9	29 6.3
17 W	19 37 47.4	24 1.8	16 37.6	28 52.2	19 29.4	27 3.0	29 56.3	5 58.0	0 58.5	1 47.3	23 32.1	29 7.7
18 T	19 41 43.9	24 59.1	16 34.4	13♍35.4	20 47.3	28 16.9	0♍33.3	5 55.0	1 4.2	1 44.9	23 34.3	29 9.0
19 F	19 45 40.5	25 56.4	16 31.3	27 53.1	22 2.9	29 30.8	1 10.4	5 52.3	1 9.8	1 42.6	23 36.5	29 10.3
20 S	19 49 37.1	26 53.6	16 28.1	11♎43.9	23 16.2	0♌44.7	1 47.5	5 49.7	1 15.3	1 40.2	23 38.8	29 11.6
21 S	19 53 33.6	27 50.9	16 24.9	25 8.6	24 26.9	1 58.6	2 24.6	5 47.4	1 20.7	1 37.8	23 41.0	29 12.9
22 M	19 57 30.2	28 48.2	16 21.7	8♏10.1	25 35.2	3 12.5	3 1.7	5 45.2	1 26.0	1 35.4	23 43.2	29 14.2
23 T	20 1 26.7	29 45.5	16 18.6	20 52.1	26 40.9	4 26.4	3 38.9	5 43.1	1 31.3	1 33.0	23 45.4	29 15.5
24 W	20 5 23.3	0♌42.8	16 15.4	3♐18.6	27 43.9	5 40.3	4 16.1	5 41.3	1 36.5	1 30.6	23 47.7	29 16.7
25 T	20 9 19.9	1 40.1	16 12.2	15 33.1	28 44.0	6 54.2	4 53.3	5 39.6	1 41.7	1 28.2	23 49.9	29 18.0
26 F	20 13 16.4	2 37.4	16 9.0	27 38.9	29 41.3	8 8.2	5 30.6	5 38.1	1 46.8	1 25.8	23 52.1	29 19.2
27 S	20 17 13.0	3 34.7	16 5.8	9♑38.6	0♍35.6	9 22.1	6 7.9	5 36.8	1 51.8	1 23.4	23 54.3	29 20.4
28 S	20 21 9.6	4 32.0	16 2.7	21 34.1	1 26.8	10 36.0	6 45.2	5 35.7	1 56.7	1 21.0	23 56.5	29 21.7
29 M	20 25 6.1	5 29.4	15 59.5	3♒27.1	2 14.6	11 50.0	7 22.6	5 34.8	2 1.5	1 18.6	23 58.7	29 22.9
30 T	20 29 2.7	6 26.7	15 56.3	15 19.1	2 59.0	13 3.9	8 0.0	5 34.1	2 6.3	1 16.2	24 0.9	29 24.1
31 W	20 32 59.2	7 24.1	15 53.1	27 11.5	3 39.8	14 17.9	8 37.4	5 33.5	2 11.0	1 13.8	24 3.0	29 25.2
						DECLINATION						
1 M	18 34 42.5	23N 9.7	6N51.8	26S 6.1	23N12.7	23N43.0	15N56.0	20S48.9	18N 7.3	20S13.2	20N59.5	17N23.3
4 T	18 46 32.1	22 56.6	6 48.2	14 51.6	22 3.6	23 34.2	15 19.5	20 46.8	18 11.2	20 14.7	20 58.5	17 23.4
7 S	18 58 21.8	22 39.9	6 44.5	1N41.3	20 42.5	23 19.2	14 42.2	20 44.9	18 15.0	20 16.3	20 57.4	17 23.5
10 W	19 10 11.5	22 19.6	6 40.9	18 41.3	19 12.6	22 57.9	14 3.9	20 43.3	18 18.6	20 17.9	20 56.4	17 23.6
13 S	19 22 1.2	21 55.8	6 37.2	28 11.3	17 36.6	22 30.5	13 24.9	20 41.9	18 22.1	20 19.5	20 55.3	17 23.6
16 T	19 33 50.8	21 28.7	6 33.6	20 56.5	15 57.1	21 57.1	12 45.0	20 40.7	18 25.3	20 21.1	20 54.2	17 23.6
19 F	19 45 40.5	20 58.3	6 29.9	2 16.7	14 16.4	21 18.0	12 4.4	20 39.8	18 28.4	20 22.7	20 53.1	17 23.6
22 M	19 57 30.2	20 24.7	6 26.2	16S 2.8	12 36.8	20 33.4	11 23.1	20 39.2	18 31.4	20 24.4	20 51.9	17 23.6
25 T	20 9 19.9	19 48.0	6 22.6	26 59.5	11 0.5	19 43.4	10 41.1	20 38.9	18 34.1	20 26.0	20 50.8	17 23.6
28 S	20 21 9.6	19 8.3	6 18.9	26 38.7	9 30.1	18 48.5	9 58.5	20 38.9	18 36.7	20 27.6	20 49.7	17 23.5
31 W	20 32 59.2	18 25.9	6 15.2	15 56.5	8 8.1	17 48.8	9 15.3	20 39.1	18 39.2	20 29.2	20 48.6	17 23.4

AUGUST 1912

						LONGITUDE						
1 T	20 36 55.8	8♌21.5	15♈50.0	9♓ 6.4	4♍16.8	15♌31.9	9♍14.9	5♐33.1	2♊15.6	1♒11.4	24♋ 5.2	29♊26.4
2 F	20 40 52.3	9 18.9	15 46.8	21 5.8	4 49.9	16 45.8	9 52.4	5R32.9	2 20.1	1R 9.1	24 7.4	29 27.6
3 S	20 44 48.9	10 16.3	15 43.6	3♈13.0	5 18.8	17 59.8	10 30.0	5 32.9	2 24.6	1 6.7	24 9.5	29 28.7
4 S	20 48 45.4	11 13.7	15 40.4	15 31.3	5 43.4	19 13.8	11 7.5	5D33.1	2 28.9	1 4.4	24 11.7	29 29.8
5 M	20 52 42.0	12 11.2	15 37.2	28 4.8	6 3.5	20 27.8	11 45.1	5 33.4	2 33.2	1 2.0	24 13.8	29 30.9
6 T	20 56 38.6	13 8.6	15 34.1	10♉58.0	6 18.9	21 41.8	12 22.8	5 33.9	2 37.4	0 59.7	24 16.0	29 32.0
7 W	21 0 35.1	14 6.1	15 30.9	24 14.7	6 29.4	22 55.9	13 0.5	5 34.7	2 41.5	0 57.4	24 18.1	29 33.1
8 T	21 4 31.7	15 3.7	15 27.7	7♊58.2	6 34.8	24 9.9	13 38.2	5 35.6	2 45.5	0 55.1	24 20.2	29 34.2
9 F	21 8 28.2	16 1.2	15 24.5	22 9.5	6 35.0	25 23.9	14 15.9	5 36.7	2 49.5	0 52.8	24 22.3	29 35.3
10 S	21 12 24.8	16 58.8	15 21.4	6♋47.3	6R29.8	26 38.0	14 53.7	5 37.9	2 53.3	0 50.5	24 24.4	29 36.3
11 S	21 16 21.4	17 56.4	15 18.2	21 46.6	6 19.2	27 52.0	15 31.6	5 39.4	2 57.1	0 48.2	24 26.5	29 37.3
12 M	21 20 17.9	18 54.0	15 15.0	6♌59.5	6 3.1	29 6.1	16 9.4	5 41.0	3 0.7	0 46.0	24 28.6	29 38.3
13 T	21 24 14.4	19 51.6	15 11.8	22 15.4	5 41.6	0♍20.1	16 47.3	5 42.8	3 4.3	0 43.7	24 30.6	29 39.3
14 W	21 28 11.0	20 49.3	15 8.7	7♍23.6	5 14.7	1 34.2	17 25.3	5 44.8	3 7.8	0 41.5	24 32.7	29 40.3
15 T	21 32 7.6	21 46.9	15 5.5	22 14.4	4 42.7	2 48.3	18 3.3	5 47.0	3 11.2	0 39.3	24 34.7	29 41.3
16 F	21 36 4.1	22 44.6	15 2.3	6♎41.1	4 5.8	4 2.4	18 41.3	5 49.4	3 14.5	0 37.2	24 36.7	29 42.2
17 S	21 40 0.7	23 42.3	14 59.1	20 40.3	3 24.5	5 16.4	19 19.3	5 51.9	3 17.7	0 35.0	24 38.7	29 43.2
18 S	21 43 57.2	24 40.1	14 55.9	4♏11.8	2 39.2	6 30.5	19 57.4	5 54.6	3 20.8	0 32.9	24 40.7	29 44.1
19 M	21 47 53.7	25 37.8	14 52.8	17 17.4	1 50.7	7 44.6	20 35.5	5 57.5	3 23.8	0 30.8	24 42.7	29 44.9
20 T	21 51 50.3	26 35.6	14 49.6	0♐ 0.7	0 59.8	8 58.7	21 13.7	6 0.6	3 26.7	0 28.7	24 44.6	29 45.8
21 W	21 55 46.9	27 33.4	14 46.4	12 25.8	0 7.2	10 12.8	21 51.9	6 3.8	3 29.6	0 26.6	24 46.6	29 46.7
22 T	21 59 43.5	28 31.2	14 43.2	24 37.0	29♌14.1	11 26.8	22 30.1	6 7.2	3 32.3	0 24.6	24 48.5	29 47.5
23 F	22 3 40.0	29 29.0	14 40.1	6♑38.4	28 21.4	12 40.9	23 8.4	6 10.8	3 34.9	0 22.6	24 50.4	29 48.3
24 S	22 7 36.5	0♍26.8	14 36.9	18 33.8	27 30.3	13 55.0	23 46.7	6 14.6	3 37.4	0 20.6	24 52.3	29 49.1
25 S	22 11 33.1	1 24.7	14 33.7	0♒26.2	26 41.9	15 9.1	24 25.0	6 18.5	3 39.8	0 18.7	24 54.2	29 49.9
26 M	22 15 29.7	2 22.6	14 30.5	12 18.2	25 57.2	16 23.1	25 3.4	6 22.6	3 42.2	0 16.8	24 56.0	29 50.7
27 T	22 19 26.2	3 20.5	14 27.4	24 11.8	25 17.1	17 37.2	25 41.8	6 26.9	3 44.4	0 14.9	24 57.9	29 51.4
28 W	22 23 22.7	4 18.4	14 24.2	6♓ 8.8	24 42.8	18 51.3	26 20.3	6 31.3	3 46.5	0 13.0	24 59.7	29 52.2
29 T	22 27 19.3	5 16.4	14 21.0	18 10.9	24 14.9	20 5.4	26 58.8	6 35.9	3 48.5	0 11.2	25 1.5	29 52.9
30 F	22 31 15.9	6 14.4	14 17.8	0♈19.7	23 54.2	21 19.4	27 37.3	6 40.6	3 50.4	0 9.4	25 3.3	29 53.6
31 S	22 35 12.5	7 12.4	14 14.6	12 37.1	23 41.1	22 33.5	28 15.8	6 45.6	3 52.2	0 7.7	25 5.0	29 54.2
						DECLINATION						
1 T	20 36 55.8	18N11.1	6N14.0	10S52.5	7N43.2	17N27.8	9N 0.7	20S39.2	18N39.9	20S29.7	20N48.2	17N23.4
4 S	20 48 45.4	17 25.0	6 10.4	6N12.6	6 37.5	16 22.3	8 16.8	20 39.9	18 42.1	20 31.3	20 47.1	17 23.3
7 W	21 0 35.1	16 36.4	6 6.7	22 0.8	5 48.1	15 12.7	7 32.3	20 40.8	18 44.1	20 32.8	20 46.0	17 23.2
10 S	21 12 24.8	15 45.4	6 3.0	28 18.9	5 19.2	13 59.3	6 47.3	20 42.0	18 45.9	20 34.3	20 44.9	17 23.0
13 T	21 24 14.4	14 52.0	5 59.3	17 52.3	5 14.4	12 42.6	6 1.8	20 43.5	18 47.6	20 35.7	20 43.8	17 22.9
16 F	21 36 4.1	13 56.5	5 55.6	2S 5.5	5 36.5	11 22.8	5 15.9	20 45.2	18 49.0	20 37.2	20 42.8	17 22.7
19 M	21 47 53.7	12 59.1	5 52.0	19 44.8	6 25.3	10 0.3	4 29.6	20 47.2	18 50.3	20 38.5	20 41.7	17 22.5
22 T	21 59 43.5	11 59.7	5 48.3	28 12.3	7 36.3	8 35.4	3 43.1	20 49.5	18 51.4	20 39.8	20 40.7	17 22.3
25 S	22 11 33.1	10 58.7	5 44.6	24 51.7	9 0.0	7 8.4	2 56.2	20 52.1	18 52.3	20 41.1	20 39.7	17 22.1
28 W	22 23 22.7	9 56.2	5 40.9	12 8.0	10 24.1	5 39.6	2 9.0	20 54.8	18 53.1	20 42.3	20 38.7	17 21.9
31 S	22 35 12.5	8 52.2	5 37.2	4N58.8	11 36.0	4 9.5	1 21.7	20 57.8	18 53.7	20 43.4	20 37.7	17 21.7

SEPTEMBER 1912

DAY	EPHEMERIS SIDEREAL TIME	☉	☊	☽	☿	♀	♂	♃	♄	♅	♆	♇
	h m s	° ′	° ′	° ′	° ′	° ′	° ′	° ′	° ′	° ′	° ′	° ′
						LONGITUDE						
1 S	22 39 9.0	8♍10.4	14♈11.5	25♈ 5.5	23♌36.2	23♍47.6	28♍54.4	6♐50.6	3♊53.9	0♒ 5.9	25♋ 6.8	29♊54.9
2 M	22 43 5.5	9 8.5	14 8.3	7♉47.4	23D39.7	25 1.7	29 33.1	6 55.9	3 55.5	0R 4.2	25 8.5	29 55.5
3 T	22 47 2.1	10 6.6	14 5.1	20 45.6	23 51.8	26 15.7	0♎11.8	7 1.3	3 57.0	0 2.6	25 10.2	29 56.1
4 W	22 50 58.6	11 4.8	14 1.9	4♊ 3.0	24 12.6	27 29.8	0 50.5	7 6.8	3 58.4	0 1.0	25 11.9	29 56.7
5 T	22 54 55.2	12 3.0	13 58.8	17 41.7	24 41.9	28 43.9	1 29.3	7 12.5	3 59.7	29♑59.4	25 13.5	29 57.3
6 F	22 58 51.7	13 1.2	13 55.6	1♋42.9	25 19.5	29 58.0	2 8.1	7 18.4	4 0.9	29 57.8	25 15.2	29 57.8
7 S	23 2 48.3	13 59.4	13 52.4	16 5.9	26 5.4	1♎12.0	2 46.9	7 24.4	4 2.0	29 56.3	25 16.8	29 58.3
8 S	23 6 44.8	14 57.7	13 49.2	0♌47.6	26 59.0	2 26.1	3 25.8	7 30.5	4 2.9	29 54.8	25 18.4	29 58.8
9 M	23 10 41.4	15 56.0	13 46.0	15 42.6	28 0.1	3 40.2	4 4.8	7 36.9	4 3.8	29 53.4	25 19.9	29 59.3
10 T	23 14 38.0	16 54.4	13 42.9	0♍43.0	29 8.0	4 54.3	4 43.7	7 43.3	4 4.5	29 52.0	25 21.5	29 59.8
11 W	23 18 34.5	17 52.7	13 39.7	15 40.2	0♍22.4	6 8.4	5 22.7	7 49.9	4 5.2	29 50.6	25 23.0	0♋ 0.2
12 T	23 22 31.0	18 51.1	13 36.5	0♎25.5	1 42.7	7 22.4	6 1.8	7 56.7	4 5.7	29 49.3	25 24.5	0 0.6
13 F	23 26 27.6	19 49.6	13 33.3	14 51.8	3 8.3	8 36.5	6 40.9	8 3.6	4 6.1	29 48.1	25 25.9	0 1.0
14 S	23 30 24.2	20 48.1	13 30.2	28 54.3	4 38.6	9 50.6	7 20.1	8 10.6	4 6.4	29 46.8	25 27.4	0 1.4
15 S	23 34 20.8	21 46.6	13 27.0	12♏31.1	6 13.1	11 4.6	7 59.2	8 17.8	4 6.6	29 45.6	25 28.8	0 1.8
16 M	23 38 17.3	22 45.1	13 23.8	25 42.4	7 51.2	12 18.7	8 38.5	8 25.2	4 6.7	29 44.5	25 30.2	0 2.1
17 T	23 42 13.8	23 43.6	13 20.6	8♐30.3	9 32.2	13 32.7	9 17.7	8 32.6	4R 6.7	29 43.4	25 31.5	0 2.4
18 W	23 46 10.4	24 42.2	13 17.4	20 58.3	11 15.9	14 46.8	9 57.0	8 40.2	4 6.5	29 42.3	25 32.9	0 2.7
19 T	23 50 7.0	25 40.8	13 14.3	3♑10.7	13 1.5	16 0.8	10 36.4	8 48.0	4 6.3	29 41.3	25 34.2	0 3.0
20 F	23 54 3.5	26 39.5	13 11.1	15 11.8	14 48.8	17 14.8	11 15.7	8 55.8	4 5.9	29 40.4	25 35.4	0 3.2
21 S	23 58 0.0	27 38.1	13 7.9	27 6.1	16 37.3	18 28.9	11 55.2	9 3.8	4 5.5	29 39.4	25 36.7	0 3.4
22 S	0 1 56.6	28 36.8	13 4.7	8♒57.8	18 26.6	19 42.9	12 34.6	9 11.9	4 4.9	29 38.6	25 37.9	0 3.6
23 M	0 5 53.2	29 35.6	13 1.6	20 50.5	20 16.6	20 56.9	13 14.1	9 20.2	4 4.3	29 37.7	25 39.1	0 3.8
24 T	0 9 49.8	0♎34.3	12 58.4	2♓47.4	22 6.8	22 10.9	13 53.7	9 28.6	4 3.5	29 37.0	25 40.3	0 3.9
25 W	0 13 46.3	1 33.1	12 55.2	14 50.9	23 57.2	23 24.9	14 33.3	9 37.1	4 2.6	29 36.2	25 41.4	0 4.1
26 T	0 17 42.8	2 31.9	12 52.0	27 3.3	25 47.4	24 38.8	15 12.9	9 45.7	4 1.6	29 35.5	25 42.5	0 4.2
27 F	0 21 39.4	3 30.8	12 48.8	9♈26.0	27 37.4	25 52.8	15 52.6	9 54.4	4 0.5	29 34.9	25 43.6	0 4.3
28 S	0 25 36.0	4 29.6	12 45.7	22 0.1	29 27.0	27 6.8	16 32.3	10 3.3	3 59.3	29 34.3	25 44.6	0 4.3
29 S	0 29 32.5	5 28.6	12 42.5	4♉46.7	1♎16.1	28 20.7	17 12.1	10 12.3	3 58.0	29 33.8	25 45.7	0 4.4
30 M	0 33 29.1	6 27.5	12 39.3	17 46.4	3 4.6	29 34.7	17 51.9	10 21.4	3 56.5	29 33.3	25 46.6	0 4.4
						DECLINATION						
1 S	22 39 9.0	8N30.6	5N36.0	10N45.4	11N55.4	3N39.2	1N 5.8	20S58.9	18N53.8	20S43.7	20N37.4	17N21.6
4 W	22 50 58.6	7 24.9	5 32.3	24 58.2	12 35.8	2 7.6	0 18.3	21 2.1	18 54.1	20 44.7	20 36.5	17 21.4
7 S	23 2 48.3	6 18.1	5 28.6	27 39.1	12 45.7	0 35.4	0S29.5	21 5.6	18 54.3	20 45.7	20 35.6	17 21.1
10 T	23 14 38.0	5 10.4	5 24.9	14 29.3	12 22.7	0S57.2	1 17.3	21 9.2	18 54.2	20 46.5	20 34.7	17 20.9
13 F	23 26 27.6	4 1.9	5 21.2	6S 3.6	11 27.6	2 29.8	2 5.1	21 13.0	18 54.0	20 47.3	20 33.9	17 20.6
16 M	23 38 17.3	2 52.7	5 17.5	22 41.6	10 4.4	4 2.0	2 53.0	21 16.9	18 53.6	20 48.0	20 33.1	17 20.4
19 T	23 50 7.0	1 43.1	5 13.8	28 36.2	8 18.5	5 33.7	3 40.8	21 21.0	18 53.0	20 48.6	20 32.4	17 20.1
22 S	0 1 56.6	0 33.1	5 10.0	22 34.1	6 16.4	7 4.3	4 28.5	21 25.1	18 52.3	20 49.2	20 31.7	17 19.8
25 W	0 13 46.3	0S37.1	5 6.3	8 13.4	4 3.9	8 33.6	5 16.0	21 29.4	18 51.4	20 49.6	20 31.0	17 19.5
28 S	0 25 36.0	1 47.2	5 2.6	9N23.7	1 45.7	10 1.3	6 3.4	21 33.8	18 50.3	20 49.9	20 30.4	17 19.3

OCTOBER 1912

DAY	EPHEMERIS SIDEREAL TIME	☉	☊	☽	☿	♀	♂	♃	♄	♅	♆	♇
						LONGITUDE						
1 T	0 37 25.6	7♎26.5	12♈36.1	1♊ 0.0	4♎52.5	0♏48.6	18♎31.7	10♐30.6	3♊55.0	29♑32.8	25♋47.6	0♋ 4.4
2 W	0 41 22.2	8 25.5	12 33.0	14 28.0	6 39.7	2 2.5	19 11.6	10 39.9	3R53.4	29R32.4	25 48.5	0R 4.3
3 T	0 45 18.7	9 24.6	12 29.8	28 10.7	8 26.1	3 16.5	19 51.5	10 49.4	3 51.6	29 32.1	25 49.4	0 4.3
4 F	0 49 15.3	10 23.7	12 26.6	12♋ 7.9	10 11.8	4 30.4	20 31.5	10 58.9	3 49.8	29 31.8	25 50.3	0 4.2
5 S	0 53 11.8	11 22.9	12 23.4	26 18.7	11 56.8	5 44.3	21 11.6	11 8.6	3 47.9	29 31.5	25 51.1	0 4.1
6 S	0 57 8.4	12 22.1	12 20.2	10♌41.1	13 41.0	6 58.2	21 51.6	11 18.4	3 45.8	29 31.3	25 51.9	0 4.0
7 M	1 1 5.0	13 21.3	12 17.1	25 11.8	15 24.3	8 12.1	22 31.8	11 28.3	3 43.7	29 31.2	25 52.7	0 3.9
8 T	1 5 1.5	14 20.6	12 13.9	9♍46.4	17 7.0	9 26.0	23 11.9	11 38.3	3 41.4	29 31.1	25 53.4	0 3.7
9 W	1 8 58.0	15 19.8	12 10.7	24 19.4	18 48.8	10 39.9	23 52.1	11 48.3	3 39.1	29 31.0	25 54.1	0 3.5
10 T	1 12 54.6	16 19.2	12 7.5	8♎44.9	20 29.9	11 53.8	24 32.4	11 58.5	3 36.6	29 31.0	25 54.8	0 3.3
11 F	1 16 51.2	17 18.6	12 4.4	22 57.5	22 10.2	13 7.7	25 12.7	12 8.8	3 34.1	29D31.1	25 55.4	0 3.1
12 S	1 20 47.7	18 18.0	12 1.2	6♏52.4	23 49.8	14 21.6	25 53.1	12 19.2	3 31.5	29 31.2	25 56.0	0 2.8
13 S	1 24 44.3	19 17.4	11 58.0	20 26.5	25 28.6	15 35.4	26 33.5	12 29.7	3 28.7	29 31.4	25 56.6	0 2.6
14 M	1 28 40.8	20 16.9	11 54.8	3♐38.7	27 6.8	16 49.3	27 13.9	12 40.3	3 25.9	29 31.6	25 57.2	0 2.3
15 T	1 32 37.4	21 16.4	11 51.6	16 29.2	28 44.2	18 3.1	27 54.4	12 51.0	3 23.0	29 31.8	25 57.7	0 1.9
16 W	1 36 33.9	22 15.9	11 48.5	29 0.2	0♏21.0	19 17.0	28 34.9	13 1.8	3 20.0	29 32.1	25 58.1	0 1.6
17 T	1 40 30.5	23 15.5	11 45.3	11♑14.8	1 57.2	20 30.8	29 15.5	13 12.6	3 16.9	29 32.5	25 58.6	0 1.2
18 F	1 44 27.1	24 15.1	11 42.1	23 17.1	3 32.7	21 44.6	29 56.1	13 23.6	3 13.7	29 32.9	25 59.0	0 0.8
19 S	1 48 23.6	25 14.7	11 38.9	5♒11.7	5 7.5	22 58.4	0♏36.8	13 34.6	3 10.4	29 33.4	25 59.4	0 0.4
20 S	1 52 20.1	26 14.3	11 35.8	17 3.2	6 41.8	24 12.2	1 17.5	13 45.8	3 7.1	29 33.9	25 59.7	0 0.0
21 M	1 56 16.7	27 14.0	11 32.6	28 56.4	8 15.5	25 25.9	1 58.3	13 57.0	3 3.6	29 34.5	25 60.0	29♊59.6
22 T	2 0 13.3	28 13.7	11 29.4	10♓55.7	9 48.5	26 39.7	2 39.1	14 8.3	3 0.1	29 35.1	26 0.3	29 59.1
23 W	2 4 9.8	29 13.5	11 26.2	23 4.7	11 21.1	27 53.4	3 19.9	14 19.6	2 56.5	29 35.8	26 0.5	29 58.6
24 T	2 8 6.4	0♏13.2	11 23.1	5♈26.7	12 53.0	29 7.1	4 0.8	14 31.1	2 52.9	29 36.5	26 0.7	29 58.1
25 F	2 12 2.9	1 13.0	11 19.9	18 3.7	14 24.4	0♐20.8	4 41.7	14 42.6	2 49.1	29 37.3	26 0.9	29 57.6
26 S	2 15 59.5	2 12.9	11 16.7	0♉57.0	15 55.3	1 34.5	5 22.7	14 54.2	2 45.3	29 38.1	26 1.0	29 57.0
27 S	2 19 56.0	3 12.7	11 13.5	14 6.6	17 25.6	2 48.2	6 3.7	15 5.9	2 41.4	29 39.0	26 1.1	29 56.4
28 M	2 23 52.6	4 12.6	11 10.3	27 31.7	18 55.4	4 1.8	6 44.8	15 17.7	2 37.5	29 39.9	26 1.2	29 55.9
29 T	2 27 49.1	5 12.6	11 7.2	11♊10.4	20 24.6	5 15.5	7 25.9	15 29.5	2 33.4	29 40.8	26 1.2	29 55.2
30 W	2 31 45.7	6 12.5	11 4.0	25 0.5	21 53.3	6 29.1	8 7.1	15 41.4	2 29.4	29 41.9	26 1.2	29 54.6
31 T	2 35 42.3	7 12.5	11 0.8	8♋59.2	23 21.5	7 42.7	8 48.3	15 53.4	2 25.2	29 42.9	26R 1.2	29 54.0
						DECLINATION						
1 T	0 37 25.6	2S57.3	4N58.9	24N15.1	0S34.6	11S27.0	6S50.5	21S38.2	18N49.1	20S50.2	20N29.8	17N19.0
4 F	0 49 15.3	4 7.1	4 55.2	28 9.7	2 54.4	12 50.4	7 37.3	21 42.6	18 47.7	20 50.3	20 29.3	17 18.7
7 M	1 1 5.0	5 16.5	4 51.5	16 47.1	5 11.9	14 11.1	8 23.8	21 47.1	18 46.2	20 50.4	20 28.8	17 18.5
10 T	1 12 54.6	6 25.3	4 47.7	3S 9.5	7 25.7	15 28.8	9 9.8	21 51.6	18 44.5	20 50.3	20 28.4	17 18.2
13 S	1 24 44.3	7 33.3	4 44.0	21 0.4	9 34.8	16 43.1	9 55.5	21 56.2	18 42.6	20 50.2	20 28.1	17 18.0
16 W	1 36 33.9	8 40.4	4 40.3	28 34.9	11 38.5	17 53.6	10 40.6	22 0.7	18 40.6	20 50.0	20 27.8	17 17.7
19 S	1 48 23.6	9 46.4	4 36.6	23 41.6	13 36.0	19 0.1	11 25.1	22 5.1	18 38.5	20 49.6	20 27.5	17 17.5
22 T	2 0 13.3	10 51.0	4 32.8	10 1.3	15 27.0	20 2.1	12 9.0	22 9.5	18 36.3	20 49.2	20 27.3	17 17.2
25 F	2 12 2.9	11 54.3	4 29.1	7N33.9	17 10.7	20 59.4	12 52.3	22 13.9	18 34.0	20 48.7	20 27.2	17 17.0
28 M	2 23 52.6	12 55.8	4 25.4	23 14.4	18 46.6	21 51.5	13 34.7	22 18.2	18 31.5	20 48.0	20 27.1	17 16.8
31 T	2 35 42.3	13 55.6	4 21.6	28 21.3	20 14.2	22 38.3	14 16.4	22 22.4	18 29.0	20 47.3	20 27.1	17 16.6

NOVEMBER 1912

DAY	EPHEMERIS SIDEREAL TIME	☉	☊	☽	☿	♀	♂	♃	♄	♅	♆	♇
	h m s	° ′	° ′	° ′	° ′	° ′	° ′	° ′	° ′	° ′	° ′	° ′
						LONGITUDE						
1 F	2 39 38.8	8♏12.6	10♈57.6	23♋ 4.1	24♏49.1	8♐56.3	9♏29.6	16♐ 5.5	2♊21.0	29♑44.1	26♋ 1.1	29♊53.3
2 S	2 43 35.4	9 12.6	10 54.5	7♌12.9	26 16.1	10 9.9	10 10.9	16 17.6	2R16.7	29 45.2	26R 1.0	29R52.6
3 S	2 47 31.9	10 12.7	10 51.3	21 23.4	27 42.5	11 23.5	10 52.2	16 29.7	2 12.4	29 46.4	26 0.9	29 51.9
4 M	2 51 28.5	11 12.9	10 48.1	5♍34.0	29 8.2	12 37.1	11 33.6	16 42.0	2 8.0	29 47.7	26 0.7	29 51.2
5 T	2 55 25.0	12 13.1	10 44.9	19 42.6	0♐33.3	13 50.6	12 15.1	16 54.3	2 3.6	29 49.0	26 0.5	29 50.4
6 W	2 59 21.6	13 13.3	10 41.8	3♎47.1	1 57.7	15 4.2	12 56.6	17 6.7	1 59.1	29 50.4	26 0.3	29 49.7
7 T	3 3 18.2	14 13.5	10 38.6	17 44.8	3 21.2	16 17.7	13 38.2	17 19.1	1 54.5	29 51.8	25 60.0	29 48.9
8 F	3 7 14.7	15 13.8	10 35.4	1♏33.1	4 44.0	17 31.2	14 19.8	17 31.6	1 50.0	29 53.3	25 59.7	29 48.1
9 S	3 11 11.3	16 14.1	10 32.2	15 9.0	6 5.8	18 44.7	15 1.4	17 44.2	1 45.3	29 54.8	25 59.3	29 47.3
10 S	3 15 7.8	17 14.5	10 29.0	28 29.9	7 26.6	19 58.1	15 43.1	17 56.8	1 40.7	29 56.3	25 59.0	29 46.5
11 M	3 19 4.4	18 14.8	10 25.9	11♐34.1	8 46.3	21 11.6	16 24.9	18 9.4	1 36.0	29 57.9	25 58.5	29 45.6
12 T	3 23 0.9	19 15.2	10 22.7	24 20.8	10 4.8	22 25.0	17 6.7	18 22.2	1 31.2	29 59.6	25 58.1	29 44.8
13 W	3 26 57.5	20 15.7	10 19.5	6♑50.5	11 21.9	23 38.4	17 48.5	18 34.9	1 26.5	0♒ 1.3	25 57.6	29 43.9
14 T	3 30 54.1	21 16.1	10 16.3	19 5.0	12 37.4	24 51.8	18 30.4	18 47.8	1 21.7	0 3.0	25 57.1	29 43.0
15 F	3 34 50.6	22 16.6	10 13.2	1♒ 7.3	13 51.2	26 5.2	19 12.4	19 0.6	1 16.9	0 4.8	25 56.6	29 42.1
16 S	3 38 47.2	23 17.1	10 10.0	13 1.4	15 3.0	27 18.5	19 54.3	19 13.5	1 12.0	0 6.6	25 56.0	29 41.2
17 S	3 42 43.7	24 17.6	10 6.8	24 51.9	16 12.7	28 31.8	20 36.4	19 26.5	1 7.2	0 8.5	25 55.4	29 40.2
18 M	3 46 40.3	25 18.1	10 3.6	6♓43.9	17 19.8	29 45.1	21 18.4	19 39.5	1 2.3	0 10.4	25 54.8	29 39.3
19 T	3 50 36.9	26 18.7	10 0.5	18 42.5	18 24.1	0♑58.4	22 0.6	19 52.6	0 57.4	0 12.4	25 54.1	29 38.3
20 W	3 54 33.4	27 19.2	9 57.3	0♈52.8	19 25.2	2 11.6	22 42.7	20 5.7	0 52.5	0 14.4	25 53.4	29 37.3
21 T	3 58 29.9	28 19.8	9 54.1	13 19.2	20 22.6	3 24.8	23 24.9	20 18.8	0 47.6	0 16.5	25 52.7	29 36.3
22 F	4 2 26.5	29 20.4	9 50.9	26 5.3	21 15.9	4 37.9	24 7.2	20 31.9	0 42.7	0 18.6	25 51.9	29 35.3
23 S	4 6 23.1	0♐21.1	9 47.7	9♉13.3	22 4.5	5 51.1	24 49.5	20 45.2	0 37.8	0 20.7	25 51.2	29 34.3
24 S	4 10 19.6	1 21.7	9 44.6	22 43.6	22 47.7	7 4.2	25 31.9	20 58.4	0 32.8	0 22.9	25 50.3	29 33.3
25 M	4 14 16.2	2 22.4	9 41.4	6♊34.4	23 25.0	8 17.2	26 14.3	21 11.7	0 27.9	0 25.1	25 49.5	29 32.3
26 T	4 18 12.7	3 23.1	9 38.2	20 42.1	23 55.6	9 30.2	26 56.7	21 25.0	0 23.0	0 27.3	25 48.6	29 31.2
27 W	4 22 9.3	4 23.9	9 35.0	5♋ 1.5	24 18.7	10 43.2	27 39.2	21 38.3	0 18.1	0 29.6	25 47.7	29 30.1
28 T	4 26 5.9	5 24.6	9 31.9	19 26.6	24 33.5	11 56.2	28 21.7	21 51.7	0 13.2	0 32.0	25 46.8	29 29.1
29 F	4 30 2.4	6 25.4	9 28.7	3♌51.7	24 39.2	13 9.1	29 4.3	22 5.1	0 8.3	0 34.4	25 45.8	29 28.0
30 S	4 33 59.0	7 26.2	9 25.5	18 12.1	24R35.0	14 21.9	29 47.0	22 18.6	0 3.5	0 36.8	25 44.8	29 26.9
						DECLINATION						
1 F	2 39 38.8	14S15.1	4N20.4	26N32.3	20S41.5	22S52.6	14S30.1	22S23.8	18N28.1	20S47.1	20N27.1	17N16.5
4 M	2 51 28.5	15 12.2	4 16.7	12 22.6	21 57.0	23 31.7	15 10.6	22 27.8	18 25.5	20 46.2	20 27.2	17 16.4
7 T	3 3 18.2	16 7.0	4 12.9	7S26.0	23 2.6	24 4.8	15 50.1	22 31.8	18 22.8	20 45.3	20 27.3	17 16.2
10 S	3 15 7.8	16 59.5	4 9.2	23 30.0	23 57.6	24 31.7	16 28.6	22 35.6	18 20.0	20 44.3	20 27.5	17 16.0
13 W	3 26 57.5	17 49.3	4 5.4	28 24.9	24 41.1	24 52.0	17 6.0	22 39.3	18 17.2	20 43.1	20 27.7	17 15.9
16 S	3 38 47.2	18 36.3	4 1.7	21 8.4	25 12.4	25 5.8	17 42.3	22 42.9	18 14.4	20 41.9	20 28.0	17 15.8
19 T	3 50 36.9	19 20.3	3 58.0	6 19.1	25 30.7	25 13.0	18 17.3	22 46.2	18 11.5	20 40.6	20 28.3	17 15.7
22 F	4 2 26.5	20 1.3	3 54.2	11N17.0	25 35.2	25 13.3	18 50.9	22 49.5	18 8.7	20 39.3	20 28.7	17 15.6
25 M	4 14 16.2	20 38.9	3 50.5	25 33.2	25 25.2	25 7.0	19 23.3	22 52.5	18 5.8	20 37.8	20 29.1	17 15.5
28 T	4 26 5.9	21 13.0	3 46.7	27 1.4	24 59.9	24 53.9	19 54.1	22 55.4	18 3.0	20 36.3	20 29.6	17 15.5

DECEMBER 1912

DAY	SIDEREAL TIME	☉	☊	☽	☿	♀	♂	♃	♄	♅	♆	♇
						LONGITUDE						
1 S	4 37 55.5	8♐27.0	9♈22.3	2♍24.4	24♐20.3	15♑34.8	0♐29.7	22♐32.0	29♉58.6	0♒39.2	25♋43.8	29♊25.8
2 M	4 41 52.1	9 27.9	9 19.2	16 27.0	23R54.7	16 47.6	1 12.4	22 45.5	29R53.8	0 41.7	25R42.8	29R24.7
3 T	4 45 48.7	10 28.7	9 16.0	0♎19.3	23 17.8	18 0.3	1 55.2	22 59.0	29 49.0	0 44.2	25 41.7	29 23.6
4 W	4 49 45.2	11 29.6	9 12.8	14 1.4	22 30.0	19 13.0	2 38.0	23 12.6	29 44.2	0 46.8	25 40.6	29 22.5
5 T	4 53 41.8	12 30.6	9 9.6	27 33.5	21 31.8	20 25.7	3 20.9	23 26.1	29 39.5	0 49.4	25 39.5	29 21.3
6 F	4 57 38.3	13 31.5	9 6.4	10♏55.6	20 24.4	21 38.3	4 3.9	23 39.7	29 34.7	0 52.0	25 38.3	29 20.2
7 S	5 1 34.9	14 32.5	9 3.3	24 7.2	19 9.5	22 50.9	4 46.8	23 53.3	29 30.1	0 54.7	25 37.2	29 19.0
8 S	5 5 31.5	15 33.5	9 0.1	7♐ 7.6	17 49.4	24 3.5	5 29.9	24 7.0	29 25.4	0 57.4	25 36.0	29 17.9
9 M	5 9 28.0	16 34.4	8 56.9	19 55.8	16 26.7	25 15.9	6 13.0	24 20.6	29 20.8	1 0.1	25 34.7	29 16.7
10 T	5 13 24.6	17 35.5	8 53.7	2♑31.1	15 4.1	26 28.4	6 56.1	24 34.2	29 16.3	1 2.9	25 33.5	29 15.5
11 W	5 17 21.1	18 36.5	8 50.6	14 53.5	13 44.5	27 40.7	7 39.2	24 47.9	29 11.8	1 5.7	25 32.2	29 14.4
12 T	5 21 17.7	19 37.5	8 47.4	27 3.7	12 30.3	28 53.1	8 22.5	25 1.6	29 7.3	1 8.5	25 30.9	29 13.2
13 F	5 25 14.2	20 38.6	8 44.2	9♒ 3.5	11 23.9	0♒ 5.3	9 5.7	25 15.3	29 2.9	1 11.4	25 29.6	29 12.0
14 S	5 29 10.8	21 39.6	8 41.0	20 55.7	10 26.7	1 17.5	9 49.0	25 29.0	28 58.6	1 14.3	25 28.3	29 10.8
15 S	5 33 7.4	22 40.7	8 37.9	2♓44.2	9 39.9	2 29.7	10 32.4	25 42.7	28 54.3	1 17.2	25 26.9	29 9.6
16 M	5 37 3.9	23 41.7	8 34.7	14 33.7	9 4.1	3 41.7	11 15.8	25 56.4	28 50.0	1 20.2	25 25.6	29 8.4
17 T	5 41 0.5	24 42.8	8 31.5	26 29.3	8 39.4	4 53.7	11 59.2	26 10.1	28 45.9	1 23.1	25 24.2	29 7.3
18 W	5 44 57.0	25 43.9	8 28.3	8♈36.7	8 25.6	6 5.7	12 42.7	26 23.9	28 41.8	1 26.1	25 22.7	29 6.1
19 T	5 48 53.6	26 45.0	8 25.2	21 1.2	8 22.1	7 17.5	13 26.2	26 37.6	28 37.7	1 29.2	25 21.3	29 4.9
20 F	5 52 50.1	27 46.1	8 22.0	3♉47.8	8D28.3	8 29.3	14 9.8	26 51.3	28 33.7	1 32.2	25 19.9	29 3.7
21 S	5 56 46.7	28 47.2	8 18.8	17 0.1	8 43.6	9 40.9	14 53.4	27 5.0	28 29.8	1 35.3	25 18.4	29 2.5
22 S	6 0 43.3	29 48.3	8 15.6	0♊40.1	9 7.0	10 52.5	15 37.1	27 18.8	28 26.0	1 38.4	25 16.9	29 1.3
23 M	6 4 39.8	0♑49.4	8 12.5	14 46.8	9 37.7	12 4.0	16 20.8	27 32.5	28 22.3	1 41.5	25 15.4	29 0.1
24 T	6 8 36.4	1 50.5	8 9.3	29 16.4	10 15.1	13 15.5	17 4.5	27 46.2	28 18.6	1 44.7	25 13.9	28 58.9
25 W	6 12 32.9	2 51.6	8 6.1	14♋ 2.3	10 58.4	14 26.8	17 48.3	27 59.9	28 15.0	1 47.9	25 12.3	28 57.7
26 T	6 16 29.5	3 52.7	8 2.9	28 55.7	11 46.9	15 38.0	18 32.2	28 13.6	28 11.5	1 51.1	25 10.8	28 56.5
27 F	6 20 26.1	4 53.9	7 59.8	13♌47.8	12 40.1	16 49.2	19 16.0	28 27.3	28 8.0	1 54.3	25 9.3	28 55.3
28 S	6 24 22.6	5 55.0	7 56.6	28 30.6	13 37.3	18 0.2	19 60.0	28 41.0	28 4.7	1 57.5	25 7.7	28 54.1
29 S	6 28 19.2	6 56.2	7 53.4	12♍58.3	14 38.3	19 11.1	20 44.0	28 54.7	28 1.4	2 0.8	25 6.1	28 52.9
30 M	6 32 15.7	7 57.3	7 50.2	27 7.9	15 42.4	20 21.9	21 28.0	29 8.3	27 58.2	2 4.1	25 4.5	28 51.7
31 T	6 36 12.3	8 58.5	7 47.0	10♎58.8	16 49.4	21 32.7	22 12.0	29 22.0	27 55.1	2 7.4	25 2.9	28 50.6
						DECLINATION						
1 S	4 37 55.5	21S43.6	3N43.0	13N34.3	24S18.1	24S34.3	20S23.5	22S58.0	18N 0.3	20S34.6	20N30.2	17N15.5
4 W	4 49 45.2	22 10.4	3 39.2	5S48.5	23 19.3	24 8.2	20 51.3	23 0.5	17 57.6	20 33.0	20 30.7	17 15.5
7 S	5 1 34.9	22 33.4	3 35.5	22 11.6	22 5.2	23 35.8	21 17.4	23 2.8	17 55.0	20 31.2	20 31.4	17 15.5
10 T	5 13 24.6	22 52.4	3 31.7	28 24.8	20 45.9	22 57.3	21 41.8	23 4.8	17 52.5	20 29.4	20 32.1	17 15.5
13 F	5 25 14.2	23 7.4	3 28.0	22 13.2	19 38.7	22 13.0	22 4.5	23 6.7	17 50.1	20 27.4	20 32.8	17 15.6
16 M	5 37 3.9	23 18.2	3 24.2	8 1.4	18 59.1	21 23.1	22 25.3	23 8.3	17 47.8	20 25.5	20 33.5	17 15.6
19 T	5 48 53.6	23 24.8	3 20.4	9N10.5	18 50.8	20 28.0	22 44.2	23 9.8	17 45.7	20 23.5	20 34.3	17 15.7
22 S	6 0 43.3	23 27.2	3 16.7	24 9.5	19 8.3	19 28.0	23 1.1	23 11.0	17 43.7	20 21.4	20 35.1	17 15.9
25 W	6 12 32.9	23 25.3	3 12.9	27 39.6	19 42.7	18 23.4	23 16.0	23 12.0	17 41.9	20 19.2	20 35.9	17 16.0
28 S	6 24 22.6	23 19.2	3 9.2	14 59.1	20 25.9	17 14.6	23 28.8	23 12.8	17 40.3	20 17.0	20 36.8	17 16.2
31 T	6 36 12.3	23 8.9	3 5.4	4S36.5	21 11.6	16 1.9	23 39.6	23 13.3	17 38.9	20 14.8	20 37.7	17 16.4

JANUARY 1913

DAY	EPHEMERIS SIDEREAL TIME h m s	☉ ° ′	☊ ° ′	☽ ° ′	☿ ° ′	♀ ° ′	♂ ° ′	♃ ° ′	♄ ° ′	♅ ° ′	♆ ° ′	♇ ° ′
						LONGITUDE						
1 W	6 40 8.9	9♑59.6	7♈43.9	24♎31.9	17♐58.9	22♒43.3	22♐56.2	29♐35.7	27♉52.1	2♒10.7	25♋ 1.3	28♊49.4
2 T	6 44 5.4	11 0.8	7 40.7	7♏48.9	19 10.7	23 53.8	23 40.3	29 49.3	27 R 49.2	2 14.0	24 R 59.6	28 R 48.2
3 F	6 48 2.0	12 2.0	7 37.5	20 52.0	20 24.5	25 4.2	24 24.5	0♑ 2.9	27 46.4	2 17.4	24 58.0	28 47.1
4 S	6 51 58.5	13 3.2	7 34.3	3♐42.8	21 40.0	26 14.5	25 8.8	0 16.5	27 43.7	2 20.7	24 56.3	28 45.9
5 S	6 55 55.1	14 4.4	7 31.2	16 22.8	22 57.2	27 24.6	25 53.1	0 30.1	27 41.0	2 24.1	24 54.7	28 44.7
6 M	6 59 51.7	15 5.6	7 28.0	28 52.7	24 15.8	28 34.6	26 37.4	0 43.6	27 38.5	2 27.5	24 53.0	28 43.6
7 T	7 3 48.2	16 6.7	7 24.8	11♑13.0	25 35.7	29 44.5	27 21.8	0 57.1	27 36.1	2 30.9	24 51.3	28 42.5
8 W	7 7 44.8	17 7.9	7 21.6	23 24.1	26 56.7	0♓54.3	28 6.2	1 10.6	27 33.8	2 34.4	24 49.7	28 41.3
9 T	7 11 41.3	18 9.1	7 18.5	5♒26.6	28 18.9	2 3.9	28 50.7	1 24.1	27 31.5	2 37.8	24 48.0	28 40.2
10 F	7 15 37.9	19 10.3	7 15.3	17 21.8	29 42.0	3 13.4	29 35.2	1 37.6	27 29.4	2 41.2	24 46.3	28 39.1
11 S	7 19 34.5	20 11.4	7 12.1	29 11.5	1♑ 6.1	4 22.7	0♑19.7	1 51.0	27 27.4	2 44.7	24 44.6	28 38.0
12 S	7 23 31.0	21 12.6	7 8.9	10♓58.6	2 30.9	5 31.9	1 4.3	2 4.4	27 25.5	2 48.2	24 42.9	28 36.9
13 M	7 27 27.5	22 13.7	7 5.7	22 46.7	3 56.6	6 40.9	1 48.9	2 17.7	27 23.7	2 51.6	24 41.2	28 35.8
14 T	7 31 24.1	23 14.9	7 2.6	4♈40.3	5 23.1	7 49.7	2 33.6	2 31.1	27 22.0	2 55.1	24 39.5	28 34.7
15 W	7 35 20.7	24 16.0	6 59.4	16 44.4	6 50.2	8 58.4	3 18.3	2 44.4	27 20.4	2 58.6	24 37.8	28 33.7
16 T	7 39 17.2	25 17.1	6 56.2	29 4.5	8 18.1	10 6.9	4 3.0	2 57.6	27 19.0	3 2.1	24 36.1	28 32.6
17 F	7 43 13.8	26 18.2	6 53.0	11♉45.9	9 46.6	11 15.2	4 47.8	3 10.8	27 17.6	3 5.6	24 34.4	28 31.6
18 S	7 47 10.3	27 19.3	6 49.9	24 53.3	11 15.7	12 23.3	5 32.6	3 24.0	27 16.3	3 9.1	24 32.7	28 30.5
19 S	7 51 6.9	28 20.3	6 46.7	8♊30.1	12 45.5	13 31.3	6 17.4	3 37.1	27 15.2	3 12.6	24 31.0	28 29.5
20 M	7 55 3.5	29 21.4	6 43.5	22 37.1	14 15.9	14 39.0	7 2.3	3 50.2	27 14.2	3 16.1	24 29.4	28 28.5
21 T	7 59 0.0	0♒22.4	6 40.3	7♋12.1	15 46.9	15 46.5	7 47.2	4 3.3	27 13.2	3 19.7	24 27.7	28 27.5
22 W	8 2 56.6	1 23.5	6 37.2	22 9.4	17 18.5	16 53.8	8 32.2	4 16.3	27 12.4	3 23.2	24 26.0	28 26.5
23 T	8 6 53.1	2 24.5	6 34.0	7♌20.0	18 50.7	18 0.8	9 17.2	4 29.3	27 11.7	3 26.7	24 24.3	28 25.5
24 F	8 10 49.7	3 25.5	6 30.8	22 33.3	20 23.5	19 7.6	10 2.2	4 42.2	27 11.1	3 30.2	24 22.6	28 24.6
25 S	8 14 46.3	4 26.5	6 27.6	7♍38.8	21 57.0	20 14.2	10 47.3	4 55.1	27 10.7	3 33.7	24 21.0	28 23.6
26 S	8 18 42.8	5 27.4	6 24.5	22 27.9	23 31.0	21 20.6	11 32.4	5 7.9	27 10.3	3 37.3	24 19.3	28 22.7
27 M	8 22 39.4	6 28.4	6 21.3	6♎55.0	25 5.7	22 26.7	12 17.6	5 20.6	27 10.0	3 40.8	24 17.6	28 21.8
28 T	8 26 35.9	7 29.4	6 18.1	20 57.7	26 41.1	23 32.6	13 2.7	5 33.4	27 9.9	3 44.3	24 16.0	28 20.9
29 W	8 30 32.5	8 30.3	6 14.9	4♏35.9	28 17.1	24 38.2	13 48.0	5 46.0	27 9.9	3 47.8	24 14.4	28 20.0
30 T	8 34 29.0	9 31.3	6 11.8	17 51.8	29 53.8	25 43.5	14 33.2	5 58.6	27 D 10.0	3 51.3	24 12.7	28 19.2
31 F	8 38 25.6	10 32.2	6 8.6	0♐48.0	1♒31.2	26 48.5	15 18.5	6 11.2	27 10.2	3 54.8	24 11.1	28 18.3
						DECLINATION						
1 W	6 40 8.9	23S 4.6	3N 4.1	10S51.9	21S26.6	15S36.9	23S42.7	23S13.5	17N38.4	20S14.1	20N38.0	17N16.4
4 S	6 51 58.5	22 48.7	3 0.4	24 59.6	22 9.0	14 19.5	23 50.5	23 13.7	17 37.3	20 11.8	20 38.9	17 16.6
7 T	7 3 48.2	22 28.8	2 56.6	27 56.4	22 45.7	12 59.2	23 56.1	23 13.8	17 36.3	20 9.4	20 39.8	17 16.9
10 F	7 15 37.9	22 4.9	2 52.9	19 14.4	23 14.6	11 36.1	23 59.5	23 13.7	17 35.6	20 7.1	20 40.7	17 17.1
13 M	7 27 27.5	21 37.1	2 49.1	3 55.7	23 34.3	10 10.8	24 0.7	23 13.3	17 35.1	20 4.7	20 41.7	17 17.4
16 T	7 39 17.2	21 5.5	2 45.3	13N 1.1	23 44.0	8 43.4	23 59.5	23 12.8	17 34.8	20 2.3	20 42.6	17 17.7
19 S	7 51 6.9	20 30.3	2 41.5	26 10.4	23 42.7	7 14.5	23 56.1	23 12.0	17 34.7	19 59.9	20 43.5	17 18.1
22 W	8 2 56.6	19 51.7	2 37.8	26 24.1	23 29.9	5 44.3	23 50.3	23 11.1	17 34.9	19 57.4	20 44.5	17 18.4
25 S	8 14 46.3	19 9.7	2 34.0	10 52.2	23 5.2	4 13.2	23 42.3	23 10.0	17 35.3	19 55.0	20 45.4	17 18.8
28 T	8 26 35.9	18 24.5	2 30.2	9S30.0	22 28.0	2 41.5	23 31.9	23 8.7	17 36.0	19 52.5	20 46.3	17 19.1
31 F	8 38 25.6	17 36.4	2 26.5	24 28.2	21 38.1	1 9.6	23 19.3	23 7.3	17 36.9	19 50.1	20 47.2	17 19.6

FEBRUARY 1913

DAY	SIDEREAL TIME h m s	☉	☊	☽	☿	♀	♂	♃	♄	♅	♆	♇
						LONGITUDE						
1 S	8 42 22.1	11♒33.1	6♈ 5.4	13♐27.8	3♒ 9.2	27♓53.3	16♑ 3.9	6♑23.7	27♉10.5	3♒58.3	24♋ 9.5	28♊17.5
2 S	8 46 18.7	12 34.0	6 2.2	25 54.2	4 48.0	28 57.8	16 49.3	6 36.1	27 10.9	4 1.8	24 R 7.9	28 R 16.6
3 M	8 50 15.3	13 34.9	5 59.0	8♑ 9.9	6 27.5	0♈ 2.0	17 34.7	6 48.5	27 11.5	4 5.3	24 6.3	28 15.9
4 T	8 54 11.8	14 35.7	5 55.9	20 16.9	8 7.8	1 5.9	18 20.1	7 0.8	27 12.1	4 8.8	24 4.8	28 15.1
5 W	8 58 8.4	15 36.6	5 52.7	2♒16.9	9 48.7	2 9.4	19 5.6	7 13.0	27 12.9	4 12.3	24 3.2	28 14.3
6 T	9 2 4.9	16 37.4	5 49.5	14 11.6	11 30.5	3 12.6	19 51.1	7 25.2	27 13.8	4 15.7	24 1.6	28 13.5
7 F	9 6 1.5	17 38.2	5 46.3	26 2.2	13 13.0	4 15.5	20 36.6	7 37.3	27 14.8	4 19.2	24 0.1	28 12.8
8 S	9 9 58.1	18 39.0	5 43.2	7♓50.6	14 56.4	5 18.1	21 22.2	7 49.4	27 15.9	4 22.6	23 58.6	28 12.1
9 S	9 13 54.6	19 39.8	5 40.0	19 38.7	16 40.5	6 20.2	22 7.8	8 1.3	27 17.1	4 26.1	23 57.1	28 11.4
10 M	9 17 51.2	20 40.5	5 36.8	1♈29.2	18 25.4	7 22.0	22 53.4	8 13.2	27 18.5	4 29.5	23 55.6	28 10.7
11 T	9 21 47.7	21 41.2	5 33.6	13 25.4	20 11.2	8 23.4	23 39.1	8 25.0	27 19.9	4 32.9	23 54.1	28 10.1
12 W	9 25 44.3	22 41.9	5 30.4	25 31.1	21 57.7	9 24.4	24 24.8	8 36.8	27 21.5	4 36.3	23 52.7	28 9.5
13 T	9 29 40.8	23 42.6	5 27.3	7♉50.6	23 45.0	10 24.9	25 10.5	8 48.5	27 23.2	4 39.7	23 51.3	28 8.8
14 F	9 33 37.4	24 43.2	5 24.1	20 28.7	25 33.2	11 25.0	25 56.2	9 0.0	27 24.9	4 43.0	23 49.9	28 8.2
15 S	9 37 33.9	25 43.8	5 20.9	3♊29.7	27 22.1	12 24.7	26 42.0	9 11.5	27 26.8	4 46.4	23 48.5	28 7.7
16 S	9 41 30.5	26 44.4	5 17.7	16 57.3	29 11.7	13 23.9	27 27.8	9 23.0	27 28.8	4 49.7	23 47.1	28 7.1
17 M	9 45 27.1	27 44.9	5 14.6	0♋53.7	1♓ 2.0	14 22.6	28 13.6	9 34.3	27 31.0	4 53.1	23 45.7	28 6.6
18 T	9 49 23.6	28 45.4	5 11.4	15 18.5	2 53.0	15 20.8	28 59.4	9 45.6	27 33.2	4 56.4	23 44.4	28 6.1
19 W	9 53 20.1	29 45.9	5 8.2	0♌ 8.2	4 44.5	16 18.4	29 45.3	9 56.7	27 35.5	4 59.6	23 43.1	28 5.6
20 T	9 57 16.7	0♓46.4	5 5.0	15 16.2	6 36.5	17 15.6	0♒31.2	10 7.8	27 37.9	5 2.9	23 41.8	28 5.1
21 F	10 1 13.3	1 46.8	5 1.9	0♍33.1	8 29.0	18 12.1	1 17.1	10 18.8	27 40.4	5 6.1	23 40.5	28 4.7
22 S	10 5 9.8	2 47.2	4 58.7	15 48.2	10 21.6	19 8.1	2 3.1	10 29.7	27 43.1	5 9.4	23 39.3	28 4.2
23 S	10 9 6.4	3 47.6	4 55.5	0♎51.5	12 14.4	20 3.5	2 49.0	10 40.5	27 45.8	5 12.6	23 38.1	28 3.8
24 M	10 13 2.9	4 47.9	4 52.3	15 35.0	14 7.0	20 58.3	3 35.0	10 51.2	27 48.7	5 15.7	23 36.9	28 3.4
25 T	10 16 59.5	5 48.2	4 49.1	29 53.4	15 59.3	21 52.4	4 21.0	11 1.8	27 51.6	5 18.9	23 35.7	28 3.1
26 W	10 20 56.0	6 48.5	4 46.0	13♏44.8	17 51.0	22 45.9	5 7.1	11 12.3	27 54.6	5 22.0	23 34.6	28 2.7
27 T	10 24 52.6	7 48.8	4 42.8	27 9.6	19 41.9	23 38.7	5 53.2	11 22.8	27 57.8	5 25.1	23 33.4	28 2.4
28 F	10 28 49.2	8 49.0	4 39.6	10♐ 9.9	21 31.5	24 30.8	6 39.3	11 33.1	28 1.0	5 28.2	23 32.3	28 2.1
						DECLINATION						
1 S	8 42 22.1	17S19.7	2N25.2	27S 8.9	21S18.7	0S38.9	23S14.5	23S 6.8	17N37.2	19S49.2	20N47.5	17N19.7
4 T	8 54 11.8	16 27.8	2 21.4	26 46.3	20 11.5	0N52.9	22 58.9	23 5.2	17 38.4	19 46.8	20 48.4	17 20.1
7 F	9 6 1.5	15 33.4	2 17.6	15 48.7	18 51.1	2 24.2	22 40.9	23 3.4	17 39.8	19 44.3	20 49.2	17 20.6
10 M	9 17 51.2	14 36.5	2 13.9	0N24.5	17 17.4	3 54.8	22 20.8	23 1.5	17 41.5	19 41.9	20 50.1	17 21.0
13 T	9 29 40.8	13 37.5	2 10.1	16 53.4	15 30.6	5 24.2	21 58.5	22 59.5	17 43.4	19 39.5	20 50.9	17 21.5
16 S	9 41 30.5	12 36.5	2 6.3	27 45.8	13 30.7	6 52.2	21 34.0	22 57.3	17 45.4	19 37.1	20 51.6	17 22.0
19 W	9 53 20.1	11 33.7	2 2.5	24 40.3	11 18.6	8 18.3	21 7.5	22 55.1	17 47.7	19 34.8	20 52.4	17 22.5
22 S	10 5 9.8	10 29.2	1 58.7	7 3.2	8 55.3	9 42.4	20 38.9	22 52.8	17 50.2	19 32.5	20 53.1	17 23.0
25 T	10 16 59.5	9 23.3	1 55.0	13S38.1	6 23.0	11 4.0	20 8.4	22 50.5	17 52.9	19 30.2	20 53.8	17 23.5
28 F	10 28 49.2	8 16.1	1 51.2	26 45.2	3 45.3	12 23.0	19 35.9	22 48.1	17 55.8	19 28.0	20 54.4	17 24.0

MARCH 1913

LONGITUDE

DAY	EPHEMERIS SIDEREAL TIME h m s	☉ ° ′	☊ ° ′	☽ ° ′	☿ ° ′	♀ ° ′	♂ ° ′	♃ ° ′	♄ ° ′	♅ ° ′	♆ ° ′	♇ ° ′
1 S	10 32 45.7	9♓49.3	4♈36.4	22♐49.2	23♓19.5	25♈22.1	7♒25.4	11♑43.3	28♉ 4.4	5♒31.3	23♋31.3	28♊ 1.8
2 S	10 36 42.3	10 49.4	4 33.3	5♑11.3	25 5.4	26 12.7	8 11.5	11 53.4	28 7.8	5 34.3	23R30.2	28R 1.6
3 M	10 40 38.8	11 49.6	4 30.1	17 20.2	26 48.9	27 2.5	8 57.7	12 3.4	28 11.4	5 37.3	23 29.2	28 1.4
4 T	10 44 35.4	12 49.8	4 26.9	29 19.5	28 29.3	27 51.5	9 43.9	12 13.3	28 15.0	5 40.3	23 28.2	28 1.1
5 W	10 48 31.9	13 49.9	4 23.7	11♒12.4	0♈ 6.2	28 39.7	10 30.1	12 23.1	28 18.7	5 43.3	23 27.2	28 1.0
6 T	10 52 28.5	14 50.0	4 20.5	23 1.8	1 39.1	29 26.9	11 16.3	12 32.8	28 22.5	5 46.2	23 26.3	28 0.8
7 F	10 56 25.0	15 50.0	4 17.4	4♓50.1	3 7.3	0♉13.3	12 2.5	12 42.4	28 26.5	5 49.1	23 25.4	28 0.7
8 S	11 0 21.6	16 50.1	4 14.2	16 39.6	4 30.3	0 58.7	12 48.8	12 51.8	28 30.5	5 52.0	23 24.5	28 0.5
9 S	11 4 18.2	17 50.1	4 11.0	28 32.1	5 47.6	1 43.1	13 35.1	13 1.2	28 34.6	5 54.8	23 23.7	28 0.4
10 M	11 8 14.7	18 50.0	4 7.8	10♈29.8	6 58.7	2 26.5	14 21.3	13 10.4	28 38.8	5 57.6	23 22.9	28 0.4
11 T	11 12 11.2	19 49.9	4 4.7	22 34.8	8 3.0	3 8.8	15 7.6	13 19.5	28 43.1	6 0.4	23 22.1	28 0.3
12 W	11 16 7.8	20 49.8	4 1.5	4♉49.6	9 0.2	3 50.1	15 54.0	13 28.5	28 47.4	6 3.2	23 21.3	28 0.3
13 T	11 20 4.4	21 49.7	3 58.3	17 17.0	9 49.9	4 30.1	16 40.3	13 37.3	28 51.9	6 5.9	23 20.6	28D 0.3
14 F	11 24 0.9	22 49.5	3 55.1	29 59.9	10 31.7	5 9.0	17 26.6	13 46.0	28 56.4	6 8.6	23 19.9	28 0.3
15 S	11 27 57.5	23 49.3	3 51.9	13♊ 1.3	11 5.3	5 46.6	18 13.0	13 54.6	29 1.1	6 11.2	23 19.2	28 0.4
16 S	11 31 54.0	24 49.0	3 48.8	26 23.9	11 30.6	6 22.9	18 59.3	14 3.1	29 5.8	6 13.8	23 18.6	28 0.4
17 M	11 35 50.6	25 48.8	3 45.6	10♋ 9.7	11 47.6	6 57.8	19 45.7	14 11.5	29 10.6	6 16.4	23 18.0	28 0.5
18 T	11 39 47.1	26 48.4	3 42.4	24 19.0	11 56.2	7 31.4	20 32.1	14 19.7	29 15.5	6 19.0	23 17.4	28 0.6
19 W	11 43 43.7	27 48.1	3 39.2	8♌50.4	11 56.5	8 3.4	21 18.4	14 27.8	29 20.4	6 21.5	23 16.9	28 0.8
20 T	11 47 40.2	28 47.7	3 36.1	23 40.1	11R48.7	8 34.0	22 4.8	14 35.7	29 25.5	6 23.9	23 16.3	28 0.9
21 F	11 51 36.8	29 47.2	3 32.9	8♍41.7	11 33.2	9 3.0	22 51.2	14 43.5	29 30.6	6 26.4	23 15.9	28 1.1
22 S	11 55 33.3	0♈46.7	3 29.7	23 47.1	11 10.5	9 30.3	23 37.6	14 51.2	29 35.8	6 28.8	23 15.4	28 1.3
23 S	11 59 29.9	1 46.2	3 26.5	8♎47.4	10 41.2	9 55.9	24 24.0	14 58.7	29 41.0	6 31.1	23 15.0	28 1.5
24 M	12 3 26.4	2 45.7	3 23.3	23 34.1	10 5.9	10 19.8	25 10.5	15 6.1	29 46.4	6 33.5	23 14.6	28 1.8
25 T	12 7 23.0	3 45.1	3 20.2	8♏ 0.4	9 25.4	10 41.8	25 56.9	15 13.4	29 51.8	6 35.7	23 14.3	28 2.1
26 W	12 11 19.5	4 44.5	3 17.0	22 1.8	8 40.9	11 2.0	26 43.3	15 20.5	29 57.3	6 38.0	23 14.0	28 2.4
27 T	12 15 16.1	5 43.8	3 13.8	5♐36.5	7 53.1	11 20.3	27 29.8	15 27.5	0♊ 2.8	6 40.2	23 13.7	28 2.7
28 F	12 19 12.7	6 43.2	3 10.6	18 45.1	7 3.1	11 36.6	28 16.3	15 34.3	0 8.5	6 42.4	23 13.4	28 3.0
29 S	12 23 9.2	7 42.5	3 7.5	1♑29.9	6 12.1	11 50.8	29 2.7	15 41.0	0 14.2	6 44.5	23 13.2	28 3.4
30 S	12 27 5.7	8 41.7	3 4.3	13 54.4	5 21.1	12 2.9	29 49.2	15 47.5	0 19.9	6 46.6	23 13.0	28 3.8
31 M	12 31 2.3	9 41.0	3 1.1	26 3.1	4 31.0	12 12.8	0♓35.6	15 53.8	0 25.8	6 48.6	23 12.9	28 4.2

DECLINATION

DAY	EPHEMERIS SIDEREAL TIME h m s	☉ ° ′	☊ ° ′	☽ ° ′	☿ ° ′	♀ ° ′	♂ ° ′	♃ ° ′	♄ ° ′	♅ ° ′	♆ ° ′	♇ ° ′
1 S	10 32 45.7	7S53.5	1N49.9	28S24.4	2S52.3	12N48.6	19S24.7	22S47.3	17N56.8	19S27.3	20N54.6	17N24.2
4 T	10 44 35.4	6 44.9	1 46.1	24 54.8	0 15.6	14 3.5	18 49.8	22 44.8	17 59.9	19 25.1	20 55.2	17 24.7
7 F	10 56 25.0	5 35.4	1 42.4	12 4.0	2N11.6	15 14.8	18 13.1	22 42.4	18 3.1	19 23.0	20 55.8	17 25.3
10 M	11 8 14.7	4 25.2	1 38.6	4N47.2	4 21.1	16 22.3	17 34.7	22 39.9	18 6.5	19 21.0	20 56.3	17 25.8
13 T	11 20 4.4	3 14.6	1 34.8	20 32.3	6 4.4	17 25.6	16 54.7	22 37.5	18 10.1	19 19.0	20 56.7	17 26.4
16 S	11 31 54.0	2 3.6	1 31.0	28 39.3	7 14.4	18 24.1	16 13.2	22 35.1	18 13.8	19 17.1	20 57.2	17 27.0
19 W	11 43 43.7	0 52.5	1 27.2	22 12.3	7 46.3	19 17.5	15 30.2	22 32.7	18 17.6	19 15.3	20 57.5	17 27.5
22 S	11 55 33.3	0N18.6	1 23.4	3 15.5	7 38.0	20 5.0	14 45.9	22 30.4	18 21.5	19 13.5	20 57.8	17 28.1
25 T	12 7 23.0	1 29.5	1 19.6	17S 3.3	6 52.0	20 46.2	14 0.2	22 28.2	18 25.5	19 11.9	20 58.1	17 28.7
28 F	12 19 12.7	2 40.1	1 15.8	28 5.2	5 36.3	21 20.2	13 13.4	22 26.1	18 29.6	19 10.3	20 58.3	17 29.2
31 M	12 31 2.3	3 50.3	1 12.1	25 44.2	4 4.0	21 46.2	12 25.4	22 24.1	18 33.8	19 8.8	20 58.5	17 29.8

APRIL 1913

LONGITUDE

DAY	EPHEMERIS SIDEREAL TIME h m s	☉ ° ′	☊ ° ′	☽ ° ′	☿ ° ′	♀ ° ′	♂ ° ′	♃ ° ′	♄ ° ′	♅ ° ′	♆ ° ′	♇ ° ′
1 T	12 34 58.9	10♈40.2	2♈57.9	8♒ 0.4	3♈42.8	12♉20.5	1♓22.1	16♑ 0.1	0♊31.7	6♒50.6	23♋12.8	28♊ 4.6
2 W	12 38 55.4	11 39.4	2 54.8	19 50.8	2R57.3	12 26.0	2 8.6	16 6.1	0 37.6	6 52.6	23R12.7	28 5.0
3 T	12 42 52.0	12 38.5	2 51.6	1♓38.5	2 15.2	12 29.1	2 55.0	16 12.0	0 43.7	6 54.5	23 12.6	28 5.5
4 F	12 46 48.5	13 37.6	2 48.4	13 27.2	1 37.2	12 29.9	3 41.5	16 17.8	0 49.8	6 56.4	23 12.6	28 6.0
5 S	12 50 45.1	14 36.7	2 45.2	25 20.1	1 3.8	12R28.3	4 28.0	16 23.4	0 55.9	6 58.2	23D12.6	28 6.5
6 S	12 54 41.6	15 35.8	2 42.0	7♈19.8	0 35.2	12 24.2	5 14.4	16 28.8	1 2.1	6 60.0	23 12.7	28 7.1
7 M	12 58 38.2	16 34.8	2 38.9	19 28.4	0 11.9	12 17.7	6 0.9	16 34.1	1 8.4	7 1.7	23 12.8	28 7.6
8 T	13 2 34.7	17 33.8	2 35.7	1♉47.5	29♓53.8	12 8.7	6 47.4	16 39.1	1 14.8	7 3.4	23 12.9	28 8.2
9 W	13 6 31.3	18 32.8	2 32.5	14 18.6	29 41.2	11 57.2	7 33.8	16 44.1	1 21.1	7 5.1	23 13.0	28 8.8
10 T	13 10 27.9	19 31.7	2 29.3	27 2.5	29 34.1	11 43.3	8 20.2	16 48.8	1 27.6	7 6.7	23 13.2	28 9.4
11 F	13 14 24.4	20 30.6	2 26.2	10♊ 0.3	29 32.3	11 27.0	9 6.7	16 53.4	1 34.1	7 8.3	23 13.4	28 10.1
12 S	13 18 21.0	21 29.4	2 23.0	23 12.8	29D35.8	11 8.2	9 53.1	16 57.8	1 40.6	7 9.8	23 13.7	28 10.7
13 S	13 22 17.5	22 28.2	2 19.8	6♋40.6	29 44.5	10 47.1	10 39.5	17 2.1	1 47.3	7 11.2	23 14.0	28 11.4
14 M	13 26 14.1	23 27.0	2 16.6	20 24.2	29 58.2	10 23.8	11 25.9	17 6.2	1 53.9	7 12.7	23 14.3	28 12.1
15 T	13 30 10.6	24 25.7	2 13.4	4♌23.7	0♈16.7	9 58.2	12 12.3	17 10.1	2 0.6	7 14.0	23 14.7	28 12.8
16 W	13 34 7.2	25 24.4	2 10.3	18 38.3	0 39.8	9 30.7	12 58.6	17 13.8	2 7.4	7 15.4	23 15.1	28 13.6
17 T	13 38 3.7	26 23.0	2 7.1	3♍ 5.9	1 7.4	9 1.1	13 45.0	17 17.4	2 14.2	7 16.7	23 15.5	28 14.3
18 F	13 42 0.3	27 21.7	2 3.9	17 43.3	1 39.2	8 29.8	14 31.3	17 20.7	2 21.0	7 17.9	23 15.9	28 15.1
19 S	13 45 56.8	28 20.2	2 0.7	2♎25.5	2 15.1	7 56.9	15 17.7	17 23.9	2 27.9	7 19.1	23 16.4	28 15.9
20 S	13 49 53.4	29 18.8	1 57.6	17 6.6	2 54.9	7 22.6	16 4.0	17 27.0	2 34.9	7 20.2	23 16.9	28 16.7
21 M	13 53 50.0	0♉17.3	1 54.4	1♏39.8	3 38.4	6 47.1	16 50.3	17 29.8	2 41.8	7 21.3	23 17.5	28 17.6
22 T	13 57 46.5	1 15.8	1 51.2	15 58.9	4 25.5	6 10.7	17 36.6	17 32.5	2 48.9	7 22.4	23 18.1	28 18.4
23 W	14 1 43.1	2 14.2	1 48.0	29 58.4	5 15.9	5 33.5	18 22.9	17 35.0	2 55.9	7 23.3	23 18.7	28 19.3
24 T	14 5 39.6	3 12.7	1 44.8	13♐35.1	6 9.6	4 55.8	19 9.1	17 37.3	3 3.0	7 24.3	23 19.3	28 20.2
25 F	14 9 36.2	4 11.1	1 41.7	26 47.6	7 6.3	4 17.9	19 55.4	17 39.4	3 10.2	7 25.2	23 20.0	28 21.1
26 S	14 13 32.7	5 9.4	1 38.5	9♑36.6	8 6.1	3 40.0	20 41.6	17 41.3	3 17.3	7 26.0	23 20.7	28 22.0
27 S	14 17 29.3	6 7.8	1 35.3	22 4.7	9 8.6	3 2.4	21 27.8	17 43.1	3 24.5	7 26.8	23 21.5	28 23.0
28 M	14 21 25.8	7 6.1	1 32.1	4♒15.6	10 14.0	2 25.4	22 14.0	17 44.6	3 31.8	7 27.6	23 22.2	28 23.9
29 T	14 25 22.4	8 4.4	1 29.0	16 14.0	11 21.9	1 49.1	23 0.2	17 46.0	3 39.1	7 28.3	23 23.1	28 24.9
30 W	14 29 19.0	9 2.6	1 25.8	28 4.7	12 32.4	1 13.7	23 46.4	17 47.2	3 46.4	7 28.9	23 23.9	28 25.9

DECLINATION

DAY	EPHEMERIS SIDEREAL TIME h m s	☉ ° ′	☊ ° ′	☽ ° ′	☿ ° ′	♀ ° ′	♂ ° ′	♃ ° ′	♄ ° ′	♅ ° ′	♆ ° ′	♇ ° ′
1 T	12 34 58.9	4N13.6	1N10.8	22S28.2	3N32.1	21N52.9	12S 9.2	22S23.5	18N35.3	19S 8.3	20N58.6	17N30.0
4 F	12 46 48.5	5 22.8	1 7.0	8 9.4	1 60.0	22 6.8	11 19.8	22 21.6	18 39.5	19 7.0	20 58.7	17 30.6
7 M	12 58 38.2	6 31.3	1 3.2	8N60.0	0 41.6	22 10.3	10 29.5	22 19.9	18 43.9	19 5.7	20 58.7	17 31.1
10 T	13 10 27.9	7 38.7	0 59.4	23 39.0	0S16.2	22 2.4	9 38.4	22 18.4	18 48.3	19 4.5	20 58.7	17 31.7
13 S	13 22 17.5	8 45.0	0 55.6	28 31.5	0 51.0	21 42.2	8 46.6	22 17.0	18 52.7	19 3.5	20 58.7	17 32.2
16 W	13 34 7.2	9 49.9	0 51.8	18 44.6	1 2.7	21 9.2	7 54.1	22 15.9	18 57.2	19 2.5	20 58.6	17 32.8
19 S	13 45 56.8	10 53.4	0 48.0	0S54.9	0 52.7	20 23.7	7 1.0	22 14.9	19 1.7	19 1.7	20 58.4	17 33.3
22 T	13 57 46.5	11 55.2	0 44.3	20 2.8	0 23.0	19 26.9	6 7.4	22 14.1	19 6.2	19 1.0	20 58.2	17 33.8
25 F	14 9 36.2	12 55.3	0 40.5	28 35.8	0N24.4	18 21.0	5 13.5	22 13.5	19 10.7	19 0.3	20 58.0	17 34.3
28 M	14 21 25.8	13 53.5	0 36.7	23 30.8	1 27.3	17 9.2	4 19.1	22 13.2	19 15.2	18 59.8	20 57.7	17 34.8

MAY 1913

DAY	EPHEMERIS SIDEREAL TIME	☉	☊	☽	☿	♀	♂	♃	♄	♅	♆	♇
	h m s	° ′	° ′	° ′	° ′	° ′	° ′	° ′	° ′	° ′	° ′	° ′
						LONGITUDE						
1 T	14 33 15.5	10♉ 0.9	1♈22.6	9♓52.9	13♈45.4	0♉39.6	24♓32.5	17♑48.2	3♊53.7	7♒29.5	23♋24.8	28♊26.9
2 F	14 37 12.0	10 59.1	1 19.4	21 43.4	15 0.7	0R 6.9	25 18.6	17 49.0	4 1.1	7 30.1	23 25.7	28 27.9
3 S	14 41 8.6	11 57.3	1 16.2	3♈40.6	16 18.4	29♈35.8	26 4.7	17 49.6	4 8.5	7 30.6	23 26.6	28 29.0
4 S	14 45 5.2	12 55.5	1 13.1	15 47.9	17 38.3	29 6.4	26 50.8	17 50.1	4 16.0	7 31.1	23 27.6	28 30.0
5 M	14 49 1.7	13 53.6	1 9.9	28 8.3	19 0.5	28 38.9	27 36.8	17 50.3	4 23.5	7 31.5	23 28.6	28 31.1
6 T	14 52 58.3	14 51.7	1 6.7	10♉43.6	20 24.8	28 13.4	28 22.8	17 50.3	4 30.9	7 31.8	23 29.6	28 32.2
7 W	14 56 54.8	15 49.8	1 3.5	23 34.4	21 51.3	27 50.1	29 8.8	17R50.2	4 38.5	7 32.1	23 30.6	28 33.3
8 T	15 0 51.4	16 47.8	1 0.4	6♊40.6	23 19.9	27 29.0	29 54.8	17 49.9	4 46.0	7 32.4	23 31.7	28 34.4
9 F	15 4 48.0	17 45.9	0 57.2	20 1.0	24 50.6	27 10.1	0♈40.7	17 49.4	4 53.6	7 32.6	23 32.8	28 35.5
10 S	15 8 44.5	18 43.9	0 54.0	3♋34.1	26 23.4	26 53.6	1 26.6	17 48.7	5 1.2	7 32.7	23 34.0	28 36.7
11 S	15 12 41.1	19 41.8	0 50.8	17 18.1	27 58.2	26 39.5	2 12.4	17 47.8	5 8.8	7 32.8	23 35.1	28 37.8
12 M	15 16 37.6	20 39.8	0 47.7	1♌11.1	29 35.1	26 27.8	2 58.2	17 46.7	5 16.4	7 32.9	23 36.3	28 39.0
13 T	15 20 34.2	21 37.7	0 44.5	15 11.8	1♉14.0	26 18.5	3 44.0	17 45.4	5 24.0	7 32.9	23 37.5	28 40.2
14 W	15 24 30.7	22 35.6	0 41.3	29 18.8	2 55.0	26 11.6	4 29.8	17 43.9	5 31.7	7R32.8	23 38.8	28 41.4
15 T	15 28 27.3	23 33.4	0 38.1	13♍30.9	4 38.1	26 7.1	5 15.5	17 42.3	5 39.4	7 32.7	23 40.1	28 42.6
16 F	15 32 23.8	24 31.2	0 34.9	27 46.5	6 23.1	26 5.0	6 1.1	17 40.5	5 47.1	7 32.6	23 41.4	28 43.8
17 S	15 36 20.4	25 29.0	0 31.8	12♎ 3.3	8 10.3	26D 5.2	6 46.8	17 38.4	5 54.8	7 32.4	23 42.7	28 45.1
18 S	15 40 17.0	26 26.8	0 28.6	26 18.3	9 59.4	26 7.7	7 32.4	17 36.3	6 2.5	7 32.2	23 44.1	28 46.3
19 M	15 44 13.5	27 24.5	0 25.4	10♏27.6	11 50.7	26 12.6	8 17.9	17 33.9	6 10.2	7 31.9	23 45.5	28 47.6
20 T	15 48 10.1	28 22.2	0 22.2	24 26.8	13 43.9	26 19.6	9 3.5	17 31.3	6 18.0	7 31.5	23 46.9	28 48.8
21 W	15 52 6.6	29 19.9	0 19.1	8♐11.6	15 39.2	26 28.9	9 48.9	17 28.6	6 25.7	7 31.1	23 48.3	28 50.1
22 T	15 56 3.2	0♊17.6	0 15.9	21 38.6	17 36.5	26 40.3	10 34.4	17 25.7	6 33.5	7 30.7	23 49.8	28 51.4
23 F	15 59 59.8	1 15.2	0 12.7	4♑45.7	19 35.7	26 53.7	11 19.8	17 22.6	6 41.3	7 30.2	23 51.3	28 52.7
24 S	16 3 56.3	2 12.9	0 9.5	17 32.4	21 36.8	27 9.2	12 5.2	17 19.3	6 49.0	7 29.7	23 52.8	28 54.0
25 S	16 7 52.9	3 10.5	0 6.4	29 59.9	23 39.7	27 26.6	12 50.5	17 15.8	6 56.8	7 29.1	23 54.3	28 55.3
26 M	16 11 49.4	4 8.1	0 3.2	12♒11.2	25 44.4	27 45.9	13 35.8	17 12.2	7 4.6	7 28.5	23 55.8	28 56.6
27 T	16 15 46.0	5 5.6	0 0.0	24 10.0	27 50.6	28 7.0	14 21.0	17 8.4	7 12.4	7 27.8	23 57.4	28 58.0
28 W	16 19 42.5	6 3.2	29♓56.8	6♓ 1.2	29 58.4	28 29.9	15 6.3	17 4.5	7 20.2	7 27.1	23 59.0	28 59.3
29 T	16 23 39.1	7 0.8	29 53.7	17 50.1	2♊ 7.4	28 54.4	15 51.4	17 0.4	7 28.0	7 26.4	24 0.7	29 0.7
30 F	16 27 35.6	7 58.3	29 50.5	29 41.9	4 17.5	29 20.6	16 36.5	16 56.1	7 35.8	7 25.5	24 2.3	29 2.0
31 S	16 31 32.2	8 55.8	29 47.3	11♈42.0	6 28.5	29 48.4	17 21.6	16 51.6	7 43.6	7 24.7	24 4.0	29 3.4
						DECLINATION						
1 T	14 33 15.5	14N49.6	0N32.9	9S44.2	2N44.2	15N55.2	3S24.6	22S13.0	19N19.7	18S59.4	20N57.3	17N35.3
4 S	14 45 5.2	15 43.6	0 29.1	7N18.6	4 13.2	14 42.7	2 29.9	22 13.1	19 24.2	18 59.1	20 56.9	17 35.8
7 W	14 56 54.8	16 35.2	0 25.3	22 33.5	5 52.8	13 35.0	1 35.2	22 13.4	19 28.6	18 59.0	20 56.5	17 36.2
10 S	15 8 44.5	17 24.4	0 21.5	28 32.0	7 41.7	12 34.5	0 40.4	22 14.0	19 33.0	18 58.9	20 56.0	17 36.7
13 T	15 20 34.2	18 10.9	0 17.7	19 51.7	9 38.2	11 43.1	0N14.2	22 14.8	19 37.3	18 59.0	20 55.4	17 37.1
16 F	15 32 23.8	18 54.7	0 13.9	1 13.5	11 40.5	11 1.6	1 8.6	22 15.8	19 41.7	18 59.2	20 54.9	17 37.5
19 M	15 44 13.5	19 35.5	0 10.1	17S59.7	13 46.7	10 30.4	2 2.8	22 17.1	19 45.9	18 59.5	20 54.2	17 37.9
22 T	15 56 3.2	20 13.4	0 6.3	28 11.0	15 54.0	10 9.2	2 56.6	22 18.5	19 50.1	18 59.9	20 53.6	17 38.3
25 S	16 7 52.9	20 48.2	0 2.5	24 30.2	17 58.9	9 57.7	3 50.0	22 20.2	19 54.2	19 0.4	20 52.8	17 38.6
28 W	16 19 42.5	21 19.8	0S 1.3	11 17.8	19 57.0	9 55.0	4 42.9	22 22.0	19 58.3	19 1.0	20 52.1	17 39.0
31 S	16 31 32.2	21 48.1	0 5.1	5N30.9	21 43.0	10 0.3	5 35.3	22 24.0	20 2.2	19 1.7	20 51.3	17 39.3

JUNE 1913

						LONGITUDE						
1 S	16 35 28.8	9♊53.3	29♓44.1	23♈55.0	8♊40.1	0♉17.7	18♈ 6.6	16♑47.0	7♊51.4	7♒23.8	24♋ 5.7	29♊ 4.8
2 M	16 39 25.3	10 50.8	29 40.9	6♉24.6	10 52.1	0 48.4	18 51.6	16R42.2	7 59.2	7R22.8	24 7.4	29 6.1
3 T	16 43 21.9	11 48.3	29 37.8	19 13.4	13 4.2	1 20.5	19 36.5	16 37.3	8 7.0	7 21.9	24 9.1	29 7.5
4 W	16 47 18.4	12 45.8	29 34.6	2♊22.5	15 16.2	1 54.0	20 21.3	16 32.2	8 14.8	7 20.8	24 10.9	29 8.9
5 T	16 51 15.0	13 43.2	29 31.4	15 51.0	17 27.7	2 28.8	21 6.2	16 27.0	8 22.6	7 19.7	24 12.7	29 10.3
6 F	16 55 11.6	14 40.7	29 28.2	29 36.5	19 38.5	3 4.8	21 50.9	16 21.6	8 30.3	7 18.6	24 14.5	29 11.7
7 S	16 59 8.1	15 38.1	29 25.1	13♋35.4	21 48.3	3 41.9	22 35.6	16 16.1	8 38.1	7 17.5	24 16.3	29 13.1
8 S	17 3 4.6	16 35.5	29 21.9	27 43.1	23 56.9	4 20.3	23 20.2	16 10.5	8 45.8	7 16.2	24 18.1	29 14.6
9 M	17 7 1.2	17 32.9	29 18.7	11♌55.4	26 4.1	4 59.7	24 4.8	16 4.7	8 53.6	7 15.0	24 20.0	29 16.0
10 T	17 10 57.8	18 30.3	29 15.5	26 8.4	28 9.8	5 40.1	24 49.3	15 58.8	9 1.3	7 13.7	24 21.8	29 17.4
11 W	17 14 54.3	19 27.6	29 12.4	10♍19.6	0♋13.6	6 21.6	25 33.8	15 52.7	9 9.1	7 12.4	24 23.7	29 18.8
12 T	17 18 50.9	20 25.0	29 9.2	24 27.3	2 15.6	7 4.1	26 18.2	15 46.6	9 16.8	7 11.0	24 25.6	29 20.3
13 F	17 22 47.5	21 22.3	29 6.0	8♎30.4	4 15.6	7 47.5	27 2.5	15 40.3	9 24.5	7 9.6	24 27.5	29 21.7
14 S	17 26 44.0	22 19.6	29 2.8	22 28.3	6 13.4	8 31.8	27 46.8	15 33.9	9 32.1	7 8.2	24 29.5	29 23.1
15 S	17 30 40.5	23 16.9	28 59.7	6♏20.1	8 9.1	9 17.0	28 31.0	15 27.4	9 39.8	7 6.7	24 31.4	29 24.6
16 M	17 34 37.1	24 14.1	28 56.5	20 4.2	10 2.6	10 3.0	29 15.2	15 20.8	9 47.5	7 5.2	24 33.4	29 26.0
17 T	17 38 33.7	25 11.4	28 53.3	3♐38.8	11 53.7	10 49.8	29 59.3	15 14.1	9 55.1	7 3.6	24 35.4	29 27.5
18 W	17 42 30.3	26 8.7	28 50.1	17 1.5	13 42.6	11 37.4	0♉43.3	15 7.3	10 2.7	7 2.0	24 37.4	29 28.9
19 T	17 46 26.8	27 5.9	28 46.9	0♑10.3	15 29.1	12 25.8	1 27.3	15 0.4	10 10.3	7 0.4	24 39.4	29 30.4
20 F	17 50 23.4	28 3.1	28 43.8	13 3.4	17 13.3	13 14.9	2 11.2	14 53.4	10 17.8	6 58.7	24 41.4	29 31.8
21 S	17 54 19.9	29 0.4	28 40.6	25 40.4	18 55.2	14 4.7	2 55.0	14 46.3	10 25.4	6 57.0	24 43.5	29 33.3
22 S	17 58 16.5	29 57.6	28 37.4	8♒ 1.7	20 34.6	14 55.2	3 38.8	14 39.2	10 32.9	6 55.3	24 45.5	29 34.7
23 M	18 2 13.0	0♋54.8	28 34.2	20 9.2	22 11.7	15 46.3	4 22.5	14 32.0	10 40.4	6 53.5	24 47.6	29 36.1
24 T	18 6 9.6	1 52.0	28 31.1	2♓ 6.1	23 46.4	16 38.1	5 6.1	14 24.7	10 47.9	6 51.7	24 49.7	29 37.6
25 W	18 10 6.2	2 49.2	28 27.9	13 56.3	25 18.7	17 30.5	5 49.7	14 17.3	10 55.3	6 49.9	24 51.7	29 39.0
26 T	18 14 2.7	3 46.5	28 24.7	25 44.6	26 48.6	18 23.4	6 33.2	14 9.9	11 2.7	6 48.0	24 53.8	29 40.5
27 F	18 17 59.3	4 43.7	28 21.5	7♈36.4	28 16.0	19 16.9	7 16.7	14 2.4	11 10.1	6 46.1	24 56.0	29 41.9
28 S	18 21 55.8	5 40.9	28 18.4	19 37.1	29 41.0	20 11.0	8 0.0	13 54.9	11 17.5	6 44.2	24 58.1	29 43.4
29 S	18 25 52.4	6 38.1	28 15.2	1♉52.1	1♌ 3.5	21 5.6	8 43.3	13 47.4	11 24.8	6 42.3	25 0.2	29 44.8
30 M	18 29 49.0	7 35.3	28 12.0	14 25.9	2 23.4	22 0.7	9 26.6	13 39.8	11 32.1	6 40.3	25 2.3	29 46.3
						DECLINATION						
1 S	16 35 28.8	21N56.7	0S 6.3	11N 8.3	22N14.6	10N 3.7	5N52.6	22S24.7	20N 3.5	19S 2.0	20N51.0	17N39.4
4 W	16 47 18.4	22 20.5	0 10.1	25 0.1	23 36.2	10 18.2	6 44.1	22 27.0	20 7.4	19 2.8	20 50.2	17 39.7
7 S	16 59 8.1	22 40.7	0 13.9	27 36.9	24 34.6	10 38.5	7 34.9	22 29.3	20 11.2	19 3.8	20 49.3	17 40.0
10 T	17 10 57.8	22 57.3	0 17.7	15 25.6	25 8.1	11 3.8	8 24.8	22 31.8	20 14.8	19 4.8	20 48.4	17 40.2
13 F	17 22 47.5	23 10.3	0 21.5	4S 6.1	25 17.2	11 33.2	9 13.8	22 34.4	20 18.4	19 5.9	20 47.4	17 40.5
16 M	17 34 37.1	23 19.6	0 25.3	21 30.8	25 3.9	12 6.2	10 1.9	22 37.1	20 21.9	19 7.2	20 46.4	17 40.7
19 T	17 46 26.8	23 25.2	0 29.1	28 27.3	24 31.4	12 42.0	10 49.0	22 39.8	20 25.3	19 8.5	20 45.4	17 40.9
22 S	17 58 16.5	23 27.2	0 32.9	21 59.9	23 43.0	13 20.0	11 35.0	22 42.6	20 28.6	19 9.8	20 44.4	17 41.0
25 W	18 10 6.2	23 25.4	0 36.7	7 27.5	22 42.1	13 59.4	12 19.9	22 45.4	20 31.7	19 11.3	20 43.3	17 41.2
28 S	18 21 55.8	23 19.9	0 40.4	9N24.4	21 31.7	14 39.9	13 3.7	22 48.2	20 34.8	19 12.8	20 42.2	17 41.3

JULY 1913

LONGITUDE

DAY	EPHEMERIS SIDEREAL TIME h m s	☉ ° ′	☊ ° ′	☽ ° ′	☿ ° ′	♀ ° ′	♂ ° ′	♃ ° ′	♄ ° ′	♅ ° ′	♆ ° ′	♇ ° ′
1 T	18 33 45.5	8♋32.6	28♓ 8.8	27♉22.2	3♌40.8	22♉56.3	10♉ 9.7	13♑32.1	11♊39.4	6♒38.3	25♋ 4.5	29♊47.7
2 W	18 37 42.1	9 29.8	28 5.7	10♊42.8	4 55.6	23 52.3	10 52.8	13R24.5	11 46.6	6R36.3	25 6.7	29 49.1
3 T	18 41 38.6	10 27.0	28 2.5	24 27.6	6 7.6	24 48.8	11 35.7	13 16.8	11 53.8	6 34.2	25 8.8	29 50.5
4 F	18 45 35.2	11 24.2	27 59.3	8♋33.8	7 17.0	25 45.8	12 18.6	13 9.1	12 1.0	6 32.1	25 11.0	29 52.0
5 S	18 49 31.7	12 21.4	27 56.1	22 56.6	8 23.5	26 43.1	13 1.5	13 1.4	12 8.1	6 30.0	25 13.2	29 53.4
6 S	18 53 28.3	13 18.7	27 53.0	7♌29.6	9 27.1	27 40.9	13 44.2	12 53.7	12 15.2	6 27.9	25 15.4	29 54.8
7 M	18 57 24.9	14 15.9	27 49.8	22 5.9	10 27.7	28 39.0	14 26.9	12 45.9	12 22.2	6 25.8	25 17.5	29 56.2
8 T	19 1 21.4	15 13.1	27 46.6	6♍39.2	11 25.3	29 37.5	15 9.4	12 38.2	12 29.2	6 23.6	25 19.7	29 57.6
9 W	19 5 18.0	16 10.3	27 43.4	21 4.7	12 19.6	0♊36.4	15 51.9	12 30.5	12 36.2	6 21.4	25 21.9	29 59.0
10 T	19 9 14.5	17 7.5	27 40.2	5♎19.4	13 10.6	1 35.7	16 34.3	12 22.9	12 43.1	6 19.2	25 24.2	0♋ 0.4
11 F	19 13 11.1	18 4.8	27 37.1	19 21.6	13 58.2	2 35.3	17 16.6	12 15.2	12 50.0	6 17.0	25 26.4	0 1.8
12 S	19 17 7.7	19 2.0	27 33.9	3♏11.1	14 42.3	3 35.2	17 58.9	12 7.6	12 56.8	6 14.7	25 28.6	0 3.2
13 S	19 21 4.2	19 59.2	27 30.7	16 48.0	15 22.6	4 35.5	18 41.0	12 0.0	13 3.6	6 12.5	25 30.8	0 4.6
14 M	19 25 0.8	20 56.4	27 27.5	0♐12.7	15 59.1	5 36.1	19 23.0	11 52.5	13 10.4	6 10.2	25 33.0	0 6.0
15 T	19 28 57.3	21 53.6	27 24.4	13 25.4	16 31.6	6 37.0	20 5.0	11 45.0	13 17.1	6 7.9	25 35.2	0 7.3
16 W	19 32 53.9	22 50.8	27 21.2	26 25.9	16 59.9	7 38.2	20 46.9	11 37.5	13 23.7	6 5.6	25 37.5	0 8.7
17 T	19 36 50.4	23 48.1	27 18.0	9♑13.9	17 23.9	8 39.6	21 28.6	11 30.1	13 30.3	6 3.3	25 39.7	0 10.0
18 F	19 40 47.0	24 45.3	27 14.8	21 49.4	17 43.6	9 41.4	22 10.3	11 22.8	13 36.8	6 0.9	25 41.9	0 11.4
19 S	19 44 43.6	25 42.5	27 11.7	4♒12.3	17 58.6	10 43.5	22 51.9	11 15.5	13 43.3	5 58.6	25 44.2	0 12.7
20 S	19 48 40.2	26 39.8	27 8.5	16 23.5	18 8.9	11 45.8	23 33.4	11 8.3	13 49.8	5 56.3	25 46.4	0 14.0
21 M	19 52 36.7	27 37.0	27 5.3	28 24.3	18 14.4	12 48.4	24 14.8	11 1.2	13 56.2	5 53.9	25 48.6	0 15.3
22 T	19 56 33.2	28 34.3	27 2.1	10♓17.1	18 15.0	13 51.3	24 56.1	10 54.1	14 2.5	5 51.5	25 50.8	0 16.6
23 W	20 0 29.8	29 31.6	26 58.9	22 5.2	18R10.7	14 54.4	25 37.4	10 47.2	14 8.8	5 49.1	25 53.1	0 17.9
24 T	20 4 26.4	0♌28.9	26 55.8	3♈52.6	18 1.4	15 57.8	26 18.5	10 40.3	14 15.0	5 46.8	25 55.3	0 19.2
25 F	20 8 22.9	1 26.2	26 52.6	15 43.7	17 47.1	17 1.4	26 59.5	10 33.5	14 21.2	5 44.4	25 57.5	0 20.5
26 S	20 12 19.5	2 23.5	26 49.4	27 43.8	17 27.9	18 5.3	27 40.4	10 26.9	14 27.3	5 42.0	25 59.7	0 21.7
27 S	20 16 16.0	3 20.8	26 46.2	9♉57.9	17 4.1	19 9.4	28 21.3	10 20.3	14 33.3	5 39.6	26 1.9	0 23.0
28 M	20 20 12.6	4 18.2	26 43.1	22 31.3	16 35.8	20 13.7	29 2.0	10 13.8	14 39.3	5 37.2	26 4.1	0 24.2
29 T	20 24 9.2	5 15.5	26 39.9	5♊28.0	16 3.3	21 18.2	29 42.6	10 7.5	14 45.2	5 34.8	26 6.4	0 25.4
30 W	20 28 5.7	6 12.9	26 36.7	18 51.2	15 27.0	22 23.0	0♊23.1	10 1.2	14 51.1	5 32.4	26 8.6	0 26.7
31 T	20 32 2.2	7 10.3	26 33.5	2♋41.7	14 47.4	23 27.9	1 3.5	9 55.1	14 56.9	5 30.0	26 10.7	0 27.9

DECLINATION

DAY	EPHEMERIS SIDEREAL TIME h m s	☉	☊	☽	☿	♀	♂	♃	♄	♅	♆	♇
1 T	18 33 45.5	23N10.7	0S44.2	23N48.5	20N14.9	15N20.7	13N46.2	22S51.0	20N37.7	19S14.3	20N41.1	17N41.4
4 F	18 45 35.2	22 57.8	0 48.0	28 5.5	18 54.2	16 1.4	14 27.4	22 53.7	20 40.6	19 15.9	20 40.0	17 41.5
7 M	18 57 24.9	22 41.3	0 51.8	16 52.5	17 32.5	16 41.4	15 7.2	22 56.3	20 43.3	19 17.6	20 38.9	17 41.6
10 T	19 9 14.5	22 21.3	0 55.6	2S48.8	16 12.4	17 20.4	15 45.7	22 58.9	20 45.9	19 19.3	20 37.7	17 41.6
13 S	19 21 4.2	21 57.8	0 59.4	20 35.6	14 56.7	17 57.8	16 22.7	23 1.4	20 48.4	19 21.0	20 36.5	17 41.6
16 W	19 32 53.9	21 31.0	1 3.2	28 27.5	13 48.3	18 33.3	16 58.3	23 3.8	20 50.7	19 22.8	20 35.3	17 41.6
19 S	19 44 43.6	21 0.8	1 7.0	23 4.8	12 50.5	19 6.4	17 32.3	23 6.1	20 53.0	19 24.5	20 34.1	17 41.6
22 T	19 56 33.2	20 27.5	1 10.8	8 57.6	12 6.6	19 36.9	18 4.8	23 8.3	20 55.1	19 26.3	20 32.9	17 41.6
25 F	20 8 22.9	19 51.1	1 14.6	7N50.2	11 39.7	20 4.3	18 35.8	23 10.4	20 57.1	19 28.1	20 31.7	17 41.5
28 M	20 20 12.6	19 11.7	1 18.3	22 34.7	11 32.4	20 28.3	19 5.2	23 12.3	20 59.0	19 29.9	20 30.5	17 41.5
31 T	20 32 2.2	18 29.4	1 22.1	28 30.9	11 45.7	20 48.5	19 33.0	23 14.1	21 0.8	19 31.7	20 29.3	17 41.4

AUGUST 1913

LONGITUDE

DAY	EPHEMERIS SIDEREAL TIME h m s	☉ ° ′	☊ ° ′	☽ ° ′	☿ ° ′	♀ ° ′	♂ ° ′	♃ ° ′	♄ ° ′	♅ ° ′	♆ ° ′	♇ ° ′
1 F	20 35 58.8	8♌ 7.8	26♓30.4	16♋57.9	14♌ 5.2	24♊33.1	1♊43.8	9♑49.1	15♊ 2.6	5♒27.6	26♋12.9	0♋29.1
2 S	20 39 55.4	9 5.2	26 27.2	1♌35.4	13R20.8	25 38.4	2 24.0	9R43.2	15 8.3	5R25.2	26 15.1	0 30.2
3 S	20 43 51.9	10 2.7	26 24.0	16 27.2	12 35.2	26 43.9	3 4.0	9 37.5	15 13.9	5 22.8	26 17.3	0 31.4
4 M	20 47 48.5	11 0.1	26 20.8	1♍24.9	11 49.0	27 49.7	3 44.0	9 31.9	15 19.4	5 20.4	26 19.5	0 32.6
5 T	20 51 45.0	11 57.6	26 17.6	16 20.2	11 3.1	28 55.6	4 23.8	9 26.4	15 24.8	5 18.1	26 21.6	0 33.7
6 W	20 55 41.6	12 55.1	26 14.5	1♎ 5.4	10 18.4	0♋ 1.6	5 3.5	9 21.1	15 30.2	5 15.7	26 23.8	0 34.8
7 T	20 59 38.2	13 52.6	26 11.3	15 35.4	9 35.7	1 7.9	5 43.1	9 15.9	15 35.5	5 13.3	26 26.0	0 35.9
8 F	21 3 34.7	14 50.1	26 8.1	29 46.9	8 55.9	2 14.3	6 22.6	9 10.9	15 40.8	5 11.0	26 28.1	0 37.0
9 S	21 7 31.3	15 47.7	26 4.9	13♏38.7	8 19.7	3 20.9	7 1.9	9 6.1	15 45.9	5 8.6	26 30.2	0 38.1
10 S	21 11 27.8	16 45.2	26 1.8	27 11.2	7 48.0	4 27.6	7 41.1	9 1.4	15 51.0	5 6.3	26 32.3	0 39.2
11 M	21 15 24.4	17 42.8	25 58.6	10♐25.6	7 21.4	5 34.5	8 20.2	8 56.8	15 56.0	5 4.0	26 34.4	0 40.2
12 T	21 19 20.9	18 40.4	25 55.4	23 23.6	7 0.4	6 41.6	8 59.2	8 52.4	16 1.0	5 1.7	26 36.5	0 41.3
13 W	21 23 17.5	19 38.0	25 52.2	6♑ 6.9	6 45.6	7 48.8	9 38.0	8 48.2	16 5.8	4 59.4	26 38.6	0 42.3
14 T	21 27 14.1	20 35.6	25 49.1	18 37.3	6 37.5	8 56.2	10 16.7	8 44.2	16 10.6	4 57.1	26 40.7	0 43.3
15 F	21 31 10.6	21 33.2	25 45.9	0♒56.3	6 36.3	10 3.7	10 55.3	8 40.3	16 15.3	4 54.8	26 42.8	0 44.3
16 S	21 35 7.2	22 30.8	25 42.7	13 5.3	6D42.3	11 11.4	11 33.8	8 36.6	16 19.9	4 52.5	26 44.8	0 45.2
17 S	21 39 3.7	23 28.5	25 39.5	25 5.8	6 55.6	12 19.2	12 12.1	8 33.0	16 24.5	4 50.3	26 46.9	0 46.2
18 M	21 43 0.2	24 26.2	25 36.4	6♓59.6	7 16.3	13 27.2	12 50.3	8 29.6	16 28.9	4 48.1	26 48.9	0 47.1
19 T	21 46 56.8	25 23.9	25 33.2	18 48.7	7 44.6	14 35.3	13 28.4	8 26.4	16 33.3	4 45.9	26 50.9	0 48.0
20 W	21 50 53.4	26 21.7	25 30.0	0♈35.6	8 20.2	15 43.6	14 6.3	8 23.4	16 37.6	4 43.7	26 52.9	0 48.9
21 T	21 54 50.0	27 19.4	25 26.8	12 23.4	9 3.2	16 52.0	14 44.1	8 20.6	16 41.8	4 41.6	26 54.9	0 49.8
22 F	21 58 46.5	28 17.2	25 23.6	24 15.7	9 53.4	18 0.6	15 21.7	8 17.9	16 45.9	4 39.4	26 56.8	0 50.7
23 S	22 2 43.0	29 15.0	25 20.5	6♉16.5	10 50.5	19 9.3	15 59.2	8 15.4	16 50.0	4 37.3	26 58.8	0 51.6
24 S	22 6 39.6	0♍12.9	25 17.3	18 30.4	11 54.3	20 18.1	16 36.6	8 13.2	16 53.9	4 35.2	27 0.7	0 52.4
25 M	22 10 36.2	1 10.8	25 14.1	1♊ 1.7	13 4.5	21 27.1	17 13.8	8 11.0	16 57.8	4 33.2	27 2.6	0 53.2
26 T	22 14 32.7	2 8.7	25 10.9	13 55.0	14 20.9	22 36.2	17 50.8	8 9.1	17 1.5	4 31.1	27 4.5	0 54.0
27 W	22 18 29.3	3 6.6	25 7.8	27 13.5	15 42.9	23 45.4	18 27.8	8 7.4	17 5.2	4 29.1	27 6.4	0 54.8
28 T	22 22 25.8	4 4.6	25 4.6	10♋59.4	17 10.2	24 54.7	19 4.5	8 5.8	17 8.8	4 27.1	27 8.3	0 55.5
29 F	22 26 22.4	5 2.6	25 1.4	25 12.7	18 42.3	26 4.2	19 41.1	8 4.5	17 12.3	4 25.2	27 10.1	0 56.3
30 S	22 30 18.9	6 0.6	24 58.2	9♌50.7	20 18.8	27 13.8	20 17.5	8 3.3	17 15.7	4 23.2	27 12.0	0 57.0
31 S	22 34 15.5	6 58.7	24 55.0	24 47.8	21 59.1	28 23.5	20 53.8	8 2.3	17 19.0	4 21.3	27 13.8	0 57.7

DECLINATION

DAY	EPHEMERIS SIDEREAL TIME h m s	☉	☊	☽	☿	♀	♂	♃	♄	♅	♆	♇
1 F	20 35 58.8	18N14.7	1S23.4	27N 6.3	11N54.6	20N54.4	19N42.0	23S14.6	21N 1.4	19S32.3	20N28.9	17N41.3
4 M	20 47 48.5	17 28.8	1 27.2	12 53.8	12 32.9	21 9.3	20 7.6	23 16.3	21 3.0	19 34.0	20 27.7	17 41.2
7 T	20 59 38.2	16 40.3	1 31.0	7S50.5	13 24.6	21 19.8	20 31.6	23 17.7	21 4.5	19 35.8	20 26.5	17 41.1
10 S	21 11 27.8	15 49.4	1 34.8	24 0.9	14 22.9	21 25.8	20 54.0	23 19.1	21 6.0	19 37.5	20 25.3	17 41.0
13 W	21 23 17.5	14 56.3	1 38.5	28 23.5	15 20.3	21 27.1	21 14.7	23 20.3	21 7.2	19 39.2	20 24.1	17 40.8
16 S	21 35 7.2	14 1.0	1 42.3	20 11.5	16 9.6	21 23.5	21 33.9	23 21.4	21 8.4	19 40.8	20 22.9	17 40.6
19 T	21 46 56.8	13 3.7	1 46.1	4 53.1	16 44.7	21 15.0	21 51.5	23 22.4	21 9.5	19 42.4	20 21.8	17 40.5
22 F	21 58 46.5	12 4.6	1 49.9	11N51.4	17 0.2	21 1.4	22 7.5	23 23.2	21 10.5	19 43.9	20 20.6	17 40.3
25 M	22 10 36.2	11 3.7	1 53.7	25 6.1	16 51.9	20 42.8	22 21.9	23 23.9	21 11.3	19 45.4	20 19.5	17 40.1
28 T	22 22 25.8	10 1.2	1 57.5	28 1.1	16 17.2	20 19.0	22 34.8	23 24.6	21 12.1	19 46.8	20 18.5	17 39.9
31 S	22 34 15.5	8 57.3	2 1.2	15 42.1	15 15.5	19 50.2	22 46.2	23 25.0	21 12.8	19 48.2	20 17.4	17 39.6

SEPTEMBER 1913

DAY	EPHEMERIS SIDEREAL TIME	☉	☊	☽	☿	♀	♂	♃	♄	♅	♆	♇
	h m s	° ′	° ′	° ′	° ′	° ′	° ′	° ′	° ′	° ′	° ′	° ′
						LONGITUDE						
1 M	22 38 12.0	7♍56.7	24♓51.9	9♍56.0	23♌42.9	29♋33.3	21♊29.9	8♑ 1.5	17♊22.2	4♒19.5	27♋15.6	0♋58.4
2 T	22 42 8.6	8 54.9	24 48.7	25 6.1	25 29.5	0♌43.3	22 5.8	8R 0.9	17 25.3	4R17.6	27 17.3	0 59.0
3 W	22 46 5.1	9 53.0	24 45.5	10♎ 8.8	27 18.5	1 53.3	22 41.6	8 0.5	17 28.3	4 15.8	27 19.1	0 59.6
4 T	22 50 1.7	10 51.2	24 42.3	24 56.0	29 9.6	3 3.5	23 17.2	8 0.3	17 31.2	4 14.0	27 20.8	1 0.3
5 F	22 53 58.3	11 49.4	24 39.2	9♏22.3	1♍ 2.1	4 13.7	23 52.6	8 0.3	17 34.0	4 12.3	27 22.5	1 0.9
6 S	22 57 54.8	12 47.6	24 36.0	23 24.3	2 55.9	5 24.1	24 27.8	8D 0.5	17 36.7	4 10.6	27 24.2	1 1.4
7 S	23 1 51.3	13 45.8	24 32.8	7♐ 1.6	4 50.4	6 34.5	25 2.8	8 0.8	17 39.3	4 8.9	27 25.9	1 2.0
8 M	23 5 47.9	14 44.1	24 29.6	20 15.1	6 45.5	7 45.1	25 37.7	8 1.4	17 41.8	4 7.3	27 27.5	1 2.5
9 T	23 9 44.5	15 42.4	24 26.5	3♑ 7.3	8 40.8	8 55.8	26 12.3	8 2.2	17 44.3	4 5.7	27 29.2	1 3.0
10 W	23 13 41.0	16 40.7	24 23.3	15 41.2	10 36.0	10 6.6	26 46.8	8 3.1	17 46.6	4 4.1	27 30.8	1 3.5
11 T	23 17 37.5	17 39.0	24 20.1	28 0.1	12 31.0	11 17.4	27 21.1	8 4.2	17 48.8	4 2.6	27 32.3	1 4.0
12 F	23 21 34.1	18 37.4	24 16.9	10♒ 7.3	14 25.6	12 28.4	27 55.1	8 5.6	17 50.8	4 1.1	27 33.9	1 4.4
13 S	23 25 30.7	19 35.8	24 13.7	22 5.7	16 19.7	13 39.5	28 29.0	8 7.1	17 52.8	3 59.6	27 35.4	1 4.9
14 S	23 29 27.3	20 34.2	24 10.6	3♓58.2	18 13.1	14 50.7	29 2.7	8 8.8	17 54.7	3 58.2	27 36.9	1 5.3
15 M	23 33 23.8	21 32.7	24 7.4	15 47.1	20 5.8	16 1.9	29 36.2	8 10.7	17 56.5	3 56.9	27 38.4	1 5.7
16 T	23 37 20.3	22 31.1	24 4.2	27 34.7	21 57.7	17 13.3	0♋ 9.5	8 12.7	17 58.2	3 55.5	27 39.8	1 6.0
17 W	23 41 16.9	23 29.7	24 1.0	9♈23.4	23 48.6	18 24.8	0 42.6	8 15.0	17 59.8	3 54.2	27 41.2	1 6.4
18 T	23 45 13.5	24 28.2	23 57.8	21 15.4	25 38.7	19 36.3	1 15.4	8 17.4	18 1.2	3 53.0	27 42.6	1 6.7
19 F	23 49 10.0	25 26.8	23 54.7	3♉13.2	27 27.8	20 48.0	1 48.1	8 20.1	18 2.6	3 51.8	27 44.0	1 7.0
20 S	23 53 6.6	26 25.4	23 51.5	15 19.6	29 15.9	21 59.7	2 20.5	8 22.9	18 3.9	3 50.6	27 45.4	1 7.3
21 S	23 57 3.1	27 24.1	23 48.3	27 37.6	1♎ 3.1	23 11.6	2 52.7	8 25.9	18 5.0	3 49.5	27 46.7	1 7.5
22 M	0 0 59.7	28 22.8	23 45.1	10♊10.5	2 49.3	24 23.5	3 24.7	8 29.0	18 6.0	3 48.4	27 48.0	1 7.7
23 T	0 4 56.3	29 21.5	23 42.0	23 1.8	4 34.5	25 35.5	3 56.4	8 32.4	18 7.0	3 47.4	27 49.2	1 7.9
24 W	0 8 52.8	0♎20.3	23 38.8	6♋14.4	6 18.7	26 47.6	4 27.9	8 35.9	18 7.8	3 46.4	27 50.5	1 8.1
25 T	0 12 49.3	1 19.1	23 35.6	19 50.9	8 2.0	27 59.8	4 59.2	8 39.7	18 8.5	3 45.5	27 51.7	1 8.3
26 F	0 16 45.9	2 17.9	23 32.4	3♌52.3	9 44.3	29 12.1	5 30.2	8 43.6	18 9.1	3 44.6	27 52.9	1 8.4
27 S	0 20 42.5	3 16.8	23 29.2	18 18.1	11 25.7	0♍24.5	6 0.9	8 47.6	18 9.6	3 43.7	27 54.0	1 8.5
28 S	0 24 39.0	4 15.7	23 26.1	3♍ 5.2	13 6.2	1 36.9	6 31.4	8 51.9	18 10.0	3 42.9	27 55.1	1 8.6
29 M	0 28 35.6	5 14.7	23 22.9	18 7.7	14 45.8	2 49.4	7 1.6	8 56.3	18 10.2	3 42.2	27 56.2	1 8.7
30 T	0 32 32.1	6 13.6	23 19.7	3♎17.8	16 24.5	4 2.0	7 31.6	9 0.9	18 10.4	3 41.5	27 57.3	1 8.8
						DECLINATION						
1 M	22 38 12.0	8N35.7	2S 2.5	9N 3.0	14N49.2	19N39.5	22N49.7	23S25.2	21N13.0	19S48.6	20N17.0	17N39.6
4 T	22 50 1.7	7 30.0	2 6.3	12S10.8	13 15.3	19 4.1	22 59.2	23 25.5	21 13.5	19 49.8	20 16.0	17 39.3
7 S	23 1 51.3	6 23.3	2 10.1	26 28.5	11 22.3	18 23.9	23 7.3	23 25.8	21 13.9	19 51.0	20 15.0	17 39.1
10 W	23 13 41.0	5 15.7	2 13.8	27 25.0	9 15.7	17 38.9	23 14.1	23 25.9	21 14.2	19 52.1	20 14.1	17 38.8
13 S	23 25 30.7	4 7.3	2 17.6	16 48.7	7 0.1	16 49.5	23 19.6	23 25.9	21 14.5	19 53.1	20 13.2	17 38.6
16 T	23 37 20.3	2 58.2	2 21.4	0 40.1	4 39.6	15 55.7	23 23.9	23 25.8	21 14.6	19 54.0	20 12.3	17 38.4
19 F	23 49 10.0	1 48.6	2 25.2	15N44.2	2 17.1	14 57.7	23 27.2	23 25.5	21 14.7	19 54.8	20 11.5	17 38.1
22 M	0 0 59.7	0 38.7	2 28.9	27 4.2	0S 5.0	13 55.9	23 29.3	23 25.2	21 14.7	19 55.6	20 10.7	17 37.8
25 T	0 12 49.3	0S31.5	2 32.7	26 42.1	2 25.1	12 50.4	23 30.5	23 24.7	21 14.5	19 56.2	20 9.9	17 37.6
28 S	0 24 39.0	1 41.7	2 36.5	12 9.3	4 42.1	11 41.5	23 30.8	23 24.1	21 14.3	19 56.7	20 9.2	17 37.3

OCTOBER 1913

DAY	EPHEMERIS SIDEREAL TIME	☉	☊	☽	☿	♀	♂	♃	♄	♅	♆	♇
						LONGITUDE						
1 W	0 36 28.7	7♎12.7	23♓16.5	18♎26.2	18♎ 2.3	5♍14.7	8♋ 1.2	9♑ 5.7	18♊10.4	3♒40.8	27♋58.3	1♋ 8.8
2 T	0 40 25.2	8 11.7	23 13.4	3♏23.6	19 39.2	6 27.5	8 30.6	9 10.6	18R 10.3	3R 40.2	27 59.3	1 8.8
3 F	0 44 21.8	9 10.8	23 10.2	18 2.0	21 15.4	7 40.3	8 59.7	9 15.8	18 10.2	3 39.6	28 0.3	1R 8.8
4 S	0 48 18.4	10 9.9	23 7.0	2♐15.8	22 50.7	8 53.2	9 28.5	9 21.0	18 9.9	3 39.1	28 1.3	1 8.7
5 S	0 52 14.9	11 9.1	23 3.8	16 2.4	24 25.2	10 6.1	9 57.0	9 26.5	18 9.5	3 38.6	28 2.2	1 8.7
6 M	0 56 11.4	12 8.3	23 0.6	29 21.6	25 58.9	11 19.1	10 25.2	9 32.1	18 8.9	3 38.2	28 3.0	1 8.6
7 T	1 0 8.0	13 7.5	22 57.5	12♑15.4	27 31.8	12 32.2	10 53.1	9 37.9	18 8.3	3 37.9	28 3.9	1 8.4
8 W	1 4 4.6	14 6.7	22 54.3	24 47.4	29 4.0	13 45.4	11 20.7	9 43.8	18 7.6	3 37.6	28 4.7	1 8.3
9 T	1 8 1.1	15 6.0	22 51.1	7♒ 1.8	0♏35.4	14 58.6	11 47.9	9 50.0	18 6.8	3 37.3	28 5.5	1 8.2
10 F	1 11 57.7	16 5.3	22 47.9	19 3.1	2 6.0	16 11.9	12 14.9	9 56.2	18 5.8	3 37.1	28 6.2	1 8.0
11 S	1 15 54.2	17 4.6	22 44.8	0♓55.8	3 35.9	17 25.2	12 41.5	10 2.6	18 4.7	3 36.9	28 7.0	1 7.8
12 S	1 19 50.8	18 4.0	22 41.6	12 43.9	5 5.0	18 38.6	13 7.7	10 9.2	18 3.6	3 36.8	28 7.6	1 7.6
13 M	1 23 47.3	19 3.3	22 38.4	24 31.1	6 33.3	19 52.1	13 33.7	10 15.9	18 2.3	3 36.7	28 8.3	1 7.3
14 T	1 27 43.9	20 2.8	22 35.2	6♈20.4	8 0.9	21 5.6	13 59.2	10 22.8	18 0.9	3 36.7	28 8.9	1 7.0
15 W	1 31 40.4	21 2.2	22 32.0	18 14.3	9 27.7	22 19.2	14 24.4	10 29.8	17 59.4	3D 36.7	28 9.5	1 6.7
16 T	1 35 37.0	22 1.7	22 28.9	0♉14.8	10 53.7	23 32.9	14 49.3	10 37.0	17 57.8	3 36.8	28 10.1	1 6.4
17 F	1 39 33.6	23 1.2	22 25.7	12 23.6	12 18.9	24 46.6	15 13.8	10 44.4	17 56.1	3 37.0	28 10.6	1 6.1
18 S	1 43 30.1	24 0.8	22 22.5	24 42.2	13 43.3	26 0.4	15 37.9	10 51.8	17 54.3	3 37.1	28 11.1	1 5.8
19 S	1 47 26.6	25 0.4	22 19.3	7♊11.9	15 6.7	27 14.2	16 1.6	10 59.4	17 52.4	3 37.4	28 11.5	1 5.4
20 M	1 51 23.2	26 0.0	22 16.2	19 54.3	16 29.3	28 28.1	16 24.9	11 7.2	17 50.4	3 37.7	28 11.9	1 5.0
21 T	1 55 19.8	26 59.7	22 13.0	2♋51.0	17 50.9	29 42.0	16 47.8	11 15.1	17 48.3	3 38.0	28 12.3	1 4.6
22 W	1 59 16.3	27 59.4	22 9.8	16 3.7	19 11.6	0♎56.0	17 10.3	11 23.1	17 46.1	3 38.4	28 12.7	1 4.1
23 T	2 3 12.9	28 59.1	22 6.6	29 34.1	20 31.1	2 10.1	17 32.4	11 31.3	17 43.8	3 38.8	28 13.0	1 3.7
24 F	2 7 9.4	29 58.9	22 3.5	13♌23.6	21 49.5	3 24.2	17 54.0	11 39.6	17 41.3	3 39.3	28 13.3	1 3.2
25 S	2 11 6.0	0♏58.7	22 0.3	27 32.7	23 6.6	4 38.3	18 15.2	11 48.1	17 38.8	3 39.9	28 13.6	1 2.7
26 S	2 15 2.5	1 58.6	21 57.1	12♍ 0.3	24 22.5	5 52.5	18 35.9	11 56.7	17 36.2	3 40.5	28 13.8	1 2.1
27 M	2 18 59.1	2 58.5	21 53.9	26 43.6	25 36.8	7 6.8	18 56.2	12 5.4	17 33.5	3 41.1	28 14.0	1 1.6
28 T	2 22 55.6	3 58.4	21 50.7	11♎37.5	26 49.6	8 21.1	19 16.0	12 14.2	17 30.7	3 41.8	28 14.1	1 1.0
29 W	2 26 52.2	4 58.4	21 47.6	26 34.7	28 0.6	9 35.4	19 35.3	12 23.2	17 27.8	3 42.6	28 14.2	1 0.4
30 T	2 30 48.8	5 58.4	21 44.4	11♏27.0	29 9.7	10 49.8	19 54.1	12 32.3	17 24.8	3 43.4	28 14.3	0 59.8
31 F	2 34 45.3	6 58.4	21 41.2	26 5.7	0♐16.7	12 4.2	20 12.3	12 41.6	17 21.7	3 44.2	28 14.4	0 59.2
						DECLINATION						
1 W	0 36 28.7	2S51.8	2S40.3	9S14.7	6S55.0	10N29.4	23N30.4	23S23.4	21N14.1	19S57.2	20N 8.6	17N37.1
4 S	0 48 18.4	4 1.7	2 44.0	25 25.4	9 3.1	9 14.5	23 29.3	23 22.6	21 13.7	19 57.5	20 8.0	17 36.8
7 T	1 0 8.0	5 11.1	2 47.8	27 52.3	11 5.7	7 57.1	23 27.6	23 21.6	21 13.3	19 57.7	20 7.5	17 36.6
10 F	1 11 57.7	6 19.9	2 51.6	17 59.5	13 2.3	6 37.5	23 25.4	23 20.4	21 12.7	19 57.8	20 7.0	17 36.4
13 M	1 23 47.3	7 28.0	2 55.3	2 8.6	14 52.3	5 15.9	23 22.9	23 19.1	21 12.2	19 57.8	20 6.6	17 36.1
16 T	1 35 37.0	8 35.1	2 59.1	14N27.5	16 35.1	3 52.7	23 20.2	23 17.6	21 11.5	19 57.7	20 6.2	17 35.9
19 S	1 47 26.6	9 41.1	3 2.9	26 26.5	18 10.0	2 28.2	23 17.3	23 16.0	21 10.8	19 57.5	20 5.9	17 35.7
22 W	1 59 16.3	10 45.9	3 6.6	27 15.6	19 36.4	1 2.6	23 14.5	23 14.2	21 9.9	19 57.2	20 5.6	17 35.5
25 S	2 11 6.0	11 49.3	3 10.4	14 28.8	20 53.5	0S23.7	23 11.8	23 12.2	21 9.1	19 56.8	20 5.5	17 35.3
28 T	2 22 55.6	12 51.0	3 14.2	6S 4.7	22 0.1	1 50.3	23 9.4	23 10.1	21 8.1	19 56.2	20 5.3	17 35.1
31 F	2 34 45.3	13 51.0	3 17.9	23 44.2	22 55.3	3 16.9	23 7.5	23 7.7	21 7.1	19 55.6	20 5.3	17 34.9

NOVEMBER 1913

DAY	EPHEMERIS SIDEREAL TIME	☉	☊	☽	☿	♀	♂	♃	♄	♅	♆	♇
	h m s	° ′	° ′	° ′	° ′	° ′	° ′	° ′	° ′	° ′	° ′	° ′
						LONGITUDE						
1 S	2 38 41.9	7♏58.5	21♓38.0	10♐23.8	1♐21.2	13♎18.7	20♋30.1	12♑50.9	17♊18.5	3♒45.1	28♋14.4	0♋58.6
2 S	2 42 38.4	8 58.5	21 34.9	24 16.4	2 23.2	14 33.2	20 47.3	13 0.4	17R15.3	3 46.1	28R14.4	0R57.9
3 M	2 46 35.0	9 58.7	21 31.7	7♑41.7	3 22.2	15 47.7	21 4.0	13 10.0	17 11.9	3 47.1	28 14.3	0 57.2
4 T	2 50 31.5	10 58.8	21 28.5	20 40.3	4 17.9	17 2.3	21 20.2	13 19.7	17 8.5	3 48.1	28 14.2	0 56.5
5 W	2 54 28.1	11 59.0	21 25.3	3♒15.0	5 9.9	18 16.9	21 35.7	13 29.5	17 5.0	3 49.2	28 14.1	0 55.8
6 T	2 58 24.7	12 59.2	21 22.2	15 30.0	5 57.8	19 31.6	21 50.8	13 39.5	17 1.4	3 50.4	28 13.9	0 55.1
7 F	3 2 21.2	13 59.4	21 19.0	27 30.4	6 41.1	20 46.2	22 5.2	13 49.5	16 57.7	3 51.6	28 13.7	0 54.3
8 S	3 6 17.7	14 59.6	21 15.8	9♓21.5	7 19.3	22 0.9	22 19.0	13 59.7	16 54.0	3 52.8	28 13.5	0 53.5
9 S	3 10 14.3	15 59.9	21 12.6	21 8.6	7 51.7	23 15.7	22 32.3	14 10.0	16 50.2	3 54.1	28 13.3	0 52.7
10 M	3 14 10.9	17 0.2	21 9.4	2♈56.3	8 17.7	24 30.4	22 44.9	14 20.4	16 46.3	3 55.5	28 13.0	0 51.9
11 T	3 18 7.4	18 0.5	21 6.3	14 48.9	8 36.7	25 45.2	22 56.9	14 30.9	16 42.3	3 56.9	28 12.6	0 51.1
12 W	3 22 4.0	19 0.8	21 3.1	26 49.7	8 47.9	27 0.0	23 8.3	14 41.5	16 38.3	3 58.3	28 12.3	0 50.3
13 T	3 26 0.5	20 1.2	20 59.9	9♉1.1	8 50.6	28 14.9	23 19.0	14 52.2	16 34.2	3 59.8	28 11.9	0 49.4
14 F	3 29 57.1	21 1.6	20 56.7	21 24.5	8R44.2	29 29.8	23 29.0	15 3.0	16 30.0	4 1.3	28 11.5	0 48.5
15 S	3 33 53.7	22 2.0	20 53.6	4♊0.7	8 28.0	0♏44.7	23 38.4	15 13.9	16 25.8	4 2.9	28 11.0	0 47.6
16 S	3 37 50.2	23 2.5	20 50.4	16 49.6	8 1.6	1 59.6	23 47.1	15 24.9	16 21.5	4 4.5	28 10.5	0 46.7
17 M	3 41 46.8	24 3.0	20 47.2	29 50.7	7 24.8	3 14.6	23 55.1	15 36.0	16 17.2	4 6.2	28 10.0	0 45.8
18 T	3 45 43.3	25 3.5	20 44.0	13♋3.3	6 37.7	4 29.6	24 2.4	15 47.1	16 12.8	4 7.9	28 9.4	0 44.9
19 W	3 49 39.9	26 4.0	20 40.9	26 27.3	5 40.9	5 44.6	24 9.0	15 58.4	16 8.3	4 9.7	28 8.9	0 43.9
20 T	3 53 36.5	27 4.6	20 37.7	10♌2.3	4 35.1	6 59.6	24 14.8	16 9.8	16 3.8	4 11.5	28 8.2	0 43.0
21 F	3 57 33.0	28 5.2	20 34.5	23 48.8	3 22.1	8 14.7	24 19.9	16 21.3	15 59.3	4 13.3	28 7.6	0 42.0
22 S	4 1 29.5	29 5.8	20 31.3	7♍47.1	2 3.6	9 29.8	24 24.2	16 32.8	15 54.7	4 15.2	28 6.9	0 41.0
23 S	4 5 26.1	0♐6.5	20 28.1	21 57.0	0 42.2	10 44.9	24 27.7	16 44.5	15 50.0	4 17.2	28 6.2	0 40.0
24 M	4 9 22.7	1 7.2	20 25.0	6♎17.7	29♏20.4	12 0.1	24 30.5	16 56.2	15 45.3	4 19.2	28 5.5	0 39.0
25 T	4 13 19.2	2 7.9	20 21.8	20 46.6	28 1.1	13 15.2	24 32.4	17 8.0	15 40.6	4 21.2	28 4.7	0 38.0
26 W	4 17 15.8	3 8.6	20 18.6	5♏19.6	26 46.8	14 30.4	24 33.5	17 19.9	15 35.9	4 23.3	28 3.9	0 36.9
27 T	4 21 12.3	4 9.4	20 15.4	19 51.0	25 39.9	15 45.6	24 33.8	17 31.9	15 31.1	4 25.4	28 3.0	0 35.9
28 F	4 25 8.9	5 10.1	20 12.3	4♐13.9	24 42.2	17 0.8	24R33.3	17 43.9	15 26.3	4 27.6	28 2.2	0 34.8
29 S	4 29 5.5	6 11.0	20 9.1	18 21.9	23 55.0	18 16.0	24 32.0	17 56.1	15 21.4	4 29.8	28 1.3	0 33.7
30 S	4 33 2.0	7 11.8	20 5.9	2♑9.6	23 19.1	19 31.3	24 29.8	18 8.3	15 16.6	4 32.0	28 0.4	0 32.7
						DECLINATION						
1 S	2 38 41.9	14S10.5	3S19.2	26S59.0	23S10.8	3S45.7	23N 7.0	23S 6.9	21N 6.8	19S55.4	20N 5.3	17N34.9
4 T	2 50 31.5	15 7.8	3 22.9	26 22.0	23 48.3	5 11.9	23 5.9	23 4.2	21 5.7	19 54.6	20 5.3	17 34.7
7 F	3 2 21.2	16 2.8	3 26.7	14 25.3	24 10.2	6 37.2	23 5.5	23 1.4	21 4.6	19 53.7	20 5.4	17 34.6
10 M	3 14 10.9	16 55.4	3 30.5	1N59.4	24 13.9	8 1.4	23 6.0	22 58.3	21 3.4	19 52.7	20 5.5	17 34.5
13 T	3 26 0.5	17 45.4	3 34.2	17 59.8	23 55.8	9 24.2	23 7.5	22 55.0	21 2.1	19 51.6	20 5.7	17 34.3
16 S	3 37 50.2	18 32.6	3 38.0	27 48.8	23 11.4	10 45.2	23 10.2	22 51.5	21 0.9	19 50.4	20 6.0	17 34.3
19 W	3 49 39.9	19 16.9	3 41.7	24 57.9	21 57.4	12 3.9	23 14.1	22 47.8	20 59.5	19 49.1	20 6.3	17 34.2
22 S	4 1 29.5	19 58.1	3 45.5	9 47.0	20 17.5	13 20.2	23 19.4	22 43.8	20 58.2	19 47.7	20 6.7	17 34.1
25 T	4 13 19.2	20 36.0	3 49.2	10S24.2	18 28.7	14 33.6	23 26.0	22 39.6	20 56.8	19 46.2	20 7.1	17 34.1
28 F	4 25 8.9	21 10.4	3 53.0	25 43.4	16 57.8	15 43.7	23 34.2	22 35.2	20 55.4	19 44.7	20 7.6	17 34.1

DECEMBER 1913

DAY	EPHEMERIS SIDEREAL TIME	☉	☊	☽	☿	♀	♂	♃	♄	♅	♆	♇
						LONGITUDE						
1 M	4 36 58.6	8♐12.6	20♓2.7	15♑33.8	22♏54.7	20♏46.5	24♋26.8	18♑20.6	15♊11.7	4♒34.3	27♋59.4	0♋31.6
2 T	4 40 55.1	9 13.5	19 59.6	28 33.5	22R41.8	22 1.8	24R22.9	18 32.9	15R 6.8	4 36.6	27R58.4	0R30.4
3 W	4 44 51.7	10 14.4	19 56.4	11♒10.2	22 39.8	23 17.1	24 18.1	18 45.4	15 1.8	4 38.9	27 57.4	0 29.3
4 T	4 48 48.3	11 15.3	19 53.2	23 27.2	22D48.2	24 32.4	24 12.6	18 57.9	14 56.9	4 41.3	27 56.4	0 28.2
5 F	4 52 44.8	12 16.2	19 50.0	5♓28.9	23 6.2	25 47.7	24 6.1	19 10.4	14 52.0	4 43.8	27 55.4	0 27.1
6 S	4 56 41.4	13 17.1	19 46.9	17 20.7	23 32.8	27 3.0	23 58.8	19 23.1	14 47.0	4 46.2	27 54.3	0 26.0
7 S	5 0 37.9	14 18.0	19 43.7	29 8.2	24 7.3	28 18.3	23 50.7	19 35.8	14 42.1	4 48.8	27 53.2	0 24.8
8 M	5 4 34.5	15 18.9	19 40.5	10♈56.9	24 48.8	29 33.6	23 41.7	19 48.6	14 37.1	4 51.3	27 52.0	0 23.7
9 T	5 8 31.1	16 19.9	19 37.3	22 52.1	25 36.5	0♐49.0	23 31.9	20 1.4	14 32.2	4 53.9	27 50.9	0 22.5
10 W	5 12 27.6	17 20.9	19 34.1	4♉58.1	26 29.6	2 4.3	23 21.3	20 14.3	14 27.2	4 56.5	27 49.7	0 21.3
11 T	5 16 24.2	18 21.8	19 31.0	17 18.4	27 27.5	3 19.7	23 9.8	20 27.2	14 22.3	4 59.1	27 48.4	0 20.2
12 F	5 20 20.7	19 22.8	19 27.8	29 55.2	28 29.6	4 35.0	22 57.5	20 40.2	14 17.4	5 1.8	27 47.2	0 19.0
13 S	5 24 17.3	20 23.8	19 24.6	12♊49.2	29 35.4	5 50.4	22 44.4	20 53.3	14 12.5	5 4.6	27 46.0	0 17.8
14 S	5 28 13.9	21 24.8	19 21.4	25 59.8	0♐44.4	7 5.8	22 30.5	21 6.4	14 7.6	5 7.3	27 44.7	0 16.6
15 M	5 32 10.4	22 25.9	19 18.3	9♋25.1	1 56.1	8 21.2	22 15.8	21 19.6	14 2.7	5 10.1	27 43.4	0 15.5
16 T	5 36 6.9	23 26.9	19 15.1	23 2.4	3 10.3	9 36.5	22 0.4	21 32.8	13 57.8	5 12.9	27 42.1	0 14.3
17 W	5 40 3.5	24 27.9	19 11.9	6♌48.9	4 26.5	10 52.0	21 44.2	21 46.0	13 53.0	5 15.7	27 40.7	0 13.1
18 T	5 44 0.1	25 29.0	19 8.7	20 41.9	5 44.7	12 7.4	21 27.3	21 59.4	13 48.2	5 18.6	27 39.3	0 11.9
19 F	5 47 56.7	26 30.1	19 5.6	4♍39.6	7 4.4	13 22.8	21 9.7	22 12.7	13 43.4	5 21.5	27 38.0	0 10.7
20 S	5 51 53.2	27 31.2	19 2.4	18 40.7	8 25.5	14 38.2	20 51.4	22 26.1	13 38.7	5 24.4	27 36.6	0 9.5
21 S	5 55 49.7	28 32.3	18 59.2	2♎44.7	9 47.9	15 53.6	20 32.4	22 39.6	13 34.0	5 27.4	27 35.1	0 8.3
22 M	5 59 46.3	29 33.4	18 56.0	16 50.8	11 11.4	17 9.1	20 12.8	22 53.1	13 29.3	5 30.4	27 33.7	0 7.1
23 T	6 3 42.9	0♑34.6	18 52.9	0♏58.2	12 35.9	18 24.5	19 52.6	23 6.7	13 24.7	5 33.4	27 32.2	0 5.9
24 W	6 7 39.4	1 35.7	18 49.7	15 5.1	14 1.2	19 40.0	19 31.9	23 20.2	13 20.1	5 36.4	27 30.7	0 4.7
25 T	6 11 36.0	2 36.8	18 46.5	29 8.5	15 27.2	20 55.4	19 10.6	23 33.9	13 15.6	5 39.5	27 29.2	0 3.5
26 F	6 15 32.6	3 38.0	18 43.3	13♐4.8	16 54.0	22 10.9	18 48.9	23 47.5	13 11.1	5 42.6	27 27.7	0 2.3
27 S	6 19 29.1	4 39.2	18 40.2	26 49.7	18 21.4	23 26.4	18 26.7	24 1.3	13 6.7	5 45.7	27 26.2	0 1.1
28 S	6 23 25.7	5 40.4	18 37.0	10♑19.4	19 49.4	24 41.8	18 4.2	24 15.0	13 2.3	5 48.9	27 24.7	29♊59.9
29 M	6 27 22.2	6 41.5	18 33.8	23 31.0	21 17.9	25 57.3	17 41.2	24 28.8	12 58.0	5 52.0	27 23.1	29 58.7
30 T	6 31 18.8	7 42.7	18 30.6	6♒23.2	22 46.9	27 12.7	17 18.0	24 42.6	12 53.7	5 55.2	27 21.5	29 57.5
31 W	6 35 15.3	8 43.9	18 27.4	18 56.1	24 16.4	28 28.2	16 54.6	24 56.4	12 49.5	5 58.4	27 20.0	29 56.3
						DECLINATION						
1 M	4 36 58.6	21S41.3	3S56.7	27S 4.2	16S 5.1	16S50.2	23N43.8	22S30.5	20N54.0	19S43.0	20N 8.1	17N34.1
4 T	4 48 48.3	22 8.4	4 0.4	15 51.8	15 54.2	17 52.7	23 54.9	22 25.5	20 52.6	19 41.2	20 8.7	17 34.1
7 S	5 0 37.9	22 31.7	4 4.2	0N22.4	16 17.4	18 50.9	24 7.3	22 20.3	20 51.2	19 39.4	20 9.4	17 34.1
10 W	5 12 27.6	22 51.0	4 7.9	16 31.6	17 3.3	19 44.4	24 20.9	22 14.9	20 49.8	19 37.5	20 10.1	17 34.2
13 S	5 24 17.3	23 6.3	4 11.7	27 16.2	18 2.0	20 33.0	24 35.6	22 9.2	20 48.4	19 35.5	20 10.8	17 34.3
16 T	5 36 6.9	23 17.4	4 15.4	25 34.3	19 6.1	21 16.3	24 51.0	22 3.3	20 47.0	19 33.4	20 11.6	17 34.4
19 F	5 47 56.7	23 24.4	4 19.1	10 56.4	20 10.3	21 54.0	25 7.0	21 57.1	20 45.7	19 31.2	20 12.4	17 34.5
22 M	5 59 46.3	23 27.1	4 22.9	8S49.9	21 11.0	22 25.8	25 23.1	21 50.7	20 44.4	19 29.0	20 13.3	17 34.6
25 T	6 11 36.0	23 25.6	4 26.6	24 36.4	22 5.8	22 51.7	25 39.2	21 44.0	20 43.2	19 26.8	20 14.1	17 34.8
28 S	6 23 25.7	23 19.9	4 30.3	27 40.5	22 52.8	23 11.3	25 54.6	21 37.1	20 42.0	19 24.4	20 15.0	17 35.0
31 W	6 35 15.3	23 9.9	4 34.1	17 26.3	23 30.8	23 24.5	26 9.3	21 29.9	20 40.9	19 22.0	20 16.0	17 35.2

JANUARY 1914

DAY	EPHEMERIS SIDEREAL TIME	☉	☊	☽	☿	♀	♂	♃	♄	♅	♆	♇
	h m s	° ′	° ′	° ′	° ′	° ′	° ′	° ′	° ′	° ′	° ′	° ′
						LONGITUDE						
1 T	6 39 11.9	9 ♑ 45.1	18 ♓ 24.3	1 ♓ 11.9	25 ♐ 46.3	29 ♐ 43.7	16 ♋ 30.9	25 ♑ 10.3	12 ♊ 45.4	6 ♒ 1.6	27 ♋ 18.4	29 ♊ 55.1
2 F	6 43 8.5	10 46.3	18 21.1	13 13.7	27 16.6	0 ♑ 59.1	16 R 7.1	25 24.2	12 R 41.3	6 4.9	27 R 16.8	29 R 54.0
3 S	6 47 5.0	11 47.4	18 17.9	25 5.9	28 47.4	2 14.6	15 43.1	25 38.1	12 37.3	6 8.2	27 15.1	29 52.8
4 S	6 51 1.6	12 48.6	18 14.7	6 ♈ 53.8	0 ♑ 18.5	3 30.1	15 19.1	25 52.0	12 33.3	6 11.4	27 13.5	29 51.6
5 M	6 54 58.1	13 49.7	18 11.6	18 42.8	1 50.1	4 45.5	14 55.2	26 6.0	12 29.5	6 14.7	27 11.9	29 50.4
6 T	6 58 54.7	14 50.9	18 8.4	0 ♉ 38.3	3 22.0	6 1.0	14 31.2	26 20.0	12 25.7	6 18.1	27 10.2	29 49.3
7 W	7 2 51.3	15 52.1	18 5.2	12 45.6	4 54.4	7 16.4	14 7.4	26 34.0	12 22.0	6 21.4	27 8.6	29 48.1
8 T	7 6 47.8	16 53.2	18 2.0	25 9.2	6 27.2	8 31.9	13 43.7	26 48.0	12 18.4	6 24.8	27 6.9	29 47.0
9 F	7 10 44.4	17 54.3	17 58.9	7 ♊ 52.6	8 0.3	9 47.3	13 20.2	27 2.1	12 14.8	6 28.1	27 5.3	29 45.8
10 S	7 14 40.9	18 55.5	17 55.7	20 57.6	9 34.0	11 2.7	12 56.9	27 16.1	12 11.4	6 31.5	27 3.6	29 44.7
11 S	7 18 37.5	19 56.6	17 52.5	4 ♋ 24.3	11 8.0	12 18.2	12 33.9	27 30.2	12 8.0	6 34.9	27 1.9	29 43.6
12 M	7 22 34.0	20 57.7	17 49.3	18 10.8	12 42.5	13 33.6	12 11.2	27 44.3	12 4.7	6 38.3	27 0.2	29 42.5
13 T	7 26 30.6	21 58.8	17 46.2	2 ♌ 13.6	14 17.4	14 49.0	11 48.9	27 58.4	12 1.5	6 41.7	26 58.5	29 41.4
14 W	7 30 27.2	22 59.9	17 43.0	16 27.7	15 52.8	16 4.4	11 27.0	28 12.5	11 58.4	6 45.2	26 56.9	29 40.3
15 T	7 34 23.7	24 1.0	17 39.8	0 ♍ 48.0	17 28.7	17 19.9	11 5.5	28 26.6	11 55.4	6 48.6	26 55.2	29 39.2
16 F	7 38 20.3	25 2.1	17 36.6	15 9.6	19 5.1	18 35.3	10 44.5	28 40.8	11 52.4	6 52.0	26 53.5	29 38.1
17 S	7 42 16.8	26 3.2	17 33.4	29 28.6	20 42.0	19 50.7	10 24.0	28 54.9	11 49.6	6 55.5	26 51.8	29 37.1
18 S	7 46 13.4	27 4.3	17 30.3	13 ♎ 42.3	22 19.4	21 6.1	10 4.0	29 9.0	11 46.9	6 59.0	26 50.1	29 36.0
19 M	7 50 10.0	28 5.4	17 27.1	27 48.8	23 57.4	22 21.5	9 44.6	29 23.2	11 44.2	7 2.4	26 48.4	29 35.0
20 T	7 54 6.5	29 6.4	17 23.9	11 ♏ 47.4	25 35.9	23 37.0	9 25.9	29 37.4	11 41.7	7 5.9	26 46.7	29 34.0
21 W	7 58 3.1	0 ♒ 7.5	17 20.7	25 37.1	27 15.0	24 52.4	9 7.7	29 51.5	11 39.2	7 9.4	26 45.0	29 32.9
22 T	8 1 59.6	1 8.6	17 17.6	9 ♐ 17.2	28 54.7	26 7.8	8 50.2	0 ♒ 5.7	11 36.9	7 12.9	26 43.3	29 31.9
23 F	8 5 56.2	2 9.6	17 14.4	22 46.9	0 ♒ 35.0	27 23.2	8 33.4	0 19.8	11 34.6	7 16.4	26 41.6	29 30.9
24 S	8 9 52.7	3 10.7	17 11.2	6 ♑ 4.8	2 15.9	28 38.6	8 17.3	0 34.0	11 32.5	7 19.9	26 39.9	29 30.0
25 S	8 13 49.3	4 11.7	17 8.0	19 9.7	3 57.4	29 54.0	8 2.0	0 48.2	11 30.5	7 23.4	26 38.2	29 29.0
26 M	8 17 45.9	5 12.7	17 4.9	2 ♒ 0.7	5 39.6	1 ♒ 9.4	7 47.3	1 2.3	11 28.6	7 26.9	26 36.6	29 28.1
27 T	8 21 42.4	6 13.7	17 1.7	14 37.1	7 22.3	2 24.7	7 33.5	1 16.5	11 26.7	7 30.4	26 34.9	29 27.1
28 W	8 25 39.0	7 14.7	16 58.5	26 59.4	9 5.7	3 40.1	7 20.4	1 30.6	11 25.0	7 34.0	26 33.2	29 26.2
29 T	8 29 35.5	8 15.7	16 55.3	9 ♓ 8.8	10 49.7	4 55.5	7 8.1	1 44.7	11 23.4	7 37.5	26 31.6	29 25.3
30 F	8 33 32.1	9 16.6	16 52.2	21 7.6	12 34.2	6 10.8	6 56.6	1 58.9	11 21.9	7 41.0	26 29.9	29 24.4
31 S	8 37 28.6	10 17.6	16 49.0	2 ♈ 58.8	14 19.4	7 26.2	6 45.9	2 13.0	11 20.5	7 44.5	26 28.3	29 23.5
						DECLINATION						
1 T	6 39 11.9	23 S 5.7	4 S 35.3	12 S 21.8	23 S 41.2	23 S 27.4	26 N 13.9	21 S 27.5	20 N 40.6	19 S 21.2	20 N 16.3	17 N 35.3
4 S	6 51 1.6	22 50.1	4 39.0	4 N 19.4	24 5.6	23 32.0	26 26.9	21 20.0	20 39.6	19 18.8	20 17.3	17 35.5
7 W	7 2 51.3	22 30.5	4 42.8	19 40.8	24 19.0	23 30.0	26 38.3	21 12.4	20 38.7	19 16.3	20 18.2	17 35.8
10 S	7 14 40.9	22 6.9	4 46.5	28 11.9	24 20.6	23 21.4	26 48.0	21 4.5	20 38.0	19 13.7	20 19.2	17 36.0
13 T	7 26 30.6	21 39.5	4 50.2	23 7.6	24 .0.0	23 6.4	26 56.0	20 56.4	20 37.3	19 11.1	20 20.2	17 36.3
16 F	7 38 20.3	21 8.2	4 53.9	5 55.4	23 46.7	22 44.9	27 2.2	20 48.1	20 36.8	19 8.5	20 21.2	17 36.6
19 M	7 50 10.0	20 33.3	4 57.6	13 S 54.2	23 10.4	22 17.1	27 6.6	20 39.6	20 36.3	19 5.9	20 22.2	17 37.0
22 T	8 1 59.6	19 54.9	5 1.4	26 54.2	22 20.6	21 43.3	27 9.5	20 30.9	20 36.0	19 3.2	20 23.3	17 37.3
25 S	8 13 49.3	19 13.2	5 5.1	26 20.0	21 17.1	21 3.5	27 10.9	20 22.0	20 35.9	19 0.6	20 24.3	17 37.7
28 W	8 25 39.0	18 28.3	5 8.8	14 3.3	19 59.8	20 18.1	27 11.0	20 13.0	20 35.8	18 57.9	20 25.2	17 38.1
31 S	8 37 28.6	17 40.3	5 12.5	2 N 38.7	18 28.7	19 27.3	27 !0.0	20 3.8	20 35.9	18 55.2	20 26.2	17 38.5

FEBRUARY 1914

DAY	EPHEMERIS SIDEREAL TIME	☉	☊	☽	☿	♀	♂	♃	♄	♅	♆	♇
						LONGITUDE						
1 S	8 41 25.2	11 ♒ 18.5	16 ♓ 45.8	14 ♈ 46.5	16 ♒ 5.1	8 ♒ 41.5	6 ♋ 36.1	2 ♒ 27.1	11 ♊ 19.3	7 ♒ 48.0	26 ♋ 26.6	29 ♊ 22.7
2 M	8 45 21.8	12 19.4	16 42.6	26 35.1	17 51.3	9 56.9	6 R 27.0	2 41.2	11 R 18.1	7 51.5	26 R 25.0	29 R 21.8
3 T	8 49 18.3	13 20.3	16 39.4	8 ♉ 29.6	19 38.0	11 12.2	6 18.7	2 55.2	11 17.1	7 55.0	26 23.4	29 21.0
4 W	8 53 14.9	14 21.1	16 36.3	20 35.2	21 25.0	12 27.5	6 11.3	3 9.3	11 16.1	7 58.5	26 21.8	29 20.2
5 T	8 57 11.4	15 21.9	16 33.1	2 ♊ 56.8	23 12.3	13 42.8	6 4.7	3 23.3	11 15.3	8 2.0	26 20.2	29 19.4
6 F	9 1 8.0	16 22.7	16 29.9	15 38.8	24 59.9	14 58.0	5 58.9	3 37.3	11 14.6	8 5.5	26 18.6	29 18.6
7 S	9 5 4.5	17 23.5	16 26.7	28 44.5	26 47.5	16 13.3	5 53.8	3 51.3	11 14.0	8 9.0	26 17.1	29 17.9
8 S	9 9 1.1	18 24.3	16 23.6	12 ♋ 15.5	28 35.1	17 28.6	5 49.6	4 5.3	11 13.5	8 12.4	26 15.5	29 17.1
9 M	9 12 57.7	19 25.0	16 20.4	26 11.5	0 ♓ 22.3	18 43.8	5 46.2	4 19.2	11 13.1	8 15.9	26 14.0	29 16.4
10 T	9 16 54.2	20 25.7	16 17.2	10 ♌ 29.9	2 9.1	19 59.0	5 43.6	4 33.1	11 12.9	8 19.4	26 12.5	29 15.7
11 W	9 20 50.7	21 26.4	16 14.0	25 5.5	3 55.2	21 14.3	5 41.7	4 47.0	11 12.7	8 22.8	26 11.0	29 15.0
12 T	9 24 47.3	22 27.0	16 10.8	9 ♍ 51.7	5 40.2	22 29.5	5 40.6	5 0.9	11 12.7	8 26.2	26 9.5	29 14.4
13 F	9 28 43.9	23 27.7	16 7.7	24 41.1	7 23.9	23 44.7	5 40.2	5 14.7	11 D 12.7	8 29.7	26 8.0	29 13.7
14 S	9 32 40.4	24 28.3	16 4.5	9 ♎ 26.6	9 5.8	24 59.9	5 D 40.6	5 28.5	11 12.9	8 33.1	26 6.6	29 13.1
15 S	9 36 37.0	25 28.9	16 1.3	24 2.2	10 45.5	26 15.0	5 41.7	5 42.3	11 13.2	8 36.5	26 5.1	29 12.5
16 M	9 40 33.5	26 29.4	15 58.1	8 ♏ 23.5	12 22.5	27 30.2	5 43.6	5 56.0	11 13.7	8 39.9	26 3.7	29 11.9
17 T	9 44 30.1	27 30.0	15 55.0	22 27.9	13 56.3	28 45.4	5 46.2	6 9.7	11 14.2	8 43.2	26 2.3	29 11.4
18 W	9 48 26.7	28 30.5	15 51.8	6 ♐ 14.6	15 26.3	0 ♓ 0.5	5 49.4	6 23.4	11 14.8	8 46.6	26 0.9	29 10.8
19 T	9 52 23.2	29 31.0	15 48.6	19 43.6	16 51.9	1 15.6	5 53.4	6 37.1	11 15.6	8 49.9	25 59.5	29 10.3
20 F	9 56 19.8	0 ♓ 31.5	15 45.4	2 ♑ 55.9	18 12.4	2 30.8	5 58.0	6 50.7	11 16.5	8 53.3	25 58.2	29 9.8
21 S	10 0 16.3	1 32.0	15 42.3	15 52.7	19 27.2	3 45.9	6 3.4	7 4.2	11 17.5	8 56.6	25 56.9	29 9.3
22 S	10 4 12.9	2 32.4	15 39.1	28 35.4	20 35.6	5 1.0	6 9.3	7 17.7	11 18.6	8 59.9	25 55.6	29 8.9
23 M	10 8 9.4	3 32.9	15 35.9	11 ♒ 5.3	21 37.0	6 16.1	6 16.0	7 31.2	11 19.8	9 3.2	25 54.3	29 8.4
24 T	10 12 6.0	4 33.3	15 32.7	23 23.8	22 30.7	7 31.1	6 23.3	7 44.7	11 21.1	9 6.4	25 53.1	29 8.0
25 W	10 16 2.5	5 33.6	15 29.5	5 ♓ 32.3	23 16.1	8 46.2	6 31.2	7 58.0	11 22.5	9 9.6	25 51.8	29 7.6
26 T	10 19 59.1	6 34.0	15 26.4	17 32.4	23 52.9	10 1.2	6 39.7	8 11.4	11 24.1	9 12.9	25 50.6	29 7.2
27 F	10 23 55.7	7 34.3	15 23.2	29 26.0	24 20.5	11 16.2	6 48.9	8 24.7	11 25.7	9 16.1	25 49.4	29 6.9
28 S	10 27 52.2	8 34.6	15 20.0	11 ♈ 15.2	24 38.8	12 31.2	6 58.6	8 37.9	11 27.5	9 19.3	25 48.3	29 6.6
						DECLINATION						
1 S	8 41 25.2	17 S 23.7	5 S 13.7	8 N 11.9	17 S 55.3	19 S 9.2	27 N 9.4	20 S 0.7	20 N 36.0	18 S 54.3	20 N 26.6	17 N 38.6
4 W	8 53 14.9	16 32.1	5 17.4	22 28.9	16 6.1	18 11.7	27 7.1	19 51.3	20 36.3	18 51.6	20 27.5	17 39.0
7 S	9 5 4.5	15 37.8	5 21.1	28 31.8	14 4.5	17 9.6	27 4.1	19 41.8	20 36.7	18 48.9	20 28.5	17 39.5
10 T	9 16 54.2	14 41.2	5 24.8	20 28.8	11 52.0	16 3.1	27 0.5	19 32.2	20 37.3	18 46.2	20 29.4	17 39.9
13 F	9 28 43.9	13 42.4	5 28.5	1 17.7	9 31.6	14 52.5	26 56.4	19 22.5	20 38.1	18 43.6	20 30.3	17 40.4
16 M	9 40 33.5	12 41.6	5 32.2	18 S 18.8	7 7.9	13 38.4	26 51.8	19 12.7	20 38.9	18 41.0	20 31.1	17 40.9
19 T	9 52 23.2	11 38.9	5 35.9	28 17.5	4 47.9	12 20.8	26 46.9	19 2.8	20 39.9	18 38.3	20 32.0	17 41.4
22 S	10 4 12.9	10 34.5	5 39.6	24 11.7	2 40.4	11 0.3	26 41.6	18 52.8	20 41.1	18 35.8	20 32.7	17 41.9
25 W	10 16 2.5	9 28.7	5 43.3	10 17.1	0 55.8	9 37.2	26 35.9	18 42.8	20 42.3	18 33.2	20 33.5	17 42.4
28 S	10 27 52.2	8 21.5	5 47.0	6 N 37.3	0 N 16.0	8 11.8	26 30.0	18 32.8	20 43.7	18 30.7	20 34.2	17 42.9

MARCH 1914

LONGITUDE

DAY	EPHEMERIS SIDEREAL TIME h m s	☉ ° ′	☊ ° ′	☽ ° ′	☿ ° ′	♀ ° ′	♂ ° ′	♃ ° ′	♄ ° ′	♅ ° ′	♆ ° ′	♇ ° ′
1 S	10 31 48.8	9 ♓ 34.8	15 ♓ 16.8	23 ♈ 2.9	24 ♓ 47.4	13 ♓ 46.2	7 ♋ 8.9	8 ♒ 51.1	11 ♊ 29.3	9 ♒ 22.4	25 ♋ 47.1	29 ♊ 6.3
2 M	10 35 45.3	10 35.0	15 13.7	4 ♉ 52.3	24 R 46.5	15 1.2	7 19.8	9 4.3	11 31.3	9 25.5	25 R 46.0	29 R 6.0
3 T	10 39 41.9	11 35.2	15 10.5	16 47.2	24 36.2	16 16.1	7 31.3	9 17.4	11 33.4	9 28.6	25 44.9	29 5.7
4 W	10 43 38.4	12 35.3	15 7.3	28 51.7	24 16.8	17 31.1	7 43.3	9 30.4	11 35.6	9 31.7	25 43.9	29 5.5
5 T	10 47 35.0	13 35.4	15 4.1	11 ♊ 10.2	23 48.9	18 46.0	7 55.8	9 43.4	11 37.9	9 34.8	25 42.9	29 5.3
6 F	10 51 31.5	14 35.5	15 0.9	23 47.2	23 13.1	20 0.9	8 8.9	9 56.3	11 40.3	9 37.8	25 41.9	29 5.1
7 S	10 55 28.1	15 35.6	14 57.8	6 ♋ 46.7	22 30.4	21 15.7	8 22.4	10 9.1	11 42.9	9 40.8	25 40.9	29 4.9
8 S	10 59 24.6	16 35.6	14 54.6	20 11.6	21 42.0	22 30.6	8 36.5	10 21.9	11 45.5	9 43.8	25 39.9	29 4.8
9 M	11 3 21.2	17 35.5	14 51.4	4 ♌ 3.6	20 48.8	23 45.4	8 51.0	10 34.7	11 48.2	9 46.8	25 39.0	29 4.6
10 T	11 7 17.7	18 35.5	14 48.2	18 22.1	19 52.4	25 0.2	9 6.0	10 47.3	11 51.0	9 49.7	25 38.1	29 4.5
11 W	11 11 14.3	19 35.3	14 45.1	3 ♍ 3.8	18 54.0	26 15.0	9 21.5	10 59.9	11 54.0	9 52.6	25 37.3	29 4.5
12 T	11 15 10.8	20 35.2	14 41.9	18 3.0	17 54.9	27 29.7	9 37.4	11 12.5	11 57.0	9 55.5	25 36.4	29 4.4
13 F	11 19 7.4	21 35.0	14 38.7	3 ♎ 11.4	16 56.6	28 44.5	9 53.8	11 25.0	12 0.1	9 58.3	25 35.6	29 4.4
14 S	11 23 4.0	22 34.8	14 35.5	18 19.7	16 0.2	29 59.2	10 10.6	11 37.4	12 3.3	10 1.1	25 34.9	29 4.4
15 S	11 27 0.5	23 34.6	14 32.3	3 ♏ 18.8	15 6.7	1 ♈ 13.9	10 27.8	11 49.7	12 6.7	10 3.9	25 34.1	29 D 4.4
16 M	11 30 57.0	24 34.3	14 29.2	18 1.1	14 17.2	2 28.6	10 45.4	12 2.0	12 10.1	10 6.6	25 33.4	29 4.4
17 T	11 34 53.6	25 34.1	14 26.0	2 ♐ 21.3	13 32.3	3 43.2	11 3.4	12 14.2	12 13.6	10 9.4	25 32.7	29 4.5
18 W	11 38 50.2	26 33.7	14 22.8	16 16.7	12 52.7	4 57.9	11 21.8	12 26.3	12 17.2	10 12.0	25 32.1	29 4.6
19 T	11 42 46.7	27 33.4	14 19.6	29 47.1	12 18.8	6 12.5	11 40.6	12 38.3	12 20.9	10 14.7	25 31.5	29 4.7
20 F	11 46 43.3	28 33.0	14 16.5	12 ♑ 54.2	11 50.9	7 27.1	11 59.8	12 50.3	12 24.7	10 17.3	25 30.9	29 4.8
21 S	11 50 39.8	29 32.6	14 13.3	25 40.6	11 29.1	8 41.6	12 19.3	13 2.2	12 28.6	10 19.9	25 30.3	29 4.9
22 S	11 54 36.4	0 ♈ 32.2	14 10.1	8 ♒ 9.7	11 13.5	9 56.2	12 39.2	13 14.0	12 32.6	10 22.4	25 29.8	29 5.1
23 M	11 58 32.9	1 31.7	14 6.9	20 24.9	11 4.0	11 10.7	12 59.5	13 25.7	12 36.7	10 25.0	25 29.3	29 5.3
24 T	12 2 29.5	2 31.2	14 3.8	2 ♓ 29.5	11 0.5	12 25.3	13 20.1	13 37.3	12 40.9	10 27.4	25 28.8	29 5.5
25 W	12 6 26.0	3 30.7	14 0.6	14 26.5	11 D 2.8	13 39.7	13 41.0	13 48.9	12 45.1	10 29.9	25 28.4	29 5.8
26 T	12 10 22.6	4 30.1	13 57.4	26 18.4	11 10.8	14 54.2	14 2.3	14 0.3	12 49.5	10 32.3	25 28.0	29 6.1
27 F	12 14 19.2	5 29.5	13 54.2	8 ♈ 7.4	11 24.1	16 8.7	14 23.9	14 11.7	12 53.9	10 34.7	25 27.6	29 6.3
28 S	12 18 15.7	6 28.9	13 51.0	19 55.7	11 42.6	17 23.1	14 45.8	14 23.0	12 58.5	10 37.0	25 27.3	29 6.7
29 S	12 22 12.3	7 28.2	13 47.9	1 ♉ 45.2	12 6.0	18 37.5	15 8.0	14 34.2	13 3.1	10 39.3	25 27.0	29 7.0
30 M	12 26 8.8	8 27.5	13 44.7	13 38.3	12 34.0	19 51.9	15 30.5	14 45.3	13 7.8	10 41.5	25 26.7	29 7.3
31 T	12 30 5.4	9 26.8	13 41.5	25 37.2	13 6.4	21 6.2	15 53.3	14 56.3	13 12.5	10 43.7	25 26.5	29 7.7

DECLINATION

DAY	EPHEMERIS SIDEREAL TIME h m s	☉ ° ′	☊ ° ′	☽ ° ′	☿ ° ′	♀ ° ′	♂ ° ′	♃ ° ′	♄ ° ′	♅ ° ′	♆ ° ′	♇ ° ′
1 S	10 31 48.8	7 S 58.9	5 S 48.2	12 N 0.3	0 N 31.2	7 S 42.9	26 N 27.9	18 S 29.5	20 N 44.2	18 S 29.9	20 N 34.5	17 N 43.1
4 W	10 43 38.4	6 50.4	5 51.9	24 52.8	0 48.0	6 14.9	26 21.4	18 19.4	20 45.8	18 27.5	20 35.1	17 43.6
7 S	10 55 28.1	5 41.0	5 55.6	28 11.4	0 21.9	4 45.5	26 14.5	18 9.4	20 47.5	18 25.1	20 35.7	17 44.1
10 T	11 7 17.7	4 30.9	5 59.3	17 35.3	0 S 40.7	3 15.0	26 7.2	17 59.5	20 49.3	18 22.8	20 36.3	17 44.7
13 F	11 19 7.4	3 20.4	6 3.0	2 S 47.6	2 6.3	1 43.6	25 59.4	17 49.5	20 51.2	18 20.6	20 36.8	17 45.2
16 M	11 30 57.0	2 9.5	6 6.7	21 44.1	3 38.1	0 11.8	25 51.1	17 39.7	20 53.1	18 18.4	20 37.3	17 45.8
19 T	11 42 46.7	0 58.3	6 10.3	28 33.7	5 2.0	1 N 20.3	25 42.2	17 29.9	20 55.2	18 16.3	20 37.8	17 46.3
22 S	11 54 36.4	0 N 12.8	6 14.0	21 17.5	6 8.7	2 52.1	25 32.7	17 20.2	20 57.4	18 14.3	20 38.1	17 46.8
25 W	12 6 26.0	1 23.8	6 17.7	6 10.3	6 54.0	4 23.5	25 22.6	17 10.6	20 59.6	18 12.3	20 38.5	17 47.4
28 S	12 18 15.7	2 34.5	6 21.3	10 N 35.4	7 17.3	5 54.0	25 11.8	17 1.2	21 1.9	18 10.5	20 38.7	17 47.9
31 T	12 30 5.4	3 44.7	6 25.0	23 58.6	7 19.5	7 23.4	25 0.2	16 51.9	21 4.3	18 8.7	20 38.9	17 48.5

APRIL 1914

LONGITUDE

DAY	EPHEMERIS SIDEREAL TIME h m s	☉ ° ′	☊ ° ′	☽ ° ′	☿ ° ′	♀ ° ′	♂ ° ′	♃ ° ′	♄ ° ′	♅ ° ′	♆ ° ′	♇ ° ′
1 W	12 34 1.9	10 ♈ 26.0	13 ♓ 38.3	7 ♊ 44.9	13 ♓ 42.9	22 ♈ 20.5	16 ♋ 16.4	15 ♒ 7.2	13 ♊ 17.4	10 ♒ 45.9	25 ♋ 26.3	29 ♊ 8.1
2 T	12 37 58.5	11 25.2	13 35.2	20 4.4	14 23.4	23 34.8	16 39.8	15 18.0	13 22.3	10 48.1	25 R 26.1	29 8.6
3 F	12 41 55.0	12 24.4	13 32.0	2 ♋ 39.2	15 7.6	24 49.1	17 3.5	15 28.7	13 27.4	10 50.1	25 26.0	29 9.0
4 S	12 45 51.6	13 23.5	13 28.8	15 33.0	15 55.3	26 3.3	17 27.4	15 39.3	13 32.5	10 52.2	25 25.9	29 9.5
5 S	12 49 48.1	14 22.6	13 25.6	28 49.2	16 46.4	27 17.5	17 51.6	15 49.8	13 37.6	10 54.2	25 25.8	29 10.0
6 M	12 53 44.7	15 21.6	13 22.4	12 ♌ 30.5	17 40.6	28 31.7	18 16.0	16 0.2	13 42.9	10 56.2	25 25.8	29 10.5
7 T	12 57 41.3	16 20.6	13 19.3	26 38.0	18 37.7	29 45.9	18 40.7	16 10.5	13 48.2	10 58.1	25 D 25.8	29 11.0
8 W	13 1 37.8	17 19.5	13 16.1	11 ♍ 11.0	19 37.7	0 ♉ 60.0	19 5.6	16 20.7	13 53.6	10 60.0	25 25.8	29 11.6
9 T	13 5 34.3	18 18.5	13 12.9	26 5.8	20 40.5	2 14.1	19 30.8	16 30.8	13 59.1	11 1.8	25 25.9	29 12.1
10 F	13 9 30.9	19 17.4	13 9.7	11 ♎ 15.9	21 45.8	3 28.1	19 56.2	16 40.8	14 4.6	11 3.6	25 26.0	29 12.7
11 S	13 13 27.5	20 16.2	13 6.6	26 32.2	22 53.6	4 42.2	20 21.8	16 50.6	14 10.2	11 5.4	25 26.2	29 13.3
12 S	13 17 24.0	21 15.0	13 3.4	11 ♏ 44.1	24 3.7	5 56.2	20 47.6	17 0.4	14 15.9	11 7.1	25 26.3	29 14.0
13 M	13 21 20.6	22 13.8	13 0.2	26 41.6	25 16.2	7 10.2	21 13.7	17 10.0	14 21.7	11 8.7	25 26.5	29 14.6
14 T	13 25 17.1	23 12.6	12 57.0	11 ♐ 16.8	26 30.9	8 24.1	21 39.9	17 19.5	14 27.5	11 10.4	25 26.8	29 15.3
15 W	13 29 13.7	24 11.3	12 53.8	25 24.6	27 47.6	9 38.0	22 6.4	17 28.9	14 33.3	11 11.9	25 27.0	29 16.0
16 T	13 33 10.2	25 10.0	12 50.7	9 ♑ 3.3	29 6.5	10 51.9	22 33.1	17 38.2	14 39.3	11 13.5	25 27.3	29 16.7
17 F	13 37 6.8	26 8.7	12 47.5	22 14.0	0 ♈ 27.4	12 5.8	22 59.9	17 47.3	14 45.3	11 14.9	25 27.7	29 17.5
18 S	13 41 3.3	27 7.3	12 44.3	4 ♒ 59.7	1 50.2	13 19.7	23 27.0	17 56.4	14 51.4	11 16.4	25 28.0	29 18.2
19 S	13 44 59.9	28 5.9	12 41.1	17 24.6	3 14.9	14 33.5	23 54.2	18 5.3	14 57.5	11 17.8	25 28.4	29 19.0
20 M	13 48 56.5	29 4.5	12 38.0	29 33.6	4 41.5	15 47.3	24 21.7	18 14.1	15 3.7	11 19.1	25 28.9	29 19.8
21 T	13 52 53.0	0 ♉ 3.1	12 34.8	11 ♓ 31.2	6 10.0	17 1.1	24 49.3	18 22.7	15 10.0	11 20.4	25 29.4	29 20.6
22 W	13 56 49.6	1 1.6	12 31.6	23 21.9	7 40.3	18 14.8	25 17.1	18 31.2	15 16.3	11 21.7	25 29.8	29 21.4
23 T	14 0 46.1	2 0.1	12 28.4	5 ♈ 9.4	9 12.4	19 28.5	25 45.1	18 39.6	15 22.6	11 22.9	25 30.4	29 22.3
24 F	14 4 42.7	2 58.6	12 25.2	16 56.9	10 46.3	20 42.2	26 13.3	18 47.9	15 29.1	11 24.0	25 30.9	29 23.2
25 S	14 8 39.2	3 57.0	12 22.1	28 46.8	12 21.9	21 55.9	26 41.6	18 56.0	15 35.6	11 25.1	25 31.6	29 24.1
26 S	14 12 35.8	4 55.4	12 18.9	10 ♉ 41.2	13 59.4	23 9.5	27 10.1	19 4.0	15 42.1	11 26.2	25 32.2	29 25.0
27 M	14 16 32.3	5 53.8	12 15.7	22 41.7	15 38.6	24 23.1	27 38.8	19 11.9	15 48.7	11 27.2	25 32.8	29 25.9
28 T	14 20 28.9	6 52.2	12 12.5	4 ♊ 49.5	17 19.5	25 36.7	28 7.6	19 19.6	15 55.3	11 28.2	25 33.5	29 26.8
29 W	14 24 25.4	7 50.5	12 9.4	17 6.3	19 2.3	26 50.3	28 36.6	19 27.1	16 2.0	11 29.1	25 34.3	29 27.8
30 T	14 28 22.0	8 48.8	12 6.2	29 33.7	20 46.8	28 3.8	29 5.8	19 34.5	16 8.8	11 29.9	25 35.0	29 28.8

DECLINATION

DAY	EPHEMERIS SIDEREAL TIME h m s	☉ ° ′	☊ ° ′	☽ ° ′	☿ ° ′	♀ ° ′	♂ ° ′	♃ ° ′	♄ ° ′	♅ ° ′	♆ ° ′	♇ ° ′
1 W	12 34 1.9	4 N 8.0	6 S 26.2	26 N 44.2	7 S 15.8	7 N 52.9	24 N 56.1	16 S 48.9	21 N 5.1	18 S 8.2	20 N 39.0	17 N 48.7
4 S	12 45 51.6	5 17.3	6 29.9	27 0.1	6 52.6	9 20.1	24 43.5	16 39.8	21 7.5	18 6.5	20 39.2	17 49.2
7 T	12 57 41.3	6 25.8	6 33.5	14 9.7	6 12.2	10 45.5	24 30.0	16 31.0	21 10.0	18 5.0	20 39.2	17 49.7
10 F	13 9 30.9	7 33.3	6 37.2	6 S 36.7	5 16.4	12 8.6	24 15.6	16 22.5	21 12.5	18 3.6	20 39.3	17 50.3
13 M	13 21 20.6	8 39.6	6 40.9	24 13.6	4 6.6	13 29.0	24 0.4	16 14.1	21 15.0	18 2.3	20 39.3	17 50.8
16 T	13 33 10.2	9 44.6	6 44.5	27 50.0	2 43.9	14 46.5	23 44.2	16 6.1	21 17.6	18 1.1	20 39.2	17 51.3
19 S	13 44 59.9	10 48.2	6 48.2	17 50.8	1 9.4	16 0.7	23 27.1	15 58.3	21 20.1	17 60.0	20 39.1	17 51.8
22 W	13 56 49.6	11 50.3	6 51.8	1 52.6	0 N 35.8	17 11.4	23 9.0	15 50.8	21 22.7	17 59.0	20 38.9	17 52.3
25 S	14 8 39.2	12 50.6	6 55.4	14 N 25.2	2 30.7	18 18.0	22 49.9	15 43.7	21 25.2	17 58.2	20 38.6	17 52.8
28 T	14 20 28.9	13 48.9	6 59.1	26 3.6	4 34.3	19 20.4	22 29.9	15 36.9	21 27.8	17 57.4	20 38.3	17 53.2

MAY 1914

DAY	EPHEMERIS SIDEREAL TIME	☉	☊	☽	☿	♀	♂	♃	♄	♅	♆	♇
	h m s	° ′	° ′	° ′	° ′	° ′	° ′	° ′	° ′	° ′	° ′	° ′
						LONGITUDE						
1 F	14 32 18.6	9♉47.0	12♓ 3.0	12♋13.6	22♈33.1	29♉17.3	29♋35.1	19♒41.8	16♊15.6	11♒30.8	25♋35.8	29♊29.7
2 S	14 36 15.1	10 45.2	11 59.8	25 8.6	24 21.2	0♊30.7	0♌ 4.6	19 48.9	16 22.4	11 31.5	25 36.6	29 30.8
3 S	14 40 11.7	11 43.4	11 56.6	8♌21.3	26 11.1	1 44.2	0 34.2	19 55.9	16 29.3	11 32.2	25 37.5	29 31.8
4 M	14 44 8.2	12 41.6	11 53.5	21 54.3	28 2.8	2 57.5	1 3.9	20 2.8	16 36.2	11 32.9	25 38.4	29 32.8
5 T	14 48 4.8	13 39.7	11 50.3	5♍49.5	29 56.2	4 10.9	1 33.8	20 9.4	16 43.2	11 33.5	25 39.3	29 33.9
6 W	14 52 1.3	14 37.8	11 47.1	20 7.6	1♉51.5	5 24.2	2 3.8	20 16.0	16 50.2	11 34.1	25 40.3	29 34.9
7 T	14 55 57.9	15 35.8	11 43.9	4♎47.0	3 48.5	6 37.5	2 33.9	20 22.3	16 57.2	11 34.6	25 41.2	29 36.0
8 F	14 59 54.4	16 33.8	11 40.8	19 43.5	5 47.3	7 50.8	3 4.2	20 28.6	17 4.3	11 35.1	25 42.2	29 37.1
9 S	15 3 51.0	17 31.8	11 37.6	4♏50.0	7 47.8	9 4.0	3 34.6	20 34.6	17 11.5	11 35.5	25 43.3	29 38.3
10 S	15 7 47.6	18 29.8	11 34.4	19 57.3	9 50.0	10 17.2	4 5.1	20 40.5	17 18.6	11 35.9	25 44.3	29 39.4
11 M	15 11 44.1	19 27.7	11 31.2	4♐55.1	11 53.7	11 30.3	4 35.8	20 46.3	17 25.8	11 36.2	25 45.4	29 40.5
12 T	15 15 40.7	20 25.7	11 28.1	19 34.3	13 59.0	12 43.4	5 6.5	20 51.8	17 33.1	11 36.5	25 46.5	29 41.7
13 W	15 19 37.2	21 23.5	11 24.9	3♑48.3	16 5.7	13 56.5	5 37.4	20 57.3	17 40.3	11 36.7	25 47.7	29 42.9
14 T	15 23 33.8	22 21.4	11 21.7	17 33.4	18 13.6	15 9.6	6 8.4	21 2.5	17 47.7	11 36.9	25 48.9	29 44.0
15 F	15 27 30.4	23 19.3	11 18.5	0♒49.6	20 22.7	16 22.6	6 39.6	21 7.6	17 55.0	11 37.0	25 50.1	29 45.2
16 S	15 31 26.9	24 17.1	11 15.3	13 38.9	22 32.7	17 35.6	7 10.8	21 12.6	18 2.4	11 37.1	25 51.3	29 46.4
17 S	15 35 23.4	25 14.9	11 12.2	26 5.6	24 43.4	18 48.6	7 42.1	21 17.3	18 9.8	11 37.1	25 52.6	29 47.7
18 M	15 39 20.0	26 12.7	11 9.0	8♓14.5	26 54.6	20 1.5	8 13.6	21 21.9	18 17.2	11R37.1	25 53.9	29 48.9
19 T	15 43 16.6	27 10.5	11 5.8	20 11.2	29 6.0	21 14.4	8 45.2	21 26.3	18 24.7	11 37.0	25 55.2	29 50.2
20 W	15 47 13.1	28 8.2	11 2.6	2♈ 0.8	1♊17.4	22 27.3	9 16.9	21 30.5	18 32.2	11 36.9	25 56.5	29 51.4
21 T	15 51 9.7	29 5.9	10 59.5	13 48.1	3 28.4	23 40.1	9 48.7	21 34.6	18 39.7	11 36.7	25 57.9	29 52.7
22 F	15 55 6.2	0♊ 3.7	10 56.3	25 37.1	5 38.9	24 52.9	10 20.6	21 38.5	18 47.2	11 36.5	25 59.3	29 54.0
23 S	15 59 2.8	1 1.4	10 53.1	7♉31.2	7 48.5	26 5.7	10 52.6	21 42.2	18 54.8	11 36.2	26 0.7	29 55.2
24 S	16 2 59.4	1 59.0	10 49.9	19 32.7	9 56.9	27 18.4	11 24.7	21 45.7	19 2.4	11 35.9	26 2.2	29 56.5
25 M	16 6 55.9	2 56.7	10 46.8	1♊43.4	12 4.0	28 31.1	11 56.9	21 49.1	19 10.0	11 35.5	26 3.6	29 57.9
26 T	16 10 52.4	3 54.3	10 43.6	14 4.2	14 9.4	29 43.8	12 29.2	21 52.3	19 17.6	11 35.1	26 5.1	29 59.2
27 W	16 14 49.0	4 51.9	10 40.4	26 35.5	16 13.1	0♋56.4	13 1.6	21 55.2	19 25.3	11 34.6	26 6.7	0♋ 0.5
28 T	16 18 45.6	5 49.5	10 37.2	9♋17.8	18 14.7	2 9.1	13 34.1	21 58.1	19 32.9	11 34.1	26 8.2	0 1.8
29 F	16 22 42.1	6 47.1	10 34.1	22 11.3	20 14.1	3 21.6	14 6.7	22 0.7	19 40.6	11 33.6	26 9.8	0 3.2
30 S	16 26 38.7	7 44.6	10 30.9	5♌16.9	22 11.2	4 34.1	14 39.4	22 3.1	19 48.3	11 33.0	26 11.4	0 4.5
31 S	16 30 35.2	8 42.2	10 27.7	18 35.8	24 6.0	5 46.6	15 12.2	22 5.3	19 56.0	11 32.3	26 13.0	0 5.9

						DECLINATION						
1 F	14 32 18.6	14N45.3	7S 2.7	27N19.5	6N45.4	20N18.2	22N 8.8	15S30.6	21N30.3	17S56.8	20N38.0	17N53.7
4 M	14 44 8.2	15 39.4	7 6.4	15 57.3	9 2.7	21 11.1	21 46.7	15 24.6	21 32.9	17 56.3	20 37.6	17 54.1
7 T	14 55 57.9	16 31.2	7 10.0	3S38.2	11 24.3	21 58.7	21 23.6	15 19.0	21 35.3	17 56.0	20 37.1	17 54.6
10 S	15 7 47.6	17 20.5	7 13.6	22 13.5	13 47.6	22 40.9	20 59.5	15 13.8	21 37.8	17 55.7	20 36.6	17 55.0
13 W	15 19 37.2	18 7.2	7 17.2	28 5.6	16 9.1	23 17.4	20 34.3	15 9.1	21 40.2	17 55.6	20 36.1	17 55.4
16 S	15 31 26.9	18 51.2	7 20.9	19 2.6	18 24.4	23 48.0	20 8.2	15 4.9	21 42.6	17 55.6	20 35.5	17 55.8
19 T	15 43 16.6	19 32.3	7 24.5	3 13.3	20 28.1	24 12.4	19 41.0	15 1.1	21 44.9	17 55.7	20 34.8	17 56.1
22 F	15 55 6.2	20 10.5	7 28.1	13N 9.2	22 14.8	24 30.6	19 12.9	14 57.9	21 47.1	17 56.0	20 34.1	17 56.5
25 M	16 6 55.9	20 45.6	7 31.7	25 20.8	23 40.1	24 42.4	18 43.7	14 55.1	21 49.3	17 56.3	20 33.4	17 56.8
28 T	16 18 45.6	21 17.4	7 35.3	27 30.7	24 41.7	24 47.8	18 13.6	14 52.9	21 51.5	17 56.8	20 32.6	17 57.1
31 S	16 30 35.2	21 46.0	7 38.9	17 2.1	25 19.3	24 46.6	17 42.5	14 51.3	21 53.5	17 57.4	20 31.7	17 57.4

JUNE 1914

						LONGITUDE						
1 M	16 34 31.8	9♊39.7	10♓24.5	2♍ 9.4	25♊58.2	6♋59.1	15♌45.1	22♒ 7.4	20♊ 3.8	11♒31.6	26♋14.6	0♋ 7.3
2 T	16 38 28.4	10 37.2	10 21.4	15 59.0	27 47.9	8 11.5	16 18.1	22 9.3	20 11.5	11R30.9	26 16.3	0 8.7
3 W	16 42 24.9	11 34.6	10 18.2	0♎ 5.4	29 34.9	9 23.8	16 51.1	22 11.0	20 19.3	11 30.1	26 18.0	0 10.0
4 T	16 46 21.5	12 32.1	10 15.0	14 28.2	1♋19.2	10 36.2	17 24.3	22 12.5	20 27.0	11 29.2	26 19.7	0 11.4
5 F	16 50 18.0	13 29.5	10 11.8	29 4.8	3 0.9	11 48.4	17 57.5	22 13.8	20 34.8	11 28.4	26 21.4	0 12.8
6 S	16 54 14.6	14 26.9	10 8.6	13♏50.5	4 39.8	13 0.7	18 30.8	22 14.9	20 42.6	11 27.4	26 23.1	0 14.2
7 S	16 58 11.2	15 24.3	10 5.5	28 38.5	6 15.9	14 12.9	19 4.2	22 15.8	20 50.4	11 26.5	26 24.9	0 15.6
8 M	17 2 7.7	16 21.6	10 2.3	13♐20.6	7 49.3	15 25.0	19 37.7	22 16.6	20 58.2	11 25.5	26 26.7	0 17.1
9 T	17 6 4.3	17 19.0	9 59.1	27 48.7	9 19.9	16 37.1	20 11.2	22 17.1	21 6.0	11 24.4	26 28.5	0 18.5
10 W	17 10 0.8	18 16.3	9 55.9	11♑56.3	10 47.6	17 49.2	20 44.9	22 17.5	21 13.8	11 23.3	26 30.3	0 19.9
11 T	17 13 57.4	19 13.7	9 52.8	25 39.0	12 12.4	19 1.2	21 18.6	22 17.6	21 21.6	11 22.2	26 32.2	0 21.3
12 F	17 17 54.0	20 11.0	9 49.6	8♒55.4	13 34.4	20 13.2	21 52.4	22R17.6	21 29.4	11 21.0	26 34.0	0 22.8
13 S	17 21 50.5	21 8.3	9 46.4	21 46.5	14 53.4	21 25.1	22 26.2	22 17.4	21 37.2	11 19.8	26 35.9	0 24.2
14 S	17 25 47.0	22 5.6	9 43.2	4♓15.4	16 9.5	22 37.0	23 0.2	22 17.0	21 45.0	11 18.5	26 37.8	0 25.6
15 M	17 29 43.6	23 2.9	9 40.1	16 26.6	17 22.6	23 48.8	23 34.2	22 16.4	21 52.9	11 17.2	26 39.7	0 27.1
16 T	17 33 40.2	24 0.2	9 36.9	28 25.1	18 32.5	25 0.6	24 8.3	22 15.6	22 0.7	11 15.9	26 41.6	0 28.5
17 W	17 37 36.8	24 57.5	9 33.7	10♈16.3	19 39.4	26 12.4	24 42.5	22 14.6	22 8.5	11 14.5	26 43.6	0 30.0
18 T	17 41 33.3	25 54.8	9 30.5	22 5.5	20 43.0	27 24.1	25 16.7	22 13.5	22 16.3	11 13.0	26 45.5	0 31.4
19 F	17 45 29.8	26 52.0	9 27.3	3♉57.5	21 43.3	28 35.7	25 51.0	22 12.1	22 24.1	11 11.6	26 47.5	0 32.9
20 S	17 49 26.4	27 49.3	9 24.2	15 56.4	22 40.3	29 47.3	26 25.4	22 10.5	22 31.9	11 10.1	26 49.5	0 34.3
21 S	17 53 23.0	28 46.6	9 21.0	28 5.4	23 33.8	0♌58.9	26 59.9	22 8.8	22 39.7	11 8.5	26 51.5	0 35.8
22 M	17 57 19.5	29 43.9	9 17.8	10♊26.7	24 23.8	2 10.4	27 34.5	22 6.8	22 47.5	11 7.0	26 53.5	0 37.2
23 T	18 1 16.1	0♋41.1	9 14.6	23 1.5	25 10.0	3 21.9	28 9.1	22 4.7	22 55.3	11 5.3	26 55.5	0 38.7
24 W	18 5 12.6	1 38.4	9 11.5	5♋49.9	25 52.6	4 33.3	28 43.8	22 2.4	23 3.0	11 3.7	26 57.6	0 40.1
25 T	18 9 9.2	2 35.6	9 8.3	18 51.6	26 31.2	5 44.7	29 18.6	21 59.9	23 10.8	11 2.0	26 59.7	0 41.6
26 F	18 13 5.8	3 32.9	9 5.1	2♌ 5.4	27 5.8	6 56.0	29 53.4	21 57.2	23 18.5	11 0.3	27 1.7	0 43.0
27 S	18 17 2.3	4 30.1	9 1.9	15 30.4	27 36.3	8 7.3	0♍28.3	21 54.3	23 26.3	10 58.6	27 3.8	0 44.5
28 S	18 20 58.9	5 27.3	8 58.8	29 5.8	28 2.6	9 18.5	1 3.3	21 51.3	23 34.0	10 56.8	27 5.9	0 45.9
29 M	18 24 55.5	6 24.5	8 55.6	12♍51.0	28 24.5	10 29.7	1 38.4	21 48.0	23 41.7	10 55.0	27 8.0	0 47.4
30 T	18 28 52.0	7 21.8	8 52.4	26 45.8	28 42.0	11 40.8	2 13.5	21 44.6	23 49.4	10 53.1	27 10.1	0 48.8

						DECLINATION						
1 M	16 34 31.8	21N54.7	7S40.1	11N22.8	25N26.7	24N44.8	17N31.9	14S50.8	21N54.2	17S57.7	20N31.5	17N57.5
4 T	16 46 21.5	22 18.7	7 43.7	8S19.1	25 34.8	24 35.1	16 59.5	14 49.9	21 56.2	17 58.4	20 30.6	17 57.8
7 S	16 58 11.2	22 39.2	7 47.3	24 39.4	25 24.0	24 19.0	16 26.3	14 49.5	21 58.1	17 59.3	20 29.6	17 58.0
10 W	17 10 0.8	22 56.1	7 50.9	27 7.8	24 57.2	23 56.6	15 52.1	14 49.7	21 59.9	18 0.3	20 28.7	17 58.2
13 S	17 21 50.5	23 9.4	7 54.5	15 40.7	24 17.7	23 28.2	15 17.0	14 50.5	22 1.6	18 1.3	20 27.7	17 58.4
16 T	17 33 40.2	23 19.0	7 58.1	0N54.8	23 28.5	22 53.8	14 41.1	14 51.8	22 3.3	18 2.5	20 26.6	17 58.6
19 F	17 45 29.8	23 24.9	8 1.7	16 44.1	22 32.5	22 13.8	14 4.4	14 53.7	22 4.8	18 3.8	20 25.5	17 58.8
22 M	17 57 19.5	23 27.2	8 5.3	27 0.1	21 32.4	21 28.3	13 26.8	14 56.1	22 6.3	18 5.1	20 24.4	17 58.9
25 T	18 9 9.2	23 25.6	8 8.9	25 54.2	20 31.2	20 37.5	12 48.4	14 59.1	22 7.7	18 6.6	20 23.3	17 59.1
28 S	18 20 58.9	23 20.4	8 12.5	12 30.3	19 31.5	19 41.9	12 9.3	15 2.6	22 9.0	18 8.1	20 22.2	17 59.2

JULY 1914

LONGITUDE

DAY	EPHEMERIS SIDEREAL TIME h m s	☉ ° ′	☊ ° ′	☽ ° ′	☿ ° ′	♀ ° ′	♂ ° ′	♃ ° ′	♄ ° ′	♅ ° ′	♆ ° ′	♇ ° ′
1 W	18 32 48.6	8♋19.0	8♓49.2	10♎49.9	28♋54.9	12♌51.8	2♍48.7	21♒41.0	23♊57.0	10♒51.2	27♋12.2	0♋50.3
2 T	18 36 45.1	9 16.2	8 46.1	25 2.5	29 3.2	14 2.7	3 23.9	21R37.2	24 4.7	10R49.3	27 14.4	0 51.7
3 F	18 40 41.7	10 13.4	8 42.9	9♏21.9	29 6.9	15 13.6	3 59.2	21 33.3	24 12.3	10 47.4	27 16.5	0 53.2
4 S	18 44 38.2	11 10.5	8 39.7	23 44.9	29R 5.9	16 24.5	4 34.6	21 29.2	24 19.9	10 45.4	27 18.7	0 54.6
5 S	18 48 34.8	12 7.7	8 36.5	8♐ 7.4	29 0.3	17 35.3	5 10.1	21 24.9	24 27.5	10 43.5	27 20.8	0 56.0
6 M	18 52 31.4	13 4.9	8 33.4	22 24.1	28 50.0	18 46.0	5 45.6	21 20.5	24 35.1	10 41.4	27 23.0	0 57.5
7 T	18 56 27.9	14 2.1	8 30.2	6♑29.4	28 35.3	19 56.6	6 21.1	21 15.9	24 42.6	10 39.4	27 25.2	0 58.9
8 W	19 0 24.4	14 59.3	8 27.0	20 18.5	28 16.2	21 7.2	6 56.8	21 11.1	24 50.1	10 37.3	27 27.3	1 0.3
9 T	19 4 21.0	15 56.5	8 23.8	3♒47.9	27 53.1	22 17.7	7 32.5	21 6.2	24 57.6	10 35.2	27 29.5	1 1.7
10 F	19 8 17.6	16 53.6	8 20.7	16 55.9	27 26.2	23 28.1	8 8.2	21 1.1	25 5.1	10 33.1	27 31.7	1 3.1
11 S	19 12 14.2	17 50.8	8 17.5	29 42.7	26 55.8	24 38.4	8 44.0	20 55.9	25 12.5	10 31.0	27 33.9	1 4.5
12 S	19 16 10.7	18 48.0	8 14.3	12♓10.2	26 22.4	25 48.7	9 19.9	20 50.5	25 19.9	10 28.8	27 36.1	1 5.9
13 M	19 20 7.2	19 45.2	8 11.1	24 21.7	25 46.5	26 58.9	9 55.8	20 45.0	25 27.3	10 26.7	27 38.3	1 7.3
14 T	19 24 3.8	20 42.5	8 7.9	6♈21.5	25 8.6	28 9.1	10 31.8	20 39.3	25 34.7	10 24.5	27 40.5	1 8.7
15 W	19 28 0.4	21 39.7	8 4.8	18 14.3	24 29.4	29 19.1	11 7.9	20 33.5	25 42.0	10 22.3	27 42.8	1 10.1
16 T	19 31 56.9	22 36.9	8 1.6	0♉ 5.3	23 49.4	0♍29.1	11 44.0	20 27.5	25 49.3	10 20.0	27 45.0	1 11.5
17 F	19 35 53.5	23 34.2	7 58.4	11 59.5	23 9.5	1 39.1	12 20.2	20 21.5	25 56.5	10 17.8	27 47.2	1 12.8
18 S	19 39 50.1	24 31.4	7 55.2	24 1.5	22 30.2	2 48.9	12 56.5	20 15.3	26 3.8	10 15.5	27 49.4	1 14.2
19 S	19 43 46.6	25 28.7	7 52.1	6♊15.4	21 52.3	3 58.7	13 32.8	20 8.9	26 10.9	10 13.2	27 51.7	1 15.5
20 M	19 47 43.2	26 26.0	7 48.9	18 44.3	21 16.5	5 8.3	14 9.2	20 2.5	26 18.1	10 10.9	27 53.9	1 16.9
21 T	19 51 39.7	27 23.3	7 45.7	1♋30.2	20 43.4	6 17.9	14 45.6	19 55.9	26 25.2	10 8.6	27 56.1	1 18.2
22 W	19 55 36.3	28 20.6	7 42.5	14 33.8	20 13.7	7 27.5	15 22.1	19 49.2	26 32.3	10 6.3	27 58.3	1 19.5
23 T	19 59 32.9	29 17.9	7 39.4	27 54.8	19 47.9	8 36.9	15 58.7	19 42.4	26 39.3	10 4.0	28 0.6	1 20.8
24 F	20 3 29.4	0♌15.2	7 36.2	11♌31.3	19 26.4	9 46.3	16 35.4	19 35.5	26 46.3	10 1.6	28 2.8	1 22.1
25 S	20 7 26.0	1 12.5	7 33.0	25 20.8	19 9.8	10 55.5	17 12.1	19 28.5	26 53.2	9 59.3	28 5.0	1 23.4
26 S	20 11 22.5	2 9.9	7 29.8	9♍20.4	18 58.5	12 4.7	17 48.8	19 21.4	27 0.1	9 56.9	28 7.2	1 24.7
27 M	20 15 19.1	3 7.2	7 26.6	23 27.2	18 52.7	13 13.8	18 25.6	19 14.3	27 7.0	9 54.5	28 9.5	1 26.0
28 T	20 19 15.6	4 4.6	7 23.5	7♎38.3	18 52.7	14 22.7	19 2.5	19 7.0	27 13.8	9 52.2	28 11.7	1 27.2
29 W	20 23 12.2	5 2.0	7 20.3	21 51.3	18D58.7	15 31.6	19 39.4	18 59.7	27 20.6	9 49.8	28 13.9	1 28.5
30 T	20 27 8.8	5 59.3	7 17.1	6♏ 4.0	19 10.8	16 40.4	20 16.4	18 52.3	27 27.3	9 47.4	28 16.1	1 29.7
31 F	20 31 5.3	6 56.7	7 13.9	20 14.4	19 29.2	17 49.1	20 53.5	18 44.8	27 33.9	9 45.0	28 18.3	1 30.9

DECLINATION

DAY	EPHEMERIS SIDEREAL TIME h m s	☉	☊	☽	☿	♀	♂	♃	♄	♅	♆	♇
1 W	18 32 48.6	23N11.5	8S16.0	6S51.6	18N36.3	18N41.7	11N29.4	15S 6.6	22N10.3	18S 9.7	20N21.0	17N59.2
4 S	18 44 38.2	22 58.9	8 19.6	23 30.3	17 48.4	17 37.2	10 48.9	15 11.1	22 11.4	18 11.3	20 19.8	17 59.3
7 T	18 56 27.9	22 42.8	8 23.2	27 43.8	17 10.3	16 28.8	10 7.6	15 16.1	22 12.5	18 13.0	20 18.5	17 59.4
10 F	19 8 17.6	22 23.0	8 26.7	17 26.1	16 44.4	15 16.7	9 25.7	15 21.5	22 13.4	18 14.8	20 17.3	17 59.4
13 M	19 20 7.2	21 59.9	8 30.3	0 48.5	16 32.0	14 1.2	8 43.3	15 27.3	22 14.3	18 16.6	20 16.0	17 59.4
16 T	19 31 56.9	21 33.3	8 33.9	15N22.9	16 33.6	12 42.8	8 0.2	15 33.5	22 15.1	18 18.5	20 14.8	17 59.4
19 S	19 43 46.6	21 3.4	8 37.4	26 26.5	16 48.1	11 21.7	7 16.5	15 40.0	22 15.8	18 20.4	20 13.5	17 59.4
22 W	19 55 36.3	20 30.3	8 41.0	26 41.7	17 13.4	9 58.2	6 32.4	15 46.9	22 16.5	18 22.3	20 12.2	17 59.3
25 S	20 7 26.0	19 54.1	8 44.5	13 59.9	17 46.4	8 32.6	5 47.7	15 53.9	22 17.0	18 24.2	20 10.9	17 59.2
28 T	20 19 15.6	19 14.9	8 48.1	5S32.2	18 23.6	7 5.2	5 2.6	16 1.2	22 17.5	18 26.1	20 9.6	17 59.2
31 F	20 31 5.3	18 32.8	8 51.6	22 38.7	19 0.7	5 36.4	4 17.1	16 8.6	22 18.0	18 28.1	20 8.3	17 59.1

AUGUST 1914

LONGITUDE

DAY	EPHEMERIS SIDEREAL TIME h m s	☉ ° ′	☊ ° ′	☽ ° ′	☿ ° ′	♀ ° ′	♂ ° ′	♃ ° ′	♄ ° ′	♅ ° ′	♆ ° ′	♇ ° ′
1 S	20 35 1.8	7♌54.1	7♓10.8	4♐20.4	19♋53.9	18♍57.6	21♍30.6	18♒37.3	27♊40.6	9♒42.6	28♋20.5	1♋32.2
2 S	20 38 58.4	8 51.5	7 7.6	18 19.6	20 24.9	20 6.1	22 7.7	18R29.7	27 47.1	9R40.2	28 22.7	1 33.4
3 M	20 42 55.0	9 48.9	7 4.4	2♑ 9.6	21 2.2	21 14.4	22 45.0	18 22.1	27 53.6	9 37.8	28 24.9	1 34.5
4 T	20 46 51.5	10 46.3	7 1.2	15 47.8	21 45.7	22 22.6	23 22.2	18 14.4	28 0.1	9 35.4	28 27.1	1 35.7
5 W	20 50 48.1	11 43.8	6 58.1	29 11.9	22 35.5	23 30.7	23 59.6	18 6.7	28 6.5	9 33.0	28 29.3	1 36.9
6 T	20 54 44.6	12 41.2	6 54.9	12♒20.5	23 31.4	24 38.7	24 37.0	17 59.0	28 12.8	9 30.6	28 31.5	1 38.0
7 F	20 58 41.2	13 38.7	6 51.7	25 12.8	24 33.2	25 46.6	25 14.4	17 51.2	28 19.1	9 28.3	28 33.6	1 39.2
8 S	21 2 37.8	14 36.2	6 48.5	7♓48.8	25 40.9	26 54.3	25 51.9	17 43.4	28 25.4	9 25.9	28 35.8	1 40.3
9 S	21 6 34.3	15 33.7	6 45.3	20 9.9	26 54.2	28 1.9	26 29.5	17 35.6	28 31.6	9 23.5	28 37.9	1 41.4
10 M	21 10 30.8	16 31.2	6 42.2	2♈18.2	28 13.0	29 9.3	27 7.1	17 27.7	28 37.7	9 21.1	28 40.1	1 42.5
11 T	21 14 27.4	17 28.8	6 39.0	14 16.9	29 36.9	0♎16.7	27 44.8	17 19.9	28 43.7	9 18.7	28 42.2	1 43.5
12 W	21 18 24.0	18 26.4	6 35.8	26 9.8	1♌ 5.9	1 23.9	28 22.5	17 12.1	28 49.7	9 16.4	28 44.4	1 44.6
13 T	21 22 20.6	19 24.0	6 32.6	8♉ 1.1	2 39.5	2 31.0	29 0.3	17 4.2	28 55.7	9 14.0	28 46.5	1 45.7
14 F	21 26 17.1	20 21.6	6 29.5	19 55.6	4 17.3	3 37.9	29 38.1	16 56.4	29 1.6	9 11.7	28 48.6	1 46.7
15 S	21 30 13.6	21 19.2	6 26.3	1♊57.8	5 59.2	4 44.7	0♎16.0	16 48.6	29 7.4	9 9.4	28 50.7	1 47.7
16 S	21 34 10.2	22 16.9	6 23.1	14 12.4	7 44.6	5 51.4	0 54.0	16 40.8	29 13.1	9 7.1	28 52.7	1 48.7
17 M	21 38 6.7	23 14.6	6 19.9	26 43.4	9 33.2	6 57.9	1 32.1	16 33.1	29 18.8	9 4.8	28 54.8	1 49.7
18 T	21 42 3.3	24 12.3	6 16.8	9♋33.9	11 24.6	8 4.2	2 10.2	16 25.4	29 24.4	9 2.5	28 56.9	1 50.7
19 W	21 45 59.9	25 10.1	6 13.6	22 46.0	13 18.3	9 10.4	2 48.3	16 17.7	29 29.9	9 0.2	28 58.9	1 51.6
20 T	21 49 56.4	26 7.8	6 10.4	6♌20.2	15 14.0	10 16.5	3 26.5	16 10.0	29 35.4	8 57.9	29 0.9	1 52.5
21 F	21 53 53.0	27 5.6	6 7.2	20 15.2	17 11.2	11 22.3	4 4.8	16 2.5	29 40.8	8 55.7	29 3.0	1 53.4
22 S	21 57 49.5	28 3.5	6 4.0	4♍28.0	19 9.6	12 28.1	4 43.1	15 54.9	29 46.1	8 53.5	29 5.0	1 54.3
23 S	22 1 46.1	29 1.3	6 0.9	18 53.9	21 8.8	13 33.6	5 21.5	15 47.5	29 51.4	8 51.3	29 7.0	1 55.2
24 M	22 5 42.6	29 59.2	5 57.7	3♎27.5	23 8.4	14 39.0	5 60.0	15 40.1	29 56.6	8 49.1	29 8.9	1 56.1
25 T	22 9 39.2	0♍57.1	5 54.5	18 3.0	25 8.3	15 44.2	6 38.5	15 32.8	0♋ 1.7	8 46.9	29 10.9	1 56.9
26 W	22 13 35.8	1 55.0	5 51.3	2♏34.8	27 8.0	16 49.2	7 17.0	15 25.5	0 6.7	8 44.8	29 12.8	1 57.7
27 T	22 17 32.3	2 52.9	5 48.2	16 58.6	29 7.5	17 54.0	7 55.7	15 18.4	0 11.6	8 42.6	29 14.8	1 58.5
28 F	22 21 28.9	3 50.9	5 45.0	1♐10.8	1♍ 6.5	18 58.6	8 34.3	15 11.3	0 16.5	8 40.5	29 16.7	1 59.3
29 S	22 25 25.4	4 48.8	5 41.8	15 9.5	3 4.9	20 2.9	9 13.1	15 4.3	0 21.3	8 38.5	29 18.6	2 0.1
30 S	22 29 22.0	5 46.8	5 38.6	28 53.4	5 2.5	21 7.1	9 51.9	14 57.5	0 26.0	8 36.4	29 20.4	2 0.8
31 M	22 33 18.5	6 44.8	5 35.5	12♑22.4	6 59.2	22 11.1	10 30.7	14 50.7	0 30.6	8 34.4	29 22.3	2 1.6

DECLINATION

DAY	EPHEMERIS SIDEREAL TIME h m s	☉	☊	☽	☿	♀	♂	♃	♄	♅	♆	♇
1 S	20 35 1.8	18N18.2	8S52.8	26S 8.6	19N12.3	5N 6.5	4N 1.8	16S11.1	22N18.1	18S28.7	20N 7.8	17N59.0
4 T	20 46 51.5	17 32.5	8 56.3	26 30.3	19 42.2	3 36.3	3 15.8	16 18.6	22 18.4	18 30.7	20 6.5	17 58.9
7 F	20 58 41.2	16 44.3	8 59.9	14 2.4	20 1.2	2 5.3	2 29.5	16 26.2	22 18.7	18 32.6	20 5.2	17 58.8
10 M	21 10 30.8	15 53.6	9 3.4	3N 4.1	20 4.2	0 33.9	1 42.8	16 33.8	22 18.9	18 34.5	20 3.9	17 58.6
13 T	21 22 20.6	15 0.7	9 6.9	18 35.4	19 46.8	0S57.8	0 55.9	16 41.3	22 19.0	18 36.4	20 2.7	17 58.5
16 S	21 34 10.2	14 5.6	9 10.4	27 41.6	19 5.9	2 29.4	0 8.8	16 48.7	22 19.1	18 38.2	20 1.4	17 58.3
19 W	21 45 59.9	13 8.4	9 14.0	25 5.1	18 0.6	4 0.6	0S38.5	16 55.9	22 19.1	18 40.0	20 0.1	17 58.1
22 S	21 57 49.5	12 9.3	9 17.5	9 59.7	16 32.7	5 31.2	1 25.9	17 2.9	22 19.1	18 41.8	19 58.9	17 57.9
25 T	22 9 39.2	11 8.5	9 21.0	10S22.1	14 45.8	7 0.9	2 13.4	17 9.7	22 19.1	18 43.5	19 57.7	17 57.7
28 F	22 21 28.9	10 6.2	9 24.5	25 33.6	12 44.5	8 29.4	3 1.0	17 16.2	22 19.0	18 45.2	19 56.5	17 57.5
31 M	22 33 18.5	9 2.4	9 28.0	27 6.5	10 33.2	9 56.5	3 48.5	17 22.3	22 18.9	18 46.7	19 55.4	17 57.3

SEPTEMBER 1914

DAY	EPHEMERIS SIDEREAL TIME	☉	☊	☽	☿	♀	♂	♃	♄	♅	♆	♇
	h m s	° ′	° ′	° ′	° ′	° ′	° ′	° ′	° ′	° ′	° ′	° ′
						LONGITUDE						
1 T	22 37 15.1	7♍42.9	5♓32.3	25♑36.5	8♍54.9	23♎14.8	11♎ 9.6	14♒44.1	0♋35.2	8♒32.4	29♋24.1	2♋ 2.3
2 W	22 41 11.6	8 40.9	5 29.1	8♒36.4	10 49.6	24 18.3	11 48.6	14R37.5	0 39.6	8R30.4	29 26.0	2 3.0
3 T	22 45 8.2	9 39.0	5 25.9	21 22.7	12 43.2	25 21.5	12 27.6	14 31.1	0 44.0	8 28.5	29 27.8	2 3.6
4 F	22 49 4.7	10 37.2	5 22.7	3♓56.2	14 35.6	26 24.5	13 6.7	14 24.8	0 48.3	8 26.6	29 29.5	2 4.3
5 S	22 53 1.3	11 35.3	5 19.6	16 17.9	16 27.0	27 27.3	13 45.8	14 18.7	0 52.5	8 24.7	29 31.3	2 4.9
6 S	22 56 57.8	12 33.5	5 16.4	28 29.2	18 17.1	28 29.8	14 25.0	14 12.6	0 56.6	8 22.8	29 33.0	2 5.5
7 M	23 0 54.4	13 31.7	5 13.2	10♈31.6	20 6.1	29 32.0	15 4.2	14 6.7	1 0.6	8 21.0	29 34.8	2 6.1
8 T	23 4 51.0	14 29.9	5 10.0	22 27.4	21 53.9	0♏33.9	15 43.5	14 0.9	1 4.6	8 19.2	29 36.5	2 6.7
9 W	23 8 47.5	15 28.2	5 6.8	4♉19.1	23 40.5	1 35.6	16 22.9	13 55.3	1 8.4	8 17.5	29 38.1	2 7.2
10 T	23 12 44.0	16 26.5	5 3.7	16 10.0	25 26.0	2 36.9	17 2.3	13 49.8	1 12.2	8 15.8	29 39.8	2 7.7
11 F	23 16 40.6	17 24.8	5 0.5	28 3.7	27 10.4	3 38.0	17 41.8	13 44.5	1 15.8	8 14.1	29 41.4	2 8.2
12 S	23 20 37.2	18 23.2	4 57.3	10♊ 4.4	28 53.6	4 38.7	18 21.3	13 39.3	1 19.4	8 12.4	29 43.0	2 8.7
13 S	23 24 33.7	19 21.6	4 54.1	22 16.5	0♎35.7	5 39.1	19 0.9	13 34.3	1 22.9	8 10.8	29 44.6	2 9.2
14 M	23 28 30.3	20 20.0	4 51.0	4♋44.5	2 16.7	6 39.2	19 40.6	13 29.4	1 26.3	8 9.2	29 46.2	2 9.6
15 T	23 32 26.8	21 18.5	4 47.8	17 32.5	3 56.6	7 39.0	20 20.3	13 24.7	1 29.6	8 7.7	29 47.7	2 10.0
16 W	23 36 23.4	22 17.0	4 44.6	0♌43.9	5 35.5	8 38.4	21 0.1	13 20.2	1 32.8	8 6.2	29 49.2	2 10.4
17 T	23 40 19.9	23 15.6	4 41.4	14 20.9	7 13.3	9 37.5	21 39.9	13 15.8	1 35.9	8 4.7	29 50.7	2 10.8
18 F	23 44 16.5	24 14.2	4 38.2	28 23.8	8 50.1	10 36.1	22 19.8	13 11.6	1 38.9	8 3.3	29 52.2	2 11.1
19 S	23 48 13.1	25 12.8	4 35.1	12♍50.3	10 25.9	11 34.4	22 59.8	13 7.6	1 41.8	8 1.9	29 53.6	2 11.5
20 S	23 52 9.6	26 11.4	4 31.9	27 35.9	12 0.6	12 32.3	23 39.8	13 3.8	1 44.6	8 0.5	29 55.0	2 11.8
21 M	23 56 6.2	27 10.1	4 28.7	12♎33.5	13 34.4	13 29.8	24 19.9	13 0.1	1 47.3	7 59.2	29 56.4	2 12.1
22 T	0 0 2.7	28 8.8	4 25.5	27 34.6	15 7.2	14 26.9	24 60.0	12 56.6	1 49.8	7 58.0	29 57.8	2 12.3
23 W	0 3 59.3	29 7.6	4 22.4	12♏30.3	16 39.0	15 23.5	25 40.2	12 53.4	1 52.3	7 56.7	29 59.1	2 12.6
24 T	0 7 55.8	0♎ 6.3	4 19.2	27 12.9	18 9.8	16 19.6	26 20.5	12 50.3	1 54.7	7 55.6	0♌ 0.4	2 12.8
25 F	0 11 52.4	1 5.1	4 16.0	11♐36.9	19 39.6	17 15.3	27 0.8	12 47.3	1 57.0	7 54.4	0 1.7	2 13.0
26 S	0 15 48.9	2 4.0	4 12.8	25 39.0	21 8.5	18 10.4	27 41.1	12 44.6	1 59.2	7 53.3	0 3.0	2 13.1
27 S	0 19 45.5	3 2.8	4 9.6	9♑18.5	22 36.3	19 5.1	28 21.6	12 42.1	2 1.3	7 52.3	0 4.2	2 13.3
28 M	0 23 42.1	4 1.7	4 6.5	22 36.4	24 3.2	19 59.1	29 2.0	12 39.7	2 3.2	7 51.3	0 5.4	2 13.4
29 T	0 27 38.6	5 0.6	4 3.3	5♒34.9	25 29.1	20 52.6	29 42.6	12 37.6	2 5.1	7 50.3	0 6.5	2 13.5
30 W	0 31 35.2	5 59.6	4 0.1	18 16.8	26 53.9	21 45.5	0♏23.2	12 35.6	2 6.8	7 49.4	0 7.7	2 13.6
						DECLINATION						
1 T	22 37 15.1	8N40.8	9S29.2	24S23.5	9N47.9	10S25.1	4S 4.4	17S24.3	22N18.8	18S47.2	19N55.0	17N57.2
4 F	22 49 4.7	7 35.4	9 32.7	10 14.2	7 29.0	11 49.8	4 51.9	17 30.0	22 18.7	18 48.7	19 53.9	17 57.0
7 M	23 0 54.4	6 28.8	9 36.2	6N56.1	5 7.9	13 12.3	5 39.2	17 35.3	22 18.5	18 50.1	19 52.8	17 56.8
10 T	23 12 44.0	5 21.2	9 39.6	21 26.1	2 46.5	14 32.6	6 26.4	17 40.1	22 18.3	18 51.5	19 51.7	17 56.6
13 S	23 24 33.7	4 12.9	9 43.1	28 16.3	0 26.4	15 50.2	7 13.4	17 44.6	22 18.1	18 52.7	19 50.7	17 56.3
16 W	23 36 23.4	3 3.8	9 46.6	22 57.8	1S51.2	17 5.0	8 0.2	17 48.5	22 17.9	18 53.8	19 49.8	17 56.1
19 S	23 48 13.1	1 54.2	9 50.1	6 9.0	4 5.4	18 16.8	8 46.6	17 52.0	22 17.6	18 54.9	19 48.8	17 55.8
22 T	0 0 2.7	0 44.2	9 53.6	14S27.7	6 15.3	19 25.2	9 32.7	17 55.0	22 17.4	18 55.8	19 48.0	17 55.6
25 F	0 11 52.4	0S25.9	9 57.0	27 20.7	8 20.3	20 30.1	10 18.3	17 57.5	22 17.2	18 56.7	19 47.1	17 55.4
28 M	0 23 42.1	1 36.1	10 0.5	25 4.7	10 19.7	21 31.2	11 3.4	17 59.5	22 17.0	18 57.4	19 46.4	17 55.1

OCTOBER 1914

DAY	EPHEMERIS SIDEREAL TIME	☉	☊	☽	☿	♀	♂	♃	♄	♅	♆	♇
						LONGITUDE						
1 T	0 35 31.7	6♎58.5	3♓56.9	0♓44.8	28♎17.7	22♏37.8	1♏ 3.8	12♒33.9	2♋ 8.5	7♒48.5	0♌ 8.8	2♋13.6
2 F	0 39 28.3	7 57.5	3 53.8	13 1.8	29 40.4	23 29.5	1 44.5	12R32.3	2 10.0	7R47.7	0 9.9	2 13.7
3 S	0 43 24.8	8 56.6	3 50.6	25 9.9	1♏ 2.0	24 20.5	2 25.3	12 30.9	2 11.5	7 47.0	0 10.9	2 13.7
4 S	0 47 21.4	9 55.7	3 47.4	7♈11.2	2 22.5	25 10.8	3 6.1	12 29.7	2 12.8	7 46.2	0 11.9	2R13.7
5 M	0 51 17.9	10 54.8	3 44.2	19 7.4	3 41.8	26 0.4	3 47.0	12 28.8	2 14.0	7 45.5	0 12.9	2 13.6
6 T	0 55 14.5	11 53.9	3 41.0	1♉ 0.1	4 59.8	26 49.3	4 28.0	12 28.0	2 15.1	7 44.9	0 13.9	2 13.6
7 W	0 59 11.0	12 53.1	3 37.9	12 51.2	6 16.4	27 37.4	5 9.0	12 27.4	2 16.1	7 44.3	0 14.8	2 13.5
8 T	1 3 7.6	13 52.3	3 34.7	24 42.8	7 31.7	28 24.7	5 50.0	12 27.0	2 17.0	7 43.8	0 15.7	2 13.4
9 F	1 7 4.2	14 51.5	3 31.5	6♊37.3	8 45.5	29 11.1	6 31.2	12 26.9	2 17.8	7 43.3	0 16.5	2 13.3
10 S	1 11 0.7	15 50.8	3 28.3	18 37.8	9 57.7	29 56.7	7 12.3	12D26.9	2 18.4	7 42.9	0 17.4	2 13.1
11 S	1 14 57.2	16 50.1	3 25.2	0♋48.0	11 8.2	0♐41.4	7 53.6	12 27.1	2 19.0	7 42.5	0 18.2	2 12.9
12 M	1 18 53.8	17 49.5	3 22.0	13 12.0	12 16.9	1 25.2	8 34.9	12 27.5	2 19.4	7 42.1	0 18.9	2 12.8
13 T	1 22 50.4	18 48.9	3 18.8	25 54.0	13 23.6	2 8.0	9 16.2	12 28.1	2 19.7	7 41.9	0 19.7	2 12.5
14 W	1 26 46.9	19 48.3	3 15.6	8♌58.3	14 28.1	2 49.8	9 57.7	12 28.9	2 20.0	7 41.6	0 20.4	2 12.3
15 T	1 30 43.5	20 47.8	3 12.5	22 28.4	15 30.3	3 30.6	10 39.1	12 29.9	2 20.1	7 41.4	0 21.1	2 12.0
16 F	1 34 40.0	21 47.3	3 9.3	6♍26.5	16 29.9	4 10.3	11 20.7	12 31.2	2R20.1	7 41.3	0 21.7	2 11.8
17 S	1 38 36.6	22 46.9	3 6.1	20 52.5	17 26.7	4 48.8	12 2.3	12 32.6	2 19.9	7 41.2	0 22.3	2 11.5
18 S	1 42 33.1	23 46.5	3 2.9	5♎43.0	18 20.4	5 26.2	12 44.0	12 34.2	2 19.7	7 41.2	0 22.9	2 11.1
19 M	1 46 29.7	24 46.1	2 59.7	20 51.7	19 10.6	6 2.3	13 25.7	12 36.0	2 19.4	7D41.2	0 23.4	2 10.8
20 T	1 50 26.2	25 45.7	2 56.6	6♏ 9.1	19 57.1	6 37.2	14 7.5	12 38.0	2 18.9	7 41.2	0 23.9	2 10.4
21 W	1 54 22.8	26 45.4	2 53.4	21 24.0	20 39.4	7 10.7	14 49.3	12 40.2	2 18.3	7 41.3	0 24.4	2 10.0
22 T	1 58 19.4	27 45.2	2 50.2	6♐25.9	21 17.1	7 42.9	15 31.2	12 42.6	2 17.7	7 41.5	0 24.8	2 9.6
23 F	2 2 15.9	28 44.9	2 47.0	21 6.1	21 49.7	8 13.6	16 13.2	12 45.2	2 16.9	7 41.7	0 25.2	2 9.2
24 S	2 6 12.5	29 44.8	2 43.9	5♑19.6	22 16.7	8 42.7	16 55.2	12 48.0	2 16.0	7 42.0	0 25.6	2 8.7
25 S	2 10 9.0	0♏44.5	2 40.7	19 4.7	22 37.5	9 10.4	17 37.3	12 51.0	2 15.0	7 42.3	0 25.9	2 8.2
26 M	2 14 5.6	1 44.3	2 37.5	2♒22.3	22 51.7	9 36.3	18 19.4	12 54.2	2 13.8	7 42.7	0 26.2	2 7.7
27 T	2 18 2.1	2 44.2	2 34.3	15 15.8	22 58.4	10 0.6	19 1.6	12 57.5	2 12.6	7 43.1	0 26.5	2 7.2
28 W	2 21 58.7	3 44.1	2 31.2	27 49.1	22R57.3	10 23.1	19 43.8	13 1.1	2 11.3	7 43.6	0 26.7	2 6.7
29 T	2 25 55.2	4 44.0	2 28.0	10♓ 6.7	22 47.6	10 43.8	20 26.1	13 4.8	2 9.8	7 44.1	0 26.9	2 6.1
30 F	2 29 51.8	5 44.0	2 24.8	22 12.9	22 29.0	11 2.6	21 8.5	13 8.7	2 8.3	7 44.7	0 27.1	2 5.5
31 S	2 33 48.3	6 43.9	2 21.6	4♈11.5	22 1.1	11 19.4	21 50.9	13 12.9	2 6.6	7 45.3	0 27.2	2 4.9
						DECLINATION						
1 T	0 35 31.7	2S46.2	10S 4.0	11S38.0	12S12.9	22S28.2	11S48.0	18S 0.9	22N16.8	18S58.1	19N45.6	17N54.9
4 S	0 47 21.4	3 56.1	10 7.4	5N21.3	13 59.1	23 21.1	12 31.9	18 1.9	22 16.6	18 58.6	19 45.0	17 54.7
7 W	0 59 11.0	5 5.5	10 10.9	20 14.9	15 37.5	24 9.7	13 15.2	18 2.3	22 16.4	18 59.0	19 44.3	17 54.5
10 S	1 11 0.7	6 14.3	10 14.3	27 57.6	17 7.1	24 53.7	13 57.8	18 2.2	22 16.3	18 59.3	19 43.8	17 54.2
13 T	1 22 50.4	7 22.5	10 17.8	24 10.3	18 26.6	25 33.0	14 39.5	18 1.6	22 16.1	18 59.5	19 43.3	17 54.0
16 F	1 34 40.0	8 29.7	10 21.2	9 1.6	19 34.5	26 7.5	15 20.3	18 0.4	22 16.0	18 59.5	19 42.8	17 53.8
19 M	1 46 29.7	9 35.9	10 24.7	11S33.8	20 28.7	26 37.0	16 0.3	17 58.8	22 15.9	18 59.5	19 42.5	17 53.6
22 T	1 58 19.4	10 40.8	10 28.1	26 24.8	21 6.2	27 1.4	16 39.2	17 56.6	22 15.8	18 59.3	19 42.2	17 53.5
25 S	2 10 9.0	11 44.3	10 31.5	25 40.7	21 23.1	27 20.4	17 17.0	17 54.0	22 15.8	18 59.0	19 41.9	17 53.3
28 W	2 21 58.7	12 46.2	10 35.0	12 46.1	21 14.0	27 33.7	17 53.6	17 50.8	22 15.8	18 58.6	19 41.7	17 53.1
31 S	2 33 48.3	13 46.2	10 38.4	4N 0.3	20 32.5	27 41.1	18 29.0	17 47.2	22 15.8	18 58.1	19 41.6	17 53.0

NOVEMBER 1914

LONGITUDE

DAY	EPHEMERIS SIDEREAL TIME	☉	☊	☽	☿	♀	♂	♃	♄	♅	♆	♇
	h m s	° ′	° ′	° ′	° ′	° ′	° ′	° ′	° ′	° ′	° ′	° ′
1 S	2 37 44.9	7♏43.9	2♓18.4	16♈ 5.5	21♏23.7	11♐34.2	22♏33.4	13♒17.2	2♋ 4.8	7♒46.0	0♌27.3	2♋ 4.3
2 M	2 41 41.5	8 44.0	2 15.3	27 57.3	20R36.9	11 46.9	23 15.9	13 21.6	2R 3.0	7 46.7	0 27.4	2R 3.7
3 T	2 45 38.0	9 44.0	2 12.1	9♉48.9	19 41.2	11 57.5	23 58.5	13 26.3	2 1.0	7 47.5	0 27.4	2 3.0
4 W	2 49 34.6	10 44.1	2 8.9	21 41.7	18 37.4	12 5.9	24 41.1	13 31.1	1 58.9	7 48.3	0R27.4	2 2.3
5 T	2 53 31.1	11 44.3	2 5.7	3♊37.0	17 26.8	12 12.1	25 23.8	13 36.2	1 56.7	7 49.2	0 27.4	2 1.6
6 F	2 57 27.7	12 44.4	2 2.6	15 36.4	16 11.1	12 15.9	26 6.6	13 41.4	1 54.4	7 50.1	0 27.3	2 0.9
7 S	3 1 24.2	13 44.6	1 59.4	27 41.6	14 52.5	12 17.4	26 49.4	13 46.7	1 52.1	7 51.1	0 27.2	2 0.2
8 S	3 5 20.8	14 44.8	1 56.2	9♋55.1	13 33.3	12R16.5	27 32.3	13 52.3	1 49.6	7 52.1	0 27.1	1 59.4
9 M	3 9 17.4	15 45.1	1 53.0	22 19.7	12 16.0	12 13.2	28 15.2	13 58.0	1 47.0	7 53.2	0 26.9	1 58.7
10 T	3 13 13.9	16 45.4	1 49.8	4♌59.1	11 3.3	12 7.5	28 58.2	14 3.9	1 44.3	7 54.4	0 26.7	1 57.9
11 W	3 17 10.5	17 45.7	1 46.7	17 57.1	9 57.4	11 59.4	29 41.3	14 9.9	1 41.5	7 55.5	0 26.5	1 57.1
12 T	3 21 7.0	18 46.1	1 43.5	1♍17.7	9 0.1	11 48.8	0♐24.4	14 16.2	1 38.7	7 56.8	0 26.2	1 56.3
13 F	3 25 3.6	19 46.5	1 40.3	15 4.1	8 13.1	11 35.8	1 7.5	14 22.5	1 35.7	7 58.0	0 25.9	1 55.4
14 S	3 29 0.1	20 46.9	1 37.1	29 17.7	7 37.3	11 20.4	1 50.8	14 29.1	1 32.6	7 59.4	0 25.5	1 54.6
15 S	3 32 56.7	21 47.3	1 34.0	13♎57.5	7 13.0	11 2.7	2 34.1	14 35.8	1 29.5	8 0.7	0 25.2	1 53.7
16 M	3 36 53.3	22 47.8	1 30.8	28 59.0	7 0.5	10 42.6	3 17.4	14 42.7	1 26.2	8 2.2	0 24.7	1 52.8
17 T	3 40 49.8	23 48.3	1 27.6	14♏14.4	6 59.4	10 20.4	4 0.8	14 49.7	1 22.9	8 3.6	0 24.3	1 51.9
18 W	3 44 46.4	24 48.9	1 24.4	29 32.9	7D 9.1	9 56.0	4 44.3	14 56.9	1 19.5	8 5.1	0 23.8	1 51.0
19 T	3 48 42.9	25 49.4	1 21.3	14♐43.0	7 29.0	9 29.7	5 27.8	15 4.3	1 16.0	8 6.7	0 23.3	1 50.0
20 F	3 52 39.5	26 50.0	1 18.1	29 34.1	7 58.0	9 1.4	6 11.4	15 11.8	1 12.4	8 8.3	0 22.8	1 49.1
21 S	3 56 36.0	27 50.6	1 14.9	13♑58.9	8 35.5	8 31.4	6 55.0	15 19.5	1 8.8	8 10.0	0 22.2	1 48.1
22 S	4 0 32.6	28 51.3	1 11.7	27 53.8	9 20.4	7 59.8	7 38.7	15 27.3	1 5.0	8 11.7	0 21.6	1 47.2
23 M	4 4 29.1	29 51.9	1 8.5	11♒18.5	10 11.9	7 26.9	8 22.4	15 35.3	1 1.2	8 13.4	0 21.0	1 46.2
24 T	4 8 25.7	0♐52.6	1 5.4	24 15.6	11 9.1	6 52.8	9 6.2	15 43.4	0 57.3	8 15.2	0 20.3	1 45.2
25 W	4 12 22.3	1 53.3	1 2.2	6♓49.5	12 11.5	6 17.7	9 50.0	15 51.6	0 53.4	8 17.1	0 19.6	1 44.2
26 T	4 16 18.8	2 54.0	0 59.0	19 5.2	13 18.2	5 41.9	10 33.9	16 0.0	0 49.3	8 18.9	0 18.9	1 43.1
27 F	4 20 15.4	3 54.7	0 55.8	1♈ 7.9	14 28.7	5 5.6	11 17.9	16 8.6	0 45.2	8 20.9	0 18.1	1 42.1
28 S	4 24 11.9	4 55.4	0 52.7	13 2.5	15 42.5	4 29.1	12 1.9	16 17.2	0 41.1	8 22.8	0 17.3	1 41.0
29 S	4 28 8.5	5 56.2	0 49.5	24 53.3	16 59.1	3 52.6	12 45.9	16 26.1	0 36.9	8 24.8	0 16.5	1 40.0
30 M	4 32 5.1	6 57.0	0 46.3	6♉43.6	18 18.0	3 16.5	13 30.0	16 35.0	0 32.6	8 26.9	0 15.7	1 38.9

DECLINATION

DAY	EPHEMERIS SIDEREAL TIME	☉	☊	☽	☿	♀	♂	♃	♄	♅	♆	♇
1 S	2 37 44.9	14S 5.8	10S39.5	9N27.9	20S10.5	27S42.2	18S40.5	17S45.8	22N15.8	18S57.9	19N41.6	17N52.9
4 W	2 49 34.6	15 3.2	10 42.9	22 56.7	18 39.4	27 41.0	19 14.1	17 41.5	22 15.9	18 57.2	19 41.6	17 52.8
7 S	3 1 24.2	15 58.4	10 46.3	27 59.6	16 38.3	27 32.7	19 46.3	17 36.8	22 15.9	18 56.4	19 41.6	17 52.7
10 T	3 13 13.9	16 51.2	10 49.8	21 17.9	14 31.0	27 16.7	20 17.0	17 31.5	22 16.0	18 55.5	19 41.7	17 52.6
13 F	3 25 3.6	17 41.4	10 53.2	4 52.3	12 49.0	26 52.5	20 46.1	17 25.8	22 16.1	18 54.4	19 41.9	17 52.5
16 M	3 36 53.3	18 28.9	10 56.6	15S 2.1	11 53.0	26 19.4	21 13.6	17 19.7	22 16.2	18 53.3	19 42.1	17 52.5
19 T	3 48 42.9	19 13.5	10 59.9	27 25.2	11 45.8	25 37.5	21 39.4	17 13.1	22 16.4	18 52.0	19 42.4	17 52.4
22 S	4 0 32.6	19 54.9	11 3.3	23 18.6	12 17.9	24 46.9	22 3.4	17 6.0	22 16.5	18 50.7	19 42.8	17 52.4
25 W	4 12 22.3	20 33.0	11 6.7	8 33.3	13 16.8	23 48.9	22 25.6	16 58.5	22 16.7	18 49.2	19 43.2	17 52.4
28 S	4 24 11.9	21 7.8	11 10.1	8N14.5	14 31.6	22 45.3	22 45.8	16 50.6	22 16.8	18 47.6	19 43.7	17 52.4

DECEMBER 1914

LONGITUDE

DAY	EPHEMERIS SIDEREAL TIME	☉	☊	☽	☿	♀	♂	♃	♄	♅	♆	♇
1 T	4 36 1.6	7♐57.8	0♓43.1	18♉36.3	19♏39.0	2♐40.9	14♐14.2	16♒44.1	0♋28.2	8♒29.0	0♌14.8	1♋37.8
2 W	4 39 58.2	8 58.6	0 40.0	0♊33.2	21 1.7	2R 6.0	14 58.4	16 53.3	0R23.8	8 31.1	0R13.9	1R36.7
3 T	4 43 54.7	9 59.4	0 36.8	12 35.6	22 26.0	1 32.2	15 42.6	17 2.7	0 19.4	8 33.3	0 12.9	1 35.6
4 F	4 47 51.3	11 0.3	0 33.6	24 44.5	23 51.4	0 59.7	16 27.0	17 12.2	0 14.9	8 35.5	0 12.0	1 34.5
5 S	4 51 47.9	12 1.1	0 30.4	7♋ 0.6	25 18.0	0 28.6	17 11.3	17 21.8	0 10.3	8 37.8	0 11.0	1 33.4
6 S	4 55 44.4	13 2.0	0 27.3	19 25.2	26 45.4	29♏59.2	17 55.7	17 31.5	0 5.7	8 40.1	0 10.0	1 32.3
7 M	4 59 41.0	14 2.9	0 24.1	1♌59.5	28 13.6	29 31.7	18 40.2	17 41.3	0 1.1	8 42.4	0 8.9	1 31.1
8 T	5 3 37.5	15 3.9	0 20.9	14 45.8	29 42.5	29 6.1	19 24.7	17 51.3	29♊56.4	8 44.8	0 7.8	1 30.0
9 W	5 7 34.1	16 4.8	0 17.7	27 46.5	1♐11.9	28 42.6	20 9.3	18 1.4	29 51.7	8 47.2	0 6.7	1 28.8
10 T	5 11 30.6	17 5.8	0 14.5	11♍ 4.5	2 41.9	28 21.4	20 53.9	18 11.6	29 46.9	8 49.7	0 5.6	1 27.7
11 F	5 15 27.2	18 6.8	0 11.4	24 42.4	4 12.2	28 2.4	21 38.6	18 22.0	29 42.1	8 52.2	0 4.5	1 26.5
12 S	5 19 23.8	19 7.8	0 8.2	8♎42.3	5 42.9	27 45.9	22 23.4	18 32.4	29 37.3	8 54.7	0 3.3	1 25.3
13 S	5 23 20.3	20 8.8	0 5.0	23 4.1	7 13.9	27 31.8	23 8.1	18 43.0	29 32.5	8 57.2	0 2.1	1 24.2
14 M	5 27 16.9	21 9.9	0 1.8	7♏45.6	8 45.2	27 20.2	23 53.0	18 53.6	29 27.6	8 59.8	0 0.9	1 23.0
15 T	5 31 13.4	22 10.9	29♒58.7	22 41.6	10 16.8	27 11.1	24 37.9	19 4.4	29 22.7	9 2.5	29♋59.6	1 21.8
16 W	5 35 10.0	23 12.0	29 55.5	7♐44.0	11 48.5	27 4.5	25 22.8	19 15.3	29 17.8	9 5.1	29 58.3	1 20.6
17 T	5 39 6.5	24 13.1	29 52.3	22 43.1	13 20.5	27 0.3	26 7.8	19 26.3	29 12.9	9 7.8	29 57.1	1 19.4
18 F	5 43 3.1	25 14.2	29 49.1	7♑29.3	14 52.7	26 58.7	26 52.8	19 37.4	29 7.9	9 10.6	29 55.7	1 18.2
19 S	5 46 59.7	26 15.3	29 46.0	21 54.5	16 25.1	26D59.4	27 37.9	19 48.6	29 3.0	9 13.3	29 54.4	1 17.0
20 S	5 50 56.2	27 16.4	29 42.8	5♒53.4	17 57.7	27 2.6	28 23.1	19 59.9	28 58.0	9 16.1	29 53.0	1 15.8
21 M	5 54 52.8	28 17.5	29 39.6	19 24.2	19 30.5	27 8.1	29 8.2	20 11.3	28 53.0	9 19.0	29 51.7	1 14.6
22 T	5 58 49.3	29 18.7	29 36.4	2♓27.7	21 3.4	27 15.9	29 53.5	20 22.8	28 48.1	9 21.8	29 50.3	1 13.4
23 W	6 2 45.9	0♑19.8	29 33.3	15 7.1	22 36.6	27 26.0	0♑38.7	20 34.4	28 43.1	9 24.7	29 48.9	1 12.2
24 T	6 6 42.5	1 20.9	29 30.1	27 26.6	24 10.0	27 38.3	1 24.0	20 46.1	28 38.1	9 27.6	29 47.4	1 11.0
25 F	6 10 39.0	2 22.1	29 26.9	9♈31.5	25 43.5	27 52.7	2 9.4	20 57.9	28 33.2	9 30.6	29 46.0	1 9.8
26 S	6 14 35.6	3 23.2	29 23.7	21 26.9	27 17.3	28 9.2	2 54.8	21 9.8	28 28.2	9 33.6	29 44.5	1 8.6
27 S	6 18 32.1	4 24.3	29 20.5	3♉17.9	28 51.4	28 27.8	3 40.2	21 21.7	28 23.3	9 36.6	29 43.0	1 7.4
28 M	6 22 28.7	5 25.5	29 17.4	15 9.0	0♑25.7	28 48.3	4 25.7	21 33.8	28 18.4	9 39.6	29 41.5	1 6.2
29 T	6 26 25.3	6 26.6	29 14.2	27 3.8	2 0.3	29 10.7	5 11.2	21 45.9	28 13.5	9 42.6	29 40.0	1 5.0
30 W	6 30 21.8	7 27.7	29 11.0	9♊ 5.4	3 35.1	29 34.9	5 56.8	21 58.1	28 8.6	9 45.7	29 38.4	1 3.8
31 T	6 34 18.4	8 28.9	29 7.8	21 15.7	5 10.3	0♐ 0.9	6 42.4	22 10.4	28 3.8	9 48.8	29 36.9	1 2.6

DECLINATION

DAY	EPHEMERIS SIDEREAL TIME	☉	☊	☽	☿	♀	♂	♃	♄	♅	♆	♇
1 T	4 36 1.6	21S38.9	11S13.5	22N 3.5	15S53.9	21S38.9	23S 4.0	16S42.3	22N17.0	18S45.9	19N44.2	17N52.4
4 F	4 47 51.3	22 6.3	11 16.8	27 52.9	17 18.0	20 33.0	23 20.1	16 33.6	22 17.2	18 44.2	19 44.8	17 52.5
7 M	4 59 41.0	22 29.9	11 20.2	21 59.5	18 40.1	19 30.5	23 34.2	16 24.4	22 17.4	18 42.3	19 45.5	17 52.5
10 T	5 11 30.6	22 49.6	11 23.6	6 28.0	19 57.4	18 34.2	23 46.0	16 14.9	22 17.6	18 40.3	19 46.2	17 52.6
13 S	5 23 20.3	23 5.2	11 26.9	12S45.2	21 8.0	17 46.0	23 55.7	16 5.0	22 17.7	18 38.3	19 47.0	17 52.7
16 W	5 35 10.0	23 16.7	11 30.3	26 31.4	22 10.5	17 6.9	24 3.1	15 54.8	22 17.9	18 36.1	19 47.8	17 52.8
19 S	5 46 59.7	23 24.0	11 33.6	24 38.8	23 3.8	16 37.4	24 8.2	15 44.1	22 18.1	18 33.9	19 48.6	17 53.0
22 T	5 58 49.3	23 27.0	11 37.0	10 15.3	23 47.1	16 17.1	24 10.9	15 33.1	22 18.3	18 31.6	19 49.5	17 53.1
25 F	6 10 39.0	23 25.9	11 40.3	6N52.4	24 19.5	16 5.5	24 11.3	15 21.8	22 18.4	18 29.2	19 50.4	17 53.3
28 M	6 22 28.7	23 20.5	11 43.6	21 8.0	24 40.6	16 1.7	24 9.3	15 10.1	22 18.6	18 26.8	19 51.4	17 53.5
31 T	6 34 18.4	23 10.8	11 47.0	27 49.7	24 49.6	16 4.7	24 4.8	14 58.2	22 18.8	18 24.3	19 52.3	17 53.8

JANUARY 1915

DAY	EPHEMERIS SIDEREAL TIME	☉	☊	☽	☿	♀	♂	♃	♄	♅	♆	♇
	h m s	° ′	° ′	° ′	° ′	° ′	° ′	° ′	° ′	° ′	° ′	° ′
						LONGITUDE						
1 F	6 38 14.9	9♑30.0	29♒ 4.7	3♋36.2	6♑45.7	0♐28.7	7♑28.1	22♒22.8	27♊59.0	9♒51.9	29♋35.3	1♋ 1.4
2 S	6 42 11.5	10 31.2	29 1.5	16 7.4	8 21.5	0 58.1	8 13.8	22 35.2	27R54.2	9 55.1	29R33.8	1R 0.2
3 S	6 46 8.0	11 32.3	28 58.3	28 49.5	9 57.6	1 29.1	8 59.5	22 47.8	27 49.4	9 58.2	29 32.2	0 59.0
4 M	6 50 4.6	12 33.4	28 55.1	11♌42.7	11 34.1	2 1.6	9 45.3	23 0.4	27 44.7	10 1.4	29 30.6	0 57.9
5 T	6 54 1.2	13 34.6	28 52.0	24 47.2	13 11.0	2 35.7	10 31.1	23 13.0	27 40.0	10 4.6	29 29.0	0 56.7
6 W	6 57 57.7	14 35.7	28 48.8	8♍ 3.3	14 48.2	3 11.1	11 17.0	23 25.8	27 35.4	10 7.9	29 27.4	0 55.5
7 T	7 1 54.3	15 36.9	28 45.6	21 32.0	16 25.9	3 47.9	12 2.9	23 38.6	27 30.8	10 11.1	29 25.7	0 54.4
8 F	7 5 50.8	16 38.0	28 42.4	5♎13.9	18 3.9	4 26.1	12 48.8	23 51.5	27 26.2	10 14.4	29 24.1	0 53.2
9 S	7 9 47.4	17 39.2	28 39.3	19 9.5	19 42.4	5 5.5	13 34.8	24 4.5	27 21.7	10 17.7	29 22.4	0 52.0
10 S	7 13 44.0	18 40.3	28 36.1	3♏18.8	21 21.3	5 46.1	14 20.8	24 17.5	27 17.3	10 21.0	29 20.8	0 50.9
11 M	7 17 40.5	19 41.5	28 32.9	17 40.1	23 0.6	6 27.9	15 6.9	24 30.6	27 12.9	10 24.3	29 19.1	0 49.8
12 T	7 21 37.1	20 42.6	28 29.7	2♐10.4	24 40.3	7 10.7	15 53.0	24 43.7	27 8.5	10 27.7	29 17.4	0 48.6
13 W	7 25 33.6	21 43.8	28 26.6	16 44.9	26 20.5	7 54.7	16 39.2	24 56.9	27 4.2	10 31.0	29 15.8	0 47.5
14 T	7 29 30.2	22 44.9	28 23.4	1♑17.3	28 1.0	8 39.7	17 25.3	25 10.2	27 0.0	10 34.4	29 14.1	0 46.4
15 F	7 33 26.7	23 46.1	28 20.2	15 41.1	29 42.0	9 25.6	18 11.6	25 23.5	26 55.9	10 37.8	29 12.4	0 45.3
16 S	7 37 23.3	24 47.2	28 17.0	29 50.1	1♒23.4	10 12.5	18 57.8	25 36.9	26 51.8	10 41.2	29 10.7	0 44.2
17 S	7 41 19.9	25 48.4	28 13.8	13♒39.6	3 5.0	11 0.3	19 44.1	25 50.4	26 47.7	10 44.6	29 9.0	0 43.1
18 M	7 45 16.4	26 49.5	28 10.7	27 6.7	4 47.0	11 48.9	20 30.4	26 3.9	26 43.8	10 48.0	29 7.3	0 42.1
19 T	7 49 13.0	27 50.6	28 7.5	10♓10.9	6 29.2	12 38.4	21 16.8	26 17.4	26 39.9	10 51.4	29 5.6	0 41.0
20 W	7 53 9.6	28 51.7	28 4.3	22 53.3	8 11.6	13 28.7	22 3.2	26 31.0	26 36.1	10 54.9	29 3.9	0 40.0
21 T	7 57 6.1	29 52.8	28 1.1	5♈16.9	9 54.1	14 19.7	22 49.6	26 44.7	26 32.4	10 58.3	29 2.2	0 38.9
22 F	8 1 2.6	0♒53.8	27 58.0	17 25.6	11 36.6	15 11.5	23 36.0	26 58.4	26 28.7	11 1.8	29 0.5	0 37.9
23 S	8 4 59.2	1 54.9	27 54.8	29 23.9	13 18.9	16 4.0	24 22.5	27 12.1	26 25.1	11 5.2	28 58.8	0 36.9
24 S	8 8 55.8	2 55.9	27 51.6	11♉16.7	15 1.0	16 57.1	25 9.0	27 25.9	26 21.7	11 8.7	28 57.2	0 35.9
25 M	8 12 52.3	3 56.9	27 48.4	23 8.9	16 42.5	17 51.0	25 55.5	27 39.8	26 18.3	11 12.2	28 55.5	0 34.9
26 T	8 16 48.9	4 57.9	27 45.3	5♊ 5.1	18 23.5	18 45.4	26 42.1	27 53.6	26 15.0	11 15.7	28 53.8	0 33.9
27 W	8 20 45.4	5 58.9	27 42.1	17 9.4	20 3.4	19 40.5	27 28.7	28 7.5	26 11.7	11 19.1	28 52.1	0 33.0
28 T	8 24 42.0	6 59.8	27 38.9	29 25.0	21 42.2	20 36.1	28 15.3	28 21.5	26 8.6	11 22.6	28 50.4	0 32.0
29 F	8 28 38.5	8 0.8	27 35.7	11♋54.5	23 19.4	21 32.3	29 1.9	28 35.5	26 5.5	11 26.1	28 48.7	0 31.1
30 S	8 32 35.1	9 1.7	27 32.6	24 39.3	24 54.6	22 29.1	29 48.6	28 49.5	26 2.6	11 29.6	28 47.1	0 30.2
31 S	8 36 31.7	10 2.6	27 29.4	7♌39.9	26 27.4	23 26.3	0♒35.3	29 3.5	25 59.7	11 33.1	28 45.4	0 29.3
						DECLINATION						
1 F	6 38 14.9	23S 6.7	11S48.1	27N31.9	24S49.8	16S 7.1	24S 2.8	14S54.1	22N18.8	18S23.4	19N52.7	17N53.8
4 M	6 50 4.6	22 51.5	11 51.4	18 36.3	24 41.9	16 17.6	23 55.2	14 41.7	22 19.0	18 20.8	19 53.7	17 54.1
7 T	7 1 54.3	22 32.3	11 54.7	1 23.7	24 20.8	16 32.5	23 45.2	14 29.0	22 19.2	18 18.2	19 54.7	17 54.4
10 S	7 13 44.0	22 9.0	11 58.0	17S 4.3	23 46.0	16 50.8	23 32.7	14 16.0	22 19.3	18 15.5	19 55.8	17 54.7
13 W	7 25 33.6	21 41.9	12 1.3	27 38.5	22 57.3	17 11.5	23 17.9	14 2.8	22 19.5	18 12.7	19 56.8	17 55.0
16 S	7 37 23.3	21 10.9	12 4.6	22 30.0	21 54.4	17 33.7	23 0.7	13 49.3	22 19.7	18 10.0	19 57.9	17 55.3
19 T	7 49 13.0	20 36.3	12 7.9	6 37.5	20 37.4	17 56.6	22 41.2	13 35.5	22 19.9	18 7.2	19 59.0	17 55.6
22 F	8 1 2.6	19 58.1	12 11.2	10N35.3	19 6.7	18 19.5	22 19.4	13 21.5	22 20.2	18 4.3	20 0.1	17 56.0
25 M	8 12 52.3	19 16.6	12 14.5	23 37.4	17 23.3	18 41.7	21 55.3	13 7.3	22 20.4	18 1.4	20 1.1	17 56.4
28 T	8 24 42.0	18 32.0	12 17.8	27 51.7	15 29.2	19 2.6	21 29.0	12 52.8	22 20.7	17 58.6	20 2.2	17 56.8
31 S	8 36 31.7	17 44.3	12 21.1	20 0.5	13 27.7	19 21.7	21 0.6	12 38.2	22 21.0	17 55.7	20 3.3	17 57.2

FEBRUARY 1915

DAY	EPHEMERIS SIDEREAL TIME	☉	☊	☽	☿	♀	♂	♃	♄	♅	♆	♇
						LONGITUDE						
1 M	8 40 28.2	11♒ 3.5	27♒26.2	20♌55.8	27♒57.4	24♐24.1	1♒22.0	29♒17.6	25♊57.0	11♒36.6	28♋43.8	0♋28.4
2 T	8 44 24.8	12 4.4	27 23.0	4♍25.8	29 23.8	25 22.4	2 8.7	29 31.7	25R54.3	11 40.1	28R42.1	0R27.6
3 W	8 48 21.3	13 5.2	27 19.8	18 8.0	0♓46.1	26 21.2	2 55.5	29 45.9	25 51.7	11 43.6	28 40.5	0 26.7
4 T	8 52 17.9	14 6.1	27 16.7	2♎ 0.4	2 3.7	27 20.4	3 42.3	0♓ 0.1	25 49.3	11 47.1	28 38.9	0 25.9
5 F	8 56 14.5	15 6.9	27 13.5	16 0.9	3 15.8	28 20.0	4 29.1	0 14.3	25 46.9	11 50.6	28 37.3	0 25.1
6 S	9 0 11.0	16 7.7	27 10.3	0♏ 7.2	4 21.7	29 20.1	5 15.9	0 28.5	25 44.6	11 54.1	28 35.6	0 24.3
7 S	9 4 7.6	17 8.5	27 7.1	14 17.4	5 20.5	0♑20.6	6 2.8	0 42.7	25 42.5	11 57.6	28 34.1	0 23.5
8 M	9 8 4.1	18 9.3	27 4.0	28 29.3	6 11.5	1 21.5	6 49.7	0 57.0	25 40.4	12 1.1	28 32.5	0 22.7
9 T	9 12 0.7	19 10.0	27 0.8	12♐40.7	6 54.1	2 22.7	7 36.6	1 11.3	25 38.4	12 4.6	28 30.9	0 22.0
10 W	9 15 57.2	20 10.8	26 57.6	26 49.0	7 27.4	3 24.3	8 23.5	1 25.7	25 36.6	12 8.1	28 29.3	0 21.2
11 T	9 19 53.8	21 11.5	26 54.4	10♑51.4	7 51.0	4 26.3	9 10.5	1 40.0	25 34.8	12 11.5	28 27.8	0 20.5
12 F	9 23 50.3	22 12.2	26 51.2	24 45.0	8 4.3	5 28.6	9 57.4	1 54.4	25 33.2	12 15.0	28 26.3	0 19.9
13 S	9 27 46.9	23 12.9	26 48.1	8♒26.8	8 7.0	6 31.2	10 44.4	2 8.8	25 31.7	12 18.5	28 24.8	0 19.2
14 S	9 31 43.5	24 13.6	26 44.9	21 54.4	7R59.2	7 34.1	11 31.4	2 23.1	25 30.3	12 21.9	28 23.3	0 18.5
15 M	9 35 40.0	25 14.2	26 41.7	5♓ 5.9	7 40.9	8 37.3	12 18.5	2 37.6	25 29.0	12 25.3	28 21.8	0 17.9
16 T	9 39 36.5	26 14.8	26 38.5	18 0.6	7 12.5	9 40.8	13 5.5	2 52.0	25 27.8	12 28.8	28 20.3	0 17.3
17 W	9 43 33.1	27 15.4	26 35.4	0♈38.5	6 34.8	10 44.6	13 52.5	3 6.4	25 26.7	12 32.2	28 18.9	0 16.7
18 T	9 47 29.7	28 16.0	26 32.2	13 1.1	5 48.6	11 48.6	14 39.6	3 20.9	25 25.7	12 35.6	28 17.5	0 16.1
19 F	9 51 26.2	29 16.5	26 29.0	25 10.6	4 55.3	12 52.9	15 26.7	3 35.3	25 24.9	12 39.0	28 16.0	0 15.6
20 S	9 55 22.8	0♓17.0	26 25.8	7♉10.4	3 56.3	13 57.4	16 13.8	3 49.8	25 24.1	12 42.4	28 14.7	0 15.1
21 S	9 59 19.3	1 17.5	26 22.6	19 4.3	2 53.1	15 2.2	17 0.8	4 4.2	25 23.5	12 45.7	28 13.3	0 14.5
22 M	10 3 15.9	2 18.0	26 19.5	0♊56.8	1 47.4	16 7.2	17 47.9	4 18.7	25 22.9	12 49.1	28 11.9	0 14.1
23 T	10 7 12.5	3 18.4	26 16.3	12 52.6	0 41.1	17 12.5	18 35.1	4 33.2	25 22.5	12 52.4	28 10.6	0 13.6
24 W	10 11 9.0	4 18.7	26 13.1	24 56.3	29♒35.6	18 17.9	19 22.2	4 47.6	25 22.2	12 55.8	28 9.3	0 13.2
25 T	10 15 5.6	5 19.1	26 9.9	7♋12.4	28 32.5	19 23.6	20 9.3	5 2.1	25 22.1	12 59.1	28 8.0	0 12.7
26 F	10 19 2.1	6 19.4	26 6.8	19 44.9	27 33.2	20 29.4	20 56.4	5 16.6	25 22.0	13 2.3	28 6.8	0 12.3
27 S	10 22 58.7	7 19.7	26 3.6	2♌36.6	26 38.6	21 35.5	21 43.6	5 31.1	25D22.0	13 5.6	28 5.5	0 12.0
28 S	10 26 55.2	8 19.9	26 0.4	15 49.4	25 49.8	22 41.8	22 30.7	5 45.5	25 22.2	13 8.9	28 4.3	0 11.6
						DECLINATION						
1 M	8 40 28.2	17S27.8	12S22.2	15N 0.7	12S46.5	19S27.6	20S50.6	12S33.3	22N21.1	17S54.7	20N 3.6	17N57.3
4 T	8 52 17.9	16 36.4	12 25.4	3S36.7	10 44.4	19 43.4	20 19.4	12 18.4	22 21.4	17 51.8	20 4.7	17 57.7
7 S	9 4 7.6	15 42.4	12 28.7	21 3.2	8 51.9	19 56.2	19 46.2	12 3.4	22 21.7	17 48.9	20 5.7	17 58.2
10 W	9 15 57.2	14 45.9	12 32.0	27 58.4	7 20.1	20 5.6	19 11.0	11 48.2	22 22.1	17 46.0	20 6.7	17 58.6
13 S	9 27 46.9	13 47.2	12 35.2	19 44.7	6 20.2	20 11.4	18 34.0	11 32.9	22 22.6	17 43.1	20 7.7	17 59.1
16 T	9 39 36.5	12 46.5	12 38.5	2 57.4	6 0.9	20 13.1	17 55.1	11 17.4	22 23.0	17 40.2	20 8.6	17 59.6
19 F	9 51 26.2	11 43.9	12 41.7	13N56.8	6 23.8	20 10.6	17 14.6	11 1.8	22 23.5	17 37.4	20 9.5	18 0.0
22 M	10 3 15.9	10 39.7	12 44.9	25 30.4	7 21.3	20 3.7	16 32.4	10 46.2	22 24.0	17 34.5	20 10.4	18 0.5
25 T	10 15 5.6	9 34.0	12 48.2	27 15.5	8 38.2	19 52.3	15 48.7	10 30.4	22 24.6	17 31.7	20 11.2	18 1.0
28 S	10 26 55.2	8 27.0	12 51.4	17 2.5	9 58.0	19 36.2	15 3.5	10 14.6	22 25.2	17 29.0	20 12.0	18 1.5

MARCH 1915

DAY	EPHEMERIS SIDEREAL TIME	☉	☊	☽	☿	♀	♂	♃	♄	♅	♆	♇
	h m s	° ′	° ′	° ′	° ′	° ′	° ′	° ′	° ′	° ′	° ′	° ′
						LONGITUDE						
1 M	10 30 51.8	9♓20.2	25♒57.2	29♌23.5	25♒ 7.2	23♑48.2	23♒17.9	5♓60.0	25♊22.5	13♒12.1	28♋ 3.1	0♋11.3
2 T	10 34 48.3	10 20.3	25 54.0	13♍17.5	24R31.4	24 54.8	24 5.0	6 14.4	25 22.8	13 15.3	28R 1.9	0R10.9
3 W	10 38 44.9	11 20.5	25 50.9	27 28.0	24 2.5	26 1.7	24 52.2	6 28.9	25 23.3	13 18.5	28 0.8	0 10.7
4 T	10 42 41.5	12 20.6	25 47.7	11♎50.5	23 40.7	27 8.7	25 39.3	6 43.3	25 24.0	13 21.7	27 59.7	0 10.4
5 F	10 46 38.0	13 20.7	25 44.5	26 19.3	23 25.8	28 15.8	26 26.5	6 57.7	25 24.7	13 24.8	27 58.6	0 10.2
6 S	10 50 34.5	14 20.8	25 41.3	10♏48.9	23 17.7	29 23.1	27 13.7	7 12.2	25 25.5	13 28.0	27 57.5	0 9.9
7 S	10 54 31.1	15 20.9	25 38.2	25 14.1	23 16.2	0♒30.6	28 0.8	7 26.6	25 26.4	13 31.1	27 56.5	0 9.7
8 M	10 58 27.6	16 20.9	25 35.0	9♐31.0	23D21.0	1 38.2	28 48.0	7 41.0	25 27.5	13 34.1	27 55.5	0 9.5
9 T	11 2 24.2	17 20.9	25 31.8	23 37.0	23 31.8	2 46.0	29 35.2	7 55.4	25 28.7	13 37.2	27 54.5	0 9.4
10 W	11 6 20.8	18 20.9	25 28.6	7♑30.5	23 48.2	3 54.0	0♓22.4	8 9.7	25 30.0	13 40.2	27 53.5	0 9.3
11 T	11 10 17.3	19 20.8	25 25.5	21 11.1	24 10.0	5 2.0	1 9.6	8 24.1	25 31.3	13 43.3	27 52.6	0 9.2
12 F	11 14 13.9	20 20.7	25 22.3	4♒38.6	24 36.7	6 10.2	1 56.7	8 38.4	25 32.8	13 46.2	27 51.7	0 9.1
13 S	11 18 10.4	21 20.6	25 19.1	17 53.4	25 8.2	7 18.5	2 43.9	8 52.7	25 34.5	13 49.2	27 50.8	0 9.0
14 S	11 22 7.0	22 20.5	25 15.9	0♓55.8	25 44.1	8 27.0	3 31.1	9 7.0	25 36.2	13 52.1	27 50.0	0 9.0
15 M	11 26 3.5	23 20.3	25 12.7	13 45.8	26 24.0	9 35.5	4 18.3	9 21.3	25 38.0	13 55.0	27 49.1	0 9.0
16 T	11 30 0.1	24 20.1	25 9.6	26 23.8	27 7.8	10 44.2	5 5.4	9 35.5	25 39.9	13 57.9	27 48.3	0D 9.0
17 W	11 33 56.6	25 19.8	25 6.4	8♈50.2	27 55.2	11 53.0	5 52.6	9 49.8	25 42.0	14 0.7	27 47.6	0 9.0
18 T	11 37 53.2	26 19.6	25 3.2	21 5.7	28 46.0	13 1.9	6 39.7	10 4.0	25 44.1	14 3.5	27 46.9	0 9.0
19 F	11 41 49.8	27 19.3	25 0.0	3♉11.6	29 39.9	14 10.9	7 26.9	10 18.1	25 46.4	14 6.3	27 46.2	0 9.1
20 S	11 45 46.3	28 18.9	24 56.9	15 9.8	0♓36.8	15 19.9	8 14.0	10 32.3	25 48.8	14 9.1	27 45.5	0 9.2
21 S	11 49 42.8	29 18.5	24 53.7	27 3.1	1 36.5	16 29.1	9 1.1	10 46.4	25 51.2	14 11.8	27 44.9	0 9.3
22 M	11 53 39.4	0♈18.1	24 50.5	8♊54.8	2 38.8	17 38.4	9 48.2	11 0.5	25 53.8	14 14.5	27 44.3	0 9.5
23 T	11 57 36.0	1 17.6	24 47.3	20 49.0	3 43.6	18 47.8	10 35.3	11 14.5	25 56.5	14 17.1	27 43.7	0 9.7
24 W	12 1 32.5	2 17.2	24 44.2	2♋50.2	4 50.8	19 57.2	11 22.4	11 28.5	25 59.3	14 19.8	27 43.2	0 9.9
25 T	12 5 29.1	3 16.6	24 41.0	15 3.2	6 0.3	21 6.7	12 9.5	11 42.5	26 2.1	14 22.3	27 42.6	0 10.1
26 F	12 9 25.6	4 16.0	24 37.8	27 33.0	7 11.8	22 16.4	12 56.5	11 56.4	26 5.1	14 24.9	27 42.2	0 10.3
27 S	12 13 22.2	5 15.4	24 34.6	10♌23.8	8 25.5	23 26.1	13 43.6	12 10.3	26 8.2	14 27.4	27 41.7	0 10.6
28 S	12 17 18.7	6 14.8	24 31.4	23 39.2	9 41.1	24 35.8	14 30.6	12 24.2	26 11.4	14 29.9	27 41.3	0 10.9
29 M	12 21 15.3	7 14.1	24 28.3	7♍20.9	10 58.7	25 45.7	15 17.6	12 38.0	26 14.7	14 32.3	27 40.9	0 11.2
30 T	12 25 11.8	8 13.4	24 25.1	21 28.6	12 18.1	26 55.6	16 4.6	12 51.8	26 18.0	14 34.7	27 40.6	0 11.5
31 W	12 29 8.4	9 12.6	24 21.9	5♎59.3	13 39.2	28 5.6	16 51.5	13 5.5	26 21.5	14 37.1	27 40.3	0 11.8
						DECLINATION						
1 M	10 30 51.8	8S 4.4	12S52.5	11N26.8	10S22.8	19S29.8	14S48.1	10S 9.4	22N25.4	17S28.1	20N12.3	18N 1.7
4 T	10 42 41.5	6 56.0	12 55.7	8S 7.7	11 27.9	19 7.4	14 1.1	9 53.5	22 26.1	17 25.4	20 13.0	18 2.2
7 S	10 54 31.1	5 46.7	12 58.9	24 10.5	12 15.4	18 40.3	13 12.9	9 37.6	22 26.7	17 22.8	20 13.7	18 2.7
10 W	11 6 20.8	4 36.6	13 2.1	27 11.6	12 43.9	18 8.5	12 23.5	9 21.7	22 27.5	17 20.2	20 14.4	18 3.3
13 S	11 18 10.4	3 26.1	13 5.3	16 13.4	12 53.9	17 32.0	11 33.0	9 5.8	22 28.2	17 17.7	20 15.0	18 3.8
16 T	11 30 0.1	2 15.1	13 8.5	0N57.8	12 46.5	16 51.2	10 41.5	8 49.9	22 29.0	17 15.2	20 15.5	18 4.3
19 F	11 41 49.8	1 3.9	13 11.7	17 4.5	12 23.0	16 5.9	9 49.2	8 34.1	22 29.7	17 12.9	20 16.0	18 4.8
22 M	11 53 39.4	0N 7.2	13 14.9	26 47.6	11 44.5	15 16.6	8 56.1	8 18.3	22 30.5	17 10.6	20 16.5	18 5.4
25 T	12 5 29.1	1 18.2	13 18.1	25 58.8	10 52.0	14 23.2	8 2.2	8 2.5	22 31.4	17 8.4	20 16.9	18 5.9
28 S	12 17 18.7	2 28.9	13 21.3	13 50.3	9 46.3	13 26.2	7 7.8	7 46.9	22 32.2	17 6.3	20 17.2	18 6.4
31 W	12 29 8.4	3 39.1	13 24.5	5S25.7	8 28.3	12 25.6	6 12.8	7 31.4	22 33.0	17 4.2	20 17.4	18 6.9

APRIL 1915

DAY	EPHEMERIS SIDEREAL TIME	☉	☊	☽	☿	♀	♂	♃	♄	♅	♆	♇
						LONGITUDE						
1 T	12 33 4.9	10♈11.8	24♒18.7	20♎47.0	15♓ 2.1	29♒15.7	17♓38.5	13♓19.2	26♊25.1	14♒39.4	27♋40.0	0♋12.2
2 F	12 37 1.5	11 11.0	24 15.5	5♏43.7	16 26.7	0♓25.9	18 25.4	13 32.9	26 28.7	14 41.7	27R39.7	0 12.6
3 S	12 40 58.0	12 10.1	24 12.4	20 40.3	17 52.9	1 36.1	19 12.4	13 46.5	26 32.5	14 44.0	27 39.5	0 13.0
4 S	12 44 54.6	13 9.2	24 9.2	5♐28.4	19 20.8	2 46.4	19 59.3	14 0.0	26 36.3	14 46.2	27 39.3	0 13.5
5 M	12 48 51.2	14 8.3	24 6.0	20 1.2	20 50.3	3 56.8	20 46.1	14 13.5	26 40.3	14 48.4	27 39.2	0 13.9
6 T	12 52 47.7	15 7.4	24 2.8	4♑14.6	22 21.3	5 7.2	21 33.0	14 27.0	26 44.3	14 50.5	27 39.1	0 14.4
7 W	12 56 44.3	16 6.4	23 59.7	18 6.8	23 54.0	6 17.7	22 19.9	14 40.4	26 48.4	14 52.6	27 39.0	0 14.9
8 T	13 0 40.8	17 5.4	23 56.5	1♒38.5	25 28.1	7 28.2	23 6.7	14 53.7	26 52.6	14 54.7	27 38.9	0 15.4
9 F	13 4 37.4	18 4.3	23 53.3	14 51.2	27 3.9	8 38.9	23 53.5	15 7.0	26 56.9	14 56.7	27 38.9	0 16.0
10 S	13 8 33.9	19 3.3	23 50.1	27 47.6	28 41.1	9 49.5	24 40.3	15 20.3	27 1.3	14 58.7	27D39.0	0 16.6
11 S	13 12 30.5	20 2.2	23 47.0	10♓30.2	0♈19.9	11 0.3	25 27.0	15 33.5	27 5.8	15 0.6	27 39.0	0 17.2
12 M	13 16 27.1	21 1.1	23 43.8	23 1.2	2 0.3	12 11.0	26 13.8	15 46.6	27 10.3	15 2.5	27 39.1	0 17.8
13 T	13 20 23.6	21 59.9	23 40.6	5♈22.4	3 42.1	13 21.9	27 0.5	15 59.7	27 15.0	15 4.4	27 39.2	0 18.4
14 W	13 24 20.1	22 58.7	23 37.4	17 35.3	5 25.6	14 32.7	27 47.1	16 12.7	27 19.7	15 6.2	27 39.4	0 19.0
15 T	13 28 16.7	23 57.5	23 34.2	29 41.0	7 10.5	15 43.7	28 33.8	16 25.7	27 24.5	15 7.9	27 39.5	0 19.7
16 F	13 32 13.3	24 56.2	23 31.1	11♉40.7	8 57.1	16 54.6	29 20.4	16 38.5	27 29.4	15 9.7	27 39.8	0 20.4
17 S	13 36 9.8	25 54.9	23 27.9	23 35.5	10 45.2	18 5.6	0♈ 7.0	16 51.4	27 34.4	15 11.3	27 40.0	0 21.1
18 S	13 40 6.4	26 53.6	23 24.7	5♊27.3	12 34.9	19 16.7	0 53.6	17 4.1	27 39.4	15 13.0	27 40.3	0 21.9
19 M	13 44 2.9	27 52.3	23 21.5	17 18.4	14 26.2	20 27.8	1 40.1	17 16.8	27 44.5	15 14.5	27 40.6	0 22.6
20 T	13 47 59.5	28 50.9	23 18.3	29 11.9	16 19.1	21 38.9	2 26.6	17 29.4	27 49.7	15 16.1	27 41.0	0 23.4
21 W	13 51 56.0	29 49.4	23 15.2	11♋11.5	18 13.6	22 50.1	3 13.1	17 41.9	27 55.0	15 17.6	27 41.4	0 24.2
22 T	13 55 52.6	0♉48.0	23 12.0	23 21.7	20 9.7	24 1.2	3 59.5	17 54.4	28 0.3	15 19.0	27 41.8	0 25.0
23 F	13 59 49.1	1 46.5	23 8.8	5♌47.3	22 7.3	25 12.5	4 45.9	18 6.8	28 5.8	15 20.4	27 42.2	0 25.8
24 S	14 3 45.7	2 44.9	23 5.6	18 33.3	24 6.5	26 23.8	5 32.3	18 19.1	28 11.3	15 21.8	27 42.7	0 26.7
25 S	14 7 42.3	3 43.3	23 2.5	1♍44.2	26 7.3	27 35.1	6 18.6	18 31.4	28 16.8	15 23.1	27 43.3	0 27.6
26 M	14 11 38.8	4 41.7	22 59.3	15 23.3	28 9.4	28 46.4	7 4.9	18 43.5	28 22.5	15 24.4	27 43.8	0 28.4
27 T	14 15 35.3	5 40.1	22 56.1	29 31.9	0♉13.0	29 57.8	7 51.1	18 55.6	28 28.1	15 25.6	27 44.4	0 29.3
28 W	14 19 31.9	6 38.4	22 52.9	14♎ 8.3	2 17.9	1♈ 9.2	8 37.3	19 7.6	28 33.9	15 26.7	27 45.0	0 30.3
29 T	14 23 28.5	7 36.7	22 49.8	29 7.3	4 24.1	2 20.6	9 23.5	19 19.5	28 39.7	15 27.8	27 45.6	0 31.2
30 F	14 27 25.0	8 35.0	22 46.6	14♏20.4	6 31.3	3 32.1	10 9.7	19 31.4	28 45.6	15 28.9	27 46.3	0 32.2
						DECLINATION						
1 T	12 33 4.9	4N 2.4	13S25.5	12S 1.1	7S59.7	12S 4.6	5S54.4	7S26.2	22N33.3	17S 3.6	20N17.5	18N 7.1
4 S	12 44 54.6	5 11.8	13 28.7	26 11.6	6 26.2	10 59.7	4 58.9	7 10.9	22 34.1	17 1.7	20 17.7	18 7.6
7 W	12 56 44.3	6 20.3	13 31.8	25 18.2	4 41.7	9 51.9	4 3.1	6 55.6	22 34.9	16 59.9	20 17.9	18 8.1
10 S	13 8 33.9	7 27.9	13 35.0	12 2.2	2 47.0	8 41.3	3 7.0	6 40.6	22 35.7	16 58.2	20 17.9	18 8.6
13 T	13 20 23.6	8 34.4	13 38.1	5N 9.1	0 42.6	7 28.3	2 10.8	6 25.7	22 36.5	16 56.6	20 17.9	18 9.1
16 F	13 32 13.3	9 39.6	13 41.3	20 1.4	1N30.7	6 13.3	1 14.5	6 11.0	22 37.3	16 55.2	20 17.9	18 9.6
19 M	13 44 2.9	10 43.4	13 44.4	27 28.3	3 52.2	4 56.4	0 18.3	5 56.5	22 38.1	16 53.8	20 17.8	18 10.1
22 T	13 55 52.6	11 45.5	13 47.5	23 58.3	6 20.4	3 38.0	0N37.8	5 42.2	22 38.8	16 52.6	20 17.6	18 10.5
25 S	14 7 42.3	12 45.9	13 50.7	10 12.9	8 53.7	2 18.4	1 33.6	5 28.2	22 39.5	16 51.5	20 17.4	18 11.0
28 W	14 19 31.9	13 44.4	13 53.8	9S 9.3	11 29.6	0 57.8	2 29.2	5 14.5	22 40.1	16 50.5	20 17.1	18 11.4

MAY 1915

DAY	EPHEMERIS SIDEREAL TIME	☉	☊	☽	☿	♀	♂	♃	♄	♅	♆	♇
	h m s	° ′	° ′	° ′	° ′	° ′	° ′	° ′	° ′	° ′	° ′	° ′
						LONGITUDE						
1 S	14 31 21.6	9♉33.2	22♒43.4	29♏36.6	8♉39.5	4♈43.6	10♈55.8	19♓43.1	28♊51.6	15♒30.0	27♋47.0	0♋33.1
2 S	14 35 18.1	10 31.4	22 40.2	14♐44.9	10 48.4	5 55.1	11 41.8	19 54.8	28 57.6	15 30.9	27 47.8	0 34.1
3 M	14 39 14.7	11 29.6	22 37.0	29 35.9	12 57.8	7 6.7	12 27.9	20 6.4	29 3.7	15 31.8	27 48.6	0 35.1
4 T	14 43 11.2	12 27.7	22 33.9	14♑ 3.1	15 7.6	8 18.3	13 13.9	20 17.9	29 9.9	15 32.7	27 49.4	0 36.2
5 W	14 47 7.8	13 25.8	22 30.7	28 3.7	17 17.5	9 29.9	13 59.8	20 29.3	29 16.1	15 33.6	27 50.2	0 37.2
6 T	14 51 4.4	14 23.9	22 27.5	11♒37.7	19 27.1	10 41.6	14 45.7	20 40.6	29 22.3	15 34.3	27 51.1	0 38.3
7 F	14 55 0.9	15 22.0	22 24.3	24 47.5	21 36.2	11 53.3	15 31.6	20 51.8	29 28.6	15 35.1	27 52.0	0 39.3
8 S	14 58 57.5	16 20.1	22 21.2	7♓36.6	23 44.6	13 5.0	16 17.5	21 3.0	29 35.0	15 35.8	27 52.9	0 40.4
9 S	15 2 54.0	17 18.1	22 18.0	20 8.8	25 51.9	14 16.8	17 3.3	21 14.0	29 41.5	15 36.4	27 53.9	0 41.5
10 M	15 6 50.6	18 16.1	22 14.8	2♈28.1	27 57.8	15 28.6	17 49.0	21 24.9	29 48.0	15 37.0	27 54.8	0 42.6
11 T	15 10 47.1	19 14.1	22 11.6	14 37.6	0♊ 2.1	16 40.4	18 34.7	21 35.7	29 54.5	15 37.5	27 55.9	0 43.8
12 W	15 14 43.7	20 12.1	22 8.4	26 40.0	2 4.4	17 52.2	19 20.4	21 46.5	0♋ 1.1	15 38.0	27 56.9	0 44.9
13 T	15 18 40.2	21 10.0	22 5.3	8♉37.5	4 4.7	19 4.1	20 6.0	21 57.1	0 7.7	15 38.5	27 58.0	0 46.1
14 F	15 22 36.8	22 7.9	22 2.1	20 31.6	6 2.6	20 16.0	20 51.6	22 7.6	0 14.4	15 38.8	27 59.1	0 47.2
15 S	15 26 33.4	23 5.8	21 58.9	2♊23.8	7 57.9	21 27.9	21 37.1	22 18.0	0 21.2	15 39.2	28 0.2	0 48.4
16 S	15 30 29.9	24 3.7	21 55.7	14 15.4	9 50.6	22 39.8	22 22.6	22 28.3	0 28.0	15 39.5	28 1.4	0 49.6
17 M	15 34 26.5	25 1.5	21 52.6	26 8.0	11 40.5	23 51.8	23 8.1	22 38.5	0 34.8	15 39.7	28 2.6	0 50.8
18 T	15 38 23.0	25 59.3	21 49.4	8♋ 3.9	13 27.4	25 3.7	23 53.4	22 48.6	0 41.7	15 39.9	28 3.8	0 52.0
19 W	15 42 19.6	26 57.1	21 46.2	20 5.8	15 11.3	26 15.7	24 38.8	22 58.6	0 48.6	15 40.0	28 5.1	0 53.3
20 T	15 46 16.2	27 54.9	21 43.0	2♌17.2	16 52.1	27 27.7	25 24.1	23 8.5	0 55.6	15 40.1	28 6.4	0 54.5
21 F	15 50 12.7	28 52.6	21 39.9	14 42.2	18 29.7	28 39.7	26 9.3	23 18.2	1 2.6	15 40.2	28 7.7	0 55.8
22 S	15 54 9.2	29 50.3	21 36.7	27 25.4	20 4.1	29 51.8	26 54.5	23 27.8	1 9.7	15R40.2	28 9.0	0 57.1
23 S	15 58 5.8	0♊48.0	21 33.5	10♍31.2	21 35.2	1♉ 3.8	27 39.6	23 37.3	1 16.8	15 40.1	28 10.3	0 58.3
24 M	16 2 2.3	1 45.7	21 30.3	24 3.5	23 2.9	2 15.9	28 24.7	23 46.7	1 23.9	15 40.0	28 11.7	0 59.6
25 T	16 5 58.9	2 43.3	21 27.2	8♎ 4.6	24 27.4	3 28.0	29 9.7	23 56.0	1 31.1	15 39.9	28 13.1	1 0.9
26 W	16 9 55.5	3 40.9	21 24.0	22 34.2	25 48.4	4 40.1	29 54.7	24 5.1	1 38.3	15 39.6	28 14.6	1 2.2
27 T	16 13 52.0	4 38.5	21 20.8	7♏28.9	27 5.9	5 52.3	0♉39.6	24 14.1	1 45.5	15 39.4	28 16.0	1 3.6
28 F	16 17 48.6	5 36.0	21 17.6	22 41.4	28 20.0	7 4.4	1 24.5	24 23.0	1 52.8	15 39.1	28 17.5	1 4.9
29 S	16 21 45.1	6 33.6	21 14.4	8♐ 1.5	29 30.5	8 16.6	2 9.3	24 31.8	2 0.1	15 38.8	28 19.0	1 6.2
30 S	16 25 41.7	7 31.1	21 11.3	23 17.6	0♋37.4	9 28.8	2 54.1	24 40.4	2 7.4	15 38.4	28 20.5	1 7.6
31 M	16 29 38.2	8 28.6	21 8.1	8♑19.0	1 40.6	10 41.0	3 38.8	24 48.9	2 14.8	15 37.9	28 22.1	1 8.9
						DECLINATION						
1 S	14 31 21.6	14N40.8	13S56.9	24S56.6	14N 4.5	0N23.5	3N24.4	5S 1.0	22N40.8	16S49.7	20N16.8	18N11.9
4 T	14 43 11.2	15 35.1	14 0.0	25 51.0	16 33.7	1 45.2	4 19.2	4 47.9	22 41.3	16 49.0	20 16.4	18 12.3
7 F	14 55 0.9	16 27.1	14 3.1	13 5.9	18 51.8	3 7.0	5 13.5	4 35.0	22 41.9	16 48.4	20 15.9	18 12.7
10 M	15 6 50.6	17 16.7	14 6.2	3N56.0	20 53.5	4 28.6	6 7.2	4 22.5	22 42.3	16 47.9	20 15.4	18 13.0
13 T	15 18 40.2	18 3.6	14 9.3	18 58.4	22 34.7	5 49.6	7 0.2	4 10.4	22 42.7	16 47.6	20 14.9	18 13.4
16 S	15 30 29.9	18 47.9	14 12.4	27 5.7	23 53.1	7 9.9	7 52.5	3 58.6	22 43.1	16 47.4	20 14.3	18 13.8
19 W	15 42 19.6	19 29.2	14 15.4	24 30.3	24 48.5	8 29.0	8 43.9	3 47.2	22 43.4	16 47.3	20 13.6	18 14.1
22 S	15 54 9.2	20 7.6	14 18.5	11 50.3	25 22.3	9 46.7	9 34.5	3 36.3	22 43.6	16 47.4	20 12.9	18 14.4
25 T	16 5 58.9	20 42.9	14 21.6	6S36.0	25 36.7	11 2.6	10 24.0	3 25.8	22 43.7	16 47.6	20 12.1	18 14.7
28 F	16 17 48.6	21 15.0	14 24.6	23 17.9	25 34.3	12 16.5	11 12.6	3 15.7	22 43.8	16 47.9	20 11.3	18 15.0
31 M	16 29 38.2	21 43.8	14 27.7	26 32.4	25 17.8	13 28.0	12 0.0	3 6.1	22 43.8	16 48.4	20 10.4	18 15.3

JUNE 1915

DAY	EPHEMERIS SIDEREAL TIME	☉	☊	☽	☿	♀	♂	♃	♄	♅	♆	♇
						LONGITUDE						
1 T	16 33 34.8	9♊26.1	21♒ 4.9	22♑57.4	2♋40.1	11♉53.3	4♉23.4	24♓57.2	2♋22.2	15♒37.4	28♋23.7	1♋10.3
2 W	16 37 31.4	10 23.5	21 1.7	7♒ 8.2	3 35.8	13 5.5	5 8.0	25 5.5	2 29.6	15R36.9	28 25.3	1 11.7
3 T	16 41 28.0	11 21.0	20 58.6	20 50.1	4 27.7	14 17.8	5 52.6	25 13.6	2 37.1	15 36.3	28 26.9	1 13.1
4 F	16 45 24.5	12 18.4	20 55.4	4♓ 4.6	5 15.5	15 30.1	6 37.1	25 21.5	2 44.6	15 35.7	28 28.5	1 14.4
5 S	16 49 21.0	13 15.9	20 52.2	16 55.0	5 59.4	16 42.5	7 21.5	25 29.3	2 52.1	15 35.0	28 30.2	1 15.8
6 S	16 53 17.6	14 13.3	20 49.0	29 25.7	6 39.1	17 54.8	8 5.9	25 37.0	2 59.6	15 34.3	28 31.9	1 17.2
7 M	16 57 14.2	15 10.7	20 45.9	11♈41.1	7 14.6	19 7.2	8 50.3	25 44.6	3 7.2	15 33.5	28 33.6	1 18.7
8 T	17 1 10.8	16 8.1	20 42.7	23 45.5	7 45.8	20 19.6	9 34.6	25 51.9	3 14.8	15 32.7	28 35.4	1 20.1
9 W	17 5 7.3	17 5.5	20 39.5	5♉42.6	8 12.7	21 32.0	10 18.8	25 59.2	3 22.4	15 31.8	28 37.1	1 21.5
10 T	17 9 3.8	18 2.9	20 36.3	17 35.6	8 35.1	22 44.5	11 2.9	26 6.3	3 30.0	15 30.9	28 38.9	1 22.9
11 F	17 13 0.4	19 0.3	20 33.1	29 27.1	8 53.1	23 57.0	11 47.1	26 13.2	3 37.6	15 30.0	28 40.7	1 24.3
12 S	17 16 56.9	19 57.6	20 30.0	11♊19.0	9 6.5	25 9.4	12 31.1	26 20.0	3 45.3	15 29.0	28 42.5	1 25.8
13 S	17 20 53.5	20 55.0	20 26.8	23 12.9	9 15.3	26 22.0	13 15.1	26 26.6	3 53.0	15 28.0	28 44.3	1 27.2
14 M	17 24 50.1	21 52.3	20 23.6	5♋10.5	9 19.5	27 34.5	13 59.0	26 33.1	4 0.7	15 26.9	28 46.2	1 28.6
15 T	17 28 46.6	22 49.6	20 20.4	17 13.3	9R19.3	28 47.0	14 42.9	26 39.4	4 8.4	15 25.8	28 48.0	1 30.1
16 W	17 32 43.2	23 47.0	20 17.3	29 23.1	9 14.5	29 59.6	15 26.7	26 45.6	4 16.1	15 24.6	28 49.9	1 31.5
17 T	17 36 39.7	24 44.3	20 14.1	11♌42.4	9 5.4	1♊12.2	16 10.4	26 51.6	4 23.9	15 23.4	28 51.8	1 33.0
18 F	17 40 36.3	25 41.6	20 10.9	24 14.0	8 52.1	2 24.8	16 54.1	26 57.4	4 31.6	15 22.1	28 53.7	1 34.4
19 S	17 44 32.9	26 38.8	20 7.7	7♍ 1.2	8 34.8	3 37.4	17 37.7	27 3.1	4 39.4	15 20.8	28 55.7	1 35.9
20 S	17 48 29.4	27 36.1	20 4.6	20 7.5	8 13.8	4 50.0	18 21.3	27 8.6	4 47.2	15 19.5	28 57.6	1 37.3
21 M	17 52 26.0	28 33.3	20 1.4	3♎36.1	7 49.3	6 2.7	19 4.7	27 14.0	4 55.0	15 18.1	28 59.6	1 38.8
22 T	17 56 22.6	29 30.6	19 58.2	17 28.9	7 21.7	7 15.3	19 48.2	27 19.1	5 2.8	15 16.7	29 1.6	1 40.3
23 W	18 0 19.1	0♋27.8	19 55.0	1♏46.6	6 51.6	8 28.0	20 31.5	27 24.1	5 10.5	15 15.3	29 3.6	1 41.7
24 T	18 4 15.7	1 25.0	19 51.9	16 26.8	6 19.3	9 40.7	21 14.8	27 29.0	5 18.3	15 13.8	29 5.6	1 43.2
25 F	18 8 12.2	2 22.2	19 48.7	1♐24.6	5 45.3	10 53.4	21 58.0	27 33.6	5 26.1	15 12.3	29 7.6	1 44.6
26 S	18 12 8.8	3 19.4	19 45.5	16 32.0	5 10.3	12 6.2	22 41.2	27 38.1	5 34.0	15 10.7	29 9.6	1 46.1
27 S	18 16 5.4	4 16.6	19 42.3	1♑39.3	4 34.9	13 19.0	23 24.3	27 42.4	5 41.8	15 9.1	29 11.7	1 47.6
28 M	18 20 1.9	5 13.8	19 39.2	16 36.7	3 59.5	14 31.8	24 7.3	27 46.6	5 49.6	15 7.5	29 13.8	1 49.0
29 T	18 23 58.4	6 11.0	19 36.0	1♒15.7	3 24.9	15 44.6	24 50.2	27 50.5	5 57.4	15 5.8	29 15.8	1 50.5
30 W	18 27 55.0	7 8.2	19 32.8	15 30.4	2 51.7	16 57.4	25 33.2	27 54.3	6 5.2	15 4,1	29 17.9	1 51.9
						DECLINATION						
1 T	16 33 34.8	21N52.6	14S28.7	23S45.5	25N 9.7	13N51.3	12N15.6	3S 3.0	22N43.8	16S48.6	20N10.1	18N15.3
4 F	16 45 24.5	22 16.9	14 31.8	8 51.5	24 38.6	14 59.2	13 1.5	2 54.0	22 43.7	16 49.2	20 9.2	18 15.6
7 M	16 57 14.2	22 37.7	14 34.8	8N17.4	23 59.4	16 4.0	13 46.2	2 45.6	22 43.5	16 49.9	20 8.2	18 15.8
10 T	17 9 3.8	22 54.9	14 37.8	21 55.8	23 14.7	17 5.5	14 29.5	2 37.7	22 43.2	16 50.8	20 7.2	18 16.0
13 S	17 20 53.5	23 8.5	14 40.8	27 27.5	22 26.6	18 3.1	15 11.6	2 30.3	22 42.9	16 51.8	20 6.1	18 16.2
16 W	17 32 43.2	23 18.4	14 43.9	21 55.9	21 37.7	18 56.8	15 52.2	2 23.6	22 42.5	16 52.9	20 5.0	18 16.3
19 S	17 44 32.9	23 24.6	14 46.9	7 25.4	20 50.2	19 46.1	16 31.3	2 17.4	22 42.0	16 54.1	20 3.9	18 16.5
22 T	17 56 22.6	23 27.1	14 49.9	10S55.8	20 6.8	20 30.8	17 8.9	2 11.8	22 41.4	16 55.4	20 2.7	18 16.6
25 F	18 8 12.2	23 25.8	14 52.9	25 20.5	19 30.0	21 10.5	17 45.0	2 6.8	22 40.7	16 56.8	20 1.5	18 16.7
28 M	18 20 1.9	23 20.9	14 55.9	25 5.0	19 2.4	21 45.2	18 19.5	2 2.4	22 40.0	16 58.3	20 0.3	18 16.8

JULY 1915

DAY	EPHEMERIS SIDEREAL TIME h m s	☉ ° ′	☊ ° ′	☽ ° ′	☿ ° ′	♀ ° ′	♂ ° ′	♃ ° ′	♄ ° ′	♅ ° ′	♆ ° ′	♇ ° ′
LONGITUDE												
1 T	18 31 51.6	8♋ 5.4	19♒29.6	29♒18.0	2♋20.4	18♊10.3	26♉16.0	27♓57.9	6♋13.0	15♒ 2.4	29♋20.0	1♋53.4
2 F	18 35 48.2	9 2.5	19 26.5	12♓38.5	1R51.6	19 23.2	26 58.8	28 1.4	6 20.8	15R 0.7	29 22.1	1 54.8
3 S	18 39 44.7	9 59.7	19 23.3	25 34.0	1 25.8	20 36.1	27 41.5	28 4.6	6 28.6	14 58.9	29 24.2	1 56.3
4 S	18 43 41.2	10 56.9	19 20.1	8♈ 8.0	1 3.4	21 49.1	28 24.1	28 7.7	6 36.4	14 57.0	29 26.4	1 57.7
5 M	18 47 37.8	11 54.1	19 16.9	20 25.0	0 44.8	23 2.1	29 6.7	28 10.5	6 44.2	14 55.2	29 28.5	1 59.2
6 T	18 51 34.4	12 51.3	19 13.7	2♉29.3	0 30.5	24 15.1	29 49.2	28 13.2	6 52.0	14 53.3	29 30.6	2 0.6
7 W	18 55 30.9	13 48.5	19 10.6	14 25.5	0 20.6	25 28.1	0♊31.7	28 15.7	6 59.8	14 51.4	29 32.8	2 2.1
8 T	18 59 27.5	14 45.7	19 7.4	26 17.6	0 15.4	26 41.2	1 14.0	28 18.0	7 7.6	14 49.4	29 35.0	2 3.5
9 F	19 3 24.0	15 43.0	19 4.2	8♊ 9.2	0 15.3	27 54.2	1 56.3	28 20.1	7 15.4	14 47.4	29 37.1	2 4.9
10 S	19 7 20.6	16 40.2	19 1.0	20 3.1	0D20.1	29 7.3	2 38.6	28 22.1	7 23.1	14 45.4	29 39.3	2 6.3
11 S	19 11 17.1	17 37.4	18 57.9	2♋ 1.8	0 30.2	0♋20.5	3 20.7	28 23.8	7 30.9	14 43.4	29 41.5	2 7.8
12 M	19 15 13.7	18 34.6	18 54.7	14 7.3	0 45.6	1 33.6	4 2.8	28 25.4	7 38.6	14 41.4	29 43.7	2 9.2
13 T	19 19 10.3	19 31.9	18 51.5	26 21.0	1 6.2	2 46.8	4 44.8	28 26.7	7 46.3	14 39.3	29 45.9	2 10.6
14 W	19 23 6.8	20 29.1	18 48.3	8♌44.3	1 32.2	4 0.0	5 26.8	28 27.9	7 54.0	14 37.2	29 48.1	2 12.0
15 T	19 27 3.4	21 26.4	18 45.2	21 18.5	2 3.6	5 13.3	6 8.7	28 28.8	8 1.7	14 35.1	29 50.3	2 13.4
16 F	19 30 60.0	22 23.6	18 42.0	4♍ 5.2	2 40.2	6 26.5	6 50.5	28 29.6	8 9.4	14 32.9	29 52.5	2 14.8
17 S	19 34 56.5	23 20.9	18 38.8	17 5.7	3 22.1	7 39.8	7 32.2	28 30.1	8 17.0	14 30.7	29 54.7	2 16.1
18 S	19 38 53.1	24 18.1	18 35.6	0♎21.7	4 9.3	8 53.1	8 13.8	28 30.5	8 24.7	14 28.6	29 56.9	2 17.5
19 M	19 42 49.6	25 15.4	18 32.4	13 54.6	5 1.6	10 6.4	8 55.4	28 30.7	8 32.3	14 26.4	29 59.1	2 18.9
20 T	19 46 46.2	26 12.6	18 29.3	27 45.3	5 59.1	11 19.7	9 36.9	28R30.7	8 39.9	14 24.1	0♌ 1.4	2 20.2
21 W	19 50 42.7	27 9.9	18 26.1	11♏53.6	7 1.6	12 33.1	10 18.3	28 30.5	8 47.4	14 21.9	0 3.6	2 21.6
22 T	19 54 39.3	28 7.1	18 22.9	26 17.9	8 9.1	13 46.5	10 59.7	28 30.0	8 55.0	14 19.6	0 5.8	2 22.9
23 F	19 58 35.8	29 4.4	18 19.7	10♐54.9	9 21.4	14 59.9	11 40.9	28 29.4	9 2.5	14 17.4	0 8.0	2 24.2
24 S	20 2 32.4	0♌ 1.7	18 16.6	25 39.3	10 38.6	16 13.3	12 22.1	28 28.6	9 10.0	14 15.1	0 10.3	2 25.6
25 S	20 6 29.0	0 59.0	18 13.4	10♑24.6	12 0.5	17 26.8	13 3.3	28 27.6	9 17.5	14 12.8	0 12.5	2 26.9
26 M	20 10 25.5	1 56.3	18 10.2	25 3.5	13 26.9	18 40.3	13 44.3	28 26.4	9 24.9	14 10.5	0 14.7	2 28.2
27 T	20 14 22.0	2 53.6	18 7.0	9♒29.3	14 57.7	19 53.8	14 25.3	28 25.0	9 32.3	14 8.1	0 16.9	2 29.5
28 W	20 18 18.6	3 50.9	18 3.9	23 36.6	16 32.8	21 7.4	15 6.2	28 23.5	9 39.7	14 5.8	0 19.2	2 30.7
29 T	20 22 15.2	4 48.2	18 0.7	7♓21.7	18 11.8	22 20.9	15 47.0	28 21.7	9 47.0	14 3.5	0 21.4	2 32.0
30 F	20 26 11.8	5 45.6	17 57.5	20 43.1	19 54.7	23 34.5	16 27.7	28 19.7	9 54.4	14 1.1	0 23.6	2 33.3
31 S	20 30 8.3	6 42.9	17 54.3	3♈41.5	21 41.2	24 48.2	17 8.4	28 17.6	10 1.6	13 58.7	0 25.8	2 34.5
DECLINATION												
1 T	18 31 51.6	23N12.3	14S58.9	10S45.8	18N46.1	22N14.5	18N52.3	1S58.7	22N39.2	16S59.9	19N59.1	18N16.8
4 S	18 43 41.2	23 0.0	15 1.9	6N53.4	18 42.2	22 38.2	19 23.5	1 55.7	22 38.3	17 1.5	19 57.8	18 16.9
7 W	18 55 30.9	22 44.1	15 4.8	21 6.8	18 50.9	22 56.1	19 53.0	1 53.3	22 37.4	17 3.3	19 56.5	18 16.9
10 S	19 7 20.6	22 24.7	15 7.8	27 27.2	19 10.7	23 8.2	20 20.7	1 51.6	22 36.3	17 5.1	19 55.2	18 16.9
13 T	19 19 10.3	22 1.8	15 10.8	22 44.4	19 39.5	23 14.2	20 46.7	1 50.6	22 35.2	17 6.9	19 53.8	18 16.9
16 F	19 30 60.0	21 35.4	15 13.7	8 36.7	20 13.9	23 14.1	21 10.8	1 50.3	22 34.1	17 8.8	19 52.5	18 16.9
19 M	19 42 49.6	21 5.8	15 16.7	9S31.2	20 50.0	23 8.0	21 33.2	1 50.7	22 32.8	17 10.8	19 51.1	18 16.8
22 T	19 54 39.3	20 32.9	15 19.6	24 22.4	21 23.3	22 55.7	21 53.8	1 51.8	22 31.5	17 12.8	19 49.7	18 16.8
25 S	20 6 29.0	19 57.0	15 22.5	26 11.8	21 48.8	22 37.3	22 12.5	1 53.6	22 30.2	17 14.9	19 48.3	18 16.7
28 W	20 18 18.6	19 18.1	15 25.5	13 6.6	22 1.1	22 13.0	22 29.4	1 56.1	22 28.8	17 16.9	19 46.9	18 16.6
31 S	20 30 8.3	18 36.3	15 28.4	4N58.5	21 55.4	21 42.8	22 44.5	1 59.2	22 27.4	17 19.0	19 45.5	18 16.5

AUGUST 1915

DAY	EPHEMERIS SIDEREAL TIME h m s	☉ ° ′	☊ ° ′	☽ ° ′	☿ ° ′	♀ ° ′	♂ ° ′	♃ ° ′	♄ ° ′	♅ ° ′	♆ ° ′	♇ ° ′
LONGITUDE												
1 S	20 34 4.8	7♌40.3	17♒51.1	16♈19.0	23♋30.8	26♋ 1.8	17♊49.0	28♓15.2	10♋ 8.9	13♒56.4	0♌28.0	2♋35.7
2 M	20 38 1.4	8 37.7	17 48.0	28 38.8	25 23.5	27 15.5	18 29.5	28R12.7	10 16.1	13R54.0	0 30.3	2 37.0
3 T	20 41 58.0	9 35.1	17 44.8	10♉45.2	27 18.8	28 29.2	19 9.9	28 9.9	10 23.3	13 51.6	0 32.5	2 38.2
4 W	20 45 54.5	10 32.5	17 41.6	22 42.5	29 16.3	29 43.0	19 50.3	28 7.0	10 30.5	13 49.2	0 34.7	2 39.4
5 T	20 49 51.1	11 30.0	17 38.4	4♊35.3	1♌15.8	0♌56.7	20 30.6	28 3.9	10 37.6	13 46.8	0 36.9	2 40.6
6 F	20 53 47.6	12 27.5	17 35.3	16 28.0	3 16.8	2 10.5	21 10.8	28 0.6	10 44.6	13 44.4	0 39.0	2 41.7
7 S	20 57 44.2	13 25.0	17 32.1	28 24.5	5 19.0	3 24.3	21 50.9	27 57.1	10 51.7	13 42.0	0 41.2	2 42.9
8 S	21 1 40.7	14 22.5	17 28.9	10♋28.3	7 22.1	4 38.2	22 30.9	27 53.4	10 58.7	13 39.6	0 43.4	2 44.0
9 M	21 5 37.3	15 20.0	17 25.7	22 42.2	9 25.7	5 52.1	23 10.9	27 49.6	11 5.6	13 37.3	0 45.6	2 45.2
10 T	21 9 33.9	16 17.6	17 22.6	5♌ 8.3	11 29.6	7 6.0	23 50.7	27 45.6	11 12.5	13 34.9	0 47.8	2 46.3
11 W	21 13 30.4	17 15.2	17 19.4	17 48.2	13 33.3	8 19.9	24 30.5	27 41.3	11 19.4	13 32.5	0 49.9	2 47.4
12 T	21 17 27.0	18 12.8	17 16.2	0♍42.4	15 36.8	9 33.9	25 10.2	27 37.0	11 26.2	13 30.1	0 52.1	2 48.5
13 F	21 21 23.5	19 10.4	17 13.0	13 51.0	17 39.8	10 47.9	25 49.8	27 32.4	11 32.9	13 27.7	0 54.2	2 49.6
14 S	21 25 20.1	20 8.0	17 9.8	27 13.6	19 42.1	12 1.9	26 29.3	27 27.7	11 39.7	13 25.3	0 56.3	2 50.6
15 S	21 29 16.6	21 5.7	17 6.7	10♎49.3	21 43.5	13 15.9	27 8.7	27 22.8	11 46.3	13 23.0	0 58.4	2 51.6
16 M	21 33 13.2	22 3.3	17 3.5	24 37.1	23 44.0	14 29.9	27 48.1	27 17.7	11 52.9	13 20.6	1 0.6	2 52.7
17 T	21 37 9.8	23 1.0	17 0.3	8♏35.4	25 43.3	15 44.0	28 27.3	27 12.5	11 59.5	13 18.2	1 2.7	2 53.7
18 W	21 41 6.3	23 58.7	16 57.1	22 42.7	27 41.5	16 58.1	29 6.5	27 7.2	12 6.0	13 15.9	1 4.8	2 54.7
19 T	21 45 2.9	24 56.4	16 54.0	6♐56.9	29 38.5	18 12.2	29 45.5	27 1.6	12 12.5	13 13.6	1 6.8	2 55.6
20 F	21 48 59.4	25 54.2	16 50.8	21 15.5	1♍34.2	19 26.3	0♋24.5	26 56.0	12 18.9	13 11.2	1 8.9	2 56.6
21 S	21 52 56.0	26 51.9	16 47.6	5♑35.6	3 28.5	20 40.5	1 3.4	26 50.1	12 25.2	13 8.9	1 10.9	2 57.5
22 S	21 56 52.5	27 49.7	16 44.4	19 53.7	5 21.6	21 54.7	1 42.2	26 44.2	12 31.5	13 6.7	1 13.0	2 58.5
23 M	22 0 49.1	28 47.5	16 41.3	4♒ 5.9	7 13.3	23 8.9	2 20.9	26 38.1	12 37.8	13 4.4	1 15.0	2 59.4
24 T	22 4 45.6	29 45.3	16 38.1	18 8.1	9 3.6	24 23.1	2 59.5	26 31.9	12 43.9	13 2.1	1 17.0	3 0.3
25 W	22 8 42.2	0♍43.1	16 34.9	1♓56.9	10 52.5	25 37.3	3 38.0	26 25.5	12 50.0	12 59.9	1 19.0	3 1.1
26 T	22 12 38.8	1 41.0	16 31.7	15 29.2	12 40.2	26 51.6	4 16.4	26 19.0	12 56.1	12 57.6	1 21.0	3 2.0
27 F	22 16 35.3	2 38.9	16 28.5	28 43.1	14 26.5	28 5.9	4 54.7	26 12.4	13 2.1	12 55.4	1 23.0	3 2.8
28 S	22 20 31.8	3 36.8	16 25.4	11♈38.1	16 11.4	29 20.2	5 33.0	26 5.7	13 8.0	12 53.2	1 24.9	3 3.6
29 S	22 24 28.4	4 34.7	16 22.2	24 14.8	17 55.1	0♍34.5	6 11.1	25 58.8	13 13.9	12 51.1	1 26.8	3 4.4
30 M	22 28 25.0	5 32.7	16 19.0	6♉35.3	19 37.4	1 48.9	6 49.2	25 51.9	13 19.7	12 48.9	1 28.8	3 5.2
31 T	22 32 21.5	6 30.7	16 15.8	18 42.5	21 18.5	3 3.2	7 27.1	25 44.8	13 25.4	12 46.8	1 30.7	3 6.0
DECLINATION												
1 S	20 34 4.8	18N21.7	15S29.4	10N35.5	21N48.7	21N31.4	22N49.1	2S 0.4	22N26.9	17S19.7	19N45.1	18N16.5
4 W	20 45 54.5	17 36.3	15 32.3	23 32.1	21 13.0	20 53.6	23 1.8	2 4.5	22 25.4	17 21.8	19 43.7	18 16.3
7 S	20 57 44.2	16 48.2	15 35.2	27 25.6	20 13.6	20 10.4	23 12.6	2 9.2	22 23.8	17 23.9	19 42.3	18 16.2
10 T	21 9 33.9	15 57.7	15 38.1	20 4.7	18 52.0	19 21.9	23 21.6	2 14.5	22 22.3	17 25.9	19 40.9	18 16.1
13 F	21 21 23.5	15 4.9	15 41.0	4 10.4	17 11.6	18 28.4	23 28.9	2 20.4	22 20.7	17 28.0	19 39.5	18 15.9
16 M	21 33 13.2	14 9.9	15 43.9	14S 4.1	15 16.7	17 30.2	23 34.4	2 27.0	22 19.1	17 30.0	19 38.2	18 15.7
19 T	21 45 2.9	13 12.9	15 46.8	26 22.9	13 11.5	16 27.6	23 38.1	2 34.0	22 17.5	17 32.0	19 36.8	18 15.5
22 S	21 56 52.5	12 14.1	15 49.6	24 23.2	10 59.5	15 20.8	23 40.2	2 41.5	22 15.9	17 34.0	19 35.5	18 15.3
25 W	22 8 42.2	11 13.5	15 52.5	9 32.6	8 43.5	14 10.2	23 40.7	2 49.5	22 14.2	17 35.9	19 34.2	18 15.2
28 S	22 20 31.8	10 11.3	15 55.4	8N32.1	6 25.9	12 56.1	23 39.5	2 57.9	22 12.6	17 37.8	19 32.9	18 14.9
31 T	22 32 21.5	9 7.6	15 58.2	22 26.3	4 8.3	11 38.8	23 36.7	3 6.7	22 11.0	17 39.6	19 31.7	18 14.7

SEPTEMBER 1915

DAY	EPHEMERIS SIDEREAL TIME	☉	☊	☾	☿	♀	♂	♃	♄	♅	♆	♇
	h m s	° ′	° ′	° ′	° ′	° ′	° ′	° ′	° ′	° ′	° ′	° ′
						LONGITUDE						
1 W	22 36 18.1	7♍28.8	16♒12.7	0♊40.4	22♍58.4	4♍17.6	8♋ 5.0	25♓37.7	13♋31.1	12♒44.7	1♌32.5	3♋ 6.7
2 T	22 40 14.6	8 26.8	16 9.5	12 33.4	24 36.9	5 32.0	8 42.7	25R30.4	13 36.7	12R42.6	1 34.4	3 7.4
3 F	22 44 11.2	9 24.9	16 6.3	24 26.1	26 14.3	6 46.5	9 20.4	25 23.1	13 42.2	12 40.5	1 36.3	3 8.1
4 S	22 48 7.8	10 23.1	16 3.1	6♋23.4	27 50.4	8 0.9	9 57.9	25 15.6	13 47.7	12 38.5	1 38.1	3 8.8
5 S	22 52 4.3	11 21.3	15 60.0	18 29.9	29 25.3	9 15.4	10 35.4	25 8.1	13 53.1	12 36.5	1 39.9	3 9.5
6 M	22 56 0.9	12 19.5	15 56.8	0♌49.5	0♎59.0	10 29.9	11 12.8	25 0.6	13 58.4	12 34.5	1 41.7	3 10.1
7 T	22 59 57.4	13 17.7	15 53.6	13 25.4	2 31.5	11 44.5	11 50.0	24 52.9	14 3.7	12 32.5	1 43.5	3 10.7
8 W	23 3 54.0	14 15.9	15 50.4	26 20.0	4 2.8	12 59.0	12 27.1	24 45.2	14 8.8	12 30.6	1 45.2	3 11.3
9 T	23 7 50.5	15 14.2	15 47.2	9♍34.1	5 32.9	14 13.6	13 4.1	24 37.4	14 13.9	12 28.7	1 46.9	3 11.9
10 F	23 11 47.1	16 12.6	15 44.1	23 7.1	7 1.8	15 28.1	13 41.1	24 29.6	14 18.9	12 26.9	1 48.7	3 12.4
11 S	23 15 43.6	17 10.9	15 40.9	6♎56.7	8 29.5	16 42.7	14 17.9	24 21.7	14 23.9	12 25.0	1 50.4	3 13.0
12 S	23 19 40.2	18 9.3	15 37.7	20 59.6	9 55.9	17 57.3	14 54.6	24 13.8	14 28.7	12 23.2	1 52.0	3 13.5
13 M	23 23 36.7	19 7.7	15 34.5	5♏11.6	11 21.2	19 11.9	15 31.1	24 5.9	14 33.5	12 21.4	1 53.7	3 14.0
14 T	23 27 33.3	20 6.2	15 31.3	19 28.2	12 45.1	20 26.6	16 7.6	23 57.9	14 38.2	12 19.7	1 55.3	3 14.4
15 W	23 31 29.8	21 4.6	15 28.2	3♐45.4	14 7.8	21 41.2	16 43.9	23 50.0	14 42.8	12 18.0	1 56.9	3 14.9
16 T	23 35 26.4	22 3.1	15 25.0	17 59.8	15 29.2	22 55.9	17 20.1	23 42.0	14 47.3	12 16.4	1 58.5	3 15.3
17 F	23 39 22.9	23 1.6	15 21.8	2♑ 9.1	16 49.2	24 10.6	17 56.2	23 34.0	14 51.8	12 14.7	1 60.0	3 15.7
18 S	23 43 19.5	24 0.2	15 18.6	16 11.5	18 7.8	25 25.2	18 32.2	23 26.0	14 56.1	12 13.1	2 1.5	3 16.1
19 S	23 47 16.1	24 58.8	15 15.5	0♒ 6.0	19 25.0	26 39.9	19 8.1	23 18.0	15 0.4	12 11.6	2 3.0	3 16.5
20 M	23 51 12.6	25 57.4	15 12.3	13 51.5	20 40.6	27 54.6	19 43.8	23 10.0	15 4.6	12 10.1	2 4.5	3 16.8
21 T	23 55 9.1	26 56.0	15 9.1	27 27.1	21 54.7	29 9.3	20 19.4	23 2.0	15 8.7	12 8.6	2 6.0	3 17.1
22 W	23 59 5.7	27 54.6	15 5.9	10♓51.6	23 7.0	0♎24.1	20 54.9	22 54.1	15 12.7	12 7.1	2 7.4	3 17.4
23 T	0 3 2.3	28 53.3	15 2.7	24 3.8	24 17.7	1 38.8	21 30.3	22 46.2	15 16.6	12 5.7	2 8.8	3 17.7
24 F	0 6 58.8	29 52.1	14 59.6	7♈ 2.5	25 26.5	2 53.5	22 5.5	22 38.3	15 20.4	12 4.4	2 10.2	3 17.9
25 S	0 10 55.4	0♎50.8	14 56.4	19 46.9	26 33.3	4 8.3	22 40.7	22 30.4	15 24.1	12 3.0	2 11.5	3 18.2
26 S	0 14 51.9	1 49.6	14 53.2	2♉17.1	27 38.0	5 23.1	23 15.6	22 22.6	15 27.8	12 1.8	2 12.8	3 18.3
27 M	0 18 48.5	2 48.4	14 50.0	14 33.8	28 40.4	6 37.8	23 50.5	22 14.9	15 31.3	12 0.5	2 14.1	3 18.5
28 T	0 22 45.0	3 47.3	14 46.9	26 39.0	29 40.5	7 52.6	24 25.2	22 7.2	15 34.8	11 59.3	2 15.4	3 18.7
29 W	0 26 41.6	4 46.2	14 43.7	8♊35.5	0♏37.9	9 7.4	24 59.8	21 59.6	15 38.1	11 58.2	2 16.6	3 18.8
30 T	0 30 38.2	5 45.1	14 40.5	20 27.1	1 32.5	10 22.2	25 34.3	21 52.0	15 41.4	11 57.1	2 17.8	3 18.9
						DECLINATION						
1 W	22 36 18.1	8N46.1	15S59.2	25N17.5	3N22.6	11N12.4	23N35.4	3S 9.7	22N10.5	17S40.2	19N31.3	18N14.7
4 S	22 48 7.8	7 40.7	16 2.0	26 43.6	1 7.2	9 51.3	23 30.6	3 18.8	22 8.9	17 41.9	19 30.0	18 14.4
7 T	22 59 57.4	6 34.1	16 4.9	17 8.1	1S 5.5	8 27.7	23 24.4	3 28.2	22 7.4	17 43.5	19 28.9	18 14.2
10 F	23 11 47.1	5 26.6	16 7.7	0S 4.8	3 14.4	7 2.0	23 16.7	3 37.7	22 5.9	17 45.1	19 27.7	18 14.0
13 M	23 23 36.7	4 18.3	16 10.5	18 2.7	5 18.7	5 34.6	23 7.7	3 47.3	22 4.4	17 46.6	19 26.6	18 13.8
16 T	23 35 26.4	3 9.3	16 13.3	27 20.3	7 17.6	4 5.7	22 57.5	3 57.0	22 3.0	17 47.9	19 25.6	18 13.5
19 S	23 47 16.1	1 59.8	16 16.1	21 36.2	9 10.1	2 35.6	22 46.0	4 6.6	22 1.7	17 49.2	19 24.5	18 13.3
22 W	23 59 5.7	0 49.9	16 19.0	5 32.9	10 55.2	1 4.8	22 33.4	4 16.1	22 0.4	17 50.4	19 23.6	18 13.1
25 S	0 10 55.4	0S20.2	16 21.7	11N58.8	12 31.6	0S26.5	22 19.7	4 25.4	21 59.2	17 51.5	19 22.6	18 12.9
28 T	0 22 45.0	1 30.4	16 24.5	24 18.8	13 57.9	1 58.0	22 5.0	4 34.6	21 58.1	17 52.4	19 21.8	18 12.7

OCTOBER 1915

DAY	EPHEMERIS SIDEREAL TIME	☉	☊	☾	☿	♀	♂	♃	♄	♅	♆	♇
						LONGITUDE						
1 F	0 34 34.7	6♎44.1	14♒37.3	2♋18.2	2♏24.0	11♎37.1	26♋ 8.6	21♓44.5	15♋44.6	11♒56.0	2♌19.0	3♋19.0
2 S	0 38 31.3	7 43.1	14 34.1	14 13.8	3 12.2	12 51.9	26 42.8	21R37.1	15 47.6	11R55.0	2 20.1	3 19.1
3 S	0 42 27.8	8 42.2	14 31.0	26 19.1	3 56.8	14 6.7	27 16.8	21 29.8	15 50.6	11 54.0	2 21.3	3 19.1
4 M	0 46 24.4	9 41.3	14 27.8	8♌39.1	4 37.5	15 21.6	27 50.7	21 22.6	15 53.4	11 53.1	2 22.4	3 19.2
5 T	0 50 20.9	10 40.4	14 24.6	21 18.6	5 13.8	16 36.5	28 24.4	21 15.5	15 56.2	11 52.2	2 23.4	3R19.1
6 W	0 54 17.5	11 39.5	14 21.4	4♍20.9	5 45.5	17 51.3	28 58.0	21 8.4	15 58.9	11 51.3	2 24.5	3 19.1
7 T	0 58 14.0	12 38.8	14 18.3	17 48.1	6 12.1	19 6.2	29 31.5	21 1.5	16 1.4	11 50.5	2 25.5	3 19.1
8 F	1 2 10.6	13 38.0	14 15.1	1♎40.0	6 33.2	20 21.1	0♌ 4.7	20 54.7	16 3.9	11 49.8	2 26.4	3 19.0
9 S	1 6 7.1	14 37.3	14 11.9	15 53.9	6 48.2	21 36.0	0 37.8	20 48.0	16 6.2	11 49.1	2 27.4	3 18.9
10 S	1 10 3.7	15 36.6	14 8.7	0♏24.5	6 56.8	22 50.9	1 10.8	20 41.4	16 8.5	11 48.4	2 28.3	3 18.8
11 M	1 14 0.2	16 35.9	14 5.5	15 4.8	6 58.3	24 5.8	1 43.6	20 35.0	16 10.6	11 47.8	2 29.2	3 18.6
12 T	1 17 56.8	17 35.3	14 2.4	29 47.1	6R52.5	25 20.7	2 16.2	20 28.7	16 12.6	11 47.3	2 30.0	3 18.5
13 W	1 21 53.4	18 34.7	13 59.2	14♐24.2	6 38.7	26 35.6	2 48.6	20 22.5	16 14.5	11 46.8	2 30.8	3 18.3
14 T	1 25 49.9	19 34.1	13 56.0	28 50.6	6 16.8	27 50.6	3 20.9	20 16.5	16 16.4	11 46.3	2 31.6	3 18.1
15 F	1 29 46.5	20 33.6	13 52.8	13♑ 2.7	5 46.4	29 5.5	3 53.0	20 10.6	16 18.1	11 45.9	2 32.4	3 17.9
16 S	1 33 43.0	21 33.1	13 49.7	26 59.2	5 7.6	0♏20.4	4 24.9	20 4.9	16 19.7	11 45.5	2 33.1	3 17.6
17 S	1 37 39.6	22 32.6	13 46.5	10♒40.2	4 20.5	1 35.3	4 56.6	19 59.3	16 21.1	11 45.2	2 33.8	3 17.3
18 M	1 41 36.1	23 32.2	13 43.3	24 6.9	3 25.5	2 50.3	5 28.2	19 53.9	16 22.5	11 45.0	2 34.4	3 17.0
19 T	1 45 32.7	24 31.7	13 40.1	7♓20.5	2 23.5	4 5.2	5 59.6	19 48.6	16 23.8	11 44.8	2 35.0	3 16.7
20 W	1 49 29.2	25 31.3	13 37.0	20 22.3	1 15.7	5 20.1	6 30.7	19 43.5	16 25.0	11 44.6	2 35.6	3 16.4
21 T	1 53 25.8	26 31.0	13 33.8	3♈13.0	0 3.5	6 35.0	7 1.7	19 38.6	16 26.0	11 44.5	2 36.2	3 16.0
22 F	1 57 22.3	27 30.6	13 30.6	15 53.1	28♎48.8	7 50.0	7 32.5	19 33.8	16 27.0	11 44.5	2 36.7	3 15.6
23 S	2 1 18.9	28 30.4	13 27.4	28 22.7	27 33.6	9 4.9	8 3.1	19 29.3	16 27.8	11 44.5	2 37.2	3 15.2
24 S	2 5 15.4	29 30.1	13 24.2	10♉41.9	26 20.3	10 19.8	8 33.5	19 24.9	16 28.5	11D44.5	2 37.6	3 14.8
25 M	2 9 12.0	0♏29.9	13 21.1	22 51.2	25 11.1	11 34.8	9 3.7	19 20.6	16 29.1	11 44.6	2 38.1	3 14.3
26 T	2 13 8.6	1 29.7	13 17.9	4♊51.7	24 8.1	12 49.7	9 33.7	19 16.6	16 29.6	11 44.7	2 38.5	3 13.9
27 W	2 17 5.1	2 29.5	13 14.7	16 45.3	23 13.2	14 4.6	10 3.5	19 12.7	16 30.0	11 44.9	2 38.8	3 13.4
28 T	2 21 1.7	3 29.4	13 11.5	28 34.8	22 27.8	15 19.6	10 33.1	19 9.0	16 30.3	11 45.2	2 39.1	3 12.9
29 F	2 24 58.2	4 29.3	13 8.4	10♋23.8	21 53.1	16 34.5	11 2.4	19 5.5	16 30.4	11 45.5	2 39.4	3 12.3
30 S	2 28 54.8	5 29.2	13 5.2	22 16.7	21 29.7	17 49.5	11 31.6	19 2.2	16 30.4	11 45.8	2 39.7	3 11.8
31 S	2 32 51.3	6 29.2	13 2.0	4♌18.8	21 17.8	19 4.4	12 0.5	18 59.1	16R30.4	11 46.2	2 39.9	3 11.2
						DECLINATION						
1 F	0 34 34.7	2S40.5	16S27.3	26N58.7	15S11.7	3S29.2	21N49.4	4S43.4	21N57.1	17S53.3	19N21.0	18N12.4
4 M	0 46 24.4	3 50.4	16 30.1	18 44.4	16 10.5	4 60.0	21 32.9	4 51.8	21 56.1	17 54.1	19 20.2	18 12.2
7 T	0 58 14.0	4 59.9	16 32.9	2 20.5	16 50.2	6 29.9	21 15.7	4 59.9	21 55.3	17 54.7	19 19.5	18 12.0
10 S	1 10 3.7	6 8.9	16 35.6	16S11.6	17 5.6	7 58.6	20 57.8	5 7.5	21 54.5	17 55.2	19 18.9	18 11.8
13 W	1 21 53.4	7 17.1	16 38.4	26 55.7	16 50.3	9 25.7	20 39.3	5 14.6	21 53.9	17 55.6	19 18.3	18 11.6
16 S	1 33 43.0	8 24.4	16 41.1	22 18.8	15 57.4	10 50.9	20 20.3	5 21.1	21 53.4	17 55.8	19 17.8	18 11.5
19 T	1 45 32.7	9 30.6	16 43.9	7 1.7	14 23.9	12 13.8	20 0.9	5 27.1	21 53.0	17 55.9	19 17.3	18 11.3
22 F	1 57 22.3	10 35.6	16 46.6	10N18.8	12 17.7	13 34.2	19 41.1	5 32.4	21 52.7	17 55.9	19 17.0	18 11.1
25 M	2 9 12.0	11 39.1	16 49.3	23 16.5	10 1.6	14 51.5	19 21.1	5 37.1	21 52.5	17 55.8	19 16.7	18 11.0
28 T	2 21 1.7	12 41.1	16 52.0	26 59.6	8 7.4	16 5.5	19 0.9	5 41.1	21 52.5	17 55.6	19 16.4	18 10.9
31 S	2 32 51.3	13 41.4	16 54.7	19 57.5	6 58.8	17 15.8	18 40.8	5 44.4	21 52.6	17 55.2	19 16.2	18 10.7

NOVEMBER 1915

LONGITUDE

DAY	EPHEMERIS SIDEREAL TIME h m s	☉ ° ′	☊ ° ′	☽ ° ′	☿ ° ′	♀ ° ′	♂ ° ′	♃ ° ′	♄ ° ′	♅ ° ′	♆ ° ′	♇ ° ′
1 M	2 36 47.9	7♏29.2	12♒58.8	16♌35.3	21♎17.4	20♏19.4	12♌29.1	18♓56.2	16♋30.2	11♒46.7	2♌40.1	3♋10.6
2 T	2 40 44.5	8 29.3	12 55.7	29 11.6	21D28.0	21 34.4	12 57.6	18R53.5	16R29.9	11 47.2	2 40.2	3R10.0
3 W	2 44 41.0	9 29.4	12 52.5	12♍12.6	21 49.0	22 49.3	13 25.7	18 51.0	16 29.5	11 47.7	2 40.3	3 9.3
4 T	2 48 37.5	10 29.5	12 49.3	25 41.7	22 19.8	24 4.3	13 53.7	18 48.6	16 29.0	11 48.3	2 40.4	3 8.7
5 F	2 52 34.1	11 29.7	12 46.1	9♎40.1	22 59.4	25 19.2	14 21.4	18 46.5	16 28.4	11 49.0	2 40.5	3 8.0
6 S	2 56 30.7	12 29.9	12 42.9	24 6.1	23 46.9	26 34.2	14 48.8	18 44.6	16 27.6	11 49.7	2 40.5	3 7.3
7 S	3 0 27.2	13 30.1	12 39.8	8♏54.5	24 41.6	27 49.2	15 15.9	18 42.9	16 26.8	11 50.5	2R40.5	3 6.6
8 M	3 4 23.8	14 30.3	12 36.6	23 57.2	25 42.4	29 4.2	15 42.8	18 41.4	16 25.8	11 51.3	2 40.4	3 5.9
9 T	3 8 20.3	15 30.6	12 33.4	9♐ 4.0	26 48.7	0♐19.1	16 9.4	18 40.1	16 24.7	11 52.1	2 40.3	3 5.1
10 W	3 12 16.9	16 30.9	12 30.2	24 4.8	27 59.7	1 34.1	16 35.7	18 39.0	16 23.5	11 53.1	2 40.2	3 4.4
11 T	3 16 13.5	17 31.3	12 27.1	8♑51.1	29 14.7	2 49.1	17 1.8	18 38.1	16 22.2	11 54.0	2 40.0	3 3.6
12 F	3 20 10.0	18 31.6	12 23.9	23 17.3	0♏33.2	4 4.0	17 27.5	18 37.4	16 20.8	11 55.0	2 39.8	3 2.8
13 S	3 24 6.6	19 32.0	12 20.7	7♒20.8	1 54.5	5 19.0	17 52.9	18 36.9	16 19.3	11 56.1	2 39.6	3 2.0
14 S	3 28 3.1	20 32.4	12 17.5	21 1.8	3 18.4	6 34.0	18 18.1	18 36.7	16 17.7	11 57.2	2 39.3	3 1.1
15 M	3 31 59.7	21 32.8	12 14.3	4♓21.9	4 44.2	7 48.9	18 42.9	18 36.6	16 15.9	11 58.4	2 39.0	3 0.3
16 T	3 35 56.2	22 33.3	12 11.2	17 23.8	6 11.8	9 3.9	19 7.4	18D36.8	16 14.1	11 59.6	2 38.7	2 59.4
17 W	3 39 52.8	23 33.8	12 8.0	0♈10.6	7 40.8	10 18.8	19 31.6	18 37.1	16 12.1	12 0.8	2 38.4	2 58.5
18 T	3 43 49.3	24 34.2	12 4.8	12 44.7	9 10.9	11 33.8	19 55.5	18 37.7	16 10.1	12 2.1	2 38.0	2 57.6
19 F	3 47 45.9	25 34.8	12 1.6	25 8.5	10 42.0	12 48.7	20 19.0	18 38.5	16 7.9	12 3.5	2 37.5	2 56.7
20 S	3 51 42.5	26 35.3	11 58.5	7♉23.4	12 13.9	14 3.6	20 42.2	18 39.4	16 5.7	12 4.9	2 37.1	2 55.8
21 S	3 55 39.0	27 35.9	11 55.3	19 30.7	13 46.3	15 18.6	21 5.1	18 40.6	16 3.3	12 6.4	2 36.6	2 54.8
22 M	3 59 35.6	28 36.5	11 52.1	1♊31.4	15 19.2	16 33.5	21 27.6	18 42.0	16 0.9	12 7.8	2 36.1	2 53.9
23 T	4 3 32.1	29 37.1	11 48.9	13 26.5	16 52.5	17 48.4	21 49.7	18 43.6	15 58.3	12 9.4	2 35.5	2 52.9
24 W	4 7 28.7	0♐37.7	11 45.8	25 17.4	18 26.1	19 3.3	22 11.5	18 45.4	15 55.7	12 11.0	2 34.9	2 51.9
25 T	4 11 25.3	1 38.4	11 42.6	7♋ 6.1	19 59.9	20 18.2	22 32.9	18 47.4	15 52.9	12 12.6	2 34.3	2 50.9
26 F	4 15 21.8	2 39.1	11 39.4	18 55.3	21 33.8	21 33.1	22 53.9	18 49.6	15 50.1	12 14.3	2 33.6	2 49.9
27 S	4 19 18.4	3 39.8	11 36.2	0♌48.2	23 7.8	22 48.0	23 14.5	18 52.0	15 47.1	12 16.0	2 33.0	2 48.9
28 S	4 23 14.9	4 40.5	11 33.0	12 49.3	24 41.9	24 3.0	23 34.7	18 54.5	15 44.1	12 17.8	2 32.2	2 47.8
29 M	4 27 11.5	5 41.3	11 29.9	25 3.1	26 16.1	25 17.9	23 54.5	18 57.3	15 41.0	12 19.6	2 31.5	2 46.8
30 T	4 31 8.0	6 42.1	11 26.7	7♍35.0	27 50.2	26 32.8	24 13.9	19 0.3	15 37.8	12 21.5	2 30.7	2 45.7

DECLINATION

DAY	SIDEREAL TIME	☉	☊	☽	☿	♀	♂	♃	♄	♅	♆	♇
1 M	2 36 47.9	14S 1.0	16S55.6	15N35.8	6S47.7	17S38.4	18N34.0	5S45.3	21N52.7	17S55.0	19N16.2	18N10.7
4 T	2 48 37.5	14 58.6	16 58.3	1S24.4	6 47.7	18 43.2	18 13.9	5 47.7	21 52.9	17 54.5	19 16.1	18 10.6
7 S	3 0 27.2	15 54.0	17 1.0	19 11.8	7 29.6	19 43.6	17 54.1	5 49.3	21 53.3	17 53.8	19 16.1	18 10.5
10 W	3 12 16.9	16 47.0	17 3.7	27 3.1	8 40.7	20 39.0	17 34.5	5 50.1	21 53.8	17 53.0	19 16.2	18 10.5
13 S	3 24 6.6	17 37.5	17 6.4	18 50.4	10 9.9	21 29.3	17 15.4	5 50.3	21 54.5	17 52.0	19 16.3	18 10.4
16 T	3 35 56.2	18 25.2	17 9.1	2 17.3	11 48.5	22 14.0	16 56.8	5 49.6	21 55.3	17 51.0	19 16.5	18 10.4
19 F	3 47 45.9	19 9.9	17 11.7	14N12.2	13 30.6	22 53.0	16 38.8	5 48.3	21 56.1	17 49.8	19 16.8	18 10.4
22 M	3 59 35.6	19 51.6	17 14.4	25 4.2	15 11.9	23 25.9	16 21.6	5 46.2	21 57.2	17 48.5	19 17.1	18 10.4
25 T	4 11 25.3	20 30.0	17 17.0	26 2.0	16 49.7	23 52.5	16 5.3	5 43.4	21 58.3	17 47.1	19 17.5	18 10.4
28 S	4 23 14.9	21 5.0	17 19.7	16 45.2	18 21.8	24 12.7	15 50.0	5 39.9	21 59.5	17 45.5	19 18.0	18 10.4

DECEMBER 1915

LONGITUDE

DAY	SIDEREAL TIME	☉	☊	☽	☿	♀	♂	♃	♄	♅	♆	♇
1 W	4 35 4.6	7♐42.9	11♒23.5	20♍29.7	29♏24.3	27♐47.7	24♌32.9	19♓ 3.5	15♋34.5	12♒23.4	2♌29.9	2♋44.6
2 T	4 39 1.1	8 43.7	11 20.3	3♎51.8	0♐58.5	29 2.5	24 51.4	19 6.9	15R31.1	12 25.3	2R29.1	2R43.6
3 F	4 42 57.7	9 44.6	11 17.2	17 43.7	2 32.6	0♑17.4	25 9.4	19 10.5	15 27.6	12 27.3	2 28.2	2 42.5
4 S	4 46 54.3	10 45.5	11 14.0	2♏ 5.5	4 6.7	1 32.3	25 27.0	19 14.3	15 24.1	12 29.4	2 27.3	2 41.4
5 S	4 50 50.8	11 46.4	11 10.8	16 54.0	5 40.8	2 47.2	25 44.2	19 18.2	15 20.4	12 31.5	2 26.4	2 40.3
6 M	4 54 47.4	12 47.3	11 7.6	2♐ 2.2	7 14.8	4 2.1	26 0.8	19 22.4	15 16.7	12 33.6	2 25.5	2 39.1
7 T	4 58 43.9	13 48.2	11 4.5	17 20.2	8 48.9	5 17.0	26 16.9	19 26.7	15 12.9	12 35.7	2 24.5	2 38.0
8 W	5 2 40.5	14 49.2	11 1.3	2♑36.8	10 22.9	6 31.8	26 32.6	19 31.3	15 9.0	12 37.9	2 23.5	2 36.9
9 T	5 6 37.1	15 50.2	10 58.1	17 41.2	11 57.0	7 46.7	26 47.7	19 36.0	15 5.1	12 40.2	2 22.4	2 35.7
10 F	5 10 33.6	16 51.2	10 54.9	2♒25.2	13 31.1	9 1.6	27 2.3	19 40.9	15 1.1	12 42.5	2 21.4	2 34.6
11 S	5 14 30.2	17 52.2	10 51.8	16 43.9	15 5.2	10 16.4	27 16.3	19 46.0	14 57.0	12 44.8	2 20.3	2 33.4
12 S	5 18 26.7	18 53.2	10 48.6	0♓35.7	16 39.4	11 31.2	27 29.8	19 51.3	14 52.8	12 47.2	2 19.2	2 32.2
13 M	5 22 23.3	19 54.2	10 45.4	14 1.4	18 13.6	12 46.1	27 42.8	19 56.8	14 48.6	12 49.6	2 18.0	2 31.1
14 T	5 26 19.9	20 55.2	10 42.2	27 3.7	19 47.9	14 0.9	27 55.2	20 2.4	14 44.4	12 52.0	2 16.9	2 29.9
15 W	5 30 16.4	21 56.2	10 39.0	9♈46.1	21 22.3	15 15.7	28 7.0	20 8.2	14 40.0	12 54.5	2 15.7	2 28.7
16 T	5 34 13.0	22 57.3	10 35.9	22 12.6	22 56.8	16 30.4	28 18.3	20 14.2	14 35.6	12 57.0	2 14.5	2 27.5
17 F	5 38 9.5	23 58.3	10 32.7	4♉26.5	24 31.5	17 45.2	28 28.9	20 20.4	14 31.2	12 59.5	2 13.2	2 26.3
18 S	5 42 6.1	24 59.4	10 29.5	16 31.2	26 6.2	18 60.0	28 38.9	20 26.7	14 26.7	13 2.1	2 12.0	2 25.1
19 S	5 46 2.7	26 0.5	10 26.3	28 29.4	27 41.2	20 14.7	28 48.4	20 33.2	14 22.2	13 4.7	2 10.7	2 23.9
20 M	5 49 59.2	27 1.5	10 23.2	10♊23.0	29 16.3	21 29.4	28 57.2	20 39.9	14 17.6	13 7.4	2 9.4	2 22.7
21 T	5 53 55.8	28 2.6	10 20.0	22 14.1	0♑51.5	22 44.1	29 5.3	20 46.7	14 13.0	13 10.1	2 8.0	2 21.5
22 W	5 57 52.3	29 3.7	10 16.8	4♋ 4.3	2 27.0	23 58.8	29 12.8	20 53.7	14 8.3	13 12.8	2 6.7	2 20.3
23 T	6 1 48.9	0♑ 4.8	10 13.6	15 55.2	4 2.6	25 13.5	29 19.7	21 0.9	14 3.6	13 15.5	2 5.3	2 19.1
24 F	6 5 45.5	1 5.9	10 10.5	27 48.9	5 38.5	26 28.1	29 25.8	21 8.2	13 58.8	13 18.3	2 4.0	2 17.9
25 S	6 9 42.0	2 7.0	10 7.3	9♌47.5	7 14.6	27 42.8	29 31.3	21 15.7	13 54.0	13 21.1	2 2.5	2 16.7
26 S	6 13 38.5	3 8.1	10 4.1	21 54.1	8 50.9	28 57.4	29 36.1	21 23.3	13 49.2	13 23.9	2 1.1	2 15.5
27 M	6 17 35.1	4 9.3	10 0.9	4♍12.1	10 27.4	0♒12.0	29 40.1	21 31.1	13 44.4	13 26.8	1 59.7	2 14.3
28 T	6 21 31.7	5 10.4	9 57.8	16 45.1	12 4.2	1 26.6	29 43.5	21 39.0	13 39.5	13 29.7	1 58.2	2 13.1
29 W	6 25 28.2	6 11.5	9 54.6	29 37.3	13 41.1	2 41.2	29 46.1	21 47.1	13 34.7	13 32.7	1 56.7	2 11.9
30 T	6 29 24.8	7 12.7	9 51.4	12♎52.4	15 18.3	3 55.7	29 47.9	21 55.4	13 29.7	13 35.6	1 55.2	2 10.7
31 F	6 33 21.3	8 13.9	9 48.2	26 33.1	16 55.6	5 10.3	29 49.0	22 3.7	13 24.8	13 38.6	1 53.7	2 9.5

DECLINATION

DAY	SIDEREAL TIME	☉	☊	☽	☿	♀	♂	♃	♄	♅	♆	♇
1 W	4 35 4.6	21S36.5	17S22.3	0N44.4	19S47.0	24S26.2	15N35.9	5S35.6	22N 0.8	17S43.9	19N18.5	18N10.5
4 S	4 46 54.3	22 4.2	17 24.9	16S55.4	21 4.0	24 33.0	15 23.0	5 30.7	22 2.2	17 42.1	19 19.1	18 10.5
7 T	4 58 43.9	22 28.1	17 27.5	26 51.4	22 12.0	24 33.1	15 11.6	5 25.1	22 3.6	17 40.3	19 19.8	18 10.6
10 F	5 10 33.6	22 48.1	17 30.1	20 13.9	23 10.2	24 26.3	15 1.7	5 18.9	22 5.2	17 38.3	19 20.5	18 10.8
13 M	5 22 23.3	23 4.0	17 32.7	3 35.1	23 57.9	24 12.8	14 53.6	5 12.0	22 6.8	17 36.2	19 21.2	18 10.9
16 T	5 34 13.0	23 15.8	17 35.3	13N12.3	24 34.5	23 52.7	14 47.2	5 4.4	22 8.4	17 34.0	19 22.1	18 11.0
19 S	5 46 2.7	23 23.5	17 37.9	24 33.1	24 59.4	23 26.0	14 42.8	4 56.3	22 10.1	17 31.8	19 22.9	18 11.2
22 W	5 57 52.3	23 26.9	17 40.5	26 18.9	25 11.9	22 53.0	14 40.5	4 47.6	22 11.9	17 29.4	19 23.8	18 11.4
25 S	6 9 42.0	23 26.1	17 43.1	17 41.0	25 11.5	22 13.8	14 40.4	4 38.3	22 13.6	17 27.0	19 24.8	18 11.6
28 T	6 21 31.7	23 21.0	17 45.6	2 14.7	24 57.8	21 28.7	14 42.5	4 28.5	22 15.4	17 24.5	19 25.8	18 11.8
31 F	6 33 21.3	23 11.8	17 48.2	15S 0.4	24 30.2	20 38.0	14 47.1	4 18.2	22 17.2	17 21.9	19 26.8	18 12.1

JANUARY 1916

DAY	EPHEMERIS SIDEREAL TIME	☉	☊	☽	☿	♀	♂	♃	♄	♅	♆	♇
	h m s	° ′	° ′	° ′	° ′	° ′	° ′	° ′	° ′	° ′	° ′	° ′
						LONGITUDE						
1 S	6 37 17.9	9♑15.0	9♒45.0	10♏40.7	18♑33.1	6♒24.8	29♌49.4	22♓12.3	13♋19.9	13♒41.6	1♌52.2	2♋ 8.3
2 S	6 41 14.5	10 16.2	9 41.9	25 14.0	20 10.7	7 39.3	29R48.9	22 20.9	13R14.9	13 44.6	1R50.7	2R 7.1
3 M	6 45 11.0	11 17.4	9 38.7	10♐ 8.6	21 48.3	8 53.8	29 47.7	22 29.8	13 10.0	13 47.7	1 49.1	2 5.9
4 T	6 49 7.6	12 18.6	9 35.5	25 17.3	23 26.0	10 8.2	29 45.7	22 38.7	13 5.0	13 50.8	1 47.5	2 4.7
5 W	6 53 4.1	13 19.8	9 32.3	10♑30.7	25 3.7	11 22.7	29 42.8	22 47.8	13 0.0	13 53.9	1 46.0	2 3.5
6 T	6 57 0.7	14 20.9	9 29.2	25 38.6	26 41.1	12 37.1	29 39.2	22 57.0	12 55.1	13 57.0	1 44.4	2 2.3
7 F	7 0 57.3	15 22.1	9 26.0	10♒31.7	28 18.4	13 51.5	29 34.8	23 6.4	12 50.1	14 0.2	1 42.8	2 1.1
8 S	7 4 53.8	16 23.3	9 22.8	25 2.7	29 55.2	15 5.8	29 29.5	23 15.9	12 45.2	14 3.4	1 41.1	1 60.0
9 S	7 8 50.4	17 24.5	9 19.6	9♓ 7.5	1♒31.5	16 20.1	29 23.5	23 25.5	12 40.2	14 6.6	1 39.5	1 58.8
10 M	7 12 46.9	18 25.6	9 16.5	22 44.7	3 7.2	17 34.4	29 16.6	23 35.3	12 35.3	14 9.8	1 37.9	1 57.7
11 T	7 16 43.5	19 26.8	9 13.3	5♈55.6	4 41.9	18 48.7	29 8.9	23 45.2	12 30.4	14 13.0	1 36.2	1 56.5
12 W	7 20 40.1	20 27.9	9 10.1	18 42.8	6 15.4	20 3.0	29 0.4	23 55.2	12 25.5	14 16.3	1 34.6	1 55.4
13 T	7 24 36.6	21 29.1	9 6.9	1♉10.2	7 47.4	21 17.1	28 51.1	24 5.3	12 20.6	14 19.6	1 32.9	1 54.2
14 F	7 28 33.1	22 30.2	9 3.8	13 22.1	9 17.7	22 31.3	28 41.0	24 15.6	12 15.7	14 22.9	1 31.3	1 53.1
15 S	7 32 29.7	23 31.3	9 0.6	25 22.8	10 45.7	23 45.4	28 30.1	24 25.9	12 10.9	14 26.2	1 29.6	1 52.0
16 S	7 36 26.3	24 32.4	8 57.4	7♊16.3	12 11.1	24 59.5	28 18.4	24 36.4	12 6.1	14 29.5	1 27.9	1 50.9
17 M	7 40 22.9	25 33.5	8 54.2	19 6.2	13 33.3	26 13.6	28 6.0	24 47.0	12 1.4	14 32.8	1 26.2	1 49.8
18 T	7 44 19.4	26 34.6	8 51.1	0♋55.7	14 51.7	27 27.6	27 52.7	24 57.7	11 56.7	14 36.2	1 24.5	1 48.7
19 W	7 48 15.9	27 35.6	8 47.9	12 47.4	16 5.8	28 41.5	27 38.7	25 8.5	11 52.0	14 39.6	1 22.9	1 47.6
20 T	7 52 12.5	28 36.7	8 44.7	24 43.5	17 14.7	29 55.4	27 24.0	25 19.4	11 47.3	14 42.9	1 21.2	1 46.6
21 F	7 56 9.1	29 37.7	8 41.5	6♌45.8	18 17.7	1♓ 9.3	27 8.5	25 30.5	11 42.7	14 46.3	1 19.5	1 45.5
22 S	8 0 5.6	0♒38.8	8 38.3	18 56.2	19 14.0	2 23.1	26 52.3	25 41.6	11 38.2	14 49.7	1 17.8	1 44.5
23 S	8 4 2.2	1 39.8	8 35.2	1♍16.2	20 2.7	3 36.9	26 35.4	25 52.8	11 33.7	14 53.2	1 16.1	1 43.4
24 M	8 7 58.7	2 40.8	8 32.0	13 47.7	20 43.0	4 50.6	26 17.8	26 4.2	11 29.2	14 56.6	1 14.4	1 42.4
25 T	8 11 55.3	3 41.8	8 28.8	26 32.5	21 14.0	6 4.3	25 59.6	26 15.6	11 24.8	15 0.0	1 12.7	1 41.4
26 W	8 15 51.9	4 42.8	8 25.6	9♎32.6	21 35.0	7 18.0	25 40.8	26 27.1	11 20.4	15 3.5	1 11.0	1 40.4
27 T	8 19 48.4	5 43.8	8 22.5	22 49.8	21 45.4	8 31.6	25 21.3	26 38.8	11 16.1	15 6.9	1 9.3	1 39.4
28 F	8 23 45.0	6 44.8	8 19.3	6♏25.8	21R44.6	9 45.1	25 1.2	26 50.5	11 11.9	15 10.4	1 7.6	1 38.5
29 S	8 27 41.5	7 45.8	8 16.1	20 21.3	21 32.4	10 58.6	24 40.6	27 2.3	11 7.7	15 13.8	1 5.9	1 37.5
30 S	8 31 38.1	8 46.7	8 12.9	4♐36.1	21 9.0	12 12.1	24 19.5	27 14.2	11 3.6	15 17.3	1 4.3	1 36.6
31 M	8 35 34.7	9 47.7	8 9.8	19 7.9	20 34.6	13 25.5	23 58.0	27 26.2	10 59.6	15 20.8	1 2.6	1 35.7
						DECLINATION						
1 S	6 37 17.9	23S 7.7	17S49.0	19S59.1	24S17.9	20S19.9	14N49.2	4S14.6	22N17.8	17S21.0	19N27.1	18N12.2
4 T	6 49 7.6	22 52.9	17 51.6	26 56.1	23 31.5	19 22.1	14 57.0	4 3.6	22 19.6	17 18.3	19 28.2	18 12.4
7 F	7 0 57.3	22 33.9	17 54.1	17 23.7	22 31.2	18 19.4	15 7.4	3 52.1	22 21.3	17 15.5	19 29.3	18 12.7
10 M	7 12 46.9	22 11.0	17 56.6	0N31.1	21 17.5	17 12.2	15 20.2	3 40.1	22 23.1	17 12.7	19 30.4	18 13.0
13 T	7 24 36.6	21 44.1	17 59.1	16 46.9	19 51.9	16 0.7	15 35.4	3 27.7	22 24.8	17 9.9	19 31.5	18 13.4
16 S	7 36 26.3	21 13.5	18 1.7	26 4.6	18 17.2	14 45.4	15 52.9	3 14.9	22 26.4	17 6.9	19 32.6	18 13.7
19 W	7 48 15.9	20 39.2	18 4.2	25 5.0	16 38.0	13 26.6	16 12.4	3 1.6	22 28.1	17 4.0	19 33.8	18 14.0
22 S	8 0 5.6	20 1.4	18 6.7	14 12.0	15 1.6	12 4.7	16 33.7	2 48.0	22 29.7	17 1.0	19 34.9	18 14.4
25 T	8 11 55.3	19 20.2	18 9.1	2S16.0	13 37.8	10 40.0	16 56.5	2 34.1	22 31.2	16 58.0	19 36.1	18 14.8
28 F	8 23 45.0	18 35.8	18 11.6	18 39.6	12 38.0	9 12.8	17 20.5	2 19.8	22 32.7	16 54.9	19 37.2	18 15.2
31 M	8 35 34.7	17 48.3	18 14.1	26 59.4	12 11.7	7 43.6	17 45.2	2 5.2	22 34.1	16 51.8	19 38.4	18 15.6

FEBRUARY 1916

DAY	EPHEMERIS SIDEREAL TIME	☉	☊	☽	☿	♀	♂	♃	♄	♅	♆	♇
						LONGITUDE						
1 T	8 39 31.2	10♒48.6	8♒ 6.6	3♑52.8	19♒50.0	14♓38.8	23♌35.9	27♓38.3	10♋55.6	15♒24.3	1♌ 0.9	1♋34.8
2 W	8 43 27.7	11 49.5	8 3.4	18 44.8	18R56.4	15 52.1	23R13.5	27 50.5	10R51.7	15 27.8	0R59.3	1R33.9
3 T	8 47 24.3	12 50.4	8 0.2	3♒36.8	17 55.2	17 5.3	22 50.7	28 2.7	10 47.9	15 31.2	0 57.6	1 33.0
4 F	8 51 20.9	13 51.3	7 57.0	18 20.8	16 48.2	18 18.5	22 27.6	28 15.1	10 44.2	15 34.7	0 56.0	1 32.2
5 S	8 55 17.4	14 52.2	7 53.9	2♓49.8	15 37.3	19 31.6	22 4.3	28 27.5	10 40.5	15 38.2	0 54.3	1 31.3
6 S	8 59 14.0	15 53.0	7 50.7	16 58.1	14 24.7	20 44.6	21 40.7	28 40.0	10 36.9	15 41.7	0 52.7	1 30.5
7 M	9 3 10.5	16 53.8	7 47.5	0♈42.1	13 12.4	21 57.6	21 16.9	28 52.6	10 33.4	15 45.2	0 51.1	1 29.7
8 T	9 7 7.1	17 54.6	7 44.3	14 0.8	12 2.2	23 10.5	20 53.0	29 5.2	10 30.0	15 48.7	0 49.5	1 28.9
9 W	9 11 3.6	18 55.4	7 41.2	26 55.2	10 56.0	24 23.4	20 29.0	29 17.9	10 26.6	15 52.2	0 47.9	1 28.1
10 T	9 15 0.2	19 56.1	7 38.0	9♉27.9	9 55.0	25 36.2	20 5.0	29 30.7	10 23.4	15 55.7	0 46.3	1 27.4
11 F	9 18 56.8	20 56.9	7 34.8	21 42.6	9 0.4	26 48.9	19 41.0	29 43.6	10 20.2	15 59.2	0 44.7	1 26.6
12 S	9 22 53.3	21 57.6	7 31.6	3♊44.1	8 13.0	28 1.5	19 17.1	29 56.5	10 17.2	16 2.6	0 43.2	1 25.9
13 S	9 26 49.9	22 58.2	7 28.5	15 37.0	7 33.3	29 14.0	18 53.2	0♈ 9.5	10 14.2	16 6.1	0 41.6	1 25.2
14 M	9 30 46.4	23 58.9	7 25.3	27 26.1	7 1.4	0♈26.5	18 29.6	0 22.6	10 11.3	16 9.6	0 40.1	1 24.6
15 T	9 34 43.0	24 59.5	7 22.1	9♋15.7	6 37.6	1 38.9	18 6.1	0 35.7	10 8.5	16 13.0	0 38.6	1 23.9
16 W	9 38 39.5	26 0.1	7 18.9	21 10.0	6 21.5	2 51.1	17 42.8	0 48.9	10 5.8	16 16.5	0 37.1	1 23.3
17 T	9 42 36.1	27 0.6	7 15.7	3♌12.2	6 13.1	4 3.4	17 19.9	1 2.2	10 3.2	16 19.9	0 35.6	1 22.6
18 F	9 46 32.7	28 1.2	7 12.6	15 24.9	6 11.9	5 15.5	16 57.2	1 15.5	10 0.8	16 23.4	0 34.1	1 22.0
19 S	9 50 29.2	29 1.7	7 9.4	27 49.9	6D17.5	6 27.5	16 34.9	1 28.8	9 58.4	16 26.8	0 32.7	1 21.5
20 S	9 54 25.7	0♓ 2.1	7 6.2	10♍28.5	6 29.6	7 39.4	16 13.0	1 42.3	9 56.1	16 30.2	0 31.2	1 20.9
21 M	9 58 22.3	1 2.6	7 3.0	23 21.0	6 47.8	8 51.3	15 51.6	1 55.7	9 53.9	16 33.6	0 29.8	1 20.4
22 T	10 2 18.9	2 3.0	6 59.9	6♎27.4	7 11.5	10 3.0	15 30.6	2 9.3	9 51.8	16 37.0	0 28.4	1 19.9
23 W	10 6 15.4	3 3.4	6 56.7	19 47.0	7 40.5	11 14.7	15 10.1	2 22.8	9 49.8	16 40.4	0 27.0	1 19.4
24 T	10 10 12.0	4 3.8	6 53.5	3♏19.2	8 14.3	12 26.3	14 50.2	2 36.5	9 47.9	16 43.8	0 25.7	1 18.9
25 F	10 14 8.5	5 4.1	6 50.3	17 3.1	8 52.6	13 37.7	14 30.8	2 50.2	9 46.1	16 47.2	0 24.3	1 18.4
26 S	10 18 5.1	6 4.5	6 47.1	0♐58.0	9 35.0	14 49.1	14 11.9	3 3.9	9 44.5	16 50.5	0 23.0	1 18.0
27 S	10 22 1.6	7 4.8	6 44.0	15 2.9	10 21.3	16 0.3	13 53.7	3 17.7	9 42.9	16 53.8	0 21.7	1 17.6
28 M	10 25 58.2	8 5.1	6 40.8	29 16.5	11 11.1	17 11.5	13 36.2	3 31.5	9 41.5	16 57.2	0 20.5	1 17.2
29 T	10 29 54.7	9 5.3	6 37.6	13♑36.9	12 4.1	18 22.5	13 19.3	3 45.3	9 40.1	17 0.5	0 19.2	1 16.8
						DECLINATION						
1 T	8 39 31.2	17S31.9	18S14.9	26S22.5	12S11.2	7S13.4	17N53.5	2S 0.3	22N34.5	16S50.8	19N38.7	18N15.8
4 F	8 51 20.9	16 40.6	18 17.4	14 26.2	12 32.7	5 41.9	18 18.5	1 45.3	22 35.9	16 47.7	19 39.9	18 16.2
7 M	9 3 10.5	15 46.8	18 19.8	4N 8.3	13 20.3	4 9.1	18 43.1	1 30.0	22 37.1	16 44.6	19 41.0	18 16.6
10 T	9 15 0.2	14 50.5	18 22.3	19 39.2	14 19.6	2 35.3	19 6.8	1 14.5	22 38.3	16 41.5	19 42.0	18 17.1
13 S	9 26 49.9	13 52.0	18 24.7	26 50.3	15 17.9	1 1.0	19 29.1	0 58.7	22 39.4	16 38.4	19 43.1	18 17.5
16 W	9 38 39.5	12 51.5	18 27.1	23 18.2	16 7.4	0N33.6	19 49.8	0 42.7	22 40.5	16 35.3	19 44.1	18 18.0
19 S	9 50 29.2	11 49.1	18 29.6	10 33.6	16 44.5	2 8.1	20 8.4	0 26.6	22 41.5	16 32.2	19 45.1	18 18.5
22 T	10 2 18.9	10 45.0	18 32.0	6S39.9	17 7.9	3 42.3	20 24.8	0 10.2	22 42.4	16 29.2	19 46.1	18 19.0
25 F	10 14 8.5	9 39.5	18 34.4	21 52.8	17 17.4	5 15.8	20 38.7	0N 6.3	22 43.2	16 26.2	19 47.0	18 19.5
28 M	10 25 58.2	8 32.5	18 36.8	26 42.5	17 13.3	6 48.3	20 50.2	0 22.9	22 44.0	16 23.2	19 47.9	18 20.0

MARCH 1916

LONGITUDE

DAY	EPHEMERIS SIDEREAL TIME h m s	☉ ° ′	☊ ° ′	☽ ° ′	☿ ° ′	♀ ° ′	♂ ° ′	♃ ° ′	♄ ° ′	♅ ° ′	♆ ° ′	♇ ° ′
1 W	10 33 51.3	10♓ 5.6	6♒34.4	28♑ 1.2	13♒ 0.3	19♈33.5	13♌ 3.1	3♈59.2	9♋38.9	17♒ 3.7	0♌18.0	1♋16.5
2 T	10 37 47.8	11 5.8	6 31.3	12♒25.7	13 59.3	20 44.3	12R47.6	4 13.2	9R37.7	17 7.0	0R16.8	1R16.2
3 F	10 41 44.4	12 6.0	6 28.1	26 45.9	15 0.9	21 55.1	12 32.8	4 27.2	9 36.7	17 10.3	0 15.6	1 15.9
4 S	10 45 41.0	13 6.1	6 24.9	10♓56.6	16 5.0	23 5.7	12 18.8	4 41.2	9 35.8	17 13.5	0 14.4	1 15.6
5 S	10 49 37.5	14 6.2	6 21.7	24 53.0	17 11.5	24 16.2	12 5.5	4 55.2	9 35.0	17 16.7	0 13.3	1 15.4
6 M	10 53 34.0	15 6.3	6 18.5	8♈31.1	18 20.1	25 26.6	11 53.0	5 9.3	9 34.4	17 19.9	0 12.2	1 15.1
7 T	10 57 30.6	16 6.4	6 15.4	21 48.4	19 30.8	26 36.8	11 41.3	5 23.5	9 33.8	17 23.1	0 11.1	1 14.9
8 W	11 1 27.2	17 6.4	6 12.2	4♉44.2	20 43.5	27 46.9	11 30.3	5 37.6	9 33.3	17 26.2	0 10.1	1 14.7
9 T	11 5 23.7	18 6.4	6 9.0	17 19.5	21 58.0	28 56.9	11 20.2	5 51.8	9 33.0	17 29.3	0 9.0	1 14.6
10 F	11 9 20.3	19 6.3	6 5.8	29 36.8	23 14.3	0♉ 6.8	11 10.8	6 6.0	9 32.8	17 32.4	0 8.0	1 14.4
11 S	11 13 16.8	20 6.2	6 2.7	11♊40.0	24 32.3	1 16.5	11 2.2	6 20.3	9 32.6	17 35.5	0 7.1	1 14.3
12 S	11 17 13.4	21 6.1	5 59.5	23 33.7	25 51.9	2 26.1	10 54.5	6 34.5	9 32.6	17 38.6	0 6.1	1 14.2
13 M	11 21 9.9	22 6.0	5 56.3	5♋23.1	27 13.1	3 35.5	10 47.5	6 48.8	9D32.8	17 41.6	0 5.2	1 14.2
14 T	11 25 6.5	23 5.8	5 53.1	17 13.2	28 35.9	4 44.8	10 41.3	7 3.1	9 33.0	17 44.6	0 4.3	1 14.1
15 W	11 29 3.0	24 5.5	5 49.9	29 9.3	0♓ 0.1	5 53.9	10 35.9	7 17.5	9 33.3	17 47.6	0 3.5	1 14.1
16 T	11 32 59.6	25 5.3	5 46.8	11♌15.8	1 25.8	7 2.9	10 31.3	7 31.8	9 33.7	17 50.5	0 2.6	1 14.1
17 F	11 36 56.1	26 5.0	5 43.6	23 36.7	2 52.9	8 11.7	10 27.4	7 46.2	9 34.3	17 53.5	0 1.8	1D14.1
18 S	11 40 52.7	27 4.6	5 40.4	6♍14.6	4 21.4	9 20.4	10 24.4	8 0.6	9 35.0	17 56.4	0 1.1	1 14.2
19 S	11 44 49.3	28 4.2	5 37.2	19 11.1	5 51.2	10 28.8	10 22.1	8 15.0	9 35.7	17 59.2	0 0.3	1 14.2
20 M	11 48 45.8	29 3.8	5 34.1	2♎26.2	7 22.4	11 37.1	10 20.5	8 29.4	9 36.6	18 2.1	29♋59.6	1 14.3
21 T	11 52 42.4	0♈ 3.4	5 30.9	15 58.2	8 55.0	12 45.3	10 19.7	8 43.8	9 37.6	18 4.9	29 58.9	1 14.4
22 W	11 56 38.9	1 2.9	5 27.7	29 44.6	10 28.9	13 53.2	10 19.6	8 58.3	9 38.8	18 7.7	29 58.3	1 14.6
23 T	12 0 35.5	2 2.4	5 24.5	13♏41.7	12 4.1	15 1.0	10D20.3	9 12.7	9 40.0	18 10.4	29 57.7	1 14.8
24 F	12 4 32.0	3 1.9	5 21.3	27 45.8	13 40.7	16 8.6	10 21.6	9 27.2	9 41.3	18 13.1	29 57.1	1 14.9
25 S	12 8 28.6	4 1.3	5 18.2	11♐53.5	15 18.6	17 16.0	10 23.7	9 41.7	9 42.7	18 15.8	29 56.5	1 15.1
26 S	12 12 25.1	5 0.7	5 15.0	26 2.3	16 57.8	18 23.2	10 26.5	9 56.2	9 44.3	18 18.5	29 56.0	1 15.4
27 M	12 16 21.7	6 0.1	5 11.8	10♑10.1	18 38.4	19 30.2	10 29.9	10 10.7	9 45.9	18 21.1	29 55.5	1 15.6
28 T	12 20 18.3	6 59.4	5 8.6	24 16.0	20 20.3	20 37.0	10 34.1	10 25.2	9 47.7	18 23.7	29 55.1	1 15.9
29 W	12 24 14.8	7 58.7	5 5.5	8♒18.8	22 3.6	21 43.6	10 38.9	10 39.7	9 49.6	18 26.3	29 54.6	1 16.2
30 T	12 28 11.3	8 58.0	5 2.3	22 17.4	23 48.3	22 50.0	10 44.3	10 54.2	9 51.5	18 28.8	29 54.2	1 16.5
31 F	12 32 7.9	9 57.3	4 59.1	6♓10.2	25 34.3	23 56.2	10 50.5	11 8.7	9 53.6	18 31.3	29 53.9	1 16.9

DECLINATION

DAY	EPHEMERIS SIDEREAL TIME	☉	☊	☽	☿	♀	♂	♃	♄	♅	♆	♇
1 W	10 33 51.3	7S47.3	18S38.4	21S26.3	17S 3.2	7N49.2	20N56.5	0N34.1	22N44.4	16S21.2	19N48.4	18N20.3
4 S	10 45 41.0	6 38.6	18 40.7	4 49.8	16 37.1	9 19.4	21 3.7	0 50.9	22 45.1	16 18.3	19 49.3	18 20.8
7 T	10 57 30.6	5 29.0	18 43.1	13N 7.0	15 58.3	10 47.7	21 8.5	1 7.8	22 45.6	16 15.4	19 50.0	18 21.3
10 F	11 9 20.3	4 18.8	18 45.5	24 44.7	15 7.1	12 13.9	21 10.9	1 24.8	22 46.1	16 12.6	19 50.7	18 21.8
13 M	11 21 9.9	3 8.1	18 47.8	26 4.1	14 3.9	13 37.6	21 10.9	1 41.9	22 46.5	16 9.9	19 51.4	18 22.3
16 T	11 32 59.6	1 57.2	18 50.2	17 3.2	12 48.9	14 58.5	21 8.8	1 59.0	22 46.9	16 7.2	19 52.0	18 22.8
19 S	11 44 49.3	0 46.1	18 52.5	1 7.1	11 22.5	16 16.4	21 4.7	2 16.1	22 47.1	16 4.6	19 52.5	18 23.3
22 W	11 56 38.9	0N25.0	18 54.9	16S 6.7	9 44.8	17 30.9	20 58.7	2 33.3	22 47.3	16 2.1	19 53.0	18 23.8
25 S	12 8 28.6	1 36.0	18 57.2	26 20.1	7 56.3	18 41.8	20 50.9	2 50.4	22 47.4	15 59.6	19 53.5	18 24.3
28 T	12 20 18.3	2 46.6	18 59.5	22 18.9	5 57.2	19 48.9	20 41.4	3 7.5	22 47.4	15 57.3	19 53.8	18 24.8
31 F	12 32 7.9	3 56.7	19 1.8	6 53.4	3 47.9	20 51.8	20 30.4	3 24.6	22 47.4	15 55.0	19 54.1	18 25.3

APRIL 1916

LONGITUDE

DAY	EPHEMERIS SIDEREAL TIME h m s	☉ ° ′	☊ ° ′	☽ ° ′	☿ ° ′	♀ ° ′	♂ ° ′	♃ ° ′	♄ ° ′	♅ ° ′	♆ ° ′	♇ ° ′
1 S	12 36 4.5	10♈56.5	4♒55.9	19♓54.9	27♓21.7	25♉ 2.2	10♌57.2	11♈23.3	9♋55.8	18♒33.7	29♋53.5	1♋17.2
2 S	12 40 1.0	11 55.7	4 52.7	3♈28.8	29 10.5	26 8.0	11 4.6	11 37.8	9 58.1	18 36.1	29R53.3	1 17.6
3 M	12 43 57.6	12 54.9	4 49.6	16 49.3	1♈ 0.8	27 13.5	11 12.6	11 52.3	10 0.5	18 38.5	29 53.0	1 18.0
4 T	12 47 54.1	13 54.0	4 46.4	29 54.0	2 52.4	28 18.8	11 21.3	12 6.8	10 3.0	18 40.8	29 52.8	1 18.5
5 W	12 51 50.7	14 53.1	4 43.2	12♉41.8	4 45.5	29 23.8	11 30.5	12 21.3	10 5.6	18 43.1	29 52.6	1 18.9
6 T	12 55 47.2	15 52.1	4 40.0	25 12.6	6 39.9	0♊28.6	11 40.3	12 35.8	10 8.3	18 45.4	29 52.4	1 19.4
7 F	12 59 43.8	16 51.1	4 36.9	7♊27.9	8 35.8	1 33.1	11 50.7	12 50.3	10 11.1	18 47.6	29 52.3	1 19.9
8 S	13 3 40.3	17 50.1	4 33.7	19 30.2	10 33.1	2 37.4	12 1.6	13 4.8	10 14.0	18 49.8	29 52.2	1 20.4
9 S	13 7 36.9	18 49.1	4 30.5	1♋23.5	12 31.8	3 41.4	12 13.1	13 19.3	10 17.1	18 52.0	29 52.1	1 21.0
10 M	13 11 33.4	19 48.0	4 27.3	13 12.4	14 31.8	4 45.1	12 25.2	13 33.7	10 20.2	18 54.1	29 52.1	1 21.6
11 T	13 15 30.0	20 46.8	4 24.1	25 2.1	16 33.1	5 48.5	12 37.7	13 48.2	10 23.4	18 56.1	29D52.1	1 22.1
12 W	13 19 26.5	21 45.7	4 21.0	6♌58.1	18 35.6	6 51.6	12 50.8	14 2.6	10 26.7	18 58.2	29 52.1	1 22.8
13 T	13 23 23.1	22 44.4	4 17.8	19 5.9	20 39.2	7 54.4	13 4.4	14 17.1	10 30.1	19 0.1	29 52.2	1 23.4
14 F	13 27 19.6	23 43.2	4 14.6	1♍30.3	22 43.9	8 56.8	13 18.5	14 31.5	10 33.6	19 2.1	29 52.3	1 24.0
15 S	13 31 16.2	24 41.9	4 11.4	14 15.4	24 49.5	9 59.0	13 33.0	14 45.9	10 37.2	19 4.0	29 52.4	1 24.7
16 S	13 35 12.8	25 40.6	4 8.3	27 23.6	26 55.8	11 0.8	13 48.1	15 0.2	10 40.9	19 5.8	29 52.6	1 25.4
17 M	13 39 9.3	26 39.2	4 5.1	10♎55.5	29 2.7	12 2.2	14 3.6	15 14.6	10 44.6	19 7.6	29 52.8	1 26.1
18 T	13 43 5.8	27 37.8	4 1.9	24 49.4	1♉10.0	13 3.3	14 19.5	15 28.9	10 48.5	19 9.4	29 53.0	1 26.8
19 W	13 47 2.4	28 36.4	3 58.7	9♏ 1.5	3 17.4	14 4.0	14 35.9	15 43.2	10 52.4	19 11.1	29 53.3	1 27.6
20 T	13 50 59.0	29 35.0	3 55.5	23 25.9	5 24.7	15 4.4	14 52.7	15 57.5	10 56.5	19 12.8	29 53.6	1 28.4
21 F	13 54 55.5	0♉33.5	3 52.4	7♐56.3	7 31.6	16 4.3	15 9.9	16 11.8	11 0.6	19 14.5	29 53.9	1 29.1
22 S	13 58 52.1	1 32.0	3 49.2	22 26.3	9 37.7	17 3.8	15 27.6	16 26.1	11 4.8	19 16.1	29 54.3	1 30.0
23 S	14 2 48.6	2 30.4	3 46.0	6♑50.8	11 42.8	18 3.0	15 45.6	16 40.3	11 9.1	19 17.6	29 54.7	1 30.8
24 M	14 6 45.2	3 28.9	3 42.8	21 6.4	13 46.5	19 1.7	16 4.0	16 54.5	11 13.5	19 19.1	29 55.1	1 31.6
25 T	14 10 41.8	4 27.3	3 39.7	5♒11.2	15 48.6	19 59.9	16 22.9	17 8.6	11 18.0	19 20.6	29 55.6	1 32.5
26 W	14 14 38.3	5 25.7	3 36.5	19 4.9	17 48.7	20 57.7	16 42.1	17 22.8	11 22.6	19 22.0	29 56.1	1 33.4
27 T	14 18 34.8	6 24.0	3 33.3	2♓47.5	19 46.6	21 55.1	17 1.6	17 36.9	11 27.2	19 23.4	29 56.6	1 34.3
28 F	14 22 31.4	7 22.4	3 30.1	16 19.3	21 41.9	22 52.0	17 21.6	17 51.0	11 31.9	19 24.7	29 57.2	1 35.2
29 S	14 26 28.0	8 20.7	3 27.0	29 40.5	23 34.4	23 48.3	17 41.9	18 5.0	11 36.7	19 26.0	29 57.8	1 36.1
30 S	14 30 24.5	9 19.0	3 23.8	12♈50.7	25 23.9	24 44.2	18 2.6	18 19.0	11 41.6	19 27.2	29 58.4	1 37.1

DECLINATION

DAY	EPHEMERIS SIDEREAL TIME	☉	☊	☽	☿	♀	♂	♃	♄	♅	♆	♇
1 S	12 36 4.5	4N19.9	19S 2.6	0S46.1	3S 2.6	21N11.8	20N26.4	3N30.3	22N47.4	15S54.3	19N54.2	18N25.5
4 T	12 47 54.1	5 29.2	19 4.9	16N 7.7	0 40.6	22 8.9	20 13.3	3 47.3	22 47.2	15 52.2	19 54.4	18 26.0
7 F	12 59 43.8	6 37.5	19 7.1	25 46.1	1N49.9	23 1.3	19 58.9	4 4.3	22 47.0	15 50.1	19 54.6	18 26.5
10 M	13 11 33.4	7 44.8	19 9.4	24 39.4	4 27.6	23 48.9	19 43.1	4 21.1	22 46.6	15 48.2	19 54.7	18 26.9
13 T	13 23 23.1	8 51.0	19 11.7	13 55.0	7 10.6	24 31.5	19 25.9	4 37.9	22 46.2	15 46.4	19 54.7	18 27.4
16 S	13 35 12.8	9 55.8	19 13.9	2S38.3	9 55.7	25 9.0	19 7.6	4 54.5	22 45.8	15 44.7	19 54.7	18 27.8
19 W	13 47 2.4	10 59.1	19 16.2	19 14.0	12 38.9	25 41.3	18 48.0	5 11.0	22 45.2	15 43.2	19 54.6	18 28.3
22 S	13 58 52.1	12 0.8	19 18.4	26 32.4	15 15.0	26 8.3	18 27.3	5 27.3	22 44.5	15 41.7	19 54.5	18 28.7
25 T	14 10 41.8	13 0.7	19 20.7	18 50.1	17 38.3	26 30.2	18 5.5	5 43.5	22 43.8	15 40.4	19 54.3	18 29.1
28 F	14 22 31.4	13 58.8	19 22.9	2 14.4	19 43.9	26 46.8	17 42.5	5 59.5	22 42.9	15 39.2	19 54.0	18 29.5

MAY 1916

LONGITUDE

DAY	EPHEMERIS SIDEREAL TIME	☉	☊	☽	☿	♀	♂	♃	♄	♅	♆	♇
	h m s	° ′	° ′	° ′	° ′	° ′	° ′	° ′	° ′	° ′	° ′	° ′
1 M	14 34 21.1	10♉17.2	3♒20.6	25♈49.2	27♉10.2	25♊39.5	18♌23.6	18♈33.0	11♋46.6	19♒28.4	29♋59.1	1♋38.1
2 T	14 38 17.6	11 15.4	3 17.4	8♉35.2	28 53.1	26 34.3	18 44.9	18 46.9	11 51.6	19 29.5	29 59.8	1 39.0
3 W	14 42 14.2	12 13.6	3 14.2	21 8.3	0♊32.4	27 28.5	19 6.6	19 0.8	11 56.7	19 30.6	0♌ 0.5	1 40.1
4 T	14 46 10.8	13 11.8	3 11.1	3♊28.5	2 8.1	28 22.2	19 28.6	19 14.7	12 1.9	19 31.6	0 1.3	1 41.1
5 F	14 50 7.3	14 9.9	3 7.9	15 36.7	3 40.1	29 15.2	19 51.0	19 28.5	12 7.2	19 32.6	0 2.1	1 42.1
6 S	14 54 3.9	15 8.0	3 4.7	27 34.8	5 8.1	0♋ 7.6	20 13.6	19 42.3	12 12.6	19 33.6	0 2.9	1 43.2
7 S	14 58 0.4	16 6.1	3 1.5	9♋25.6	6 32.2	0 59.3	20 36.5	19 56.1	12 18.0	19 34.5	0 3.8	1 44.2
8 M	15 1 57.0	17 4.1	2 58.4	21 13.0	7 52.2	1 50.3	20 59.8	20 9.7	12 23.5	19 35.3	0 4.6	1 45.3
9 T	15 5 53.5	18 2.2	2 55.2	3♌ 1.7	9 8.2	2 40.7	21 23.3	20 23.4	12 29.0	19 36.1	0 5.6	1 46.4
10 W	15 9 50.1	19 0.2	2 52.0	14 56.7	10 20.0	3 30.2	21 47.1	20 37.0	12 34.6	19 36.9	0 6.5	1 47.5
11 T	15 13 46.6	19 58.1	2 48.8	27 3.4	11 27.6	4 19.1	22 11.2	20 50.5	12 40.3	19 37.5	0 7.5	1 48.7
12 F	15 17 43.2	20 56.0	2 45.6	9♍27.4	12 30.8	5 7.1	22 35.6	21 4.0	12 46.1	19 38.2	0 8.5	1 49.8
13 S	15 21 39.7	21 53.9	2 42.5	22 13.2	13 29.8	5 54.3	23 0.3	21 17.5	12 51.9	19 38.8	0 9.5	1 51.0
14 S	15 25 36.3	22 51.8	2 39.3	5♎24.7	14 24.2	6 40.7	23 25.1	21 30.9	12 57.8	19 39.4	0 10.6	1 52.2
15 M	15 29 32.9	23 49.6	2 36.1	19 3.4	15 14.2	7 26.1	23 50.3	21 44.2	13 3.8	19 39.9	0 11.7	1 53.3
16 T	15 33 29.4	24 47.4	2 32.9	3♏ 8.8	15 59.7	8 10.6	24 15.7	21 57.5	13 9.8	19 40.3	0 12.8	1 54.5
17 W	15 37 26.0	25 45.2	2 29.8	17 37.2	16 40.6	8 54.2	24 41.3	22 10.8	13 15.8	19 40.7	0 13.9	1 55.7
18 T	15 41 22.5	26 43.0	2 26.6	2♐22.4	17 16.7	9 36.8	25 7.2	22 24.0	13 22.0	19 41.1	0 15.1	1 57.0
19 F	15 45 19.1	27 40.7	2 23.4	17 16.1	17 48.2	10 18.3	25 33.3	22 37.1	13 28.2	19 41.4	0 16.3	1 58.2
20 S	15 49 15.6	28 38.4	2 20.2	2♑ 9.7	18 14.9	10 58.8	25 59.7	22 50.1	13 34.4	19 41.6	0 17.6	1 59.5
21 S	15 53 12.2	29 36.1	2 17.1	16 55.6	18 36.8	11 38.2	26 26.2	23 3.1	13 40.7	19 41.8	0 18.8	2 0.7
22 M	15 57 8.8	0♊33.8	2 13.9	1♒27.9	18 53.9	12 16.4	26 53.0	23 16.1	13 47.1	19 42.0	0 20.1	2 2.0
23 T	16 1 5.3	1 31.4	2 10.7	15 43.1	19 6.2	12 53.4	27 20.0	23 29.0	13 53.5	19 42.1	0 21.4	2 3.3
24 W	16 5 1.8	2 29.1	2 7.5	29 39.9	19 13.7	13 29.2	27 47.3	23 41.8	13 60.0	19 42.2	0 22.8	2 4.6
25 T	16 8 58.4	3 26.7	2 4.3	13♓18.5	19 16.5	14 3.7	28 14.7	23 54.6	14 6.5	19 42.2	0 24.1	2 5.9
26 F	16 12 54.9	4 24.3	2 1.2	26 40.1	19R14.7	14 36.9	28 42.3	24 7.2	14 13.1	19R42.1	0 25.5	2 7.2
27 S	16 16 51.5	5 21.9	1 58.0	9♈46.3	19 8.4	15 8.7	29 10.2	24 19.9	14 19.7	19 42.1	0 26.9	2 8.5
28 S	16 20 48.1	6 19.5	1 54.8	22 38.5	18 57.8	15 39.1	29 38.2	24 32.4	14 26.4	19 41.9	0 28.4	2 9.8
29 M	16 24 44.6	7 17.0	1 51.6	5♉18.0	18 43.1	16 8.0	0♍ 6.5	24 44.9	14 33.1	19 41.8	0 29.9	2 11.2
30 T	16 28 41.2	8 14.6	1 48.5	17 46.0	18 24.5	16 35.3	0 34.9	24 57.3	14 39.9	19 41.5	0 31.3	2 12.5
31 W	16 32 37.8	9 12.1	1 45.3	0♊ 3.3	18 2.5	17 1.1	1 3.6	25 9.7	14 46.7	19 41.2	0 32.9	2 13.9

DECLINATION

DAY	EPHEMERIS SIDEREAL TIME	☉	☊	☽	☿	♀	♂	♃	♄	♅	♆	♇
1 M	14 34 21.1	14N54.7	19S25.1	14N36.2	21N28.6	26N58.4	17N18.5	6N15.4	22N42.0	15S38.2	19N53.6	18N29.9
4 T	14 46 10.8	15 48.5	19 27.3	25 4.4	22 50.8	27 5.0	16 53.3	6 31.0	22 40.9	15 37.3	19 53.2	18 30.3
7 S	14 58 0.4	16 39.9	19 29.5	25 2.8	23 50.8	27 6.8	16 27.1	6 46.5	22 39.8	15 36.5	19 52.8	18 30.7
10 W	15 9 50.1	17 28.8	19 31.7	15 15.6	24 30.0	27 4.0	15 59.9	7 1.7	22 38.6	15 35.9	19 52.2	18 31.0
13 S	15 21 39.7	18 15.0	19 33.9	0S30.2	24 49.9	26 56.9	15 31.6	7 16.6	22 37.3	15 35.4	19 51.7	18 31.3
16 T	15 33 29.4	18 58.5	19 36.0	17 18.5	24 52.6	26 45.7	15 2.4	7 31.3	22 35.9	15 35.0	19 51.0	18 31.7
19 F	15 45 19.1	19 39.1	19 38.2	26 19.8	24 39.8	26 30.9	14 32.2	7 45.8	22 34.4	15 34.8	19 50.3	18 31.9
22 M	15 57 8.8	20 16.7	19 40.4	19 47.1	24 13.2	26 12.8	14 1.1	7 60.0	22 32.7	15 34.7	19 49.6	18 32.2
25 T	16 8 58.4	20 51.2	19 42.5	3 22.2	23 34.6	25 51.7	13 29.1	8 13.8	22 31.0	15 34.7	19 48.8	18 32.5
28 S	16 20 48.1	21 22.5	19 44.6	13N29.7	22 46.0	25 28.0	12 56.1	8 27.4	22 29.2	15 34.9	19 47.9	18 32.7
31 W	16 32 37.8	21 50.5	19 46.8	24 29.8	21 50.1	25 2.1	12 22.2	8 40.7	22 27.3	15 35.3	19 47.0	18 33.0

JUNE 1916

LONGITUDE

DAY	EPHEMERIS SIDEREAL TIME	☉	☊	☽	☿	♀	♂	♃	♄	♅	♆	♇
1 T	16 36 34.3	10♊ 9.6	1♒42.1	12♊10.9	17♊37.4	17♋25.2	1♍32.4	25♈21.9	14♋53.5	19♒40.9	0♌34.4	2♋15.3
2 F	16 40 30.9	11 7.1	1 38.9	24 10.0	17R 9.6	17 47.6	2 1.4	25 34.1	15 0.4	19R40.5	0 36.0	2 16.6
3 S	16 44 27.4	12 4.6	1 35.8	6♋ 2.4	16 39.6	18 8.2	2 30.6	25 46.2	15 7.4	19 40.1	0 37.6	2 18.0
4 S	16 48 24.0	13 2.1	1 32.6	17 50.3	16 7.8	18 27.0	3 0.0	25 58.2	15 14.4	19 39.6	0 39.2	2 19.4
5 M	16 52 20.6	13 59.5	1 29.4	29 36.8	15 35.0	18 43.9	3 29.6	26 10.2	15 21.4	19 39.1	0 40.8	2 20.8
6 T	16 56 17.1	14 56.9	1 26.2	11♌25.5	15 1.5	18 58.8	3 59.3	26 22.0	15 28.5	19 38.6	0 42.5	2 22.2
7 W	17 0 13.7	15 54.3	1 23.1	23 20.6	14 28.0	19 11.7	4 29.2	26 33.8	15 35.6	19 37.9	0 44.2	2 23.6
8 T	17 4 10.2	16 51.7	1 19.9	5♍26.9	13 55.1	19 22.5	4 59.3	26 45.5	15 42.7	19 37.3	0 45.9	2 25.0
9 F	17 8 6.7	17 49.1	1 16.7	17 49.4	13 23.3	19 31.2	5 29.5	26 57.1	15 49.9	19 36.6	0 47.6	2 26.5
10 S	17 12 3.3	18 46.5	1 13.5	0♎32.8	12 53.1	19 37.7	5 59.9	27 8.6	15 57.1	19 35.8	0 49.3	2 27.9
11 S	17 15 59.9	19 43.8	1 10.4	13 41.4	12 25.2	19 41.9	6 30.5	27 20.0	16 4.4	19 35.0	0 51.1	2 29.3
12 M	17 19 56.5	20 41.1	1 7.2	27 17.7	11 59.8	19 43.8	7 1.2	27 31.4	16 11.7	19 34.2	0 52.9	2 30.8
13 T	17 23 53.0	21 38.4	1 4.0	11♏22.6	11 37.5	19R43.4	7 32.1	27 42.6	16 19.0	19 33.3	0 54.7	2 32.2
14 W	17 27 49.5	22 35.7	1 0.8	25 53.8	11 18.7	19 40.6	8 3.1	27 53.7	16 26.3	19 32.4	0 56.5	2 33.6
15 T	17 31 46.1	23 33.0	0 57.6	10♐46.1	11 3.6	19 35.4	8 34.2	28 4.8	16 33.7	19 31.4	0 58.3	2 35.1
16 F	17 35 42.7	24 30.2	0 54.5	25 51.8	10 52.5	19 27.8	9 5.6	28 15.8	16 41.1	19 30.4	1 0.2	2 36.5
17 S	17 39 39.3	25 27.5	0 51.3	11♑ 1.5	10 45.7	19 17.8	9 37.0	28 26.6	16 48.6	19 29.3	1 2.0	2 38.0
18 S	17 43 35.8	26 24.7	0 48.1	26 5.6	10 43.2	19 5.4	10 8.6	28 37.4	16 56.0	19 28.2	1 3.9	2 39.5
19 M	17 47 32.3	27 22.0	0 44.9	10♒56.0	10D45.3	18 50.6	10 40.3	28 48.0	17 3.5	19 27.1	1 5.8	2 40.9
20 T	17 51 28.9	28 19.2	0 41.8	25 26.8	10 52.1	18 33.4	11 12.2	28 58.6	17 11.0	19 25.9	1 7.8	2 42.4
21 W	17 55 25.5	29 16.5	0 38.6	9♓34.8	11 3.5	18 13.9	11 44.2	29 9.0	17 18.6	19 24.7	1 9.7	2 43.8
22 T	17 59 22.0	0♋13.7	0 35.4	23 19.1	11 19.6	17 52.2	12 16.3	29 19.4	17 26.1	19 23.4	1 11.7	2 45.3
23 F	18 3 18.6	1 10.9	0 32.2	6♈40.6	11 40.4	17 28.4	12 48.6	29 29.6	17 33.7	19 22.1	1 13.6	2 46.8
24 S	18 7 15.2	2 8.2	0 29.1	19 41.3	12 5.9	17 2.5	13 21.0	29 39.7	17 41.3	19 20.7	1 15.6	2 48.2
25 S	18 11 11.7	3 5.4	0 25.9	2♉24.0	12 36.0	16 34.7	13 53.5	29 49.8	17 48.9	19 19.3	1 17.6	2 49.7
26 M	18 15 8.3	4 2.6	0 22.7	14 51.4	13 10.7	16 5.0	14 26.2	29 59.7	17 56.6	19 17.9	1 19.6	2 51.2
27 T	18 19 4.8	4 59.8	0 19.5	27 6.3	13 49.9	15 33.7	14 59.0	0♉ 9.5	18 4.2	19 16.4	1 21.7	2 52.6
28 W	18 23 1.4	5 57.1	0 16.3	9♊11.2	14 33.7	15 0.9	15 31.9	0 19.1	18 11.9	19 14.9	1 23.7	2 54.1
29 T	18 26 58.0	6 54.3	0 13.2	21 8.4	15 21.9	14 26.8	16 4.9	0 28.7	18 19.6	19 13.4	1 25.8	2 55.6
30 F	18 30 54.5	7 51.5	0 10.0	3♋ 0.0	16 14.4	13 51.6	16 38.1	0 38.1	18 27.3	19 11.8	1 27.8	2 57.0

DECLINATION

DAY	EPHEMERIS SIDEREAL TIME	☉	☊	☽	☿	♀	♂	♃	♄	♅	♆	♇
1 T	16 36 34.3	21N59.1	19S47.5	26N 1.5	21N30.5	24N53.1	12N10.8	8N45.1	22N26.7	15S35.4	19N46.7	18N33.0
4 S	16 48 24.0	22 22.4	19 49.6	23 19.0	20 30.8	24 24.9	11 35.7	8 57.9	22 24.6	15 35.9	19 45.7	18 33.2
7 W	17 0 13.7	22 42.3	19 51.7	11 46.8	19 33.8	23 55.5	10 59.9	9 10.4	22 22.5	15 36.5	19 44.7	18 33.4
10 S	17 12 3.3	22 58.6	19 53.8	4S22.2	18 44.9	23 25.1	10 23.2	9 22.6	22 20.2	15 37.3	19 43.6	18 33.6
13 T	17 23 53.0	23 11.2	19 55.9	20 4.2	18 8.6	22 54.1	9 45.8	9 34.4	22 17.9	15 38.2	19 42.5	18 33.7
16 F	17 35 42.7	23 20.2	19 57.9	26 15.4	17 48.0	22 22.6	9 7.6	9 45.8	22 15.5	15 39.2	19 41.3	18 33.9
19 M	17 47 32.3	23 25.5	20 0.0	16 28.8	17 44.1	21 50.9	8 28.7	9 56.8	22 13.0	15 40.4	19 40.2	18 34.0
22 T	17 59 22.0	23 27.1	20 2.1	1N14.2	17 56.5	21 19.1	7 49.1	10 7.4	22 10.4	15 41.6	19 38.9	18 34.1
25 S	18 11 11.7	23 24.9	20 4.1	17 12.6	18 23.0	20 47.2	7 8.8	10 17.7	22 7.7	15 43.0	19 37.7	18 34.1
28 W	18 23 1.4	23 19.1	20 6.2	25 48.2	19 1.1	20 15.7	6 27.9	10 27.5	22 4.9	15 44.4	19 36.4	18 34.2

JULY 1916

DAY	EPHEMERIS SIDEREAL TIME	☉	☊	☽	☿	♀	♂	♃	♄	♅	♆	♇
	h m s	° ′	° ′	° ′	° ′	° ′	° ′	° ′	° ′	° ′	° ′	° ′
						LONGITUDE						
1 S	18 34 51.1	8♋48.7	0♒ 6.8	14♋48.2	17♊11.3	13♋15.5	17♍11.4	0♉47.5	18♋35.0	19♒10.2	1♌29.9	2♋58.5
2 S	18 38 47.6	9 46.0	0 3.6	26 35.1	18 12.3	12R38.7	17 44.8	0 56.6	18 42.7	19R 8.5	1 32.0	2 60.0
3 M	18 42 44.2	10 43.2	0 0.5	8♌23.1	19 17.6	12 1.5	18 18.4	1 5.7	18 50.5	19 6.9	1 34.1	3 1.4
4 T	18 46 40.7	11 40.4	29♑57.3	20 15.1	20 27.0	11 24.0	18 52.1	1 14.6	18 58.2	19 5.1	1 36.2	3 2.9
5 W	18 50 37.3	12 37.6	29 54.1	2♍14.2	21 40.5	10 46.6	19 25.8	1 23.5	19 6.0	19 3.4	1 38.4	3 4.3
6 T	18 54 33.9	13 34.8	29 50.9	14 23.8	22 58.1	10 9.4	19 59.7	1 32.1	19 13.7	19 1.6	1 40.5	3 5.8
7 F	18 58 30.4	14 32.0	29 47.8	26 48.0	24 19.6	9 32.7	20 33.8	1 40.7	19 21.5	18 59.8	1 42.6	3 7.2
8 S	19 2 26.9	15 29.2	29 44.6	9♎30.7	25 45.0	8 56.7	21 7.9	1 49.1	19 29.3	18 57.9	1 44.8	3 8.6
9 S	19 6 23.5	16 26.4	29 41.4	22 35.4	27 14.2	8 21.7	21 42.1	1 57.4	19 37.1	18 56.1	1 46.9	3 10.1
10 M	19 10 20.1	17 23.6	29 38.2	6♏ 5.2	28 47.3	7 47.8	22 16.5	2 5.5	19 44.9	18 54.2	1 49.1	3 11.5
11 T	19 14 16.7	18 20.8	29 35.1	20 1.5	0♋24.0	7 15.3	22 50.9	2 13.5	19 52.7	18 52.2	1 51.3	3 12.9
12 W	19 18 13.2	19 18.0	29 31.9	4♐23.9	2 4.3	6 44.3	23 25.5	2 21.4	20 0.4	18 50.3	1 53.4	3 14.4
13 T	19 22 9.7	20 15.2	29 28.7	19 9.2	3 48.1	6 15.0	24 0.1	2 29.1	20 8.2	18 48.3	1 55.6	3 15.8
14 F	19 26 6.3	21 12.4	29 25.5	4♑11.6	5 35.1	5 47.5	24 34.9	2 36.7	20 16.0	18 46.3	1 57.8	3 17.2
15 S	19 30 2.9	22 9.6	29 22.4	19 22.9	7 25.3	5 22.1	25 9.8	2 44.1	20 23.8	18 44.2	2 0.0	3 18.6
16 S	19 33 59.4	23 6.8	29 19.2	4♒33.8	9 18.5	4 58.7	25 44.7	2 51.4	20 31.6	18 42.2	2 2.2	3 20.0
17 M	19 37 56.0	24 4.0	29 16.0	19 35.0	11 14.3	4 37.5	26 19.8	2 58.6	20 39.4	18 40.1	2 4.4	3 21.4
18 T	19 41 52.5	25 1.3	29 12.8	4♓18.5	13 12.7	4 18.6	26 55.0	3 5.6	20 47.2	18 38.0	2 6.6	3 22.7
19 W	19 45 49.1	25 58.5	29 9.6	18 38.7	15 13.2	4 2.1	27 30.3	3 12.4	20 54.9	18 35.8	2 8.9	3 24.1
20 T	19 49 45.7	26 55.8	29 6.5	2♈32.9	17 15.6	3 47.9	28 5.6	3 19.1	21 2.7	18 33.7	2 11.1	3 25.5
21 F	19 53 42.2	27 53.0	29 3.3	16 0.6	19 19.6	3 36.1	28 41.1	3 25.7	21 10.5	18 31.5	2 13.3	3 26.8
22 S	19 57 38.8	28 50.3	29 0.1	29 3.3	21 24.8	3 26.7	29 16.7	3 32.0	21 18.2	18 29.3	2 15.5	3 28.2
23 S	20 1 35.3	29 47.6	28 56.9	11♉44.1	23 31.0	3 19.7	29 52.4	3 38.3	21 26.0	18 27.1	2 17.7	3 29.5
24 M	20 5 31.9	0♌44.9	28 53.8	24 6.6	25 37.8	3 15.1	0♎28.1	3 44.3	21 33.7	18 24.9	2 20.0	3 30.9
25 T	20 9 28.4	1 42.2	28 50.6	6♊14.7	27 44.9	3 12.9	1 4.0	3 50.2	21 41.4	18 22.6	2 22.2	3 32.2
26 W	20 13 25.0	2 39.5	28 47.4	18 12.5	29 52.0	3D13.0	1 40.0	3 56.0	21 49.1	18 20.3	2 24.4	3 33.5
27 T	20 17 21.6	3 36.9	28 44.2	0♋ 3.5	1♌58.9	3 15.4	2 16.1	4 1.5	21 56.8	18 18.1	2 26.6	3 34.8
28 F	20 21 18.1	4 34.3	28 41.1	11 51.1	4 5.2	3 20.1	2 52.2	4 6.9	22 4.5	18 15.8	2 28.9	3 36.1
29 S	20 25 14.7	5 31.6	28 37.9	23 38.1	6 10.9	3 27.0	3 28.5	4 12.2	22 12.2	18 13.5	2 31.1	3 37.4
30 S	20 29 11.2	6 29.0	28 34.7	5♌27.3	8 15.8	3 36.0	4 4.9	4 17.2	22 19.8	18 11.1	2 33.3	3 38.6
31 M	20 33 7.8	7 26.4	28 31.5	17 20.7	10 19.5	3 47.1	4 41.3	4 22.1	22 27.5	18 8.8	2 35.5	3 39.9
						DECLINATION						
1 S	18 34 51.1	23N 9.5	20S 8.2	23N54.6	19N47.2	19N44.9	5N46.4	10N36.9	22N 2.0	15S46.0	19N35.0	18N34.2
4 T	18 46 40.7	22 56.3	20 10.2	12 55.2	20 37.6	19 15.4	5 4.3	10 45.8	21 59.1	15 47.7	19 33.7	18 34.2
7 F	18 58 30.4	22 39.5	20 12.2	2S49.9	21 28.1	18 48.0	4 21.6	10 54.3	21 56.1	15 49.4	19 32.3	18 34.2
10 M	19 10 20.1	22 19.2	20 14.2	18 29.9	22 13.8	18 23.6	3 38.4	11 2.3	21 53.0	15 51.2	19 30.9	18 34.2
13 T	19 22 9.7	21 55.4	20 16.2	26 23.3	22 49.5	18 2.8	2 54.8	11 9.8	21 49.8	15 53.1	19 29.5	18 34.2
16 S	19 33 59.4	21 28.2	20 18.2	18 37.7	23 10.0	17 46.3	2 10.7	11 16.9	21 46.6	15 55.1	19 28.0	18 34.1
19 W	19 45 49.1	20 57.8	20 20.2	0 46.4	23 10.3	17 34.3	1 26.3	11 23.4	21 43.3	15 57.1	19 26.6	18 34.0
22 S	19 57 38.8	20 24.2	20 22.1	16N 5.4	22 47.3	17 26.7	0 41.5	11 29.5	21 40.0	15 59.2	19 25.1	18 34.0
25 T	20 9 28.4	19 47.4	20 24.1	25 31.0	22 0.0	17 23.2	0S 3.7	11 35.0	21 36.6	16 1.3	19 23.7	18 33.9
28 F	20 21 18.1	19 7.8	20 26.0	24 29.0	20 50.2	17 23.3	0 49.1	11 40.0	21 33.2	16 3.5	19 22.2	18 33.8
31 M	20 33 7.8	18 25.2	20 28.0	14 3.3	19 21.2	17 26.4	1 34.8	11 44.5	21 29.7	16 5.7	19 20.7	18 33.6

AUGUST 1916

DAY	EPHEMERIS SIDEREAL TIME	☉	☊	☽	☿	♀	♂	♃	♄	♅	♆	♇
						LONGITUDE						
1 T	20 37 4.3	8♌23.9	28♑28.3	29♌20.7	12♌22.2	4♋ 0.3	5♎17.9	4♉26.8	22♋35.1	18♒ 6.5	2♌37.8	3♋41.1
2 W	20 41 0.9	9 21.3	28 25.2	11♍29.3	14 23.6	4 15.4	5 54.5	4 31.4	22 42.7	18R 4.1	2 40.0	3 42.4
3 T	20 44 57.5	10 18.7	28 22.0	23 48.6	16 23.6	4 32.5	6 31.3	4 35.7	22 50.2	18 1.8	2 42.2	3 43.6
4 F	20 48 54.0	11 16.2	28 18.8	6♎21.0	18 22.2	4 51.4	7 8.1	4 39.9	22 57.8	17 59.4	2 44.4	3 44.8
5 S	20 52 50.5	12 13.7	28 15.6	19 8.8	20 19.3	5 12.2	7 45.0	4 43.9	23 5.3	17 57.0	2 46.6	3 46.0
6 S	20 56 47.1	13 11.1	28 12.5	2♏14.4	22 15.0	5 34.6	8 22.0	4 47.7	23 12.8	17 54.6	2 48.8	3 47.2
7 M	21 0 43.7	14 8.7	28 9.3	15 40.0	24 9.2	5 58.8	8 59.2	4 51.4	23 20.3	17 52.2	2 51.0	3 48.3
8 T	21 4 40.3	15 6.2	28 6.1	29 27.0	26 1.8	6 24.6	9 36.3	4 54.9	23 27.7	17 49.9	2 53.2	3 49.5
9 W	21 8 36.8	16 3.7	28 2.9	13♐35.7	27 52.9	6 52.0	10 13.6	4 58.1	23 35.1	17 47.5	2 55.4	3 50.6
10 T	21 12 33.3	17 1.2	27 59.7	28 5.0	29 42.4	7 20.8	10 51.0	5 1.2	23 42.5	17 45.1	2 57.5	3 51.7
11 F	21 16 29.9	17 58.8	27 56.6	12♑51.5	1♍30.5	7 51.2	11 28.4	5 4.1	23 49.9	17 42.7	2 59.7	3 52.9
12 S	21 20 26.5	18 56.3	27 53.4	27 49.7	3 17.0	8 23.0	12 6.0	5 6.8	23 57.2	17 40.3	3 1.9	3 54.0
13 S	21 24 23.0	19 53.9	27 50.2	12♒52.0	5 2.0	8 56.1	12 43.6	5 9.3	24 4.5	17 37.9	3 4.0	3 55.0
14 M	21 28 19.6	20 51.5	27 47.0	27 50.2	6 45.5	9 30.6	13 21.3	5 11.7	24 11.8	17 35.5	3 6.2	3 56.1
15 T	21 32 16.1	21 49.1	27 43.9	12♓35.7	8 27.5	10 6.3	13 59.0	5 13.8	24 19.0	17 33.1	3 8.3	3 57.2
16 W	21 36 12.7	22 46.8	27 40.7	27 1.4	10 8.1	10 43.3	14 36.9	5 15.8	24 26.2	17 30.7	3 10.4	3 58.2
17 T	21 40 9.2	23 44.5	27 37.5	11♈ 2.5	11 47.2	11 21.5	15 14.9	5 17.5	24 33.4	17 28.4	3 12.5	3 59.2
18 F	21 44 5.8	24 42.2	27 34.3	24 36.7	13 24.9	12 0.8	15 52.9	5 19.1	24 40.5	17 26.0	3 14.6	4 0.2
19 S	21 48 2.3	25 39.9	27 31.2	7♉44.3	15 1.1	12 41.2	16 31.0	5 20.5	24 47.6	17 23.6	3 16.7	4 1.2
20 S	21 51 58.9	26 37.7	27 28.0	20 27.5	16 35.9	13 22.7	17 9.2	5 21.6	24 54.6	17 21.3	3 18.8	4 2.2
21 M	21 55 55.4	27 35.4	27 24.8	2♊50.1	18 9.2	14 5.2	17 47.5	5 22.6	25 1.6	17 18.9	3 20.9	4 3.1
22 T	21 59 52.0	28 33.3	27 21.6	14 56.6	19 41.2	14 48.7	18 25.9	5 23.4	25 8.6	17 16.6	3 23.0	4 4.1
23 W	22 3 48.6	29 31.1	27 18.4	26 51.9	21 11.7	15 33.1	19 4.4	5 24.0	25 15.5	17 14.3	3 25.0	4 5.0
24 T	22 7 45.1	0♍28.9	27 15.3	8♋40.7	22 40.8	16 18.5	19 42.9	5 24.3	25 22.4	17 12.0	3 27.0	4 5.9
25 F	22 11 41.6	1 26.8	27 12.1	20 27.5	24 8.4	17 4.7	20 21.5	5 24.5	25 29.2	17 9.7	3 29.0	4 6.8
26 S	22 15 38.2	2 24.8	27 8.9	2♌16.2	25 34.6	17 51.8	21 0.3	5R24.5	25 36.0	17 7.4	3 31.1	4 7.6
27 S	22 19 34.8	3 22.7	27 5.7	14 10.3	26 59.3	18 39.6	21 39.1	5 24.3	25 42.8	17 5.1	3 33.0	4 8.5
28 M	22 23 31.4	4 20.7	27 2.6	26 12.5	28 22.5	19 28.3	22 18.0	5 23.8	25 49.5	17 2.8	3 35.0	4 9.3
29 T	22 27 27.9	5 18.7	26 59.4	8♍24.5	29 44.2	20 17.7	22 56.9	5 23.2	25 56.1	17 0.6	3 37.0	4 10.1
30 W	22 31 24.4	6 16.7	26 56.2	20 48.0	1♎ 4.3	21 7.8	23 36.0	5 22.4	26 2.7	16 58.4	3 38.9	4 10.9
31 T	22 35 21.0	7 14.8	26 53.0	3♎23.7	2 22.8	21 58.6	24 15.1	5 21.3	26 9.2	16 56.2	3 40.9	4 11.7
						DECLINATION						
1 T	20 37 4.3	18N10.4	20S28.6	9N12.0	18N48.0	17N28.0	1S50.1	11N45.9	21N28.5	16S 6.4	19N20.2	18N33.6
4 F	20 48 54.0	17 24.3	20 30.6	6S59.8	16 59.6	17 33.9	2 36.1	11 49.6	21 25.0	16 8.6	19 18.7	18 33.5
7 M	21 0 43.7	16 35.6	20 32.5	21 22.0	15 1.2	17 41.1	3 22.1	11 52.8	21 21.5	16 10.8	19 17.2	18 33.3
10 T	21 12 33.3	15 44.5	20 34.4	26 8.7	12 56.0	17 48.9	4 8.3	11 55.4	21 18.0	16 13.0	19 15.8	18 33.1
13 S	21 24 23.0	14 51.2	20 36.3	15 44.5	10 46.8	17 56.5	4 54.5	11 57.5	21 14.4	16 15.2	19 14.3	18 33.0
16 W	21 36 12.7	13 55.8	20 38.2	2N54.5	8 35.5	18 3.4	5 40.7	11 59.0	21 10.8	16 17.4	19 12.9	18 32.8
19 S	21 48 2.3	12 58.3	20 40.0	18 59.1	6 24.0	18 8.8	6 26.9	11 59.9	21 7.3	16 19.6	19 11.4	18 32.6
22 T	21 59 52.0	11 59.0	20 41.9	26 13.6	4 13.6	18 12.3	7 12.9	12 0.2	21 3.8	16 21.7	19 10.0	18 32.4
25 F	22 11 41.6	10 57.9	20 43.8	22 38.4	2 5.6	18 13.4	7 58.8	11 59.9	21 0.3	16 23.8	19 8.6	18 32.2
28 M	22 23 31.4	9 55.3	20 45.6	10 31.5	0 1.1	18 11.7	8 44.5	11 59.1	20 56.8	16 25.9	19 7.2	18 32.0
31 T	22 35 21.0	8 51.2	20 47.5	5S38.9	1S58.8	18 6.8	9 29.9	11 57.6	20 53.3	16 27.9	19 5.9	18 31.8

SEPTEMBER 1916

DAY	EPHEMERIS SIDEREAL TIME	☉	☊	☽	☿	♀	♂	♃	♄	♅	♆	♇
	h m s	° ′	° ′	° ′	° ′	° ′	° ′	° ′	° ′	° ′	° ′	° ′
						LONGITUDE						
1 F	22 39 17.6	8 ♍ 12.9	26 ♑ 49.8	16 ♎ 12.1	3 ♎ 39.6	22 ♋ 50.1	24 ♎ 54.3	5 ♉ 20.1	26 ♋ 15.7	16 ♒ 54.0	3 ♌ 42.8	4 ♋ 12.4
2 S	22 43 14.1	9 11.0	26 46.7	29 13.7	4 54.7	23 42.3	25 33.6	5 R 18.7	26 22.2	16 R 51.8	3 44.7	4 13.1
3 S	22 47 10.6	10 9.1	26 43.5	12 ♏ 28.9	6 8.0	24 35.1	26 13.0	5 17.0	26 28.5	16 49.7	3 46.5	4 13.8
4 M	22 51 7.2	11 7.3	26 40.3	25 58.1	7 19.5	25 28.5	26 52.5	5 15.2	26 34.9	16 47.6	3 48.4	4 14.5
5 T	22 55 3.8	12 5.5	26 37.1	9 ♐ 41.8	8 29.1	26 22.4	27 32.0	5 13.2	26 41.1	16 45.5	3 50.2	4 15.2
6 W	22 59 0.3	13 3.7	26 34.0	23 40.4	9 36.6	27 17.0	28 11.6	5 10.9	26 47.3	16 43.4	3 52.1	4 15.8
7 T	23 2 56.9	14 1.9	26 30.8	7 ♑ 53.3	10 41.9	28 12.1	28 51.3	5 8.5	26 53.5	16 41.4	3 53.9	4 16.5
8 F	23 6 53.4	15 0.2	26 27.6	22 19.2	11 45.0	29 7.8	29 31.1	5 5.9	26 59.6	16 39.4	3 55.6	4 17.1
9 S	23 10 50.0	15 58.4	26 24.4	6 ♒ 55.3	12 45.7	0 ♌ 3.9	0 ♏ 10.9	5 3.1	27 5.6	16 37.4	3 57.4	4 17.7
10 S	23 14 46.5	16 56.7	26 21.3	21 36.7	13 43.8	1 0.6	0 50.8	5 0.1	27 11.6	16 35.4	3 59.1	4 18.2
11 M	23 18 43.1	17 55.1	26 18.1	6 ♓ 17.6	14 39.2	1 57.8	1 30.8	4 56.9	27 17.4	16 33.5	4 0.9	4 18.8
12 T	23 22 39.6	18 53.4	26 14.9	20 50.7	15 31.7	2 55.5	2 10.9	4 53.5	27 23.3	16 31.6	4 2.5	4 19.3
13 W	23 26 36.2	19 51.8	26 11.7	5 ♈ 9.4	16 21.1	3 53.6	2 51.0	4 50.0	27 29.0	16 29.7	4 4.2	4 19.8
14 T	23 30 32.7	20 50.3	26 8.5	19 7.9	17 7.1	4 52.2	3 31.3	4 46.2	27 34.8	16 27.8	4 5.9	4 20.3
15 F	23 34 29.3	21 48.7	26 5.4	2 ♉ 42.5	17 49.6	5 51.2	4 11.6	4 42.3	27 40.4	16 26.0	4 7.5	4 20.7
16 S	23 38 25.9	22 47.2	26 2.2	15 52.0	18 28.2	6 50.7	4 51.9	4 38.1	27 46.0	16 24.3	4 9.1	4 21.2
17 S	23 42 22.4	23 45.7	25 59.0	28 37.4	19 2.6	7 50.5	5 32.4	4 33.8	27 51.4	16 22.5	4 10.7	4 21.6
18 M	23 46 18.9	24 44.3	25 55.8	11 ♊ 1.6	19 32.6	8 50.8	6 12.9	4 29.4	27 56.9	16 20.8	4 12.3	4 22.0
19 T	23 50 15.5	25 42.9	25 52.6	23 8.8	19 57.8	9 51.5	6 53.5	4 24.7	28 2.2	16 19.1	4 13.8	4 22.4
20 W	23 54 12.1	26 41.6	25 49.5	5 ♋ 4.2	20 17.8	10 52.5	7 34.2	4 19.9	28 7.5	16 17.5	4 15.3	4 22.7
21 T	23 58 8.6	27 40.2	25 46.3	16 52.9	20 32.3	11 54.0	8 15.0	4 14.9	28 12.7	16 15.8	4 16.8	4 23.0
22 F	0 2 5.2	28 39.0	25 43.1	28 40.5	20 40.9	12 55.7	8 55.8	4 9.7	28 17.8	16 14.3	4 18.3	4 23.3
23 S	0 6 1.8	29 37.7	25 39.9	10 ♌ 31.8	20 43.1	13 57.9	9 36.7	4 4.4	28 22.9	16 12.7	4 19.7	4 23.6
24 S	0 9 58.3	0 ♎ 36.5	25 36.8	22 31.3	20 R 38.7	15 0.3	10 17.7	3 58.9	28 27.9	16 11.2	4 21.1	4 23.9
25 M	0 13 54.9	1 35.3	25 33.6	4 ♍ 42.4	20 27.3	16 3.1	10 58.8	3 53.2	28 32.8	16 9.8	4 22.5	4 24.1
26 T	0 17 51.4	2 34.2	25 30.4	17 7.6	20 8.7	17 6.2	11 39.9	3 47.4	28 37.6	16 8.4	4 23.9	4 24.3
27 W	0 21 48.0	3 33.1	25 27.2	29 48.2	19 42.7	18 9.7	12 21.2	3 41.5	28 42.3	16 7.0	4 25.2	4 24.5
28 T	0 25 44.5	4 32.0	25 24.1	12 ♎ 44.3	19 9.1	19 13.4	13 2.5	3 35.4	28 47.0	16 5.6	4 26.5	4 24.7
29 F	0 29 41.1	5 31.0	25 20.9	25 55.0	18 28.2	20 17.4	13 43.9	3 29.1	28 51.5	16 4.3	4 27.8	4 24.8
30 S	0 33 37.6	6 30.0	25 17.7	9 ♏ 18.6	17 40.2	21 21.7	14 25.3	3 22.7	28 56.0	16 3.1	4 29.1	4 24.9
						DECLINATION						
1 F	22 39 17.6	8 N 29.6	20 S 48.1	11 S 1.9	2 S 37.5	18 N 4.4	9 S 45.0	11 N 57.0	20 N 52.2	16 S 28.5	19 N 5.5	18 N 31.7
4 M	22 51 7.2	7 23.9	20 49.9	23 41.4	4 29.3	17 54.9	10 30.0	11 54.8	20 48.8	16 30.4	19 4.2	18 31.5
7 T	23 2 56.9	6 17.1	20 51.7	24 59.9	6 13.3	17 41.7	11 14.5	11 52.0	20 45.5	16 32.3	19 2.9	18 31.3
10 S	23 14 46.5	5 9.4	20 53.5	12 21.5	7 47.9	17 24.4	11 58.6	11 48.6	20 42.3	16 34.0	19 1.7	18 31.1
13 W	23 26 36.2	4 1.0	20 55.3	6 N 22.8	9 10.9	17 3.1	12 42.1	11 44.7	20 39.1	16 35.7	19 0.5	18 30.9
16 S	23 38 25.9	2 51.9	20 57.1	21 13.7	10 19.2	16 37.5	13 25.0	11 40.3	20 36.1	16 37.3	18 59.3	18 30.6
19 T	23 50 15.5	1 42.2	20 58.9	26 8.3	11 9.2	16 7.7	14 7.3	11 35.3	20 33.1	16 38.8	18 58.2	18 30.4
22 F	0 2 5.2	0 32.2	21 0.7	20 18.4	11 35.6	15 33.7	14 48.8	11 29.8	20 30.2	16 40.2	18 57.2	18 30.2
25 M	0 13 54.9	0 S 37.9	21 2.4	6 54.1	11 32.4	14 55.4	15 29.5	11 23.9	20 27.5	16 41.5	18 56.2	18 30.0
28 T	0 25 44.5	1 48.2	21 4.2	9 S 32.2	10 53.3	14 12.9	16 9.3	11 17.5	20 24.9	16 42.6	18 55.3	18 29.8

OCTOBER 1916

DAY	EPHEMERIS SIDEREAL TIME	☉	☊	☽	☿	♀	♂	♃	♄	♅	♆	♇
						LONGITUDE						
1 S	0 37 34.2	7 ♎ 29.0	25 ♑ 14.5	22 ♏ 53.2	16 ♎ 45.6	22 ♌ 26.2	15 ♏ 6.8	3 ♉ 16.2	29 ♋ 0.4	16 ♒ 1.9	4 ♌ 30.3	4 ♋ 25.0
2 M	0 41 30.7	8 28.0	25 11.3	6 ♐ 36.9	15 R 45.3	23 31.1	15 48.4	3 R 9.6	29 4.7	16 R 0.7	4 31.5	4 25.1
3 T	0 45 27.3	9 27.1	25 8.2	20 28.3	14 40.4	24 36.2	16 30.1	3 2.8	29 8.9	15 59.6	4 32.6	4 25.2
4 W	0 49 23.9	10 26.3	25 5.0	4 ♑ 26.5	13 32.3	25 41.5	17 11.9	2 55.9	29 13.1	15 58.5	4 33.8	4 25.2
5 T	0 53 20.4	11 25.4	25 1.8	18 30.8	12 22.5	26 47.1	17 53.7	2 48.9	29 17.1	15 57.5	4 34.9	4 25.2
6 F	0 57 16.9	12 24.6	24 58.6	2 ♒ 40.7	11 12.8	27 53.0	18 35.5	2 41.8	29 21.1	15 56.5	4 36.0	4 R 25.2
7 S	1 1 13.5	13 23.8	24 55.4	16 55.0	10 5.3	28 59.0	19 17.5	2 34.5	29 24.9	15 55.5	4 37.0	4 25.1
8 S	1 5 10.1	14 23.0	24 52.3	1 ♓ 11.4	9 1.7	0 ♍ 5.4	19 59.5	2 27.2	29 28.7	15 54.6	4 38.0	4 25.1
9 M	1 9 6.6	15 22.3	24 49.1	15 26.6	8 3.9	1 11.9	20 41.6	2 19.8	29 32.4	15 53.8	4 39.0	4 25.0
10 T	1 13 3.2	16 21.6	24 45.9	29 36.2	7 13.5	2 18.7	21 23.8	2 12.3	29 35.9	15 52.9	4 40.0	4 24.9
11 W	1 16 59.7	17 20.9	24 42.7	13 ♈ 35.3	6 32.0	3 25.7	22 6.0	2 4.7	29 39.4	15 52.2	4 40.9	4 24.7
12 T	1 20 56.3	18 20.2	24 39.6	27 19.1	6 0.4	4 32.9	22 48.3	1 57.1	29 42.8	15 51.5	4 41.8	4 24.6
13 F	1 24 52.8	19 19.6	24 36.4	10 ♉ 43.9	5 39.3	5 40.3	23 30.7	1 49.3	29 46.1	15 50.8	4 42.6	4 24.4
14 S	1 28 49.4	20 19.1	24 33.2	23 47.7	5 29.2	6 48.0	24 13.1	1 41.5	29 49.3	15 50.2	4 43.5	4 24.2
15 S	1 32 45.9	21 18.5	24 30.0	6 ♊ 30.5	5 D 30.2	7 55.8	24 55.7	1 33.7	29 52.4	15 49.6	4 44.3	4 24.0
16 M	1 36 42.5	22 18.0	24 26.8	18 53.8	5 42.0	9 3.9	25 38.2	1 25.8	29 55.4	15 49.1	4 45.0	4 23.7
17 T	1 40 39.0	23 17.6	24 23.7	1 ♋ 1.1	6 4.2	10 12.1	26 20.9	1 17.8	29 58.3	15 48.6	4 45.8	4 23.5
18 W	1 44 35.6	24 17.2	24 20.5	12 56.6	6 36.3	11 20.5	27 3.6	1 9.8	0 ♌ 1.1	15 48.2	4 46.5	4 23.2
19 T	1 48 32.1	25 16.8	24 17.3	24 45.6	7 17.4	12 29.2	27 46.4	1 1.7	0 3.8	15 47.8	4 47.2	4 22.9
20 F	1 52 28.7	26 16.4	24 14.1	6 ♌ 33.5	8 6.9	13 37.9	28 29.3	0 53.6	0 6.4	15 47.5	4 47.8	4 22.5
21 S	1 56 25.2	27 16.1	24 11.0	18 26.1	9 4.0	14 46.9	29 12.2	0 45.5	0 8.9	15 47.2	4 48.4	4 22.2
22 S	2 0 21.8	28 15.9	24 7.8	0 ♍ 28.4	10 7.6	15 56.1	29 55.3	0 37.4	0 11.3	15 47.0	4 49.0	4 21.8
23 M	2 4 18.4	29 15.6	24 4.6	12 45.1	11 17.2	17 5.4	0 ♐ 38.3	0 29.3	0 13.6	15 46.8	4 49.5	4 21.4
24 T	2 8 14.9	0 ♏ 15.4	24 1.4	25 19.6	12 31.9	18 14.8	1 21.5	0 21.1	0 15.7	15 46.7	4 50.0	4 21.0
25 W	2 12 11.5	1 15.3	23 58.2	8 ♎ 14.0	13 50.9	19 24.5	2 4.7	0 13.0	0 17.8	15 46.6	4 50.5	4 20.5
26 T	2 16 8.0	2 15.2	23 55.1	21 28.6	15 13.7	20 34.3	2 48.0	0 4.8	0 19.8	15 46.6	4 50.9	4 20.1
27 F	2 20 4.6	3 15.1	23 51.9	5 ♏ 1.9	16 39.7	21 44.2	3 31.4	29 ♈ 56.7	0 21.6	15 D 46.6	4 51.3	4 19.6
28 S	2 24 1.1	4 15.0	23 48.7	18 51.0	18 8.3	22 54.3	4 14.8	29 48.6	0 23.4	15 46.7	4 51.7	4 19.1
29 S	2 27 57.7	5 15.0	23 45.5	2 ♐ 51.7	19 39.1	24 4.5	4 58.3	29 40.5	0 25.0	15 46.8	4 52.0	4 18.6
30 M	2 31 54.2	6 15.0	23 42.4	16 59.6	21 11.6	25 14.8	5 41.8	29 32.5	0 26.5	15 47.0	4 52.3	4 18.0
31 T	2 35 50.8	7 15.0	23 39.2	1 ♑ 10.7	22 45.6	26 25.3	6 25.5	29 24.5	0 27.9	15 47.2	4 52.6	4 17.4
						DECLINATION						
1 S	0 37 34.2	2 S 58.3	21 S 5.9	22 S 51.1	9 S 34.6	13 N 26.5	16 S 48.2	11 N 10.7	20 N 22.4	16 S 43.7	18 N 54.4	18 N 29.6
4 W	0 49 23.9	4 8.1	21 7.6	25 13.4	7 40.5	12 36.1	17 26.0	11 3.6	20 20.1	16 44.6	18 53.5	18 29.4
7 S	1 1 13.5	5 17.4	21 9.3	14 2.2	5 28.0	11 42.1	18 2.6	10 56.1	20 17.9	16 45.4	18 52.8	18 29.2
10 T	1 13 3.2	6 26.1	21 11.1	3 N 59.0	3 23.8	10 44.4	18 38.1	10 48.4	20 15.8	16 46.1	18 52.1	18 29.1
13 F	1 24 52.8	7 34.1	21 12.8	19 37.5	1 54.1	9 43.3	19 12.3	10 40.4	20 14.0	16 46.7	18 51.5	18 28.9
16 M	1 36 42.5	8 41.1	21 14.4	25 54.6	1 13.0	8 39.1	19 45.2	10 32.2	20 12.3	16 47.1	18 50.9	18 28.8
19 T	1 48 32.1	9 47.1	21 16.1	21 9.0	1 21.5	7 32.0	20 16.6	10 24.0	20 10.8	16 47.4	18 50.4	18 28.6
22 S	2 0 21.8	10 51.8	21 17.8	8 31.3	2 11.6	6 22.2	20 46.5	10 15.6	20 9.5	16 47.5	18 50.0	18 28.5
25 W	2 12 11.5	11 55.0	21 19.5	7 S 42.1	3 32.1	5 10.0	21 14.8	10 7.3	20 8.4	16 47.5	18 49.6	18 28.4
28 S	2 24 1.1	12 56.6	21 21.1	21 47.1	5 12.5	3 55.8	21 41.4	9 59.0	20 7.6	16 47.4	18 49.3	18 28.3
31 T	2 35 50.8	13 56.3	21 22.7	25 19.0	7 4.2	2 39.7	22 6.2	9 50.8	20 6.9	16 47.2	18 49.1	18 28.2

NOVEMBER 1916

LONGITUDE

DAY	EPHEMERIS SIDEREAL TIME	☉	☊	☽	☿	♀	♂	♃	♄	♅	♆	♇
	h m s	° '	° '	° '	° '	° '	° '	° '	° '	° '	° '	° '
1 W	2 39 47.4	8♏15.1	23♑36.0	15♑21.7	24♎20.7	27♍35.9	7♐ 9.2	29♈16.5	0♌29.2	15♒47.5	4♌52.8	4♋16.9
2 T	2 43 43.9	9 15.1	23 32.8	29 30.5	25 56.6	28 46.7	7 52.9	29R 8.6	0 30.4	15 47.8	4 53.0	4R16.2
3 F	2 47 40.4	10 15.2	23 29.6	13♒36.1	27 33.3	29 57.5	8 36.7	29 0.8	0 31.5	15 48.2	4 53.2	4 15.6
4 S	2 51 37.0	11 15.4	23 26.5	27 37.5	29 10.4	1♎ 8.5	9 20.6	28 53.0	0 32.5	15 48.6	4 53.3	4 15.0
5 S	2 55 33.6	12 15.5	23 23.3	11♓34.2	0♏47.8	2 19.6	10 4.5	28 45.3	0 33.3	15 49.1	4 53.4	4 14.3
6 M	2 59 30.1	13 15.7	23 20.1	25 24.9	2 25.4	3 30.9	10 48.5	28 37.7	0 34.1	15 49.7	4 53.5	4 13.6
7 T	3 3 26.7	14 15.9	23 16.9	9♈ 7.8	4 3.2	4 42.2	11 32.6	28 30.1	0 34.7	15 50.3	4 53.5	4 12.9
8 W	3 7 23.2	15 16.2	23 13.8	22 40.8	5 40.9	5 53.7	12 16.7	28 22.7	0 35.2	15 50.9	4R53.5	4 12.2
9 T	3 11 19.8	16 16.4	23 10.6	6♉ 1.4	7 18.6	7 5.2	13 0.9	28 15.3	0 35.6	15 51.6	4 53.5	4 11.4
10 F	3 15 16.4	17 16.7	23 7.4	19 7.2	8 56.2	8 16.9	13 45.1	28 8.0	0 35.9	15 52.3	4 53.4	4 10.7
11 S	3 19 12.9	18 17.1	23 4.2	1♊57.0	10 33.7	9 28.7	14 29.5	28 0.9	0 36.1	15 53.1	4 53.3	4 9.9
12 S	3 23 9.5	19 17.4	23 1.1	14 30.3	12 10.9	10 40.6	15 13.8	27 53.8	0 36.2	15 54.0	4 53.1	4 9.1
13 M	3 27 6.0	20 17.8	22 57.9	26 48.0	13 48.0	11 52.6	15 58.2	27 46.8	0R36.2	15 54.8	4 53.0	4 8.3
14 T	3 31 2.6	21 18.2	22 54.7	8♋52.2	15 24.9	13 4.7	16 42.7	27 40.0	0 36.0	15 55.8	4 52.7	4 7.4
15 W	3 34 59.1	22 18.6	22 51.5	20 46.4	17 1.5	14 16.9	17 27.3	27 33.3	0 35.7	15 56.8	4 52.5	4 6.6
16 T	3 38 55.7	23 19.1	22 48.4	2♌34.8	18 37.9	15 29.2	18 11.9	27 26.7	0 35.4	15 57.8	4 52.2	4 5.7
17 F	3 42 52.2	24 19.6	22 45.2	14 22.3	20 14.0	16 41.6	18 56.6	27 20.3	0 34.9	15 58.9	4 51.9	4 4.8
18 S	3 46 48.8	25 20.1	22 42.0	26 14.2	21 50.0	17 54.0	19 41.3	27 14.0	0 34.3	16 0.1	4 51.6	4 3.9
19 S	3 50 45.4	26 20.7	22 38.8	8♍16.0	23 25.7	19 6.6	20 26.1	27 7.8	0 33.6	16 1.2	4 51.2	4 3.0
20 M	3 54 41.9	27 21.3	22 35.6	20 32.9	25 1.1	20 19.3	21 10.9	27 1.8	0 32.7	16 2.5	4 50.8	4 2.1
21 T	3 58 38.5	28 21.9	22 32.5	3♎ 9.3	26 36.4	21 32.0	21 55.8	26 55.9	0 31.8	16 3.8	4 50.3	4 1.2
22 W	4 2 35.0	29 22.5	22 29.3	16 8.7	28 11.5	22 44.8	22 40.8	26 50.2	0 30.7	16 5.1	4 49.9	4 0.2
23 T	4 6 31.6	0♐23.2	22 26.1	29 32.6	29 46.4	23 57.7	23 25.8	26 44.7	0 29.6	16 6.5	4 49.4	3 59.2
24 F	4 10 28.2	1 23.9	22 22.9	13♏20.5	1♐21.1	25 10.7	24 10.9	26 39.3	0 28.3	16 7.9	4 48.8	3 58.2
25 S	4 14 24.7	2 24.7	22 19.8	27 29.6	2 55.7	26 23.7	24 56.1	26 34.1	0 26.9	16 9.4	4 48.2	3 57.2
26 S	4 18 21.3	3 25.4	22 16.6	11♐54.8	4 30.1	27 36.8	25 41.3	26 29.0	0 25.4	16 10.9	4 47.6	3 56.2
27 M	4 22 17.8	4 26.2	22 13.4	26 29.7	6 4.4	28 50.0	26 26.5	26 24.2	0 23.8	16 12.5	4 47.0	3 55.2
28 T	4 26 14.4	5 27.0	22 10.2	11♑ 7.7	7 38.6	0♏ 3.2	27 11.8	26 19.5	0 22.1	16 14.1	4 46.3	3 54.2
29 W	4 30 10.9	6 27.8	22 7.1	25 42.6	9 12.7	1 16.5	27 57.2	26 15.0	0 20.3	16 15.8	4 45.6	3 53.1
30 T	4 34 7.5	7 28.6	22 3.9	10♒ 9.4	10 46.7	2 29.9	28 42.6	26 10.6	0 18.4	16 17.5	4 44.9	3 52.1

DECLINATION

DAY	EPHEMERIS SIDEREAL TIME	☉	☊	☽	☿	♀	♂	♃	♄	♅	♆	♇
1 W	2 39 47.4	14S15.8	21S23.3	23S13.4	7S42.8	2N14.0	22S14.1	9N48.1	20N 6.7	16S47.1	18N49.1	18N28.2
4 S	2 51 37.0	15 12.9	21 24.9	9 35.2	9 40.1	0 56.0	22 36.5	9 40.2	20 6.3	16 46.6	18 48.9	18 28.1
7 T	3 3 26.7	16 7.6	21 26.5	8N 7.7	11 37.0	0S23.1	22 57.0	9 32.5	20 6.1	16 46.0	18 48.9	18 28.0
10 F	3 15 16.4	16 60.0	21 28.1	21 50.0	13 30.8	1 42.9	23 15.4	9 25.1	20 6.2	16 45.3	18 48.9	18 28.0
13 M	3 27 6.0	17 49.7	21 29.7	25 32.9	15 19.7	3 3.3	23 31.8	9 18.1	20 6.5	16 44.5	18 49.1	18 28.0
16 T	3 38 55.7	18 36.7	21 31.3	18 38.0	17 2.3	4 23.8	23 46.0	9 11.5	20 7.0	16 43.5	18 49.2	18 28.0
19 S	3 50 45.4	19 20.7	21 32.9	5 0.3	18 37.7	5 44.1	23 58.1	9 5.3	20 7.7	16 42.4	18 49.5	18 28.0
22 W	4 2 35.0	20 1.6	21 34.4	11S 3.2	20 4.9	7 3.9	24 7.9	8 59.7	20 8.6	16 41.1	18 49.8	18 28.1
25 S	4 14 24.7	20 39.2	21 36.0	23 37.1	21 23.3	8 22.8	24 15.3	8 54.6	20 9.7	16 39.8	18 50.2	18 28.1
28 T	4 26 14.4	21 13.3	21 37.5	23 50.1	22 32.2	9 40.4	24 20.5	8 50.0	20 11.1	16 38.3	18 50.7	18 28.2

DECEMBER 1916

LONGITUDE

DAY	EPHEMERIS SIDEREAL TIME	☉	☊	☽	☿	♀	♂	♃	♄	♅	♆	♇
1 F	4 38 4.1	8♐29.4	22♑ 0.7	24♒25.1	12♐20.6	3♏43.3	29♐28.1	26♈ 6.5	0♌16.4	16♒19.3	4♌44.1	3♋51.0
2 S	4 42 0.6	9 30.3	21 57.5	8♓27.8	13 54.5	4 56.8	0♑13.6	26R 2.5	0R14.2	16 21.1	4R43.3	3R49.9
3 S	4 45 57.2	10 31.1	21 54.3	22 17.0	15 28.3	6 10.3	0 59.1	25 58.8	0 12.0	16 22.9	4 42.5	3 48.8
4 M	4 49 53.7	11 32.0	21 51.2	5♈52.5	17 2.1	7 23.9	1 44.8	25 55.2	0 9.7	16 24.8	4 41.7	3 47.7
5 T	4 53 50.3	12 32.9	21 48.0	19 14.8	18 35.9	8 37.5	2 30.4	25 51.8	0 7.2	16 26.8	4 40.8	3 46.6
6 W	4 57 46.8	13 33.8	21 44.8	2♉24.1	20 9.7	9 51.2	3 16.1	25 48.7	0 4.7	16 28.7	4 39.9	3 45.5
7 T	5 1 43.4	14 34.7	21 41.6	15 20.5	21 43.5	11 5.0	4 1.9	25 45.7	0 2.1	16 30.8	4 38.9	3 44.3
8 F	5 5 40.0	15 35.7	21 38.5	28 4.1	23 17.3	12 18.7	4 47.7	25 42.9	29♋59.3	16 32.8	4 38.0	3 43.2
9 S	5 9 36.5	16 36.6	21 35.3	10♊35.1	24 51.1	13 32.6	5 33.5	25 40.4	29 56.5	16 34.9	4 37.0	3 42.1
10 S	5 13 33.1	17 37.6	21 32.1	22 54.2	26 24.9	14 46.5	6 19.4	25 38.0	29 53.6	16 37.1	4 36.0	3 40.9
11 M	5 17 29.6	18 38.5	21 28.9	5♋ 2.1	27 58.7	16 0.4	7 5.4	25 35.8	29 50.6	16 39.3	4 34.9	3 39.7
12 T	5 21 26.2	19 39.5	21 25.8	17 0.7	29 32.6	17 14.4	7 51.3	25 33.8	29 47.5	16 41.5	4 33.8	3 38.6
13 W	5 25 22.8	20 40.5	21 22.6	28 52.1	1♑ 6.4	18 28.4	8 37.4	25 32.1	29 44.3	16 43.8	4 32.7	3 37.4
14 T	5 29 19.3	21 41.6	21 19.4	10♌39.6	2 40.1	19 42.5	9 23.5	25 30.5	29 41.0	16 46.1	4 31.6	3 36.2
15 F	5 33 15.9	22 42.6	21 16.2	22 26.8	4 13.9	20 56.6	10 9.6	25 29.2	29 37.7	16 48.4	4 30.5	3 35.0
16 S	5 37 12.4	23 43.6	21 13.1	4♍18.1	5 47.5	22 10.7	10 55.7	25 28.0	29 34.2	16 50.8	4 29.3	3 33.8
17 S	5 41 9.0	24 44.7	21 9.9	16 18.3	7 21.0	23 24.9	11 42.0	25 27.1	29 30.7	16 53.2	4 28.1	3 32.6
18 M	5 45 5.5	25 45.8	21 6.7	28 32.3	8 54.3	24 39.1	12 28.2	25 26.4	29 27.1	16 55.7	4 26.9	3 31.5
19 T	5 49 2.1	26 46.9	21 3.5	11♎ 4.8	10 27.4	25 53.4	13 14.5	25 25.9	29 23.4	16 58.2	4 25.6	3 30.3
20 W	5 52 58.7	27 48.0	21 0.3	24 0.2	12 0.2	27 7.7	14 0.9	25 25.6	29 19.6	17 0.7	4 24.3	3 29.0
21 T	5 56 55.2	28 49.1	20 57.2	7♏21.5	13 32.6	28 22.0	14 47.3	25 25.5	29 15.7	17 3.3	4 23.0	3 27.8
22 F	6 0 51.8	29 50.2	20 54.0	21 !0.0	15 4.5	29 36.4	15 33.7	25D25.6	29 11.8	17 5.9	4 21.7	3 26.6
23 S	6 4 48.3	0♑51.4	20 50.8	5♐24.6	16 35.7	0♐50.7	16 20.2	25 25.9	29 7.8	17 8.5	4 20.4	3 25.4
24 S	6 8 44.9	1 52.5	20 47.6	20 1.6	18 6.1	2 5.2	17 6.7	25 26.4	29 3.8	17 11.2	4 19.0	3 24.2
25 M	6 12 41.4	2 53.7	20 44.5	4♑54.7	19 35.5	3 19.6	17 53.2	25 27.2	28 59.6	17 13.9	4 17.6	3 23.0
26 T	6 16 38.0	3 54.9	20 41.3	19 56.0	21 3.8	4 34.1	18 39.8	25 28.1	28 55.5	17 16.6	4 16.2	3 21.8
27 W	6 20 34.6	4 56.0	20 38.1	4♒56.5	22 30.5	5 48.6	19 26.4	25 29.3	28 51.2	17 19.4	4 14.8	3 20.6
28 T	6 24 31.1	5 57.2	20 34.9	19 48.4	23 55.5	7 3.1	20 13.1	25 30.7	28 46.9	17 22.2	4 13.4	3 19.4
29 F	6 28 27.7	6 58.4	20 31.8	4♓25.0	25 18.4	8 17.6	20 59.8	25 32.2	28 42.5	17 25.0	4 11.9	3 18.1
30 S	6 32 24.2	7 59.5	20 28.6	18 42.1	26 38.8	9 32.2	21 46.5	25 34.0	28 38.1	17 27.9	4 10.5	3 16.9
31 S	6 36 20.8	9 0.7	20 25.4	2♈37.6	27 56.2	10 46.7	22 33.2	25 36.0	28 33.6	17 30.7	4 9.0	3 15.7

DECLINATION

DAY	EPHEMERIS SIDEREAL TIME	☉	☊	☽	☿	♀	♂	♃	♄	♅	♆	♇
1 F	4 38 4.1	21S43.9	21S39.1	10S40.0	23S30.9	10S56.5	24S23.3	8N46.1	20N12.7	16S36.6	18N51.2	18N28.3
4 M	4 49 53.7	22 10.6	21 40.6	6N56.0	24 18.9	12 10.6	24 23.6	8 42.8	20 14.4	16 34.9	18 51.8	18 28.4
7 T	5 1 43.4	22 33.5	21 42.1	20 56.0	24 55.4	13 22.4	24 21.5	8 40.2	20 16.4	16 33.0	18 52.5	18 28.5
10 S	5 13 33.1	22 52.5	21 43.6	25 38.4	25 20.0	14 31.5	24 17.0	8 38.3	20 18.5	16 31.0	18 53.2	18 28.7
13 W	5 25 22.8	23 7.4	21 45.1	19 36.2	25 31.9	15 37.6	24 .0.0	8 37.0	20 20.8	16 29.0	18 54.0	18 28.8
16 S	5 37 12.4	23 18.1	21 46.6	6 30.9	25 30.7	16 40.4	24 0.5	8 36.4	20 23.3	16 26.8	18 54.8	18 29.0
19 T	5 49 2.1	23 24.7	21 48.1	9S 9.6	25 16.0	17 39.4	23 48.6	8 36.4	20 25.9	16 24.5	18 55.7	18 29.2
22 F	6 0 51.8	23 27.1	21 49.5	22 24.0	24 47.5	18 34.3	23 34.2	8 37.2	20 28.6	16 22.1	18 56.7	18 29.4
25 M	6 12 41.4	23 25.2	21 51.0	24 43.4	24 5.7	19 24.8	23 17.4	8 38.7	20 31.5	16 19.6	18 57.7	18 29.7
28 T	6 24 31.1	23 19.0	21 52.4	12 22.3	23 11.2	20 10.6	22 58.1	8 40.8	20 34.5	16 17.0	18 58.7	18 29.9
31 S	6 36 20.8	23 8.7	21 53.8	5N40.8	22 6.1	20 51.4	22 36.6	8 43.6	20 37.5	16 14.3	18 59.8	18 30.2

JANUARY 1917

LONGITUDE

DAY	EPHEMERIS SIDEREAL TIME h m s	☉ ° ′	☊ ° ′	☽ ° ′	☿ ° ′	♀ ° ′	♂ ° ′	♃ ° ′	♄ ° ′	♅ ° ′	♆ ° ′	♇ ° ′
1 M	6 40 17.4	10♑ 1.9	20♑22.2	16♈11.5	29♑10.2	12♐ 1.3	23♑20.0	25♈38.2	28♋29.1	17♒33.7	4♌ 7.5	3♋14.5
2 T	6 44 13.9	11 3.0	20 19.1	29 25.0	0♒20.0	13 15.9	24 6.8	25 40.6	28R24.5	17 36.6	4R 6.0	3R13.3
3 W	6 48 10.5	12 4.2	20 15.9	12♉19.9	1 25.1	14 30.5	24 53.7	25 43.2	28 19.9	17 39.6	4 4.4	3 12.1
4 T	6 52 7.0	13 5.3	20 12.7	24 58.8	2 24.7	15 45.2	25 40.5	25 46.0	28 15.3	17 42.6	4 2.9	3 10.9
5 F	6 56 3.6	14 6.5	20 9.5	7♊24.0	3 18.0	16 59.8	26 27.4	25 49.0	28 10.6	17 45.6	4 1.3	3 9.7
6 S	7 0 0.2	15 7.6	20 6.4	19 38.0	4 4.2	18 14.5	27 14.4	25 52.2	28 5.9	17 48.7	3 59.7	3 8.6
7 S	7 3 56.7	16 8.7	20 3.2	1♋42.7	4 42.3	19 29.2	28 1.3	25 55.6	28 1.1	17 51.7	3 58.2	3 7.4
8 M	7 7 53.3	17 9.9	19 60.0	13 40.2	5 11.5	20 43.8	28 48.3	25 59.2	27 56.3	17 54.8	3 56.6	3 6.2
9 T	7 11 49.8	18 11.0	19 56.8	25 32.4	5 30.8	21 58.6	29 35.3	26 2.9	27 51.5	17 57.9	3 55.0	3 5.0
10 W	7 15 46.4	19 12.1	19 53.6	7♌21.3	5 39.5	23 13.3	0♒22.4	26 6.9	27 46.6	18 1.1	3 53.3	3 3.9
11 T	7 19 42.9	20 13.2	19 50.5	19 9.1	5R37.0	24 28.0	1 9.4	26 11.1	27 41.8	18 4.2	3 51.7	3 2.7
12 F	7 23 39.5	21 14.4	19 47.3	0♍58.4	5 22.7	25 42.8	1 56.5	26 15.4	27 36.9	18 7.4	3 50.1	3 1.6
13 S	7 27 36.0	22 15.5	19 44.1	12 52.2	4 56.7	26 57.5	2 43.6	26 19.9	27 32.0	18 10.6	3 48.4	3 0.4
14 S	7 31 32.6	23 16.6	19 40.9	24 53.8	4 19.1	28 12.3	3 30.7	26 24.6	27 27.1	18 13.9	3 46.8	2 59.3
15 M	7 35 29.2	24 17.7	19 37.8	7♎ 7.1	3 30.6	29 27.1	4 17.9	26 29.6	27 22.2	18 17.1	3 45.1	2 58.2
16 T	7 39 25.7	25 18.8	19 34.6	19 36.1	2 32.5	0♑41.9	5 5.1	26 34.6	27 17.2	18 20.4	3 43.4	2 57.1
17 W	7 43 22.3	26 19.9	19 31.4	2♏24.8	1 26.2	1 56.7	5 52.3	26 39.9	27 12.3	18 23.6	3 41.8	2 56.0
18 T	7 47 18.8	27 21.0	19 28.2	15 37.0	0 13.7	3 11.6	6 39.5	26 45.3	27 7.3	18 26.9	3 40.1	2 54.9
19 F	7 51 15.4	28 22.1	19 25.1	29 15.2	28♑57.4	4 26.4	7 26.7	26 50.9	27 2.4	18 30.3	3 38.4	2 53.8
20 S	7 55 12.0	29 23.2	19 21.9	13♐20.6	27 39.6	5 41.3	8 14.0	26 56.7	26 57.4	18 33.6	3 36.7	2 52.7
21 S	7 59 8.5	0♒24.2	19 18.7	27 51.9	26 22.8	6 56.1	9 1.3	27 2.7	26 52.5	18 36.9	3 35.0	2 51.7
22 M	8 3 5.1	1 25.3	19 15.5	12♑45.2	25 9.0	8 11.0	9 48.6	27 8.9	26 47.6	18 40.3	3 33.3	2 50.6
23 T	8 7 1.6	2 26.4	19 12.3	27 53.6	24 0.2	9 25.8	10 35.9	27 15.2	26 42.7	18 43.7	3 31.6	2 49.6
24 W	8 10 58.2	3 27.4	19 9.2	13♒ 8.1	22 58.0	10 40.7	11 23.2	27 21.6	26 37.8	18 47.0	3 29.9	2 48.5
25 T	8 14 54.7	4 28.4	19 6.0	28 18.7	22 3.5	11 55.6	12 10.6	27 28.3	26 32.9	18 50.4	3 28.3	2 47.5
26 F	8 18 51.3	5 29.5	19 2.8	13♓15.9	21 17.5	13 10.4	12 58.0	27 35.1	26 28.0	18 53.8	3 26.6	2 46.5
27 S	8 22 47.8	6 30.4	18 59.6	27 52.2	20 40.2	14 25.3	13 45.3	27 42.1	26 23.2	18 57.3	3 24.9	2 45.5
28 S	8 26 44.4	7 31.4	18 56.5	12♈ 2.8	20 11.9	15 40.2	14 32.7	27 49.2	26 18.4	19 0.7	3 23.2	2 44.6
29 M	8 30 41.0	8 32.4	18 53.3	25 45.9	19 52.5	16 55.1	15 20.1	27 56.5	26 13.6	19 4.1	3 21.5	2 43.6
30 T	8 34 37.5	9 33.3	18 50.1	9♉ 2.2	19 41.5	18 9.9	16 7.5	28 4.0	26 8.8	19 7.6	3 19.8	2 42.7
31 W	8 38 34.1	10 34.2	18 46.9	21 54.4	19 38.7	19 24.8	16 54.9	28 11.6	26 4.1	19 11.0	3 18.1	2 41.7

DECLINATION

DAY	EPHEMERIS SIDEREAL TIME h m s	☉	☊	☽	☿	♀	♂	♃	♄	♅	♆	♇
1 M	6 40 17.4	23S 4.3	21S54.3	11N14.4	21S42.6	21S 3.8	22S28.8	8N44.7	20N38.5	16S13.4	19N 0.1	18N30.3
4 T	6 52 7.0	22 48.4	21 55.7	23 13.4	20 29.3	21 37.4	22 4.2	8 48.4	20 41.7	16 10.6	19 1.2	18 30.6
7 S	7 3 56.7	22 28.4	21 57.1	25 5.6	19 16.9	22 5.4	21 37.3	8 52.7	20 44.8	16 7.8	19 2.4	18 30.9
10 W	7 15 46.4	22 4.5	21 58.5	16 53.8	18 14.1	22 27.5	21 8.2	8 57.7	20 48.0	16 4.9	19 3.5	18 31.2
13 S	7 27 36.0	21 36.7	21 59.9	2 48.9	17 30.3	22 43.6	20 36.9	9 3.2	20 51.3	16 1.9	19 4.7	18 31.6
16 T	7 39 25.7	21 5.1	22 1.3	12S34.2	17 11.3	22 53.6	20 3.6	9 9.4	20 54.5	15 58.8	19 5.9	18 31.9
19 F	7 51 15.4	20 29.9	22 2.7	23 59.8	17 16.9	22 57.3	19 28.3	9 16.1	20 57.7	15 55.7	19 7.1	18 32.3
22 M	8 3 5.1	19 51.2	22 4.0	23 29.7	17 40.1	22 54.8	18 51.0	9 23.3	21 0.9	15 52.6	19 8.3	18 32.7
25 T	8 14 54.7	19 9.1	22 5.4	8 58.7	18 12.4	22 45.9	18 11.9	9 31.0	21 4.0	15 49.4	19 9.5	18 33.1
28 S	8 26 44.4	18 23.9	22 6.7	9N34.2	18 47.0	22 30.8	17 31.0	9 39.3	21 7.0	15 46.2	19 10.7	18 33.5
31 W	8 38 34.1	17 35.7	22 8.0	22 33.7	19 19.5	22 9.6	16 48.5	9 48.0	21 10.0	15 43.0	19 12.0	18 33.9

FEBRUARY 1917

LONGITUDE

DAY	EPHEMERIS SIDEREAL TIME h m s	☉	☊	☽	☿	♀	♂	♃	♄	♅	♆	♇
1 T	8 42 30.6	11♒35.1	18♑43.8	4♊26.2	19♑43.5	20♑39.7	17♒42.3	28♈19.3	25♋59.4	19♒14.5	3♌16.5	2♋40.8
2 F	8 46 27.2	12 36.0	18 40.6	16 41.6	19D55.5	21 54.5	18 29.7	28 27.2	25R54.8	19 17.9	3R14.8	2R39.9
3 S	8 50 23.8	13 36.8	18 37.4	28 44.8	20 14.0	23 9.4	19 17.2	28 35.3	25 50.2	19 21.4	3 13.1	2 39.1
4 S	8 54 20.3	14 37.7	18 34.2	10♋39.6	20 38.6	24 24.3	20 4.6	28 43.5	25 45.7	19 24.9	3 11.5	2 38.2
5 M	8 58 16.9	15 38.5	18 31.0	22 29.6	21 8.8	25 39.2	20 52.0	28 51.8	25 41.2	19 28.3	3 9.8	2 37.3
6 T	9 2 13.4	16 39.2	18 27.9	4♌17.5	21 44.1	26 54.0	21 39.4	29 0.3	25 36.7	19 31.8	3 8.2	2 36.5
7 W	9 6 10.0	17 40.0	18 24.7	16 5.8	22 24.1	28 8.9	22 26.9	29 8.9	25 32.3	19 35.3	3 6.6	2 35.7
8 T	9 10 6.5	18 40.8	18 21.5	27 56.5	23 8.3	29 23.8	23 14.3	29 17.7	25 28.0	19 38.8	3 4.9	2 34.9
9 F	9 14 3.1	19 41.5	18 18.3	9♍51.6	23 56.5	0♒38.6	24 1.8	29 26.6	25 23.7	19 42.3	3 3.3	2 34.1
10 S	9 17 59.6	20 42.2	18 15.2	21 52.7	24 48.2	1 53.5	24 49.2	29 35.6	25 19.5	19 45.7	3 1.7	2 33.4
11 S	9 21 56.2	21 42.8	18 12.0	4♎ 1.9	25 43.2	3 8.3	25 36.6	29 44.7	25 15.3	19 49.2	3 0.1	2 32.6
12 M	9 25 52.7	22 43.5	18 8.8	16 21.2	26 41.2	4 23.2	26 24.1	29 54.0	25 11.2	19 52.7	2 58.6	2 31.9
13 T	9 29 49.3	23 44.1	18 5.6	28 53.3	27 42.0	5 38.1	27 11.5	0♉ 3.5	25 7.2	19 56.2	2 57.0	2 31.2
14 W	9 33 45.9	24 44.8	18 2.5	11♏40.9	28 45.4	6 53.0	27 59.0	0 13.0	25 3.2	19 59.6	2 55.4	2 30.5
15 T	9 37 42.4	25 45.4	17 59.3	24 47.1	29 51.1	8 7.8	28 46.4	0 22.7	24 59.3	20 3.1	2 53.9	2 29.8
16 F	9 41 39.0	26 45.9	17 56.1	8♐14.6	0♒59.0	9 22.7	29 33.9	0 32.4	24 55.5	20 6.6	2 52.4	2 29.2
17 S	9 45 35.5	27 46.5	17 52.9	22 5.5	2 9.0	10 37.5	0♓21.3	0 42.4	24 51.8	20 10.0	2 50.9	2 28.6
18 S	9 49 32.1	28 47.0	17 49.7	6♑20.6	3 20.9	11 52.4	1 8.7	0 52.4	24 48.1	20 13.5	2 49.4	2 28.0
19 M	9 53 28.6	29 47.6	17 46.6	20 58.6	4 34.6	13 7.3	1 56.2	1 2.5	24 44.5	20 16.9	2 47.9	2 27.4
20 T	9 57 25.2	0♓48.0	17 43.4	5♒55.5	5 49.9	14 22.1	2 43.6	1 12.8	24 41.0	20 20.4	2 46.4	2 26.8
21 W	10 1 21.7	1 48.5	17 40.2	21 4.3	7 6.9	15 37.0	3 31.0	1 23.2	24 37.6	20 23.8	2 45.0	2 26.3
22 T	10 5 18.3	2 49.0	17 37.0	6♓15.8	8 25.4	16 51.8	4 18.4	1 33.7	24 34.2	20 27.2	2 43.6	2 25.7
23 F	10 9 14.9	3 49.4	17 33.9	21 19.8	9 45.4	18 6.6	5 5.8	1 44.3	24 31.0	20 30.7	2 42.2	2 25.2
24 S	10 13 11.4	4 49.8	17 30.7	6♈ 6.8	11 6.7	19 21.5	5 53.2	1 55.0	24 27.8	20 34.1	2 40.8	2 24.8
25 S	10 17 7.9	5 50.1	17 27.5	20 29.4	12 29.4	20 36.3	6 40.6	2 5.8	24 24.7	20 37.4	2 39.4	2 24.3
26 M	10 21 4.5	6 50.4	17 24.3	4♉23.6	13 53.3	21 51.1	7 28.0	2 16.7	24 21.7	20 40.8	2 38.1	2 23.9
27 T	10 25 1.1	7 50.7	17 21.1	17 48.3	15 18.5	23 5.9	8 15.3	2 27.7	24 18.8	20 44.2	2 36.8	2 23.4
28 W	10 28 57.6	8 51.0	17 18.0	0♊45.4	16 45.0	24 20.7	9 2.7	2 38.8	24 16.0	20 47.6	2 35.5	2 23.1

DECLINATION

DAY	EPHEMERIS SIDEREAL TIME h m s	☉	☊	☽	☿	♀	♂	♃	♄	♅	♆	♇
1 T	8 42 30.6	17S19.0	22S 8.5	24N43.5	19S29.3	22S 1.1	16S33.9	9N51.0	21N11.0	15S41.9	19N12.4	18N34.1
4 S	8 54 20.3	16 27.2	22 9.8	23 51.5	19 54.4	21 31.8	15 49.3	10 0.3	21 13.9	15 38.7	19 13.5	18 34.5
7 W	9 6 10.0	15 32.7	22 11.1	13 48.0	20 11.8	20 56.7	15 3.2	10 10.0	21 16.6	15 35.4	19 14.7	18 35.0
10 S	9 17 59.6	14 35.9	22 12.4	1S 1.0	20 19.9	20 16.0	14 15.7	10 20.1	21 19.2	15 32.1	19 15.9	18 35.4
13 T	9 29 49.3	13 36.9	22 13.6	15 52.3	20 18.0	19 29.9	13 27.0	10 30.5	21 21.8	15 28.8	19 17.0	18 35.9
16 F	9 41 39.0	12 35.9	22 14.9	25 3.8	20 5.4	18 38.7	12 37.0	10 41.3	21 24.1	15 25.5	19 18.1	18 36.3
19 M	9 53 28.6	11 33.0	22 16.2	21 39.7	19 41.6	17 42.7	11 46.0	10 52.4	21 26.4	15 22.3	19 19.2	18 36.8
22 T	10 5 18.3	10 28.5	22 17.4	5 42.0	19 6.4	16 42.0	10 53.9	11 3.8	21 28.5	15 19.0	19 20.2	18 37.3
25 S	10 17 7.9	9 22.5	22 18.7	12N45.8	18 19.7	15 37.2	10 0.9	11 15.5	21 30.4	15 15.8	19 21.2	18 37.8
28 W	10 28 57.6	8 15.3	22 19.9	24 3.1	17 21.4	14 28.5	9 7.2	11 27.4	21 32.2	15 12.6	19 22.1	18 38.3

MARCH 1917

LONGITUDE

DAY	EPHEMERIS SIDEREAL TIME h m s	☉ ° ′	☊ ° ′	☽ ° ′	☿ ° ′	♀ ° ′	♂ ° ′	♃ ° ′	♄ ° ′	♅ ° ′	♆ ° ′	♇ ° ′
1 T	10 32 54.2	9 ♓ 51.2	17 ♑ 14.8	13 ♓ 18.6	18 ♒ 12.6	25 ♒ 35.5	9 ♓ 50.0	2 ♉ 50.0	24 ♋ 13.3	20 ♒ 50.9	2 ♌ 34.2	2 ♋ 22.7
2 F	10 36 50.7	10 51.4	17 11.6	25 32.5	19 41.4	26 50.2	10 37.3	3 1.3	24 R 10.7	20 54.2	2 R 32.9	2 R 22.3
3 S	10 40 47.3	11 51.6	17 8.4	7 ♋ 32.5	21 11.3	28 5.0	11 24.6	3 12.7	24 8.2	20 57.5	2 31.7	2 22.0
4 S	10 44 43.8	12 51.7	17 5.3	19 23.7	22 42.4	29 19.8	12 11.8	3 24.2	24 5.8	21 0.8	2 30.5	2 21.7
5 M	10 48 40.4	13 51.8	17 2.1	1 ♌ 10.7	24 14.7	0 ♓ 34.5	12 59.1	3 35.8	24 3.5	21 4.1	2 29.3	2 21.4
6 T	10 52 36.9	14 51.8	16 58.9	12 57.7	25 48.0	1 49.2	13 46.3	3 47.5	24 1.2	21 7.4	2 28.1	2 21.2
7 W	10 56 33.5	15 51.8	16 55.7	24 47.9	27 22.5	3 4.0	14 33.5	3 59.3	23 59.1	21 10.6	2 27.0	2 20.9
8 T	11 0 30.0	16 51.8	16 52.5	6 ♍ 44.1	28 58.1	4 18.7	15 20.7	4 11.1	23 57.1	21 13.8	2 25.9	2 20.7
9 F	11 4 26.6	17 51.8	16 49.4	18 48.0	0 ♓ 34.9	5 33.4	16 7.9	4 23.0	23 55.2	21 17.0	2 24.8	2 20.5
10 S	11 8 23.1	18 51.7	16 46.2	1 ♎ 0.9	2 12.8	6 48.1	16 55.0	4 35.0	23 53.4	21 20.2	2 23.7	2 20.3
11 S	11 12 19.7	19 51.6	16 43.0	13 23.6	3 51.8	8 2.8	17 42.2	4 47.1	23 51.7	21 23.4	2 22.7	2 20.2
12 M	11 16 16.2	20 51.4	16 39.8	25 56.7	5 32.0	9 17.4	18 29.3	4 59.3	23 50.1	21 26.5	2 21.7	2 20.1
13 T	11 20 12.8	21 51.3	16 36.7	8 ♏ 41.1	7 13.4	10 32.1	19 16.4	5 11.5	23 48.6	21 29.7	2 20.7	2 20.0
14 W	11 24 9.4	22 51.1	16 33.5	21 37.7	8 55.9	11 46.8	20 3.4	5 23.8	23 47.3	21 32.8	2 19.7	2 19.9
15 T	11 28 5.9	23 50.9	16 30.3	4 ♐ 47.9	10 39.6	13 1.4	20 50.5	5 36.2	23 46.0	21 35.8	2 18.8	2 19.8
16 F	11 32 2.4	24 50.6	16 27.1	18 13.5	12 24.5	14 16.1	21 37.5	5 48.7	23 44.8	21 38.9	2 17.9	2 19.8
17 S	11 35 59.0	25 50.3	16 23.9	1 ♑ 56.1	14 10.7	15 30.7	22 24.5	6 1.2	23 43.8	21 41.9	2 17.0	2 19.8
18 S	11 39 55.6	26 50.0	16 20.8	15 57.0	15 58.0	16 45.3	23 11.5	6 13.8	23 42.8	21 44.9	2 16.2	2 D 19.8
19 M	11 43 52.1	27 49.7	16 17.6	0 ♒ 16.4	17 46.6	17 60.0	23 58.4	6 26.5	23 42.0	21 47.9	2 15.4	2 19.9
20 T	11 47 48.7	28 49.3	16 14.4	14 52.3	19 36.5	19 14.6	24 45.3	6 39.3	23 41.3	21 50.9	2 14.6	2 19.9
21 W	11 51 45.2	29 48.9	16 11.2	29 40.8	21 27.6	20 29.2	25 32.2	6 52.1	23 40.6	21 53.8	2 13.8	2 20.0
22 T	11 55 41.8	0 ♈ 48.5	16 8.1	14 ♓ 35.1	23 20.0	21 43.8	26 19.1	7 4.9	23 40.1	21 56.7	2 13.1	2 20.1
23 F	11 59 38.3	1 48.0	16 4.9	29 26.9	25 13.6	22 58.3	27 5.9	7 17.9	23 39.7	21 59.6	2 12.4	2 20.3
24 S	12 3 34.9	2 47.5	16 1.7	14 ♈ 7.4	27 8.4	24 12.9	27 52.7	7 30.8	23 39.5	22 2.4	2 11.8	2 20.4
25 S	12 7 31.4	3 47.0	15 58.5	28 28.5	29 4.5	25 27.5	28 39.5	7 43.9	23 39.3	22 5.2	2 11.1	2 20.6
26 M	12 11 28.0	4 46.4	15 55.3	12 ♉ 24.8	1 ♈ 1.8	26 42.0	29 26.3	7 57.0	23 39.2	22 8.0	2 10.5	2 20.8
27 T	12 15 24.6	5 45.8	15 52.2	25 53.7	3 0.2	27 56.5	0 ♈ 13.0	8 10.2	23 D 39.3	22 10.7	2 10.0	2 21.0
28 W	12 19 21.1	6 45.2	15 49.0	8 ♊ 55.4	4 59.8	29 11.0	0 59.7	8 23.4	23 39.4	22 13.5	2 9.4	2 21.3
29 T	12 23 17.7	7 44.5	15 45.8	21 32.4	7 0.4	0 ♈ 25.5	1 46.3	8 36.6	23 39.7	22 16.1	2 8.9	2 21.5
30 F	12 27 14.2	8 43.8	15 42.6	3 ♋ 49.2	9 1.9	1 40.0	2 32.9	8 49.9	23 40.1	22 18.8	2 8.4	2 21.8
31 S	12 31 10.8	9 43.0	15 39.5	15 50.8	11 4.3	2 54.5	3 19.5	9 3.3	23 40.6	22 21.4	2 8.0	2 22.1

DECLINATION

DAY	EPHEMERIS SIDEREAL TIME h m s	☉	☊	☽	☿	♀	♂	♃	♄	♅	♆	♇
1 T	10 32 54.2	7 S 52.7	22 S 20.3	25 N 21.7	16 S 59.4	14 S 4.8	8 S 49.1	11 N 31.4	21 N 32.8	15 S 11.6	19 N 22.4	18 N 38.4
4 S	10 44 43.8	6 44.1	22 21.5	21 58.6	15 45.6	12 51.4	7 54.4	11 43.6	21 34.3	15 8.4	19 23.3	18 38.9
7 W	10 56 33.5	5 34.7	22 22.7	10 24.6	14 20.4	11 34.8	6 59.1	11 55.9	21 35.7	15 5.3	19 24.2	18 39.4
10 S	11 8 23.1	4 24.6	22 23.9	4 S 50.7	12 43.6	10 15.5	6 3.4	12 8.5	21 36.9	15 2.3	19 25.0	18 39.9
13 T	11 20 12.8	3 13.9	22 25.1	18 51.9	10 55.4	8 53.7	5 7.2	12 21.2	21 38.0	14 59.3	19 25.7	18 40.4
16 F	11 32 2.4	2 3.0	22 26.2	25 22.9	8 56.1	7 29.7	4 10.7	12 34.0	21 38.8	14 56.4	19 26.4	18 40.9
19 M	11 43 52.1	0 51.9	22 27.4	18 58.8	6 45.8	6 3.9	3 13.9	12 46.9	21 39.5	14 53.5	19 27.0	18 41.4
22 T	11 55 41.8	0 N 19.3	22 28.5	2 8.7	4 25.0	4 36.7	2 17.0	12 59.9	21 40.1	14 50.8	19 27.6	18 41.9
25 S	12 7 31.4	1 30.3	22 29.7	15 N 31.3	1 54.4	3 8.3	1 20.1	13 13.0	21 40.4	14 48.1	19 28.1	18 42.4
28 W	12 19 21.1	2 40.9	22 30.8	24 48.4	0 N 44.7	1 39.1	0 23.2	13 26.1	21 40.6	14 45.5	19 28.5	18 42.8
31 S	12 31 10.8	3 51.1	22 31.9	22 31.1	3 30.7	0 9.4	0 N 33.6	13 39.2	21 40.6	14 42.9	19 28.9	18 43.3

APRIL 1917

LONGITUDE

DAY	EPHEMERIS SIDEREAL TIME h m s	☉ ° ′	☊ ° ′	☽ ° ′	☿ ° ′	♀ ° ′	♂ ° ′	♃ ° ′	♄ ° ′	♅ ° ′	♆ ° ′	♇ ° ′
1 S	12 35 7.3	10 ♈ 42.2	15 ♑ 36.3	27 ♋ 42.7	13 ♈ 7.4	4 ♈ 8.9	4 ♈ 6.0	9 ♉ 16.7	23 ♋ 41.2	22 ♒ 24.0	2 ♌ 7.6	2 ♋ 22.5
2 M	12 39 3.9	11 41.4	15 33.1	9 ♌ 30.5	15 11.0	5 23.4	4 52.5	9 30.2	23 41.9	22 26.6	2 R 7.2	2 22.9
3 T	12 43 0.4	12 40.5	15 29.9	21 19.0	17 15.0	6 37.8	5 39.0	9 43.7	23 42.7	22 29.1	2 6.9	2 23.2
4 W	12 46 57.0	13 39.6	15 26.7	3 ♍ 12.7	19 19.1	7 52.2	6 25.4	9 57.2	23 43.7	22 31.6	2 6.5	2 23.6
5 T	12 50 53.5	14 38.6	15 23.6	15 15.1	21 23.2	9 6.5	7 11.8	10 10.8	23 44.7	22 34.0	2 6.3	2 24.1
6 F	12 54 50.1	15 37.7	15 20.4	27 28.7	23 26.9	10 20.9	7 58.1	10 24.4	23 45.9	22 36.5	2 6.0	2 24.5
7 S	12 58 46.7	16 36.6	15 17.2	9 ♎ 54.8	25 29.8	11 35.3	8 44.4	10 38.1	23 47.2	22 38.8	2 5.8	2 25.0
8 S	13 2 43.2	17 35.6	15 14.0	22 34.0	27 31.8	12 49.6	9 30.7	10 51.8	23 48.5	22 41.2	2 5.6	2 25.5
9 M	13 6 39.7	18 34.5	15 10.8	5 ♏ 26.0	29 32.4	14 4.0	10 16.9	11 5.5	23 50.0	22 43.5	2 5.5	2 26.0
10 T	13 10 36.3	19 33.4	15 7.7	18 30.1	1 ♉ 31.3	15 18.3	11 3.1	11 19.3	23 51.6	22 45.7	2 5.4	2 26.6
11 W	13 14 32.9	20 32.2	15 4.5	1 ♐ 45.3	3 28.2	16 32.6	11 49.3	11 33.1	23 53.3	22 48.0	2 5.3	2 27.1
12 T	13 18 29.4	21 31.1	15 1.3	15 11.0	5 22.6	17 46.9	12 35.4	11 47.0	23 55.1	22 50.2	2 5.2	2 27.7
13 F	13 22 26.0	22 29.8	14 58.1	28 47.0	7 14.3	19 1.2	13 21.5	12 0.8	23 57.0	22 52.3	2 5.2	2 28.3
14 S	13 26 22.5	23 28.6	14 55.0	12 ♑ 33.6	9 2.9	20 15.4	14 7.5	12 14.7	23 59.0	22 54.4	2 D 5.2	2 28.9
15 S	13 30 19.1	24 27.3	14 51.8	26 31.0	10 48.1	21 29.7	14 53.5	12 28.7	24 1.1	22 56.5	2 5.3	2 29.6
16 M	13 34 15.6	25 26.1	14 48.6	10 ♒ 39.1	12 29.6	22 43.9	15 39.4	12 42.6	24 3.3	22 58.5	2 5.4	2 30.2
17 T	13 38 12.2	26 24.7	14 45.4	24 57.2	14 7.2	23 58.2	16 25.3	12 56.6	24 5.6	23 0.5	2 5.5	2 30.9
18 W	13 42 8.7	27 23.4	14 42.2	9 ♓ 22.7	15 40.6	25 12.4	17 11.2	13 10.6	24 8.0	23 2.5	2 5.7	2 31.6
19 T	13 46 5.3	28 22.0	14 39.1	23 51.8	17 9.7	26 26.6	17 57.1	13 24.7	24 10.6	23 4.4	2 5.8	2 32.4
20 F	13 50 1.8	29 20.6	14 35.9	8 ♈ 18.9	18 34.3	27 40.8	18 42.8	13 38.7	24 13.2	23 6.3	2 6.1	2 33.1
21 S	13 53 58.4	0 ♉ 19.2	14 32.7	22 37.7	19 54.2	28 55.0	19 28.6	13 52.8	24 15.9	23 8.1	2 6.3	2 33.9
22 S	13 57 54.9	1 17.7	14 29.5	6 ♉ 41.9	21 9.3	0 ♉ 9.2	20 14.3	14 6.9	24 18.7	23 9.9	2 6.6	2 34.7
23 M	14 1 51.5	2 16.2	14 26.4	20 26.7	22 19.4	1 23.3	20 59.9	14 21.0	24 21.7	23 11.6	2 6.9	2 35.5
24 T	14 5 48.0	3 14.7	14 23.2	3 ♊ 49.0	23 24.5	2 37.5	21 45.5	14 35.2	24 24.7	23 13.3	2 7.3	2 36.3
25 W	14 9 44.6	4 13.1	14 20.0	16 48.0	24 24.4	3 51.6	22 31.1	14 49.3	24 27.8	23 14.9	2 7.7	2 37.1
26 T	14 13 41.2	5 11.5	14 16.8	29 25.0	25 19.2	5 5.7	23 16.6	15 3.5	24 31.0	23 16.6	2 8.1	2 38.0
27 F	14 17 37.7	6 9.9	14 13.7	11 ♋ 43.1	26 8.6	6 19.8	24 2.1	15 17.7	24 34.3	23 18.1	2 8.5	2 38.9
28 S	14 21 34.3	7 8.2	14 10.5	23 46.6	26 52.6	7 33.9	24 47.5	15 31.9	24 37.7	23 19.6	2 9.0	2 39.8
29 S	14 25 30.8	8 6.5	14 7.3	5 ♌ 40.4	27 31.3	8 48.0	25 32.8	15 46.1	24 41.2	23 21.1	2 9.5	2 40.7
30 M	14 29 27.4	9 4.8	14 4.1	17 30.0	28 4.5	10 2.0	26 18.1	16 0.3	24 44.8	23 22.5	2 10.1	2 41.6

DECLINATION

DAY	EPHEMERIS SIDEREAL TIME h m s	☉	☊	☽	☿	♀	♂	♃	♄	♅	♆	♇
1 S	12 35 7.3	4 N 14.3	22 S 32.3	19 N 37.0	4 N 27.0	0 N 20.6	0 N 52.5	13 N 43.6	21 N 40.5	14 S 42.1	19 N 29.0	18 N 43.5
4 W	12 46 57.0	5 23.6	22 33.4	6 52.5	7 17.1	1 50.5	1 48.9	13 56.8	21 40.3	14 39.7	19 29.3	18 43.9
7 S	12 58 46.7	6 31.9	22 34.5	8 S 30.2	10 5.3	3 20.1	2 45.1	14 9.9	21 39.9	14 37.5	19 29.5	18 44.4
10 T	13 10 36.3	7 39.3	22 35.5	21 20.1	12 45.9	4 49.1	3 40.9	14 23.0	21 39.3	14 35.3	19 29.6	18 44.8
13 F	13 22 26.0	8 45.5	22 36.6	24 47.7	15 13.1	6 17.2	4 36.2	14 36.1	21 38.6	14 33.2	19 29.7	18 45.2
16 M	13 34 15.6	9 50.5	22 37.7	15 24.6	17 21.9	7 44.2	5 30.9	14 49.1	21 37.6	14 31.3	19 29.7	18 45.7
19 T	13 46 5.3	10 53.9	22 38.7	1 N 53.8	19 9.1	9 9.6	6 25.1	15 2.1	21 36.5	14 29.5	19 29.7	18 46.1
22 S	13 57 54.9	11 55.8	22 39.7	18 7.1	20 32.8	10 33.1	7 18.5	15 14.9	21 35.3	14 27.8	19 29.6	18 46.5
25 W	14 9 44.6	12 55.9	22 40.8	25 1.8	21 32.8	11 54.4	8 11.2	15 27.7	21 33.8	14 26.2	19 29.4	18 46.9
28 S	14 21 34.3	13 54.1	22 41.8	20 25.2	22 9.4	13 13.1	9 3.0	15 40.3	21 32.3	14 24.7	19 29.1	18 47.2

MAY 1917

LONGITUDE

DAY	EPHEMERIS SIDEREAL TIME h m s	☉ ° ′	☊ ° ′	☾ ° ′	☿ ° ′	♀ ° ′	♂ ° ′	♃ ° ′	♄ ° ′	♅ ° ′	♆ ° ′	♇ ° ′
1 T	14 33 23.9	10♉ 3.0	14♑ 0.9	29♌20.7	28♉32.3	11♉16.1	27♈ 3.4	16♉14.5	24♋48.5	23♒23.9	2♌10.7	2♋42.6
2 W	14 37 20.5	11 1.2	13 57.8	11♍17.4	28 54.5	12 30.1	27 48.6	16 28.7	24 52.3	23 25.2	2 11.3	2 43.6
3 T	14 41 17.0	11 59.4	13 54.6	23 24.5	29 11.3	13 44.1	28 33.8	16 43.0	24 56.2	23 26.5	2 11.9	2 44.5
4 F	14 45 13.6	12 57.5	13 51.4	5♎45.4	29 22.7	14 58.1	29 18.9	16 57.2	25 0.1	23 27.8	2 12.6	2 45.5
5 S	14 49 10.2	13 55.6	13 48.2	18 22.4	29 28.7	16 12.0	0♉ 3.9	17 11.4	25 4.2	23 28.9	2 13.3	2 46.6
6 S	14 53 6.7	14 53.7	13 45.1	1♏16.5	29 29.5	17 26.0	0 48.9	17 25.7	25 8.3	23 30.1	2 14.1	2 47.6
7 M	14 57 3.2	15 51.7	13 41.9	14 27.3	29R25.2	18 39.9	1 33.9	17 39.9	25 12.5	23 31.2	2 14.8	2 48.7
8 T	15 0 59.8	16 49.7	13 38.7	27 53.3	29 16.1	19 53.9	2 18.8	17 54.2	25 16.8	23 32.2	2 15.6	2 49.7
9 W	15 4 56.4	17 47.7	13 35.5	11♐32.4	29 2.4	21 7.8	3 3.7	18 8.4	25 21.2	23 33.2	2 16.5	2 50.8
10 T	15 8 53.0	18 45.7	13 32.4	25 21.8	28 44.3	22 21.7	3 48.5	18 22.7	25 25.7	23 34.2	2 17.4	2 51.9
11 F	15 12 49.5	19 43.6	13 29.2	9♑19.0	28 22.4	23 35.6	4 33.2	18 36.9	25 30.2	23 35.1	2 18.2	2 53.0
12 S	15 16 46.0	20 41.6	13 26.0	23 21.7	27 56.9	24 49.5	5 17.9	18 51.2	25 34.8	23 36.0	2 19.2	2 54.1
13 S	15 20 42.6	21 39.5	13 22.8	7♒28.4	27 28.5	26 3.4	6 2.6	19 5.4	25 39.6	23 36.8	2 20.1	2 55.3
14 M	15 24 39.2	22 37.3	13 19.6	21 37.6	26 57.5	27 17.2	6 47.2	19 19.6	25 44.3	23 37.6	2 21.1	2 56.5
15 T	15 28 35.7	23 35.2	13 16.5	5♓47.8	26 24.6	28 31.1	7 31.8	19 33.9	25 49.2	23 38.3	2 22.1	2 57.6
16 W	15 32 32.3	24 33.0	13 13.3	19 57.3	25 50.4	29 44.9	8 16.3	19 48.1	25 54.2	23 38.9	2 23.2	2 58.8
17 T	15 36 28.8	25 30.9	13 10.1	4♈ 3.8	25 15.4	0♊58.8	9 0.7	20 2.3	25 59.2	23 39.5	2 24.3	3 0.0
18 F	15 40 25.4	26 28.7	13 6.9	18 4.5	24 40.3	2 12.6	9 45.1	20 16.5	26 4.3	23 40.1	2 25.4	3 1.2
19 S	15 44 21.9	27 26.4	13 3.8	1♉55.8	24 5.7	3 26.4	10 29.5	20 30.7	26 9.5	23 40.6	2 26.5	3 2.4
20 S	15 48 18.5	28 24.2	13 0.6	15 34.5	23 32.2	4 40.2	11 13.8	20 44.9	26 14.7	23 41.1	2 27.7	3 3.7
21 M	15 52 15.0	29 21.9	12 57.4	28 57.7	23 0.3	5 54.0	11 58.0	20 59.0	26 20.0	23 41.5	2 28.9	3 4.9
22 T	15 56 11.6	0♊19.7	12 54.2	12♊ 3.4	22 30.6	7 7.8	12 42.2	21 13.2	26 25.4	23 41.9	2 30.1	3 6.2
23 W	16 0 8.1	1 17.4	12 51.1	24 51.0	22 3.5	8 21.6	13 26.4	21 27.3	26 30.9	23 42.2	2 31.3	3 7.5
24 T	16 4 4.7	2 15.0	12 47.9	7♋21.2	21 39.5	9 35.4	14 10.5	21 41.4	26 36.4	23 42.5	2 32.6	3 8.8
25 F	16 8 1.3	3 12.7	12 44.7	19 36.0	21 18.9	10 49.1	14 54.5	21 55.5	26 42.0	23 42.7	2 33.9	3 10.0
26 S	16 11 57.8	4 10.3	12 41.5	1♌38.5	21 2.0	12 2.9	15 38.4	22 9.6	26 47.7	23 42.9	2 35.2	3 11.3
27 S	16 15 54.4	5 7.9	12 38.3	13 32.7	20 49.1	13 16.6	16 22.4	22 23.6	26 53.4	23 43.0	2 36.6	3 12.7
28 M	16 19 50.9	6 5.5	12 35.2	25 23.2	20 40.4	14 30.3	17 6.2	22 37.7	26 59.2	23 43.1	2 38.0	3 14.0
29 T	16 23 47.5	7 3.0	12 32.0	7♍14.8	20 35.9	15 44.0	17 50.0	22 51.7	27 5.1	23 43.1	2 39.4	3 15.3
30 W	16 27 44.0	8 0.6	12 28.8	19 12.6	20 35.9	16 57.7	18 33.8	23 5.6	27 11.0	23R43.1	2 40.8	3 16.7
31 T	16 31 40.6	8 58.1	12 25.6	1♎21.4	20D40.4	18 11.4	19 17.4	23 19.6	27 17.0	23 43.0	2 42.2	3 18.0

DECLINATION

DAY	h m s	☉	☊	☾	☿	♀	♂	♃	♄	♅	♆	♇
1 T	14 33 23.9	14N50.2	22S42.8	8N15.1	22N23.2	14N29.0	9N53.9	15N52.8	21N30.5	14S23.4	19N28.8	18N47.6
4 F	14 45 13.6	15 44.1	22 43.8	6S54.6	22 14.9	15 41.6	10 43.8	16 5.2	21 28.6	14 22.3	19 28.4	18 47.9
7 M	14 57 3.2	16 35.7	22 44.7	20 17.2	21 45.6	16 50.7	11 32.7	16 17.4	21 26.5	14 21.2	19 28.0	18 48.3
10 T	15 8 53.0	17 24.8	22 45.7	24 49.6	20 57.3	17 56.0	12 20.5	16 29.4	21 24.3	14 20.4	19 27.4	18 48.6
13 S	15 20 42.6	18 11.2	22 46.7	16 15.6	19 53.7	18 57.0	13 7.0	16 41.3	21 21.9	14 19.6	19 26.9	18 48.9
16 W	15 32 32.3	18 55.0	22 47.6	0N24.4	18 40.4	19 53.5	13 52.4	16 53.0	21 19.3	14 19.0	19 26.2	18 49.2
19 S	15 44 21.9	19 35.9	22 48.5	16 39.9	17 24.8	20 45.2	14 36.4	17 4.5	21 16.6	14 18.6	19 25.5	18 49.4
22 T	15 56 11.6	20 13.7	22 49.5	24 44.8	16 14.9	21 31.8	15 19.1	17 15.8	21 13.8	14 18.3	19 24.8	18 49.7
25 F	16 8 1.3	20 48.5	22 50.4	21 15.8	15 17.9	22 13.0	16 0.3	17 26.9	21 10.8	14 18.1	19 24.0	18 49.9
28 M	16 19 50.9	21 20.1	22 51.3	9 38.4	14 38.5	22 48.5	16 40.1	17 37.8	21 7.7	14 18.1	19 23.1	18 50.1
31 T	16 31 40.6	21 48.3	22 52.2	5S14.8	14 19.1	23 18.2	17 18.4	17 48.5	21 4.4	14 18.2	19 22.1	18 50.3

JUNE 1917

LONGITUDE

DAY	h m s	☉	☊	☾	☿	♀	♂	♃	♄	♅	♆	♇
1 F	16 35 37.1	9♊55.5	12♑22.5	13♎45.3	20♉49.3	19♊25.0	20♉ 1.1	23♉33.5	27♋23.0	23♒42.9	2♌43.7	3♋19.4
2 S	16 39 33.7	10 53.0	12 19.3	26 27.6	21 2.8	20 38.7	20 44.6	23 47.4	27 29.1	23R42.7	2 45.2	3 20.8
3 S	16 43 30.3	11 50.5	12 16.1	9♏30.5	21 20.6	21 52.4	21 28.2	24 1.3	27 35.3	23 42.5	2 46.8	3 22.1
4 M	16 47 26.8	12 47.9	12 12.9	22 54.5	21 42.9	23 6.0	22 11.6	24 15.1	27 41.5	23 42.3	2 48.3	3 23.5
5 T	16 51 23.4	13 45.3	12 9.8	6♐38.5	22 9.5	24 19.6	22 55.0	24 28.9	27 47.8	23 42.0	2 49.9	3 24.9
6 W	16 55 20.0	14 42.7	12 6.6	20 40.0	22 40.4	25 33.2	23 38.4	24 42.7	27 54.1	23 41.6	2 51.5	3 26.3
7 T	16 59 16.5	15 40.1	12 3.4	4♑54.8	23 15.5	26 46.8	24 21.7	24 56.4	28 0.5	23 41.2	2 53.1	3 27.7
8 F	17 3 13.1	16 37.4	12 0.2	19 18.3	23 54.7	28 0.4	25 4.9	25 10.1	28 6.9	23 40.7	2 54.8	3 29.1
9 S	17 7 9.6	17 34.8	11 57.0	3♒45.5	24 37.8	29 14.0	25 48.1	25 23.8	28 13.4	23 40.2	2 56.4	3 30.6
10 S	17 11 6.2	18 32.1	11 53.9	18 11.9	25 24.9	0♋27.5	26 31.2	25 37.4	28 19.9	23 39.7	2 58.1	3 32.0
11 M	17 15 2.7	19 29.5	11 50.7	2♓33.6	26 15.9	1 41.1	27 14.3	25 51.0	28 26.5	23 39.1	2 59.8	3 33.4
12 T	17 18 59.3	20 26.8	11 47.5	16 47.6	27 10.6	2 54.6	27 57.3	26 4.6	28 33.2	23 38.5	3 1.6	3 34.9
13 W	17 22 55.8	21 24.1	11 44.3	0♈51.8	28 8.9	4 8.2	28 40.3	26 18.1	28 39.8	23 37.8	3 3.3	3 36.3
14 T	17 26 52.4	22 21.5	11 41.2	14 44.6	29 10.9	5 21.7	29 23.2	26 31.6	28 46.6	23 37.0	3 5.1	3 37.7
15 F	17 30 48.9	23 18.8	11 38.0	28 24.9	0♊16.4	6 35.3	0♊ 6.0	26 45.0	28 53.4	23 36.3	3 6.9	3 39.2
16 S	17 34 45.5	24 16.1	11 34.8	11♉51.9	1 25.4	7 48.8	0 48.8	26 58.4	29 0.2	23 35.4	3 8.7	3 40.7
17 S	17 38 42.1	25 13.4	11 31.6	25 5.1	2 37.8	9 2.3	1 31.6	27 11.8	29 7.1	23 34.6	3 10.5	3 42.1
18 M	17 42 38.7	26 10.7	11 28.5	8♊ 4.1	3 53.7	10 15.8	2 14.2	27 25.1	29 14.0	23 33.7	3 12.3	3 43.6
19 T	17 46 35.2	27 8.0	11 25.3	20 49.0	5 12.8	11 29.3	2 56.9	27 38.3	29 20.9	23 32.7	3 14.2	3 45.0
20 W	17 50 31.7	28 5.2	11 22.1	3♋20.3	6 35.3	12 42.8	3 39.4	27 51.5	29 27.9	23 31.7	3 16.1	3 46.5
21 T	17 54 28.3	29 2.5	11 18.9	15 38.8	8 1.0	13 56.3	4 22.0	28 4.7	29 34.9	23 30.7	3 18.0	3 48.0
22 F	17 58 24.9	29 59.8	11 15.8	27 46.2	9 30.0	15 9.8	5 4.4	28 17.8	29 42.0	23 29.6	3 19.9	3 49.4
23 S	18 2 21.4	0♋57.0	11 12.6	9♌44.7	11 2.1	16 23.2	5 46.8	28 30.8	29 49.1	23 28.4	3 21.8	3 50.9
24 S	18 6 18.0	1 54.3	11 9.4	21 37.2	12 37.5	17 36.7	6 29.1	28 43.8	29 56.3	23 27.3	3 23.8	3 52.4
25 M	18 10 14.5	2 51.5	11 6.2	3♍27.2	14 15.9	18 50.1	7 11.4	28 56.7	0♌ 3.4	23 26.1	3 25.8	3 53.9
26 T	18 14 11.1	3 48.8	11 3.0	15 18.8	15 57.5	20 3.6	7 53.6	29 9.6	0 10.7	23 24.8	3 27.7	3 55.3
27 W	18 18 7.6	4 46.0	10 59.9	27 16.1	17 42.1	21 17.0	8 35.8	29 22.4	0 17.9	23 23.5	3 29.7	3 56.8
28 T	18 22 4.2	5 43.2	10 56.7	9♎23.9	19 29.6	22 30.4	9 17.9	29 35.2	0 25.2	23 22.2	3 31.7	3 58.3
29 F	18 26 0.8	6 40.4	10 53.5	21 46.6	21 20.0	23 43.8	9 59.9	29 47.9	0 32.5	23 20.8	3 33.8	3 59.7
30 S	18 29 57.4	7 37.6	10 50.3	4♏28.2	23 13.2	24 57.1	10 41.9	0♊ 0.5	0 39.8	23 19.4	3 35.8	4 1.2

DECLINATION

DAY	h m s	☉	☊	☾	☿	♀	♂	♃	♄	♅	♆	♇
1 F	16 35 37.1	21N56.9	22S52.5	10S13.2	14N17.1	23N26.7	17N30.8	17N52.0	21N 3.3	14S18.3	19N21.8	18N50.4
4 M	16 47 26.8	22 20.6	22 53.3	22 15.7	14 24.3	23 48.3	18 6.9	18 2.3	20 59.8	14 18.6	19 20.8	18 50.6
7 T	16 59 16.5	22 40.8	22 54.2	23 53.9	14 49.5	24 3.6	18 41.5	18 12.4	20 56.2	14 19.1	19 19.8	18 50.7
10 S	17 11 6.2	22 57.3	22 55.1	12 20.6	15 30.4	24 12.5	19 14.3	18 22.2	20 52.5	14 19.7	19 18.7	18 50.8
13 W	17 22 55.8	23 10.3	22 55.9	5N 5.4	16 23.9	24 15.0	19 45.5	18 31.8	20 48.6	14 20.4	19 17.5	18 51.0
16 S	17 34 45.5	23 19.6	22 56.7	19 41.1	17 27.2	24 11.0	20 14.9	18 41.2	20 44.6	14 21.3	19 16.3	18 51.1
19 T	17 46 35.2	23 25.2	22 57.5	24 55.5	18 37.0	24 0.6	20 42.5	18 50.3	20 40.5	14 22.3	19 15.1	18 51.1
22 F	17 58 24.9	23 27.0	22 58.4	19 5.6	19 49.6	23 43.8	21 8.3	18 59.1	20 36.3	14 23.4	19 13.8	18 51.2
25 M	18 10 14.5	23 25.2	22 59.2	6 19.0	21 1.3	23 20.7	21 32.3	19 7.6	20 32.0	14 24.7	19 12.5	18 51.2
28 T	18 22 4.2	23 19.6	22 59.9	8S34.9	22 7.2	22 51.5	21 54.3	19 15.9	20 27.5	14 26.1	19 11.2	18 51.3

JULY 1917

LONGITUDE

DAY	EPHEMERIS SIDEREAL TIME h m s	☉ ° ′	☊ ° ′	☽ ° ′	☿ ° ′	♀ ° ′	♂ ° ′	♃ ° ′	♄ ° ′	♅ ° ′	♆ ° ′	♇ ° ′
1 S	18 33 53.9	8♋34.8	10♑47.2	17♏32.1	25♊ 8.9	26♋10.5	11♊23.8	0♊13.1	0♌47.2	23♒17.9	3♌37.8	4♋ 2.7
2 M	18 37 50.4	9 32.0	10 44.0	1♐ 0.3	27 7.2	27 23.9	12 5.7	0 25.6	0 54.6	23R16.4	3 39.9	4 4.2
3 T	18 41 47.0	10 29.1	10 40.8	14 53.0	29 7.7	28 37.2	12 47.5	0 38.0	1 2.0	23 14.9	3 42.0	4 5.6
4 W	18 45 43.6	11 26.3	10 37.6	29 8.6	1♋10.4	29 50.5	13 29.2	0 50.4	1 9.4	23 13.3	3 44.1	4 7.1
5 T	18 49 40.2	12 23.5	10 34.5	13♑42.9	3 14.8	1♌ 3.8	14 10.9	1 2.7	1 16.9	23 11.8	3 46.2	4 8.5
6 F	18 53 36.7	13 20.7	10 31.3	28 30.1	5 20.9	2 17.1	14 52.5	1 14.9	1 24.4	23 10.1	3 48.3	4 10.0
7 S	18 57 33.2	14 17.9	10 28.1	13♒22.8	7 28.3	3 30.4	15 34.1	1 27.1	1 31.9	23 8.4	3 50.4	4 11.5
8 S	19 1 29.8	15 15.0	10 24.9	28 13.4	9 36.6	4 43.6	16 15.6	1 39.1	1 39.4	23 6.7	3 52.5	4 12.9
9 M	19 5 26.3	16 12.2	10 21.7	12♓55.0	11 45.7	5 56.9	16 57.1	1 51.2	1 47.0	23 5.0	3 54.6	4 14.4
10 T	19 9 22.9	17 9.4	10 18.6	27 22.2	13 55.2	7 10.2	17 38.5	2 3.1	1 54.6	23 3.2	3 56.8	4 15.8
11 W	19 13 19.5	18 6.6	10 15.4	11♈31.3	16 4.8	8 23.4	18 19.8	2 15.0	2 2.2	23 1.4	3 58.9	4 17.2
12 T	19 17 16.0	19 3.8	10 12.2	25 20.6	18 14.3	9 36.6	19 1.1	2 26.8	2 9.8	22 59.6	4 1.1	4 18.7
13 F	19 21 12.6	20 1.1	10 9.0	8♉50.2	20 23.4	10 49.8	19 42.3	2 38.5	2 17.4	22 57.7	4 3.3	4 20.1
14 S	19 25 9.1	20 58.3	10 5.9	22 1.1	22 31.9	12 3.0	20 23.5	2 50.1	2 25.1	22 55.9	4 5.4	4 21.5
15 S	19 29 5.7	21 55.5	10 2.7	4♊55.0	24 39.5	13 16.2	21 4.6	3 1.6	2 32.7	22 53.9	4 7.6	4 22.9
16 M	19 33 2.3	22 52.8	9 59.5	17 34.0	26 46.0	14 29.4	21 45.7	3 13.1	2 40.4	22 52.0	4 9.8	4 24.4
17 T	19 36 58.8	23 50.0	9 56.3	29 60.0	28 51.4	15 42.6	22 26.7	3 24.5	2 48.1	22 50.0	4 12.0	4 25.8
18 W	19 40 55.4	24 47.3	9 53.2	12♋15.1	0♌55.4	16 55.7	23 7.7	3 35.7	2 55.8	22 48.0	4 14.2	4 27.2
19 T	19 44 51.9	25 44.6	9 50.0	24 21.2	2 58.1	18 8.9	23 48.5	3 46.9	3 3.5	22 46.0	4 16.4	4 28.5
20 F	19 48 48.5	26 41.9	9 46.8	6♌20.1	4 59.2	19 22.0	24 29.4	3 58.0	3 11.2	22 43.9	4 18.6	4 29.9
21 S	19 52 45.1	27 39.2	9 43.6	18 13.7	6 58.7	20 35.1	25 10.1	4 9.1	3 18.9	22 41.8	4 20.8	4 31.3
22 S	19 56 41.6	28 36.5	9 40.5	0♍ 4.1	8 56.6	21 48.2	25 50.8	4 20.0	3 26.7	22 39.7	4 23.0	4 32.7
23 M	20 0 38.2	29 33.8	9 37.3	11 53.9	10 52.8	23 1.3	26 31.5	4 30.8	3 34.4	22 37.6	4 25.3	4 34.0
24 T	20 4 34.7	0♌31.1	9 34.1	23 45.8	12 47.3	24 14.3	27 12.1	4 41.5	3 42.1	22 35.5	4 27.5	4 35.4
25 W	20 8 31.3	1 28.4	9 30.9	5♎43.2	14 40.2	25 27.4	27 52.6	4 52.1	3 49.9	22 33.3	4 29.7	4 36.7
26 T	20 12 27.8	2 25.7	9 27.8	17 49.9	16 31.3	26 40.4	28 33.1	5 2.7	3 57.6	22 31.1	4 31.9	4 38.0
27 F	20 16 24.4	3 23.1	9 24.6	0♏10.0	18 20.7	27 53.4	29 13.5	5 13.1	4 5.4	22 28.9	4 34.2	4 39.4
28 S	20 20 20.9	4 20.4	9 21.4	12 47.6	20 8.3	29 6.3	29 53.8	5 23.4	4 13.1	22 26.7	4 36.4	4 40.7
29 S	20 24 17.5	5 17.8	9 18.2	25 46.8	21 54.3	0♍19.3	0♋34.1	5 33.6	4 20.9	22 24.4	4 38.6	4 42.0
30 M	20 28 14.1	6 15.1	9 15.0	9♐10.8	23 38.6	1 32.2	1 14.3	5 43.7	4 28.6	22 22.2	4 40.8	4 43.3
31 T	20 32 10.6	7 12.5	9 11.9	23 1.6	25 21.2	2 45.2	1 54.5	5 53.7	4 36.4	22 19.9	4 43.1	4 44.5

DECLINATION

DAY	EPHEMERIS SIDEREAL TIME h m s	☉	☊	☽	☿	♀	♂	♃	♄	♅	♆	♇
1 S	18 33 53.9	23N10.3	23S 0.7	21S 8.1	23N 2.5	22N16.3	22N14.7	19N23.9	20N23.0	14S27.6	19N 9.8	18N51.3
4 W	18 45 43.6	22 57.5	23 1.5	24 30.8	23 41.6	21 35.4	22 33.0	19 31.6	20 18.3	14 29.1	19 8.4	18 51.3
7 S	18 57 33.2	22 41.0	23 2.2	14 4.4	23 59.8	20 49.0	22 49.5	19 39.0	20 13.6	14 30.8	19 6.[illegible]	18 51.2
10 T	19 9 22.9	22 20.9	23 3.0	3N40.3	23 53.9	19 57.4	23 4.0	19 46.2	20 8.7	14 32.6	19 5.4	18 51.2
13 F	19 21 12.6	21 57.4	23 3.7	18 51.8	23 23.2	19 0.7	23 16.6	19 53.1	20 3.8	14 34.5	19 4.0	18 51.2
16 M	19 33 2.3	21 30.5	23 4.4	24 56.7	22 29.3	17 59.4	23 27.3	19 59.7	19 58.8	14 36.5	19 2.5	18 51.1
19 T	19 44 51.9	21 0.3	23 5.1	20 2.1	21 15.4	16 53.7	23 36.1	20 6.0	19 53.7	14 38.5	19 0.9	18 51.0
22 S	19 56 41.6	20 26.9	23 5.8	7 42.8	19 45.4	15 44.0	23 43.0	20 12.0	19 48.6	14 40.6	18 59.4	18 50.9
25 W	20 8 31.3	19 50.4	23 6.5	7S 4.2	18 3.1	14 30.5	23 48.0	20 17.7	19 43.4	14 42.8	18 57.8	18 50.8
28 S	20 20 20.9	19 11.0	23 7.2	19 54.5	16 11.9	13 13.7	23 51.2	20 23.2	19 38.1	14 45.0	18 56.3	18 50.7
31 T	20 32 10.6	18 28.7	23 7.9	24 50.8	14 14.7	11 53.7	23 52.5	20 28.4	19 32.9	14 47.2	18 54.7	18 50.5

AUGUST 1917

LONGITUDE

DAY	EPHEMERIS SIDEREAL TIME h m s	☉ ° ′	☊ ° ′	☽ ° ′	☿ ° ′	♀ ° ′	♂ ° ′	♃ ° ′	♄ ° ′	♅ ° ′	♆ ° ′	♇ ° ′
1 W	20 36 7.2	8♌ 9.9	9♑ 8.7	7♑19.1	27♌ 2.1	3♍58.0	2♋34.6	6♊ 3.6	4♌44.1	22♒17.6	4♌45.3	4♋45.8
2 T	20 40 3.8	9 7.3	9 5.5	22 0.6	28 41.3	5 10.9	3 14.6	6 13.4	4 51.8	22R15.3	4 47.5	4 47.1
3 F	20 44 0.3	10 4.7	9 2.3	7♒ 0.7	0♍18.8	6 23.7	3 54.6	6 23.0	4 59.6	22 13.0	4 49.7	4 48.3
4 S	20 47 56.8	11 2.1	8 59.2	22 11.1	1 54.7	7 36.6	4 34.5	6 32.6	5 7.3	22 10.7	4 51.9	4 49.5
5 S	20 51 53.4	11 59.5	8 56.0	7♓22.1	3 28.9	8 49.4	5 14.4	6 42.0	5 15.0	22 8.3	4 54.2	4 50.8
6 M	20 55 50.0	12 57.0	8 52.8	22 23.9	5 1.5	10 2.1	5 54.2	6 51.3	5 22.7	22 6.0	4 56.4	4 52.0
7 T	20 59 46.5	13 54.5	8 49.6	7♈ 8.0	6 32.3	11 14.9	6 33.9	7 0.5	5 30.4	22 3.6	4 58.6	4 53.2
8 W	21 3 43.1	14 52.0	8 46.5	21 28.7	8 1.5	12 27.6	7 13.6	7 9.6	5 38.1	22 1.3	5 0.8	4 54.3
9 T	21 7 39.6	15 49.5	8 43.3	5♉23.4	9 29.0	13 40.3	7 53.3	7 18.6	5 45.8	21 58.9	5 3.0	4 55.5
10 F	21 11 36.1	16 47.0	8 40.1	18 51.9	10 54.8	14 53.0	8 32.8	7 27.4	5 53.5	21 56.5	5 5.2	4 56.6
11 S	21 15 32.7	17 44.6	8 36.9	1♊56.3	12 18.9	16 5.7	9 12.3	7 36.1	6 1.1	21 54.1	5 7.3	4 57.8
12 S	21 19 29.3	18 42.2	8 33.7	14 39.7	13 41.2	17 18.3	9 51.8	7 44.7	6 8.8	21 51.7	5 9.5	4 58.9
13 M	21 23 25.9	19 39.8	8 30.6	27 6.1	15 1.7	18 30.9	10 31.2	7 53.1	6 16.4	21 49.4	5 11.7	5 0.0
14 T	21 27 22.4	20 37.5	8 27.4	9♋19.1	16 20.4	19 43.5	11 10.5	8 1.4	6 24.0	21 47.0	5 13.9	5 1.1
15 W	21 31 18.9	21 35.1	8 24.2	21 22.3	17 37.2	20 56.1	11 49.8	8 9.6	6 31.6	21 44.6	5 16.0	5 2.2
16 T	21 35 15.5	22 32.8	8 21.0	3♌18.8	18 52.0	22 8.7	12 29.0	8 17.6	6 39.1	21 42.2	5 18.2	5 3.3
17 F	21 39 12.1	23 30.5	8 17.9	15 11.2	20 4.9	23 21.2	13 8.2	8 25.5	6 46.7	21 39.8	5 20.3	5 4.3
18 S	21 43 8.6	24 28.2	8 14.7	27 1.5	21 15.7	24 33.7	13 47.3	8 33.3	6 54.2	21 37.4	5 22.4	5 5.3
19 S	21 47 5.2	25 26.0	8 11.5	8♍51.6	22 24.3	25 46.2	14 26.3	8 40.9	7 1.7	21 35.0	5 24.6	5 6.3
20 M	21 51 1.7	26 23.8	8 8.3	20 43.2	23 30.7	26 58.6	15 5.3	8 48.4	7 9.2	21 32.6	5 26.7	5 7.3
21 T	21 54 58.3	27 21.6	8 5.1	2♎38.4	24 34.7	28 11.0	15 44.2	8 55.7	7 16.6	21 30.2	5 28.8	5 8.3
22 W	21 58 54.9	28 19.4	8 2.0	14 39.1	25 36.3	29 23.4	16 23.0	9 2.9	7 24.1	21 27.9	5 30.9	5 9.3
23 T	22 2 51.4	29 17.2	7 58.8	26 48.0	26 35.3	0♎35.8	17 1.8	9 10.0	7 31.5	21 25.5	5 32.9	5 10.2
24 F	22 6 47.9	0♍15.1	7 55.6	9♏ 8.3	27 31.6	1 48.1	17 40.5	9 16.9	7 38.9	21 23.1	5 35.0	5 11.2
25 S	22 10 44.5	1 13.0	7 52.4	21 43.4	28 25.0	3 0.4	18 19.1	9 23.6	7 46.2	21 20.8	5 37.1	5 12.1
26 S	22 14 41.0	2 10.9	7 49.3	4♐37.3	29 15.3	4 12.7	18 57.7	9 30.2	7 53.5	21 18.4	5 39.1	5 13.0
27 M	22 18 37.6	3 8.8	7 46.1	17 53.7	0♎ 2.5	5 24.9	19 36.2	9 36.6	8 0.8	21 16.1	5 41.1	5 13.8
28 T	22 22 34.2	4 6.7	7 42.9	1♑35.6	0 46.2	6 37.1	20 14.6	9 42.9	8 8.0	21 13.8	5 43.1	5 14.7
29 W	22 26 30.7	5 4.7	7 39.7	15 44.6	1 26.2	7 49.3	20 53.0	9 49.0	8 15.3	21 11.5	5 45.1	5 15.5
30 T	22 30 27.2	6 2.7	7 36.5	0♒19.9	2 2.3	9 1.4	21 31.3	9 54.9	8 22.4	21 9.2	5 47.1	5 16.3
31 F	22 34 23.8	7 0.7	7 33.4	15 17.7	2 34.4	10 13.5	22 9.6	10 0.7	8 29.6	21 6.9	5 49.1	5 17.2

DECLINATION

DAY	EPHEMERIS SIDEREAL TIME h m s	☉	☊	☽	☿	♀	♂	♃	♄	♅	♆	♇
1 W	20 36 7.2	18N14.0	23S 8.1	23S32.7	13N34.7	11N26.5	23N52.5	20N30.1	19N31.1	14S48.0	18N54.2	18N50.5
4 S	20 47 56.8	17 28.1	23 8.7	10 50.2	11 33.2	10 3.0	23 51.4	20 34.9	19 25.7	14 50.3	18 52.6	18 50.3
7 T	20 59 46.5	16 39.7	23 9.4	7N35.9	9 30.6	8 37.2	23 48.5	20 39.4	19 20.4	14 52.6	18 51.0	18 50.2
10 F	21 11 36.1	15 48.8	23 10.0	21 20.7	7 28.7	7 9.4	23 43.8	20 43.7	19 15.0	14 54.9	18 49.5	18 50.0
13 M	21 23 25.9	14 55.6	23 10.6	24 36.1	5 29.1	5 39.9	23 37.4	20 47.7	19 9.5	14 57.2	18 47.9	18 49.8
16 T	21 35 15.5	14 0.3	23 11.2	17 27.0	3 33.2	4 9.1	23 29.4	20 51.4	19 4.1	14 59.6	18 46.4	18 49.6
19 S	21 47 5.2	13 2.9	23 11.8	4 10.4	1 42.5	2 37.2	23 19.7	20 54.8	18 58.7	15 1.9	18 44.9	18 49.4
22 W	21 58 54.9	12 3.7	23 12.4	10S28.3	0S 1.1	1 4.6	23 8.4	20 58.0	18 53.3	15 4.2	18 43.3	18 49.2
25 S	22 10 44.5	11 2.8	23 13.0	21 51.3	1 35.5	0S28.4	22 55.6	21 1.0	18 47.9	15 6.5	18 41.9	18 49.0
28 T	22 22 34.2	10 0.4	23 13.5	24 7.5	2 58.3	2 1.6	22 41.3	21 3.6	18 42.6	15 8.7	18 40.4	18 48.8
31 F	22 34 23.8	8 56.5	23 14.1	13 23.0	4 6.2	3 34.5	22 25.5	21 6.1	18 37.3	15 10.9	18 38.9	18 48.6

SEPTEMBER 1917

DAY	EPHEMERIS SIDEREAL TIME	☉	☊	☾	☿	♀	♂	♃	♄	♅	♆	♇
	h m s	° ′	° ′	° ′	° ′	° ′	° ′	° ′	° ′	° ′	° ′	° ′
						LONGITUDE						
1 S	22 38 20.4	7♍58.7	7♑30.2	0♓31.0	3♎ 2.0	11♎25.5	22♋47.7	10♊ 6.3	8♌36.7	21♒ 4.7	5♌51.0	5♋17.9
2 S	22 42 16.9	8 56.8	7 27.0	15 49.7	3 25.0	12 37.5	23 25.9	10 11.8	8 43.8	21R 2.4	5 53.0	5 18.7
3 M	22 46 13.4	9 54.9	7 23.8	1♈ 2.7	3 43.0	13 49.5	24 3.9	10 17.1	8 50.8	21 0.2	5 54.9	5 19.4
4 T	22 50 10.0	10 53.0	7 20.7	15 59.4	3 55.7	15 1.4	24 41.9	10 22.2	8 57.8	20 58.0	5 56.8	5 20.1
5 W	22 54 6.6	11 51.2	7 17.5	0♉32.0	4 2.9	16 13.4	25 19.8	10 27.2	9 4.8	20 55.8	5 58.7	5 20.9
6 T	22 58 3.2	12 49.3	7 14.3	14 35.7	4 4.3	17 25.2	25 57.7	10 32.0	9 11.7	20 53.6	6 0.5	5 21.5
7 F	23 1 59.7	13 47.6	7 11.1	28 9.6	3R59.5	18 37.0	26 35.5	10 36.6	9 18.5	20 51.5	6 2.4	5 22.2
8 S	23 5 56.2	14 45.8	7 7.9	11♊15.5	3 48.5	19 48.8	27 13.2	10 41.0	9 25.4	20 49.3	6 4.2	5 22.8
9 S	23 9 52.8	15 44.1	7 4.8	23 57.1	3 31.0	21 0.6	27 50.9	10 45.3	9 32.1	20 47.2	6 6.0	5 23.5
10 M	23 13 49.4	16 42.4	7 1.6	6♋19.0	3 6.9	22 12.3	28 28.5	10 49.3	9 38.9	20 45.2	6 7.8	5 24.1
11 T	23 17 45.9	17 40.8	6 58.4	18 26.1	2 36.2	23 24.0	29 6.0	10 53.2	9 45.6	20 43.1	6 9.6	5 24.6
12 W	23 21 42.4	18 39.2	6 55.2	0♌23.3	1 59.0	24 35.6	29 43.5	10 56.9	9 52.2	20 41.1	6 11.4	5 25.2
13 T	23 25 39.0	19 37.6	6 52.1	12 14.8	1 15.7	25 47.2	0♌20.9	11 0.5	9 58.8	20 39.1	6 13.1	5 25.7
14 F	23 29 35.6	20 36.1	6 48.9	24 4.1	0 26.7	26 58.8	0 58.2	11 3.8	10 5.3	20 37.1	6 14.8	5 26.2
15 S	23 33 32.1	21 34.6	6 45.7	5♍53.9	29♍32.6	28 10.3	1 35.5	11 7.0	10 11.8	20 35.2	6 16.5	5 26.7
16 S	23 37 28.7	22 33.1	6 42.5	17 46.5	28 34.3	29 21.8	2 12.7	11 9.9	10 18.3	20 33.2	6 18.2	5 27.2
17 M	23 41 25.2	23 31.6	6 39.3	29 43.4	27 32.9	0♏33.3	2 49.8	11 12.7	10 24.6	20 31.3	6 19.8	5 27.6
18 T	23 45 21.8	24 30.2	6 36.2	11♎45.8	26 29.6	1 44.7	3 26.8	11 15.3	10 31.0	20 29.5	6 21.4	5 28.1
19 W	23 49 18.3	25 28.9	6 33.0	23 54.9	25 25.8	2 56.0	4 3.8	11 17.7	10 37.2	20 27.7	6 23.0	5 28.5
20 T	23 53 14.9	26 27.5	6 29.8	6♏12.1	24 23.1	4 7.3	4 40.6	11 19.9	10 43.4	20 25.9	6 24.6	5 28.9
21 F	23 57 11.4	27 26.2	6 26.6	18 39.2	23 23.1	5 18.6	5 17.4	11 21.9	10 49.6	20 24.1	6 26.2	5 29.2
22 S	0 1 8.0	28 24.9	6 23.4	1♐18.5	22 27.2	6 29.8	5 54.2	11 23.7	10 55.7	20 22.4	6 27.7	5 29.5
23 S	0 5 4.6	29 23.6	6 20.3	14 12.7	21 37.0	7 41.0	6 30.8	11 25.3	11 1.7	20 20.7	6 29.2	5 29.9
24 M	0 9 1.1	0♎22.4	6 17.1	27 25.1	20 53.8	8 52.1	7 7.4	11 26.8	11 7.7	20 19.0	6 30.7	5 30.1
25 T	0 12 57.7	1 21.2	6 13.9	10♑58.6	20 18.7	10 3.2	7 43.9	11 28.0	11 13.6	20 17.4	6 32.1	5 30.4
26 W	0 16 54.2	2 20.0	6 10.7	24 55.6	19 52.6	11 14.2	8 20.3	11 29.0	11 19.4	20 15.8	6 33.5	5 30.7
27 T	0 20 50.8	3 18.9	6 7.6	9♒16.5	19 36.2	12 25.1	8 56.6	11 29.8	11 25.2	20 14.3	6 34.9	5 30.9
28 F	0 24 47.3	4 17.7	6 4.4	23 59.5	19 29.9	13 36.0	9 32.9	11 30.5	11 30.9	20 12.8	6 36.3	5 31.1
29 S	0 28 43.9	5 16.7	6 1.2	8♓59.6	19D33.8	14 46.8	10 9.1	11 30.9	11 36.5	20 11.3	6 37.7	5 31.3
30 S	0 32 40.4	6 15.6	5 58.0	24 8.8	19 47.9	15 57.6	10 45.2	11 31.1	11 42.1	20 9.8	6 39.0	5 31.4
						DECLINATION						
1 S	22 38 20.4	8N34.9	23S14.3	7S34.4	4S24.9	4S 5.4	22N19.9	21N 6.8	18N35.6	15S11.6	18N38.5	18N48.5
4 T	22 50 10.0	7 29.3	23 14.8	10N55.7	5 6.5	5 37.5	22 2.4	21 8.9	18 30.3	15 13.7	18 37.1	18 48.3
7 F	23 1 59.7	6 22.6	23 15.3	22 57.5	5 22.4	7 8.8	21 43.4	21 10.7	18 25.2	15 15.8	18 35.7	18 48.1
10 M	23 13 49.4	5 15.0	23 15.8	23 28.8	5 7.1	8 38.8	21 23.2	21 12.3	18 20.1	15 17.7	18 34.4	18 47.9
13 T	23 25 39.0	4 6.5	23 16.3	14 25.1	4 16.4	10 7.2	21 1.9	21 13.6	18 15.1	15 19.6	18 33.1	18 47.7
16 S	23 37 28.7	2 57.4	23 16.8	0 29.7	2 50.8	11 33.9	20 39.3	21 14.7	18 10.2	15 21.5	18 31.9	18 47.5
19 W	23 49 18.3	1 47.8	23 17.3	13S44.1	0 59.0	12 58.3	20 15.7	21 15.6	18 5.4	15 23.2	18 30.7	18 47.3
22 S	0 1 8.0	0 37.8	23 17.8	23 17.1	1N 1.0	14 20.2	19 51.1	21 16.2	18 0.7	15 24.8	18 29.5	18 47.1
25 T	0 12 57.7	0S32.3	23 18.2	22 36.8	2 46.8	15 39.3	19 25.5	21 16.6	17 56.2	15 26.3	18 28.5	18 46.9
28 F	0 24 47.3	1 42.5	23 18.7	10 2.0	3 59.2	16 55.2	18 59.1	21 16.7	17 51.7	15 27.7	18 27.4	18 46.7

OCTOBER 1917

DAY	EPHEMERIS SIDEREAL TIME	☉	☊	☾	☿	♀	♂	♃	♄	♅	♆	♇
						LONGITUDE						
1 M	0 36 37.0	7♎14.6	5♑54.8	9♈16.9	20♍12.0	17♏ 8.3	11♌21.2	11♊31.2	11♌47.6	20♒ 8.4	6♌40.3	5♋31.5
2 T	0 40 33.5	8 13.6	5 51.7	24 13.5	20 45.7	18 18.9	11 57.1	11R31.0	11 53.0	20R 7.1	6 41.5	5 31.6
3 W	0 44 30.1	9 12.6	5 48.5	8♉49.4	21 28.4	19 29.5	12 33.0	11 30.6	11 58.3	20 5.8	6 42.8	5 31.7
4 T	0 48 26.7	10 11.7	5 45.3	22 58.5	22 19.5	20 40.0	13 8.8	11 30.1	12 3.6	20 4.5	6 44.0	5 31.8
5 F	0 52 23.2	11 10.8	5 42.1	6♊38.2	23 18.4	21 50.4	13 44.5	11 29.3	12 8.8	20 3.3	6 45.2	5 31.8
6 S	0 56 19.7	12 10.0	5 39.0	19 49.1	24 24.2	23 0.8	14 20.1	11 28.3	12 14.0	20 2.1	6 46.3	5 31.8
7 S	1 0 16.3	13 9.2	5 35.8	2♋34.1	25 36.3	24 11.1	14 55.6	11 27.1	12 19.0	20 1.0	6 47.4	5R31.8
8 M	1 4 12.9	14 8.4	5 32.6	14 57.7	26 53.9	25 21.4	15 31.1	11 25.8	12 24.0	19 59.9	6 48.5	5 31.8
9 T	1 8 9.4	15 7.7	5 29.4	27 5.1	28 16.3	26 31.6	16 6.5	11 24.2	12 28.9	19 58.8	6 49.6	5 31.8
10 W	1 12 6.0	16 7.0	5 26.3	9♌ 1.5	29 42.9	27 41.7	16 41.7	11 22.4	12 33.7	19 57.8	6 50.6	5 31.7
11 T	1 16 2.5	17 6.3	5 23.1	20 52.2	1♎12.9	28 51.8	17 16.9	11 20.4	12 38.4	19 56.8	6 51.6	5 31.6
12 F	1 19 59.1	18 5.7	5 19.9	2♍41.5	2 45.9	0♐ 1.7	17 52.0	11 18.2	12 43.1	19 55.9	6 52.6	5 31.5
13 S	1 23 55.6	19 5.2	5 16.7	14 33.2	4 21.3	1 11.6	18 27.0	11 15.8	12 47.7	19 55.0	6 53.5	5 31.3
14 S	1 27 52.2	20 4.6	5 13.5	26 30.2	5 58.6	2 21.5	19 1.9	11 13.3	12 52.2	19 54.2	6 54.4	5 31.1
15 M	1 31 48.7	21 4.1	5 10.4	8♎34.5	7 37.5	3 31.2	19 36.7	11 10.5	12 56.6	19 53.4	6 55.3	5 31.0
16 T	1 35 45.3	22 3.6	5 7.2	20 47.4	9 17.6	4 40.9	20 11.4	11 7.5	13 0.9	19 52.7	6 56.2	5 30.7
17 W	1 39 41.8	23 3.2	5 4.0	3♏ 9.6	10 58.7	5 50.5	20 46.0	11 4.3	13 5.1	19 52.0	6 57.0	5 30.5
18 T	1 43 38.4	24 2.8	5 0.8	15 41.6	12 40.3	6 60.0	21 20.6	11 1.0	13 9.2	19 51.4	6 57.8	5 30.2
19 F	1 47 34.9	25 2.4	4 57.7	28 23.7	14 22.4	8 9.4	21 55.0	10 57.4	13 13.3	19 50.8	6 58.5	5 30.0
20 S	1 51 31.5	26 2.1	4 54.5	11♐16.6	16 4.7	9 18.7	22 29.3	10 53.7	13 17.2	19 50.2	6 59.2	5 29.6
21 S	1 55 28.0	27 1.8	4 51.3	24 21.4	17 47.1	10 27.9	23 3.5	10 49.7	13 21.1	19 49.7	6 59.9	5 29.3
22 M	1 59 24.6	28 1.5	4 48.1	7♑39.8	19 29.5	11 37.1	23 37.6	10 45.6	13 24.9	19 49.3	7 0.6	5 29.0
23 T	2 3 21.2	29 1.3	4 44.9	21 13.4	21 11.7	12 46.1	24 11.6	10 41.3	13 28.6	19 48.9	7 1.2	5 28.6
24 W	2 7 17.7	0♏ 1.0	4 41.8	5♒ 3.7	22 53.7	13 55.0	24 45.4	10 36.9	13 32.1	19 48.6	7 1.8	5 28.2
25 T	2 11 14.2	1 0.8	4 38.6	19 11.4	24 35.4	15 3.8	25 19.2	10 32.2	13 35.6	19 48.3	7 2.3	5 27.8
26 F	2 15 10.8	2 0.7	4 35.4	3♓35.7	26 16.8	16 12.5	25 52.8	10 27.4	13 39.0	19 48.0	7 2.8	5 27.4
27 S	2 19 7.4	3 0.5	4 32.2	18 13.6	27 57.8	17 21.1	26 26.4	10 22.4	13 42.3	19 47.8	7 3.3	5 26.9
28 S	2 23 3.9	4 0.4	4 29.1	2♈59.6	29 38.3	18 29.5	26 59.8	10 17.2	13 45.5	19 47.7	7 3.8	5 26.4
29 M	2 27 0.5	5 0.4	4 25.9	17 46.6	1♏18.5	19 37.8	27 33.2	10 11.9	13 48.6	19 47.6	7 4.2	5 25.9
30 T	2 30 57.0	6 0.3	4 22.7	2♉26.3	2 58.1	20 46.0	28 6.4	10 6.4	13 51.6	19 47.5	7 4.6	5 25.4
31 W	2 34 53.6	7 0.3	4 19.5	16 50.9	4 37.4	21 54.1	28 39.5	10 0.7	13 54.5	19D47.6	7 4.9	5 24.8
						DECLINATION						
1 M	0 36 37.0	2S52.5	23S19.1	8N16.1	4N28.1	18S 7.6	18N31.8	21N16.6	17N47.5	15S29.0	18N26.4	18N46.5
4 T	0 48 26.7	4 2.4	23 19.5	21 48.8	4 12.3	19 16.2	18 3.7	21 16.3	17 43.4	15 30.2	18 25.5	18 46.4
7 S	1 0 16.3	5 11.7	23 19.9	23 40.5	3 17.4	20 20.7	17 34.9	21 15.7	17 39.5	15 31.2	18 24.7	18 46.2
10 W	1 12 6.0	6 20.6	23 20.3	15 18.4	1 51.9	21 20.7	17 5.4	21 14.9	17 35.8	15 32.2	18 23.9	18 46.1
13 S	1 23 55.6	7 28.6	23 20.7	1 44.6	0 5.1	22 16.1	16 35.4	21 13.9	17 32.2	15 32.9	18 23.2	18 45.9
16 T	1 35 45.3	8 35.8	23 21.1	12S34.4	1S54.9	23 6.4	16 4.9	21 12.7	17 28.9	15 33.6	18 22.5	18 45.8
19 F	1 47 34.9	9 41.8	23 21.4	22 40.0	4 2.0	23 51.5	15 33.9	21 11.2	17 25.8	15 34.1	18 21.9	18 45.7
22 M	1 59 24.6	10 46.6	23 21.8	22 52.7	6 11.4	24 31.1	15 2.5	21 9.4	17 22.9	15 34.5	18 21.4	18 45.6
25 T	2 11 14.2	11 49.9	23 22.1	11 37.5	8 19.9	25 5.0	14 30.9	21 7.5	17 20.3	15 34.7	18 21.0	18 45.5
28 S	2 23 3.9	12 51.6	23 22.5	5N50.5	10 25.5	25 32.9	13 58.9	21 5.3	17 17.9	15 34.8	18 20.7	18 45.4
31 W	2 34 53.6	13 51.5	23 22.8	20 23.5	12 26.3	25 54.9	13 26.8	21 2.9	17 15.7	15 34.7	18 20.4	18 45.3

NOVEMBER 1917

DAY	EPHEMERIS SIDEREAL TIME	☉	☊	☽	☿	♀	♂	♃	♄	♅	♆	♇
	h m s	° '	° '	° '	° '	° '	° '	° '	° '	° '	° '	° '
						LONGITUDE						
1 T	2 38 50.2	8♏ 0.3	4♑16.3	0♊54.3	6♏16.2	23♐ 2.0	29♌12.4	9♊54.9	13♌57.3	19♒47.6	7♌ 5.3	5♋24.3
2 F	2 42 46.7	9 0.3	4 13.2	14 32.8	7 54.5	24 9.7	29 45.3	9R49.0	14 0.0	19 47.7	7 5.6	5R23.7
3 S	2 46 43.3	10 0.4	4 10.0	27 45.5	9 32.4	25 17.4	0♍18.0	9 42.9	14 2.6	19 47.9	7 5.8	5 23.1
4 S	2 50 39.8	11 0.5	4 6.8	10♋33.8	11 9.9	26 24.9	0 50.6	9 36.6	14 5.1	19 48.1	7 6.0	5 22.5
5 M	2 54 36.4	12 0.7	4 3.6	23 1.1	12 46.9	27 32.2	1 23.1	9 30.2	14 7.5	19 48.4	7 6.2	5 21.8
6 T	2 58 32.9	13 0.9	4 0.5	5♌11.5	14 23.5	28 39.4	1 55.5	9 23.7	14 9.8	19 48.7	7 6.4	5 21.2
7 W	3 2 29.5	14 1.1	3 57.3	17 10.3	15 59.8	29 46.4	2 27.7	9 17.1	14 11.9	19 49.0	7 6.5	5 20.5
8 T	3 6 26.0	15 1.3	3 54.1	29 2.5	17 35.6	0♑53.2	2 59.8	9 10.3	14 14.0	19 49.5	7 6.5	5 19.8
9 F	3 10 22.6	16 1.6	3 50.9	10♍53.3	19 11.1	1 59.9	3 31.8	9 3.4	14 16.0	19 49.9	7 6.6	5 19.1
10 S	3 14 19.2	17 1.9	3 47.8	22 47.2	20 46.2	3 6.4	4 3.6	8 56.3	14 17.8	19 50.4	7 6.6	5 18.3
11 S	3 18 15.7	18 2.3	3 44.6	4♎48.1	22 21.0	4 12.8	4 35.3	8 49.2	14 19.6	19 51.0	7R 6.6	5 17.6
12 M	3 22 12.3	19 2.7	3 41.4	16 59.0	23 55.5	5 18.9	5 6.8	8 41.9	14 21.2	19 51.6	7 6.5	5 16.8
13 T	3 26 8.8	20 3.1	3 38.2	29 22.0	25 29.7	6 24.8	5 38.2	8 34.6	14 22.7	19 52.3	7 6.4	5 16.0
14 W	3 30 5.4	21 3.5	3 35.0	11♏58.3	27 3.6	7 30.6	6 9.5	8 27.1	14 24.2	19 53.0	7 6.3	5 15.2
15 T	3 34 1.9	22 4.0	3 31.9	24 48.1	28 37.2	8 36.1	6 40.6	8 19.6	14 25.5	19 53.8	7 6.1	5 14.4
16 F	3 37 58.5	23 4.5	3 28.7	7♐51.0	0♐10.6	9 41.5	7 11.5	8 12.0	14 26.7	19 54.6	7 5.9	5 13.5
17 S	3 41 55.0	24 5.0	3 25.5	21 6.2	1 43.7	10 46.6	7 42.3	8 4.2	14 27.8	19 55.5	7 5.7	5 12.6
18 S	3 45 51.6	25 5.5	3 22.3	4♑32.7	3 16.6	11 51.4	8 12.9	7 56.5	14 28.7	19 56.4	7 5.4	5 11.8
19 M	3 49 48.1	26 6.1	3 19.2	18 9.7	4 49.3	12 56.0	8 43.3	7 48.6	14 29.6	19 57.4	7 5.2	5 10.9
20 T	3 53 44.7	27 6.7	3 16.0	1♒56.5	6 21.7	14 0.4	9 13.6	7 40.7	14 30.3	19 58.4	7 4.8	5 10.0
21 W	3 57 41.3	28 7.3	3 12.8	15 52.7	7 54.0	15 4.5	9 43.7	7 32.7	14 31.0	19 59.5	7 4.5	5 9.0
22 T	4 1 37.8	29 7.9	3 9.6	29 57.5	9 26.0	16 8.4	10 13.6	7 24.7	14 31.5	20 0.6	7 4.1	5 8.1
23 F	4 5 34.4	0♐ 8.6	3 6.4	14♓ 9.6	10 57.8	17 11.9	10 43.4	7 16.7	14 31.9	20 1.8	7 3.6	5 7.1
24 S	4 9 30.9	1 9.3	3 3.3	28 27.0	12 29.5	18 15.2	11 13.0	7 8.6	14 32.2	20 3.1	7 3.2	5 6.2
25 S	4 13 27.5	2 9.9	3 0.1	12♈46.7	14 0.9	19 18.1	11 42.4	7 0.5	14 32.4	20 4.3	7 2.7	5 5.2
26 M	4 17 24.1	3 10.6	2 56.9	27 4.5	15 32.1	20 20.7	12 11.6	6 52.3	14 32.5	20 5.6	7 2.2	5 4.2
27 T	4 21 20.6	4 11.3	2 53.7	11♉15.8	17 3.1	21 23.0	12 40.6	6 44.1	14R32.4	20 7.0	7 1.6	5 3.2
28 W	4 25 17.2	5 12.1	2 50.6	25 15.6	18 33.8	22 24.9	13 9.5	6 36.0	14 32.3	20 8.4	7 1.0	5 2.1
29 T	4 29 13.7	6 12.9	2 47.4	8♊60.0	20 4.2	23 26.5	13 38.1	6 27.8	14 32.0	20 9.9	7 0.4	5 1.1
30 F	4 33 10.3	7 13.6	2 44.2	22 25.7	21 34.4	24 27.7	14 6.6	6 19.6	14 31.6	20 11.4	6 59.7	5 0.1
						DECLINATION						
1 T	2 38 50.2	14S11.0	23S22.9	22N59.5	13S 5.4	26S 0.8	13N16.1	21N 2.1	17N15.1	15S34.7	18N20.3	18N45.3
4 S	2 50 39.8	15 8.2	23 23.2	22 19.9	14 58.4	26 14.6	12 43.8	20 59.5	17 13.3	15 34.4	18 20.1	18 45.3
7 W	3 2 29.5	16 3.2	23 23.5	12 15.7	16 44.5	26 22.2	12 11.5	20 56.6	17 11.8	15 34.0	18 20.0	18 45.3
10 S	3 14 19.2	16 55.8	23 23.7	1S47.1	18 23.1	26 23.6	11 39.2	20 53.6	17 10.5	15 33.5	18 20.0	18 45.3
13 T	3 26 8.8	17 45.8	23 24.0	15 31.9	19 53.4	26 18.8	11 7.0	20 50.4	17 9.6	15 32.8	18 20.1	18 45.3
16 F	3 37 58.5	18 33.0	23 24.3	23 42.9	21 15.0	26 8.0	10 35.0	20 47.0	17 8.9	15 32.0	18 20.2	18 45.3
19 M	3 49 48.1	19 17.3	23 24.5	20 46.3	22 27.1	25 51.4	10 3.2	20 43.5	17 8.5	15 31.0	18 20.4	18 45.3
22 T	4 1 37.8	19 58.4	23 24.7	7 21.0	23 29.1	25 29.0	9 31.8	20 39.9	17 8.5	15 29.9	18 20.7	18 45.4
25 S	4 13 27.5	20 36.2	23 25.0	9N45.4	24 20.5	25 1.2	9 0.7	20 36.2	17 8.7	15 28.6	18 21.1	18 45.5
28 W	4 25 17.2	21 10.6	23 25.2	22 5.9	25 0.6	24 28.3	8 30.1	20 32.5	17 9.2	15 27.2	18 21.5	18 45.6

DECEMBER 1917

DAY	EPHEMERIS SIDEREAL TIME	☉	☊	☽	☿	♀	♂	♃	♄	♅	♆	♇
						LONGITUDE						
1 S	4 37 6.8	8♐14.4	2♑41.0	5♋31.4	23♐ 4.2	25♑28.6	14♍34.9	6♊11.4	14♌31.1	20♒13.0	6♌59.0	4♋59.0
2 S	4 41 3.4	9 15.2	2 37.9	18 17.3	24 33.6	26 29.0	15 2.9	6R 3.3	14R30.5	20 14.6	6R58.3	4R57.9
3 M	4 44 59.9	10 16.1	2 34.7	0♌45.0	26 2.6	27 29.0	15 30.8	5 55.1	14 29.8	20 16.2	6 57.6	4 56.8
4 T	4 48 56.5	11 17.0	2 31.5	12 57.5	27 31.1	28 28.6	15 58.4	5 47.0	14 29.0	20 17.9	6 56.8	4 55.8
5 W	4 52 53.1	12 17.9	2 28.3	24 58.5	28 59.0	29 27.8	16 25.8	5 38.9	14 28.1	20 19.7	6 56.0	4 54.7
6 T	4 56 49.6	13 18.8	2 25.2	6♍52.6	0♑26.2	0♒26.5	16 53.0	5 30.9	14 27.0	20 21.4	6 55.2	4 53.5
7 F	5 0 46.2	14 19.7	2 22.0	18 44.4	1 52.6	1 24.8	17 20.0	5 22.9	14 25.9	20 23.3	6 54.3	4 52.4
8 S	5 4 42.7	15 20.6	2 18.8	0♎38.9	3 18.0	2 22.5	17 46.7	5 14.9	14 24.6	20 25.2	6 53.4	4 51.3
9 S	5 8 39.3	16 21.6	2 15.6	12 40.8	4 42.4	3 19.8	18 13.2	5 7.0	14 23.2	20 27.1	6 52.5	4 50.1
10 M	5 12 35.9	17 22.6	2 12.4	24 54.1	6 5.4	4 16.5	18 39.5	4 59.2	14 21.7	20 29.0	6 51.5	4 49.0
11 T	5 16 32.4	18 23.6	2 9.3	7♏22.3	7 26.9	5 12.7	19 5.5	4 51.4	14 20.1	20 31.0	6 50.5	4 47.8
12 W	5 20 29.0	19 24.6	2 6.1	20 7.9	8 46.6	6 8.3	19 31.3	4 43.7	14 18.4	20 33.1	6 49.5	4 46.7
13 T	5 24 25.5	20 25.7	2 2.9	3♐12.0	10 4.2	7 3.3	19 56.7	4 36.1	14 16.6	20 35.2	6 48.5	4 45.5
14 F	5 28 22.1	21 26.7	1 59.7	16 34.6	11 19.3	7 57.8	20 22.0	4 28.6	14 14.7	20 37.3	6 47.4	4 44.3
15 S	5 32 18.6	22 27.8	1 56.6	0♑14.3	12 31.6	8 51.5	20 46.9	4 21.1	14 12.7	20 39.5	6 46.3	4 43.1
16 S	5 36 15.2	23 28.9	1 53.4	14 8.6	13 40.6	9 44.6	21 11.6	4 13.8	14 10.6	20 41.7	6 45.2	4 42.0
17 M	5 40 11.8	24 30.0	1 50.2	28 13.9	14 45.7	10 37.1	21 36.0	4 6.6	14 8.4	20 44.0	6 44.1	4 40.8
18 T	5 44 8.3	25 31.1	1 47.0	12♒26.6	15 46.4	11 28.8	22 0.1	3 59.5	14 6.0	20 46.3	6 42.9	4 39.6
19 W	5 48 4.9	26 32.2	1 43.9	26 42.8	16 42.0	12 19.7	22 23.9	3 52.5	14 3.6	20 48.6	6 41.7	4 38.4
20 T	5 52 1.4	27 33.3	1 40.7	10♓59.1	17 31.7	13 9.8	22 47.4	3 45.6	14 1.1	20 51.0	6 40.5	4 37.2
21 F	5 55 58.0	28 34.4	1 37.5	25 12.6	18 14.7	13 59.2	23 10.6	3 38.8	13 58.5	20 53.4	6 39.3	4 35.9
22 S	5 59 54.5	29 35.5	1 34.3	9♈21.0	18 50.1	14 47.6	23 33.5	3 32.2	13 55.7	20 55.8	6 38.0	4 34.7
23 S	6 3 51.1	0♑36.6	1 31.2	23 22.1	19 17.2	15 35.2	23 56.0	3 25.7	13 52.9	20 58.3	6 36.7	4 33.5
24 M	6 7 47.7	1 37.8	1 28.0	7♉14.5	19 34.9	16 21.8	24 18.3	3 19.3	13 50.0	21 0.8	6 35.4	4 32.3
25 T	6 11 44.2	2 38.9	1 24.8	20 56.6	19 42.3	17 7.5	24 40.2	3 13.1	13 47.0	21 3.4	6 34.1	4 31.1
26 W	6 15 40.8	3 40.0	1 21.6	4♊27.2	19R38.9	17 52.1	25 1.8	3 7.1	13 43.9	21 5.9	6 32.7	4 29.9
27 T	6 19 37.3	4 41.1	1 18.4	17 44.9	19 23.9	18 35.7	25 23.0	3 1.2	13 40.7	21 8.6	6 31.4	4 28.7
28 F	6 23 33.9	5 42.2	1 15.3	0♋49.0	18 57.0	19 18.2	25 43.9	2 55.4	13 37.5	21 11.2	6 30.0	4 27.5
29 S	6 27 30.5	6 43.4	1 12.1	13 38.8	18 18.4	19 59.5	26 4.4	2 49.8	13 34.1	21 13.9	6 28.6	4 26.2
30 S	6 31 27.0	7 44.5	1 8.9	26 14.4	17 28.6	20 39.6	26 24.6	2 44.4	13 30.7	21 16.6	6 27.2	4 25.0
31 M	6 35 23.6	8 45.6	1 5.7	8♌36.6	16 28.5	21 18.6	26 44.4	2 39.1	13 27.2	21 19.4	6 25.7	4 23.8
						DECLINATION						
1 S	4 37 6.8	21S41.4	23S25.4	22N58.3	25S28.7	23S50.5	7N60.0	20N28.7	17N10.1	15S25.7	18N22.0	18N45.7
4 T	4 48 56.5	22 8.5	23 25.6	13 35.6	25 44.4	23 8.2	7 30.5	20 24.9	17 11.2	15 24.0	18 22.6	18 45.9
7 F	5 0 46.2	22 31.8	23 25.7	0S16.0	25 47.1	22 21.8	7 1.6	20 21.1	17 12.6	15 22.3	18 23.3	18 46.0
10 M	5 12 35.9	22 51.0	23 25.9	14 8.5	25 36.8	21 31.6	6 33.5	20 17.4	17 14.3	15 20.3	18 24.0	18 46.2
13 T	5 24 25.5	23 6.3	23 26.0	23 15.9	25 13.6	20 38.1	6 6.2	20 13.7	17 16.2	15 18.3	18 24.7	18 46.4
16 S	5 36 15.2	23 17.4	23 26.2	21 32.7	24 38.6	19 41.7	5 39.9	20 10.2	17 18.5	15 16.1	18 25.6	18 46.6
19 W	5 48 4.9	23 24.3	23 26.3	8 31.6	23 53.8	18 42.9	5 14.5	20 6.8	17 21.0	15 13.9	18 26.5	18 46.8
22 S	5 59 54.5	23 26.9	23 26.4	8N31.1	23 2.7	17 42.3	4 50.3	20 3.6	17 23.8	15 11.5	18 27.4	18 47.1
25 T	6 11 44.2	23 25.4	23 26.5	21 19.2	22 10.4	16 40.4	4 27.2	20 0.7	17 26.7	15 9.0	18 28.4	18 47.3
28 F	6 23 33.9	23 19.6	23 26.6	23 30.9	21 22.5	15 37.7	4 5.4	19 57.9	17 30.0	15 6.4	18 29.5	18 47.6
31 M	6 35 23.6	23 9.6	23 26.7	15 2.2	20 43.8	14 35.0	3 44.8	19 55.4	17 33.4	15 3.7	18 30.6	18 47.9

JANUARY 1918

DAY	EPHEMERIS SIDEREAL TIME	☉	☊	☽	☿	♀	♂	♃	♄	♅	♆	♇
	h m s	° ′	° ′	° ′	° ′	° ′	° ′	° ′	° ′	° ′	° ′	° ′
						LONGITUDE						
1 T	6 39 20.1	9♑46.8	1♑ 2.6	20♌46.9	15♑19.7	21♒56.2	27♍ 3.8	2♊34.0	13♌23.6	21♒22.2	6♌24.3	4♋22.6
2 W	6 43 16.7	10 47.9	0 59.4	2♍47.7	14R 4.3	22 32.5	27 22.8	2R29.1	13R19.9	21 25.0	6R22.8	4R21.4
3 T	6 47 13.2	11 49.1	0 56.2	14 42.1	12 44.7	23 7.4	27 41.4	2 24.3	13 16.2	21 27.8	6 21.3	4 20.2
4 F	6 51 9.8	12 50.2	0 53.0	26 34.0	11 23.4	23 40.8	27 59.6	2 19.7	13 12.3	21 30.7	6 19.8	4 19.0
5 S	6 55 6.4	13 51.4	0 49.9	8♎27.5	10 3.2	24 12.8	28 17.4	2 15.3	13 8.4	21 33.6	6 18.2	4 17.8
6 S	6 59 2.9	14 52.5	0 46.7	20 27.4	8 46.6	24 43.2	28 34.7	2 11.1	13 4.5	21 36.5	6 16.7	4 16.6
7 M	7 2 59.5	15 53.7	0 43.5	2♏38.4	7 35.6	25 12.0	28 51.6	2 7.1	13 0.5	21 39.5	6 15.2	4 15.4
8 T	7 6 56.0	16 54.9	0 40.3	15 5.1	6 32.1	25 39.2	29 8.1	2 3.2	12 56.3	21 42.5	6 13.6	4 14.2
9 W	7 10 52.6	17 56.0	0 37.1	27 51.3	5 37.3	26 4.6	29 24.1	1 59.6	12 52.2	21 45.5	6 12.0	4 13.0
10 T	7 14 49.1	18 57.2	0 34.0	11♐ 0.2	4 52.0	26 28.1	29 39.6	1 56.1	12 48.0	21 48.5	6 10.4	4 11.8
11 F	7 18 45.7	19 58.4	0 30.8	24 33.2	4 16.5	26 49.9	29 54.6	1 52.9	12 43.7	21 51.6	6 8.8	4 10.7
12 S	7 22 42.3	20 59.5	0 27.6	8♑29.8	3 50.9	27 9.7	0♎ 9.2	1 49.8	12 39.3	21 54.7	6 7.2	4 9.5
13 S	7 26 38.8	22 0.7	0 24.4	22 47.4	3 35.0	27 27.5	0 23.2	1 46.9	12 34.9	21 57.8	6 5.6	4 8.4
14 M	7 30 35.4	23 1.8	0 21.3	7♒21.1	3 28.2	27 43.2	0 36.7	1 44.3	12 30.5	22 0.9	6 3.9	4 7.2
15 T	7 34 31.9	24 2.9	0 18.1	22 4.2	3D30.1	27 56.9	0 49.7	1 41.8	12 26.0	22 4.1	6 2.3	4 6.1
16 W	7 38 28.5	25 4.1	0 14.9	6♓49.3	3 40.1	28 8.3	1 2.2	1 39.5	12 21.4	22 7.2	6 0.6	4 5.0
17 T	7 42 25.1	26 5.2	0 11.7	21 29.2	3 57.5	28 17.4	1 14.1	1 37.5	12 16.9	22 10.4	5 59.0	4 3.8
18 F	7 46 21.6	27 6.3	0 8.6	5♈58.2	4 21.7	28 24.3	1 25.5	1 35.6	12 12.2	22 13.6	5 57.3	4 2.7
19 S	7 50 18.2	28 7.4	0 5.4	20 12.1	4 52.1	28 28.7	1 36.3	1 34.0	12 7.6	22 16.9	5 55.6	4 1.6
20 S	7 54 14.7	29 8.5	0 2.2	4♉ 8.8	5 28.0	28 30.8	1 46.5	1 32.5	12 2.9	22 20.1	5 54.0	4 0.5
21 M	7 58 11.3	0♒ 9.5	29♐59.0	17 48.0	6 9.0	28R30.4	1 56.1	1 31.3	11 58.1	22 23.4	5 52.3	3 59.5
22 T	8 2 7.8	1 10.5	29 55.9	1♊10.5	6 54.6	28 27.4	2 5.2	1 30.3	11 53.4	22 26.7	5 50.6	3 58.4
23 W	8 6 4.4	2 11.6	29 52.7	14 17.8	7 44.3	28 21.9	2 13.6	1 29.4	11 48.6	22 30.0	5 48.9	3 57.3
24 T	8 10 0.9	3 12.6	29 49.5	27 11.3	8 37.7	28 13.9	2 21.5	1 28.8	11 43.8	22 33.3	5 47.2	3 56.3
25 F	8 13 57.5	4 13.6	29 46.3	9♋52.8	9 34.5	28 3.4	2 28.7	1 28.4	11 38.9	22 36.6	5 45.6	3 55.3
26 S	8 17 54.1	5 14.5	29 43.1	22 23.4	10 34.4	27 50.3	2 35.2	1 28.2	11 34.1	22 40.0	5 43.9	3 54.2
27 S	8 21 50.6	6 15.5	29 40.0	4♌44.2	11 37.0	27 34.7	2 41.2	1 28.2	11 29.2	22 43.3	5 42.2	3 53.2
28 M	8 25 47.2	7 16.4	29 36.8	16 56.2	12 42.1	27 16.6	2 46.4	1D28.4	11 24.3	22 46.7	5 40.5	3 52.2
29 T	8 29 43.7	8 17.4	29 33.6	29 0.5	13 49.6	26 56.2	2 51.0	1 28.8	11 19.4	22 50.1	5 38.8	3 51.2
30 W	8 33 40.3	9 18.3	29 30.4	10♍58.4	14 59.2	26 33.5	2 54.9	1 29.4	11 14.5	22 53.5	5 37.1	3 50.3
31 T	8 37 36.9	10 19.2	29 27.3	22 51.9	16 10.7	26 8.5	2 58.2	1 30.2	11 9.6	22 56.9	5 35.4	3 49.3
						DECLINATION						
1 T	6 39 20.1	23S 5.4	23S26.7	10N46.4	20S33.4	14S14.1	3N38.3	19N54.7	17N34.5	15S 2.8	18N31.0	18N48.0
4 F	6 51 9.8	22 49.8	23 26.8	3S27.4	20 10.4	13 12.2	3 19.7	19 52.6	17 38.2	15 0.0	18 32.1	18 48.3
7 M	7 2 59.5	22 30.2	23 26.9	16 37.8	20 0.2	12 11.6	3 2.7	19 50.8	17 42.0	14 57.1	18 33.3	18 48.7
10 T	7 14 49.1	22 6.6	23 26.9	23 56.0	20 3.2	11 13.3	2 47.4	19 49.3	17 46.0	14 54.1	18 34.5	18 49.0
13 S	7 26 38.8	21 39.0	23 27.0	19 38.4	20 17.9	10 18.1	2 33.9	19 48.2	17 50.1	14 51.1	18 35.7	18 49.4
16 W	7 38 28.5	21 7.7	23 27.0	4 35.0	20 40.3	9 26.8	2 22.3	19 47.4	17 54.3	14 48.0	18 36.9	18 49.8
19 S	7 50 18.2	20 32.8	23 27.0	12N28.6	21 6.0	8 40.5	2 12.7	19 47.0	17 58.6	14 44.8	18 38.2	18 50.2
22 T	8 2 7.8	19 54.4	23 27.0	22 58.5	21 30.8	8 0.4	2 5.2	19 47.0	18 2.9	14 41.6	18 39.5	18 50.6
25 F	8 13 57.5	19 12.6	23 27.0	22 18.4	21 51.4	7 27.3	1 59.9	19 47.4	18 7.3	14 38.3	18 40.8	18 51.0
28 M	8 25 47.2	18 27.7	23 27.0	12 13.4	22 5.3	7 2.4	1 56.8	19 48.1	18 11.6	14 35.0	18 42.0	18 51.4
31 T	8 37 36.9	17 39.8	23 26.9	1S51.5	22 11.0	6 46.1	1 56.0	19 49.2	18 16.0	14 31.7	18 43.3	18 51.8

FEBRUARY 1918

						LONGITUDE						
1 F	8 41 33.4	11♒20.1	29♐24.1	4♎43.3	17♑23.9	25♒41.5	3♎ 0.7	1♊31.2	11♌ 4.7	23♒ 0.3	5♌33.7	3♋48.4
2 S	8 45 30.0	12 20.9	29 20.9	16 36.0	18 38.9	25R12.5	3 2.5	1 32.5	10R59.8	23 3.7	5R32.1	3R47.5
3 S	8 49 26.5	13 21.8	29 17.7	28 33.8	19 55.4	24 41.8	3 3.5	1 33.9	10 54.9	23 7.2	5 30.4	3 46.6
4 M	8 53 23.1	14 22.6	29 14.6	10♏41.1	21 13.3	24 9.5	3 3.9	1 35.5	10 50.0	23 10.6	5 28.7	3 45.7
5 T	8 57 19.6	15 23.5	29 11.4	23 2.6	22 32.6	23 35.7	3R 3.5	1 37.3	10 45.1	23 14.0	5 27.0	3 44.8
6 W	9 1 16.2	16 24.3	29 8.2	5♐43.3	23 53.2	23 0.8	3 2.3	1 39.3	10 40.2	23 17.5	5 25.4	3 44.0
7 T	9 5 12.7	17 25.1	29 5.0	18 47.5	25 14.9	22 25.0	3 0.4	1 41.6	10 35.4	23 20.9	5 23.7	3 43.1
8 F	9 9 9.3	18 25.9	29 1.8	2♑18.6	26 37.9	21 48.4	2 57.7	1 44.0	10 30.5	23 24.4	5 22.1	3 42.3
9 S	9 13 5.9	19 26.6	28 58.7	16 18.1	28 1.9	21 11.4	2 54.2	1 46.6	10 25.7	23 27.9	5 20.5	3 41.5
10 S	9 17 2.4	20 27.4	28 55.5	0♒44.9	29 27.0	20 34.2	2 49.9	1 49.4	10 20.9	23 31.3	5 18.8	3 40.7
11 M	9 20 58.9	21 28.1	28 52.3	15 34.6	0♒53.1	19 57.0	2 44.9	1 52.4	10 16.1	23 34.8	5 17.2	3 39.9
12 T	9 24 55.5	22 28.8	28 49.1	0♓39.6	2 20.3	19 20.1	2 39.1	1 55.6	10 11.3	23 38.3	5 15.6	3 39.2
13 W	9 28 52.1	23 29.5	28 46.0	15 50.2	3 48.4	18 43.7	2 32.4	1 59.0	10 6.6	23 41.8	5 14.0	3 38.5
14 T	9 32 48.6	24 30.1	28 42.8	0♈55.8	5 17.5	18 8.1	2 25.0	2 2.6	10 1.9	23 45.2	5 12.4	3 37.7
15 F	9 36 45.2	25 30.8	28 39.6	15 47.0	6 47.5	17 33.5	2 16.8	2 6.3	9 57.3	23 48.7	5 10.9	3 37.0
16 S	9 40 41.7	26 31.3	28 36.4	0♉17.1	8 18.5	17 0.2	2 7.8	2 10.3	9 52.7	23 52.2	5 9.3	3 36.4
17 S	9 44 38.3	27 31.9	28 33.2	14 22.5	9 50.3	16 28.3	1 58.0	2 14.4	9 48.1	23 55.6	5 7.8	3 35.7
18 M	9 48 34.8	28 32.4	28 30.1	28 2.6	11 23.1	15 58.0	1 47.5	2 18.8	9 43.6	23 59.1	5 6.2	3 35.1
19 T	9 52 31.4	29 33.0	28 26.9	11♊19.2	12 56.9	15 29.5	1 36.2	2 23.3	9 39.1	24 2.6	5 4.7	3 34.5
20 W	9 56 28.0	0♓33.4	28 23.7	24 15.2	14 31.5	15 2.9	1 24.1	2 27.9	9 34.7	24 6.0	5 3.2	3 33.9
21 T	10 0 24.5	1 33.9	28 20.5	6♋54.2	16 7.1	14 38.4	1 11.3	2 32.8	9 30.3	24 9.5	5 1.7	3 33.3
22 F	10 4 21.1	2 34.3	28 17.4	19 19.8	17 43.7	14 16.1	0 57.8	2 37.8	9 26.0	24 12.9	5 0.3	3 32.7
23 S	10 8 17.6	3 34.7	28 14.2	1♌35.0	19 21.2	13 56.1	0 43.5	2 43.0	9 21.7	24 16.4	4 58.8	3 32.2
24 S	10 12 14.2	4 35.0	28 11.0	13 42.5	20 59.6	13 38.5	0 28.5	2 48.4	9 17.5	24 19.8	4 57.4	3 31.7
25 M	10 16 10.7	5 35.3	28 7.8	25 44.1	22 39.0	13 23.3	0 12.8	2 54.0	9 13.4	24 23.2	4 56.0	3 31.2
26 T	10 20 7.3	6 35.6	28 4.6	7♍41.4	24 19.4	13 10.6	29♍56.4	2 59.7	9 9.3	24 26.6	4 54.6	3 30.7
27 W	10 24 3.8	7 35.9	28 1.5	19 35.8	26 0.8	13 0.3	29 39.4	3 5.6	9 5.3	24 30.0	4 53.2	3 30.3
28 T	10 28 0.4	8 36.1	27 58.3	1♎28.4	27 43.3	12 52.6	29 21.7	3 11.6	9 1.4	24 33.4	4 51.9	3 29.9
						DECLINATION						
1 F	8 41 33.4	17S23.2	23S26.9	6S35.7	22S10.8	6S42.8	1N56.3	19N49.6	18N17.5	14S30.5	18N43.7	18N52.0
4 M	8 53 23.1	16 31.5	23 26.9	18 46.8	22 3.6	6 38.7	1 58.9	19 51.2	18 21.8	14 27.1	18 45.0	18 52.4
7 T	9 5 12.7	15 37.2	23 26.8	24 1.4	21 45.8	6 43.5	2 4.0	19 53.1	18 26.1	14 23.7	18 46.2	18 52.9
10 S	9 17 2.4	14 40.6	23 26.7	17 28.4	21 16.9	6 56.4	2 11.7	19 55.4	18 30.3	14 20.3	18 47.5	18 53.3
13 W	9 28 52.1	13 41.7	23 26.7	1 2.0	20 36.6	7 16.1	2 22.0	19 58.0	18 34.4	14 16.9	18 48.7	18 53.8
16 S	9 40 41.7	12 40.8	23 26.6	15N41.2	19 44.6	7 41.0	2 34.8	20 0.9	18 38.3	14 13.4	18 49.9	18 54.2
19 T	9 52 31.4	11 38.1	23 26.5	23 44.7	18 40.7	8 9.3	2 50.1	20 4.2	18 42.2	14 10.0	18 51.0	18 54.7
22 F	10 4 21.1	10 33.8	23 26.3	20 21.8	17 24.8	8 39.3	3 7.6	20 7.7	18 45.9	14 6.6	18 52.1	18 55.2
25 M	10 16 10.7	9 28.0	23 26.2	8 59.5	15 56.9	9 9.1	3 27.2	20 11.4	18 49.4	14 3.2	18 53.2	18 55.7
28 T	10 28 0.4	8 20.9	23 26.1	5S11.0	14 16.9	9 37.5	3 48.7	20 15.5	18 52.7	13 59.8	18 54.2	18 56.2

MARCH 1918

DAY	EPHEMERIS SIDEREAL TIME h m s	☉ ° ′	☊ ° ′	☽ ° ′	☿ ° ′	♀ ° ′	♂ ° ′	♃ ° ′	♄ ° ′	♅ ° ′	♆ ° ′	♇ ° ′
						LONGITUDE						
1 F	10 31 56.9	9♓36.3	27♐55.1	13♎20.7	29♒26.7	12♒47.3	29♍ 3.4	3♓17.8	8♌57.5	24♒36.8	4♌50.5	3♋29.5
2 S	10 35 53.5	10 36.5	27 51.9	25 15.0	1♓11.2	12R44.5	28R44.5	3 24.2	8R53.7	24 40.2	4R49.2	3R29.1
3 S	10 39 50.0	11 36.7	27 48.8	7♏13.8	2 56.7	12 44.2	28 25.0	3 30.7	8 50.0	24 43.6	4 47.9	3 28.7
4 M	10 43 46.6	12 36.8	27 45.6	19 20.6	4 43.3	12D46.2	28 5.0	3 37.4	8 46.3	24 46.9	4 46.7	3 28.4
5 T	10 47 43.2	13 36.9	27 42.4	1♐39.5	6 31.0	12 50.7	27 44.5	3 44.3	8 42.7	24 50.3	4 45.4	3 28.1
6 W	10 51 39.7	14 37.0	27 39.2	14 15.2	8 19.8	12 57.4	27 23.5	3 51.2	8 39.2	24 53.6	4 44.2	3 27.8
7 T	10 55 36.2	15 37.0	27 36.0	27 12.3	10 9.6	13 6.5	27 2.1	3 58.4	8 35.8	24 56.9	4 43.0	3 27.5
8 F	10 59 32.8	16 37.0	27 32.9	10♑35.1	12 0.6	13 17.7	26 40.2	4 5.7	8 32.5	25 0.2	4 41.8	3 27.3
9 S	11 3 29.4	17 37.0	27 29.7	24 26.6	13 52.6	13 31.1	26 18.0	4 13.1	8 29.2	25 3.4	4 40.7	3 27.0
10 S	11 7 25.9	18 37.0	27 26.5	8♒47.6	15 45.7	13 46.5	25 55.5	4 20.7	8 26.0	25 6.7	4 39.6	3 26.8
11 M	11 11 22.5	19 36.9	27 23.3	23 35.6	17 39.9	14 4.0	25 32.6	4 28.5	8 23.0	25 9.9	4 38.5	3 26.7
12 T	11 15 19.0	20 36.9	27 20.2	8♓44.5	19 35.0	14 23.3	25 9.5	4 36.3	8 20.0	25 13.2	4 37.4	3 26.5
13 W	11 19 15.6	21 36.7	27 17.0	24 4.6	21 31.2	14 44.6	24 46.3	4 44.3	8 17.1	25 16.4	4 36.3	3 26.4
14 T	11 23 12.1	22 36.6	27 13.8	9♈24.3	23 28.2	15 7.7	24 22.8	4 52.5	8 14.3	25 19.6	4 35.3	3 26.3
15 F	11 27 8.7	23 36.4	27 10.6	24 31.9	25 26.1	15 32.5	23 59.3	5 0.8	8 11.6	25 22.7	4 34.3	3 26.2
16 S	11 31 5.2	24 36.2	27 7.4	9♉18.2	27 24.8	15 58.9	23 35.7	5 9.2	8 8.9	25 25.9	4 33.4	3 26.1
17 S	11 35 1.8	25 35.9	27 4.3	23 37.3	29 24.0	16 27.0	23 12.1	5 17.8	8 6.4	25 29.0	4 32.4	3 26.1
18 M	11 38 58.3	26 35.6	27 1.1	7♊27.2	1♈23.8	16 56.7	22 48.5	5 26.5	8 4.0	25 32.1	4 31.5	3 26.1
19 T	11 42 54.9	27 35.3	26 57.9	20 48.7	3 23.8	17 27.8	22 25.0	5 35.3	8 1.7	25 35.2	4 30.6	3D26.1
20 W	11 46 51.4	28 34.9	26 54.7	3♋45.2	5 24.0	18 0.3	22 1.7	5 44.2	7 59.4	25 38.2	4 29.8	3 26.1
21 T	11 50 48.0	29 34.5	26 51.5	16 20.8	7 24.1	18 34.3	21 38.5	5 53.3	7 57.3	25 41.2	4 28.9	3 26.2
22 F	11 54 44.5	0♈34.0	26 48.4	28 40.1	9 23.7	19 9.6	21 15.5	6 2.5	7 55.3	25 44.2	4 28.1	3 26.3
23 S	11 58 41.1	1 33.5	26 45.2	10♌47.7	11 22.7	19 46.1	20 52.8	6 11.8	7 53.4	25 47.2	4 27.4	3 26.4
24 S	12 2 37.7	2 33.0	26 42.0	22 47.4	13 20.7	20 23.9	20 30.4	6 21.2	7 51.6	25 50.2	4 26.6	3 26.5
25 M	12 6 34.2	3 32.5	26 38.8	4♍42.3	15 17.2	21 2.9	20 8.3	6 30.8	7 49.8	25 53.1	4 25.9	3 26.6
26 T	12 10 30.7	4 31.9	26 35.7	16 35.0	17 12.0	21 43.0	19 46.5	6 40.4	7 48.2	25 56.0	4 25.3	3 26.8
27 W	12 14 27.3	5 31.2	26 32.5	28 27.3	19 4.7	22 24.2	19 25.2	6 50.2	7 46.7	25 58.8	4 24.6	3 27.0
28 T	12 18 23.9	6 30.6	26 29.3	10♎20.8	20 54.8	23 6.5	19 4.4	7 0.1	7 45.3	26 1.7	4 24.0	3 27.2
29 F	12 22 20.4	7 29.9	26 26.1	22 16.7	22 41.9	23 49.8	18 44.0	7 10.1	7 44.0	26 4.5	4 23.4	3 27.5
30 S	12 26 17.0	8 29.1	26 23.0	4♏16.3	24 25.5	24 34.1	18 24.1	7 20.2	7 42.8	26 7.3	4 22.9	3 27.7
31 S	12 30 13.5	9 28.3	26 19.8	16 21.3	26 5.4	25 19.3	18 4.8	7 30.4	7 41.7	26 10.0	4 22.3	3 28.0
						DECLINATION						
1 F	10 31 56.9	7S58.3	23S26.0	9S44.3	13S40.9	9S46.5	3N56.3	20N16.8	18N53.8	13S58.6	18N54.6	18N56.3
4 M	10 43 46.6	6 49.8	23 25.9	20 36.6	11 44.8	10 11.1	4 19.9	20 21.2	18 56.8	13 55.3	18 55.5	18 56.8
7 T	10 55 36.2	5 40.4	23 25.7	23 29.6	9 37.0	10 32.1	4 44.6	20 25.7	18 59.7	13 52.0	18 56.5	18 57.3
10 S	11 7 25.9	4 30.3	23 25.5	14 53.4	7 17.8	10 48.8	5 10.0	20 30.4	19 2.4	13 48.7	18 57.3	18 57.8
13 W	11 19 15.6	3 19.7	23 25.3	2N14.0	4 47.9	11 0.8	5 35.6	20 35.3	19 4.8	13 45.5	18 58.1	18 58.2
16 S	11 31 5.2	2 8.7	23 25.1	18 6.9	2 8.7	11 8.0	6 1.0	20 40.4	19 7.0	13 42.4	18 58.9	18 58.7
19 T	11 42 54.9	0 57.6	23 24.9	23 39.5	0N37.6	11 10.2	6 25.5	20 45.5	19 8.9	13 39.3	18 59.6	18 59.2
22 F	11 54 44.5	0N13.5	23 24.7	17 49.8	3 27.6	11 7.3	6 48.9	20 50.8	19 10.6	13 36.3	19 0.2	18 59.7
25 M	12 6 34.2	1 24.5	23 24.4	5 27.5	6 16.5	10 59.2	7 10.6	20 56.2	19 12.0	13 33.4	19 0.8	19 0.1
28 T	12 18 23.9	2 35.1	23 24.2	8S32.5	8 58.3	10 46.0	7 30.3	21 1.6	19 13.2	13 30.5	19 1.3	19 0.6
31 S	12 30 13.5	3 45.3	23 23.9	19 45.3	11 26.6	10 27.7	7 47.8	21 7.1	19 14.2	13 27.8	19 1.8	19 1.0

APRIL 1918

DAY	EPHEMERIS SIDEREAL TIME h m s	☉ ° ′	☊ ° ′	☽ ° ′	☿ ° ′	♀ ° ′	♂ ° ′	♃ ° ′	♄ ° ′	♅ ° ′	♆ ° ′	♇ ° ′
						LONGITUDE						
1 M	12 34 10.1	10♈27.6	26♐16.6	28♏34.2	27♈41.1	26♒ 5.4	17♍46.0	7♓40.7	7♌40.8	26♒12.8	4♌21.9	3♋28.3
2 T	12 38 6.6	11 26.7	26 13.4	10♐57.6	29 12.3	26 52.3	17R27.9	7 51.1	7R39.9	26 15.5	4R21.4	3 28.7
3 W	12 42 3.2	12 25.9	26 10.2	23 35.1	0♉38.6	27 40.1	17 10.3	8 1.6	7 39.1	26 18.1	4 21.0	3 29.0
4 T	12 45 59.7	13 25.0	26 7.1	6♑30.7	1 59.7	28 28.7	16 53.4	8 12.2	7 38.5	26 20.7	4 20.6	3 29.4
5 F	12 49 56.3	14 24.1	26 3.9	19 48.0	3 15.4	29 18.1	16 37.1	8 22.9	7 37.9	26 23.3	4 20.2	3 29.8
6 S	12 53 52.8	15 23.1	26 0.7	3♒30.2	4 25.5	0♓ 8.2	16 21.6	8 33.7	7 37.5	26 25.9	4 19.9	3 30.2
7 S	12 57 49.4	16 22.1	25 57.5	17 39.1	5 29.7	0 59.0	16 6.7	8 44.6	7 37.2	26 28.4	4 19.6	3 30.7
8 M	13 1 45.9	17 21.1	25 54.4	2♓13.6	6 27.8	1 50.5	15 52.6	8 55.6	7 36.9	26 30.9	4 19.3	3 31.1
9 T	13 5 42.5	18 20.1	25 51.2	17 9.9	7 19.7	2 42.6	15 39.2	9 6.6	7 36.8	26 33.4	4 19.1	3 31.6
10 W	13 9 39.0	19 19.0	25 48.0	2♈20.4	8 5.4	3 35.4	15 26.5	9 17.8	7D36.8	26 35.8	4 18.9	3 32.1
11 T	13 13 35.6	20 17.9	25 44.8	17 35.0	8 44.7	4 28.7	15 14.7	9 29.1	7 36.9	26 38.2	4 18.7	3 32.7
12 F	13 17 32.2	21 16.8	25 41.6	2♉42.8	9 17.4	5 22.7	15 3.6	9 40.4	7 37.2	26 40.5	4 18.6	3 33.2
13 S	13 21 28.7	22 15.6	25 38.5	17 33.6	9 43.7	6 17.1	14 53.2	9 51.8	7 37.5	26 42.8	4 18.5	3 33.8
14 S	13 25 25.2	23 14.4	25 35.3	2♊ 0.2	10 3.6	7 12.1	14 43.7	10 3.3	7 37.9	26 45.1	4 18.4	3 34.4
15 M	13 29 21.8	24 13.2	25 32.1	15 58.6	10 17.0	8 7.6	14 35.0	10 14.9	7 38.5	26 47.3	4 18.4	3 35.0
16 T	13 33 18.4	25 11.9	25 28.9	29 28.2	10 24.0	9 3.7	14 27.0	10 26.6	7 39.1	26 49.5	4D18.4	3 35.7
17 W	13 37 14.9	26 10.6	25 25.8	12♋31.0	10 24.9	10 0.1	14 19.9	10 38.3	7 39.9	26 51.7	4 18.5	3 36.3
18 T	13 41 11.5	27 9.3	25 22.6	25 10.4	10R19.8	10 57.1	14 13.6	10 50.1	7 40.8	26 53.8	4 18.5	3 37.0
19 F	13 45 8.0	28 7.9	25 19.4	7♌31.3	10 8.9	11 54.4	14 8.0	11 2.0	7 41.8	26 55.9	4 18.6	3 37.7
20 S	13 49 4.6	29 6.5	25 16.2	19 38.3	9 52.6	12 52.2	14 3.3	11 14.0	7 42.9	26 57.9	4 18.8	3 38.4
21 S	13 53 1.1	0♉ 5.0	25 13.0	1♍36.2	9 31.4	13 50.4	13 59.3	11 26.0	7 44.1	26 59.9	4 18.9	3 39.2
22 M	13 56 57.7	1 3.5	25 9.9	13 29.1	9 5.6	14 49.0	13 56.1	11 38.1	7 45.4	27 1.9	4 19.2	3 40.0
23 T	14 0 54.2	2 2.0	25 6.7	25 20.5	8 35.8	15 48.0	13 53.7	11 50.2	7 46.8	27 3.8	4 19.4	3 40.7
24 W	14 4 50.8	3 0.4	25 3.5	7♎13.4	8 2.7	16 47.4	13 52.0	12 2.5	7 48.3	27 5.7	4 19.7	3 41.5
25 T	14 8 47.4	3 58.8	25 0.3	19 9.9	7 26.7	17 47.1	13 51.1	12 14.8	7 49.9	27 7.5	4 20.0	3 42.4
26 F	14 12 43.9	4 57.2	24 57.2	1♏11.7	6 48.8	18 47.2	13 51.0	12 27.1	7 51.6	27 9.3	4 20.3	3 43.2
27 S	14 16 40.5	5 55.6	24 54.0	13 20.3	6 9.5	19 47.6	13D51.6	12 39.5	7 53.5	27 11.0	4 20.7	3 44.1
28 S	14 20 37.0	6 53.9	24 50.8	25 36.7	5 29.5	20 48.4	13 52.9	12 52.0	7 55.4	27 12.7	4 21.1	3 44.9
29 M	14 24 33.6	7 52.2	24 47.6	8♐ 2.4	4 49.8	21 49.5	13 55.0	13 4.5	7 57.4	27 14.4	4 21.5	3 45.8
30 T	14 28 30.1	8 50.4	24 44.4	20 38.8	4 10.8	22 50.8	13 57.7	13 17.1	7 59.6	27 16.0	4 22.0	3 46.7
						DECLINATION						
1 M	12 34 10.1	4N 8.6	23S23.8	22S 2.7	12N12.0	10S20.5	7N53.0	21N 9.0	19N14.4	13S26.9	19N 1.9	19N 1.2
4 T	12 45 59.7	5 17.9	23 23.6	22 16.6	14 13.4	9 55.6	8 7.1	21 14.5	19 15.0	13 24.2	19 2.2	19 1.6
7 S	12 57 49.4	6 26.4	23 23.3	11 42.7	15 49.7	9 26.0	8 18.5	21 20.1	19 15.3	13 21.7	19 2.5	19 2.0
10 W	13 9 39.0	7 33.9	23 23.0	5N31.0	16 58.5	8 51.9	8 27.1	21 25.6	19 15.4	13 19.3	19 2.7	19 2.4
13 S	13 21 28.7	8 40.2	23 22.7	19 58.6	17 38.3	8 13.5	8 32.8	21 31.1	19 15.2	13 16.9	19 2.9	19 2.8
16 T	13 33 18.4	9 45.3	23 22.4	22 57.6	17 48.2	7 31.0	8 35.6	21 36.6	19 14.8	13 14.7	19 2.9	19 3.2
19 F	13 45 8.0	10 48.9	23 22.0	14 59.5	17 28.6	6 44.6	8 35.7	21 42.1	19 14.1	13 12.6	19 2.9	19 3.6
22 M	13 56 57.7	11 50.8	23 21.7	1 51.7	16 41.6	5 54.7	8 33.0	21 47.4	19 13.1	13 10.7	19 2.9	19 4.0
25 T	14 8 47.4	12 51.1	23 21.3	11S45.2	15 32.2	5 1.5	8 27.7	21 52.7	19 11.9	13 8.9	19 2.7	19 4.4
28 S	14 20 37.0	13 49.4	23 21.0	21 27.9	14 8.6	4 5.2	8 20.0	21 57.9	19 10.5	13 7.2	19 2.5	19 4.7

MAY 1918

DAY	EPHEMERIS SIDEREAL TIME h m s	☉ ° ′	☊ ° ′	☽ ° ′	☿ ° ′	♀ ° ′	♂ ° ′	♃ ° ′	♄ ° ′	♅ ° ′	♆ ° ′	♇ ° ′
						LONGITUDE						
1 W	14 32 26.7	9♉48.7	24♐41.3	3♑27.9	3♉33.4	23♓52.5	14♍ 1.2	13♊29.7	8♌ 1.8	27♒17.6	4♌22.5	3♋47.7
2 T	14 36 23.2	10 46.9	24 38.1	16 31.8	2R58.0	24 54.5	14 5.4	13 42.4	8 4.1	27 19.1	4 23.0	3 48.6
3 F	14 40 19.8	11 45.0	24 34.9	29 52.9	2 25.3	25 56.7	14 10.2	13 55.2	8 6.6	27 20.6	4 23.6	3 49.6
4 S	14 44 16.3	12 43.2	24 31.7	13♒33.1	1 55.9	26 59.3	14 15.7	14 8.0	8 9.1	27 22.0	4 24.2	3 50.6
5 S	14 48 12.9	13 41.3	24 28.6	27 33.4	1 30.0	28 2.0	14 21.9	14 20.8	8 11.8	27 23.4	4 24.8	3 51.6
6 M	14 52 9.5	14 39.5	24 25.4	11♓53.4	1 8.0	29 5.1	14 28.8	14 33.7	8 14.5	27 24.8	4 25.5	3 52.6
7 T	14 56 6.0	15 37.5	24 22.2	26 30.4	0 50.2	0♈ 8.3	14 36.3	14 46.7	8 17.3	27 26.1	4 26.2	3 53.6
8 W	15 0 2.6	16 35.6	24 19.0	11♈19.5	0 36.8	1 11.9	14 44.4	14 59.7	8 20.3	27 27.3	4 26.9	3 54.7
9 T	15 3 59.1	17 33.7	24 15.8	26 13.5	0 28.0	2 15.6	14 53.2	15 12.7	8 23.3	27 28.5	4 27.6	3 55.8
10 F	15 7 55.7	18 31.7	24 12.7	11♉ 4.2	0 23.8	3 19.5	15 2.6	15 25.8	8 26.4	27 29.7	4 28.4	3 56.8
11 S	15 11 52.2	19 29.7	24 9.5	25 43.2	0D24.2	4 23.7	15 12.6	15 38.9	8 29.6	27 30.8	4 29.2	3 57.9
12 S	15 15 48.8	20 27.6	24 6.3	10♊ 3.7	0 29.3	5 28.0	15 23.1	15 52.1	8 33.0	27 31.9	4 30.1	3 59.1
13 M	15 19 45.3	21 25.6	24 3.1	24 1.0	0 39.0	6 32.6	15 34.3	16 5.3	8 36.4	27 32.9	4 31.0	4 0.2
14 T	15 23 41.9	22 23.5	23 60.0	7♋33.1	0 53.3	7 37.3	15 46.1	16 18.6	8 39.9	27 33.8	4 31.9	4 1.3
15 W	15 27 38.5	23 21.4	23 56.8	20 40.1	1 12.1	8 42.2	15 58.4	16 31.8	8 43.5	27 34.8	4 32.8	4 2.5
16 T	15 31 35.0	24 19.2	23 53.6	3♌24.2	1 35.2	9 47.3	16 11.3	16 45.2	8 47.2	27 35.6	4 33.8	4 3.7
17 F	15 35 31.5	25 17.0	23 50.4	15 49.1	2 2.6	10 52.6	16 24.7	16 58.5	8 50.9	27 36.5	4 34.8	4 4.8
18 S	15 39 28.1	26 14.8	23 47.2	27 59.1	2 34.1	11 58.0	16 38.7	17 11.9	8 54.8	27 37.2	4 35.8	4 6.0
19 S	15 43 24.7	27 12.6	23 44.1	9♍58.6	3 9.7	13 3.6	16 53.1	17 25.3	8 58.7	27 38.0	4 36.9	4 7.3
20 M	15 47 21.2	28 10.3	23 40.9	21 52.4	3 49.1	14 9.4	17 8.1	17 38.7	9 2.8	27 38.7	4 38.0	4 8.5
21 T	15 51 17.8	29 8.1	23 37.7	3♎44.8	4 32.4	15 15.3	17 23.6	17 52.2	9 6.9	27 39.3	4 39.1	4 9.7
22 W	15 55 14.3	0♊ 5.7	23 34.5	15 39.5	5 19.2	16 21.4	17 39.6	18 5.7	9 11.1	27 39.9	4 40.3	4 11.0
23 T	15 59 10.9	1 3.4	23 31.4	27 40.0	6 9.6	17 27.6	17 56.0	18 19.2	9 15.4	27 40.4	4 41.4	4 12.2
24 F	16 3 7.4	2 1.1	23 28.2	9♏48.7	7 3.5	18 34.0	18 12.9	18 32.8	9 19.8	27 40.9	4 42.6	4 13.5
25 S	16 7 4.0	2 58.7	23 25.0	22 7.7	8 0.6	19 40.5	18 30.3	18 46.4	9 24.2	27 41.3	4 43.9	4 14.8
26 S	16 11 0.6	3 56.3	23 21.8	4♐38.4	9 1.1	20 47.1	18 48.1	18 59.9	9 28.8	27 41.7	4 45.1	4 16.1
27 M	16 14 57.1	4 53.9	23 18.7	17 21.5	10 4.6	21 53.9	19 6.3	19 13.6	9 33.4	27 42.0	4 46.4	4 17.4
28 T	16 18 53.7	5 51.4	23 15.5	0♑17.6	11 11.3	23 0.8	19 25.0	19 27.2	9 38.1	27 42.3	4 47.7	4 18.7
29 W	16 22 50.2	6 49.0	23 12.3	13 26.9	12 20.9	24 7.9	19 44.1	19 40.9	9 42.8	27 42.6	4 49.1	4 20.0
30 T	16 26 46.8	7 46.5	23 9.1	26 49.6	13 33.5	25 15.1	20 3.6	19 54.5	9 47.7	27 42.8	4 50.4	4 21.4
31 F	16 30 43.3	8 44.0	23 5.9	10♒25.6	14 49.0	26 22.4	20 23.5	20 8.2	9 52.6	27 42.9	4 51.8	4 22.7
						DECLINATION						
1 W	14 32 26.7	14N45.7	23S20.6	22S27.2	12N41.1	3S 6.1	8N 9.9	22N 3.0	19N 8.8	13S 5.6	19N 2.2	19N 5.0
4 S	14 44 16.3	15 39.8	23 20.2	12 55.3	11 20.2	2 4.5	7 57.5	22 8.0	19 6.9	13 4.2	19 1.8	19 5.3
7 T	14 56 6.0	16 31.5	23 19.8	3N21.0	10 14.2	1 0.8	7 43.0	22 12.8	19 4.7	13 2.9	19 1.4	19 5.6
10 F	15 7 55.7	17 20.9	23 19.4	18 25.4	9 28.4	0N 4.8	7 26.5	22 17.5	19 2.3	13 1.8	19 0.9	19 5.9
13 M	15 19 45.3	18 7.6	23 19.0	23 10.4	9 4.9	1 12.0	7 8.0	22 22.0	18 59.7	13 0.8	19 0.4	19 6.2
16 T	15 31 35.0	18 51.5	23 18.5	16 4.1	9 3.5	2 20.4	6 47.6	22 26.4	18 56.8	12 59.9	18 59.7	19 6.4
19 S	15 43 24.7	19 32.6	23 18.1	3 6.0	9 22.8	3 29.7	6 25.6	22 30.6	18 53.7	12 59.2	18 59.0	19 6.7
22 W	15 55 14.3	20 10.8	23 17.6	10S35.9	10 0.5	4 39.7	6 1.9	22 34.6	18 50.4	12 58.7	18 58.3	19 6.9
25 S	16 7 4.0	20 45.8	23 17.1	20 51.3	10 54.2	5 50.0	5 36.7	22 38.5	18 46.9	12 58.3	18 57.4	19 7.1
28 T	16 18 53.7	21 17.6	23 16.7	22 42.4	12 1.3	7 0.4	5 10.1	22 42.1	18 43.2	12 58.1	18 56.6	19 7.3
31 F	16 30 43.3	21 46.1	23 16.2	13 50.7	13 19.4	8 10.5	4 42.1	22 45.6	18 39.3	12 58.0	18 55.6	19 7.4

JUNE 1918

DAY	SIDEREAL TIME	☉	☊	☽	☿	♀	♂	♃	♄	♅	♆	♇
						LONGITUDE						
1 S	16 34 39.9	9♊41.5	23♐ 2.8	24♒14.5	16♉ 7.3	27♈29.8	20♍43.8	20♊21.9	9♌57.6	27♒43.0	4♌53.2	4♋24.1
2 S	16 38 36.5	10 39.0	22 59.6	8♓15.8	17 28.4	28 37.4	21 4.5	20 35.7	10 2.7	27 43.0	4 54.7	4 25.5
3 M	16 42 33.0	11 36.5	22 56.4	22 28.1	18 52.3	29 45.0	21 25.6	20 49.4	10 7.8	27 43.0	4 56.2	4 26.8
4 T	16 46 29.5	12 33.9	22 53.2	6♈49.2	20 18.9	0♉52.8	21 47.0	21 3.2	10 13.0	27R43.0	4 57.6	4 28.2
5 W	16 50 26.1	13 31.4	22 50.1	21 15.7	21 48.2	2 0.7	22 8.9	21 16.9	10 18.3	27 42.9	4 59.1	4 29.6
6 T	16 54 22.7	14 28.8	22 46.9	5♉43.4	23 20.2	3 8.7	22 31.0	21 30.7	10 23.7	27 42.7	5 0.7	4 31.0
7 F	16 58 19.3	15 26.2	22 43.7	20 7.4	24 54.9	4 16.8	22 53.6	21 44.5	10 29.1	27 42.5	5 2.3	4 32.4
8 S	17 2 15.8	16 23.7	22 40.5	4♊22.5	26 32.2	5 25.0	23 16.5	21 58.3	10 34.6	27 42.3	5 3.8	4 33.8
9 S	17 6 12.3	17 21.1	22 37.4	18 24.0	28 12.2	6 33.3	23 39.8	22 12.1	10 40.2	27 42.0	5 5.5	4 35.2
10 M	17 10 8.9	18 18.5	22 34.2	2♋ 8.1	29 54.8	7 41.7	24 3.3	22 25.9	10 45.8	27 41.7	5 7.1	4 36.7
11 T	17 14 5.5	19 15.8	22 31.0	15 32.5	1♊40.0	8 50.1	24 27.3	22 39.7	10 51.5	27 41.3	5 8.7	4 38.1
12 W	17 18 2.0	20 13.2	22 27.8	28 36.5	3 27.8	9 58.7	24 51.5	22 53.5	10 57.3	27 40.8	5 10.4	4 39.5
13 T	17 21 58.6	21 10.6	22 24.7	11♌20.6	5 18.1	11 7.4	25 16.1	23 7.3	11 3.1	27 40.3	5 12.1	4 41.0
14 F	17 25 55.1	22 7.9	22 21.5	23 47.0	7 10.9	12 16.1	25 41.0	23 21.1	11 9.0	27 39.8	5 13.8	4 42.4
15 S	17 29 51.7	23 5.2	22 18.3	5♍58.9	9 6.2	13 24.9	26 6.1	23 35.0	11 14.9	27 39.2	5 15.6	4 43.9
16 S	17 33 48.2	24 2.5	22 15.1	18 0.2	11 3.8	14 33.8	26 31.6	23 48.8	11 20.9	27 38.6	5 17.3	4 45.3
17 M	17 37 44.8	24 59.8	22 12.0	29 55.1	13 3.6	15 42.8	26 57.4	24 2.6	11 27.0	27 37.9	5 19.1	4 46.8
18 T	17 41 41.4	25 57.1	22 8.8	11♎48.3	15 5.5	16 51.8	27 23.5	24 16.4	11 33.1	27 37.2	5 20.9	4 48.2
19 W	17 45 37.9	26 54.3	22 5.6	23 44.4	17 9.4	18 1.0	27 49.8	24 30.2	11 39.3	27 36.5	5 22.7	4 49.7
20 T	17 49 34.5	27 51.6	22 2.4	5♏47.4	19 15.0	19 10.2	28 16.5	24 44.0	11 45.5	27 35.6	5 24.6	4 51.2
21 F	17 53 31.0	28 48.8	21 59.2	18 1.3	21 22.3	20 19.5	28 43.4	24 57.8	11 51.8	27 34.8	5 26.4	4 52.6
22 S	17 57 27.6	29 46.1	21 56.1	0♐29.0	23 30.8	21 28.9	29 10.5	25 11.6	11 58.2	27 33.9	5 28.3	4 54.1
23 S	18 1 24.2	0♋43.3	21 52.9	13 12.8	25 40.5	22 38.3	29 37.9	25 25.3	12 4.6	27 33.0	5 30.2	4 55.6
24 M	18 5 20.7	1 40.5	21 49.7	26 13.8	27 50.9	23 47.8	0♎ 5.6	25 39.1	12 11.0	27 32.0	5 32.1	4 57.1
25 T	18 9 17.3	2 37.7	21 46.5	9♑32.0	0♋ 1.9	24 57.4	0 33.5	25 52.8	12 17.5	27 30.9	5 34.0	4 58.5
26 W	18 13 13.8	3 34.9	21 43.4	23 6.4	2 13.2	26 7.1	1 1.7	26 6.6	12 24.0	27 29.9	5 35.9	5 0.0
27 T	18 17 10.4	4 32.1	21 40.2	6♒55.0	4 24.5	27 16.9	1 30.1	26 20.3	12 30.6	27 28.8	5 37.9	5 1.5
28 F	18 21 6.9	5 29.3	21 37.0	20 55.0	6 35.4	28 26.7	1 58.8	26 34.0	12 37.3	27 27.6	5 39.9	5 3.0
29 S	18 25 3.5	6 26.5	21 33.8	5♓ 3.1	8 45.8	29 36.6	2 27.6	26 47.7	12 44.0	27 26.4	5 41.8	5 4.5
30 S	18 29 0.1	7 23.7	21 30.7	19 16.2	10 55.4	0♊46.6	2 56.8	27 1.4	12 50.7	27 25.2	5 43.8	5 5.9
						DECLINATION						
1 S	16 34 39.9	21N54.8	23S16.0	9S 3.0	13N47.5	8N33.7	4N32.5	22N46.7	18N38.0	12S58.0	18N55.3	19N 7.5
4 T	16 46 29.5	22 18.8	23 15.5	7N23.6	15 16.3	9 43.0	4 2.8	22 49.8	18 33.8	12 58.1	18 54.3	19 7.6
7 F	16 58 19.3	22 39.2	23 15.0	20 29.2	16 50.2	10 51.2	3 31.9	22 52.8	18 29.5	12 58.4	18 53.2	19 7.7
10 M	17 10 8.9	22 56.1	23 14.5	22 31.2	18 25.8	11 58.1	2 59.8	22 55.6	18 24.9	12 58.8	18 52.1	19 7.8
13 T	17 21 58.6	23 9.3	23 13.9	13 32.2	19 59.7	13 3.3	2 26.7	22 58.1	18 20.2	12 59.3	18 50.9	19 7.9
16 S	17 33 48.2	23 18.9	23 13.4	0S 6.4	21 27.4	14 6.5	1 52.6	23 0.4	18 15.3	13 0.0	18 49.7	19 8.0
19 W	17 45 37.9	23 24.8	23 12.8	13 24.2	22 43.8	15 7.4	1 17.5	23 2.5	18 10.3	13 0.9	18 48.4	19 8.0
22 S	17 57 27.6	23 26.9	23 12.2	22 10.8	23 43.6	16 5.7	0 41.5	23 4.4	18 5.1	13 1.9	18 47.1	19 8.1
25 T	18 9 17.3	23 25.4	23 11.6	21 32.5	24 22.0	17 1.1	0 4.8	23 6.1	17 59.7	13 3.0	18 45.7	19 8.1
28 F	18 21 6.9	23 20.1	23 11.0	10 15.6	24 35.8	17 53.2	0S32.7	23 7.5	17 54.2	13 4.2	18 44.3	19 8.1

JULY 1918

LONGITUDE

DAY	EPHEMERIS SIDEREAL TIME h m s	☉ ° ′	☊ ° ′	☽ ° ′	☿ ° ′	♀ ° ′	♂ ° ′	♃ ° ′	♄ ° ′	♅ ° ′	♆ ° ′	♇ ° ′
1 M	18 32 56.6	8♋20.9	21♐27.5	3♈31.0	13♋ 4.0	1♊56.6	3♎26.1	27♊15.0	12♌57.5	27♒23.9	5♌45.9	5♋ 7.4
2 T	18 36 53.2	9 18.1	21 24.3	17 44.9	15 11.5	3 6.7	3 55.7	27 28.7	13 4.3	27R22.6	5 47.9	5 8.9
3 W	18 40 49.7	10 15.3	21 21.1	1♉55.3	17 17.6	4 16.9	4 25.5	27 42.3	13 11.1	27 21.2	5 49.9	5 10.4
4 T	18 44 46.3	11 12.6	21 17.9	16 0.3	19 22.2	5 27.1	4 55.5	27 55.9	13 18.0	27 19.8	5 52.0	5 11.8
5 F	18 48 42.9	12 9.8	21 14.8	29 57.6	21 25.2	6 37.5	5 25.7	28 9.5	13 25.0	27 18.4	5 54.1	5 13.3
6 S	18 52 39.4	13 7.0	21 11.6	13♊45.3	23 26.5	7 47.9	5 56.2	28 23.1	13 32.0	27 16.9	5 56.1	5 14.8
7 S	18 56 36.0	14 4.2	21 8.4	27 21.5	25 26.0	8 58.3	6 26.8	28 36.6	13 39.0	27 15.4	5 58.2	5 16.3
8 M	19 0 32.5	15 1.5	21 5.2	10♋44.5	27 23.7	10 8.8	6 57.7	28 50.1	13 46.0	27 13.8	6 0.3	5 17.7
9 T	19 4 29.1	15 58.7	21 2.1	23 52.8	29 19.6	11 19.4	7 28.8	29 3.6	13 53.1	27 12.3	6 2.4	5 19.2
10 W	19 8 25.6	16 55.9	20 58.9	6♌45.6	1♌13.6	12 30.0	8 0.1	29 17.0	14 0.3	27 10.6	6 4.6	5 20.6
11 T	19 12 22.2	17 53.2	20 55.7	19 23.0	3 5.7	13 40.7	8 31.6	29 30.4	14 7.4	27 9.0	6 6.7	5 22.1
12 F	19 16 18.8	18 50.4	20 52.5	1♍45.9	4 55.8	14 51.4	9 3.2	29 43.8	14 14.6	27 7.3	6 8.8	5 23.5
13 S	19 20 15.3	19 47.6	20 49.4	13 56.2	6 44.1	16 2.2	9 35.1	29 57.2	14 21.8	27 5.6	6 11.0	5 25.0
14 S	19 24 11.8	20 44.9	20 46.2	25 56.8	8 30.4	17 13.1	10 7.2	0♋10.5	14 29.1	27 3.8	6 13.1	5 26.4
15 M	19 28 8.4	21 42.1	20 43.0	7♎51.2	10 14.8	18 24.0	10 39.4	0 23.8	14 36.4	27 2.0	6 15.3	5 27.8
16 T	19 32 5.0	22 39.4	20 39.8	19 43.7	11 57.3	19 35.0	11 11.9	0 37.1	14 43.7	27 0.2	6 17.5	5 29.3
17 W	19 36 1.6	23 36.6	20 36.7	1♏39.0	13 37.8	20 46.0	11 44.5	0 50.3	14 51.0	26 58.3	6 19.6	5 30.7
18 T	19 39 58.1	24 33.8	20 33.5	13 41.9	15 16.4	21 57.1	12 17.3	1 3.4	14 58.4	26 56.5	6 21.8	5 32.1
19 F	19 43 54.6	25 31.1	20 30.3	25 57.0	16 53.2	23 8.2	12 50.2	1 16.6	15 5.8	26 54.5	6 24.0	5 33.5
20 S	19 47 51.2	26 28.3	20 27.1	8♐28.8	18 28.0	24 19.4	13 23.4	1 29.7	15 13.2	26 52.6	6 26.2	5 34.9
21 S	19 51 47.8	27 25.6	20 23.9	21 20.6	20 0.9	25 30.7	13 56.7	1 42.7	15 20.7	26 50.6	6 28.4	5 36.3
22 M	19 55 44.3	28 22.9	20 20.8	4♑34.7	21 31.8	26 42.0	14 30.1	1 55.7	15 28.1	26 48.6	6 30.6	5 37.7
23 T	19 59 40.9	29 20.1	20 17.6	18 11.5	23 0.8	27 53.4	15 3.8	2 8.7	15 35.6	26 46.6	6 32.8	5 39.1
24 W	20 3 37.4	0♌17.4	20 14.4	2♒ 9.5	24 27.8	29 4.8	15 37.6	2 21.6	15 43.1	26 44.6	6 35.0	5 40.4
25 T	20 7 34.0	1 14.7	20 11.2	16 25.2	25 52.9	0♋16.3	16 11.5	2 34.5	15 50.6	26 42.5	6 37.3	5 41.8
26 F	20 11 30.5	2 12.0	20 8.1	0♓53.1	27 15.9	1 27.8	16 45.6	2 47.3	15 58.2	26 40.4	6 39.5	5 43.1
27 S	20 15 27.1	3 9.3	20 4.9	15 27.0	28 36.9	2 39.4	17 19.9	3 0.1	16 5.7	26 38.3	6 41.7	5 44.5
28 S	20 19 23.7	4 6.6	20 1.7	0♈ 0.5	29 55.8	3 51.1	17 54.3	3 12.8	16 13.3	26 36.2	6 43.9	5 45.8
29 M	20 23 20.2	5 4.0	19 58.5	14 27.9	1♍12.5	5 2.8	18 28.9	3 25.5	16 20.9	26 34.0	6 46.1	5 47.1
30 T	20 27 16.8	6 1.4	19 55.4	28 45.2	2 27.1	6 14.6	19 3.7	3 38.2	16 28.5	26 31.8	6 48.4	5 48.4
31 W	20 31 13.3	6 58.7	19 52.2	12♉50.0	3 39.4	7 26.5	19 38.5	3 50.7	16 36.1	26 29.6	6 50.6	5 49.7

DECLINATION

DAY	SIDEREAL TIME	☉	☊	☽	☿	♀	♂	♃	♄	♅	♆	♇
1 M	18 32 56.6	23N11.2	23S10.4	6N 7.8	24N24.4	18N41.8	1S11.0	23N 8.7	17N48.5	13S 5.6	18N42.9	19N 8.1
4 T	18 44 46.3	22 58.6	23 9.8	19 36.6	23 49.3	19 26.5	1 49.8	23 9.7	17 42.7	13 7.1	18 41.4	19 8.0
7 S	18 56 36.0	22 42.3	23 9.2	22 57.1	22 53.6	20 7.2	2 29.3	23 10.5	17 36.8	13 8.7	18 39.9	19 8.0
10 W	19 8 25.6	22 22.6	23 8.5	15 1.8	21 40.8	20 43.4	3 9.4	23 11.1	17 30.8	13 10.4	18 38.4	19 7.9
13 S	19 20 15.3	21 59.3	23 7.9	1 33.2	20 14.8	21 14.9	3 49.9	23 11.5	17 24.6	13 12.2	18 36.8	19 7.8
16 T	19 32 5.0	21 32.7	23 7.2	11S59.0	18 38.8	21 41.5	4 30.9	23 11.6	17 18.3	13 14.2	18 35.3	19 7.8
19 F	19 43 54.6	21 2.8	23 6.6	21 28.0	16 55.8	22 3.0	5 12.2	23 11.6	17 12.0	13 16.2	18 33.7	19 7.6
22 M	19 55 44.3	20 29.6	23 5.9	22 13.7	15 8.4	22 19.2	5 53.8	23 11.4	17 5.5	13 18.2	18 32.1	19 7.5
25 T	20 7 34.0	19 53.4	23 5.2	11 53.8	13 18.8	22 29.9	6 35.7	23 11.0	16 59.0	13 20.4	18 30.4	19 7.4
28 S	20 19 23.7	19 14.2	23 4.5	4N40.5	11 29.1	22 35.1	7 17.8	23 10.4	16 52.4	13 22.6	18 28.8	19 7.3
31 W	20 31 13.3	18 32.2	23 3.8	18 45.3	9 41.3	22 34.5	7 60.0	23 9.6	16 45.7	13 24.9	18 27.1	19 7.1

AUGUST 1918

LONGITUDE

DAY	EPHEMERIS SIDEREAL TIME h m s	☉ ° ′	☊ ° ′	☽ ° ′	☿ ° ′	♀ ° ′	♂ ° ′	♃ ° ′	♄ ° ′	♅ ° ′	♆ ° ′	♇ ° ′
1 T	20 35 9.9	7♌56.1	19♐49.0	26♉41.2	4♍49.5	8♋38.4	20♎13.6	4♋ 3.2	16♌43.7	26♒27.4	6♌52.8	5♋51.0
2 F	20 39 6.4	8 53.6	19 45.8	10♊18.8	5 57.1	9 50.3	20 48.8	4 15.7	16 51.3	26R25.2	6 55.0	5 52.3
3 S	20 43 3.0	9 51.0	19 42.6	23 43.5	7 2.2	11 2.3	21 24.1	4 28.1	16 59.0	26 22.9	6 57.3	5 53.6
4 S	20 46 59.6	10 48.5	19 39.5	6♋55.8	8 4.8	12 14.4	21 59.6	4 40.5	17 6.7	26 20.7	6 59.5	5 54.8
5 M	20 50 56.1	11 45.9	19 36.3	19 56.2	9 4.7	13 26.5	22 35.2	4 52.8	17 14.3	26 18.4	7 1.7	5 56.1
6 T	20 54 52.7	12 43.4	19 33.1	2♌45.0	10 1.8	14 38.7	23 11.0	5 5.0	17 22.0	26 16.1	7 3.9	5 57.3
7 W	20 58 49.2	13 41.0	19 29.9	15 22.1	10 55.9	15 50.9	23 46.9	5 17.1	17 29.7	26 13.8	7 6.2	5 58.5
8 T	21 2 45.8	14 38.5	19 26.8	27 48.0	11 47.0	17 3.2	24 23.0	5 29.2	17 37.4	26 11.4	7 8.4	5 59.7
9 F	21 6 42.3	15 36.0	19 23.6	10♍ 2.9	12 34.8	18 15.5	24 59.2	5 41.3	17 45.1	26 9.1	7 10.6	6 0.9
10 S	21 10 38.9	16 33.6	19 20.4	22 8.2	13 19.2	19 27.9	25 35.6	5 53.2	17 52.7	26 6.7	7 12.8	6 2.1
11 S	21 14 35.4	17 31.2	19 17.2	4♎ 5.5	14 0.1	20 40.4	26 12.0	6 5.1	18 0.4	26 4.4	7 15.0	6 3.2
12 M	21 18 32.0	18 28.8	19 14.1	15 57.7	14 37.2	21 52.8	26 48.7	6 16.9	18 8.1	26 2.0	7 17.2	6 4.4
13 T	21 22 28.6	19 26.4	19 10.9	27 48.1	15 10.3	23 5.4	27 25.4	6 28.7	18 15.8	25 59.7	7 19.4	6 5.5
14 W	21 26 25.1	20 24.0	19 7.7	9♏41.2	15 39.2	24 18.0	28 2.3	6 40.3	18 23.5	25 57.3	7 21.6	6 6.6
15 T	21 30 21.6	21 21.7	19 4.5	21 41.6	16 3.8	25 30.6	28 39.3	6 51.9	18 31.2	25 54.9	7 23.7	6 7.7
16 F	21 34 18.2	22 19.3	19 1.3	3♐54.5	16 23.6	26 43.3	29 16.4	7 3.4	18 38.9	25 52.5	7 25.9	6 8.8
17 S	21 38 14.8	23 17.0	18 58.2	16 25.0	16 38.7	27 56.0	29 53.7	7 14.9	18 46.6	25 50.1	7 28.1	6 9.9
18 S	21 42 11.4	24 14.7	18 55.0	29 17.8	16 48.6	29 8.8	0♏31.1	7 26.2	18 54.2	25 47.7	7 30.2	6 11.0
19 M	21 46 7.9	25 12.4	18 51.8	12♑36.4	16 53.3	0♌21.6	1 8.6	7 37.5	19 1.9	25 45.3	7 32.4	6 12.0
20 T	21 50 4.4	26 10.1	18 48.6	26 22.6	16R52.5	1 34.5	1 46.2	7 48.7	19 9.5	25 42.9	7 34.5	6 13.0
21 W	21 54 1.0	27 7.9	18 45.4	10♒35.5	16 46.0	2 47.4	2 24.0	7 59.8	19 17.2	25 40.5	7 36.6	6 14.0
22 T	21 57 57.6	28 5.7	18 42.3	25 11.3	16 33.7	4 0.4	3 1.9	8 10.8	19 24.8	25 38.2	7 38.7	6 15.0
23 F	22 1 54.1	29 3.5	18 39.1	10♓ 3.3	16 15.6	5 13.4	3 39.9	8 21.8	19 32.5	25 35.8	7 40.8	6 16.0
24 S	22 5 50.6	0♍ 1.3	18 35.9	25 2.7	15 51.6	6 26.5	4 18.0	8 32.6	19 40.1	25 33.4	7 42.9	6 17.0
25 S	22 9 47.2	0 59.1	18 32.7	9♈59.9	15 21.9	7 39.6	4 56.2	8 43.4	19 47.7	25 31.0	7 45.0	6 17.9
26 M	22 13 43.8	1 57.0	18 29.6	24 46.6	14 46.7	8 52.8	5 34.5	8 54.1	19 55.2	25 28.6	7 47.1	6 18.8
27 T	22 17 40.3	2 54.9	18 26.4	9♉16.5	14 6.2	10 6.0	6 13.0	9 4.6	20 2.8	25 26.3	7 49.1	6 19.7
28 W	22 21 36.9	3 52.9	18 23.2	23 26.3	13 21.0	11 19.3	6 51.6	9 15.1	20 10.4	25 23.9	7 51.2	6 20.6
29 T	22 25 33.4	4 50.8	18 20.0	7♊15.0	12 31.6	12 32.6	7 30.3	9 25.5	20 17.9	25 21.5	7 53.2	6 21.5
30 F	22 29 30.0	5 48.8	18 16.9	20 43.6	11 38.8	13 46.0	8 9.1	9 35.8	20 25.4	25 19.2	7 55.2	6 22.3
31 S	22 33 26.5	6 46.9	18 13.7	3♋54.4	10 43.6	14 59.4	8 48.0	9 46.0	20 32.9	25 16.9	7 57.2	6 23.2

DECLINATION

DAY	SIDEREAL TIME	☉	☊	☽	☿	♀	♂	♃	♄	♅	♆	♇
1 T	20 35 9.9	18N17.5	23S 3.5	21N31.0	9N 6.1	22N33.1	8S14.1	23N 9.3	16N43.4	13S25.7	18N26.6	19N 7.1
4 S	20 46 59.6	17 31.8	23 2.8	21 53.3	7 23.8	22 24.9	8 56.4	23 8.3	16 36.7	13 28.0	18 24.9	19 6.9
7 W	20 58 49.2	16 43.5	23 2.0	12 16.5	5 48.3	22 10.9	9 38.7	23 7.1	16 29.8	13 30.4	18 23.3	19 6.7
10 S	21 10 38.9	15 52.8	23 1.3	1S32.7	4 22.0	21 51.2	10 20.9	23 5.9	16 23.0	13 32.8	18 21.6	19 6.5
13 T	21 22 28.6	14 59.8	23 0.5	14 27.7	3 8.1	21 25.8	11 3.0	23 4.4	16 16.1	13 35.2	18 20.0	19 6.3
16 F	21 34 18.2	14 4.6	22 59.7	22 20.7	2 10.1	20 54.9	11 44.9	23 2.9	16 9.2	13 37.7	18 18.4	19 6.2
19 M	21 46 7.9	13 7.5	22 58.9	20 55.2	1 32.1	20 18.6	12 26.5	23 1.3	16 2.2	13 40.1	18 16.8	19 6.0
22 T	21 57 57.6	12 8.5	22 58.1	8 48.6	1 18.8	19 37.0	13 7.8	22 59.5	15 55.3	13 42.6	18 15.2	19 5.8
25 S	22 9 47.2	11 7.7	22 57.3	8N17.6	1 34.3	18 50.3	13 48.6	22 57.7	15 48.4	13 45.0	18 13.6	19 5.5
28 W	22 21 36.9	10 5.4	22 56.5	20 45.8	2 20.5	17 58.8	14 29.0	22 55.8	15 41.5	13 47.4	18 12.0	19 5.3
31 S	22 33 26.5	9 1.6	22 55.7	22 6.1	3 35.0	17 2.6	15 8.8	22 53.8	15 34.6	13 49.7	18 10.5	19 5.1

SEPTEMBER 1918

DAY	EPHEMERIS SIDEREAL TIME	☉	☊	☽	☿	♀	♂	♃	♄	♅	♆	♇
	h m s	° '	° '	° '	° '	° '	° '	° '	° '	° '	° '	° '
						LONGITUDE						
1 S	22 37 23.1	7♍44.9	18♐10.5	16♋49.7	9♍46.8	16♌12.9	9♏27.1	9♋56.1	20♌40.4	25♒14.5	7♌59.2	6♋24.0
2 M	22 41 19.6	8 43.0	18 7.3	29 32.0	8R49.8	17 26.4	10 6.2	10 6.1	20 47.9	25R12.2	8 1.2	6 24.8
3 T	22 45 16.1	9 41.1	18 4.1	12♌ 3.2	7 53.6	18 40.0	10 45.5	10 15.9	20 55.3	25 9.9	8 3.2	6 25.5
4 W	22 49 12.7	10 39.3	18 1.0	24 24.8	6 59.6	19 53.6	11 24.9	10 25.7	21 2.7	25 7.6	8 5.1	6 26.3
5 T	22 53 9.3	11 37.5	17 57.8	6♍38.0	6 9.0	21 7.3	12 4.4	10 35.4	21 10.1	25 5.4	8 7.1	6 27.0
6 F	22 57 5.9	12 35.7	17 54.6	18 43.4	5 23.0	22 21.0	12 44.0	10 44.9	21 17.5	25 3.1	8 9.0	6 27.7
7 S	23 1 2.4	13 33.9	17 51.4	0♎42.2	4 42.7	23 34.8	13 23.7	10 54.4	21 24.8	25 0.9	8 10.9	6 28.4
8 S	23 4 58.9	14 32.2	17 48.2	12 35.6	4 9.1	24 48.5	14 3.5	11 3.7	21 32.1	24 58.7	8 12.7	6 29.1
9 M	23 8 55.5	15 30.5	17 45.1	24 25.5	3 43.0	26 2.4	14 43.4	11 12.9	21 39.4	24 56.5	8 14.6	6 29.8
10 T	23 12 52.1	16 28.8	17 41.9	6♏14.5	3 25.1	27 16.2	15 23.5	11 22.0	21 46.6	24 54.3	8 16.4	6 30.4
11 W	23 16 48.6	17 27.2	17 38.7	18 6.2	3 15.9	28 30.1	16 3.6	11 31.0	21 53.8	24 52.1	8 18.3	6 31.0
12 T	23 20 45.1	18 25.6	17 35.5	0♐ 4.6	3 15.7	29 44.1	16 43.9	11 39.8	22 1.0	24 50.0	8 20.1	6 31.6
13 F	23 24 41.7	19 24.0	17 32.4	12 14.6	3D24.8	0♍58.1	17 24.2	11 48.5	22 8.2	24 47.9	8 21.8	6 32.2
14 S	23 28 38.3	20 22.4	17 29.2	24 41.3	3 43.1	2 12.1	18 4.6	11 57.1	22 15.3	24 45.8	8 23.6	6 32.7
15 S	23 32 34.8	21 20.9	17 26.0	7♑30.0	4 10.6	3 26.2	18 45.2	12 5.6	22 22.3	24 43.7	8 25.3	6 33.2
16 M	23 36 31.4	22 19.4	17 22.8	20 45.1	4 46.9	4 40.2	19 25.8	12 13.9	22 29.4	24 41.7	8 27.1	6 33.7
17 T	23 40 27.9	23 17.9	17 19.6	4♒29.6	5 31.8	5 54.4	20 6.6	12 22.1	22 36.4	24 39.7	8 28.8	6 34.2
18 W	23 44 24.5	24 16.4	17 16.5	18 44.2	6 24.8	7 8.5	20 47.4	12 30.2	22 43.3	24 37.7	8 30.4	6 34.7
19 T	23 48 21.0	25 15.0	17 13.3	3♓26.3	7 25.4	8 22.8	21 28.4	12 38.2	22 50.2	24 35.8	8 32.1	6 35.1
20 F	23 52 17.6	26 13.6	17 10.1	18 29.5	8 33.0	9 37.0	22 9.4	12 46.0	22 57.1	24 33.8	8 33.7	6 35.5
21 S	23 56 14.1	27 12.2	17 6.9	3♈44.6	9 47.1	10 51.3	22 50.5	12 53.7	23 3.9	24 31.9	8 35.3	6 35.9
22 S	0 0 10.7	28 10.9	17 3.8	19 0.2	11 6.9	12 5.6	23 31.7	13 1.2	23 10.7	24 30.0	8 36.9	6 36.3
23 M	0 4 7.2	29 9.6	17 0.6	4♉ 5.7	12 31.8	13 19.9	24 13.0	13 8.6	23 17.5	24 28.2	8 38.5	6 36.6
24 T	0 8 3.8	0♎ 8.3	16 57.4	18 52.3	14 1.3	14 34.3	24 54.5	13 15.9	23 24.2	24 26.4	8 40.0	6 36.9
25 W	0 12 0.4	1 7.1	16 54.2	3♊14.8	15 34.6	15 48.7	25 36.0	13 23.0	23 30.8	24 24.6	8 41.6	6 37.3
26 T	0 15 56.9	2 5.9	16 51.0	17 11.0	17 11.3	17 3.2	26 17.6	13 30.0	23 37.4	24 22.9	8 43.0	6 37.5
27 F	0 19 53.5	3 4.7	16 47.9	0♋41.6	18 50.7	18 17.7	26 59.2	13 36.8	23 44.0	24 21.2	8 44.5	6 37.8
28 S	0 23 50.0	4 3.6	16 44.7	13 49.3	20 32.4	19 32.2	27 41.0	13 43.5	23 50.5	24 19.5	8 45.9	6 38.0
29 S	0 27 46.6	5 2.5	16 41.5	26 37.4	22 15.9	20 46.8	28 22.9	13 50.0	23 56.9	24 17.9	8 47.4	6 38.2
30 M	0 31 43.1	6 1.5	16 38.3	9♌ 9.5	24 0.8	22 1.4	29 4.9	13 56.4	24 3.3	24 16.3	8 48.7	6 38.4

DAY	EPHEMERIS SIDEREAL TIME	☉	☊	☽	☿	♀	♂	♃	♄	♅	♆	♇
						DECLINATION						
1 S	22 37 23.1	8N40.0	22S55.4	20N 3.5	4N 4.8	16N42.9	15S21.9	22N53.1	15N32.3	13S50.5	18N10.0	19N 5.1
4 W	22 49 12.7	7 34.5	22 54.5	9 5.0	5 42.5	15 41.0	16 0.8	22 51.1	15 25.5	13 52.8	18 8.5	19 4.8
7 S	23 1 2.4	6 27.8	22 53.7	4S45.0	7 20.2	14 35.0	16 38.9	22 49.0	15 18.7	13 55.0	18 7.0	19 4.6
10 T	23 12 52.1	5 20.3	22 52.8	16 44.0	8 41.9	13 25.4	17 16.3	22 47.0	15 12.0	13 57.2	18 5.6	19 4.4
13 F	23 24 41.7	4 11.9	22 51.9	22 43.0	9 35.2	12 12.4	17 52.7	22 44.9	15 5.3	13 59.3	18 4.2	19 4.2
16 M	23 36 31.4	3 2.9	22 51.0	19 5.9	9 52.9	10 56.3	18 28.1	22 42.9	14 58.8	14 1.3	18 2.9	19 4.0
19 T	23 48 21.0	1 53.3	22 50.1	5 42.0	9 33.3	9 37.4	19 2.5	22 40.9	14 52.3	14 3.3	18 1.6	19 3.8
22 S	0 0 10.7	0 43.4	22 49.2	11N21.5	8 38.5	8 16.0	19 35.6	22 38.9	14 45.9	14 5.1	18 0.4	19 3.7
25 W	0 12 0.4	0S26.7	22 48.3	21 55.5	7 14.1	6 52.4	20 7.5	22 37.0	14 39.7	14 6.9	17 59.2	19 3.5
28 S	0 23 50.0	1 36.9	22 47.3	20 23.5	5 27.1	5 27.0	20 38.1	22 35.2	14 33.6	14 8.5	17 58.1	19 3.3

OCTOBER 1918

DAY	EPHEMERIS SIDEREAL TIME	☉	☊	☽	☿	♀	♂	♃	♄	♅	♆	♇
						LONGITUDE						
1 T	0 35 39.7	7♎ 0.5	16♐35.2	21♌29.1	25♍46.8	23♍16.0	29♏46.9	14♋ 2.6	24♌ 9.7	24♒14.7	8♌50.1	6♋38.6
2 W	0 39 36.2	7 59.5	16 32.0	3♍39.2	27 33.5	24 30.7	0♐29.1	14 8.7	24 16.0	24R13.2	8 51.4	6 38.7
3 T	0 43 32.8	8 58.6	16 28.8	15 41.9	29 20.6	25 45.4	1 11.3	14 14.6	24 22.2	24 11.7	8 52.7	6 38.8
4 F	0 47 29.3	9 57.7	16 25.6	27 39.2	1♎ 8.0	27 0.1	1 53.7	14 20.3	24 28.4	24 10.2	8 54.0	6 38.9
5 S	0 51 25.9	10 56.9	16 22.4	9♎32.6	2 55.5	28 14.8	2 36.1	14 25.9	24 34.5	24 8.8	8 55.3	6 39.0
6 S	0 55 22.4	11 56.0	16 19.3	21 23.4	4 42.8	29 29.6	3 18.6	14 31.3	24 40.5	24 7.5	8 56.5	6 39.0
7 M	0 59 19.0	12 55.2	16 16.1	3♏13.2	6 29.9	0♎44.4	4 1.2	14 36.5	24 46.5	24 6.1	8 57.7	6 39.1
8 T	1 3 15.6	13 54.5	16 12.9	15 4.0	8 16.6	1 59.2	4 43.9	14 41.6	24 52.5	24 4.9	8 58.9	6 39.1
9 W	1 7 12.1	14 53.8	16 9.7	26 58.2	10 2.9	3 14.1	5 26.7	14 46.5	24 58.3	24 3.6	9 0.0	6R39.1
10 T	1 11 8.7	15 53.1	16 6.6	8♐58.9	11 48.6	4 28.9	6 9.6	14 51.2	25 4.1	24 2.4	9 1.1	6 39.0
11 F	1 15 5.2	16 52.4	16 3.4	21 10.0	13 33.8	5 43.8	6 52.5	14 55.8	25 9.9	24 1.2	9 2.2	6 38.9
12 S	1 19 1.7	17 51.8	16 0.2	3♑35.8	15 18.4	6 58.7	7 35.5	15 0.1	25 15.5	24 0.1	9 3.2	6 38.8
13 S	1 22 58.3	18 51.2	15 57.0	16 21.0	17 2.4	8 13.7	8 18.6	15 4.4	25 21.1	23 59.1	9 4.2	6 38.7
14 M	1 26 54.9	19 50.6	15 53.8	29 29.9	18 45.7	9 28.6	9 1.8	15 8.4	25 26.7	23 58.0	9 5.2	6 38.6
15 T	1 30 51.4	20 50.1	15 50.7	13♒ 6.0	20 28.4	10 43.6	9 45.1	15 12.2	25 32.1	23 57.1	9 6.2	6 38.4
16 W	1 34 48.0	21 49.5	15 47.5	27 11.2	22 10.4	11 58.5	10 28.4	15 15.9	25 37.5	23 56.1	9 7.1	6 38.2
17 T	1 38 44.5	22 49.1	15 44.3	11♓44.5	23 51.7	13 13.6	11 11.9	15 19.4	25 42.8	23 55.2	9 8.0	6 38.0
18 F	1 42 41.1	23 48.6	15 41.1	26 41.7	25 32.3	14 28.6	11 55.4	15 22.7	25 48.1	23 54.4	9 8.9	6 37.8
19 S	1 46 37.6	24 48.2	15 38.0	11♈55.0	27 12.3	15 43.6	12 38.9	15 25.8	25 53.3	23 53.6	9 9.7	6 37.6
20 S	1 50 34.2	25 47.8	15 34.8	27 14.0	28 51.7	16 58.7	13 22.6	15 28.7	25 58.4	23 52.9	9 10.5	6 37.3
21 M	1 54 30.7	26 47.4	15 31.6	12♉27.8	0♏30.4	18 13.8	14 6.3	15 31.5	26 3.4	23 52.2	9 11.3	6 37.0
22 T	1 58 27.3	27 47.1	15 28.4	27 26.0	2 8.6	19 28.8	14 50.1	15 34.1	26 8.3	23 51.5	9 12.0	6 36.7
23 W	2 2 23.9	28 46.8	15 25.2	12♊ 1.3	3 46.1	20 44.0	15 34.0	15 36.4	26 13.2	23 50.9	9 12.7	6 36.3
24 T	2 6 20.4	29 46.6	15 22.1	26 9.4	5 23.1	21 59.1	16 17.9	15 38.6	26 18.0	23 50.3	9 13.4	6 36.0
25 F	2 10 16.9	0♏46.3	15 18.9	9♋49.6	6 59.4	23 14.2	17 2.0	15 40.6	26 22.6	23 49.8	9 14.0	6 35.6
26 S	2 14 13.5	1 46.2	15 15.7	23 3.1	8 35.3	24 29.4	17 46.1	15 42.4	26 27.3	23 49.4	9 14.6	6 35.2
27 S	2 18 10.1	2 46.0	15 12.5	5♌53.3	10 10.6	25 44.6	18 30.2	15 44.0	26 31.8	23 49.0	9 15.2	6 34.7
28 M	2 22 6.6	3 45.9	15 9.4	18 24.0	11 45.4	26 59.8	19 14.5	15 45.4	26 36.3	23 48.6	9 15.7	6 34.3
29 T	2 26 3.2	4 45.9	15 6.2	0♍39.4	13 19.7	28 15.0	19 58.8	15 46.6	26 40.6	23 48.3	9 16.2	6 33.8
30 W	2 29 59.7	5 45.8	15 3.0	12 43.7	14 53.6	29 30.3	20 43.2	15 47.6	26 44.9	23 48.0	9 16.7	6 33.3
31 T	2 33 56.3	6 45.8	14 59.8	24 40.4	16 26.9	0♏45.5	21 27.7	15 48.4	26 49.1	23 47.8	9 17.1	6 32.8

DAY	EPHEMERIS SIDEREAL TIME	☉	☊	☽	☿	♀	♂	♃	♄	♅	♆	♇
						DECLINATION						
1 T	0 35 39.7	2S47.0	22S46.4	9N59.8	3N24.6	4N 0.1	21S 7.2	22N33.5	14N27.6	14S10.1	17N57.0	19N 3.1
4 F	0 47 29.3	3 56.9	22 45.4	3S34.9	1 12.7	2 32.0	21 34.9	22 31.9	14 21.8	14 11.5	17 56.0	19 3.0
7 M	0 59 19.0	5 6.3	22 44.5	15 45.3	1S 3.7	1 3.0	22 0.9	22 30.4	14 16.2	14 12.8	17 55.0	19 2.8
10 T	1 11 8.7	6 15.2	22 43.5	22 18.1	3 21.2	0S26.5	22 25.3	22 29.1	14 10.7	14 13.9	17 54.2	19 2.7
13 S	1 22 58.3	7 23.3	22 42.5	19 46.1	5 37.3	1 56.2	22 47.9	22 27.9	14 5.5	14 14.9	17 53.3	19 2.6
16 W	1 34 48.0	8 30.5	22 41.5	7 51.5	7 50.1	3 25.7	23 8.6	22 26.9	14 0.4	14 15.8	17 52.6	19 2.5
19 S	1 46 37.6	9 36.6	22 40.5	8N53.0	9 58.5	4 54.8	23 27.4	22 26.0	13 55.6	14 16.6	17 52.0	19 2.4
22 T	1 58 27.3	10 41.4	22 39.4	21 1.1	12 1.6	6 23.1	23 44.2	22 25.4	13 51.0	14 17.2	17 51.4	19 2.3
25 F	2 10 16.9	11 44.8	22 38.4	20 49.5	13 58.5	7 50.2	23 59.0	22 24.9	13 46.6	14 17.6	17 50.9	19 2.2
28 M	2 22 6.6	12 46.7	22 37.3	10 52.2	15 48.7	9 15.7	24 11.6	22 24.6	13 42.5	14 17.9	17 50.4	19 2.2
31 T	2 33 56.3	13 46.7	22 36.3	2S32.7	17 31.6	10 39.5	24 22.0	22 24.6	13 38.6	14 18.1	17 50.1	19 2.2

NOVEMBER 1918

LONGITUDE

DAY	EPHEMERIS SIDEREAL TIME h m s	☉ ° ′	☊ ° ′	☽ ° ′	☿ ° ′	♀ ° ′	♂ ° ′	♃ ° ′	♄ ° ′	♅ ° ′	♆ ° ′	♇ ° ′
1 F	2 37 52.8	7♏45.9	14♐56.6	6♎32.7	17♏59.8	2♏ 0.8	22♐12.2	15♋49.0	26♌53.2	23♒47.7	9♌17.5	6♋32.3
2 S	2 41 49.4	8 45.9	14 53.5	18 23.2	19 32.3	3 16.1	22 56.8	15 49.5	26 57.2	23R47.5	9 17.9	6R31.7
3 S	2 45 45.9	9 46.0	14 50.3	0♏14.0	21 4.4	4 31.4	23 41.5	15 49.7	27 1.1	23 47.5	9 18.2	6 31.1
4 M	2 49 42.5	10 46.2	14 47.1	12 6.9	22 36.0	5 46.7	24 26.2	15 49.7	27 5.0	23 47.5	9 18.5	6 30.5
5 T	2 53 39.0	11 46.3	14 43.9	24 3.6	24 7.2	7 2.0	25 11.0	15R49.5	27 8.7	23D47.5	9 18.8	6 29.9
6 W	2 57 35.6	12 46.5	14 40.8	6♐ 6.0	25 38.0	8 17.3	25 55.9	15 49.1	27 12.4	23 47.6	9 19.0	6 29.3
7 T	3 1 32.2	13 46.8	14 37.6	18 16.1	27 8.3	9 32.6	26 40.9	15 48.5	27 15.9	23 47.8	9 19.2	6 28.6
8 F	3 5 28.7	14 47.0	14 34.4	0♑36.3	28 38.3	10 48.0	27 25.9	15 47.7	27 19.4	23 48.0	9 19.4	6 27.9
9 S	3 9 25.3	15 47.3	14 31.2	13 9.3	0♐ 7.8	12 3.3	28 10.9	15 46.7	27 22.7	23 48.2	9 19.5	6 27.2
10 S	3 13 21.8	16 47.6	14 28.1	25 58.3	1 36.9	13 18.7	28 56.1	15 45.5	27 26.0	23 48.5	9 19.6	6 26.5
11 M	3 17 18.4	17 47.9	14 24.9	9♒ 6.3	3 5.6	14 34.0	29 41.3	15 44.1	27 29.1	23 48.9	9 19.7	6 25.8
12 T	3 21 14.9	18 48.3	14 21.7	22 36.1	4 33.7	15 49.4	0♑26.5	15 42.5	27 32.2	23 49.3	9 19.7	6 25.0
13 W	3 25 11.5	19 48.7	14 18.5	6♓29.4	6 1.4	17 4.7	1 11.8	15 40.7	27 35.2	23 49.7	9R19.7	6 24.3
14 T	3 29 8.0	20 49.1	14 15.3	20 46.2	7 28.6	18 20.1	1 57.2	15 38.7	27 38.0	23 50.2	9 19.6	6 23.5
15 F	3 33 4.6	21 49.5	14 12.2	5♈24.4	8 55.2	19 35.5	2 42.6	15 36.5	27 40.8	23 50.8	9 19.6	6 22.7
16 S	3 37 1.2	22 49.9	14 9.0	20 19.0	10 21.2	20 50.9	3 28.1	15 34.2	27 43.4	23 51.4	9 19.5	6 21.8
17 S	3 40 57.7	23 50.4	14 5.8	5♉22.7	11 46.6	22 6.2	4 13.6	15 31.6	27 46.0	23 52.0	9 19.3	6 21.0
18 M	3 44 54.3	24 50.9	14 2.6	20 26.6	13 11.2	23 21.6	4 59.2	15 28.8	27 48.4	23 52.8	9 19.1	6 20.1
19 T	3 48 50.8	25 51.4	13 59.5	5♊21.6	14 35.0	24 37.0	5 44.9	15 25.8	27 50.8	23 53.5	9 18.9	6 19.3
20 W	3 52 47.4	26 51.9	13 56.3	19 59.6	15 58.0	25 52.4	6 30.6	15 22.7	27 53.0	23 54.3	9 18.7	6 18.4
21 T	3 56 44.0	27 52.5	13 53.1	4♋14.7	17 19.9	27 7.8	7 16.3	15 19.4	27 55.2	23 55.2	9 18.4	6 17.5
22 F	4 0 40.5	28 53.1	13 49.9	18 3.7	18 40.6	28 23.2	8 2.1	15 15.8	27 57.2	23 56.1	9 18.1	6 16.5
23 S	4 4 37.0	29 53.7	13 46.7	1♌26.1	20 0.1	29 38.7	8 47.9	15 12.1	27 59.1	23 57.1	9 17.7	6 15.6
24 S	4 8 33.6	0♐54.4	13 43.6	14 23.5	21 18.2	0♐54.1	9 33.9	15 8.2	28 1.0	23 58.1	9 17.4	6 14.6
25 M	4 12 30.2	1 55.0	13 40.4	26 58.9	22 34.6	2 9.5	10 19.8	15 4.1	28 2.7	23 59.1	9 16.9	6 13.7
26 T	4 16 26.7	2 55.8	13 37.2	9♍16.3	23 49.0	3 25.0	11 5.8	14 59.8	28 4.3	24 0.2	9 16.5	6 12.7
27 W	4 20 23.3	3 56.5	13 34.0	21 20.4	25 1.4	4 40.4	11 51.9	14 55.4	28 5.8	24 1.4	9 16.0	6 11.7
28 T	4 24 19.8	4 57.2	13 30.9	3♎15.5	26 11.2	5 55.8	12 38.0	14 50.7	28 7.1	24 2.6	9 15.5	6 10.7
29 F	4 28 16.4	5 58.0	13 27.7	15 6.0	27 18.2	7 11.3	13 24.1	14 45.9	28 8.4	24 3.9	9 15.0	6 9.7
30 S	4 32 13.0	6 58.8	13 24.5	26 55.8	28 21.9	8 26.8	14 10.3	14 41.0	28 9.6	24 5.2	9 14.4	6 8.6

DECLINATION

DAY	SIDEREAL TIME	☉	☊	☽	☿	♀	♂	♃	♄	♅	♆	♇
1 F	2 37 52.8	14S 6.3	22S35.9	6S58.5	18S 4.2	11S 6.9	24S25.0	22N24.6	13N37.4	14S18.1	17N50.0	19N 2.1
4 M	2 49 42.5	15 3.7	22 34.9	18 2.5	19 36.4	12 27.6	24 32.4	22 24.9	13 33.9	14 18.1	17 49.7	19 2.1
7 T	3 1 32.2	15 58.9	22 33.8	22 28.0	21 0.0	13 45.6	24 37.4	22 25.4	13 30.7	14 17.9	17 49.6	19 2.1
10 S	3 13 21.8	16 51.7	22 32.7	17 27.5	22 14.4	15 0.5	24 40.1	22 26.0	13 27.8	14 17.5	17 49.5	19 2.2
13 W	3 25 11.5	17 41.8	22 31.6	4 17.1	23 18.8	16 11.9	24 40.4	22 26.9	13 25.2	14 17.0	17 49.5	19 2.2
16 S	3 37 1.2	18 29.3	22 30.5	11N49.1	24 12.7	17 19.6	24 38.3	22 28.1	13 23.0	14 16.4	17 49.6	19 2.3
19 T	3 48 50.8	19 13.7	22 29.3	21 54.0	24 55.3	18 23.2	24 33.7	22 29.4	13 21.0	14 15.6	17 49.7	19 2.4
22 F	4 0 40.5	19 55.1	22 28.2	19 13.4	25 26.0	19 22.2	24 26.7	22 30.9	13 19.4	14 14.6	17 50.0	19 2.5
25 M	4 12 30.2	20 33.2	22 27.0	7 44.8	25 44.2	20 16.4	24 17.2	22 32.6	13 18.1	14 13.5	17 50.3	19 2.6
28 T	4 24 19.8	21 7.9	22 25.9	5S50.9	25 49.6	21 5.4	24 5.2	22 34.4	13 17.2	14 12.3	17 50.7	19 2.7

DECEMBER 1918

LONGITUDE

DAY	SIDEREAL TIME	☉	☊	☽	☿	♀	♂	♃	♄	♅	♆	♇
1 S	4 36 9.5	7♐59.7	13♐21.3	8♏48.2	29♐21.9	9♐42.2	14♑56.6	14♋35.8	28♌10.6	24♒ 6.5	9♌13.8	6♋ 7.6
2 M	4 40 6.1	9 0.5	13 18.2	20 46.2	0♑17.7	10 57.7	15 42.9	14R30.5	28 11.6	24 7.9	9R13.1	6R 6.5
3 T	4 44 2.6	10 1.4	13 15.0	2♐51.8	1 8.6	12 13.1	16 29.2	14 25.0	28 12.4	24 9.4	9 12.5	6 5.4
4 W	4 47 59.2	11 2.3	13 11.8	15 6.9	1 54.0	13 28.6	17 15.6	14 19.4	28 13.1	24 10.9	9 11.8	6 4.4
5 T	4 51 55.8	12 3.2	13 8.6	27 32.8	2 33.2	14 44.1	18 2.1	14 13.6	28 13.7	24 12.4	9 11.0	6 3.3
6 F	4 55 52.3	13 4.1	13 5.5	10♑10.6	3 5.3	15 59.5	18 48.5	14 7.7	28 14.2	24 14.0	9 10.3	6 2.2
7 S	4 59 48.8	14 5.1	13 2.3	23 1.2	3 29.5	17 15.0	19 35.0	14 1.6	28 14.6	24 15.6	9 9.5	6 1.0
8 S	5 3 45.4	15 6.0	12 59.1	6♒ 5.5	3 45.0	18 30.5	20 21.6	13 55.4	28 14.8	24 17.3	9 8.6	5 59.9
9 M	5 7 42.0	16 7.0	12 55.9	19 24.1	3 50.9	19 45.9	21 8.2	13 49.0	28 15.0	24 19.1	9 7.8	5 58.8
10 T	5 11 38.5	17 8.0	12 52.7	2♓57.9	3R46.4	21 1.4	21 54.8	13 42.5	28 15.0	24 20.8	9 6.9	5 57.6
11 W	5 15 35.1	18 9.0	12 49.6	16 47.0	3 31.0	22 16.9	22 41.5	13 35.9	28R15.0	24 22.7	9 6.0	5 56.5
12 T	5 19 31.6	19 9.9	12 46.4	0♈51.2	3 4.1	23 32.3	23 28.2	13 29.1	28 14.8	24 24.5	9 5.1	5 55.3
13 F	5 23 28.2	20 11.0	12 43.2	15 9.1	2 25.8	24 47.8	24 14.9	13 22.3	28 14.5	24 26.4	9 4.1	5 54.2
14 S	5 27 24.8	21 12.0	12 40.0	29 38.4	1 36.2	26 3.2	25 1.6	13 15.3	28 14.1	24 28.4	9 3.1	5 53.0
15 S	5 31 21.3	22 13.0	12 36.9	14♉14.9	0 36.2	27 18.7	25 48.4	13 8.2	28 13.6	24 30.4	9 2.1	5 51.8
16 M	5 35 17.9	23 14.0	12 33.7	28 53.5	29♐27.2	28 34.1	26 35.3	13 1.0	28 12.9	24 32.4	9 1.0	5 50.6
17 T	5 39 14.4	24 15.1	12 30.5	13♊28.0	28 11.1	29 49.6	27 22.1	12 53.7	28 12.2	24 34.5	8 59.9	5 49.4
18 W	5 43 11.0	25 16.1	12 27.3	27 52.3	26 50.3	1♑ 5.0	28 9.0	12 46.3	28 11.3	24 36.6	8 58.8	5 48.3
19 T	5 47 7.6	26 17.2	12 24.2	12♋ 0.5	25 27.4	2 20.4	28 55.9	12 38.9	28 10.4	24 38.8	8 57.7	5 47.1
20 F	5 51 4.1	27 18.2	12 21.0	25 48.6	24 5.3	3 35.9	29 42.8	12 31.3	28 9.3	24 41.0	8 56.6	5 45.9
21 S	5 55 0.6	28 19.3	12 17.8	9♌14.0	22 46.7	4 51.3	0♒29.8	12 23.6	28 8.1	24 43.2	8 55.4	5 44.6
22 S	5 58 57.2	29 20.4	12 14.6	22 16.3	21 33.9	6 6.7	1 16.7	12 15.9	28 6.8	24 45.5	8 54.2	5 43.4
23 M	6 2 53.8	0♑21.5	12 11.5	4♍56.8	20 29.1	7 22.1	2 3.8	12 8.2	28 5.5	24 47.8	8 53.0	5 42.2
24 T	6 6 50.4	1 22.6	12 8.3	17 18.4	19 33.5	8 37.6	2 50.8	12 0.3	28 4.0	24 50.2	8 51.7	5 41.0
25 W	6 10 46.9	2 23.8	12 5.1	29 24.9	18 48.2	9 53.0	3 37.8	11 52.4	28 2.3	24 52.5	8 50.4	5 39.8
26 T	6 14 43.4	3 24.9	12 1.9	11♎21.0	18 13.5	11 8.4	4 24.9	11 44.4	28 0.6	24 55.0	8 49.1	5 38.6
27 F	6 18 40.0	4 26.0	11 58.7	23 11.6	17 49.5	12 23.8	5 12.0	11 36.5	27 58.8	24 57.4	8 47.8	5 37.3
28 S	6 22 36.6	5 27.2	11 55.6	5♏ 1.5	17 36.0	13 39.3	5 59.2	11 28.4	27 56.9	24 60.0	8 46.5	5 36.1
29 S	6 26 33.1	6 28.4	11 52.4	16 55.4	17 32.4	14 54.7	6 46.3	11 20.4	27 54.8	25 2.5	8 45.1	5 34.9
30 M	6 30 29.7	7 29.5	11 49.2	28 57.6	17D38.1	16 10.1	7 33.5	11 12.3	27 52.7	25 5.1	8 43.7	5 33.7
31 T	6 34 26.2	8 30.7	11 46.0	11♐11.3	17 52.3	17 25.5	8 20.7	11 4.1	27 50.5	25 7.7	8 42.3	5 32.5

DECLINATION

DAY	SIDEREAL TIME	☉	☊	☽	☿	♀	♂	♃	♄	♅	♆	♇
1 S	4 36 9.5	21S39.0	22S24.7	17S15.7	25S42.0	21S49.0	23S50.8	22N36.5	13N16.6	14S10.9	17N51.2	19N 2.9
4 W	4 47 59.2	22 6.4	22 23.5	22 25.6	25 21.8	22 26.8	23 33.9	22 38.6	13 16.4	14 9.3	17 51.7	19 3.0
7 S	4 59 48.8	22 30.0	22 22.3	18 7.5	24 49.8	22 58.7	23 14.6	22 40.9	13 16.5	14 7.6	17 52.4	19 3.2
10 T	5 11 38.5	22 49.6	22 21.1	5 33.4	24 7.3	23 24.2	22 53.0	22 43.3	13 16.9	14 5.8	17 53.1	19 3.4
13 F	5 23 28.2	23 5.1	22 19.9	10N 6.2	23 15.6	23 43.4	22 29.0	22 45.7	13 17.8	14 3.9	17 53.8	19 3.6
16 M	5 35 17.9	23 16.6	22 18.7	21 11.1	22 17.0	23 56.0	22 2.7	22 48.3	13 18.9	14 1.8	17 54.7	19 3.9
19 T	5 47 7.6	23 23.8	22 17.5	20 21.4	21 17.0	24 2.0	21 34.2	22 50.8	13 20.4	13 59.6	17 55.6	19 4.1
22 S	5 58 57.2	23 26.8	22 16.2	9 25.5	20 26.6	24 1.3	21 3.5	22 53.4	13 22.3	13 57.2	17 56.5	19 4.4
25 W	6 10 46.9	23 25.6	22 15.0	4S24.0	19 56.7	23 53.8	20 30.7	22 55.9	13 24.5	13 54.8	17 57.5	19 4.7
28 S	6 22 36.6	23 20.2	22 13.7	16 15.0	19 51.2	23 39.7	19 55.9	22 58.4	13 26.9	13 52.2	17 58.6	19 5.0
31 T	6 34 26.2	23 10.5	22 12.4	22 17.5	20 6.2	23 19.0	19 19.1	23 0.9	13 29.8	13 49.6	17 59.7	19 5.3

JANUARY 1919

DAY	EPHEMERIS SIDEREAL TIME	☉	☊	☽	☿	♀	♂	♃	♄	♅	♆	♇
	h m s	° ′	° ′	° ′	° ′	° ′	° ′	° ′	° ′	° ′	° ′	° ′
						LONGITUDE						
1 W	6 38 22.8	9 ♑ 31.9	11 ♐ 42.9	23 ♐ 39.2	18 ♐ 14.3	18 ♑ 40.9	9 ♒ 7.9	10 ♋ 56.0	27 ♌ 48.1	25 ♒ 10.3	8 ♌ 40.9	5 ♋ 31.2
2 T	6 42 19.4	10 33.1	11 39.7	6 ♑ 22.9	18 43.4	19 56.3	9 55.1	10 R 47.9	27 R 45.7	25 13.0	8 R 39.5	5 R 30.0
3 F	6 46 15.9	11 34.3	11 36.5	19 22.8	19 18.9	21 11.7	10 42.4	10 39.8	27 43.2	25 15.7	8 38.0	5 28.8
4 S	6 50 12.5	12 35.4	11 33.3	2 ♒ 38.2	20 0.1	22 27.1	11 29.6	10 31.6	27 40.5	25 18.4	8 36.6	5 27.6
5 S	6 54 9.0	13 36.6	11 30.2	16 7.7	20 46.4	23 42.5	12 16.9	10 23.5	27 37.8	25 21.2	8 35.1	5 26.4
6 M	6 58 5.6	14 37.8	11 27.0	29 49.3	21 37.2	24 57.9	13 4.2	10 15.4	27 35.0	25 24.0	8 33.6	5 25.2
7 T	7 2 2.2	15 39.0	11 23.8	13 ♓ 40.5	22 32.0	26 13.2	13 51.5	10 7.4	27 32.1	25 26.9	8 32.1	5 24.0
8 W	7 5 58.7	16 40.1	11 20.6	27 39.2	23 30.5	27 28.6	14 38.8	9 59.3	27 29.1	25 29.7	8 30.5	5 22.8
9 T	7 9 55.2	17 41.3	11 17.4	11 ♈ 43.3	24 32.2	28 43.9	15 26.1	9 51.3	27 26.0	25 32.6	8 29.0	5 21.6
10 F	7 13 51.8	18 42.4	11 14.3	25 51.3	25 36.8	29 59.3	16 13.5	9 43.4	27 22.8	25 35.5	8 27.4	5 20.4
11 S	7 17 48.4	19 43.6	11 11.1	10 ♉ 1.5	26 43.9	1 ♒ 14.6	17 0.8	9 35.5	27 19.5	25 38.5	8 25.8	5 19.2
12 S	7 21 44.9	20 44.7	11 7.9	24 12.3	27 53.4	2 29.9	17 48.1	9 27.6	27 16.2	25 41.5	8 24.3	5 18.1
13 M	7 25 41.5	21 45.8	11 4.7	8 ♊ 21.7	29 4.9	3 45.2	18 35.5	9 19.9	27 12.8	25 44.5	8 22.7	5 16.9
14 T	7 29 38.0	22 46.9	11 1.6	22 27.1	0 ♑ 18.4	5 0.5	19 22.8	9 12.1	27 9.2	25 47.5	8 21.0	5 15.7
15 W	7 33 34.6	23 48.0	10 58.4	6 ♋ 25.4	1 33.5	6 15.7	20 10.1	9 4.5	27 5.7	25 50.5	8 19.4	5 14.6
16 T	7 37 31.2	24 49.1	10 55.2	20 13.0	2 50.1	7 31.0	20 57.5	8 56.9	27 2.0	25 53.6	8 17.8	5 13.4
17 F	7 41 27.7	25 50.2	10 52.0	3 ♌ 46.5	4 8.2	8 46.3	21 44.8	8 49.5	26 58.3	25 56.7	8 16.2	5 12.3
18 S	7 45 24.3	26 51.2	10 48.9	17 3.2	5 27.6	10 1.5	22 32.2	8 42.1	26 54.5	25 59.8	8 14.5	5 11.2
19 S	7 49 20.8	27 52.3	10 45.7	0 ♍ 1.6	6 48.2	11 16.7	23 19.5	8 34.8	26 50.6	26 3.0	8 12.9	5 10.0
20 M	7 53 17.4	28 53.4	10 42.5	12 41.4	8 9.9	12 31.9	24 6.9	8 27.6	26 46.6	26 6.1	8 11.2	5 8.9
21 T	7 57 13.9	29 54.4	10 39.3	25 3.9	9 32.6	13 47.1	24 54.2	8 20.5	26 42.6	26 9.3	8 9.5	5 7.8
22 W	8 1 10.5	0 ♒ 55.4	10 36.1	7 ♎ 11.7	10 56.3	15 2.3	25 41.6	8 13.5	26 38.5	26 12.5	8 7.9	5 6.8
23 T	8 5 7.0	1 56.5	10 33.0	19 8.6	12 21.0	16 17.5	26 28.9	8 6.7	26 34.4	26 15.7	8 6.2	5 5.7
24 F	8 9 3.6	2 57.5	10 29.8	0 ♏ 59.2	13 46.5	17 32.6	27 16.2	7 59.9	26 30.2	26 19.0	8 4.5	5 4.6
25 S	8 13 0.2	3 58.5	10 26.6	12 48.7	15 12.9	18 47.8	28 3.6	7 53.3	26 25.9	26 22.2	8 2.8	5 3.6
26 S	8 16 56.7	4 59.5	10 23.4	24 42.4	16 40.1	20 2.9	28 50.9	7 46.8	26 21.6	26 25.5	8 1.2	5 2.5
27 M	8 20 53.3	6 0.5	10 20.3	6 ♐ 45.6	18 8.1	21 18.0	29 38.3	7 40.4	26 17.2	26 28.8	7 59.5	5 1.5
28 T	8 24 49.8	7 1.5	10 17.1	19 3.1	19 36.8	22 33.1	0 ♓ 25.6	7 34.2	26 12.8	26 32.1	7 57.8	5 0.5
29 W	8 28 46.4	8 2.5	10 13.9	1 ♑ 38.8	21 6.3	23 48.2	1 12.9	7 28.1	26 8.3	26 35.4	7 56.1	4 59.5
30 T	8 32 43.0	9 3.4	10 10.7	14 35.4	22 36.5	25 3.3	2 0.2	7 22.2	26 3.8	26 38.8	7 54.4	4 58.5
31 F	8 36 39.5	10 4.4	10 7.6	27 53.9	24 7.5	26 18.3	2 47.5	7 16.4	25 59.3	26 42.1	7 52.7	4 57.5
						DECLINATION						
1 W	6 38 22.8	23 S 6.4	22 S 12.0	22 S 19.5	20 S 14.5	23 S 10.7	19 S 6.4	23 N 1.7	13 N 30.8	13 S 48.7	18 N 0.1	19 N 5.4
4 S	6 50 12.5	22 51.2	22 10.7	15 41.8	20 45.8	22 41.4	18 27.1	23 4.1	13 34.0	13 45.9	18 1.2	19 5.8
7 T	7 2 2.2	22 31.8	22 9.4	1 37.1	21 21.6	22 5.9	17 46.0	23 6.4	13 37.5	13 43.0	18 2.5	19 6.1
10 F	7 13 51.8	22 8.5	22 8.1	13 N 31.0	21 56.9	21 24.5	17 3.3	23 8.6	13 41.2	13 40.0	18 3.7	19 6.5
13 M	7 25 41.5	21 41.3	22 6.8	22 5.1	22 28.3	20 37.3	16 18.9	23 10.7	13 45.2	13 36.9	18 5.0	19 6.9
16 T	7 37 31.2	21 10.4	22 5.4	18 47.9	22 53.1	19 44.7	15 33.1	23 12.7	13 49.4	13 33.8	18 6.2	19 7.3
19 S	7 49 20.8	20 35.7	22 4.1	6 45.7	23 9.7	18 47.0	14 45.8	23 14.6	13 53.8	13 30.6	18 7.6	19 7.7
22 W	8 1 10.5	19 57.6	22 2.7	7 S 6.9	23 16.9	17 44.4	13 57.2	23 16.3	13 58.4	13 27.3	18 8.9	19 8.1
25 S	8 13 0.2	19 16.1	22 1.4	18 3.4	23 13.6	16 37.3	13 7.4	23 17.9	14 3.2	13 23.9	18 10.2	19 8.5
28 T	8 24 49.8	18 31.4	21 60.0	22 20.5	22 59.2	15 26.1	12 16.5	23 19.4	14 8.1	13 20.5	18 11.6	19 9.0
31 F	8 36 39.5	17 43.7	21 58.6	16 58.7	22 33.3	14 11.1	11 24.5	23 20.8	14 13.1	13 17.1	18 12.9	19 9.4

FEBRUARY 1919

DAY	EPHEMERIS SIDEREAL TIME	☉	☊	☽	☿	♀	♂	♃	♄	♅	♆	♇
						LONGITUDE						
1 S	8 40 36.1	11 ♒ 5.3	10 ♐ 4.4	11 ♒ 33.3	25 ♑ 39.2	27 ♒ 33.4	3 ♓ 34.8	7 ♋ 10.7	25 ♌ 54.7	26 ♒ 45.5	7 ♌ 51.0	4 ♋ 56.5
2 S	8 44 32.6	12 6.2	10 1.2	25 30.6	27 11.6	28 48.4	4 22.1	7 R 5.3	25 R 50.0	26 48.8	7 R 49.3	4 R 55.6
3 M	8 48 29.1	13 7.1	9 58.0	9 ♓ 41.3	28 44.8	0 ♓ 3.4	5 9.4	6 60.0	25 45.4	26 52.2	7 47.6	4 54.7
4 T	8 52 25.7	14 8.0	9 54.8	23 59.9	0 ♒ 18.6	1 18.4	5 56.6	6 54.8	25 40.7	26 55.6	7 46.0	4 53.8
5 W	8 56 22.3	15 8.8	9 51.7	8 ♈ 20.8	1 53.3	2 33.3	6 43.9	6 49.8	25 35.9	26 59.0	7 44.3	4 52.9
6 T	9 0 18.8	16 9.7	9 48.5	22 39.4	3 28.6	3 48.3	7 31.1	6 45.0	25 31.2	27 2.4	7 42.6	4 52.0
7 F	9 4 15.4	17 10.5	9 45.3	6 ♉ 52.4	5 4.7	5 3.2	8 18.3	6 40.4	25 26.4	27 5.9	7 40.9	4 51.1
8 S	9 8 11.9	18 11.2	9 42.1	20 57.9	6 41.6	6 18.1	9 5.5	6 35.9	25 21.6	27 9.3	7 39.3	4 50.3
9 S	9 12 8.5	19 12.0	9 39.0	4 ♊ 55.0	8 19.3	7 32.9	9 52.7	6 31.6	25 16.8	27 12.7	7 37.6	4 49.4
10 M	9 16 5.1	20 12.7	9 35.8	18 43.7	9 57.7	8 47.7	10 39.8	6 27.5	25 12.0	27 16.2	7 36.0	4 48.6
11 T	9 20 1.6	21 13.4	9 32.6	2 ♋ 23.9	11 36.9	10 2.5	11 27.0	6 23.6	25 7.1	27 19.6	7 34.3	4 47.8
12 W	9 23 58.2	22 14.1	9 29.4	15 55.3	13 17.0	11 17.3	12 14.1	6 19.9	25 2.3	27 23.1	7 32.7	4 47.1
13 T	9 27 54.7	23 14.7	9 26.2	29 17.0	14 57.9	12 32.0	13 1.2	6 16.3	24 57.4	27 26.5	7 31.1	4 46.3
14 F	9 31 51.3	24 15.3	9 23.1	12 ♌ 27.9	16 39.7	13 46.8	13 48.2	6 13.0	24 52.5	27 30.0	7 29.5	4 45.6
15 S	9 35 47.8	25 15.9	9 19.9	25 26.4	18 22.3	15 1.4	14 35.3	6 9.8	24 47.7	27 33.4	7 27.9	4 44.8
16 S	9 39 44.4	26 16.5	9 16.7	8 ♍ 11.4	20 5.8	16 16.1	15 22.3	6 6.8	24 42.8	27 36.9	7 26.3	4 44.1
17 M	9 43 40.9	27 17.0	9 13.5	20 42.4	21 50.1	17 30.7	16 9.3	6 4.0	24 37.9	27 40.4	7 24.7	4 43.4
18 T	9 47 37.5	28 17.6	9 10.4	2 ♎ 59.6	23 35.4	18 45.3	16 56.3	6 1.4	24 33.1	27 43.8	7 23.2	4 42.8
19 W	9 51 34.1	29 18.1	9 7.2	15 4.7	25 21.6	19 59.9	17 43.2	5 59.0	24 28.3	27 47.3	7 21.6	4 42.1
20 T	9 55 30.6	0 ♓ 18.5	9 4.0	27 0.2	27 8.7	21 14.4	18 30.1	5 56.8	24 23.4	27 50.8	7 20.1	4 41.5
21 F	9 59 27.1	1 19.0	9 0.8	8 ♏ 49.9	28 56.7	22 28.9	19 17.0	5 54.8	24 18.6	27 54.2	7 18.6	4 40.9
22 S	10 3 23.7	2 19.4	8 57.6	20 38.2	0 ♓ 45.7	23 43.4	20 3.9	5 53.0	24 13.8	27 57.7	7 17.1	4 40.3
23 S	10 7 20.3	3 19.8	8 54.5	2 ♐ 30.4	2 35.5	24 57.9	20 50.8	5 51.3	24 9.0	28 1.1	7 15.6	4 39.8
24 M	10 11 16.8	4 20.2	8 51.3	14 32.0	4 26.2	26 12.3	21 37.6	5 49.9	24 4.3	28 4.6	7 14.1	4 39.2
25 T	10 15 13.4	5 20.6	8 48.1	26 48.5	6 17.8	27 26.7	22 24.4	5 48.7	23 59.5	28 8.0	7 12.7	4 38.7
26 W	10 19 9.9	6 20.9	8 44.9	9 ♑ 25.1	8 10.2	28 41.0	23 11.1	5 47.7	23 54.8	28 11.5	7 11.2	4 38.2
27 T	10 23 6.5	7 21.2	8 41.8	22 25.7	10 3.3	29 55.3	23 57.9	5 46.8	23 50.2	28 14.9	7 9.8	4 37.7
28 F	10 27 3.0	8 21.5	8 38.6	5 ♒ 52.8	11 57.2	1 ♈ 9.6	24 44.6	5 46.2	23 45.5	28 18.3	7 8.4	4 37.3
						DECLINATION						
1 S	8 40 36.1	17 S 27.2	21 S 58.1	13 S 5.4	22 S 22.0	13 S 45.3	11 S 7.0	23 N 21.2	14 N 14.8	13 S 15.9	18 N 13.3	19 N 9.6
4 T	8 52 25.7	16 35.7	21 56.7	2 N 8.5	21 40.1	12 25.8	10 13.8	23 22.5	14 20.0	13 12.4	18 14.7	19 10.0
7 F	9 4 15.4	15 41.6	21 55.3	16 28.6	20 45.8	11 3.3	9 19.8	23 23.6	14 25.1	13 8.9	18 16.0	19 10.5
10 M	9 16 5.1	14 45.2	21 53.9	22 15.1	19 38.9	9 38.3	8 25.1	23 24.5	14 30.3	13 5.4	18 17.3	19 10.9
13 T	9 27 54.7	13 46.5	21 52.5	16 35.5	18 19.3	8 10.9	7 29.7	23 25.4	14 35.5	13 1.8	18 18.6	19 11.4
16 S	9 39 44.4	12 45.8	21 51.0	3 51.1	16 46.9	6 41.7	6 33.9	23 26.2	14 40.7	12 58.2	18 19.8	19 11.9
19 W	9 51 34.1	11 43.3	21 49.6	9 S 41.8	15 1.6	5 10.9	5 37.6	23 26.9	14 45.8	12 54.7	18 21.1	19 12.3
22 S	10 3 23.7	10 39.1	21 48.1	19 26.9	13 3.7	3 38.9	4 41.0	23 27.5	14 50.8	12 51.1	18 22.3	19 12.8
25 T	10 15 13.4	9 33.4	21 46.7	21 51.4	10 53.3	2 5.9	3 44.1	23 28.0	14 55.7	12 47.5	18 23.4	19 13.3
28 F	10 27 3.0	8 26.3	21 45.2	14 42.9	8 31.4	0 32.4	2 47.0	23 28.4	15 0.5	12 44.0	18 24.5	19 13.8

MARCH 1919

LONGITUDE

DAY	EPHEMERIS SIDEREAL TIME h m s	☉ ° ′	☊ ° ′	☽ ° ′	☿ ° ′	♀ ° ′	♂ ° ′	♃ ° ′	♄ ° ′	♅ ° ′	♆ ° ′	♇ ° ′
1 S	10 30 59.6	9 ♓ 21.8	8 ♐ 35.4	19 ♒ 46.2	13 ♓ 51.6	2 ♈ 23.9	25 ♓ 31.3	5 ♋ 45.8	23 ♌ 40.9	28 ♒ 21.7	7 ♌ 7.0	4 ♋ 36.8
2 S	10 34 56.1	10 22.0	8 32.2	4 ♓ 3.4	15 46.6	3 38.1	26 17.9	5 R 45.5	23 R 36.3	28 25.2	7 R 5.7	4 R 36.4
3 M	10 38 52.7	11 22.2	8 29.0	18 38.6	17 42.0	4 52.3	27 4.6	5 45.5	23 31.8	28 28.6	7 4.3	4 36.0
4 T	10 42 49.2	12 22.4	8 25.9	3 ♈ 24.4	19 37.5	6 6.4	27 51.2	5 D 45.7	23 27.3	28 32.0	7 3.0	4 35.7
5 W	10 46 45.8	13 22.5	8 22.7	18 12.2	21 33.1	7 20.5	28 37.7	5 46.1	23 22.9	28 35.3	7 1.7	4 35.3
6 T	10 50 42.3	14 22.6	8 19.5	2 ♉ 54.3	23 28.5	8 34.6	29 24.2	5 46.6	23 18.5	28 38.7	7 0.4	4 35.0
7 F	10 54 38.9	15 22.7	8 16.3	17 24.8	25 23.5	9 48.6	0 ♈ 10.7	5 47.4	23 14.2	28 42.1	6 59.2	4 34.7
8 S	10 58 35.4	16 22.7	8 13.2	1 ♊ 40.1	27 17.7	11 2.6	0 57.2	5 48.3	23 9.9	28 45.4	6 57.9	4 34.4
9 S	11 2 32.0	17 22.7	8 10.0	15 38.7	29 10.8	12 16.6	1 43.6	5 49.5	23 5.7	28 48.7	6 56.7	4 34.2
10 M	11 6 28.6	18 22.7	8 6.8	29 20.9	1 ♈ 2.5	13 30.5	2 30.0	5 50.9	23 1.5	28 52.1	6 55.6	4 33.9
11 T	11 10 25.1	19 22.6	8 3.6	12 ♋ 47.8	2 52.4	14 44.3	3 16.3	5 52.4	22 57.4	28 55.4	6 54.4	4 33.7
12 W	11 14 21.6	20 22.5	8 0.4	26 1.0	4 39.9	15 58.1	4 2.6	5 54.1	22 53.4	28 58.6	6 53.3	4 33.5
13 T	11 18 18.2	21 22.3	7 57.3	9 ♌ 1.7	6 24.7	17 11.8	4 48.8	5 56.1	22 49.4	29 1.9	6 52.1	4 33.4
14 F	11 22 14.8	22 22.1	7 54.1	21 51.1	8 6.3	18 25.5	5 35.0	5 58.2	22 45.5	29 5.2	6 51.1	4 33.2
15 S	11 26 11.3	23 21.9	7 50.9	4 ♍ 29.5	9 44.2	19 39.2	6 21.2	6 0.5	22 41.7	29 8.4	6 50.0	4 33.1
16 S	11 30 7.9	24 21.6	7 47.7	16 57.3	11 17.9	20 52.8	7 7.3	6 3.0	22 37.9	29 11.6	6 49.0	4 33.0
17 M	11 34 4.4	25 21.4	7 44.6	29 14.7	12 46.8	22 6.4	7 53.4	6 5.7	22 34.2	29 14.8	6 48.0	4 33.0
18 T	11 38 1.0	26 21.0	7 41.4	11 ♎ 22.3	14 10.5	23 19.9	8 39.5	6 8.5	22 30.6	29 18.0	6 47.0	4 32.9
19 W	11 41 57.5	27 20.7	7 38.2	23 21.3	15 28.6	24 33.3	9 25.5	6 11.6	22 27.0	29 21.2	6 46.0	4 32.9
20 T	11 45 54.1	28 20.3	7 35.0	5 ♏ 13.5	16 40.7	25 46.7	10 11.5	6 14.8	22 23.6	29 24.3	6 45.1	4 D 32.9
21 F	11 49 50.6	29 19.9	7 31.8	17 1.6	17 46.3	27 0.1	10 57.4	6 18.2	22 20.2	29 27.4	6 44.2	4 32.9
22 S	11 53 47.2	0 ♈ 19.4	7 28.7	28 49.2	18 45.2	28 13.4	11 43.3	6 21.8	22 16.9	29 30.5	6 43.3	4 33.0
23 S	11 57 43.7	1 19.0	7 25.5	10 ♐ 40.7	19 37.0	29 26.7	12 29.1	6 25.6	22 13.7	29 33.6	6 42.5	4 33.0
24 M	12 1 40.3	2 18.4	7 22.3	22 40.9	20 21.5	0 ♉ 39.9	13 15.0	6 29.5	22 10.5	29 36.6	6 41.7	4 33.1
25 T	12 5 36.8	3 17.9	7 19.1	4 ♑ 55.2	20 58.5	1 53.0	14 0.7	6 33.6	22 7.5	29 39.7	6 40.9	4 33.3
26 W	12 9 33.4	4 17.3	7 16.0	17 28.8	21 27.9	3 6.1	14 46.4	6 37.9	22 4.5	29 42.7	6 40.2	4 33.4
27 T	12 13 29.9	5 16.7	7 12.8	0 ♒ 26.6	21 49.7	4 19.2	15 32.1	6 42.4	22 1.6	29 45.6	6 39.4	4 33.6
28 F	12 17 26.5	6 16.1	7 9.6	13 52.0	22 3.8	5 32.2	16 17.8	6 47.0	21 58.8	29 48.6	6 38.8	4 33.8
29 S	12 21 23.1	7 15.5	7 6.4	27 46.5	22 10.3	6 45.2	17 3.4	6 51.8	21 56.1	29 51.5	6 38.1	4 34.0
30 S	12 25 19.6	8 14.8	7 3.2	12 ♓ 8.9	22 R 9.3	7 58.0	17 48.9	6 56.8	21 53.5	29 54.4	6 37.5	4 34.2
31 M	12 29 16.1	9 14.1	7 0.1	26 54.6	22 1.2	9 10.9	18 34.4	7 1.9	21 51.0	29 57.3	6 36.9	4 34.4

DECLINATION

DAY	EPHEMERIS SIDEREAL TIME h m s	☉	☊	☽	☿	♀	♂	♃	♄	♅	♆	♇
1 S	10 30 59.6	8 S 3.7	21 S 44.7	10 S 22.9	7 S 41.7	0 S 1.2	2 S 28.0	23 N 28.5	15 N 2.1	12 S 42.8	18 N 24.9	19 N 13.9
4 T	10 42 49.2	6 55.3	21 43.2	5 N 30.3	5 6.6	1 N 32.5	1 30.8	23 28.8	15 6.7	12 39.3	18 26.0	19 14.4
7 F	10 54 38.9	5 45.9	21 41.7	18 42.3	2 24.6	3 6.0	0 33.7	23 29.0	15 11.1	12 35.8	18 27.0	19 14.9
10 M	11 6 28.6	4 35.9	21 40.2	21 34.2	0 N 20.1	4 38.9	0 N 23.3	23 29.1	15 15.4	12 32.3	18 27.9	19 15.3
13 T	11 18 18.2	3 25.4	21 38.6	13 43.8	3 1.5	6 10.9	1 20.1	23 29.2	15 19.4	12 28.9	18 28.8	19 15.8
16 S	11 30 7.9	2 14.5	21 37.1	0 36.0	5 32.6	7 41.7	2 16.6	23 29.1	15 23.1	12 25.6	18 29.7	19 16.3
19 W	11 41 57.5	1 3.4	21 35.6	12 S 15.9	7 45.8	9 11.0	3 12.8	23 29.0	15 26.7	12 22.3	18 30.4	19 16.7
22 S	11 53 47.2	0 N 7.7	21 34.0	20 31.2	9 34.0	10 38.4	4 8.5	23 28.7	15 30.0	12 19.0	18 31.1	19 17.2
25 T	12 5 36.8	1 18.7	21 32.4	20 53.0	10 51.7	12 3.6	5 3.7	23 28.4	15 33.0	12 15.9	18 31.8	19 17.6
28 F	12 17 26.5	2 29.4	21 30.8	12 8.6	11 34.9	13 26.2	5 58.3	23 28.0	15 35.7	12 12.8	18 32.4	19 18.0
31 M	12 29 16.1	3 39.7	21 29.3	3 N 7.1	11 41.3	14 46.0	6 52.3	23 27.4	15 38.1	12 9.8	18 32.9	19 18.5

APRIL 1919

LONGITUDE

DAY	EPHEMERIS SIDEREAL TIME h m s	☉ ° ′	☊ ° ′	☽ ° ′	☿ ° ′	♀ ° ′	♂ ° ′	♃ ° ′	♄ ° ′	♅ ° ′	♆ ° ′	♇ ° ′
1 T	12 33 12.7	10 ♈ 13.3	6 ♐ 56.9	11 ♈ 55.9	21 ♈ 46.3	10 ♉ 23.7	19 ♈ 19.9	7 ♋ 7.2	21 ♌ 48.6	0 ♓ 0.1	6 ♌ 36.3	4 ♋ 34.7
2 W	12 37 9.3	11 12.5	6 53.7	27 3.5	21 R 24.9	11 36.4	20 5.3	7 12.7	21 R 46.2	0 2.9	6 R 35.8	4 35.0
3 T	12 41 5.8	12 11.7	6 50.5	12 ♉ 7.3	20 57.7	12 49.1	20 50.7	7 18.3	21 44.0	0 5.7	6 35.3	4 35.4
4 F	12 45 2.4	13 10.9	6 47.4	26 58.8	20 25.3	14 1.7	21 36.0	7 24.1	21 41.9	0 8.5	6 34.8	4 35.7
5 S	12 48 58.9	14 10.0	6 44.2	11 ♊ 31.8	19 48.3	15 14.2	22 21.3	7 30.1	21 39.9	0 11.2	6 34.3	4 36.1
6 S	12 52 55.5	15 9.0	6 41.0	25 42.9	19 7.6	16 26.7	23 6.5	7 36.2	21 37.9	0 13.9	6 33.9	4 36.5
7 M	12 56 52.0	16 8.1	6 37.8	9 ♋ 31.3	18 24.1	17 39.1	23 51.7	7 42.4	21 36.1	0 16.6	6 33.6	4 36.9
8 T	13 0 48.6	17 7.0	6 34.6	22 57.9	17 38.5	18 51.5	24 36.8	7 48.8	21 34.4	0 19.2	6 33.2	4 37.3
9 W	13 4 45.1	18 6.0	6 31.5	6 ♌ 4.8	16 52.0	20 3.8	25 21.9	7 55.4	21 32.8	0 21.8	6 32.9	4 37.8
10 T	13 8 41.7	19 4.9	6 28.3	18 54.6	16 5.2	21 16.0	26 6.9	8 2.1	21 31.3	0 24.3	6 32.6	4 38.3
11 F	13 12 38.2	20 3.8	6 25.1	1 ♍ 30.0	15 19.3	22 28.1	26 51.9	8 8.9	21 29.9	0 26.9	6 32.4	4 38.8
12 S	13 16 34.8	21 2.6	6 21.9	13 53.2	14 34.9	23 40.2	27 36.8	8 15.9	21 28.6	0 29.4	6 32.2	4 39.3
13 S	13 20 31.3	22 1.4	6 18.8	26 6.2	13 52.8	24 52.2	28 21.7	8 23.0	21 27.4	0 31.8	6 32.0	4 39.9
14 M	13 24 27.9	23 0.2	6 15.6	8 ♎ 10.9	13 13.7	26 4.2	29 6.5	8 30.3	21 26.2	0 34.2	6 31.8	4 40.4
15 T	13 28 24.4	23 58.9	6 12.4	20 8.7	12 38.2	27 16.0	29 51.3	8 37.7	21 25.3	0 36.6	6 31.7	4 41.0
16 W	13 32 21.0	24 57.6	6 9.2	2 ♏ 1.3	12 6.7	28 27.8	0 ♉ 36.0	8 45.2	21 24.4	0 39.0	6 31.7	4 41.7
17 T	13 36 17.6	25 56.3	6 6.0	13 50.4	11 39.7	29 39.5	1 20.7	8 52.9	21 23.6	0 41.3	6 31.6	4 42.3
18 F	13 40 14.1	26 54.9	6 2.9	25 38.2	11 17.4	0 ♊ 51.1	2 5.3	9 0.7	21 22.9	0 43.6	6 31.6	4 43.0
19 S	13 44 10.6	27 53.5	5 59.7	7 ♐ 27.5	11 0.0	2 2.7	2 49.9	9 8.6	21 22.3	0 45.8	6 D 31.6	4 43.6
20 S	13 48 7.2	28 52.1	5 56.5	19 21.5	10 47.7	3 14.2	3 34.4	9 16.7	21 21.9	0 48.0	6 31.7	4 44.3
21 M	13 52 3.8	29 50.7	5 53.3	1 ♑ 23.9	10 40.5	4 25.6	4 18.9	9 24.9	21 21.5	0 50.2	6 31.8	4 45.0
22 T	13 56 0.3	0 ♉ 49.2	5 50.2	13 39.2	10 38.4	5 36.9	5 3.4	9 33.2	21 21.3	0 52.3	6 31.9	4 45.8
23 W	13 59 56.9	1 47.7	5 47.0	26 11.7	10 D 41.4	6 48.2	5 47.7	9 41.7	21 21.1	0 54.4	6 32.0	4 46.5
24 T	14 3 53.4	2 46.1	5 43.8	9 ♒ 5.9	10 49.3	7 59.4	6 32.1	9 50.2	21 21.1	0 56.4	6 32.2	4 47.3
25 F	14 7 50.0	3 44.6	5 40.6	22 25.4	11 2.1	9 10.5	7 16.4	9 58.9	21 D 21.2	0 58.5	6 32.4	4 48.1
26 S	14 11 46.5	4 43.0	5 37.4	6 ♓ 12.7	11 19.7	10 21.5	8 0.6	10 7.7	21 21.3	1 0.4	6 32.7	4 48.9
27 S	14 15 43.1	5 41.4	5 34.3	20 27.8	11 41.7	11 32.4	8 44.8	10 16.6	21 21.6	1 2.3	6 33.0	4 49.8
28 M	14 19 39.6	6 39.7	5 31.1	5 ♈ 8.2	12 8.2	12 43.3	9 28.9	10 25.6	21 22.0	1 4.2	6 33.3	4 50.6
29 T	14 23 36.2	7 38.1	5 27.9	20 8.3	12 38.9	13 54.1	10 13.0	10 34.8	21 22.5	1 6.1	6 33.6	4 51.5
30 W	14 27 32.8	8 36.4	5 24.7	5 ♉ 19.7	13 13.7	15 4.8	10 57.1	10 44.1	21 23.1	1 7.9	6 34.0	4 52.4

DECLINATION

DAY	EPHEMERIS SIDEREAL TIME h m s	☉	☊	☽	☿	♀	♂	♃	♄	♅	♆	♇
1 T	12 33 12.7	4 N 3.0	21 S 28.7	8 N 29.1	11 N 35.3	15 N 11.9	7 N 10.1	23 N 27.2	15 N 38.9	12 S 8.8	18 N 33.0	19 N 18.6
4 F	12 45 2.4	5 12.4	21 27.1	20 11.5	10 54.3	16 27.4	8 3.1	23 26.5	15 40.9	12 6.0	18 33.5	19 19.0
7 M	12 56 52.0	6 20.9	21 25.5	20 11.8	9 44.3	17 39.2	8 55.2	23 25.7	15 42.6	12 3.2	18 33.8	19 19.4
10 T	13 8 41.7	7 28.5	21 23.9	10 27.4	8 15.7	18 47.0	9 46.4	23 24.7	15 44.0	12 0.5	18 34.1	19 19.8
13 S	13 20 31.3	8 34.9	21 22.3	2 S 50.8	6 41.6	19 50.6	10 36.7	23 23.7	15 45.1	11 57.9	18 34.3	19 20.2
16 W	13 32 21.0	9 40.0	21 20.6	14 46.5	5 14.5	20 49.6	11 25.9	23 22.4	15 45.9	11 55.5	18 34.4	19 20.5
19 S	13 44 10.6	10 43.7	21 19.0	21 16.1	4 3.7	21 43.7	12 14.0	23 21.1	15 46.4	11 53.2	18 34.5	19 20.9
22 T	13 56 0.3	11 45.8	21 17.3	19 26.5	3 14.6	22 32.7	13 1.0	23 19.6	15 46.5	11 50.9	18 34.4	19 21.2
25 F	14 7 50.0	12 46.2	21 15.6	9 12.0	2 48.9	23 16.3	13 46.7	23 17.9	15 46.3	11 48.8	18 34.3	19 21.6
28 M	14 19 39.6	13 44.7	21 13.9	6 N 9.3	2 46.2	23 54.3	14 31.2	23 16.0	15 45.8	11 46.9	18 34.2	19 21.9

MAY 1919

DAY	EPHEMERIS SIDEREAL TIME h m s	☉ ° ′	☊ ° ′	☽ ° ′	☿ ° ′	♀ ° ′	♂ ° ′	♃ ° ′	♄ ° ′	♅ ° ′	♆ ° ′	♇ ° ′
						LONGITUDE						
1 T	14 31 29.3	9♉34.7	5♐21.6	20♉32.7	13♈52.5	16♊15.4	11♉41.0	10♋53.4	21♌23.9	1♓ 9.6	6♌34.5	4♋53.3
2 F	14 35 25.9	10 32.9	5 18.4	5♊37.4	14 34.9	17 25.9	12 25.0	11 2.9	21 24.7	1 11.3	6 34.9	4 54.2
3 S	14 39 22.4	11 31.1	5 15.2	20 25.6	15 20.9	18 36.3	13 8.8	11 12.5	21 25.6	1 13.0	6 35.4	4 55.2
4 S	14 43 18.9	12 29.3	5 12.0	4♋51.4	16 10.4	19 46.6	13 52.7	11 22.2	21 26.6	1 14.6	6 35.9	4 56.2
5 M	14 47 15.5	13 27.5	5 8.8	18 51.8	17 3.2	20 56.9	14 36.5	11 32.0	21 27.8	1 16.2	6 36.5	4 57.1
6 T	14 51 12.1	14 25.6	5 5.7	2♌26.3	17 59.2	22 7.0	15 20.2	11 41.9	21 29.0	1 17.8	6 37.0	4 58.2
7 W	14 55 8.6	15 23.7	5 2.5	15 36.5	18 58.2	23 17.0	16 3.8	11 51.8	21 30.4	1 19.2	6 37.7	4 59.2
8 T	14 59 5.2	16 21.7	4 59.3	28 24.9	20 0.2	24 27.0	16 47.4	12 1.9	21 31.8	1 20.7	6 38.3	5 0.2
9 F	15 3 1.7	17 19.7	4 56.1	10♍55.0	21 5.0	25 36.8	17 31.0	12 12.1	21 33.4	1 22.1	6 39.0	5 1.2
10 S	15 6 58.3	18 17.7	4 53.0	23 10.4	22 12.6	26 46.5	18 14.5	12 22.4	21 35.1	1 23.4	6 39.7	5 2.3
11 S	15 10 54.9	19 15.7	4 49.8	5♎14.6	23 22.9	27 56.1	18 58.0	12 32.8	21 36.8	1 24.7	6 40.4	5 3.4
12 M	15 14 51.4	20 13.6	4 46.6	17 10.9	24 35.7	29 5.6	19 41.4	12 43.2	21 38.7	1 26.0	6 41.2	5 4.5
13 T	15 18 47.9	21 11.5	4 43.4	29 2.0	25 51.1	0♋15.0	20 24.7	12 53.8	21 40.7	1 27.2	6 42.0	5 5.6
14 W	15 22 44.5	22 9.4	4 40.2	10♏50.7	27 9.0	1 24.2	21 8.0	13 4.4	21 42.8	1 28.4	6 42.8	5 6.7
15 T	15 26 41.1	23 7.3	4 37.1	22 39.2	28 29.3	2 33.4	21 51.2	13 15.1	21 44.9	1 29.5	6 43.7	5 7.9
16 F	15 30 37.6	24 5.1	4 33.9	4♐29.7	29 52.0	3 42.4	22 34.4	13 25.9	21 47.2	1 30.6	6 44.6	5 9.0
17 S	15 34 34.2	25 2.9	4 30.7	16 24.5	1♉17.1	4 51.3	23 17.6	13 36.8	21 49.6	1 31.6	6 45.5	5 10.2
18 S	15 38 30.7	26 0.7	4 27.5	28 25.9	2 44.5	6 0.1	24 0.6	13 47.8	21 52.0	1 32.6	6 46.5	5 11.4
19 M	15 42 27.3	26 58.4	4 24.4	10♑36.5	4 14.1	7 8.7	24 43.7	13 58.8	21 54.6	1 33.5	6 47.5	5 12.6
20 T	15 46 23.9	27 56.2	4 21.2	22 59.2	5 46.1	8 17.3	25 26.7	14 9.9	21 57.3	1 34.4	6 48.5	5 13.8
21 W	15 50 20.4	28 53.9	4 18.0	5♒36.8	7 20.3	9 25.6	26 9.6	14 21.1	22 0.0	1 35.3	6 49.5	5 15.0
22 T	15 54 16.9	29 51.6	4 14.8	18 32.6	8 56.7	10 33.9	26 52.5	14 32.4	22 2.9	1 36.1	6 50.6	5 16.3
23 F	15 58 13.5	0♊49.3	4 11.6	1♓49.2	10 35.5	11 42.0	27 35.3	14 43.7	22 5.8	1 36.8	6 51.7	5 17.5
24 S	16 2 10.1	1 46.9	4 8.5	15 28.8	12 16.4	12 50.0	28 18.1	14 55.2	22 8.9	1 37.5	6 52.8	5 18.8
25 S	16 6 6.6	2 44.6	4 5.3	29 32.1	13 59.7	13 57.9	29 0.8	15 6.7	22 12.0	1 38.2	6 54.0	5 20.1
26 M	16 10 3.1	3 42.2	4 2.1	13♈58.2	15 45.1	15 5.6	29 43.5	15 18.2	22 15.2	1 38.7	6 55.2	5 21.4
27 T	16 13 59.7	4 39.8	3 58.9	28 43.8	17 32.8	16 13.2	0♊26.1	15 29.9	22 18.6	1 39.3	6 56.4	5 22.6
28 W	16 17 56.3	5 37.4	3 55.8	13♉43.3	19 22.7	17 20.6	1 8.7	15 41.6	22 22.0	1 39.8	6 57.6	5 24.0
29 T	16 21 52.8	6 35.0	3 52.6	28 48.9	21 14.8	18 27.9	1 51.3	15 53.3	22 25.5	1 40.2	6 58.9	5 25.3
30 F	16 25 49.4	7 32.6	3 49.4	13♊51.8	23 9.0	19 35.1	2 33.8	16 5.2	22 29.1	1 40.7	7 0.2	5 26.6
31 S	16 29 45.9	8 30.2	3 46.2	28 43.5	25 5.5	20 42.0	3 16.2	16 17.0	22 32.8	1 41.0	7 1.5	5 27.9
						DECLINATION						
1 T	14 31 29.3	14N41.2	21S12.3	19N 4.1	3N 4.6	24N26.5	15N14.4	23N14.0	15N45.0	11S45.1	18N33.9	19N22.2
4 S	14 43 18.9	15 35.5	21 10.5	20 39.2	3 42.1	24 52.7	15 56.1	23 11.8	15 43.9	11 43.4	18 33.6	19 22.5
7 W	14 55 8.6	16 27.5	21 8.8	11 23.0	4 36.4	25 12.8	16 36.4	23 9.4	15 42.5	11 41.9	18 33.2	19 22.7
10 S	15 6 58.3	17 17.0	21 7.1	1S51.6	5 45.4	25 26.8	17 15.3	23 6.9	15 40.7	11 40.5	18 32.7	19 23.0
13 T	15 18 47.9	18 3.9	21 5.4	13 57.3	7 7.1	25 34.5	17 52.5	23 4.1	15 38.7	11 39.2	18 32.2	19 23.2
16 F	15 30 37.6	18 48.0	21 3.6	20 59.1	8 39.7	25 36.0	18 28.2	23 1.1	15 36.4	11 38.1	18 31.5	19 23.4
19 M	15 42 27.3	19 29.4	21 1.9	19 51.5	10 21.4	25 31.3	19 2.2	22 58.0	15 33.7	11 37.2	18 30.9	19 23.6
22 T	15 54 16.9	20 7.7	21 0.1	10 24.6	12 10.2	25 20.6	19 34.6	22 54.6	15 30.8	11 36.4	18 30.1	19 23.8
25 S	16 6 6.6	20 43.0	20 58.4	4N11.8	14 4.1	25 3.8	20 5.3	22 51.0	15 27.7	11 35.7	18 29.3	19 24.0
28 W	16 17 56.3	21 15.1	20 56.6	17 42.4	16 0.5	24 41.2	20 34.2	22 47.2	15 24.2	11 35.3	18 28.4	19 24.1
31 S	16 29 45.9	21 43.8	20 54.8	21 12.6	17 56.2	24 12.9	21 1.3	22 43.2	15 20.5	11 35.0	18 27.5	19 24.2

JUNE 1919

DAY	SIDEREAL TIME	☉	☊	☽	☿	♀	♂	♃	♄	♅	♆	♇
						LONGITUDE						
1 S	16 33 42.5	9♊27.7	3♐43.1	13♋16.5	27♉ 4.0	21♋48.8	3♊58.6	16♋29.0	22♌36.5	1♓41.3	7♌ 2.9	5♋29.3
2 M	16 37 39.1	10 25.2	3 39.9	27 25.8	29 4.5	22 55.5	4 40.9	16 41.0	22 40.4	1 41.6	7 4.3	5 30.7
3 T	16 41 35.6	11 22.7	3 36.7	11♌ 8.8	1♊ 7.0	24 2.0	5 23.2	16 53.1	22 44.3	1 41.8	7 5.7	5 32.0
4 W	16 45 32.2	12 20.2	3 33.5	24 25.4	3 11.2	25 8.3	6 5.4	17 5.2	22 48.4	1 41.9	7 7.1	5 33.4
5 T	16 49 28.7	13 17.6	3 30.4	7♍17.6	5 17.2	26 14.4	6 47.6	17 17.4	22 52.5	1 42.0	7 8.5	5 34.8
6 F	16 53 25.3	14 15.0	3 27.2	19 48.5	7 24.7	27 20.3	7 29.7	17 29.6	22 56.7	1 42.1	7 10.0	5 36.2
7 S	16 57 21.9	15 12.5	3 24.0	2♎ 2.2	9 33.6	28 26.0	8 11.7	17 41.9	23 1.0	1 42.1	7 11.5	5 37.6
8 S	17 1 18.4	16 9.8	3 20.8	14 3.3	11 43.6	29 31.5	8 53.8	17 54.3	23 5.3	1R42.1	7 13.1	5 39.0
9 M	17 5 15.0	17 7.2	3 17.6	25 55.9	13 54.5	0♌36.9	9 35.7	18 6.6	23 9.8	1 42.0	7 14.6	5 40.4
10 T	17 9 11.5	18 4.6	3 14.5	7♏44.4	16 6.1	1 42.0	10 17.6	18 19.1	23 14.3	1 41.8	7 16.2	5 41.8
11 W	17 13 8.0	19 1.9	3 11.3	19 32.4	18 18.0	2 46.9	10 59.5	18 31.5	23 18.9	1 41.7	7 17.8	5 43.2
12 T	17 17 4.6	19 59.2	3 8.1	1♐23.2	20 30.1	3 51.5	11 41.3	18 44.1	23 23.6	1 41.4	7 19.4	5 44.7
13 F	17 21 1.2	20 56.6	3 4.9	13 19.5	22 42.0	4 56.0	12 23.1	18 56.6	23 28.4	1 41.2	7 21.0	5 46.1
14 S	17 24 57.8	21 53.9	3 1.8	25 23.6	24 53.4	6 0.2	13 4.8	19 9.3	23 33.2	1 40.8	7 22.7	5 47.6
15 S	17 28 54.3	22 51.1	2 58.6	7♑37.4	27 4.2	7 4.2	13 46.4	19 21.9	23 38.1	1 40.5	7 24.4	5 49.0
16 M	17 32 50.8	23 48.4	2 55.4	20 2.3	29 14.0	8 7.9	14 28.0	19 34.6	23 43.1	1 40.0	7 26.1	5 50.5
17 T	17 36 47.4	24 45.7	2 52.2	2♒39.6	1♋22.7	9 11.4	15 9.6	19 47.3	23 48.1	1 39.6	7 27.8	5 51.9
18 W	17 40 44.0	25 43.0	2 49.1	15 30.6	3 30.1	10 14.7	15 51.1	20 0.1	23 53.2	1 39.1	7 29.6	5 53.4
19 T	17 44 40.6	26 40.2	2 45.9	28 36.3	5 35.9	11 17.6	16 32.6	20 12.9	23 58.4	1 38.5	7 31.3	5 54.9
20 F	17 48 37.1	27 37.5	2 42.7	11♓57.8	7 40.0	12 20.4	17 14.0	20 25.8	24 3.7	1 37.9	7 33.1	5 56.3
21 S	17 52 33.6	28 34.7	2 39.5	25 36.0	9 42.3	13 22.8	17 55.4	20 38.7	24 9.0	1 37.2	7 34.9	5 57.8
22 S	17 56 30.2	29 32.0	2 36.4	9♈31.2	11 42.8	14 24.9	18 36.7	20 51.6	24 14.4	1 36.5	7 36.7	5 59.3
23 M	18 0 26.8	0♋29.2	2 33.2	23 43.1	13 41.3	15 26.8	19 18.0	21 4.5	24 19.9	1 35.8	7 38.6	6 0.8
24 T	18 4 23.3	1 26.5	2 30.0	8♉ 9.9	15 37.7	16 28.4	19 59.2	21 17.5	24 25.4	1 35.0	7 40.4	6 2.2
25 W	18 8 19.9	2 23.7	2 26.8	22 48.7	17 32.1	17 29.7	20 40.4	21 30.5	24 31.0	1 34.2	7 42.3	6 3.7
26 T	18 12 16.5	3 21.0	2 23.6	7♊34.5	19 24.3	18 30.6	21 21.5	21 43.6	24 36.7	1 33.3	7 44.2	6 5.2
27 F	18 16 13.0	4 18.2	2 20.5	22 21.2	21 14.4	19 31.3	22 2.6	21 56.6	24 42.4	1 32.4	7 46.1	6 6.7
28 S	18 20 9.5	5 15.5	2 17.3	7♋ 1.6	23 2.4	20 31.6	22 43.7	22 9.7	24 48.2	1 31.4	7 48.1	6 8.2
29 S	18 24 6.1	6 12.7	2 14.1	21 28.7	24 48.1	21 31.5	23 24.7	22 22.8	24 54.1	1 30.4	7 50.0	6 9.7
30 M	18 28 2.7	7 9.9	2 10.9	5♌36.7	26 31.7	22 31.1	24 5.6	22 36.0	24 60.0	1 29.3	7 52.0	6 11.2
						DECLINATION						
1 S	16 33 42.5	21N52.7	20S54.2	19N26.1	18N34.0	24N 2.3	21N 9.9	22N41.8	15N19.2	11S34.9	18N27.1	19N24.3
4 W	16 45 32.2	22 16.9	20 52.4	8 27.4	20 22.5	23 26.9	21 34.6	22 37.5	15 15.1	11 34.8	18 26.1	19 24.4
7 S	16 57 21.9	22 37.6	20 50.6	5S 5.3	21 59.7	22 46.5	21 57.5	22 33.0	15 10.8	11 34.8	18 25.0	19 24.5
10 T	17 9 11.5	22 54.8	20 48.7	16 18.1	23 20.3	22 1.3	22 18.4	22 28.3	15 6.2	11 35.0	18 23.9	19 24.5
13 F	17 21 1.2	23 8.3	20 46.9	21 32.8	24 19.4	21 11.7	22 37.5	22 23.3	15 1.4	11 35.4	18 22.7	19 24.6
16 M	17 32 50.8	23 18.2	20 45.1	18 11.6	24 54.0	20 18.0	22 54.7	22 18.1	14 56.4	11 35.9	18 21.4	19 24.6
19 T	17 44 40.6	23 24.4	20 43.2	7 3.5	25 3.4	19 20.4	23 9.9	22 12.7	14 51.2	11 36.5	18 20.1	19 24.7
22 S	17 56 30.2	23 26.9	20 41.4	7N40.9	24 49.0	18 19.4	23 23.3	22 7.1	14 45.7	11 37.4	18 18.8	19 24.7
25 W	18 8 19.9	23 25.6	20 39.5	19 26.2	24 13.7	17 15.2	23 34.7	22 1.3	14 40.0	11 38.3	18 17.4	19 24.6
28 S	18 20 9.5	23 20.6	20 37.6	20 23.3	23 20.8	16 8.2	23 44.1	21 55.3	14 34.2	11 39.4	18 15.9	19 24.6

JULY 1919

LONGITUDE

DAY	EPHEMERIS SIDEREAL TIME h m s	☉ ° ′	☊ ° ′	☾ ° ′	☿ ° ′	♀ ° ′	♂ ° ′	♃ ° ′	♄ ° ′	♅ ° ′	♆ ° ′	♇ ° ′
1 T	18 31 59.2	8♋ 7.2	2♐ 7.8	19♌21.4	28♋13.1	23♌30.4	24♊46.5	22♋49.2	25♌ 5.9	1♓28.2	7♌54.0	6♋12.7
2 W	18 35 55.8	9 4.4	2 4.6	2♍41.1	29 52.4	24 29.3	25 27.4	23 2.4	25 12.0	1R27.1	7 55.9	6 14.1
3 T	18 39 52.3	10 1.6	2 1.4	15 36.3	1♌29.4	25 27.7	26 8.2	23 15.6	25 18.1	1 25.9	7 58.0	6 15.6
4 F	18 43 48.9	10 58.8	1 58.2	28 9.4	3 4.2	26 25.8	26 49.0	23 28.8	25 24.2	1 24.7	7 60.0	6 17.1
5 S	18 47 45.5	11 56.0	1 55.1	10♎24.1	4 36.8	27 23.4	27 29.7	23 42.0	25 30.4	1 23.4	8 2.0	6 18.6
6 S	18 51 42.0	12 53.2	1 51.9	22 25.0	6 7.2	28 20.6	28 10.3	23 55.3	25 36.6	1 22.1	8 4.0	6 20.1
7 M	18 55 38.6	13 50.4	1 48.7	4♏17.1	7 35.3	29 17.4	28 50.9	24 8.6	25 42.9	1 20.7	8 6.1	6 21.5
8 T	18 59 35.1	14 47.6	1 45.5	16 5.5	9 1.2	0♍13.6	29 31.5	24 21.9	25 49.3	1 19.4	8 8.2	6 23.0
9 W	19 3 31.7	15 44.8	1 42.3	27 54.8	10 24.7	1 9.4	0♋12.0	24 35.2	25 55.7	1 17.9	8 10.3	6 24.5
10 T	19 7 28.2	16 42.0	1 39.2	9♐49.4	11 45.9	2 4.7	0 52.5	24 48.5	26 2.1	1 16.5	8 12.4	6 26.0
11 F	19 11 24.8	17 39.2	1 36.0	21 53.0	13 4.8	2 59.5	1 32.9	25 1.8	26 8.6	1 15.0	8 14.5	6 27.4
12 S	19 15 21.4	18 36.4	1 32.8	4♑ 8.2	14 21.2	3 53.7	2 13.3	25 15.2	26 15.2	1 13.4	8 16.6	6 28.9
13 S	19 19 17.9	19 33.6	1 29.6	16 37.0	15 35.2	4 47.4	2 53.6	25 28.5	26 21.8	1 11.9	8 18.7	6 30.3
14 M	19 23 14.4	20 30.8	1 26.5	29 20.3	16 46.6	5 40.5	3 33.9	25 41.9	26 28.4	1 10.3	8 20.8	6 31.8
15 T	19 27 11.0	21 28.0	1 23.3	12♒18.0	17 55.4	6 33.0	4 14.2	25 55.2	26 35.1	1 8.6	8 23.0	6 33.2
16 W	19 31 7.6	22 25.2	1 20.1	25 29.7	19 1.6	7 24.9	4 54.4	26 8.6	26 41.8	1 6.9	8 25.1	6 34.7
17 T	19 35 4.2	23 22.5	1 16.9	8♓54.1	20 4.9	8 16.1	5 34.5	26 22.0	26 48.6	1 5.2	8 27.3	6 36.1
18 F	19 39 0.7	24 19.7	1 13.8	22 30.1	21 5.4	9 6.7	6 14.6	26 35.3	26 55.4	1 3.5	8 29.4	6 37.5
19 S	19 42 57.2	25 16.9	1 10.6	6♈16.4	22 3.0	9 56.7	6 54.7	26 48.7	27 2.2	1 1.7	8 31.6	6 39.0
20 S	19 46 53.8	26 14.2	1 7.4	20 12.3	22 57.5	10 45.9	7 34.7	27 2.1	27 9.1	0 59.9	8 33.8	6 40.4
21 M	19 50 50.4	27 11.5	1 4.2	4♉16.9	23 48.8	11 34.4	8 14.7	27 15.5	27 16.1	0 58.1	8 36.0	6 41.8
22 T	19 54 46.9	28 8.8	1 1.0	18 29.1	24 36.7	12 22.2	8 54.7	27 28.9	27 23.0	0 56.2	8 38.2	6 43.2
23 W	19 58 43.5	29 6.1	0 57.9	2♊47.6	25 21.2	13 9.1	9 34.6	27 42.2	27 30.0	0 54.3	8 40.4	6 44.6
24 T	20 2 40.0	0♌ 3.4	0 54.7	17 9.9	26 2.1	13 55.3	10 14.4	27 55.6	27 37.1	0 52.4	8 42.6	6 46.0
25 F	20 6 36.6	1 0.7	0 51.5	1♋32.5	26 39.2	14 40.6	10 54.3	28 9.0	27 44.1	0 50.4	8 44.8	6 47.3
26 S	20 10 33.1	1 58.0	0 48.3	15 50.9	27 12.4	15 25.1	11 34.0	28 22.4	27 51.2	0 48.4	8 47.0	6 48.7
27 S	20 14 29.7	2 55.4	0 45.2	29 59.9	27 41.4	16 8.7	12 13.8	28 35.7	27 58.4	0 46.4	8 49.2	6 50.1
28 M	20 18 26.3	3 52.8	0 42.0	13♌54.5	28 6.2	16 51.3	12 53.5	28 49.1	28 5.6	0 44.4	8 51.4	6 51.4
29 T	20 22 22.8	4 50.1	0 38.8	27 30.4	28 26.5	17 32.9	13 33.1	29 2.4	28 12.8	0 42.3	8 53.7	6 52.8
30 W	20 26 19.4	5 47.5	0 35.6	10♍45.2	28 42.1	18 13.6	14 12.7	29 15.8	28 20.0	0 40.2	8 55.9	6 54.1
31 T	20 30 15.9	6 44.9	0 32.5	23 38.1	28 53.0	18 53.1	14 52.3	29 29.1	28 27.2	0 38.1	8 58.1	6 55.4

DECLINATION

DAY	EPHEMERIS SIDEREAL TIME h m s	☉	☊	☾	☿	♀	♂	♃	♄	♅	♆	♇
1 T	18 31 59.2	23N12.0	20S35.7	10N13.5	22N13.8	14N58.8	23N51.7	21N49.1	14N28.1	11S40.6	18N14.5	19N24.6
4 F	18 43 48.9	22 59.7	20 33.8	3S35.6	20 56.2	13 47.4	23 57.3	21 42.6	14 21.9	11 42.0	18 13.0	19 24.5
7 M	18 55 38.6	22 43.7	20 31.9	15 19.3	19 30.8	12 34.3	24 1.0	21 36.0	14 15.5	11 43.5	18 11.4	19 24.4
10 T	19 7 28.2	22 24.3	20 30.0	21 20.6	18 0.4	11 19.8	24 2.8	21 29.2	14 8.9	11 45.1	18 9.8	19 24.4
13 S	19 19 17.9	22 1.3	20 28.1	18 53.8	16 27.6	10 4.5	24 2.7	21 22.1	14 2.1	11 46.8	18 8.2	19 24.3
16 W	19 31 7.6	21 35.0	20 26.1	8 14.4	14 54.8	8 48.6	24 0.8	21 14.9	13 55.3	11 48.6	18 6.6	19 24.1
19 S	19 42 57.2	21 5.3	20 24.2	6N23.9	13 24.4	7 32.5	23 57.0	21 7.6	13 48.2	11 50.6	18 4.9	19 24.0
22 T	19 54 46.9	20 32.4	20 22.2	18 31.1	11 59.2	6 16.6	23 51.5	21 0.0	13 41.1	11 52.6	18 3.2	19 23.9
25 F	20 6 36.6	19 56.4	20 20.3	20 56.8	10 41.7	5 1.3	23 44.1	20 52.3	13 33.8	11 54.7	18 1.5	19 23.7
28 M	20 18 26.3	19 17.4	20 18.3	12 2.3	9 35.3	3 47.2	23 35.0	20 44.4	13 26.4	11 56.9	17 59.8	19 23.6
31 T	20 30 15.9	18 35.6	20 16.3	1S47.1	8 43.3	2 34.7	23 24.2	20 36.4	13 18.9	11 59.2	17 58.1	19 23.4

AUGUST 1919

LONGITUDE

DAY	EPHEMERIS SIDEREAL TIME h m s	☉ ° ′	☊ ° ′	☾ ° ′	☿ ° ′	♀ ° ′	♂ ° ′	♃ ° ′	♄ ° ′	♅ ° ′	♆ ° ′	♇ ° ′
1 F	20 34 12.5	7♌42.3	0♐29.3	6♎10.4	28♌58.9	19♍31.6	15♋31.8	29♋42.4	28♌34.5	0♓36.0	9♌ 0.3	6♋56.7
2 S	20 38 9.0	8 39.7	0 26.1	18 24.9	28 59.8	20 8.9	16 11.3	29 55.7	28 41.8	0R33.8	9 2.6	6 58.0
3 S	20 42 5.6	9 37.2	0 22.9	0♏25.8	28R55.4	20 45.0	16 50.7	0♌ 9.0	28 49.2	0 31.7	9 4.8	6 59.3
4 M	20 46 2.2	10 34.6	0 19.8	12 17.8	28 45.8	21 19.9	17 30.1	0 22.2	28 56.5	0 29.5	9 7.0	7 0.6
5 T	20 49 58.7	11 32.1	0 16.6	24 6.4	28 31.0	21 53.5	18 9.4	0 35.5	29 3.9	0 27.2	9 9.2	7 1.9
6 W	20 53 55.3	12 29.5	0 13.4	5♐56.9	28 11.0	22 25.7	18 48.7	0 48.7	29 11.3	0 25.0	9 11.5	7 3.1
7 T	20 57 51.8	13 27.0	0 10.2	17 54.6	27 45.8	22 56.5	19 27.9	1 1.9	29 18.7	0 22.8	9 13.7	7 4.3
8 F	21 1 48.4	14 24.5	0 7.0	0♑ 3.9	27 15.8	23 25.9	20 7.2	1 15.1	29 26.2	0 20.5	9 15.9	7 5.6
9 S	21 5 44.9	15 22.0	0 3.9	12 28.5	26 41.2	23 53.8	20 46.3	1 28.3	29 33.6	0 18.2	9 18.1	7 6.8
10 S	21 9 41.5	16 19.5	0 0.7	25 11.0	26 2.3	24 20.1	21 25.4	1 41.4	29 41.1	0 15.9	9 20.3	7 8.0
11 M	21 13 38.0	17 17.1	29♏57.5	8♒12.4	25 19.8	24 44.8	22 4.5	1 54.5	29 48.6	0 13.6	9 22.5	7 9.2
12 T	21 17 34.6	18 14.6	29 54.3	21 32.1	24 34.2	25 7.9	22 43.6	2 7.6	29 56.1	0 11.3	9 24.7	7 10.3
13 W	21 21 31.1	19 12.2	29 51.1	5♓ 8.1	23 46.3	25 29.2	23 22.6	2 20.7	0♍ 3.6	0 9.0	9 26.9	7 11.5
14 T	21 25 27.7	20 9.8	29 48.0	18 57.2	22 56.8	25 48.7	24 1.5	2 33.7	0 11.2	0 6.6	9 29.1	7 12.7
15 F	21 29 24.2	21 7.4	29 44.8	2♈55.8	22 6.6	26 6.3	24 40.5	2 46.7	0 18.7	0 4.3	9 31.3	7 13.8
16 S	21 33 20.8	22 5.0	29 41.6	17 0.3	21 16.7	26 22.1	25 19.3	2 59.7	0 26.3	0 1.9	9 33.5	7 14.9
17 S	21 37 17.4	23 2.7	29 38.4	1♉ 7.6	20 28.1	26 35.8	25 58.2	3 12.7	0 33.8	29♒59.6	9 35.7	7 16.0
18 M	21 41 13.9	24 0.4	29 35.3	15 15.6	19 41.8	26 47.6	26 37.0	3 25.6	0 41.4	29 57.2	9 37.9	7 17.1
19 T	21 45 10.4	24 58.1	29 32.1	29 22.9	18 58.7	26 57.3	27 15.8	3 38.5	0 49.0	29 54.8	9 40.0	7 18.2
20 W	21 49 7.0	25 55.9	29 28.9	13♊28.6	18 19.8	27 4.9	27 54.5	3 51.3	0 56.6	29 52.4	9 42.2	7 19.2
21 T	21 53 3.6	26 53.7	29 25.7	27 31.7	17 45.8	27 10.3	28 33.2	4 4.1	1 4.2	29 50.0	9 44.3	7 20.2
22 F	21 57 0.2	27 51.5	29 22.6	11♋30.9	17 17.7	27 13.5	29 11.8	4 16.9	1 11.8	29 47.6	9 46.5	7 21.3
23 S	22 0 56.7	28 49.3	29 19.4	25 24.1	16 56.0	27 14.4	29 50.4	4 29.6	1 19.4	29 45.2	9 48.6	7 22.3
24 S	22 4 53.2	29 47.2	29 16.2	9♌ 8.5	16 41.2	27R13.1	0♌29.0	4 42.3	1 27.1	29 42.8	9 50.7	7 23.3
25 M	22 8 49.8	0♍45.0	29 13.0	22 41.2	16 33.9	27 9.4	1 7.5	4 55.0	1 34.7	29 40.4	9 52.8	7 24.2
26 T	22 12 46.3	1 43.0	29 9.8	5♍59.3	16D34.4	27 3.3	1 46.0	5 7.6	1 42.3	29 38.0	9 54.9	7 25.2
27 W	22 16 42.9	2 40.9	29 6.7	19 0.6	16 42.8	26 54.9	2 24.5	5 20.2	1 49.9	29 35.7	9 57.0	7 26.1
28 T	22 20 39.5	3 38.9	29 3.5	1♎44.2	16 59.3	26 44.1	3 2.9	5 32.7	1 57.5	29 33.3	9 59.1	7 27.0
29 F	22 24 36.0	4 36.8	29 0.3	14 10.6	17 23.9	26 30.9	3 41.2	5 45.2	2 5.2	29 30.9	10 1.2	7 27.9
30 S	22 28 32.5	5 34.8	28 57.1	26 21.5	17 56.6	26 15.4	4 19.5	5 57.6	2 12.8	29 28.5	10 3.2	7 28.8
31 S	22 32 29.1	6 32.9	28 53.9	8♏20.3	18 37.2	25 57.5	4 57.8	6 10.0	2 20.4	29 26.1	10 5.3	7 29.7

DECLINATION

DAY	EPHEMERIS SIDEREAL TIME h m s	☉	☊	☾	☿	♀	♂	♃	♄	♅	♆	♇
1 F	20 34 12.5	18N21.0	20S15.6	6S16.8	8N29.8	2N11.0	23N20.3	20N33.7	13N16.4	11S60.0	17N57.5	19N23.3
4 M	20 46 2.2	17 35.5	20 13.7	17 6.5	8 2.9	1 1.5	23 7.2	20 25.5	13 8.8	12 2.3	17 55.8	19 23.2
7 T	20 57 51.8	16 47.5	20 11.6	21 26.7	7 58.7	0S 5.0	22 52.6	20 17.2	13 1.1	12 4.8	17 54.1	19 23.0
10 S	21 9 41.5	15 57.0	20 9.6	17 5.1	8 19.0	1 7.7	22 36.4	20 8.8	12 53.3	12 7.2	17 52.3	19 22.8
13 W	21 21 31.1	15 4.2	20 7.6	4 58.5	9 2.8	2 5.8	22 18.7	20 0.3	12 45.5	12 9.7	17 50.6	19 22.6
16 S	21 33 20.8	14 9.2	20 5.6	9N51.2	10 5.3	2 58.5	21 59.5	19 51.7	12 37.6	12 12.2	17 48.9	19 22.4
19 T	21 45 10.4	13 12.2	20 3.5	20 4.1	11 18.2	3 44.8	21 38.8	19 43.0	12 29.6	12 14.7	17 47.2	19 22.2
22 F	21 57 0.2	12 13.3	20 1.5	19 36.5	12 31.2	4 23.6	21 16.8	19 34.3	12 21.7	12 17.3	17 45.5	19 22.0
25 M	22 8 49.8	11♍12.7	19 59.4	9 15.0	13 34.3	4 53.7	20 53.5	19 25.5	12 13.7	12 19.8	17 43.8	19 21.7
28 T	22 20 39.5	10 10.4	19 57.4	4S33.2	14 19.0	5 13.9	20 28.8	19 16.6	12 5.7	12 22.3	17 42.2	19 21.5
31 S	22 32 29.1	9 6.7	19 55.3	15 55.9	14 39.2	5 23.2	20 2.9	19 7.8	11 57.7	12 24.8	17 40.5	19 21.3

SEPTEMBER 1919

LONGITUDE

DAY	EPHEMERIS SIDEREAL TIME h m s	☉ ° ′	☊ ° ′	☽ ° ′	☿ ° ′	♀ ° ′	♂ ° ′	♃ ° ′	♄ ° ′	♅ ° ′	♆ ° ′	♇ ° ′
1 M	22 36 25.7	7♍30.9	28♏50.8	20♏11.2	19♌25.6	25♍37.3	5♌36.0	6♌22.3	2♍28.0	29♒23.8	10♌ 7.3	7♋30.5
2 T	22 40 22.2	8 29.0	28 47.6	1♐59.0	20 21.3	25R15.0	6 14.2	6 34.6	2 35.6	29R21.4	10 9.3	7 31.3
3 W	22 44 18.7	9 27.1	28 44.4	13 49.2	21 24.2	24 50.5	6 52.4	6 46.8	2 43.2	29 19.1	10 11.3	7 32.1
4 T	22 48 15.3	10 25.2	28 41.2	25 47.3	22 33.8	24 24.0	7 30.5	6 59.0	2 50.7	29 16.7	10 13.3	7 32.9
5 F	22 52 11.9	11 23.4	28 38.1	7♑58.5	23 49.6	23 55.6	8 8.6	7 11.1	2 58.3	29 14.4	10 15.3	7 33.7
6 S	22 56 8.4	12 21.6	28 34.9	20 27.6	25 11.2	23 25.4	8 46.6	7 23.1	3 5.9	29 12.1	10 17.2	7 34.4
7 S	23 0 4.9	13 19.8	28 31.7	3♒17.9	26 38.1	22 53.6	9 24.6	7 35.1	3 13.4	29 9.8	10 19.2	7 35.1
8 M	23 4 1.5	14 18.0	28 28.5	16 31.5	28 9.7	22 20.4	10 2.5	7 47.0	3 20.9	29 7.5	10 21.1	7 35.8
9 T	23 7 58.1	15 16.2	28 25.3	0♓ 8.2	29 45.5	21 46.0	10 40.4	7 58.9	3 28.5	29 5.2	10 23.0	7 36.5
10 W	23 11 54.7	16 14.5	28 22.2	14 5.6	1♍25.0	21 10.6	11 18.3	8 10.7	3 36.0	29 3.0	10 24.9	7 37.2
11 T	23 15 51.2	17 12.8	28 19.0	28 19.6	3 7.7	20 34.3	11 56.1	8 22.4	3 43.5	29 0.7	10 26.7	7 37.8
12 F	23 19 47.7	18 11.2	28 15.8	12♈44.3	4 52.9	19 57.5	12 33.9	8 34.1	3 50.9	28 58.5	10 28.6	7 38.5
13 S	23 23 44.3	19 9.5	28 12.6	27 13.6	6 40.3	19 20.4	13 11.6	8 45.7	3 58.4	28 56.3	10 30.4	7 39.1
14 S	23 27 40.8	20 7.9	28 9.5	11♉41.8	8 29.5	18 43.3	13 49.3	8 57.3	4 5.8	28 54.1	10 32.2	7 39.6
15 M	23 31 37.4	21 6.4	28 6.3	26 4.6	10 19.9	18 6.3	14 27.0	9 8.7	4 13.2	28 51.9	10 34.0	7 40.2
16 T	23 35 33.9	22 4.9	28 3.1	10♊19.0	12 11.4	17 29.8	15 4.6	9 20.1	4 20.6	28 49.8	10 35.8	7 40.7
17 W	23 39 30.5	23 3.4	27 59.9	24 23.4	14 3.4	16 53.9	15 42.2	9 31.5	4 28.0	28 47.7	10 37.5	7 41.3
18 T	23 43 27.1	24 1.9	27 56.7	8♋17.3	15 55.8	16 18.9	16 19.7	9 42.7	4 35.3	28 45.6	10 39.3	7 41.7
19 F	23 47 23.6	25 0.5	27 53.6	22 0.4	17 48.3	15 45.1	16 57.2	9 53.9	4 42.6	28 43.5	10 41.0	7 42.2
20 S	23 51 20.1	25 59.2	27 50.4	5♌32.6	19 40.7	15 12.5	17 34.7	10 5.0	4 49.9	28 41.4	10 42.7	7 42.7
21 S	23 55 16.7	26 57.8	27 47.2	18 53.5	21 32.8	14 41.5	18 12.1	10 16.0	4 57.2	28 39.4	10 44.3	7 43.1
22 M	23 59 13.3	27 56.5	27 44.0	2♍ 2.4	23 24.5	14 12.1	18 49.5	10 26.9	5 4.5	28 37.4	10 46.0	7 43.5
23 T	0 3 9.8	28 55.3	27 40.9	14 58.6	25 15.6	13 44.5	19 26.8	10 37.8	5 11.7	28 35.4	10 47.6	7 43.9
24 W	0 7 6.4	29 54.0	27 37.7	27 41.3	27 6.2	13 18.9	20 4.1	10 48.5	5 18.9	28 33.5	10 49.2	7 44.2
25 T	0 11 3.0	0♎52.8	27 34.5	10♎10.4	28 56.0	12 55.4	20 41.4	10 59.2	5 26.0	28 31.6	10 50.8	7 44.6
26 F	0 14 59.5	1 51.7	27 31.3	22 26.3	0♎45.1	12 34.1	21 18.6	11 9.8	5 33.1	28 29.7	10 52.3	7 44.9
27 S	0 18 56.0	2 50.5	27 28.1	4♏30.5	2 33.4	12 14.9	21 55.7	11 20.3	5 40.2	28 27.9	10 53.9	7 45.2
28 S	0 22 52.6	3 49.4	27 25.0	16 25.2	4 20.8	11 58.2	22 32.8	11 30.7	5 47.2	28 26.0	10 55.4	7 45.4
29 M	0 26 49.2	4 48.3	27 21.8	28 13.7	6 7.4	11 43.7	23 9.9	11 41.0	5 54.3	28 24.3	10 56.9	7 45.7
30 T	0 30 45.7	5 47.3	27 18.6	10♐ 0.1	7 53.1	11 31.7	23 46.9	11 51.3	6 1.2	28 22.5	10 58.3	7 45.9

DECLINATION

DAY	EPHEMERIS SIDEREAL TIME	☉	☊	☽	☿	♀	♂	♃	♄	♅	♆	♇
1 M	22 36 25.7	8N45.2	19S54.6	18S29.5	14N39.7	5S23.7	19N54.0	19N 4.8	11N55.0	12S25.6	17N40.0	19N21.2
4 T	22 48 15.3	7 39.8	19 52.5	21 2.7	14 21.5	5 17.1	19 26.6	18 56.0	11 47.0	12 28.1	17 38.4	19 21.0
7 S	23 0 4.9	6 33.3	19 50.4	14 58.1	13 33.3	4 58.4	18 58.1	18 47.2	11 39.0	12 30.5	17 36.9	19 20.8
10 W	23 11 54.7	5 25.8	19 48.3	1 48.0	12 17.2	4 28.3	18 28.5	18 38.3	11 31.1	12 32.9	17 35.4	19 20.6
13 S	23 23 44.3	4 17.5	19 46.2	12N51.0	10 37.4	3 48.2	17 57.9	18 29.6	11 23.2	12 35.2	17 33.9	19 20.4
16 T	23 35 33.9	3 8.6	19 44.0	20 50.9	8 39.7	3 0.4	17 26.4	18 20.9	11 15.4	12 37.4	17 32.5	19 20.2
19 F	23 47 23.6	1 59.0	19 41.9	17 32.1	6 29.6	2 7.6	16 53.9	18 12.3	11 7.7	12 39.5	17 31.1	19 20.1
22 M	23 59 13.3	0 49.1	19 39.7	6 1.6	4 12.1	1 12.8	16 20.7	18 3.8	10 60.0	12 41.6	17 29.7	19 19.9
25 T	0 11 3.0	0S21.0	19 37.6	7S24.3	1 51.1	0 18.7	15 46.6	17 55.4	10 52.4	12 43.6	17 28.5	19 19.7
28 S	0 22 52.6	1 31.2	19 35.4	17 34.0	0S30.6	0N32.1	15 11.8	17 47.1	10 44.9	12 45.5	17 27.2	19 19.5

OCTOBER 1919

LONGITUDE

DAY	EPHEMERIS SIDEREAL TIME	☉	☊	☽	☿	♀	♂	♃	♄	♅	♆	♇
1 W	0 34 42.3	6♎46.3	27♏15.4	21♐49.1	9♎38.0	11♍22.1	24♌23.9	12♌ 1.4	6♍ 8.2	28♒20.8	10♌59.7	7♋46.1
2 T	0 38 38.8	7 45.3	27 12.2	3♑45.8	11 21.9	11R14.9	25 0.8	12 11.4	6 15.0	28R19.1	11 1.1	7 46.3
3 F	0 42 35.3	8 44.3	27 9.1	15 55.5	13 5.0	11 10.1	25 37.7	12 21.3	6 21.9	28 17.5	11 2.5	7 46.4
4 S	0 46 31.9	9 43.4	27 5.9	28 23.3	14 47.3	11 7.8	26 14.5	12 31.2	6 28.7	28 15.8	11 3.9	7 46.5
5 S	0 50 28.5	10 42.5	27 2.7	11♒13.5	16 28.7	11D 7.8	26 51.3	12 40.9	6 35.5	28 14.3	11 5.2	7 46.7
6 M	0 54 25.0	11 41.7	26 59.5	24 29.4	18 9.3	11 10.2	27 28.1	12 50.5	6 42.2	28 12.7	11 6.5	7 46.7
7 T	0 58 21.6	12 40.8	26 56.4	8♓12.1	19 49.0	11 14.9	28 4.8	12 60.0	6 48.9	28 11.2	11 7.7	7 46.8
8 W	1 2 18.1	13 40.0	26 53.2	22 20.4	21 28.0	11 21.9	28 41.4	13 9.4	6 55.5	28 9.8	11 9.0	7 46.8
9 T	1 6 14.7	14 39.2	26 50.0	6♈50.5	23 6.2	11 31.1	29 18.0	13 18.7	7 2.1	28 8.4	11 10.2	7 46.8
10 F	1 10 11.2	15 38.5	26 46.8	21 36.2	24 43.6	11 42.5	29 54.6	13 27.9	7 8.6	28 7.0	11 11.4	7R46.8
11 S	1 14 7.8	16 37.8	26 43.6	6♉29.6	26 20.3	11 56.0	0♍31.1	13 36.9	7 15.1	28 5.6	11 12.5	7 46.8
12 S	1 18 4.3	17 37.1	26 40.5	21 22.7	27 56.3	12 11.7	1 7.5	13 45.9	7 21.5	28 4.3	11 13.6	7 46.7
13 M	1 22 0.9	18 36.5	26 37.3	6♊ 8.0	29 31.5	12 29.3	1 44.0	13 54.7	7 27.9	28 3.1	11 14.7	7 46.6
14 T	1 25 57.4	19 35.9	26 34.1	20 40.1	1♏ 6.1	12 48.9	2 20.3	14 3.4	7 34.3	28 1.9	11 15.8	7 46.5
15 W	1 29 54.0	20 35.4	26 30.9	4♋55.4	2 39.9	13 10.4	2 56.7	14 12.0	7 40.5	28 0.7	11 16.8	7 46.4
16 T	1 33 50.5	21 34.8	26 27.8	18 52.3	4 13.1	13 33.8	3 32.9	14 20.5	7 46.8	27 59.6	11 17.8	7 46.3
17 F	1 37 47.1	22 34.4	26 24.6	2♌30.8	5 45.7	13 58.9	4 9.2	14 28.9	7 52.9	27 58.5	11 18.8	7 46.1
18 S	1 41 43.7	23 33.9	26 21.4	15 51.6	7 17.6	14 25.7	4 45.4	14 37.1	7 59.0	27 57.4	11 19.7	7 45.9
19 S	1 45 40.2	24 33.5	26 18.2	28 56.1	8 48.9	14 54.2	5 21.5	14 45.2	8 5.1	27 56.4	11 20.6	7 45.7
20 M	1 49 36.8	25 33.2	26 15.1	11♍45.8	10 19.5	15 24.3	5 57.6	14 53.1	8 11.1	27 55.5	11 21.5	7 45.4
21 T	1 53 33.3	26 32.8	26 11.9	24 22.1	11 49.6	15 55.9	6 33.6	15 1.0	8 17.0	27 54.6	11 22.4	7 45.2
22 W	1 57 29.8	27 32.6	26 8.7	6♎46.3	13 18.9	16 29.0	7 9.6	15 8.7	8 22.9	27 53.7	11 23.2	7 44.9
23 T	2 1 26.4	28 32.3	26 5.5	18 59.7	14 47.7	17 3.5	7 45.5	15 16.2	8 28.7	27 52.9	11 24.0	7 44.6
24 F	2 5 23.0	29 32.1	26 2.3	1♏ 3.7	16 15.8	17 39.3	8 21.4	15 23.7	8 34.4	27 52.1	11 24.7	7 44.2
25 S	2 9 19.5	0♏31.9	25 59.2	12 59.9	17 43.3	18 16.5	8 57.2	15 31.0	8 40.1	27 51.4	11 25.4	7 43.9
26 S	2 13 16.1	1 31.7	25 56.0	24 50.1	19 10.1	18 54.9	9 32.9	15 38.1	8 45.7	27 50.8	11 26.1	7 43.5
27 M	2 17 12.6	2 31.6	25 52.8	6♐36.9	20 36.2	19 34.6	10 8.6	15 45.1	8 51.2	27 50.1	11 26.8	7 43.1
28 T	2 21 9.2	3 31.5	25 49.6	18 23.1	22 1.7	20 15.4	10 44.3	15 52.0	8 56.7	27 49.6	11 27.4	7 42.7
29 W	2 25 5.7	4 31.5	25 46.5	0♑12.5	23 26.3	20 57.3	11 19.8	15 58.7	9 2.1	27 49.0	11 28.0	7 42.2
30 T	2 29 2.3	5 31.4	25 43.3	12 8.9	24 50.2	21 40.4	11 55.4	16 5.2	9 7.4	27 48.6	11 28.5	7 41.7
31 F	2 32 58.8	6 31.4	25 40.1	24 17.0	26 13.3	22 24.5	12 30.8	16 11.6	9 12.6	27 48.1	11 29.0	7 41.3

DECLINATION

DAY	EPHEMERIS SIDEREAL TIME	☉	☊	☽	☿	♀	♂	♃	♄	♅	♆	♇
1 W	0 34 42.3	2S41.3	19S33.2	20S56.5	2S50.9	1N18.0	14N36.3	17N39.0	10N37.6	12S47.2	17N26.1	19N19.4
4 S	0 46 31.9	3 51.2	19 31.1	16 0.1	5 8.2	1 57.3	14 0.2	17 31.1	10 30.4	12 48.9	17 25.0	19 19.3
7 T	0 58 21.6	5 0.7	19 28.9	3 49.2	7 21.6	2 29.4	13 23.5	17 23.4	10 23.3	12 50.4	17 23.9	19 19.1
10 F	1 10 11.2	6 9.5	19 26.7	11N 5.8	9 30.2	2 53.7	12 46.3	17 16.0	10 16.4	12 51.8	17 23.0	19 19.0
13 M	1 22 0.9	7 17.7	19 24.5	20 22.3	11 33.2	3 10.0	12 8.6	17 8.7	10 9.6	12 53.0	17 22.1	19 18.9
16 T	1 33 50.5	8 25.0	19 22.2	17 57.5	13 30.2	3 18.4	11 30.5	17 1.8	10 3.1	12 54.2	17 21.2	19 18.8
19 S	1 45 40.2	9 31.2	19 20.0	6 57.8	15 20.5	3 19.2	10 52.0	16 55.1	9 56.7	12 55.2	17 20.5	19 18.8
22 W	1 57 29.8	10 36.2	19 17.8	6S16.4	17 3.7	3 12.7	10 13.2	16 48.7	9 50.5	12 56.0	17 19.8	19 18.7
25 S	2 9 19.5	11 39.8	19 15.5	16 46.6	18 39.1	2 59.4	9 34.1	16 42.6	9 44.6	12 56.7	17 19.2	19 18.7
28 T	2 21 9.2	12 41.7	19 13.3	20 50.3	20 6.0	2 39.6	8 54.7	16 36.9	9 38.9	12 57.3	17 18.7	19 18.6
31 F	2 32 58.8	13 41.9	19 11.0	16 47.3	21 23.9	2 13.7	8 15.2	16 31.6	9 33.4	12 57.6	17 18.3	19 18.6

NOVEMBER 1919

LONGITUDE

DAY	EPHEMERIS SIDEREAL TIME h m s	☉ ° ′	☊ ° ′	☽ ° ′	☿ ° ′	♀ ° ′	♂ ° ′	♃ ° ′	♄ ° ′	♅ ° ′	♆ ° ′	♇ ° ′
1 S	2 36 55.4	7♏31.4	25♏36.9	6♒41.3	27♏35.4	23♍ 9.5	13♍ 6.2	16♌17.9	9♍17.8	27♒47.8	11♌29.5	7♋40.8
2 S	2 40 52.0	8 31.5	25 33.7	19 26.3	28 56.7	23 55.6	13 41.6	16 24.0	9 22.9	27R47.5	11 30.0	7R40.2
3 M	2 44 48.5	9 31.5	25 30.6	2♓36.0	0♐16.8	24 42.6	14 16.8	16 29.9	9 27.9	27 47.2	11 30.4	7 39.7
4 T	2 48 45.0	10 31.6	25 27.4	16 12.8	1 35.9	25 30.5	14 52.1	16 35.7	9 32.9	27 47.0	11 30.8	7 39.1
5 W	2 52 41.6	11 31.8	25 24.2	0♈17.6	2 53.7	26 19.3	15 27.2	16 41.3	9 37.7	27 46.8	11 31.1	7 38.5
6 T	2 56 38.2	12 31.9	25 21.0	14 48.3	4 10.2	27 8.9	16 2.3	16 46.8	9 42.5	27 46.7	11 31.4	7 37.9
7 F	3 0 34.7	13 32.1	25 17.9	29 40.4	5 25.3	27 59.3	16 37.3	16 52.1	9 47.2	27 46.6	11 31.7	7 37.3
8 S	3 4 31.3	14 32.3	25 14.7	14♉46.6	6 38.6	28 50.6	17 12.3	16 57.3	9 51.8	27 46.6	11 32.0	7 36.6
9 S	3 8 27.8	15 32.5	25 11.5	29 57.8	7 50.1	29 42.5	17 47.2	17 2.2	9 56.4	27D46.6	11 32.2	7 35.9
10 M	3 12 24.4	16 32.8	25 8.3	15♊ 4.4	8 59.6	0♎35.3	18 22.0	17 7.1	10 0.8	27 46.7	11 32.4	7 35.2
11 T	3 16 20.9	17 33.1	25 5.1	29 57.9	10 6.7	1 28.7	18 56.8	17 11.7	10 5.2	27 46.8	11 32.5	7 34.5
12 W	3 20 17.5	18 33.4	25 2.0	14♋31.9	11 11.3	2 22.8	19 31.5	17 16.2	10 9.5	27 47.0	11 32.6	7 33.8
13 T	3 24 14.1	19 33.8	24 58.8	28 42.2	12 12.9	3 17.6	20 6.2	17 20.5	10 13.7	27 47.2	11 32.7	7 33.0
14 F	3 28 10.6	20 34.2	24 55.6	12♌27.5	13 11.3	4 13.0	20 40.7	17 24.6	10 17.8	27 47.5	11 32.7	7 32.3
15 S	3 32 7.2	21 34.6	24 52.4	25 48.4	14 6.0	5 9.0	21 15.3	17 28.6	10 21.9	27 47.8	11 32.7	7 31.5
16 S	3 36 3.7	22 35.1	24 49.3	8♍47.1	14 56.5	6 5.6	21 49.7	17 32.3	10 25.8	27 48.2	11R32.7	7 30.7
17 M	3 40 0.3	23 35.6	24 46.1	21 26.4	15 42.3	7 2.8	22 24.1	17 35.9	10 29.7	27 48.7	11 32.7	7 29.9
18 T	3 43 56.8	24 36.1	24 42.9	3♎49.7	16 22.9	8 0.6	22 58.3	17 39.3	10 33.4	27 49.2	11 32.6	7 29.0
19 W	3 47 53.4	25 36.6	24 39.7	16 0.3	16 57.4	8 58.8	23 32.6	17 42.6	10 37.1	27 49.7	11 32.4	7 28.2
20 T	3 51 50.0	26 37.2	24 36.6	28 1.2	17 25.4	9 57.6	24 6.7	17 45.6	10 40.6	27 50.3	11 32.3	7 27.3
21 F	3 55 46.5	27 37.8	24 33.4	9♏55.3	17 46.0	10 56.9	24 40.8	17 48.5	10 44.1	27 50.9	11 32.1	7 26.4
22 S	3 59 43.1	28 38.4	24 30.2	21 44.9	17 58.5	11 56.6	25 14.7	17 51.2	10 47.5	27 51.6	11 31.8	7 25.5
23 S	4 3 39.6	29 39.1	24 27.0	3♐32.3	18 2.0	12 56.8	25 48.6	17 53.7	10 50.8	27 52.4	11 31.6	7 24.6
24 M	4 7 36.2	0♐39.8	24 23.8	15 19.6	17R55.9	13 57.4	26 22.4	17 56.0	10 54.0	27 53.2	11 31.3	7 23.6
25 T	4 11 32.7	1 40.5	24 20.7	27 9.1	17 39.6	14 58.4	26 56.2	17 58.1	10 57.0	27 54.0	11 30.9	7 22.7
26 W	4 15 29.3	2 41.2	24 17.5	9♑ 3.1	17 12.5	15 59.9	27 29.8	17 60.0	11 0.0	27 54.9	11 30.6	7 21.7
27 T	4 19 25.8	3 41.9	24 14.3	21 4.1	16 34.6	17 1.8	28 3.4	18 1.7	11 2.9	27 55.9	11 30.2	7 20.7
28 F	4 23 22.4	4 42.7	24 11.1	3♒15.4	15 45.9	18 4.0	28 36.8	18 3.2	11 5.7	27 56.9	11 29.7	7 19.7
29 S	4 27 18.9	5 43.5	24 8.0	15 40.1	14 47.2	19 6.6	29 10.2	18 4.6	11 8.4	27 57.9	11 29.3	7 18.7
30 S	4 31 15.5	6 44.3	24 4.8	28 21.8	13 39.5	20 9.6	29 43.5	18 5.7	11 11.0	27 59.0	11 28.8	7 17.7

DECLINATION

DAY	EPHEMERIS SIDEREAL TIME h m s	☉	☊	☽	☿	♀	♂	♃	♄	♅	♆	♇
1 S	2 36 55.4	14S 1.6	19S10.3	13S44.8	21S47.7	2N 3.9	8N 2.0	16N29.9	9N31.6	12S57.7	17N18.2	19N18.6
4 T	2 48 45.0	14 59.1	19 8.0	0 54.1	22 52.3	1 30.8	7 22.4	16 25.2	9 26.5	12 57.9	17 17.8	19 18.7
7 F	3 0 34.7	15 54.4	19 5.7	13N28.2	23 45.9	0 52.7	6 42.7	16 20.8	9 21.7	12 57.9	17 17.6	19 18.7
10 M	3 12 24.4	16 47.4	19 3.4	20 47.1	24 27.5	0 10.0	6 2.9	16 16.8	9 17.1	12 57.8	17 17.5	19 18.7
13 T	3 24 14.1	17 37.8	19 1.1	15 45.8	24 56.1	0S36.7	5 23.2	16 13.4	9 12.9	12 57.5	17 17.4	19 18.8
16 S	3 36 3.7	18 25.4	18 58.8	3 30.2	25 10.4	1 27.2	4 43.6	16 10.4	9 8.9	12 57.1	17 17.4	19 18.9
19 W	3 47 53.4	19 10.2	18 56.5	9S22.3	25 8.9	2 20.8	4 4.0	16 7.8	9 5.3	12 56.5	17 17.5	19 19.0
22 S	3 59 43.1	19 51.8	18 54.2	18 29.2	24 49.5	3 17.1	3 24.7	16 5.8	9 2.0	12 55.7	17 17.7	19 19.1
25 T	4 11 32.7	20 30.2	18 51.8	20 34.9	24 9.9	4 15.8	2 45.5	16 4.4	8 59.0	12 54.7	17 18.0	19 19.3
28 F	4 23 22.4	21 5.2	18 49.5	14 38.6	23 7.6	5 16.4	2 6.7	16 3.4	8 56.4	12 53.7	17 18.4	19 19.5

DECEMBER 1919

LONGITUDE

DAY	EPHEMERIS SIDEREAL TIME h m s	☉ ° ′	☊ ° ′	☽ ° ′	☿ ° ′	♀ ° ′	♂ ° ′	♃ ° ′	♄ ° ′	♅ ° ′	♆ ° ′	♇ ° ′
1 M	4 35 12.1	7♐45.1	24♏ 1.6	11♓24.0	12♐24.6	21♎12.9	0♎16.7	18♌ 6.7	11♍13.4	28♒ 0.2	11♌28.3	7♋16.7
2 T	4 39 8.6	8 45.9	23 58.4	24 49.8	11R 4.5	22 16.5	0 49.8	18 7.4	11 15.8	28 1.4	11R27.7	7R15.6
3 W	4 43 5.2	9 46.7	23 55.2	8♈41.1	9 41.9	23 20.5	1 22.8	18 8.0	11 18.1	28 2.6	11 27.1	7 14.6
4 T	4 47 1.7	10 47.6	23 52.1	22 58.3	8 19.6	24 24.8	1 55.7	18 8.4	11 20.2	28 3.9	11 26.5	7 13.5
5 F	4 50 58.3	11 48.5	23 48.9	7♉39.5	7 0.3	25 29.4	2 28.5	18 8.5	11 22.3	28 5.2	11 25.8	7 12.4
6 S	4 54 54.9	12 49.3	23 45.7	22 39.8	5 46.6	26 34.3	3 1.2	18R 8.5	11 24.3	28 6.6	11 25.1	7 11.3
7 S	4 58 51.4	13 50.2	23 42.5	7♊51.9	4 40.7	27 39.5	3 33.8	18 8.3	11 26.1	28 8.1	11 24.4	7 10.2
8 M	5 2 48.0	14 51.2	23 39.4	23 6.3	3 44.3	28 45.0	4 6.4	18 7.9	11 27.8	28 9.5	11 23.7	7 9.1
9 T	5 6 44.5	15 52.1	23 36.2	8♋13.0	2 58.5	29 50.8	4 38.8	18 7.3	11 29.5	28 11.1	11 22.9	7 8.0
10 W	5 10 41.1	16 53.0	23 33.0	23 2.8	2 23.9	0♏56.8	5 11.1	18 6.4	11 31.0	28 12.7	11 22.1	7 6.8
11 T	5 14 37.6	17 54.0	23 29.8	7♌28.8	2 0.7	2 3.1	5 43.3	18 5.4	11 32.4	28 14.3	11 21.2	7 5.7
12 F	5 18 34.2	18 55.0	23 26.7	21 27.0	1 48.5	3 9.6	6 15.4	18 4.2	11 33.7	28 15.9	11 20.4	7 4.5
13 S	5 22 30.7	19 56.0	23 23.5	4♍56.5	1 47.0	4 16.4	6 47.4	18 2.8	11 34.9	28 17.7	11 19.5	7 3.4
14 S	5 26 27.3	20 57.0	23 20.3	17 59.0	1D55.4	5 23.4	7 19.3	18 1.2	11 36.0	28 19.4	11 18.5	7 2.2
15 M	5 30 23.9	21 58.1	23 17.1	0♎37.6	2 12.9	6 30.7	7 51.0	17 59.4	11 37.0	28 21.2	11 17.6	7 1.0
16 T	5 34 20.4	22 59.1	23 14.0	12 56.7	2 38.7	7 38.2	8 22.7	17 57.4	11 37.9	28 23.1	11 16.6	6 59.9
17 W	5 38 17.0	24 0.2	23 10.8	25 1.0	3 12.0	8 45.8	8 54.2	17 55.3	11 38.6	28 25.0	11 15.6	6 58.7
18 T	5 42 13.5	25 1.3	23 7.6	6♏55.2	3 52.0	9 53.7	9 25.6	17 52.9	11 39.3	28 26.9	11 14.6	6 57.5
19 F	5 46 10.1	26 2.4	23 4.4	18 43.5	4 37.8	11 1.8	9 56.9	17 50.3	11 39.8	28 28.9	11 13.5	6 56.3
20 S	5 50 6.7	27 3.5	23 1.2	0♐29.8	5 29.0	12 10.1	10 28.0	17 47.5	11 40.2	28 30.9	11 12.4	6 55.1
21 S	5 54 3.2	28 4.6	22 58.1	12 17.0	6 24.7	13 18.5	10 59.0	17 44.6	11 40.5	28 33.0	11 11.3	6 53.9
22 M	5 57 59.8	29 5.7	22 54.9	24 7.9	7 24.6	14 27.2	11 29.9	17 41.4	11 40.7	28 35.1	11 10.1	6 52.7
23 T	6 1 56.3	0♑ 6.9	22 51.7	6♑ 4.4	8 28.0	15 36.0	12 0.7	17 38.1	11 40.8	28 37.2	11 9.0	6 51.4
24 W	6 5 52.9	1 8.0	22 48.5	18 8.1	9 34.5	16 44.9	12 31.3	17 34.6	11R40.8	28 39.4	11 7.8	6 50.2
25 T	6 9 49.4	2 9.2	22 45.4	0♒20.4	10 43.8	17 54.1	13 1.7	17 30.9	11 40.7	28 41.7	11 6.6	6 49.0
26 F	6 13 46.0	3 10.3	22 42.2	12 42.6	11 55.6	19 3.3	13 32.0	17 27.0	11 40.4	28 43.9	11 5.3	6 47.8
27 S	6 17 42.5	4 11.5	22 39.0	25 16.4	13 9.5	20 12.8	14 2.2	17 22.9	11 40.1	28 46.2	11 4.1	6 46.6
28 S	6 21 39.1	5 12.6	22 35.8	8♓ 3.3	14 25.3	21 22.3	14 32.2	17 18.7	11 39.6	28 48.6	11 2.8	6 45.3
29 M	6 25 35.7	6 13.8	22 32.7	21 5.6	15 42.7	22 32.0	15 2.1	17 14.3	11 39.0	28 51.0	11 1.5	6 44.1
30 T	6 29 32.2	7 15.0	22 29.5	4♈25.3	17 1.7	23 41.9	15 31.8	17 9.7	11 38.3	28 53.4	11 0.1	6 42.9
31 W	6 33 28.8	8 16.1	22 26.3	18 4.6	18 22.0	24 51.9	16 1.3	17 4.9	11 37.5	28 55.8	10 58.8	6 41.6

DECLINATION

DAY	EPHEMERIS SIDEREAL TIME h m s	☉	☊	☽	☿	♀	♂	♃	♄	♅	♆	♇
1 M	4 35 12.1	21S36.6	18S47.2	2S36.1	21S44.2	6S18.5	1N28.1	16N 3.0	8N54.1	12S52.4	17N18.8	19N19.6
4 T	4 47 1.7	22 4.3	18 44.8	11N31.5	20 11.3	7 21.7	0 49.9	16 3.2	8 52.2	12 51.0	17 19.3	19 19.8
7 S	4 58 51.4	22 28.2	18 42.4	20 27.0	18 50.3	8 25.5	0 12.1	16 3.8	8 50.7	12 49.5	17 19.9	19 20.1
10 W	5 10 41.1	22 48.1	18 40.1	17 3.7	18 0.1	9 29.6	0S25.3	16 5.1	8 49.5	12 47.8	17 20.6	19 20.3
13 S	5 22 30.7	23 4.0	18 37.7	4 53.3	17 46.3	10 33.5	1 2.2	16 6.8	8 48.7	12 46.0	17 21.3	19 20.6
16 T	5 34 20.4	23 15.7	18 35.3	8S19.9	18 3.0	11 36.9	1 38.6	16 9.2	8 48.3	12 44.0	17 22.1	19 20.8
19 F	5 46 10.1	23 23.3	18 32.9	17 55.3	18 40.3	12 39.3	2 14.4	16 12.0	8 48.3	12 41.9	17 23.0	19 21.1
22 M	5 57 59.8	23 26.7	18 30.5	20 45.0	19 29.1	13 40.3	2 49.6	16 15.4	8 48.7	12 39.6	17 24.0	19 21.4
25 T	6 9 49.4	23 25.8	18 28.1	15 27.6	20 22.2	14 39.6	3 24.1	16 19.3	8 49.4	12 37.3	17 25.0	19 21.7
28 S	6 21 39.1	23 20.7	18 25.6	3 53.8	21 14.7	15 36.6	3 58.0	16 23.6	8 50.6	12 34.8	17 26.1	19 22.1
31 W	6 33 28.8	23 11.4	18 23.2	9N53.5	22 3.2	16 31.1	4 31.0	16 28.4	8 52.1	12 32.2	17 27.2	19 22.4

JANUARY 1920

LONGITUDE

DAY	EPHEMERIS SIDEREAL TIME h m s	☉ ° ′	☊ ° ′	☽ ° ′	☿ ° ′	♀ ° ′	♂ ° ′	♃ ° ′	♄ ° ′	♅ ° ′	♆ ° ′	♇ ° ′
1 T	6 37 25.3	9♑17.3	22♏23.1	2♉ 4.7	19♐43.4	26♏ 2.0	16♎30.7	17♌ 0.0	11♍36.6	28♒58.3	10♌57.4	6♋40.4
2 F	6 41 21.9	10 18.4	22 19.9	16 25.8	21 6.0	27 12.2	16 59.9	16R54.9	11R35.6	29 0.9	10R56.0	6R39.2
3 S	6 45 18.5	11 19.6	22 16.8	1♊ 5.9	22 29.5	28 22.5	17 29.0	16 49.7	11 34.5	29 3.4	10 54.6	6 38.0
4 S	6 49 15.0	12 20.7	22 13.6	16 0.6	23 53.9	29 33.0	17 57.9	16 44.3	11 33.2	29 6.0	10 53.2	6 36.8
5 M	6 53 11.6	13 21.8	22 10.4	1♋ 3.1	25 19.1	0♐43.6	18 26.6	16 38.7	11 31.9	29 8.7	10 51.7	6 35.5
6 T	6 57 8.1	14 23.0	22 7.2	16 4.4	26 45.1	1 54.3	18 55.1	16 33.0	11 30.4	29 11.3	10 50.3	6 34.3
7 W	7 1 4.7	15 24.1	22 4.1	0♌55.2	28 11.7	3 5.1	19 23.5	16 27.2	11 28.9	29 14.0	10 48.8	6 33.1
8 T	7 5 1.2	16 25.2	22 0.9	15 26.9	29 39.1	4 16.0	19 51.7	16 21.2	11 27.2	29 16.7	10 47.3	6 31.9
9 F	7 8 57.8	17 26.4	21 57.7	29 33.4	1♑ 7.0	5 27.0	20 19.7	16 15.1	11 25.5	29 19.5	10 45.8	6 30.7
10 S	7 12 54.4	18 27.5	21 54.5	13♍11.6	2 35.5	6 38.1	20 47.5	16 8.8	11 23.6	29 22.3	10 44.3	6 29.5
11 S	7 16 50.9	19 28.6	21 51.4	26 21.3	4 4.6	7 49.4	21 15.1	16 2.4	11 21.6	29 25.1	10 42.7	6 28.3
12 M	7 20 47.5	20 29.8	21 48.2	9♎ 4.9	5 34.3	9 0.7	21 42.5	15 55.9	11 19.6	29 28.0	10 41.2	6 27.1
13 T	7 24 44.0	21 30.9	21 45.0	21 26.5	7 4.5	10 12.1	22 9.7	15 49.3	11 17.4	29 30.8	10 39.6	6 25.9
14 W	7 28 40.6	22 32.0	21 41.8	3♏31.2	8 35.2	11 23.6	22 36.7	15 42.5	11 15.1	29 33.8	10 38.0	6 24.8
15 T	7 32 37.1	23 33.2	21 38.6	15 24.4	10 6.5	12 35.2	23 3.5	15 35.6	11 12.8	29 36.7	10 36.4	6 23.6
16 F	7 36 33.7	24 34.3	21 35.5	27 11.5	11 38.3	13 46.8	23 30.1	15 28.7	11 10.3	29 39.7	10 34.8	6 22.4
17 S	7 40 30.3	25 35.4	21 32.3	8♐57.6	13 10.6	14 58.6	23 56.4	15 21.6	11 7.7	29 42.6	10 33.2	6 21.3
18 S	7 44 26.8	26 36.5	21 29.1	20 46.8	14 43.4	16 10.4	24 22.5	15 14.4	11 5.1	29 45.7	10 31.6	6 20.1
19 M	7 48 23.3	27 37.6	21 25.9	2♑42.8	16 16.8	17 22.3	24 48.4	15 7.1	11 2.3	29 48.7	10 30.0	6 19.0
20 T	7 52 19.9	28 38.7	21 22.8	14 48.2	17 50.7	18 34.2	25 14.0	14 59.7	10 59.5	29 51.8	10 28.3	6 17.9
21 W	7 56 16.5	29 39.8	21 19.6	27 4.5	19 25.2	19 46.3	25 39.4	14 52.3	10 56.6	29 54.8	10 26.7	6 16.8
22 T	8 0 13.1	0♒40.9	21 16.4	9♒32.7	21 0.2	20 58.3	26 4.5	14 44.8	10 53.5	29 58.0	10 25.0	6 15.7
23 F	8 4 9.6	1 42.0	21 13.2	22 12.7	22 35.8	22 10.5	26 29.4	14 37.2	10 50.4	0♓ 1.1	10 23.4	6 14.6
24 S	8 8 6.1	2 43.0	21 10.1	5♓ 4.4	24 12.0	23 22.7	26 54.0	14 29.5	10 47.2	0 4.2	10 21.7	6 13.5
25 S	8 12 2.7	3 44.1	21 6.9	18 7.5	25 48.7	24 35.0	27 18.4	14 21.8	10 43.9	0 7.4	10 20.0	6 12.4
26 M	8 15 59.3	4 45.1	21 3.7	1♈21.9	27 26.1	25 47.3	27 42.4	14 14.0	10 40.6	0 10.6	10 18.3	6 11.3
27 T	8 19 55.8	5 46.1	21 0.5	14 48.0	29 4.1	26 59.6	28 6.2	14 6.2	10 37.1	0 13.8	10 16.7	6 10.3
28 W	8 23 52.4	6 47.1	20 57.3	28 26.3	0♒42.8	28 12.1	28 29.7	13 58.3	10 33.6	0 17.1	10 15.0	6 9.3
29 T	8 27 48.9	7 48.0	20 54.2	12♉17.9	2 22.1	29 24.5	28 52.9	13 50.4	10 30.0	0 20.3	10 13.3	6 8.2
30 F	8 31 45.5	8 49.0	20 51.0	26 23.2	4 2.0	0♑37.0	29 15.9	13 42.5	10 26.4	0 23.6	10 11.6	6 7.2
31 S	8 35 42.0	9 49.9	20 47.8	10♊41.8	5 42.7	1 49.6	29 38.5	13 34.5	10 22.6	0 26.9	10 9.9	6 6.2

DECLINATION

DAY	EPHEMERIS SIDEREAL TIME h m s	☉	☊	☽	☿	♀	♂	♃	♄	♅	♆	♇
1 T	6 37 25.3	23S 7.4	18S22.4	14N 0.3	22S18.1	16S48.7	4S41.9	16N30.1	8N52.6	12S31.3	17N27.6	19N22.5
4 S	6 49 15.0	22 52.5	18 19.9	20 46.9	22 57.5	17 39.2	5 14.0	16 35.5	8 54.6	12 28.5	17 28.8	19 22.9
7 W	7 1 4.7	22 33.5	18 17.5	15 20.9	23 28.4	18 26.4	5 45.2	16 41.2	8 57.0	12 25.6	17 30.0	19 23.3
10 S	7 12 54.4	22 10.5	18 15.0	2 10.0	23 49.5	19 9.7	6 15.5	16 47.3	8 59.7	12 22.7	17 31.3	19 23.7
13 T	7 24 44.0	21 43.6	18 12.6	10S51.2	23 60.0	19 49.0	6 45.0	16 53.7	9 2.7	12 19.6	17 32.6	19 24.1
16 F	7 36 33.7	21 12.9	18 10.1	19 10.7	23 59.1	20 23.9	7 13.5	17 0.4	9 6.1	12 16.5	17 33.9	19 24.5
19 M	7 48 23.3	20 38.6	18 7.6	20 10.2	23 46.4	20 54.0	7 40.9	17 7.3	9 9.7	12 13.2	17 35.2	19 24.9
22 T	8 0 13.1	20 0.7	18 5.1	13 7.9	23 21.4	21 19.3	8 7.4	17 14.3	9 13.7	12 9.9	17 36.6	19 25.4
25 S	8 12 2.7	19 19.5	18 2.6	0 32.4	22 43.7	21 39.3	8 32.7	17 21.5	9 17.9	12 6.6	17 38.0	19 25.8
28 W	8 23 52.4	18 35.0	18 0.1	12N46.5	21 53.0	21 53.9	8 57.0	17 28.7	9 22.4	12 3.1	17 39.4	19 26.2
31 S	8 35 42.0	17 47.6	17 57.6	20 24.5	20 49.0	22 3.0	9 20.1	17 35.9	9 27.2	11 59.6	17 40.8	19 26.7

FEBRUARY 1920

LONGITUDE

DAY	EPHEMERIS SIDEREAL TIME h m s	☉ ° ′	☊ ° ′	☽ ° ′	☿ ° ′	♀ ° ′	♂ ° ′	♃ ° ′	♄ ° ′	♅ ° ′	♆ ° ′	♇ ° ′
1 S	8 39 38.6	10♒50.8	20♏44.6	25♊11.8	7♒24.0	3♑ 2.2	0♏ 0.8	13♌26.6	10♍18.8	0♓30.1	10♌ 8.2	6♋ 5.2
2 M	8 43 35.1	11 51.7	20 41.5	9♋49.1	9 6.1	4 14.8	0 22.8	13R18.6	10R14.9	0 33.5	10R 6.5	6R 4.3
3 T	8 47 31.7	12 52.5	20 38.3	24 28.0	10 48.8	5 27.5	0 44.5	13 10.6	10 11.0	0 36.8	10 4.8	6 3.3
4 W	8 51 28.3	13 53.4	20 35.1	9♌ 1.2	12 32.3	6 40.3	1 5.8	13 2.6	10 7.0	0 40.1	10 3.2	6 2.4
5 T	8 55 24.8	14 54.2	20 31.9	23 21.3	14 16.5	7 53.1	1 26.8	12 54.6	10 2.9	0 43.5	10 1.5	6 1.5
6 F	8 59 21.4	15 55.0	20 28.8	7♍21.9	16 1.5	9 5.9	1 47.5	12 46.7	9 58.8	0 46.8	9 59.8	6 0.6
7 S	9 3 17.9	16 55.8	20 25.6	20 58.9	17 47.2	10 18.7	2 7.8	12 38.7	9 54.6	0 50.2	9 58.1	5 59.7
8 S	9 7 14.5	17 56.5	20 22.4	4♎10.4	19 33.5	11 31.6	2 27.8	12 30.8	9 50.3	0 53.6	9 56.4	5 58.8
9 M	9 11 11.0	18 57.3	20 19.2	16 57.3	21 20.6	12 44.6	2 47.4	12 22.9	9 46.0	0 57.0	9 54.8	5 57.9
10 T	9 15 7.6	19 58.0	20 16.0	29 22.4	23 8.4	13 57.6	3 6.7	12 15.0	9 41.7	1 0.4	9 53.1	5 57.1
11 W	9 19 4.1	20 58.7	20 12.9	11♏30.0	24 56.8	15 10.6	3 25.5	12 7.1	9 37.3	1 3.8	9 51.5	5 56.3
12 T	9 23 0.7	21 59.4	20 9.7	23 25.3	26 45.8	16 23.6	3 43.9	11 59.4	9 32.9	1 7.2	9 49.8	5 55.5
13 F	9 26 57.2	23 0.1	20 6.5	5♐14.0	28 35.3	17 36.7	4 2.0	11 51.6	9 28.4	1 10.7	9 48.2	5 54.7
14 S	9 30 53.8	24 0.7	20 3.3	17 1.6	0♓25.2	18 49.8	4 19.6	11 43.9	9 23.9	1 14.1	9 46.5	5 53.9
15 S	9 34 50.4	25 1.4	20 0.2	28 53.3	2 15.5	20 3.0	4 36.8	11 36.3	9 19.3	1 17.5	9 44.9	5 53.2
16 M	9 38 46.9	26 2.0	19 57.0	10♑53.7	4 6.1	21 16.1	4 53.6	11 28.8	9 14.7	1 21.0	9 43.3	5 52.4
17 T	9 42 43.5	27 2.6	19 53.8	23 6.5	5 56.7	22 29.3	5 9.9	11 21.3	9 10.1	1 24.4	9 41.7	5 51.7
18 W	9 46 40.0	28 3.1	19 50.6	5♒34.0	7 47.2	23 42.6	5 25.8	11 13.9	9 5.4	1 27.9	9 40.1	5 51.0
19 T	9 50 36.6	29 3.7	19 47.4	18 17.6	9 37.4	24 55.8	5 41.2	11 6.6	9 0.7	1 31.3	9 38.5	5 50.4
20 F	9 54 33.1	0♓ 4.2	19 44.3	1♓17.0	11 27.0	26 9.1	5 56.1	10 59.3	8 56.0	1 34.8	9 37.0	5 49.7
21 S	9 58 29.7	1 4.7	19 41.1	14 31.1	13 15.8	27 22.4	6 10.6	10 52.2	8 51.2	1 38.2	9 35.4	5 49.1
22 S	10 2 26.2	2 5.1	19 37.9	27 57.8	15 3.4	28 35.7	6 24.5	10 45.2	8 46.5	1 41.7	9 33.9	5 48.4
23 M	10 6 22.8	3 5.6	19 34.7	11♈34.8	16 49.5	29 49.0	6 38.0	10 38.3	8 41.7	1 45.2	9 32.4	5 47.9
24 T	10 10 19.4	4 6.0	19 31.6	25 20.0	18 33.6	1♒ 2.4	6 50.9	10 31.4	8 36.9	1 48.6	9 30.9	5 47.3
25 W	10 14 15.9	5 6.4	19 28.4	9♉11.9	20 15.3	2 15.7	7 3.3	10 24.7	8 32.1	1 52.1	9 29.4	5 46.7
26 T	10 18 12.4	6 6.7	19 25.2	23 9.6	21 54.0	3 29.1	7 15.2	10 18.2	8 27.3	1 55.5	9 27.9	5 46.2
27 F	10 22 9.0	7 7.0	19 22.0	7♊12.4	23 29.3	4 42.5	7 26.5	10 11.7	8 22.5	1 59.0	9 26.4	5 45.7
28 S	10 26 5.6	8 7.3	19 18.8	21 19.8	25 0.5	5 55.9	7 37.3	10 5.4	8 17.7	2 2.4	9 25.0	5 45.2
29 S	10 30 2.1	9 7.5	19 15.7	5♋30.8	26 27.1	7 9.3	7 47.5	9 59.2	8 12.9	2 5.9	9 23.6	5 44.8

DECLINATION

DAY	EPHEMERIS SIDEREAL TIME h m s	☉	☊	☽	☿	♀	♂	♃	♄	♅	♆	♇
1 S	8 39 38.6	17S31.1	17S56.8	20N33.4	20S24.7	22S 4.8	9S27.5	17N38.3	9N28.8	11S58.4	17N41.3	19N26.8
4 W	8 51 28.3	16 39.9	17 54.2	13 16.5	19 2.8	22 6.3	9 49.1	17 45.5	9 33.8	11 54.9	17 42.7	19 27.3
7 S	9 3 17.9	15 46.1	17 51.7	0S23.8	17 27.3	22 2.1	10 9.4	17 52.6	9 38.9	11 51.3	17 44.0	19 27.8
10 T	9 15 7.6	14 49.8	17 49.1	12 55.6	15 38.4	21 52.1	10 28.4	17 59.6	9 44.3	11 47.6	17 45.4	19 28.2
13 F	9 26 57.2	13 51.3	17 46.6	19 52.6	13 36.7	21 36.3	10 46.1	18 6.4	9 49.7	11 44.0	17 46.8	19 28.7
16 M	9 38 46.9	12 50.7	17 44.0	19 6.1	11 23.0	21 14.8	11 2.5	18 12.9	9 55.3	11 40.3	17 48.1	19 29.2
19 T	9 50 36.6	11 48.3	17 41.5	10 35.0	8 59.2	20 47.7	11 17.4	18 19.2	10 0.9	11 36.6	17 49.4	19 29.6
22 S	10 2 26.2	10 44.2	17 38.9	2N45.6	6 28.4	20 15.1	11 30.9	18 25.2	10 6.5	11 32.9	17 50.7	19 30.1
25 W	10 14 15.9	9 38.5	17 36.3	15 20.2	3 55.4	19 37.1	11 43.0	18 30.9	10 12.2	11 29.2	17 51.9	19 30.6
28 S	10 26 5.6	8 31.0	17 33.7	20 24.8	1 27.0	18 54.1	11 53.5	18 36.2	10 17.9	11 25.5	17 53.1	19 31.1

MARCH 1920

LONGITUDE

DAY	EPHEMERIS SIDEREAL TIME h m s	☉ ° ′	☊ ° ′	☽ ° ′	☿ ° ′	♀ ° ′	♂ ° ′	♃ ° ′	♄ ° ′	♅ ° ′	♆ ° ′	♇ ° ′
1 M	10 33 58.7	10♓ 7.7	19♏12.5	19♋43.3	27♓48.5	8♒22.7	7♏57.2	9♌53.1	8♍ 8.1	2♓ 9.3	9♌22.1	5♋44.3
2 T	10 37 55.2	11 7.9	19 9.3	3♌54.4	29 4.0	9 36.2	8 6.2	9R47.2	8R 3.3	2 12.7	9R20.7	5R43.9
3 W	10 41 51.7	12 8.0	19 6.1	17 59.7	0♈13.1	10 49.6	8 14.7	9 41.4	7 58.5	2 16.1	9 19.4	5 43.5
4 T	10 45 48.3	13 8.1	19 3.0	1♍54.9	1 15.2	12 3.1	8 22.6	9 35.8	7 53.7	2 19.6	9 18.0	5 43.1
5 F	10 49 44.9	14 8.2	18 59.8	15 35.4	2 9.9	13 16.6	8 29.8	9 30.3	7 48.9	2 23.0	9 16.7	5 42.8
6 S	10 53 41.4	15 8.2	18 56.6	28 57.8	2 56.6	14 30.1	8 36.4	9 25.0	7 44.2	2 26.3	9 15.4	5 42.4
7 S	10 57 38.0	16 8.3	18 53.4	12♎ 0.3	3 35.0	15 43.6	8 42.4	9 19.8	7 39.4	2 29.7	9 14.1	5 42.1
8 M	11 1 34.5	17 8.2	18 50.2	24 42.7	4 4.8	16 57.1	8 47.8	9 14.8	7 34.7	2 33.1	9 12.9	5 41.8
9 T	11 5 31.1	18 8.2	18 47.1	7♏ 6.5	4 25.8	18 10.7	8 52.4	9 9.9	7 30.0	2 36.5	9 11.6	5 41.6
10 W	11 9 27.6	19 8.1	18 43.9	19 14.8	4 37.9	19 24.2	8 56.4	9 5.2	7 25.3	2 39.8	9 10.4	5 41.3
11 T	11 13 24.2	20 8.0	18 40.7	1♐11.6	4 41.1	20 37.8	8 59.7	9 0.7	7 20.7	2 43.2	9 9.2	5 41.1
12 F	11 17 20.7	21 7.9	18 37.5	13 2.0	4R35.6	21 51.3	9 2.4	8 56.3	7 16.1	2 46.5	9 8.0	5 40.9
13 S	11 21 17.3	22 7.7	18 34.4	24 51.1	4 21.7	23 4.9	9 4.3	8 52.1	7 11.5	2 49.8	9 6.9	5 40.7
14 S	11 25 13.9	23 7.5	18 31.2	6♑44.3	3 59.7	24 18.5	9 5.5	8 48.1	7 7.0	2 53.1	9 5.8	5 40.6
15 M	11 29 10.4	24 7.3	18 28.0	18 46.7	3 30.4	25 32.1	9 5.9	8 44.2	7 2.5	2 56.4	9 4.7	5 40.5
16 T	11 33 6.9	25 7.1	18 24.8	1♒ 3.0	2 54.4	26 45.8	9R 5.6	8 40.5	6 58.0	2 59.7	9 3.6	5 40.4
17 W	11 37 3.5	26 6.8	18 21.6	13 36.6	2 12.6	27 59.4	9 4.6	8 37.1	6 53.6	3 2.9	9 2.5	5 40.3
18 T	11 41 0.0	27 6.5	18 18.5	26 29.8	1 26.0	29 13.0	9 2.8	8 33.7	6 49.2	3 6.1	9 1.5	5 40.2
19 F	11 44 56.6	28 6.1	18 15.3	9♓43.4	0 35.8	0♓26.7	9 0.3	8 30.6	6 44.9	3 9.4	9 0.5	5 40.2
20 S	11 48 53.2	29 5.8	18 12.1	23 16.5	29♓42.9	1 40.3	8 57.0	8 27.7	6 40.6	3 12.6	8 59.6	5 40.2
21 S	11 52 49.7	0♈ 5.4	18 8.9	7♈ 6.4	28 48.7	2 53.9	8 52.9	8 24.9	6 36.4	3 15.7	8 58.6	5D40.2
22 M	11 56 46.2	1 4.9	18 5.7	21 9.4	27 54.3	4 7.6	8 48.0	8 22.3	6 32.2	3 18.9	8 57.7	5 40.3
23 T	12 0 42.8	2 4.5	18 2.6	5♉21.2	27 0.8	5 21.2	8 42.4	8 20.0	6 28.1	3 22.0	8 56.8	5 40.3
24 W	12 4 39.4	3 3.9	17 59.4	19 37.5	26 9.3	6 34.9	8 36.0	8 17.8	6 24.1	3 25.2	8 56.0	5 40.4
25 T	12 8 35.9	4 3.4	17 56.2	3♊54.6	25 20.6	7 48.5	8 28.9	8 15.8	6 20.1	3 28.2	8 55.2	5 40.5
26 F	12 12 32.5	5 2.8	17 53.0	18 9.6	24 35.5	9 2.2	8 20.9	8 13.9	6 16.2	3 31.3	8 54.4	5 40.6
27 S	12 16 29.0	6 2.2	17 49.9	2♋20.3	23 54.8	10 15.8	8 12.2	8 12.3	6 12.3	3 34.4	8 53.6	5 40.8
28 S	12 20 25.6	7 1.5	17 46.7	16 25.1	23 18.8	11 29.5	8 2.8	8 10.9	6 8.5	3 37.4	8 52.9	5 41.0
29 M	12 24 22.1	8 0.8	17 43.5	0♌22.8	22 48.2	12 43.1	7 52.5	8 9.6	6 4.8	3 40.4	8 52.2	5 41.2
30 T	12 28 18.7	9 0.1	17 40.3	14 12.0	22 23.0	13 56.7	7 41.6	8 8.6	6 1.2	3 43.4	8 51.5	5 41.4
31 W	12 32 15.2	9 59.3	17 37.1	27 51.3	22 3.5	15 10.4	7 29.9	8 7.7	5 57.6	3 46.3	8 50.9	5 41.7

DECLINATION

DAY	EPHEMERIS SIDEREAL TIME h m s	☉ ° ′	☊ ° ′	☽ ° ′	☿ ° ′	♀ ° ′	♂ ° ′	♃ ° ′	♄ ° ′	♅ ° ′	♆ ° ′	♇ ° ′
1 M	10 33 58.7	7S46.4	17S32.0	17N36.1	0N 5.2	18S22.7	11S59.6	18N39.5	10N21.6	11S23.0	17N53.9	19N31.4
4 T	10 45 48.3	6 37.7	17 29.4	6 13.1	2 6.5	17 31.6	12 7.5	18 44.2	10 27.2	11 19.4	17 55.0	19 31.8
7 S	10 57 38.0	5 28.3	17 26.8	7S27.3	3 39.5	16 36.0	12 13.8	18 48.4	10 32.6	11 15.7	17 56.1	19 32.3
10 W	11 9 27.6	4 18.1	17 24.2	17 22.1	4 36.3	15 36.2	12 18.4	18 52.3	10 38.0	11 12.1	17 57.1	19 32.8
13 S	11 21 17.3	3 7.4	17 21.5	20 12.9	4 52.1	14 32.4	12 21.3	18 55.7	10 43.2	11 8.6	17 58.1	19 33.2
16 T	11 33 6.9	1 56.4	17 18.9	15 7.6	4 26.4	13 25.1	12 22.4	18 58.6	10 48.3	11 5.1	17 59.0	19 33.7
19 F	11 44 56.6	0 45.3	17 16.3	3 33.4	3 24.7	12 14.3	12 21.6	19 1.1	10 53.1	11 1.6	17 59.8	19 34.1
22 M	11 56 46.2	0N25.8	17 13.6	10N17.5	1 58.9	11 0.6	12 19.1	19 3.1	10 57.8	10 58.2	18 0.6	19 34.5
25 T	12 8 35.9	1 36.8	17 11.0	19 23.8	0 24.2	9 44.1	12 14.7	19 4.7	11 2.2	10 54.8	18 1.3	19 34.9
28 S	12 20 25.6	2 47.4	17 8.3	17 58.5	1S 4.9	8 25.3	12 8.5	19 5.8	11 6.4	10 51.6	18 1.9	19 35.3
31 W	12 32 15.2	3 57.4	17 5.6	7 27.3	2 18.0	7 4.3	12 0.4	19 6.5	11 10.3	10 48.4	18 2.5	19 35.7

APRIL 1920

LONGITUDE

DAY	EPHEMERIS SIDEREAL TIME h m s	☉ ° ′	☊ ° ′	☽ ° ′	☿ ° ′	♀ ° ′	♂ ° ′	♃ ° ′	♄ ° ′	♅ ° ′	♆ ° ′	♇ ° ′
1 T	12 36 11.8	10♈58.5	17♏34.0	11♍19.0	21♓49.7	16♓24.0	7♏17.4	8♌ 7.1	5♍54.1	3♓49.2	8♌50.2	5♋42.0
2 F	12 40 8.3	11 57.6	17 30.8	24 33.5	21R41.6	17 37.7	7R 4.3	8R 6.6	5R50.7	3 52.1	8R49.7	5 42.3
3 S	12 44 4.9	12 56.7	17 27.6	7♎33.5	21 39.1	18 51.3	6 50.4	8 6.3	5 47.3	3 55.0	8 49.1	5 42.6
4 S	12 48 1.4	13 55.8	17 24.4	20 18.5	21D42.2	20 5.0	6 35.9	8 6.2	5 44.1	3 57.8	8 48.6	5 42.9
5 M	12 51 58.0	14 54.8	17 21.3	2♏48.6	21 50.6	21 18.6	6 20.6	8D 6.3	5 40.9	4 0.7	8 48.1	5 43.3
6 T	12 55 54.5	15 53.8	17 18.1	15 4.9	22 4.2	22 32.3	6 4.7	8 6.6	5 37.8	4 3.5	8 47.7	5 43.7
7 W	12 59 51.1	16 52.8	17 14.9	27 9.5	22 22.7	23 45.9	5 48.2	8 7.0	5 34.8	4 6.2	8 47.2	5 44.1
8 T	13 3 47.6	17 51.8	17 11.7	9♐ 5.1	22 46.0	24 59.6	5 31.0	8 7.7	5 31.9	4 8.9	8 46.8	5 44.5
9 F	13 7 44.2	18 50.7	17 8.5	20 55.7	23 13.9	26 13.2	5 13.2	8 8.5	5 29.0	4 11.6	8 46.5	5 45.0
10 S	13 11 40.7	19 49.6	17 5.4	2♑45.4	23 46.0	27 26.9	4 54.9	8 9.5	5 26.3	4 14.3	8 46.1	5 45.4
11 S	13 15 37.3	20 48.4	17 2.2	14 38.9	24 22.3	28 40.5	4 36.0	8 10.8	5 23.6	4 16.9	8 45.9	5 45.9
12 M	13 19 33.9	21 47.3	16 59.0	26 41.3	25 2.4	29 54.2	4 16.5	8 12.2	5 21.0	4 19.5	8 45.6	5 46.5
13 T	13 23 30.4	22 46.1	16 55.8	8♒57.2	25 46.3	1♈ 7.8	3 56.6	8 13.7	5 18.5	4 22.1	8 45.4	5 47.0
14 W	13 27 26.9	23 44.8	16 52.7	21 31.0	26 33.7	2 21.5	3 36.3	8 15.5	5 16.2	4 24.6	8 45.2	5 47.6
15 T	13 31 23.5	24 43.6	16 49.5	4♓26.1	27 24.5	3 35.2	3 15.5	8 17.5	5 13.9	4 27.1	8 45.0	5 48.2
16 F	13 35 20.1	25 42.3	16 46.3	17 44.7	28 18.4	4 48.8	2 54.3	8 19.6	5 11.7	4 29.6	8 44.9	5 48.8
17 S	13 39 16.6	26 41.0	16 43.1	1♈27.1	29 15.4	6 2.5	2 32.8	8 21.9	5 9.6	4 32.0	8 44.8	5 49.4
18 S	13 43 13.2	27 39.6	16 39.9	15 31.8	0♈15.3	7 16.1	2 11.0	8 24.4	5 7.6	4 34.4	8 44.7	5 50.1
19 M	13 47 9.7	28 38.2	16 36.8	29 55.0	1 18.0	8 29.8	1 49.0	8 27.1	5 5.6	4 36.8	8 44.7	5 50.7
20 T	13 51 6.3	29 36.8	16 33.6	14♉31.3	2 23.3	9 43.4	1 26.7	8 29.9	5 3.8	4 39.1	8D44.7	5 51.4
21 W	13 55 2.8	0♉35.4	16 30.4	29 14.2	3 31.2	10 57.1	1 4.3	8 32.9	5 2.1	4 41.4	8 44.7	5 52.1
22 T	13 58 59.4	1 33.9	16 27.2	13♊57.1	4 41.6	12 10.7	0 41.8	8 36.2	5 0.5	4 43.6	8 44.8	5 52.9
23 F	14 2 55.9	2 32.4	16 24.0	28 33.8	5 54.3	13 24.3	0 19.2	8 39.5	4 59.0	4 45.8	8 44.9	5 53.6
24 S	14 6 52.5	3 30.8	16 20.9	12♋59.6	7 9.3	14 38.0	29♎56.5	8 43.1	4 57.6	4 48.0	8 45.0	5 54.4
25 S	14 10 49.0	4 29.2	16 17.7	27 11.1	8 26.6	15 51.6	29 34.0	8 46.8	4 56.3	4 50.1	8 45.2	5 55.2
26 M	14 14 45.6	5 27.6	16 14.5	11♌ 6.6	9 46.0	17 5.2	29 11.4	8 50.7	4 55.1	4 52.2	8 45.4	5 56.0
27 T	14 18 42.2	6 26.0	16 11.3	24 45.3	11 7.5	18 18.8	28 49.0	8 54.8	4 54.0	4 54.3	8 45.6	5 56.9
28 W	14 22 38.7	7 24.3	16 8.2	8♍ 7.5	12 31.2	19 32.4	28 26.8	8 59.0	4 53.0	4 56.3	8 45.9	5 57.7
29 T	14 26 35.2	8 22.5	16 5.0	21 14.0	13 56.8	20 46.0	28 4.7	9 3.4	4 52.2	4 58.3	8 46.2	5 58.6
30 F	14 30 31.8	9 20.8	16 1.8	4♎ 5.7	15 24.5	21 59.6	27 43.0	9 7.9	4 51.4	5 0.2	8 46.6	5 59.5

DECLINATION

DAY	EPHEMERIS SIDEREAL TIME h m s	☉ ° ′	☊ ° ′	☽ ° ′	☿ ° ′	♀ ° ′	♂ ° ′	♃ ° ′	♄ ° ′	♅ ° ′	♆ ° ′	♇ ° ′
1 T	12 36 11.8	4N20.7	17S 4.7	2N58.9	2S37.8	6S36.9	11S57.4	19N 6.6	11N11.5	10S47.4	18N 2.7	19N35.9
4 S	12 48 1.4	5 29.8	17 2.0	10S 1.2	3 21.8	5 13.7	11 47.0	19 6.6	11 15.0	10 44.3	18 3.1	19 36.3
7 W	12 59 51.1	6 38.1	16 59.4	18 31.3	3 42.9	3 49.1	11 35.1	19 6.2	11 18.3	10 41.3	18 3.5	19 36.6
10 S	13 11 40.7	7 45.4	16 56.7	19 34.9	3 41.9	2 23.5	11 21.6	19 5.4	11 21.2	10 38.4	18 3.8	19 37.0
13 T	13 23 30.4	8 51.5	16 54.0	12 59.5	3 20.9	0 57.1	11 6.9	19 4.1	11 23.8	10 35.7	18 4.1	19 37.3
16 F	13 35 20.1	9 56.3	16 51.2	0 44.3	2 41.7	0N29.7	10 51.1	19 2.3	11 26.0	10 33.0	18 4.2	19 37.7
19 M	13 47 9.7	10 59.6	16 48.5	12N47.1	1 46.2	1 56.7	10 34.4	19 0.2	11 27.9	10 30.5	18 4.3	19 38.0
22 T	13 58 59.4	12 1.3	16 45.8	19 59.4	0 36.3	3 23.4	10 17.4	18 57.6	11 29.5	10 28.1	18 4.3	19 38.3
25 S	14 10 49.0	13 1.3	16 43.1	15 48.6	0N46.7	4 49.6	10 0.2	18 54.6	11 30.7	10 25.8	18 4.3	19 38.6
28 W	14 22 38.7	13 59.2	16 40.3	3 59.4	2 21.3	6 15.0	9 43.4	18 51.1	11 31.6	10 23.6	18 4.1	19 38.9

MAY 1920

DAY	EPHEMERIS SIDEREAL TIME	☉	☊	☽	☿	♀	♂	♃	♄	♅	♆	♇
	h m s	° ′	° ′	° ′	° ′	° ′	° ′	° ′	° ′	° ′	° ′	° ′
						LONGITUDE						
1 S	14 34 28.4	10♉19.0	15♏58.6	16♎44.0	16♈54.1	23♈13.2	27♎21.4	9♌12.6	4♍50.7	5♓ 2.1	8♌46.9	6♋ 0.4
2 S	14 38 24.9	11 17.2	15 55.5	29 9.9	18 25.7	24 26.8	27R 0.3	9 17.5	4R50.1	5 3.9	8 47.3	6 1.3
3 M	14 42 21.5	12 15.3	15 52.3	11♏24.9	19 59.3	25 40.4	26 39.5	9 22.5	4 49.7	5 5.7	8 47.8	6 2.3
4 T	14 46 18.0	13 13.4	15 49.1	23 30.5	21 34.7	26 54.0	26 19.0	9 27.7	4 49.3	5 7.5	8 48.2	6 3.2
5 W	14 50 14.6	14 11.5	15 45.9	5♐28.6	23 12.2	28 7.5	25 59.1	9 33.1	4 49.0	5 9.2	8 48.7	6 4.2
6 T	14 54 11.1	15 9.6	15 42.7	17 21.2	24 51.5	29 21.1	25 39.6	9 38.5	4 48.9	5 10.9	8 49.3	6 5.2
7 F	14 58 7.7	16 7.6	15 39.6	29 11.0	26 32.8	0♉34.7	25 20.6	9 44.2	4 48.8	5 12.5	8 49.8	6 6.2
8 S	15 2 4.2	17 5.6	15 36.4	11♑ 1.2	28 16.0	1 48.3	25 2.1	9 50.0	4D48.9	5 14.1	8 50.4	6 7.2
9 S	15 6 0.8	18 3.6	15 33.2	22 55.4	0♉ 1.1	3 1.9	24 44.2	9 55.9	4 49.1	5 15.7	8 51.1	6 8.3
10 M	15 9 57.4	19 1.6	15 30.0	4♒57.6	1 48.2	4 15.4	24 27.0	10 2.0	4 49.3	5 17.2	8 51.7	6 9.4
11 T	15 13 53.9	19 59.5	15 26.9	17 12.0	3 37.2	5 29.0	24 10.3	10 8.2	4 49.7	5 18.6	8 52.4	6 10.4
12 W	15 17 50.4	20 57.5	15 23.7	29 42.9	5 28.1	6 42.6	23 54.3	10 14.6	4 50.2	5 20.0	8 53.1	6 11.5
13 T	15 21 47.0	21 55.4	15 20.5	12♓34.4	7 21.0	7 56.2	23 38.9	10 21.1	4 50.8	5 21.4	8 53.9	6 12.6
14 F	15 25 43.6	22 53.3	15 17.3	25 49.8	9 15.8	9 9.8	23 24.3	10 27.8	4 51.4	5 22.7	8 54.7	6 13.8
15 S	15 29 40.1	23 51.1	15 14.2	9♈31.1	11 12.5	10 23.4	23 10.3	10 34.6	4 52.2	5 24.0	8 55.5	6 14.9
16 S	15 33 36.7	24 49.0	15 11.0	23 38.3	13 11.1	11 36.9	22 57.2	10 41.5	4 53.1	5 25.2	8 56.3	6 16.1
17 M	15 37 33.2	25 46.8	15 7.8	8♉ 9.3	15 11.5	12 50.5	22 44.7	10 48.6	4 54.1	5 26.4	8 57.2	6 17.2
18 T	15 41 29.8	26 44.6	15 4.6	22 59.3	17 13.7	14 4.1	22 33.0	10 55.8	4 55.2	5 27.6	8 58.1	6 18.4
19 W	15 45 26.4	27 42.4	15 1.4	8♊ 1.1	19 17.6	15 17.7	22 22.2	11 3.1	4 56.4	5 28.7	8 59.1	6 19.6
20 T	15 49 22.9	28 40.1	14 58.3	23 6.1	21 23.1	16 31.3	22 12.1	11 10.6	4 57.8	5 29.7	9 0.0	6 20.8
21 F	15 53 19.5	29 37.8	14 55.1	8♋ 5.2	23 30.0	17 44.8	22 2.8	11 18.2	4 59.2	5 30.7	9 1.0	6 22.1
22 S	15 57 16.0	0♊35.5	14 51.9	22 50.7	25 38.3	18 58.4	21 54.3	11 25.9	5 0.7	5 31.6	9 2.1	6 23.3
23 S	16 1 12.6	1 33.2	14 48.7	7♌16.6	27 47.8	20 12.0	21 46.7	11 33.7	5 2.3	5 32.5	9 3.1	6 24.6
24 M	16 5 9.1	2 30.9	14 45.6	21 19.4	29 58.2	21 25.6	21 39.9	11 41.7	5 4.0	5 33.4	9 4.2	6 25.8
25 T	16 9 5.6	3 28.5	14 42.4	4♍58.3	2♊ 9.3	22 39.1	21 33.9	11 49.8	5 5.9	5 34.2	9 5.3	6 27.1
26 W	16 13 2.2	4 26.1	14 39.2	18 14.1	4 21.0	23 52.7	21 28.7	11 58.0	5 7.8	5 34.9	9 6.5	6 28.4
27 T	16 16 58.8	5 23.7	14 36.0	1♎ 9.2	6 32.9	25 6.2	21 24.3	12 6.3	5 9.8	5 35.7	9 7.6	6 29.7
28 F	16 20 55.4	6 21.2	14 32.8	13 46.4	8 44.7	26 19.8	21 20.8	12 14.8	5 11.9	5 36.3	9 8.8	6 31.0
29 S	16 24 51.9	7 18.8	14 29.7	26 9.0	10 56.3	27 33.4	21 18.0	12 23.3	5 14.2	5 36.9	9 10.1	6 32.3
30 S	16 28 48.4	8 16.3	14 26.5	8♏20.1	13 7.3	28 46.9	21 16.1	12 32.0	5 16.5	5 37.5	9 11.3	6 33.7
31 M	16 32 45.0	9 13.8	14 23.3	20 22.4	15 17.4	0♊ 0.5	21 15.0	12 40.7	5 18.9	5 38.0	9 12.6	6 35.0
						DECLINATION						
1 S	14 34 28.4	14N55.1	16S37.6	8S56.5	4N 6.2	7N39.3	9S27.2	18N47.3	11N32.1	10S21.6	18N 3.9	19N39.1
4 T	14 46 18.0	15 48.8	16 34.8	17 57.0	6 0.3	9 2.1	9 12.1	18 43.1	11 32.2	10 19.7	18 3.6	19 39.4
7 F	14 58 7.7	16 40.2	16 32.1	19 47.5	8 2.1	10 23.1	8 58.3	18 38.5	11 32.0	10 17.9	18 3.2	19 39.6
10 M	15 9 57.4	17 29.0	16 29.3	13 58.8	10 10.3	11 42.0	8 46.2	18 33.5	11 31.5	10 16.3	18 2.7	19 39.8
13 T	15 21 47.0	18 15.2	16 26.5	2 28.9	12 22.7	12 58.5	8 36.0	18 28.1	11 30.5	10 14.9	18 2.2	19 40.0
16 S	15 33 36.7	18 58.7	16 23.7	11N 1.5	14 37.1	14 12.3	8 27.9	18 22.4	11 29.3	10 13.6	18 1.6	19 40.2
19 W	15 45 26.4	19 39.3	16 20.9	19 39.8	16 50.0	15 23.0	8 22.1	18 16.3	11 27.7	10 12.4	18 0.9	19 40.3
22 S	15 57 16.0	20 16.9	16 18.1	16 42.7	18 57.3	16 30.3	8 18.7	18 9.8	11 25.7	10 11.4	18 0.1	19 40.5
25 T	16 9 5.6	20 51.4	16 15.3	5 3.6	20 53.6	17 33.9	8 17.9	18 3.0	11 23.4	10 10.6	17 59.3	19 40.6
28 F	16 20 55.4	21 22.6	16 12.5	7S59.8	22 33.6	18 33.5	8 19.5	17 55.9	11 20.8	10 9.9	17 58.4	19 40.7
31 M	16 32 45.0	21 50.5	16 9.7	17 25.5	23 52.6	19 28.7	8 23.6	17 48.4	11 17.9	10 9.4	17 57.4	19 40.8

JUNE 1920

DAY	EPHEMERIS SIDEREAL TIME	☉	☊	☽	☿	♀	♂	♃	♄	♅	♆	♇
						LONGITUDE						
1 T	16 36 41.6	10♊11.2	14♏20.1	2♐18.6	17♊26.5	1♊14.0	21♎14.6	12♌49.6	5♍21.4	5♓38.5	9♌13.9	6♋36.3
2 W	16 40 38.1	11 8.7	14 17.0	14 10.7	19 34.2	2 27.6	21D15.1	12 58.6	5 24.0	5 38.9	9 15.3	6 37.7
3 T	16 44 34.7	12 6.1	14 13.8	26 0.9	21 40.3	3 41.2	21 16.3	13 7.7	5 26.7	5 39.3	9 16.6	6 39.1
4 F	16 48 31.2	13 3.5	14 10.6	7♑51.2	23 44.7	4 54.7	21 18.3	13 16.9	5 29.5	5 39.6	9 18.0	6 40.5
5 S	16 52 27.8	14 1.0	14 7.4	19 43.7	25 47.3	6 8.3	21 21.0	13 26.2	5 32.4	5 39.8	9 19.4	6 41.8
6 S	16 56 24.3	14 58.3	14 4.3	1♒40.8	27 47.8	7 21.9	21 24.5	13 35.6	5 35.4	5 40.1	9 20.9	6 43.2
7 M	17 0 20.9	15 55.7	14 1.1	13 45.4	29 46.1	8 35.5	21 28.8	13 45.1	5 38.4	5 40.2	9 22.3	6 44.6
8 T	17 4 17.5	16 53.1	13 57.9	26 0.7	1♋42.2	9 49.1	21 33.8	13 54.7	5 41.6	5 40.4	9 23.8	6 46.1
9 W	17 8 14.0	17 50.5	13 54.7	8♓30.3	3 36.0	11 2.7	21 39.5	14 4.4	5 44.9	5 40.4	9 25.3	6 47.5
10 T	17 12 10.5	18 47.8	13 51.5	21 17.8	5 27.4	12 16.3	21 45.9	14 14.2	5 48.2	5 40.5	9 26.9	6 48.9
11 F	17 16 7.1	19 45.2	13 48.4	4♈27.0	7 16.4	13 29.9	21 53.1	14 24.1	5 51.6	5R40.5	9 28.4	6 50.3
12 S	17 20 3.7	20 42.5	13 45.2	18 0.8	9 3.0	14 43.5	22 0.9	14 34.1	5 55.2	5 40.4	9 30.0	6 51.8
13 S	17 24 0.3	21 39.9	13 42.0	2♉ 1.0	10 47.0	15 57.1	22 9.4	14 44.2	5 58.8	5 40.3	9 31.6	6 53.2
14 M	17 27 56.8	22 37.2	13 38.8	16 27.2	12 28.6	17 10.7	22 18.6	14 54.3	6 2.5	5 40.1	9 33.2	6 54.7
15 T	17 31 53.3	23 34.5	13 35.7	1♊16.5	14 7.7	18 24.4	22 28.5	15 4.6	6 6.3	5 39.9	9 34.9	6 56.1
16 W	17 35 49.9	24 31.8	13 32.5	16 22.8	15 44.2	19 38.0	22 39.0	15 14.9	6 10.1	5 39.6	9 36.6	6 57.6
17 T	17 39 46.5	25 29.1	13 29.3	1♋37.5	17 18.2	20 51.7	22 50.2	15 25.3	6 14.1	5 39.3	9 38.3	6 59.1
18 F	17 43 43.0	26 26.4	13 26.1	16 50.1	18 49.6	22 5.3	23 2.1	15 35.8	6 18.1	5 39.0	9 40.0	7 0.5
19 S	17 47 39.6	27 23.7	13 23.0	1♌50.6	20 18.5	23 19.0	23 14.5	15 46.4	6 22.3	5 38.6	9 41.7	7 2.0
20 S	17 51 36.1	28 21.0	13 19.8	16 30.3	21 44.7	24 32.6	23 27.6	15 57.1	6 26.5	5 38.1	9 43.5	7 3.5
21 M	17 55 32.7	29 18.2	13 16.6	0♍43.9	23 8.3	25 46.3	23 41.3	16 7.9	6 30.8	5 37.6	9 45.2	7 4.9
22 T	17 59 29.3	0♋15.5	13 13.4	14 29.1	24 29.2	26 60.0	23 55.6	16 18.7	6 35.1	5 37.1	9 47.0	7 6.4
23 W	18 3 25.8	1 12.7	13 10.2	27 46.6	25 47.4	28 13.7	24 10.5	16 29.6	6 39.6	5 36.5	9 48.8	7 7.9
24 T	18 7 22.4	2 9.9	13 7.1	10♎39.0	27 2.8	29 27.3	24 26.0	16 40.5	6 44.1	5 35.8	9 50.7	7 9.4
25 F	18 11 18.9	3 7.2	13 3.9	23 10.4	28 15.5	0♋41.0	24 42.0	16 51.6	6 48.7	5 35.1	9 52.5	7 10.9
26 S	18 15 15.5	4 4.4	13 0.7	5♏25.2	29 25.2	1 54.7	24 58.6	17 2.7	6 53.4	5 34.4	9 54.4	7 12.4
27 S	18 19 12.0	5 1.6	12 57.5	17 28.0	0♌32.0	3 8.4	25 15.7	17 13.9	6 58.1	5 33.6	9 56.3	7 13.9
28 M	18 23 8.6	5 58.8	12 54.4	29 22.9	1 35.8	4 22.1	25 33.3	17 25.1	7 3.0	5 32.8	9 58.2	7 15.4
29 T	18 27 5.2	6 55.9	12 51.2	11♐13.4	2 36.5	5 35.8	25 51.4	17 36.5	7 7.9	5 31.9	10 0.1	7 16.9
30 W	18 31 1.7	7 53.1	12 48.0	23 2.7	3 33.9	6 49.5	26 10.1	17 47.8	7 12.8	5 31.0	10 2.0	7 18.4
						DECLINATION						
1 T	16 36 41.6	21N59.1	16S 8.8	19S 8.9	24N13.7	19N46.0	8S25.5	17N45.8	11N16.8	10S 9.3	17N57.1	19N40.8
4 F	16 48 31.2	22 22.4	16 5.9	19 4.9	25 0.5	20 35.0	8 32.8	17 37.9	11 13.5	10 9.0	17 56.0	19 40.9
7 M	17 0 20.9	22 42.3	16 3.1	11 42.5	25 22.9	21 18.9	8 42.4	17 29.7	11 9.8	10 8.9	17 54.9	19 41.0
10 T	17 12 10.5	22 58.5	16 0.3	0N25.1	25 22.7	21 57.4	8 54.2	17 21.2	11 5.8	10 8.9	17 53.8	19 41.0
13 S	17 24 0.3	23 11.1	15 57.4	13 17.4	25 2.7	22 30.5	9 8.0	17 12.3	11 1.6	10 9.1	17 52.5	19 41.0
16 W	17 35 49.9	23 20.1	15 54.5	20 4.3	24 26.1	22 57.8	9 23.9	17 3.2	10 57.0	10 9.4	17 51.2	19 41.0
19 S	17 47 39.6	23 25.3	15 51.7	14 51.2	23 36.3	23 19.1	9 41.7	16 53.7	10 52.2	10 9.9	17 49.9	19 41.0
22 T	17 59 29.3	23 26.8	15 48.8	1 58.6	22 36.3	23 34.3	10 1.3	16 44.0	10 47.1	10 10.6	17 48.5	19 40.9
25 F	18 11 18.9	23 24.6	15 45.9	10S45.8	21 29.2	23 43.3	10 22.4	16 34.0	10 41.8	10 11.4	17 47.1	19 40.9
28 M	18 23 8.6	23 18.8	15 43.1	18 44.7	20 17.8	23 46.0	10 45.1	16 23.8	10 36.2	10 12.4	17 45.6	19 40.8

JULY 1920

DAY	EPHEMERIS SIDEREAL TIME h m s	☉ ° ′	☊ ° ′	☽ ° ′	☿ ° ′	♀ ° ′	♂ ° ′	♃ ° ′	♄ ° ′	♅ ° ′	♆ ° ′	♇ ° ′
LONGITUDE												
1 T	18 34 58.3	8♋50.3	12♏44.8	4♑53.1	4♌28.1	8♋ 3.2	26♎29.2	17♌59.3	7♍17.9	5♓30.1	10♌ 4.0	7♋19.8
2 F	18 38 54.8	9 47.5	12 41.7	16 46.5	5 18.9	9 16.9	26 48.8	18 10.8	7 23.0	5R29.1	10 6.0	7 21.3
3 S	18 42 51.4	10 44.7	12 38.5	28 44.5	6 6.1	10 30.7	27 8.9	18 22.4	7 28.2	5 28.0	10 7.9	7 22.8
4 S	18 46 47.9	11 41.8	12 35.3	10♒48.6	6 49.7	11 44.4	27 29.5	18 34.0	7 33.4	5 27.0	10 9.9	7 24.3
5 M	18 50 44.5	12 39.0	12 32.1	23 0.5	7 29.6	12 58.2	27 50.5	18 45.7	7 38.7	5 25.8	10 12.0	7 25.8
6 T	18 54 41.1	13 36.2	12 29.0	5♓22.1	8 5.5	14 11.9	28 12.0	18 57.4	7 44.1	5 24.7	10 14.0	7 27.3
7 W	18 58 37.6	14 33.4	12 25.8	17 55.6	8 37.5	15 25.7	28 33.9	19 9.2	7 49.6	5 23.5	10 16.0	7 28.8
8 T	19 2 34.1	15 30.6	12 22.6	0♈43.9	9 5.2	16 39.5	28 56.3	19 21.1	7 55.1	5 22.2	10 18.1	7 30.3
9 F	19 6 30.7	16 27.8	12 19.4	13 50.1	9 28.7	17 53.3	29 19.0	19 33.0	8 0.6	5 20.9	10 20.1	7 31.7
10 S	19 10 27.3	17 25.0	12 16.2	27 17.1	9 47.8	19 7.1	29 42.2	19 45.0	8 6.3	5 19.6	10 22.2	7 33.2
11 S	19 14 23.9	18 22.2	12 13.1	11♉ 7.4	10 2.3	20 20.9	0♏ 5.8	19 57.0	8 12.0	5 18.2	10 24.3	7 34.7
12 M	19 18 20.4	19 19.5	12 9.9	25 21.8	10 12.2	21 34.7	0 29.8	20 9.1	8 17.8	5 16.8	10 26.4	7 36.2
13 T	19 22 16.9	20 16.7	12 6.7	9♊59.3	10 17.4	22 48.5	0 54.2	20 21.2	8 23.6	5 15.4	10 28.5	7 37.6
14 W	19 26 13.5	21 13.9	12 3.5	24 55.9	10 17.8	24 2.4	1 19.0	20 33.4	8 29.5	5 13.9	10 30.6	7 39.1
15 T	19 30 10.1	22 11.2	12 0.4	10♋ 4.4	10R13.4	25 16.3	1 44.2	20 45.6	8 35.4	5 12.3	10 32.7	7 40.5
16 F	19 34 6.6	23 8.5	11 57.2	25 15.3	10 4.2	26 30.1	2 9.8	20 57.8	8 41.4	5 10.8	10 34.9	7 42.0
17 S	19 38 3.2	24 5.7	11 54.0	10♌18.0	9 50.2	27 44.0	2 35.7	21 10.1	8 47.5	5 9.2	10 37.0	7 43.4
18 S	19 41 59.7	25 3.0	11 50.8	25 2.9	9 31.6	28 57.9	3 2.0	21 22.5	8 53.6	5 7.6	10 39.2	7 44.9
19 M	19 45 56.3	26 0.3	11 47.7	9♍22.8	9 8.5	0♌11.8	3 28.7	21 34.9	8 59.7	5 5.9	10 41.3	7 46.3
20 T	19 49 52.8	26 57.6	11 44.5	23 14.0	8 41.3	1 25.7	3 55.7	21 47.3	9 6.0	5 4.2	10 43.5	7 47.7
21 W	19 53 49.4	27 54.8	11 41.3	6♎35.9	8 10.1	2 39.6	4 23.1	21 59.8	9 12.2	5 2.5	10 45.7	7 49.1
22 T	19 57 46.0	28 52.1	11 38.1	19 30.7	7 35.4	3 53.5	4 50.8	22 12.3	9 18.5	5 0.7	10 47.9	7 50.6
23 F	20 1 42.5	29 49.4	11 34.9	2♏ 2.3	6 57.7	5 7.4	5 18.8	22 24.8	9 24.9	4 58.9	10 50.1	7 52.0
24 S	20 5 39.1	0♌46.7	11 31.8	14 15.7	6 17.6	6 21.3	5 47.2	22 37.4	9 31.3	4 57.1	10 52.3	7 53.4
25 S	20 9 35.6	1 44.0	11 28.6	26 16.1	5 35.6	7 35.2	6 15.8	22 50.0	9 37.8	4 55.2	10 54.5	7 54.7
26 M	20 13 32.2	2 41.4	11 25.4	8♐ 8.7	4 52.5	8 49.1	6 44.8	23 2.7	9 44.3	4 53.3	10 56.7	7 56.1
27 T	20 17 28.8	3 38.7	11 22.2	19 57.8	4 9.0	10 3.1	7 14.1	23 15.3	9 50.8	4 51.4	10 58.9	7 57.5
28 W	20 21 25.3	4 36.0	11 19.1	1♑47.5	3 25.9	11 17.0	7 43.7	23 28.0	9 57.4	4 49.4	11 1.1	7 58.8
29 T	20 25 21.8	5 33.3	11 15.9	13 40.8	2 43.9	12 30.9	8 13.5	23 40.8	10 4.1	4 47.5	11 3.3	8 0.2
30 F	20 29 18.4	6 30.7	11 12.7	25 40.0	2 4.0	13 44.9	8 43.7	23 53.5	10 10.8	4 45.5	11 5.5	8 1.5
31 S	20 33 15.0	7 28.1	11 9.5	7♒46.7	1 26.7	14 58.8	9 14.1	24 6.3	10 17.5	4 43.4	11 7.7	8 2.9
DECLINATION												
1 T	18 34 58.3	23N 9.2	15S40.2	19S25.4	19N 4.9	23N42.3	11S 9.1	16N13.3	10N30.4	10S13.5	17N44.0	19N40.8
4 S	18 46 47.9	22 56.0	15 37.3	12 38.8	17 53.2	23 32.4	11 34.4	16 2.5	10 24.3	10 14.7	17 42.5	19 40.7
7 W	18 58 37.6	22 39.1	15 34.4	0 54.7	16 45.6	23 16.1	12 0.8	15 51.5	10 18.0	10 16.1	17 40.9	19 40.6
10 S	19 10 27.3	22 18.8	15 31.5	11N49.8	15 45.1	22 53.7	12 28.2	15 40.3	10 11.5	10 17.6	17 39.2	19 40.4
13 T	19 22 16.9	21 55.0	15 28.5	19 42.2	14 54.8	22 25.1	12 56.4	15 28.8	10 4.8	10 19.2	17 37.6	19 40.3
16 F	19 34 6.6	21 27.8	15 25.6	16 22.1	14 17.7	21 50.7	13 25.5	15 17.1	9 57.9	10 21.0	17 35.9	19 40.2
19 M	19 45 56.3	20 57.3	15 22.7	3 52.9	13 56.4	21 10.5	13 55.3	15 5.2	9 50.8	10 22.9	17 34.1	19 40.0
22 T	19 57 46.0	20 23.6	15 19.8	9S27.4	13 52.5	20 24.8	14 25.6	14 53.2	9 43.6	10 24.9	17 32.4	19 39.8
25 S	20 9 35.6	19 46.9	15 16.8	18 8.2	14 6.2	19 33.9	14 56.3	14 40.9	9 36.1	10 26.9	17 30.6	19 39.7
28 W	20 21 25.3	19 7.2	15 13.9	19 36.2	14 35.4	18 38.0	15 27.4	14 28.4	9 28.6	10 29.1	17 28.8	19 39.5
31 S	20 33 15.0	18 24.6	15 10.9	13 30.3	15 16.2	17 37.4	15 58.7	14 15.8	9 20.8	10 31.4	17 27.0	19 39.3

AUGUST 1920

DAY	EPHEMERIS SIDEREAL TIME h m s	☉ ° ′	☊ ° ′	☽ ° ′	☿ ° ′	♀ ° ′	♂ ° ′	♃ ° ′	♄ ° ′	♅ ° ′	♆ ° ′	♇ ° ′
LONGITUDE												
1 S	20 37 11.5	8♌25.4	11♏ 6.3	20♒ 1.9	0♌52.9	16♌12.8	9♏44.9	24♌19.1	10♍24.3	4♓41.4	11♌10.0	8♋ 4.2
2 M	20 41 8.1	9 22.8	11 3.2	2♓26.4	0R23.2	17 26.8	10 15.8	24 31.9	10 31.1	4R39.3	11 12.2	8 5.5
3 T	20 45 4.6	10 20.3	10 60.0	15 0.8	29♋58.2	18 40.7	10 47.1	24 44.8	10 37.9	4 37.2	11 14.4	8 6.8
4 W	20 49 1.2	11 17.7	10 56.8	27 46.0	29 38.5	19 54.7	11 18.6	24 57.7	10 44.8	4 35.1	11 16.6	8 8.1
5 T	20 52 57.7	12 15.1	10 53.6	10♈43.3	29 24.5	21 8.7	11 50.4	25 10.6	10 51.7	4 32.9	11 18.9	8 9.4
6 F	20 56 54.3	13 12.6	10 50.5	23 54.4	29 16.6	22 22.7	12 22.4	25 23.5	10 58.6	4 30.8	11 21.1	8 10.6
7 S	21 0 50.9	14 10.1	10 47.3	7♉21.4	29 15.1	23 36.7	12 54.7	25 36.5	11 5.6	4 28.6	11 23.3	8 11.9
8 S	21 4 47.4	15 7.6	10 44.1	21 6.1	29D20.2	24 50.7	13 27.2	25 49.4	11 12.7	4 26.4	11 25.5	8 13.1
9 M	21 8 43.9	16 5.2	10 40.9	5♊ 9.7	29 32.2	26 4.7	14 0.0	26 2.4	11 19.7	4 24.2	11 27.8	8 14.3
10 T	21 12 40.5	17 2.7	10 37.7	19 32.1	29 51.0	27 18.8	14 33.0	26 15.4	11 26.8	4 21.9	11 30.0	8 15.6
11 W	21 16 37.1	18 0.3	10 34.6	4♋10.7	0♌16.9	28 32.8	15 6.3	26 28.4	11 33.9	4 19.6	11 32.2	8 16.8
12 T	21 20 33.6	18 57.9	10 31.4	19 0.8	0 49.7	29 46.8	15 39.8	26 41.4	11 41.1	4 17.4	11 34.4	8 17.9
13 F	21 24 30.2	19 55.6	10 28.2	3♌55.0	1 29.4	1♍ 0.9	16 13.5	26 54.5	11 48.2	4 15.1	11 36.6	8 19.1
14 S	21 28 26.7	20 53.2	10 25.0	18 44.5	2 15.9	2 14.9	16 47.5	27 7.5	11 55.4	4 12.8	11 38.8	8 20.3
15 S	21 32 23.3	21 50.9	10 21.9	3♍20.7	3 9.1	3 29.0	17 21.7	27 20.5	12 2.7	4 10.5	11 41.0	8 21.4
16 M	21 36 19.8	22 48.6	10 18.7	17 36.2	4 8.9	4 43.0	17 56.1	27 33.6	12 9.9	4 8.1	11 43.2	8 22.5
17 T	21 40 16.4	23 46.3	10 15.5	1♎26.4	5 15.0	5 57.1	18 30.8	27 46.7	12 17.2	4 5.8	11 45.4	8 23.7
18 W	21 44 12.9	24 44.0	10 12.3	14 49.4	6 27.1	7 11.2	19 5.6	27 59.8	12 24.5	4 3.4	11 47.6	8 24.8
19 T	21 48 9.5	25 41.8	10 9.2	27 46.3	7 45.0	8 25.2	19 40.7	28 12.8	12 31.8	4 1.1	11 49.8	8 25.8
20 F	21 52 6.0	26 39.6	10 6.0	10♏20.1	9 8.4	9 39.3	20 16.0	28 25.9	12 39.2	3 58.7	11 51.9	8 26.9
21 S	21 56 2.6	27 37.4	10 2.8	22 35.2	10 37.0	10 53.3	20 51.4	28 39.0	12 46.5	3 56.3	11 54.1	8 27.9
22 S	21 59 59.2	28 35.2	9 59.6	4♐36.8	12 10.2	12 7.4	21 27.1	28 52.1	12 53.9	3 54.0	11 56.2	8 29.0
23 M	22 3 55.7	29 33.0	9 56.4	16 30.1	13 47.8	13 21.5	22 3.0	29 5.2	13 1.3	3 51.6	11 58.4	8 30.0
24 T	22 7 52.2	0♍30.8	9 53.3	28 20.3	15 29.2	14 35.5	22 39.1	29 18.3	13 8.7	3 49.2	12 0.5	8 31.0
25 W	22 11 48.8	1 28.7	9 50.1	10♑12.0	17 14.1	15 49.6	23 15.3	29 31.3	13 16.1	3 46.8	12 2.6	8 32.0
26 T	22 15 45.4	2 26.6	9 46.9	22 9.2	19 2.0	17 3.6	23 51.8	29 44.4	13 23.6	3 44.4	12 4.8	8 32.9
27 F	22 19 42.0	3 24.5	9 43.7	4♒15.0	20 52.4	18 17.7	24 28.4	29 57.5	13 31.0	3 42.0	12 6.9	8 33.9
28 S	22 23 38.5	4 22.5	9 40.6	16 31.4	22 44.9	19 31.7	25 5.2	0♍10.6	13 38.5	3 39.6	12 9.0	8 34.8
29 S	22 27 35.0	5 20.4	9 37.4	28 59.7	24 39.1	20 45.8	25 42.2	0 23.6	13 46.0	3 37.2	12 11.0	8 35.7
30 M	22 31 31.6	6 18.4	9 34.2	11♓40.2	26 34.5	21 59.8	26 19.4	0 36.7	13 53.5	3 34.8	12 13.1	8 36.6
31 T	22 35 28.2	7 16.4	9 31.0	24 32.8	28 30.9	23 13.9	26 56.7	0 49.7	14 1.0	3 32.4	12 15.2	8 37.5
DECLINATION												
1 S	20 37 11.5	18N 9.8	15S 9.9	10S 6.9	15N31.5	17N16.3	16S 9.1	14N11.6	9N18.2	10S32.1	17N26.4	19N39.2
4 W	20 49 1.2	17 23.7	15 7.0	2N15.4	16 19.6	16 9.9	16 40.5	13 58.8	9 10.4	10 34.5	17 24.6	19 39.0
7 S	21 0 50.9	16 35.0	15 4.0	14 14.6	17 6.5	14 59.6	17 11.9	13 45.8	9 2.3	10 36.9	17 22.8	19 38.8
10 T	21 12 40.5	15 43.9	15 1.0	19 52.5	17 46.8	13 45.6	17 43.1	13 32.7	8 54.2	10 39.4	17 21.0	19 38.6
13 F	21 24 30.2	14 50.6	14 58.0	14 25.9	18 15.1	12 28.2	18 14.1	13 19.5	8 46.0	10 41.9	17 19.2	19 38.4
16 M	21 36 19.8	13 55.0	14 55.0	1 14.6	18 26.6	11 7.9	18 44.8	13 6.2	8 37.7	10 44.5	17 17.4	19 38.2
19 T	21 48 9.5	12 57.5	14 52.0	11S38.5	18 16.8	9 44.9	19 15.0	12 52.8	8 29.3	10 47.1	17 15.6	19 38.0
22 S	21 59 59.2	11 58.2	14 49.0	18 56.5	17 42.6	8 19.5	19 44.7	12 39.3	8 20.8	10 49.7	17 13.9	19 37.8
25 W	22 11 48.8	10 57.2	14 46.0	18 38.8	16 42.8	6 52.2	20 13.7	12 25.7	8 12.3	10 52.3	17 12.1	19 37.5
28 S	22 23 38.5	9 54.6	14 43.0	11 6.9	15 18.8	5 23.2	20 42.0	12 12.1	8 3.8	10 54.9	17 10.4	19 37.3
31 T	22 35 28.2	8 50.6	14 40.0	1N 3.1	13 34.3	3 52.8	21 9.4	11 58.4	7 55.2	10 57.5	17 8.7	19 37.1

SEPTEMBER 1920

LONGITUDE

DAY	EPHEMERIS SIDEREAL TIME	☉	☊	☽	☿	♀	♂	♃	♄	♅	♆	♇
	h m s	° ′	° ′	° ′	° ′	° ′	° ′	° ′	° ′	° ′	° ′	° ′
1 W	22 39 24.7	8♍14.5	9♏27.8	7♈37.1	0♍27.9	24♍27.9	27♏34.2	1♍ 2.8	14♍ 8.5	3♓30.1	12♌17.2	8♋38.3
2 T	22 43 21.2	9 12.6	9 24.7	20 52.5	2 25.1	25 41.9	28 11.9	1 15.8	14 16.0	3R27.7	12 19.3	8 39.2
3 F	22 47 17.8	10 10.7	9 21.5	4♉18.9	4 22.3	26 56.0	28 49.8	1 28.8	14 23.5	3 25.3	12 21.3	8 40.0
4 S	22 51 14.3	11 8.8	9 18.3	17 56.5	6 19.4	28 10.0	29 27.8	1 41.8	14 31.0	3 22.9	12 23.3	8 40.8
5 S	22 55 10.9	12 7.0	9 15.1	1♊45.5	8 16.1	29 24.1	0♐ 5.9	1 54.8	14 38.6	3 20.6	12 25.3	8 41.6
6 M	22 59 7.4	13 5.2	9 12.0	15 46.0	10 12.2	0♎38.1	0 44.3	2 7.7	14 46.1	3 18.2	12 27.3	8 42.3
7 T	23 3 4.0	14 3.4	9 8.8	29 57.6	12 7.7	1 52.1	1 22.8	2 20.7	14 53.7	3 15.9	12 29.2	8 43.1
8 W	23 7 0.6	15 1.7	9 5.6	14♋18.7	14 2.4	3 6.2	2 1.4	2 33.6	15 1.2	3 13.5	12 31.2	8 43.8
9 T	23 10 57.1	16 0.0	9 2.4	28 46.1	15 56.2	4 20.2	2 40.2	2 46.5	15 8.7	3 11.2	12 33.1	8 44.5
10 F	23 14 53.7	16 58.4	8 59.2	13♌15.1	17 49.1	5 34.3	3 19.2	2 59.4	15 16.3	3 8.9	12 35.0	8 45.2
11 S	23 18 50.2	17 56.8	8 56.1	27 39.9	19 41.0	6 48.3	3 58.3	3 12.3	15 23.8	3 6.6	12 36.9	8 45.8
12 S	23 22 46.8	18 55.2	8 52.9	11♍54.4	21 31.9	8 2.3	4 37.6	3 25.1	15 31.4	3 4.3	12 38.8	8 46.4
13 M	23 26 43.3	19 53.6	8 49.7	25 53.0	23 21.8	9 16.3	5 17.0	3 37.9	15 38.9	3 2.0	12 40.6	8 47.0
14 T	23 30 39.9	20 52.1	8 46.5	9♎31.5	25 10.6	10 30.4	5 56.6	3 50.7	15 46.4	2 59.8	12 42.5	8 47.6
15 W	23 34 36.4	21 50.6	8 43.4	22 47.8	26 58.3	11 44.4	6 36.4	4 3.5	15 53.9	2 57.6	12 44.3	8 48.2
16 T	23 38 33.0	22 49.1	8 40.2	5♏41.9	28 45.0	12 58.4	7 16.2	4 16.2	16 1.4	2 55.4	12 46.1	8 48.8
17 F	23 42 29.5	23 47.7	8 37.0	18 15.3	0♎30.6	14 12.4	7 56.2	4 28.9	16 8.9	2 53.2	12 47.9	8 49.3
18 S	23 46 26.1	24 46.3	8 33.8	0♐31.5	2 15.2	15 26.4	8 36.4	4 41.6	16 16.4	2 51.0	12 49.6	8 49.8
19 S	23 50 22.6	25 44.9	8 30.6	12 34.5	3 58.7	16 40.4	9 16.7	4 54.3	16 23.9	2 48.8	12 51.4	8 50.3
20 M	23 54 19.2	26 43.5	8 27.5	24 29.2	5 41.2	17 54.4	9 57.1	5 6.9	16 31.4	2 46.7	12 53.1	8 50.7
21 T	23 58 15.7	27 42.2	8 24.3	6♑20.7	7 22.7	19 8.4	10 37.7	5 19.4	16 38.8	2 44.6	12 54.8	8 51.2
22 W	0 2 12.3	28 40.9	8 21.1	18 14.0	9 3.2	20 22.4	11 18.3	5 32.0	16 46.3	2 42.5	12 56.5	8 51.6
23 T	0 6 8.8	29 39.6	8 17.9	0♒13.6	10 42.7	21 36.3	11 59.2	5 44.5	16 53.7	2 40.5	12 58.1	8 52.0
24 F	0 10 5.4	0♎38.4	8 14.7	12 23.5	12 21.2	22 50.3	12 40.1	5 56.9	17 1.1	2 38.4	12 59.8	8 52.3
25 S	0 14 2.0	1 37.2	8 11.6	24 46.9	13 58.8	24 4.2	13 21.1	6 9.3	17 8.5	2 36.4	13 1.4	8 52.7
26 S	0 17 58.5	2 36.0	8 8.4	7♓25.9	15 35.5	25 18.1	14 2.3	6 21.7	17 15.9	2 34.4	13 3.0	8 53.0
27 M	0 21 55.1	3 34.9	8 5.2	20 21.4	17 11.2	26 32.1	14 43.6	6 34.0	17 23.2	2 32.5	13 4.5	8 53.3
28 T	0 25 51.6	4 33.7	8 2.0	3♈33.3	18 46.1	27 46.0	15 25.0	6 46.3	17 30.6	2 30.6	13 6.1	8 53.6
29 W	0 29 48.2	5 32.7	7 58.9	17 0.3	20 20.1	28 59.9	16 6.6	6 58.5	17 37.9	2 28.7	13 7.6	8 53.8
30 T	0 33 44.7	6 31.6	7 55.7	0♉40.5	21 53.2	0♏13.8	16 48.2	7 10.7	17 45.1	2 26.8	13 9.1	8 54.1

DECLINATION

DAY	EPHEMERIS SIDEREAL TIME	☉	☊	☽	☿	♀	♂	♃	♄	♅	♆	♇
1 W	22 39 24.7	8N28.9	14S39.0	5N23.9	12N55.7	3N22.4	21S18.3	11N53.9	7N52.3	10S58.4	17N 8.1	19N37.0
4 S	22 51 14.3	7 23.3	14 36.0	16 20.3	10 51.2	1 50.7	21 44.4	11 40.2	7 43.7	11 1.0	17 6.4	19 36.8
7 T	23 3 4.0	6 16.5	14 32.9	19 25.0	8 37.1	0 18.4	22 9.3	11 26.4	7 35.1	11 3.5	17 4.8	19 36.6
10 F	23 14 53.7	5 8.8	14 29.9	11 58.0	6 17.5	1S14.2	22 33.0	11 12.7	7 26.5	11 6.0	17 3.2	19 36.4
13 M	23 26 43.3	4 0.2	14 26.8	1S29.3	3 55.4	2 46.8	22 55.5	10 59.0	7 17.9	11 8.4	17 1.7	19 36.2
16 T	23 38 33.0	2 51.1	14 23.8	13 33.6	1 33.1	4 18.9	23 16.5	10 45.4	7 9.3	11 10.8	17 0.1	19 36.0
19 S	23 50 22.6	1 41.4	14 20.7	19 20.4	0S47.8	5 50.4	23 36.1	10 31.7	7 0.8	11 13.1	16 58.7	19 35.9
22 W	0 2 12.3	0 31.5	14 17.6	17 21.0	3 6.0	7 20.9	23 54.0	10 18.2	6 52.3	11 15.4	16 57.3	19 35.7
25 S	0 14 2.0	0S38.7	14 14.6	8 36.4	5 20.5	8 49.9	24 10.3	10 4.7	6 43.9	11 17.5	16 55.9	19 35.5
28 T	0 25 51.6	1 48.8	14 11.5	4N 2.0	7 30.5	10 17.3	24 24.7	9 51.4	6 35.5	11 19.6	16 54.6	19 35.4

OCTOBER 1920

LONGITUDE

DAY	EPHEMERIS SIDEREAL TIME	☉	☊	☽	☿	♀	♂	♃	♄	♅	♆	♇
1 F	0 37 41.3	7♎30.6	7♏52.5	14♉31.5	23♎25.5	1♏27.6	17♐29.9	7♍22.9	17♍52.4	2♓25.0	13♌10.5	8♋54.3
2 S	0 41 37.8	8 29.6	7 49.3	28 30.8	24 56.9	2 41.5	18 11.8	7 35.0	17 59.6	2R23.2	13 12.0	8 54.5
3 S	0 45 34.4	9 28.7	7 46.1	12♊36.3	26 27.4	3 55.4	18 53.8	7 47.0	18 6.9	2 21.4	13 13.4	8 54.6
4 M	0 49 30.9	10 27.8	7 43.0	26 45.6	27 57.1	5 9.3	19 35.9	7 59.0	18 14.1	2 19.7	13 14.8	8 54.8
5 T	0 53 27.5	11 26.9	7 39.8	10♋57.0	29 26.0	6 23.1	20 18.1	8 10.9	18 21.2	2 18.0	13 16.2	8 54.9
6 W	0 57 24.0	12 26.1	7 36.6	25 8.3	0♏54.0	7 37.0	21 0.4	8 22.8	18 28.3	2 16.3	13 17.5	8 55.0
7 T	1 1 20.6	13 25.3	7 33.4	9♌17.5	2 21.1	8 50.8	21 42.8	8 34.6	18 35.4	2 14.7	13 18.8	8 55.0
8 F	1 5 17.1	14 24.6	7 30.3	23 21.9	3 47.4	10 4.7	22 25.3	8 46.4	18 42.5	2 13.1	13 20.1	8 55.1
9 S	1 9 13.7	15 23.9	7 27.1	7♍18.7	5 12.8	11 18.5	23 7.9	8 58.1	18 49.5	2 11.6	13 21.3	8 55.1
10 S	1 13 10.3	16 23.2	7 23.9	21 5.1	6 37.2	12 32.3	23 50.7	9 9.7	18 56.5	2 10.1	13 22.6	8R55.1
11 M	1 17 6.8	17 22.6	7 20.7	4♎38.2	8 0.8	13 46.1	24 33.5	9 21.3	19 3.5	2 8.6	13 23.7	8 55.1
12 T	1 21 3.3	18 22.0	7 17.5	17 56.0	9 23.3	14 59.9	25 16.4	9 32.8	19 10.4	2 7.2	13 24.9	8 55.0
13 W	1 24 59.9	19 21.4	7 14.4	0♏57.0	10 44.9	16 13.7	25 59.5	9 44.3	19 17.3	2 5.8	13 26.0	8 55.0
14 T	1 28 56.5	20 20.9	7 11.2	13 41.1	12 5.4	17 27.5	26 42.6	9 55.7	19 24.1	2 4.4	13 27.2	8 54.9
15 F	1 32 53.0	21 20.4	7 8.0	26 9.0	13 24.7	18 41.3	27 25.9	10 7.0	19 31.0	2 3.1	13 28.2	8 54.7
16 S	1 36 49.6	22 19.9	7 4.8	8♐22.8	14 42.9	19 55.1	28 9.2	10 18.2	19 37.7	2 1.8	13 29.3	8 54.6
17 S	1 40 46.1	23 19.5	7 1.6	20 25.3	15 59.8	21 8.8	28 52.6	10 29.4	19 44.4	2 0.6	13 30.3	8 54.4
18 M	1 44 42.7	24 19.1	6 58.5	2♑20.3	17 15.4	22 22.6	29 36.1	10 40.4	19 51.1	1 59.4	13 31.3	8 54.2
19 T	1 48 39.2	25 18.7	6 55.3	14 11.9	18 29.5	23 36.3	0♑19.7	10 51.5	19 57.8	1 58.3	13 32.2	8 54.0
20 W	1 52 35.8	26 18.4	6 52.1	26 4.9	19 42.0	24 50.0	1 3.4	11 2.4	20 4.3	1 57.2	13 33.1	8 53.8
21 T	1 56 32.3	27 18.1	6 48.9	8♒ 3.9	20 52.8	26 3.7	1 47.2	11 13.2	20 10.9	1 56.1	13 34.0	8 53.5
22 F	2 0 28.9	28 17.8	6 45.8	20 13.6	22 1.8	27 17.4	2 31.0	11 24.0	20 17.4	1 55.1	13 34.9	8 53.3
23 S	2 4 25.5	29 17.5	6 42.6	2♓38.1	23 8.7	28 31.1	3 15.0	11 34.7	20 23.8	1 54.2	13 35.7	8 53.0
24 S	2 8 22.0	0♏17.3	6 39.4	15 21.0	24 13.3	29 44.7	3 59.0	11 45.3	20 30.2	1 53.2	13 36.5	8 52.6
25 M	2 12 18.5	1 17.1	6 36.2	28 24.6	25 15.4	0♐58.3	4 43.1	11 55.8	20 36.6	1 52.4	13 37.3	8 52.3
26 T	2 16 15.1	2 16.9	6 33.0	11♈49.7	26 14.8	2 12.0	5 27.2	12 6.2	20 42.8	1 51.5	13 38.0	8 51.9
27 W	2 20 11.6	3 16.8	6 29.9	25 35.8	27 11.2	3 25.6	6 11.5	12 16.6	20 49.1	1 50.8	13 38.7	8 51.5
28 T	2 24 8.2	4 16.7	6 26.7	9♉40.3	28 4.1	4 39.1	6 55.8	12 26.8	20 55.3	1 50.0	13 39.4	8 51.1
29 F	2 28 4.8	5 16.6	6 23.5	23 59.3	28 53.3	5 52.7	7 40.2	12 37.0	21 1.4	1 49.4	13 40.0	8 50.7
30 S	2 32 1.3	6 16.5	6 20.3	8♊27.6	29 38.3	7 6.3	8 24.6	12 47.1	21 7.5	1 48.7	13 40.6	8 50.2
31 S	2 35 57.9	7 16.5	6 17.2	22 59.6	0♐18.7	8 19.8	9 9.1	12 57.0	21 13.5	1 48.1	13 41.2	8 49.7

DECLINATION

DAY	EPHEMERIS SIDEREAL TIME	☉	☊	☽	☿	♀	♂	♃	♄	♅	♆	♇
1 F	0 37 41.3	2S58.9	14S 8.4	15N31.2	9S35.5	11S42.6	24S37.4	9N38.1	6N27.3	11S21.5	16N53.4	19N35.3
4 M	0 49 30.9	4 8.6	14 5.3	19 23.5	11 34.7	13 5.5	24 48.1	9 25.0	6 19.1	11 23.3	16 52.2	19 35.1
7 T	1 1 20.6	5 18.0	14 2.2	12 53.0	13 27.7	14 25.7	24 56.7	9 12.0	6 11.1	11 25.1	16 51.1	19 35.0
10 S	1 13 10.3	6 26.7	13 59.1	0 5.4	15 13.8	15 42.8	25 3.4	8 59.2	6 3.2	11 26.7	16 50.1	19 35.0
13 W	1 24 59.9	7 34.7	13 56.0	12S17.3	16 52.2	16 56.5	25 7.8	8 46.6	5 55.4	11 28.1	16 49.1	19 34.9
16 S	1 36 49.6	8 41.8	13 52.9	18 57.3	18 22.3	18 6.3	25 10.1	8 34.2	5 47.8	11 29.5	16 48.2	19 34.8
19 T	1 48 39.2	9 47.7	13 49.8	17 49.9	19 43.0	19 12.0	25 10.2	8 22.0	5 40.3	11 30.6	16 47.4	19 34.8
22 F	2 0 28.9	10 52.3	13 46.6	9 52.3	20 53.3	20 13.3	25 8.0	8 10.1	5 33.0	11 31.7	16 46.7	19 34.7
25 M	2 12 18.5	11 55.5	13 43.5	2N22.0	21 51.7	21 9.7	25 3.5	7 58.5	5 25.9	11 32.6	16 46.0	19 34.7
28 T	2 24 8.2	12 57.0	13 40.4	14 26.4	22 36.4	22 0.9	24 56.6	7 47.1	5 19.0	11 33.3	16 45.4	19 34.7
31 S	2 35 57.9	13 56.7	13 37.2	19 25.7	23 5.0	22 46.7	24 47.4	7 36.0	5 12.4	11 33.9	16 45.0	19 34.8

NOVEMBER 1920

LONGITUDE

DAY	EPHEMERIS SIDEREAL TIME h m s	☉ ° ′	☊ ° ′	☽ ° ′	☿ ° ′	♀ ° ′	♂ ° ′	♃ ° ′	♄ ° ′	♅ ° ′	♆ ° ′	♇ ° ′
1 M	2 39 54.4	8♏16.6	6♏14.0	7♋29.9	0♐53.9	9♐33.3	9♑53.7	13♍ 6.9	21♍19.4	1♓47.6	13♌41.7	8♋49.2
2 T	2 43 51.0	9 16.6	6 10.8	21 53.8	1 23.4	10 46.8	10 38.4	13 16.7	21 25.3	1R47.1	13 42.2	8R48.7
3 W	2 47 47.5	10 16.7	6 7.6	6♌ 7.9	1 46.5	12 0.3	11 23.1	13 26.3	21 31.1	1 46.7	13 42.7	8 48.1
4 T	2 51 44.1	11 16.9	6 4.4	20 9.8	2 2.6	13 13.8	12 7.9	13 35.9	21 36.9	1 46.3	13 43.1	8 47.6
5 F	2 55 40.6	12 17.0	6 1.3	3♍58.2	2 11.2	14 27.2	12 52.8	13 45.4	21 42.6	1 45.9	13 43.5	8 47.0
6 S	2 59 37.2	13 17.2	5 58.1	17 32.7	2 11.4	15 40.7	13 37.8	13 54.8	21 48.2	1 45.7	13 43.9	8 46.4
7 S	3 3 33.7	14 17.5	5 54.9	0♎53.3	2R 2.7	16 54.1	14 22.8	14 4.0	21 53.8	1 45.4	13 44.2	8 45.7
8 M	3 7 30.3	15 17.7	5 51.7	14 0.4	1 44.5	18 7.5	15 7.8	14 13.1	21 59.3	1 45.2	13 44.5	8 45.1
9 T	3 11 26.8	16 18.1	5 48.6	26 54.1	1 16.5	19 20.9	15 53.0	14 22.2	22 4.7	1 45.1	13 44.8	8 44.4
10 W	3 15 23.4	17 18.4	5 45.4	9♏35.2	0 38.5	20 34.3	16 38.2	14 31.1	22 10.1	1 45.0	13 45.0	8 43.7
11 T	3 19 20.0	18 18.8	5 42.2	22 4.1	29♏50.6	21 47.6	17 23.4	14 39.9	22 15.4	1 45.0	13 45.2	8 43.0
12 F	3 23 16.5	19 19.1	5 39.0	4♐21.8	28 53.3	23 1.0	18 8.7	14 48.6	22 20.6	1D45.0	13 45.4	8 42.3
13 S	3 27 13.1	20 19.6	5 35.8	16 29.5	27 47.6	24 14.3	18 54.1	14 57.1	22 25.7	1 45.0	13 45.5	8 41.6
14 S	3 31 9.6	21 20.0	5 32.7	28 29.0	26 34.9	25 27.6	19 39.5	15 5.6	22 30.8	1 45.2	13 45.6	8 40.8
15 M	3 35 6.2	22 20.5	5 29.5	10♑22.7	25 17.1	26 40.8	20 25.0	15 13.9	22 35.8	1 45.3	13 45.7	8 40.0
16 T	3 39 2.7	23 21.0	5 26.3	22 13.5	23 56.5	27 54.1	21 10.5	15 22.1	22 40.7	1 45.6	13 45.7	8 39.2
17 W	3 42 59.3	24 21.5	5 23.1	4♒ 5.2	22 35.8	29 7.3	21 56.1	15 30.2	22 45.6	1 45.8	13R45.7	8 38.4
18 T	3 46 55.8	25 22.0	5 20.0	16 1.9	21 17.5	0♑20.5	22 41.7	15 38.1	22 50.3	1 46.2	13 45.6	8 37.6
19 F	3 50 52.4	26 22.6	5 16.8	28 8.1	20 4.4	1 33.6	23 27.4	15 45.9	22 55.0	1 46.5	13 45.5	8 36.7
20 S	3 54 49.0	27 23.1	5 13.6	10♓28.4	18 58.5	2 46.7	24 13.1	15 53.6	22 59.6	1 47.0	13 45.4	8 35.8
21 S	3 58 45.5	28 23.7	5 10.4	23 7.4	18 1.9	3 59.8	24 58.9	16 1.1	23 4.1	1 47.4	13 45.3	8 34.9
22 M	4 2 42.1	29 24.4	5 7.3	6♈ 9.0	17 15.8	5 12.9	25 44.7	16 8.5	23 8.5	1 48.0	13 45.1	8 34.0
23 T	4 6 38.6	0♐25.0	5 4.1	19 36.1	16 41.1	6 25.9	26 30.6	16 15.8	23 12.9	1 48.5	13 44.9	8 33.1
24 W	4 10 35.2	1 25.7	5 0.9	3♉29.5	16 18.0	7 38.9	27 16.5	16 22.9	23 17.2	1 49.2	13 44.6	8 32.2
25 T	4 14 31.8	2 26.3	4 57.7	17 48.1	16 6.5	8 51.8	28 2.4	16 29.9	23 21.3	1 49.9	13 44.4	8 31.2
26 F	4 18 28.3	3 27.0	4 54.6	2♊27.8	16 6.2	10 4.7	28 48.3	16 36.8	23 25.4	1 50.6	13 44.0	8 30.3
27 S	4 22 24.8	4 27.7	4 51.4	17 22.1	16D16.3	11 17.6	29 34.3	16 43.4	23 29.4	1 51.4	13 43.7	8 29.3
28 S	4 26 21.4	5 28.5	4 48.2	2♋22.6	16 36.2	12 30.4	0♒20.4	16 50.0	23 33.3	1 52.2	13 43.3	8 28.3
29 M	4 30 18.0	6 29.3	4 45.0	17 20.2	17 4.9	13 43.2	1 6.4	16 56.4	23 37.2	1 53.1	13 42.9	8 27.3
30 T	4 34 14.5	7 30.0	4 41.8	2♌ 6.6	17 41.6	14 55.9	1 52.5	17 2.7	23 40.9	1 54.0	13 42.4	8 26.3

DECLINATION

DAY	EPHEMERIS SIDEREAL TIME h m s	☉ ° ′	☊ ° ′	☽ ° ′	☿ ° ′	♀ ° ′	♂ ° ′	♃ ° ′	♄ ° ′	♅ ° ′	♆ ° ′	♇ ° ′
1 M	2 39 54.4	14S16.2	13S36.2	18N36.9	23S10.4	23S 0.7	24S43.8	7N32.4	5N10.2	11S34.0	16N44.8	19N34.8
4 T	2 51 44.1	15 13.2	13 33.0	9 53.1	23 12.2	23 38.8	24 31.5	7 21.8	5 3.8	11 34.4	16 44.4	19 34.8
7 S	3 3 33.7	16 8.0	13 29.9	3S11.2	22 48.1	24 10.9	24 16.8	7 11.5	4 57.7	11 34.6	16 44.2	19 34.9
10 W	3 15 23.4	17 0.3	13 26.7	14 25.6	21 53.0	24 36.6	23 59.7	7 1.6	4 51.8	11 34.7	16 44.0	19 35.0
13 S	3 27 13.1	17 50.1	13 23.5	19 23.5	20 24.4	24 55.9	23 40.4	6 52.1	4 46.2	11 34.5	16 43.9	19 35.1
16 T	3 39 2.7	18 37.0	13 20.4	16 34.8	18 30.5	25 8.6	23 18.7	6 43.0	4 40.9	11 34.2	16 43.8	19 35.2
19 F	3 50 52.4	19 21.0	13 17.2	7 32.3	16 34.6	25 14.7	22 54.8	6 34.4	4 35.9	11 33.8	16 43.9	19 35.4
22 M	4 2 42.1	20 1.8	13 14.0	4N52.7	15 5.9	25 13.9	22 28.6	6 26.3	4 31.2	11 33.2	16 44.1	19 35.5
25 T	4 14 31.8	20 39.3	13 10.8	16 9.1	14 21.3	25 6.5	22 0.3	6 18.6	4 26.7	11 32.4	16 44.3	19 35.7
28 S	4 26 21.4	21 13.4	13 7.6	19 5.8	14 20.7	24 52.4	21 29.8	6 11.4	4 22.7	11 31.4	16 44.7	19 35.9

DECEMBER 1920

LONGITUDE

DAY	EPHEMERIS SIDEREAL TIME h m s	☉ ° ′	☊ ° ′	☽ ° ′	☿ ° ′	♀ ° ′	♂ ° ′	♃ ° ′	♄ ° ′	♅ ° ′	♆ ° ′	♇ ° ′
1 W	4 38 11.1	8♐30.9	4♏38.7	16♌35.7	18♏25.4	16♑ 8.6	2♒38.6	17♍ 8.8	23♍44.5	1♓55.0	13♌42.0	8♋25.2
2 T	4 42 7.6	9 31.7	4 35.5	0♍43.6	19 15.4	17 21.2	3 24.8	17 14.7	23 48.1	1 56.0	13R41.4	8R24.2
3 F	4 46 4.2	10 32.6	4 32.3	14 29.2	20 11.0	18 33.8	4 11.0	17 20.5	23 51.5	1 57.1	13 40.9	8 23.1
4 S	4 50 0.7	11 33.4	4 29.1	27 53.4	21 11.4	19 46.4	4 57.2	17 26.2	23 54.9	1 58.3	13 40.3	8 22.0
5 S	4 53 57.3	12 34.4	4 26.0	10♎58.0	22 16.0	20 58.9	5 43.5	17 31.7	23 58.2	1 59.4	13 39.7	8 21.0
6 M	4 57 53.9	13 35.3	4 22.8	23 46.0	23 24.2	22 11.4	6 29.8	17 37.0	24 1.3	2 0.7	13 39.1	8 19.9
7 T	5 1 50.4	14 36.2	4 19.6	6♏20.0	24 35.6	23 23.8	7 16.1	17 42.2	24 4.4	2 2.0	13 38.4	8 18.8
8 W	5 5 47.0	15 37.2	4 16.4	18 42.6	25 49.7	24 36.2	8 2.4	17 47.2	24 7.4	2 3.3	13 37.7	8 17.6
9 T	5 9 43.5	16 38.2	4 13.3	0♐55.9	27 6.2	25 48.5	8 48.8	17 52.0	24 10.2	2 4.7	13 37.0	8 16.5
10 F	5 13 40.1	17 39.2	4 10.1	13 1.8	28 24.7	27 0.8	9 35.2	17 56.7	24 13.0	2 6.1	13 36.2	8 15.4
11 S	5 17 36.6	18 40.2	4 6.9	25 1.8	29 45.0	28 13.0	10 21.6	18 1.1	24 15.7	2 7.6	13 35.4	8 14.2
12 S	5 21 33.2	19 41.2	4 3.7	6♑57.0	1♐ 6.8	29 25.2	11 8.1	18 5.5	24 18.2	2 9.1	13 34.6	8 13.1
13 M	5 25 29.8	20 42.3	4 0.5	18 49.2	2 29.9	0♒37.2	11 54.5	18 9.6	24 20.7	2 10.7	13 33.7	8 11.9
14 T	5 29 26.3	21 43.3	3 57.4	0♒40.0	3 54.1	1 49.3	12 41.0	18 13.6	24 23.1	2 12.3	13 32.8	8 10.8
15 W	5 33 22.9	22 44.4	3 54.2	12 31.9	5 19.3	3 1.2	13 27.5	18 17.4	24 25.3	2 13.9	13 31.9	8 9.6
16 T	5 37 19.4	23 45.5	3 51.0	24 27.8	6 45.4	4 13.1	14 14.0	18 21.0	24 27.5	2 15.6	13 31.0	8 8.4
17 F	5 41 16.0	24 46.5	3 47.8	6♓31.4	8 12.3	5 24.9	15 0.5	18 24.5	24 29.5	2 17.4	13 30.0	8 7.2
18 S	5 45 12.6	25 47.6	3 44.7	18 47.0	9 39.8	6 36.6	15 47.1	18 27.7	24 31.5	2 19.2	13 29.0	8 6.0
19 S	5 49 9.1	26 48.7	3 41.5	1♈19.2	11 7.9	7 48.3	16 33.6	18 30.8	24 33.3	2 21.0	13 28.0	8 4.8
20 M	5 53 5.7	27 49.8	3 38.3	14 12.7	12 36.5	8 59.9	17 20.2	18 33.7	24 35.1	2 22.9	13 26.9	8 3.6
21 T	5 57 2.2	28 50.9	3 35.1	27 31.6	14 5.6	10 11.3	18 6.7	18 36.4	24 36.7	2 24.8	13 25.8	8 2.4
22 W	6 0 58.8	29 52.0	3 31.9	11♉18.9	15 35.1	11 22.7	18 53.3	18 39.0	24 38.2	2 26.8	13 24.7	8 1.2
23 T	6 4 55.3	0♑53.1	3 28.8	25 35.6	17 5.1	12 34.0	19 39.9	18 41.3	24 39.6	2 28.8	13 23.6	7 60.0
24 F	6 8 51.9	1 54.2	3 25.6	10♊19.4	18 35.4	13 45.2	20 26.5	18 43.5	24 40.9	2 30.9	13 22.4	7 58.7
25 S	6 12 48.4	2 55.3	3 22.4	25 24.6	20 6.0	14 56.3	21 13.1	18 45.5	24 42.1	2 33.0	13 21.3	7 57.5
26 S	6 16 45.0	3 56.5	3 19.2	10♋42.3	21 37.0	16 7.3	21 59.7	18 47.3	24 43.2	2 35.1	13 20.0	7 56.3
27 M	6 20 41.6	4 57.6	3 16.1	26 1.2	23 8.4	17 18.2	22 46.3	18 48.9	24 44.2	2 37.3	13 18.8	7 55.1
28 T	6 24 38.1	5 58.7	3 12.9	11♌ 9.9	24 40.0	18 29.0	23 32.9	18 50.3	24 45.0	2 39.5	13 17.6	7 53.8
29 W	6 28 34.7	6 59.8	3 9.7	25 59.0	26 11.9	19 39.7	24 19.5	18 51.5	24 45.8	2 41.7	13 16.3	7 52.6
30 T	6 32 31.2	8 1.0	3 6.5	10♍22.2	27 44.2	20 50.2	25 6.1	18 52.6	24 46.4	2 44.0	13 15.0	7 51.4
31 F	6 36 27.8	9 2.1	3 3.4	24 16.9	29 16.8	22 0.7	25 52.7	18 53.4	24 47.0	2 46.4	13 13.7	7 50.1

DECLINATION

DAY	EPHEMERIS SIDEREAL TIME h m s	☉ ° ′	☊ ° ′	☽ ° ′	☿ ° ′	♀ ° ′	♂ ° ′	♃ ° ′	♄ ° ′	♅ ° ′	♆ ° ′	♇ ° ′
1 W	4 38 11.1	21S43.9	13S 4.4	10N58.7	14S54.1	24S31.7	20S57.3	6N 4.8	4N18.9	11S30.3	16N45.1	19N36.2
4 S	4 50 0.7	22 10.6	13 1.2	2S 7.2	15 49.6	24 4.6	20 22.8	5 58.7	4 15.5	11 29.1	16 45.6	19 36.4
7 T	5 1 50.4	22 33.5	12 58.0	13 37.2	16 57.1	23 31.3	19 46.4	5 53.1	4 12.5	11 27.6	16 46.2	19 36.7
10 F	5 13 40.1	22 52.4	12 54.8	19 17.2	18 9.6	22 51.9	19 8.1	5 48.2	4 9.8	11 26.0	16 46.9	19 36.9
13 M	5 25 29.8	23 7.3	12 51.6	17 15.8	19 21.9	22 6.7	18 28.1	5 43.9	4 7.5	11 24.3	16 47.6	19 37.2
16 T	5 37 19.4	23 18.0	12 48.3	8 48.3	20 30.7	21 16.1	17 46.3	5 40.1	4 5.5	11 22.4	16 48.4	19 37.5
19 S	5 49 9.1	23 24.5	12 45.1	3N 8.7	21 33.5	20 20.2	17 2.9	5 37.1	4 4.0	11 20.4	16 49.3	19 37.9
22 W	6 0 58.8	23 26.8	12 41.9	14 42.2	22 28.6	19 19.5	16 18.1	5 34.6	4 2.8	11 18.2	16 50.3	19 38.2
25 S	6 12 48.4	23 24.9	12 38.6	19 26.8	23 14.8	18 14.4	15 31.8	5 32.8	4 2.0	11 15.9	16 51.3	19 38.6
28 T	6 24 38.1	23 18.7	12 35.4	12 35.3	23 51.1	17 5.0	14 44.2	5 31.7	4 1.6	11 13.5	16 52.4	19 38.9
31 F	6 36 27.8	23 8.4	12 32.1	0S43.4	24 16.6	15 51.9	13 55.3	5 31.3	4 1.6	11 10.9	16 53.5	19 39.3

JANUARY 1921

DAY	EPHEMERIS SIDEREAL TIME	☉	☊	☽	☿	♀	♂	♃	♄	♅	♆	♇
	h m s	° ′	° ′	° ′	° ′	° ′	° ′	° ′	° ′	° ′	° ′	° ′
						LONGITUDE						
1 S	6 40 24.3	10♑ 3.3	3♏ 0.2	7♎43.7	0♑49.7	23♒11.0	26♒39.3	18♍54.1	24♍47.4	2♓48.7	13♌12.3	7♋48.9
2 S	6 44 20.9	11 4.5	2 57.0	20 45.2	2 23.0	24 21.2	27 25.9	18 54.5	24 47.7	2 51.2	13R11.0	7R47.7
3 M	6 48 17.5	12 5.6	2 53.8	3♏25.5	3 56.6	25 31.3	28 12.5	18 54.8	24 48.0	2 53.6	13 9.6	7 46.5
4 T	6 52 14.0	13 6.8	2 50.7	15 49.1	5 30.5	26 41.3	28 59.1	18 54.9	24 48.0	2 56.1	13 8.2	7 45.2
5 W	6 56 10.6	14 8.0	2 47.5	28 0.2	7 4.8	27 51.1	29 45.7	18R54.7	24R48.0	2 58.6	13 6.8	7 44.0
6 T	7 0 7.1	15 9.1	2 44.3	10♐ 2.5	8 39.5	29 0.8	0♓32.2	18 54.4	24 47.9	3 1.1	13 5.4	7 42.8
7 F	7 4 3.7	16 10.3	2 41.1	21 59.2	10 14.5	0♓10.4	1 18.8	18 53.9	24 47.7	3 3.7	13 3.9	7 41.6
8 S	7 8 0.3	17 11.5	2 38.0	3♑52.7	11 50.0	1 19.8	2 5.4	18 53.2	24 47.3	3 6.4	13 2.4	7 40.3
9 S	7 11 56.8	18 12.7	2 34.8	15 44.6	13 25.9	2 29.1	2 52.0	18 52.3	24 46.9	3 9.0	13 0.9	7 39.1
10 M	7 15 53.3	19 13.8	2 31.6	27 36.6	15 2.2	3 38.2	3 38.6	18 51.2	24 46.3	3 11.7	12 59.4	7 37.9
11 T	7 19 49.9	20 15.0	2 28.4	9♒29.6	16 38.9	4 47.2	4 25.1	18 49.9	24 45.7	3 14.4	12 57.9	7 36.7
12 W	7 23 46.5	21 16.1	2 25.2	21 25.3	18 16.1	5 56.0	5 11.7	18 48.4	24 44.9	3 17.2	12 56.4	7 35.5
13 T	7 27 43.0	22 17.3	2 22.1	3♓25.2	19 53.8	7 4.6	5 58.2	18 46.7	24 44.0	3 20.0	12 54.8	7 34.3
14 F	7 31 39.6	23 18.4	2 18.9	15 31.9	21 32.0	8 13.1	6 44.7	18 44.9	24 43.0	3 22.8	12 53.3	7 33.2
15 S	7 35 36.1	24 19.6	2 15.7	27 48.3	23 10.6	9 21.4	7 31.3	18 42.8	24 41.9	3 25.6	12 51.7	7 32.0
16 S	7 39 32.7	25 20.7	2 12.5	10♈18.3	24 49.8	10 29.5	8 17.8	18 40.6	24 40.7	3 28.5	12 50.1	7 30.8
17 M	7 43 29.3	26 21.8	2 9.4	23 6.0	26 29.5	11 37.3	9 4.2	18 38.1	24 39.4	3 31.4	12 48.5	7 29.7
18 T	7 47 25.8	27 22.9	2 6.2	6♉15.7	28 9.7	12 45.0	9 50.7	18 35.5	24 37.9	3 34.3	12 46.9	7 28.5
19 W	7 51 22.4	28 23.9	2 3.0	19 51.3	29 50.5	13 52.5	10 37.1	18 32.7	24 36.4	3 37.3	12 45.3	7 27.4
20 T	7 55 18.9	29 25.0	1 59.8	3♊55.1	1♒31.7	14 59.8	11 23.6	18 29.7	24 34.8	3 40.2	12 43.7	7 26.2
21 F	7 59 15.5	0♒26.0	1 56.7	18 27.1	3 13.6	16 6.8	12 10.0	18 26.5	24 33.0	3 43.3	12 42.0	7 25.1
22 S	8 3 12.0	1 27.1	1 53.5	3♋23.8	4 55.9	17 13.6	12 56.3	18 23.2	24 31.2	3 46.3	12 40.4	7 24.0
23 S	8 7 8.6	2 28.1	1 50.3	18 38.2	6 38.7	18 20.2	13 42.7	18 19.7	24 29.3	3 49.3	12 38.7	7 22.9
24 M	8 11 5.1	3 29.1	1 47.1	3♌59.9	8 22.1	19 26.5	14 29.0	18 15.9	24 27.2	3 52.4	12 37.1	7 21.8
25 T	8 15 1.7	4 30.1	1 43.9	19 16.9	10 5.9	20 32.5	15 15.3	18 12.1	24 25.1	3 55.5	12 35.4	7 20.7
26 W	8 18 58.3	5 31.0	1 40.8	4♍18.0	11 50.2	21 38.4	16 1.6	18 8.0	24 22.9	3 58.6	12 33.7	7 19.7
27 T	8 22 54.8	6 32.0	1 37.6	18 54.6	13 34.8	22 43.9	16 47.9	18 3.8	24 20.6	4 1.8	12 32.1	7 18.6
28 F	8 26 51.4	7 32.9	1 34.4	3♎ 1.8	15 19.8	23 49.2	17 34.1	17 59.4	24 18.1	4 4.9	12 30.4	7 17.5
29 S	8 30 47.9	8 33.9	1 31.2	16 38.5	17 5.0	24 54.1	18 20.3	17 54.8	24 15.6	4 8.1	12 28.7	7 16.5
30 S	8 34 44.5	9 34.8	1 28.1	29 46.6	18 50.4	25 58.8	19 6.5	17 50.1	24 13.0	4 11.3	12 27.0	7 15.5
31 M	8 38 41.0	10 35.7	1 24.9	12♏29.9	20 35.8	27 3.3	19 52.7	17 45.2	24 10.3	4 14.5	12 25.3	7 14.5
						DECLINATION						
1 S	6 40 24.3	23S 4.0	12S31.0	5S 8.9	24S22.7	15S26.7	13S38.7	5N31.3	4N 1.7	11S10.0	16N53.9	19N39.4
4 T	6 52 14.0	22 48.1	12 27.8	15 35.8	24 32.9	14 9.1	12 48.3	5 31.7	4 2.2	11 7.3	16 55.1	19 39.8
7 F	7 4 3.7	22 28.0	12 24.5	19 28.0	24 31.0	12 48.4	11 56.9	5 32.9	4 3.1	11 4.5	16 56.4	19 40.2
10 M	7 15 53.3	22 4.1	12 21.2	15 45.9	24 16.4	11 25.1	11 4.5	5 34.7	4 4.5	11 1.5	16 57.7	19 40.7
13 T	7 27 43.0	21 36.2	12 18.0	6 14.3	23 48.8	9 59.6	10 11.2	5 37.2	4 6.1	10 58.5	16 59.0	19 41.1
16 S	7 39 32.7	21 4.6	12 14.7	5N49.2	23 7.7	8 32.2	9 17.2	5 40.4	4 8.2	10 55.3	17 0.4	19 41.5
19 W	7 51 22.4	20 29.3	12 11.4	16 14.4	22 12.8	7 3.3	8 22.6	5 44.2	4 10.6	10 52.1	17 1.8	19 42.0
22 S	8 3 12.0	19 50.6	12 8.1	19 0.4	21 3.9	5 33.2	7 27.3	5 48.7	4 13.4	10 48.7	17 3.2	19 42.4
25 T	8 15 1.7	19 8.6	12 4.8	10 30.9	19 41.1	4 2.2	6 31.6	5 53.7	4 16.5	10 45.3	17 4.7	19 42.9
28 F	8 26 51.4	18 23.4	12 1.5	3S22.7	18 4.5	2 30.7	5 35.5	5 59.4	4 20.0	10 41.9	17 6.1	19 43.3
31 M	8 38 41.0	17 35.2	11 58.2	14 38.1	16 14.8	0 59.1	4 39.1	6 5.6	4 23.8	10 38.3	17 7.6	19 43.8

FEBRUARY 1921

DAY	EPHEMERIS SIDEREAL TIME	☉	☊	☽	☿	♀	♂	♃	♄	♅	♆	♇
						LONGITUDE						
1 T	8 42 37.6	11♒36.6	1♏21.7	24♏53.1	22♒21.1	28♓ 7.3	20♓38.8	17♍40.1	24♍ 7.5	4♓17.8	12♌23.6	7♋13.5
2 W	8 46 34.1	12 37.5	1 18.5	7♐ 1.4	24 6.1	29 11.1	21 25.0	17R34.9	24R 4.6	4 21.0	12R21.9	7R12.5
3 T	8 50 30.7	13 38.4	1 15.3	18 59.7	25 50.7	0♈14.6	22 11.0	17 29.6	24 1.7	4 24.3	12 20.3	7 11.6
4 F	8 54 27.3	14 39.2	1 12.2	0♑52.2	27 34.5	1 17.7	22 57.1	17 24.1	23 58.6	4 27.6	12 18.6	7 10.6
5 S	8 58 23.8	15 40.1	1 9.0	12 42.6	29 17.3	2 20.5	23 43.1	17 18.4	23 55.5	4 30.9	12 16.9	7 9.7
6 S	9 2 20.3	16 40.9	1 5.8	24 33.7	0♓58.8	3 22.9	24 29.2	17 12.6	23 52.2	4 34.2	12 15.2	7 8.8
7 M	9 6 16.9	17 41.7	1 2.6	6♒27.4	2 38.6	4 25.0	25 15.1	17 6.7	23 48.9	4 37.5	12 13.5	7 7.9
8 T	9 10 13.5	18 42.5	0 59.5	18 25.2	4 16.2	5 26.7	26 1.1	17 0.6	23 45.5	4 40.9	12 11.8	7 7.0
9 W	9 14 10.0	19 43.3	0 56.3	0♓28.3	5 51.3	6 28.0	26 47.0	16 54.4	23 42.1	4 44.3	12 10.2	7 6.1
10 T	9 18 6.6	20 44.0	0 53.1	12 37.8	7 23.2	7 28.9	27 32.9	16 48.1	23 38.5	4 47.6	12 8.5	7 5.3
11 F	9 22 3.1	21 44.7	0 49.9	24 54.7	8 51.3	8 29.3	28 18.7	16 41.7	23 34.9	4 51.0	12 6.8	7 4.4
12 S	9 25 59.7	22 45.4	0 46.7	7♈20.9	10 15.1	9 29.3	29 4.6	16 35.1	23 31.2	4 54.4	12 5.2	7 3.6
13 S	9 29 56.2	23 46.1	0 43.6	19 58.5	11 33.9	10 28.9	29 50.4	16 28.4	23 27.5	4 57.8	12 3.5	7 2.8
14 M	9 33 52.8	24 46.7	0 40.4	2♉50.3	12 46.9	11 28.0	0♈36.1	16 21.7	23 23.7	5 1.2	12 1.9	7 2.0
15 T	9 37 49.4	25 47.3	0 37.2	15 59.4	13 53.4	12 26.6	1 21.8	16 14.8	23 19.8	5 4.6	12 0.2	7 1.3
16 W	9 41 45.9	26 47.9	0 34.0	29 28.8	14 52.8	13 24.7	2 7.5	16 7.8	23 15.8	5 8.0	11 58.6	7 0.5
17 T	9 45 42.4	27 48.4	0 30.9	13♊20.9	15 44.4	14 22.3	2 53.2	16 0.7	23 11.8	5 11.4	11 57.0	6 59.8
18 F	9 49 39.0	28 49.0	0 27.7	27 36.4	16 27.5	15 19.3	3 38.8	15 53.6	23 7.7	5 14.9	11 55.4	6 59.1
19 S	9 53 35.6	29 49.5	0 24.5	12♋13.7	17 1.6	16 15.8	4 24.3	15 46.3	23 3.6	5 18.3	11 53.8	6 58.4
20 S	9 57 32.1	0♓49.9	0 21.3	27 8.3	17 26.1	17 11.7	5 9.9	15 39.0	22 59.4	5 21.8	11 52.2	6 57.8
21 M	10 1 28.7	1 50.3	0 18.1	12♌12.6	17 40.8	18 6.9	5 55.3	15 31.6	22 55.2	5 25.2	11 50.7	6 57.1
22 T	10 5 25.2	2 50.7	0 15.0	27 17.1	17 45.4	19 1.6	6 40.8	15 24.1	22 50.9	5 28.6	11 49.1	6 56.5
23 W	10 9 21.8	3 51.1	0 11.8	12♍11.8	17R40.1	19 55.5	7 26.2	15 16.6	22 46.6	5 32.1	11 47.6	6 55.9
24 T	10 13 18.3	4 51.4	0 8.6	26 47.9	17 24.8	20 48.9	8 11.6	15 9.1	22 42.2	5 35.5	11 46.0	6 55.3
25 F	10 17 14.9	5 51.8	0 5.4	10♎59.2	17 0.1	21 41.5	8 56.9	15 1.4	22 37.8	5 39.0	11 44.5	6 54.7
26 S	10 21 11.4	6 52.1	0 2.3	24 42.8	16 26.7	22 33.3	9 42.2	14 53.7	22 33.3	5 42.4	11 43.0	6 54.2
27 S	10 25 8.0	7 52.3	29♎59.1	7♏58.5	15 45.2	23 24.5	10 27.4	14 46.0	22 28.8	5 45.9	11 41.5	6 53.7
28 M	10 29 4.6	8 52.6	29 55.9	20 48.8	14 56.9	24 14.9	11 12.6	14 38.3	22 24.3	5 49.3	11 40.1	6 53.2
						DECLINATION						
1 T	8 42 37.6	17S18.5	11S57.1	17S 0.6	15S35.5	0S28.5	4S20.3	6N 7.8	4N25.1	10S37.1	17N 8.1	19N44.0
4 F	8 54 27.3	16 26.6	11 53.8	19 5.4	13 30.7	1N 2.9	3 23.6	6 14.7	4 29.2	10 33.5	17 9.5	19 44.4
7 M	9 6 16.9	15 32.1	11 50.5	13 50.4	11 18.0	2 33.8	2 26.7	6 22.0	4 33.7	10 29.8	17 11.0	19 44.9
10 T	9 18 6.6	14 35.2	11 47.1	3 25.4	9 2.3	4 3.8	1 29.9	6 29.8	4 38.4	10 26.1	17 12.4	19 45.4
13 S	9 29 56.2	13 36.2	11 43.8	8N34.2	6 50.9	5 32.5	0 33.1	6 38.0	4 43.3	10 22.4	17 13.8	19 45.9
16 W	9 41 45.9	12 35.1	11 40.5	17 30.3	4 53.2	6 59.8	0N23.6	6 46.5	4 48.4	10 18.6	17 15.2	19 46.3
19 S	9 53 35.6	11 32.3	11 37.1	18 2.6	3 20.3	8 25.2	1 20.1	6 55.3	4 53.7	10 14.8	17 16.6	19 46.8
22 T	10 5 25.2	10 27.8	11 33.8	8 13.3	2 22.5	9 48.3	2 16.2	7 4.3	4 59.2	10 11.0	17 17.9	19 47.3
25 F	10 17 14.9	9 21.9	11 30.5	5S45.5	2 6.9	11 9.0	3 12.0	7 13.4	5 4.8	10 7.2	17 19.2	19 47.8
28 M	10 29 4.6	8 14.7	11 27.1	16 3.9	2 34.5	12 26.8	4 7.4	7 22.6	5 10.5	10 3.4	17 20.5	19 48.2

MARCH 1921

LONGITUDE

DAY	EPHEMERIS SIDEREAL TIME (h m s)	☉ (° ′)	☊ (° ′)	☽ (° ′)	☿ (° ′)	♀ (° ′)	♂ (° ′)	♃ (° ′)	♄ (° ′)	♅ (° ′)	♆ (° ′)	♇ (° ′)
1 T	10 33 1.1	9♓52.8	29♎52.7	3♐17.4	14♓ 3.0	25♈ 4.4	11♈57.8	14♍30.5	22♍19.7	5♓52.8	11♌38.6	6♋52.7
2 W	10 36 57.6	10 53.0	29 49.5	15 29.3	13R 4.9	25 53.2	12 42.9	14R22.7	22R15.1	5 56.2	11R37.2	6R52.3
3 T	10 40 54.2	11 53.1	29 46.4	27 29.3	12 4.0	26 41.1	13 28.0	14 14.9	22 10.5	5 59.7	11 35.8	6 51.8
4 F	10 44 50.7	12 53.3	29 43.2	9♑22.4	11 1.9	27 28.1	14 13.0	14 7.0	22 5.9	6 3.1	11 34.4	6 51.4
5 S	10 48 47.3	13 53.4	29 40.0	21 13.2	10 0.0	28 14.1	14 58.0	13 59.2	22 1.2	6 6.5	11 33.0	6 51.0
6 S	10 52 43.9	14 53.5	29 36.8	3♒ 5.3	8 59.7	28 59.2	15 43.0	13 51.3	21 56.5	6 !0.0	11 31.6	6 50.7
7 M	10 56 40.4	15 53.5	29 33.7	15 2.1	8 2.3	29 43.3	16 27.9	13 43.5	21 51.8	6 13.4	11 30.3	6 50.3
8 T	11 0 36.9	16 53.6	29 30.5	27 5.8	7 8.7	0♉26.4	17 12.8	13 35.7	21 47.0	6 16.8	11 29.0	6 50.0
9 W	11 4 33.5	17 53.6	29 27.3	9♓18.2	6 20.0	1 8.4	17 57.6	13 27.8	21 42.3	6 20.2	11 27.7	6 49.7
10 T	11 8 30.1	18 53.5	29 24.1	21 40.3	5 36.7	1 49.3	18 42.4	13 20.0	21 37.6	6 23.6	11 26.4	6 49.4
11 F	11 12 26.6	19 53.5	29 20.9	4♈12.9	4 59.4	2 29.0	19 27.2	13 12.3	21 32.8	6 27.0	11 25.1	6 49.2
12 S	11 16 23.2	20 53.4	29 17.8	16 56.6	4 28.3	3 7.5	20 11.9	13 4.5	21 28.0	6 30.3	11 23.9	6 49.0
13 S	11 20 19.7	21 53.2	29 14.6	29 51.9	4 3.8	3 44.7	20 56.5	12 56.8	21 23.3	6 33.7	11 22.7	6 48.8
14 M	11 24 16.3	22 53.1	29 11.4	12♉59.8	3 45.7	4 20.6	21 41.2	12 49.2	21 18.5	6 37.0	11 21.5	6 48.6
15 T	11 28 12.8	23 52.9	29 8.2	26 21.1	3 34.1	4 55.2	22 25.7	12 41.6	21 13.8	6 40.4	11 20.4	6 48.4
16 W	11 32 9.4	24 52.6	29 5.0	9♊56.9	3 28.7	5 28.3	23 10.2	12 34.0	21 9.0	6 43.7	11 19.2	6 48.3
17 T	11 36 5.9	25 52.3	29 1.9	23 47.8	3D29.5	5 60.0	23 54.7	12 26.6	21 4.3	6 47.0	11 18.1	6 48.2
18 F	11 40 2.5	26 52.0	28 58.7	7♋54.0	3 36.2	6 30.1	24 39.2	12 19.2	20 59.6	6 50.3	11 17.1	6 48.1
19 S	11 43 59.0	27 51.7	28 55.5	22 14.1	3 48.5	6 58.6	25 23.5	12 11.8	20 54.9	6 53.6	11 16.0	6 48.0
20 S	11 47 55.6	28 51.3	28 52.3	6♌45.2	4 6.1	7 25.4	26 7.9	12 4.5	20 50.2	6 56.8	11 15.0	6 48.0
21 M	11 51 52.1	29 50.8	28 49.2	21 22.7	4 28.8	7 50.6	26 52.1	11 57.3	20 45.5	7 0.1	11 14.0	6 48.0
22 T	11 55 48.7	0♈50.3	28 46.0	6♍ 0.6	4 56.2	8 13.9	27 36.4	11 50.2	20 40.8	7 3.3	11 13.0	6D48.0
23 W	11 59 45.2	1 49.8	28 42.8	20 32.0	5 28.2	8 35.4	28 20.6	11 43.2	20 36.2	7 6.5	11 12.0	6 48.0
24 T	12 3 41.8	2 49.3	28 39.6	4♎50.6	6 4.4	8 55.0	29 4.7	11 36.3	20 31.6	7 9.7	11 11.1	6 48.1
25 F	12 7 38.3	3 48.7	28 36.4	18 51.0	6 44.6	9 12.7	29 48.8	11 29.5	20 27.1	7 12.9	11 10.2	6 48.2
26 S	12 11 34.9	4 48.1	28 33.3	2♏29.7	7 28.6	9 28.3	0♉32.8	11 22.8	20 22.5	7 16.1	11 9.4	6 48.3
27 S	12 15 31.4	5 47.5	28 30.1	15 45.3	8 16.2	9 41.8	1 16.8	11 16.2	20 18.0	7 19.2	11 8.5	6 48.4
28 M	12 19 28.0	6 46.8	28 26.9	28 38.5	9 7.1	9 53.2	2 0.8	11 9.7	20 13.5	7 22.3	11 7.7	6 48.5
29 T	12 23 24.5	7 46.1	28 23.7	11♐11.4	10 1.1	10 2.4	2 44.7	11 3.3	20 9.1	7 25.4	11 6.9	6 48.7
30 W	12 27 21.1	8 45.3	28 20.6	23 27.6	10 58.2	10 9.3	3 28.5	10 57.1	20 4.7	7 28.5	11 6.2	6 48.9
31 T	12 31 17.6	9 44.6	28 17.4	5♑31.2	11 58.0	10 14.0	4 12.3	10 50.9	20 0.4	7 31.5	11 5.5	6 49.1

DECLINATION

DAY	SIDEREAL TIME (h m s)	☉	☊	☽	☿	♀	♂	♃	♄	♅	♆	♇
1 T	10 33 1.1	7S52.0	11S26.0	17S55.6	2S52.1	12N52.0	4N25.7	7N25.7	5N12.4	10S 2.1	17N20.9	19N48.4
4 F	10 44 50.7	6 43.4	11 22.6	18 15.9	4 3.9	14 5.5	5 20.4	7 35.0	5 18.2	9 58.4	17 22.1	19 48.8
7 M	10 56 40.4	5 33.9	11 19.3	11 37.7	5 30.7	15 15.3	6 14.5	7 44.2	5 24.0	9 54.6	17 23.3	19 49.3
10 T	11 8 30.1	4 23.8	11 15.9	0 30.9	6 56.3	16 21.0	7 7.9	7 53.4	5 29.8	9 50.8	17 24.4	19 49.7
13 S	11 20 19.7	3 13.2	11 12.5	11N13.5	8 9.0	17 22.2	8 0.6	8 2.3	5 35.7	9 47.1	17 25.4	19 50.2
16 W	11 32 9.4	2 2.2	11 9.1	18 27.9	9 2.7	18 18.4	8 52.4	8 11.1	5 41.4	9 43.4	17 26.4	19 50.6
19 S	11 43 59.0	0 51.1	11 5.8	16 29.2	9 35.4	19 9.1	9 43.4	8 19.6	5 47.1	9 39.8	17 27.3	19 51.0
22 T	11 55 48.7	0N20.0	11 2.4	5 30.9	9 47.6	19 53.4	10 33.5	8 27.7	5 52.7	9 36.2	17 28.2	19 51.4
25 F	12 7 38.3	1 30.9	10 59.0	8S 5.6	9 40.4	20 30.8	11 22.5	8 35.5	5 58.1	9 32.7	17 29.0	19 51.8
28 M	12 19 28.0	2 41.5	10 55.6	17 11.1	9 15.6	21 0.3	12 10.5	8 42.8	6 3.4	9 29.2	17 29.7	19 52.2
31 T	12 31 17.6	3 51.7	10 52.2	18 26.9	8 34.6	21 21.0	12 57.3	8 49.8	6 8.5	9 25.9	17 30.3	19 52.6

APRIL 1921

LONGITUDE

DAY	EPHEMERIS SIDEREAL TIME (h m s)	☉ (° ′)	☊ (° ′)	☽ (° ′)	☿ (° ′)	♀ (° ′)	♂ (° ′)	♃ (° ′)	♄ (° ′)	♅ (° ′)	♆ (° ′)	♇ (° ′)
1 F	12 35 14.2	10♈43.8	28♎14.2	17♑26.9	13♓ 0.6	10♉16.3	4♉56.1	10♍44.9	19♍56.1	7♓34.6	11♌ 4.8	6♋49.4
2 S	12 39 10.8	11 43.0	28 11.0	29 19.4	14 5.7	10R16.2	5 39.8	10R39.0	19R51.8	7 37.6	11R 4.1	6 49.6
3 S	12 43 7.3	12 42.1	28 7.8	11♒13.2	15 13.2	10 13.7	6 23.5	10 33.3	19 47.6	7 40.5	11 3.5	6 49.9
4 M	12 47 3.8	13 41.2	28 4.7	23 12.5	16 23.0	10 8.8	7 7.1	10 27.7	19 43.5	7 43.5	11 2.9	6 50.2
5 T	12 51 0.4	14 40.3	28 1.5	5♓20.9	17 35.1	10 1.4	7 50.7	10 22.2	19 39.4	7 46.4	11 2.3	6 50.6
6 W	12 54 57.0	15 39.4	27 58.3	17 41.1	18 49.3	9 51.6	8 34.2	10 16.9	19 35.4	7 49.3	11 1.8	6 50.9
7 T	12 58 53.5	16 38.4	27 55.1	0♈15.2	20 5.6	9 39.3	9 17.7	10 11.8	19 31.4	7 52.2	11 1.3	6 51.3
8 F	13 2 50.1	17 37.4	27 52.0	13 4.2	21 23.9	9 24.5	10 1.1	10 6.7	19 27.5	7 55.0	11 0.8	6 51.7
9 S	13 6 46.6	18 36.3	27 48.8	26 8.5	22 44.1	9 7.3	10 44.5	10 1.9	19 23.6	7 57.9	11 0.4	6 52.1
10 S	13 10 43.1	19 35.3	27 45.6	9♉27.4	24 6.1	8 47.8	11 27.8	9 57.2	19 19.8	8 0.6	10 60.0	6 52.6
11 M	13 14 39.7	20 34.2	27 42.4	22 60.0	25 30.0	8 26.0	12 11.1	9 52.6	19 16.1	8 3.4	10 59.6	6 53.1
12 T	13 18 36.3	21 33.0	27 39.2	6♊44.6	26 55.7	8 1.9	12 54.4	9 48.3	19 12.5	8 6.1	10 59.3	6 53.6
13 W	13 22 32.8	22 31.8	27 36.1	20 39.4	28 23.2	7 35.7	13 37.6	9 44.1	19 8.9	8 8.8	10 59.0	6 54.1
14 T	13 26 29.4	23 30.6	27 32.9	4♋42.5	29 52.3	7 7.5	14 20.7	9 40.0	19 5.4	8 11.5	10 58.7	6 54.6
15 F	13 30 25.9	24 29.3	27 29.7	18 51.9	1♈23.2	6 37.4	15 3.8	9 36.1	19 2.0	8 14.1	10 58.4	6 55.2
16 S	13 34 22.5	25 28.0	27 26.5	3♌ 5.3	2 55.8	6 5.6	15 46.8	9 32.4	18 58.6	8 16.7	10 58.2	6 55.8
17 S	13 38 19.0	26 26.7	27 23.4	17 20.2	4 30.1	5 32.3	16 29.8	9 28.9	18 55.4	8 19.3	10 58.0	6 56.4
18 M	13 42 15.6	27 25.3	27 20.2	1♍34.0	6 6.0	4 57.6	17 12.8	9 25.5	18 52.2	8 21.8	10 57.9	6 57.0
19 T	13 46 12.1	28 23.9	27 17.0	15 43.5	7 43.6	4 21.8	17 55.7	9 22.3	18 49.0	8 24.3	10 57.8	6 57.6
20 W	13 50 8.7	29 22.5	27 13.8	29 45.6	9 22.8	3 45.1	18 38.5	9 19.3	18 46.0	8 26.8	10 57.7	6 58.3
21 T	13 54 5.3	0♉21.0	27 10.6	13♎37.1	11 3.7	3 7.7	19 21.3	9 16.5	18 43.1	8 29.2	10 57.7	6 59.0
22 F	13 58 1.8	1 19.5	27 7.5	27 14.9	12 46.3	2 29.9	20 4.0	9 13.8	18 40.2	8 31.6	10 57.6	6 59.7
23 S	14 1 58.3	2 17.9	27 4.3	10♏37.0	14 30.6	1 51.9	20 46.7	9 11.4	18 37.4	8 34.0	10D57.7	7 0.4
24 S	14 5 54.9	3 16.4	27 1.1	23 42.0	16 16.6	1 14.1	21 29.4	9 9.1	18 34.7	8 36.3	10 57.7	7 1.2
25 M	14 9 51.5	4 14.8	26 57.9	6♐29.6	18 4.2	0 36.6	22 12.0	9 7.0	18 32.1	8 38.6	10 57.8	7 2.0
26 T	14 13 48.0	5 13.1	26 54.8	19 0.7	19 53.6	29♈59.7	22 54.5	9 5.0	18 29.6	8 40.9	10 57.9	7 2.8
27 W	14 17 44.6	6 11.5	26 51.6	1♑17.3	21 44.7	29 23.6	23 37.0	9 3.3	18 27.2	8 43.1	10 58.1	7 3.6
28 T	14 21 41.1	7 9.8	26 48.4	13 22.3	23 37.4	28 48.6	24 19.5	9 1.7	18 24.8	8 45.3	10 58.3	7 4.4
29 F	14 25 37.7	8 8.1	26 45.2	25 19.4	25 31.9	28 14.9	25 1.9	9 0.3	18 22.6	8 47.4	10 58.5	7 5.2
30 S	14 29 34.2	9 6.3	26 42.0	7♒12.9	27 28.1	27 42.7	25 44.3	8 59.1	18 20.4	8 49.5	10 58.7	7 6.1

DECLINATION

DAY	SIDEREAL TIME (h m s)	☉	☊	☽	☿	♀	♂	♃	♄	♅	♆	♇
1 F	12 35 14.2	4N14.9	10S51.1	17S.0.0	8S17.6	21N25.8	13N12.7	8N52.0	6N10.1	9S24.7	17N30.5	19N52.7
4 M	12 47 3.8	5 24.2	10 47.7	9 18.6	7 17.1	21 33.0	13 57.9	8 58.2	6 14.9	9 21.5	17 31.1	19 53.1
7 T	12 58 53.5	6 32.6	10 44.2	2N17.6	6 3.4	21 28.9	14 42.0	9 3.9	6 19.5	9 18.3	17 31.5	19 53.4
10 S	13 10 43.1	7 40.0	10 40.8	13 34.6	4 37.5	21 12.6	15 24.7	9 9.1	6 23.8	9 15.2	17 31.9	19 53.8
13 W	13 22 32.8	8 46.2	10 37.4	18 52.6	3 0.1	20 43.4	16 6.1	9 13.7	6 27.9	9 12.2	17 32.2	19 54.1
16 S	13 34 22.5	9 51.1	10 34.0	14 21.3	1 12.2	20 1.4	16 46.0	9 17.6	6 31.6	9 9.3	17 32.5	19 54.4
19 T	13 46 12.1	10 54.5	10 30.6	2 24.0	0N45.5	19 7.6	17 24.5	9 21.0	6 35.1	9 6.6	17 32.6	19 54.7
22 F	13 58 1.8	11 56.3	10 27.1	10S29.5	2 52.1	18 3.9	18 1.4	9 23.8	6 38.2	9 3.9	17 32.7	19 55.0
25 M	14 9 51.5	12 56.4	10 23.7	18 5.8	5 6.6	16 53.4	18 36.8	9 25.9	6 41.0	9 1.4	17 32.7	19 55.2
28 T	14 21 41.1	13 54.5	10 20.3	17 40.6	7 27.8	15 39.6	19 10.7	9 27.4	6 43.5	8 59.0	17 32.6	19 55.5

MAY 1921

LONGITUDE

DAY	EPHEMERIS SIDEREAL TIME	☉	☊	☽	☿	♀	♂	♃	♄	♅	♆	♇
	h m s	° ′	° ′	° ′	° ′	° ′	° ′	° ′	° ′	° ′	° ′	° ′
1 S	14 33 30.8	10♉ 4.6	26♎38.9	19♒ 7.2	29♈26.0	27♈12.1	26♉26.6	8♍58.1	18♍18.4	8♓51.6	10♌59.0	7♋ 7.0
2 M	14 37 27.3	11 2.8	26 35.7	1♓ 7.0	1♉25.5	26R43.3	27 8.9	8R57.2	18R16.4	8 53.6	10 59.3	7 7.9
3 T	14 41 23.9	12 0.9	26 32.5	13 16.9	3 26.7	26 16.5	27 51.1	8 56.6	18 14.6	8 55.6	10 59.7	7 8.8
4 W	14 45 20.4	12 59.1	26 29.3	25 40.9	5 29.4	25 51.8	28 33.3	8 56.1	18 12.8	8 57.5	11 0.1	7 9.8
5 T	14 49 17.0	13 57.2	26 26.2	8♈22.4	7 33.6	25 29.2	29 15.4	8 55.8	18 11.1	8 59.4	11 0.5	7 10.7
6 F	14 53 13.6	14 55.4	26 23.0	21 23.5	9 39.2	25 8.9	29 57.5	8 55.7	18 9.6	9 1.3	11 0.9	7 11.7
7 S	14 57 10.1	15 53.4	26 19.8	4♉45.2	11 46.2	24 50.9	0♊39.6	8D55.8	18 8.1	9 3.1	11 1.4	7 12.7
8 S	15 1 6.7	16 51.5	26 16.6	18 26.8	13 54.2	24 35.3	1 21.6	8 56.1	18 6.7	9 4.9	11 1.9	7 13.7
9 M	15 5 3.2	17 49.5	26 13.4	2♊25.9	16 3.3	24 22.1	2 3.6	8 56.5	18 5.5	9 6.6	11 2.5	7 14.8
10 T	15 8 59.8	18 47.5	26 10.3	16 38.8	18 13.1	24 11.3	2 45.5	8 57.2	18 4.3	9 8.3	11 3.1	7 15.8
11 W	15 12 56.3	19 45.5	26 7.1	1♋ 0.5	20 23.6	24 3.0	3 27.4	8 58.0	18 3.2	9 9.9	11 3.7	7 16.9
12 T	15 16 52.9	20 43.4	26 3.9	15 25.9	22 34.4	23 57.0	4 9.2	8 59.0	18 2.3	9 11.5	11 4.3	7 17.9
13 F	15 20 49.4	21 41.4	26 0.7	29 50.1	24 45.2	23 53.4	4 50.9	9 0.2	18 1.4	9 13.1	11 5.0	7 19.0
14 S	15 24 46.0	22 39.3	25 57.6	14♌ 8.8	26 55.9	23 52.2	5 32.7	9 1.6	18 0.6	9 14.6	11 5.7	7 20.2
15 S	15 28 42.6	23 37.1	25 54.4	28 19.2	29 6.2	23D53.3	6 14.4	9 3.1	17 60.0	9 16.1	11 6.4	7 21.3
16 M	15 32 39.1	24 34.9	25 51.2	12♍19.3	1♊15.6	23 56.7	6 56.0	9 4.8	17 59.4	9 17.5	11 7.2	7 22.4
17 T	15 36 35.6	25 32.7	25 48.0	26 8.1	3 24.1	24 2.4	7 37.6	9 6.7	17 59.0	9 18.9	11 8.0	7 23.6
18 W	15 40 32.2	26 30.5	25 44.8	9♎45.1	5 31.2	24 10.3	8 19.1	9 8.8	17 58.6	9 20.2	11 8.8	7 24.8
19 T	15 44 28.8	27 28.2	25 41.7	23 10.1	7 36.8	24 20.3	9 0.6	9 11.0	17 58.4	9 21.5	11 9.7	7 25.9
20 F	15 48 25.3	28 26.0	25 38.5	6♏22.9	9 40.5	24 32.4	9 42.1	9 13.5	17 58.3	9 22.7	11 10.6	7 27.1
21 S	15 52 21.9	29 23.7	25 35.3	19 23.2	11 42.3	24 46.6	10 23.5	9 16.1	17 58.2	9 23.9	11 11.5	7 28.4
22 S	15 56 18.4	0♊21.3	25 32.1	2♐10.9	13 41.9	25 2.7	11 4.8	9 18.8	17D58.3	9 25.1	11 12.5	7 29.6
23 M	16 0 14.9	1 19.0	25 29.0	14 46.0	15 39.1	25 20.8	11 46.2	9 21.8	17 58.5	9 26.2	11 13.5	7 30.8
24 T	16 4 11.5	2 16.6	25 25.8	27 9.0	17 33.9	25 40.7	12 27.4	9 24.9	17 58.7	9 27.2	11 14.5	7 32.1
25 W	16 8 8.1	3 14.2	25 22.6	9♑21.0	19 26.0	26 2.4	13 8.7	9 28.2	17 59.1	9 28.2	11 15.5	7 33.3
26 T	16 12 4.6	4 11.8	25 19.4	21 23.7	21 15.5	26 25.9	13 49.9	9 31.6	17 59.6	9 29.2	11 16.6	7 34.6
27 F	16 16 1.2	5 9.4	25 16.2	3♒19.7	23 2.2	26 51.1	14 31.0	9 35.2	18 0.2	9 30.1	11 17.7	7 35.9
28 S	16 19 57.7	6 6.9	25 13.1	15 12.4	24 46.1	27 17.8	15 12.1	9 39.0	18 0.8	9 31.0	11 18.8	7 37.2
29 S	16 23 54.3	7 4.5	25 9.9	27 5.7	26 27.1	27 46.1	15 53.2	9 42.9	18 1.6	9 31.8	11 20.0	7 38.5
30 M	16 27 50.9	8 2.0	25 6.7	9♓ 4.1	28 5.2	28 16.0	16 34.2	9 47.0	18 2.5	9 32.6	11 21.1	7 39.8
31 T	16 31 47.4	8 59.5	25 3.5	21 12.6	29 40.4	28 47.2	17 15.2	9 51.2	18 3.5	9 33.3	11 22.4	7 41.2

DECLINATION

DAY	EPHEMERIS SIDEREAL TIME	☉	☊	☽	☿	♀	♂	♃	♄	♅	♆	♇
1 S	14 33 30.8	14N50.6	10S16.8	10S26.6	9N54.0	14N26.3	19N42.8	9N28.2	6N45.6	8S56.7	17N32.4	19N55.7
4 W	14 45 20.4	15 44.5	10 13.4	0N48.7	12 22.8	13 17.0	20 13.3	9 28.4	6 47.4	8 54.5	17 32.1	19 55.9
7 S	14 57 10.1	16 36.0	10 9.9	12 27.3	14 50.9	12 14.5	20 42.1	9 28.0	6 48.7	8 52.5	17 31.8	19 56.1
10 T	15 8 59.8	17 25.1	10 6.5	18 48.3	17 13.9	11 20.6	21 9.2	9 26.9	6 49.8	8 50.7	17 31.3	19 56.3
13 F	15 20 49.4	18 11.6	10 3.0	15 4.8	19 26.6	10 36.6	21 34.5	9 25.3	6 50.4	8 49.0	17 30.8	19 56.5
16 M	15 32 39.1	18 55.3	9 59.5	3 32.3	21 23.6	10 2.8	21 57.9	9 23.0	6 50.7	8 47.4	17 30.3	19 56.6
19 T	15 44 28.8	19 36.1	9 56.1	9S19.8	23 0.2	9 39.1	22 19.6	9 20.1	6 50.6	8 46.0	17 29.6	19 56.7
22 S	15 56 18.4	20 13.9	9 52.6	17 39.6	24 13.8	9 25.2	22 39.4	9 16.6	6 50.1	8 44.8	17 28.9	19 56.8
25 W	16 8 8.1	20 48.6	9 49.1	18 11.4	25 3.8	9 20.3	22 57.3	9 12.6	6 49.3	8 43.7	17 28.1	19 56.9
28 S	16 19 57.7	21 20.1	9 45.6	11 35.9	25 31.2	9 23.6	23 13.4	9 7.9	6 48.1	8 42.8	17 27.2	19 57.0
31 T	16 31 47.4	21 48.3	9 42.1	0 44.8	25 38.5	9 34.3	23 27.5	9 2.8	6 46.5	8 42.0	17 26.2	19 57.1

JUNE 1921

LONGITUDE

DAY	EPHEMERIS SIDEREAL TIME	☉	☊	☽	☿	♀	♂	♃	♄	♅	♆	♇
1 W	16 35 44.0	9♊57.0	25♎ 0.4	3♈36.0	1♋12.5	29♈19.9	17♊56.1	9♍55.7	18♍ 4.6	9♓34.0	11♌23.6	7♋42.5
2 T	16 39 40.5	10 54.5	24 57.2	16 18.8	2 41.7	29 53.8	18 37.0	10 0.2	18 5.8	9 34.6	11 24.9	7 43.9
3 F	16 43 37.1	11 52.0	24 54.0	29 24.7	4 7.8	0♉29.1	19 17.9	10 5.0	18 7.1	9 35.2	11 26.2	7 45.2
4 S	16 47 33.6	12 49.5	24 50.8	12♉55.8	5 30.9	1 5.6	19 58.7	10 9.9	18 8.5	9 35.7	11 27.5	7 46.6
5 S	16 51 30.2	13 46.9	24 47.7	26 52.4	6 50.8	1 43.2	20 39.5	10 14.9	18 10.0	9 36.2	11 28.8	7 48.0
6 M	16 55 26.7	14 44.3	24 44.5	11♊12.0	8 7.6	2 22.0	21 20.3	10 20.1	18 11.6	9 36.6	11 30.2	7 49.4
7 T	16 59 23.3	15 41.8	24 41.3	25 49.7	9 21.2	3 1.9	22 1.0	10 25.4	18 13.3	9 37.0	11 31.6	7 50.8
8 W	17 3 19.9	16 39.2	24 38.1	10♋38.3	10 31.5	3 42.8	22 41.7	10 30.9	18 15.1	9 37.3	11 33.0	7 52.2
9 T	17 7 16.4	17 36.6	24 35.0	25 29.3	11 38.5	4 24.7	23 22.3	10 36.6	18 17.0	9 37.6	11 34.5	7 53.6
10 F	17 11 13.0	18 34.0	24 31.8	10♌14.7	12 42.2	5 7.6	24 2.9	10 42.3	18 19.0	9 37.9	11 36.0	7 55.0
11 S	17 15 9.5	19 31.3	24 28.6	24 48.0	13 42.3	5 51.3	24 43.4	10 48.3	18 21.1	9 38.1	11 37.5	7 56.5
12 S	17 19 6.1	20 28.7	24 25.4	9♍ 4.6	14 39.0	6 36.0	25 23.9	10 54.3	18 23.3	9 38.2	11 39.0	7 57.9
13 M	17 23 2.6	21 26.0	24 22.2	23 2.5	15 32.0	7 21.5	26 4.4	11 0.6	18 25.6	9 38.3	11 40.5	7 59.3
14 T	17 26 59.2	22 23.3	24 19.1	6♎41.6	16 21.3	8 7.9	26 44.8	11 6.9	18 28.0	9 38.3	11 42.1	8 0.8
15 W	17 30 55.8	23 20.6	24 15.9	20 3.3	17 6.8	8 55.0	27 25.2	11 13.4	18 30.4	9R38.3	11 43.7	8 2.2
16 T	17 34 52.3	24 17.9	24 12.7	3♏ 9.3	17 48.4	9 42.9	28 5.6	11 20.0	18 33.0	9 38.3	11 45.3	8 3.7
17 F	17 38 48.9	25 15.1	24 9.5	16 1.7	18 26.0	10 31.6	28 45.9	11 26.8	18 35.7	9 38.2	11 46.9	8 5.2
18 S	17 42 45.4	26 12.4	24 6.4	28 42.3	18 59.4	11 20.9	29 26.1	11 33.7	18 38.4	9 38.0	11 48.6	8 6.6
19 S	17 46 42.0	27 9.6	24 3.2	11♐12.4	19 28.7	12 11.0	0♋ 6.4	11 40.7	18 41.3	9 37.8	11 50.3	8 8.1
20 M	17 50 38.5	28 6.9	24 0.0	23 33.1	19 53.6	13 1.7	0 46.5	11 47.9	18 44.2	9 37.6	11 52.0	8 9.6
21 T	17 54 35.1	29 4.1	23 56.8	5♑45.3	20 14.1	13 53.1	1 26.7	11 55.1	18 47.3	9 37.3	11 53.7	8 11.1
22 W	17 58 31.7	0♋ 1.3	23 53.7	17 49.8	20 30.2	14 45.1	2 6.8	12 2.5	18 50.4	9 36.9	11 55.5	8 12.6
23 T	18 2 28.2	0 58.5	23 50.5	29 47.9	20 41.7	15 37.6	2 46.9	12 10.1	18 53.6	9 36.5	11 57.2	8 14.0
24 F	18 6 24.7	1 55.8	23 47.3	11♒41.4	20 48.6	16 30.8	3 27.0	12 17.7	18 56.9	9 36.1	11 59.0	8 15.5
25 S	18 10 21.3	2 53.0	23 44.1	23 32.6	20 51.0	17 24.5	4 7.0	12 25.5	19 0.3	9 35.6	12 0.8	8 17.0
26 S	18 14 17.9	3 50.2	23 40.9	5♓24.7	20R48.8	18 18.8	4 47.0	12 33.4	19 3.8	9 35.1	12 2.6	8 18.5
27 M	18 18 14.5	4 47.4	23 37.8	17 21.7	20 42.1	19 13.5	5 26.9	12 41.4	19 7.4	9 34.5	12 4.5	8 20.0
28 T	18 22 11.0	5 44.6	23 34.6	29 28.0	20 30.9	20 8.8	6 6.8	12 49.5	19 11.0	9 33.9	12 6.3	8 21.5
29 W	18 26 7.5	6 41.8	23 31.4	11♈48.7	20 15.5	21 4.6	6 46.7	12 57.8	19 14.8	9 33.2	12 8.2	8 23.0
30 T	18 30 4.1	7 39.0	23 28.2	24 28.8	19 56.0	22 0.8	7 26.5	13 6.1	19 18.6	9 32.5	12 10.1	8 24.5

DECLINATION

DAY	EPHEMERIS SIDEREAL TIME	☉	☊	☽	☿	♀	♂	♃	♄	♅	♆	♇
1 W	16 35 44.0	21N57.0	9S41.0	3N16.1	25N36.9	9N39.3	23N31.8	9N 0.9	6N45.9	8S41.8	17N25.9	19N57.1
4 S	16 47 33.6	22 20.6	9 37.5	14 19.3	25 21.6	9 58.5	23 43.4	8 55.1	6 43.8	8 41.2	17 24.8	19 57.1
7 T	16 59 23.3	22 40.7	9 34.0	18 57.8	24 53.0	10 22.9	23 53.1	8 48.6	6 41.4	8 40.9	17 23.7	19 57.1
10 F	17 11 13.0	22 57.3	9 30.5	12 54.8	24 13.8	10 51.8	24 1.0	8 41.7	6 38.7	8 40.6	17 22.5	19 57.1
13 M	17 23 2.6	23 10.2	9 27.0	0 13.7	23 27.0	11 24.5	24 6.9	8 34.3	6 35.6	8 40.6	17 21.3	19 57.1
16 T	17 34 52.3	23 19.4	9 23.5	11S56.4	22 35.4	12 0.3	24 10.9	8 26.4	6 32.2	8 40.7	17 20.0	19 57.1
19 S	17 46 42.0	23 25.0	9 20.0	18 31.8	21 41.5	12 38.5	24 13.0	8 18.1	6 28.4	8 41.0	17 18.7	19 57.0
22 W	17 58 31.7	23 26.8	9 16.5	17 17.9	20 48.2	13 18.5	24 13.2	8 9.3	6 24.4	8 41.4	17 17.2	19 56.9
25 S	18 10 21.3	23 24.9	9 13.0	9 30.4	19 57.9	13 59.7	24 11.6	8 0.1	6 20.0	8 42.0	17 15.8	19 56.9
28 T	18 22 11.0	23 19.3	9 9.5	1N44.2	19 13.2	14 41.5	24 8.1	7 50.5	6 15.3	8 42.8	17 14.3	19 56.8

JULY 1921

DAY	EPHEMERIS SIDEREAL TIME	☉	☊	☽	☿	♀	♂	♃	♄	♅	♆	♇
	h m s	° ′	° ′	° ′	° ′	° ′	° ′	° ′	° ′	° ′	° ′	° ′
						LONGITUDE						
1 F	18 34 0.7	8♋36.2	23♎25.1	7♉32.8	19♋32.7	22♉57.5	8♋ 6.4	13♍14.6	19♍22.5	9♓31.8	12♌12.0	8♋26.0
2 S	18 37 57.2	9 33.4	23 21.9	21 4.4	19R 5.9	23 54.6	8 46.1	13 23.2	19 26.5	9R31.0	12 13.9	8 27.5
3 S	18 41 53.8	10 30.7	23 18.7	5♊ 5.0	18 36.0	24 52.1	9 25.9	13 31.9	19 30.5	9 30.1	12 15.9	8 29.0
4 M	18 45 50.3	11 27.9	23 15.5	19 33.3	18 3.4	25 50.0	10 5.6	13 40.7	19 34.7	9 29.2	12 17.8	8 30.5
5 T	18 49 46.9	12 25.1	23 12.4	4♋24.6	17 28.7	26 48.3	10 45.3	13 49.6	19 38.9	9 28.3	12 19.8	8 32.0
6 W	18 53 43.5	13 22.3	23 9.2	19 31.0	16 52.3	27 47.0	11 25.0	13 58.6	19 43.2	9 27.3	12 21.8	8 33.5
7 T	18 57 40.0	14 19.6	23 6.0	4♌42.4	16 15.0	28 46.1	12 4.6	14 7.7	19 47.6	9 26.3	12 23.8	8 35.0
8 F	19 1 36.6	15 16.8	23 2.8	19 47.9	15 37.2	29 45.5	12 44.2	14 16.9	19 52.1	9 25.2	12 25.8	8 36.5
9 S	19 5 33.1	16 14.0	22 59.6	4♍38.5	14 59.7	0♊45.2	13 23.7	14 26.2	19 56.6	9 24.1	12 27.8	8 38.0
10 S	19 9 29.7	17 11.2	22 56.5	19 7.7	14 23.1	1 45.3	14 3.3	14 35.7	20 1.3	9 22.9	12 29.9	8 39.5
11 M	19 13 26.3	18 8.5	22 53.3	3♎12.5	13 48.0	2 45.7	14 42.7	14 45.2	20 6.0	9 21.7	12 32.0	8 41.0
12 T	19 17 22.8	19 5.7	22 50.1	16 52.4	13 15.1	3 46.4	15 22.2	14 54.8	20 10.7	9 20.5	12 34.0	8 42.4
13 W	19 21 19.4	20 2.9	22 46.9	0♏ 9.3	12 44.9	4 47.4	16 1.6	15 4.5	20 15.6	9 19.2	12 36.1	8 43.9
14 T	19 25 15.9	21 0.1	22 43.8	13 6.3	12 18.1	5 48.7	16 41.0	15 14.3	20 20.5	9 17.9	12 38.2	8 45.4
15 F	19 29 12.5	21 57.3	22 40.6	25 46.8	11 55.1	6 50.3	17 20.4	15 24.2	20 25.5	9 16.5	12 40.3	8 46.9
16 S	19 33 9.0	22 54.6	22 37.4	8♐14.0	11 36.3	7 52.2	17 59.7	15 34.2	20 30.5	9 15.1	12 42.4	8 48.3
17 S	19 37 5.6	23 51.8	22 34.2	20 30.9	11 22.2	8 54.3	18 39.0	15 44.2	20 35.6	9 13.7	12 44.5	8 49.8
18 M	19 41 2.1	24 49.0	22 31.1	2♑39.6	11 13.0	9 56.8	19 18.3	15 54.4	20 40.8	9 12.2	12 46.7	8 51.2
19 T	19 44 58.7	25 46.3	22 27.9	14 42.1	11 9.0	10 59.4	19 57.5	16 4.6	20 46.1	9 10.7	12 48.8	8 52.7
20 W	19 48 55.3	26 43.5	22 24.7	26 39.6	11D10.6	12 2.4	20 36.7	16 14.9	20 51.4	9 9.2	12 50.9	8 54.1
21 T	19 52 51.8	27 40.8	22 21.5	8♒33.6	11 17.7	13 5.6	21 15.9	16 25.3	20 56.8	9 7.6	12 53.1	8 55.6
22 F	19 56 48.3	28 38.0	22 18.3	20 25.3	11 30.5	14 9.0	21 55.0	16 35.8	21 2.2	9 6.0	12 55.3	8 57.0
23 S	20 0 44.9	29 35.3	22 15.2	2♓16.6	11 49.2	15 12.7	22 34.1	16 46.3	21 7.8	9 4.3	12 57.4	8 58.4
24 S	20 4 41.5	0♌32.6	22 12.0	14 9.8	12 13.8	16 16.6	23 13.2	16 57.0	21 13.3	9 2.6	12 59.6	8 59.8
25 M	20 8 38.1	1 29.9	22 8.8	26 8.0	12 44.2	17 20.7	23 52.3	17 7.7	21 19.0	9 0.9	13 1.8	9 1.2
26 T	20 12 34.6	2 27.2	22 5.6	8♈14.8	13 20.5	18 25.1	24 31.4	17 18.5	21 24.7	8 59.2	13 4.0	9 2.6
27 W	20 16 31.1	3 24.5	22 2.5	20 34.7	14 2.7	19 29.6	25 10.4	17 29.3	21 30.4	8 57.4	13 6.2	9 4.0
28 T	20 20 27.7	4 21.9	21 59.3	3♉12.3	14 50.6	20 34.4	25 49.4	17 40.3	21 36.2	8 55.5	13 8.4	9 5.4
29 F	20 24 24.3	5 19.2	21 56.1	16 12.4	15 44.3	21 39.4	26 28.3	17 51.3	21 42.1	8 53.7	13 10.6	9 6.8
30 S	20 28 20.8	6 16.6	21 52.9	29 38.9	16 43.6	22 44.6	27 7.3	18 2.4	21 48.0	8 51.8	13 12.8	9 8.1
31 S	20 32 17.4	7 14.0	21 49.8	13♊34.4	17 48.4	23 50.0	27 46.2	18 13.5	21 54.0	8 49.9	13 15.0	9 9.5
						DECLINATION						
1 F	18 34 0.7	23N10.1	9S 5.9	12N55.6	18N36.5	15N23.6	24N 2.8	7N40.4	6N10.4	8S43.7	17N12.7	19N56.7
4 M	18 45 50.3	22 57.1	9 2.4	18 53.9	18 9.7	16 5.2	23 55.8	7 30.0	6 5.1	8 44.8	17 11.1	19 56.5
7 T	18 57 40.0	22 40.6	8 58.9	14 18.9	17 54.4	16 46.1	23 46.9	7 19.2	5 59.6	8 46.0	17 9.5	19 56.4
10 S	19 9 29.7	22 20.5	8 55.3	1 42.6	17 51.2	17 25.6	23 36.4	7 8.1	5 53.8	8 47.3	17 7.8	19 56.2
13 W	19 21 19.4	21 57.0	8 51.8	10S56.8	17 59.7	18 3.5	23 24.1	6 56.6	5 47.8	8 48.8	17 6.0	19 56.1
16 S	19 33 9.0	21 30.1	8 48.3	18 9.5	18 18.8	18 39.2	23 10.2	6 44.7	5 41.5	8 50.4	17 4.3	19 55.9
19 T	19 44 58.7	20 59.8	8 44.7	17 42.8	18 46.2	19 12.5	22 54.6	6 32.6	5 35.0	8 52.2	17 2.5	19 55.7
22 F	19 56 48.3	20 26.5	8 41.2	10 30.9	19 18.9	19 42.9	22 37.5	6 20.2	5 28.3	8 54.0	17 0.7	19 55.6
25 M	20 8 38.1	19 50.0	8 37.6	0N26.3	19 53.2	20 10.1	22 18.8	6 7.5	5 21.4	8 56.0	16 58.9	19 55.4
28 T	20 20 27.7	19 10.5	8 34.1	11 36.2	20 24.8	20 33.8	21 58.6	5 54.5	5 14.3	8 58.1	16 57.1	19 55.2
31 S	20 32 17.4	18 28.2	8 30.5	18 28.0	20 48.9	20 53.6	21 36.9	5 41.2	5 6.9	9 0.3	16 55.2	19 54.9

AUGUST 1921

DAY	EPHEMERIS SIDEREAL TIME	☉	☊	☽	☿	♀	♂	♃	♄	♅	♆	♇
						LONGITUDE						
1 M	20 36 13.9	8♌11.4	21♎46.6	27♊58.9	18♋58.7	24♊55.6	28♋25.1	18♍24.7	22♍ 0.1	8♓48.0	13♌17.2	9♋10.8
2 T	20 40 10.5	9 8.9	21 43.4	12♋49.2	20 14.2	26 1.3	29 3.9	18 36.0	22 6.1	8R46.0	13 19.5	9 12.1
3 W	20 44 7.0	10 6.3	21 40.2	27 58.4	21 34.9	27 7.3	29 42.8	18 47.4	22 12.3	8 44.0	13 21.7	9 13.5
4 T	20 48 3.6	11 3.8	21 37.0	13♌16.6	23 0.4	28 13.4	0♌21.6	18 58.8	22 18.5	8 42.0	13 23.9	9 14.8
5 F	20 52 0.1	12 1.3	21 33.9	28 32.5	24 30.7	29 19.7	1 0.4	19 10.2	22 24.8	8 39.9	13 26.1	9 16.1
6 S	20 55 56.7	12 58.8	21 30.7	13♍35.2	26 5.4	0♋26.2	1 39.1	19 21.8	22 31.0	8 37.9	13 28.4	9 17.4
7 S	20 59 53.2	13 56.3	21 27.5	28 16.6	27 44.3	1 32.8	2 17.9	19 33.4	22 37.4	8 35.8	13 30.6	9 18.6
8 M	21 3 49.8	14 53.8	21 24.3	12♎31.7	29 27.0	2 39.6	2 56.6	19 45.0	22 43.8	8 33.7	13 32.8	9 19.9
9 T	21 7 46.4	15 51.4	21 21.2	26 18.9	1♌13.4	3 46.5	3 35.3	19 56.7	22 50.2	8 31.5	13 35.0	9 21.2
10 W	21 11 42.9	16 48.9	21 18.0	9♏39.5	3 2.9	4 53.6	4 13.9	20 8.5	22 56.7	8 29.3	13 37.3	9 22.4
11 T	21 15 39.4	17 46.5	21 14.8	22 36.4	4 55.2	6 0.9	4 52.6	20 20.3	23 3.2	8 27.2	13 39.5	9 23.6
12 F	21 19 36.0	18 44.1	21 11.6	5♐13.5	6 50.0	7 8.3	5 31.2	20 32.2	23 9.8	8 25.0	13 41.7	9 24.8
13 S	21 23 32.6	19 41.7	21 8.4	17 35.0	8 46.8	8 15.8	6 9.8	20 44.1	23 16.4	8 22.7	13 43.9	9 26.0
14 S	21 27 29.1	20 39.3	21 5.3	29 44.7	10 45.2	9 23.5	6 48.3	20 56.1	23 23.1	8 20.5	13 46.1	9 27.2
15 M	21 31 25.6	21 36.9	21 2.1	11♑46.2	12 45.0	10 31.3	7 26.8	21 8.1	23 29.8	8 18.2	13 48.3	9 28.4
16 T	21 35 22.2	22 34.6	20 58.9	23 42.4	14 45.7	11 39.3	8 5.3	21 20.1	23 36.5	8 16.0	13 50.5	9 29.5
17 W	21 39 18.8	23 32.3	20 55.7	5♒35.5	16 47.0	12 47.4	8 43.8	21 32.3	23 43.3	8 13.7	13 52.7	9 30.7
18 T	21 43 15.4	24 30.0	20 52.6	17 27.6	18 48.5	13 55.7	9 22.3	21 44.4	23 50.1	8 11.4	13 54.9	9 31.8
19 F	21 47 11.9	25 27.7	20 49.4	29 20.1	20 50.1	15 4.1	10 0.7	21 56.6	23 57.0	8 9.1	13 57.1	9 32.9
20 S	21 51 8.4	26 25.4	20 46.2	11♓14.8	22 51.4	16 12.7	10 39.1	22 8.8	24 3.8	8 6.8	13 59.3	9 34.0
21 S	21 55 5.0	27 23.2	20 43.0	23 13.3	24 52.4	17 21.3	11 17.5	22 21.1	24 10.7	8 4.4	14 1.5	9 35.1
22 M	21 59 1.6	28 21.0	20 39.8	5♈17.9	26 52.7	18 30.1	11 55.9	22 33.4	24 17.7	8 2.1	14 3.7	9 36.1
23 T	22 2 58.1	29 18.8	20 36.7	17 31.1	28 52.2	19 39.1	12 34.3	22 45.8	24 24.7	7 59.7	14 5.8	9 37.2
24 W	22 6 54.7	0♍16.6	20 33.5	29 56.2	0♍50.8	20 48.2	13 12.6	22 58.2	24 31.7	7 57.4	14 8.0	9 38.2
25 T	22 10 51.2	1 14.5	20 30.3	12♉36.7	2 48.5	21 57.4	13 50.9	23 10.6	24 38.7	7 55.0	14 10.1	9 39.2
26 F	22 14 47.8	2 12.4	20 27.1	25 36.3	4 45.0	23 6.7	14 29.2	23 23.1	24 45.8	7 52.6	14 12.3	9 40.2
27 S	22 18 44.3	3 10.3	20 24.0	8♊58.6	6 40.5	24 16.1	15 7.5	23 35.6	24 52.9	7 50.2	14 14.4	9 41.2
28 S	22 22 40.9	4 8.3	20 20.8	22 46.0	8 34.7	25 25.7	15 45.7	23 48.2	25 0.0	7 47.8	14 16.5	9 42.2
29 M	22 26 37.4	5 6.3	20 17.6	6♋59.4	10 27.8	26 35.4	16 24.0	24 0.7	25 7.2	7 45.4	14 18.6	9 43.1
30 T	22 30 33.9	6 4.3	20 14.4	21 36.9	12 19.6	27 45.2	17 2.2	24 13.4	25 14.3	7 43.0	14 20.7	9 44.0
31 W	22 34 30.5	7 2.4	20 11.2	6♌33.8	14 10.1	28 55.1	17 40.4	24 26.0	25 21.6	7 40.6	14 22.8	9 44.9
						DECLINATION						
1 M	20 36 13.9	18N13.4	8S29.3	18N47.7	20N54.4	20N59.3	21N29.4	5N36.8	5N 4.5	9S 1.0	16N54.6	19N54.9
4 T	20 48 3.6	17 27.5	8 25.8	12 22.5	21 0.7	21 13.7	21 5.9	5 23.2	4 56.9	9 3.3	16 52.7	19 54.7
7 S	20 59 53.2	16 39.0	8 22.2	1S 3.7	20 47.9	21 23.6	20 41.0	5 9.4	4 49.2	9 5.7	16 50.8	19 54.4
10 W	21 11 42.9	15 48.1	8 18.6	13 6.3	20 12.6	21 28.9	20 14.7	4 55.4	4 41.3	9 8.2	16 48.9	19 54.2
13 S	21 23 32.6	14 54.9	8 15.1	18 36.1	19 13.3	21 29.4	19 47.3	4 41.2	4 33.3	9 10.7	16 47.1	19 54.0
16 T	21 35 22.2	13 59.6	8 11.5	16 22.6	17 51.3	21 25.1	19 18.6	4 26.8	4 25.2	9 13.3	16 45.2	19 53.8
19 F	21 47 11.9	13 2.3	8 7.9	8 3.0	16 9.7	21 15.6	18 48.7	4 12.3	4 16.9	9 15.9	16 43.3	19 53.5
22 M	21 59 1.6	12 3.1	8 4.3	3N13.5	14 12.9	21 1.2	18 17.8	3 57.6	4 8.5	9 18.5	16 41.5	19 53.3
25 T	22 10 51.2	11 2.2	8 0.7	13 39.4	12 5.3	20 41.6	17 45.7	3 42.8	4 0.1	9 21.2	16 39.6	19 53.1
28 S	22 22 40.9	9 59.7	7 57.1	18 37.7	9 50.6	20 16.9	17 12.6	3 27.8	3 51.5	9 23.9	16 37.8	19 52.9
31 W	22 34 30.5	8 55.8	7 53.5	13 52.7	7 32.0	19 47.1	16 38.6	3 12.7	3 42.9	9 26.6	16 36.0	19 52.6

SEPTEMBER 1921

DAY	EPHEMERIS SIDEREAL TIME	☉	☊	☽	☿	♀	♂	♃	♄	♅	♆	♇
	h m s	° ′	° ′	° ′	° ′	° ′	° ′	° ′	° ′	° ′	° ′	° ′
						LONGITUDE						
1 T	22 38 27.1	8♍ 0.5	20♎ 8.1	21♌42.2	15♍59.5	0♌ 5.2	18♌18.6	24♍38.7	25♍28.8	7♓38.3	14♌24.9	9♋45.8
2 F	22 42 23.6	8 58.6	20 4.9	6♍52.6	17 47.5	1 15.3	18 56.7	24 51.4	25 36.0	7R35.9	14 27.0	9 46.7
3 S	22 46 20.1	9 56.7	20 1.7	21 54.7	19 34.4	2 25.6	19 34.8	25 4.1	25 43.3	7 33.4	14 29.0	9 47.5
4 S	22 50 16.7	10 54.9	19 58.5	6♎39.7	21 20.0	3 35.9	20 13.0	25 16.8	25 50.6	7 31.1	14 31.1	9 48.3
5 M	22 54 13.3	11 53.1	19 55.4	21 1.2	23 4.4	4 46.4	20 51.1	25 29.6	25 57.9	7 28.7	14 33.1	9 49.2
6 T	22 58 9.9	12 51.3	19 52.2	4♏55.9	24 47.5	5 57.0	21 29.1	25 42.4	26 5.2	7 26.3	14 35.1	9 50.0
7 W	23 2 6.4	13 49.6	19 49.0	18 23.4	26 29.5	7 7.6	22 7.2	25 55.2	26 12.6	7 23.9	14 37.1	9 50.7
8 T	23 6 2.9	14 47.8	19 45.8	1♐25.4	28 10.3	8 18.4	22 45.2	26 8.0	26 19.9	7 21.5	14 39.1	9 51.5
9 F	23 9 59.5	15 46.1	19 42.6	14 5.3	29 50.0	9 29.2	23 23.2	26 20.9	26 27.3	7 19.2	14 41.1	9 52.2
10 S	23 13 56.1	16 44.5	19 39.5	26 27.2	1♎28.5	10 40.2	24 1.2	26 33.7	26 34.7	7 16.8	14 43.0	9 52.9
11 S	23 17 52.6	17 42.8	19 36.3	8♑35.4	3 5.9	11 51.2	24 39.2	26 46.6	26 42.1	7 14.5	14 45.0	9 53.6
12 M	23 21 49.1	18 41.2	19 33.1	20 34.4	4 42.2	13 2.4	25 17.1	26 59.5	26 49.5	7 12.1	14 46.9	9 54.3
13 T	23 25 45.7	19 39.6	19 29.9	2♒27.9	6 17.4	14 13.6	25 55.0	27 12.4	26 56.9	7 9.8	14 48.8	9 54.9
14 W	23 29 42.3	20 38.0	19 26.8	14 19.5	7 51.4	15 25.0	26 32.9	27 25.3	27 4.3	7 7.5	14 50.7	9 55.5
15 T	23 33 38.8	21 36.5	19 23.6	26 12.0	9 24.4	16 36.4	27 10.8	27 38.3	27 11.7	7 5.2	14 52.5	9 56.1
16 F	23 37 35.4	22 35.0	19 20.4	8♓ 8.0	10 56.4	17 47.9	27 48.7	27 51.2	27 19.2	7 2.9	14 54.4	9 56.7
17 S	23 41 31.9	23 33.5	19 17.2	20 9.3	12 27.2	18 59.5	28 26.5	28 4.2	27 26.6	7 0.6	14 56.2	9 57.3
18 S	23 45 28.5	24 32.0	19 14.0	2♈17.5	13 57.0	20 11.2	29 4.4	28 17.1	27 34.1	6 58.4	14 58.0	9 57.8
19 M	23 49 25.0	25 30.6	19 10.9	14 34.4	15 25.7	21 23.0	29 42.2	28 30.1	27 41.5	6 56.1	14 59.8	9 58.3
20 T	23 53 21.6	26 29.2	19 7.7	27 1.3	16 53.3	22 34.9	0♍20.0	28 43.1	27 49.0	6 53.9	15 1.6	9 58.8
21 W	23 57 18.1	27 27.9	19 4.5	9♉40.1	18 19.8	23 46.9	0 57.8	28 56.0	27 56.4	6 51.7	15 3.4	9 59.3
22 T	0 1 14.7	28 26.6	19 1.3	22 32.4	19 45.2	24 59.0	1 35.5	29 9.0	28 3.9	6 49.5	15 5.1	9 59.7
23 F	0 5 11.2	29 25.3	18 58.1	5♊40.4	21 9.5	26 11.1	2 13.3	29 22.0	28 11.3	6 47.4	15 6.8	10 0.2
24 S	0 9 7.8	0♎24.1	18 55.0	19 5.7	22 32.7	27 23.3	2 51.0	29 35.0	28 18.8	6 45.2	15 8.5	10 0.6
25 S	0 13 4.4	1 22.9	18 51.8	2♋49.7	23 54.7	28 35.7	3 28.7	29 48.0	28 26.3	6 43.1	15 10.2	10 0.9
26 M	0 17 0.9	2 21.7	18 48.6	16 52.7	25 15.4	29 48.1	4 6.4	0♎ 0.9	28 33.7	6 41.0	15 11.8	10 1.3
27 T	0 20 57.4	3 20.6	18 45.4	1♌13.7	26 35.0	1♍ 0.6	4 44.1	0 13.9	28 41.2	6 39.0	15 13.4	10 1.6
28 W	0 24 54.0	4 19.5	18 42.3	15 49.8	27 53.2	2 13.1	5 21.7	0 26.9	28 48.6	6 36.9	15 15.0	10 1.9
29 T	0 28 50.6	5 18.4	18 39.1	0♍36.0	29 10.0	3 25.8	5 59.4	0 39.9	28 56.0	6 34.9	15 16.6	10 2.2
30 F	0 32 47.1	6 17.4	18 35.9	15 25.8	0♏25.4	4 38.5	6 37.0	0 52.8	29 3.5	6 32.9	15 18.2	10 2.5
						DECLINATION						
1 T	22 38 27.1	8N34.2	7S52.3	10N10.3	6N45.3	19N36.1	16N27.0	3N 7.7	3N40.0	9S27.5	16N35.4	19N52.6
4 S	22 50 16.7	7 28.5	7 48.7	3S37.5	4 25.1	18 59.7	15 51.7	2 52.5	3 31.3	9 30.1	16 33.7	19 52.3
7 W	23 2 6.4	6 21.8	7 45.1	14 48.5	2 5.5	18 18.5	15 15.6	2 37.2	3 22.5	9 32.8	16 31.9	19 52.1
10 S	23 13 56.1	5 14.2	7 41.5	18 34.2	0S12.1	17 32.6	14 38.6	2 21.8	3 13.8	9 35.4	16 30.3	19 51.9
13 T	23 25 45.7	4 5.8	7 37.9	14 41.3	2 26.6	16 42.2	14 0.9	2 6.5	3 4.9	9 38.0	16 28.6	19 51.8
16 F	23 37 35.4	2 56.7	7 34.3	5 23.9	4 37.2	15 47.5	13 22.5	1 51.0	2 56.1	9 40.6	16 27.0	19 51.6
19 M	23 49 25.0	1 47.1	7 30.7	6N 2.4	6 43.3	14 48.8	12 43.4	1 35.6	2 47.3	9 43.0	16 25.4	19 51.4
22 T	0 1 14.7	0 37.2	7 27.1	15 31.5	8 43.9	13 46.1	12 3.6	1 20.1	2 38.5	9 45.4	16 23.9	19 51.2
25 S	0 13 4.4	0S33.0	7 23.5	18 20.1	10 38.6	12 39.8	11 23.3	1 4.7	2 29.7	9 47.8	16 22.5	19 51.1
28 W	0 24 54.0	1 43.2	7 19.9	11 38.1	12 26.3	11 30.2	10 42.4	0 49.3	2 21.0	9 50.0	16 21.1	19 51.0

OCTOBER 1921

						LONGITUDE						
1 S	0 36 43.7	7♎16.5	18♎32.7	0♎11.6	1♏39.3	5♍51.3	7♍14.6	1♎ 5.8	29♍10.9	6♓30.9	15♌19.7	10♋ 2.7
2 S	0 40 40.2	8 15.5	18 29.5	14 46.1	2 51.6	7 4.1	7 52.2	1 18.7	29 18.3	6R29.0	15 21.2	10 3.0
3 M	0 44 36.8	9 14.6	18 26.4	29 3.0	4 2.2	8 17.1	8 29.8	1 31.7	29 25.7	6 27.1	15 22.7	10 3.2
4 T	0 48 33.3	10 13.7	18 23.2	12♏58.0	5 11.0	9 30.1	9 7.3	1 44.6	29 33.1	6 25.2	15 24.1	10 3.3
5 W	0 52 29.9	11 12.9	18 20.0	26 28.8	6 17.8	10 43.1	9 44.9	1 57.5	29 40.5	6 23.4	15 25.5	10 3.5
6 T	0 56 26.4	12 12.1	18 16.8	9♐35.5	7 22.5	11 56.3	10 22.4	2 10.4	29 47.8	6 21.6	15 26.9	10 3.6
7 F	1 0 23.0	13 11.3	18 13.6	22 19.8	8 24.8	13 9.5	10 59.9	2 23.3	29 55.1	6 19.8	15 28.3	10 3.7
8 S	1 4 19.5	14 10.5	18 10.5	4♑45.0	9 24.8	14 22.7	11 37.3	2 36.2	0♎ 2.5	6 18.1	15 29.7	10 3.8
9 S	1 8 16.1	15 9.8	18 7.3	16 54.9	10 21.9	15 36.0	12 14.8	2 49.0	0 9.8	6 16.4	15 31.0	10 3.8
10 M	1 12 12.6	16 9.1	18 4.1	28 54.2	11 16.2	16 49.4	12 52.2	3 1.8	0 17.0	6 14.7	15 32.3	10 3.9
11 T	1 16 9.2	17 8.4	18 0.9	10♒47.3	12 7.2	18 2.9	13 29.6	3 14.6	0 24.3	6 13.1	15 33.5	10 3.9
12 W	1 20 5.7	18 7.8	17 57.8	22 38.8	12 54.6	19 16.4	14 7.0	3 27.4	0 31.5	6 11.5	15 34.8	10R 3.9
13 T	1 24 2.3	19 7.2	17 54.6	4♓32.7	13 38.2	20 29.9	14 44.4	3 40.2	0 38.8	6 9.9	15 36.0	10 3.8
14 F	1 27 58.9	20 6.6	17 51.4	16 32.6	14 17.5	21 43.5	15 21.7	3 52.9	0 46.0	6 8.4	15 37.2	10 3.8
15 S	1 31 55.4	21 6.1	17 48.2	28 41.4	14 52.1	22 57.2	15 59.1	4 5.6	0 53.1	6 6.9	15 38.3	10 3.7
16 S	1 35 51.9	22 5.6	17 45.0	11♈ 1.3	15 21.6	24 10.9	16 36.4	4 18.3	1 0.3	6 5.5	15 39.4	10 3.6
17 M	1 39 48.5	23 5.1	17 41.9	23 34.1	15 45.4	25 24.7	17 13.7	4 30.9	1 7.4	6 4.0	15 40.5	10 3.4
18 T	1 43 45.1	24 4.7	17 38.7	6♉20.4	16 3.1	26 38.6	17 50.9	4 43.5	1 14.5	6 2.7	15 41.6	10 3.3
19 W	1 47 41.6	25 4.3	17 35.5	19 20.7	16 14.1	27 52.5	18 28.2	4 56.1	1 21.5	6 1.4	15 42.6	10 3.1
20 T	1 51 38.2	26 3.9	17 32.3	2♊34.7	16 17.9	29 6.4	19 5.4	5 8.7	1 28.6	6 0.1	15 43.6	10 2.9
21 F	1 55 34.7	27 3.6	17 29.2	16 2.0	16R13.8	0♎20.4	19 42.7	5 21.2	1 35.5	5 58.8	15 44.6	10 2.7
22 S	1 59 31.3	28 3.3	17 26.0	29 41.6	16 1.6	1 34.5	20 19.9	5 33.7	1 42.5	5 57.6	15 45.5	10 2.4
23 S	2 3 27.8	29 3.0	17 22.8	13♋32.7	15 40.6	2 48.6	20 57.1	5 46.2	1 49.4	5 56.5	15 46.4	10 2.1
24 M	2 7 24.4	0♏ 2.8	17 19.6	27 34.0	15 10.7	4 2.8	21 34.2	5 58.6	1 56.3	5 55.4	15 47.3	10 1.8
25 T	2 11 20.9	1 2.6	17 16.4	11♌44.1	14 31.8	5 17.0	22 11.4	6 11.0	2 3.2	5 54.3	15 48.1	10 1.5
26 W	2 15 17.5	2 2.4	17 13.3	26 1.0	13 44.0	6 31.3	22 48.5	6 23.3	2 10.0	5 53.3	15 49.0	10 1.2
27 T	2 19 14.0	3 2.3	17 10.1	10♍22.1	12 47.8	7 45.6	23 25.6	6 35.6	2 16.8	5 52.3	15 49.7	10 0.8
28 F	2 23 10.6	4 2.3	17 6.9	24 44.0	11 44.1	8 60.0	24 2.7	6 47.8	2 23.6	5 51.4	15 50.5	10 0.4
29 S	2 27 7.1	5 2.2	17 3.7	9♎ 2.8	10 34.1	10 14.4	24 39.8	7 0.0	2 30.3	5 50.5	15 51.2	10 0.0
30 S	2 31 3.7	6 2.2	17 0.6	23 14.0	9 19.4	11 28.8	25 16.9	7 12.2	2 36.9	5 49.7	15 51.9	9 59.6
31 M	2 35 0.2	7 2.2	16 57.4	7♏13.2	8 2.2	12 43.3	25 53.9	7 24.3	2 43.5	5 48.9	15 52.5	9 59.1
						DECLINATION						
1 S	0 36 43.7	2S53.3	7S16.2	1S33.8	14S 6.3	10N17.5	10N 1.1	0N33.9	2N12.3	9S52.2	16N19.8	19N50.8
4 T	0 48 33.3	4 3.1	7 12.6	13 36.3	15 37.2	9 2.0	9 19.3	0 18.6	2 3.6	9 54.2	16 18.5	19 50.7
7 F	1 0 23.0	5 12.5	7 9.0	18 27.9	16 57.7	7 44.0	8 37.1	0 3.3	1 55.1	9 56.2	16 17.3	19 50.6
10 M	1 12 12.6	6 21.3	7 5.3	15 17.8	18 5.9	6 23.9	7 54.5	0S11.9	1 46.6	9 58.0	16 16.2	19 50.6
13 T	1 24 2.3	7 29.3	7 1.7	6 26.9	18 59.1	5 1.8	7 11.6	0 26.9	1 38.2	9 59.7	16 15.1	19 50.5
16 S	1 35 51.9	8 36.4	6 58.1	4N57.7	19 33.8	3 38.2	6 28.5	0 41.9	1 29.9	10 1.2	16 14.1	19 50.5
19 W	1 47 41.6	9 42.4	6 54.4	14 55.4	19 45.0	2 13.4	5 45.1	0 56.7	1 21.8	10 2.7	16 13.2	19 50.4
22 S	1 59 31.3	10 47.1	6 50.8	18 26.1	19 26.6	0 47.6	5 1.6	1 11.4	1 13.8	10 3.9	16 12.4	19 50.4
25 T	2 11 20.9	11 50.4	6 47.1	12 37.5	18 31.9	0S38.9	4 17.8	1 25.9	1 5.9	10 5.1	16 11.6	19 50.5
28 F	2 23 10.6	12 52.1	6 43.5	0 10.4	16 57.9	2 5.6	3 34.0	1 40.3	0 58.2	10 6.1	16 11.0	19 50.5
31 M	2 35 0.2	13 52.0	6 39.8	12S17.4	14 52.7	3 32.3	2 50.1	1 54.4	0 50.7	10 6.9	16 10.4	19 50.5

NOVEMBER 1921

DAY	EPHEMERIS SIDEREAL TIME	☉	☊	☽	☿	♀	♂	♃	♄	♅	♆	♇
	h m s	° ′	° ′	° ′	° ′	° ′	° ′	° ′	° ′	° ′	° ′	° ′
						LONGITUDE						
1 T	2 38 56.8	8♏ 2.3	16♎54.2	20♏56.7	6♏44.7	13♎57.8	26♍30.9	7♎36.4	2♎50.1	5♓48.1	15♌53.2	9♋58.7
2 W	2 42 53.4	9 2.4	16 51.0	4♐21.6	5R29.4	15 12.4	27 7.9	7 48.4	2 56.6	5R47.4	15 53.7	9R58.2
3 T	2 46 49.9	10 2.5	16 47.9	17 26.5	4 18.6	16 26.9	27 44.8	8 0.3	3 3.1	5 46.8	15 54.3	9 57.7
4 F	2 50 46.5	11 2.6	16 44.7	0♑11.6	3 14.5	17 41.6	28 21.8	8 12.2	3 9.5	5 46.2	15 54.8	9 57.1
5 S	2 54 43.0	12 2.8	16 41.5	12 38.4	2 19.1	18 56.2	28 58.7	8 24.1	3 15.9	5 45.6	15 55.3	9 56.6
6 S	2 58 39.6	13 3.0	16 38.3	24 50.0	1 33.7	20 10.9	29 35.6	8 35.9	3 22.3	5 45.1	15 55.7	9 56.0
7 M	3 2 36.1	14 3.2	16 35.1	6♒50.0	0 59.4	21 25.6	0♎12.4	8 47.6	3 28.5	5 44.7	15 56.1	9 55.4
8 T	3 6 32.7	15 3.5	16 32.0	18 43.0	0 36.7	22 40.4	0 49.3	8 59.3	3 34.8	5 44.3	15 56.5	9 54.7
9 W	3 10 29.2	16 3.8	16 28.8	0♓34.0	0 25.6	23 55.2	1 26.1	9 10.9	3 40.9	5 43.9	15 56.9	9 54.1
10 T	3 14 25.8	17 4.1	16 25.6	12 27.9	0D26.0	25 10.0	2 2.9	9 22.4	3 47.1	5 43.6	15 57.2	9 53.4
11 F	3 18 22.4	18 4.4	16 22.4	24 29.5	0 37.3	26 24.8	2 39.6	9 33.9	3 53.1	5 43.4	15 57.5	9 52.8
12 S	3 22 18.9	19 4.7	16 19.3	6♈42.9	0 58.7	27 39.7	3 16.4	9 45.3	3 59.1	5 43.2	15 57.7	9 52.1
13 S	3 26 15.4	20 5.1	16 16.1	19 11.8	1 29.6	28 54.6	3 53.1	9 56.6	4 5.1	5 43.0	15 57.9	9 51.3
14 M	3 30 12.0	21 5.5	16 12.9	1♉58.6	2 8.9	0♏ 9.5	4 29.8	10 7.9	4 10.9	5 42.9	15 58.1	9 50.6
15 T	3 34 8.6	22 5.9	16 9.7	15 4.5	2 55.7	1 24.4	5 6.5	10 19.1	4 16.8	5 42.9	15 58.2	9 49.8
16 W	3 38 5.1	23 6.4	16 6.5	28 29.0	3 49.3	2 39.4	5 43.1	10 30.2	4 22.5	5 42.9	15 58.3	9 49.1
17 T	3 42 1.7	24 6.8	16 3.4	12♊10.4	4 48.8	3 54.4	6 19.7	10 41.3	4 28.2	5D43.0	15 58.4	9 48.3
18 F	3 45 58.2	25 7.3	16 0.2	26 5.5	5 53.4	5 9.4	6 56.3	10 52.3	4 33.9	5 43.1	15 58.5	9 47.4
19 S	3 49 54.8	26 7.9	15 57.0	10♋10.5	7 2.5	6 24.5	7 32.9	11 3.2	4 39.4	5 43.2	15 58.5	9 46.6
20 S	3 53 51.3	27 8.4	15 53.8	24 21.2	8 15.4	7 39.5	8 9.4	11 14.0	4 44.9	5 43.4	15R58.4	9 45.8
21 M	3 57 47.9	28 9.0	15 50.7	8♌33.8	9 31.5	8 54.6	8 46.0	11 24.7	4 50.4	5 43.7	15 58.4	9 44.9
22 T	4 1 44.5	29 9.6	15 47.5	22 45.3	10 50.4	10 9.8	9 22.4	11 35.4	4 55.8	5 44.0	15 58.3	9 44.0
23 W	4 5 41.0	0♐10.3	15 44.3	6♍53.6	12 11.7	11 24.9	9 58.9	11 46.0	5 1.1	5 44.3	15 58.1	9 43.1
24 T	4 9 37.6	1 11.0	15 41.1	20 57.1	13 35.0	12 40.1	10 35.4	11 56.5	5 6.3	5 44.8	15 58.0	9 42.2
25 F	4 13 34.1	2 11.7	15 37.9	4♎55.0	15 0.0	13 55.3	11 11.8	12 6.9	5 11.4	5 45.2	15 57.8	9 41.2
26 S	4 17 30.7	3 12.4	15 34.8	18 46.1	16 26.4	15 10.5	11 48.2	12 17.2	5 16.5	5 45.7	15 57.5	9 40.3
27 S	4 21 27.2	4 13.2	15 31.6	2♏29.3	17 54.0	16 25.7	12 24.5	12 27.4	5 21.5	5 46.3	15 57.3	9 39.3
28 M	4 25 23.8	5 13.9	15 28.4	16 3.0	19 22.5	17 40.9	13 0.8	12 37.6	5 26.5	5 46.9	15 57.0	9 38.4
29 T	4 29 20.3	6 14.7	15 25.2	29 25.2	20 51.9	18 56.2	13 37.1	12 47.6	5 31.3	5 47.6	15 56.6	9 37.4
30 W	4 33 16.9	7 15.6	15 22.1	12♐34.1	22 22.0	20 11.4	14 13.4	12 57.5	5 36.1	5 48.3	15 56.3	9 36.4
						DECLINATION						
1 T	2 38 56.8	14S11.5	6S38.6	15S14.2	14S 7.9	4S 1.1	2N35.5	1S59.1	0N48.2	10S 7.1	16N10.3	19N50.6
4 F	2 50 46.5	15 8.7	6 35.0	18 27.2	12 0.8	5 27.2	1 51.6	2 12.9	0 40.9	10 7.8	16 9.8	19 50.6
7 M	3 2 36.1	16 3.7	6 31.3	13 46.5	10 27.8	6 52.5	1 7.8	2 26.5	0 33.8	10 8.2	16 9.4	19 50.7
10 T	3 14 25.8	16 56.2	6 27.6	4 5.0	9 45.0	8 16.6	0 24.0	2 39.9	0 27.0	10 8.5	16 9.2	19 50.9
13 S	3 26 15.4	17 46.2	6 24.0	7N24.1	9 50.9	9 39.1	0S19.6	2 53.0	0 20.3	10 8.6	16 9.0	19 51.0
16 W	3 38 5.1	18 33.3	6 20.3	16 31.2	10 34.7	10 59.8	1 3.1	3 5.8	0 13.9	10 8.5	16 8.9	19 51.2
19 S	3 49 54.8	19 17.5	6 16.6	17 56.6	11 43.7	12 18.2	1 46.4	3 18.3	0 7.8	10 8.3	16 8.9	19 51.3
22 T	4 1 44.5	19 58.6	6 13.0	9 57.0	13 7.3	13 34.0	2 29.5	3 30.5	0 1.9	10 7.9	16 9.0	19 51.5
25 F	4 13 34.1	20 36.4	6 9.3	2S58.2	14 37.8	14 46.8	3 12.3	3 42.4	0S 3.7	10 7.3	16 9.2	19 51.8
28 M	4 25 23.8	21 10.8	6 5.6	14 16.2	16 9.8	15 56.4	3 54.8	3 53.9	0 9.1	10 6.6	16 9.5	19 52.0

DECEMBER 1921

DAY	EPHEMERIS SIDEREAL TIME	☉	☊	☽	☿	♀	♂	♃	♄	♅	♆	♇
						LONGITUDE						
1 T	4 37 13.5	8♐16.4	15♎18.9	25♐28.3	23♏52.6	21♏26.7	14♎49.6	13♎ 7.4	5♎40.8	5♓49.1	15♌55.9	9♋35.3
2 F	4 41 10.0	9 17.3	15 15.7	8♑ 6.9	25 23.7	22 42.0	15 25.8	13 17.1	5 45.4	5 49.9	15R55.4	9R34.3
3 S	4 45 6.6	10 18.1	15 12.5	20 30.5	26 55.2	23 57.3	16 2.0	13 26.8	5 50.0	5 50.8	15 55.0	9 33.2
4 S	4 49 3.1	11 19.0	15 9.4	2♒40.4	28 26.9	25 12.6	16 38.1	13 36.3	5 54.4	5 51.7	15 54.5	9 32.2
5 M	4 52 59.7	12 20.0	15 6.2	14 39.5	29 59.0	26 28.0	17 14.2	13 45.7	5 58.8	5 52.7	15 53.9	9 31.1
6 T	4 56 56.2	13 20.9	15 3.0	26 31.4	1♐31.2	27 43.3	17 50.2	13 55.0	6 3.1	5 53.7	15 53.4	9 30.0
7 W	5 0 52.8	14 21.8	14 59.8	8♓20.7	3 3.7	28 58.6	18 26.2	14 4.3	6 7.3	5 54.8	15 52.8	9 28.9
8 T	5 4 49.3	15 22.7	14 56.6	20 12.5	4 36.2	0♐14.0	19 2.2	14 13.4	6 11.4	5 55.9	15 52.1	9 27.8
9 F	5 8 45.9	16 23.7	14 53.5	2♈12.3	6 9.0	1 29.3	19 38.1	14 22.3	6 15.4	5 57.1	15 51.5	9 26.7
10 S	5 12 42.5	17 24.7	14 50.3	14 25.3	7 41.8	2 44.7	20 14.0	14 31.2	6 19.4	5 58.3	15 50.8	9 25.6
11 S	5 16 39.0	18 25.6	14 47.1	26 56.4	9 14.7	4 0.1	20 49.9	14 40.0	6 23.2	5 59.6	15 50.1	9 24.5
12 M	5 20 35.6	19 26.6	14 43.9	9♉49.6	10 47.8	5 15.5	21 25.7	14 48.6	6 27.0	6 0.9	15 49.3	9 23.3
13 T	5 24 32.1	20 27.6	14 40.8	23 7.3	12 20.9	6 30.8	22 1.5	14 57.1	6 30.7	6 2.3	15 48.5	9 22.1
14 W	5 28 28.7	21 28.6	14 37.6	6♊49.9	13 54.2	7 46.2	22 37.3	15 5.5	6 34.3	6 3.7	15 47.7	9 21.0
15 T	5 32 25.3	22 29.7	14 34.4	20 55.1	15 27.5	9 1.6	23 13.0	15 13.8	6 37.8	6 5.1	15 46.9	9 19.8
16 F	5 36 21.8	23 30.7	14 31.2	5♋18.4	17 1.0	10 17.0	23 48.6	15 22.0	6 41.2	6 6.7	15 46.0	9 18.6
17 S	5 40 18.4	24 31.7	14 28.1	19 53.1	18 34.6	11 32.4	24 24.3	15 30.0	6 44.5	6 8.2	15 45.1	9 17.5
18 S	5 44 14.9	25 32.8	14 24.9	4♌31.8	20 8.3	12 47.9	24 59.9	15 37.9	6 47.7	6 9.8	15 44.2	9 16.3
19 M	5 48 11.5	26 33.9	14 21.7	19 7.4	21 42.2	14 3.3	25 35.4	15 45.7	6 50.8	6 11.5	15 43.2	9 15.1
20 T	5 52 8.0	27 34.9	14 18.5	3♍34.2	23 16.2	15 18.7	26 10.9	15 53.3	6 53.8	6 13.1	15 42.2	9 13.9
21 W	5 56 4.6	28 36.0	14 15.3	17 48.5	24 50.4	16 34.1	26 46.4	16 0.8	6 56.7	6 14.9	15 41.2	9 12.6
22 T	6 0 1.1	29 37.1	14 12.2	1♎48.8	26 24.8	17 49.6	27 21.8	16 8.2	6 59.5	6 16.7	15 40.2	9 11.4
23 F	6 3 57.7	0♑38.3	14 9.0	15 35.0	27 59.4	19 5.0	27 57.2	16 15.5	7 2.3	6 18.5	15 39.1	9 10.2
24 S	6 7 54.3	1 39.4	14 5.8	29 7.9	29 34.2	20 20.5	28 32.5	16 22.6	7 4.9	6 20.4	15 38.0	9 9.0
25 S	6 11 50.8	2 40.5	14 2.6	12♏28.6	1♑ 9.2	21 36.0	29 7.8	16 29.5	7 7.4	6 22.3	15 36.9	9 7.8
26 M	6 15 47.4	3 41.7	13 59.5	25 38.2	2 44.5	22 51.4	29 43.1	16 36.3	7 9.8	6 24.2	15 35.7	9 6.5
27 T	6 19 43.9	4 42.8	13 56.3	8♐37.0	4 20.0	24 6.9	0♏18.2	16 43.0	7 12.1	6 26.2	15 34.6	9 5.3
28 W	6 23 40.5	5 44.0	13 53.1	21 25.2	5 55.8	25 22.4	0 53.4	16 49.5	7 14.4	6 28.3	15 33.4	9 4.1
29 T	6 27 37.1	6 45.2	13 49.9	4♑ 2.4	7 31.9	26 37.8	1 28.5	16 55.9	7 16.5	6 30.4	15 32.2	9 2.8
30 F	6 31 33.6	7 46.4	13 46.8	16 28.3	9 8.3	27 53.3	2 3.5	17 2.1	7 18.5	6 32.5	15 30.9	9 1.6
31 S	6 35 30.2	8 47.5	13 43.6	28 43.2	10 45.0	29 8.8	2 38.5	17 8.2	7 20.4	6 34.7	15 29.6	9 0.4
						DECLINATION						
1 T	4 37 13.5	21S41.6	6S 2.0	18S37.2	17S39.5	17S 2.2	4S36.9	4S 5.0	0S14.1	10S 5.7	16N 9.9	19N52.2
4 S	4 49 3.1	22 8.6	5 58.3	14 48.0	19 4.3	18 4.0	5 18.6	4 15.7	0 18.9	10 4.6	16 10.3	19 52.5
7 W	5 0 52.8	22 31.8	5 54.6	5 32.0	20 22.6	19 1.4	5 59.9	4 26.1	0 23.3	10 3.4	16 10.9	19 52.8
10 S	5 12 42.5	22 51.0	5 50.9	5N49.8	21 32.9	19 54.1	6 40.7	4 36.0	0 27.4	10 2.0	16 11.5	19 53.1
13 T	5 24 32.1	23 6.2	5 47.2	15 35.8	22 34.2	20 41.8	7 21.0	4 45.5	0 31.1	10 0.4	16 12.2	19 53.4
16 F	5 36 21.8	23 17.3	5 43.5	18 23.2	23 25.7	21 24.0	8 0.7	4 54.5	0 34.5	9 58.7	16 13.0	19 53.8
19 M	5 48 11.5	23 24.1	5 39.8	11 6.9	24 6.7	22 0.7	8 39.9	5 3.0	0 37.6	9 56.8	16 13.9	19 54.1
22 T	6 0 1.1	23 26.8	5 36.1	1S46.7	24 36.4	22 31.5	9 18.5	5 11.1	0 40.3	9 54.8	16 14.8	19 54.5
25 S	6 11 50.8	23 25.2	5 32.5	13 21.7	24 54.3	22 56.2	9 56.4	5 18.7	0 42.7	9 52.6	16 15.8	19 54.9
28 W	6 23 40.5	23 19.3	5 28.8	18 34.4	24 59.8	23 14.7	10 33.7	5 25.7	0 44.6	9 50.3	16 16.9	19 55.3
31 S	6 35 30.2	23 9.3	5 25.1	15 41.5	24 52.3	23 26.7	11 10.2	5 32.2	0 46.2	9 47.9	16 18.0	19 55.7

JANUARY 1922

DAY	EPHEMERIS SIDEREAL TIME	☉	☊	☽	☿	♀	♂	♃	♄	♅	♆	♇
	h m s	° ′	° ′	° ′	° ′	° ′	° ′	° ′	° ′	° ′	° ′	° ′
						LONGITUDE						
1 S	6 39 26.7	9♑48.7	13♎40.4	10♒47.7	12♑22.1	0♑24.3	3♏13.4	17♎14.1	7♎22.2	6♓36.9	15♌28.4	8♋59.1
2 M	6 43 23.3	10 49.9	13 37.2	22 43.5	13 59.4	1 39.7	3 48.2	17 19.9	7 23.9	6 39.1	15R27.0	8R57.9
3 T	6 47 19.8	11 51.1	13 34.1	4♓33.3	15 37.1	2 55.2	4 23.0	17 25.5	7 25.5	6 41.4	15 25.7	8 56.7
4 W	6 51 16.4	12 52.2	13 30.9	16 20.7	17 15.1	4 10.7	4 57.8	17 30.9	7 26.9	6 43.7	15 24.4	8 55.4
5 T	6 55 12.9	13 53.4	13 27.7	28 10.1	18 53.5	5 26.1	5 32.5	17 36.2	7 28.3	6 46.1	15 23.0	8 54.2
6 F	6 59 9.5	14 54.6	13 24.5	10♈ 6.7	20 32.2	6 41.6	6 7.1	17 41.3	7 29.6	6 48.5	15 21.6	8 53.0
7 S	7 3 6.1	15 55.7	13 21.3	22 15.9	22 11.2	7 57.0	6 41.6	17 46.3	7 30.7	6 50.9	15 20.2	8 51.7
8 S	7 7 2.6	16 56.9	13 18.2	4♉43.4	23 50.5	9 12.5	7 16.1	17 51.1	7 31.8	6 53.4	15 18.8	8 50.5
9 M	7 10 59.2	17 58.0	13 15.0	17 34.2	25 30.1	10 27.9	7 50.6	17 55.7	7 32.7	6 55.9	15 17.3	8 49.3
10 T	7 14 55.7	18 59.1	13 11.8	0♊52.3	27 9.9	11 43.4	8 24.9	18 0.1	7 33.5	6 58.5	15 15.8	8 48.1
11 W	7 18 52.3	20 0.2	13 8.6	14 39.6	28 50.0	12 58.8	8 59.2	18 4.4	7 34.3	7 1.0	15 14.4	8 46.9
12 T	7 22 48.9	21 1.4	13 5.5	28 55.2	0♒30.2	14 14.3	9 33.5	18 8.6	7 34.9	7 3.7	15•12.9	8 45.7
13 F	7 26 45.4	22 2.5	13 2.3	13♋34.9	2 10.5	15 29.7	10 7.6	18 12.5	7 35.4	7 6.3	15 11.4	8 44.5
14 S	7 30 41.9	23 3.5	12 59.1	28 31.6	3 50.9	16 45.1	10 41.7	18 16.3	7 35.8	7 9.0	15 9.8	8 43.2
15 S	7 34 38.5	24 4.6	12 55.9	13♌35.7	5 31.1	18 0.5	11 15.8	18 19.9	7 36.1	7 11.7	15 8.3	8 42.1
16 M	7 38 35.1	25 5.7	12 52.8	28 37.3	7 11.2	19 16.0	11 49.8	18 23.3	7 36.3	7 14.4	15 6.7	8 40.9
17 T	7 42 31.6	26 6.8	12 49.6	13♍27.4	8 51.0	20 31.4	12 23.7	18 26.6	7 36.4	7 17.2	15 5.2	8 39.7
18 W	7 46 28.2	27 7.9	12 46.4	27 59.8	10 30.2	21 46.8	12 57.5	18 29.7	7R36.3	7 20.0	15 3.6	8 38.5
19 T	7 50 24.7	28 8.9	12 43.2	12♎11.2	12 8.7	23 2.2	13 31.3	18 32.6	7 36.2	7 22.8	15 2.0	8 37.4
20 F	7 54 21.3	29 10.0	12 40.0	26 0.8	13 46.3	24 17.6	14 4.9	18 35.3	7 35.9	7 25.7	15 0.4	8 36.2
21 S	7 58 17.9	0♒11.1	12 36.9	9♏29.9	15 22.7	25 33.0	14 38.5	18 37.8	7 35.6	7 28.6	14 58.8	8 35.1
22 S	8 2 14.4	1 12.1	12 33.7	22 40.6	16 57.6	26 48.4	15 12.1	18 40.2	7 35.1	7 31.5	14 57.2	8 34.0
23 M	8 6 11.0	2 13.2	12 30.5	5♐35.5	18 30.5	28 3.8	15 45.5	18 42.3	7 34.5	7 34.4	14 55.5	8 32.8
24 T	8 10 7.5	3 14.2	12 27.3	18 17.0	20 1.1	29 19.2	16 18.9	18 44.3	7 33.9	7 37.4	14 53.9	8 31.7
25 W	8 14 4.1	4 15.2	12 24.2	0♑47.3	21 28.8	0♒34.6	16 52.1	18 46.1	7 33.1	7 40.4	14 52.2	8 30.6
26 T	8 18 0.6	5 16.2	12 21.0	13 7.6	22 53.1	1 50.0	17 25.3	18 47.7	7 32.2	7 43.4	14 50.6	8 29.5
27 F	8 21 57.2	6 17.2	12 17.8	25 19.3	24 13.4	3 5.4	17 58.4	18 49.1	7 31.2	7 46.5	14 48.9	8 28.4
28 S	8 25 53.7	7 18.2	12 14.6	7♒23.2	25 29.1	4 20.8	18 31.4	18 50.3	7 30.1	7 49.5	14 47.3	8 27.4
29 S	8 29 50.3	8 19.2	12 11.4	19 20.3	26 39.2	5 36.1	19 4.3	18 51.4	7 28.8	7 52.6	14 45.6	8 26.3
30 M	8 33 46.9	9 20.1	12 8.3	1♓12.0	27 43.2	6 51.5	19 37.1	18 52.2	7 27.5	7 55.8	14 43.9	8 25.3
31 T	8 37 43.4	10 21.1	12 5.1	13 0.1	28 40.2	8 6.9	20 9.8	18 52.9	7 26.1	7 58.9	14 42.2	8 24.3
						DECLINATION						
1 S	6 39 26.7	23S 5.0	5S23.8	13S14.6	24S46.9	23S29.3	11S22.2	5S34.3	0S46.7	9S47.0	16N18.4	19N55.9
4 W	6 51 16.4	22 49.4	5 20.1	3 17.4	24 21.4	23 32.6	11 57.8	5 40.0	0 47.8	9 44.4	16 19.7	19 56.3
7 S	7 3 6.1	22 29.8	5 16.4	7N55.5	23 42.1	23 29.4	12 32.5	5 45.2	0 48.5	9 41.6	16 20.9	19 56.7
10 T	7 14 55.7	22 6.1	5 12.7	16 41.0	22 48.6	23 19.7	13 6.4	5 49.8	0 48.8	9 38.8	16 22.2	19 57.2
13 F	7 26 45.4	21 38.6	5 9.0	17 46.0	21 41.0	23 3.4	13 39.5	5 53.8	0 48.7	9 35.8	16 23.6	19 57.6
16 M	7 38 35.1	21 7.3	5 5.3	8 42.7	20 19.7	22 40.8	14 11.7	5 57.2	0 48.3	9 32.7	16 25.0	19 58.1
19 T	7 50 24.7	20 32.3	5 1.6	4S47.4	18 45.6	22 11.9	14 43.0	6 0.0	0 47.5	9 29.5	16 26.4	19 58.5
22 S	8 2 14.4	19 53.9	4 57.9	15 14.4	17 0.9	21 36.9	15 13.4	6 2.2	0 46.3	9 26.2	16 27.9	19 59.0
25 W	8 14 4.1	19 12.1	4 54.2	18 29.5	15 9.0	20 56.1	15 42.9	6 3.7	0 44.7	9 22.8	16 29.4	19 59.5
28 S	8 25 53.7	18 27.1	4 50.4	14 3.5	13 15.7	20 9.7	16 11.5	6 4.6	0 42.7	9 19.4	16 30.9	19 60.0
31 T	8 37 43.4	17 39.1	4 46.7	4 31.0	11 29.6	19 17.9	16 39.0	6 4.9	0 40.4	9 15.8	16 32.4	20 0.5

FEBRUARY 1922

DAY	EPHEMERIS SIDEREAL TIME	☉	☊	☽	☿	♀	♂	♃	♄	♅	♆	♇
						LONGITUDE						
1 W	8 41 40.0	11♒22.0	12♎ 1.9	24♓47.3	29♒29.4	9♒22.2	20♏42.4	18♎53.4	7♎24.6	8♓ 2.0	14♌40.5	8♋23.2
2 T	8 45 36.5	12 22.9	11 58.7	6♈36.8	0♓ 9.9	10 37.5	21 14.9	18 53.6	7R22.9	8 5.2	14R38.9	8R22.2
3 F	8 49 33.0	13 23.8	11 55.6	18 32.9	0 41.1	11 52.8	21 47.3	18 53.7	7 21.2	8 8.4	14 37.2	8 21.2
4 S	8 53 29.6	14 24.6	11 52.4	0♉40.3	1 2.3	13 8.1	22 19.6	18R53.6	7 19.4	8 11.6	14 35.5	8 20.3
5 S	8 57 26.2	15 25.5	11 49.2	13 4.0	1 13.0	14 23.4	22 51.8	18 53.3	7 17.5	8 14.9	14 33.8	8 19.3
6 M	9 1 22.7	16 26.3	11 46.0	25 49.2	1R12.7	15 38.7	23 23.9	18 52.8	7 15.4	8 18.1	14 32.1	8 18.4
7 T	9 5 19.3	17 27.0	11 42.9	9♊ 0.4	1 1.5	16 54.0	23 55.8	18 52.2	7 13.3	8 21.4	14 30.4	8 17.5
8 W	9 9 15.8	18 27.8	11 39.7	22 40.7	0 39.4	18 9.2	24 27.7	18 51.3	7 11.1	8 24.7	14 28.7	8 16.5
9 T	9 13 12.4	19 28.5	11 36.5	6♋51.2	0 6.9	19 24.5	24 59.4	18 50.3	7 8.8	8 27.9	14 27.1	8 15.7
10 F	9 17 8.9	20 29.2	11 33.3	21 29.5	29♒24.8	20 39.7	25 31.0	18 49.0	7 6.4	8 31.3	14 25.4	8 14.8
11 S	9 21 5.5	21 29.9	11 30.1	6♌30.1	28 34.1	21 54.9	26 2.5	18 47.6	7 3.9	8 34.6	14 23.7	8 13.9
12 S	9 25 2.0	22 30.5	11 27.0	21 44.1	27 36.3	23 10.1	26 33.9	18 46.0	7 1.3	8 37.9	14 22.0	8 13.1
13 M	9 28 58.6	23 31.2	11 23.8	7♍ 0.9	26 32.9	24 25.3	27 5.2	18 44.2	6 58.6	8 41.3	14 20.4	8 12.3
14 T	9 32 55.2	24 31.8	11 20.6	22 9.9	25 25.8	25 40.5	27 36.3	18 42.2	6 55.8	8 44.6	14 18.7	8 11.4
15 W	9 36 51.7	25 32.4	11 17.4	7♎ 2.1	24 16.8	26 55.7	28 7.3	18 40.0	6 53.0	8 48.0	14 17.1	8 10.7
16 T	9 40 48.3	26 32.9	11 14.2	21 31.4	23 7.7	28 10.8	28 38.2	18 37.6	6 50.0	8 51.4	14 15.4	8 9.9
17 F	9 44 44.8	27 33.5	11 11.1	5♏35.0	22 0.3	29 26.0	29 9.0	18 35.1	6 47.0	8 54.8	14 13.8	8 9.1
18 S	9 48 41.4	28 34.0	11 7.9	19 12.6	20 56.2	0♓41.1	29 39.6	18 32.4	6 43.9	8 58.2	14 12.1	8 8.4
19 S	9 52 37.9	29 34.5	11 4.7	2♐26.1	19 56.6	1 56.3	0♐10.1	18 29.5	6 40.7	9 1.6	14 10.5	8 7.7
20 M	9 56 34.5	0♓35.0	11 1.5	15 18.4	19 2.7	3 11.4	0 40.4	18 26.4	6 37.4	9 5.0	14 8.9	8 7.0
21 T	10 0 31.0	1 35.4	10 58.4	27 52.9	18 15.2	4 26.5	1 10.5	18 23.1	6 34.1	9 8.4	14 7.3	8 6.3
22 W	10 4 27.6	2 35.9	10 55.2	10♑13.2	17 34.7	5 41.6	1 40.6	18 19.7	6 30.7	9 11.8	14 5.7	8 5.7
23 T	10 8 24.1	3 36.3	10 52.0	22 22.4	17 1.5	6 56.6	2 10.4	18 16.1	6 27.2	9 15.3	14 4.2	8 5.0
24 F	10 12 20.7	4 36.7	10 48.8	4♒23.3	16 35.7	8 11.7	2 40.2	18 12.3	6 23.6	9 18.7	14 2.6	8 4.4
25 S	10 16 17.3	5 37.0	10 45.7	16 18.1	16 17.3	9 26.8	3 9.7	18 8.3	6 20.0	9 22.1	14 1.0	8 3.8
26 S	10 20 13.8	6 37.4	10 42.5	28 9.0	16 6.1	10 41.8	3 39.1	18 4.2	6 16.2	9 25.6	13 59.5	8 3.3
27 M	10 24 10.3	7 37.7	10 39.3	9♓57.8	16 1.9	11 56.8	4 8.3	17 59.9	6 12.5	9 29.0	13 58.0	8 2.7
28 T	10 28 6.9	8 38.0	10 36.1	21 46.3	16D 4.3	13 11.8	4 37.3	17 55.4	6 8.6	9 32.5	13 56.5	8 2.2
						DECLINATION						
1 W	8 41 40.0	17S22.5	4S45.5	0S49.0	10S57.6	18S59.5	16S48.0	6S 4.8	0S39.6	9S14.6	16N32.9	20N 0.6
4 S	8 53 29.6	16 30.8	4 41.7	10N 1.9	9 37.9	18 1.1	17 14.2	6 4.2	0 36.8	9 11.0	16 34.4	20 1.1
7 T	9 5 19.3	15 36.5	4 38.0	17 28.2	8 51.3	16 58.1	17 39.4	6 2.9	0 33.7	9 7.3	16 35.9	20 1.6
10 F	9 17 8.9	14 39.9	4 34.3	16 46.1	8 44.9	15 50.8	18 3.7	6 1.1	0 30.3	9 3.6	16 37.4	20 2.1
13 M	9 28 58.6	13 41.1	4 30.6	6 21.5	9 17.3	14 39.5	18 26.9	5 58.5	0 26.6	8 59.8	16 38.9	20 2.6
16 T	9 40 48.3	12 40.2	4 26.8	7S23.6	10 17.8	13 24.7	18 49.2	5 55.4	0 22.5	8 56.0	16 40.3	20 3.0
19 S	9 52 37.9	11 37.5	4 23.1	16 35.8	11 30.2	12 6.6	19 10.4	5 51.6	0 18.3	8 52.1	16 41.8	20 3.5
22 W	10 4 27.6	10 33.1	4 19.4	17 53.2	12 40.0	10 45.5	19 30.7	5 47.3	0 13.7	8 48.3	16 43.2	20 4.0
25 S	10 16 17.3	9 27.3	4 15.6	12 0.1	13 38.0	9 21.9	19 49.9	5 42.4	0 9.0	8 44.4	16 44.6	20 4.5
28 T	10 28 6.9	8 20.1	4 11.9	1 51.0	14 20.0	7 56.1	20 8.2	5 36.9	0 4.0	8 40.5	16 45.9	20 4.9

MARCH 1922

DAY	EPHEMERIS SIDEREAL TIME	☉	☊	☽	☿	♀	♂	♃	♄	♅	♆	♇
	h m s	° ′	° ′	° ′	° ′	° ′	° ′	° ′	° ′	° ′	° ′	° ′
LONGITUDE												
1 W	10 32 3.5	9♓38.2	10♎32.9	3♈36.6	16♒13.0	14♓26.8	5♐ 6.1	17♎50.8	6♎ 4.7	9♓35.9	13♌55.0	8♋ 1.7
2 T	10 36 0.0	10 38.4	10 29.8	15 31.1	16 27.7	15 41.7	5 34.8	17R46.0	6R 0.8	9 39.4	13R53.5	8R 1.2
3 F	10 39 56.6	11 38.6	10 26.6	27 32.6	16 48.0	16 56.7	6 3.3	17 41.1	5 56.7	9 42.8	13 52.0	8 0.7
4 S	10 43 53.1	12 38.7	10 23.4	9♉44.5	17 13.6	18 11.6	6 31.5	17 36.0	5 52.7	9 46.2	13 50.6	8 0.3
5 S	10 47 49.7	13 38.9	10 20.2	22 10.6	17 44.0	19 26.5	6 59.6	17 30.7	5 48.5	9 49.7	13 49.2	7 59.9
6 M	10 51 46.2	14 38.9	10 17.1	4♊54.8	18 18.9	20 41.4	7 27.5	17 25.3	5 44.3	9 53.1	13 47.8	7 59.5
7 T	10 55 42.8	15 39.0	10 13.9	18 0.9	18 58.1	21 56.3	7 55.2	17 19.8	5 40.1	9 56.5	13 46.4	7 59.1
8 W	10 59 39.3	16 39.0	10 10.7	1♋32.0	19 41.3	23 11.1	8 22.7	17 14.2	5 35.8	9 60.0	13 45.0	7 58.7
9 T	11 3 35.9	17 39.0	10 7.5	15 29.9	20 28.1	24 25.9	8 49.9	17 8.4	5 31.5	10 3.4	13 43.7	7 58.4
10 F	11 7 32.4	18 38.9	10 4.3	29 54.0	21 18.3	25 40.7	9 17.0	17 2.4	5 27.1	10 6.8	13 42.4	7 58.1
11 S	11 11 29.0	19 38.8	10 1.2	14♌41.3	22 11.8	26 55.5	9 43.8	16 56.4	5 22.7	10 10.2	13 41.1	7 57.8
12 S	11 15 25.5	20 38.7	9 58.0	29 45.7	23 8.2	28 10.2	10 10.5	16 50.2	5 18.3	10 13.6	13 39.8	7 57.6
13 M	11 19 22.1	21 38.5	9 54.8	14♍58.5	24 7.5	29 25.0	10 36.8	16 43.9	5 13.8	10 17.0	13 38.5	7 57.3
14 T	11 23 18.6	22 38.3	9 51.6	0♎10.0	25 9.4	0♈39.7	11 3.0	16 37.5	5 9.3	10 20.4	13 37.3	7 57.1
15 W	11 27 15.2	23 38.1	9 48.4	15 10.5	26 13.9	1 54.4	11 28.9	16 31.0	5 4.8	10 23.8	13 36.1	7 56.9
16 T	11 31 11.7	24 37.8	9 45.3	29 52.0	27 20.6	3 9.0	11 54.6	16 24.4	5 0.2	10 27.2	13 34.9	7 56.8
17 F	11 35 8.3	25 37.5	9 42.1	14♏ 9.1	28 29.6	4 23.6	12 20.1	16 17.7	4 55.6	10 30.5	13 33.7	7 56.6
18 S	11 39 4.8	26 37.2	9 38.9	27 59.2	29 40.8	5 38.3	12 45.2	16 10.8	4 51.0	10 33.9	13 32.6	7 56.5
19 S	11 43 1.4	27 36.8	9 35.7	11♐22.4	0♓53.9	6 52.9	13 10.2	16 3.9	4 46.4	10 37.2	13 31.4	7 56.4
20 M	11 46 57.9	28 36.4	9 32.6	24 20.6	2 9.0	8 7.5	13 34.8	15 56.9	4 41.7	10 40.5	13 30.3	7 56.3
21 T	11 50 54.5	29 36.0	9 29.4	6♑57.1	3 25.9	9 22.0	13 59.2	15 49.8	4 37.1	10 43.8	13 29.3	7 56.3
22 W	11 54 51.0	0♈35.6	9 26.2	19 15.8	4 44.6	10 36.5	14 23.2	15 42.6	4 32.4	10 47.1	13 28.2	7 56.3
23 T	11 58 47.6	1 35.1	9 23.0	1♒21.0	6 5.1	11 51.1	14 47.0	15 35.4	4 27.7	10 50.4	13 27.2	7D56.3
24 F	12 2 44.2	2 34.6	9 19.8	13 16.8	7 27.2	13 5.6	15 10.5	15 28.1	4 23.0	10 53.7	13 26.2	7 56.3
25 S	12 6 40.7	3 34.1	9 16.7	25 6.9	8 50.9	14 20.0	15 33.7	15 20.7	4 18.3	10 56.9	13 25.3	7 56.3
26 S	12 10 37.2	4 33.5	9 13.5	6♓54.8	10 16.3	15 34.5	15 56.6	15 13.3	4 13.6	11 0.1	13 24.3	7 56.4
27 M	12 14 33.8	5 32.9	9 10.3	18 43.3	11 43.1	16 48.9	16 19.1	15 5.8	4 8.9	11 3.4	13 23.4	7 56.5
28 T	12 18 30.4	6 32.3	9 7.1	0♈34.9	13 11.5	18 3.3	16 41.3	14 58.2	4 4.2	11 6.6	13 22.5	7 56.6
29 W	12 22 26.9	7 31.6	9 4.0	12 31.9	14 41.4	19 17.7	17 3.2	14 50.6	3 59.5	11 9.7	13 21.7	7 56.8
30 T	12 26 23.5	8 30.9	9 0.8	24 36.2	16 12.8	20 32.1	17 24.7	14 43.0	3 54.9	11 12.9	13 20.9	7 56.9
31 F	12 30 20.0	9 30.2	8 57.6	6♉49.6	17 45.6	21 46.4	17 45.9	14 35.4	3 50.2	11 16.0	13 20.1	7 57.1
DECLINATION												
1 W	10 32 3.5	7S57.5	4S10.6	1N52.5	14S30.3	7S27.1	20S14.1	5S35.0	0S 2.3	8S39.2	16N46.4	20N 5.1
4 S	10 43 53.1	6 49.0	4 6.9	12 10.5	14 49.8	5 58.8	20 31.1	5 28.8	0N 3.0	8 35.3	16 47.7	20 5.5
7 T	10 55 42.8	5 39.6	4 3.2	18 0.7	14 52.9	4 29.1	20 47.2	5 22.1	0 8.3	8 31.4	16 48.9	20 6.0
10 F	11 7 32.4	4 29.5	3 59.4	15 22.4	14 40.5	2 58.3	21 2.5	5 15.1	0 13.8	8 27.5	16 50.1	20 6.4
13 M	11 19 22.1	3 19.0	3 55.7	3 57.3	14 13.5	1 26.8	21 16.8	5 7.6	0 19.4	8 23.7	16 51.2	20 6.8
16 T	11 31 11.7	2 8.0	3 51.9	9S38.5	13 32.6	0N 5.1	21 30.4	4 59.7	0 25.1	8 19.9	16 52.3	20 7.3
19 S	11 43 1.4	0 57.0	3 48.2	17 29.8	12 38.5	1 37.2	21 43.2	4 51.6	0 30.8	8 16.1	16 53.3	20 7.7
22 W	11 54 51.0	0N14.2	3 44.4	16 54.6	11 31.9	3 9.0	21 55.3	4 43.1	0 36.5	8 12.3	16 54.2	20 8.1
25 S	12 6 40.7	1 25.1	3 40.7	9 42.3	10 13.3	4 40.2	22 6.7	4 34.5	0 42.2	8 8.7	16 55.1	20 8.5
28 T	12 18 30.4	2 35.8	3 36.9	0N55.4	8 43.2	6 10.6	22 17.5	4 25.7	0 47.9	8 5.0	16 55.9	20 8.8
31 F	12 30 20.0	3 46.0	3 33.2	11 26.1	7 2.1	7 39.8	22 27.8	4 16.7	0 53.5	8 1.5	16 56.6	20 9.2

APRIL 1922

DAY	SID. TIME	☉	☊	☽	☿	♀	♂	♃	♄	♅	♆	♇
LONGITUDE												
1 S	12 34 16.6	10♈29.4	8♎54.4	19♉14.1	19♓19.8	23♈ 0.7	18♐ 6.7	14♎27.7	3♎45.5	11♓19.1	13♌19.3	7♋57.3
2 S	12 38 13.1	11 28.6	8 51.2	1♊51.7	20 55.6	24 15.0	18 27.1	14R20.0	3R40.9	11 22.2	13R18.6	7 57.6
3 M	12 42 9.7	12 27.8	8 48.1	14 44.3	22 32.7	25 29.2	18 47.2	14 12.3	3 36.3	11 25.3	13 17.9	7 57.8
4 T	12 46 6.2	13 26.9	8 44.9	27 54.1	24 11.3	26 43.4	19 6.9	14 4.6	3 31.7	11 28.4	13 17.2	7 58.1
5 W	12 50 2.8	14 26.0	8 41.7	11♋22.8	25 51.4	27 57.6	19 26.2	13 56.8	3 27.1	11 31.4	13 16.6	7 58.4
6 T	12 53 59.3	15 25.0	8 38.5	25 11.6	27 32.9	29 11.8	19 45.0	13 49.1	3 22.5	11 34.4	13 16.0	7 58.7
7 F	12 57 55.9	16 24.1	8 35.3	9♌20.5	29 15.9	0♉25.9	20 3.5	13 41.4	3 18.0	11 37.4	13 15.4	7 59.1
8 S	13 1 52.4	17 23.0	8 32.2	23 48.1	1♈ 0.3	1 40.0	20 21.6	13 33.7	3 13.5	11 40.3	13 14.8	7 59.5
9 S	13 5 49.0	18 21.9	8 29.0	8♍31.0	2 46.2	2 54.1	20 39.2	13 26.0	3 9.1	11 43.2	13 14.3	7 59.9
10 M	13 9 45.5	19 20.8	8 25.8	23 23.9	4 33.6	4 8.1	20 56.4	13 18.4	3 4.6	11 46.1	13 13.8	8 0.3
11 T	13 13 42.1	20 19.7	8 22.6	8♎19.9	6 22.5	5 22.1	21 13.2	13 10.8	3 0.3	11 49.0	13 13.4	8 0.7
12 W	13 17 38.7	21 18.5	8 19.5	23 11.1	8 12.9	6 36.1	21 29.5	13 3.2	2 55.9	11 51.9	13 13.0	8 1.2
13 T	13 21 35.2	22 17.3	8 16.3	7♏49.7	10 4.9	7 50.1	21 45.4	12 55.6	2 51.6	11 54.7	13 12.6	8 1.7
14 F	13 25 31.7	23 16.0	8 13.1	22 9.3	11 58.3	9 4.0	22 0.7	12 48.1	2 47.4	11 57.5	13 12.2	8 2.2
15 S	13 29 28.3	24 14.8	8 9.9	6♐ 5.3	13 53.3	10 17.9	22 15.6	12 40.7	2 43.2	12 0.2	13 11.9	8 2.7
16 S	13 33 24.9	25 13.5	8 6.7	19 35.7	15 49.7	11 31.8	22 30.0	12 33.2	2 39.0	12 3.0	13 11.6	8 3.3
17 M	13 37 21.4	26 12.1	8 3.6	2♑40.7	17 47.7	12 45.6	22 43.9	12 25.9	2 34.9	12 5.7	13 11.3	8 3.9
18 T	13 41 18.0	27 10.8	8 0.4	15 22.2	19 47.2	13 59.4	22 57.2	12 18.6	2 30.8	12 8.3	13 11.1	8 4.5
19 W	13 45 14.5	28 9.4	7 57.2	27 43.9	21 48.1	15 13.2	23 10.0	12 11.4	2 26.8	12 11.0	13 10.9	8 5.1
20 T	13 49 11.0	29 8.0	7 54.0	9♒49.9	23 50.3	16 27.0	23 22.3	12 4.3	2 22.9	12 13.6	13 10.7	8 5.7
21 F	13 53 7.6	0♉ 6.5	7 50.9	21 45.2	25 53.9	17 40.7	23 34.0	11 57.2	2 19.0	12 16.2	13 10.6	8 6.4
22 S	13 57 4.2	1 5.1	7 47.7	3♓34.4	27 58.7	18 54.4	23 45.1	11 50.2	2 15.2	12 18.7	13 10.5	8 7.1
23 S	14 1 0.7	2 3.5	7 44.5	15 22.2	0♉ 4.6	20 8.1	23 55.7	11 43.3	2 11.4	12 21.2	13 10.4	8 7.8
24 M	14 4 57.3	3 2.0	7 41.3	27 12.6	2 11.5	21 21.8	24 5.6	11 36.5	2 7.7	12 23.7	13 10.4	8 8.5
25 T	14 8 53.8	4 0.5	7 38.1	9♈ 9.3	4 19.3	22 35.4	24 14.9	11 29.8	2 4.1	12 26.1	13D10.4	8 9.2
26 W	14 12 50.4	4 58.9	7 35.0	21 15.1	6 27.6	23 49.0	24 23.7	11 23.2	2 0.5	12 28.5	13 10.5	8 10.0
27 T	14 16 46.9	5 57.3	7 31.8	3♉32.1	8 36.4	25 2.6	24 31.7	11 16.7	1 57.0	12 30.9	13 10.5	8 10.8
28 F	14 20 43.5	6 55.6	7 28.6	16 1.9	10 45.3	26 16.1	24 39.2	11 10.3	1 53.6	12 33.2	13 10.6	8 11.6
29 S	14 24 40.0	7 53.9	7 25.4	28 45.2	12 54.1	27 29.6	24 45.9	11 4.1	1 50.3	12 35.5	13 10.8	8 12.4
30 S	14 28 36.6	8 52.2	7 22.3	11♊42.3	15 2.6	28 43.1	24 52.1	10 57.9	1 47.0	12 37.8	13 10.9	8 13.3
DECLINATION												
1 S	12 34 16.6	4N 9.3	3S31.9	14N13.4	6S26.0	8N 9.1	22S31.1	4S13.8	0N55.3	8S 0.3	16N56.9	20N 9.3
4 T	12 46 6.2	5 18.6	3 28.2	18 13.7	4 30.8	9 36.1	22 40.7	4 4.8	1 0.8	7 56.9	16 57.5	20 9.6
7 F	12 57 55.9	6 27.0	3 24.4	13 31.3	2 25.8	11 1.1	22 49.9	3 55.9	1 6.2	7 53.5	16 58.0	20 10.0
10 M	13 9 45.5	7 34.5	3 20.7	1 19.8	0 11.4	12 23.8	22 58.8	3 47.0	1 11.3	7 50.2	16 58.5	20 10.3
13 T	13 21 35.2	8 40.8	3 16.9	11S41.4	2N11.5	13 43.8	23 7.5	3 38.3	1 16.4	7 47.0	16 58.9	20 10.6
16 S	13 33 24.9	9 45.8	3 13.1	18 4.1	4 42.0	15 0.7	23 16.0	3 29.8	1 21.2	7 43.9	16 59.2	20 10.9
19 W	13 45 14.5	10 49.3	3 9.4	15 44.1	7 18.2	16 14.3	23 24.5	3 21.6	1 25.8	7 40.9	16 59.4	20 11.1
22 S	13 57 4.2	11 51.3	3 5.6	7 22.3	9 57.9	17 24.3	23 32.9	3 13.6	1 30.1	7 38.0	16 59.5	20 11.4
25 T	14 8 53.8	12 51.5	3 1.8	3N35.5	12 37.7	18 30.2	23 41.3	3 6.0	1 34.2	7 35.3	16 59.5	20 11.6
28 F	14 20 43.5	13 49.8	2 58.1	13 35.7	15 13.0	19 31.8	23 49.6	2 58.8	1 38.0	7 32.6	16 59.5	20 11.8

MAY 1922

LONGITUDE

DAY	EPHEMERIS SIDEREAL TIME	☉	☊	☽	☿	♀	♂	♃	♄	♅	♆	♇
	h m s	° ′	° ′	° ′	° ′	° ′	° ′	° ′	° ′	° ′	° ′	° ′
1 M	14 32 33.2	9♉50.5	7♎19.1	24♊53.2	17♉10.4	29♉56.5	24♐57.5	10♎51.9	1♎43.8	12♓40.0	13♌11.1	8♋14.1
2 T	14 36 29.7	10 48.7	7 15.9	8♋17.3	19 17.3	1♊ 9.9	25 2.3	10R46.0	1R40.7	12 42.2	13 11.4	8 15.0
3 W	14 40 26.2	11 46.9	7 12.7	21 54.5	21 22.9	2 23.3	25 6.4	10 40.2	1 37.7	12 44.4	13 11.6	8 15.9
4 T	14 44 22.8	12 45.1	7 9.5	5♌44.1	23 26.9	3 36.7	25 9.8	10 34.6	1 34.7	12 46.5	13 11.9	8 16.8
5 F	14 48 19.4	13 43.2	7 6.4	19 45.7	25 29.0	4 50.0	25 12.5	10 29.1	1 31.8	12 48.5	13 12.3	8 17.8
6 S	14 52 15.9	14 41.3	7 3.2	3♍58.2	27 29.1	6 3.3	25 14.4	10 23.7	1 29.1	12 50.6	13 12.6	8 18.8
7 S	14 56 12.5	15 39.4	7 0.0	18 19.9	29 26.8	7 16.5	25 15.7	10 18.5	1 26.4	12 52.6	13 13.0	8 19.7
8 M	15 0 9.0	16 37.4	6 56.8	2♎48.1	1♊21.8	8 29.7	25 16.3	10 13.4	1 23.7	12 54.5	13 13.5	8 20.7
9 T	15 4 5.6	17 35.4	6 53.7	17 19.1	3 14.2	9 42.9	25R16.1	10 8.5	1 21.2	12 56.4	13 13.9	8 21.7
10 W	15 8 2.1	18 33.4	6 50.5	1♏47.8	5 3.6	10 56.0	25 15.2	10 3.7	1 18.8	12 58.3	13 14.4	8 22.8
11 T	15 11 58.7	19 31.3	6 47.3	16 8.6	6 49.9	12 9.1	25 13.5	9 59.1	1 16.4	13 0.1	13 15.0	8 23.8
12 F	15 15 55.2	20 29.2	6 44.1	0♐16.1	8 33.0	13 22.2	25 11.1	9 54.6	1 14.2	13 1.9	13 15.5	8 24.9
13 S	15 19 51.8	21 27.1	6 40.9	14 5.5	10 12.8	14 35.2	25 8.0	9 50.3	1 12.0	13 3.6	13 16.1	8 25.9
14 S	15 23 48.3	22 25.0	6 37.8	27 33.5	11 49.2	15 48.2	25 4.1	9 46.2	1 9.9	13 5.3	13 16.8	8 27.0
15 M	15 27 44.9	23 22.8	6 34.6	10♑38.9	13 22.2	17 1.2	24 59.4	9 42.2	1 7.9	13 7.0	13 17.4	8 28.2
16 T	15 31 41.5	24 20.6	6 31.4	23 22.2	14 51.6	18 14.1	24 54.0	9 38.4	1 6.0	13 8.6	13 18.1	8 29.3
17 W	15 35 38.0	25 18.4	6 28.2	5♒45.9	16 17.4	19 27.0	24 47.8	9 34.7	1 4.3	13 10.2	13 18.8	8 30.4
18 T	15 39 34.6	26 16.2	6 25.1	17 53.5	17 39.7	20 39.9	24 40.8	9 31.2	1 2.5	13 11.7	13 19.6	8 31.6
19 F	15 43 31.1	27 14.0	6 21.9	29 49.7	18 58.2	21 52.7	24 33.1	9 27.9	1 0.9	13 13.2	13 20.4	8 32.7
20 S	15 47 27.7	28 11.7	6 18.7	11♓39.6	20 13.0	23 5.5	24 24.7	9 24.7	0 59.4	13 14.6	13 21.2	8 33.9
21 S	15 51 24.2	29 9.5	6 15.5	23 28.3	21 24.0	24 18.3	24 15.5	9 21.7	0 58.0	13 16.0	13 22.0	8 35.1
22 M	15 55 20.8	0♊ 7.2	6 12.3	5♈21.1	22 31.2	25 31.0	24 5.5	9 18.9	0 56.7	13 17.4	13 22.9	8 36.3
23 T	15 59 17.3	1 4.9	6 9.2	17 22.5	23 34.5	26 43.7	23 54.9	9 16.3	0 55.5	13 18.7	13 23.8	8 37.6
24 W	16 3 13.9	2 2.5	6 6.0	29 36.4	24 33.8	27 56.4	23 43.5	9 13.8	0 54.4	13 19.9	13 24.7	8 38.8
25 T	16 7 10.4	3 0.2	6 2.8	12♉ 5.7	25 29.1	29 9.0	23 31.4	9 11.5	0 53.4	13 21.1	13 25.7	8 40.1
26 F	16 11 7.0	3 57.8	5 59.6	24 52.2	26 20.3	0♋21.6	23 18.7	9 9.4	0 52.5	13 22.3	13 26.7	8 41.3
27 S	16 15 3.5	4 55.4	5 56.5	7♊56.3	27 7.3	1 34.2	23 5.2	9 7.5	0 51.6	13 23.4	13 27.7	8 42.6
28 S	16 19 0.1	5 53.0	5 53.3	21 16.9	27 50.0	2 46.7	22 51.2	9 5.7	0 50.9	13 24.5	13 28.8	8 43.9
29 M	16 22 56.6	6 50.6	5 50.1	4♋52.1	28 28.5	3 59.2	22 36.5	9 4.2	0 50.3	13 25.5	13 29.9	8 45.2
30 T	16 26 53.2	7 48.2	5 46.9	18 39.1	29 2.5	5 11.7	22 21.3	9 2.8	0 49.8	13 26.5	13 31.0	8 46.5
31 W	16 30 49.8	8 45.7	5 43.8	2♌34.9	29 32.1	6 24.1	22 5.5	9 1.6	0 49.4	13 27.4	13 32.1	8 47.8

DECLINATION

DAY	EPHEMERIS SIDEREAL TIME	☉	☊	☽	☿	♀	♂	♃	♄	♅	♆	♇
1 M	14 32 33.2	14N46.1	2S54.3	18N17.2	17N38.4	20N28.7	23S58.7	2S52.0	1N41.5	7S30.1	16N59.4	20N12.0
4 T	14 44 22.8	15 40.2	2 50.5	14 21.5	19 48.5	21 20.7	24 7.6	2 45.7	1 44.7	7 27.7	16 59.2	20 12.2
7 S	14 56 12.5	16 31.9	2 46.8	2 58.7	21 39.0	22 7.4	24 16.7	2 39.9	1 47.5	7 25.5	16 58.9	20 12.4
10 W	15 8 2.1	17 21.2	2 43.0	10S 9.3	23 7.3	22 48.6	24 26.0	2 34.7	1 50.1	7 23.4	16 58.5	20 12.5
13 S	15 19 51.8	18 7.9	2 39.2	17 49.0	24 13.0	23 24.0	24 35.6	2 30.0	1 52.3	7 21.4	16 58.0	20 12.6
16 T	15 31 41.5	18 51.8	2 35.5	16 32.0	24 56.9	23 53.5	24 45.2	2 25.9	1 54.1	7 19.6	16 57.5	20 12.7
19 F	15 43 31.1	19 32.8	2 31.7	8 34.6	25 21.1	24 16.9	24 54.9	2 22.4	1 55.6	7 18.0	16 56.9	20 12.8
22 M	15 55 20.8	20 10.9	2 27.9	2N18.7	25 27.8	24 33.9	25 4.6	2 19.6	1 56.7	7 16.5	16 56.2	20 12.9
25 T	16 7 10.4	20 45.9	2 24.1	12 42.1	25 19.5	24 44.6	25 14.0	2 17.3	1 57.4	7 15.1	16 55.4	20 12.9
28 S	16 19 0.1	21 17.7	2 20.4	18 17.0	24 58.5	24 48.8	25 23.1	2 15.8	1 57.8	7 13.9	16 54.5	20 13.0
31 W	16 30 49.8	21 46.2	2 16.6	15 8.2	24 27.1	24 46.6	25 31.7	2 14.8	1 57.8	7 12.9	16 53.6	20 13.0

JUNE 1922

LONGITUDE

DAY	EPHEMERIS SIDEREAL TIME	☉	☊	☽	☿	♀	♂	♃	♄	♅	♆	♇
1 T	16 34 46.3	9♊43.2	5♎40.6	16♌36.6	29♊57.2	7♋36.4	21♐49.2	9♎ 0.5	0♎49.1	13♓28.3	13♌33.3	8♋49.2
2 F	16 38 42.9	10 40.7	5 37.4	0♍42.2	0♋17.6	8 48.8	21R32.4	8R59.7	0R48.9	13 29.1	13 34.5	8 50.5
3 S	16 42 39.4	11 38.2	5 34.2	14 50.0	0 33.5	10 1.0	21 15.1	8 59.0	0 48.8	13 29.9	13 35.7	8 51.9
4 S	16 46 36.0	12 35.6	5 31.1	28 58.9	0 44.7	11 13.3	20 57.4	8 58.5	0 48.8	13 30.6	13 37.0	8 53.2
5 M	16 50 32.6	13 33.1	5 27.9	13♎ 7.5	0 51.3	12 25.5	20 39.4	8 58.2	0D48.9	13 31.3	13 38.2	8 54.6
6 T	16 54 29.1	14 30.5	5 24.7	27 14.3	0 53.3	13 37.6	20 21.0	8 58.1	0 49.1	13 31.9	13 39.5	8 56.0
7 W	16 58 25.7	15 27.9	5 21.5	11♏17.2	0R50.8	14 49.7	20 2.3	8D58.2	0 49.4	13 32.5	13 40.9	8 57.4
8 T	17 2 22.2	16 25.2	5 18.3	25 13.1	0 43.9	16 1.8	19 43.3	8 58.4	0 49.8	13 33.1	13 42.3	8 58.8
9 F	17 6 18.8	17 22.6	5 15.2	8♐58.6	0 32.7	17 13.8	19 24.1	8 58.8	0 50.3	13 33.6	13 43.6	9 0.2
10 S	17 10 15.3	18 19.9	5 12.0	22 30.4	0 17.4	18 25.7	19 4.7	8 59.4	0 50.9	13 34.0	13 45.0	9 1.6
11 S	17 14 11.9	19 17.2	5 8.8	5♑45.5	29♊58.4	19 37.7	18 45.2	9 0.2	0 51.7	13 34.4	13 46.5	9 3.0
12 M	17 18 8.5	20 14.6	5 5.6	18 42.3	29 35.9	20 49.5	18 25.6	9 1.2	0 52.5	13 34.8	13 47.9	9 4.5
13 T	17 22 5.0	21 11.9	5 2.5	1♒20.5	29 10.2	22 1.4	18 5.9	9 2.3	0 53.4	13 35.1	13 49.4	9 5.9
14 W	17 26 1.6	22 9.2	4 59.3	13 41.5	28 41.9	23 13.1	17 46.2	9 3.6	0 54.4	13 35.3	13 50.9	9 7.4
15 T	17 29 58.1	23 6.5	4 56.1	25 48.0	28 11.3	24 24.9	17 26.6	9 5.1	0 55.5	13 35.5	13 52.5	9 8.8
16 F	17 33 54.7	24 3.8	4 52.9	7♓43.7	27 39.0	25 36.5	17 7.0	9 6.7	0 56.7	13 35.7	13 54.0	9 10.3
17 S	17 37 51.3	25 1.0	4 49.8	19 33.5	27 5.4	26 48.2	16 47.5	9 8.6	0 58.0	13 35.8	13 55.6	9 11.7
18 S	17 41 47.8	25 58.3	4 46.6	1♈22.6	26 31.3	27 59.8	16 28.2	9 10.6	0 59.5	13 35.9	13 57.2	9 13.2
19 M	17 45 44.3	26 55.6	4 43.4	13 16.4	25 57.1	29 11.3	16 9.1	9 12.8	1 1.0	13 35.9	13 58.8	9 14.7
20 T	17 49 40.9	27 52.9	4 40.2	25 20.3	25 23.5	0♌22.8	15 50.3	9 15.1	1 2.6	13R35.8	14 0.5	9 16.2
21 W	17 53 37.5	28 50.1	4 37.0	7♉39.0	24 50.9	1 34.2	15 31.8	9 17.6	1 4.3	13 35.8	14 2.1	9 17.7
22 T	17 57 34.0	29 47.4	4 33.9	20 16.6	24 20.1	2 45.6	15 13.6	9 20.3	1 6.1	13 35.6	14 3.8	9 19.1
23 F	18 1 30.6	0♋44.6	4 30.7	3♊15.6	23 51.4	3 57.0	14 55.8	9 23.2	1 8.0	13 35.4	14 5.5	9 20.6
24 S	18 5 27.1	1 41.9	4 27.5	16 36.7	23 25.5	5 8.3	14 38.5	9 26.2	1 10.0	13 35.2	14 7.3	9 22.1
25 S	18 9 23.7	2 39.1	4 24.3	0♋18.8	23 2.7	6 19.5	14 21.6	9 29.4	1 12.1	13 34.9	14 9.0	9 23.6
26 M	18 13 20.2	3 36.4	4 21.2	14 18.7	22 43.4	7 30.7	14 5.2	9 32.8	1 14.3	13 34.6	14 10.8	9 25.1
27 T	18 17 16.8	4 33.6	4 18.0	28 31.6	22 28.0	8 41.8	13 49.4	9 36.3	1 16.6	13 34.2	14 12.6	9 26.6
28 W	18 21 13.4	5 30.9	4 14.8	12♌51.9	22 16.7	9 52.9	13 34.2	9 40.0	1 18.9	13 33.8	14 14.4	9 28.1
29 T	18 25 9.9	6 28.1	4 11.6	27 14.4	22 9.9	11 3.9	13 19.6	9 43.9	1 21.4	13 33.3	14 16.2	9 29.6
30 F	18 29 6.4	7 25.3	4 8.4	11♍34.5	22 7.7	12 14.8	13 5.7	9 47.9	1 24.0	13 32.8	14 18.1	9 31.1

DECLINATION

DAY	EPHEMERIS SIDEREAL TIME	☉	☊	☽	☿	♀	♂	♃	♄	♅	♆	♇
1 T	16 34 46.3	21N54.9	2S15.3	12N 8.7	24N14.7	24N44.4	25S34.4	2S14.7	1N57.7	7S12.6	16N53.2	20N13.0
4 S	16 46 36.0	22 18.8	2 11.6	0S12.4	23 32.6	24 33.5	25 42.0	2 14.6	1 57.2	7 11.8	16 52.2	20 13.0
7 W	16 58 25.7	22 39.2	2 7.8	12 27.9	22 45.1	24 16.4	25 48.8	2 15.2	1 56.4	7 11.2	16 51.1	20 13.0
10 S	17 10 15.3	22 56.1	2 4.0	18 20.8	21 54.5	23 53.0	25 54.6	2 16.4	1 55.1	7 10.7	16 49.9	20 12.9
13 T	17 22 5.0	23 9.3	2 0.2	15 26.5	21 3.5	23 23.5	25 59.3	2 18.2	1 53.5	7 10.4	16 48.7	20 12.9
16 F	17 33 54.7	23 18.8	1 56.4	6 30.3	20 15.3	22 48.1	26 2.9	2 20.7	1 51.6	7 10.3	16 47.4	20 12.8
19 M	17 45 44.3	23 24.7	1 52.7	4N34.8	19 33.6	22 7.1	26 5.5	2 23.8	1 49.3	7 10.3	16 46.0	20 12.7
22 T	17 57 34.0	23 26.8	1 48.9	14 22.0	19 1.8	21 20.7	26 7.2	2 27.5	1 46.6	7 10.5	16 44.6	20 12.6
25 S	18 9 23.7	23 25.2	1 45.1	18 26.9	18 42.7	20 29.2	26 8.0	2 31.8	1 43.6	7 10.9	16 43.1	20 12.5
28 W	18 21 13.4	23 19.9	1 41.3	13 12.0	18 37.8	19 32.8	26 8.1	2 36.6	1 40.3	7 11.5	16 41.6	20 12.4

JULY 1922

LONGITUDE

DAY	EPHEMERIS SIDEREAL TIME h m s	☉ ° ′	☊ ° ′	☽ ° ′	☿ ° ′	♀ ° ′	♂ ° ′	♃ ° ′	♄ ° ′	♅ ° ′	♆ ° ′	♇ ° ′
1 S	18 33 3.0	8♋22.5	4♎ 5.3	25♍49.2	22♊10.2	13♌25.7	12♐52.4	9♎52.1	1♎26.7	13♓32.3	14♌20.0	9♋32.7
2 S	18 36 59.6	9 19.7	4 2.1	9♎56.6	22D17.6	14 36.6	12R39.9	9 56.5	1 29.4	13R31.7	14 21.8	9 34.2
3 M	18 40 56.2	10 16.9	3 58.9	23 55.8	22 29.9	15 47.3	12 28.1	10 1.0	1 32.3	13 31.0	14 23.7	9 35.7
4 T	18 44 52.7	11 14.1	3 55.7	7♏46.4	22 47.2	16 58.0	12 17.0	10 5.6	1 35.2	13 30.3	14 25.7	9 37.2
5 W	18 48 49.2	12 11.3	3 52.6	21 28.2	23 9.5	18 8.6	12 6.7	10 10.4	1 38.2	13 29.6	14 27.6	9 38.7
6 T	18 52 45.8	13 8.5	3 49.4	5♐ 0.4	23 36.8	19 19.1	11 57.2	10 15.4	1 41.4	13 28.8	14 29.5	9 40.2
7 F	18 56 42.4	14 5.7	3 46.2	18 21.9	24 9.1	20 29.6	11 48.4	10 20.5	1 44.6	13 27.9	14 31.5	9 41.7
8 S	19 0 38.9	15 2.8	3 43.0	1♑31.3	24 46.4	21 40.0	11 40.5	10 25.8	1 47.8	13 27.0	14 33.5	9 43.2
9 S	19 4 35.5	16 0.0	3 39.9	14 27.2	25 28.6	22 50.3	11 33.4	10 31.2	1 51.2	13 26.1	14 35.5	9 44.7
10 M	19 8 32.1	16 57.2	3 36.7	27 8.9	26 15.6	24 0.6	11 27.1	10 36.7	1 54.7	13 25.2	14 37.5	9 46.2
11 T	19 12 28.6	17 54.4	3 33.5	9♒36.0	27 7.5	25 10.8	11 21.6	10 42.5	1 58.2	13 24.2	14 39.5	9 47.7
12 W	19 16 25.1	18 51.6	3 30.3	21 49.5	28 4.2	26 20.9	11 16.9	10 48.3	2 1.9	13 23.1	14 41.5	9 49.2
13 T	19 20 21.7	19 48.8	3 27.2	3♓51.3	29 5.5	27 30.9	11 13.1	10 54.3	2 5.6	13 22.0	14 43.6	9 50.7
14 F	19 24 18.3	20 46.0	3 24.0	15 44.5	0♋11.5	28 40.8	11 10.1	11 0.4	2 9.4	13 20.9	14 45.6	9 52.2
15 S	19 28 14.8	21 43.2	3 20.8	27 32.8	1 22.1	29 50.7	11 7.9	11 6.7	2 13.3	13 19.7	14 47.7	9 53.6
16 S	19 32 11.4	22 40.5	3 17.6	9♈21.1	2 37.2	1♍ 0.5	11 6.6	11 13.1	2 17.2	13 18.5	14 49.8	9 55.1
17 M	19 36 7.9	23 37.7	3 14.4	21 14.5	3 56.8	2 10.2	11 6.1	11 19.6	2 21.3	13 17.2	14 51.9	9 56.6
18 T	19 40 4.5	24 34.9	3 11.3	3♉18.3	5 20.6	3 19.8	11D 6.4	11 26.3	2 25.4	13 15.9	14 54.0	9 58.1
19 W	19 44 1.1	25 32.2	3 8.1	15 37.8	6 48.8	4 29.3	11 7.6	11 33.1	2 29.6	13 14.5	14 56.1	9 59.5
20 T	19 47 57.6	26 29.5	3 4.9	28 17.9	8 21.0	5 38.8	11 9.6	11 40.1	2 33.9	13 13.2	14 58.2	10 1.0
21 F	19 51 54.2	27 26.8	3 1.7	11♊21.9	9 57.2	6 48.2	11 12.5	11 47.2	2 38.3	13 11.7	15 0.4	10 2.4
22 S	19 55 50.7	28 24.1	2 58.6	24 51.8	11 37.3	7 57.5	11 16.1	11 54.4	2 42.7	13 10.3	15 2.5	10 3.9
23 S	19 59 47.3	29 21.4	2 55.4	8♋47.1	13 21.0	9 6.6	11 20.6	12 1.7	2 47.2	13 8.8	15 4.7	10 5.3
24 M	20 3 43.8	0♌18.7	2 52.2	23 4.7	15 8.2	10 15.7	11 25.9	12 9.2	2 51.8	13 7.2	15 6.8	10 6.7
25 T	20 7 40.4	1 16.0	2 49.0	7♌39.2	16 58.5	11 24.8	11 32.0	12 16.8	2 56.5	13 5.7	15 9.0	10 8.2
26 W	20 11 36.9	2 13.4	2 45.9	22 23.4	18 51.8	12 33.7	11 38.9	12 24.5	3 1.2	13 4.1	15 11.2	10 9.6
27 T	20 15 33.5	3 10.7	2 42.7	7♍ 9.6	20 47.8	13 42.5	11 46.6	12 32.3	3 6.0	13 2.4	15 13.4	10 11.0
28 F	20 19 30.0	4 8.1	2 39.5	21 50.7	22 46.1	14 51.2	11 55.1	12 40.3	3 10.9	13 0.7	15 15.6	10 12.4
29 S	20 23 26.6	5 5.5	2 36.3	6♎21.4	24 46.4	15 59.8	12 4.4	12 48.4	3 15.8	12 59.0	15 17.8	10 13.8
30 S	20 27 23.2	6 2.8	2 33.1	20 38.1	26 48.3	17 8.3	12 14.4	12 56.6	3 20.9	12 57.3	15 20.0	10 15.2
31 M	20 31 19.7	7 0.2	2 30.0	4♏39.2	28 51.6	18 16.7	12 25.2	13 4.9	3 26.0	12 55.5	15 22.2	10 16.5

DECLINATION

DAY	EPHEMERIS SIDEREAL TIME h m s	☉	☊	☽	☿	♀	♂	♃	♄	♅	♆	♇
1 S	18 33 3.0	23N10.9	1S37.5	1N 1.2	18N46.9	18N31.9	26S 7.8	2S42.1	1N36.6	7S12.2	16N40.0	20N12.2
4 T	18 44 52.7	22 58.3	1 33.7	11S25.9	19 8.5	17 26.8	26 7.2	2 48.1	1 32.6	7 13.0	16 38.4	20 12.1
7 F	18 56 42.4	22 42.0	1 30.0	18 6.3	19 40.2	16 17.8	26 6.7	2 54.6	1 28.3	7 14.0	16 36.7	20 11.9
10 M	19 8 32.1	22 22.3	1 26.2	16 14.4	20 18.5	15 5.2	26 6.2	3 1.6	1 23.7	7 15.2	16 35.0	20 11.7
13 T	19 20 21.7	21 59.0	1 22.4	7 50.5	20 59.5	13 49.3	26 6.0	3 9.1	1 18.8	7 16.5	16 33.2	20 11.6
16 S	19 32 11.4	21 32.4	1 18.6	3N 7.9	21 38.6	12 30.5	26 6.3	3 17.1	1 13.6	7 17.9	16 31.4	20 11.4
19 W	19 44 1.1	21 2.4	1 14.8	13 10.6	22 10.9	11 9.1	26 6.9	3 25.6	1 8.2	7 19.5	16 29.6	20 11.2
22 S	19 55 50.0	20 29.2	1 11.0	18 19.0	22 31.0	9 45.3	26 8.1	3 34.5	1 2.5	7 21.3	16 27.8	20 10.9
25 T	20 7 40.4	19 53.0	1 7.2	14 23.3	22 33.7	8 19.6	26 9.7	3 43.8	0 56.5	7 23.1	16 25.9	20 10.7
28 F	20 19 30.0	19 13.7	1 3.4	2 27.8	22 15.0	6 52.1	26 11.9	3 53.5	0 50.3	7 25.1	16 24.0	20 10.5
31 M	20 31 19.7	18 31.7	0 59.7	10S24.8	21 32.5	5 23.2	26 14.6	4 3.6	0 43.9	7 27.1	16 22.1	20 10.3

AUGUST 1922

LONGITUDE

DAY	EPHEMERIS SIDEREAL TIME h m s	☉ ° ′	☊ ° ′	☽ ° ′	☿ ° ′	♀ ° ′	♂ ° ′	♃ ° ′	♄ ° ′	♅ ° ′	♆ ° ′	♇ ° ′
1 T	20 35 16.2	7♌57.6	2♎26.8	18♏24.4	0♌55.8	19♍25.0	12♐36.7	13♎13.3	3♎31.1	12♓53.7	15♌24.4	10♋17.9
2 W	20 39 12.8	8 55.0	2 23.6	1♐54.2	3 0.7	20 33.2	12 48.9	13 21.8	3 36.3	12R51.9	15 26.6	10 19.3
3 T	20 43 9.4	9 52.4	2 20.4	15 9.5	5 6.0	21 41.2	13 1.8	13 30.5	3 41.6	12 50.0	15 28.8	10 20.6
4 F	20 47 6.0	10 49.9	2 17.3	28 11.2	7 11.3	22 49.1	13 15.5	13 39.2	3 47.0	12 48.1	15 31.0	10 21.9
5 S	20 51 2.5	11 47.3	2 14.1	11♑ 0.0	9 16.4	23 56.9	13 29.8	13 48.1	3 52.4	12 46.2	15 33.2	10 23.3
6 S	20 54 59.0	12 44.8	2 10.9	23 36.5	11 21.1	25 4.6	13 44.7	13 57.1	3 57.9	12 44.2	15 35.4	10 24.6
7 M	20 58 55.6	13 42.2	2 7.7	6♒ 1.1	13 25.1	26 12.1	14 0.4	14 6.1	4 3.4	12 42.2	15 37.7	10 25.9
8 T	21 2 52.2	14 39.7	2 4.5	18 14.8	15 28.3	27 19.5	14 16.7	14 15.3	4 9.0	12 40.2	15 39.9	10 27.2
9 W	21 6 48.7	15 37.2	2 1.4	0♓18.5	17 30.5	28 26.8	14 33.6	14 24.6	4 14.7	12 38.2	15 42.1	10 28.4
10 T	21 10 45.3	16 34.7	1 58.2	12 14.0	19 31.7	29 33.9	14 51.1	14 34.0	4 20.4	12 36.1	15 44.3	10 29.7
11 F	21 14 41.8	17 32.3	1 55.0	24 3.6	21 31.7	0♎40.9	15 9.2	14 43.5	4 26.1	12 34.0	15 46.6	10 30.9
12 S	21 18 38.4	18 29.9	1 51.8	5♈50.5	23 30.4	1 47.7	15 27.9	14 53.0	4 32.0	12 31.9	15 48.8	10 32.2
13 S	21 22 34.9	19 27.4	1 48.7	17 38.3	25 27.7	2 54.4	15 47.2	15 2.7	4 37.8	12 29.8	15 51.0	10 33.4
14 M	21 26 31.5	20 25.1	1 45.5	29 31.4	27 23.8	4 0.9	16 7.1	15 12.5	4 43.8	12 27.6	15 53.2	10 34.6
15 T	21 30 28.0	21 22.7	1 42.3	11♉34.6	29 18.4	5 7.3	16 27.6	15 22.3	4 49.8	12 25.4	15 55.4	10 35.8
16 W	21 34 24.6	22 20.4	1 39.1	23 52.8	1♍11.6	6 13.5	16 48.5	15 32.3	4 55.8	12 23.3	15 57.7	10 37.0
17 T	21 38 21.1	23 18.0	1 35.9	6♊30.9	3 3.4	7 19.6	17 10.1	15 42.3	5 1.9	12 21.0	15 59.9	10 38.2
18 F	21 42 17.7	24 15.8	1 32.8	19 33.0	4 53.8	8 25.5	17 32.1	15 52.5	5 8.1	12 18.8	16 2.1	10 39.3
19 S	21 46 14.3	25 13.5	1 29.6	3♋ 2.1	6 42.7	9 31.3	17 54.7	16 2.7	5 14.3	12 16.6	16 4.3	10 40.4
20 S	21 50 10.8	26 11.3	1 26.4	16 58.8	8 30.3	10 36.9	18 17.8	16 13.0	5 20.5	12 14.3	16 6.5	10 41.6
21 M	21 54 7.3	27 9.1	1 23.2	1♌21.8	10 16.4	11 42.3	18 41.4	16 23.4	5 26.8	12 12.0	16 8.7	10 42.7
22 T	21 58 3.9	28 6.9	1 20.1	16 6.3	12 1.1	12 47.5	19 5.6	16 33.8	5 33.2	12 9.7	16 10.9	10 43.8
23 W	22 2 0.5	29 4.7	1 16.9	1♍ 5.3	13 44.5	13 52.6	19 30.2	16 44.4	5 39.6	12 7.4	16 13.1	10 44.8
24 T	22 5 57.0	0♍ 2.6	1 13.7	16 10.1	15 26.5	14 57.4	19 55.2	16 55.0	5 46.0	12 5.1	16 15.2	10 45.9
25 F	22 9 53.5	1 0.5	1 10.5	1♎11.6	17 7.1	16 2.1	20 20.8	17 5.8	5 52.5	12 2.7	16 17.4	10 46.9
26 S	22 13 50.1	1 58.4	1 7.3	16 1.8	18 46.4	17 6.6	20 46.8	17 16.6	5 59.0	12 0.4	16 19.6	10 48.0
27 S	22 17 46.7	2 56.4	1 4.2	0♏34.8	20 24.3	18 10.8	21 13.2	17 27.4	6 5.6	11 58.0	16 21.7	10 49.0
28 M	22 21 43.3	3 54.3	1 1.0	14 46.9	22 1.0	19 14.9	21 40.2	17 38.4	6 12.2	11 55.7	16 23.9	10 50.0
29 T	22 25 39.8	4 52.3	0 57.8	28 36.8	23 36.3	20 18.7	22 7.5	17 49.4	6 18.8	11 53.3	16 26.0	10 50.9
30 W	22 29 36.3	5 50.3	0 54.6	12♐ 4.9	25 10.3	21 22.3	22 35.2	18 0.5	6 25.5	11 50.9	16 28.1	10 51.9
31 T	22 33 32.9	6 48.3	0 51.5	25 12.8	26 43.0	22 25.6	23 3.4	18 11.7	6 32.2	11 48.5	16 30.2	10 52.8

DECLINATION

DAY	EPHEMERIS SIDEREAL TIME h m s	☉	☊	☽	☿	♀	♂	♃	♄	♅	♆	♇
1 T	20 35 16.2	18N17.0	0S58.4	13S41.6	21N13.0	4N53.3	26S15.5	4S 7.1	0N41.7	7S27.9	16N21.4	20N10.2
4 F	20 47 6.0	17 31.3	0 54.6	18 19.2	19 59.8	3 23.1	26 18.7	4 17.7	0 35.0	7 30.1	16 19.5	20 10.0
7 M	20 58 55.6	16 43.0	0 50.8	14 42.7	18 27.0	1 52.2	26 22.2	4 28.6	0 28.0	7 32.4	16 17.5	20 9.7
10 T	21 10 45.3	15 52.3	0 47.0	5 29.0	16 38.6	0 20.8	26 25.8	4 39.9	0 20.9	7 34.8	16 15.6	20 9.5
13 S	21 22 34.9	14 59.4	0 43.2	5N29.6	14 38.8	1S10.7	26 29.5	4 51.5	0 13.6	7 37.3	16 13.6	20 9.2
16 W	21 34 24.6	14 4.2	0 39.4	14 41.3	12 31.2	2 42.1	26 33.1	5 3.3	0 6.1	7 39.8	16 11.7	20 9.0
19 S	21 46 14.3	13 7.0	0 35.6	18 12.9	10 18.7	4 13.0	26 36.6	5 15.5	0S 1.5	7 42.4	16 9.8	20 8.7
22 T	21 58 3.9	12 8.0	0 31.9	12 33.1	8 3.8	5 43.3	26 39.7	5 27.8	0 9.3	7 45.0	16 7.8	20 8.5
25 F	22 9 53.5	11 7.2	0 28.1	0S22.2	5 48.3	7 12.6	26 42.3	5 40.5	0 17.2	7 47.7	16 5.9	20 8.3
28 M	22 21 43.3	10 4.8	0 24.3	12 44.1	3 33.6	8 40.8	26 44.4	5 53.3	0 25.3	7 50.5	16 4.0	20 8.0
31 T	22 33 32.9	9 1.0	0 20.5	18 7.8	1 21.0	10 7.4	26 45.7	6 6.4	0 33.4	7 53.2	16 2.1	20 7.8

SEPTEMBER 1922

DAY	EPHEMERIS SIDEREAL TIME	☉	☊	☽	☿	♀	♂	♃	♄	♅	♆	♇
	h m s	° ′	° ′	° ′	° ′	° ′	° ′	° ′	° ′	° ′	° ′	° ′
						LONGITUDE						
1 F	22 37 29.5	7 ♍ 46.4	0 ♎ 48.3	8 ♑ 2.6	28 ♍ 14.4	23 ♎ 28.7	23 ♐ 31.9	18 ♎ 22.9	6 ♎ 39.0	11 ♓ 46.1	16 ♌ 32.3	10 ♋ 53.7
2 S	22 41 26.0	8 44.4	0 45.1	20 36.8	29 44.5	24 31.6	24 0.9	18 34.2	6 45.8	11 R 43.8	16 34.4	10 54.6
3 S	22 45 22.5	9 42.5	0 41.9	2 ♒ 58.0	1 ♎ 13.4	25 34.2	24 30.2	18 45.6	6 52.6	11 41.4	16 36.5	10 55.5
4 M	22 49 19.1	10 40.7	0 38.7	15 8.2	2 40.8	26 36.5	24 59.9	18 57.0	6 59.5	11 39.0	16 38.6	10 56.4
5 T	22 53 15.6	11 38.8	0 35.6	27 9.8	4 7.0	27 38.6	25 29.9	19 8.5	7 6.4	11 36.6	16 40.7	10 57.2
6 W	22 57 12.2	12 37.0	0 32.4	9 ♓ 4.6	5 31.8	28 40.3	26 0.3	19 20.1	7 13.3	11 34.2	16 42.7	10 58.0
7 T	23 1 8.8	13 35.2	0 29.2	20 54.8	6 55.3	29 41.8	26 31.0	19 31.7	7 20.2	11 31.8	16 44.7	10 58.8
8 F	23 5 5.3	14 33.4	0 26.0	2 ♈ 42.4	8 17.3	0 ♏ 42.9	27 2.1	19 43.4	7 27.2	11 29.4	16 46.8	10 59.6
9 S	23 9 1.8	15 31.7	0 22.8	14 29.8	9 38.0	1 43.8	27 33.5	19 55.1	7 34.2	11 27.0	16 48.8	11 0.4
10 S	23 12 58.4	16 30.0	0 19.7	26 19.9	10 57.1	2 44.3	28 5.2	20 6.9	7 41.3	11 24.6	16 50.8	11 1.1
11 M	23 16 55.0	17 28.3	0 16.5	8 ♉ 15.9	12 14.8	3 44.5	28 37.3	20 18.7	7 48.3	11 22.2	16 52.7	11 1.8
12 T	23 20 51.5	18 26.7	0 13.3	20 21.3	13 30.9	4 44.4	29 9.6	20 30.7	7 55.4	11 19.8	16 54.7	11 2.5
13 W	23 24 48.0	19 25.1	0 10.1	2 ♊ 40.1	14 45.3	5 43.9	29 42.3	20 42.6	8 2.5	11 17.5	16 56.6	11 3.2
14 T	23 28 44.6	20 23.5	0 7.0	15 16.3	15 58.1	6 43.1	0 ♑ 15.2	20 54.6	8 9.7	11 15.1	16 58.6	11 3.9
15 F	23 32 41.2	21 22.0	0 3.8	28 13.9	17 9.1	7 41.9	0 48.5	21 6.7	8 16.8	11 12.7	17 0.5	11 4.5
16 S	23 36 37.7	22 20.5	0 0.6	11 ♋ 36.0	18 18.2	8 40.3	1 22.0	21 18.8	8 24.0	11 10.4	17 2.4	11 5.1
17 S	23 40 34.3	23 19.0	29 ♍ 57.4	25 24.8	19 25.3	9 38.3	1 55.8	21 31.0	8 31.2	11 8.1	17 4.3	11 5.7
18 M	23 44 30.8	24 17.6	29 54.2	9 ♌ 40.1	20 30.3	10 35.9	2 29.9	21 43.2	8 38.5	11 5.8	17 6.1	11 6.3
19 T	23 48 27.4	25 16.2	29 51.1	24 19.6	21 33.1	11 33.1	3 4.3	21 55.4	8 45.7	11 3.4	17 8.0	11 6.8
20 W	23 52 23.9	26 14.9	29 47.9	9 ♍ 18.2	22 33.5	12 29.9	3 38.9	22 7.8	8 53.0	11 1.2	17 9.8	11 7.4
21 T	23 56 20.5	27 13.5	29 44.7	24 28.1	23 31.3	13 26.2	4 13.8	22 20.1	9 0.2	10 58.9	17 11.6	11 7.9
22 F	0 0 17.0	28 12.3	29 41.5	9 ♎ 40.1	24 26.4	14 22.0	4 49.0	22 32.5	9 7.5	10 56.6	17 13.4	11 8.4
23 S	0 4 13.6	29 11.0	29 38.4	24 44.6	25 18.5	15 17.3	5 24.4	22 44.9	9 14.8	10 54.4	17 15.1	11 8.8
24 S	0 8 10.2	0 ♎ 9.8	29 35.2	9 ♏ 33.3	26 7.5	16 12.2	6 0.1	22 57.4	9 22.1	10 52.1	17 16.9	11 9.3
25 M	0 12 6.7	1 8.6	29 32.0	23 60.0	26 52.9	17 6.5	6 36.0	23 9.9	9 29.5	10 49.9	17 18.6	11 9.7
26 T	0 16 3.3	2 7.4	29 28.8	8 ♐ 0.9	27 34.6	18 0.2	7 12.1	23 22.5	9 36.8	10 47.7	17 20.3	11 10.1
27 W	0 19 59.8	3 6.3	29 25.6	21 35.4	28 12.3	18 53.4	7 48.5	23 35.1	9 44.2	10 45.6	17 22.0	11 10.4
28 T	0 23 56.3	4 5.2	29 22.5	4 ♑ 44.6	28 45.5	19 46.0	8 25.1	23 47.7	9 51.5	10 43.4	17 23.6	11 10.8
29 F	0 27 52.9	5 4.1	29 19.3	17 31.1	29 13.9	20 37.9	9 1.9	24 0.3	9 58.9	10 41.3	17 25.3	11 11.1
30 S	0 31 49.5	6 3.1	29 16.1	29 58.6	29 37.2	21 29.2	9 39.0	24 13.0	10 6.3	10 39.2	17 26.9	11 11.4
						DECLINATION						
1 F	22 37 29.5	8 N 39.4	0 S 19.2	18 S 0.7	0 N 37.4	10 S 35.9	26 S 46.0	6 S 10.8	0 S 36.2	7 S 54.1	16 N 1.5	20 N 7.7
4 M	22 49 19.1	7 33.9	0 15.4	12 45.4	1 S 30.8	12 0.0	26 46.3	6 24.1	0 44.5	7 56.9	15 59.7	20 7.5
7 T	23 1 8.8	6 27.3	0 11.6	2 51.5	3 34.7	13 22.1	26 45.5	6 37.5	0 52.8	7 59.6	15 57.9	20 7.3
10 S	23 12 58.4	5 19.8	0 7.8	7 N 57.2	5 33.1	14 41.8	26 43.7	6 51.1	1 1.3	8 2.3	15 56.1	20 7.1
13 W	23 24 48.0	4 11.4	0 4.0	16 4.3	7 25.2	15 58.8	26 40.6	7 4.8	1 9.8	8 5.0	15 54.3	20 6.9
16 S	23 36 37.7	3 2.4	0 0.2	17 46.4	9 9.8	17 13.0	26 36.2	7 18.7	1 18.4	8 7.7	15 52.6	20 6.7
19 T	23 48 27.4	1 52.8	0 N 3.6	10 30.7	10 45.2	18 24.0	26 30.4	7 32.6	1 27.0	8 10.3	15 51.0	20 6.6
22 F	0 0 17.0	0 42.9	0 7.3	2 S 59.5	12 9.8	19 31.7	26 23.1	7 46.7	1 35.6	8 12.9	15 49.4	20 6.4
25 M	0 12 6.7	0 S 27.3	0 11.1	14 36.2	13 21.0	20 35.9	26 14.3	8 0.7	1 44.3	8 15.4	15 47.8	20 6.3
28 T	0 23 56.3	1 37.5	0 14.9	18 5.0	14 15.3	21 36.2	26 3.9	8 14.9	1 52.9	8 17.8	15 46.4	20 6.2

OCTOBER 1922

DAY	EPHEMERIS SIDEREAL TIME	☉	☊	☽	☿	♀	♂	♃	♄	♅	♆	♇
						LONGITUDE						
1 S	0 35 46.0	7 ♎ 2.0	29 ♍ 12.9	12 ♒ 11.0	29 ♎ 54.9	22 ♏ 19.9	10 ♑ 16.2	24 ♎ 25.7	10 ♎ 13.6	10 ♓ 37.1	17 ♌ 28.5	11 ♋ 11.7
2 M	0 39 42.6	8 1.1	29 9.8	24 12.0	0 ♏ 6.5	23 9.8	10 53.6	24 38.5	10 21.0	10 R 35.1	17 30.0	11 11.9
3 T	0 43 39.1	9 0.1	29 6.6	6 ♓ 5.5	0 11.7	23 59.0	11 31.2	24 51.2	10 28.4	10 33.1	17 31.6	11 12.2
4 W	0 47 35.7	9 59.2	29 3.4	17 54.6	0 R 9.9	24 47.4	12 9.1	25 4.0	10 35.8	10 31.1	17 33.1	11 12.4
5 T	0 51 32.2	10 58.3	29 0.2	29 42.2	0 0.9	25 35.1	12 47.1	25 16.9	10 43.1	10 29.1	17 34.6	11 12.6
6 F	0 55 28.8	11 57.4	28 57.0	11 ♈ 30.7	29 ♎ 44.2	26 21.9	13 25.2	25 29.7	10 50.5	10 27.2	17 36.0	11 12.7
7 S	0 59 25.3	12 56.6	28 53.9	23 22.4	29 19.6	27 7.9	14 3.6	25 42.6	10 57.9	10 25.2	17 37.5	11 12.9
8 S	1 3 21.9	13 55.8	28 50.7	5 ♉ 19.3	28 47.0	27 53.0	14 42.1	25 55.5	11 5.3	10 23.4	17 38.9	11 13.0
9 M	1 7 18.4	14 55.0	28 47.5	17 23.5	28 6.4	28 37.2	15 20.8	26 8.4	11 12.6	10 21.5	17 40.3	11 13.1
10 T	1 11 15.0	15 54.3	28 44.3	29 37.2	27 18.0	29 20.4	15 59.7	26 21.3	11 20.0	10 19.7	17 41.6	11 13.1
11 W	1 15 11.5	16 53.6	28 41.1	12 ♊ 2.7	26 22.4	0 ♐ 2.7	16 38.7	26 34.3	11 27.4	10 17.9	17 43.0	11 13.2
12 T	1 19 8.1	17 53.0	28 38.0	24 42.6	25 20.5	0 43.9	17 17.9	26 47.2	11 34.7	10 16.2	17 44.3	11 13.2
13 F	1 23 4.6	18 52.4	28 34.8	7 ♋ 39.5	24 13.3	1 24.0	17 57.2	27 0.2	11 42.1	10 14.4	17 45.5	11 R 13.2
14 S	1 27 1.2	19 51.8	28 31.6	20 56.1	23 2.4	2 3.1	18 36.7	27 13.2	11 49.4	10 12.8	17 46.8	11 13.2
15 S	1 30 57.7	20 51.3	28 28.4	4 ♌ 34.3	21 49.6	2 40.9	19 16.4	27 26.2	11 56.8	10 11.1	17 48.0	11 13.1
16 M	1 34 54.3	21 50.8	28 25.3	18 35.5	20 36.8	3 17.6	19 56.2	27 39.3	12 4.1	10 9.5	17 49.2	11 13.0
17 T	1 38 50.8	22 50.4	28 22.1	2 ♍ 59.1	19 26.1	3 53.0	20 36.1	27 52.3	12 11.4	10 7.9	17 50.4	11 12.9
18 W	1 42 47.4	23 50.0	28 18.9	17 42.5	18 19.7	4 27.1	21 16.2	28 5.4	12 18.7	10 6.4	17 51.5	11 12.8
19 T	1 46 44.0	24 49.6	28 15.7	2 ♎ 40.9	17 19.5	4 59.9	21 56.5	28 18.4	12 26.0	10 4.9	17 52.6	11 12.7
20 F	1 50 40.5	25 49.2	28 12.6	17 46.8	16 27.3	5 31.2	22 36.8	28 31.5	12 33.2	10 3.4	17 53.7	11 12.5
21 S	1 54 37.0	26 48.9	28 9.4	2 ♏ 51.4	15 44.4	6 1.1	23 17.3	28 44.6	12 40.5	10 2.0	17 54.7	11 12.3
22 S	1 58 33.6	27 48.7	28 6.2	17 45.5	15 12.0	6 29.5	23 58.0	28 57.6	12 47.7	10 0.6	17 55.7	11 12.1
23 M	2 2 30.2	28 48.4	28 3.0	2 ♐ 20.9	14 50.7	6 56.2	24 38.7	29 10.7	12 54.9	9 59.3	17 56.7	11 11.8
24 T	2 6 26.7	29 48.2	27 59.8	16 31.7	14 40.7	7 21.4	25 19.6	29 23.8	13 2.1	9 58.0	17 57.7	11 11.6
25 W	2 10 23.3	0 ♏ 48.0	27 56.7	0 ♑ 14.9	14 D 42.0	7 44.8	26 0.7	29 36.9	13 9.3	9 56.8	17 58.6	11 11.3
26 T	2 14 19.8	1 47.9	27 53.5	13 30.2	14 54.3	8 6.4	26 41.8	29 50.0	13 16.4	9 55.5	17 59.5	11 11.0
27 F	2 18 16.4	2 47.7	27 50.3	26 19.9	15 16.9	8 26.1	27 23.0	0 ♏ 3.1	13 23.5	9 54.4	18 0.4	11 10.6
28 S	2 22 12.9	3 47.7	27 47.1	8 ♒ 47.4	15 49.3	8 44.0	28 4.4	0 16.1	13 30.6	9 53.3	18 1.2	11 10.3
29 S	2 26 9.5	4 47.6	27 43.9	20 57.4	16 30.5	8 59.8	28 45.9	0 29.2	13 37.7	9 52.2	18 2.0	11 9.9
30 M	2 30 6.0	5 47.5	27 40.8	2 ♓ 54.9	17 19.8	9 13.7	29 27.4	0 42.3	13 44.7	9 51.2	18 2.7	11 9.5
31 T	2 34 2.6	6 47.5	27 37.6	14 44.8	18 16.3	9 25.4	0 ♒ 9.1	0 55.3	13 51.7	9 50.2	18 3.5	11 9.1
						DECLINATION						
1 S	0 35 46.0	2 S 47.6	0 N 18.7	13 S 23.0	14 S 48.3	22 S 32.5	25 S 51.7	8 S 29.1	2 S 1.6	8 S 20.1	15 N 44.9	20 N 6.1
4 W	0 47 35.7	3 57.4	0 22.5	3 46.3	14 54.2	23 24.6	25 37.8	8 43.2	2 10.2	8 22.4	15 43.6	20 6.0
7 S	0 59 25.3	5 6.8	0 26.3	7 N 6.9	14 26.0	24 12.3	25 22.2	8 57.4	2 18.8	8 24.5	15 42.3	20 5.9
10 T	1 11 15.0	6 15.6	0 30.1	15 36.9	13 18.2	24 55.3	25 4.8	9 11.6	2 27.4	8 26.5	15 41.0	20 5.8
13 F	1 23 4.6	7 23.7	0 33.9	18 1.1	11 31.3	25 33.6	24 45.5	9 25.8	2 35.8	8 28.5	15 39.9	20 5.8
16 M	1 34 54.3	8 30.9	0 37.7	11 57.8	9 18.5	26 7.0	24 24.3	9 39.9	2 44.3	8 30.3	15 38.8	20 5.8
19 T	1 46 44.0	9 37.0	0 41.5	0 S 48.8	7 6.5	26 35.1	24 1.4	9 54.0	2 52.6	8 31.9	15 37.8	20 5.8
22 S	1 58 33.6	10 41.9	0 45.3	13 22.9	5 24.9	26 57.9	23 36.5	10 8.0	3 0.9	8 33.4	15 36.9	20 5.8
25 W	2 10 23.3	11 45.3	0 49.1	18 13.5	4 32.2	27 15.1	23 9.8	10 21.9	3 9.0	8 34.8	15 36.1	20 5.8
28 S	2 22 12.9	12 47.2	0 52.9	14 10.3	4 30.8	27 26.2	22 41.3	10 35.7	3 17.0	8 36.0	15 35.3	20 5.9
31 T	2 34 2.6	13 47.2	0 56.7	4 47.6	5 12.6	27 30.8	22 11.0	10 49.4	3 24.9	8 37.1	15 34.7	20 5.9

NOVEMBER 1922

DAY	EPHEMERIS SIDEREAL TIME h m s	☉ ° ′	☊ ° ′	☽ ° ′	☿ ° ′	♀ ° ′	♂ ° ′	♃ ° ′	♄ ° ′	♅ ° ′	♆ ° ′	♇ ° ′
LONGITUDE												
1 W	2 37 59.2	7♏47.5	27♍34.4	26♓31.6	19♎19.1	9♐34.9	0♒50.9	1♏ 8.4	13♎58.7	9♓49.2	18♌ 4.2	11♋ 8.6
2 T	2 41 55.7	8 47.6	27 31.2	8♈19.4	20 27.4	9 42.2	1 32.7	1 21.4	14 5.7	9R48.3	18 4.8	11R 8.2
3 F	2 45 52.3	9 47.6	27 28.1	20 11.5	21 40.5	9 47.2	2 14.7	1 34.5	14 12.6	9 47.5	18 5.5	11 7.7
4 S	2 49 48.8	10 47.7	27 24.9	2♉10.5	22 57.7	9 49.9	2 56.7	1 47.5	14 19.5	9 46.7	18 6.1	11 7.2
5 S	2 53 45.3	11 47.9	27 21.7	14 18.3	24 18.4	9 50.2	3 38.8	2 0.5	14 26.3	9 45.9	18 6.6	11 6.6
6 M	2 57 41.9	12 48.0	27 18.5	26 36.3	25 42.1	9R48.2	4 21.0	2 13.5	14 33.1	9 45.2	18 7.2	11 6.1
7 T	3 1 38.5	13 48.2	27 15.4	9♊ 5.3	27 8.2	9 43.7	5 3.3	2 26.4	14 39.9	9 44.6	18 7.7	11 5.5
8 W	3 5 35.0	14 48.4	27 12.2	21 45.9	28 36.4	9 36.7	5 45.7	2 39.4	14 46.7	9 44.0	18 8.1	11 4.9
9 T	3 9 31.6	15 48.7	27 9.0	4♋38.7	0♏ 6.2	9 27.3	6 28.1	2 52.3	14 53.4	9 43.4	18 8.5	11 4.3
10 F	3 13 28.1	16 49.0	27 5.8	17 44.4	1 37.5	9 15.5	7 10.6	3 5.2	15 0.0	9 42.9	18 8.9	11 3.6
11 S	3 17 24.7	17 49.3	27 2.6	1♌ 3.9	3 9.8	9 1.3	7 53.2	3 18.1	15 6.7	9 42.4	18 9.3	11 3.0
12 S	3 21 21.3	18 49.7	26 59.5	14 38.4	4 43.1	8 44.7	8 35.9	3 31.0	15 13.2	9 42.0	18 9.6	11 2.3
13 M	3 25 17.8	19 50.0	26 56.3	28 28.7	6 17.0	8 25.8	9 18.6	3 43.9	15 19.8	9 41.6	18 9.9	11 1.6
14 T	3 29 14.3	20 50.5	26 53.1	12♍35.4	7 51.4	8 4.6	10 1.4	3 56.7	15 26.3	9 41.3	18 10.2	11 0.9
15 W	3 33 10.9	21 50.9	26 49.9	26 57.8	9 26.3	7 41.2	10 44.3	4 9.5	15 32.7	9 41.1	18 10.4	11 0.2
16 T	3 37 7.5	22 51.4	26 46.8	11♎33.7	11 1.4	7 15.8	11 27.2	4 22.3	15 39.1	9 40.9	18 10.6	10 59.4
17 F	3 41 4.0	23 51.9	26 43.6	26 18.6	12 36.8	6 48.5	12 10.2	4 35.0	15 45.5	9 40.7	18 10.8	10 58.6
18 S	3 45 0.6	24 52.4	26 40.4	11♏ 6.2	14 12.2	6 19.4	12 53.3	4 47.7	15 51.8	9 40.6	18 10.9	10 57.8
19 S	3 48 57.1	25 53.0	26 37.2	25 49.0	15 47.7	5 48.6	13 36.4	5 0.4	15 58.0	9 40.5	18 11.0	10 57.0
20 M	3 52 53.7	26 53.6	26 34.0	10♐18.9	17 23.2	5 16.4	14 19.6	5 13.0	16 4.2	9 40.5	18 11.0	10 56.2
21 T	3 56 50.3	27 54.2	26 30.9	24 29.1	18 58.7	4 42.9	15 2.8	5 25.7	16 10.4	9D40.6	18 11.1	10 55.3
22 W	4 0 46.8	28 54.9	26 27.7	8♑15.0	20 34.1	4 8.4	15 46.1	5 38.2	16 16.5	9 40.6	18R11.0	10 54.5
23 T	4 4 43.3	29 55.5	26 24.5	21 34.4	22 9.4	3 33.0	16 29.5	5 50.8	16 22.5	9 40.8	18 11.0	10 53.6
24 F	4 8 39.9	0♐56.2	26 21.3	4♒28.0	23 44.6	2 57.0	17 12.9	6 3.2	16 28.5	9 41.0	18 10.9	10 52.7
25 S	4 12 36.5	1 56.9	26 18.2	16 58.5	25 19.8	2 20.7	17 56.4	6 15.7	16 34.4	9 41.2	18 10.8	10 51.8
26 S	4 16 33.0	2 57.6	26 15.0	29 10.0	26 54.8	1 44.2	18 39.9	6 28.1	16 40.3	9 41.5	18 10.6	10 50.8
27 M	4 20 29.6	3 58.3	26 11.8	11♓ 7.9	28 29.6	1 8.0	19 23.4	6 40.5	16 46.1	9 41.9	18 10.5	10 49.9
28 T	4 24 26.1	4 59.1	26 8.6	22 57.5	0♐ 4.4	0 32.1	20 7.0	6 52.8	16 51.8	9 42.3	18 10.2	10 48.9
29 W	4 28 22.7	5 59.9	26 5.4	4♈44.4	1 39.1	29♏56.8	20 50.6	7 5.0	16 57.5	9 42.8	18 10.0	10 48.0
30 T	4 32 19.2	7 0.6	26 2.3	16 33.7	3 13.6	29 22.5	21 34.2	7 17.3	17 3.1	9 43.3	18 9.7	10 47.0
DECLINATION												
1 W	2 37 59.2	14S 6.8	0N57.9	1S 8.7	5S34.0	27S30.8	22S 0.5	10S53.9	3S27.6	8S37.4	15N34.5	20N 6.0
4 S	2 49 48.8	15 4.1	1 1.7	9N35.4	6 54.7	27 26.0	21 27.9	11 7.5	3 35.3	8 38.3	15 33.9	20 6.1
7 T	3 1 38.5	15 59.2	1 5.5	17 2.3	8 32.1	27 13.1	20 53.6	11 20.9	3 42.8	8 39.0	15 33.5	20 6.2
10 F	3 13 28.1	16 52.0	1 9.3	17 27.6	10 18.1	26 51.7	20 17.6	11 34.1	3 50.2	8 39.5	15 33.1	20 6.4
13 M	3 25 17.8	17 42.1	1 13.1	9 35.6	12 7.1	26 21.1	19 40.0	11 47.2	3 57.4	8 39.9	15 32.9	20 6.5
16 T	3 37 7.5	18 29.5	1 16.9	3S30.1	13 55.1	25 41.1	19 0.8	12 0.1	4 4.5	8 40.1	15 32.7	20 6.7
19 S	3 48 57.1	19 14.0	1 20.6	15 2.2	15 39.5	24 52.0	18 20.1	12 12.7	4 11.3	8 40.1	15 32.6	20 6.9
22 W	4 0 46.8	19 55.4	1 24.4	18 12.3	17 18.4	23 54.7	17 38.0	12 25.2	4 17.9	8 39.9	15 32.7	20 7.2
25 S	4 12 36.5	20 33.5	1 28.2	12 35.9	18 50.5	22 51.1	16 54.5	12 37.5	4 24.3	8 39.6	15 32.8	20 7.4
28 T	4 24 26.1	21 8.1	1 32.0	2 26.0	20 14.8	21 43.8	16 9.7	12 49.5	4 30.4	8 39.1	15 33.0	20 7.7

DECEMBER 1922

DAY	EPHEMERIS SIDEREAL TIME h m s	☉ ° ′	☊ ° ′	☽ ° ′	☿ ° ′	♀ ° ′	♂ ° ′	♃ ° ′	♄ ° ′	♅ ° ′	♆ ° ′	♇ ° ′
LONGITUDE												
1 F	4 36 15.8	8♐ 1.5	25♍59.1	28♈29.8	4♐48.1	28♏49.3	22♒17.9	7♏29.4	17♎ 8.7	9♓43.8	18♌ 9.4	10♋46.0
2 S	4 40 12.4	9 2.3	25 55.9	10♉36.3	6 22.5	28R17.4	23 1.6	7 41.6	17 14.2	9 44.4	18R 9.0	10R44.9
3 S	4 44 8.9	10 3.1	25 52.7	22 55.7	7 56.8	27 47.1	23 45.4	7 53.6	17 19.6	9 45.1	18 8.6	10 43.9
4 M	4 48 5.5	11 4.0	25 49.6	5♊29.5	9 31.1	27 18.5	24 29.2	8 5.6	17 24.9	9 45.8	18 8.2	10 42.9
5 T	4 52 2.0	12 4.8	25 46.4	18 17.8	11 5.4	26 51.8	25 13.0	8 17.6	17 30.2	9 46.6	18 7.8	10 41.8
6 W	4 55 58.6	13 5.7	25 43.2	1♋20.0	12 39.6	26 27.1	25 56.8	8 29.5	17 35.4	9 47.4	18 7.3	10 40.7
7 T	4 59 55.1	14 6.6	25 40.0	14 34.6	14 13.8	26 4.6	26 40.6	8 41.3	17 40.6	9 48.2	18 6.7	10 39.6
8 F	5 3 51.7	15 7.5	25 36.9	28 0.1	15 48.0	25 44.4	27 24.5	8 53.1	17 45.6	9 49.1	18 6.2	10 38.5
9 S	5 7 48.3	16 8.5	25 33.7	11♌35.0	17 22.3	25 26.5	28 8.4	9 4.8	17 50.6	9 50.1	18 5.6	10 37.4
10 S	5 11 44.8	17 9.5	25 30.5	25 18.5	18 56.6	25 11.0	28 52.3	9 16.5	17 55.6	9 51.1	18 5.0	10 36.3
11 M	5 15 41.4	18 10.4	25 27.3	9♍ 9.9	20 31.0	24 58.0	29 36.3	9 28.0	18 0.4	9 52.2	18 4.4	10 35.2
12 T	5 19 37.9	19 11.4	25 24.1	23 9.3	22 5.4	24 47.5	0♓20.2	9 39.6	18 5.2	9 53.3	18 3.7	10 34.1
13 W	5 23 34.5	20 12.5	25 21.0	7♎16.5	23 39.9	24 39.5	1 4.2	9 51.0	18 9.9	9 54.4	18 3.0	10 32.9
14 T	5 27 31.0	21 13.5	25 17.8	21 30.7	25 14.5	24 34.0	1 48.2	10 2.4	18 14.5	9 55.7	18 2.2	10 31.8
15 F	5 31 27.6	22 14.6	25 14.6	5♏49.9	26 49.2	24 31.0	2 32.2	10 13.7	18 19.1	9 56.9	18 1.5	10 30.6
16 S	5 35 24.2	23 15.6	25 11.4	20 10.8	28 24.1	24 30.5	3 16.2	10 25.0	18 23.5	9 58.2	18 0.7	10 29.4
17 S	5 39 20.7	24 16.7	25 8.3	4♐28.6	29 59.0	24D32.4	4 0.3	10 36.1	18 27.9	9 59.6	17 59.8	10 28.2
18 M	5 43 17.3	25 17.8	25 5.1	18 37.7	1♑34.1	24 36.7	4 44.3	10 47.2	18 32.2	10 1.0	17 59.0	10 27.0
19 T	5 47 13.8	26 18.9	25 1.9	2♑32.5	3 9.3	24 43.4	5 28.4	10 58.2	18 36.4	10 2.4	17 58.1	10 25.9
20 W	5 51 10.4	27 20.0	24 58.7	16 8.5	4 44.7	24 52.3	6 12.5	11 9.1	18 40.5	10 3.9	17 57.2	10 24.7
21 T	5 55 6.9	28 21.2	24 55.6	29 22.8	6 20.2	25 3.5	6 56.6	11 20.0	18 44.5	10 5.5	17 56.2	10 23.4
22 F	5 59 3.5	29 22.3	24 52.4	12♒14.7	7 55.8	25 16.8	7 40.7	11 30.7	18 48.5	10 7.1	17 55.2	10 22.2
23 S	6 3 0.1	0♑23.4	24 49.2	24 45.6	9 31.5	25 32.3	8 24.9	11 41.4	18 52.3	10 8.7	17 54.2	10 21.0
24 S	6 6 56.6	1 24.6	24 46.0	6♓58.3	11 7.3	25 49.8	9 9.0	11 52.0	18 56.1	10 10.4	17 53.2	10 19.8
25 M	6 10 53.2	2 25.7	24 42.9	18 57.4	12 43.1	26 9.3	9 53.1	12 2.5	18 59.8	10 12.1	17 52.1	10 18.6
26 T	6 14 49.7	3 26.8	24 39.7	0♈47.9	14 19.0	26 30.7	10 37.2	12 12.9	19 3.4	10 13.9	17 51.1	10 17.3
27 W	6 18 46.3	4 28.0	24 36.5	12 35.5	15 54.8	26 54.0	11 21.4	12 23.2	19 6.9	10 15.7	17 50.0	10 16.1
28 T	6 22 42.8	5 29.1	24 33.3	24 25.6	17 30.6	27 19.1	12 5.5	12 33.4	19 10.3	10 17.6	17 48.8	10 14.9
29 F	6 26 39.4	6 30.3	24 30.2	6♉23.8	19 6.2	27 46.0	12 49.6	12 43.6	19 13.6	10 19.5	17 47.7	10 13.6
30 S	6 30 36.0	7 31.4	24 27.0	18 34.5	20 41.6	28 14.5	13 33.8	12 53.6	19 16.8	10 21.5	17 46.5	10 12.4
31 S	6 34 32.5	8 32.6	24 23.8	1♊ 1.5	22 16.6	28 44.6	14 17.9	13 3.5	19 20.0	10 23.4	17 45.3	10 11.1
DECLINATION												
1 F	4 36 15.8	21S39.2	1N35.8	8N29.4	21S30.2	20S36.1	15S23.7	13S 1.3	4S36.3	8S38.4	15N33.3	20N 8.0
4 M	4 48 5.5	22 6.5	1 39.6	16 37.1	22 36.3	19 31.1	14 36.5	13 12.9	4 42.0	8 37.5	15 33.7	20 8.3
7 T	4 59 55.1	22 30.0	1 43.4	17 54.8	23 32.1	18 31.7	13 48.3	13 24.1	4 47.3	8 36.5	15 34.2	20 8.6
10 S	5 11 44.8	22 49.6	1 47.1	10 40.3	24 17.2	17 40.2	12 59.0	13 35.1	4 52.4	8 35.3	15 34.8	20 8.9
13 W	5 23 34.5	23 5.1	1 50.9	1S57.9	24 50.9	16 57.8	12 8.9	13 45.8	4 57.3	8 34.0	15 35.5	20 9.3
16 S	5 35 24.2	23 16.5	1 54.7	13 50.9	25 12.5	16 25.1	11 17.8	13 56.2	5 1.8	8 32.4	15 36.2	20 9.7
19 T	5 47 13.8	23 23.7	1 58.5	18 27.7	25 21.5	16 2.1	10 26.0	14 6.4	5 6.0	8 30.7	15 37.1	20 10.1
22 F	5 59 3.5	23 26.7	2 2.3	13 52.8	25 17.3	15 48.1	9 33.5	14 16.1	5 9.9	8 28.9	15 38.0	20 10.5
25 M	6 10 53.2	23 25.5	2 6.0	3 56.3	24 59.6	15 42.3	8 40.4	14 25.6	5 13.5	8 26.9	15 39.0	20 10.9
28 T	6 22 42.8	23 20.0	2 9.8	7N 6.1	24 27.9	15 43.8	7 46.8	14 34.7	5 16.8	8 24.7	15 40.1	20 11.3
31 S	6 34 32.5	23 10.3	2 13.6	15 49.8	23 42.4	15 51.5	6 52.7	14 43.5	5 19.7	8 22.4	15 41.2	20 11.8

JANUARY 1923

DAY	EPHEMERIS SIDEREAL TIME	☉	☊	☽	☿	♀	♂	♃	♄	♅	♆	♇
	h m s	° ′	° ′	° ′	° ′	° ′	° ′	° ′	° ′	° ′	° ′	° ′
						LONGITUDE						
1 M	6 38 29.0	9♑33.7	24♍20.6	13♊47.1	23♑51.3	29♏16.3	15♓ 2.0	13♏13.3	19♎23.0	10♓25.5	17♌44.0	10♋ 9.9
2 T	6 42 25.6	10 34.8	24 17.4	26 52.1	25 25.3	29 49.5	15 46.1	13 23.1	19 25.9	10 27.6	17R42.8	10R 8.7
3 W	6 46 22.2	11 36.0	24 14.3	10♋15.5	26 58.6	0♐24.2	16 30.2	13 32.7	19 28.8	10 29.7	17 41.5	10 7.4
4 T	6 50 18.7	12 37.1	24 11.1	23 54.9	28 30.8	1 0.3	17 14.3	13 42.2	19 31.5	10 31.8	17 40.2	10 6.2
5 F	6 54 15.3	13 38.3	24 7.9	7♌46.8	0♒ 1.9	1 37.7	17 58.3	13 51.6	19 34.1	10 34.0	17 38.9	10 4.9
6 S	6 58 11.8	14 39.4	24 4.7	21 47.4	1 31.5	2 16.4	18 42.4	14 0.9	19 36.7	10 36.3	17 37.5	10 3.7
7 S	7 2 8.4	15 40.5	24 1.6	5♍52.9	2 59.3	2 56.3	19 26.4	14 10.1	19 39.1	10 38.5	17 36.2	10 2.5
8 M	7 6 5.0	16 41.7	23 58.4	20 0.3	4 24.9	3 37.4	20 10.5	14 19.2	19 41.5	10 40.9	17 34.8	10 1.2
9 T	7 10 1.5	17 42.8	23 55.2	4♎ 7.7	5 47.8	4 19.7	20 54.5	14 28.2	19 43.7	10 43.2	17 33.4	9 60.0
10 W	7 13 58.1	18 44.0	23 52.0	18 13.8	7 7.7	5 3.1	21 38.5	14 37.0	19 45.9	10 45.6	17 32.0	9 58.8
11 T	7 17 54.6	19 45.1	23 48.8	2♏17.7	8 23.8	5 47.6	22 22.5	14 45.8	19 47.9	10 48.0	17 30.5	9 57.5
12 F	7 21 51.2	20 46.3	23 45.7	16 18.6	9 35.6	6 33.0	23 6.6	14 54.4	19 49.8	10 50.5	17 29.1	9 56.3
13 S	7 25 47.7	21 47.4	23 42.5	0♐15.0	10 42.4	7 19.4	23 50.5	15 2.9	19 51.7	10 53.0	17 27.6	9 55.1
14 S	7 29 44.3	22 48.5	23 39.3	14 5.1	11 43.4	8 6.8	24 34.5	15 11.3	19 53.4	10 55.5	17 26.1	9 53.9
15 M	7 33 40.8	23 49.7	23 36.1	27 46.2	12 37.7	8 55.0	25 18.5	15 19.5	19 55.0	10 58.1	17 24.6	9 52.7
16 T	7 37 37.4	24 50.8	23 33.0	11♑15.5	13 24.5	9 44.1	26 2.4	15 27.6	19 56.5	11 0.7	17 23.1	9 51.5
17 W	7 41 34.0	25 52.0	23 29.8	24 30.4	14 3.0	10 34.1	26 46.4	15 35.6	19 58.0	11 3.3	17 21.6	9 50.3
18 T	7 45 30.5	26 53.1	23 26.6	7♒29.0	14 32.2	11 24.7	27 30.3	15 43.5	19 59.3	11 6.0	17 20.0	9 49.1
19 F	7 49 27.1	27 54.2	23 23.4	20 10.3	14 51.3	12 16.2	28 14.2	15 51.2	20 0.5	11 8.7	17 18.4	9 47.9
20 S	7 53 23.6	28 55.3	23 20.2	2♓35.1	14 59.6	13 8.4	28 58.1	15 58.8	20 1.5	11 11.4	17 16.9	9 46.8
21 S	7 57-20.2	29 56.4	23 17.1	14 45.1	14R56.7	14 1.2	29 41.9	16 6.2	20 2.5	11 14.2	17 15.3	9 45.6
22 M	8 1 16.8	0♒57.4	23 13.9	26 43.4	14 42.2	14 54.8	0♈25.8	16 13.6	20 3.4	11 17.0	17 13.7	9 44.5
23 T	8 5 13.3	1 58.5	23 10.7	8♈34.0	14 16.1	15 48.9	1 9.6	16 20.7	20 4.2	11 19.8	17 12.1	9 43.3
24 W	8 9 9.9	2 59.5	23 7.5	20 21.6	13 38.8	16 43.7	1 53.4	16 27.8	20 4.8	11 22.7	17 10.5	9 42.2
25 T	8 13 6.4	4 0.5	23 4.4	2♉11.6	12 51.1	17 39.1	2 37.2	16 34.7	20 5.4	11 25.6	17 8.8	9 41.1
26 F	8 17 3.0	5 1.5	23 1.2	14 9.3	11 54.2	18 35.0	3 21.0	16 41.4	20 5.9	11 28.5	17 7.2	9 40.0
27 S	8 20 59.5	6 2.5	22 58.0	26 19.8	10 49.7	19 31.5	4 4.7	16 48.0	20 6.2	11 31.4	17 5.6	9 38.9
28 S	8 24 56.1	7 3.5	22 54.8	8♊47.8	9 39.5	20 28.6	4 48.4	16 54.5	20 6.4	11 34.4	17 3.9	9 37.8
29 M	8 28 52.6	8 4.4	22 51.7	21 36.9	8 25.7	21 26.1	5 32.1	17 0.8	20 6.6	11 37.4	17 2.2	9 36.7
30 T	8 32 49.2	9 5.3	22 48.5	4♋49.2	7 10.6	22 24.2	6 15.7	17 6.9	20 6.6	11 40.4	17 0.6	9 35.6
31 W	8 36 45.8	10 6.2	22 45.3	18 25.0	5 56.3	23 22.7	6 59.3	17 12.9	20R 6.5	11 43.4	16 58.9	9 34.6
						DECLINATION						
1 M	6 38 29.0	23S 6.1	2N14.9	17N32.7	23S24.1	15S55.3	6S34.6	14S46.3	5S20.6	8S21.6	15N41.6	20N11.9
4 T	6 50 18.7	22 50.9	2 18.6	17 3.8	22 20.7	16 9.6	5 40.0	14 54.7	5 23.0	8 19.1	15 42.8	20 12.4
7 S	7 2 8.4	22 31.5	2 22.4	7 58.8	21 5.6	16 27.8	4 45.1	15 2.6	5 25.2	8 16.4	15 44.1	20 12.8
10 W	7 13 58.1	22 8.2	2 26.2	5S 7.6	19 41.4	16 48.8	3 50.0	15 10.2	5 26.9	8 13.7	15 45.4	20 13.3
13 S	7 25 47.7	21 40.9	2 30.0	15 36.9	18 12.9	17 11.8	2 54.8	15 17.4	5 28.4	8 10.8	15 46.8	20 13.8
16 T	7 37 37.4	21 9.9	2 33.7	18 11.1	16 47.4	17 35.9	1 59.5	15 24.2	5 29.4	8 7.8	15 48.2	20 14.3
19 F	7 49 27.1	20 35.2	2 37.5	12 13.1	15 34.6	18 0.3	1 4.2	15 30.6	5 30.1	8 4.7	15 49.6	20 14.8
22 M	8 1 16.8	19 57.1	2 41.3	1 43.4	14 45.3	18 24.4	0 9.0	15 36.6	5 30.4	8 1.5	15 51.1	20 15.3
25 T	8 13 6.4	19 15.5	2 45.0	9N 5.0	14 27.2	18 47.5	0N46.0	15 42.2	5 30.4	7 58.1	15 52.6	20 15.8
28 S	8 24 56.1	18 30.8	2 48.8	16 48.1	14 40.8	19 9.0	1 40.8	15 47.4	5 30.0	7 54.7	15 54.2	20 16.3
31 W	8 36 45.8	17 43.1	2 52.6	17 37.5	15 18.0	19 28.4	2 35.4	15 52.1	5 29.3	7 51.2	15 55.7	20 16.8

FEBRUARY 1923

DAY	EPHEMERIS SIDEREAL TIME	☉	☊	☽	☿	♀	♂	♃	♄	♅	♆	♇
						LONGITUDE						
1 T	8 40 42.3	11♒ 7.1	22♍42.1	2♌22.5	4♒44.9	24♐21.7	7♈42.9	17♏18.8	20♎ 6.3	11♓46.5	16♌57.2	9♋33.6
2 F	8 44 38.8	12 8.0	22 38.9	16 37.7	3R38.0	25 21.1	8 26.5	17 24.5	20R 6.0	11 49.5	16R55.6	9R32.5
3 S	8 48 35.4	13 8.8	22 35.8	1♍ 5.3	2 37.2	26 21.0	9 10.0	17 30.0	20 5.6	11 52.7	16 53.9	9 31.5
4 S	8 52 32.0	14 9.7	22 32.6	15 39.1	1 43.5	27 21.3	9 53.5	17 35.4	20 5.1	11 55.8	16 52.2	9 30.5
5 M	8 56 28.5	15 10.5	22 29.4	0♎13.0	0 57.5	28 22.0	10 37.0	17 40.6	20 4.5	11 58.9	16 50.5	9 29.5
6 T	9 0 25.1	16 11.3	22 26.2	14 42.0	0 19.9	29 23.0	11 20.5	17 45.7	20 3.8	12 2.1	16 48.8	9 28.6
7 W	9 4 21.6	17 12.1	22 23.1	29 2.2	29♑50.6	0♑24.5	12 3.9	17 50.6	20 3.0	12 5.3	16 47.1	9 27.6
8 T	9 8 18.2	18 12.8	22 19.9	13♏11.3	29 29.6	1 26.3	12 47.3	17 55.3	20 2.0	12 8.5	16 45.4	9 26.7
9 F	9 12 14.7	19 13.6	22 16.7	27 7.9	29 16.8	2 28.4	13 30.6	17 59.9	20 1.0	12 11.7	16 43.8	9 25.8
10 S	9 16 11.3	20 14.3	22 13.5	10♐51.5	29 11.8	3 30.9	14 14.0	18 4.3	19 59.9	12 15.0	16 42.1	9 24.9
11 S	9 20 7.9	21 15.1	22 10.4	24 21.8	29D14.1	4 33.7	14 57.3	18 8.5	19 58.6	12 18.2	16 40.4	9 24.0
12 M	9 24 4.4	22 15.8	22 7.2	7♑38.9	29 23.3	5 36.9	15 40.5	18 12.6	19 57.3	12 21.5	16 38.7	9 23.1
13 T	9 28 0.9	23 16.4	22 4.0	20 42.8	29 39.0	6 40.3	16 23.8	18 16.4	19 55.8	12 24.8	16 37.0	9 22.2
14 W	9 31 57.5	24 17.1	22 0.8	3♒33.5	0♒ 0.7	7 44.0	17 7.0	18 20.2	19 54.3	12 28.1	16 35.4	9 21.4
15 T	9 35 54.1	25 17.7	21 57.6	16 11.1	0 28.0	8 47.9	17 50.2	18 23.7	19 52.6	12 31.4	16 33.7	9 20.6
16 F	9 39 50.6	26 18.4	21 54.5	28 36.1	1 0.3	9 52.2	18 33.4	18 27.1	19 50.9	12 34.7	16 32.0	9 19.8
17 S	9 43 47.2	27 18.9	21 51.3	10♓49.3	1 37.4	10 56.6	19 16.5	18 30.2	19 49.0	12 38.1	16 30.4	9 19.0
18 S	9 47 43.7	28 19.5	21 48.1	22 52.2	2 18.8	12 1.4	19 59.6	18 33.2	19 47.1	12 41.4	16 28.7	9 18.3
19 M	9 51 40.3	29 20.0	21 44.9	4♈46.9	3 4.2	13 6.3	20 42.7	18 36.1	19 45.1	12 44.8	16 27.1	9 17.5
20 T	9 55 36.8	0♓20.6	21 41.8	16 36.3	3 53.2	14 11.5	21 25.7	18 38.7	19 42.9	12 48.2	16 25.5	9 16.8
21 W	9 59 33.4	1 21.0	21 38.6	28 23.9	4 45.7	15 16.9	22 8.7	18 41.2	19 40.7	12 51.5	16 23.8	9 16.1
22 T	10 3 29.9	2 21.5	21 35.4	10♉13.8	5 41.2	16 22.6	22 51.6	18 43.4	19 38.4	12 54.9	16 22.2	9 15.4
23 F	10 7 26.5	3 21.9	21 32.2	22 10.5	6 39.7	17 28.4	23 34.6	18 45.5	19 36.0	12 58.3	16 20.6	9 14.7
24 S	10 11 23.1	4 22.3	21 29.0	4♊18.9	7 40.9	18 34.4	24 17.5	18 47.4	19 33.5	13 1.8	16 19.0	9 14.1
25 S	10 15 19.6	5 22.6	21 25.9	16 43.6	8 44.5	19 40.6	25 0.3	18 49.2	19 30.9	13 5.2	16 17.4	9 13.5
26 M	10 19 16.1	6 22.9	21 22.7	29 29.0	9 50.5	20 47.0	25 43.1	18 50.7	19 28.2	13 8.6	16 15.9	9 12.9
27 T	10 23 12.7	7 23.2	21 19.5	12♋38.5	10 58.7	21 53.6	26 25.9	18 52.1	19 25.4	13 12.0	16 14.3	9 12.3
28 W	10 27 9.2	8 23.5	21 16.3	26 14.2	12 9.0	23 0.4	27 8.7	18 53.2	19 22.6	13 15.4	16 12.8	9 11.7
						DECLINATION						
1 T	8 40 42.3	17S26.6	2N53.8	15N50.6	15S33.5	19S34.3	2N53.5	15S53.6	5S28.9	7S50.0	15N56.2	20N16.9
4 S	8 52 32.0	16 35.1	2 57.6	5 12.9	16 22.9	19 50.2	3 47.5	15 57.8	5 27.7	7 46.4	15 57.8	20 17.4
7 W	9 4 21.6	15 41.1	3 1.4	8S 7.3	17 10.0	20 2.9	4 41.1	16 1.6	5 26.2	7 42.8	15 59.4	20 17.9
10 S	9 16 11.3	14 44.6	3 5.1	16 59.5	17 49.6	20 12.0	5 34.2	16 4.9	5 24.2	7 39.0	16 0.9	20 18.4
13 T	9 28 0.9	13 45.9	3 8.9	17 22.3	18 19.1	20 17.4	6 26.7	16 7.8	5 22.0	7 35.2	16 2.5	20 18.9
16 F	9 39 50.6	12 45.1	3 12.7	10 7.0	18 37.3	20 18.6	7 18.7	16 10.2	5 19.4	7 31.4	16 4.0	20 19.4
19 M	9 51 40.3	11 42.5	3 16.4	0N42.7	18 43.8	20 15.4	8 9.9	16 12.2	5 16.6	7 27.5	16 5.5	20 19.9
22 T	10 3 29.9	10 38.3	3 20.2	11 4.0	18 38.4	20 7.8	9 0.3	16 13.7	5 13.4	7 23.6	16 7.0	20 20.4
25 S	10 15 19.6	9 32.6	3 23.9	17 32.4	18 20.8	19 55.5	9 50.0	16 14.8	5 9.9	7 19.6	16 8.5	20 20.8
28 W	10 27 9.2	8 25.6	3 27.7	16 41.2	17 51.2	19 38.6	10 38.8	16 15.4	5 6.2	7 15.7	16 9.9	20 21.3

MARCH 1923

DAY	EPHEMERIS SIDEREAL TIME h m s	☉ ° ′	☊ ° ′	☽ ° ′	☿ ° ′	♀ ° ′	♂ ° ′	♃ ° ′	♄ ° ′	♅ ° ′	♆ ° ′	♇ ° ′
						LONGITUDE						
1 T	10 31 5.8	9♓23.7	21♍13.2	10♌16.0	13♒21.2	24♑7.3	27♈51.4	18♏54.2	19♎19.6	13♓18.9	16♌11.3	9♋11.2
2 F	10 35 2.4	10 23.9	21 !0.0	24 41.5	14 35.2	25 14.4	28 34.0	18 55.0	19R16.6	13 22.3	16R 9.7	9R10.7
3 S	10 38 58.9	11 24.0	21 6.8	9♍25.9	15 50.9	26 21.7	29 16.7	18 55.6	19 13.5	13 25.7	16 8.2	9 10.2
4 S	10 42 55.4	12 24.2	21 3.6	24 22.1	17 8.4	27 29.1	29 59.3	18 56.0	19 10.3	13 29.2	16 6.8	9 9.7
5 M	10 46 52.0	13 24.3	21 0.4	9♎21.9	18 27.4	28 36.7	0♉41.8	18 56.3	19 7.1	13 32.6	16 5.3	9 9.3
6 T	10 50 48.6	14 24.3	20 57.3	24 17.0	19 47.9	29 44.5	1 24.3	18 56.3	19 3.8	13 36.1	16 3.9	9 8.8
7 W	10 54 45.1	15 24.4	20 54.1	9♏0.4	21 9.9	0♒52.4	2 6.8	18R56.2	19 0.3	13 39.5	16 2.4	9 8.4
8 T	10 58 41.7	16 24.4	20 50.9	23 26.5	22 33.4	2 0.4	2 49.2	18 55.9	18 56.9	13 42.9	16 1.0	9 8.0
9 F	11 2 38.2	17 24.4	20 47.7	7♐32.3	23 58.2	3 8.6	3 31.7	18 55.4	18 53.3	13 46.4	15 59.6	9 7.7
10 S	11 6 34.8	18 24.3	20 44.6	21 16.6	25 24.4	4 16.9	4 14.0	18 54.7	18 49.7	13 49.8	15 58.2	9 7.3
11 S	11 10 31.3	19 24.3	20 41.4	4♑39.9	26 51.9	5 25.3	4 56.4	18 53.8	18 46.0	13 53.2	15 56.9	9 7.0
12 M	11 14 27.9	20 24.2	20 38.2	17 43.8	28 20.7	6 33.8	5 38.7	18 52.7	18 42.3	13 56.7	15 55.5	9 6.7
13 T	11 18 24.4	21 24.0	20 35.0	0♒30.4	29 50.8	7 42.5	6 20.9	18 51.4	18 38.5	14 0.1	15 54.2	9 6.5
14 W	11 22 21.0	22 23.9	20 31.8	13 2.2	1♓22.2	8 51.3	7 3.2	18 49.9	18 34.6	14 3.5	15 52.9	9 6.2
15 T	11 26 17.6	23 23.7	20 28.7	25 21.5	2 54.8	10 0.2	7 45.4	18 48.3	18 30.7	14 6.9	15 51.7	9 6.0
16 F	11 30 14.1	24 23.5	20 25.5	7♓30.5	4 28.6	11 9.2	8 27.5	18 46.5	18 26.7	14 10.3	15 50.4	9 5.8
17 S	11 34 10.6	25 23.3	20 22.3	19 31.4	6 3.7	12 18.3	9 9.6	18 44.5	18 22.6	14 13.7	15 49.2	9 5.6
18 S	11 38 7.2	26 23.0	20 19.1	1♈26.0	7 40.1	13 27.5	9 51.7	18 42.3	18 18.5	14 17.1	15 48.0	9 5.5
19 M	11 42 3.7	27 22.7	20 15.9	13 16.4	9 17.7	14 36.8	10 33.8	18 39.9	18 14.4	14 20.5	15 46.8	9 5.3
20 T	11 46 0.3	28 22.3	20 12.8	25 4.8	10 56.5	15 46.2	11 15.8	18 37.3	18 10.2	14 23.8	15 45.7	9 5.2
21 W	11 49 56.9	29 21.9	20 9.6	6♉53.5	12 36.6	16 55.7	11 57.8	18 34.6	18 6.0	14 27.2	15 44.5	9 5.2
22 T	11 53 53.4	0♈21.5	20 6.4	18 45.3	14 17.9	18 5.2	12 39.7	18 31.6	18 1.7	14 30.5	15 43.4	9 5.1
23 F	11 57 49.9	1 21.1	20 3.2	0♊43.6	16 0.6	19 14.9	13 21.6	18 28.5	17 57.4	14 33.9	15 42.3	9 5.1
24 S	12 1 46.5	2 20.6	20 0.1	12 51.9	17 44.5	20 24.6	14 3.5	18 25.3	17 53.0	14 37.2	15 41.3	9 5.1
25 S	12 5 43.1	3 20.1	19 56.9	25 14.2	19 29.7	21 34.4	14 45.3	18 21.8	17 48.6	14 40.5	15 40.3	9D 5.1
26 M	12 9 39.6	4 19.5	19 53.7	7♋54.6	21 16.2	22 44.3	15 27.1	18 18.2	17 44.2	14 43.8	15 39.3	9 5.1
27 T	12 13 36.1	5 18.9	19 50.5	20 56.9	23 4.0	23 54.2	16 8.8	18 14.4	17 39.7	14 47.1	15 38.3	9 5.2
28 W	12 17 32.7	6 18.2	19 47.3	4♌24.3	24 53.1	25 4.3	16 50.5	18 10.5	17 35.3	14 50.3	15 37.3	9 5.3
29 T	12 21 29.3	7 17.6	19 44.2	18 18.5	26 43.6	26 14.4	17 32.2	18 6.3	17 30.7	14 53.6	15 36.4	9 5.4
30 F	12 25 25.8	8 16.8	19 41.0	2♍39.4	28 35.5	27 24.5	18 13.8	18 2.1	17 26.2	14 56.8	15 35.5	9 5.5
31 S	12 29 22.3	9 16.1	19 37.8	17 24.1	0♈28.6	28 34.7	18 55.4	17 57.6	17 21.6	14 60.0	15 34.7	9 5.7
						DECLINATION						
1 T	10 31 5.8	8S 3.0	3N28.9	14N22.4	17S38.7	19S31.8	10N54.8	16S15.5	5S 4.9	7S14.4	16N10.3	20N21.5
4 S	10 42 55.4	6 54.5	3 32.7	2 33.7	16 53.1	19 8.5	11 42.4	16 15.5	5 0.8	7 10.4	16 11.7	20 21.9
7 W	10 54 45.1	5 45.2	3 36.5	10S44.3	15 55.8	18 40.4	12 28.9	16 15.1	4 56.5	7 6.4	16 13.0	20 22.4
10 S	11 6 34.8	4 35.2	3 40.2	17 52.3	14 46.7	18 7.7	13 14.3	16 14.2	4 52.0	7 2.5	16 14.3	20 22.8
13 T	11 18 24.4	3 24.6	3 44.0	16 4.4	13 26.0	17 30.3	13 58.7	16 12.8	4 47.3	6 58.5	16 15.5	20 23.2
16 F	11 30 14.1	2 13.7	3 47.7	7 38.3	11 54.1	16 48.4	14 41.9	16 11.1	4 42.4	6 54.6	16 16.7	20 23.6
19 M	11 42 3.7	1 2.6	3 51.5	3N21.4	10 10.9	16 2.2	15 23.9	16 8.8	4 37.4	6 50.7	16 17.8	20 24.0
22 T	11 53 53.4	0N 8.6	3 55.2	13 4.9	8 16.9	15 11.9	16 4.6	16 6.2	4 32.3	6 46.8	16 18.8	20 24.4
25 S	12 5 43.1	1 19.6	3 58.9	18 5.9	6 12.2	14 17.7	16 44.0	16 3.1	4 27.0	6 43.0	16 19.7	20 24.8
28 W	12 17 32.7	2 30.2	4 2.7	15 27.7	3 57.3	13 19.7	17 22.1	15 59.6	4 21.7	6 39.2	16 20.6	20 25.1
31 S	12 29 22.3	3 40.4	4 6.4	4 42.7	1 32.8	12 18.3	17 58.7	15 55.7	4 16.3	6 35.5	16 21.4	20 25.5

APRIL 1923

DAY	EPHEMERIS SIDEREAL TIME h m s	☉ ° ′	☊ ° ′	☽ ° ′	☿ ° ′	♀ ° ′	♂ ° ′	♃ ° ′	♄ ° ′	♅ ° ′	♆ ° ′	♇ ° ′
						LONGITUDE						
1 S	12 33 18.9	10♈15.3	19♍34.6	2♎27.1	2♈23.1	29♒45.0	19♉36.9	17♏53.0	17♎17.1	15♓3.2	15♌33.8	9♋5.8
2 M	12 37 15.5	11 14.4	19 31.5	17 40.1	4 19.0	0♓55.4	20 18.4	17R48.3	17R12.5	15 6.4	15R33.0	9 6.0
3 T	12 41 12.0	12 13.6	19 28.3	2♏53.3	6 16.2	2 5.9	20 59.9	17 43.4	17 7.9	15 9.5	15 32.3	9 6.3
4 W	12 45 8.6	13 12.7	19 25.1	17 56.8	8 14.7	3 16.3	21 41.3	17 38.3	17 3.3	15 12.7	15 31.5	9 6.5
5 T	12 49 5.1	14 11.7	19 21.9	2♐42.1	10 14.4	4 26.9	22 22.7	17 33.1	16 58.6	15 15.8	15 30.8	9 6.8
6 F	12 53 1.7	15 10.8	19 18.7	17 3.2	12 15.3	5 37.5	23 4.0	17 27.8	16 54.0	15 18.9	15 30.1	9 7.1
7 S	12 56 58.2	16 9.8	19 15.6	0♑57.4	14 17.4	6 48.2	23 45.4	17 22.3	16 49.4	15 21.9	15 29.4	9 7.4
8 S	13 0 54.8	17 8.8	19 12.4	14 24.4	16 20.5	7 59.0	24 26.6	17 16.7	16 44.7	15 25.0	15 28.8	9 7.8
9 M	13 4 51.3	18 7.7	19 9.2	27 26.1	18 24.6	9 9.8	25 7.9	17 11.0	16 40.1	15 28.0	15 28.2	9 8.1
10 T	13 8 47.9	19 6.7	19 6.0	10♒6.0	20 29.4	10 20.6	25 49.1	17 5.1	16 35.4	15 31.0	15 27.7	9 8.5
11 W	13 12 44.4	20 5.6	19 2.8	22 28.0	22 34.9	11 31.5	26 30.2	16 59.1	16 30.8	15 34.0	15 27.1	9 8.9
12 T	13 16 41.0	21 4.4	18 59.7	4♓36.3	24 40.8	12 42.5	27 11.4	16 53.0	16 26.2	15 37.0	15 26.6	9 9.4
13 F	13 20 37.5	22 3.3	18 56.5	16 34.8	26 46.9	13 53.5	27 52.5	16 46.7	16 21.6	15 39.9	15 26.2	9 9.8
14 S	13 24 34.1	23 2.1	18 53.3	28 27.0	28 53.0	15 4.5	28 33.6	16 40.4	16 17.0	15 42.8	15 25.7	9 10.3
15 S	13 28 30.6	24 0.9	18 50.1	10♈15.8	0♉58.8	16 15.6	29 14.6	16 33.9	16 12.4	15 45.7	15 25.3	9 10.8
16 M	13 32 27.2	24 59.6	18 47.0	22 3.8	3 3.9	17 26.7	29 55.6	16 27.3	16 7.8	15 48.5	15 24.9	9 11.3
17 T	13 36 23.8	25 58.3	18 43.8	3♉53.1	5 8.2	18 37.9	0♊36.6	16 20.6	16 3.3	15 51.4	15 24.6	9 11.9
18 W	13 40 20.3	26 57.0	18 40.6	15 45.6	7 11.2	19 49.1	1 17.5	16 13.9	15 58.8	15 54.2	15 24.3	9 12.5
19 T	13 44 16.8	27 55.6	18 37.4	27 43.0	9 12.7	21 0.4	1 58.4	16 7.0	15 54.3	15 56.9	15 24.0	9 13.0
20 F	13 48 13.4	28 54.2	18 34.2	9♊47.5	11 12.2	22 11.6	2 39.2	16 0.0	15 49.8	15 59.7	15 23.8	9 13.7
21 S	13 52 10.0	29 52.8	18 31.1	22 1.1	13 9.5	23 23.0	3 20.0	15 53.0	15 45.4	16 2.4	15 23.6	9 14.3
22 S	13 56 6.5	0♉51.4	18 27.9	4♋26.6	15 4.3	24 34.3	4 0.8	15 45.9	15 41.0	16 5.1	15 23.4	9 15.0
23 M	14 0 3.1	1 49.9	18 24.7	17 6.8	16 56.2	25 45.7	4 41.6	15 38.7	15 36.6	16 7.7	15 23.2	9 15.6
24 T	14 3 59.6	2 48.3	18 21.5	0♌5.0	18 45.0	26 57.1	5 22.3	15 31.5	15 32.2	16 10.3	15 23.1	9 16.3
25 W	14 7 56.2	3 46.8	18 18.4	13 24.4	20 30.5	28 8.5	6 2.9	15 24.2	15 28.0	16 12.9	15 23.0	9 17.1
26 T	14 11 52.7	4 45.2	18 15.2	27 7.4	22 12.4	29 20.0	6 43.6	15 16.8	15 23.7	16 15.4	15 23.0	9 17.8
27 F	14 15 49.3	5 43.5	18 12.0	11♍15.6	23 50.6	0♈31.5	7 24.2	15 9.4	15 19.5	16 18.0	15 23.0	9 18.6
28 S	14 19 45.8	6 41.9	18 8.8	25 48.3	25 24.9	1 43.0	8 4.7	15 1.9	15 15.3	16 20.4	15D23.0	9 19.4
29 S	14 23 42.4	7 40.1	18 5.6	10♎42.1	26 55.1	2 54.6	8 45.3	14 54.4	15 11.2	16 22.9	15 23.1	9 20.2
30 M	14 27 38.9	8 38.4	18 2.5	25 50.7	28 21.2	4 6.2	9 25.7	14 46.9	15 7.2	16 25.3	15 23.1	9 21.0
						DECLINATION						
1 S	12 33 18.9	4N 3.7	4N 7.7	0N 1.5	0S42.6	11S57.1	18N10.6	15S54.3	4S14.5	6S34.3	16N21.7	20N25.6
4 W	12 45 8.6	5 13.1	4 11.4	12S55.4	1N53.4	10 51.4	18 45.3	15 50.0	4 9.1	6 30.7	16 22.4	20 25.9
7 S	12 56 58.2	6 21.6	4 15.2	18 17.1	4 36.1	9 42.7	19 18.5	15 45.2	4 3.8	6 27.1	16 23.0	20 26.2
10 T	13 8 47.9	7 29.1	4 18.9	14 27.0	7 23.0	8 31.5	19 50.1	15 40.2	3 58.4	6 23.7	16 23.6	20 26.5
13 F	13 20 37.5	8 35.6	4 22.6	4 58.7	10 10.5	7 17.9	20 20.2	15 34.8	3 53.2	6 20.3	16 24.0	20 26.7
16 M	13 32 27.2	9 40.7	4 26.4	6N 3.1	12 53.6	6 2.3	20 48.6	15 29.2	3 48.0	6 17.0	16 24.4	20 27.0
19 T	13 44 16.8	10 44.4	4 30.1	14 59.3	15 26.9	4 44.9	21 15.4	15 23.3	3 42.9	6 13.8	16 24.7	20 27.2
22 S	13 56 6.5	11 46.5	4 33.8	18 22.5	17 44.7	3 26.0	21 40.6	15 17.2	3 38.0	6 10.7	16 24.9	20 27.5
25 W	14 7 56.2	12 46.9	4 37.6	13 52.1	19 43.0	2 5.9	22 4.0	15 10.9	3 33.2	6 7.8	16 25.0	20 27.7
28 S	14 19 45.8	13 45.3	4 41.3	2 10.6	21 19.2	0 45.0	22 25.6	15 4.5	3 28.6	6 4.9	16 25.0	20 27.8

MAY 1923

LONGITUDE

DAY	EPHEMERIS SIDEREAL TIME h m s	☉ ° ′	☊ ° ′	☽ ° ′	☿ ° ′	♀ ° ′	♂ ° ′	♃ ° ′	♄ ° ′	♅ ° ′	♆ ° ′	♇ ° ′
1 T	14 31 35.5	9♉36.6	17♍59.3	11♏ 5.2	29♉43.0	5♈17.8	10♊ 6.2	14♏39.3	15♎ 3.2	16♓27.7	15♌23.3	9♋21.8
2 W	14 35 32.0	10 34.8	17 56.1	26 15.0	1♊ 0.5	6 29.5	10 46.6	14R31.7	14R59.2	16 30.0	15 23.4	9 22.7
3 T	14 39 28.6	11 33.0	17 52.9	11♐10.0	2 13.4	7 41.2	11 27.0	14 24.1	14 55.3	16 32.3	15 23.6	9 23.6
4 F	14 43 25.1	12 31.1	17 49.8	25 42.2	3 21.9	8 52.9	12 7.3	14 16.5	14 51.5	16 34.6	15 23.8	9 24.5
5 S	14 47 21.7	13 29.3	17 46.6	9♑46.3	4 25.7	10 4.6	12 47.6	14 8.9	14 47.7	16 36.8	15 24.1	9 25.4
6 S	14 51 18.3	14 27.4	17 43.4	23 20.8	5 24.9	11 16.4	13 27.9	14 1.2	14 44.0	16 39.0	15 24.4	9 26.3
7 M	14 55 14.8	15 25.4	17 40.2	6♒26.9	6 19.4	12 28.2	14 8.2	13 53.6	14 40.3	16 41.2	15 24.7	9 27.3
8 T	14 59 11.4	16 23.5	17 37.0	19 7.8	7 9.0	13 40.0	14 48.4	13 45.9	14 36.7	16 43.3	15 25.0	9 28.2
9 W	15 3 7.9	17 21.5	17 33.9	1♓28.2	7 53.8	14 51.9	15 28.6	13 38.3	14 33.2	16 45.4	15 25.4	9 29.2
10 T	15 7 4.5	18 19.5	17 30.7	13 33.1	8 33.7	16 3.8	16 8.7	13 30.7	14 29.7	16 47.4	15 25.8	9 30.2
11 F	15 11 1.1	19 17.5	17 27.5	25 27.6	9 8.7	17 15.7	16 48.9	13 23.1	14 26.3	16 49.4	15 26.3	9 31.3
12 S	15 14 57.6	20 15.5	17 24.3	7♈16.3	9 38.6	18 27.6	17 29.0	13 15.5	14 23.0	16 51.4	15 26.7	9 32.3
13 S	15 18 54.1	21 13.4	17 21.2	19 3.3	10 3.5	19 39.6	18 9.0	13 8.0	14 19.7	16 53.3	15 27.2	9 33.4
14 M	15 22 50.7	22 11.3	17 18.0	0♉52.0	10 23.4	20 51.6	18 49.1	13 0.5	14 16.6	16 55.2	15 27.8	9 34.5
15 T	15 26 47.2	23 9.2	17 14.8	12 45.0	10 38.3	22 3.6	19 29.1	12 53.0	14 13.5	16 57.0	15 28.4	9 35.5
16 W	15 30 43.8	24 7.1	17 11.6	24 44.3	10 48.1	23 15.6	20 9.0	12 45.6	14 10.5	16 58.8	15 29.0	9 36.7
17 T	15 34 40.4	25 4.9	17 8.5	6♊51.2	10 53.1	24 27.7	20 49.0	12 38.2	14 7.5	17 0.6	15 29.6	9 37.8
18 F	15 38 36.9	26 2.7	17 5.3	19 6.8	10 53.1	25 39.7	21 28.9	12 30.9	14 4.7	17 2.3	15 30.3	9 38.9
19 S	15 42 33.5	27 0.5	17 2.1	1♋32.0	10R48.5	26 51.8	22 8.8	12 23.7	14 1.9	17 3.9	15 31.0	9 40.1
20 S	15 46 30.0	27 58.3	16 58.9	14 8.1	10 39.4	28 3.9	22 48.6	12 16.5	13 59.2	17 5.6	15 31.7	9 41.3
21 M	15 50 26.6	28 56.0	16 55.7	26 56.3	10 25.9	29 16.0	23 28.5	12 9.4	13 56.6	17 7.1	15 32.5	9 42.4
22 T	15 54 23.1	29 53.7	16 52.6	9♌58.6	10 8.5	0♉28.1	24 8.3	12 2.4	13 54.1	17 8.7	15 33.3	9 43.6
23 W	15 58 19.7	0♊51.4	16 49.4	23 17.2	9 47.3	1 40.3	24 48.0	11 55.5	13 51.7	17 10.2	15 34.1	9 44.8
24 T	16 2 16.2	1 49.1	16 46.2	6♍54.1	9 22.8	2 52.5	25 27.7	11 48.7	13 49.3	17 11.6	15 35.0	9 46.1
25 F	16 6 12.8	2 46.7	16 43.0	20 51.1	8 55.5	4 4.6	26 7.5	11 41.9	13 47.1	17 13.0	15 35.9	9 47.3
26 S	16 10 9.4	3 44.3	16 39.9	5♎ 8.7	8 25.7	5 16.8	26 47.1	11 35.2	13 44.9	17 14.4	15 36.8	9 48.6
27 S	16 14 5.9	4 41.9	16 36.7	19 45.2	7 54.1	6 29.1	27 26.7	11 28.7	13 42.8	17 15.7	15 37.8	9 49.8
28 M	16 18 2.4	5 39.5	16 33.5	4♏36.7	7 21.1	7 41.3	28 6.4	11 22.2	13 40.8	17 16.9	15 38.7	9 51.1
29 T	16 21 59.0	6 37.0	16 30.3	19 36.4	6 47.4	8 53.5	28 45.9	11 15.9	13 39.0	17 18.2	15 39.8	9 52.4
30 W	16 25 55.6	7 34.5	16 27.2	4♐35.5	6 13.6	10 5.8	29 25.5	11 9.7	13 37.2	17 19.3	15 40.8	9 53.7
31 T	16 29 52.1	8 32.0	16 24.0	19 24.6	5 40.2	11 18.1	0♋ 5.0	11 3.6	13 35.5	17 20.5	15 41.9	9 55.0

DECLINATION

DAY	SIDEREAL TIME	☉	☊	☽	☿	♀	♂	♃	♄	♅	♆	♇
1 T	14 31 35.5	14N41.7	4N45.0	11S20.0	22N32.8	0N36.6	22N45.5	14S58.0	3S24.2	6S 2.2	16N25.0	20N28.0
4 F	14 43 25.1	15 36.0	4 48.7	18 17.9	23 24.3	1 58.5	23 3.7	14 51.5	3 20.1	5 59.5	16 24.8	20 28.1
7 M	14 55 14.8	16 27.9	4 52.4	15 18.8	23 54.8	3 20.5	23 20.0	14 44.9	3 16.1	5 57.1	16 24.6	20 28.3
10 T	15 7 4.5	17 17.4	4 56.2	6 1.7	24 5.8	4 42.2	23 34.5	14 38.3	3 12.5	5 54.7	16 24.2	20 28.4
13 S	15 18 54.1	18 4.3	4 59.9	5N 5.4	23 58.6	6 3.3	23 47.2	14 31.8	3 9.1	5 52.5	16 23.8	20 28.5
16 W	15 30 43.8	18 48.4	5 3.6	14 28.1	23 34.6	7 23.5	23 58.1	14 25.4	3 6.0	5 50.5	16 23.3	20 28.5
19 S	15 42 33.5	19 29.7	5 7.3	18 32.5	22 55.3	8 42.6	24 7.1	14 19.2	3 3.2	5 48.6	16 22.7	20 28.6
22 T	15 54 23.1	20 8.1	5 11.0	14 47.0	22 3.1	10 0.1	24 14.3	14 13.1	3 0.7	5 46.8	16 22.1	20 28.6
25 F	16 6 12.8	20 43.3	5 14.7	3 54.4	21 1.2	11 15.9	24 19.6	14 7.3	2 58.6	5 45.2	16 21.3	20 28.7
28 M	16 18 2.4	21 15.3	5 18.4	9S34.2	19 54.6	12 29.5	24 23.1	14 1.8	2 56.8	5 43.8	16 20.5	20 28.7
31 T	16 29 52.1	21 44.0	5 22.1	18 1.7	18 49.5	13 40.7	24 24.8	13 56.6	2 55.3	5 42.5	16 19.6	20 28.6

JUNE 1923

LONGITUDE

DAY	SIDEREAL TIME	☉	☊	☽	☿	♀	♂	♃	♄	♅	♆	♇
1 F	16 33 48.7	9♊29.5	16♍20.8	3♑55.0	5♊ 7.8	12♉30.4	0♋44.5	10♏57.6	13♎33.8	17♓21.6	15♌43.0	9♋56.4
2 S	16 37 45.2	10 27.0	16 17.6	18 0.7	4R36.9	13 42.8	1 24.0	10R51.7	13R32.3	17 22.6	15 44.1	9 57.7
3 S	16 41 41.8	11 24.4	16 14.4	1♒38.5	4 8.2	14 55.1	2 3.4	10 45.9	13 30.9	17 23.6	15 45.2	9 59.0
4 M	16 45 38.3	12 21.9	16 11.3	14 48.3	3 41.9	16 7.5	2 42.8	10 40.3	13 29.6	17 24.5	15 46.4	10 0.4
5 T	16 49 34.9	13 19.3	16 8.1	27 32.4	3 18.7	17 19.9	3 22.2	10 34.8	13 28.3	17 25.4	15 47.6	10 1.8
6 W	16 53 31.5	14 16.7	16 4.9	9♓55.0	2 58.8	18 32.3	4 1.6	10 29.5	13 27.2	17 26.3	15 48.9	10 3.1
7 T	16 57 28.0	15 14.1	16 1.7	22 1.1	2 42.6	19 44.8	4 40.9	10 24.3	13 26.2	17 27.1	15 50.1	10 4.5
8 F	17 1 24.6	16 11.5	15 58.6	3♈56.1	2 30.2	20 57.2	5 20.2	10 19.2	13 25.2	17 27.8	15 51.4	10 5.9
9 S	17 5 21.1	17 8.9	15 55.4	15 45.4	2 22.1	22 9.7	5 59.5	10 14.3	13 24.4	17 28.5	15 52.7	10 7.3
10 S	17 9 17.7	18 6.3	15 52.2	27 33.7	2 18.2	23 22.2	6 38.8	10 9.5	13 23.7	17 29.2	15 54.1	10 8.7
11 M	17 13 14.2	19 3.7	15 49.0	9♉25.4	2D18.8	24 34.8	7 18.0	10 4.9	13 23.0	17 29.8	15 55.4	10 10.2
12 T	17 17 10.8	20 1.0	15 45.8	21 23.9	2 23.8	25 47.3	7 57.3	10 0.4	13 22.5	17 30.4	15 56.9	10 11.6
13 W	17 21 7.4	20 58.4	15 42.7	3♊31.6	2 33.4	26 59.9	8 36.5	9 56.1	13 22.1	17 30.9	15 58.3	10 13.0
14 T	17 25 3.9	21 55.7	15 39.5	15 50.1	2 47.5	28 12.5	9 15.6	9 51.9	13 21.7	17 31.3	15 59.7	10 14.5
15 F	17 29 0.5	22 53.0	15 36.3	28 20.2	3 6.2	29 25.1	9 54.8	9 47.9	13 21.5	17 31.7	16 1.2	10 15.9
16 S	17 32 57.0	23 50.4	15 33.1	11♋ 2.0	3 29.4	0♊37.7	10 33.9	9 44.1	13 21.3	17 32.1	16 2.7	10 17.4
17 S	17 36 53.6	24 47.7	15 30.0	23 55.3	3 57.1	1 50.3	11 13.0	9 40.4	13 21.3	17 32.4	16 4.2	10 18.9
18 M	17 40 50.2	25 45.0	15 26.8	7♌ 0.0	4 29.1	3 3.0	11 52.1	9 36.9	13D21.4	17 32.7	16 5.8	10 20.3
19 T	17 44 46.7	26 42.3	15 23.6	20 16.2	5 5.6	4 15.7	12 31.2	9 33.6	13 21.5	17 32.9	16 7.3	10 21.8
20 W	17 48 43.2	27 39.5	15 20.4	3♍44.2	5 46.3	5 28.4	13 10.2	9 30.4	13 21.8	17 33.1	16 8.9	10 23.3
21 T	17 52 39.8	28 36.8	15 17.3	17 24.9	6 31.2	6 41.1	13 49.2	9 27.4	13 22.2	17 33.2	16 10.5	10 24.8
22 F	17 56 36.4	29 34.0	15 14.1	1♎19.1	7 20.2	7 53.8	14 28.2	9 24.6	13 22.6	17 33.3	16 12.2	10 26.3
23 S	18 0 32.9	0♋31.3	15 10.9	15 26.9	8 13.4	9 6.6	15 7.2	9 22.0	13 23.2	17 33.3	16 13.8	10 27.8
24 S	18 4 29.5	1 28.5	15 7.7	29 47.5	9 10.5	10 19.3	15 46.2	9 19.5	13 23.9	17R33.3	16 15.5	10 29.3
25 M	18 8 26.0	2 25.7	15 4.5	14♏18.4	10 11.6	11 32.1	16 25.1	9 17.2	13 24.6	17 33.2	16 17.2	10 30.8
26 T	18 12 22.6	3 22.9	15 1.4	28 55.0	11 16.6	12 44.9	17 4.0	9 15.1	13 25.5	17 33.1	16 18.9	10 32.3
27 W	18 16 19.2	4 20.1	14 58.2	13♐31.4	12 25.4	13 57.7	17 42.9	9 13.1	13 26.5	17 32.9	16 20.7	10 33.8
28 T	18 20 15.7	5 17.3	14 55.0	28 0.3	13 38.0	15 10.6	18 21.7	9 11.4	13 27.5	17 32.7	16 22.4	10 35.3
29 F	18 24 12.2	6 14.5	14 51.8	12♑15.0	14 54.4	16 23.5	19 0.6	9 9.8	13 28.7	17 32.4	16 24.2	10 36.8
30 S	18 28 8.8	7 11.6	14 48.7	26 9.8	16 14.5	17 36.4	19 39.4	9 8.4	13 30.0	17 32.1	16 26.0	10 38.3

DECLINATION

DAY	SIDEREAL TIME	☉	☊	☽	☿	♀	♂	♃	♄	♅	♆	♇
1 F	16 33 48.7	21N52.9	5N23.4	18S35.9	18N29.2	14N 3.8	24N24.9	13S54.9	2S54.9	5S42.1	16N19.3	20N28.6
4 M	16 45 38.3	22 17.0	5 27.1	13 52.6	17 35.8	15 11.3	24 24.1	13 50.1	2 53.9	5 41.1	16 18.2	20 28.6
7 T	16 57 28.0	22 37.7	5 30.8	3 38.3	16 57.1	16 15.6	24 21.6	13 45.7	2 53.3	5 40.2	16 17.1	20 28.5
10 S	17 9 17.7	22 54.8	5 34.5	7N29.6	16 36.2	17 16.5	24 17.2	13 41.8	2 53.0	5 39.5	16 16.0	20 28.5
13 W	17 21 7.4	23 8.3	5 38.1	16 3.4	16 33.6	18 13.5	24 11.1	13 38.2	2 53.0	5 38.9	16 14.8	20 28.4
16 S	17 32 57.0	23 18.2	5 41.8	18 29.9	16 48.6	19 6.5	24 3.2	13 35.1	2 53.4	5 38.5	16 13.5	20 28.3
19 T	17 44 46.7	23 24.3	5 45.5	12 45.5	17 18.8	19 55.0	23 53.7	13 32.5	2 54.2	5 38.3	16 12.1	20 28.1
22 F	17 56 36.4	23 26.8	5 49.2	0 49.0	18 1.6	20 38.9	23 42.4	13 30.4	2 55.3	5 38.3	16 10.7	20 28.0
25 M	18 8 26.0	23 25.5	5 52.9	11S57.8	18 53.7	21 17.8	23 29.4	13 28.8	2 56.8	5 38.4	16 9.2	20 27.9
28 T	18 20 15.7	23 20.5	5 56.6	18 32.5	19 51.6	21 51.6	23 14.9	13 27.7	2 58.6	5 38.7	16 7.6	20 27.7

JULY 1923

DAY	EPHEMERIS SIDEREAL TIME h m s	☉ ° ′	☊ ° ′	☽ ° ′	☿ ° ′	♀ ° ′	♂ ° ′	♃ ° ′	♄ ° ′	♅ ° ′	♆ ° ′	♇ ° ′
						LONGITUDE						
1 S	18 32 5.4	8♋ 8.8	14♍45.5	9♒41.4	17♊38.2	18♊49.3	20♋18.2	9♏ 7.2	13♎31.3	17♓31.8	16♌27.8	10♋39.8
2 M	18 36 1.9	9 6.0	14 42.3	22 48.6	19 5.6	20 2.2	20 57.0	9R 6.1	13 32.8	17R31.4	16 29.7	10 41.3
3 T	18 39 58.5	10 3.2	14 39.1	5♓32.6	20 36.5	21 15.2	21 35.7	9 5.2	13 34.3	17 30.9	16 31.5	10 42.8
4 W	18 43 55.0	11 0.4	14 36.0	17 56.5	22 10.9	22 28.2	22 14.5	9 4.6	13 36.0	17 30.4	16 33.4	10 44.3
5 T	18 47 51.6	11 57.6	14 32.8	0♈ 4.4	23 48.8	23 41.2	22 53.2	9 4.0	13 37.7	17 29.9	16 35.3	10 45.9
6 F	18 51 48.1	12 54.8	14 29.6	12 1.3	25 30.0	24 54.2	23 31.9	9 3.7	13 39.6	17 29.3	16 37.2	10 47.4
7 S	18 55 44.7	13 52.0	14 26.4	23 52.5	27 14.5	26 7.3	24 10.7	9 3.6	13 41.5	17 28.7	16 39.1	10 48.9
8 S	18 59 41.3	14 49.2	14 23.3	5♉43.1	29 2.2	27 20.4	24 49.3	9D 3.6	13 43.5	17 28.0	16 41.0	10 50.4
9 M	19 3 37.8	15 46.4	14 20.1	17 37.9	0♋52.9	28 33.5	25 28.0	9 3.8	13 45.7	17 27.2	16 43.0	10 51.9
10 T	19 7 34.4	16 43.6	14 16.9	29 41.2	2 46.4	29 46.7	26 6.7	9 4.2	13 47.9	17 26.5	16 45.0	10 53.4
11 W	19 11 30.9	17 40.8	14 13.7	11♊56.3	4 42.7	0♋59.9	26 45.3	9 4.8	13 50.2	17 25.7	16 47.0	10 54.9
12 T	19 15 27.5	18 38.0	14 10.5	24 25.4	6 41.4	2 13.1	27 23.9	9 5.6	13 52.6	17 24.8	16 49.0	10 56.4
13 F	19 19 24.1	19 35.3	14 7.4	7♋ 9.7	8 42.3	3 26.3	28 2.6	9 6.5	13 55.1	17 23.9	16 51.0	10 57.9
14 S	19 23 20.6	20 32.5	14 4.2	20 9.3	10 45.1	4 39.5	28 41.1	9 7.6	13 57.7	17 22.9	16 53.0	10 59.4
15 S	19 27 17.2	21 29.8	14 1.0	3♌23.4	12 49.7	5 52.8	29 19.7	9 8.9	14 0.4	17 21.9	16 55.0	11 0.9
16 M	19 31 13.7	22 27.0	13 57.8	16 50.3	14 55.6	7 6.1	29 58.3	9 10.4	14 3.2	17 20.9	16 57.1	11 2.4
17 T	19 35 10.3	23 24.3	13 54.7	0♍28.5	17 2.6	8 19.4	0♌36.9	9 12.0	14 6.1	17 19.8	16 59.2	11 3.9
18 W	19 39 6.8	24 21.5	13 51.5	14 16.0	19 10.3	9 32.7	1 15.4	9 13.9	14 9.0	17 18.7	17 1.2	11 5.4
19 T	19 43 3.4	25 18.8	13 48.3	28 11.7	21 18.4	10 46.1	1 53.9	9 15.9	14 12.1	17 17.5	17 3.3	11 6.9
20 F	19 46 60.0	26 16.0	13 45.1	12♎14.1	23 26.7	11 59.5	2 32.4	9 18.1	14 15.2	17 16.3	17 5.4	11 8.4
21 S	19 50 56.5	27 13.3	13 42.0	26 22.2	25 34.9	13 12.9	3 10.9	9 20.4	14 18.4	17 15.0	17 7.5	11 9.8
22 S	19 54 53.1	28 10.6	13 38.8	10♏34.6	27 42.7	14 26.3	3 49.4	9 23.0	14 21.7	17 13.8	17 9.7	11 11.3
23 M	19 58 49.6	29 7.8	13 35.6	24 49.3	29 49.8	15 39.8	4 27.9	9 25.7	14 25.1	17 12.4	17 11.8	11 12.7
24 T	20 2 46.2	0♌ 5.1	13 32.4	9♐ 3.5	1♌56.2	16 53.2	5 6.3	9 28.5	14 28.6	17 11.0	17 13.9	11 14.2
25 W	20 6 42.7	1 2.4	13 29.2	23 13.6	4 1.6	18 6.8	5 44.8	9 31.6	14 32.2	17 9.6	17 16.1	11 15.6
26 T	20 10 39.3	1 59.7	13 26.1	7♑15.6	6 5.8	19 20.3	6 23.2	9 34.8	14 35.8	17 8.2	17 18.2	11 17.1
27 F	20 14 35.8	2 57.0	13 22.9	21 5.3	8 8.7	20 33.8	7 1.6	9 38.2	14 39.6	17 6.7	17 20.4	11 18.5
28 S	20 18 32.4	3 54.3	13 19.7	4♒39.3	10 10.3	21 47.4	7 40.0	9 41.7	14 43.4	17 5.2	17 22.6	11 19.9
29 S	20 22 29.0	4 51.6	13 16.5	17 55.0	12 10.5	23 1.0	8 18.4	9 45.4	14 47.3	17 3.6	17 24.7	11 21.3
30 M	20 26 25.5	5 49.0	13 13.4	0♓51.6	14 9.2	24 14.6	8 56.7	9 49.3	14 51.2	17 2.0	17 26.9	11 22.7
31 T	20 30 22.1	6 46.3	13 10.2	13 29.4	16 6.3	25 28.3	9 35.1	9 53.4	14 55.3	17 0.4	17 29.1	11 24.1

						DECLINATION						
1 S	18 32 5.4	23N11.8	6N 0.3	15S 6.1	20N51.2	22N19.9	22N58.7	13S27.1	3S 0.8	5S39.2	16N 6.0	20N27.5
4 W	18 43 55.0	22 59.4	6 3.9	5 8.2	21 48.3	22 42.5	22 40.9	13 27.0	3 3.3	5 39.8	16 4.4	20 27.3
7 S	18 55 44.7	22 43.5	6 7.6	6N11.1	22 37.9	22 59.4	22 21.7	13 27.5	3 6.1	5 40.6	16 2.7	20 27.1
10 T	19 7 34.4	22 23.9	6 11.3	15 15.0	23 14.6	23 10.4	22 0.9	13 28.4	3 9.3	5 41.6	16 0.9	20 26.9
13 F	19 19 24.1	22 1.0	6 15.0	18 36.9	23 33.1	23 15.3	21 38.7	13 29.9	3 12.8	5 42.7	15 59.1	20 26.7
16 M	19 31 13.7	21 34.6	6 18.6	13 40.6	23 29.5	23 14.1	21 15.0	13 31.9	3 16.5	5 43.9	15 57.3	20 26.5
19 T	19 43 3.4	21 4.9	6 22.3	2 0.5	23 1.5	23 6.8	20 50.0	13 34.4	3 20.6	5 45.4	15 55.4	20 26.2
22 S	19 54 53.1	20 32.0	6 26.0	10S49.8	22 9.6	22 53.3	20 23.7	13 37.4	3 25.0	5 46.9	15 53.5	20 26.0
25 W	20 6 42.7	19 56.0	6 29.6	18 13.1	20 56.2	22 33.9	19 56.1	13 40.9	3 29.7	5 48.6	15 51.6	20 25.8
28 S	20 18 32.4	19 17.0	6 33.3	16 3.4	19 25.2	22 8.4	19 27.2	13 44.8	3 34.6	5 50.4	15 49.7	20 25.5
31 T	20 30 22.1	18 35.1	6 36.9	6 38.0	17 40.6	21 37.1	18 57.2	13 49.2	3 39.8	5 52.3	15 47.7	20 25.3

AUGUST 1923

						LONGITUDE						
1 W	20 34 18.6	7♌43.7	13♍ 7.0	25♓50.5	18♌ 1.9	26♋42.0	10♌13.5	9♏57.6	14♎59.4	16♓58.7	17♌31.3	11♋25.5
2 T	20 38 15.2	8 41.1	13 3.8	7♈57.8	19 55.8	27 55.7	10 51.8	10 1.9	15 3.6	16R57.0	17 33.5	11 26.9
3 F	20 42 11.7	9 38.5	13 0.6	19 55.3	21 48.2	29 9.4	11 30.2	10 6.4	15 7.9	16 55.3	17 35.7	11 28.2
4 S	20 46 8.3	10 35.9	12 57.5	1♉47.5	23 39.0	0♌23.2	12 8.5	10 11.1	15 12.3	16 53.5	17 37.9	11 29.6
5 S	20 50 4.8	11 33.4	12 54.3	13 39.3	25 28.1	1 37.0	12 46.8	10 16.0	15 16.7	16 51.7	17 40.1	11 30.9
6 M	20 54 1.4	12 30.8	12 51.1	25 35.5	27 15.7	2 50.8	13 25.1	10 20.9	15 21.2	16 49.9	17 42.4	11 32.3
7 T	20 57 57.9	13 28.3	12 47.9	7♊40.9	29 1.7	4 4.6	14 3.4	10 26.1	15 25.8	16 48.0	17 44.6	11 33.6
8 W	21 1 54.5	14 25.8	12 44.8	19 59.5	0♍46.1	5 18.5	14 41.8	10 31.4	15 30.5	16 46.2	17 46.8	11 34.9
9 T	21 5 51.1	15 23.4	12 41.6	2♋34.6	2 28.9	6 32.4	15 20.1	10 36.9	15 35.2	16 44.2	17 49.0	11 36.2
10 F	21 9 47.6	16 20.9	12 38.4	15 28.5	4 10.2	7 46.3	15 58.3	10 42.5	15 40.0	16 42.3	17 51.2	11 37.5
11 S	21 13 44.1	17 18.5	12 35.2	28 42.1	5 49.9	9 0.3	16 36.6	10 48.2	15 44.9	16 40.3	17 53.5	11 38.8
12 S	21 17 40.7	18 16.1	12 32.0	12♌14.8	7 28.1	10 14.2	17 14.9	10 54.1	15 49.8	16 38.3	17 55.7	11 40.0
13 M	21 21 37.3	19 13.7	12 28.9	26 4.5	9 4.7	11 28.2	17 53.2	11 0.2	15 54.9	16 36.3	17 57.9	11 41.3
14 T	21 25 33.9	20 11.3	12 25.7	10♍ 8.2	10 39.9	12 42.3	18 31.4	11 6.4	15 59.9	16 34.2	18 0.1	11 42.5
15 W	21 29 30.4	21 9.0	12 22.5	24 21.9	12 13.5	13 56.3	19 9.7	11 12.7	16 5.1	16 32.1	18 2.4	11 43.7
16 T	21 33 26.9	22 6.6	12 19.3	8♎41.4	13 45.5	15 10.4	19 47.9	11 19.2	16 10.3	16 30.0	18 4.6	11 44.9
17 F	21 37 23.5	23 4.3	12 16.2	23 2.7	15 16.1	16 24.5	20 26.2	11 25.8	16 15.6	16 27.9	18 6.8	11 46.1
18 S	21 41 20.1	24 2.0	12 13.0	7♏22.3	16 45.1	17 38.6	21 4.4	11 32.6	16 20.9	16 25.7	18 9.0	11 47.3
19 S	21 45 16.6	24 59.8	12 9.8	21 37.2	18 12.5	18 52.7	21 42.6	11 39.5	16 26.3	16 23.6	18 11.2	11 48.5
20 M	21 49 13.1	25 57.5	12 6.6	5♐45.0	19 38.4	20 6.9	22 20.9	11 46.5	16 31.8	16 21.4	18 13.4	11 49.6
21 T	21 53 9.7	26 55.3	12 3.4	19 43.8	21 2.6	21 21.0	22 59.1	11 53.7	16 37.3	16 19.2	18 15.6	11 50.8
22 W	21 57 6.3	27 53.0	12 0.3	3♑32.0	22 25.3	22 35.2	23 37.3	12 1.0	16 42.9	16 16.9	18 17.9	11 51.9
23 T	22 1 2.8	28 50.8	11 57.1	17 8.3	23 46.3	23 49.4	24 15.5	12 8.4	16 48.5	16 14.7	18 20.1	11 53.0
24 F	22 4 59.4	29 48.6	11 53.9	0♒31.4	25 5.6	25 3.7	24 53.7	12 16.0	16 54.2	16 12.4	18 22.2	11 54.1
25 S	22 8 55.9	0♍46.5	11 50.7	13 40.5	26 23.1	26 17.9	25 31.9	12 23.7	16 60.0	16 10.2	18 24.4	11 55.1
26 S	22 12 52.4	1 44.3	11 47.6	26 35.2	27 38.9	27 32.2	26 10.0	12 31.5	17 5.8	16 7.9	18 26.6	11 56.2
27 M	22 16 49.0	2 42.2	11 44.4	9♓15.4	28 52.9	28 46.5	26 48.2	12 39.4	17 11.7	16 5.6	18 28.8	11 57.2
28 T	22 20 45.6	3 40.2	11 41.2	21 41.8	0♎ 4.9	0♍ 0.8	27 26.4	12 47.5	17 17.6	16 3.3	18 30.9	11 58.3
29 W	22 24 42.1	4 38.1	11 38.0	3♈55.7	1 15.0	1 15.1	28 4.6	12 55.7	17 23.6	16 0.9	18 33.1	11 59.3
30 T	22 28 38.6	5 36.1	11 34.8	15 59.3	2 22.9	2 29.5	28 42.7	13 4.0	17 29.6	15 58.6	18 35.2	12 0.2
31 F	22 32 35.2	6 34.1	11 31.7	27 55.2	3 28.7	3 43.8	29 20.9	13 12.4	17 35.7	15 56.2	18 37.4	12 1.2

						DECLINATION						
1 W	20 34 18.6	18N20.6	6N38.2	2S48.9	17N 3.3	21N25.4	18N46.9	13S50.7	3S41.6	5S53.0	15N47.0	20N25.2
4 S	20 46 8.3	17 35.1	6 41.8	8N20.6	15 6.1	20 46.5	18 15.3	13 55.7	3 47.1	5 55.1	15 45.1	20 24.9
7 T	20 57 57.9	16 47.0	6 45.5	16 27.3	13 2.9	20 2.3	17 42.6	14 1.1	3 52.9	5 57.3	15 43.1	20 24.6
10 F	21 9 47.6	15 56.5	6 49.1	18 13.7	10 56.3	19 12.8	17 8.9	14 6.9	3 58.9	5 59.6	15 41.0	20 24.4
13 M	21 21 37.3	15 3.6	6 52.7	11 30.7	8 48.2	18 18.4	16 34.1	14 13.0	4 5.1	6 2.0	15 39.0	20 24.1
16 T	21 33 26.9	14 8.7	6 56.4	1S14.1	6 40.3	17 19.4	15 58.4	14 19.6	4 11.5	6 4.5	15 37.0	20 23.9
19 S	21 45 16.6	13 11.6	7 0.0	13 23.3	4 33.9	16 15.9	15 21.7	14 26.5	4 18.1	6 7.1	15 35.0	20 23.6
22 W	21 57 6.3	12 12.7	7 3.7	18 30.9	2 30.5	15 8.4	14 44.2	14 33.7	4 24.9	6 9.7	15 33.0	20 23.4
25 S	22 8 55.9	11 12.1	7 7.3	14 21.7	0 31.2	13 57.1	14 5.9	14 41.2	4 31.9	6 12.3	15 31.0	20 23.1
28 T	22 20 45.6	10 9.9	7 10.9	4 9.6	1S22.6	12 42.4	13 26.8	14 49.0	4 39.0	6 15.1	15 29.0	20 22.9
31 F	22 32 35.2	9 6.2	7 14.6	7N 9.1	3 9.3	11 24.5	12 46.9	14 57.1	4 46.3	6 17.8	15 27.1	20 22.6

SEPTEMBER 1923

DAY	EPHEMERIS SIDEREAL TIME	☉	☊	☽	☿	♀	♂	♃	♄	♅	♆	♇
	h m s	° '	° '	° '	° '	° '	° '	° '	° '	° '	° '	° '
						LONGITUDE						
1 S	22 36 31.8	7♍32.1	11♍28.5	9♉47.0	4♎32.2	4♍58.3	29♌59.1	13♏20.9	17♎41.8	15♓53.9	18♌39.5	12♋2.1
2 S	22 40 28.4	8 30.1	11 25.3	21 38.5	5 33.3	6 12.7	0♍37.3	13 29.6	17 48.0	15R51.5	18 41.6	12 3.1
3 M	22 44 24.9	9 28.2	11 22.1	3♊34.2	6 31.9	7 27.1	1 15.4	13 38.3	17 54.2	15 49.1	18 43.7	12 4.0
4 T	22 48 21.4	10 26.4	11 19.0	15 38.5	7 27.7	8 41.6	1 53.6	13 47.2	18 0.5	15 46.7	18 45.8	12 4.9
5 W	22 52 18.0	11 24.5	11 15.8	27 56.0	8 20.7	9 56.0	2 31.8	13 56.2	18 6.8	15 44.3	18 47.9	12 5.8
6 T	22 56 14.6	12 22.7	11 12.6	10♋30.9	9 10.6	11 10.6	3 9.9	14 5.3	18 13.1	15 41.9	18 50.0	12 6.6
7 F	23 0 11.1	13 20.9	11 9.4	23 26.6	9 57.3	12 25.1	3 48.1	14 14.5	18 19.6	15 39.5	18 52.1	12 7.4
8 S	23 4 7.6	14 19.2	11 6.2	6♌45.6	10 40.5	13 39.6	4 26.3	14 23.9	18 26.0	15 37.1	18 54.1	12 8.3
9 S	23 8 4.2	15 17.5	11 3.1	20 28.6	11 19.9	14 54.2	5 4.4	14 33.3	18 32.5	15 34.7	18 56.2	12 9.1
10 M	23 12 0.8	16 15.8	10 59.9	4♍34.4	11 55.4	16 8.7	5 42.6	14 42.8	18 39.0	15 32.3	18 58.2	12 9.8
11 T	23 15 57.3	17 14.2	10 56.7	18 59.6	12 26.6	17 23.3	6 20.8	14 52.5	18 45.6	15 29.9	19 0.2	12 10.6
12 W	23 19 53.9	18 12.5	10 53.5	3♎38.9	12 53.2	18 37.9	6 58.9	15 2.2	18 52.2	15 27.5	19 2.2	12 11.3
13 T	23 23 50.4	19 11.0	10 50.4	18 25.5	13 14.9	19 52.6	7 37.1	15 12.0	18 58.9	15 25.1	19 4.2	12 12.0
14 F	23 27 47.0	20 9.4	10 47.2	3♏12.3	13 31.3	21 7.2	8 15.3	15 22.0	19 5.6	15 22.8	19 6.2	12 12.7
15 S	23 31 43.5	21 7.9	10 44.0	17 52.4	13 42.2	22 21.8	8 53.4	15 32.0	19 12.3	15 20.4	19 8.1	12 13.4
16 S	23 35 40.1	22 6.4	10 40.8	2♐20.3	13 47.1	23 36.5	9 31.6	15 42.1	19 19.1	15 18.0	19 10.1	12 14.1
17 M	23 39 36.6	23 4.9	10 37.6	16 32.2	13R45.8	24 51.2	10 9.7	15 52.4	19 25.8	15 15.6	19 12.0	12 14.7
18 T	23 43 33.2	24 3.4	10 34.5	0♑26.2	13 37.9	26 5.8	10 47.9	16 2.7	19 32.7	15 13.2	19 13.9	12 15.3
19 W	23 47 29.7	25 2.0	10 31.3	14 1.8	13 23.2	27 20.5	11 26.0	16 13.1	19 39.5	15 10.9	19 15.8	12 15.9
20 T	23 51 26.3	26 0.6	10 28.1	27 19.7	13 1.4	28 35.2	12 4.2	16 23.6	19 46.4	15 8.5	19 17.6	12 16.4
21 F	23 55 22.8	26 59.3	10 24.9	10♒21.4	12 32.6	29 49.9	12 42.4	16 34.1	19 53.3	15 6.2	19 19.5	12 17.0
22 S	23 59 19.4	27 57.9	10 21.8	23 8.4	11 56.7	1♎4.7	13 20.5	16 44.8	20 0.3	15 3.9	19 21.3	12 17.5
23 S	0 3 15.9	28 56.6	10 18.6	5♓42.5	11 13.9	2 19.4	13 58.7	16 55.6	20 7.2	15 1.6	19 23.1	12 18.0
24 M	0 7 12.5	29 55.3	10 15.4	18 5.3	10 24.6	3 34.1	14 36.8	17 6.4	20 14.2	14 59.3	19 24.9	12 18.5
25 T	0 11 9.1	0♎54.1	10 12.2	0♈18.3	9 29.5	4 48.9	15 15.0	17 17.3	20 21.3	14 57.0	19 26.7	12 18.9
26 W	0 15 5.6	1 52.9	10 9.0	12 23.1	8 29.4	6 3.6	15 53.2	17 28.3	20 28.3	14 54.7	19 28.5	12 19.3
27 T	0 19 2.2	2 51.7	10 5.9	24 21.3	7 25.4	7 18.4	16 31.3	17 39.4	20 35.4	14 52.5	19 30.2	12 19.7
28 F	0 22 58.7	3 50.6	10 2.7	6♉14.7	6 18.9	8 33.2	17 9.5	17 50.5	20 42.5	14 50.2	19 31.9	12 20.1
29 S	0 26 55.3	4 49.4	9 59.5	18 5.6	5 11.5	9 47.9	17 47.7	18 1.7	20 49.6	14 48.0	19 33.6	12 20.5
30 S	0 30 51.8	5 48.4	9 56.3	29 56.9	4 4.7	11 2.7	18 25.8	18 13.0	20 56.7	14 45.8	19 35.3	12 20.8

						DECLINATION						
1 S	22 36 31.8	8N44.7	7N15.8	10N28.5	3S43.1	10N57.8	12N33.5	14S59.9	4S48.7	6S18.7	15N26.4	20N22.6
4 T	22 48 21.4	7 39.3	7 19.4	17 25.6	5 17.8	9 36.3	11 52.7	15 8.3	4 56.2	6 21.5	15 24.5	20 22.3
7 F	23 0 11.1	6 32.8	7 23.0	17 31.6	6 40.7	8 12.3	11 11.2	15 16.9	5 3.8	6 24.3	15 22.6	20 22.1
10 M	23 12 0.8	5 25.3	7 26.6	9 14.4	7 48.7	6 46.2	10 29.2	15 25.8	5 11.5	6 27.1	15 20.7	20 21.9
13 T	23 23 50.4	4 17.0	7 30.3	4S17.0	8 37.9	5 18.4	9 46.5	15 34.9	5 19.3	6 29.9	15 18.9	20 21.7
16 S	23 35 40.1	3 8.0	7 33.9	15 31.4	9 3.2	3 49.3	9 3.4	15 44.1	5 27.1	6 32.6	15 17.1	20 21.6
19 W	23 47 29.7	1 58.4	7 37.5	18 16.8	8 58.4	2 19.0	8 19.8	15 53.5	5 35.1	6 35.4	15 15.4	20 21.4
22 S	23 59 19.4	0 48.6	7 41.1	12 14.1	8 17.9	0 48.1	7 35.8	16 3.0	5 43.1	6 38.0	15 13.7	20 21.2
25 T	0 11 9.1	0S21.5	7 44.7	1 26.1	6 59.1	0S43.3	6 51.4	16 12.7	5 51.2	6 40.7	15 12.0	20 21.1
28 F	0 22 58.7	1 31.7	7 48.3	9N33.4	5 7.1	2 14.8	6 6.6	16 22.4	5 59.3	6 43.2	15 10.5	20 21.0

OCTOBER 1923

						LONGITUDE						
1 M	0 34 48.4	6♎47.3	9♍53.1	11♊51.9	3♎0.5	12♎17.5	19♍4.0	18♏24.4	21♎3.9	14♓43.7	19♌36.9	12♋21.1
2 T	0 38 44.9	7 46.3	9 50.0	23 54.3	2R 0.5	13 32.4	19 42.2	18 35.9	21 11.0	14R41.5	19 38.5	12 21.4
3 W	0 42 41.5	8 45.4	9 46.8	6♋8.5	1 6.4	14 47.2	20 20.4	18 47.4	21 18.2	14 39.4	19 40.1	12 21.7
4 T	0 46 38.0	9 44.5	9 43.6	18 38.8	0 19.8	16 2.0	20 58.6	18 59.0	21 25.4	14 37.3	19 41.7	12 21.9
5 F	0 50 34.6	10 43.6	9 40.4	1♌29.7	29♍41.8	17 16.9	21 36.8	19 10.6	21 32.7	14 35.2	19 43.3	12 22.2
6 S	0 54 31.1	11 42.8	9 37.3	14 44.7	29 13.4	18 31.7	22 15.0	19 22.4	21 39.9	14 33.1	19 44.8	12 22.4
7 S	0 58 27.7	12 42.0	9 34.1	28 26.4	28 55.3	19 46.6	22 53.2	19 34.1	21 47.1	14 31.1	19 46.3	12 22.5
8 M	1 2 24.2	13 41.2	9 30.9	12♍35.5	28 47.8	21 1.5	23 31.4	19 46.0	21 54.4	14 29.1	19 47.7	12 22.7
9 T	1 6 20.8	14 40.5	9 27.7	27 10.0	28D51.1	22 16.3	24 9.6	19 57.9	22 1.7	14 27.1	19 49.2	12 22.8
10 W	1 10 17.3	15 39.8	9 24.5	12♎4.8	29 4.9	23 31.2	24 47.9	20 9.9	22 8.9	14 25.2	19 50.6	12 22.9
11 T	1 14 13.9	16 39.1	9 21.4	27 12.2	29 29.0	24 46.1	25 26.1	20 21.9	22 16.2	14 23.2	19 52.0	12 23.0
12 F	1 18 10.4	17 38.5	9 18.2	12♏22.4	0♎2.8	26 1.0	26 4.3	20 34.0	22 23.5	14 21.3	19 53.4	12 23.0
13 S	1 22 7.0	18 37.9	9 15.0	27 25.5	0 45.6	27 15.9	26 42.5	20 46.2	22 30.8	14 19.5	19 54.7	12 23.0
14 S	1 26 3.5	19 37.3	9 11.8	12♐12.6	1 36.7	28 30.8	27 20.8	20 58.4	22 38.1	14 17.7	19 56.1	12 23.1
15 M	1 30 0.1	20 36.8	9 8.7	26 37.6	2 35.4	29 45.7	27 59.0	21 10.7	22 45.4	14 15.9	19 57.4	12R23.0
16 T	1 33 56.6	21 36.3	9 5.5	10♑37.4	3 40.8	1♏0.6	28 37.2	21 23.0	22 52.7	14 14.1	19 58.6	12 23.0
17 W	1 37 53.2	22 35.8	9 2.3	24 11.7	4 52.1	2 15.6	29 15.5	21 35.4	23 0.0	14 12.4	19 59.9	12 22.9
18 T	1 41 49.8	23 35.4	8 59.1	7♒22.1	6 8.7	3 30.5	29 53.7	21 47.8	23 7.4	14 10.7	20 1.1	12 22.8
19 F	1 45 46.3	24 35.0	8 55.9	20 11.8	7 29.7	4 45.4	0♎32.0	22 0.3	23 14.7	14 9.0	20 2.2	12 22.7
20 S	1 49 42.9	25 34.6	8 52.8	2♓44.4	8 54.6	6 0.3	1 10.2	22 12.8	23 22.0	14 7.4	20 3.4	12 22.6
21 S	1 53 39.4	26 34.2	8 49.6	15 3.4	10 22.7	7 15.2	1 48.5	22 25.3	23 29.3	14 5.8	20 4.5	12 22.4
22 M	1 57 35.9	27 33.9	8 46.4	27 12.4	11 53.4	8 30.1	2 26.7	22 37.9	23 36.6	14 4.3	20 5.6	12 22.2
23 T	2 1 32.5	28 33.6	8 43.2	9♈14.0	13 26.4	9 45.0	3 5.0	22 50.6	23 43.9	14 2.8	20 6.6	12 22.0
24 W	2 5 29.1	29 33.4	8 40.1	21 10.6	15 1.2	10 59.9	3 43.3	23 3.3	23 51.2	14 1.3	20 7.7	12 21.8
25 T	2 9 25.6	0♏33.1	8 36.9	3♉4.0	16 37.4	12 14.9	4 21.5	23 16.0	23 58.5	13 59.9	20 8.7	12 21.5
26 F	2 13 22.2	1 32.9	8 33.7	14 55.8	18 14.7	13 29.8	4 59.8	23 28.8	24 5.7	13 58.5	20 9.6	12 21.3
27 S	2 17 18.7	2 32.8	8 30.5	26 47.5	19 52.9	14 44.7	5 38.1	23 41.6	24 13.0	13 57.1	20 10.6	12 21.0
28 S	2 21 15.3	3 32.6	8 27.3	8♊41.0	21 31.7	15 59.6	6 16.4	23 54.5	24 20.2	13 55.8	20 11.5	12 20.6
29 M	2 25 11.8	4 32.6	8 24.2	20 38.2	23 10.9	17 14.5	6 54.7	24 7.3	24 27.5	13 54.6	20 12.4	12 20.3
30 T	2 29 8.4	5 32.5	8 21.0	2♋41.9	24 50.4	18 29.5	7 33.0	24 20.3	24 34.7	13 53.4	20 13.2	12 19.9
31 W	2 33 4.9	6 32.5	8 17.8	14 55.2	26 30.0	19 44.4	8 11.3	24 33.2	24 41.9	13 52.2	20 14.0	12 19.5

						DECLINATION						
1 M	0 34 48.4	2S41.8	7N51.9	17N 2.1	2S58.8	3S46.0	5N21.5	16S32.2	6S 7.4	6S45.7	15N 8.9	20N20.9
4 T	0 46 38.0	3 51.6	7 55.5	18 2.1	0 59.1	5 16.6	4 36.2	16 42.1	6 15.6	6 48.2	15 7.5	20 20.8
7 S	0 58 27.7	5 1.1	7 59.1	10 56.1	0N28.1	6 46.3	3 50.6	16 52.1	6 23.8	6 50.5	15 6.1	20 20.7
10 W	1 10 17.3	6 10.0	8 2.7	2S18.9	1 9.0	8 14.7	3 4.9	17 2.1	6 31.9	6 52.7	15 4.8	20 20.7
13 S	1 22 7.0	7 18.2	8 6.2	14 41.1	1 1.9	9 41.6	2 19.0	17 12.1	6 40.1	6 54.9	15 3.5	20 20.7
16 T	1 33 56.6	8 25.5	8 9.8	18 32.6	0 13.0	11 6.4	1 32.9	17 22.1	6 48.2	6 56.9	15 2.3	20 20.7
19 F	1 45 46.3	9 31.7	8 13.4	13 1.8	1S 7.6	12 28.9	0 46.9	17 32.0	6 56.2	6 58.7	15 1.2	20 20.7
22 M	1 57 35.9	10 36.6	8 17.0	2 27.1	2 49.6	13 48.8	0 0.8	17 42.0	7 4.3	7 0.5	15 0.2	20 20.7
25 T	2 9 25.6	11♏40.2	8 20.5	8N43.2	4 44.5	15 5.5	0S45.2	17 51.9	7 12.2	7 2.1	14 59.3	20 20.8
28 S	2 21 15.3	12 42.1	8 24.1	16 43.8	6 45.7	16 18.9	1 31.2	18 1.8	7 20.1	7 3.6	14 58.5	20 20.9
31 W	2 33 4.9	13 42.3	8 27.7	18 28.5	8 48.7	17 28.5	2 17.1	18 11.5	7 27.9	7 4.9	14 57.7	20 21.0

NOVEMBER 1923

DAY	EPHEMERIS SIDEREAL TIME h m s	☉ ° ′	☊ ° ′	☾ ° ′	☿ ° ′	♀ ° ′	♂ ° ′	♃ ° ′	♄ ° ′	♅ ° ′	♆ ° ′	♇ ° ′
						LONGITUDE						
1 T	2 37 1.5	7♏32.5	8♍14.6	27♋22.1	28♎ 9.7	20♏59.3	8♎49.6	24♏46.2	24♎49.1	13♓51.0	20♌14.8	12♋19.1
2 F	2 40 58.1	8 32.5	8 11.5	10♌ 6.7	29 49.3	22 14.2	9 27.9	24 59.2	24 56.3	13R50.0	20 15.5	12R18.7
3 S	2 44 54.6	9 32.6	8 8.3	23 13.3	1♏28.8	23 29.2	10 6.3	25 12.3	25 3.5	13 48.9	20 16.2	12 18.2
4 S	2 48 51.2	10 32.7	8 5.1	6♍45.6	3 8.1	24 44.1	10 44.6	25 25.3	25 10.6	13 47.9	20 16.9	12 17.7
5 M	2 52 47.7	11 32.9	8 1.9	20 45.9	4 47.1	25 59.1	11 22.9	25 38.4	25 17.8	13 47.0	20 17.6	12 17.2
6 T	2 56 44.3	12 33.1	7 58.7	5♎14.3	6 25.9	27 14.0	12 1.3	25 51.6	25 24.9	13 46.0	20 18.2	12 16.7
7 W	3 0 40.8	13 33.3	7 55.6	20 7.7	8 4.4	28 29.0	12 39.7	26 4.7	25 32.0	13 45.2	20 18.8	12 16.2
8 T	3 4 37.4	14 33.6	7 52.4	5♏19.6	9 42.5	29 43.9	13 18.0	26 17.9	25 39.0	13 44.4	20 19.3	12 15.6
9 F	3 8 33.9	15 33.9	7 49.2	20 40.0	11 20.4	0♐58.8	13 56.4	26 31.1	25 46.1	13 43.6	20 19.8	12 15.0
10 S	3 12 30.5	16 34.2	7 46.0	5♐57.4	12 57.9	2 13.8	14 34.8	26 44.3	25 53.1	13 42.9	20 20.3	12 14.4
11 S	3 16 27.0	17 34.5	7 42.9	21 0.6	14 35.1	3 28.7	15 13.1	26 57.6	26 0.1	13 42.2	20 20.8	12 13.8
12 M	3 20 23.6	18 34.9	7 39.7	5♑40.7	16 12.0	4 43.7	15 51.5	27 10.8	26 7.1	13 41.6	20 21.2	12 13.1
13 T	3 24 20.2	19 35.3	7 36.5	19 52.4	17 48.5	5 58.6	16 29.9	27 24.1	26 14.0	13 41.0	20 21.5	12 12.4
14 W	3 28 16.7	20 35.7	7 33.3	3♒34.1	19 24.7	7 13.6	17 8.3	27 37.4	26 20.9	13 40.5	20 21.9	12 11.7
15 T	3 32 13.2	21 36.1	7 30.1	16 47.3	21 0.6	8 28.5	17 46.7	27 50.7	26 27.7	13 40.0	20 22.2	12 11.0
16 F	3 36 9.8	22 36.6	7 27.0	29 35.5	22 36.3	9 43.4	18 25.1	28 4.0	26 34.6	13 39.6	20 22.5	12 10.3
17 S	3 40 6.4	23 37.1	7 23.8	12♓ 3.3	24 11.6	10 58.4	19 3.5	28 17.3	26 41.4	13 39.2	20 22.7	12 9.5
18 S	3 44 2.9	24 37.6	7 20.6	24 15.5	25 46.7	12 13.3	19 41.9	28 30.6	26 48.2	13 38.9	20 22.9	12 8.8
19 M	3 47 59.5	25 38.1	7 17.4	6♈17.0	27 21.6	13 28.2	20 20.3	28 44.0	26 54.9	13 38.6	20 23.1	12 8.0
20 T	3 51 56.0	26 38.7	7 14.3	18 11.8	28 56.2	14 43.1	20 58.7	28 57.3	27 1.6	13 38.4	20 23.2	12 7.2
21 W	3 55 52.6	27 39.2	7 11.1	0♉ 3.3	0♐30.6	15 58.0	21 37.1	29 10.7	27 8.2	13 38.2	20 23.3	12 6.3
22 T	3 59 49.2	28 39.8	7 7.9	11 54.3	2 4.8	17 12.9	22 15.5	29 24.0	27 14.9	13 38.1	20 23.4	12 5.5
23 F	4 3 45.7	29 40.4	7 4.7	23 46.7	3 38.8	18 27.8	22 53.9	29 37.4	27 21.4	13 38.0	20 23.4	12 4.6
24 S	4 7 42.3	0♐41.1	7 1.5	5♊42.0	5 12.6	19 42.7	23 32.4	29 50.7	27 28.0	13 38.0	20R23.4	12 3.8
25 S	4 11 38.8	1 41.7	6 58.4	17 41.4	6 46.4	20 57.6	24 10.8	0♐ 4.1	27 34.4	13D38.1	20 23.4	12 2.9
26 M	4 15 35.4	2 42.4	6 55.2	29 45.9	8 19.9	22 12.5	24 49.2	0 17.5	27 40.9	13 38.2	20 23.3	12 1.9
27 T	4 19 31.9	3 43.1	6 52.0	11♋57.0	9 53.4	23 27.3	25 27.7	0 30.8	27 47.3	13 38.3	20 23.2	12 1.0
28 W	4 23 28.5	4 43.9	6 48.8	24 16.6	11 26.7	24 42.2	26 6.1	0 44.2	27 53.6	13 38.5	20 23.1	12 0.1
29 T	4 27 25.0	5 44.6	6 45.7	6♌47.2	12 59.9	25 57.1	26 44.6	0 57.5	27 60.0	13 38.7	20 22.9	11 59.1
30 F	4 31 21.6	6 45.4	6 42.5	19 31.9	14 33.1	27 12.0	27 23.1	1 10.9	28 6.2	13 39.0	20 22.7	11 58.1
						DECLINATION						
1 T	2 37 1.5	14S 1.9	8N28.9	17N19.8	9S29.5	17S50.9	2S32.4	18S14.8	7S30.5	7S 5.3	14N57.5	20N21.0
4 S	2 48 51.2	14 59.4	8 32.4	8 48.1	11 30.1	18 54.9	3 18.1	18 24.5	7 38.1	7 6.4	14 56.9	20 21.1
7 W	3 0 40.8	15 54.8	8 36.0	4S48.4	13 26.3	19 54.4	4 3.6	18 34.0	7 45.7	7 7.3	14 56.3	20 21.3
10 S	3 12 30.5	16 47.7	8 39.5	16 20.8	15 17.0	20 49.0	4 48.8	18 43.5	7 53.1	7 8.1	14 55.9	20 21.5
13 T	3 24 20.2	17 38.1	8 43.1	18 12.9	17 0.9	21 38.3	5 33.8	18 52.8	8 0.4	7 8.7	14 55.6	20 21.7
16 F	3 36 9.8	18 25.8	8 46.6	10 53.0	18 37.3	22 22.0	6 18.4	19 2.0	8 7.6	7 9.2	14 55.3	20 21.9
19 M	3 47 59.5	19 10.5	8 50.2	0N19.8	20 5.5	22 59.9	7 2.6	19 11.1	8 14.6	7 9.4	14 55.2	20 22.1
22 T	3 59 49.2	19 52.1	8 53.7	11 7.9	21 24.7	23 31.7	7 46.4	19 19.9	8 21.4	7 9.5	14 55.1	20 22.4
25 S	4 11 38.8	20 30.4	8 57.2	17 59.2	22 34.4	23 57.2	8 29.8	19 28.7	8 28.0	7 9.4	14 55.2	20 22.7
28 W	4 23 28.5	21 5.4	9 0.8	17 55.7	23 34.0	24 16.3	9 12.6	19 37.2	8 34.5	7 9.2	14 55.4	20 23.0

DECEMBER 1923

DAY	EPHEMERIS SIDEREAL TIME h m s	☉ ° ′	☊ ° ′	☾ ° ′	☿ ° ′	♀ ° ′	♂ ° ′	♃ ° ′	♄ ° ′	♅ ° ′	♆ ° ′	♇ ° ′
						LONGITUDE						
1 S	4 35 18.2	7♐46.2	6♍39.3	2♍34.3	16♐ 6.1	28♐26.8	28♎ 1.6	1♐24.2	28♎12.4	13♓39.3	20♌22.5	11♋57.2
2 S	4 39 14.7	8 47.1	6 36.1	15 57.9	17 39.1	29 41.7	28 40.0	1 37.5	28 18.6	13 39.7	20R22.2	11R56.1
3 M	4 43 11.3	9 47.9	6 33.0	29 45.6	19 12.0	0♑56.5	29 18.5	1 50.9	28 24.7	13 40.2	20 21.9	11 55.1
4 T	4 47 7.8	10 48.8	6 29.8	13♎58.9	20 44.8	2 11.4	29 57.0	2 4.2	28 30.7	13 40.7	20 21.6	11 54.1
5 W	4 51 4.4	11 49.7	6 26.6	28 36.7	22 17.6	3 26.2	0♏35.5	2 17.5	28 36.7	13 41.2	20 21.2	11 53.0
6 T	4 55 0.9	12 50.7	6 23.4	13♏34.8	23 50.2	4 41.1	1 14.0	2 30.8	28 42.7	13 41.8	20 20.8	11 52.0
7 F	4 58 57.5	13 51.6	6 20.3	28 45.5	25 22.8	5 55.9	1 52.5	2 44.0	28 48.6	13 42.5	20 20.3	11 50.9
8 S	5 2 54.0	14 52.6	6 17.1	13♐58.7	26 55.2	7 10.8	2 31.0	2 57.3	28 54.4	13 43.1	20 19.9	11 49.8
9 S	5 6 50.6	15 53.5	6 13.9	29 3.1	28 27.5	8 25.6	3 9.6	3 10.5	29 0.2	13 43.9	20 19.4	11 48.7
10 M	5 10 47.2	16 54.5	6 10.7	13♑48.9	29 59.6	9 40.4	3 48.1	3 23.7	29 5.9	13 44.7	20 18.8	11 47.6
11 T	5 14 43.7	17 55.6	6 7.5	28 8.8	1♑31.5	10 55.2	4 26.6	3 36.9	29 11.5	13 45.6	20 18.3	11 46.5
12 W	5 18 40.3	18 56.6	6 4.4	11♒59.2	3 3.1	12 10.0	5 5.1	3 50.1	29 17.1	13 46.5	20 17.7	11 45.4
13 T	5 22 36.8	19 57.6	6 1.2	25 20.1	4 34.4	13 24.8	5 43.6	4 3.2	29 22.6	13 47.4	20 17.0	11 44.2
14 F	5 26 33.4	20 58.6	5 58.0	8♓13.8	6 5.3	14 39.6	6 22.1	4 16.3	29 28.1	13 48.4	20 16.4	11 43.1
15 S	5 30 30.0	21 59.7	5 54.8	20 44.7	7 35.6	15 54.4	7 0.7	4 29.4	29 33.5	13 49.5	20 15.7	11 41.9
16 S	5 34 26.5	23 0.7	5 51.7	2♈57.8	9 5.4	17 9.1	7 39.2	4 42.5	29 38.8	13 50.6	20 14.9	11 40.8
17 M	5 38 23.1	24 1.8	5 48.5	14 58.5	10 34.4	18 23.8	8 17.7	4 55.5	29 44.0	13 51.7	20 14.2	11 39.6
18 T	5 42 19.6	25 2.9	5 45.3	26 51.6	12 2.6	19 38.5	8 56.2	5 8.5	29 49.2	13 52.9	20 13.4	11 38.4
19 W	5 46 16.2	26 3.9	5 42.1	8♉41.9	13 29.7	20 53.2	9 34.8	5 21.5	29 54.3	13 54.2	20 12.6	11 37.2
20 T	5 50 12.8	27 5.0	5 39.0	20 32.9	14 55.5	22 7.9	10 13.3	5 34.4	29 59.4	13 55.5	20 11.7	11 36.0
21 F	5 54 9.3	28 6.1	5 35.8	2♊27.8	16 19.8	23 22.6	10 51.8	5 47.3	0♏ 4.3	13 56.8	20 10.8	11 34.8
22 S	5 58 5.8	29 7.2	5 32.6	14 28.4	17 42.3	24 37.2	11 30.4	6 0.1	0 9.2	13 58.2	20 9.9	11 33.6
23 S	6 2 2.4	0♑ 8.3	5 29.4	26 36.4	19 2.6	25 51.9	12 8.9	6 13.0	0 14.1	13 59.7	20 9.0	11 32.4
24 M	6 5 59.0	1 9.4	5 26.2	8♋52.5	20 20.5	27 6.5	12 47.4	6 25.7	0 18.8	14 1.2	20 8.0	11 31.2
25 T	6 9 55.5	2 10.5	5 23.1	21 17.3	21 35.3	28 21.1	13 26.0	6 38.5	0 23.5	14 2.7	20 7.1	11 29.9
26 W	6 13 52.1	3 11.6	5 19.9	3♌51.5	22 46.8	29 35.7	14 4.5	6 51.2	0 28.1	14 4.3	20 6.0	11 28.7
27 T	6 17 48.6	4 12.8	5 16.7	16 36.0	23 54.1	0♒50.2	14 43.1	7 3.8	0 32.6	14 5.9	20 5.0	11 27.5
28 F	6 21 45.2	5 13.9	5 13.5	29 32.1	24 56.8	2 4.7	15 21.6	7 16.4	0 37.0	14 7.6	20 3.9	11 26.2
29 S	6 25 41.8	6 15.1	5 10.4	12♍41.7	25 54.1	3 19.3	16 0.2	7 29.0	0 41.4	14 9.3	20 2.8	11 25.0
30 S	6 29 38.3	7 16.2	5 7.2	26 6.8	26 45.2	4 33.8	16 38.8	7 41.5	0 45.6	14 11.1	20 1.7	11 23.8
31 M	6 33 34.9	8 17.4	5 4.0	9♎49.3	27 29.2	5 48.2	17 17.3	7 54.0	0 49.8	14 12.9	20 0.6	11 22.5
						DECLINATION						
1 S	4 35 18.2	21S36.7	9N 4.3	10N13.9	24S22.8	24S28.6	9S55.0	19S45.5	8S40.8	7S 8.7	14N55.6	20N23.3
4 T	4 47 7.8	22 4.4	9 7.8	2S41.7	25 0.2	24 34.3	10 36.7	19 53.7	8 46.9	7 8.1	14 55.9	20 23.7
7 F	4 58 57.5	22 28.2	9 11.4	15 2.5	25 25.5	24 33.1	11 17.8	20 1.7	8 52.7	7 7.3	14 56.4	20 24.0
10 M	5 10 47.2	22 48.1	9 14.9	18 48.3	25 38.3	24 25.2	11 58.1	20 9.4	8 58.4	7 6.3	14 56.9	20 24.4
13 T	5 22 36.8	23 4.0	9 18.4	12 15.1	25 37.9	24 10.5	12 37.8	20 17.0	9 3.8	7 5.2	14 57.5	20 24.8
16 S	5 34 26.5	23 15.7	9 21.9	0 58.7	25 24.2	23 49.2	13 16.7	20 24.3	9 8.9	7 3.8	14 58.3	20 25.2
19 W	5 46 16.2	23 23.3	9 25.4	10N 7.3	24 57.1	23 21.4	13 54.8	20 31.4	9 13.8	7 2.3	14 59.1	20 25.6
22 S	5 58 5.8	23 26.6	9 28.9	17 37.0	24 17.2	22 47.3	14 32.0	20 38.3	9 18.5	7 0.7	14 59.9	20 26.1
25 T	6 9 55.5	23 25.7	9 32.4	18 22.2	23 25.9	22 7.0	15 8.3	20 44.9	9 22.8	6 58.9	15 0.9	20 26.5
28 F	6 21 45.2	23 20.6	9 35.9	11 17.3	22 26.1	21 20.9	15 43.6	20 51.3	9 26.9	6 56.9	15 1.9	20 27.0
31 M	6 33 34.9	23 11.2	9 39.4	1S 7.1	21 22.3	20 29.2	16 18.0	20 57.4	9 30.8	6 54.7	15 3.1	20 27.5

JANUARY 1924

DAY	EPHEMERIS SIDEREAL TIME	☉	☊	☽	☿	♀	♂	♃	♄	♅	♆	♇
	h m s	° ′	° ′	° ′	° ′	° ′	° ′	° ′	° ′	° ′	° ′	° ′
						LONGITUDE						
1 T	6 37 31.4	9♑18.5	5♍ 0.8	23♎50.3	28♑ 5.4	7♒ 2.7	17♏55.9	8♐ 6.4	0♏53.9	14♓14.7	19♌59.4	11♋21.3
2 W	6 41 28.0	10 19.7	4 57.7	8♏ 9.7	28 32.6	8 17.2	18 34.5	8 18.8	0 57.9	14 16.6	19R58.2	11R20.0
3 T	6 45 24.6	11 20.9	4 54.5	22 45.1	28 50.2	9 31.6	19 13.0	8 31.1	1 1.9	14 18.6	19 57.0	11 18.8
4 F	6 49 21.1	12 22.1	4 51.3	7♐31.6	28 57.2	10 46.0	19 51.6	8 43.3	1 5.7	14 20.5	19 55.7	11 17.5
5 S	6 53 17.6	13 23.3	4 48.1	22 22.2	28R52.9	12 0.3	20 30.2	8 55.5	1 9.5	14 22.6	19 54.4	11 16.3
6 S	6 57 14.2	14 24.4	4 44.9	7♑ 8.6	28 37.0	13 14.7	21 8.7	9 7.7	1 13.1	14 24.6	19 53.2	11 15.0
7 M	7 1 10.8	15 25.6	4 41.8	21 42.5	28 9.1	14 29.0	21 47.3	9 19.7	1 16.7	14 26.7	19 51.8	11 13.8
8 T	7 5 7.3	16 26.8	4 38.6	5♒56.8	27 29.7	15 43.3	22 25.9	9 31.8	1 20.2	14 28.9	19 50.5	11 12.5
9 W	7 9 3.9	17 28.0	4 35.4	19 46.9	26 39.2	16 57.6	23 4.4	9 43.7	1 23.6	14 31.1	19 49.2	11 11.3
10 T	7 13 0.4	18 29.2	4 32.2	3♓11.1	25 38.9	18 11.8	23 43.0	9 55.6	1 26.9	14 33.3	19 47.8	11 10.1
11 F	7 16 57.0	19 30.3	4 29.1	16 10.0	24 30.5	19 26.0	24 21.5	10 7.4	1 30.1	14 35.6	19 46.4	11 8.8
12 S	7 20 53.5	20 31.5	4 25.9	28 46.2	23 16.0	20 40.2	25 0.1	10 19.1	1 33.2	14 37.9	19 45.0	11 7.6
13 S	7 24 50.1	21 32.6	4 22.7	11♈ 3.9	21 57.7	21 54.3	25 38.6	10 30.8	1 36.3	14 40.2	19 43.5	11 6.4
14 M	7 28 46.7	22 33.8	4 19.5	23 7.8	20 38.2	23 8.4	26 17.2	10 42.4	1 39.2	14 42.6	19 42.1	11 5.1
15 T	7 32 43.2	23 34.9	4 16.4	5♉ 2.9	19 20.0	24 22.5	26 55.7	10 53.9	1 42.0	14 45.0	19 40.6	11 3.9
16 W	7 36 39.8	24 36.0	4 13.2	16 54.3	18 5.4	25 36.5	27 34.2	11 5.4	1 44.7	14 47.5	19 39.1	11 2.7
17 T	7 40 36.3	25 37.1	4 10.0	28 46.6	16 56.3	26 50.5	28 12.7	11 16.8	1 47.4	14 50.0	19 37.7	11 1.5
18 F	7 44 32.9	26 38.2	4 6.8	10♊43.8	15 54.4	28 4.4	28 51.3	11 28.1	1 49.9	14 52.5	19 36.1	11 0.3
19 S	7 48 29.4	27 39.3	4 3.6	22 49.2	15 0.7	29 18.3	29 29.8	11 39.3	1 52.4	14 55.1	19 34.6	10 59.1
20 S	7 52 26.0	28 40.3	4 0.5	5♋ 5.1	14 16.1	0♓32.1	0♐ 8.3	11 50.4	1 54.7	14 57.7	19 33.1	10 57.9
21 M	7 56 22.6	29 41.4	3 57.3	17 33.2	13 40.7	1 45.9	0 46.8	12 1.5	1 56.9	15 0.3	19 31.5	10 56.8
22 T	8 0 19.1	0♒42.4	3 54.1	0♌14.1	13 14.7	2 59.6	1 25.3	12 12.4	1 59.1	15 3.0	19 29.9	10 55.6
23 W	8 4 15.7	1 43.4	3 50.9	13 8.0	12 57.8	4 13.3	2 3.8	12 23.3	2 1.1	15 5.7	19 28.4	10 54.4
24 T	8 8 12.2	2 44.4	3 47.8	26 14.4	12 49.7	5 27.0	2 42.3	12 34.1	2 3.1	15 8.4	19 26.8	10 53.3
25 F	8 12 8.8	3 45.4	3 44.6	9♍32.8	12D49.9	6 40.6	3 20.8	12 44.8	2 4.9	15 11.1	19 25.2	10 52.1
26 S	8 16 5.3	4 46.4	3 41.4	23 2.7	12 57.9	7 54.1	3 59.3	12 55.4	2 6.6	15 13.9	19 23.6	10 51.0
27 S	8 20 1.9	5 47.4	3 38.2	6♎43.6	13 13.1	9 7.6	4 37.8	13 6.0	2 8.3	15 16.7	19 21.9	10 49.9
28 M	8 23 58.5	6 48.4	3 35.1	20 35.0	13 34.8	10 21.1	5 16.3	13 16.4	2 9.8	15 19.6	19 20.3	10 48.8
29 T	8 27 55.0	7 49.4	3 31.9	4♏36.2	14 2.7	11 34.4	5 54.8	13 26.7	2 11.2	15 22.5	19 18.7	10 47.7
30 W	8 31 51.5	8 50.3	3 28.7	18 46.3	14 36.0	12 47.8	6 33.3	13 37.0	2 12.5	15 25.4	19 17.0	10 46.6
31 T	8 35 48.1	9 51.2	3 25.5	3♐ 3.3	15 14.4	14 1.1	7 11.8	13 47.1	2 13.8	15 28.3	19 15.4	10 45.5
						DECLINATION						
1 T	6 37 31.4	23S 7.2	9N40.5	5S36.1	21S 1.2	20S10.8	16S29.2	20S59.4	9S32.0	6S54.0	15N 3.4	20N27.6
4 F	6 49 21.1	22 52.3	9 44.0	16 32.7	20 2.7	19 12.2	17 2.2	21 5.3	9 35.4	6 51.6	15 4.7	20 28.1
7 M	7 1 10.8	22 33.3	9 47.5	18 20.8	19 17.5	18 8.7	17 34.1	21 10.9	9 38.6	6 49.2	15 5.9	20 28.6
10 T	7 13 0.4	22 10.2	9 51.0	10 21.7	18 51.0	17 0.7	18 4.9	21 16.2	9 41.4	6 46.5	15 7.2	20 29.1
13 S	7 24 50.1	21 43.3	9 54.5	1N26.2	18 44.0	15 48.6	18 34.5	21 21.4	9 43.9	6 43.8	15 8.6	20 29.6
16 W	7 36 39.8	21 12.6	9 57.9	12 6.9	18 52.5	14 32.6	19 2.8	21 26.2	9 46.1	6 40.9	15 10.0	20 30.1
19 S	7 48 29.4	20 38.2	10 1.4	18 23.8	19 11.5	13 13.3	19 30.0	21 30.9	9 48.1	6 37.9	15 11.5	20 30.6
22 T	8 0 19.1	20 0.3	10 4.9	17 23.9	19 36.6	11 50.8	19 55.8	21 35.3	9 49.6	6 34.7	15 13.0	20 31.2
25 F	8 12 8.8	19 19.1	10 8.3	8 36.3	20 3.9	10 25.7	20 20.3	21 39.4	9 50.9	6 31.5	15 14.6	20 31.7
28 M	8 23 58.5	18 34.6	10 11.8	4S24.8	20 29.8	8 58.1	20 43.5	21 43.3	9 51.8	6 28.2	15 16.1	20 32.2
31 T	8 35 48.1	17 47.1	10 15.2	15 37.8	20 51.5	7 28.6	21 5.3	21 47.0	9 52.5	6 24.7	15 17.7	20 32.7

FEBRUARY 1924

DAY	EPHEMERIS SIDEREAL TIME	☉	☊	☽	☿	♀	♂	♃	♄	♅	♆	♇
						LONGITUDE						
1 F	8 39 44.7	10♒52.2	3♍22.3	17♐24.3	15♑57.4	15♓14.3	7♐50.2	13♐57.2	2♏14.9	15♓31.2	19♌13.7	10♋44.5
2 S	8 43 41.2	11 53.1	3 19.2	1♑45.6	16 44.5	16 27.5	8 28.7	14 7.1	2 15.9	15 34.2	19R12.0	10R43.4
3 S	8 47 37.8	12 54.0	3 16.0	16 2.3	17 35.4	17 40.6	9 7.2	14 16.9	2 16.8	15 37.2	19 10.3	10 42.4
4 M	8 51 34.3	13 54.9	3 12.8	0♒ 9.7	18 29.7	18 53.6	9 45.6	14 26.7	2 17.6	15 40.3	19 8.7	10 41.4
5 T	8 55 30.9	14 55.7	3 9.6	14 3.1	19 27.2	20 6.6	10 24.0	14 36.3	2 18.3	15 43.3	19 7.0	10 40.4
6 W	8 59 27.4	15 56.6	3 6.5	27 39.0	20 27.6	21 19.5	11 2.4	14 45.8	2 18.9	15 46.4	19 5.3	10 39.4
7 T	9 3 24.0	16 57.4	3 3.3	10♓55.3	21 30.5	22 32.4	11 40.8	14 55.2	2 19.3	15 49.5	19 3.6	10 38.4
8 F	9 7 20.5	17 58.2	3 0.1	23 51.4	22 35.9	23 45.2	12 19.2	15 4.5	2 19.7	15 52.6	19 1.9	10 37.4
9 S	9 11 17.1	18 59.0	2 56.9	6♈28.4	23 43.6	24 57.9	12 57.6	15 13.6	2 20.0	15 55.8	19 0.2	10 36.5
10 S	9 15 13.7	19 59.8	2 53.8	18 48.6	24 53.3	26 10.5	13 36.0	15 22.7	2 20.1	15 58.9	18 58.6	10 35.6
11 M	9 19 10.2	21 0.5	2 50.6	0♉55.4	26 4.9	27 23.1	14 14.3	15 31.6	2 20.2	16 2.1	18 56.9	10 34.6
12 T	9 23 6.7	22 1.2	2 47.4	12 53.0	27 18.2	28 35.6	14 52.7	15 40.4	2R20.1	16 5.3	18 55.2	10 33.7
13 W	9 27 3.3	23 1.8	2 44.2	24 45.9	28 33.3	29 48.0	15 31.0	15 49.1	2 20.0	16 8.5	18 53.5	10 32.9
14 T	9 30 59.9	24 2.5	2 41.0	6♊39.0	29 49.9	1♈ 0.3	16 9.3	15 57.7	2 19.7	16 11.8	18 51.8	10 32.0
15 F	9 34 56.4	25 3.1	2 37.9	18 36.8	1♒ 8.0	2 12.5	16 47.6	16 6.1	2 19.4	16 15.0	18 50.2	10 31.2
16 S	9 38 53.0	26 3.7	2 34.7	0♋43.8	2 27.5	3 24.7	17 25.9	16 14.4	2 18.9	16 18.3	18 48.5	10 30.3
17 S	9 42 49.5	27 4.3	2 31.5	13 3.7	3 48.4	4 36.7	18 4.1	16 22.6	2 18.3	16 21.6	18 46.8	10 29.5
18 M	9 46 46.1	28 4.8	2 28.3	25 39.3	5 10.5	5 48.7	18 42.4	16 30.7	2 17.6	16 24.8	18 45.1	10 28.7
19 T	9 50 42.6	29 5.3	2 25.1	8♌32.5	6 33.8	7 0.6	19 20.6	16 38.6	2 16.8	16 28.2	18 43.5	10 28.0
20 W	9 54 39.2	0♓ 5.8	2 22.0	21 44.1	7 58.4	8 12.3	19 58.9	16 46.4	2 16.0	16 31.5	18 41.8	10 27.2
21 T	9 58 35.7	1 6.2	2 18.8	5♍13.5	9 24.1	9 24.0	20 37.1	16 54.0	2 15.0	16 34.8	18 40.2	10 26.5
22 F	10 2 32.3	2 6.6	2 15.6	18 58.8	10 50.9	10 35.6	21 15.3	17 1.5	2 13.9	16 38.2	18 38.6	10 25.8
23 S	10 6 28.9	3 7.0	2 12.4	2♎57.2	12 18.9	11 47.0	21 53.5	17 8.9	2 12.7	16 41.5	18 36.9	10 25.1
24 S	10 10 25.4	4 7.4	2 9.3	17 5.2	13 47.9	12 58.4	22 31.6	17 16.2	2 11.4	16 44.9	18 35.3	10 24.4
25 M	10 14 22.0	5 7.8	2 6.1	1♏19.1	15 18.0	14 9.7	23 9.8	17 23.3	2 10.0	16 48.3	18 33.7	10 23.7
26 T	10 18 18.5	6 8.1	2 2.9	15 35.2	16 49.1	15 20.8	23 47.9	17 30.2	2 8.5	16 51.7	18 32.1	10 23.1
27 W	10 22 15.0	7 8.4	1 59.7	29 50.3	18 21.3	16 31.9	24 26.1	17 37.0	2 6.9	16 55.0	18 30.5	10 22.5
28 T	10 26 11.6	8 8.7	1 56.5	14♐ 1.8	19 54.6	17 42.8	25 4.2	17 43.7	2 5.3	16 58.5	18 29.0	10 21.9
29 F	10 30 8.2	9 8.9	1 53.4	28 7.4	21 28.9	18 53.7	25 42.2	17 50.2	2 3.5	17 1.9	18 27.4	10 21.3
						DECLINATION						
1 F	8 39 44.7	17S30.7	10N16.4	17S48.6	20S57.4	6S58.3	21S12.3	21S48.2	9S52.6	6S23.6	15N18.2	20N32.9
4 M	8 51 34.3	16 39.4	10 19.8	17 23.7	21 9.9	5 26.6	21 32.2	21 51.6	9 52.8	6 20.0	15 19.8	20 33.4
7 T	9 3 24.0	15 45.5	10 23.3	8 13.1	21 13.8	3 53.6	21 50.7	21 54.8	9 52.6	6 16.4	15 21.5	20 33.9
10 S	9 15 13.7	14 49.2	10 26.7	3N48.9	21 7.9	2 19.8	22 7.8	21 57.8	9 52.2	6 12.7	15 23.1	20 34.4
13 W	9 27 3.3	13 50.7	10 30.1	13 52.9	20 51.5	0 45.4	22 23.3	22 0.5	9 51.4	6 8.9	15 24.7	20 34.9
16 S	9 38 53.0	12 50.1	10 33.5	18 48.1	20 24.2	0N49.2	22 37.3	22 3.1	9 50.3	6 5.1	15 26.3	20 35.4
19 T	9 50 42.6	11 47.7	10 37.0	16 4.9	19 45.6	2 23.7	22 49.9	22 5.4	9 48.9	6 1.2	15 27.8	20 35.9
22 F	10 2 32.3	10 43.6	10 40.4	5 46.3	18 55.4	3 57.8	23 0.9	22 7.6	9 47.2	5 57.3	15 29.4	20 36.4
25 M	10 14 22.0	9 38.0	10 43.8	7S40.5	17 53.7	5 31.1	23 10.4	22 9.6	9 45.2	5 53.3	15 30.9	20 36.9
28 T	10 26 11.6	8 31.1	10 47.2	17 21.3	16 40.2	7 3.4	23 18.3	22 11.4	9 42.9	5 49.3	15 32.4	20 37.3

MARCH 1924

LONGITUDE

DAY	EPHEMERIS SIDEREAL TIME	☉	☊	☽	☿	♀	♂	♃	♄	♅	♆	♇
	h m s	° ′	° ′	° ′	° ′	° ′	° ′	° ′	° ′	° ′	° ′	° ′
1 S	10 34 4.7	10♓ 9.1	1♍50.2	12♑ 5.2	23♒ 4.3	20♈ 4.4	26♐20.3	17♐56.6	2♏ 1.6	17♓ 5.3	18♌25.9	10♋20.8
2 S	10 38 1.3	11 9.3	1 47.0	25 53.8	24 40.7	21 15.0	26 58.3	18 2.8	1R59.6	17 8.7	18R24.3	10R20.2
3 M	10 41 57.8	12 9.5	1 43.8	9♒31.6	26 18.1	22 25.5	27 36.4	18 8.9	1 57.5	17 12.1	18 22.8	10 19.7
4 T	10 45 54.4	13 9.7	1 40.7	22 57.4	27 56.6	23 35.9	28 14.3	18 14.8	1 55.4	17 15.6	18 21.3	10 19.3
5 W	10 49 50.9	14 9.8	1 37.5	6♓10.0	29 36.2	24 46.1	28 52.3	18 20.6	1 53.1	17 19.0	18 19.8	10 18.8
6 T	10 53 47.5	15 9.9	1 34.3	19 8.4	1♓16.9	25 56.3	29 30.2	18 26.1	1 50.8	17 22.4	18 18.3	10 18.4
7 F	10 57 44.0	16 9.9	1 31.1	1♈52.5	2 58.7	27 6.3	0♑ 8.2	18 31.6	1 48.3	17 25.9	18 16.9	10 17.9
8 S	11 1 40.6	17 10.0	1 27.9	14 22.4	4 41.6	28 16.1	0 46.0	18 36.8	1 45.8	17 29.3	18 15.4	10 17.5
9 S	11 5 37.1	18 9.9	1 24.8	26 39.5	6 25.6	29 25.9	1 23.9	18 41.9	1 43.2	17 32.7	18 14.0	10 17.2
10 M	11 9 33.7	19 9.9	1 21.6	8♉45.5	8 10.7	0♉35.5	2 1.7	18 46.9	1 40.5	17 36.2	18 12.6	10 16.8
11 T	11 13 30.2	20 9.8	1 18.4	20 43.3	9 57.0	1 44.9	2 39.5	18 51.7	1 37.7	17 39.6	18 11.2	10 16.5
12 W	11 17 26.8	21 9.7	1 15.2	2♊36.4	11 44.4	2 54.2	3 17.2	18 56.3	1 34.9	17 43.0	18 9.9	10 16.2
13 T	11 21 23.3	22 9.5	1 12.1	14 29.0	13 33.0	4 3.3	3 54.9	19 0.7	1 31.9	17 46.5	18 8.5	10 15.9
14 F	11 25 19.9	23 9.4	1 8.9	26 25.5	15 22.8	5 12.3	4 32.6	19 5.0	1 28.9	17 49.9	18 7.2	10 15.7
15 S	11 29 16.5	24 9.1	1 5.7	8♋30.8	17 13.7	6 21.2	5 10.3	19 9.1	1 25.8	17 53.3	18 5.9	10 15.4
16 S	11 33 13.0	25 8.9	1 2.5	20 49.6	19 5.8	7 29.8	5 47.9	19 13.0	1 22.6	17 56.7	18 4.6	10 15.2
17 M	11 37 9.5	26 8.6	0 59.3	3♌26.0	20 59.1	8 38.3	6 25.5	19 16.8	1 19.3	18 0.1	18 3.4	10 15.0
18 T	11 41 6.1	27 8.2	0 56.2	16 23.7	22 53.6	9 46.6	7 3.0	19 20.4	1 16.0	18 3.5	18 2.1	10 14.9
19 W	11 45 2.7	28 7.9	0 53.0	29 44.7	24 49.2	10 54.8	7 40.6	19 23.8	1 12.6	18 6.9	18 0.9	10 14.7
20 T	11 48 59.2	29 7.4	0 49.8	13♍29.6	26 46.0	12 2.7	8 18.0	19 27.0	1 9.1	18 10.3	17 59.7	10 14.6
21 F	11 52 55.7	0♈ 7.0	0 46.6	27 36.6	28 43.8	13 10.5	8 55.5	19 30.0	1 5.6	18 13.7	17 58.6	10 14.5
22 S	11 56 52.3	1 6.5	0 43.4	12♎ 1.9	0♈42.6	14 18.1	9 32.9	19 32.9	1 2.0	18 17.1	17 57.4	10 14.5
23 S	12 0 48.9	2 6.0	0 40.3	26 39.4	2 42.3	15 25.5	10 10.3	19 35.6	0 58.3	18 20.4	17 56.3	10 14.4
24 M	12 4 45.4	3 5.4	0 37.1	11♏22.2	4 42.9	16 32.7	10 47.6	19 38.2	0 54.6	18 23.8	17 55.2	10 14.4
25 T	12 8 42.0	4 4.9	0 33.9	26 3.1	6 44.2	17 39.7	11 24.9	19 40.5	0 50.8	18 27.1	17 54.2	10D14.4
26 W	12 12 38.5	5 4.3	0 30.7	10♐35.6	8 46.1	18 46.5	12 2.2	19 42.6	0 47.0	18 30.5	17 53.1	10 14.4
27 T	12 16 35.1	6 3.6	0 27.6	24 55.1	10 48.4	19 53.1	12 39.4	19 44.6	0 43.1	18 33.8	17 52.1	10 14.5
28 F	12 20 31.6	7 3.0	0 24.4	8♑58.9	12 50.9	20 59.4	13 16.6	19 46.4	0 39.1	18 37.1	17 51.1	10 14.6
29 S	12 24 28.2	8 2.3	0 21.2	22 46.1	14 53.4	22 5.6	13 53.7	19 48.0	0 35.1	18 40.4	17 50.2	10 14.7
30 S	12 28 24.7	9 1.5	0 18.0	6♒17.0	16 55.6	23 11.5	14 30.8	19 49.4	0 31.0	18 43.7	17 49.2	10 14.8
31 M	12 32 21.3	10 0.8	0 14.8	19 32.7	18 57.3	24 17.2	15 7.8	19 50.7	0 26.9	18 46.9	17 48.3	10 14.9

DECLINATION

DAY	EPHEMERIS SIDEREAL TIME	☉	☊	☽	☿	♀	♂	♃	♄	♅	♆	♇
1 S	10 34 4.7	7S45.8	10N49.5	18S51.4	15S44.7	8N 4.2	23S22.8	22S12.5	9S41.2	5S46.7	15N33.4	20N37.7
4 T	10 45 54.4	6 37.1	10 52.9	13 3.9	14 11.7	9 34.0	23 28.2	22 14.0	9 38.5	5 42.6	15 34.8	20 38.1
7 F	10 57 44.0	5 27.6	10 56.3	1 39.1	12 27.0	11 2.0	23 32.1	22 15.4	9 35.5	5 38.6	15 36.2	20 38.5
10 M	11 9 33.7	4 17.4	10 59.7	9N50.8	10 30.9	12 27.7	23 34.4	22 16.6	9 32.2	5 34.6	15 37.5	20 39.0
13 T	11 21 23.3	3 6.7	11 3.1	17 26.9	8 23.4	13 51.0	23 35.3	22 17.6	9 28.7	5 30.6	15 38.8	20 39.4
16 S	11 33 13.0	1 55.7	11 6.5	18 24.6	6 4.9	15 11.5	23 34.7	22 18.5	9 25.0	5 26.6	15 40.0	20 39.8
19 W	11 45 2.7	0 44.6	11 9.8	11 22.0	3 36.1	16 28.8	23 32.7	22 19.3	9 21.1	5 22.6	15 41.2	20 40.1
22 S	11 56 52.3	0N26.5	11 13.2	1S39.9	0 58.1	17 42.8	23 29.2	22 19.9	9 17.0	5 18.6	15 42.3	20 40.5
25 T	12 8 42.0	1 37.4	11 16.6	14 14.4	1N47.3	18 53.2	23 24.3	22 20.4	9 12.7	5 14.7	15 43.3	20 40.9
28 F	12 20 31.6	2 47.9	11 19.9	19 0.7	4 37.2	19 59.6	23 18.0	22 20.7	9 8.3	5 10.8	15 44.2	20 41.2
31 M	12 32 21.3	3 58.0	11 23.3	13 55.2	7 27.6	21 1.9	23 10.5	22 21.0	9 3.8	5 7.0	15 45.1	20 41.5

APRIL 1924

LONGITUDE

DAY	EPHEMERIS SIDEREAL TIME	☉	☊	☽	☿	♀	♂	♃	♄	♅	♆	♇
1 T	12 36 17.8	11♈ 0.0	0♍11.7	2♓34.6	20♈58.0	25♉22.7	15♑44.8	19♐51.7	0♏22.8	18♓50.2	17♌47.4	10♋15.1
2 W	12 40 14.4	11 59.2	0 8.5	15 24.0	22 57.5	26 28.0	16 21.7	19 52.6	0R18.6	18 53.4	17R46.6	10 15.3
3 T	12 44 10.9	12 58.3	0 5.3	28 2.2	24 55.4	27 33.0	16 58.6	19 53.2	0 14.3	18 56.6	17 45.8	10 15.5
4 F	12 48 7.5	13 57.5	0 2.1	10♈29.8	26 51.3	28 37.7	17 35.4	19 53.7	0 10.0	18 59.8	17 45.0	10 15.8
5 S	12 52 4.0	14 56.5	29♌59.0	22 47.8	28 44.9	29 42.2	18 12.1	19 54.0	0 5.7	19 3.0	17 44.2	10 16.0
6 S	12 56 0.6	15 55.6	29 55.8	4♉56.9	0♉35.7	0♊46.4	18 48.8	19 54.1	0 1.3	19 6.2	17 43.5	10 16.3
7 M	12 59 57.2	16 54.6	29 52.6	16 58.4	2 23.4	1 50.4	19 25.4	19R54.0	29♎57.0	19 9.3	17 42.8	10 16.6
8 T	13 3 53.7	17 53.6	29 49.4	28 54.0	4 7.6	2 54.0	20 2.0	19 53.7	29 52.5	19 12.4	17 42.1	10 17.0
9 W	13 7 50.2	18 52.5	29 46.2	10♊45.9	5 48.0	3 57.4	20 38.4	19 53.3	29 48.1	19 15.5	17 41.5	10 17.3
10 T	13 11 46.8	19 51.5	29 43.1	22 37.4	7 24.4	5 0.4	21 14.8	19 52.6	29 43.6	19 18.6	17 40.9	10 17.7
11 F	13 15 43.4	20 50.3	29 39.9	4♋32.3	8 56.4	6 3.2	21 51.2	19 51.8	29 39.1	19 21.6	17 40.3	10 18.1
12 S	13 19 39.9	21 49.2	29 36.7	16 34.9	10 23.8	7 5.6	22 27.5	19 50.8	29 34.6	19 24.7	17 39.7	10 18.6
13 S	13 23 36.5	22 48.0	29 33.5	28 50.1	11 46.3	8 7.7	23 3.7	19 49.5	29 30.1	19 27.7	17 39.2	10 19.0
14 M	13 27 33.0	23 46.7	29 30.4	11♌22.8	13 3.8	9 9.5	23 39.8	19 48.1	29 25.5	19 30.7	17 38.7	10 19.5
15 T	13 31 29.6	24 45.4	29 27.2	24 17.7	14 16.1	10 10.9	24 15.8	19 46.6	29 21.0	19 33.6	17 38.3	10 20.0
16 W	13 35 26.1	25 44.1	29 24.0	7♍38.6	15 23.0	11 12.0	24 51.8	19 44.8	29 16.4	19 36.6	17 37.9	10 20.5
17 T	13 39 22.7	26 42.8	29 20.8	21 27.4	16 24.5	12 12.6	25 27.7	19 42.8	29 11.8	19 39.5	17 37.5	10 21.1
18 F	13 43 19.2	27 41.4	29 17.6	5♎44.0	17 20.3	13 12.9	26 3.5	19 40.7	29 7.3	19 42.4	17 37.1	10 21.6
19 S	13 47 15.8	28 39.9	29 14.5	20 24.8	18 10.5	14 12.8	26 39.3	19 38.4	29 2.7	19 45.2	17 36.8	10 22.2
20 S	13 51 12.3	29 38.5	29 11.3	5♏23.4	18 55.0	15 12.2	27 14.9	19 35.9	28 58.1	19 48.0	17 36.5	10 22.8
21 M	13 55 8.9	0♉37.0	29 8.1	20 30.5	19 33.6	16 11.3	27 50.5	19 33.2	28 53.5	19 50.8	17 36.2	10 23.5
22 T	13 59 5.4	1 35.5	29 4.9	5♐35.9	20 6.3	17 9.9	28 26.0	19 30.4	28 48.9	19 53.6	17 36.0	10 24.1
23 W	14 3 2.0	2 33.9	29 1.7	20 30.2	20 33.2	18 8.0	29 1.4	19 27.4	28 44.3	19 56.3	17 35.8	10 24.8
24 T	14 6 58.5	3 32.4	28 58.6	5♑ 5.9	20 54.2	19 5.7	29 36.7	19 24.2	28 39.8	19 59.1	17 35.7	10 25.5
25 F	14 10 55.1	4 30.8	28 55.4	19 19.0	21 9.4	20 3.0	0♒12.0	19 20.8	28 35.2	20 1.7	17 35.5	10 26.2
26 S	14 14 51.7	5 29.1	28 52.2	3♒ 7.9	21 18.8	20 59.7	0 47.1	19 17.3	28 30.7	20 4.4	17 35.4	10 26.9
27 S	14 18 48.2	6 27.5	28 49.0	16 33.7	21 22.6	21 55.9	1 22.1	19 13.5	28 26.2	20 7.0	17 35.4	10 27.7
28 M	14 22 44.7	7 25.8	28 45.9	29 38.8	21R20.8	22 51.6	1 57.0	19 9.7	28 21.7	20 9.6	17 35.3	10 28.5
29 T	14 26 41.3	8 24.1	28 42.7	12♓26.6	21 13.8	23 46.8	2 31.8	19 5.6	28 17.2	20 12.2	17 35.3	10 29.3
30 W	14 30 37.9	9 22.4	28 39.5	25 0.1	21 1.8	24 41.4	3 6.5	19 1.4	28 12.7	20 14.7	17D35.4	10 30.1

DECLINATION

DAY	EPHEMERIS SIDEREAL TIME	☉	☊	☽	☿	♀	♂	♃	♄	♅	♆	♇
1 T	12 36 17.8	4N21.3	11N24.4	10S37.9	8N23.6	21N21.7	23S 7.6	22S21.0	9S 2.2	5S 5.8	15N45.4	20N41.6
4 F	12 48 7.5	5 30.4	11 27.8	1N10.7	11 6.1	22 18.1	22 58.4	22 21.1	8 57.5	5 2.0	15 46.2	20 41.9
7 M	12 59 57.2	6 38.8	11 31.1	12 8.5	13 35.6	23 9.8	22 47.9	22 21.0	8 52.8	4 58.3	15 46.8	20 42.2
10 T	13 11 46.8	7 46.1	11 34.5	18 29.3	15 46.8	23 56.8	22 36.2	22 20.9	8 48.0	4 54.7	15 47.4	20 42.4
13 S	13 23 36.5	8 52.2	11 37.8	17 44.4	17 35.9	24 38.8	22 23.5	22 20.6	8 43.1	4 51.2	15 47.9	20 42.7
16 W	13 35 26.1	9 57.0	11 41.2	9 16.5	19 0.5	25 15.6	22 9.7	22 20.2	8 38.3	4 47.8	15 48.4	20 42.9
19 S	13 47 15.8	11 0.2	11 44.5	4S22.5	19 59.8	25 47.4	21 54.9	22 19.7	8 33.4	4 44.4	15 48.7	20 43.1
22 T	13 59 5.4	12 1.9	11 47.8	16 16.7	20 33.3	26 13.9	21 39.2	22 19.0	8 28.6	4 41.2	15 48.9	20 43.3
25 F	14 10 55.1	13 1.8	11 51.1	18 46.9	20 41.3	26 35.3	21 22.6	22 18.3	8 23.9	4 38.1	15 49.1	20 43.4
28 M	14 22 44.7	13 59.7	11 54.5	11 34.9	20 24.3	26 51.6	21 5.3	22 17.4	8 19.2	4 35.1	15 49.2	20 43.6

MAY 1924

DAY	EPHEMERIS SIDEREAL TIME	☉	☊	☽	☿	♀	♂	♃	♄	♅	♆	♇
	h m s	° ′	° ′	° ′	° ′	° ′	° ′	° ′	° ′	° ′	° ′	° ′
						LONGITUDE						
1 T	14 34 34.4	10♉20.6	28♌36.3	7♈22.4	20♉45.0	25♊35.5	3♒41.1	18♐57.0	28♎ 8.3	20♓17.2	17♌35.4	10♋30.9
2 F	14 38 31.0	11 18.8	28 33.2	19 35.7	20R23.9	26 29.0	4 15.5	18R52.5	28R 3.9	20 19.6	17 35.5	10 31.8
3 S	14 42 27.5	12 17.0	28 30.0	1♉41.8	19 58.8	27 21.8	4 49.8	18 47.8	27 59.5	20 22.1	17 35.7	10 32.6
4 S	14 46 24.1	13 15.2	28 26.8	13 42.2	19 30.3	28 14.0	5 24.0	18 43.0	27 55.1	20 24.4	17 35.8	10 33.5
5 M	14 50 20.6	14 13.3	28 23.6	25 38.2	18 58.9	29 5.5	5 58.1	18 38.0	27 50.8	20 26.8	17 36.0	10 34.5
6 T	14 54 17.2	15 11.4	28 20.4	7♊30.9	18 25.3	29 56.4	6 32.0	18 32.8	27 46.5	20 29.1	17 36.3	10 35.4
7 W	14 58 13.7	16 9.5	28 17.3	19 22.1	17 49.9	0♋46.5	7 5.8	18 27.5	27 42.3	20 31.4	17 36.5	10 36.4
8 T	15 2 10.3	17 7.6	28 14.1	1♋13.8	17 13.5	1 35.9	7 39.4	18 22.1	27 38.1	20 33.6	17 36.8	10 37.3
9 F	15 6 6.9	18 5.6	28 10.9	13 9.0	16 36.7	2 24.6	8 12.9	18 16.5	27 33.9	20 35.8	17 37.2	10 38.3
10 S	15 10 3.4	19 3.6	28 7.7	25 11.1	16 0.1	3 12.4	8 46.2	18 10.8	27 29.8	20 38.0	17 37.6	10 39.3
11 S	15 13 60.0	20 1.5	28 4.6	7♌24.5	15 24.4	3 59.4	9 19.4	18 5.0	27 25.8	20 40.1	17 38.0	10 40.3
12 M	15 17 56.5	20 59.4	28 1.4	19 53.8	14 50.3	4 45.5	9 52.4	17 59.1	27 21.7	20 42.2	17 38.4	10 41.4
13 T	15 21 53.1	21 57.3	27 58.2	2♍43.9	14 18.2	5 30.8	10 25.3	17 53.0	27 17.8	20 44.3	17 38.8	10 42.4
14 W	15 25 49.6	22 55.2	27 55.0	15 59.4	13 48.6	6 15.1	10 58.0	17 46.8	27 13.9	20 46.3	17 39.3	10 43.5
15 T	15 29 46.2	23 53.1	27 51.9	29 43.4	13 22.1	6 58.4	11 30.6	17 40.5	27 10.0	20 48.2	17 39.9	10 44.6
16 F	15 33 42.7	24 50.9	27 48.7	13♎57.1	12 59.0	7 40.7	12 2.9	17 34.1	27 6.2	20 50.2	17 40.4	10 45.7
17 S	15 37 39.3	25 48.6	27 45.5	28 38.8	12 39.7	8 22.0	12 35.1	17 27.6	27 2.5	20 52.0	17 41.0	10 46.8
18 S	15 41 35.8	26 46.4	27 42.3	13♏42.7	12 24.3	9 2.2	13 7.1	17 20.9	26 58.8	20 53.9	17 41.6	10 48.0
19 M	15 45 32.4	27 44.1	27 39.1	29 0.1	12 13.2	9 41.3	13 39.0	17 14.2	26 55.2	20 55.7	17 42.3	10 49.1
20 T	15 49 29.0	28 41.8	27 36.0	14♐19.4	12 6.4	10 19.1	14 10.7	17 7.4	26 51.7	20 57.5	17 43.0	10 50.3
21 W	15 53 25.5	29 39.5	27 32.8	29 29.4	12 4.1	10 55.8	14 42.1	17 0.5	26 48.2	20 59.2	17 43.7	10 51.5
22 T	15 57 22.1	0♊37.2	27 29.6	14♑20.5	12D 6.3	11 31.2	15 13.4	16 53.5	26 44.8	21 0.9	17 44.5	10 52.7
23 F	16 1 18.6	1 34.8	27 26.4	28 46.3	12 13.1	12 5.3	15 44.5	16 46.5	26 41.4	21 2.5	17 45.2	10 53.9
24 S	16 5 15.1	2 32.5	27 23.3	12♒44.1	12 24.4	12 38.1	16 15.3	16 39.3	26 38.2	21 4.1	17 46.1	10 55.1
25 S	16 9 11.7	3 30.1	27 20.1	26 14.3	12 40.1	13 9.4	16 46.0	16 32.1	26 35.0	21 5.7	17 46.9	10 56.4
26 M	16 13 8.3	4 27.7	27 16.9	9♓19.3	13 0.3	13 39.3	17 16.4	16 24.8	26 31.8	21 7.2	17 47.8	10 57.6
27 T	16 17 4.8	5 25.3	27 13.7	22 3.2	13 24.8	14 7.7	17 46.6	16 17.5	26 28.8	21 8.6	17 48.7	10 58.9
28 W	16 21 1.4	6 22.9	27 10.5	4♈29.9	13 53.6	14 34.6	18 16.5	16 10.1	26 25.8	21 10.0	17 49.6	11 0.2
29 T	16 24 57.9	7 20.4	27 7.4	16 43.8	14 26.5	14 59.8	18 46.2	16 2.7	26 22.9	21 11.4	17 50.6	11 1.5
30 F	16 28 54.5	8 18.0	27 4.2	28 48.3	15 3.5	15 23.4	19 15.6	15 55.2	26 20.1	21 12.7	17 51.6	11 2.8
31 S	16 32 51.1	9 15.5	27 1.0	10♉46.5	15 44.4	15 45.2	19 44.8	15 47.7	26 17.3	21 14.0	17 52.6	11 4.1
						DECLINATION						
1 T	14 34 34.4	14N55.6	11N57.8	0N 5.6	19N43.8	27N 2.8	20S47.2	22S16.4	8S14.7	4S32.1	15N49.1	20N43.7
4 S	14 46 24.1	15 49.3	12 1.1	11 20.7	18 43.1	27 9.2	20 28.6	22 15.3	8 10.2	4 29.4	15 49.0	20 43.8
7 W	14 58 13.7	16 40.7	12 4.4	18 20.9	17 28.2	27 10.8	20 9.5	22 14.1	8 5.9	4 26.7	15 48.8	20 43.9
10 S	15 10 3.4	17 29.5	12 7.7	18 24.1	16 7.0	27 8.1	19 49.9	22 12.8	8 1.8	4 24.2	15 48.5	20 44.0
13 T	15 21 53.1	18 15.7	12 11.0	10 52.8	14 48.6	27 1.1	19 30.1	22 11.3	7 57.9	4 21.8	15 48.1	20 44.0
16 F	15 33 42.7	18 59.2	12 14.3	2S10.5	13 41.6	26 50.2	19 .0.0	22 9.7	7 54.2	4 19.6	15 47.6	20 44.1
19 M	15 45 32.4	19 39.7	12 17.5	15 3.4	12 51.9	26 35.7	18 49.7	22 8.1	7 50.7	4 17.5	15 47.1	20 44.1
22 T	15 57 22.1	20 17.2	12 20.8	19 16.8	12 22.9	26 18.1	18 29.4	22 6.3	7 47.4	4 15.5	15 46.4	20 44.1
25 S	16 9 11.7	20 51.6	12 24.1	12 42.8	12 15.2	25 57.5	18 9.3	22 4.4	7 44.4	4 13.7	15 45.7	20 44.0
28 W	16 21 1.4	21 22.8	12 27.3	1 2.0	12 27.9	25 34.5	17 49.3	22 2.4	7 41.6	4 12.1	15 44.9	20 44.0
31 S	16 32 51.1	21 50.7	12 30.6	10N28.5	12 58.9	25 9.4	17 29.6	22 0.4	7 39.2	4 10.6	15 43.9	20 43.9

JUNE 1924

						LONGITUDE						
1 S	16 36 47.6	10♊13.0	26♌57.8	22♉40.8	16♉29.1	16♋ 5.2	20♒13.7	15♐40.1	26♎14.6	21♓15.3	17♌53.6	11♋ 5.4
2 M	16 40 44.2	11 10.5	26 54.7	4♊33.0	17 17.6	16 23.4	20 42.3	15R32.5	26R12.1	21 16.5	17 54.7	11 6.8
3 T	16 44 40.7	12 8.0	26 51.5	16 24.7	18 9.8	16 39.7	21 10.7	15 24.9	26 9.6	21 17.6	17 55.8	11 8.1
4 W	16 48 37.3	13 5.4	26 48.3	28 17.3	19 5.4	16 54.0	21 38.7	15 17.3	26 7.2	21 18.7	17 57.0	11 9.5
5 T	16 52 33.8	14 2.9	26 45.1	10♋12.4	20 4.5	17 6.3	22 6.4	15 9.6	26 4.8	21 19.7	17 58.1	11 10.8
6 F	16 56 30.4	15 0.3	26 41.9	22 12.0	21 7.1	17 16.4	22 33.9	15 2.0	26 2.6	21 20.7	17 59.3	11 12.2
7 S	17 0 26.9	15 57.7	26 38.8	4♌18.7	22 12.9	17 24.5	23 1.0	14 54.3	26 0.5	21 21.7	18 0.6	11 13.6
8 S	17 4 23.5	16 55.1	26 35.6	16 35.7	23 22.0	17 30.3	23 27.8	14 46.7	25 58.4	21 22.6	18 1.8	11 15.0
9 M	17 8 20.0	17 52.5	26 32.4	29 6.7	24 34.3	17 33.8	23 54.3	14 39.0	25 56.5	21 23.5	18 3.1	11 16.4
10 T	17 12 16.6	18 49.8	26 29.2	11♍55.9	25 49.7	17 35.1	24 20.4	14 31.4	25 54.6	21 24.3	18 4.4	11 17.8
11 W	17 16 13.2	19 47.2	26 26.1	25 7.4	27 8.2	17R34.0	24 46.2	14 23.8	25 52.8	21 25.1	18 5.7	11 19.3
12 T	17 20 9.7	20 44.5	26 22.9	8♎44.5	28 29.8	17 30.5	25 11.6	14 16.2	25 51.1	21 25.8	18 7.1	11 20.7
13 F	17 24 6.3	21 41.8	26 19.7	22 49.1	29 54.5	17 24.6	25 36.7	14 8.7	25 49.5	21 26.5	18 8.5	11 22.2
14 S	17 28 2.8	22 39.1	26 16.5	7♏20.6	1♊22.1	17 16.3	26 1.4	14 1.2	25 48.0	21 27.1	18 9.9	11 23.6
15 S	17 31 59.4	23 36.4	26 13.4	22 15.3	2 52.7	17 5.6	26 25.8	13 53.7	25 46.6	21 27.6	18 11.3	11 25.1
16 M	17 35 56.0	24 33.7	26 10.2	7♐26.0	4 26.3	16 52.4	26 49.7	13 46.3	25 45.3	21 28.2	18 12.8	11 26.5
17 T	17 39 52.5	25 30.9	26 7.0	22 42.7	6 2.9	16 36.8	27 13.3	13 38.9	25 44.1	21 28.7	18 14.3	11 28.0
18 W	17 43 49.1	26 28.2	26 3.8	7♑54.4	7 42.3	16 18.9	27 36.5	13 31.6	25 42.9	21 29.1	18 15.8	11 29.5
19 T	17 47 45.6	27 25.4	26 0.6	22 50.8	9 24.6	15 58.7	27 59.2	13 24.4	25 41.9	21 29.5	18 17.3	11 30.9
20 F	17 51 42.2	28 22.6	25 57.5	7♒24.2	11 9.8	15 36.3	28 21.5	13 17.2	25 41.0	21 29.8	18 18.8	11 32.4
21 S	17 55 38.7	29 19.9	25 54.3	21 30.2	12 57.8	15 11.7	28 43.4	13 10.1	25 40.2	21 30.1	18 20.4	11 33.9
22 S	17 59 35.3	0♋17.1	25 51.1	5♓ 7.8	14 48.5	14 45.1	29 4.8	13 3.0	25 39.4	21 30.3	18 22.0	11 35.4
23 M	18 3 31.9	1 14.3	25 47.9	18 18.4	16 41.8	14 16.6	29 25.8	12 56.1	25 38.8	21 30.5	18 23.6	11 36.9
24 T	18 7 28.4	2 11.5	25 44.8	1♈ 5.1	18 37.7	13 46.4	29 46.3	12 49.2	25 38.2	21 30.7	18 25.3	11 38.4
25 W	18 11 24.9	3 8.7	25 41.6	13 32.4	20 36.0	13 14.5	0♓ 6.3	12 42.4	25 37.8	21 30.7	18 26.9	11 39.9
26 T	18 15 21.5	4 6.0	25 38.4	25 44.7	22 36.6	12 41.2	0 25.7	12 35.7	25 37.4	21 30.8	18 28.6	11 41.4
27 F	18 19 18.1	5 3.2	25 35.2	7♉46.3	24 39.3	12 6.7	0 44.7	12 29.1	25 37.2	21 30.8	18 30.3	11 42.9
28 S	18 23 14.7	6 0.4	25 32.1	19 41.3	26 43.8	11 31.1	1 3.1	12 22.6	25 37.1	21R30.7	18 32.1	11 44.5
29 S	18 27 11.2	6 57.6	25 28.9	1♊33.1	28 50.1	10 54.7	1 21.0	12 16.2	25 37.0	21 30.6	18 33.8	11 46.0
30 M	18 31 7.7	7 54.8	25 25.7	13 24.5	0♋57.7	10 17.7	1 38.3	12 9.9	25D37.1	21 30.5	18 35.6	11 47.5
						DECLINATION						
1 S	16 36 47.6	21N59.3	12N31.7	13N36.6	13N12.9	25N 0.6	17S23.2	21S59.7	7S38.4	4S10.2	15N43.6	20N43.9
4 W	16 48 37.3	22 22.6	12 34.9	19 12.1	14 4.3	24 33.2	17 4.2	21 57.6	7 36.3	4 8.9	15 42.6	20 43.8
7 S	17 0 26.9	22 42.4	12 38.2	17 25.2	15 7.9	24 4.5	16 45.9	21 55.4	7 34.5	4 7.8	15 41.5	20 43.7
10 T	17 12 16.6	22 58.6	12 41.4	8 26.2	16 20.7	23 34.7	16 28.3	21 53.2	7 33.1	4 6.9	15 40.3	20 43.6
13 F	17 24 6.3	23 11.2	12 44.7	4S53.6	17 39.9	23 4.0	16 11.7	21 51.0	7 31.9	4 6.2	15 39.1	20 43.5
16 M	17 35 56.0	23 20.1	12 47.9	16 40.5	19 2.1	22 32.5	15 56.0	21 48.7	7 31.1	4 5.6	15 37.8	20 43.3
19 T	17 47 45.6	23 25.3	12 51.1	18 52.3	20 23.7	22 0.4	15 41.5	21 46.5	7 30.6	4 5.2	15 36.4	20 43.2
22 S	17 59 35.3	23 26.8	12 54.4	10 31.2	21 40.2	21 27.7	15 28.3	21 44.4	7 30.4	4 5.0	15 35.0	20 43.0
25 W	18 11 24.9	23 24.6	12 57.6	1N46.2	22 46.8	20 54.8	15 16.6	21 42.3	7 30.5	4 4.9	15 33.5	20 42.8
28 S	18 23 14.7	23 18.6	13 0.8	12 44.7	23 37.9	20 22.0	15 6.6	21 40.2	7 31.0	4 5.0	15 31.9	20 42.6

JULY 1924

DAY	EPHEMERIS SIDEREAL TIME h m s	☉ ° ′	☊ ° ′	☽ ° ′	☿ ° ′	♀ ° ′	♂ ° ′	♃ ° ′	♄ ° ′	♅ ° ′	♆ ° ′	♇ ° ′
LONGITUDE												
1 T	18 35 4.3	8♋52.1	25♌22.5	25♊17.7	3♋ 6.4	9♋40.4	1♓55.1	12♐ 3.8	25♎37.2	21♓30.3	18♌37.4	11♋49.0
2 W	18 39 0.9	9 49.3	25 19.4	7♋14.6	5 16.0	9R 2.9	2 11.3	11R57.7	25 37.5	21R30.0	18 39.2	11 50.5
3 T	18 42 57.4	10 46.5	25 16.2	19 16.8	7 26.2	8 25.6	2 26.8	11 51.8	25 37.8	21 29.7	18 41.0	11 52.1
4 F	18 46 54.0	11 43.7	25 13.0	1♌25.8	9 36.6	7 48.5	2 41.8	11 46.0	25 38.3	21 29.4	18 42.9	11 53.6
5 S	18 50 50.6	12 40.9	25 9.8	13 43.3	11 47.1	7 12.1	2 56.2	11 40.4	25 38.8	21 29.0	18 44.7	11 55.1
6 S	18 54 47.1	13 38.2	25 6.7	26 11.3	13 57.2	6 36.5	3 9.9	11 34.8	25 39.5	21 28.6	18 46.6	11 56.6
7 M	18 58 43.6	14 35.4	25 3.5	8♍52.1	16 6.8	6 1.8	3 23.0	11 29.5	25 40.2	21 28.1	18 48.5	11 58.2
8 T	19 2 40.2	15 32.6	25 0.3	21 48.4	18 15.6	5 28.4	3 35.4	11 24.2	25 41.1	21 27.6	18 50.4	11 59.7
9 W	19 6 36.8	16 29.8	24 57.1	5♎ 2.9	20 23.5	4 56.4	3 47.2	11 19.1	25 42.0	21 27.0	18 52.3	12 1.2
10 T	19 10 33.3	17 27.0	24 53.9	18 37.9	22 30.2	4 26.0	3 58.3	11 14.1	25 43.1	21 26.4	18 54.3	12 2.7
11 F	19 14 29.9	18 24.2	24 50.8	2♏34.8	24 35.6	3 57.3	4 8.7	11 9.3	25 44.2	21 25.7	18 56.3	12 4.2
12 S	19 18 26.4	19 21.4	24 47.6	16 53.3	26 39.6	3 30.5	4 18.5	11 4.7	25 45.4	21 25.0	18 58.2	12 5.8
13 S	19 22 23.0	20 18.6	24 44.4	1♐31.0	28 42.1	3 5.7	4 27.5	11 0.2	25 46.8	21 24.2	19 0.2	12 7.3
14 M	19 26 19.6	21 15.8	24 41.2	16 22.9	0♌42.9	2 43.0	4 35.9	10 55.8	25 48.2	21 23.4	19 2.2	12 8.8
15 T	19 30 16.1	22 13.0	24 38.1	1♑21.9	2 42.1	2 22.6	4 43.5	10 51.7	25 49.7	21 22.6	19 4.3	12 10.3
16 W	19 34 12.7	23 10.2	24 34.9	16 19.3	4 39.5	2 4.4	4 50.5	10 47.6	25 51.4	21 21.7	19 6.3	12 11.8
17 T	19 38 9.2	24 7.4	24 31.7	1♒ 6.4	6 35.2	1 48.5	4 56.6	10 43.8	25 53.1	21 20.7	19 8.3	12 13.3
18 F	19 42 5.8	25 4.6	24 28.5	15 35.8	8 29.2	1 35.0	5 2.1	10 40.1	25 54.9	21 19.7	19 10.4	12 14.8
19 S	19 46 2.3	26 1.9	24 25.3	29 42.2	10 21.3	1 23.9	5 6.7	10 36.6	25 56.8	21 18.7	19 12.5	12 16.3
20 S	19 49 58.9	26 59.1	24 22.2	13♓23.1	12 11.6	1 15.2	5 10.7	10 33.2	25 58.8	21 17.7	19 14.5	12 17.7
21 M	19 53 55.5	27 56.4	24 19.0	26 38.4	14 0.1	1 8.9	5 13.8	10 30.0	26 0.9	21 16.5	19 16.6	12 19.2
22 T	19 57 52.0	28 53.6	24 15.8	9♈29.8	15 46.9	1 5.1	5 16.1	10 27.0	26 3.1	21 15.4	19 18.7	12 20.7
23 W	20 1 48.5	29 50.9	24 12.6	22 0.7	17 31.8	1 3.5	5 17.7	10 24.2	26 5.4	21 14.2	19 20.9	12 22.1
24 T	20 5 45.1	0♌48.2	24 9.5	4♉15.1	19 15.0	1D 4.4	5 18.5	10 21.5	26 7.8	21 13.0	19 23.0	12 23.6
25 F	20 9 41.7	1 45.5	24 6.3	16 17.7	20 56.4	1 7.5	5R18.4	10 19.0	26 10.2	21 11.7	19 25.1	12 25.1
26 S	20 13 38.3	2 42.9	24 3.1	28 12.8	22 36.0	1 12.8	5 17.6	10 16.7	26 12.8	21 10.4	19 27.3	12 26.5
27 S	20 17 34.7	3 40.2	23 59.9	10♊ 4.7	24 13.9	1 20.4	5 15.9	10 14.6	26 15.4	21 9.0	19 29.4	12 27.9
28 M	20 21 31.3	4 37.6	23 56.7	21 57.2	25 50.0	1 30.1	5 13.5	10 12.6	26 18.2	21 7.6	19 31.6	12 29.4
29 T	20 25 27.9	5 34.9	23 53.6	3♋53.6	27 24.3	1 41.9	5 10.3	10 10.9	26 21.0	21 6.2	19 33.7	12 30.8
30 W	20 29 24.5	6 32.3	23 50.4	15 56.5	28 56.9	1 55.7	5 6.3	10 9.3	26 23.9	21 4.7	19 35.9	12 32.2
31 T	20 33 21.0	7 29.7	23 47.2	28 8.2	0♍27.7	2 11.5	5 1.5	10 7.9	26 27.0	21 3.2	19 38.1	12 33.6
DECLINATION												
1 T	18 35 4.3	23N 9.0	13N 4.0	18N59.4	24N 8.7	19N49.9	14S58.3	21S38.3	7S31.8	4S 5.3	15N30.2	20N42.4
4 F	18 46 54.0	22 55.7	13 7.2	17 57.1	24 15.6	19 19.5	14 51.9	21 36.5	7 32.9	4 5.7	15 28.6	20 42.2
7 M	18 58 43.6	22 38.9	13 10.4	9 31.6	23 57.4	18 51.6	14 47.5	21 34.8	7 34.4	4 6.4	15 26.8	20 41.9
10 T	19 10 33.3	22 18.5	13 13.6	3S21.2	23 15.4	18 27.2	14 45.2	21 33.3	7 36.1	4 7.1	15 25.0	20 41.7
13 S	19 22 23.0	21 54.7	13 16.8	15 25.8	22 12.3	18 7.0	14 45.1	21 31.9	7 38.2	4 8.1	15 23.2	20 41.4
16 W	19 34 12.7	21 27.4	13 19.9	19 20.4	20 52.1	17 51.4	14 47.2	21 30.8	7 40.6	4 9.2	15 21.3	20 41.2
19 S	19 46 2.3	20 56.9	13 23.1	12 8.5	19 18.4	17 40.6	14 51.6	21 29.8	7 43.3	4 10.4	15 19.4	20 40.9
22 T	19 57 52.0	20 23.2	13 26.3	0N16.4	17 34.8	17 34.4	14 58.2	21 29.0	7 46.3	4 11.8	15 17.5	20 40.6
25 F	20 9 41.7	19 46.5	13 29.5	11 43.4	15 44.1	17 32.3	15 7.1	21 28.5	7 49.6	4 13.4	15 15.5	20 40.3
28 M	20 21 31.3	19 6.7	13 32.6	18 36.7	13 49.1	17 33.8	15 18.1	21 28.2	7 53.2	4 15.1	15 13.5	20 40.1
31 T	20 33 21.0	18 24.2	13 35.8	18 22.2	11 51.8	17 38.0	15 31.0	21 28.1	7 57.1	4 16.9	15 11.5	20 39.8

AUGUST 1924

DAY	EPHEMERIS SIDEREAL TIME h m s	☉ ° ′	☊ ° ′	☽ ° ′	☿ ° ′	♀ ° ′	♂ ° ′	♃ ° ′	♄ ° ′	♅ ° ′	♆ ° ′	♇ ° ′
LONGITUDE												
1 F	20 37 17.5	8♌27.1	23♌44.0	10♌30.2	1♍56.6	2♋29.2	4♓55.9	10♐ 6.6	26♎30.0	21♓ 1.6	19♌40.3	12♋35.0
2 S	20 41 14.1	9 24.6	23 40.9	23 3.8	3 23.8	2 48.8	4R49.6	10R 5.6	26 33.2	21R 0.1	19 42.5	12 36.4
3 S	20 45 10.7	10 22.0	23 37.7	5♍49.8	4 49.2	3 10.1	4 42.5	10 4.8	26 36.5	20 58.4	19 44.7	12 37.8
4 M	20 49 7.2	11 19.5	23 34.5	18 49.0	6 12.7	3 33.1	4 34.7	10 4.1	26 39.9	20 56.8	19 46.9	12 39.1
5 T	20 53 3.8	12 17.0	23 31.3	2♎ 2.1	7 34.3	3 57.8	4 26.2	10 3.6	26 43.3	20 55.1	19 49.1	12 40.5
6 W	20 57 0.3	13 14.5	23 28.2	15 29.5	8 54.0	4 24.2	4 17.1	10 3.3	26 46.8	20 53.4	19 51.3	12 41.8
7 T	21 0 56.9	14 12.0	23 25.0	29 11.6	10 11.8	4 52.0	4 7.3	10 3.2	26 50.4	20 51.6	19 53.5	12 43.2
8 F	21 4 53.4	15 9.5	23 21.8	13♏ 8.0	11 27.5	5 21.4	3 56.8	10D 3.3	26 54.1	20 49.8	19 55.7	12 44.5
9 S	21 8 50.0	16 7.0	23 18.6	27 18.0	12 41.1	5 52.2	3 45.8	10 3.6	26 57.9	20 48.0	19 57.9	12 45.8
10 S	21 12 46.5	17 4.5	23 15.4	11♐39.5	13 52.6	6 24.4	3 34.1	10 4.0	27 1.8	20 46.1	20 0.2	12 47.1
11 M	21 16 43.1	18 2.1	23 12.3	26 9.3	15 1.8	6 57.9	3 22.0	10 4.7	27 5.7	20 44.3	20 2.4	12 48.4
12 T	21 20 39.6	18 59.7	23 9.1	10♑43.0	16 8.8	7 32.8	3 9.3	10 5.5	27 9.7	20 42.3	20 4.6	12 49.7
13 W	21 24 36.2	19 57.2	23 5.9	25 15.3	17 13.4	8 8.9	2 56.1	10 6.5	27 13.8	20 40.4	20 6.8	12 50.9
14 T	21 28 32.8	20 54.9	23 2.7	9♒40.4	18 15.4	8 46.2	2 42.6	10 7.7	27 18.0	20 38.4	20 9.1	12 52.2
15 F	21 32 29.3	21 52.5	22 59.6	23 52.9	19 14.8	9 24.7	2 28.5	10 9.1	27 22.2	20 36.4	20 11.3	12 53.4
16 S	21 36 25.8	22 50.1	22 56.4	7♓48.4	20 11.5	10 4.3	2 14.1	10 10.6	27 26.5	20 34.4	20 13.5	12 54.6
17 S	21 40 22.4	23 47.8	22 53.2	21 23.6	21 5.3	10 45.0	1 59.4	10 12.3	27 30.9	20 32.4	20 15.7	12 55.8
18 M	21 44 19.0	24 45.5	22 50.0	4♈37.3	21 56.1	11 26.7	1 44.4	10 14.3	27 35.4	20 30.3	20 17.9	12 57.0
19 T	21 48 15.6	25 43.2	22 46.9	17 29.8	22 43.6	12 9.5	1 29.1	10 16.4	27 39.9	20 28.2	20 20.2	12 58.2
20 W	21 52 12.1	26 40.9	22 43.7	0♉ 2.9	23 27.8	12 53.2	1 13.6	10 18.6	27 44.6	20 26.1	20 22.4	12 59.4
21 T	21 56 8.6	27 38.7	22 40.5	12 19.6	24 8.3	13 37.8	0 57.9	10 21.1	27 49.2	20 23.9	20 24.6	13 0.5
22 F	22 0 5.2	28 36.5	22 37.3	24 23.7	24 45.1	14 23.4	0 42.1	10 23.7	27 54.0	20 21.8	20 26.8	13 1.7
23 S	22 4 1.8	29 34.3	22 34.1	6♊19.8	25 17.8	15 9.9	0 26.2	10 26.5	27 58.8	20 19.6	20 29.0	13 2.8
24 S	22 7 58.3	0♍32.2	22 31.0	18 12.2	25 46.3	15 57.1	0 10.3	10 29.5	28 3.7	20 17.4	20 31.2	13 3.9
25 M	22 11 54.8	1 30.1	22 27.8	0♋ 5.7	26 10.2	16 45.2	29♒54.3	10 32.6	28 8.7	20 15.2	20 33.4	13 5.0
26 T	22 15 51.4	2 28.0	22 24.6	12 4.6	26 29.4	17 34.1	29 38.5	10 36.0	28 13.7	20 12.9	20 35.6	13 6.0
27 W	22 19 48.0	3 25.9	22 21.4	24 12.6	26 43.5	18 23.7	29 22.7	10 39.5	28 18.8	20 10.7	20 37.8	13 7.1
28 T	22 23 44.5	4 23.9	22 18.2	6♌33.0	26 52.3	19 14.0	29 7.1	10 43.2	28 24.0	20 8.4	20 39.9	13 8.1
29 F	22 27 41.1	5 21.9	22 15.1	19 8.1	26 55.6	20 5.0	28 51.7	10 47.0	28 29.2	20 6.1	20 42.1	13 9.1
30 S	22 31 37.6	6 19.9	22 11.9	1♍59.4	26R53.1	20 56.7	28 36.5	10 51.0	28 34.5	20 3.8	20 44.3	13 10.1
31 S	22 35 34.1	7 18.0	22 8.7	15 7.2	26 44.6	21 49.0	28 21.7	10 55.2	28 39.9	20 1.5	20 46.4	13 11.1
DECLINATION												
1 F	20 37 17.5	18N 9.4	13N36.8	16N30.9	11N12.5	17N39.9	15S35.8	21S28.1	7S58.4	4S17.5	15N10.8	20N39.7
4 M	20 49 7.2	17 23.2	13 40.0	6 32.8	9 15.1	17 46.6	15 50.9	21 28.3	8 2.6	4 19.5	15 8.8	20 39.4
7 T	21 0 56.9	16 34.5	13 43.1	6S40.0	7 19.7	17 54.4	16 7.3	21 28.8	8 7.1	4 21.6	15 6.7	20 39.1
10 S	21 12 46.5	15 43.4	13 46.2	17 13.8	5 28.0	18 2.4	16 24.5	21 29.5	8 11.8	4 23.8	15 4.7	20 38.8
13 W	21 24 36.2	14 50.0	13 49.4	18 40.2	3 41.7	18 10.1	16 42.1	21 30.5	8 16.7	4 26.2	15 2.6	20 38.6
16 S	21 36 25.8	13 54.5	13 52.5	9 54.1	2 2.9	18 16.8	16 59.6	21 31.6	8 21.9	4 28.6	15 0.5	20 38.3
19 T	21 48 15.6	12 57.0	13 55.6	2N53.3	0 34.0	18 21.9	17 16.6	21 33.1	8 27.3	4 31.1	14 58.4	20 38.0
22 F	22 0 5.2	11 57.7	13 58.7	13 45.0	0S42.3	18 24.9	17 32.6	21 34.7	8 32.9	4 33.6	14 56.3	20 37.8
25 M	22 11 54.8	10 56.6	14 1.8	19 13.8	1 42.3	18 25.4	17 47.0	21 36.5	8 38.6	4 36.3	14 54.3	20 37.5
28 T	22 23 44.5	9 54.0	14 4.9	17 11.3	2 21.7	18 22.9	17 59.4	21 38.6	8 44.6	4 39.0	14 52.2	20 37.2
31 S	22 35 34.1	8 50.0	14 8.0	7 41.7	2 35.4	18 17.2	18 9.5	21 40.8	8 50.7	4 41.7	14 50.2	20 37.0

SEPTEMBER 1924

DAY	EPHEMERIS SIDEREAL TIME	☉	☊	☽	☿	♀	♂	♃	♄	♅	♆	♇
	h m s	° ′	° ′	° ′	° ′	° ′	° ′	° ′	° ′	° ′	° ′	° ′
						LONGITUDE						
1 M	22 39 30.7	8♍16.1	22♌ 5.5	28♍30.9	26♍29.9	22♋42.0	28♒ 7.2	10♐59.6	28♎45.3	19♓59.1	20♌48.6	13♋12.1
2 T	22 43 27.3	9 14.2	22 2.4	12♎ 8.9	26R 9.0	23 35.5	27R53.1	11 4.1	28 50.8	19R56.8	20 50.7	13 13.0
3 W	22 47 23.8	10 12.3	21 59.2	25 59.1	25 41.8	24 29.7	27 39.4	11 8.8	28 56.3	19 54.4	20 52.8	13 13.9
4 T	22 51 20.3	11 10.5	21 56.0	9♏58.9	25 8.5	25 24.4	27 26.2	11 13.7	29 1.9	19 52.1	20 54.9	13 14.8
5 F	22 55 16.9	12 8.7	21 52.8	24 5.5	24 29.2	26 19.6	27 13.5	11 18.7	29 7.6	19 49.7	20 57.1	13 15.7
6 S	22 59 13.5	13 6.9	21 49.7	8♐16.5	23 44.4	27 15.4	27 1.4	11 23.9	29 13.3	19 47.3	20 59.2	13 16.6
7 S	23 3 10.1	14 5.1	21 46.5	22 29.3	22 54.5	28 11.7	26 49.9	11 29.2	29 19.0	19 44.9	21 1.2	13 17.5
8 M	23 7 6.6	15 3.4	21 43.3	6♑41.8	22 0.4	29 8.5	26 38.9	11 34.7	29 24.9	19 42.6	21 3.3	13 18.3
9 T	23 11 3.1	16 1.7	21 40.1	20 51.7	21 2.8	0♌ 5.7	26 28.6	11 40.4	29 30.7	19 40.2	21 5.4	13 19.1
10 W	23 14 59.7	16 60.0	21 36.9	4♒56.7	20 2.9	1 3.5	26 18.9	11 46.2	29 36.7	19 37.8	21 7.4	13 19.9
11 T	23 18 56.3	17 58.3	21 33.8	18 54.3	19 1.9	2 1.7	26 10.0	11 52.1	29 42.7	19 35.4	21 9.4	13 20.6
12 F	23 22 52.8	18 56.7	21 30.6	2♓41.8	18 1.2	3 0.3	26 1.7	11 58.3	29 48.7	19 33.0	21 11.5	13 21.4
13 S	23 26 49.3	19 55.1	21 27.4	16 16.7	17 2.1	3 59.4	25 54.1	12 4.5	29 54.8	19 30.6	21 13.5	13 22.1
14 S	23 30 45.9	20 53.5	21 24.2	29 36.8	16 6.2	4 58.9	25 47.3	12 10.9	0♏ 0.9	19 28.2	21 15.5	13 22.8
15 M	23 34 42.5	21 51.9	21 21.0	12♈40.6	15 14.8	5 58.8	25 41.2	12 17.5	0 7.1	19 25.8	21 17.4	13 23.5
16 T	23 38 39.0	22 50.4	21 17.9	25 27.5	14 29.2	6 59.1	25 35.8	12 24.2	0 13.3	19 23.4	21 19.4	13 24.2
17 W	23 42 35.5	23 49.0	21 14.7	7♉58.0	13 50.6	7 59.8	25 31.2	12 31.0	0 19.6	19 21.0	21 21.3	13 24.8
18 T	23 46 32.1	24 47.5	21 11.5	20 13.9	13 19.9	9 0.9	25 27.3	12 38.0	0 25.9	19 18.6	21 23.3	13 25.4
19 F	23 50 28.7	25 46.1	21 8.3	2♊17.8	12 58.1	10 2.3	25 24.3	12 45.2	0 32.2	19 16.2	21 25.2	13 26.0
20 S	23 54 25.2	26 44.7	21 5.2	14 13.5	12 45.5	11 4.1	25 22.0	12 52.5	0 38.6	19 13.8	21 27.1	13 26.6
21 S	23 58 21.8	27 43.4	21 2.0	26 5.3	12 42.7	12 6.3	25 20.5	12 59.9	0 45.1	19 11.5	21 29.0	13 27.2
22 M	0 2 18.3	28 42.1	20 58.8	7♋58.1	12D49.7	13 8.8	25 19.8	13 7.4	0 51.5	19 9.1	21 30.8	13 27.7
23 T	0 6 14.9	29 40.8	20 55.6	19 56.8	13 6.5	14 11.6	25D19.9	13 15.1	0 58.1	19 6.7	21 32.7	13 28.2
24 W	0 10 11.4	0♎39.6	20 52.4	2♌ 6.3	13 33.0	15 14.7	25 20.8	13 22.9	1 4.6	19 4.4	21 34.5	13 28.7
25 T	0 14 8.0	1 38.5	20 49.3	14 31.0	14 8.7	16 18.2	25 22.5	13 30.9	1 11.2	19 2.1	21 36.3	13 29.2
26 F	0 18 4.6	2 37.3	20 46.1	27 14.6	14 53.3	17 21.9	25 25.0	13 39.0	1 17.9	18 59.7	21 38.1	13 29.6
27 S	0 22 1.1	3 36.2	20 42.9	10♍19.5	15 46.1	18 26.0	25 28.2	13 47.2	1 24.5	18 57.4	21 39.8	13 30.0
28 S	0 25 57.6	4 35.1	20 39.7	23 46.6	16 46.6	19 30.3	25 32.3	13 55.5	1 31.3	18 55.1	21 41.6	13 30.4
29 M	0 29 54.2	5 34.1	20 36.5	7♎34.5	17 54.0	20 34.9	25 37.2	14 4.0	1 38.0	18 52.9	21 43.3	13 30.8
30 T	0 33 50.8	6 33.1	20 33.4	21 40.3	19 7.7	21 39.8	25 42.8	14 12.6	1 44.8	18 50.6	21 45.0	13 31.1
						DECLINATION						
1 M	22 39 30.7	8N28.3	14N 9.0	3N24.0	2S33.5	18N14.5	18S12.3	21S41.6	8S52.8	4S42.6	14N49.5	20N36.9
4 T	22 51 20.3	7 22.6	14 12.1	9S56.9	2 5.6	18 4.0	18 18.8	21 44.1	8 59.2	4 45.4	14 47.5	20 36.7
7 S	23 3 10.1	6 15.8	14 15.2	18 40.4	1 3.8	17 49.7	18 22.3	21 46.8	9 5.7	4 48.2	14 45.6	20 36.5
10 W	23 14 59.7	5 8.1	14 18.3	17 27.8	0N28.0	17 31.3	18 22.7	21 49.6	9 12.3	4 51.1	14 43.6	20 36.3
13 S	23 26 49.3	3 59.7	14 21.3	7 19.8	2 18.1	17 8.8	18 20.1	21 52.5	9 19.1	4 53.9	14 41.7	20 36.1
16 T	23 38 39.0	2 50.5	14 24.4	5N32.1	4 7.8	16 42.1	18 14.5	21 55.6	9 25.9	4 56.7	14 39.9	20 35.9
19 F	23 50 28.7	1 40.9	14 27.4	15 36.2	5 37.6	16 11.1	18 6.0	21 58.8	9 32.9	4 59.5	14 38.1	20 35.8
22 M	0 2 18.3	0 31.0	14 30.5	19 34.1	6 33.0	15 35.8	17 54.6	22 2.1	9 40.0	5 2.3	14 36.3	20 35.6
25 T	0 14 8.0	0S39.2	14 33.5	15 47.6	6 47.0	14 56.3	17 40.6	22 5.4	9 47.1	5 5.0	14 34.6	20 35.5
28 S	0 25 57.6	1 49.4	14 36.6	4 56.4	6 19.8	14 12.7	17 24.1	22 8.9	9 54.3	5 7.7	14 32.9	20 35.4

OCTOBER 1924

DAY	EPHEMERIS SIDEREAL TIME	☉	☊	☽	☿	♀	♂	♃	♄	♅	♆	♇
						LONGITUDE						
1 W	0 37 47.3	7♎32.1	20♌30.2	5♏59.0	20♍26.9	22♌44.9	25♒49.2	14♐21.4	1♏51.6	18♓48.4	21♌46.7	13♋31.5
2 T	0 41 43.9	8 31.2	20 27.0	20 24.9	21 51.0	23 50.3	25 56.4	14 30.2	1 58.4	18R46.1	21 48.3	13 31.8
3 F	0 45 40.4	9 30.2	20 23.8	4♐52.2	23 19.4	24 55.9	26 4.4	14 39.2	2 5.3	18 43.9	21 50.0	13 32.0
4 S	0 49 37.0	10 29.4	20 20.7	19 15.6	24 51.3	26 1.7	26 13.1	14 48.3	2 12.2	18 41.8	21 51.6	13 32.3
5 S	0 53 33.5	11 28.5	20 17.5	3♑3x.4	26 26.3	27 7.8	26 22.6	14 57.5	2 19.1	18 39.6	21 53.2	13 32.5
6 M	0 57 30.1	12 27.7	20 14.3	17 37.3	28 3.7	28 14.1	26 32.8	15 6.8	2 26.1	18 37.5	21 54.7	13 32.7
7 T	1 1 26.6	13 26.9	20 11.1	1♒32.3	29 43.2	29 20.7	26 43.7	15 16.2	2 33.0	18 35.3	21 56.3	13 32.9
8 W	1 5 23.2	14 26.1	20 7.9	15 16.1	1♎24.2	0♍27.5	26 55.3	15 25.8	2 40.0	18 33.3	21 57.8	13 33.1
9 T	1 9 19.7	15 25.4	20 4.8	28 49.0	3 6.5	1 34.5	27 7.6	15 35.4	2 47.0	18 31.2	21 59.3	13 33.2
10 F	1 13 16.3	16 24.7	20 1.6	12♓11.0	4 49.7	2 41.7	27 20.6	15 45.2	2 54.1	18 29.2	22 0.7	13 33.3
11 S	1 17 12.8	17 24.0	19 58.4	25 22.0	6 33.6	3 49.1	27 34.2	15 55.0	3 1.1	18 27.1	22 2.2	13 33.4
12 S	1 21 9.4	18 23.4	19 55.2	8♈21.5	8 17.8	4 56.7	27 48.4	16 5.0	3 8.2	18 25.1	22 3.6	13 33.5
13 M	1 25 5.9	19 22.8	19 52.1	21 9.0	10 2.3	6 4.5	28 3.4	16 15.1	3 15.3	18 23.2	22 5.0	13 33.5
14 T	1 29 2.5	20 22.2	19 48.9	3♉44.1	11 46.8	7 12.5	28 18.9	16 25.3	3 22.4	18 21.3	22 6.3	13 33.5
15 W	1 32 59.1	21 21.7	19 45.7	16 6.7	13 31.2	8 20.7	28 35.0	16 35.5	3 29.6	18 19.4	22 7.7	13R33.5
16 T	1 36 55.6	22 21.1	19 42.5	28 17.7	15 15.4	9 29.1	28 51.7	16 45.9	3 36.7	18 17.5	22 8.9	13 33.5
17 F	1 40 52.1	23 20.7	19 39.3	10♊18.7	16 59.3	10 37.7	29 9.0	16 56.4	3 43.9	18 15.7	22 10.2	13 33.4
18 S	1 44 48.7	24 20.3	19 36.2	22 12.3	18 42.9	11 46.5	29 26.9	17 7.0	3 51.0	18 13.9	22 11.5	13 33.4
19 S	1 48 45.3	25 19.9	19 33.0	4♋ 2.2	20 26.0	12 55.4	29 45.3	17 17.6	3 58.2	18 12.1	22 12.7	13 33.3
20 M	1 52 41.8	26 19.5	19 29.8	15 52.7	22 8.7	14 4.5	0♓ 4.3	17 28.4	4 5.4	18 10.3	22 13.9	13 33.1
21 T	1 56 38.4	27 19.2	19 26.6	27 48.8	23 50.8	15 13.8	0 23.8	17 39.3	4 12.6	18 8.6	22 15.0	13 33.0
22 W	2 0 34.9	28 18.9	19 23.5	9♌55.8	25 32.5	16 23.3	0 43.8	17 50.2	4 19.8	18 7.0	22 16.2	13 32.8
23 T	2 4 31.5	29 18.7	19 20.3	22 19.1	27 13.6	17 32.9	1 4.3	18 1.2	4 27.1	18 5.3	22 17.3	13 32.6
24 F	2 8 28.0	0♏18.5	19 17.1	5♍ 3.6	28 54.2	18 42.6	1 25.4	18 12.4	4 34.3	18 3.7	22 18.4	13 32.4
25 S	2 12 24.6	1 18.3	19 13.9	18 13.1	0♏34.3	19 52.6	1 46.9	18 23.6	4 41.5	18 2.2	22 19.4	13 32.1
26 S	2 16 21.1	2 18.2	19 10.7	1♎49.7	2 13.8	21 2.6	2 8.9	18 34.9	4 48.8	18 0.7	22 20.4	13 31.9
27 M	2 20 17.7	3 18.1	19 7.6	15 53.2	3 52.7	22 12.8	2 31.4	18 46.3	4 56.0	17 59.2	22 21.4	13 31.6
28 T	2 24 14.3	4 18.0	19 4.4	0♏20.2	5 31.2	23 23.2	2 54.3	18 57.7	5 3.3	17 57.8	22 22.4	13 31.3
29 W	2 28 10.8	5 18.0	19 1.2	15 4.5	7 9.1	24 33.7	3 17.7	19 9.3	5 10.5	17 56.4	22 23.3	13 30.9
30 T	2 32 7.3	6 18.0	18 58.0	29 57.9	8 46.5	25 44.3	3 41.6	19 20.9	5 17.8	17 55.0	22 24.2	13 30.6
31 F	2 36 3.9	7 18.0	18 54.9	14♐51.1	10 23.5	26 55.0	4 5.8	19 32.6	5 25.0	17 53.7	22 25.0	13 30.2
						DECLINATION						
1 W	0 37 47.3	2S59.5	14N39.6	8S51.8	5N16.6	13N25.1	17S 5.1	22S12.4	10S 1.6	5S10.3	14N31.3	20N35.3
4 S	0 49 37.0	4 9.2	14 42.6	18 28.2	3 44.9	12 33.6	16 43.8	22 15.9	10 8.9	5 12.8	14 29.8	20 35.2
7 T	1 1 26.6	5 18.6	14 45.6	18 5.3	1 53.3	11 38.4	16 20.4	22 19.4	10 16.2	5 15.3	14 28.3	20 35.2
10 F	1 13 16.3	6 27.3	14 48.6	8 38.6	0S10.9	10 39.7	15 55.1	22 23.0	10 23.6	5 17.7	14 26.9	20 35.2
13 M	1 25 5.9	7 35.2	14 51.6	4N11.4	2 21.7	9 37.7	15 27.9	22 26.5	10 31.0	5 20.0	14 25.6	20 35.2
16 T	1 36 55.6	8 42.2	14 54.6	14 53.5	4 35.0	8 32.5	14 59.0	22 30.0	10 38.4	5 22.1	14 24.4	20 35.2
19 S	1 48 45.3	9 48.1	14 57.6	19 42.2	6 47.5	7 24.5	14 28.6	22 33.5	10 45.7	5 24.2	14 23.2	20 35.2
22 W	2 0 34.9	10 52.7	15 0.6	16 52.1	8 57.2	6 13.9	13 56.6	22 36.9	10 53.1	5 26.1	14 22.2	20 35.3
25 S	2 12 24.6	11 55.9	15 3.6	6 50.0	11 2.5	5 1.0	13 23.2	22 40.2	11 0.4	5 27.9	14 21.2	20 35.4
28 T	2 24 14.3	12 57.5	15 6.6	7S 9.6	13 2.4	3 46.0	12 48.5	22 43.5	11 7.7	5 29.5	14 20.3	20 35.5
31 F	2 36 3.9	13 57.2	15 9.5	18 4.5	14 56.0	2 29.3	12 12.5	22 46.7	11 14.9	5 31.0	14 19.5	20 35.6

NOVEMBER 1924

DAY	EPHEMERIS SIDEREAL TIME	☉	☊	☽	☿	♀	♂	♃	♄	♅	♆	♇
	h m s	° ′	° ′	° ′	° ′	° ′	° ′	° ′	° ′	° ′	° ′	° ′
						LONGITUDE						
1 S	2 40 0.5	8♏18.1	18♌51.7	29♐36.1	11♏59.9	28♍ 5.9	4♓30.5	19♐44.4	5♏32.3	17♓52.4	22♌25.8	13♋29.8
2 S	2 43 57.0	9 18.2	18 48.5	14♑ 6.4	13 36.0	29 16.9	4 55.6	19 56.2	5 39.5	17R51.2	22 26.6	13R29.3
3 M	2 47 53.6	10 18.3	18 45.3	28 18.7	15 11.5	0♎28.0	5 21.2	20 8.2	5 46.8	17 50.0	22 27.4	13 28.9
4 T	2 51 50.1	11 18.4	18 42.1	12♒11.8	16 46.7	1 39.2	5 47.0	20 20.1	5 54.0	17 48.8	22 28.1	13 28.4
5 W	2 55 46.7	12 18.6	18 39.0	25 46.4	18 21.4	2 50.5	6 13.3	20 32.2	6 1.2	17 47.7	22 28.8	13 27.9
6 T	2 59 43.2	13 18.8	18 35.8	9♓ 4.3	19 55.7	4 1.9	6 40.0	20 44.3	6 8.4	17 46.7	22 29.5	13 27.4
7 F	3 3 39.8	14 19.0	18 32.6	22 7.7	21 29.7	5 13.5	7 7.0	20 56.5	6 15.6	17 45.7	22 30.1	13 26.9
8 S	3 7 36.3	15 19.2	18 29.4	4♈58.6	23 3.3	6 25.2	7 34.3	21 8.8	6 22.8	17 44.7	22 30.7	13 26.3
9 S	3 11 32.9	16 19.5	18 26.3	17 38.4	24 36.5	7 36.9	8 2.0	21 21.1	6 30.0	17 43.8	22 31.2	13 25.7
10 M	3 15 29.4	17 19.8	18 23.1	0♉ 8.1	26 9.4	8 48.8	8 30.0	21 33.5	6 37.2	17 42.9	22 31.8	13 25.1
11 T	3 19 26.0	18 20.1	18 19.9	12 28.6	27 42.0	10 0.8	8 58.3	21 46.0	6 44.3	17 42.1	22 32.3	13 24.5
12 W	3 23 22.6	19 20.5	18 16.7	24 40.2	29 14.3	11 12.8	9 26.9	21 58.5	6 51.5	17 41.3	22 32.7	13 23.8
13 T	3 27 19.1	20 20.8	18 13.5	6♊43.7	0♐46.3	12 25.0	9 55.8	22 11.0	6 58.6	17 40.6	22 33.2	13 23.2
14 F	3 31 15.7	21 21.2	18 10.4	18 40.0	2 17.9	13 37.3	10 25.0	22 23.6	7 5.7	17 39.9	22 33.5	13 22.5
15 S	3 35 12.2	22 21.7	18 7.2	0♋31.0	3 49.3	14 49.6	10 54.5	22 36.3	7 12.8	17 39.3	22 33.9	13 21.8
16 S	3 39 8.8	23 22.2	18 4.0	12 19.4	5 20.4	16 2.1	11 24.2	22 49.1	7 19.9	17 38.7	22 34.2	13 21.0
17 M	3 43 5.3	24 22.7	18 0.8	24 8.4	6 51.2	17 14.6	11 54.2	23 1.8	7 26.9	17 38.2	22 34.5	13 20.3
18 T	3 47 1.9	25 23.2	17 57.7	6♌ 2.4	8 21.7	18 27.3	12 24.5	23 14.7	7 34.0	17 37.7	22 34.8	13 19.5
19 W	3 50 58.4	26 23.7	17 54.5	18 6.2	9 51.9	19 40.0	12 55.1	23 27.6	7 41.0	17 37.2	22 35.0	13 18.7
20 T	3 54 55.0	27 24.3	17 51.3	0♍25.4	11 21.8	20 52.8	13 25.9	23 40.5	7 48.0	17 36.9	22 35.2	13 17.9
21 F	3 58 51.6	28 24.9	17 48.1	13 5.1	12 51.4	22 5.7	13 56.9	23 53.5	7 54.9	17 36.5	22 35.4	13 17.1
22 S	4 2 48.1	29 25.6	17 45.0	26 10.2	14 20.6	23 18.6	14 28.2	24 6.5	8 1.8	17 36.2	22 35.5	13 16.3
23 S	4 6 44.7	0♐26.2	17 41.8	9♎44.4	15 49.4	24 31.7	14 59.7	24 19.6	8 8.7	17 36.0	22 35.6	13 15.4
24 M	4 10 41.2	1 26.9	17 38.6	23 48.8	17 17.8	25 44.8	15 31.4	24 32.7	8 15.6	17 35.8	22 35.6	13 14.5
25 T	4 14 37.8	2 27.7	17 35.4	8♏21.8	18 45.7	26 57.9	16 3.4	24 45.9	8 22.5	17 35.7	22 35.6	13 13.7
26 W	4 18 34.3	3 28.4	17 32.2	23 17.8	20 13.0	28 11.2	16 35.5	24 59.1	8 29.3	17 35.6	22R35.6	13 12.7
27 T	4 22 30.9	4 29.2	17 29.1	8♐28.2	21 39.8	29 24.5	17 7.9	25 12.3	8 36.1	17 35.6	22 35.5	13 11.8
28 F	4 26 27.4	5 30.0	17 25.9	23 42.2	23 5.8	0♏37.9	17 40.5	25 25.6	8 42.8	17D35.6	22 35.5	13 10.9
29 S	4 30 24.0	6 30.8	17 22.7	8♑49.0	24 31.1	1 51.3	18 13.4	25 38.9	8 49.5	17 35.7	22 35.3	13 9.9
30 S	4 34 20.6	7 31.6	17 19.5	23 39.6	25 55.5	3 4.8	18 46.4	25 52.3	8 56.2	17 35.8	22 35.2	13 8.9
						DECLINATION						
1 S	2 40 0.5	14S16.7	15N10.5	19S36.3	15S32.3	2N 3.4	12S 0.2	22S47.7	11S17.3	5S31.5	14N19.2	20N35.7
4 T	2 51 50.1	15 13.7	15 13.5	16 33.0	17 16.4	0 44.9	11 22.6	22 50.8	11 24.5	5 32.8	14 18.5	20 35.8
7 F	3 3 39.8	16 8.4	15 16.4	5 38.4	18 52.7	0S34.7	10 43.9	22 53.7	11 31.5	5 33.9	14 17.9	20 36.0
10 M	3 15 29.4	17 0.7	15 19.4	7N 5.1	20 20.6	1 55.0	10 4.2	22 56.4	11 38.5	5 34.9	14 17.4	20 36.2
13 T	3 27 19.1	17 50.4	15 22.3	16 46.4	21 39.6	3 15.6	9 23.6	22 59.1	11 45.4	5 35.7	14 17.1	20 36.5
16 S	3 39 8.8	18 37.3	15 25.2	19 59.2	22 48.9	4 36.4	8 42.1	23 1.6	11 52.2	5 36.3	14 16.8	20 36.7
19 W	3 50 58.4	19 21.2	15 28.2	15 28.2	23 48.0	5 56.9	7 59.7	23 3.9	11 58.8	5 36.8	14 16.6	20 37.0
22 S	4 2 48.1	20 2.1	15 31.1	4 25.8	24 36.2	7 16.7	7 16.6	23 6.0	12 5.3	5 37.1	14 16.5	20 37.3
25 T	4 14 37.8	20 39.6	15 34.0	9S35.2	25 13.0	8 35.7	6 32.8	23 8.0	12 11.7	5 37.2	14 16.5	20 37.7
28 F	4 26 27.4	21 13.7	15 36.9	19 17.3	25 37.6	9 53.3	5 48.4	23 9.8	12 18.0	5 37.1	14 16.6	20 38.0

DECEMBER 1924

DAY	EPHEMERIS SIDEREAL TIME	☉	☊	☽	☿	♀	♂	♃	♄	♅	♆	♇
						LONGITUDE						
1 M	4 38 17.1	8♐32.5	17♌16.4	8♒ 8.0	27♐18.8	4♏18.3	19♓19.6	26♐ 5.6	9♏ 2.9	17♓36.0	22♌35.0	13♋ 8.0
2 T	4 42 13.7	9 33.3	17 13.2	22 11.5	28 40.9	5 31.9	19 52.9	26 19.0	9 9.5	17 36.2	22R34.8	13R 6.9
3 W	4 46 10.2	10 34.2	17 10.0	5♓50.2	0♑ 1.6	6 45.6	20 26.5	26 32.5	9 16.0	17 36.5	22 34.5	13 5.9
4 T	4 50 6.8	11 35.1	17 6.8	19 6.2	1 20.7	7 59.3	21 0.2	26 46.0	9 22.5	17 36.8	22 34.2	13 4.9
5 F	4 54 3.4	12 36.0	17 3.7	2♈ 2.3	2 38.0	9 13.0	21 34.1	26 59.5	9 29.0	17 37.2	22 33.9	13 3.9
6 S	4 57 59.9	13 36.9	17 0.5	14 42.1	3 53.1	10 26.8	22 8.2	27 13.0	9 35.5	17 37.6	22 33.5	13 2.8
7 S	5 1 56.5	14 37.8	16 57.3	27 8.6	5 5.6	11 40.6	22 42.4	27 26.5	9 41.9	17 38.1	22 33.1	13 1.7
8 M	5 5 53.0	15 38.8	16 54.1	9♉24.6	6 15.3	12 54.5	23 16.8	27 40.1	9 48.2	17 38.6	22 32.7	13 0.6
9 T	5 9 49.6	16 39.7	16 50.9	21 32.3	7 21.7	14 8.4	23 51.3	27 53.7	9 54.5	17 39.2	22 32.2	12 59.5
10 W	5 13 46.1	17 40.7	16 47.8	3♊33.4	8 24.2	15 22.4	24 26.0	28 7.3	10 0.8	17 39.9	22 31.8	12 58.4
11 T	5 17 42.7	18 41.7	16 44.6	15 29.4	9 22.2	16 36.4	25 0.8	28 20.9	10 7.0	17 40.6	22 31.2	12 57.3
12 F	5 21 39.2	19 42.7	16 41.4	27 21.5	10 15.2	17 50.5	25 35.7	28 34.6	10 13.1	17 41.3	22 30.7	12 56.2
13 S	5 25 35.8	20 43.7	16 38.2	9♋11.2	11 2.4	19 4.6	26 10.7	28 48.3	10 19.2	17 42.1	22 30.1	12 55.0
14 S	5 29 32.4	21 44.7	16 35.1	21 0.5	11 43.0	20 18.7	26 45.9	29 2.0	10 25.3	17 42.9	22 29.5	12 53.9
15 M	5 33 28.9	22 45.7	16 31.9	2♌51.7	12 16.3	21 32.9	27 21.2	29 15.7	10 31.3	17 43.8	22 28.8	12 52.7
16 T	5 37 25.5	23 46.8	16 28.7	14 48.0	12 41.2	22 47.2	27 56.6	29 29.4	10 37.2	17 44.8	22 28.1	12 51.6
17 W	5 41 22.0	24 47.8	16 25.5	26 53.2	12 56.9	24 1.4	28 32.1	29 43.1	10 43.1	17 45.8	22 27.4	12 50.4
18 T	5 45 18.6	25 48.9	16 22.4	9♍11.5	13 2.6	25 15.7	29 7.8	29 56.8	10 49.0	17 46.8	22 26.7	12 49.2
19 F	5 49 15.2	26 50.0	16 19.2	21 47.8	12R57.5	26 30.1	29 43.6	0♑10.6	10 54.7	17 47.9	22 25.9	12 48.0
20 S	5 53 11.7	27 51.1	16 16.0	4♎46.6	12 41.0	27 44.4	0♈19.4	0 24.3	11 0.5	17 49.1	22 25.1	12 46.8
21 S	5 57 8.2	28 52.2	16 12.8	18 11.8	12 12.7	28 58.8	0 55.4	0 38.1	11 6.1	17 50.2	22 24.3	12 45.6
22 M	6 1 4.8	29 53.4	16 9.6	2♏ 5.9	11 32.9	0♐13.3	1 31.5	0 51.8	11 11.7	17 51.5	22 23.4	12 44.4
23 T	6 5 1.4	0♑54.5	16 6.5	16 28.9	10 41.8	1 27.7	2 7.6	1 5.6	11 17.3	17 52.8	22 22.5	12 43.2
24 W	6 8 58.0	1 55.7	16 3.3	1♐17.6	9 40.5	2 42.2	2 43.9	1 19.4	11 22.7	17 54.1	22 21.6	12 42.0
25 T	6 12 54.5	2 56.8	16 0.1	16 25.5	8 30.6	3 56.7	3 20.3	1 33.2	11 28.1	17 55.5	22 20.6	12 40.7
26 F	6 16 51.0	3 58.0	15 56.9	1♑43.0	7 14.1	5 11.3	3 56.8	1 46.9	11 33.5	17 56.9	22 19.7	12 39.5
27 S	6 20 47.6	4 59.2	15 53.8	16 59.3	5 53.4	6 25.8	4 33.3	2 0.7	11 38.7	17 58.4	22 18.7	12 38.2
28 S	6 24 44.2	6 0.3	15 50.6	2♒ 3.7	4 31.3	7 40.4	5 10.0	2 14.5	11 44.0	17 59.9	22 17.6	12 37.0
29 M	6 28 40.7	7 1.5	15 47.4	16 48.0	3 10.4	8 55.0	5 46.7	2 28.2	11 49.1	18 1.5	22 16.6	12 35.8
30 T	6 32 37.3	8 2.7	15 44.2	1♓ 6.9	1 53.4	10 9.6	6 23.6	2 42.0	11 54.2	18 3.1	22 15.5	12 34.5
31 W	6 36 33.8	9 3.9	15 41.1	14 58.2	0 42.4	11 24.3	7 0.5	2 55.7	11 59.2	18 4.8	22 14.4	12 33.3
						DECLINATION						
1 M	4 38 17.1	21S44.1	15N39.8	17S33.0	25S49.7	11S 9.2	5S 3.3	23S11.4	12S24.1	5S36.8	14N16.8	20N38.4
4 T	4 50 6.8	22 10.8	15 42.7	6 51.4	25 48.8	12 23.1	4 17.7	23 12.8	12 30.1	5 36.4	14 17.1	20 38.7
7 S	5 1 56.5	22 33.7	15 45.6	5N58.7	25 35.2	13 34.6	3 31.6	23 13.9	12 35.8	5 35.8	14 17.5	20 39.2
10 W	5 13 46.1	22 52.6	15 48.4	16 8.3	25 9.6	14 43.4	2 45.1	23 14.9	12 41.4	5 35.0	14 18.0	20 39.6
13 S	5 25 35.8	23 7.4	15 51.3	20 9.0	24 33.4	15 49.1	1 58.3	23 15.7	12 46.8	5 34.0	14 18.7	20 40.0
16 T	5 37 25.5	23 18.1	15 54.2	16 24.1	23 49.5	16 51.3	1 11.2	23 16.2	12 52.1	5 32.8	14 19.3	20 40.5
19 F	5 49 15.2	23 24.5	15 57.0	6 6.6	23 1.4	17 49.8	0 23.9	23 16.6	12 57.1	5 31.5	14 20.1	20 40.9
22 M	6 1 4.8	23 26.8	15 59.9	7S28.7	22 13.1	18 44.1	0N23.6	23 16.7	13 1.9	5 30.0	14 21.0	20 41.4
25 T	6 12 54.5	23 24.8	16 2.7	18 23.8	21 28.0	19 33.9	1 11.2	23 16.6	13 6.5	5 28.3	14 22.0	20 41.9
28 S	6 24 44.2	23 18.6	16 5.5	18 38.5	20 49.5	20 18.9	1 58.9	23 16.3	13 10.9	5 26.5	14 23.0	20 42.4
31 W	6 36 33.8	23 8.2	16 8.4	8 23.0	20 23.0	20 58.8	2 46.7	23 15.8	13 15.0	5 24.5	14 24.1	20 42.9

JANUARY 1925

LONGITUDE

DAY	EPHEMERIS SIDEREAL TIME	☉	☊	☽	☿	♀	♂	♃	♄	♅	♆	♇
	h m s	° ′	° ′	° ′	° ′	° ′	° ′	° ′	° ′	° ′	° ′	° ′
1 T	6 40 30.4	10♑ 5.1	15♌37.9	28♓22.7	29♐39.3	12♐38.9	7♈37.5	3♑ 9.5	12♏ 4.1	18♓ 6.5	22♌13.2	12♋32.0
2 F	6 44 27.0	11 6.2	15 34.7	11♈22.7	28R45.3	13 53.6	8 14.5	3 23.2	12 8.9	18 8.3	22R12.1	12R30.8
3 S	6 48 23.5	12 7.4	15 31.5	24 1.8	28 1.1	15 8.2	8 51.6	3 36.9	12 13.7	18 10.1	22 10.9	12 29.5
4 S	6 52 20.1	13 8.6	15 28.4	6♉24.0	27 27.2	16 22.9	9 28.8	3 50.6	12 18.4	18 11.9	22 9.7	12 28.3
5 M	6 56 16.6	14 9.7	15 25.2	18 33.3	27 3.6	17 37.6	10 6.1	4 4.3	12 23.0	18 13.8	22 8.4	12 27.0
6 T	7 0 13.2	15 10.9	15 22.0	0♊33.5	26 49.8	18 52.4	10 43.4	4 18.0	12 27.6	18 15.7	22 7.2	12 25.7
7 W	7 4 9.8	16 12.0	15 18.8	12 27.6	26 45.6	20 7.1	11 20.8	4 31.6	12 32.1	18 17.7	22 5.9	12 24.5
8 T	7 8 6.3	17 13.1	15 15.6	24 18.5	26D50.1	21 21.8	11 58.2	4 45.3	12 36.4	18 19.7	22 4.6	12 23.3
9 F	7 12 2.8	18 14.3	15 12.5	6♋ 8.3	27 2.9	22 36.6	12 35.7	4 58.9	12 40.7	18 21.8	22 3.3	12 22.0
10 S	7 15 59.4	19 15.4	15 9.3	17 59.3	27 23.1	23 51.4	13 13.3	5 12.5	12 45.0	18 23.9	22 1.9	12 20.8
11 S	7 19 56.0	20 16.5	15 6.1	29 53.0	27 50.2	25 6.2	13 50.9	5 26.0	12 49.1	18 26.0	22 0.6	12 19.5
12 M	7 23 52.5	21 17.7	15 2.9	11♌51.5	28 23.5	26 21.0	14 28.5	5 39.6	12 53.2	18 28.2	21 59.2	12 18.3
13 T	7 27 49.1	22 18.8	14 59.8	23 56.7	29 2.3	27 35.8	15 6.2	5 53.1	12 57.2	18 30.4	21 57.8	12 17.1
14 W	7 31 45.6	23 19.9	14 56.6	6♍11.1	29 46.1	28 50.6	15 43.9	6 6.6	13 1.1	18 32.7	21 56.3	12 15.8
15 T	7 35 42.2	24 21.0	14 53.4	18 37.3	0♑34.4	0♑ 5.4	16 21.7	6 20.1	13 4.9	18 35.0	21 54.9	12 14.6
16 F	7 39 38.7	25 22.1	14 50.2	1♎18.5	1 26.8	1 20.3	16 59.6	6 33.5	13 8.6	18 37.3	21 53.4	12 13.4
17 S	7 43 35.3	26 23.2	14 47.1	14 17.7	2 22.9	2 35.1	17 37.4	6 46.9	13 12.2	18 39.7	21 52.0	12 12.2
18 S	7 47 31.9	27 24.3	14 43.9	27 37.8	3 22.1	3 50.0	18 15.3	7 0.3	13 15.8	18 42.1	21 50.5	12 11.0
19 M	7 51 28.4	28 25.4	14 40.7	11♏21.0	4 24.4	5 4.9	18 53.3	7 13.7	13 19.2	18 44.6	21 49.0	12 9.8
20 T	7 55 25.0	29 26.4	14 37.5	25 28.1	5 29.2	6 19.8	19 31.3	7 27.0	13 22.6	18 47.1	21 47.5	12 8.6
21 W	7 59 21.5	0♒27.5	14 34.3	9♐57.8	6 36.5	7 34.7	20 9.3	7 40.3	13 25.9	18 49.6	21 45.9	12 7.4
22 T	8 3 18.1	1 28.6	14 31.2	24 46.4	7 46.0	8 49.6	20 47.4	7 53.5	13 29.1	18 52.1	21 44.4	12 6.2
23 F	8 7 14.6	2 29.6	14 28.0	9♑47.5	8 57.4	10 4.5	21 25.5	8 6.7	13 32.1	18 54.7	21 42.8	12 5.0
24 S	8 11 11.2	3 30.7	14 24.8	24 53.0	10 10.7	11 19.4	22 3.7	8 19.9	13 35.1	18 57.3	21 41.2	12 3.9
25 S	8 15 7.8	4 31.7	14 21.6	9♒53.7	11 25.6	12 34.3	22 41.9	8 33.0	13 38.1	18 60.0	21 39.6	12 2.7
26 M	8 19 4.3	5 32.8	14 18.5	24 40.8	12 42.1	13 49.2	23 20.1	8 46.0	13 40.9	19 2.7	21 38.0	12 1.6
27 T	8 23 0.9	6 33.8	14 15.3	9♓ 7.6	13 60.0	15 4.1	23 58.3	8 59.1	13 43.6	19 5.4	21 36.4	12 0.5
28 W	8 26 57.4	7 34.8	14 12.1	23 9.3	15 19.2	16 19.0	24 36.6	9 12.0	13 46.2	19 8.1	21 34.8	11 59.3
29 T	8 30 54.0	8 35.7	14 8.9	6♈44.4	16 39.6	17 33.9	25 14.9	9 25.0	13 48.7	19 10.9	21 33.2	11 58.2
30 F	8 34 50.5	9 36.7	14 5.8	19 53.4	18 1.2	18 48.9	25 53.3	9 37.9	13 51.1	19 13.7	21 31.5	11 57.1
31 S	8 38 47.1	10 37.6	14 2.6	2♉38.6	19 23.9	20 3.8	26 31.7	9 50.7	13 53.4	19 16.6	21 29.9	11 56.1

DECLINATION

DAY	EPHEMERIS SIDEREAL TIME	☉	☊	☽	☿	♀	♂	♃	♄	♅	♆	♇
1 T	6 40 30.4	23S 3.8	16N 9.3	3S58.8	20S17.7	21S10.9	3N 2.6	23S15.5	13S16.3	5S23.8	14N24.5	20N43.1
4 S	6 52 20.1	22 47.9	16 12.1	8N46.6	20 13.5	21 43.6	3 50.2	23 14.7	13 20.2	5 21.6	14 25.7	20 43.6
7 W	7 4 9.8	22 27.8	16 14.9	17 44.7	20 25.1	22 10.6	4 37.7	23 13.7	13 23.8	5 19.2	14 27.0	20 44.1
10 S	7 15 59.4	22 3.8	16 17.8	19 58.4	20 47.7	22 31.7	5 25.0	23 12.5	13 27.1	5 16.7	14 28.3	20 44.7
13 T	7 27 49.1	21 35.9	16 20.6	14 25.6	21 15.7	22 46.8	6 12.1	23 11.0	13 30.2	5 14.0	14 29.7	20 45.2
16 F	7 39 38.7	21 4.3	16 23.3	3 3.2	21 44.2	22 55.7	6 58.8	23 9.4	13 33.0	5 11.3	14 31.2	20 45.7
19 M	7 51 28.4	20 29.0	16 26.1	10S13.3	22 9.3	22 58.3	7 45.2	23 7.6	13 35.6	5 8.3	14 32.7	20 46.3
22 T	8 3 18.1	19 50.2	16 28.9	19 21.5	22 28.5	22 54.6	8 31.1	23 5.6	13 37.9	5 5.3	14 34.2	20 46.8
25 S	8 15 7.8	19 8.1	16 31.7	17 26.2	22 39.8	22 44.6	9 16.7	23 3.4	13 40.0	5 2.1	14 35.8	20 47.4
28 W	8 26 57.4	18 22.9	16 34.4	5 48.7	22 41.8	22 28.4	10 1.7	23 1.1	13 41.7	4 58.9	14 37.4	20 47.9
31 S	8 38 47.1	17 34.7	16 37.2	7N30.3	22 33.7	22 6.0	10 46.1	22 58.6	13 43.2	4 55.5	14 39.0	20 48.5

FEBRUARY 1925

LONGITUDE

DAY	EPHEMERIS SIDEREAL TIME	☉	☊	☽	☿	♀	♂	♃	♄	♅	♆	♇
1 S	8 42 43.6	11♒38.5	13♌59.4	15♉ 3.8	20♑47.6	21♑18.7	27♈10.1	10♑ 3.5	13♏55.7	19♓19.5	21♌28.2	11♋55.0
2 M	8 46 40.2	12 39.4	13 56.2	27 13.2	22 12.4	22 33.6	27 48.5	10 16.2	13 57.8	19 22.3	21R26.6	11R53.9
3 T	8 50 36.7	13 40.2	13 53.0	9♊11.4	23 38.1	23 48.5	28 26.9	10 28.9	13 59.8	19 25.3	21 24.9	11 52.9
4 W	8 54 33.3	14 41.1	13 49.9	21 2.9	25 4.7	25 3.4	29 5.4	10 41.5	14 1.7	19 28.2	21 23.2	11 51.9
5 T	8 58 29.9	15 41.9	13 46.7	2♋51.8	26 32.3	26 18.3	29 43.8	10 54.0	14 3.6	19 31.2	21 21.6	11 50.8
6 F	9 2 26.4	16 42.7	13 43.5	14 41.7	28 0.7	27 33.2	0♉22.3	11 6.5	14 5.3	19 34.2	21 19.9	11 49.8
7 S	9 6 23.0	17 43.5	13 40.3	26 35.6	29 30.0	28 48.1	1 0.8	11 18.9	14 6.9	19 37.2	21 18.2	11 48.8
8 S	9 10 19.5	18 44.2	13 37.2	8♌36.3	1♒ 0.1	0♒ 3.0	1 39.3	11 31.3	14 8.4	19 40.3	21 16.5	11 47.9
9 M	9 14 16.1	19 44.9	13 34.0	20 45.6	2 31.1	1 17.9	2 17.8	11 43.6	14 9.8	19 43.3	21 14.9	11 46.9
10 T	9 18 12.6	20 45.6	13 30.8	3♍ 5.3	4 3.0	2 32.8	2 56.4	11 55.9	14 11.1	19 46.4	21 13.2	11 46.0
11 W	9 22 9.2	21 46.3	13 27.6	15 36.4	5 35.7	3 47.7	3 34.9	12 8.0	14 12.4	19 49.5	21 11.5	11 45.1
12 T	9 26 5.7	22 47.0	13 24.4	28 20.1	7 9.2	5 2.6	4 13.5	12 20.1	14 13.5	19 52.7	21 9.8	11 44.1
13 F	9 30 2.3	23 47.6	13 21.3	11♎17.3	8 43.6	6 17.5	4 52.1	12 32.2	14 14.5	19 55.8	21 8.1	11 43.3
14 S	9 33 58.9	24 48.2	13 18.1	24 28.7	10 18.9	7 32.4	5 30.6	12 44.1	14 15.4	19 59.0	21 6.4	11 42.4
15 S	9 37 55.4	25 48.8	13 14.9	7♏55.2	11 55.0	8 47.2	6 9.2	12 56.0	14 16.2	20 2.2	21 4.7	11 41.5
16 M	9 41 51.9	26 49.4	13 11.7	21 37.1	13 32.0	10 2.1	6 47.8	13 7.8	14 16.9	20 5.4	21 3.1	11 40.7
17 T	9 45 48.5	27 49.9	13 8.6	5♐34.5	15 9.8	11 17.0	7 26.4	13 19.6	14 17.5	20 8.6	21 1.4	11 39.9
18 W	9 49 45.1	28 50.5	13 5.4	19 46.8	16 48.6	12 31.9	8 5.1	13 31.2	14 17.9	20 11.9	20 59.7	11 39.1
19 T	9 53 41.6	29 51.0	13 2.2	4♑12.1	18 28.3	13 46.8	8 43.7	13 42.8	14 18.3	20 15.1	20 58.1	11 38.3
20 F	9 57 38.2	0♓51.5	12 59.0	18 47.1	20 8.9	15 1.7	9 22.3	13 54.3	14 18.6	20 18.4	20 56.4	11 37.5
21 S	10 1 34.7	1 52.0	12 55.8	3♒27.2	21 50.4	16 16.5	10 1.0	14 5.8	14 18.8	20 21.7	20 54.7	11 36.8
22 S	10 5 31.3	2 52.4	12 52.7	18 6.5	23 32.9	17 31.4	10 39.6	14 17.1	14 18.8	20 25.0	20 53.1	11 36.0
23 M	10 9 27.8	3 52.8	12 49.5	2♓38.6	25 16.3	18 46.3	11 18.3	14 28.4	14R18.8	20 28.3	20 51.5	11 35.3
24 T	10 13 24.4	4 53.2	12 46.3	16 57.1	27 0.7	20 1.1	11 57.0	14 39.5	14 18.7	20 31.7	20 49.8	11 34.7
25 W	10 17 20.9	5 53.6	12 43.1	0♈56.8	28 46.1	21 16.0	12 35.6	14 50.6	14 18.4	20 35.0	20 48.2	11 34.0
26 T	10 21 17.5	6 53.9	12 40.0	14 34.2	0♓32.5	22 30.8	13 14.3	15 1.6	14 18.1	20 38.4	20 46.6	11 33.3
27 F	10 25 14.0	7 54.2	12 36.8	27 47.9	2 19.9	23 45.6	13 53.0	15 12.5	14 17.6	20 41.7	20 45.0	11 32.7
28 S	10 29 10.6	8 54.5	12 33.6	10♉38.4	4 8.3	25 0.5	14 31.7	15 23.3	14 17.1	20 45.1	20 43.4	11 32.1

DECLINATION

DAY	EPHEMERIS SIDEREAL TIME	☉	☊	☽	☿	♀	♂	♃	♄	♅	♆	♇
1 S	8 42 43.6	17S18.0	16N38.1	11N17.5	22S28.6	21S57.2	11N 0.8	22S57.7	13S43.7	4S54.3	14N39.5	20N48.6
4 W	8 54 33.3	16 26.0	16 40.9	18 56.2	22 6.0	21 26.9	11 44.3	22 55.0	13 44.8	4 50.8	14 41.2	20 49.2
7 S	9 6 23.0	15 31.5	16 43.6	19 18.3	21 31.8	20 50.7	12 27.2	22 52.2	13 45.7	4 47.2	14 42.8	20 49.7
10 T	9 18 12.6	14 34.7	16 46.3	12 0.8	20 45.9	20 8.9	13 9.3	22 49.2	13 46.3	4 43.6	14 44.5	20 50.2
13 F	9 30 2.3	13 35.6	16 49.1	0S21.5	19 47.9	19 21.9	13 50.6	22 46.2	13 46.6	4 39.8	14 46.1	20 50.7
16 M	9 41 51.9	12 34.6	16 51.8	13 7.2	18 37.8	18 29.7	14 31.0	22 43.0	13 46.6	4 36.0	14 47.8	20 51.3
19 T	9 53 41.6	11 31.7	16 54.5	20 1.2	17 15.3	17 32.7	15 10.5	22 39.8	13 46.4	4 32.1	14 49.4	20 51.8
22 S	10 5 31.3	10 27.2	16 57.2	15 47.6	15 40.4	16 31.3	15 49.1	22 36.5	13 45.9	4 28.2	14 51.0	20 52.2
25 W	10 17 20.9	9 21.2	16 59.9	3 10.1	13 53.1	15 25.7	16 26.7	22 33.2	13 45.1	4 24.3	14 52.6	20 52.7
28 S	10 29 10.6	8 14.0	17 2.6	10N 2.5	11 53.6	14 16.2	17 3.2	22 29.8	13 44.0	4 20.3	14 54.1	20 53.2

MARCH 1925

LONGITUDE

DAY	EPHEMERIS SIDEREAL TIME h m s	☉ ° ′	☊ ° ′	☽ ° ′	☿ ° ′	♀ ° ′	♂ ° ′	♃ ° ′	♄ ° ′	♅ ° ′	♆ ° ′	♇ ° ′
1 S	10 33 7.1	9♓54.7	12♌30.4	23♉ 8.0	5♓57.8	26♒15.3	15♉10.4	15♑34.0	14♏16.4	20♓48.5	20♌41.8	11♋31.5
2 M	10 37 3.7	10 54.9	12 27.2	5♊20.4	7 48.2	27 30.1	15 49.1	15 44.6	14R15.6	20 51.9	20R40.3	11R31.0
3 T	10 41 0.2	11 55.1	12 24.1	17 20.0	9 39.6	28 44.8	16 27.8	15 55.1	14 14.8	20 55.3	20 38.7	11 30.4
4 W	10 44 56.8	12 55.2	12 20.9	29 11.7	11 32.0	29 59.6	17 6.5	16 5.5	14 13.8	20 58.7	20 37.2	11 29.9
5 T	10 48 53.4	13 55.3	12 17.7	11♋ 0.6	13 25.4	1♓14.4	17 45.2	16 15.8	14 12.8	21 2.1	20 35.7	11 29.4
6 F	10 52 49.9	14 55.4	12 14.5	22 51.4	15 19.7	2 29.1	18 23.8	16 26.0	14 11.6	21 5.5	20 34.1	11 29.0
7 S	10 56 46.4	15 55.4	12 11.4	4♌48.5	17 14.8	3 43.9	19 2.5	16 36.1	14 10.3	21 8.9	20 32.6	11 28.5
8 S	11 0 43.0	16 55.4	12 8.2	16 55.8	19 10.8	4 58.6	19 41.2	16 46.0	14 9.0	21 12.3	20 31.2	11 28.1
9 M	11 4 39.6	17 55.3	12 5.0	29 16.2	21 7.4	6 13.3	20 19.9	16 55.9	14 7.5	21 15.8	20 29.7	11 27.7
10 T	11 8 36.1	18 55.3	12 1.8	11♍51.5	23 4.7	7 28.1	20 58.5	17 5.7	14 6.0	21 19.2	20 28.3	11 27.3
11 W	11 12 32.7	19 55.2	11 58.6	24 42.7	25 2.5	8 42.8	21 37.2	17 15.4	14 4.3	21 22.6	20 26.8	11 26.9
12 T	11 16 29.2	20 55.0	11 55.5	7♎49.5	27 0.6	9 57.4	22 15.8	17 24.9	14 2.6	21 26.1	20 25.4	11 26.6
13 F	11 20 25.8	21 54.8	11 52.3	21 11.0	28 58.9	11 12.1	22 54.5	17 34.3	14 0.7	21 29.5	20 24.0	11 26.3
14 S	11 24 22.3	22 54.6	11 49.1	4♏45.3	0♈57.1	12 26.8	23 33.1	17 43.7	13 58.8	21 32.9	20 22.7	11 26.0
15 S	11 28 18.9	23 54.4	11 45.9	18 30.5	2 54.9	13 41.5	24 11.8	17 52.9	13 56.8	21 36.4	20 21.3	11 25.7
16 M	11 32 15.4	24 54.2	11 42.8	2♐24.3	4 52.2	14 56.1	24 50.4	18 1.9	13 54.7	21 39.8	20 20.0	11 25.5
17 T	11 36 12.0	25 53.9	11 39.6	16 25.0	6 48.6	16 10.8	25 29.0	18 10.9	13 52.5	21 43.2	20 18.7	11 25.3
18 W	11 40 8.5	26 53.5	11 36.4	0♑31.1	8 43.6	17 25.4	26 7.7	18 19.7	13 50.2	21 46.6	20 17.4	11 25.1
19 T	11 44 5.1	27 53.2	11 33.2	14 41.3	10 37.1	18 40.0	26 46.3	18 28.5	13 47.8	21 50.1	20 16.1	11 24.9
20 F	11 48 1.6	28 52.8	11 30.0	28 54.1	12 28.4	19 54.7	27 24.9	18 37.0	13 45.3	21 53.5	20 14.9	11 24.8
21 S	11 51 58.2	29 52.4	11 26.9	13♒ 7.4	14 17.2	21 9.3	28 3.5	18 45.5	13 42.7	21 56.9	20 13.6	11 24.6
22 S	11 55 54.7	0♈52.0	11 23.7	27 18.8	16 3.1	22 23.9	28 42.1	18 53.8	13 40.1	22 0.3	20 12.4	11 24.5
23 M	11 59 51.3	1 51.5	11 20.5	11♓24.7	17 45.6	23 38.5	29 20.7	19 2.0	13 37.4	22 3.7	20 11.3	11 24.5
24 T	12 3 47.9	2 51.0	11 17.3	25 21.5	19 24.3	24 53.1	29 59.3	19 10.1	13 34.6	22 7.1	20 10.1	11 24.4
25 W	12 7 44.4	3 50.5	11 14.2	9♈ 5.0	20 58.7	26 7.6	0♊37.9	19 18.0	13 31.7	22 10.5	20 9.0	11 24.4
26 T	12 11 40.9	4 49.9	11 11.0	22 31.8	22 28.4	27 22.2	1 16.5	19 25.8	13 28.7	22 13.8	20 7.9	11 24.4
27 F	12 15 37.5	5 49.3	11 7.8	5♉39.8	23 53.0	28 36.7	1 55.1	19 33.5	13 25.6	22 17.2	20 6.8	11D24.4
28 S	12 19 34.1	6 48.7	11 4.6	18 28.1	25 12.2	29 51.2	2 33.6	19 41.0	13 22.5	22 20.6	20 5.8	11 24.4
29 S	12 23 30.6	7 48.0	11 1.4	0♊57.7	26 25.7	1♈ 5.7	3 12.2	19 48.3	13 19.3	22 23.9	20 4.7	11 24.5
30 M	12 27 27.2	8 47.3	10 58.3	13 10.8	27 33.1	2 20.2	3 50.8	19 55.6	13 16.0	22 27.2	20 3.7	11 24.6
31 T	12 31 23.7	9 46.6	10 55.1	25 11.2	28 34.2	3 34.7	4 29.3	20 2.6	13 12.7	22 30.5	20 2.8	11 24.7

DECLINATION

DAY	SID. TIME	☉	☊	☽	☿	♀	♂	♃	♄	♅	♆	♇
1 S	10 33 7.1	7S51.3	17N 3.5	13N33.5	11S11.1	13S52.3	17N15.1	22S28.6	13S43.6	4S18.9	14N54.7	20N53.3
4 W	10 44 56.8	6 42.7	17 6.1	19 47.1	8 55.8	12 38.2	17 50.1	22 25.2	13 42.3	4 14.9	14 56.2	20 53.8
7 S	10 56 46.4	5 33.2	17 8.8	18 18.1	6 29.3	11 21.1	18 24.0	22 21.8	13 40.6	4 10.8	14 57.6	20 54.2
10 T	11 8 36.1	4 23.1	17 11.5	9 24.4	3 53.1	10 1.2	18 56.6	22 18.4	13 38.7	4 6.8	14 59.0	20 54.6
13 F	11 20 25.8	3 12.5	17 14.1	3S49.1	1 9.1	8 38.9	19 28.0	22 15.0	13 36.6	4 2.7	15 0.4	20 55.0
16 M	11 32 15.4	2 1.6	17 16.8	15 52.2	1N39.0	7 14.5	19 58.0	22 11.7	13 34.3	3 58.6	15 1.7	20 55.4
19 T	11 44 5.1	0 50.4	17 19.4	20 12.5	4 26.5	5 48.4	20 26.7	22 8.4	13 31.7	3 54.6	15 2.9	20 55.8
22 S	11 55 54.7	0N20.7	17 22.1	13 37.1	7 7.1	4 20.8	20 54.1	22 5.2	13 28.9	3 50.6	15 4.1	20 56.1
25 W	12 7 44.4	1 31.7	17 24.7	0 19.2	9 34.0	2 52.2	21 20.0	22 2.1	13 26.0	3 46.5	15 5.2	20 56.5
28 S	12 19 34.1	2 42.3	17 27.3	12N27.2	11 40.7	1 22.8	21 44.5	21 59.2	13 22.8	3 42.6	15 6.2	20 56.8
31 T	12 31 23.7	3 52.4	17 29.9	19 38.4	13 22.0	0N 7.0	22 7.5	21 56.3	13 19.5	3 38.7	15 7.2	20 57.1

APRIL 1925

LONGITUDE

DAY	SID. TIME	☉	☊	☽	☿	♀	♂	♃	♄	♅	♆	♇
1 W	12 35 20.3	10♈45.8	10♌51.9	7♋ 3.2	29♈28.8	4♈49.2	5♊ 7.8	20♑ 9.6	13♏ 9.3	22♓33.9	20♌ 1.8	11♋24.9
2 T	12 39 16.8	11 44.9	10 48.7	18 52.2	0♉16.8	6 3.6	5 46.4	20 16.4	13R 5.8	22 37.1	20R 0.9	11 25.0
3 F	12 43 13.4	12 44.1	10 45.5	0♌43.4	0 57.9	7 18.0	6 24.9	20 23.0	13 2.3	22 40.4	20 0.0	11 25.2
4 S	12 47 9.9	13 43.2	10 42.4	12 42.1	1 32.0	8 32.5	7 3.4	20 29.5	12 58.6	22 43.7	19 59.2	11 25.4
5 S	12 51 6.5	14 42.2	10 39.2	24 53.2	1 59.2	9 46.9	7 41.9	20 35.8	12 55.0	22 46.9	19 58.3	11 25.7
6 M	12 55 3.0	15 41.3	10 36.0	7♍20.9	2 19.4	11 1.2	8 20.4	20 42.0	12 51.2	22 50.2	19 57.5	11 25.9
7 T	12 58 59.6	16 40.2	10 32.8	20 8.2	2 32.7	12 15.6	8 58.8	20 48.0	12 47.5	22 53.4	19 56.8	11 26.2
8 W	13 2 56.1	17 39.2	10 29.7	3♎16.4	2 39.1	13 30.0	9 37.3	20 53.9	12 43.6	22 56.6	19 56.0	11 26.5
9 T	13 6 52.7	18 38.1	10 26.5	16 45.2	2R38.8	14 44.3	10 15.7	20 59.6	12 39.7	22 59.8	19 55.3	11 26.8
10 F	13 10 49.2	19 37.0	10 23.3	0♏32.3	2 32.0	15 58.6	10 54.2	21 5.2	12 35.8	23 2.9	19 54.6	11 27.2
11 S	13 14 45.8	20 35.8	10 20.1	14 34.1	2 19.2	17 12.9	11 32.6	21 10.6	12 31.8	23 6.1	19 54.0	11 27.6
12 S	13 18 42.4	21 34.6	10 16.9	28 45.5	2 0.5	18 27.2	12 11.0	21 15.8	12 27.7	23 9.2	19 53.3	11 28.0
13 M	13 22 38.9	22 33.4	10 13.8	13♐ 1.7	1 36.6	19 41.5	12 49.4	21 20.9	12 23.6	23 12.3	19 52.7	11 28.4
14 T	13 26 35.4	23 32.2	10 10.6	27 18.2	1 7.8	20 55.8	13 27.8	21 25.8	12 19.5	23 15.4	19 52.2	11 28.8
15 W	13 30 32.0	24 30.9	10 7.4	11♑31.7	0 35.0	22 10.0	14 6.1	21 30.5	12 15.3	23 18.4	19 51.6	11 29.3
16 T	13 34 28.5	25 29.6	10 4.2	25 40.1	29♈58.6	23 24.3	14 44.5	21 35.1	12 11.1	23 21.4	19 51.1	11 29.8
17 F	13 38 25.1	26 28.3	10 1.1	9♒42.3	29 19.5	24 38.5	15 22.9	21 39.5	12 6.8	23 24.5	19 50.7	11 30.3
18 S	13 42 21.7	27 26.9	9 57.9	23 37.8	28 38.5	25 52.7	16 1.2	21 43.7	12 2.5	23 27.5	19 50.2	11 30.9
19 S	13 46 18.2	28 25.5	9 54.7	7♓26.1	27 56.2	27 6.9	16 39.6	21 47.8	11 58.2	23 30.4	19 49.8	11 31.4
20 M	13 50 14.8	29 24.1	9 51.5	21 6.5	27 13.6	28 21.1	17 17.9	21 51.6	11 53.9	23 33.4	19 49.4	11 32.0
21 T	13 54 11.3	0♉22.7	9 48.3	4♈37.6	26 31.4	29 35.3	17 56.2	21 55.3	11 49.5	23 36.3	19 49.1	11 32.6
22 W	13 58 7.9	1 21.2	9 45.2	17 57.8	25 50.4	0♉49.5	18 34.6	21 58.9	11 45.1	23 39.2	19 48.8	11 33.2
23 T	14 2 4.4	2 19.7	9 42.0	1♉ 5.1	25 11.2	2 3.7	19 12.9	22 2.2	11 40.6	23 42.0	19 48.5	11 33.9
24 F	14 6 1.0	3 18.2	9 38.8	13 58.1	24 34.5	3 17.8	19 51.2	22 5.4	11 36.2	23 44.9	19 48.3	11 34.5
25 S	14 9 57.5	4 16.6	9 35.6	26 35.8	24 0.8	4 31.9	20 29.5	22 8.4	11 31.7	23 47.7	19 48.1	11 35.2
26 S	14 13 54.1	5 15.0	9 32.5	8♊58.6	23 30.7	5 46.0	21 7.8	22 11.2	11 27.2	23 50.4	19 47.9	11 35.9
27 M	14 17 50.6	6 13.4	9 29.3	21 7.7	23 4.5	7 0.1	21 46.0	22 13.8	11 22.7	23 53.2	19 47.7	11 36.7
28 T	14 21 47.2	7 11.7	9 26.1	3♋ 5.8	22 42.5	8 14.2	22 24.3	22 16.2	11 18.2	23 55.9	19 47.6	11 37.4
29 W	14 25 43.7	8 10.0	9 22.9	14 56.6	22 25.0	9 28.3	23 2.5	22 18.5	11 13.6	23 58.6	19 47.6	11 38.2
30 T	14 29 40.3	9 8.3	9 19.7	26 44.7	22 12.2	10 42.3	23 40.8	22 20.6	11 9.1	24 1.3	19 47.5	11 39.0

DECLINATION

DAY	SID. TIME	☉	☊	☽	☿	♀	♂	♃	♄	♅	♆	♇
1 W	12 35 20.3	4N15.7	17N30.8	20N20.5	13N49.4	0N37.0	22N14.8	21S55.4	13S18.3	3S37.4	15N 7.5	20N57.2
4 S	12 47 9.9	5 24.9	17 33.4	17 4.5	14 51.3	2 6.9	22 35.8	21 52.8	13 14.8	3 33.5	15 8.3	20 57.5
7 T	12 58 59.6	6 33.3	17 36.0	6 48.5	15 21.0	3 36.5	22 55.2	21 50.3	13 11.1	3 29.7	15 9.1	20 57.7
10 F	13 10 49.2	7 40.6	17 38.5	7S 1.2	15 17.6	5 5.5	23 13.0	21 48.0	13 7.3	3 26.0	15 9.8	20 57.9
13 M	13 22 38.9	8 46.8	17 41.1	18 7.9	14 42.5	6 33.5	23 29.2	21 45.9	13 3.4	3 22.3	15 10.4	20 58.2
16 T	13 34 28.5	9 51.7	17 43.7	19 43.8	13 39.9	8 0.2	23 43.8	21 44.1	12 59.5	3 18.7	15 10.9	20 58.4
19 S	13 46 18.2	10 55.1	17 46.2	10 54.0	12 17.7	9 25.3	23 56.7	21 42.4	12 55.4	3 15.2	15 11.3	20 58.5
22 W	13 58 7.9	11 56.9	17 48.8	2N45.4	10 47.0	10 48.4	24 7.9	21 41.0	12 51.3	3 11.8	15 11.6	20 58.7
25 S	14 9 57.5	12 57.0	17 51.3	14 44.3	9 19.5	12 9.3	24 17.5	21 39.9	12 47.2	3 8.5	15 11.9	20 58.8
28 T	14 21 47.2	13 55.1	17 53.9	20 26.7	8 5.0	13 27.6	24 25.4	21 39.0	12 43.0	3 5.3	15 12.0	20 58.9

MAY 1925

DAY	EPHEMERIS SIDEREAL TIME	☉	☊	☽	☿	♀	♂	♃	♄	♅	♆	♇
	h m s	° ′	° ′	° ′	° ′	° ′	° ′	° ′	° ′	° ′	° ′	° ′
						LONGITUDE						
1 F	14 33 36.9	10♉ 6.6	9♌16.6	8♌35.1	22♈ 4.1	11♉56.4	24♊19.0	22♑22.5	11♏ 4.6	24♓ 3.9	19♌47.5	11♋39.8
2 S	14 37 33.4	11 4.8	9 13.4	20 33.3	22R 0.9	13 10.4	24 57.2	22 24.2	11R 0.0	24 6.5	19D47.5	11 40.6
3 S	14 41 30.0	12 2.9	9 10.2	2♍44.9	22D 2.4	14 24.4	25 35.4	22 25.7	10 55.5	24 9.0	19 47.6	11 41.5
4 M	14 45 26.5	13 1.1	9 7.0	15 14.8	22 8.8	15 38.4	26 13.6	22 27.0	10 51.0	24 11.6	19 47.7	11 42.4
5 T	14 49 23.1	13 59.2	9 3.9	28 7.2	22 19.9	16 52.4	26 51.8	22 28.2	10 46.4	24 14.1	19 47.8	11 43.3
6 W	14 53 19.6	14 57.2	9 0.7	11♎24.6	22 35.6	18 6.3	27 30.0	22 29.1	10 41.9	24 16.5	19 47.9	11 44.2
7 T	14 57 16.2	15 55.3	8 57.5	25 7.5	22 55.8	19 20.3	28 8.1	22 29.9	10 37.4	24 19.0	19 48.1	11 45.1
8 F	15 1 12.7	16 53.3	8 54.3	9♏13.7	23 20.3	20 34.2	28 46.3	22 30.5	10 32.9	24 21.4	19 48.3	11 46.1
9 S	15 5 9.3	17 51.3	8 51.1	23 38.7	23 49.2	21 48.1	29 24.4	22 30.9	10 28.4	24 23.7	19 48.6	11 47.0
10 S	15 9 5.8	18 49.2	8 48.0	8♐15.9	24 22.1	23 2.0	0♋ 2.5	22 31.1	10 23.9	24 26.0	19 48.9	11 48.0
11 M	15 13 2.4	19 47.2	8 44.8	22 57.7	24 59.0	24 15.9	0 40.6	22 31.1	10 19.5	24 28.3	19 49.2	11 49.0
12 T	15 16 59.0	20 45.1	8 41.6	7♑37.0	25 39.8	25 29.8	1 18.7	22R30.9	10 15.1	24 30.6	19 49.5	11 50.0
13 W	15 20 55.5	21 43.0	8 38.4	22 8.0	26 24.2	26 43.6	1 56.8	22 30.6	10 10.7	24 32.8	19 49.9	11 51.1
14 T	15 24 52.1	22 40.8	8 35.3	6♒26.8	27 12.3	27 57.5	2 34.9	22 30.0	10 6.3	24 35.0	19 50.3	11 52.1
15 F	15 28 48.6	23 38.7	8 32.1	20 31.5	28 3.7	29 11.3	3 13.0	22 29.3	10 1.9	24 37.1	19 50.8	11 53.2
16 S	15 32 45.2	24 36.5	8 28.9	4♓21.6	28 58.5	0♊25.2	3 51.1	22 28.4	9 57.6	24 39.2	19 51.2	11 54.3
17 S	15 36 41.7	25 34.3	8 25.7	17 57.6	29 56.5	1 39.0	4 29.1	22 27.3	9 53.3	24 41.3	19 51.8	11 55.4
18 M	15 40 38.3	26 32.1	8 22.5	1♈20.5	0♉57.6	2 52.8	5 7.2	22 26.0	9 49.0	24 43.3	19 52.3	11 56.5
19 T	15 44 34.8	27 29.9	8 19.4	14 30.8	2 1.7	4 6.6	5 45.2	22 24.5	9 44.8	24 45.3	19 52.9	11 57.7
20 W	15 48 31.4	28 27.7	8 16.2	27 29.2	3 8.8	5 20.4	6 23.3	22 22.8	9 40.6	24 47.2	19 53.5	11 58.8
21 T	15 52 28.0	29 25.4	8 13.0	10♉15.6	4 18.6	6 34.2	7 1.3	22 20.9	9 36.5	24 49.1	19 54.1	11 60.0
22 F	15 56 24.5	0♊23.1	8 9.8	22 50.2	5 31.3	7 48,0	7 39.3	22 18.9	9 32.4	24 51.0	19 54.8	12 1.2
23 S	16 0 21.0	1 20.8	8 6.7	5♊13.0	6 46.7	9 1.7	8 17.3	22 16.6	9 28.3	24 52.8	19 55.5	12 2.4
24 S	16 4 17.6	2 18.5	8 3.5	17 24.6	8 4.7	10 15.5	8 55.4	22 14.2	9 24.3	24 54.6	19 56.2	12 3.6
25 M	16 8 14.2	3 16.1	8 0.3	29 26.2	9 25.4	11 29.3	9 33.4	22 11.6	9 20.4	24 56.3	19 57.0	12 4.8
26 T	16 12 10.7	4 13.7	7 57.1	11♋19.7	10 48.6	12 43.0	10 11.4	22 8.8	9 16.5	24 58.0	19 57.8	12 6.1
27 W	16 16 7.2	5 11.3	7 54.0	23 8.1	12 14.4	13 56.7	10 49.3	22 5.9	9 12.6	24 59.7	19 58.6	12 7.3
28 T	16 20 3.8	6 8.9	7 50.8	4♌54.9	13 42.8	15 10.4	11 27.3	22 2.7	9 8.8	25 1.3	19 59.5	12 8.6
29 F	16 24 0.4	7 6.5	7 47.6	16 44.5	15 13.6	16 24.1	12 5.3	21 59.4	9 5.1	25 2.8	20 0.4	12 9.9
30 S	16 27 57.0	8 4.0	7 44.4	28 41.9	16 46.9	17 37.8	12 43.3	21 55.9	9 1.4	25 4.3	20 1.3	12 11.2
31 S	16 31 53.5	9 1.5	7 41.2	10♍52.2	18 22.7	18 51.4	13 21.2	21 52.3	8 57.8	25 5.8	20 2.2	12 12.5
						DECLINATION						
1 F	14 33 36.9	14N51.2	17N56.4	18N 5.0	7N 9.9	14N43.0	24N31.6	21S38.3	12S38.9	3S 2.2	15N12.0	20N59.0
4 M	14 45 26.5	15 45.1	17 58.9	8 34.1	6 37.4	15 55.1	24 36.1	21 38.0	12 34.8	2 59.2	15 12.0	20 59.1
7 T	14 57 16.2	16 36.6	18 1.4	5S10.8	6 27.8	17 3.5	24 38.9	21 37.9	12 30.7	2 56.4	15 11.8	20 59.2
10 S	15 9 5.8	17 25.6	18 3.9	17 24.2	6 39.9	18 8.0	24 39.9	21 38.1	12 26.7	2 53.6	15 11.6	20 59.2
13 W	15 20 55.5	18 12.0	18 6.4	20 17.0	7 11.6	19 8.3	24 39.3	21 38.6	12 22.8	2 51.0	15 11.3	20 59.2
16 S	15 32 45.2	18 55.7	18 8.9	12 1.8	8 0.6	20 3.9	24 37.0	21 39.4	12 19.0	2 48.6	15 10.9	20 59.2
19 T	15 44 34.8	19 36.5	18 11.4	1N26.3	9 4.6	20 54.7	24 32.9	21 40.5	12 15.3	2 46.2	15 10.3	20 59.2
22 F	15 56 24.5	20 14.3	18 13.9	13 47.4	10 21.1	21 40.4	24 27.2	21 41.8	12 11.8	2 44.1	15 9.7	20 59.1
25 M	16 8 14.2	20 49.0	18 16.3	20 23.1	11 48.1	22 20.6	24 19.9	21 43.4	12 8.4	2 42.0	15 9.0	20 59.1
28 T	16 20 3.8	21 20.5	18 18.8	18 55.3	13 23.3	22 55.1	24 10.9	21 45.3	12 5.2	2 40.2	15 8.3	20 59.0
31 S	16 31 53.5	21 48.7	18 21.2	10 10.9	15 4.3	23 23.6	24 0.3	21 47.4	12 2.2	2 38.4	15 7.4	20 58.9

JUNE 1925

DAY	EPHEMERIS SIDEREAL TIME	☉	☊	☽	☿	♀	♂	♃	♄	♅	♆	♇
						LONGITUDE						
1 M	16 35 50.0	9♊59.0	7♌38.1	23♍20.9	20♉ 0.9	20♊ 5.1	13♋59.2	21♑48.4	8♏54.2	25♓ 7.3	20♌ 3.2	12♋13.8
2 T	16 39 46.6	10 56.5	7 34.9	6♎12.4	21 41.6	21 18.7	14 37.1	21R44.4	8R50.7	25 8.6	20 4.2	12 15.1
3 W	16 43 43.2	11 53.9	7 31.7	19 30.4	23 24.8	22 32.4	15 15.1	21 40.3	8 47.3	25 10.0	20 5.3	12 16.5
4 T	16 47 39.7	12 51.4	7 28.5	3♏16.6	25 10.4	23 46.0	15 53.0	21 35.9	8 43.9	25 11.3	20 6.3	12 17.8
5 F	16 51 36.3	13 48.8	7 25.4	17 29.9	26 58.4	24 59.6	16 30.9	21 31.4	8 40.6	25 12.5	20 7.4	12 19.2
6 S	16 55 32.8	14 46.2	7 22.2	2♐ 6.8	28 48.8	26 13.2	17 8.8	21 26.8	8 37.4	25 13.7	20 8.5	12 20.6
7 S	16 59 29.4	15 43.5	7 19.0	17 0.3	0♊41.6	27 26.7	17 46.7	21 22.0	8 34.3	25 14.9	20 9.7	12 21.9
8 M	17 3 26.0	16 40.9	7 15.8	2♑ 2.1	2 36.7	28 40.3	18 24.6	21 17.1	8 31.2	25 16.0	20 10.9	12 23.3
9 T	17 7 22.5	17 38.3	7 12.7	17 2.9	4 34.1	29 53.9	19 2.5	21 12.0	8 28.2	25 17.1	20 12.1	12 24.7
10 W	17 11 19.1	18 35.6	7 9.5	1♒54.4	6 33.6	1♋ 7.4	19 40.4	21 6.7	8 25.3	25 18.1	20 13.3	12 26.1
11 T	17 15 15.6	19 32.9	7 6.3	16 30.4	8 35.2	2 20.9	20 18.2	21 1.3	8 22.4	25 19.1	20 14.6	12 27.6
12 F	17 19 12.2	20 30.3	7 3.1	0♓47.0	10 38.8	3 34.5	20 56.1	20 55.8	8 19.6	25 20.0	20 15.9	12 29.0
13 S	17 23 8.7	21 27.6	6 60.0	14 42.7	12 44.2	4 48.0	21 34.0	20 50.1	8 16.9	25 20.9	20 17.2	12 30.4
14 S	17 27 5.3	22 24.9	6 56.8	28 17.7	14 51.2	6 1.5	22 11.9	20 44.3	8 14.3	25 21.7	20 18.5	12 31.9
15 M	17 31 1.9	23 22.2	6 53.6	11♈33.5	16 59.6	7 15.0	22 49.7	20 38.4	8 11.8	25 22.5	20 19.9	12 33.3
16 T	17 34 58.4	24 19.5	6 50.4	24 31.9	19 9.2	8 28.5	23 27.6	20 32.3	8 9.3	25 23.2	20 21.3	12 34.8
17 W	17 38 55.0	25 16.8	6 47.2	7♉15.2	21 19.7	9 42.0	24 5.5	20 26.1	8 7.0	25 23.9	20 22.7	12 36.3
18 T	17 42 51.5	26 14.1	6 44.1	19 45.2	23 30.9	10 55.5	24 43.3	20 19.8	8 4.7	25 24.6	20 24.2	12 37.7
19 F	17 46 48.1	27 11.3	6 40.9	2♊ 3.8	25 42.6	12 9.0	25 21.2	20 13.4	8 2.5	25 25.1	20 25.6	12 39.2
20 S	17 50 44.6	28 8.6	6 37.7	14 12.6	27 54.3	13 22.4	25 59.0	20 6.8	8 0.4	25 25.7	20 27.1	12 40.7
21 S	17 54 41.2	29 5.9	6 34.5	26 13.0	0♋ 5.9	14 35.9	26 36.9	20 0.2	7 58.4	25 26.2	20 28.6	12 42.2
22 M	17 58 37.8	0♋ 3.2	6 31.4	8♋ 6.8	2 17.1	15 49.3	27 14.8	19 53.4	7 56.4	25 26.6	20 30.2	12 43.7
23 T	18 2 34.3	1 0.4	6 28.2	19 55.9	4 27.6	17 2.8	27 52.6	19 46.6	7 54.6	25 27.0	20 31.7	12 45.2
24 W	18 6 30.8	1 57.7	6 25.0	1♌42.6	6 37.2	18 16.2	28 30.5	19 39.7	7 52.8	25 27.4	20 33.3	12 46.7
25 T	18 10 27.4	2 54.9	6 21.8	13 29.7	8 45.6	19 29.6	29 8.3	19 32.6	7 51.2	25 27.7	20 34.9	12 48.2
26 F	18 14 24.0	3 52.1	6 18.7	25 20.7	10 52.8	20 43.0	29 46.2	19 25.5	7 49.6	25 27.9	20 36.6	12 49.7
27 S	18 18 20.6	4 49.4	6 15.5	7♍19.5	12 58.5	21 56.4	0♌24.0	19 18.4	7 48.1	25 28.1	20 38.2	12 51.2
28 S	18 22 17.1	5 46.6	6 12.3	19 30.4	15 2.6	23 9.7	1 1.9	19 11.1	7 46.8	25 28.3	20 39.9	12 52.8
29 M	18 26 13.6	6 43.8	6 9.1	1♎58.0	17 5.0	24 23.1	1 39.7	19 3.8	7 45.5	25 28.4	20 41.6	12 54.3
30 T	18 30 10.2	7 41.0	6 5.9	14 46.7	19 5.6	25 36.4	2 17.5	18 56.4	7 44.3	25 28.5	20 43.3	12 55.8
						DECLINATION						
1 M	16 35 50.0	21N57.3	18N22.0	6N 5.1	15N38.9	23N31.8	23N56.4	21S48.2	12S 1.2	2S37.9	15N 7.1	20N58.8
4 T	16 47 39.7	22 20.9	18 24.5	7S48.2	17 23.5	23 52.3	23 43.6	21 50.6	11 58.4	2 36.4	15 6.1	20 58.7
7 S	16 59 29.4	22 40.9	18 26.9	18 58.5	19 7.0	24 6.4	23 29.3	21 53.3	11 55.9	2 35.1	15 5.0	20 58.6
10 W	17 11 19.1	22 57.4	18 29.3	19 25.3	20 45.1	24 14.1	23 13.4	21 56.1	11 53.6	2 33.9	15 3.9	20 58.4
13 S	17 23 8.7	23 10.3	18 31.7	9 2.1	22 13.0	24 15.4	22 56.0	21 59.1	11 51.6	2 32.9	15 2.7	20 58.3
16 T	17 34 58.4	23 19.5	18 34.1	4N47.2	23 25.1	24 10.3	22 37.1	22 2.3	11 49.8	2 32.1	15 1.4	20 58.1
19 F	17 46 48.1	23 25.0	18 36.5	16 3.3	24 16.6	23 58.7	22 16.8	22 5.6	11 48.2	2 31.4	14 60.0	20 57.9
22 M	17 58 37.8	23 26.8	18 38.9	20 51.2	24 43.9	23 40.8	21 55.0	22 9.0	11 47.0	2 30.9	14 58.6	20 57.7
25 T	18 10 27.4	23 24.9	18 41.3	17 31.9	24 45.8	23 16.5	21 31.8	22 12.4	11 46.0	2 30.6	14 57.0	20 57.4
28 S	18 22 17.1	23 19.3	18 43.7	7 32.6	24 23.6	22 46.2	21 7.3	22 16.0	11 45.3	2 30.5	14 55.5	20 57.2

JULY 1925

DAY	EPHEMERIS SIDEREAL TIME h m s	☉ ° ′	☊ ° ′	☽ ° ′	☿ ° ′	♀ ° ′	♂ ° ′	♃ ° ′	♄ ° ′	♅ ° ′	♆ ° ′	♇ ° ′
LONGITUDE												
1 W	18 34 6.8	8♋38.2	6♌ 2.8	28♎ 0.4	21♋ 4.3	26♋49.8	2♌55.4	18♑49.0	7♏43.2	25♓28.5	20♌45.1	12♋57.3
2 T	18 38 3.3	9 35.4	5 59.6	11♏41.4	23 1.1	28 3.1	3 33.2	18R41.5	7R42.2	25R28.4	20 46.8	12 58.9
3 F	18 41 59.9	10 32.6	5 56.4	25 50.4	24 55.9	29 16.4	4 11.0	18 34.0	7 41.3	25 28.4	20 48.6	13 0.4
4 S	18 45 56.4	11 29.7	5 53.2	10♐25.1	26 48.8	0♌29.7	4 48.9	18 26.4	7 40.5	25 28.2	20 50.4	13 1.9
5 S	18 49 53.0	12 26.9	5 50.1	25 20.6	28 39.6	1 42.9	5 26.7	18 18.8	7 39.8	25 28.0	20 52.2	13 3.5
6 M	18 53 49.5	13 24.1	5 46.9	10♑29.1	0♌28.4	2 56.2	6 4.5	18 11.1	7 39.2	25 27.8	20 54.0	13 5.0
7 T	18 57 46.1	14 21.3	5 43.7	25 41.3	2 15.3	4 9.4	6 42.3	18 3.5	7 38.6	25 27.5	20 55.9	13 6.5
8 W	19 1 42.7	15 18.4	5 40.5	10♒47.7	4 0.0	5 22.6	7 20.2	17 55.8	7 38.2	25 27.2	20 57.8	13 8.1
9 T	19 5 39.2	16 15.6	5 37.4	25 39.7	5 42.8	6 35.9	7 58.0	17 48.1	7 37.9	25 26.8	20 59.7	13 9.6
10 F	19 9 35.8	17 12.8	5 34.2	10♓11.1	7 23.5	7 49.1	8 35.8	17 40.4	7 37.7	25 26.4	21 1.6	13 11.1
11 S	19 13 32.3	18 10.0	5 31.0	24 18.4	9 2.2	9 2.2	9 13.7	17 32.6	7 37.6	25 26.0	21 3.5	13 12.6
12 S	19 17 28.9	19 7.2	5 27.8	8♈ 0.4	10 38.9	10 15.4	9 51.5	17 24.9	7 37.5	25 25.4	21 5.4	13 14.2
13 M	19 21 25.5	20 4.4	5 24.6	21 18.0	12 13.5	11 28.6	10 29.3	17 17.2	7D37.6	25 24.9	21 7.4	13 15.7
14 T	19 25 22.0	21 1.6	5 21.5	4♉13.4	13 46.1	12 41.7	11 7.2	17 9.5	7 37.7	25 24.3	21 9.3	13 17.2
15 W	19 29 18.6	21 58.9	5 18.3	16 49.7	15 16.7	13 54.9	11 45.0	17 1.8	7 38.0	25 23.6	21 11.3	13 18.7
16 T	19 33 15.1	22 56.1	5 15.1	29 10.2	16 45.2	15 8.0	12 22.9	16 54.2	7 38.4	25 22.9	21 13.3	13 20.2
17 F	19 37 11.7	23 53.4	5 11.9	11♊18.4	18 11.6	16 21.1	13 0.7	16 46.5	7 38.8	25 22.2	21 15.3	13 21.8
18 S	19 41 8.2	24 50.6	5 8.8	23 17.2	19 35.9	17 34.2	13 38.6	16 38.9	7 39.4	25 21.4	21 17.4	13 23.3
19 S	19 45 4.8	25 47.9	5 5.6	5♋ 9.6	20 58.0	18 47.3	14 16.5	16 31.4	7 40.0	25 20.5	21 19.4	13 24.8
20 M	19 49 1.4	26 45.2	5 2.4	16 58.2	22 18.0	20 0.3	14 54.4	16 23.9	7 40.8	25 19.7	21 21.5	13 26.3
21 T	19 52 57.9	27 42.5	4 59.2	28 45.2	23 35.8	21 13.4	15 32.2	16 16.4	7 41.7	25 18.7	21 23.5	13 27.8
22 W	19 56 54.5	28 39.8	4 56.1	10♌33.1	24 51.2	22 26.4	16 10.1	16 9.0	7 42.6	25 17.8	21 25.6	13 29.3
23 T	20 0 51.0	29 37.1	4 52.9	22 24.2	26 4.4	23 39.4	16 48.0	16 1.7	7 43.7	25 16.8	21 27.7	13 30.7
24 F	20 4 47.6	0♌34.4	4 49.7	4♍20.8	27 15.1	24 52.4	17 25.9	15 54.4	7 44.8	25 15.7	21 29.8	13 32.2
25 S	20 8 44.2	1 31.7	4 46.5	16 25.9	28 23.4	26 5.4	18 3.8	15 47.2	7 46.1	25 14.6	21 31.9	13 33.7
26 S	20 12 40.7	2 29.1	4 43.4	28 42.4	29 29.1	27 18.4	18 41.7	15 40.1	7 47.4	25 13.5	21 34.0	13 35.1
27 M	20 16 37.2	3 26.4	4 40.2	11♎13.5	0♍32.2	28 31.3	19 19.6	15 33.0	7 48.8	25 12.3	21 36.1	13 36.6
28 T	20 20 33.8	4 23.8	4 37.0	24 2.5	1 32.5	29 44.2	19 57.5	15 26.1	7 50.4	25 11.1	21 38.3	13 38.1
29 W	20 24 30.4	5 21.1	4 33.8	7♏12.6	2 29.9	0♍57.1	20 35.5	15 19.2	7 52.0	25 9.8	21 40.4	13 39.5
30 T	20 28 26.9	6 18.5	4 30.6	20 46.2	3 24.4	2 10.0	21 13.4	15 12.5	7 53.7	25 8.5	21 42.6	13 40.9
31 F	20 32 23.5	7 15.8	4 27.5	4♐44.5	4 15.7	3 22.8	21 51.3	15 5.8	7 55.5	25 7.1	21 44.7	13 42.4
DECLINATION												
1 W	18 34 6.8	23N10.0	18N46.0	5S54.1	23N39.9	22N10.0	20N41.5	22S19.5	11S44.9	2S30.5	14N53.8	20N56.9
4 S	18 45 56.4	22 57.0	18 48.4	17 47.4	22 38.2	21 28.1	20 14.3	22 23.1	11 44.7	2 30.7	14 52.1	20 56.7
7 T	18 57 46.1	22 40.4	18 50.7	20 12.0	21 22.2	20 40.7	19 46.0	22 26.6	11 44.9	2 31.1	14 50.4	20 56.4
10 F	19 9 35.8	22 20.3	18 53.1	10 35.4	19 55.3	19 48.1	19 16.4	22 30.1	11 45.3	2 31.6	14 48.6	20 56.1
13 M	19 21 25.5	21 56.8	18 55.4	3N32.8	18 20.5	18 50.6	18 45.7	22 33.5	11 46.1	2 32.3	14 46.8	20 55.8
16 T	19 33 15.1	21 29.8	18 57.7	15 16.9	16 40.5	17 48.5	18 13.8	22 36.8	11 47.1	2 33.2	14 44.9	20 55.6
19 S	19 45 4.8	20 59.6	19 0.0	20 44.4	14 57.7	16 42.0	17 40.8	22 40.0	11 48.4	2 34.2	14 42.9	20 55.3
22 W	19 56 54.5	20 26.1	19 2.3	18 7.5	13 14.4	15 31.6	17 6.8	22 43.1	11 50.0	2 35.4	14 41.0	20 55.0
25 S	20 8 44.2	19 49.6	19 4.6	8 36.8	11 32.8	14 17.5	16 31.8	22 46.1	11 51.8	2 36.8	14 38.9	20 54.6
28 T	20 20 33.8	19 10.1	19 6.9	4S29.0	9 55.0	13 0.1	15 55.8	22 48.9	11 54.0	2 38.2	14 36.9	20 54.3
31 F	20 32 23.5	18 27.7	19 9.2	16 34.7	8 23.5	11 39.7	15 18.8	22 51.6	11 56.4	2 39.9	14 34.8	20 54.0

AUGUST 1925

DAY	EPHEMERIS SIDEREAL TIME h m s	☉ ° ′	☊ ° ′	☽ ° ′	☿ ° ′	♀ ° ′	♂ ° ′	♃ ° ′	♄ ° ′	♅ ° ′	♆ ° ′	♇ ° ′
LONGITUDE												
1 S	20 36 20.0	8♌13.2	4♌24.3	19♐ 7.0	5♍ 3.8	4♍35.6	22♌29.2	14♑59.3	7♏57.5	25♓ 5.8	21♌46.9	13♋43.8
2 S	20 40 16.6	9 10.6	4 21.1	3♑51.0	5 48.4	5 48.4	23 7.2	14R52.8	7 59.5	25R 4.3	21 49.1	13 45.2
3 M	20 44 13.1	10 8.0	4 17.9	18 51.0	6 29.5	7 1.2	23 45.1	14 46.5	8 1.6	25 2.9	21 51.3	13 46.6
4 T	20 48 9.7	11 5.5	4 14.8	3♒59.5	7 6.8	8 14.0	24 23.1	14 40.3	8 3.8	25 1.4	21 53.5	13 48.0
5 W	20 52 6.3	12 2.9	4 11.6	19 7.6	7 40.1	9 26.7	25 1.0	14 34.2	8 6.0	24 59.8	21 55.7	13 49.3
6 T	20 56 2.8	13 0.3	4 8.4	4♓ 6.1	8 9.3	10 39.4	25 39.0	14 28.2	8 8.4	24 58.3	21 57.9	13 50.7
7 F	20 59 59.3	13 57.8	4 5.2	18 47.1	8 34.2	11 52.0	26 17.0	14 22.4	8 10.9	24 56.7	22 0.1	13 52.1
8 S	21 3 55.9	14 55.3	4 2.0	3♈ 4.6	8 54.6	13 4.7	26 55.0	14 16.7	8 13.4	24 55.0	22 2.3	13 53.4
9 S	21 7 52.5	15 52.8	3 58.9	16 55.6	9 10.2	14 17.3	27 33.0	14 11.1	8 16.1	24 53.3	22 4.5	13 54.8
10 M	21 11 49.0	16 50.3	3 55.7	0♉19.5	9 20.9	15 29.9	28 11.0	14 5.7	8 18.8	24 51.6	22 6.7	13 56.1
11 T	21 15 45.6	17 47.9	3 52.5	13 17.9	9 26.4	16 42.5	28 49.0	14 0.4	8 21.6	24 49.9	22 8.9	13 57.4
12 W	21 19 42.1	18 45.5	3 49.3	25 53.8	9 26.7	17 55.0	29 27.0	13 55.3	8 24.6	24 48.1	22 11.1	13 58.7
13 T	21 23 38.7	19 43.1	3 46.2	8♊11.4	9R21.6	19 7.6	0♍ 5.0	13 50.3	8 27.6	24 46.3	22 13.4	13 60.0
14 F	21 27 35.3	20 40.7	3 43.0	20 14.9	9 11.0	20 20.1	0 43.1	13 45.4	8 30.6	24 44.4	22 15.6	14 1.3
15 S	21 31 31.8	21 38.4	3 39.8	2♋ 8.8	8 54.8	21 32.6	1 21.2	13 40.8	8 33.8	24 42.6	22 17.8	14 2.5
16 S	21 35 28.3	22 36.0	3 36.6	13 57.3	8 33.1	22 45.0	1 59.2	13 36.3	8 37.1	24 40.7	22 20.0	14 3.8
17 M	21 39 24.9	23 33.8	3 33.4	25 44.0	8 5.9	23 57.4	2 37.3	13 31.9	8 40.4	24 38.7	22 22.2	14 5.0
18 T	21 43 21.5	24 31.5	3 30.3	7♌32.3	7 33.4	25 9.8	3 15.4	13 27.7	8 43.9	24 36.8	22 24.5	14 6.2
19 W	21 47 18.0	25 29.2	3 27.1	19 24.8	6 56.0	26 22.2	3 53.5	13 23.7	8 47.4	24 34.8	22 26.7	14 7.4
20 T	21 51 14.5	26 27.0	3 23.9	1♍23.8	6 14.0	27 34.6	4 31.7	13 19.8	8 51.0	24 32.8	22 28.9	14 8.6
21 F	21 55 11.1	27 24.8	3 20.7	13 31.2	5 28.0	28 46.9	5 9.8	13 16.1	8 54.7	24 30.7	22 31.1	14 9.8
22 S	21 59 7.7	28 22.6	3 17.6	25 48.7	4 38.6	29 59.2	5 47.9	13 12.6	8 58.4	24 28.7	22 33.4	14 11.0
23 S	22 3 4.2	29 20.5	3 14.4	8♎17.7	3 46.8	1♎11.4	6 26.1	13 9.3	9 2.3	24 26.6	22 35.6	14 12.1
24 M	22 7 0.8	0♍18.3	3 11.2	20 59.8	2 53.3	2 23.7	7 4.3	13 6.2	9 6.2	24 24.4	22 37.8	14 13.2
25 T	22 10 57.3	1 16.2	3 8.0	3♏56.5	1 59.1	3 35.9	7 42.5	13 3.2	9 10.2	24 22.3	22 40.0	14 14.4
26 W	22 14 53.8	2 14.1	3 4.8	17 9.4	1 5.5	4 48.0	8 20.7	13 0.4	9 14.3	24 20.1	22 42.2	14 15.4
27 T	22 18 50.4	3 12.0	3 1.7	0♐39.8	0 13.4	6 0.1	8 58.9	12 57.8	9 18.4	24 18.0	22 44.4	14 16.5
28 F	22 22 47.0	4 10.0	2 58.5	14 28.9	29♌24.1	7 12.2	9 37.1	12 55.4	9 22.7	24 15.8	22 46.6	14 17.6
29 S	22 26 43.6	5 8.0	2 55.3	28 37.0	28 38.6	8 24.3	10 15.3	12 53.2	9 27.0	24 13.5	22 48.8	14 18.6
30 S	22 30 40.1	6 6.0	2 52.1	13♑ 2.8	27 58.0	9 36.3	10 53.6	12 51.1	9 31.4	24 11.3	22 50.9	14 19.7
31 M	22 34 36.6	7 4.0	2 49.0	27 43.6	27 23.3	10 48.2	11 31.8	12 49.3	9 35.8	24 9.0	22 53.1	14 20.7
DECLINATION												
1 S	20 36 20.0	18N13.0	19N 9.9	19S13.6	7N54.8	11N12.3	15N 6.3	22S52.4	11S57.2	2S40.5	14N34.2	20N53.9
4 T	20 48 9.7	17 27.1	19 12.2	19 12.1	6 35.9	9 48.3	14 28.2	22 54.9	12 0.0	2 42.3	14 32.1	20 53.6
7 F	20 59 59.3	16 38.6	19 14.5	7 49.8	5 30.2	8 22.2	13 49.3	22 57.1	12 3.0	2 44.2	14 30.0	20 53.3
10 M	21 11 49.0	15 47.7	19 16.7	6N38.9	4 41.4	6 54.1	13 9.5	22 59.2	12 6.3	2 46.3	14 27.8	20 53.0
13 T	21 23 38.7	14 54.5	19 19.0	17 19.7	4 13.7	5 24.4	12 29.0	23 1.1	12 9.8	2 48.5	14 25.7	20 52.7
16 S	21 35 28.3	13 59.1	19 21.2	20 51.3	4 11.1	3 53.4	11 47.8	23 2.9	12 13.5	2 50.8	14 23.6	20 52.4
19 W	21 47 18.0	13 1.8	19 23.4	16 16.7	4 36.2	2 21.4	11 5.9	23 4.4	12 17.5	2 53.1	14 21.4	20 52.1
22 S	21 59 7.7	12 2.5	19 25.6	5 25.2	5 28.9	0 48.7	10 23.4	23 5.8	12 21.6	2 55.6	14 19.3	20 51.8
25 T	22 10 57.3	11 1.6	19 27.8	7S54.6	6 44.3	0S44.4	9 40.3	23 6.9	12 26.0	2 58.2	14 17.2	20 51.6
28 F	22 22 47.0	9 59.1	19 30.0	18 34.1	8 12.3	2 17.5	8 56.6	23 7.9	12 30.6	3 0.8	14 15.0	20 51.3
31 M	22 34 36.6	8 55.2	19 32.2	20 1.8	9 39.6	3 50.3	8 12.4	23 8.8	12 35.4	3 3.5	14 12.9	20 51.0

SEPTEMBER 1925

DAY	EPHEMERIS SIDEREAL TIME	☉	☊	☽	☿	♀	♂	♃	♄	♅	♆	♇
	h m s	° ′	° ′	° ′	° ′	° ′	° ′	° ′	° ′	° ′	° ′	° ′
						LONGITUDE						
1 T	22 38 33.2	8♍ 2.0	2♌45.8	12♒34.7	26♌55.2	12♎ 0.2	12♍10.1	12♑47.6	9♏40.4	24♓ 6.8	22♌55.3	14♋21.7
2 W	22 42 29.8	9 0.1	2 42.6	27 29.3	26R34.5	13 12.1	12 48.4	12R46.1	9 45.0	24R 4.5	22 57.4	14 22.7
3 T	22 46 26.3	9 58.1	2 39.4	12♓19.7	26 21.7	14 23.9	13 26.7	12 44.8	9 49.6	24 2.2	22 59.6	14 23.6
4 F	22 50 22.8	10 56.3	2 36.2	26 57.9	26 17.2	15 35.7	14 5.0	12 43.7	9 54.4	23 59.9	23 1.7	14 24.5
5 S	22 54 19.4	11 54.4	2 33.1	11♈16.9	26D21.4	16 47.5	14 43.3	12 42.8	9 59.2	23 57.5	23 3.8	14 25.5
6 S	22 58 16.0	12 52.6	2 29.9	25 11.8	26 34.4	17 59.2	15 21.7	12 42.1	10 4.1	23 55.2	23 6.0	14 26.4
7 M	23 2 12.5	13 50.8	2 26.7	8♉40.4	26 56.2	19 10.9	16 0.0	12 41.6	10 9.0	23 52.9	23 8.1	14 27.3
8 T	23 6 9.0	14 49.0	2 23.5	21 42.8	27 26.6	20 22.6	16 38.4	12 41.2	10 14.0	23 50.5	23 10.2	14 28.1
9 W	23 10 5.6	15 47.3	2 20.4	4♊21.4	28 5.5	21 34.2	17 16.8	12 41.1	10 19.1	23 48.1	23 12.3	14 29.0
10 T	23 14 2.2	16 45.6	2 17.2	16 39.8	28 52.7	22 45.8	17 55.2	12D41.1	10 24.2	23 45.8	23 14.3	14 29.8
11 F	23 17 58.7	17 44.0	2 14.0	28 42.8	29 47.6	23 57.3	18 33.7	12 41.3	10 29.5	23 43.4	23 16.4	14 30.6
12 S	23 21 55.3	18 42.4	2 10.8	10♋35.6	0♍49.9	25 8.8	19 12.1	12 41.8	10 34.7	23 41.0	23 18.5	14 31.4
13 S	23 25 51.8	19 40.8	2 7.6	22 23.2	1 59.1	26 20.2	19 50.6	12 42.4	10 40.1	23 38.6	23 20.5	14 32.1
14 M	23 29 48.4	20 39.2	2 4.5	4♌10.6	3 14.6	27 31.6	20 29.1	12 43.2	10 45.5	23 36.2	23 22.5	14 32.9
15 T	23 33 44.9	21 37.7	2 1.3	16 2.0	4 35.9	28 43.0	21 7.6	12 44.2	10 50.9	23 33.8	23 24.6	14 33.6
16 W	23 37 41.5	22 36.2	1 58.1	28 1.0	6 2.3	29 54.3	21 46.1	12 45.4	10 56.5	23 31.4	23 26.6	14 34.3
17 T	23 41 38.0	23 34.8	1 54.9	10♍10.3	7 33.3	1♏ 5.6	22 24.7	12 46.8	11 2.0	23 29.0	23 28.5	14 35.0
18 F	23 45 34.6	24 33.4	1 51.8	22 31.8	9 8.3	2 16.9	23 3.2	12 48.4	11 7.7	23 26.6	23 30.5	14 35.6
19 S	23 49 31.1	25 32.0	1 48.6	5♎ 6.5	10 46.7	3 28.0	23 41.8	12 50.1	11 13.4	23 24.2	23 32.5	14 36.3
20 S	23 53 27.7	26 30.6	1 45.4	17 54.6	12 27.9	4 39.2	24 20.4	12 52.1	11 19.1	23 21.8	23 34.4	14 36.9
21 M	23 57 24.3	27 29.3	1 42.2	0♏55.7	14 11.5	5 50.3	24 59.0	12 54.2	11 24.9	23 19.4	23 36.3	14 37.5
22 T	0 1 20.8	28 28.0	1 39.0	14 9.3	15 57.0	7 1.3	25 37.7	12 56.6	11 30.8	23 17.0	23 38.2	14 38.0
23 W	0 5 17.4	29 26.8	1 35.9	27 34.8	17 43.9	8 12.3	26 16.3	12 59.1	11 36.7	23 14.6	23 40.1	14 38.6
24 T	0 9 13.9	0♎25.5	1 32.7	11♐11.7	19 32.0	9 23.2	26 55.0	13 1.8	11 42.6	23 12.2	23 42.0	14 39.1
25 F	0 13 10.5	1 24.3	1 29.5	24 59.9	21 20.8	10 34.1	27 33.7	13 4.7	11 48.6	23 9.8	23 43.8	14 39.6
26 S	0 17 7.0	2 23.2	1 26.3	8♑59.3	23 10.1	11 44.9	28 12.4	13 7.8	11 54.7	23 7.4	23 45.7	14 40.1
27 S	0 21 3.6	3 22.0	1 23.1	23 9.5	24 59.7	12 55.7	28 51.1	13 11.0	12 0.8	23 5.1	23 47.5	14 40.5
28 M	0 25 0.1	4 20.9	1 20.0	7♒29.4	26 49.2	14 6.4	29 29.9	13 14.5	12 7.0	23 2.7	23 49.3	14 41.0
29 T	0 28 56.7	5 19.8	1 16.8	21 56.7	28 38.7	15 17.0	0♎ 8.7	13 18.1	12 13.2	23 0.4	23 51.0	14 41.4
30 W	0 32 53.3	6 18.8	1 13.6	6♓27.6	0♎27.8	16 27.6	0 47.5	13 21.9	12 19.4	22 58.1	23 52.8	14 41.8
						DECLINATION						
1 T	22 38 33.2	8N33.6	19N32.9	17S45.3	10N 6.2	4S21.2	7N57.6	23S 9.0	12S37.0	3S 4.4	14N12.2	20N51.0
4 F	22 50 22.8	7 28.0	19 35.1	4 60.0	11 12.3	5 53.2	7 12.8	23 9.6	12 42.0	3 7.2	14 10.2	20 50.7
7 M	23 2 12.5	6 21.3	19 37.3	9N30.2	11 51.2	7 24.2	6 27.5	23 10.0	12 47.1	3 10.0	14 8.1	20 50.5
10 T	23 14 2.2	5 13.7	19 39.4	18 59.6	11 57.7	8 54.0	5 41.9	23 10.3	12 52.4	3 12.8	14 6.1	20 50.3
13 S	23 25 51.8	4 5.3	19 41.6	20 34.2	11 30.0	10 22.1	4 55.9	23 10.3	12 57.9	3 15.6	14 4.1	20 50.1
16 W	23 37 41.5	2 56.2	19 43.7	14 8.9	10 29.9	11 48.4	4 9.7	23 10.2	13 3.5	3 18.5	14 2.2	20 49.9
19 S	23 49 31.1	1 46.6	19 45.8	2 5.7	9 2.1	13 12.4	3 23.1	23 9.9	13 9.2	3 21.3	14 0.3	20 49.8
22 T	0 1 20.8	0 36.6	19 48.0	11S18.8	7 12.8	14 33.9	2 36.4	23 9.5	13 15.0	3 24.2	13 58.4	20 49.6
25 F	0 13 10.5	0S33.6	19 50.1	20 13.3	5 8.4	15 52.5	1 49.4	23 8.9	13 20.9	3 27.0	13 56.6	20 49.5
28 M	0 25 0.1	1 43.7	19 52.2	18 48.5	2 54.7	17 7.8	1 2.4	23 8.1	13 26.9	3 29.8	13 54.9	20 49.4

OCTOBER 1925

DAY	EPHEMERIS SIDEREAL TIME	☉	☊	☽	☿	♀	♂	♃	♄	♅	♆	♇
						LONGITUDE						
1 T	0 36 49.8	7♎17.7	1♌10.4	20♓56.7	2♎16.6	17♏38.1	1♎26.3	13♑25.9	12♏25.7	22♓55.8	23♌54.5	14♋42.1
2 F	0 40 46.3	8 16.7	1 7.3	5♈18.1	4 4.8	18 48.5	2 5.1	13 30.1	12 32.0	22R53.5	23 56.2	14 42.5
3 S	0 44 42.9	9 15.8	1 4.1	19 25.4	5 52.5	19 58.9	2 43.9	13 34.4	12 38.4	22 51.2	23 57.9	14 42.8
4 S	0 48 39.4	10 14.8	1 0.9	3♉13.6	7 39.5	21 9.2	3 22.8	13 38.9	12 44.8	22 48.9	23 59.6	14 43.1
5 M	0 52 36.0	11 14.0	0 57.7	16 39.3	9 25.9	22 19.4	4 1.7	13 43.6	12 51.3	22 46.7	24 1.2	14 43.3
6 T	0 56 32.6	12 13.1	0 54.6	29 41.3	11 11.5	23 29.6	4 40.6	13 48.5	12 57.8	22 44.5	24 2.8	14 43.6
7 W	1 0 29.1	13 12.3	0 51.4	12♊20.6	12 56.4	24 39.7	5 19.5	13 53.5	13 4.3	22 42.2	24 4.4	14 43.8
8 T	1 4 25.7	14 11.5	0 48.2	24 40.0	14 40.6	25 49.7	5 58.5	13 58.7	13 10.9	22 40.1	24 6.0	14 44.0
9 F	1 8 22.2	15 10.8	0 45.0	6♋43.8	16 24.0	26 59.6	6 37.5	14 4.0	13 17.5	22 37.9	24 7.6	14 44.2
10 S	1 12 18.8	16 10.1	0 41.8	18 37.0	18 6.7	28 9.5	7 16.5	14 9.6	13 24.1	22 35.7	24 9.1	14 44.3
11 S	1 16 15.3	17 9.4	0 38.7	0♌25.1	19 48.7	29 19.3	7 55.5	14 15.3	13 30.8	22 33.6	24 10.6	14 44.4
12 M	1 20 11.9	18 8.8	0 35.5	12 13.5	21 29.8	0♐29.0	8 34.6	14 21.1	13 37.5	22 31.5	24 12.1	14 44.5
13 T	1 24 8.4	19 8.2	0 32.3	24 7.6	23 10.3	1 38.6	9 13.7	14 27.2	13 44.3	22 29.4	24 13.5	14 44.6
14 W	1 28 5.0	20 7.7	0 29.1	6♍11.8	24 50.1	2 48.2	9 52.8	14 33.3	13 51.0	22 27.4	24 15.0	14 44.7
15 T	1 32 1.5	21 7.1	0 26.0	18 30.0	26 29.1	3 57.6	10 31.9	14 39.7	13 57.8	22 25.4	24 16.4	14 44.7
16 F	1 35 58.1	22 6.7	0 22.8	1♎ 4.7	28 7.5	5 7.0	11 11.1	14 46.2	14 4.7	22 23.4	24 17.7	14R44.7
17 S	1 39 54.6	23 6.2	0 19.6	13 56.9	29 45.2	6 16.3	11 50.3	14 52.8	14 11.5	22 21.4	24 19.1	14 44.7
18 S	1 43 51.2	24 5.8	0 16.4	27 6.4	1♏22.2	7 25.5	12 29.5	14 59.6	14 18.4	22 19.5	24 20.4	14 44.6
19 M	1 47 47.8	25 5.5	0 13.2	10♏31.4	2 58.7	8 34.6	13 8.7	15 6.6	14 25.3	22 17.5	24 21.7	14 44.6
20 T	1 51 44.3	26 5.1	0 10.1	24 9.4	4 34.4	9 43.6	13 48.0	15 13.7	14 32.3	22 15.7	24 22.9	14 44.5
21 W	1 55 40.8	27 4.8	0 6.9	7♐57.3	6 9.6	10 52.5	14 27.2	15 21.0	14 39.2	22 13.8	24 24.2	14 44.4
22 T	1 59 37.4	28 4.5	0 3.7	21 52.1	7 44.2	12 1.4	15 6.5	15 28.4	14 46.2	22 12.0	24 25.4	14 44.2
23 F	2 3 33.9	29 4.3	0 0.5	5♑51.7	9 18.3	13 10.0	15 45.8	15 36.0	14 53.2	22 10.2	24 26.5	14 44.1
24 S	2 7 30.5	0♏ 4.1	29♋57.4	19 54.3	10 51.7	14 18.6	16 25.2	15 43.7	15 0.2	22 8.5	24 27.7	14 43.9
25 S	2 11 27.1	1 3.9	29 54.2	3♒59.2	12 24.7	15 27.1	17 4.5	15 51.6	15 7.3	22 6.8	24 28.8	14 43.7
26 M	2 15 23.6	2 3.7	29 51.0	18 5.6	13 57.0	16 35.4	17 43.9	15 59.5	15 14.3	22 5.1	24 29.9	14 43.4
27 T	2 19 20.2	3 3.6	29 47.8	2♓12.5	15 28.9	17 43.6	18 23.3	16 7.7	15 21.4	22 3.4	24 30.9	14 43.2
28 W	2 23 16.7	4 3.5	29 44.6	16 18.5	17 0.2	18 51.7	19 2.8	16 16.0	15 28.5	22 1.8	24 32.0	14 42.9
29 T	2 27 13.3	5 3.4	29 41.5	0♈21.0	18 31.1	19 59.7	19 42.2	16 24.4	15 35.6	22 0.3	24 33.0	14 42.6
30 F	2 31 9.8	6 3.3	29 38.3	14 16.5	20 1.4	21 7.5	20 21.7	16 32.9	15 42.7	21 58.7	24 33.9	14 42.2
31 S	2 35 6.4	7 3.3	29 35.1	28 1.2	21 31.2	22 15.1	21 1.2	16 41.6	15 49.9	21 57.3	24 34.9	14 41.9
						DECLINATION						
1 T	0 36 49.8	2S53.8	19N54.3	7S 4.2	0N36.3	18S19.7	0N15.2	23S 7.1	13S33.0	3S32.5	13N53.2	20N49.3
4 S	0 48 39.4	4 3.6	19 56.4	7N50.7	1S43.4	19 27.7	0S32.0	23 5.9	13 39.1	3 35.2	13 51.6	20 49.3
7 W	1 0 29.1	5 12.9	19 58.4	18 28.3	4 2.0	20 31.5	1 19.3	23 4.5	13 45.3	3 37.8	13 50.0	20 49.2
10 S	1 12 18.8	6 21.7	20 0.5	21 1.4	6 17.8	21 30.9	2 6.5	23 3.0	13 51.6	3 40.3	13 48.5	20 49.2
13 T	1 24 8.4	7 29.7	20 2.6	15 19.1	8 29.5	22 25.6	2 53.6	23 1.3	13 57.9	3 42.7	13 47.1	20 49.2
16 F	1 35 58.1	8 36.8	20 4.6	3 33.3	10 36.2	23 15.2	3 40.6	22 59.3	14 4.2	3 45.1	13 45.8	20 49.3
19 M	1 47 47.8	9 42.9	20 6.6	10S17.7	12 37.2	23 59.5	4 27.5	22 57.2	14 10.6	3 47.3	13 44.5	20 49.3
22 T	1 59 37.4	10 47.6	20 8.7	20 5.2	14 31.8	24 38.4	5 14.1	22 54.8	14 16.9	3 49.4	13 43.3	20 49.4
25 S	2 11 27.1	11 50.9	20 10.7	19 36.3	16 19.5	25 11.5	6 0.5	22 52.3	14 23.2	3 51.4	13 42.3	20 49.5
28 W	2 23 16.7	12 52.6	20 12.7	8 45.6	17 59.7	25 38.8	6 46.6	22 49.5	14 29.6	3 53.3	13 41.3	20 49.6
31 S	2 35 6.4	13 52.4	20 14.7	6N 5.6	19 31.8	25 60.0	7 32.3	22 46.5	14 35.9	3 55.0	13 40.4	20 49.8

NOVEMBER 1925

LONGITUDE

DAY	EPHEMERIS SIDEREAL TIME	☉	☊	☽	☿	♀	♂	♃	♄	♅	♆	♇
	h m s	° ′	° ′	° ′	° ′	° ′	° ′	° ′	° ′	° ′	° ′	° ′
1 S	2 39 2.9	8♏ 3.3	29♋31.9	11♉31.3	23♏ 0.5	23♐22.6	21♎40.7	16♑50.4	15♏57.0	21♓55.8	24♌35.8	14♋41.5
2 M	2 42 59.5	9 3.4	29 28.8	24 43.9	24 29.3	24 30.0	22 20.3	16 59.3	16 4.2	21R54.4	24 36.6	14R41.1
3 T	2 46 56.1	10 3.4	29 25.6	7♊37.4	25 57.6	25 37.2	22 59.9	17 8.4	16 11.3	21 53.0	24 37.5	14 40.7
4 W	2 50 52.6	11 3.5	29 22.4	20 12.0	27 25.3	26 44.2	23 39.5	17 17.6	16 18.5	21 51.7	24 38.3	14 40.3
5 T	2 54 49.1	12 3.7	29 19.2	2♋29.2	28 52.4	27 51.1	24 19.1	17 26.9	16 25.6	21 50.4	24 39.0	14 39.8
6 F	2 58 45.7	13 3.9	29 16.0	14 32.2	0♐19.0	28 57.8	24 58.8	17 36.3	16 32.8	21 49.2	24 39.8	14 39.3
7 S	3 2 42.3	14 4.1	29 12.9	26 25.2	1 45.0	0♑ 4.3	25 38.5	17 45.9	16 40.0	21 48.0	24 40.5	14 38.8
8 S	3 6 38.8	15 4.3	29 9.7	8♌13.2	3 10.3	1 10.7	26 18.2	17 55.5	16 47.2	21 46.8	24 41.2	14 38.3
9 M	3 10 35.4	16 4.6	29 6.5	20 1.7	4 34.9	2 16.8	26 58.0	18 5.3	16 54.4	21 45.7	24 41.8	14 37.7
10 T	3 14 31.9	17 4.9	29 3.3	1♍56.2	5 58.8	3 22.8	27 37.8	18 15.2	17 1.6	21 44.6	24 42.4	14 37.1
11 W	3 18 28.5	18 5.2	29 0.2	14 2.1	7 21.8	4 28.6	28 17.6	18 25.2	17 8.8	21 43.6	24 43.0	14 36.5
12 T	3 22 25.0	19 5.6	28 57.0	26 24.0	8 43.9	5 34.1	28 57.4	18 35.4	17 16.0	21 42.7	24 43.6	14 35.9
13 F	3 26 21.6	20 6.0	28 53.8	9♎ 5.7	10 5.1	6 39.5	29 37.3	18 45.6	17 23.2	21 41.7	24 44.1	14 35.3
14 S	3 30 18.2	21 6.4	28 50.6	22 9.3	11 25.1	7 44.6	0♏17.2	18 56.0	17 30.4	21 40.8	24 44.5	14 34.6
15 S	3 34 14.7	22 6.9	28 47.4	5♏35.1	12 43.9	8 49.6	0 57.1	19 6.5	17 37.5	21 40.0	24 45.0	14 33.9
16 M	3 38 11.3	23 7.4	28 44.3	19 21.4	14 1.3	9 54.2	1 37.0	19 17.0	17 44.7	21 39.2	24 45.4	14 33.2
17 T	3 42 7.8	24 7.9	28 41.1	3♐24.5	15 17.2	10 58.7	2 17.0	19 27.7	17 51.9	21 38.5	24 45.8	14 32.5
18 W	3 46 4.4	25 8.5	28 37.9	17 39.4	16 31.3	12 2.9	2 57.0	19 38.5	17 59.1	21 37.8	24 46.1	14 31.8
19 T	3 50 0.9	26 9.0	28 34.7	2♑ 0.7	17 43.4	13 6.8	3 37.0	19 49.4	18 6.2	21 37.1	24 46.4	14 31.0
20 F	3 53 57.5	27 9.6	28 31.6	16 23.2	18 53.3	14 10.5	4 17.1	20 0.4	18 13.4	21 36.5	24 46.7	14 30.2
21 S	3 57 54.1	28 10.2	28 28.4	0♒42.8	20 0.6	15 13.9	4 57.2	20 11.5	18 20.5	21 36.0	24 46.9	14 29.4
22 S	4 1 50.6	29 10.9	28 25.2	14 56.5	21 5.0	16 16.9	5 37.3	20 22.6	18 27.6	21 35.5	24 47.1	14 28.6
23 M	4 5 47.1	0♐11.5	28 22.0	29 2.9	22 6.1	17 19.7	6 17.4	20 33.9	18 34.7	21 35.1	24 47.3	14 27.8
24 T	4 9 43.7	1 12.2	28 18.8	13♓ 1.0	23 3.4	18 22.1	6 57.5	20 45.3	18 41.8	21 34.7	24 47.4	14 26.9
25 W	4 13 40.3	2 12.9	28 15.7	26 50.3	23 56.4	19 24.3	7 37.7	20 56.7	18 48.9	21 34.3	24 47.5	14 26.0
26 T	4 17 36.8	3 13.6	28 12.5	10♈30.2	24 44.6	20 26.0	8 17.9	21 8.3	18 55.9	21 34.0	24 47.6	14 25.2
27 F	4 21 33.4	4 14.3	28 9.3	24 0.1	25 27.4	21 27.4	8 58.1	21 19.9	19 3.0	21 33.8	24 47.6	14 24.2
28 S	4 25 29.9	5 15.0	28 6.1	7♉18.6	26 3.9	22 28.4	9 38.4	21 31.6	19 10.0	21 33.6	24R47.6	14 23.3
29 S	4 29 26.5	6 15.8	28 3.0	20 24.5	26 33.4	23 29.1	10 18.7	21 43.4	19 17.0	21 33.4	24 47.6	14 22.4
30 M	4 33 23.1	7 16.6	27 59.8	3♊16.8	26 55.2	24 29.3	10 59.0	21 55.3	19 23.9	21 33.4	24 47.5	14 21.4

DECLINATION

DAY	EPHEMERIS SIDEREAL TIME	☉	☊	☽	☿	♀	♂	♃	♄	♅	♆	♇
1 S	2 39 2.9	14S11.9	20N15.4	10N38.0	20S 0.6	26S 5.7	7S47.5	22S45.4	14S38.0	3S55.5	13N40.1	20N49.9
4 W	2 50 52.6	15 9.1	20 17.3	19 57.3	21 21.1	26 18.8	8 32.7	22 42.1	14 44.2	3 57.1	13 39.3	20 50.1
7 S	3 2 42.3	16 4.0	20 19.3	20 41.6	22 32.1	26 25.7	9 17.4	22 38.6	14 50.4	3 58.4	13 38.6	20 50.3
10 T	3 14 31.9	16 56.5	20 21.3	13 24.1	23 32.9	26 26.5	10 1.6	22 34.8	14 56.6	3 59.7	13 38.1	20 50.5
13 F	3 26 21.6	17 46.4	20 23.3	0 47.1	24 22.9	26 21.2	10 45.3	22 30.8	15 2.7	4 0.7	13 37.6	20 50.8
16 M	3 38 11.3	18 33.6	20 25.2	13S 2.8	25 1.1	26 9.9	11 28.4	22 26.5	15 8.7	4 1.6	13 37.2	20 51.1
19 T	3 50 0.9	19 17.8	20 27.1	21 15.4	25 27.0	25 52.9	12 10.7	22 22.0	15 14.7	4 2.3	13 36.9	20 51.4
22 S	4 1 50.6	19 58.9	20 29.1	17 50.8	25 39.8	25 30.2	12 52.4	22 17.2	15 20.5	4 2.8	13 36.8	20 51.7
25 W	4 13 40.3	20 36.7	20 31.0	5 18.3	25 39.1	25 2.2	13 33.3	22 12.2	15 26.3	4 3.2	13 36.7	20 52.1
28 S	4 25 29.9	21 11.1	20 32.9	9N12.2	25 24.4	24 29.2	14 13.3	22 6.9	15 32.0	4 3.4	13 36.7	20 52.5

DECEMBER 1925

LONGITUDE

DAY	EPHEMERIS SIDEREAL TIME	☉	☊	☽	☿	♀	♂	♃	♄	♅	♆	♇
1 T	4 37 19.6	8♐17.4	27♋56.6	15♊54.6	27♐ 8.5	25♑29.1	11♏39.3	22♑ 7.3	19♏30.9	21♓33.3	24♌47.4	14♋20.5
2 W	4 41 16.2	9 18.2	27 53.4	28 18.2	27 12.3	26 28.5	12 19.7	22 19.4	19 37.8	21 33.3	24R47.3	14R19.5
3 T	4 45 12.7	10 19.0	27 50.3	10♋28.7	27R 6.0	27 27.4	13 0.1	22 31.5	19 44.7	21D33.4	24 47.1	14 18.5
4 F	4 49 9.3	11 19.9	27 47.1	22 28.1	26 49.0	28 25.9	13 40.5	22 43.7	19 51.6	21 33.5	24 46.9	14 17.5
5 S	4 53 5.8	12 20.8	27 43.9	4♌19.6	26 20.8	29 23.9	14 21.0	22 56.0	19 58.5	21 33.7	24 46.6	14 16.4
6 S	4 57 2.4	13 21.7	27 40.7	16 6.9	25 41.3	0♒21.4	15 1.5	23 8.3	20 5.3	21 33.9	24 46.4	14 15.4
7 M	5 0 58.9	14 22.6	27 37.6	27 54.8	24 50.8	1 18.4	15 42.0	23 20.7	20 12.1	21 34.1	24 46.0	14 14.3
8 T	5 4 55.5	15 23.6	27 34.4	9♍48.2	23 50.2	2 14.8	16 22.6	23 33.2	20 18.8	21 34.5	24 45.7	14 13.3
9 W	5 8 52.1	16 24.5	27 31.2	21 52.4	22 40.7	3 10.7	17 3.1	23 45.8	20 25.5	21 34.8	24 45.3	14 12.2
10 T	5 12 48.6	17 25.5	27 28.0	4♎12.6	21 24.3	4 6.0	17 43.8	23 58.4	20 32.2	21 35.3	24 44.9	14 11.1
11 F	5 16 45.2	18 26.5	27 24.8	16 53.2	20 3.2	5 0.7	18 24.4	24 11.1	20 38.9	21 35.7	24 44.5	14 10.0
12 S	5 20 41.7	19 27.5	27 21.7	29 57.9	18 40.2	5 54.8	19 5.1	24 23.9	20 45.5	21 36.3	24 44.0	14 8.8
13 S	5 24 38.3	20 28.6	27 18.5	13♏28.4	17 18.0	6 48.2	19 45.8	24 36.7	20 52.1	21 36.8	24 43.5	14 7.7
14 M	5 28 34.9	21 29.6	27 15.3	27 24.4	15 59.6	7 41.0	20 26.5	24 49.6	20 58.7	21 37.5	24 42.9	14 6.6
15 T	5 32 31.4	22 30.7	27 12.1	11♐43.1	14 47.2	8 33.0	21 7.3	25 2.6	21 5.2	21 38.2	24 42.4	14 5.4
16 W	5 36 28.0	23 31.8	27 9.0	26 19.4	13 42.8	9 24.4	21 48.0	25 15.6	21 11.6	21 38.9	24 41.8	14 4.3
17 T	5 40 24.5	24 32.9	27 5.8	11♑ 6.2	12 48.1	10 14.9	22 28.8	25 28.7	21 18.1	21 39.7	24 41.1	14 3.1
18 F	5 44 21.1	25 34.0	27 2.6	25 55.9	12 3.9	11 4.7	23 9.7	25 41.8	21 24.4	21 40.5	24 40.4	14 1.9
19 S	5 48 17.6	26 35.1	26 59.4	10♒41.3	11 30.6	11 53.7	23 50.6	25 55.0	21 30.8	21 41.4	24 39.7	14 0.7
20 S	5 52 14.2	27 36.2	26 56.3	25 16.3	11 8.3	12 41.8	24 31.4	26 8.3	21 37.1	21 42.3	24 39.0	13 59.5
21 M	5 56 10.8	28 37.3	26 53.1	9♓36.8	10 56.7	13 28.9	25 12.4	26 21.5	21 43.3	21 43.3	24 38.3	13 58.3
22 T	6 0 7.3	29 38.4	26 49.9	23 40.6	10 55.2	14 15.2	25 53.3	26 34.9	21 49.5	21 44.3	24 37.5	13 57.1
23 W	6 4 3.9	0♑39.6	26 46.7	7♈26.8	11D 3.1	15 0.4	26 34.3	26 48.3	21 55.7	21 45.4	24 36.6	13 55.9
24 T	6 8 0.4	1 40.7	26 43.6	20 55.8	11 19.8	15 44.6	27 15.3	27 1.7	22 1.8	21 46.6	24 35.8	13 54.7
25 F	6 11 57.0	2 41.8	26 40.4	4♉ 8.5	11 44.4	16 27.8	27 56.3	27 15.2	22 7.8	21 47.7	24 34.9	13 53.5
26 S	6 15 53.5	3 43.0	26 37.2	17 6.2	12 16.1	17 9.8	28 37.3	27 28.7	22 13.8	21 49.0	24 34.0	13 52.2
27 S	6 19 50.1	4 44.1	26 34.0	29 50.1	12 54.2	17 50.7	29 18.4	27 42.3	22 19.8	21 50.3	24 33.1	13 51.0
28 M	6 23 46.7	5 45.2	26 30.8	12♊21.4	13 38.0	18 30.3	29 59.5	27 55.9	22 25.7	21 51.6	24 32.1	13 49.7
29 T	6 27 43.2	6 46.4	26 27.7	24 41.3	14 26.9	19 8.7	0♐40.7	28 9.5	22 31.5	21 53.0	24 31.1	13 48.5
30 W	6 31 39.8	7 47.5	26 24.5	6♋51.0	15 20.3	19 45.8	1 21.8	28 23.2	22 37.3	21 54.4	24 30.1	13 47.3
31 T	6 35 36.3	8 48.6	26 21.3	18 52.0	16 17.7	20 21.5	2 3.0	28 36.9	22 43.0	21 55.9	24 29.0	13 46.0

DECLINATION

DAY	EPHEMERIS SIDEREAL TIME	☉	☊	☽	☿	♀	♂	♃	♄	♅	♆	♇
1 T	4 37 19.6	21S41.8	20N34.8	19N23.0	24S55.3	23S51.4	14S52.5	22S 1.4	15S37.5	4S 3.4	13N36.9	20N52.9
4 F	4 49 9.3	22 8.8	20 36.7	21 14.4	24 11.4	23 9.2	15 30.7	21 55.6	15 42.9	4 3.2	13 37.1	20 53.3
7 M	5 0 58.9	22 32.0	20 38.6	14 45.8	23 12.7	22 23.0	16 7.9	21 49.5	15 48.2	4 2.8	13 37.4	20 53.7
10 T	5 12 48.6	22 51.2	20 40.5	2 44.8	22 1.7	21 33.3	16 44.1	21 43.2	15 53.4	4 2.3	13 37.9	20 54.2
13 S	5 24 38.3	23 6.3	20 42.3	11S 9.3	20 48.1	20 40.4	17 19.1	21 36.6	15 58.4	4 1.5	13 38.4	20 54.7
16 W	5 36 28.0	23 17.4	20 44.2	20 49.6	19 48.5	19 44.8	17 53.0	21 29.8	16 3.3	4 0.6	13 39.1	20 55.1
19 S	5 48 17.6	23 24.2	20 46.0	18 51.8	19 15.7	18 47.0	18 25.7	21 22.7	16 8.0	3 59.5	13 39.8	20 55.6
22 T	6 0 7.3	23 26.8	20 47.9	6 35.6	19 12.0	17 47.6	18 57.1	21 15.3	16 12.6	3 58.2	13 40.6	20 56.2
25 F	6 11 57.0	23 25.2	20 49.7	8N 0.8	19 31.5	16 47.0	19 27.1	21 7.7	16 17.0	3 56.8	13 41.5	20 56.7
28 M	6 23 46.7	23 19.4	20 51.5	18 42.5	20 5.8	15 46.0	19 55.7	20 59.9	16 21.2	3 55.2	13 42.5	20 57.2
31 T	6 35 36.3	23 9.3	20 53.3	21 30.9	20 47.1	14 45.2	20 22.9	20 51.8	16 25.2	3 53.4	13 43.6	20 57.8

JANUARY 1926

DAY	EPHEMERIS SIDEREAL TIME	☉	☊	☽	☿	♀	♂	♃	♄	♅	♆	♇
	h m s	° ′	° ′	° ′	° ′	° ′	° ′	° ′	° ′	° ′	° ′	° ′
						LONGITUDE						
1 F	6 39 32.9	9♑49.8	26♋18.1	0♌46.1	17♐18.7	20♒55.8	2♐44.3	28♑50.6	22♏48.6	21♓57.4	24♌27.9	13♋44.7
2 S	6 43 29.4	10 50.9	26 15.0	12 35.4	18 22.8	21 28.7	3 25.5	29 4.4	22 54.3	21 58.9	24R26.8	13R43.5
3 S	6 47 26.0	11 52.1	26 11.8	24 22.7	19 29.6	21 60.0	4 6.8	29 18.3	22 59.8	22 0.6	24 25.7	13 42.2
4 M	6 51 22.6	12 53.2	26 8.6	6♍11.2	20 39.0	22 29.7	4 48.1	29 32.1	23 5.3	22 2.2	24 24.6	13 41.0
5 T	6 55 19.1	13 54.4	26 5.4	18 4.9	21 50.6	22 57.8	5 29.5	29 46.0	23 10.7	22 3.9	24 23.4	13 39.7
6 W	6 59 15.7	14 55.5	26 2.3	0♎8.0	23 4.1	23 24.1	6 10.8	29 59.9	23 16.0	22 5.7	24 22.2	13 38.5
7 T	7 3 12.2	15 56.7	25 59.1	12 25.1	24 19.5	23 48.7	6 52.3	0♒13.8	23 21.3	22 7.5	24 21.0	13 37.2
8 F	7 7 8.8	16 57.8	25 55.9	25 0.6	25 36.4	24 11.5	7 33.7	0 27.8	23 26.6	22 9.3	24 19.7	13 35.9
9 S	7 11 5.3	17 59.0	25 52.7	7♏58.7	26 54.7	24 32.4	8 15.2	0 41.8	23 31.7	22 11.2	24 18.5	13 34.7
10 S	7 15 1.9	19 0.2	25 49.5	21 22.6	28 14.4	24 51.3	8 56.7	0 55.8	23 36.8	22 13.1	24 17.2	13 33.4
11 M	7 18 58.5	20 1.3	25 46.4	5♐13.8	29 35.3	25 8.2	9 38.2	1 9.9	23 41.8	22 15.1	24 15.9	13 32.2
12 T	7 22 55.0	21 2.5	25 43.2	19 31.9	0♑57.2	25 23.0	10 19.7	1 23.9	23 46.8	22 17.1	24 14.5	13 30.9
13 W	7 26 51.6	22 3.6	25 40.0	4♑13.5	2 20.2	25 35.7	11 1.3	1 38.0	23 51.6	22 19.1	24 13.2	13 29.7
14 T	7 30 48.1	23 4.8	25 36.8	19 12.6	3 44.0	25 46.1	11 42.9	1 52.1	23 56.4	22 21.2	24 11.8	13 28.4
15 F	7 34 44.7	24 5.9	25 33.7	4♒20.9	5 8.8	25 54.3	12 24.6	2 6.2	24 1.1	22 23.3	24 10.4	13 27.2
16 S	7 38 41.2	25 7.1	25 30.5	19 29.1	6 34.4	26 0.2	13 6.2	2 20.3	24 5.8	22 25.5	24 9.0	13 26.0
17 S	7 42 37.8	26 8.2	25 27.3	4♓28.2	8 0.7	26 3.6	13 47.9	2 34.5	24 10.4	22 27.7	24 7.5	13 24.8
18 M	7 46 34.4	27 9.3	25 24.1	19 10.4	9 27.8	26 4.7	14 29.6	2 48.6	24 14.9	22 30.0	24 6.1	13 23.5
19 T	7 50 30.9	28 10.4	25 21.0	3♈30.8	10 55.6	26R 3.2	15 11.4	3 2.8	24 19.3	22 32.3	24 4.6	13 22.3
20 W	7 54 27.5	29 11.5	25 17.8	17 26.7	12 24.1	25 59.3	15 53.1	3 16.9	24 23.6	22 34.6	24 3.1	13 21.1
21 T	7 58 24.0	0♒12.6	25 14.6	0♉57.8	13 53.3	25 52.8	16 34.9	3 31.1	24 27.9	22 37.0	24 1.6	13 19.9
22 F	8 2 20.6	1 13.6	25 11.4	14 5.8	15 23.1	25 43.8	17 16.8	3 45.3	24 32.1	22 39.4	24 0.1	13 18.7
23 S	8 6 17.2	2 14.7	25 8.3	26 53.4	16 53.6	25 32.2	17 58.6	3 59.5	24 36.2	22 41.8	23 58.6	13 17.5
24 S	8 10 13.7	3 15.7	25 5.1	9♊23.6	18 24.7	25 18.2	18 40.5	4 13.7	24 40.2	22 44.3	23 57.0	13 16.4
25 M	8 14 10.2	4 16.7	25 1.9	21 40.0	19 56.4	25 1.6	19 22.4	4 27.9	24 44.1	22 46.8	23 55.5	13 15.2
26 T	8 18 6.8	5 17.7	24 58.7	3♋45.6	21 28.8	24 42.6	20 4.3	4 42.1	24 47.9	22 49.4	23 53.9	13 14.0
27 W	8 22 3.4	6 18.6	24 55.5	15 43.3	23 1.8	24 21.2	20 46.2	4 56.3	24 51.7	22 52.0	23 52.3	13 12.9
28 T	8 25 59.9	7 19.6	24 52.4	27 35.8	24 35.5	23 57.5	21 28.2	5 10.5	24 55.4	22 54.6	23 50.7	13 11.7
29 F	8 29 56.5	8 20.5	24 49.2	9♌25.1	26 9.8	23 31.7	22 10.2	5 24.7	24 59.0	22 57.2	23 49.1	13 10.6
30 S	8 33 53.0	9 21.4	24 46.0	21 13.4	27 44.8	23 3.9	22 52.3	5 38.8	25 2.5	22 59.9	23 47.5	13 9.5
31 S	8 37 49.6	10 22.4	24 42.8	3♍2.8	29 20.5	22 34.1	23 34.3	5 53.0	25 5.9	23 2.6	23 45.9	13 8.4
						DECLINATION						
1 F	6 39 32.9	23S 5.0	20N53.9	20N28.1	21S 1.5	14S25.0	20S31.7	20S49.1	16S26.5	3S52.7	13N44.0	20N58.0
4 M	6 51 22.6	22 49.4	20 55.7	12 27.2	21 43.7	13 25.5	20 56.9	20 40.7	16 30.3	3 50.7	13 45.2	20 58.5
7 T	7 3 12.2	22 29.7	20 57.5	0S 9.4	22 22.2	12 27.7	21 20.5	20 32.0	16 34.0	3 48.5	13 46.4	20 59.1
10 S	7 15 1.9	22 6.0	20 59.3	13 30.2	22 54.3	11 32.6	21 42.5	20 23.2	16 37.4	3 46.2	13 47.8	20 59.6
13 W	7 26 51.6	21 38.4	21 1.0	21 27.0	23 18.3	10 41.0	22 2.8	20 14.1	16 40.6	3 43.7	13 49.2	21 0.2
16 S	7 38 41.2	21 7.1	21 2.8	17 1.8	23 32.9	9 53.9	22 21.4	20 4.9	16 43.6	3 41.1	13 50.6	21 0.8
19 T	7 50 30.9	20 32.1	21 4.5	3 6.9	23 37.2	9 12.2	22 38.2	19 55.4	16 46.5	3 38.4	13 52.1	21 1.4
22 F	8 2 20.6	19 53.6	21 6.3	11N16.3	23 30.4	8 37.0	22 53.3	19 45.7	16 49.1	3 35.5	13 53.6	21 1.9
25 M	8 14 10.2	19 11.8	21 8.0	20 13.9	23 12.0	8 9.3	23 6.5	19 35.9	16 51.5	3 32.4	13 55.2	21 2.5
28 T	8 25 59.9	18 26.8	21 9.7	20 49.9	22 41.5	7 49.8	23 17.8	19 25.9	16 53.7	3 29.3	13 56.8	21 3.1
31 S	8 37 49.6	17 38.8	21 11.4	13 23.3	21 58.7	7 38.9	23 27.2	19 15.7	16 55.7	3 26.0	13 58.5	21 3.6

FEBRUARY 1926

DAY	EPHEMERIS SIDEREAL TIME	☉	☊	☽	☿	♀	♂	♃	♄	♅	♆	♇
						LONGITUDE						
1 M	8 41 46.2	11♒23.2	24♋39.7	14♍55.5	0♒56.8	22♒ 2.7	24♐16.4	6♒ 7.2	25♏ 9.2	23♓ 5.4	23♌44.3	13♋ 7.3
2 T	8 45 42.7	12 24.1	24 36.5	26 53.7	2 33.9	21R29.7	24 58.5	6 21.4	25 12.4	23 8.1	23R42.6	13R 6.2
3 W	8 49 39.2	13 25.0	24 33.3	9♎0.5	4 11.6	20 55.4	25 40.7	6 35.5	25 15.6	23 10.9	23 41.0	13 5.2
4 T	8 53 35.8	14 25.8	24 30.1	21 18.9	5 50.1	20 20.0	26 22.9	6 49.7	25 18.6	23 13.8	23 39.3	13 4.1
5 F	8 57 32.4	15 26.6	24 26.9	3♏52.3	7 29.4	19 43.8	27 5.1	7 3.8	25 21.6	23 16.6	23 37.7	13 3.1
6 S	9 1 28.9	16 27.5	24 23.8	16 44.5	9 9.4	19 7.0	27 47.3	7 17.9	25 24.5	23 19.5	23 36.0	13 2.0
7 S	9 5 25.5	17 28.3	24 20.6	29 58.7	10 50.1	18 29.8	28 29.6	7 32.0	25 27.2	23 22.4	23 34.3	13 1.0
8 M	9 9 22.0	18 29.0	24 17.4	13♐37.7	12 31.7	17 52.5	29 11.9	7 46.1	25 29.9	23 25.4	23 32.7	13 0.0
9 T	9 13 18.6	19 29.8	24 14.2	27 42.8	14 14.1	17 15.4	29 54.2	8 0.2	25 32.5	23 28.3	23 31.0	12 59.0
10 W	9 17 15.2	20 30.6	24 11.1	12♑13.4	15 57.2	16 38.7	0♑36.5	8 14.3	25 35.0	23 31.3	23 29.3	12 58.1
11 T	9 21 11.7	21 31.3	24 7.9	27 5.9	17 41.2	16 2.7	1 18.9	8 28.3	25 37.4	23 34.3	23 27.6	12 57.1
12 F	9 25 8.2	22 32.0	24 4.7	12♒14.2	19 26.1	15 27.6	2 1.3	8 42.4	25 39.6	23 37.4	23 25.9	12 56.2
13 S	9 29 4.8	23 32.7	24 1.5	27 29.4	21 11.7	14 53.7	2 43.7	8 56.3	25 41.8	23 40.4	23 24.2	12 55.3
14 S	9 33 1.4	24 33.3	23 58.3	12♓41.2	22 58.2	14 21.0	3 26.2	9 10.3	25 43.9	23 43.5	23 22.6	12 54.4
15 M	9 36 57.9	25 34.0	23 55.2	27 39.7	24 45.5	13 49.9	4 8.6	9 24.3	25 45.9	23 46.6	23 20.9	12 53.5
16 T	9 40 54.5	26 34.6	23 52.0	12♈16.7	26 33.7	13 20.5	4 51.1	9 38.2	25 47.8	23 49.8	23 19.2	12 52.6
17 W	9 44 51.0	27 35.2	23 48.8	26 26.9	28 22.7	12 52.9	5 33.6	9 52.1	25 49.6	23 52.9	23 17.5	12 51.8
18 T	9 48 47.6	28 35.7	23 45.6	10♉8.2	0♓12.4	12 27.4	6 16.1	10 6.0	25 51.3	23 56.1	23 15.8	12 50.9
19 F	9 52 44.1	29 36.2	23 42.5	23 21.4	2 2.9	12 4.0	6 58.7	10 19.8	25 52.9	23 59.3	23 14.2	12 50.1
20 S	9 56 40.7	0♓36.7	23 39.3	6♊9.3	3 54.1	11 42.8	7 41.3	10 33.6	25 54.4	24 2.5	23 12.5	12 49.3
21 S	10 0 37.2	1 37.2	23 36.1	18 35.9	5 45.9	11 23.9	8 23.9	10 47.3	25 55.8	24 5.7	23 10.8	12 48.6
22 M	10 4 33.8	2 37.6	23 32.9	0♋46.1	7 38.3	11 7.4	9 6.5	11 1.1	25 57.1	24 8.9	23 9.1	12 47.8
23 T	10 8 30.3	3 38.0	23 29.7	12 44.5	9 31.2	10 53.4	9 49.1	11 14.8	25 58.3	24 12.2	23 7.5	12 47.1
24 W	10 12 26.9	4 38.4	23 26.6	24 35.5	11 24.5	10 41.8	10 31.8	11 28.4	25 59.4	24 15.5	23 5.9	12 46.4
25 T	10 16 23.5	5 38.7	23 23.4	6♌23.0	13 17.9	10 32.6	11 14.5	11 42.0	26 0.3	24 18.8	23 4.2	12 45.7
26 F	10 20 20.0	6 39.0	23 20.2	18 10.4	15 11.4	10 26.0	11 57.2	11 55.6	26 1.2	24 22.1	23 2.6	12 45.0
27 S	10 24 16.5	7 39.3	23 17.0	0♍0.2	17 4.7	10 21.8	12 39.9	12 9.1	26 2.0	24 25.4	23 1.0	12 44.3
28 S	10 28 13.1	8 39.5	23 13.9	11 54.6	18 57.6	10 20.1	13 22.7	12 22.6	26 2.7	24 28.7	22 59.3	12 43.7
						DECLINATION						
1 M	8 41 46.2	17S22.2	21N12.0	9N38.1	21S41.6	7S37.2	23S29.9	19S12.3	16S56.3	3S24.9	13N59.0	21N 3.8
4 T	8 53 35.8	16 30.5	21 13.7	3S26.6	20 41.8	7 38.0	23 36.8	19 2.0	16 58.1	3 21.5	14 0.7	21 4.4
7 S	9 5 25.5	15 36.2	21 15.4	15 54.9	19 29.0	7 46.7	23 41.6	18 51.5	16 59.6	3 18.1	14 2.4	21 4.9
10 W	9 17 15.2	14 39.5	21 17.0	21 41.4	18 3.1	8 2.3	23 44.5	18 40.9	17 0.8	3 14.5	14 4.1	21 5.5
13 S	9 29 4.8	13 40.6	21 18.7	14 57.9	16 24.1	8 23.4	23 45.4	18 30.2	17 1.9	3 10.8	14 5.8	21 6.0
16 T	9 40 54.5	12 39.7	21 20.4	0N10.1	14 32.0	8 48.2	23 44.3	18 19.4	17 2.7	3 7.0	14 7.5	21 6.5
19 F	9 52 44.1	11 36.9	21 22.0	14 10.1	12 27.2	9 15.2	23 41.2	18 8.5	17 3.4	3 3.2	14 9.2	21 7.0
22 M	10 4 33.8	10 32.5	21 23.6	21 17.9	10 10.5	9 42.7	23 36.0	17 57.6	17 3.8	2 59.4	14 10.8	21 7.5
25 T	10 16 23.5	9 26.7	21 25.3	19 40.3	7 43.1	10 9.4	23 28.9	17 46.6	17 4.0	2 55.4	14 12.5	21 8.0
28 S	10 28 13.1	8 19.6	21 26.9	10 34.9	5 7.4	10 34.1	23 19.7	17 35.6	17 3.9	2 51.4	14 14.1	21 8.5

MARCH 1926

LONGITUDE

DAY	EPHEMERIS SIDEREAL TIME	☉	☊	☽	☿	♀	♂	♃	♄	♅	♆	♇
	h m s	° ′	° ′	° ′	° ′	° ′	° ′	° ′	° ′	° ′	° ′	° ′
1 M	10 32 9.7	9♓39.7	23♋10.7	23♍55.1	20♓49.8	10♒20.9	14♑ 5.5	12♒36.1	26♏ 3.3	24♓32.0	22♌57.7	12♋43.1
2 T	10 36 6.2	10 39.9	23 7.5	6♎ 3.3	22 41.1	10D24.0	14 48.3	12 49.5	26 3.7	24 35.4	22R56.2	12R42.5
3 W	10 40 2.8	11 40.1	23 4.3	18 20.4	24 30.9	10 29.5	15 31.1	13 2.8	26 4.1	24 38.7	22 54.6	12 41.9
4 T	10 43 59.3	12 40.2	23 1.1	0♏47.9	26 19.1	10 37.2	16 14.0	13 16.1	26 4.4	24 42.1	22 53.0	12 41.4
5 F	10 47 55.9	13 40.3	22 58.0	13 27.7	28 5.0	10 47.3	16 56.9	13 29.4	26 4.6	24 45.5	22 51.4	12 40.8
6 S	10 51 52.4	14 40.4	22 54.8	26 21.9	29 48.2	10 59.4	17 39.8	13 42.6	26 4.6	24 48.9	22 49.9	12 40.3
7 S	10 55 49.0	15 40.4	22 51.6	9♐32.9	1♈28.3	11 13.8	18 22.7	13 55.8	26R 4.6	24 52.3	22 48.4	12 39.9
8 M	10 59 45.5	16 40.4	22 48.4	23 3.1	3 4.7	11 30.1	19 5.7	14 8.9	26 4.4	24 55.7	22 46.9	12 39.4
9 T	11 3 42.1	17 40.4	22 45.3	6♑54.5	4 36.9	11 48.5	19 48.6	14 21.9	26 4.2	24 59.1	22 45.4	12 39.0
10 W	11 7 38.7	18 40.4	22 42.1	21 7.9	6 4.4	12 8.8	20 31.6	14 34.9	26 3.9	25 2.5	22 43.9	12 38.5
11 T	11 11 35.2	19 40.4	22 38.9	5♒42.3	7 26.5	12 30.9	21 14.6	14 47.9	26 3.4	25 5.9	22 42.4	12 38.1
12 F	11 15 31.7	20 40.3	22 35.7	20 34.1	8 42.8	12 54.9	21 57.7	15 0.7	26 2.9	25 9.3	22 40.9	12 37.8
13 S	11 19 28.3	21 40.1	22 32.5	5♓37.0	9 52.8	13 20.5	22 40.7	15 13.6	26 2.2	25 12.8	22 39.5	12 37.4
14 S	11 23 24.8	22 40.0	22 29.4	20 42.3	10 56.1	13 47.8	23 23.8	15 26.3	26 1.5	25 16.2	22 38.1	12 37.1
15 M	11 27 21.4	23 39.8	22 26.2	5♈40.3	11 52.3	14 16.7	24 6.9	15 39.0	26 0.6	25 19.6	22 36.7	12 36.8
16 T	11 31 18.0	24 39.6	22 23.0	20 21.5	12 40.9	14 47.1	24 50.0	15 51.6	25 59.7	25 23.1	22 35.3	12 36.5
17 W	11 35 14.5	25 39.4	22 19.8	4♉38.8	13 21.8	15 19.0	25 33.1	16 4.2	25 58.6	25 26.5	22 33.9	12 36.3
18 T	11 39 11.0	26 39.1	22 16.7	18 28.1	13 54.7	15 52.3	26 16.2	16 16.7	25 57.5	25 29.9	22 32.6	12 36.0
19 F	11 43 7.6	27 38.7	22 13.5	1♊48.4	14 19.4	16 26.9	26 59.3	16 29.1	25 56.2	25 33.3	22 31.3	12 35.8
20 S	11 47 4.2	28 38.4	22 10.3	14 41.3	14 36.0	17 2.9	27 42.5	16 41.4	25 54.9	25 36.8	22 30.0	12 35.7
21 S	11 51 0.7	29 38.0	22 7.1	27 10.8	14 44.3	17 40.1	28 25.7	16 53.7	25 53.4	25 40.2	22 28.7	12 35.5
22 M	11 54 57.3	0♈37.5	22 3.9	9♋21.6	14 44.6	18 18.4	29 8.8	17 5.9	25 51.9	25 43.6	22 27.5	12 35.4
23 T	11 58 53.8	1 37.1	22 0.8	21 19.2	14R37.0	18 58.0	29 52.0	17 18.0	25 50.3	25 47.0	22 26.2	12 35.3
24 W	12 2 50.4	2 36.6	21 57.6	3♌ 8.9	14 22.0	19 38.7	0♒35.3	17 30.1	25 48.5	25 50.5	22 25.0	12 35.2
25 T	12 6 46.9	3 36.0	21 54.4	14 55.7	13 59.9	20 20.4	1 18.5	17 42.1	25 46.7	25 53.9	22 23.8	12 35.1
26 F	12 10 43.5	4 35.4	21 51.2	26 44.1	13 31.3	21 3.2	2 1.7	17 53.9	25 44.8	25 57.3	22 22.7	12 35.1
27 S	12 14 40.0	5 34.8	21 48.1	8♍37.5	12 56.9	21 47.0	2 45.0	18 5.8	25 42.8	26 0.7	22 21.5	12 35.1
28 S	12 18 36.6	6 34.1	21 44.9	20 38.8	12 17.6	22 31.7	3 28.2	18 17.5	25 40.7	26 4.1	22 20.4	12D35.1
29 M	12 22 33.2	7 33.4	21 41.7	2♎49.8	11 34.1	23 17.3	4 11.5	18 29.1	25 38.5	26 7.4	22 19.3	12 35.1
30 T	12 26 29.7	8 32.7	21 38.5	15 11.5	10 47.6	24 3.9	4 54.8	18 40.7	25 36.3	26 10.8	22 18.3	12 35.2
31 W	12 30 26.2	9 31.9	21 35.3	27 44.3	9 58.8	24 51.2	5 38.1	18 52.1	25 33.9	26 14.2	22 17.2	12 35.3

DECLINATION

DAY	EPHEMERIS SIDEREAL TIME	☉	☊	☽	☿	♀	♂	♃	♄	♅	♆	♇
1 M	10 32 9.7	7S57.0	21N27.4	6N28.1	4S14.3	10S41.8	23S16.2	17S32.0	17S 3.9	2S50.1	14N14.6	21N 8.6
4 T	10 43 59.3	6 48.4	21 29.0	6S58.7	1 33.9	11 2.5	23 4.4	17 20.9	17 3.6	2 46.1	14 16.2	21 9.1
7 S	10 55 49.0	5 39.0	21 30.6	18 19.5	1N 3.3	11 19.5	22 50.7	17 9.9	17 3.1	2 42.0	14 17.8	21 9.5
10 W	11 7 38.7	4 28.9	21 32.2	21 31.4	3 29.6	11 32.3	22 35.0	16 59.0	17 2.4	2 38.0	14 19.2	21 9.9
13 S	11 19 28.3	3 18.3	21 33.7	12 36.3	5 36.7	11 40.5	22 17.4	16 48.0	17 1.4	2 33.9	14 20.7	21 10.3
16 T	11 31 18.0	2 7.3	21 35.3	3N15.6	7 16.9	11 44.0	21 57.9	16 37.1	17 0.3	2 29.8	14 22.1	21 10.7
19 F	11 43 7.6	0 56.2	21 36.9	16 38.2	8 23.8	11 42.5	21 36.6	16 26.3	16 59.0	2 25.7	14 23.4	21 11.1
22 M	11 54 57.3	0N14.9	21 38.4	21 54.6	8 52.9	11 36.2	21 13.5	16 15.7	16 57.5	2 21.6	14 24.6	21 11.4
25 T	12 6 46.9	1 25.9	21 39.9	18 10.2	8 42.6	11 24.9	20 48.6	16 5.1	16 55.8	2 17.5	14 25.8	21 11.7
28 S	12 18 36.6	2 36.5	21 41.4	7 37.5	7 55.5	11 8.6	20 22.0	15 54.6	16 53.9	2 13.5	14 26.9	21 12.0
31 W	12 30 26.2	3 46.7	21 43.0	6S 0.8	6 39.5	10 47.4	19 53.8	15 44.4	16 51.9	2 9.5	14 28.0	21 12.3

APRIL 1926

LONGITUDE

DAY	EPHEMERIS SIDEREAL TIME	☉	☊	☽	☿	♀	♂	♃	♄	♅	♆	♇
1 T	12 34 22.8	10♈31.1	21♋32.2	10♏28.3	9♈ 9.0	25♒39.4	6♒21.4	19♒ 3.5	25♏31.5	26♓17.5	22♌16.2	12♋35.4
2 F	12 38 19.3	11 30.3	21 29.0	23 23.6	8R19.0	26 28.4	7 4.8	19 14.8	25R29.0	26 20.9	22R15.2	12 35.5
3 S	12 42 15.9	12 29.5	21 25.8	6♐30.5	7 29.9	27 18.1	7 48.1	19 26.0	25 26.4	26 24.2	22 14.3	12 35.7
4 S	12 46 12.5	13 28.6	21 22.6	19 49.5	6 42.6	28 8.6	8 31.5	19 37.1	25 23.7	26 27.5	22 13.4	12 35.8
5 M	12 50 9.0	14 27.6	21 19.4	3♑21.7	5 57.8	28 59.7	9 14.9	19 48.1	25 20.9	26 30.8	22 12.5	12 36.0
6 T	12 54 5.5	15 26.7	21 16.3	17 8.3	5 16.4	29 51.6	9 58.2	19 59.1	25 18.0	26 34.1	22 11.6	12 36.3
7 W	12 58 2.1	16 25.7	21 13.1	1♒10.2	4 38.9	0♓44.0	10 41.6	20 9.9	25 15.1	26 37.4	22 10.7	12 36.5
8 T	13 1 58.7	17 24.7	21 9.9	15 27.2	4 5.7	1 37.1	11 25.0	20 20.6	25 12.1	26 40.7	22 9.9	12 36.8
9 F	13 5 55.2	18 23.7	21 6.7	29 57.6	3 37.4	2 30.8	12 8.4	20 31.2	25 9.0	26 43.9	22 9.1	12 37.1
10 S	13 9 51.8	19 22.6	21 3.6	14♓37.7	3 14.1	3 25.1	12 51.8	20 41.8	25 5.9	26 47.2	22 8.4	12 37.4
11 S	13 13 48.3	20 21.5	21 0.4	29 21.5	2 56.0	4 19.8	13 35.3	20 52.2	25 2.6	26 50.4	22 7.6	12 37.7
12 M	13 17 44.9	21 20.4	20 57.2	14♈ 1.5	2 43.3	5 15.2	14 18.7	21 2.5	24 59.3	26 53.6	22 6.9	12 38.1
13 T	13 21 41.4	22 19.2	20 54.0	28 29.8	2 35.9	6 11.0	15 2.1	21 12.7	24 56.0	26 56.8	22 6.3	12 38.5
14 W	13 25 38.0	23 18.0	20 50.8	12♉39.6	2 33.8	7 7.3	15 45.5	21 22.8	24 52.5	26 59.9	22 5.6	12 38.9
15 T	13 29 34.5	24 16.8	20 47.7	26 25.8	2D37.0	8 4.0	16 28.9	21 32.8	24 49.0	27 3.1	22 5.0	12 39.4
16 F	13 33 31.1	25 15.5	20 44.5	9♊46.3	2 45.2	9 1.3	17 12.3	21 42.6	24 45.5	27 6.2	22 4.5	12 39.8
17 S	13 37 27.7	26 14.2	20 41.3	22 41.3	2 58.4	9 58.9	17 55.7	21 52.4	24 41.8	27 9.3	22 3.9	12 40.3
18 S	13 41 24.2	27 12.9	20 38.1	5♋13.5	3 16.5	10 57.0	18 39.1	22 2.0	24 38.2	27 12.4	22 3.4	12 40.8
19 M	13 45 20.7	28 11.5	20 35.0	17 26.9	3 39.1	11 55.4	19 22.5	22 11.5	24 34.4	27 15.4	22 2.9	12 41.4
20 T	13 49 17.3	29 10.1	20 31.8	29 26.5	4 6.2	12 54.3	20 5.9	22 20.9	24 30.6	27 18.5	22 2.5	12 41.9
21 W	13 53 13.8	0♉ 8.7	20 28.6	11♌17.9	4 37.6	13 53.5	20 49.3	22 30.2	24 26.8	27 21.5	22 2.0	12 42.5
22 T	13 57 10.4	1 7.2	20 25.4	23 6.4	5 13.0	14 53.1	21 32.7	22 39.4	24 22.9	27 24.5	22 1.7	12 43.1
23 F	14 1 7.0	2 5.7	20 22.3	4♍57.2	5 52.3	15 53.0	22 16.1	22 48.4	24 18.9	27 27.5	22 1.3	12 43.7
24 S	14 5 3.5	3 4.1	20 19.1	16 54.7	6 35.4	16 53.3	22 59.5	22 57.3	24 14.9	27 30.4	22 1.0	12 44.3
25 S	14 9 0.1	4 2.5	20 15.9	29 2.6	7 22.0	17 53.9	23 42.8	23 6.1	24 10.8	27 33.3	22 0.7	12 45.0
26 M	14 12 56.6	5 0.9	20 12.7	11♎23.5	8 12.0	18 54.9	24 26.2	23 14.8	24 6.8	27 36.2	22 0.4	12 45.7
27 T	14 16 53.2	5 59.2	20 9.5	23 58.8	9 5.2	19 56.1	25 9.6	23 23.3	24 2.6	27 39.1	22 0.2	12 46.4
28 W	14 20 49.7	6 57.6	20 6.4	6♏48.8	10 1.6	20 57.7	25 52.9	23 31.7	23 58.5	27 41.9	22 0.0	12 47.1
29 T	14 24 46.3	7 55.8	20 3.2	19 52.8	11 1.0	21 59.5	26 36.3	23 39.9	23 54.3	27 44.7	21 59.8	12 47.9
30 F	14 28 42.8	8 54.1	20 0.0	3♐ 9.7	12 3.3	23 1.6	27 19.6	23 48.1	23 50.0	27 47.5	21 59.7	12 48.6

DECLINATION

DAY	EPHEMERIS SIDEREAL TIME	☉	☊	☽	☿	♀	♂	♃	♄	♅	♆	♇
1 T	12 34 22.8	4N10.0	21N43.5	10S26.9	6N 9.8	10S39.3	19S44.1	15S41.0	16S51.2	2S 8.2	14N28.3	21N12.4
4 S	12 46 12.5	5 19.2	21 44.9	20 24.9	4 35.2	10 11.8	19 13.7	15 30.9	16 48.9	2 4.2	14 29.2	21 12.6
7 W	12 58 2.1	6 27.7	21 46.4	20 44.3	3 3.1	9 39.8	18 41.8	15 21.1	16 46.5	2 0.3	14 30.1	21 12.9
10 S	13 9 51.8	7 35.2	21 47.9	9 46.2	1 44.7	9 3.3	18 8.5	15 11.5	16 44.0	1 56.5	14 30.9	21 13.1
13 T	13 21 41.4	8 41.5	21 49.4	6N18.3	0 46.7	8 22.7	17 33.8	15 2.1	16 41.3	1 52.7	14 31.5	21 13.3
16 F	13 33 31.1	9 46.5	21 50.8	18 41.4	0 11.8	7 38.1	16 57.7	14 53.0	16 38.5	1 49.0	14 32.1	21 13.5
19 M	13 45 20.7	10 50.1	21 52.3	22 4.5	0 0.1	6 49.8	16 20.4	14 44.2	16 35.6	1 45.3	14 32.6	21 13.6
22 T	13 57 10.4	11 52.1	21 53.7	16 25.3	0 10.2	5 58.1	15 42.0	14 35.7	16 32.6	1 41.8	14 33.0	21 13.7
25 S	14 9 0.1	12 52.3	21 55.1	4 41.6	0 40.1	5 3.2	15 2.3	14 27.5	16 29.6	1 38.3	14 33.3	21 13.8
28 W	14 20 49.7	13 50.5	21 56.5	9S15.9	1 27.6	4 5.3	14 21.7	14 19.7	16 26.4	1 35.0	14 33.5	21 13.9

MAY 1926

DAY	EPHEMERIS SIDEREAL TIME	☉	☊	☽	☿	♀	♂	♃	♄	♅	♆	♇
	h m s	° ′	° ′	° ′	° ′	° ′	° ′	° ′	° ′	° ′	° ′	° ′
LONGITUDE												
1 S	14 32 39.4	9♉52.3	19♋56.8	16♐37.8	13♈ 8.3	24♓ 4.0	28♒ 2.9	23♒56.1	23♏45.7	27♓50.3	21♌59.6	12♋49.4
2 S	14 36 36.0	10 50.5	19 53.7	0♑15.6	14 16.0	25 6.7	28 46.3	24 3.9	23R41.4	27 53.0	21R59.6	12 50.2
3 M	14 40 32.5	11 48.7	19 50.5	14 2.2	15 26.3	26 9.6	29 29.6	24 11.6	23 37.1	27 55.7	21 59.5	12 51.1
4 T	14 44 29.0	12 46.8	19 47.3	27 56.7	16 39.1	27 12.8	0♓12.9	24 19.2	23 32.7	27 58.4	21D59.5	12 51.9
5 W	14 48 25.6	13 45.0	19 44.1	11♒58.8	17 54.4	28 16.2	0 56.1	24 26.7	23 28.3	28 1.0	21 59.6	12 52.8
6 T	14 52 22.2	14 43.1	19 40.9	26 7.8	19 12.0	29 19.9	1 39.4	24 33.9	23 23.9	28 3.6	21 59.6	12 53.7
7 F	14 56 18.7	15 41.2	19 37.8	10♓22.6	20 31.9	0♈23.7	2 22.7	24 41.1	23 19.5	28 6.2	21 59.7	12 54.6
8 S	15 0 15.3	16 39.2	19 34.6	24 40.7	21 54.1	1 27.8	3 5.9	24 48.1	23 15.1	28 8.7	21 59.9	12 55.5
9 S	15 4 11.8	17 37.3	19 31.4	8♈58.8	23 18.5	2 32.1	3 49.1	24 54.9	23 10.6	28 11.2	22 0.0	12 56.5
10 M	15 8 8.4	18 35.3	19 28.2	23 12.2	24 45.1	3 36.6	4 32.3	25 1.6	23 6.1	28 13.7	22 0.2	12 57.4
11 T	15 12 5.0	19 33.3	19 25.1	7♉15.8	26 13.8	4 41.3	5 15.4	25 8.2	23 1.6	28 16.2	22 0.5	12 58.4
12 W	15 16 1.5	20 31.2	19 21.9	21 4.9	27 44.7	5 46.2	5 58.6	25 14.6	22 57.2	28 18.6	22 0.7	12 59.4
13 T	15 19 58.0	21 29.2	19 18.7	4♊35.7	29 17.7	6 51.3	6 41.7	25 20.8	22 52.7	28 20.9	22 1.0	13 0.4
14 F	15 23 54.6	22 27.1	19 15.5	17 45.9	0♉52.9	7 56.5	7 24.7	25 26.8	22 48.1	28 23.3	22 1.4	13 1.5
15 S	15 27 51.2	23 25.0	19 12.3	0♋35.2	2 30.1	9 1.9	8 7.8	25 32.8	22 43.6	28 25.6	22 1.7	13 2.5
16 S	15 31 47.7	24 22.8	19 9.2	13 5.0	4 9.4	10 7.5	8 50.8	25 38.5	22 39.2	28 27.8	22 2.1	13 3.6
17 M	15 35 44.3	25 20.7	19 6.0	25 18.3	5 50.8	11 13.2	9 33.7	25 44.1	22 34.7	28 30.1	22 2.6	13 4.7
18 T	15 39 40.8	26 18.5	19 2.8	7♌18.9	7 34.3	12 19.1	10 16.6	25 49.5	22 30.2	28 32.2	22 3.0	13 5.8
19 W	15 43 37.4	27 16.2	18 59.6	19 11.8	9 19.9	13 25.2	10 59.5	25 54.8	22 25.7	28 34.4	22 3.5	13 6.9
20 T	15 47 33.9	28 14.0	18 56.5	1♍ 1.9	11 7.6	14 31.3	11 42.4	25 59.9	22 21.2	28 36.5	22 4.0	13 8.1
21 F	15 51 30.5	29 11.7	18 53.3	12 54.5	12 57.4	15 37.7	12 25.2	26 4.8	22 16.8	28 38.6	22 4.6	13 9.2
22 S	15 55 27.0	0♊ 9.4	18 50.1	24 54.6	14 49.3	16 44.1	13 8.0	26 9.5	22 12.3	28 40.6	22 5.2	13 10.4
23 S	15 59 23.6	1 7.1	18 46.9	7♎ 6.4	16 43.2	17 50.7	13 50.7	26 14.1	22 7.9	28 42.6	22 5.8	13 11.6
24 M	16 3 20.1	2 4.7	18 43.8	19 33.6	18 39.2	18 57.5	14 33.4	26 18.5	22 3.5	28 44.6	22 6.5	13 12.8
25 T	16 7 16.7	3 2.3	18 40.6	2♏18.5	20 37.2	20 4.4	15 16.1	26 22.8	21 59.1	28 46.5	22 7.2	13 14.0
26 W	16 11 13.2	3 59.9	18 37.4	15 22.2	22 37.1	21 11.4	15 58.7	26 26.9	21 54.8	28 48.3	22 7.9	13 15.2
27 T	16 15 9.8	4 57.5	18 34.2	28 44.3	24 39.0	22 18.5	16 41.2	26 30.7	21 50.4	28 50.2	22 8.6	13 16.5
28 F	16 19 6.4	5 55.1	18 31.0	12♐23.1	26 42.6	23 25.8	17 23.7	26 34.5	21 46.1	28 52.0	22 9.4	13 17.7
29 S	16 23 2.9	6 52.6	18 27.9	26 15.8	28 48.0	24 33.1	18 6.2	26 38.0	21 41.9	28 53.7	22 10.2	13 19.0
30 S	16 26 59.5	7 50.1	18 24.7	10♑18.9	0♊54.9	25 40.6	18 48.7	26 41.4	21 37.6	28 55.4	22 11.1	13 20.3
31 M	16 30 56.0	8 47.6	18 21.5	24 28.9	3 3.2	26 48.3	19 31.0	26 44.5	21 33.4	28 57.1	22 11.9	13 21.6
DECLINATION												
1 S	14 32 39.4	14N46.8	21N57.9	20S 6.0	2N30.8	3S 4.8	13S40.0	14S12.2	16S23.2	1S31.7	14N33.7	21N14.0
4 T	14 44 29.0	15 40.8	21 59.3	21 23.3	3 47.7	2 2.0	12 57.5	14 5.1	16 20.0	1 28.5	14 33.7	21 14.0
7 F	14 56 18.7	16 32.5	22 0.7	11 22.5	5 16.7	0 57.1	12 14.1	13 58.4	16 16.7	1 25.5	14 33.6	21 14.0
10 M	15 8 8.4	17 21.8	22 2.1	4N19.4	6 56.1	0N 9.6	11 30.0	13 52.2	16 13.4	1 22.6	14 33.4	21 14.0
13 T	15 19 58.0	18 8.4	22 3.4	17 38.1	8 44.4	1 17.8	10 45.2	13 46.4	16 10.1	1 19.8	14 33.2	21 14.0
16 S	15 31 47.7	18 52.4	22 4.8	22 24.1	10 40.0	2 27.1	9 59.9	13 41.1	16 6.9	1 17.1	14 32.8	21 14.0
19 W	15 43 37.4	19 33.4	22 6.1	17 38.0	12 40.8	3 37.2	9 14.0	13 36.3	16 3.7	1 14.6	14 32.4	21 13.9
22 S	15 55 27.0	20 11.5	22 7.4	6 22.7	14 44.7	4 47.9	8 27.7	13 32.0	16 0.5	1 12.2	14 31.8	21 13.8
25 T	16 7 16.7	20 46.4	22 8.7	7S36.7	16 48.7	5 58.8	7 41.1	13 28.2	15 57.4	1 9.9	14 31.2	21 13.7
28 F	16 19 6.4	21 18.1	22 10.0	19 22.7	18 49.1	7 9.7	6 54.2	13 24.9	15 54.4	1 7.8	14 30.4	21 13.6
31 M	16 30 56.0	21 46.5	22 11.3	21 54.6	20 41.1	8 20.1	6 7.0	13 22.2	15 51.4	1 5.9	14 29.6	21 13.5

JUNE 1926

DAY	EPHEMERIS SIDEREAL TIME	☉	☊	☽	☿	♀	♂	♃	♄	♅	♆	♇
LONGITUDE												
1 T	16 34 52.6	9♊45.1	18♋18.3	8♒42.5	5♊12.7	27♈56.0	20♓13.3	26♒47.5	21♏29.3	28♓58.7	22♌12.8	13♋22.9
2 W	16 38 49.2	10 42.6	18 15.2	22 57.0	7 23.2	29 3.8	20 55.6	26 50.3	21R25.1	29 0.3	22 13.8	13 24.2
3 T	16 42 45.7	11 40.1	18 12.0	7♓10.1	9 34.5	0♉11.8	21 37.8	26 53.0	21 21.1	29 1.8	22 14.7	13 25.5
4 F	16 46 42.3	12 37.5	18 8.8	21 19.8	11 46.4	1 19.9	22 20.0	26 55.4	21 17.0	29 3.3	22 15.7	13 26.9
5 S	16 50 38.8	13 35.0	18 5.6	5♈24.3	13 58.5	2 28.0	23 2.1	26 57.7	21 13.0	29 4.8	22 16.7	13 28.2
6 S	16 54 35.4	14 32.4	18 2.5	19 21.6	16 10.5	3 36.3	23 44.1	26 59.8	21 9.1	29 6.2	22 17.8	13 29.6
7 M	16 58 31.9	15 29.8	17 59.3	3♉ 9.6	18 22.3	4 44.6	24 26.0	27 1.7	21 5.2	29 7.5	22 18.9	13 31.0
8 T	17 2 28.5	16 27.2	17 56.1	16 46.2	20 33.6	5 53.1	25 7.9	27 3.3	21 1.3	29 8.8	22 20.0	13 32.4
9 W	17 6 25.1	17 24.6	17 52.9	0♊ 9.4	22 44.0	7 1.7	25 49.7	27 4.9	20 57.5	29 10.1	22 21.1	13 33.8
10 T	17 10 21.6	18 22.0	17 49.7	13 17.6	24 53.4	8 10.3	26 31.4	27 6.2	20 53.8	29 11.3	22 22.3	13 35.2
11 F	17 14 18.1	19 19.4	17 46.6	26 9.9	27 1.4	9 19.0	27 13.1	27 7.3	20 50.1	29 12.5	22 23.5	13 36.6
12 S	17 18 14.7	20 16.8	17 43.4	8♋46.3	29 8.0	10 27.8	27 54.7	27 8.2	20 46.5	29 13.6	22 24.7	13 38.0
13 S	17 22 11.3	21 14.1	17 40.2	21 7.9	1♋13.0	11 36.7	28 36.1	27 9.0	20 42.9	29 14.7	22 26.0	13 39.5
14 M	17 26 7.9	22 11.4	17 37.0	3♌16.7	3 16.1	12 45.7	29 17.5	27 9.5	20 39.4	29 15.7	22 27.2	13 40.9
15 T	17 30 4.4	23 8.8	17 33.9	15 15.4	5 17.4	13 54.7	29 58.8	27 9.9	20 36.0	29 16.7	22 28.5	13 42.3
16 W	17 34 0.9	24 6.1	17 30.7	27 7.9	7 16.6	15 3.8	0♈40.0	27 10.0	20 32.6	29 17.7	22 29.8	13 43.8
17 T	17 37 57.5	25 3.4	17 27.5	8♍58.3	9 13.7	16 13.0	1 21.1	27R10.0	20 29.3	29 18.6	22 31.2	13 45.3
18 F	17 41 54.1	26 0.6	17 24.3	20 51.3	11 8.6	17 22.3	2 2.2	27 9.8	20 26.1	29 19.4	22 32.6	13 46.7
19 S	17 45 50.6	26 57.9	17 21.2	2♎51.5	13 1.3	18 31.7	2 43.1	27 9.4	20 22.9	29 20.2	22 34.0	13 48.2
20 S	17 49 47.2	27 55.2	17 18.0	15 3.7	14 51.8	19 41.1	3 23.9	27 8.7	20 19.8	29 21.0	22 35.4	13 49.7
21 M	17 53 43.7	28 52.4	17 14.8	27 32.1	16 40.0	20 50.6	4 4.6	27 7.9	20 16.8	29 21.7	22 36.9	13 51.2
22 T	17 57 40.3	29 49.6	17 11.6	10♏20.2	18 25.9	22 0.1	4 45.2	27 6.9	20 13.8	29 22.3	22 38.4	13 52.7
23 W	18 1 36.8	0♋46.9	17 8.5	23 30.3	20 9.5	23 9.8	5 25.8	27 5.8	20 11.0	29 22.9	22 39.9	13 54.2
24 T	18 5 33.4	1 44.1	17 5.3	7♐ 3.2	21 50.8	24 19.5	6 6.2	27 4.4	20 8.2	29 23.5	22 41.4	13 55.7
25 F	18 9 30.0	2 41.3	17 2.1	20 57.8	23 29.8	25 29.2	6 46.5	27 2.8	20 5.5	29 24.0	22 42.9	13 57.2
26 S	18 13 26.5	3 38.5	16 58.9	5♑11.3	25 6.4	26 39.1	7 26.7	27 1.1	20 2.8	29 24.5	22 44.5	13 58.7
27 S	18 17 23.1	4 35.7	16 55.7	19 39.1	26 40.7	27 49.0	8 6.8	26 59.1	20 0.3	29 24.9	22 46.1	14 0.3
28 M	18 21 19.6	5 32.9	16 52.6	4♒15.5	28 12.6	28 59.0	8 46.7	26 57.0	19 57.8	29 25.3	22 47.7	14 1.8
29 T	18 25 16.2	6 30.1	16 49.4	18 54.4	29 42.1	0♊ 9.1	9 26.6	26 54.7	19 55.4	29 25.6	22 49.4	14 3.3
30 W	18 29 12.8	7 27.2	16 46.2	3♓30.1	1♌ 9.3	1 19.2	10 6.3	26 52.2	19 53.1	29 25.8	22 51.0	14 4.8
DECLINATION												
1 T	16 34 52.6	21N55.3	22N11.8	19S57.5	21N15.6	8N43.5	5S51.3	13S21.4	15S50.5	1S 5.3	14N29.3	21N13.4
4 F	16 46 42.3	22 19.1	22 13.1	7 45.0	22 48.1	9 53.0	5 4.0	13 19.4	15 47.7	1 3.5	14 28.4	21 13.2
7 M	16 58 31.9	22 39.5	22 14.3	7N52.5	24 0.1	11 1.4	4 16.8	13 18.0	15 45.0	1 1.9	14 27.3	21 13.1
10 T	17 10 21.6	22 56.3	22 15.6	19 33.5	24 48.1	12 8.4	3 29.6	13 17.2	15 42.5	1 0.5	14 26.2	21 12.9
13 S	17 22 11.3	23 9.5	22 16.8	22 12.5	25 11.1	13 13.6	2 42.5	13 17.0	15 40.2	0 59.3	14 25.0	21 12.7
16 W	17 34 0.9	23 19.0	22 18.1	15 41.3	25 10.0	14 16.8	1 55.7	13 17.4	15 38.0	0 58.2	14 23.7	21 12.4
19 S	17 45 50.6	23 24.8	22 19.3	3 33.1	24 47.4	15 17.6	1 9.3	13 18.4	15 36.0	0 57.3	14 22.4	21 12.2
22 T	17 57 40.3	23 26.9	22 20.5	10S21.0	24 6.4	16 15.6	0 23.2	13 20.0	15 34.2	0 56.5	14 21.0	21 11.9
25 F	18 9 30.0	23 25.2	22 21.7	20 52.5	23 10.7	17 10.7	0N22.5	13 22.2	15 32.6	0 55.9	14 19.5	21 11.7
28 M	18 21 19.6	23 19.9	22 22.9	20 46.6	22 3.3	18 2.4	1 7.6	13 24.9	15 31.2	0 55.5	14 17.9	21 11.4

JULY 1926

LONGITUDE

DAY	EPHEMERIS SIDEREAL TIME h m s	☉ ° ′	☊ ° ′	☽ ° ′	☿ ° ′	♀ ° ′	♂ ° ′	♃ ° ′	♄ ° ′	♅ ° ′	♆ ° ′	♇ ° ′
1 T	18 33 9.3	8♋24.4	16♋43.0	17♓57.6	2♌34.0	2♊29.4	10♈45.9	26♒49.5	19♏50.9	29♓26.1	22♌52.7	14♋ 6.4
2 F	18 37 5.9	9 21.6	16 39.9	2♈13.2	3 56.3	3 39.7	11 25.4	26R46.7	19R48.7	29 26.2	22 54.4	14 7.9
3 S	18 41 2.5	10 18.8	16 36.7	16 14.6	5 16.2	4 50.0	12 4.7	26 43.6	19 46.7	29 26.4	22 56.2	14 9.4
4 S	18 44 59.0	11 16.0	16 33.5	0♉ 0.5	6 33.4	6 0.4	12 43.9	26 40.4	19 44.7	29 26.4	22 57.9	14 11.0
5 M	18 48 55.5	12 13.3	16 30.3	13 30.6	7 48.2	7 10.8	13 22.9	26 36.9	19 42.8	29 26.5	22 59.7	14 12.5
6 T	18 52 52.1	13 10.5	16 27.2	26 45.2	9 0.2	8 21.4	14 1.8	26 33.4	19 41.0	29R26.5	23 1.5	14 14.0
7 W	18 56 48.7	14 7.7	16 24.0	9♊45.0	10 9.6	9 32.0	14 40.6	26 29.6	19 39.3	29 26.4	23 3.3	14 15.6
8 T	19 0 45.3	15 4.9	16 20.8	22 30.7	11 16.2	10 42.6	15 19.2	26 25.6	19 37.7	29 26.3	23 5.1	14 17.1
9 F	19 4 41.8	16 2.1	16 17.6	5♋ 3.3	12 20.0	11 53.3	15 57.6	26 21.5	19 36.2	29 26.1	23 6.9	14 18.7
10 S	19 8 38.3	16 59.4	16 14.4	17 24.1	13 20.8	13 4.1	16 35.8	26 17.2	19 34.8	29 25.9	23 8.8	14 20.2
11 S	19 12 34.9	17 56.6	16 11.3	29 34.4	14 18.6	14 14.9	17 13.9	26 12.8	19 33.4	29 25.6	23 10.7	14 21.8
12 M	19 16 31.5	18 53.8	16 8.1	11♌35.9	15 13.2	15 25.8	17 51.8	26 8.1	19 32.2	29 25.3	23 12.6	14 23.3
13 T	19 20 28.0	19 51.1	16 4.9	23 30.8	16 4.5	16 36.7	18 29.6	26 3.4	19 31.1	29 25.0	23 14.5	14 24.8
14 W	19 24 24.6	20 48.3	16 1.7	5♍21.6	16 52.5	17 47.7	19 7.1	25 58.4	19 30.0	29 24.6	23 16.4	14 26.4
15 T	19 28 21.1	21 45.6	15 58.6	17 11.5	17 36.9	18 58.8	19 44.5	25 53.3	19 29.1	29 24.1	23 18.4	14 27.9
16 F	19 32 17.7	22 42.8	15 55.4	29 4.2	18 17.7	20 9.9	20 21.6	25 48.1	19 28.2	29 23.6	23 20.3	14 29.4
17 S	19 36 14.2	23 40.0	15 52.2	11♎ 3.6	18 54.6	21 21.0	20 58.6	25 42.6	19 27.4	29 23.1	23 22.3	14 30.9
18 S	19 40 10.8	24 37.3	15 49.0	23 14.1	19 27.6	22 32.2	21 35.4	25 37.1	19 26.8	29 22.5	23 24.3	14 32.5
19 M	19 44 7.3	25 34.5	15 45.9	5♏40.0	19 56.5	23 43.5	22 12.0	25 31.4	19 26.2	29 21.8	23 26.3	14 34.0
20 T	19 48 3.9	26 31.8	15 42.7	18 25.4	20 21.0	24 54.8	22 48.3	25 25.6	19 25.7	29 21.2	23 28.3	14 35.5
21 W	19 52 0.5	27 29.1	15 39.5	1♐34.0	20 41.2	26 6.2	23 24.5	25 19.6	19 25.4	29 20.4	23 30.4	14 37.0
22 T	19 55 57.0	28 26.3	15 36.3	15 7.8	20 56.7	27 17.6	24 0.5	25 13.5	19 25.1	29 19.6	23 32.4	14 38.5
23 F	19 59 53.6	29 23.6	15 33.1	29 7.6	21 7.5	28 29.1	24 36.2	25 7.3	19 24.9	29 18.8	23 34.5	14 40.0
24 S	20 3 50.1	0♌20.9	15 30.0	13♑31.7	21 13.5	29 40.6	25 11.7	25 0.9	19 24.8	29 18.0	23 36.5	14 41.5
25 S	20 7 46.7	1 18.1	15 26.8	28 15.7	21 14.6	0♋52.2	25 47.0	24 54.5	19D24.8	29 17.1	23 38.6	14 43.0
26 M	20 11 43.2	2 15.4	15 23.6	13♒13.2	21R10.6	2 3.9	26 22.1	24 47.9	19 24.9	29 16.1	23 40.7	14 44.5
27 T	20 15 39.8	3 12.8	15 20.4	28 15.9	21 1.6	3 15.6	26 56.9	24 41.2	19 25.2	29 15.1	23 42.8	14 46.0
28 W	20 19 36.4	4 10.1	15 17.3	13♓14.8	20 47.5	4 27.3	27 31.5	24 34.4	19 25.5	29 14.1	23 44.9	14 47.4
29 T	20 23 32.9	5 7.4	15 14.1	28 2.2	20 28.5	5 39.1	28 5.8	24 27.5	19 25.9	29 13.0	23 47.0	14 48.9
30 F	20 27 29.5	6 4.8	15 10.9	12♈31.6	20 4.6	6 51.0	28 39.9	24 20.5	19 26.4	29 11.9	23 49.2	14 50.3
31 S	20 31 26.0	7 2.1	15 7.7	26 39.3	19 36.2	8 2.9	29 13.8	24 13.4	19 26.9	29 10.7	23 51.3	14 51.8

DECLINATION

DAY	EPHEMERIS SIDEREAL TIME h m s	☉	☊	☽	☿	♀	♂	♃	♄	♅	♆	♇
1 T	18 33 9.3	23N10.9	22N24.1	9S 2.2	20N47.5	18N50.6	1N52.1	13S28.2	15S30.0	0S55.3	14N16.3	21N11.1
4 S	18 44 59.0	22 58.2	22 25.3	6N39.9	19 26.0	19 34.8	2 36.0	13 32.1	15 29.0	0 55.3	14 14.6	21 10.8
7 W	18 56 48.7	22 41.9	22 26.4	18 47.6	18 1.6	20 14.8	3 19.1	13 36.5	15 28.3	0 55.4	14 12.8	21 10.5
10 S	19 8 38.3	22 22.1	22 27.6	22 24.4	16 36.9	20 50.3	4 1.5	13 41.4	15 27.7	0 55.7	14 11.0	21 10.2
13 T	19 20 28.0	21 58.8	22 28.7	16 42.1	15 14.4	21 21.1	4 42.9	13 46.8	15 27.5	0 56.2	14 9.2	21 9.9
16 F	19 32 17.7	21 32.1	22 29.9	4 59.8	13 57.0	21 46.9	5 23.4	13 52.7	15 27.4	0 56.8	14 7.3	21 9.5
19 M	19 44 7.3	21 2.1	22 31.0	8S42.4	12 47.6	22 7.5	6 2.8	13 59.0	15 27.6	0 57.6	14 5.3	21 9.2
22 T	19 55 57.0	20 28.9	22 32.1	19 53.3	11 49.5	22 22.8	6 41.3	14 5.7	15 28.1	0 58.5	14 3.3	21 8.9
25 S	20 7 46.7	19 52.6	22 33.2	21 34.7	11 6.1	22 32.6	7 18.6	14 12.7	15 28.7	0 59.7	14 1.3	21 8.5
28 W	20 19 36.4	19 13.3	22 34.3	10 39.2	10 40.6	22 36.7	7 54.8	14 20.0	15 29.6	1 0.9	13 59.2	21 8.2
31 S	20 31 26.0	18 31.2	22 35.4	5N27.5	10 35.8	22 35.2	8 29.8	14 27.5	15 30.8	1 2.4	13 57.1	21 7.9

AUGUST 1926

LONGITUDE

DAY	EPHEMERIS SIDEREAL TIME h m s	☉ ° ′	☊ ° ′	☽ ° ′	☿ ° ′	♀ ° ′	♂ ° ′	♃ ° ′	♄ ° ′	♅ ° ′	♆ ° ′	♇ ° ′
1 S	20 35 22.6	7♌59.5	15♋ 4.6	10♉23.9	19♌ 3.5	9♋14.9	29♈47.3	24♒ 6.2	19♏27.6	29♓ 9.5	23♌53.5	14♋53.2
2 M	20 39 19.1	8 56.9	15 1.4	23 46.0	18R26.8	10 27.0	0♉20.6	23R59.0	19 28.4	29R 8.2	23 55.6	14 54.7
3 T	20 43 15.7	9 54.4	14 58.2	6♊47.5	17 46.7	11 39.1	0 53.6	23 51.6	19 29.3	29 6.9	23 57.8	14 56.1
4 W	20 47 12.3	10 51.8	14 55.0	19 31.0	17 3.8	12 51.2	1 26.3	23 44.2	19 30.3	29 5.6	23 60.0	14 57.5
5 T	20 51 8.8	11 49.3	14 51.9	1♋59.6	16 18.7	14 3.5	1 58.7	23 36.7	19 31.4	29 4.2	24 2.1	14 58.9
6 F	20 55 5.3	12 46.8	14 48.7	14 16.0	15 32.1	15 15.7	2 30.7	23 29.2	19 32.6	29 2.8	24 4.3	15 0.3
7 S	20 59 1.9	13 44.3	14 45.5	26 23.0	14 45.0	16 28.0	3 2.5	23 21.6	19 33.8	29 1.4	24 6.5	15 1.7
8 S	21 2 58.5	14 41.8	14 42.3	8♌22.8	13 58.0	17 40.4	3 33.9	23 13.9	19 35.2	28 59.9	24 8.7	15 3.0
9 M	21 6 55.1	15 39.4	14 39.1	20 17.3	13 12.2	18 52.8	4 5.1	23 6.2	19 36.7	28 58.4	24 10.9	15 4.4
10 T	21 10 51.6	16 36.9	14 36.0	2♍ 8.6	12 28.4	20• 5.3	4 35.8	22 58.5	19 38.2	28 56.8	24 13.1	15 5.7
11 W	21 14 48.1	17 34.5	14 32.8	13 58.5	11 47.5	21 17.8	5 6.2	22 50.7	19 39.9	28 55.2	24 15.3	15 7.1
12 T	21 18 44.7	18 32.1	14 29.6	25 49.2	11 10.3	22 30.4	5 36.3	22 42.9	19 41.6	28 53.6	24 17.6	15 8.4
13 F	21 22 41.3	19 29.7	14 26.4	7♎43.2	10 37.6	23 43.0	6 6.0	22 35.0	19 43.5	28 51.9	24 19.8	15 9.7
14 S	21 26 37.8	20 27.4	14 23.3	19 43.5	10 10.1	24 55.6	6 35.4	22 27.2	19 45.4	28 50.2	24 22.0	15 11.0
15 S	21 30 34.4	21 25.0	14 20.1	1♏53.3	9 48.4	26 8.4	7 4.3	22 19.3	19 47.5	28 48.4	24 24.2	15 12.3
16 M	21 34 30.9	22 22.7	14 16.9	14 16.6	9 33.0	27 21.1	7 32.9	22 11.5	19 49.6	28 46.7	24 26.4	15 13.6
17 T	21 38 27.5	23 20.3	14 13.7	26 57.5	9 24.5	28 33.9	8 1.1	22 3.6	19 51.8	28 44.9	24 28.7	15 14.8
18 W	21 42 24.0	24 18.0	14 10.5	9♐59.8	9 23.0	29 46.8	8 28.9	21 55.8	19 54.1	28 43.0	24 30.9	15 16.1
19 T	21 46 20.6	25 15.8	14 7.4	23 27.2	9D29.0	0♌59.7	8 56.2	21 47.9	19 56.6	28 41.2	24 33.1	15 17.3
20 F	21 50 17.1	26 13.5	14 4.2	7♑21.6	9 42.4	2 12.6	9 23.2	21 40.1	19 59.0	28 39.3	24 35.3	15 18.6
21 S	21 54 13.7	27 11.2	14 1.0	21 43.4	10 3.5	3 25.6	9 49.7	21 32.3	20 1.6	28 37.3	24 37.6	15 19.8
22 S	21 58 10.2	28 9.0	13 57.8	6♒29.9	10 32.2	4 38.6	10 15.8	21 24.6	20 4.3	28 35.4	24 39.8	15 21.0
23 M	22 2 6.8	29 6.8	13 54.7	21 35.4	11 8.5	5 51.7	10 41.5	21 16.9	20 7.1	28 33.4	24 42.0	15 22.1
24 T	22 6 3.4	0♍ 4.6	13 51.5	6♓51.2	11 52.2	7 4.9	11 6.7	21 9.2	20 9.9	28 31.4	24 44.2	15 23.3
25 W	22 9 59.9	1 2.5	13 48.3	22 6.8	12 43.2	8 18.1	11 31.5	21 1.5	20 12.9	28 29.4	24 46.4	15 24.4
26 T	22 13 56.4	2 0.3	13 45.1	7♈11.5	13 41.2	9 31.3	11 55.7	20 53.9	20 15.9	28 27.3	24 48.6	15 25.6
27 F	22 17 53.0	2 58.2	13 41.9	21 56.5	14 46.1	10 44.6	12 19.5	20 46.4	20 19.0	28 25.2	24 50.8	15 26.7
28 S	22 21 49.6	3 56.2	13 38.8	6♉15.7	15 57.3	11 57.9	12 42.8	20 39.0	20 22.2	28 23.1	24 53.1	15 27.8
29 S	22 25 46.1	4 54.1	13 35.6	20 6.6	17 14.7	13 11.3	13 5.6	20 31.6	20 25.5	28 21.0	24 55.3	15 28.9
30 M	22 29 42.6	5 52.1	13 32.4	3♊29.7	18 37.6	14 24.7	13 27.9	20 24.2	20 28.8	28 18.8	24 57.4	15 29.9
31 T	22 33 39.2	6 50.1	13 29.2	16 27.4	20 5.8	15 38.2	13 49.6	20 17.0	20 32.3	28 16.6	24 59.6	15 31.0

DECLINATION

DAY	EPHEMERIS SIDEREAL TIME h m s	☉	☊	☽	☿	♀	♂	♃	♄	♅	♆	♇
1 S	20 35 22.6	18N16.6	22N35.7	10N23.1	10N39.0	22N33.4	8N41.2	14S30.1	15S31.2	1S 2.9	13N56.4	21N 7.7
4 W	20 47 12.3	17 30.8	22 36.8	20 40.2	11 2.9	22 24.1	9 14.6	14 37.9	15 32.7	1 4.5	13 54.3	21 7.4
7 S	20 59 1.9	16 42.5	22 37.9	21 46.9	11 45.9	22 9.1	9 46.6	14 45.8	15 34.4	1 6.3	13 52.1	21 7.1
10 T	21 10 51.6	15 51.8	22 38.9	14 12.5	12 42.5	21 48.3	10 17.3	14 53.9	15 36.3	1 8.1	13 49.9	21 6.7
13 F	21 22 41.3	14 58.7	22 39.9	1 39.3	13 45.2	21 21.9	10 46.6	15 1.9	15 38.5	1 10.2	13 47.8	21 6.4
16 M	21 34 30.9	14 3.5	22 40.9	11S46.1	14 45.6	20 50.0	11 14.5	15 9.9	15 40.8	1 12.3	13 45.6	21 6.1
19 T	21 46 20.6	13 6.3	22 42.0	21 18.9	15 36.3	20 12.6	11 41.0	15 17.9	15 43.4	1 14.6	13 43.4	21 5.8
22 S	21 58 10.2	12 7.3	22 43.0	20 25.7	16 10.6	19 30.0	12 6.0	15 25.7	15 46.2	1 16.9	13 41.2	21 5.5
25 W	22 9 59.9	11 6.5	22 43.9	7 27.6	16 23.3	18 42.4	12 29.6	15 33.3	15 49.1	1 19.4	13 39.0	21 5.2
28 S	22 21 49.6	10 4.1	22 44.9	9N 4.9	16 10.5	17 49.9	12 51.7	15 40.7	15 52.3	1 21.9	13 36.8	21 4.9
31 T	22 33 39.2	9 0.3	22 45.9	20 17.9	15 30.1	16 52.9	13 12.4	15 47.8	15 55.6	1 24.5	13 34.6	21 4.6

SEPTEMBER 1926

DAY	EPHEMERIS SIDEREAL TIME	☉	☊	☽	☿	♀	♂	♃	♄	♅	♆	♇
	h m s	° ′	° ′	° ′	° ′	° ′	° ′	° ′	° ′	° ′	° ′	° ′
LONGITUDE												
1 W	22 37 35.8	7♍48.2	13♋26.1	29♊ 3.7	21♌38.7	16♌51.8	14♉10.7	20♒ 9.8	20♏35.8	28♓14.4	25♌ 1.8	15♋32.0
2 T	22 41 32.4	8 46.3	13 22.9	11♋23.0	23 15.8	18 5.3	14 31.3	20R 2.7	20 39.4	28R12.2	25 4.0	15 33.0
3 F	22 45 28.9	9 44.4	13 19.7	23 29.6	24 56.7	19 19.0	14 51.3	19 55.8	20 43.1	28 !0.0	25 6.2	15 34.0
4 S	22 49 25.4	10 42.5	13 16.5	5♌27.5	26 40.7	20 32.6	15 10.7	19 48.9	20 46.9	28 7.7	25 8.3	15 35.0
5 S	22 53 22.0	11 40.7	13 13.3	17 20.2	28 27.5	21 46.3	15 29.6	19 42.1	20 50.8	28 5.5	25 10.5	15 35.9
6 M	22 57 18.6	12 38.9	13 10.2	29 10.5	0♍16.6	23 0.1	15 47.7	19 35.4	20 54.7	28 3.2	25 12.6	15 36.9
7 T	23 1 15.1	13 37.2	13 7.0	11♍ 0.5	2 7.5	24 13.9	16 5.3	19 28.9	20 58.7	28 0.9	25 14.8	15 37.8
8 W	23 5 11.6	14 35.4	13 3.8	22 52.0	3 59.9	25 27.7	16 22.2	19 22.5	21 2.8	27 58.6	25 16.9	15 38.7
9 T	23 9 8.2	15 33.7	13 0.6	4♎46.6	5 53.2	26 41.6	16 38.5	19 16.1	21 7.0	27 56.2	25 19.0	15 39.5
10 F	23 13 4.8	16 32.1	12 57.5	16 45.7	7 47.2	27 55.5	16 54.0	19 10.0	21 11.3	27 53.9	25 21.1	15 40.4
11 S	23 17 1.3	17 30.4	12 54.3	28 51.3	9 41.7	29 9.5	17 8.9	19 3.9	21 15.6	27 51.5	25 23.2	15 41.2
12 S	23 20 57.9	18 28.8	12 51.1	11♏ 5.3	11 36.3	0♍23.5	17 23.1	18 58.0	21 20.0	27 49.2	25 25.3	15 42.1
13 M	23 24 54.4	19 27.2	12 47.9	23 30.6	13 30.7	1 37.5	17 36.6	18 52.2	21 24.5	27 46.8	25 27.4	15 42.9
14 T	23 28 51.0	20 25.6	12 44.7	6♐10.3	15 25.0	2 51.6	17 49.4	18 46.6	21 29.0	27 44.4	25 29.4	15 43.6
15 W	23 32 47.5	21 24.1	12 41.6	19 8.2	17 18.7	4 5.7	18 1.5	18 41.1	21 33.6	27 42.0	25 31.5	15 44.4
16 T	23 36 44.1	22 22.6	12 38.4	2♑27.6	19 11.9	5 19.8	18 12.8	18 35.8	21 38.3	27 39.7	25 33.5	15 45.1
17 F	23 40 40.6	23 21.1	12 35.2	16 11.7	21 4.5	6 34.0	18 23.3	18 30.7	21 43.1	27 37.3	25 35.5	15 45.8
18 S	23 44 37.1	24 19.7	12 32.0	0♒22.1	22 56.2	7 48.2	18 33.1	18 25.7	21 47.9	27 34.9	25 37.5	15 46.5
19 S	23 48 33.7	25 18.2	12 28.8	14 58.0	24 47.2	9 2.4	18 42.2	18 20.8	21 52.8	27 32.4	25 39.5	15 47.2
20 M	23 52 30.3	26 16.8	12 25.7	29 55.7	26 37.3	10 16.7	18 50.4	18 16.1	21 57.8	27 30.0	25 41.5	15 47.8
21 T	23 56 26.8	27 15.5	12 22.5	15♓ 8.1	28 26.4	11 31.0	18 57.9	18 11.6	22 2.8	27 27.6	25 43.5	15 48.5
22 W	0 0 23.4	28 14.1	12 19.3	0♈25.2	0♎14.7	12 45.4	19 4.5	18 7.3	22 7.9	27 25.2	25 45.4	15 49.1
23 T	0 4 20.0	29 12.8	12 16.1	15 35.7	2 2.0	13 59.8	19 10.3	18 3.1	22 13.1	27 22.8	25 47.3	15 49.7
24 F	0 8 16.5	0♎11.5	12 13.0	0♉29.2	3 48.3	15 14.2	19 15.3	17 59.1	22 18.3	27 20.4	25 49.2	15 50.2
25 S	0 12 13.1	1 10.3	12 9.8	14 57.7	5 33.7	16 28.6	19 19.4	17 55.3	22 23.6	27 18.0	25 51.1	15 50.8
26 S	0 16 9.6	2 9.1	12 6.6	28 56.9	7 18.2	17 43.1	19 22.7	17 51.7	22 28.9	27 15.6	25 53.0	15 51.3
27 M	0 20 6.2	3 7.9	12 3.4	12♊25.9	9 1.7	18 57.6	19 25.1	17 48.2	22 34.3	27 13.2	25 54.9	15 51.8
28 T	0 24 2.7	4 6.8	12 0.2	25 26.9	10 44.2	20 12.2	19 26.7	17 44.9	22 39.8	27 10.8	25 56.7	15 52.2
29 W	0 27 59.3	5 5.7	11 57.1	8♋ 3.6	12 25.9	21 26.8	19 27.3	17 41.8	22 45.3	27 8.5	25 58.5	15 52.7
30 T	0 31 55.8	6 4.7	11 53.9	20 21.1	14 6.7	22 41.4	19R27.1	17 38.9	22 50.9	27 6.1	26 0.3	15 53.1
DECLINATION												
1 W	22 37 35.8	8N38.8	22N46.2	22N 1.0	15N10.4	16N32.9	13N18.9	15S50.1	15S56.8	1S25.4	13N33.9	21N 4.6
4 S	22 49 25.4	7 33.2	22 47.2	20 38.0	13 54.3	15 30.1	13 37.6	15 56.8	16 0.3	1 28.1	13 31.8	21 4.3
7 T	23 1 15.1	6 26.6	22 48.1	11 20.2	12 15.2	14 23.4	13 54.7	16 3.1	16 4.1	1 30.8	13 29.7	21 4.1
10 F	23 13 4.8	5 19.0	22 49.0	1S55.6	10 18.2	13 13.1	14 10.2	16 9.0	16 8.0	1 33.6	13 27.6	21 3.9
13 M	23 24 54.4	4 10.6	22 49.9	14 52.7	8 8.7	11 59.4	14 24.2	16 14.5	16 12.0	1 36.5	13 25.5	21 3.7
16 T	23 36 44.1	3 1.6	22 50.9	22 25.8	5 51.4	10 42.7	14 36.7	16 19.5	16 16.2	1 39.3	13 23.5	21 3.5
19 S	23 48 33.7	1 52.0	22 51.7	18 51.5	3 30.2	9 23.2	14 47.6	16 24.1	16 20.5	1 42.2	13 21.5	21 3.3
22 W	0 0 23.4	0 42.1	22 52.6	4 19.4	1 7.7	8 1.3	14 57.1	16 28.1	16 24.9	1 45.0	13 19.6	21 3.2
25 S	0 12 13.1	0S28.0	22 53.5	12N15.3	1S13.8	6 37.3	15 4.9	16 31.6	16 29.4	1 47.9	13 17.7	21 3.1
28 T	0 24 2.7	1 38.1	22 54.4	21 52.6	3 32.8	5 11.6	15 11.2	16 34.6	16 34.0	1 50.7	13 15.8	21 3.0

OCTOBER 1926

DAY	EPHEMERIS SIDEREAL TIME	☉	☊	☽	☿	♀	♂	♃	♄	♅	♆	♇
LONGITUDE												
1 F	0 35 52.4	7♎ 3.7	11♋50.7	2♌24.6	15♎46.6	23♍56.0	19♉26.0	17♒36.2	22♏56.5	27♓ 3.7	26♌ 2.1	15♋53.5
2 S	0 39 48.9	8 2.7	11 47.5	14 19.1	17 25.6	25 10.7	19R23.9	17R33.7	23 2.2	27R 1.4	26 3.9	15 53.9
3 S	0 43 45.5	9 1.7	11 44.4	26 9.0	19 3.8	26 25.4	19 21.0	17 31.4	23 8.0	26 59.0	26 5.6	15 54.2
4 M	0 47 42.0	10 0.8	11 41.2	7♍58.2	20 41.1	27 40.2	19 17.1	17 29.2	23 13.8	26 56.7	26 7.3	15 54.6
5 T	0 51 38.6	10 60.0	11 38.0	19 49.6	22 17.6	28 54.9	19 12.3	17 27.3	23 19.6	26 54.4	26 9.1	15 54.9
6 W	0 55 35.2	11 59.2	11 34.8	1♎45.4	23 53.4	0♎ 9.7	19 6.7	17 25.6	23 25.6	26 52.1	26 10.7	15 55.2
7 T	0 59 31.7	12 58.4	11 31.6	13 47.2	25 28.3	1 24.5	19 0.1	17 24.0	23 31.5	26 49.8	26 12.4	15 55.4
8 F	1 3 28.2	13 57.6	11 28.5	25 55.9	27 2.5	2 39.4	18 52.7	17 22.7	23 37.5	26 47.5	26 14.0	15 55.6
9 S	1 7 24.8	14 56.9	11 25.3	8♏12.5	28 35.9	3 54.2	18 44.3	17 21.5	23 43.6	26 45.3	26 15.6	15 55.8
10 S	1 11 21.4	15 56.2	11 22.1	20 37.7	0♏ 8.6	5 9.1	18 35.1	17 20.6	23 49.7	26 43.0	26 17.2	15 56.0
11 M	1 15 17.9	16 55.5	11 18.9	3♐13.0	1 40.5	6 24.0	18 25.1	17 19.8	23 55.9	26 40.8	26 18.8	15 56.2
12 T	1 19 14.5	17 54.9	11 15.8	16 0.1	3 11.7	7 39.0	18 14.2	17 19.3	24 2.1	26 38.6	26 20.3	15 56.3
13 W	1 23 11.0	18 54.3	11 12.6	29 1.3	4 42.2	8 53.9	18 2.5	17 18.9	24 8.3	26 36.4	26 21.8	15 56.4
14 T	1 27 7.6	19 53.7	11 9.4	12♑19.1	6 12.0	10 8.9	17 50.0	17 18.8	24 14.6	26 34.3	26 23.3	15 56.5
15 F	1 31 4.1	20 53.2	11 6.2	25 56.2	7 41.0	11 23.9	17 36.7	17D18.9	24 20.9	26 32.1	26 24.8	15 56.6
16 S	1 35 0.7	21 52.7	11 3.0	9♒54.4	9 9.3	12 38.9	17 22.7	17 19.1	24 27.3	26 30.0	26 26.2	15 56.6
17 S	1 38 57.2	22 52.2	10 59.9	24 14.2	10 36.8	13 53.9	17 8.0	17 19.6	24 33.7	26 27.9	26 27.6	15 56.7
18 M	1 42 53.8	23 51.7	10 56.7	8♓53.4	12 3.7	15 8.9	16 52.6	17 20.3	24 40.2	26 25.9	26 29.0	15R56.6
19 T	1 46 50.3	24 51.3	10 53.5	23 47.4	13 29.7	16 24.0	16 36.5	17 21.1	24 46.7	26 23.9	26 30.4	15 56.6
20 W	1 50 46.9	25 50.9	10 50.3	8♈48.5	14 54.9	17 39.1	16 19.8	17 22.2	24 53.2	26 21.9	26 31.7	15 56.6
21 T	1 54 43.4	26 50.5	10 47.2	23 47.6	16 19.4	18 54.1	16 2.5	17 23.5	24 59.7	26 19.9	26 33.0	15 56.5
22 F	1 58 40.0	27 50.2	10 44.0	8♉34.7	17 43.0	20 9.2	15 44.6	17 24.9	25 6.3	26 17.9	26 34.2	15 56.4
23 S	2 2 36.5	28 49.9	10 40.8	23 1.8	19 5.7	21 24.4	15 26.3	17 26.6	25 13.0	26 16.0	26 35.5	15 56.2
24 S	2 6 33.1	29 49.7	10 37.6	7♊ 3.1	20 27.5	22 39.5	15 7.4	17 28.5	25 19.7	26 14.1	26 36.7	15 56.1
25 M	2 10 29.7	0♏49.4	10 34.5	20 36.3	21 48.2	23 54.7	14 48.1	17 30.5	25 26.3	26 12.3	26 37.9	15 55.9
26 T	2 14 26.2	1 49.2	10 31.3	3♋41.9	23 8.0	25 9.8	14 28.4	17 32.8	25 33.1	26 10.4	26 39.1	15 55.7
27 W	2 18 22.7	2 49.1	10 28.1	16 22.8	24 26.6	26 25.0	14 8.3	17 35.2	25 39.8	26 8.6	26 40.2	15 55.5
28 T	2 22 19.3	3 49.0	10 24.9	28 43.4	25 43.9	27 40.2	13 47.9	17 37.8	25 46.6	26 6.9	26 41.3	15 55.2
29 F	2 26 15.9	4 48.9	10 21.7	10♌48.7	26 60.0	28 55.4	13 27.3	17 40.7	25 53.4	26 5.2	26 42.4	15 55.0
30 S	2 30 12.4	5 48.9	10 18.6	22 44.0	28 14.6	0♏10.7	13 6.4	17 43.7	26 0.3	26 3.5	26 43.4	15 54.7
31 S	2 34 9.0	6 48.9	10 15.4	4♍34.5	29 27.6	1 25.9	12 45.4	17 46.9	26 7.1	26 1.8	26 44.4	15 54.4
DECLINATION												
1 F	0 35 52.4	2S48.2	22N55.2	21N17.7	5S48.3	3N44.3	15N16.0	16S37.0	16S38.7	1S53.5	13N14.1	21N 2.9
4 M	0 47 42.0	3 58.1	22 56.1	12 25.1	7 59.4	2 16.0	15 19.0	16 38.9	16 43.5	1 56.3	13 12.3	21 2.8
7 T	0 59 31.7	5 7.5	22 56.9	0S50.7	10 5.4	0 46.8	15 20.5	16 40.2	16 48.4	1 59.0	13 10.7	21 2.8
10 S	1 11 21.4	6 16.3	22 57.7	14 11.3	12 5.6	0S42.8	15 20.3	16 41.0	16 53.3	2 1.6	13 9.1	21 2.8
13 W	1 23 11.0	7 24.5	22 58.5	22 24.8	13 59.6	2 12.6	15 18.6	16 41.1	16 58.2	2 4.2	13 7.6	21 2.8
16 S	1 35 0.7	8 31.6	22 59.3	20 8.4	15 46.7	3 42.1	15 15.3	16 40.8	17 3.3	2 6.7	13 6.2	21 2.9
19 T	1 46 50.3	9 37.7	23 0.1	6 53.0	17 26.3	5 11.1	15 10.7	16 39.8	17 8.3	2 9.1	13 4.8	21 2.9
22 F	1 58 40.0	10 42.5	23 0.9	10N10.9	18 57.8	6 39.2	15 4.7	16 38.3	17 13.4	2 11.4	13 3.6	21 3.1
25 M	2 10 29.7	11 45.9	23 1.6	21 27.9	20 20.6	8 6.1	14 57.6	16 36.3	17 18.4	2 13.6	13 2.4	21 3.2
28 T	2 22 19.3	12 47.7	23 2.4	22 3.3	21 33.7	9 31.4	14 49.6	16 33.7	17 23.5	2 15.6	13 1.3	21 3.3
31 S	2 34 9.0	13 47.7	23 3.1	13 42.4	22 36.2	10 54.8	14 40.8	16 30.5	17 28.6	2 17.6	13 0.3	21 3.5

NOVEMBER 1926

LONGITUDE

DAY	EPHEMERIS SIDEREAL TIME h m s	☉ ° ′	☊ ° ′	☽ ° ′	☿ ° ′	♀ ° ′	♂ ° ′	♃ ° ′	♄ ° ′	♅ ° ′	♆ ° ′	♇ ° ′
1 M	2 38 5.5	7♏48.9	10♋12.2	16♍24.8	0♐38.8	2♏41.2	12♉24.3	17♒50.3	26♏14.0	26♓ 0.2	26♌45.4	15♋54.0
2 T	2 42 2.1	8 49.0	10 9.0	28 18.9	1 48.1	3 56.5	12R 3.1	17 53.9	26 21.0	25R58.6	26 46.3	15R53.6
3 W	2 45 58.6	9 49.1	10 5.9	10♎19.9	2 55.3	5 11.8	11 41.9	17 57.7	26 27.9	25 57.1	26 47.3	15 53.3
4 T	2 49 55.2	10 49.2	10 2.7	22 30.0	4 0.0	6 27.0	11 20.8	18 1.7	26 34.9	25 55.6	26 48.1	15 52.8
5 F	2 53 51.7	11 49.3	9 59.5	4♏50.4	5 2.1	7 42.4	10 59.8	18 5.9	26 41.8	25 54.1	26 49.0	15 52.4
6 S	2 57 48.3	12 49.5	9 56.3	17 21.9	6 1.1	8 57.7	10 39.0	18 10.2	26 48.8	25 52.7	26 49.8	15 51.9
7 S	3 1 44.9	13 49.8	9 53.1	0♐ 4.5	6 56.9	10 13.0	10 18.3	18 14.8	26 55.9	25 51.3	26 50.6	15 51.5
8 M	3 5 41.4	14 50.0	9 50.0	12 58.1	7 48.8	11 28.4	9 57.9	18 19.5	27 2.9	25 50.0	26 51.4	15 51.0
9 T	3 9 38.0	15 50.3	9 46.8	26 2.9	8 36.5	12 43.7	9 37.9	18 24.4	27 9.9	25 48.7	26 52.1	15 50.4
10 W	3 13 34.5	16 50.6	9 43.6	9♑19.1	9 19.5	13 59.0	9 18.2	18 29.4	27 17.0	25 47.4	26 52.8	15 49.9
11 T	3 17 31.1	17 50.9	9 40.4	22 47.2	9 57.3	15 14.4	8 58.9	18 34.7	27 24.1	25 46.2	26 53.4	15 49.3
12 F	3 21 27.7	18 51.3	9 37.3	6♒28.3	10 29.1	16 29.8	8 40.1	18 40.2	27 31.2	25 45.1	26 54.1	15 48.7
13 S	3 25 24.2	19 51.7	9 34.1	20 22.9	10 54.3	17 45.1	8 21.7	18 45.8	27 38.3	25 43.9	26 54.7	15 48.1
14 S	3 29 20.7	20 52.1	9 30.9	4♓30.9	11 12.2	19 0.5	8 3.9	18 51.5	27 45.4	25 42.9	26 55.2	15 47.5
15 M	3 33 17.3	21 52.5	9 27.7	18 51.3	11 22.1	20 15.9	7 46.7	18 57.5	27 52.5	25 41.8	26 55.7	15 46.8
16 T	3 37 13.9	22 52.9	9 24.5	3♈21.1	11 23.3	21 31.3	7 30.0	19 3.6	27 59.6	25 40.8	26 56.2	15 46.2
17 W	3 41 10.4	23 53.4	9 21.4	17 55.6	11R15.1	22 46.6	7 14.0	19 9.9	28 6.8	25 39.9	26 56.7	15 45.5
18 T	3 45 7.0	24 53.9	9 18.2	2♉28.7	10 56.9	24 2.0	6 58.7	19 16.4	28 13.9	25 39.0	26 57.1	15 44.7
19 F	3 49 3.5	25 54.4	9 15.0	16 53.7	10 28.3	25 17.4	6 44.0	19 23.0	28 21.1	25 38.2	26 57.5	15 44.0
20 S	3 53 0.1	26 54.9	9 11.8	1♊ 4.2	9 49.1	26 32.8	6 30.0	19 29.8	28 28.2	25 37.4	26 57.8	15 43.3
21 S	3 56 56.7	27 55.5	9 8.7	14 55.2	8 59.6	27 48.2	6 16.7	19 36.7	28 35.3	25 36.6	26 58.2	15 42.5
22 M	4 0 53.2	28 56.1	9 5.5	28 23.6	8 0.4	29 3.6	6 4.2	19 43.8	28 42.5	25 35.9	26 58.5	15 41.7
23 T	4 4 49.8	29 56.7	9 2.3	11♋28.6	6 52.6	0♐19.0	5 52.4	19 51.0	28 49.6	25 35.3	26 58.7	15 40.9
24 W	4 8 46.3	0♐57.3	8 59.1	24 11.6	5 37.7	1 34.4	5 41.4	19 58.5	28 56.8	25 34.7	26 58.9	15 40.0
25 T	4 12 42.9	1 58.0	8 56.0	6♌35.3	4 18.0	2 49.8	5 31.1	20 6.0	29 3.9	25 34.1	26 59.1	15 39.2
26 F	4 16 39.4	2 58.7	8 52.8	18 43.7	2 55.9	4 5.3	5 21.7	20 13.7	29 11.1	25 33.6	26 59.3	15 38.3
27 S	4 20 36.0	3 59.4	8 49.6	0♍41.6	1 34.2	5 20.7	5 13.0	20 21.6	29 18.2	25 33.1	26 59.4	15 37.5
28 S	4 24 32.5	5 0.2	8 46.4	12 34.0	0 15.7	6 36.1	5 5.2	20 29.6	29 25.3	25 32.7	26 59.5	15 36.5
29 M	4 28 29.1	6 0.9	8 43.2	24 25.7	29♏ 2.8	7 51.6	4 58.1	20 37.8	29 32.5	25 32.4	26 59.5	15 35.6
30 T	4 32 25.7	7 1.7	8 40.1	6♎21.6	27 57.8	9 7.0	4 51.9	20 46.1	29 39.6	25 32.1	26 59.5	15 34.7

DECLINATION

DAY	EPHEMERIS SIDEREAL TIME h m s	☉ ° ′	☊ ° ′	☽ ° ′	☿ ° ′	♀ ° ′	♂ ° ′	♃ ° ′	♄ ° ′	♅ ° ′	♆ ° ′	♇ ° ′
1 M	2 38 5.5	14S 7.3	23N 3.4	9N39.6	22S54.5	11S22.1	14N37.7	16S29.4	17S30.3	2S18.2	12N60.0	21N 3.6
4 T	2 49 55.2	15 4.6	23 4.1	4S11.1	23 41.0	12 42.4	14 28.4	16 25.5	17 35.4	2 19.9	12 59.1	21 3.8
7 S	3 1 44.9	15 59.7	23 4.8	17 4.8	24 14.0	13 59.9	14 19.0	16 21.2	17 40.4	2 21.5	12 58.3	21 4.0
10 W	3 13 34.5	16 52.5	23 5.5	23 12.8	24 31.6	15 14.2	14 10.0	16 16.3	17 45.4	2 23.0	12 57.7	21 4.3
13 S	3 25 24.2	17 42.6	23 6.2	17 58.1	24 31.2	16 25.1	14 1.8	16 10.8	17 50.4	2 24.3	12 57.1	21 4.6
16 T	3 37 13.9	18 30.0	23 6.9	3 21.9	24 9.6	17 32.1	13 54.5	16 4.9	17 55.3	2 25.4	12 56.6	21 4.9
19 F	3 49 3.5	19 14.4	23 7.5	13N 3.0	23 22.7	18 34.8	13 48.6	15 58.5	18 0.2	2 26.4	12 56.3	21 5.3
22 M	4 0 53.2	19 55.7	23 8.2	22 36.3	22 7.9	19 33.0	13 44.1	15 51.7	18 5.0	2 27.2	12 56.0	21 5.6
25 T	4 12 42.9	20 33.8	23 8.8	21 4.4	20 29.7	20 26.4	13 41.3	15 44.3	18 9.7	2 27.8	12 55.9	21 6.0
28 S	4 24 32.5	21 8.4	23 9.5	11 12.1	18 45.6	21 14.5	13 40.3	15 36.5	18 14.4	2 28.2	12 55.8	21 6.5

DECEMBER 1926

LONGITUDE

DAY	EPHEMERIS SIDEREAL TIME h m s	☉ ° ′	☊ ° ′	☽ ° ′	☿ ° ′	♀ ° ′	♂ ° ′	♃ ° ′	♄ ° ′	♅ ° ′	♆ ° ′	♇ ° ′
1 W	4 36 22.2	8♐ 2.6	8♋36.9	18♎25.7	27♏ 2.4	10♐22.5	4♉46.5	20♒54.6	29♏46.7	25♓31.8	26♌59.5	15♋33.7
2 T	4 40 18.8	9 3.4	8 33.7	0♏41.4	26R17.8	11 37.9	4R41.9	21 3.2	29 53.8	25R31.6	26R59.4	15R32.8
3 F	4 44 15.3	10 4.3	8 30.5	13 11.2	25 44.5	12 53.4	4 38.2	21 11.9	0♐ 0.9	25 31.4	26 59.3	15 31.8
4 S	4 48 11.9	11 5.2	8 27.4	25 56.3	25 22.7	14 8.8	4 35.2	21 20.8	0 7.9	25 31.3	26 59.2	15 30.8
5 S	4 52 8.4	12 6.1	8 24.2	8♐57.3	25 12.2	15 24.3	4 33.1	21 29.8	0 15.0	25 31.3	26 59.1	15 29.8
6 M	4 56 5.0	13 7.0	8 21.0	22 13.3	25D12.5	16 39.7	4 31.8	21 38.9	0 22.0	25 31.3	26 58.9	15 28.7
7 T	5 0 1.6	14 7.9	8 17.8	5♑43.0	25 22.9	17 55.2	4 31.4	21 48.2	0 29.1	25D31.3	26 58.6	15 27.7
8 W	5 3 58.1	15 8.9	8 14.7	19 24.6	25 42.6	19 10.7	4D31.7	21 57.6	0 36.1	25 31.4	26 58.4	15 26.6
9 T	5 7 54.7	16 9.9	8 11.5	3♒15.9	26 10.6	20 26.1	4 32.8	22 7.2	0 43.1	25 31.6	26 58.1	15 25.6
10 F	5 11 51.2	17 10.9	8 8.3	17 15.0	26 46.3	21 41.6	4 34.7	22 16.8	0 50.0	25 31.8	26 57.7	15 24.5
11 S	5 15 47.8	18 11.9	8 5.1	1♓20.0	27 28.6	22 57.0	4 37.4	22 26.6	0 57.0	25 32.1	26 57.4	15 23.4
12 S	5 19 44.3	19 12.9	8 1.9	15 29.1	28 17.0	24 12.5	4 40.9	22 36.5	1 3.9	25 32.4	26 57.0	15 22.3
13 M	5 23 40.9	20 13.9	7 58.8	29 40.3	29 10.6	25 27.9	4 45.1	22 46.6	1 10.8	25 32.7	26 56.5	15 21.2
14 T	5 27 37.5	21 14.9	7 55.6	13♈51.6	0♐ 8.8	26 43.4	4 50.0	22 56.7	1 17.7	25 33.2	26 56.1	15 20.0
15 W	5 31 34.0	22 15.9	7 52.4	28 0.4	1 11.1	27 58.8	4 55.7	23 7.0	1 24.6	25 33.6	26 55.6	15 18.9
16 T	5 35 30.6	23 16.9	7 49.2	12♉ 3.9	2 16.9	29 14.2	5 2.2	23 17.4	1 31.4	25 34.2	26 55.1	15 17.8
17 F	5 39 27.1	24 18.0	7 46.1	25 58.7	3 25.8	0♑29.7	5 9.3	23 27.9	1 38.2	25 34.7	26 54.5	15 16.6
18 S	5 43 23.7	25 19.0	7 42.9	9♊41.9	4 37.4	1 45.1	5 17.1	23 38.5	1 44.9	25 35.3	26 53.9	15 15.4
19 S	5 47 20.2	26 20.1	7 39.7	23 10.6	5 51.4	3 0.5	5 25.5	23 49.2	1 51.7	25 36.0	26 53.3	15 14.2
20 M	5 51 16.8	27 21.2	7 36.5	6♋23.1	7 7.4	4 15.9	5 34.7	24 0.1	1 58.4	25 36.7	26 52.6	15 13.1
21 T	5 55 13.4	28 22.2	7 33.4	19 18.2	8 25.2	5 31.4	5 44.4	24 11.0	2 5.0	25 37.5	26 51.9	15 11.9
22 W	5 59 9.9	29 23.3	7 30.2	1♌56.3	9 44.6	6 46.8	5 54.8	24 22.1	2 11.7	25 38.3	26 51.2	15 10.7
23 T	6 3 6.5	0♑24.4	7 27.0	14 18.8	11 5.5	8 2.2	6 5.9	24 33.2	2 18.3	25 39.2	26 50.5	15 9.4
24 F	6 7 3.0	1 25.5	7 23.8	26 28.0	12 27.5	9 17.6	6 17.5	24 44.5	2 24.9	25 40.1	26 49.7	15 8.2
25 S	6 10 59.6	2 26.7	7 20.7	8♍27.4	13 50.6	10 33.0	6 29.7	24 55.8	2 31.4	25 41.1	26 48.9	15 7.0
26 S	6 14 56.2	3 27.8	7 17.5	20 20.9	15 14.8	11 48.4	6 42.5	25 7.3	2 37.9	25 42.1	26 48.1	15 5.8
27 M	6 18 52.7	4 28.9	7 14.3	2♎13.1	16 39.7	13 3.8	6 55.9	25 18.8	2 44.3	25 43.2	26 47.2	15 4.5
28 T	6 22 49.3	5 30.1	7 11.1	14 8.6	18 5.5	14 19.2	7 9.9	25 30.5	2 50.7	25 44.3	26 46.3	15 3.3
29 W	6 26 45.8	6 31.2	7 8.0	26 12.1	19 32.0	15 34.6	7 24.3	25 42.2	2 57.1	25 45.5	26 45.4	15 2.0
30 T	6 30 42.4	7 32.4	7 4.8	8♏28.2	20 59.1	16 50.0	7 39.4	25 54.0	3 3.5	25 46.7	26 44.4	15 0.8
31 F	6 34 38.9	8 33.6	7 1.6	21 0.7	22 26.9	18 5.4	7 54.9	26 5.9	3 9.7	25 48.0	26 43.4	14 59.5

DECLINATION

DAY	EPHEMERIS SIDEREAL TIME h m s	☉ ° ′	☊ ° ′	☽ ° ′	☿ ° ′	♀ ° ′	♂ ° ′	♃ ° ′	♄ ° ′	♅ ° ′	♆ ° ′	♇ ° ′
1 W	4 36 22.2	21S39.4	23N10.1	2S29.6	17S21.6	21S57.0	13N41.2	15S28.3	18S19.0	2S28.5	12N55.9	21N 6.9
4 S	4 48 11.9	22 6.8	23 10.7	15 53.3	16 35.5	22 33.8	13 44.0	15 19.6	18 23.5	2 28.5	12 56.0	21 7.3
7 T	5 0 1.6	22 30.3	23 11.3	23 11.3	16 29.3	23 4.5	13 48.8	15 10.4	18 27.9	2 28.4	12 56.3	21 7.8
10 F	5 11 51.2	22 49.8	23 11.9	18 53.6	16 54.6	23 29.0	13 55.5	15 0.9	18 32.2	2 28.1	12 56.7	21 8.3
13 M	5 23 40.9	23 5.3	23 12.5	4 54.8	17 40.6	23 47.0	14 4.1	14 50.9	18 36.4	2 27.6	12 57.2	21 8.8
16 T	5 35 30.6	23 16.7	23 13.0	11N20.5	18 37.7	23 58.5	14 14.6	14 40.5	18 40.5	2 27.0	12 57.8	21 9.4
19 S	5 47 20.2	23 23.9	23 13.6	21 59.9	19 38.9	24 3.2	14 26.7	14 29.8	18 44.4	2 26.1	12 58.4	21 9.9
22 W	5 59 9.9	23 26.8	23 14.1	21 53.9	20 39.5	24 1.3	14 40.3	14 18.7	18 48.3	2 25.1	12 59.2	21 10.4
25 S	6 10 59.6	23 25.5	23 14.7	12 42.0	21 35.9	23 52.6	14 55.4	14 7.2	18 52.0	2 23.9	13 0.1	21 11.0
28 T	6 22 49.3	23 20.0	23 15.2	0S44.3	22 26.0	23 37.3	15 11.8	13 55.3	18 55.6	2 22.5	13 1.0	21 11.6
31 F	6 34 38.9	23 10.3	23 15.7	14 19.7	23 8.0	23 15.4	15 29.4	13 43.1	18 59.1	2 20.9	13 2.1	21 12.2

JANUARY 1927

DAY	EPHEMERIS SIDEREAL TIME	☉	☊	☽	☿	♀	♂	♃	♄	♅	♆	♇
	h m s	° ′	° ′	° ′	° ′	° ′	° ′	° ′	° ′	° ′	° ′	° ′
						LONGITUDE						
1 S	6 38 35.5	9♑34.7	6♋58.4	3♐52.5	23♐55.2	19♑20.8	8♉11.0	26♒17.9	3♐16.0	25♓49.3	26♌42.4	14♋58.3
2 S	6 42 32.1	10 35.9	6 55.2	17 5.2	25 24.0	20 36.2	8 27.6	26 30.0	3 22.2	25 50.7	26R41.4	14R57.0
3 M	6 46 28.6	11 37.1	6 52.1	0♑39.1	26 53.3	21 51.6	8 44.6	26 42.2	3 28.3	25 52.1	26 40.3	14 55.8
4 T	6 50 25.2	12 38.3	6 48.9	14 32.6	28 23.1	23 7.0	9 2.2	26 54.5	3 34.4	25 53.6	26 39.2	14 54.5
5 W	6 54 21.7	13 39.5	6 45.7	28 42.3	29 53.3	24 22.3	9 20.2	27 6.8	3 40.5	25 55.1	26 38.1	14 53.2
6 T	6 58 18.3	14 40.6	6 42.5	13♒3.8	1♑24.0	25 37.7	9 38.6	27 19.2	3 46.4	25 56.6	26 37.0	14 52.0
7 F	7 2 14.8	15 41.8	6 39.4	27 31.6	2 55.2	26 53.0	9 57.6	27 31.8	3 52.4	25 58.2	26 35.8	14 50.7
8 S	7 6 11.4	16 43.0	6 36.2	12♓0.3	4 26.7	28 8.4	10 16.9	27 44.3	3 58.3	25 59.9	26 34.6	14 49.5
9 S	7 10 8.0	17 44.2	6 33.0	26 25.0	5 58.7	29 23.7	10 36.7	27 57.0	4 4.1	26 1.6	26 33.4	14 48.2
10 M	7 14 4.5	18 45.3	6 29.8	10♈41.8	7 31.1	0♒39.0	10 56.9	28 9.7	4 9.9	26 3.3	26 32.2	14 46.9
11 T	7 18 1.1	19 46.4	6 26.7	24 48.0	9 4.0	1 54.3	11 17.6	28 22.5	4 15.6	26 5.1	26 30.9	14 45.7
12 W	7 21 57.6	20 47.6	6 23.5	8♉42.1	10 37.3	3 9.6	11 38.6	28 35.4	4 21.3	26 6.9	26 29.6	14 44.4
13 T	7 25 54.2	21 48.7	6 20.3	22 23.4	12 11.0	4 24.9	11 59.9	28 48.3	4 26.9	26 8.8	26 28.3	14 43.2
14 F	7 29 50.8	22 49.8	6 17.1	5♊51.7	13 45.3	5 40.2	12 21.7	29 1.3	4 32.4	26 10.7	26 27.0	14 41.9
15 S	7 33 47.3	23 50.9	6 13.9	19 7.1	15 19.9	6 55.5	12 43.8	29 14.4	4 37.9	26 12.7	26 25.6	14 40.7
16 S	7 37 43.9	24 52.0	6 10.8	2♋9.9	16 55.1	8 10.7	13 6.3	29 27.5	4 43.3	26 14.7	26 24.3	14 39.4
17 M	7 41 40.4	25 53.1	6 7.6	15 0.2	18 30.8	9 25.9	13 29.1	29 40.7	4 48.7	26 16.7	26 22.9	14 38.2
18 T	7 45 37.0	26 54.2	6 4.4	27 38.4	20 7.0	10 41.2	13 52.2	29 54.0	4 54.0	26 18.8	26 21.5	14 36.9
19 W	7 49 33.5	27 55.2	6 1.2	10♌4.7	21 43.7	11 56.4	14 15.7	0♓7.3	4 59.2	26 20.9	26 20.1	14 35.7
20 T	7 53 30.1	28 56.3	5 58.1	22 20.2	23 21.0	13 11.5	14 39.5	0 20.6	5 4.4	26 23.1	26 18.6	14 34.5
21 F	7 57 26.7	29 57.3	5 54.9	4♍26.1	24 58.8	14 26.7	15 3.5	0 34.0	5 9.4	26 25.3	26 17.2	14 33.3
22 S	8 1 23.2	0♒58.4	5 51.7	16 24.4	26 37.2	15 41.9	15 27.9	0 47.5	5 14.5	26 27.6	26 15.7	14 32.1
23 S	8 5 19.8	1 59.4	5 48.5	28 17.7	28 16.2	16 57.0	15 52.6	1 1.1	5 19.4	26 29.9	26 14.2	14 30.9
24 M	8 9 16.3	3 0.4	5 45.4	10♎9.3	29 55.8	18 12.2	16 17.5	1 14.6	5 24.3	26 32.2	26 12.7	14 29.7
25 T	8 13 12.9	4 1.4	5 42.2	22 3.3	1♒36.1	19 27.3	16 42.8	1 28.3	5 29.1	26 34.5	26 11.2	14 28.5
26 W	8 17 9.4	5 2.4	5 39.0	4♏4.2	3 16.9	20 42.4	17 8.3	1 41.9	5 33.9	26 36.9	26 9.6	14 27.3
27 T	8 21 6.0	6 3.4	5 35.8	16 16.6	4 58.4	21 57.5	17 34.0	1 55.7	5 38.5	26 39.4	26 8.1	14 26.1
28 F	8 25 2.6	7 4.4	5 32.7	28 45.4	6 40.5	23 12.6	18 0.1	2 9.4	5 43.1	26 41.8	26 6.5	14 25.0
29 S	8 28 59.1	8 5.4	5 29.5	11♐35.0	8 23.3	24 27.6	18 26.4	2 23.3	5 47.7	26 44.3	26 4.9	14 23.8
30 S	8 32 55.6	9 6.3	5 26.3	24 48.7	10 6.8	25 42.7	18 52.9	2 37.1	5 52.1	26 46.9	26 3.3	14 22.7
31 M	8 36 52.2	10 7.3	5 23.1	8♑28.7	11 50.9	26 57.7	19 19.7	2 51.0	5 56.5	26 49.4	26 1.7	14 21.6
						DECLINATION						
1 S	6 38 35.5	23S 6.1	23N15.9	18S 4.4	23S19.9	23S 6.7	15N35.5	13S39.0	19S 0.2	2S20.4	13N 2.4	21N12.4
4 T	6 50 25.2	22 50.9	23 16.4	23 19.6	23 49.3	22 36.3	15 54.4	13 26.4	19 3.5	2 18.6	13 3.6	21 13.0
7 F	7 2 14.8	22 31.5	23 16.9	16 9.1	24 8.0	21 59.7	16 14.3	13 13.4	19 6.6	2 16.6	13 4.8	21 13.6
10 M	7 14 4.5	22 8.1	23 17.3	0 36.5	24 15.6	21 17.2	16 35.0	13 0.2	19 9.6	2 14.5	13 6.1	21 14.2
13 T	7 25 54.2	21 40.9	23 17.8	14N46.6	24 11.3	20 29.0	16 56.4	12 46.6	19 12.5	2 12.2	13 7.5	21 14.8
16 S	7 37 43.9	21 9.8	23 18.2	22 58.0	23 54.6	19 35.4	17 18.3	12 32.8	19 15.2	2 9.8	13 8.9	21 15.4
19 W	7 49 33.5	20 35.1	23 18.7	20 28.5	23 25.2	18 36.8	17 40.5	12 18.7	19 17.8	2 7.2	13 10.4	21 16.0
22 S	8 1 23.2	19 56.9	23 19.1	9 52.5	22 42.7	17 33.3	18 3.1	12 4.4	19 20.2	2 4.5	13 11.9	21 16.6
25 T	8 13 12.9	19 15.4	23 19.5	3S54.6	21 46.8	16 25.5	18 25.9	11 49.9	19 22.4	2 1.6	13 13.5	21 17.2
28 F	8 25 2.6	18 30.7	23 19.9	16 44.4	20 37.2	15 13.6	18 48.8	11 35.1	19 24.6	1 58.6	13 15.2	21 17.8
31 M	8 36 52.2	17 42.9	23 20.3	23 19.3	19 13.9	13 57.9	19 11.6	11 20.1	19 26.5	1 55.5	13 16.8	21 18.3

FEBRUARY 1927

DAY	EPHEMERIS SIDEREAL TIME	☉	☊	☽	☿	♀	♂	♃	♄	♅	♆	♇
						LONGITUDE						
1 T	8 40 48.8	11♒8.2	5♋19.9	22♑34.7	13♒35.6	28♒12.7	19♉46.7	3♓5.0	6♐0.8	26♓52.1	26♌0.1	14♋20.5
2 W	8 44 45.3	12 9.1	5 16.8	7♒3.9	15 20.9	29 27.7	20 13.9	3 18.9	6 5.0	26 54.7	25R58.5	14R19.4
3 T	8 48 41.9	13 10.0	5 13.6	21 50.6	17 6.9	0♓42.7	20 41.4	3 33.0	6 9.1	26 57.4	25 56.9	14 18.3
4 F	8 52 38.4	14 10.9	5 10.4	6♓47.2	18 53.4	1 57.7	21 9.1	3 47.0	6 13.1	27 0.1	25 55.3	14 17.2
5 S	8 56 35.0	15 11.8	5 7.2	21 44.5	20 40.4	3 12.6	21 37.0	4 1.1	6 17.1	27 2.8	25 53.6	14 16.1
6 S	9 0 31.6	16 12.6	5 4.1	6♈34.0	22 27.9	4 27.5	22 5.2	4 15.2	6 21.0	27 5.6	25 52.0	14 15.1
7 M	9 4 28.1	17 13.4	5 0.9	21 8.6	24 15.8	5 42.4	22 33.5	4 29.4	6 24.8	27 8.4	25 50.3	14 14.0
8 T	9 8 24.6	18 14.2	4 57.7	5♉23.9	26 3.9	6 57.2	23 2.0	4 43.6	6 28.5	27 11.2	25 48.6	14 13.0
9 W	9 12 21.2	19 15.0	4 54.5	19 17.8	27 52.3	8 12.1	23 30.8	4 57.8	6 32.1	27 14.1	25 47.0	14 12.0
10 T	9 16 17.8	20 15.7	4 51.3	2♊50.7	29 40.7	9 26.9	23 59.7	5 12.0	6 35.6	27 17.0	25 45.3	14 11.0
11 F	9 20 14.3	21 16.4	4 48.2	16 4.1	1♓29.0	10 41.7	24 28.8	5 26.3	6 39.1	27 19.9	25 43.6	14 10.0
12 S	9 24 10.9	22 17.1	4 45.0	29 0.7	3 17.0	11 56.4	24 58.0	5 40.5	6 42.4	27 22.8	25 41.9	14 9.1
13 S	9 28 7.4	23 17.8	4 41.8	11♋43.0	5 4.4	13 11.1	25 27.4	5 54.8	6 45.7	27 25.7	25 40.3	14 8.1
14 M	9 32 4.0	24 18.4	4 38.6	24 13.5	6 51.0	14 25.8	25 57.1	6 9.2	6 48.9	27 28.7	25 38.6	14 7.2
15 T	9 36 0.6	25 19.0	4 35.5	6♌34.2	8 36.5	15 40.5	26 26.8	6 23.5	6 52.0	27 31.8	25 36.9	14 6.3
16 W	9 39 57.1	26 19.6	4 32.3	18 46.7	10 20.5	16 55.1	26 56.7	6 37.9	6 55.0	27 34.8	25 35.2	14 5.4
17 T	9 43 53.6	27 20.1	4 29.1	0♍52.3	12 2.5	18 9.7	27 26.8	6 52.3	6 57.9	27 37.8	25 33.5	14 4.5
18 F	9 47 50.2	28 20.6	4 25.9	12 52.1	13 42.3	19 24.2	27 57.0	7 6.7	7 0.7	27 40.9	25 31.8	14 3.7
19 S	9 51 46.8	29 21.1	4 22.7	24 47.5	15 19.2	20 38.8	28 27.4	7 21.1	7 3.4	27 44.0	25 30.2	14 2.8
20 S	9 55 43.3	0♓21.6	4 19.6	6♎39.9	16 52.6	21 53.3	28 57.9	7 35.5	7 6.1	27 47.1	25 28.5	14 2.0
21 M	9 59 39.9	1 22.1	4 16.4	18 31.6	18 22.1	23 7.7	29 28.5	7 49.9	7 8.6	27 50.3	25 26.8	14 1.2
22 T	10 3 36.4	2 22.5	4 13.2	0♏25.4	19 47.0	24 22.2	29 59.3	8 4.4	7 11.0	27 53.5	25 25.1	14 0.4
23 W	10 7 33.0	3 22.9	4 10.0	12 24.9	21 6.7	25 36.6	0♊30.2	8 18.8	7 13.4	27 56.6	25 23.5	13 59.6
24 T	10 11 29.5	4 23.3	4 6.9	24 34.2	22 20.4	26 51.0	1 1.3	8 33.3	7 15.6	27 59.8	25 21.8	13 58.9
25 F	10 15 26.1	5 23.6	4 3.7	6♐58.0	23 27.6	28 5.3	1 32.4	8 47.8	7 17.8	28 3.1	25 20.2	13 58.2
26 S	10 19 22.6	6 24.0	4 0.5	19 41.2	24 27.7	29 19.6	2 3.7	9 2.3	7 19.9	28 6.3	25 18.5	13 57.5
27 S	10 23 19.2	7 24.3	3 57.3	2♑48.4	25 20.0	0♈33.9	2 35.1	9 16.7	7 21.8	28 9.5	25 16.9	13 56.8
28 M	10 27 15.7	8 24.6	3 54.1	16 23.2	26 4.1	1 48.1	3 6.7	9 31.2	7 23.7	28 12.8	25 15.2	13 56.1
						DECLINATION						
1 T	8 40 48.8	17S26.4	23N20.5	22S56.8	18S43.1	13S31.9	19N19.2	11S15.1	19S27.1	1S54.5	13N17.4	21N18.5
4 F	8 52 38.4	16 34.8	23 20.8	13 11.2	17 1.5	12 11.8	19 42.0	10 59.8	19 28.9	1 51.2	13 19.1	21 19.1
7 M	9 4 28.1	15 40.7	23 21.2	3N37.1	15 6.8	10 48.8	20 4.5	10 44.4	19 30.5	1 47.8	13 20.8	21 19.7
10 T	9 16 17.8	14 44.2	23 21.6	17 55.9	12 59.9	9 23.2	20 26.7	10 28.8	19 31.9	1 44.3	13 22.5	21 20.2
13 S	9 28 7.4	13 45.5	23 21.9	23 24.5	10 42.8	7 55.5	20 48.6	10 13.1	19 33.2	1 40.8	13 24.3	21 20.8
16 W	9 39 57.1	12 44.8	23 22.2	18 29.4	8 18.5	6 25.9	21 10.0	9 57.2	19 34.3	1 37.1	13 26.0	21 21.3
19 S	9 51 46.8	11 42.2	23 22.6	6 38.9	5 52.3	4 54.8	21 30.8	9 41.2	19 35.3	1 33.4	13 27.7	21 21.9
22 T	10 3 36.4	10 38.0	23 22.9	7S18.5	3 31.2	3 22.5	21 51.0	9 25.2	19 36.1	1 29.6	13 29.5	21 22.4
25 F	10 15 26.1	9 32.2	23 23.2	19 6.4	1 24.3	1 49.4	22 10.5	9 9.0	19 36.8	1 25.7	13 31.2	21 22.9
28 M	10 27 15.7	8 25.2	23 23.5	23 25.8	0N18.2	0 15.8	22 29.2	8 52.7	19 37.3	1 21.8	13 32.8	21 23.3

MARCH 1927

LONGITUDE

DAY	Ephemeris Sidereal Time h m s	☉ ° ′	☊ ° ′	☽ ° ′	☿ ° ′	♀ ° ′	♂ ° ′	♃ ° ′	♄ ° ′	♅ ° ′	♆ ° ′	♇ ° ′
1 T	10 31 12.3	9♓24.8	3♋51.0	0♒27.4	26♓39.4	3♈ 2.3	3♊38.3	9♓45.7	7♐25.4	28♓16.1	25♌13.6	13♋55.5
2 W	10 35 8.9	10 25.1	3 47.8	14 59.9	27 5.8	4 16.5	4 10.1	10 0.2	7 27.1	28 19.4	25R12.0	13R54.8
3 T	10 39 5.4	11 25.3	3 44.6	29 56.3	27 22.8	5 30.6	4 42.0	10 14.7	7 28.7	28 22.7	25 10.4	13 54.2
4 F	10 43 1.9	12 25.5	3 41.4	15♓ 8.6	27 30.4	6 44.7	5 14.0	10 29.2	7 30.1	28 26.0	25 8.8	13 53.6
5 S	10 46 58.5	13 25.6	3 38.3	0♈26.1	27R28.6	7 58.8	5 46.1	10 43.7	7 31.5	28 29.4	25 7.2	13 53.1
6 S	10 50 55.1	14 25.7	3 35.1	15 37.4	27 17.7	9 12.8	6 18.3	10 58.2	7 32.8	28 32.7	25 5.6	13 52.6
7 M	10 54 51.6	15 25.8	3 31.9	0♉32.4	26 57.9	10 26.8	6 50.6	11 12.6	7 33.9	28 36.1	25 4.1	13 52.0
8 T	10 58 48.2	16 25.9	3 28.7	15 4.0	26 29.9	11 40.7	7 23.1	11 27.1	7 35.0	28 39.4	25 2.5	13 51.5
9 W	11 2 44.7	17 25.9	3 25.5	29 8.5	25 54.3	12 54.6	7 55.6	11 41.6	7 35.9	28 42.8	25 1.0	13 51.1
10 T	11 6 41.3	18 25.8	3 22.4	12♊45.6	25 12.1	14 8.5	8 28.2	11 56.0	7 36.8	28 46.2	24 59.5	13 50.6
11 F	11 10 37.8	19 25.8	3 19.2	25 57.4	24 24.2	15 22.3	9 0.9	12 10.5	7 37.6	28 49.6	24 57.9	13 50.2
12 S	11 14 34.4	20 25.7	3 16.0	8♋47.4	23 32.0	16 36.0	9 33.7	12 24.9	7 38.2	28 53.0	24 56.5	13 49.8
13 S	11 18 30.9	21 25.5	3 12.8	21 19.7	22 36.5	17 49.7	10 6.5	12 39.3	7 38.8	28 56.4	24 55.0	13 49.4
14 M	11 22 27.5	22 25.4	3 9.7	3♌38.4	21 39.2	19 3.3	10 39.5	12 53.7	7 39.2	28 59.8	24 53.5	13 49.1
15 T	11 26 24.0	23 25.2	3 6.5	15 47.1	20 41.4	20 16.9	11 12.5	13 8.1	7 39.6	29 3.2	24 52.1	13 48.7
16 W	11 30 20.6	24 24.9	3 3.3	27 49.0	19 44.2	21 30.5	11 45.6	13 22.4	7 39.8	29 6.6	24 50.7	13 48.4
17 T	11 34 17.1	25 24.6	3 0.1	9♍46.2	18 48.9	22 44.0	12 18.8	13 36.8	7 40.0	29 10.1	24 49.3	13 48.1
18 F	11 38 13.7	26 24.3	2 56.9	21 40.6	17 56.5	23 57.4	12 52.1	13 51.1	7 40.0	29 13.5	24 47.9	13 47.9
19 S	11 42 10.2	27 24.0	2 53.8	3♎33.5	17 7.9	25 10.8	13 25.4	14 5.4	7R40.0	29 16.9	24 46.5	13 47.6
20 S	11 46 6.8	28 23.6	2 50.6	15 26.3	16 23.9	26 24.2	13 58.8	14 19.7	7 39.8	29 20.3	24 45.2	13 47.4
21 M	11 50 3.4	29 23.2	2 47.4	27 20.3	15 45.0	27 37.5	14 32.3	14 33.9	7 39.6	29 23.8	24 43.8	13 47.2
22 T	11 53 59.9	0♈22.7	2 44.2	9♏17.3	15 11.7	28 50.7	15 5.8	14 48.1	7 39.2	29 27.2	24 42.5	13 47.0
23 W	11 57 56.4	1 22.3	2 41.1	21 19.9	14 44.2	0♉ 3.9	15 39.4	15 2.3	7 38.8	29 30.6	24 41.2	13 46.9
24 T	12 1 53.0	2 21.8	2 37.9	3♐31.0	14 22.7	1 17.0	16 13.1	15 16.5	7 38.2	29 34.0	24 40.0	13 46.8
25 F	12 5 49.6	3 21.2	2 34.7	15 54.5	14 7.3	2 30.1	16 46.8	15 30.7	7 37.6	29 37.5	24 38.7	13 46.7
26 S	12 9 46.1	4 20.7	2 31.5	28 34.6	13 57.9	3 43.1	17 20.6	15 44.8	7 36.8	29 40.9	24 37.5	13 46.6
27 S	12 13 42.7	5 20.1	2 28.3	11♑35.9	13 54.4	4 56.1	17 54.5	15 58.9	7 36.0	29 44.3	24 36.3	13 46.6
28 M	12 17 39.2	6 19.5	2 25.2	25 2.3	13D56.6	6 9.0	18 28.4	16 12.9	7 35.0	29 47.7	24 35.1	13 46.5
29 T	12 21 35.8	7 18.8	2 22.0	8♒56.7	14 4.5	7 21.8	19 2.4	16 27.0	7 34.0	29 51.1	24 34.0	13D46.5
30 W	12 25 32.3	8 18.1	2 18.8	23 19.8	14 17.6	8 34.6	19 36.5	16 40.9	7 32.8	29 54.5	24 32.9	13 46.6
31 T	12 29 28.9	9 17.4	2 15.6	8♓ 8.9	14 35.9	9 47.4	20 10.6	16 54.9	7 31.6	29 57.9	24 31.8	13 46.6

DECLINATION

DAY	Sid. Time	☉	☊	☽	☿	♀	♂	♃	♄	♅	♆	♇
1 T	10 31 12.3	8S 2.6	23N23.6	22S11.1	0N45.3	0N15.4	22N35.3	8S47.3	19S37.4	1S20.5	13N33.4	21N23.5
4 F	10 43 1.9	6 54.1	23 23.8	10 13.9	1 41.1	1 49.1	22 53.0	8 31.0	19 37.8	1 16.5	13 35.0	21 23.9
7 M	10 54 51.6	5 44.7	23 24.1	7N25.7	1 54.7	3 22.6	23 9.7	8 14.7	19 37.9	1 12.5	13 36.6	21 24.4
10 T	11 6 41.3	4 34.6	23 24.3	20 30.8	1 25.7	4 55.5	23 25.5	7 58.3	19 37.9	1 8.4	13 38.2	21 24.8
13 S	11 18 30.9	3 24.1	23 24.6	23 14.5	0 21.0	6 27.4	23 40.3	7 41.9	19 37.8	1 4.3	13 39.7	21 25.2
16 W	11 30 20.6	2 13.2	23 24.8	16 2.6	1S 6.0	7 58.0	23 54.1	7 25.6	19 37.5	1 0.2	13 41.2	21 25.5
19 S	11 42 10.2	1 2.1	23 25.0	3 9.7	2 38.9	9 27.0	24 6.7	7 9.2	19 37.1	0 56.1	13 42.6	21 25.9
22 T	11 53 59.9	0N 9.1	23 25.2	10S47.5	4 3.4	10 54.0	24 18.1	6 53.0	19 36.6	0 52.0	13 43.9	21 26.2
25 F	12 5 49.6	1 20.0	23 25.4	21 17.8	5 10.6	12 18.8	24 28.4	6 36.7	19 35.9	0 47.9	13 45.2	21 26.5
28 M	12 17 39.2	2 30.7	23 25.6	23 3.7	5 56.1	13 41.0	24 37.4	6 20.6	19 35.1	0 43.9	13 46.4	21 26.8
31 T	12 29 28.9	3 41.0	23 25.8	12 46.2	6 19.1	15 0.3	24 45.2	6 4.5	19 34.1	0 39.8	13 47.5	21 27.1

APRIL 1927

LONGITUDE

DAY	Sid. Time	☉	☊	☽	☿	♀	♂	♃	♄	♅	♆	♇
1 F	12 33 25.4	10♈16.7	2♋12.5	23♓18.0	14♓59.1	11♉ 0.1	20♊44.7	17♓ 8.8	7♐30.2	0♈ 1.3	24♌30.7	13♋46.7
2 S	12 37 22.0	11 15.9	2 9.3	8♈37.4	15 26.8	12 12.7	21 19.0	17 22.7	7R28.8	0 4.7	24R29.6	13 46.8
3 S	12 41 18.6	12 15.1	2 6.1	23 55.5	15 59.0	13 25.3	21 53.2	17 36.5	7 27.3	0 8.1	24 28.6	13 46.9
4 M	12 45 15.1	13 14.2	2 2.9	9♉ 1.0	16 35.3	14 37.8	22 27.6	17 50.3	7 25.7	0 11.5	24 27.6	13 47.1
5 T	12 49 11.6	14 13.3	1 59.7	23 44.6	17 15.5	15 50.3	23 2.0	18 4.1	7 23.9	0 14.8	24 26.7	13 47.2
6 W	12 53 8.2	15 12.4	1 56.6	8♊ 0.9	17 59.5	17 2.6	23 36.4	18 17.8	7 22.1	0 18.2	24 25.7	13 47.4
7 T	12 57 4.7	16 11.5	1 53.4	21 47.6	18 46.9	18 15.0	24 10.9	18 31.5	7 20.2	0 21.5	24 24.8	13 47.6
8 F	13 1 1.3	17 10.5	1 50.2	5♋ 5.9	19 37.8	19 27.2	24 45.4	18 45.1	7 18.3	0 24.8	24 23.9	13 47.9
9 S	13 4 57.9	18 9.5	1 47.0	17 58.9	20 31.7	20 39.4	25 20.0	18 58.6	7 16.2	0 28.1	24 23.1	13 48.2
10 S	13 8 54.4	19 8.4	1 43.9	0♌30.9	21 28.7	21 51.5	25 54.7	19 12.2	7 14.0	0 31.4	24 22.2	13 48.4
11 M	13 12 50.9	20 7.3	1 40.7	12 46.8	22 28.5	23 3.5	26 29.3	19 25.6	7 11.7	0 34.7	24 21.4	13 48.8
12 T	13 16 47.5	21 6.1	1 37.5	24 51.1	23 31.1	24 15.5	27 4.0	19 39.0	7 9.4	0 38.0	24 20.7	13 49.1
13 W	13 20 44.1	22 4.9	1 34.3	6♍48.0	24 36.3	25 27.4	27 38.8	19 52.4	7 7.0	0 41.2	24 19.9	13 49.5
14 T	13 24 40.6	23 3.7	1 31.1	18 41.0	25 44.0	26 39.2	28 13.6	20 5.7	7 4.5	0 44.5	24 19.2	13 49.9
15 F	13 28 37.2	24 2.5	1 28.0	0♎32.7	26 54.1	27 51.0	28 48.4	20 18.9	7 1.9	0 47.7	24 18.5	13 50.3
16 S	13 32 33.7	25 1.2	1 24.8	12 25.5	28 6.5	29 2.6	29 23.3	20 32.1	6 59.2	0 50.9	24 17.9	13 50.7
17 S	13 36 30.3	25 59.8	1 21.6	24 20.8	29 21.1	0♊14.2	29 58.2	20 45.3	6 56.5	0 54.1	24 17.3	13 51.1
18 M	13 40 26.8	26 58.5	1 18.4	6♏20.1	0♈37.9	1 25.7	0♋33.2	20 58.4	6 53.7	0 57.2	24 16.7	13 51.6
19 T	13 44 23.4	27 57.1	1 15.3	18 24.8	1 56.7	2 37.1	1 8.2	21 11.4	6 50.8	1 0.4	24 16.1	13 52.1
20 W	13 48 19.9	28 55.7	1 12.1	0♐36.2	3 17.7	3 48.5	1 43.2	21 24.3	6 47.8	1 3.5	24 15.6	13 52.6
21 T	13 52 16.5	29 54.2	1 8.9	12 56.3	4 40.6	4 59.7	2 18.2	21 37.2	6 44.7	1 6.6	24 15.1	13 53.2
22 F	13 56 13.1	0♉52.7	1 5.7	25 27.7	6 5.4	6 10.9	2 53.3	21 50.0	6 41.6	1 9.7	24 14.6	13 53.8
23 S	14 0 9.6	1 51.2	1 2.5	8♑13.2	7 32.2	7 22.0	3 28.5	22 2.8	6 38.4	1 12.8	24 14.2	13 54.4
24 S	14 4 6.2	2 49.7	0 59.4	21 16.1	9 0.9	8 33.0	4 3.6	22 15.5	6 35.1	1 15.8	24 13.8	13 55.0
25 M	14 8 2.7	3 48.1	0 56.2	4♒39.6	10 31.4	9 44.0	4 38.8	22 28.1	6 31.8	1 18.9	24 13.4	13 55.6
26 T	14 11 59.3	4 46.5	0 53.0	18 26.2	12 3.8	10 54.8	5 14.0	22 40.7	6 28.4	1 21.9	24 13.1	13 56.3
27 W	14 15 55.8	5 44.9	0 49.8	2♓36.8	13 38.0	12 5.6	5 49.3	22 53.2	6 24.9	1 24.8	24 12.8	13 56.9
28 T	14 19 52.4	6 43.3	0 46.7	17 10.3	15 14.0	13 16.3	6 24.6	23 5.6	6 21.4	1 27.8	24 12.5	13 57.6
29 F	14 23 48.9	7 41.6	0 43.5	2♈ 2.5	16 51.8	14 26.9	6 60.0	23 17.9	6 17.8	1 30.7	24 12.2	13 58.4
30 S	14 27 45.5	8 39.9	0 40.3	17 6.4	18 31.4	15 37.4	7 35.3	23 30.2	6 14.2	1 33.6	24 12.0	13 59.1

DECLINATION

DAY	Sid. Time	☉	☊	☽	☿	♀	♂	♃	♄	♅	♆	♇
1 F	12 33 25.4	4N 4.3	23N25.8	7S12.5	6S22.0	15N26.0	24N47.5	5S59.2	19S33.8	0S38.5	13N47.9	21N27.2
4 M	12 45 15.1	5 13.7	23 26.0	10N44.6	6 16.9	16 40.9	24 53.5	5 43.3	19 32.7	0 34.4	13 48.9	21 27.4
7 T	12 57 4.7	6 22.2	23 26.1	22 23.2	5 52.7	17 52.1	24 58.2	5 27.5	19 31.4	0 30.5	13 49.8	21 27.6
10 S	13 8 54.4	7 29.8	23 26.3	22 29.1	5 11.4	18 59.3	25 1.5	5 11.9	19 30.1	0 26.5	13 50.7	21 27.8
13 W	13 20 44.1	8 36.2	23 26.4	13 17.5	4 14.4	20 2.1	25 3.4	4 56.4	19 28.6	0 22.7	13 51.4	21 28.0
16 S	13 32 33.7	9 41.3	23 26.5	0S22.8	3 3.4	21 0.3	25 3.9	4 41.2	19 27.0	0 18.8	13 52.1	21 28.1
19 T	13 44 23.4	10 45.0	23 26.6	14 6.2	1 39.6	21 53.6	25 3.0	4 26.1	19 25.4	0 15.1	13 52.7	21 28.3
22 F	13 56 13.1	11 47.1	23 26.7	23 0.9	0 4.2	22 41.8	25 0.7	4 11.2	19 23.6	0 11.4	13 53.2	21 28.4
25 M	14 8 2.7	12 47.4	23 26.7	21 58.2	1N41.7	23 24.5	24 56.9	3 56.6	19 21.7	0 7.8	13 53.6	21 28.4
28 T	14 19 52.4	13 45.9	23 26.8	9 39.7	3 37.2	24 1.6	24 51.7	3 42.2	19 19.8	0 4.3	13 53.9	21 28.5

MAY 1927

LONGITUDE

DAY	EPHEMERIS SIDEREAL TIME	☉	☊	☽	☿	♀	♂	♃	♄	♅	♆	♇
	h m s	° ′	° ′	° ′	° ′	° ′	° ′	° ′	° ′	° ′	° ′	° ′
1 S	14 31 42.0	9♉38.2	0♋37.1	2♉12.7	20♈12.9	16♊47.8	8♋10.7	23♓42.4	6♐10.4	1♈36.5	24♌11.8	13♋59.9
2 M	14 35 38.6	10 36.5	0 33.9	17 11.5	21 56.1	17 58.2	8 46.2	23 54.5	6R 6.7	1 39.4	24R 11.7	14 0.7
3 T	14 39 35.2	11 34.7	0 30.8	1♊53.6	23 41.2	19 8.4	9 21.6	24 6.5	6 2.9	1 42.2	24 11.6	14 1.5
4 W	14 43 31.7	12 32.9	0 27.6	16 12.6	25 28.1	20 18.5	9 57.1	24 18.4	5 59.0	1 45.0	24 11.5	14 2.3
5 T	14 47 28.3	13 31.0	0 24.4	0♋ 4.7	27 16.8	21 28.6	10 32.7	24 30.3	5 55.1	1 47.7	24 11.5	14 3.1
6 F	14 51 24.8	14 29.2	0 21.2	13 29.4	29 7.4	22 38.5	11 8.2	24 42.1	5 51.1	1 50.5	24 11.5	14 4.0
7 S	14 55 21.4	15 27.3	0 18.1	26 28.3	0♉59.7	23 48.3	11 43.8	24 53.7	5 47.1	1 53.2	24D 11.5	14 4.9
8 S	14 59 17.9	16 25.3	0 14.9	9♌ 4.9	2 53.9	24 58.1	12 19.5	25 5.3	5 43.0	1 55.8	24 11.5	14 5.8
9 M	15 3 14.5	17 23.4	0 11.7	21 23.5	4 49.9	26 7.7	12 55.1	25 16.8	5 38.9	1 58.5	24 11.6	14 6.7
10 T	15 7 11.0	18 21.4	0 8.5	3♍28.9	6 47.8	27 17.2	13 30.8	25 28.3	5 34.8	2 1.1	24 11.7	14 7.7
11 W	15 11 7.6	19 19.3	0 5.4	15 25.7	8 47.3	28 26.6	14 6.5	25 39.6	5 30.6	2 3.7	24 11.9	14 8.6
12 T	15 15 4.2	20 17.3	0 2.2	27 18.2	10 48.6	29 35.8	14 42.2	25 50.8	5 26.4	2 6.2	24 12.1	14 9.6
13 F	15 19 0.7	21 15.2	29♊59.0	9♎10.1	12 51.6	0♋45.0	15 17.9	26 1.9	5 22.2	2 8.7	24 12.3	14 10.6
14 S	15 22 57.2	22 13.1	29 55.8	21 4.7	14 56.1	1 54.0	15 53.7	26 13.0	5 17.9	2 11.2	24 12.5	14 11.6
15 S	15 26 53.8	23 10.9	29 52.6	3♏ 4.5	17 2.1	3 2.9	16 29.5	26 23.9	5 13.6	2 13.7	24 12.8	14 12.7
16 M	15 30 50.4	24 8.8	29 49.5	15 11.3	19 9.5	4 11.7	17 5.3	26 34.8	5 9.3	2 16.1	24 13.1	14 13.7
17 T	15 34 46.9	25 6.6	29 46.3	27 26.7	21 18.1	5 20.3	17 41.1	26 45.5	5 5.0	2 18.5	24 13.5	14 14.8
18 W	15 38 43.5	26 4.3	29 43.1	9♐51.8	23 27.7	6 28.8	18 17.0	26 56.1	5 0.6	2 20.8	24 13.9	14 15.9
19 T	15 42 40.0	27 2.1	29 39.9	22 27.7	25 38.2	7 37.2	18 52.9	27 6.7	4 56.2	2 23.1	24 14.3	14 17.0
20 F	15 46 36.6	27 59.8	29 36.8	5♑15.4	27 49.3	8 45.4	19 28.8	27 17.1	4 51.8	2 25.4	24 14.7	14 18.1
21 S	15 50 33.2	28 57.6	29 33.6	18 16.1	0♊ 0.8	9 53.5	20 4.7	27 27.4	4 47.4	2 27.7	24 15.2	14 19.3
22 S	15 54 29.7	29 55.3	29 30.4	1♒31.2	2 12.4	11 1.5	20 40.7	27 37.7	4 42.9	2 29.9	24 15.7	14 20.4
23 M	15 58 26.3	0♊52.9	29 27.2	15 2.0	4 23.8	12 9.3	21 16.6	27 47.8	4 38.5	2 32.0	24 16.3	14 21.6
24 T	16 2 22.8	1 50.6	29 24.0	28 49.3	6 34.8	13 17.0	21 52.6	27 57.7	4 34.0	2 34.1	24 16.8	14 22.8
25 W	16 6 19.4	2 48.2	29 20.9	12♓53.2	8 45.0	14 24.5	22 28.7	28 7.6	4 29.6	2 36.2	24 17.4	14 24.0
26 T	16 10 15.9	3 45.9	29 17.7	27 12.7	10 54.3	15 31.9	23 4.7	28 17.4	4 25.1	2 38.3	24 18.1	14 25.2
27 F	16 14 12.5	4 43.5	29 14.5	11♈44.9	13 2.4	16 39.1	23 40.8	28 27.0	4 20.6	2 40.3	24 18.7	14 26.4
28 S	16 18 9.0	5 41.1	29 11.3	26 25.1	15 8.9	17 46.2	24 16.9	28 36.6	4 16.1	2 42.3	24 19.4	14 27.6
29 S	16 22 5.6	6 38.7	29 8.2	11♉ 7.3	17 13.8	18 53.1	24 53.0	28 46.0	4 11.7	2 44.2	24 20.2	14 28.9
30 M	16 26 2.1	7 36.2	29 5.0	25 44.6	19 16.8	19 59.9	25 29.2	28 55.3	4 7.2	2 46.1	24 21.0	14 30.2
31 T	16 29 58.7	8 33.8	29 1.8	10♊10.2	21 17.7	21 6.5	26 5.4	29 4.4	4 2.8	2 47.9	24 21.7	14 31.5

DECLINATION

DAY	EPHEMERIS SIDEREAL TIME	☉	☊	☽	☿	♀	♂	♃	♄	♅	♆	♇
1 S	14 31 42.0	14N42.3	23N26.8	8N13.6	5N41.0	24N32.8	24N45.0	3S28.1	19S17.8	0S 0.9	13N54.1	21N28.5
4 W	14 43 31.7	15 36.6	23 26.9	21 37.4	7 52.0	24 58.1	24 36.9	3 14.3	19 15.7	0N 2.4	13 54.2	21 28.5
7 S	14 55 21.4	16 28.5	23 26.9	23 13.8	10 8.5	25 17.3	24 27.3	3 0.8	19 13.5	0 5.6	13 54.2	21 28.5
10 T	15 7 11.0	17 18.0	23 26.9	14 35.1	12 28.6	25 30.3	24 16.3	2 47.6	19 11.4	0 8.7	13 54.1	21 28.5
13 F	15 19 0.7	18 4.8	23♊26.9	1 1.9	14 49.3	25 37.1	24 3.9	2 34.7	19 9.1	0 11.7	13 53.9	21 28.4
16 M	15 30 50.4	18 49.0	23 26.9	13S 0.6	17 6.9	25 37.7	23 50.0	2 22.2	19 6.9	0 14.5	13 53.6	21 28.3
19 T	15 42 40.0	19 30.2	23 26.9	22 43.5	19 16.8	25 32.1	23 34.7	2 10.1	19 4.6	0 17.3	13 53.2	21 28.2
22 S	15 54 29.7	20 8.5	23 26.9	22 38.4	21 13.3	25 20.5	23 18.0	1 58.4	19 2.3	0 19.9	13 52.7	21 28.1
25 W	16 6 19.4	20 43.7	23 26.8	11 23.0	22 51.4	25 2.9	22 59.9	1 47.0	19 0.0	0 22.3	13 52.1	21 28.0
28 S	16 18 9.0	21 15.7	23 26.8	5N54.0	24 7.1	24 39.5	22 40.5	1 36.1	18 57.8	0 24.6	13 51.4	21 27.8
31 T	16 29 58.7	21 44.4	23 26.7	20 23.8	24 58.7	24 10.6	22 19.7	1 25.7	18 55.5	0 26.8	13 50.6	21 27.6

JUNE 1927

LONGITUDE

DAY	EPHEMERIS SIDEREAL TIME	☉	☊	☽	☿	♀	♂	♃	♄	♅	♆	♇
1 W	16 33 55.3	9♊31.3	28♊58.6	24♊18.4	23♊16.5	22♋12.9	26♋41.6	29♓13.5	3♐58.3	2♈49.7	24♌22.6	14♋32.8
2 T	16 37 51.8	10 28.8	28 55.5	8♋ 5.3	25 12.9	23 19.2	27 17.8	29 22.4	3R 53.9	2 51.5	24 23.4	14 34.1
3 F	16 41 48.3	11 26.3	28 52.3	21 29.1	27 7.0	24 25.2	27 54.0	29 31.2	3 49.5	2 53.2	24 24.3	14 35.4
4 S	16 45 44.9	12 23.8	28 49.1	4♌29.9	28 58.5	25 31.1	28 30.3	29 39.8	3 45.1	2 54.9	24 25.2	14 36.7
5 S	16 49 41.5	13 21.3	28 45.9	17 9.7	0♋47.5	26 36.8	29 6.6	29 48.3	3 40.7	2 56.5	24 26.2	14 38.1
6 M	16 53 38.1	14 18.7	28 42.8	29 31.6	2 34.0	27 42.3	29 42.9	29 56.7	3 36.3	2 58.1	24 27.2	14 39.4
7 T	16 57 34.6	15 16.1	28 39.6	11♍39.6	4 17.7	28 47.6	0♌19.2	0♈ 5.0	3 32.0	2 59.7	24 28.2	14 40.8
8 W	17 1 31.1	16 13.5	28 36.4	23 38.2	5 58.9	29 52.6	0 55.6	0 13.1	3 27.7	3 1.2	24 29.2	14 42.2
9 T	17 5 27.7	17 10.9	28 33.2	5♎31.8	7 37.4	0♌57.5	1 32.0	0 21.0	3 23.4	3 2.6	24 30.3	14 43.6
10 F	17 9 24.3	18 8.3	28 30.0	17 25.0	9 13.1	2 2.1	2 8.4	0 28.9	3 19.2	3 4.1	24 31.4	14 45.0
11 S	17 13 20.8	19 5.6	28 26.9	29 21.8	10 46.1	3 6.5	2 44.8	0 36.6	3 14.9	3 5.4	24 32.5	14 46.4
12 S	17 17 17.4	20 2.9	28 23.7	11♏25.8	12 16.4	4 10.7	3 21.2	0 44.1	3 10.8	3 6.8	24 33.6	14 47.8
13 M	17 21 14.0	21 0.3	28 20.5	23 40.0	13 43.9	5 14.6	3 57.7	0 51.5	3 6.6	3 8.0	24 34.8	14 49.2
14 T	17 25 10.5	21 57.6	28 17.3	6♐ 6.6	15 8.6	6 18.3	4 34.1	0 58.8	3 2.5	3 9.3	24 36.0	14 50.7
15 W	17 29 7.0	22 54.8	28 14.2	18 47.1	16 30.5	7 21.7	5 10.6	1 5.9	2 58.4	3 10.5	24 37.3	14 52.1
16 T	17 33 3.6	23 52.1	28 11.0	1♑42.2	17 49.5	8 24.9	5 47.1	1 12.8	2 54.4	3 11.6	24 38.5	14 53.6
17 F	17 37 0.2	24 49.4	28 7.8	14 51.9	19 5.6	9 27.8	6 23.7	1 19.6	2 50.4	3 12.7	24 39.8	14 55.0
18 S	17 40 56.8	25 46.7	28 4.6	28 15.8	20 18.7	10 30.4	7 0.2	1 26.3	2 46.5	3 13.8	24 41.1	14 56.5
19 S	17 44 53.3	26 43.9	28 1.5	11♒52.7	21 28.8	11 32.7	7 36.8	1 32.8	2 42.6	3 14.8	24 42.5	14 58.0
20 M	17 48 49.8	27 41.1	27 58.3	25 41.5	22 35.8	12 34.8	8 13.4	1 39.1	2 38.8	3 15.7	24 43.8	14 59.5
21 T	17 52 46.4	28 38.4	27 55.1	9♓40.4	23 39.7	13 36.5	8 50.0	1 45.3	2 35.0	3 16.6	24 45.2	15 1.0
22 W	17 56 43.0	29 35.6	27 51.9	23 47.7	24 40.3	14 38.0	9 26.6	1 51.4	2 31.2	3 17.5	24 46.6	15 2.5
23 T	18 0 39.6	0♋32.9	27 48.8	8♈ 1.3	25 37.6	15 39.1	10 3.3	1 57.2	2 27.6	3 18.3	24 48.1	15 4.0
24 F	18 4 36.1	1 30.1	27 45.6	22 18.6	26 31.6	16 40.0	10 40.0	2 2.9	2 23.9	3 19.1	24 49.5	15 5.5
25 S	18 8 32.6	2 27.4	27 42.4	6♉36.7	27 22.0	17 40.5	11 16.7	2 8.5	2 20.4	3 19.8	24 51.0	15 7.0
26 S	18 12 29.2	3 24.6	27 39.2	20 52.4	28 8.8	18 40.6	11 53.4	2 13.8	2 16.9	3 20.5	24 52.5	15 8.5
27 M	18 16 25.7	4 21.8	27 36.0	5♊ 2.1	28 51.9	19 40.5	12 30.2	2 19.1	2 13.4	3 21.1	24 54.1	15 10.0
28 T	18 20 22.3	5 19.1	27 32.9	19 2.1	29 31.1	20 39.9	13 6.9	2 24.1	2 10.0	3 21.7	24 55.6	15 11.6
29 W	18 24 18.9	6 16.3	27 29.7	2♋48.9	0♌ 6.4	21 39.0	13 43.7	2 29.0	2 6.7	3 22.2	24 57.2	15 13.1
30 T	18 28 15.4	7 13.5	27 26.5	16 20.0	0 37.6	22 37.7	14 20.6	2 33.6	2 3.5	3 22.7	24 58.8	15 14.6

DECLINATION

DAY	EPHEMERIS SIDEREAL TIME	☉	☊	☽	☿	♀	♂	♃	♄	♅	♆	♇
1 W	16 33 55.3	21N53.2	23N26.7	22N59.7	25N10.5	23N59.8	22N12.5	1S22.3	18S54.8	0N27.5	13N50.4	21N27.6
4 S	16 45 44.9	22 17.4	23 26.6	22 11.6	25 30.5	23 23.8	21 50.0	1 12.5	18 52.6	0 29.5	13 49.4	21 27.4
7 T	16 57 34.6	22 38.1	23 26.5	11 51.8	25 29.5	22 42.9	21 26.2	1 3.1	18 50.4	0 31.3	13 48.5	21 27.1
10 F	17 9 24.3	22 55.2	23 26.4	2S14.7	25 10.3	21 57.3	21 1.1	0 54.3	18 48.3	0 32.9	13 47.4	21 26.9
13 M	17 21 14.0	23 8.6	23 26.3	15 49.0	24 36.1	21 7.3	20 34.8	0 46.0	18 46.3	0 34.4	13 46.2	21 26.6
16 T	17 33 3.6	23 18.4	23 26.2	23 47.4	23 50.1	20 13.3	20 7.2	0 38.3	18 44.4	0 35.7	13 45.0	21 26.4
19 S	17 44 53.3	23 24.5	23 26.0	20 45.5	22 55.3	19 15.6	19 38.6	0 31.1	18 42.5	0 36.9	13 43.7	21 26.1
22 W	17 56 43.0	23 26.9	23 25.9	7 17.9	21 54.6	18 14.5	19 8.7	0 24.4	18 40.8	0 37.9	13 42.3	21 25.8
25 S	18 8 32.6	23 25.6	23 25.7	9N49.8	20 50.7	17 10.4	18 37.8	0 18.4	18 39.1	0 38.7	13 40.8	21 25.5
28 T	18 20 22.3	23 20.5	23 25.6	22 10.8	19 46.6	16 3.6	18 5.7	0 13.0	18 37.6	0 39.4	13 39.2	21 25.2

JULY 1927

LONGITUDE

DAY	EPHEMERIS SIDEREAL TIME h m s	☉ ° ′	☊ ° ′	☾ ° ′	☿ ° ′	♀ ° ′	♂ ° ′	♃ ° ′	♄ ° ′	♅ ° ′	♆ ° ′	♇ ° ′
1 F	18 32 12.0	8♋10.8	27♓23.3	29♋33.4	1♌ 4.6	23♌36.0	14♌57.4	2♈38.2	2♐ 0.3	3♈23.1	25♌ 0.5	15♋16.2
2 S	18 36 8.5	9 8.0	27 20.2	12♌28.6	1 27.3	24 33.9	15 34.3	2 42.5	1R57.2	3 23.5	25 2.1	15 17.7
3 S	18 40 5.1	10 5.2	27 17.0	25 6.2	1 45.5	25 31.4	16 11.2	2 46.7	1 54.2	3 23.9	25 3.8	15 19.3
4 M	18 44 1.7	11 2.4	27 13.8	7♍27.8	1 59.3	26 28.5	16 48.1	2 50.6	1 51.2	3 24.2	25 5.5	15 20.8
5 T	18 47 58.2	11 59.6	27 10.6	19 36.5	2 8.4	27 25.0	17 25.0	2 54.4	1 48.3	3 24.4	25 7.2	15 22.3
6 W	18 51 54.8	12 56.8	27 7.5	1♎35.7	2 12.8	28 21.2	18 2.0	2 58.1	1 45.5	3 24.6	25 9.0	15 23.9
7 T	18 55 51.4	13 54.0	27 4.3	13 29.7	2R12.6	29 16.8	18 39.0	3 1.5	1 42.8	3 24.7	25 10.7	15 25.4
8 F	18 59 47.9	14 51.2	27 1.1	25 23.1	2 7.7	0♍11.9	19 16.0	3 4.8	1 40.1	3 24.8	25 12.5	15 27.0
9 S	19 3 44.5	15 48.4	26 57.9	7♏20.5	1 58.1	1 6.5	19 53.0	3 7.8	1 37.6	3 24.9	25 14.3	15 28.5
10 S	19 7 41.0	16 45.6	26 54.7	19 26.4	1 43.9	2 0.5	20 30.0	3 10.7	1 35.1	3R24.9	25 16.1	15 30.1
11 M	19 11 37.6	17 42.8	26 51.6	1♐45.0	1 25.3	2 54.0	21 7.1	3 13.4	1 32.7	3 24.8	25 17.9	15 31.6
12 T	19 15 34.2	18 40.0	26 48.4	14 19.7	1 2.5	3 46.9	21 44.2	3 15.9	1 30.4	3 24.7	25 19.8	15 33.2
13 W	19 19 30.7	19 37.2	26 45.2	27 12.9	0 35.8	4 39.2	22 21.3	3 18.3	1 28.1	3 24.6	25 21.7	15 34.7
14 T	19 23 27.2	20 34.4	26 42.0	10♑25.8	0 5.4	5 30.9	22 58.4	3 20.4	1 25.9	3 24.4	25 23.5	15 36.3
15 F	19 27 23.8	21 31.6	26 38.9	23 58.1	29♋31.9	6 21.9	23 35.6	3 22.3	1 23.9	3 24.1	25 25.4	15 37.8
16 S	19 31 20.4	22 28.8	26 35.7	7♒48.1	28 55.7	7 12.3	24 12.7	3 24.1	1 21.9	3 23.8	25 27.4	15 39.4
17 S	19 35 16.9	23 26.0	26 32.5	21 52.5	28 17.4	8 1.9	24 49.9	3 25.7	1 20.0	3 23.5	25 29.3	15 40.9
18 M	19 39 13.5	24 23.3	26 29.3	6♓ 7.0	27 37.6	8 50.9	25 27.2	3 27.1	1 18.2	3 23.1	25 31.3	15 42.4
19 T	19 43 10.0	25 20.5	26 26.2	20 27.0	26 56.8	9 39.1	26 4.4	3 28.2	1 16.4	3 22.7	25 33.2	15 44.0
20 W	19 47 6.6	26 17.7	26 23.0	4♈48.0	26 16.0	10 26.5	26 41.7	3 29.2	1 14.8	3 22.2	25 35.2	15 45.5
21 T	19 51 3.2	27 15.0	26 19.8	19 6.0	25 35.6	11 13.1	27 19.0	3 30.0	1 13.3	3 21.7	25 37.2	15 47.0
22 F	19 54 59.7	28 12.3	26 16.6	3♉18.1	24 56.6	11 58.9	27 56.3	3 30.6	1 11.8	3 21.1	25 39.2	15 48.5
23 S	19 58 56.2	29 9.6	26 13.5	17 22.2	24 19.5	12 43.9	28 33.6	3 31.0	1 10.5	3 20.5	25 41.2	15 50.1
24 S	20 2 52.8	0♌ 6.9	26 10.3	1♊17.0	23 45.1	13 28.0	29 11.0	3 31.2	1 9.2	3 19.8	25 43.3	15 51.6
25 M	20 6 49.4	1 4.2	26 7.1	15 1.7	23 14.1	14 11.1	29 48.4	3 31.2	1 8.0	3 19.1	25 45.3	15 53.1
26 T	20 10 45.9	2 1.5	26 3.9	28 35.3	22 46.9	14 53.3	0♍25.8	3R31.0	1 6.9	3 18.3	25 47.4	15 54.6
27 W	20 14 42.5	2 58.9	26 0.7	11♋57.4	22 24.2	15 34.5	1 3.3	3 30.6	1 5.9	3 17.5	25 49.5	15 56.1
28 T	20 18 39.0	3 56.2	25 57.6	25 6.9	22 6.4	16 14.7	1 40.8	3 30.0	1 5.0	3 16.7	25 51.5	15 57.6
29 F	20 22 35.6	4 53.6	25 54.4	8♌ 3.3	21 53.9	16 53.8	2 18.3	3 29.2	1 4.2	3 15.8	25 53.6	15 59.0
30 S	20 26 32.1	5 51.0	25 51.2	20 46.1	21 47.1	17 31.8	2 55.8	3 28.2	1 3.5	3 14.8	25 55.8	16 0.5
31 S	20 30 28.7	6 48.4	25 48.0	3♍15.5	21 46.2	18 8.7	3 33.4	3 27.1	1 2.9	3 13.9	25 57.9	16 2.0

DECLINATION

DAY	EPHEMERIS SIDEREAL TIME h m s	☉	☊	☾	☿	♀	♂	♃	♄	♅	♆	♇
1 F	18 32 12.0	23N11.8	23N25.4	22N57.5	18N45.1	14N54.5	17N32.6	0S 8.2	18S36.2	0N39.9	13N37.6	21N24.8
4 M	18 44 1.7	22 59.4	23 25.2	13 20.9	17 49.0	13 43.4	16 58.5	0 4.0	18 35.0	0 40.2	13 35.9	21 24.5
7 T	18 55 51.4	22 43.4	23 25.0	0S39.5	17 1.1	12 30.8	16 23.4	0 0.5	18 33.9	0 40.3	13 34.2	21 24.2
10 S	19 7 41.0	22 23.8	23 24.8	14 26.8	16 24.4	11 17.0	15 47.4	0N 2.3	18 33.0	0 40.3	13 32.4	21 23.8
13 W	19 19 30.7	22 0.8	23 24.5	23 21.5	16 0.9	10 2.4	15 10.4	0 4.5	18 32.2	0 40.0	13 30.5	21 23.5
16 S	19 31 20.4	21 34.4	23 24.3	21 34.4	15 52.1	8 47.4	14 32.6	0 6.0	18 31.6	0 39.7	13 28.6	21 23.1
19 T	19 43 10.0	21 4.7	23 24.0	8 32.3	15 58.0	7 32.4	13 54.0	0 6.8	18 31.2	0 39.1	13 26.6	21 22.7
22 F	19 54 59.7	20 31.7	23 23.8	8N38.0	16 17.3	6 17.9	13 14.5	0 6.9	18 30.9	0 38.4	13 24.6	21 22.4
25 M	20 6 49.4	19 55.7	23 23.5	21 28.6	16 47.3	5 4.3	12 34.2	0 6.3	18 30.8	0 37.5	13 22.5	21 22.0
28 T	20 18 39.0	19 16.7	23 23.2	23 28.7	17 24.3	3 52.0	11 53.2	0 5.1	18 30.9	0 36.5	13 20.4	21 21.6
31 S	20 30 28.7	18 34.7	23 22.9	14 42.0	18 4.1	2 41.6	11 11.5	0 3.1	18 31.1	0 35.3	13 18.3	21 21.2

AUGUST 1927

LONGITUDE

DAY	EPHEMERIS SIDEREAL TIME h m s	☉	☊	☾	☿	♀	♂	♃	♄	♅	♆	♇
1 M	20 34 25.3	7♌45.8	25♓44.9	15♍32.2	21♋51.4	18♍44.3	4♍11.0	3♈25.7	1♐ 2.4	3♈12.8	26♌ 0.0	16♋ 3.4
2 T	20 38 21.8	8 43.2	25 41.7	27 37.9	22D 3.0	19 18.7	4 48.6	3R24.1	1R 2.0	3R11.8	26 2.1	16 4.9
3 W	20 42 18.4	9 40.6	25 38.5	9♎35.4	22 20.9	19 51.8	5 26.2	3 22.3	1 1.7	3 10.6	26 4.3	16 6.3
4 T	20 46 14.9	10 38.1	25 35.3	21 27.9	22 45.3	20 23.5	6 3.9	3 20.4	1 1.5	3 9.5	26 6.4	16 7.8
5 F	20 50 11.5	11 35.5	25 32.2	3♏19.7	23 16.2	20 53.8	6 41.6	3 18.2	1 1.4	3 8.3	26 8.6	16 9.2
6 S	20 54 8.1	12 33.0	25 29.0	15 15.4	23 53.5	21 22.6	7 19.3	3 15.8	1 1.4	3 7.0	26 10.8	16 10.6
7 S	20 58 4.6	13 30.5	25 25.8	27 20.1	24 37.3	21 49.9	7 57.0	3 13.3	1D 1.4	3 5.8	26 13.0	16 12.0
8 M	21 2 1.2	14 28.0	25 22.6	9♐38.6	25 27.4	22 15.6	8 34.8	3 10.6	1 1.6	3 4.4	26 15.1	16 13.4
9 T	21 5 57.7	15 25.5	25 19.4	22 15.7	26 23.7	22 39.7	9 12.6	3 7.6	1 1.9	3 3.1	26 17.3	16 14.8
10 W	21 9 54.3	16 23.0	25 16.3	5♑15.0	27 26.1	23 2.1	9 50.4	3 4.5	1 2.2	3 1.7	26 19.5	16 16.2
11 T	21 13 50.8	17 20.5	25 13.1	18 39.0	28 34.5	23 22.7	10 28.2	3 1.2	1 2.7	3 0.2	26 21.7	16 17.5
12 F	21 17 47.4	18 18.1	25 9.9	2♒27.9	29 48.5	23 41.5	11 6.1	2 57.7	1 3.3	2 58.8	26 23.9	16 18.9
13 S	21 21 43.9	19 15.7	25 6.7	16 39.9	1♌ 8.1	23 58.4	11 44.0	2 54.1	1 3.9	2 57.3	26 26.1	16 20.2
14 S	21 25 40.5	20 13.2	25 3.6	1♓10.3	2 32.9	24 13.4	12 21.9	2 50.3	1 4.7	2 55.7	26 28.3	16 21.6
15 M	21 29 37.0	21 10.9	25 0.4	15 52.4	4 2.6	24 26.4	12 59.9	2 46.2	1 5.5	2 54.1	26 30.6	16 22.9
16 T	21 33 33.6	22 8.5	24 57.2	0♈38.3	5 37.0	24 37.3	13 37.8	2 42.0	1 6.5	2 52.5	26 32.8	16 24.2
17 W	21 37 30.1	23 6.1	24 54.0	15 20.5	7 15.6	24 46.2	14 15.8	2 37.7	1 7.5	2 50.8	26 35.0	16 25.5
18 T	21 41 26.7	24 3.8	24 50.8	29 52.6	8 58.1	24 52.9	14 53.9	2 33.1	1 8.7	2 49.1	26 37.2	16 26.7
19 F	21 45 23.3	25 1.5	24 47.7	14♉10.2	10 44.0	24 57.3	15 32.0	2 28.4	1 9.9	2 47.4	26 39.4	16 28.0
20 S	21 49 19.8	25 59.3	24 44.5	28 11.1	12 33.0	24 59.6	16 10.1	2 23.5	1 11.2	2 45.7	26 41.7	16 29.3
21 S	21 53 16.4	26 57.0	24 41.3	11♊55.2	14 24.7	24R59.6	16 48.2	2 18.5	1 12.6	2 43.9	26 43.9	16 30.5
22 M	21 57 12.9	27 54.8	24 38.1	25 23.2	16 18.5	24 57.2	17 26.3	2 13.3	1 14.2	2 42.0	26 46.1	16 31.7
23 T	22 1 9.5	28 52.7	24 35.0	8♋36.7	18 14.1	24 52.5	18 4.5	2 7.9	1 15.8	2 40.2	26 48.3	16 32.9
24 W	22 5 6.0	29 50.5	24 31.8	21 37.2	20 11.2	24 45.5	18 42.8	2 2.4	1 17.5	2 38.3	26 50.6	16 34.1
25 T	22 9 2.6	0♍48.4	24 28.6	4♌25.9	22 9.2	24 36.1	19 21.0	1 56.7	1 19.3	2 36.4	26 52.8	16 35.3
26 F	22 12 59.2	1 46.3	24 25.4	17 3.8	24 8.0	24 24.3	19 59.3	1 50.9	1 21.2	2 34.4	26 55.0	16 36.4
27 S	22 16 55.7	2 44.2	24 22.2	29 31.3	26 7.1	24 10.2	20 37.7	1 44.9	1 23.2	2 32.4	26 57.2	16 37.6
28 S	22 20 52.3	3 42.2	24 19.1	11♍49.1	28 6.3	23 53.7	21 16.0	1 38.8	1 25.3	2 30.4	26 59.4	16 38.7
29 M	22 24 48.8	4 40.2	24 15.9	23 57.6	0♍ 5.4	23 34.9	21 54.4	1 32.5	1 27.5	2 28.4	27 1.6	16 39.8
30 T	22 28 45.3	5 38.2	24 12.7	5♎58.0	2 4.0	23 13.9	22 32.8	1 26.2	1 29.7	2 26.3	27 3.8	16 40.9
31 W	22 32 41.9	6 36.2	24 9.5	17 52.0	4 2.2	22 50.8	23 11.3	1 19.6	1 32.1	2 24.3	27 6.0	16 42.0

DECLINATION

DAY	EPHEMERIS SIDEREAL TIME h m s	☉	☊	☾	☿	♀	♂	♃	♄	♅	♆	♇
1 M	20 34 25.3	18N20.2	23N22.8	10N21.1	18N17.3	2N18.7	10N57.5	0N 2.2	18S31.3	0N34.8	13N17.6	21N21.1
4 T	20 46 14.9	17 34.6	23 22.5	4S 1.3	18 53.8	1 11.8	10 14.9	0S 0.7	18 31.8	0 33.4	13 15.4	21 20.7
7 S	20 58 4.6	16 46.5	23 22.2	17 5.5	19 22.5	0 8.3	9 31.8	0 4.3	18 32.5	0 31.9	13 13.2	21 20.4
10 W	21 9 54.3	15 56.0	23 21.9	24 5.4	19 38.3	0S51.0	8 48.0	0 8.5	18 33.3	0 30.2	13 11.0	21 20.0
13 S	21 21 43.9	15 3.1	23 21.5	19 34.2	19 36.4	1 45.1	8 3.7	0 13.4	18 34.4	0 28.3	13 8.8	21 19.7
16 T	21 33 33.6	14 8.1	23 21.2	4 23.9	19 12.7	2 33.1	7 18.9	0 18.9	18 35.6	0 26.4	13 6.6	21 19.3
19 F	21 45 23.3	13 11.1	23 20.8	12N50.4	18 24.8	3 14.0	6 33.7	0 25.0	18 37.0	0 24.3	13 4.3	21 19.0
22 M	21 57 12.9	12 12.2	23 20.4	23 18.3	17 12.5	3 46.5	5 48.0	0 31.7	18 38.6	0 22.1	13 2.1	21 18.7
25 T	22 9 2.6	11 11.5	23 20.0	22 13.1	15 38.3	4 9.7	5 1.9	0 38.9	18 40.3	0 19.8	12 59.8	21 18.4
28 S	22 20 52.3	10 9.3	23 19.6	11 38.7	13 46.2	4 22.3	4 15.5	0 46.5	18 42.2	0 17.4	12 57.6	21 18.1
31 W	22 32 41.9	9 5.5	23 19.2	2S43.7	11 41.0	4 23.6	3 28.8	0 54.7	18 44.2	0 14.9	12 55.4	21 17.8

SEPTEMBER 1927

DAY	EPHEMERIS SIDEREAL TIME	☉	☊	☽	☿	♀	♂	♃	♄	♅	♆	♇
	h m s	° ′	° ′	° ′	° ′	° ′	° ′	° ′	° ′	° ′	° ′	° ′
						LONGITUDE						
1 T	22 36 38.5	7♍34.3	24♊ 6.4	29♎42.2	5♍59.7	22♍25.5	23♍49.7	1♈13.0	1♐34.6	2♈22.2	27♌ 8.2	16♋43.1
2 F	22 40 35.0	8 32.3	24 3.2	11♏31.9	7 56.4	21R58.3	24 28.3	1R 6.3	1 37.1	2R20.0	27 10.4	16 44.1
3 S	22 44 31.6	9 30.4	24 0.0	23 25.2	9 52.1	21 29.3	25 6.8	0 59.4	1 39.8	2 17.9	27 12.6	16 45.1
4 S	22 48 28.1	10 28.6	23 56.8	5♐27.0	11 46.9	20 58.5	25 45.4	0 52.4	1 42.5	2 15.7	27 14.8	16 46.1
5 M	22 52 24.7	11 26.7	23 53.6	17 42.3	13 40.7	20 26.2	26 24.0	0 45.3	1 45.3	2 13.5	27 17.0	16 47.1
6 T	22 56 21.2	12 24.9	23 50.5	0♑16.6	15 33.3	19 52.5	27 2.6	0 38.2	1 48.2	2 11.3	27 19.1	16 48.1
7 W	23 0 17.8	13 23.1	23 47.3	13 14.5	17 24.9	19 17.7	27 41.3	0 30.9	1 51.2	2 9.1	27 21.3	16 49.0
8 T	23 4 14.3	14 21.3	23 44.1	26 39.9	19 15.3	18 42.0	28 20.0	0 23.5	1 54.3	2 6.8	27 23.5	16 50.0
9 F	23 8 10.9	15 19.6	23 40.9	10♒34.4	21 4.6	18 5.5	28 58.7	0 16.1	1 57.5	2 4.5	27 25.6	16 50.9
10 S	23 12 7.4	16 17.8	23 37.8	24 57.0	22 52.7	17 28.6	29 37.5	0 8.6	2 0.7	2 2.2	27 27.7	16 51.8
11 S	23 16 4.0	17 16.2	23 34.6	9♓43.4	24 39.7	16 51.4	0♎16.3	0 1.0	2 4.0	1 60.0	27 29.8	16 52.7
12 M	23 20 0.5	18 14.5	23 31.4	24 45.9	26 25.6	16 14.2	0 55.1	29♓53.3	2 7.5	1 57.6	27 32.0	16 53.5
13 T	23 23 57.1	19 12.9	23 28.2	9♈54.7	28 10.3	15 37.3	1 33.9	29 45.6	2 11.0	1 55.3	27 34.1	16 54.3
14 W	23 27 53.7	20 11.3	23 25.0	24 59.3	29 53.9	15 0.9	2 12.8	29 37.8	2 14.5	1 53.0	27 36.1	16 55.2
15 T	23 31 50.2	21 9.7	23 21.9	9♉50.5	1♎36.5	14 25.2	2 51.8	29 30.0	2 18.2	1 50.6	27 38.2	16 55.9
16 F	23 35 46.8	22 8.2	23 18.7	24 22.0	3 17.9	13 50.5	3 30.7	29 22.1	2 21.9	1 48.3	27 40.3	16 56.7
17 S	23 39 43.3	23 6.7	23 15.5	8♊30.4	4 58.3	13 17.1	4 9.7	29 14.2	2 25.8	1 45.9	27 42.3	16 57.5
18 S	23 43 39.9	24 5.2	23 12.3	22 15.1	6 37.6	12 45.0	4 48.8	29 6.3	2 29.7	1 43.5	27 44.4	16 58.2
19 M	23 47 36.4	25 3.8	23 9.2	5♋37.8	8 15.9	12 14.4	5 27.8	28 58.3	2 33.7	1 41.1	27 46.4	16 58.9
20 T	23 51 33.0	26 2.4	23 6.0	18 41.1	9 53.2	11 45.7	6 7.0	28 50.3	2 37.7	1 38.7	27 48.4	16 59.6
21 W	23 55 29.5	27 1.1	23 2.8	1♌28.0	11 29.6	11 18.8	6 46.1	28 42.3	2 41.9	1 36.3	27 50.4	17 0.3
22 T	23 59 26.1	27 59.8	22 59.6	14 1.5	13 4.9	10 53.9	7 25.3	28 34.3	2 46.1	1 33.9	27 52.4	17 0.9
23 F	0 3 22.6	28 58.5	22 56.4	26 24.2	14 39.2	10 31.1	8 4.5	28 26.2	2 50.4	1 31.5	27 54.4	17 1.5
24 S	0 7 19.2	29 57.2	22 53.3	8♍37.9	16 12.6	10 10.6	8 43.8	28 18.2	2 54.7	1 29.1	27 56.3	17 2.1
25 S	0 11 15.8	0♎56.0	22 50.1	20 44.3	17 45.0	9 52.3	9 23.1	28 10.2	2 59.2	1 26.7	27 58.3	17 2.7
26 M	0 15 12.3	1 54.9	22 46.9	2♎44.3	19 16.5	9 36.4	10 2.4	28 2.2	3 3.7	1 24.3	28 0.2	17 3.3
27 T	0 19 8.9	2 53.7	22 43.7	14 39.2	20 47.1	9 22.9	10 41.8	27 54.2	3 8.3	1 21.9	28 2.1	17 3.8
28 W	0 23 5.4	3 52.6	22 40.6	26 30.3	22 16.7	9 11.8	11 21.2	27 46.3	3 13.0	1 19.5	28 4.0	17 4.3
29 T	0 27 2.0	4 51.5	22 37.4	8♏19.3	23 45.4	9 3.1	12 0.7	27 38.4	3 17.7	1 17.0	28 5.9	17 4.8
30 F	0 30 58.5	5 50.5	22 34.2	20 8.9	25 13.1	8 56.8	12 40.1	27 30.5	3 22.5	1 14.6	28 7.7	17 5.2
						DECLINATION						
1 T	22 36 38.5	8N44.0	23N19.1	7S30.2	10N57.0	4S21.4	3N13.1	0S57.5	18S44.9	0N14.0	12N54.6	21N17.7
4 S	22 48 28.1	7 38.6	23 18.6	19 35.3	8 40.9	4 6.8	2 26.0	1 6.1	18 47.2	0 11.4	12 52.4	21 17.4
7 W	23 0 17.8	6 32.0	23 18.2	24 24.1	6 20.6	3 40.9	1 38.7	1 15.1	18 49.6	0 8.8	12 50.2	21 17.2
10 S	23 12 7.4	5 24.5	23 17.7	17 19.6	3 58.8	3 4.6	0 51.2	1 24.3	18 52.1	0 6.0	12 48.1	21 17.0
13 T	23 23 57.1	4 16.2	23 17.3	0 29.8	1 37.3	2 20.1	0 3.6	1 33.8	18 54.8	0 3.3	12 45.9	21 16.7
16 F	23 35 46.8	3 7.3	23 16.8	16N30.0	0S42.3	1 29.9	0S44.1	1 43.3	18 57.5	0 0.4	12 43.8	21 16.6
19 M	23 47 36.4	1 57.8	23 16.3	24 24.1	2 59.0	0 37.0	1 31.8	1 53.0	19 0.4	0S 2.4	12 41.8	21 16.4
22 T	23 59 26.1	0 47.9	23 15.8	20 20.9	5 11.9	0N15.8	2 19.6	2 2.7	19 3.4	0 5.3	12 39.7	21 16.2
25 S	0 11 15.8	0S22.3	23 15.3	8 15.5	7 20.4	1 6.0	3 7.3	2 12.3	19 6.5	0 8.1	12 37.8	21 16.1
28 W	0 23 5.4	1 32.5	23 14.8	6S22.5	9 23.6	1 51.7	3 54.9	2 21.8	19 9.7	0 11.0	12 35.8	21 16.0

OCTOBER 1927

DAY	EPHEMERIS SIDEREAL TIME	☉	☊	☽	☿	♀	♂	♃	♄	♅	♆	♇
						LONGITUDE						
1 S	0 34 55.1	6♎49.5	22♊31.0	2♐ 2.2	26♎39.8	8♍53.0	13♎19.7	27♓22.7	3♐27.4	1♈12.2	28♌ 9.5	17♋ 5.7
2 S	0 38 51.6	7 48.5	22 27.8	14 3.1	28 5.6	8R51.5	13 59.2	27R14.9	3 32.3	1R 9.9	28 11.3	17 6.1
3 M	0 42 48.2	8 47.6	22 24.7	26 16.3	29 30.4	8D52.4	14 38.8	27 7.2	3 37.3	1 7.5	28 13.1	17 6.5
4 T	0 46 44.7	9 46.6	22 21.5	8♑46.8	0♏54.1	8 55.6	15 18.4	26 59.5	3 42.4	1 5.1	28 14.9	17 6.8
5 W	0 50 41.3	10 45.8	22 18.3	21 39.6	2 16.9	9 1.2	15 58.1	26 52.0	3 47.5	1 2.7	28 16.7	17 7.2
6 T	0 54 37.9	11 44.9	22 15.1	4♒59.0	3 38.5	9 8.9	16 37.8	26 44.5	3 52.7	1 0.4	28 18.4	17 7.5
7 F	0 58 34.4	12 44.1	22 12.0	18 48.0	4 59.0	9 18.9	17 17.5	26 37.0	3 58.0	0 58.0	28 20.1	17 7.8
8 S	1 2 30.9	13 43.2	22 8.8	3♓ 7.1	6 18.3	9 31.1	17 57.3	26 29.7	4 3.3	0 55.7	28 21.8	17 8.1
9 S	1 6 27.5	14 42.5	22 5.6	17 53.6	7 36.4	9 45.3	18 37.1	26 22.5	4 8.7	0 53.3	28 23.5	17 8.3
10 M	1 10 24.1	15 41.7	22 2.4	3♈ 0.9	8 53.2	10 1.6	19 17.0	26 15.3	4 14.1	0 51.0	28 25.1	17 8.5
11 T	1 14 20.6	16 41.0	21 59.3	18 19.4	10 8.6	10 19.8	19 56.9	26 8.3	4 19.6	0 48.7	28 26.7	17 8.7
12 W	1 18 17.2	17 40.4	21 56.1	3♉37.7	11 22.5	10 40.0	20 36.8	26 1.4	4 25.2	0 46.5	28 28.3	17 8.9
13 T	1 22 13.7	18 39.7	21 52.9	18 44.9	12 34.9	11 2.1	21 16.7	25 54.6	4 30.8	0 44.2	28 29.9	17 9.1
14 F	1 26 10.3	19 39.1	21 49.7	3♊32.1	13 45.6	11 26.0	21 56.8	25 47.9	4 36.4	0 42.0	28 31.4	17 9.2
15 S	1 30 6.8	20 38.6	21 46.5	17 54.0	14 54.4	11 51.7	22 36.8	25 41.3	4 42.2	0 39.7	28 33.0	17 9.3
16 S	1 34 3.4	21 38.0	21 43.4	1♋48.4	16 1.3	12 19.0	23 16.9	25 34.9	4 47.9	0 37.5	28 34.5	17 9.4
17 M	1 37 59.9	22 37.5	21 40.2	15 16.1	17 5.9	12 48.0	23 57.0	25 28.5	4 53.8	0 35.3	28 35.9	17 9.4
18 T	1 41 56.5	23 37.1	21 37.0	28 19.7	18 8.2	13 18.5	24 37.2	25 22.4	4 59.7	0 33.2	28 37.4	17 9.5
19 W	1 45 53.0	24 36.7	21 33.8	11♌ 2.9	19 8.0	13 50.6	25 17.4	25 16.3	5 5.6	0 31.0	28 38.8	17 9.5
20 T	1 49 49.6	25 36.3	21 30.6	23 29.6	20 4.8	14 24.1	25 57.7	25 10.4	5 11.6	0 28.9	28 40.2	17R 9.4
21 F	1 53 46.1	26 36.0	21 27.5	5♍43.5	20 58.5	14 59.1	26 38.0	25 4.7	5 17.6	0 26.8	28 41.6	17 9.4
22 S	1 57 42.7	27 35.7	21 24.3	17 48.1	21 48.8	15 35.3	27 18.3	24 59.1	5 23.7	0 24.7	28 42.9	17 9.3
23 S	2 1 39.3	28 35.4	21 21.1	29 46.1	22 35.2	16 12.9	27 58.7	24 53.6	5 29.8	0 22.7	28 44.2	17 9.2
24 M	2 5 35.8	29 35.2	21 17.9	11♎39.8	23 17.3	16 51.8	28 39.1	24 48.4	5 36.0	0 20.7	28 45.5	17 9.1
25 T	2 9 32.4	0♏35.0	21 14.8	23 31.0	23 54.7	17 31.8	29 19.6	24 43.3	5 42.2	0 18.7	28 46.8	17 9.0
26 W	2 13 28.9	1 34.8	21 11.6	5♏21.3	24 27.0	18 13.0	0♏ 0.1	24 38.3	5 48.5	0 16.7	28 48.0	17 8.8
27 T	2 17 25.5	2 34.7	21 8.4	17 12.4	24 53.5	18 55.3	0 40.6	24 33.5	5 54.8	0 14.8	28 49.2	17 8.6
28 F	2 21 22.0	3 34.6	21 5.2	29 6.1	25 13.7	19 38.7	1 21.2	24 29.0	6 1.2	0 12.9	28 50.4	17 8.4
29 S	2 25 18.6	4 34.6	21 2.1	11♐ 4.6	25 27.0	20 23.1	2 1.8	24 24.5	6 7.6	0 11.0	28 51.5	17 8.2
30 S	2 29 15.2	5 34.5	20 58.9	23 10.8	25 32.7	21 8.5	2 42.5	24 20.3	6 14.0	0 9.2	28 52.7	17 7.9
31 M	2 33 11.7	6 34.5	20 55.7	5♑27.9	25R30.3	21 54.9	3 23.2	24 16.3	6 20.5	0 7.4	28 53.7	17 7.6
						DECLINATION						
1 S	0 34 55.1	2S42.6	23N14.3	18S55.0	11S21.0	2N31.6	4S42.5	2S31.1	19S13.0	0S13.9	12N34.0	21N16.0
4 T	0 46 44.7	3 52.5	23 13.7	24 39.5	13 12.0	3 4.6	5 29.8	2 40.2	19 16.3	0 16.7	12 32.2	21 15.9
7 F	0 58 34.4	5 1.9	23 13.2	19 14.5	14 55.7	3 30.2	6 16.9	2 48.9	19 19.7	0 19.5	12 30.4	21 15.9
10 M	1 10 24.1	6 10.8	23 12.6	3 20.0	16 31.4	3 48.1	7 3.7	2 57.3	19 23.2	0 22.2	12 28.8	21 15.9
13 T	1 22 13.7	7 18.9	23 12.0	14N49.6	17 58.1	3 58.4	7 50.2	3 5.2	19 26.7	0 24.9	12 27.2	21 15.9
16 S	1 34 3.4	8 26.2	23 11.4	24 26.1	19 14.5	4 1.1	8 36.3	3 12.7	19 30.3	0 27.5	12 25.6	21 16.0
19 W	1 45 53.0	9 32.3	23 10.8	21 15.2	20 19.2	3 56.6	9 22.0	3 19.6	19 33.9	0 30.0	12 24.2	21 16.1
22 S	1 57 42.7	10 37.3	23 10.2	9 30.4	21 9.9	3 45.2	10 7.3	3 26.0	19 37.5	0 32.5	12 22.8	21 16.2
25 T	2 9 32.4	11 40.9	23 9.6	5S11.1	21 44.0	3 27.2	10 51.9	3 31.8	19 41.2	0 34.8	12 21.6	21 16.3
28 F	2 21 22.0	12 42.8	23 9.0	18 13.1	21 57.5	3 3.2	11 36.0	3 36.9	19 44.9	0 37.0	12 20.4	21 16.5
31 M	2 33 11.7	13 43.0	23 8.3	24 46.4	21 45.1	2 33.6	12 19.5	3 41.3	19 48.5	0 39.2	12 19.3	21 16.7

NOVEMBER 1927

LONGITUDE

DAY	EPHEMERIS SIDEREAL TIME h m s	☉ ° ′	☊ ° ′	☽ ° ′	☿ ° ′	♀ ° ′	♂ ° ′	♃ ° ′	♄ ° ′	♅ ° ′	♆ ° ′	♇ ° ′
1 T	2 37 8.2	7♏34.5	20♊52.5	17♑59.8	25♏19.2	22♍42.2	4♏ 3.9	24♓12.4	6♐27.0	0♈ 5.6	28♌54.8	17♋ 7.3
2 W	2 41 4.8	8 34.6	20 49.3	0♒50.5	24R59.0	23 30.4	4 44.7	24R 8.7	6 33.5	0R 3.9	28 55.8	17R 7.0
3 T	2 45 1.4	9 34.7	20 46.2	14 4.0	24 29.2	24 19.4	5 25.5	24 5.2	6 40.1	0 2.2	28 56.8	17 6.6
4 F	2 48 57.9	10 34.8	20 43.0	27 43.2	23 49.8	25 9.2	6 6.4	24 2.0	6 46.7	0 0.5	28 57.8	17 6.2
5 S	2 52 54.5	11 34.9	20 39.8	11♓49.5	23 0.9	25 59.9	6 47.3	23 58.9	6 53.4	29♓58.9	28 58.7	17 5.8
6 S	2 56 51.0	12 35.0	20 36.6	26 22.1	22 3.2	26 51.3	7 28.3	23 56.0	7 0.0	29 57.3	28 59.6	17 5.4
7 M	3 0 47.6	13 35.2	20 33.5	11♈16.6	20 57.4	27 43.5	8 9.2	23 53.3	7 6.7	29 55.8	29 0.5	17 5.0
8 T	3 4 44.1	14 35.4	20 30.3	26 26.0	19 45.1	28 36.4	8 50.3	23 50.7	7 13.5	29 54.3	29 1.3	17 4.5
9 W	3 8 40.7	15 35.7	20 27.1	11♉40.6	18 28.0	29 29.9	9 31.3	23 48.4	7 20.2	29 52.8	29 2.1	17 4.0
10 T	3 12 37.2	16 35.9	20 23.9	26 49.9	17 8.5	0♎24.2	10 12.4	23 46.3	7 27.0	29 51.3	29 2.9	17 3.5
11 F	3 16 33.8	17 36.2	20 20.7	11♊44.4	15 49.0	1 19.1	10 53.6	23 44.4	7 33.8	29 50.0	29 3.6	17 2.9
12 S	3 20 30.4	18 36.5	20 17.6	26 16.7	14 32.2	2 14.7	11 34.8	23 42.7	7 40.7	29 48.6	29 4.3	17 2.4
13 S	3 24 26.9	19 36.9	20 14.4	10♋22.4	13 20.4	3 10.8	12 16.0	23 41.2	7 47.6	29 47.3	29 5.0	17 1.8
14 M	3 28 23.5	20 37.3	20 11.2	24 0.4	12 16.0	4 7.6	12 57.3	23 39.9	7 54.4	29 46.0	29 5.6	17 1.2
15 T	3 32 20.0	21 37.7	20 8.0	7♌11.8	11 20.8	5 4.9	13 38.6	23 38.9	8 1.4	29 44.8	29 6.2	17 0.6
16 W	3 36 16.6	22 38.1	20 4.9	19 59.4	10 36.1	6 2.7	14 20.0	23 38.0	8 8.3	29 43.6	29 6.8	16 59.9
17 T	3 40 13.2	23 38.6	20 1.7	2♍27.2	10 2.8	7 1.1	15 1.4	23 37.3	8 15.3	29 42.5	29 7.3	16 59.3
18 F	3 44 9.7	24 39.1	19 58.5	14 39.5	9 41.2	7 60.0	15 42.9	23 36.8	8 22.2	29 41.4	29 7.9	16 58.6
19 S	3 48 6.2	25 39.7	19 55.3	26 40.6	9 31.2	8 59.4	16 24.4	23 36.6	8 29.2	29 40.4	29 8.3	16 57.9
20 S	3 52 2.8	26 40.2	19 52.1	8♎34.6	9D32.5	9 59.2	17 6.0	23 36.5	8 36.2	29 39.4	29 8.8	16 57.1
21 M	3 55 59.4	27 40.8	19 49.0	20 25.1	9 44.4	10 59.5	17 47.6	23D36.7	8 43.2	29 38.4	29 9.2	16 56.4
22 T	3 59 55.9	28 41.5	19 45.8	2♏15.0	10 6.1	12 0.3	18 29.2	23 37.1	8 50.3	29 37.5	29 9.5	16 55.6
23 W	4 3 52.5	29 42.1	19 42.6	14 7.1	10 36.9	13 1.5	19 10.9	23 37.6	8 57.3	29 36.7	29 9.9	16 54.8
24 T	4 7 49.0	0♐42.8	19 39.4	26 3.2	11 15.7	14 3.0	19 52.6	23 38.4	9 4.4	29 35.8	29 10.2	16 54.0
25 F	4 11 45.6	1 43.5	19 36.3	8♐ 5.4	12 1.7	15 5.0	20 34.4	23 39.4	9 11.5	29 35.1	29 10.4	16 53.2
26 S	4 15 42.1	2 44.2	19 33.1	20 15.2	12 54.0	16 7.3	21 16.2	23 40.6	9 18.6	29 34.4	29 10.7	16 52.4
27 S	4 19 38.7	3 44.9	19 29.9	2♑34.3	13 51.9	17 10.1	21 58.1	23 42.0	9 25.7	29 33.7	29 10.9	16 51.5
28 M	4 23 35.3	4 45.7	19 26.7	15 4.5	14 54.7	18 13.1	22 39.9	23 43.6	9 32.8	29 33.1	29 11.0	16 50.6
29 T	4 27 31.8	5 46.5	19 23.6	27 47.7	16 1.7	19 16.6	23 21.9	23 45.4	9 39.9	29 32.5	29 11.2	16 49.7
30 W	4 31 28.4	6 47.3	19 20.4	10♒46.2	17 12.3	20 20.3	24 3.9	23 47.4	9 47.0	29 32.0	29 11.3	16 48.8

DECLINATION

DAY	EPHEMERIS SIDEREAL TIME h m s	☉	☊	☽	☿	♀	♂	♃	♄	♅	♆	♇
1 T	2 37 8.2	14S 2.6	23N 8.1	24S42.1	21S34.1	2N22.5	12S33.8	3S42.7	19S49.7	0S39.8	12N18.9	21N16.8
4 F	2 48 57.9	15 0.1	23 7.4	16 47.4	20 37.8	1 46.0	13 16.3	3 46.2	19 53.4	0 41.8	12 18.0	21 17.0
7 M	3 0 47.6	15 55.4	23 6.8	0N 2.2	19 5.0	1 4.8	13 57.9	3 49.0	19 57.1	0 43.6	12 17.1	21 17.3
10 T	3 12 37.2	16 48.3	23 6.1	17 32.5	17 4.3	0 19.4	14 38.7	3 51.0	20 0.7	0 45.3	12 16.3	21 17.6
13 S	3 24 26.9	17 38.7	23 5.4	24 57.1	15 0.5	0S29.8	15 18.6	3 52.4	20 4.3	0 46.8	12 15.7	21 17.9
16 W	3 36 16.6	18 26.2	23 4.7	19 10.0	13 24.3	1 22.5	15 57.5	3 53.0	20 7.9	0 48.1	12 15.1	21 18.3
19 S	3 48 6.2	19 10.9	23 4.0	6 5.0	12 34.5	2 18.2	16 35.4	3 52.8	20 11.4	0 49.4	12 14.7	21 18.7
22 T	3 59 55.9	19 52.5	23 3.2	8S40.7	12 31.9	3 16.4	17 12.2	3 51.9	20 14.9	0 50.4	12 14.3	21 19.1
25 F	4 11 45.6	20 30.9	23 2.5	20 42.5	13 6.5	4 16.8	17 47.8	3 50.2	20 18.3	0 51.3	12 14.1	21 19.5
28 M	4 23 35.3	21 5.8	23 1.8	24 56.0	14 5.9	5 18.8	18 22.1	3 47.8	20 21.7	0 51.9	12 13.9	21 19.9

DECEMBER 1927

LONGITUDE

DAY	EPHEMERIS SIDEREAL TIME h m s	☉	☊	☽	☿	♀	♂	♃	♄	♅	♆	♇
1 T	4 35 25.0	7♐48.1	19♊17.2	24♒ 1.9	18♏26.0	21♎24.4	24♏45.9	23♓49.7	9♐54.1	29♓31.5	29♌11.3	16♋47.9
2 F	4 39 21.5	8 48.9	19 14.0	7♓36.8	19 42.5	22 28.8	25 28.0	23 52.1	10 1.2	29R31.1	29 11.3	16R46.9
3 S	4 43 18.0	9 49.8	19 10.9	21 31.6	21 1.2	23 33.4	26 10.1	23 54.7	10 8.3	29 30.7	29R11.3	16 45.9
4 S	4 47 14.6	10 50.6	19 7.7	5♈46.3	22 21.9	24 38.4	26 52.2	23 57.5	10 15.4	29 30.4	29 11.3	16 45.0
5 M	4 51 11.2	11 51.5	19 4.5	20 18.6	23 44.3	25 43.7	27 34.4	24 0.6	10 22.6	29 30.2	29 11.2	16 44.0
6 T	4 55 7.7	12 52.4	19 1.3	5♉ 4.4	25 8.1	26 49.2	28 16.6	24 3.8	10 29.7	29 30.0	29 11.1	16 43.0
7 W	4 59 4.3	13 53.3	18 58.2	19 57.6	26 33.2	27 55.0	28 58.9	24 7.2	10 36.8	29 29.8	29 11.0	16 41.9
8 T	5 3 0.8	14 54.2	18 55.0	4♊50.5	27 59.3	29 1.1	29 41.2	24 10.8	10 43.9	29 29.7	29 10.8	16 40.9
9 F	5 6 57.4	15 55.1	18 51.8	19 35.3	29 26.3	0♏ 7.5	0♐23.5	24 14.6	10 51.0	29 29.6	29 10.6	16 39.8
10 S	5 10 53.9	16 56.1	18 48.6	4♋ 4.9	0♐54.1	1 14.0	1 5.9	24 18.6	10 58.1	29 29.6	29 10.3	16 38.8
11 S	5 14 50.5	17 57.0	18 45.4	18 13.4	2 22.5	2 20.9	1 48.4	24 22.8	11 5.2	29D29.6	29 10.0	16 37.7
12 M	5 18 47.1	18 58.0	18 42.3	1♌57.7	3 51.5	3 27.9	2 30.9	24 27.2	11 12.3	29 29.7	29 9.7	16 36.6
13 T	5 22 43.6	19 59.0	18 39.1	15 16.6	5 21.0	4 35.2	3 13.4	24 31.8	11 19.3	29 29.9	29 9.4	16 35.5
14 W	5 26 40.2	21 0.0	18 35.9	28 11.3	6 51.0	5 42.7	3 56.0	24 36.5	11 26.4	29 30.1	29 9.0	16 34.4
15 T	5 30 36.7	22 1.0	18 32.7	10♍44.5	8 21.3	6 50.5	4 38.6	24 41.4	11 33.4	29 30.3	29 8.6	16 33.2
16 F	5 34 33.3	23 2.1	18 29.6	22 59.9	9 52.0	7 58.4	5 21.3	24 46.6	11 40.5	29 30.6	29 8.1	16 32.1
17 S	5 38 29.9	24 3.1	18 26.4	5♎ 2.0	11 23.0	9 6.5	6 4.0	24 51.9	11 47.5	29 31.0	29 7.6	16 31.0
18 S	5 42 26.4	25 4.2	18 23.2	16 55.6	12 54.2	10 14.9	6 46.7	24 57.3	11 54.5	29 31.4	29 7.1	16 29.8
19 M	5 46 23.0	26 5.3	18 20.0	28 45.4	14 25.8	11 23.4	7 29.6	25 3.0	12 1.5	29 31.8	29 6.6	16 28.6
20 T	5 50 19.6	27 6.4	18 16.9	10♏35.6	15 57.5	12 32.1	8 12.4	25 8.8	12 8.5	29 32.3	29 6.0	16 27.4
21 W	5 54 16.1	28 7.5	18 13.7	22 30.1	17 29.5	13 41.0	8 55.3	25 14.8	12 15.4	29 32.9	29 5.4	16 26.3
22 T	5 58 12.6	29 8.7	18 10.5	4♐32.2	19 1.7	14 50.0	9 38.2	25 21.0	12 22.3	29 33.5	29 4.8	16 25.1
23 F	6 2 9.2	0♑ 9.8	18 7.3	16 44.6	20 34.2	15 59.2	10 21.2	25 27.4	12 29.2	29 34.2	29 4.1	16 23.8
24 S	6 6 5.8	1 10.9	18 4.1	29 8.9	22 6.9	17 8.5	11 4.2	25 33.9	12 36.1	29 34.9	29 3.4	16 22.6
25 S	6 10 2.3	2 12.1	18 1.0	11♑46.4	23 39.8	18 18.0	11 47.3	25 40.6	12 43.0	29 35.6	29 2.7	16 21.4
26 M	6 13 58.9	3 13.3	17 57.8	24 37.6	25 12.9	19 27.7	12 30.4	25 47.5	12 49.8	29 36.5	29 1.9	16 20.2
27 T	6 17 55.4	4 14.4	17 54.6	7♒42.4	26 46.3	20 37.4	13 13.5	25 54.5	12 56.6	29 37.3	29 1.1	16 19.0
28 W	6 21 52.0	5 15.6	17 51.4	21 0.5	28 19.9	21 47.4	13 56.7	26 1.7	13 3.4	29 38.2	29 0.3	16 17.7
29 T	6 25 48.6	6 16.7	17 48.3	4♓31.4	29 53.8	22 57.4	14 39.9	26 9.0	13 10.2	29 39.2	28 59.4	16 16.5
30 F	6 29 45.1	7 17.9	17 45.1	18 14.4	1♑27.9	24 7.6	15 23.2	26 16.5	13 16.9	29 40.2	28 58.5	16 15.2
31 S	6 33 41.7	8 19.1	17 41.9	2♈ 8.7	3 2.4	25 17.9	16 6.5	26 24.2	13 23.6	29 41.3	28 57.6	16 14.0

DECLINATION

DAY	EPHEMERIS SIDEREAL TIME h m s	☉	☊	☽	☿	♀	♂	♃	♄	♅	♆	♇
1 T	4 35 25.0	21S37.2	23N 1.0	18S 2.6	15S19.4	6S22.2	18S55.2	3S44.6	20S25.0	0S52.5	12N13.9	21N20.4
4 S	4 47 14.6	22 4.8	23 0.2	2 20.9	16 39.3	7 26.5	19 26.8	3 40.8	20 28.2	0 52.8	12 14.0	21 20.9
7 W	4 59 4.3	22 28.6	22 59.4	15N16.9	18 0.2	8 31.3	19 57.0	3 36.2	20 31.4	0 52.9	12 14.2	21 21.4
10 S	5 10 53.9	22 48.4	22 58.6	24 47.6	19 18.4	9 36.2	20 25.7	3 30.9	20 34.5	0 52.9	12 14.5	21 21.9
13 T	5 22 43.6	23 4.2	22 57.8	20 28.9	20 31.3	10 40.8	20 52.9	3 25.0	20 37.5	0 52.7	12 14.9	21 22.5
16 F	5 34 33.3	23 15.9	22 57.0	7 37.5	21 37.2	11 44.7	21 18.4	3 18.4	20 40.5	0 52.3	12 15.4	21 23.0
19 M	5 46 23.0	23 23.5	22 56.2	7S14.6	22 34.6	12 47.6	21 42.2	3 11.2	20 43.3	0 51.7	12 16.0	21 23.6
22 T	5 58 12.6	23 26.8	22 55.4	19 46.6	23 22.6	13 48.9	22 4.2	3 3.4	20 46.1	0 50.9	12 16.8	21 24.2
25 S	6 10 2.3	23 25.8	22 54.5	24 59.2	24 0.3	14 48.4	22 24.4	2 54.9	20 48.7	0 49.9	12 17.6	21 24.8
28 W	6 21 52.0	23 20.7	22 53.7	18 54.8	24 27.0	15 45.5	22 42.8	2 45.9	20 51.3	0 48.8	12 18.5	21 25.4
31 S	6 33 41.7	23 11.3	22 52.8	3 50.2	24 42.0	16 40.0	22 59.2	2 36.3	20 53.8	0 47.5	12 19.5	21 26.1

JANUARY 1928

DAY	EPHEMERIS SIDEREAL TIME	☉	☊	☽	☿	♀	♂	♃	♄	♅	♆	♇
	h m s	° ′	° ′	° ′	° ′	° ′	° ′	° ′	° ′	° ′	° ′	° ′
						LONGITUDE						
1 S	6 37 38.2	9♑20.2	17♊38.7	16♈13.3	4♑37.1	26♏28.3	16♐49.8	26♓32.0	13♐30.3	29♓42.4	28♌56.7	16♋12.7
2 M	6 41 34.8	10 21.4	17 35.6	0♉26.8	6 12.2	27 38.8	17 33.2	26 40.0	13 36.9	29 43.6	28R55.7	16R11.4
3 T	6 45 31.4	11 22.5	17 32.4	14 47.3	7 47.6	28 49.4	18 16.6	26 48.1	13 43.5	29 44.8	28 54.7	16 10.2
4 W	6 49 27.9	12 23.7	17 29.2	29 11.7	9 23.3	0♐ 0.2	19 0.0	26 56.4	13 50.0	29 46.1	28 53.7	16 8.9
5 T	6 53 24.5	13 24.8	17 26.0	13♊36.2	10 59.4	1 11.0	19 43.5	27 4.8	13 56.5	29 47.4	28 52.6	16 7.7
6 F	6 57 21.0	14 25.9	17 22.9	27 56.3	12 35.8	2 22.0	20 27.1	27 13.3	14 3.0	29 48.7	28 51.5	16 6.4
7 S	7 1 17.6	15 27.1	17 19.7	12♋ 7.0	14 12.7	3 33.0	21 10.7	27 22.0	14 9.5	29 50.1	28 50.4	16 5.1
8 S	7 5 14.2	16 28.2	17 16.5	26 3.5	15 49.9	4 44.2	21 54.3	27 30.9	14 15.9	29 51.6	28 49.3	16 3.9
9 M	7 9 10.7	17 29.3	17 13.3	9♌42.0	17 27.6	5 55.5	22 37.9	27 39.9	14 22.2	29 53.1	28 48.2	16 2.6
10 T	7 13 7.2	18 30.5	17 10.1	23 0.0	19 5.7	7 6.8	23 21.6	27 49.0	14 28.6	29 54.6	28 47.0	16 1.3
11 W	7 17 3.8	19 31.6	17 7.0	5♍56.8	20 44.2	8 18.3	24 5.4	27 58.2	14 34.8	29 56.2	28 45.8	16 0.0
12 T	7 21 0.4	20 32.7	17 3.8	18 33.2	22 23.2	9 29.8	24 49.2	28 7.6	14 41.1	29 57.9	28 44.5	15 58.8
13 F	7 24 56.9	21 33.8	17 0.6	0♎51.8	24 2.6	10 41.4	25 33.0	28 17.1	14 47.3	29 59.6	28 43.3	15 57.5
14 S	7 28 53.5	22 35.0	16 57.4	12 56.1	25 42.5	11 53.1	26 16.9	28 26.8	14 53.4	0♈ 1.3	28 42.0	15 56.3
15 S	7 32 50.0	23 36.1	16 54.3	24 50.7	27 22.9	13 4.9	27 0.8	28 36.5	14 59.5	0 3.1	28 40.7	15 55.0
16 M	7 36 46.6	24 37.2	16 51.1	6♏40.6	29 3.6	14 16.8	27 44.7	28 46.4	15 5.5	0 4.9	28 39.4	15 53.7
17 T	7 40 43.2	25 38.3	16 47.9	18 30.9	0♒44.9	15 28.7	28 28.7	28 56.4	15 11.5	0 6.8	28 38.1	15 52.5
18 W	7 44 39.7	26 39.4	16 44.7	0♐26.7	2 26.5	16 40.8	29 12.8	29 6.6	15 17.5	0 8.7	28 36.7	15 51.2
19 T	7 48 36.3	27 40.5	16 41.6	12 32.6	4 8.6	17 52.8	29 56.9	29 16.8	15 23.4	0 10.6	28 35.3	15 50.0
20 F	7 52 32.8	28 41.6	16 38.4	24 52.4	5 51.0	19 5.0	0♑41.0	29 27.2	15 29.2	0 12.6	28 34.0	15 48.8
21 S	7 56 29.4	29 42.7	16 35.2	7♑29.1	7 33.7	20 17.2	1 25.1	29 37.7	15 35.0	0 14.7	28 32.5	15 47.5
22 S	8 0 26.0	0♒43.8	16 32.0	20 24.3	9 16.6	21 29.5	2 9.3	29 48.3	15 40.7	0 16.7	28 31.1	15 46.3
23 M	8 4 22.5	1 44.9	16 28.9	3♒38.1	10 59.8	22 41.8	2 53.5	29 59.0	15 46.4	0 18.9	28 29.7	15 45.1
24 T	8 8 19.1	2 45.9	16 25.7	17 9.3	12 43.0	23 54.2	3 37.8	0♈ 9.9	15 52.0	0 21.0	28 28.2	15 43.9
25 W	8 12 15.6	3 47.0	16 22.5	0♓55.1	14 26.3	25 6.6	4 22.1	0 20.8	15 57.5	0 23.2	28 26.7	15 42.7
26 T	8 16 12.2	4 48.0	16 19.3	14 52.1	16 9.3	26 19.1	5 6.4	0 31.9	16 3.0	0 25.4	28 25.2	15 41.5
27 F	8 20 8.7	5 49.0	16 16.1	28 56.4	17 52.1	27 31.6	5 50.8	0 43.0	16 8.5	0 27.7	28 23.7	15 40.3
28 S	8 24 5.3	6 50.0	16 13.0	13♈ 4.5	19 34.3	28 44.2	6 35.2	0 54.3	16 13.8	0 30.0	28 22.2	15 39.1
29 S	8 28 1.8	7 51.0	16 9.8	27 13.4	21 15.9	29 56.8	7 19.6	1 5.6	16 19.1	0 32.4	28 20.6	15 38.0
30 M	8 31 58.4	8 51.9	16 6.6	11♉21.2	22 56.4	1♑ 9.5	8 4.1	1 17.1	16 24.3	0 34.8	28 19.0	15 36.8
31 T	8 35 54.9	9 52.8	16 3.4	25 26.5	24 35.6	2 22.2	8 48.6	1 28.6	16 29.5	0 37.2	28 17.5	15 35.7
						DECLINATION						
1 S	6 37 38.2	23S 7.2	22N52.5	2N 4.7	24S44.3	16S57.5	23S 4.2	2S33.0	20S54.6	0S47.0	12N19.8	21N26.3
4 W	6 49 27.9	22 52.3	22 51.6	18 16.6	24 43.0	17 47.9	23 18.0	2 22.6	20 56.9	0 45.4	12 20.9	21 26.9
7 S	7 1 17.6	22 33.2	22 50.7	24 58.8	24 28.7	18 34.7	23 29.7	2 11.8	20 59.1	0 43.7	12 22.1	21 27.5
10 T	7 13 7.2	22 10.2	22 49.8	18 18.0	24 1.1	19 17.7	23 39.3	2 0.5	21 1.3	0 41.8	12 23.4	21 28.2
13 F	7 24 56.9	21 43.2	22 48.9	4 19.0	23 19.8	19 56.5	23 46.8	1 48.8	21 3.3	0 39.7	12 24.7	21 28.8
16 M	7 36 46.6	21 12.5	22 48.0	10S29.2	22 24.5	20 30.8	23 52.2	1 36.6	21 5.2	0 37.5	12 26.2	21 29.4
19 T	7 48 36.3	20 38.1	22 47.0	21 48.0	21 15.1	21 0.3	23 55.3	1 23.9	21 7.0	0 35.1	12 27.6	21 30.1
22 S	8 0 26.0	20 0.1	22 46.1	24 37.5	19 51.6	21 24.8	23 56.3	1 10.9	21 8.7	0 32.6	12 29.2	21 30.7
25 W	8 12 15.6	19 18.9	22 45.1	15 44.2	18 14.7	21 44.1	23 55.0	0 57.5	21 10.4	0 29.9	12 30.8	21 31.3
28 S	8 24 5.3	18 34.4	22 44.1	0N54.1	16 25.5	21 57.9	23 51.5	0 43.7	21 11.9	0 27.1	12 32.4	21 32.0
31 T	8 35 54.9	17 46.8	22 43.1	17 15.8	14 26.1	22 6.1	23 45.7	0 29.5	21 13.3	0 24.2	12 34.1	21 32.6

FEBRUARY 1928

DAY	EPHEMERIS SIDEREAL TIME	☉	☊	☽	☿	♀	♂	♃	♄	♅	♆	♇
						LONGITUDE						
1 W	8 39 51.5	10♒53.7	16♊ 0.3	9♊28.3	26♒13.1	3♑35.0	9♑33.2	1♈40.3	16♐34.6	0♈39.7	28♌15.9	15♋34.5
2 T	8 43 48.1	11 54.6	15 57.1	23 25.5	27 48.5	4 47.8	10 17.7	1 52.0	16 39.7	0 42.2	28R14.3	15R33.4
3 F	8 47 44.6	12 55.5	15 53.9	7♋16.9	29 21.4	6 0.6	11 2.3	2 3.8	16 44.6	0 44.7	28 12.7	15 32.3
4 S	8 51 41.2	13 56.3	15 50.7	21 0.4	0♓51.2	7 13.4	11 47.0	2 15.8	16 49.5	0 47.3	28 11.1	15 31.2
5 S	8 55 37.7	14 57.1	15 47.5	4♌33.6	2 17.3	8 26.4	12 31.7	2 27.8	16 54.4	0 49.9	28 9.5	15 30.1
6 M	8 59 34.3	15 58.0	15 44.4	17 54.1	3 39.2	9 39.3	13 16.4	2 39.9	16 59.1	0 52.5	28 7.8	15 29.0
7 T	9 3 30.9	16 58.7	15 41.2	0♍59.7	4 56.0	10 52.3	14 1.1	2 52.0	17 3.8	0 55.2	28 6.2	15 28.0
8 W	9 7 27.4	17 59.5	15 38.0	13 48.9	6 7.2	12 5.3	14 45.9	3 4.3	17 8.4	0 57.9	28 4.6	15 26.9
9 T	9 11 24.0	19 0.2	15 34.8	26 21.5	7 11.9	13 18.4	15 30.7	3 16.6	17 12.9	1 0.6	28 2.9	15 25.9
10 F	9 15 20.5	20 1.0	15 31.7	8♎38.7	8 9.3	14 31.5	16 15.6	3 29.1	17 17.4	1 3.4	28 1.2	15 24.9
11 S	9 19 17.1	21 1.7	15 28.5	20 42.8	8 58.9	15 44.6	17 0.5	3 41.6	17 21.8	1 6.2	27 59.6	15 23.9
12 S	9 23 13.6	22 2.3	15 25.3	2♏37.4	9 39.7	16 57.8	17 45.4	3 54.1	17 26.1	1 9.0	27 57.9	15 22.9
13 M	9 27 10.2	23 3.0	15 22.1	14 26.8	10 11.3	18 10.9	18 30.3	4 6.8	17 30.3	1 11.8	27 56.2	15 21.9
14 T	9 31 6.7	24 3.7	15 19.0	26 16.3	10 33.0	19 24.2	19 15.3	4 19.5	17 34.5	1 14.7	27 54.6	15 21.0
15 W	9 35 3.3	25 4.3	15 15.8	8♐11.3	10 44.6	20 37.4	20 0.3	4 32.3	17 38.6	1 17.6	27 52.9	15 20.0
16 T	9 38 59.9	26 4.9	15 12.6	20 17.2	10 45.6	21 50.7	20 45.4	4 45.2	17 42.6	1 20.5	27 51.2	15 19.1
17 F	9 42 56.4	27 5.5	15 9.4	2♑39.2	10R36.2	23 4.0	21 30.5	4 58.1	17 46.5	1 23.5	27 49.5	15 18.2
18 S	9 46 52.9	28 6.1	15 6.2	15 21.5	10 16.6	24 17.3	22 15.6	5 11.1	17 50.3	1 26.5	27 47.8	15 17.3
19 S	9 50 49.5	29 6.6	15 3.1	28 27.1	9 47.2	25 30.7	23 0.7	5 24.2	17 54.0	1 29.5	27 46.1	15 16.4
20 M	9 54 46.1	0♓ 7.1	14 59.9	11♒57.0	9 8.8	26 44.1	23 45.9	5 37.3	17 57.7	1 32.5	27 44.5	15 15.6
21 T	9 58 42.6	1 7.6	14 56.7	25 49.8	8 22.3	27 57.5	24 31.1	5 50.5	18 1.3	1 35.6	27 42.8	15 14.7
22 W	10 2 39.2	2 8.1	14 53.5	10♓ 1.9	7 28.9	29 10.9	25 16.3	6 3.7	18 4.8	1 38.6	27 41.1	15 13.9
23 T	10 6 35.7	3 8.5	14 50.4	24 27.6	6 30.2	0♒24.3	26 1.6	6 17.1	18 8.2	1 41.7	27 39.4	15 13.1
24 F	10 10 32.3	4 9.0	14 47.2	9♈ 0.0	5 27.6	1 37.7	26 46.9	6 30.4	18 11.5	1 44.9	27 37.8	15 12.3
25 S	10 14 28.8	5 9.3	14 44.0	23 32.4	4 22.9	2 51.2	27 32.2	6 43.9	18 14.7	1 48.0	27 36.1	15 11.6
26 S	10 18 25.4	6 9.7	14 40.8	7♉59.0	3 17.6	4 4.7	28 17.5	6 57.3	18 17.8	1 51.2	27 34.4	15 10.9
27 M	10 22 21.9	7 10.0	14 37.6	22 16.0	2 13.4	5 18.1	29 2.9	7 10.9	18 20.9	1 54.3	27 32.8	15 10.1
28 T	10 26 18.5	8 10.3	14 34.5	6♊21.4	1 11.6	6 31.6	29 48.3	7 24.5	18 23.8	1 57.5	27 31.1	15 9.4
29 W	10 30 15.1	9 10.6	14 31.3	20 14.4	0 13.6	7 45.1	0♒33.7	7 38.1	18 26.7	2 0.8	27 29.5	15 8.8
						DECLINATION						
1 W	8 39 51.5	17S30.3	22N42.8	21N10.7	13S44.7	22S 7.6	23S43.3	0S24.8	21S13.7	0S23.2	12N34.6	21N32.8
4 S	8 51 41.2	16 39.1	22 41.8	24 36.1	11 38.0	22 8.1	23 34.5	0 10.2	21 15.0	0 20.1	12 36.3	21 33.4
7 T	9 3 30.9	15 45.2	22 40.8	15 40.4	9 33.4	22 2.9	23 23.6	0N 4.6	21 16.1	0 16.8	12 38.1	21 34.0
10 F	9 15 20.5	14 48.9	22 39.8	0 52.8	7 40.3	21 51.9	23 10.3	0 19.7	21 17.2	0 13.5	12 39.8	21 34.6
13 M	9 27 10.2	13 50.4	22 38.8	13S37.6	6 9.9	21 35.1	22 54.9	0 35.1	21 18.2	0 10.1	12 41.6	21 35.1
16 T	9 38 59.9	12 49.8	22 37.7	23 27.7	5 13.1	21 12.6	22 37.3	0 50.6	21 19.1	0 6.6	12 43.4	21 35.7
19 S	9 50 49.5	11 47.3	22 36.7	23 49.0	4 57.9	20 44.5	22 17.6	1 6.4	21 19.8	0 2.9	12 45.1	21 36.2
22 W	10 2 39.2	10 43.2	22 35.6	12 25.7	5 25.0	20 10.8	21 55.7	1 22.4	21 20.5	0N 0.8	12 46.9	21 36.7
25 S	10 14 28.8	9 37.5	22 34.5	5N29.5	6 26.2	19 31.9	21 31.7	1 38.6	21 21.1	0 4.5	12 48.7	21 37.2
28 T	10 26 18.5	8 30.5	22 33.4	20 39.0	7 46.0	18 47.9	21 5.8	1 54.9	21 21.6	0 8.4	12 50.4	21 37.7

MARCH 1928

DAY	EPHEMERIS SIDEREAL TIME h m s	☉ ° ′	☊ ° ′	☽ ° ′	☿ ° ′	♀ ° ′	♂ ° ′	♃ ° ′	♄ ° ′	♅ ° ′	♆ ° ′	♇ ° ′
LONGITUDE												
1 T	10 34 11.6	10♓10.8	14♊28.1	3♋55.6	29♒20.3	8♒58.6	1♒19.1	7♈51.8	18♐29.5	2♈ 4.0	27♌27.8	15♋ 8.1
2 F	10 38 8.1	11 10.9	14 24.9	17 25.6	28R32.6	10 12.2	2 4.5	8 5.5	18 32.1	2 7.2	27R26.2	15R 7.5
3 S	10 42 4.7	12 11.1	14 21.8	0♌45.0	27 51.1	11 25.7	2 50.0	8 19.3	18 34.7	2 10.5	27 24.6	15 6.8
4 S	10 46 1.3	13 11.2	14 18.6	13 53.8	27 16.2	12 39.3	3 35.5	8 33.1	18 37.2	2 13.8	27 23.0	15 6.3
5 M	10 49 57.8	14 11.3	14 15.4	26 51.7	26 48.1	13 52.8	4 21.0	8 46.9	18 39.6	2 17.1	27 21.4	15 5.7
6 T	10 53 54.4	15 11.3	14 12.2	9♍38.1	26 26.9	15 6.4	5 6.6	9 0.8	18 41.9	2 20.4	27 19.8	15 5.1
7 W	10 57 50.9	16 11.3	14 9.0	22 12.4	26 12.5	16 20.0	5 52.1	9 14.8	18 44.1	2 23.7	27 18.2	15 4.6
8 T	11 1 47.5	17 11.3	14 5.9	4♎34.4	26 4.9	17 33.6	6 37.7	9 28.7	18 46.2	2 27.0	27 16.7	15 4.1
9 F	11 5 44.0	18 11.3	14 2.7	16 44.7	26 3.6	18 47.2	7 23.3	9 42.7	18 48.2	2 30.4	27 15.1	15 3.6
10 S	11 9 40.6	19 11.2	13 59.5	28 44.8	26D 8.6	20 0.8	8 9.0	9 56.8	18 50.2	2 33.7	27 13.6	15 3.2
11 S	11 13 37.1	20 11.1	13 56.3	10♏37.3	26 19.5	21 14.4	8 54.6	10 10.9	18 52.0	2 37.1	27 12.0	15 2.7
12 M	11 17 33.7	21 11.0	13 53.2	22 25.5	26 36.0	22 28.1	9 40.3	10 25.0	18 53.7	2 40.5	27 10.5	15 2.3
13 T	11 21 30.2	22 10.8	13 50.0	4♐13.8	26 57.7	23 41.7	10 26.0	10 39.1	18 55.3	2 43.8	27 9.0	15 1.9
14 W	11 25 26.8	23 10.6	13 46.8	16 7.3	27 24.4	24 55.4	11 11.7	10 53.3	18 56.9	2 47.2	27 7.6	15 1.6
15 T	11 29 23.4	24 10.4	13 43.6	28 11.3	27 55.8	26 9.1	11 57.5	11 7.5	18 58.3	2 50.6	27 6.1	15 1.2
16 F	11 33 19.9	25 10.2	13 40.4	10♑31.5	28 31.5	27 22.7	12 43.2	11 21.7	18 59.6	2 54.0	27 4.6	15 0.9
17 S	11 37 16.4	26 9.9	13 37.3	23 12.9	29 11.4	28 36.4	13 29.0	11 36.0	19 0.9	2 57.4	27 3.2	15 0.6
18 S	11 41 13.0	27 9.6	13 34.1	6♒19.6	29 55.0	29 50.1	14 14.8	11 50.2	19 2.0	3 0.8	27 1.8	15 0.3
19 M	11 45 9.6	28 9.2	13 30.9	19 54.2	0♓42.3	1♓ 3.8	15 0.6	12 4.6	19 3.0	3 4.3	27 0.4	15 0.1
20 T	11 49 6.1	29 8.9	13 27.7	3♓56.5	1 32.9	2 17.5	15 46.4	12 18.9	19 4.0	3 7.7	26 59.0	14 59.8
21 W	11 53 2.7	0♈ 8.5	13 24.6	18 23.5	2 26.7	3 31.2	16 32.3	12 33.2	19 4.8	3 11.1	26 57.7	14 59.6
22 T	11 56 59.2	1 8.0	13 21.4	3♈ 9.3	3 23.5	4 44.9	17 18.1	12 47.6	19 5.5	3 14.5	26 56.3	14 59.4
23 F	12 0 55.8	2 7.6	13 18.2	18 5.4	4 23.1	5 58.7	18 4.0	13 2.0	19 6.2	3 18.0	26 55.0	14 59.3
24 S	12 4 52.3	3 7.1	13 15.0	3♉ 2.7	5 25.4	7 12.4	18 49.9	13 16.4	19 6.7	3 21.4	26 53.7	14 59.2
25 S	12 8 48.9	4 6.6	13 11.9	17 52.6	6 30.1	8 26.1	19 35.8	13 30.8	19 7.1	3 24.8	26 52.5	14 59.1
26 M	12 12 45.4	5 6.0	13 8.7	2♊28.6	7 37.3	9 39.8	20 21.6	13 45.2	19 7.5	3 28.3	26 51.2	14 59.0
27 T	12 16 42.0	6 5.4	13 5.5	16 46.6	8 46.7	10 53.5	21 7.5	13 59.7	19 7.7	3 31.7	26 50.0	14 58.9
28 W	12 20 38.5	7 4.7	13 2.3	0♋45.0	9 58.3	12 7.2	21 53.4	14 14.1	19 7.8	3 35.1	26 48.8	14 58.9
29 T	12 24 35.1	8 4.0	12 59.1	14 24.1	11 12.0	13 20.9	22 39.4	14 28.6	19 7.8	3 38.5	26 47.6	14 58.9
30 F	12 28 31.7	9 3.3	12 56.0	27 45.4	12 27.7	14 34.6	23 25.3	14 43.1	19R 7.8	3 42.0	26 46.4	14D58.9
31 S	12 32 28.2	10 2.5	12 52.8	10♌50.8	13 45.3	15 48.3	24 11.2	14 57.5	19 7.6	3 45.4	26 45.3	14 58.9
DECLINATION												
1 T	10 34 11.6	7S45.3	22N32.7	25N 2.8	8S41.2	18S15.8	20S47.3	2N 5.9	21S21.9	0N11.0	12N51.6	21N38.0
4 S	10 46 1.3	6 36.6	22 31.6	20 47.3	9 57.0	17 23.8	20 18.1	2 22.4	21 22.3	0 14.9	12 53.2	21 38.5
7 W	10 57 50.9	5 27.1	22 30.5	7 37.9	10 57.4	16 27.4	19 47.0	2 39.0	21 22.6	0 18.9	12 54.9	21 38.9
10 S	11 9 40.6	4 16.9	22 29.4	7S44.3	11 38.7	15 26.7	19 14.0	2 55.7	21 22.8	0 22.9	12 56.5	21 39.3
13 T	11 21 30.2	3 6.2	22 28.2	20 14.3	12 0.4	14 22.2	18 39.3	3 12.5	21 22.9	0 27.0	12 58.1	21 39.7
16 F	11 33 19.9	1 55.2	22 27.1	25 21.8	12 3.4	13 14.1	18 2.8	3 29.4	21 22.9	0 31.0	12 59.6	21 40.1
19 M	11 45 9.6	0 44.1	22 25.9	19 15.0	11 49.1	12 2.7	17 24.8	3 46.2	21 22.9	0 35.1	13 1.0	21 40.4
22 T	11 56 59.2	0N27.1	22 24.7	3 3.7	11 18.7	10 48.3	16 45.2	4 3.1	21 22.8	0 39.2	13 2.4	21 40.7
25 S	12 8 48.9	1 38.0	22 23.6	15N11.2	10 33.4	9 31.2	16 4.1	4 20.0	21 22.6	0 43.3	13 3.8	21 41.0
28 W	12 20 38.5	2 48.6	22 22.4	25 6.0	9 34.3	8 11.9	15 21.6	4 36.9	21 22.4	0 47.4	13 5.0	21 41.3
31 S	12 32 28.2	3 58.7	22 21.2	21 42.5	8 22.4	6 50.4	14 37.8	4 53.8	21 22.1	0 51.5	13 6.2	21 41.5

APRIL 1928

DAY	EPHEMERIS SIDEREAL TIME h m s	☉ ° ′	☊ ° ′	☽ ° ′	☿ ° ′	♀ ° ′	♂ ° ′	♃ ° ′	♄ ° ′	♅ ° ′	♆ ° ′	♇ ° ′
LONGITUDE												
1 S	12 36 24.7	11♈ 1.7	12♊49.6	23♌42.3	15♓ 4.7	17♓ 2.0	24♒57.1	15♈12.0	19♐ 7.3	3♈48.8	26♌44.2	14♋59.0
2 M	12 40 21.3	12 0.9	12 46.4	6♍21.4	16 26.0	18 15.7	25 43.1	15 26.5	19R 7.0	3 52.2	26R43.1	14 59.1
3 T	12 44 17.9	13 0.0	12 43.2	18 49.6	17 49.1	19 29.4	26 29.0	15 41.0	19 6.5	3 55.6	26 42.1	14 59.2
4 W	12 48 14.4	13 59.1	12 40.1	1♎ 7.7	19 13.8	20 43.1	27 15.0	15 55.5	19 5.9	3 59.0	26 41.0	14 59.3
5 T	12 52 11.0	14 58.1	12 36.9	13 16.8	20 40.3	21 56.8	28 0.9	16 10.0	19 5.3	4 2.4	26 40.0	14 59.5
6 F	12 56 7.5	15 57.2	12 33.7	25 17.7	22 8.4	23 10.5	28 46.9	16 24.5	19 4.5	4 5.7	26 39.0	14 59.7
7 S	13 0 4.1	16 56.1	12 30.5	7♏12.0	23 38.1	24 24.2	29 32.8	16 39.0	19 3.7	4 9.1	26 38.1	14 59.9
8 S	13 4 0.6	17 55.1	12 27.4	19 1.6	25 9.4	25 37.9	0♓18.8	16 53.5	19 2.7	4 12.5	26 37.2	15 0.1
9 M	13 7 57.2	18 54.0	12 24.2	0♐49.0	26 42.4	26 51.6	1 4.8	17 8.0	19 1.6	4 15.8	26 36.3	15 0.4
10 T	13 11 53.7	19 52.9	12 21.0	12 37.6	28 16.9	28 5.3	1 50.8	17 22.5	19 0.5	4 19.1	26 35.4	15 0.7
11 W	13 15 50.3	20 51.8	12 17.8	24 31.5	29 53.0	29 19.0	2 36.7	17 37.0	18 59.3	4 22.5	26 34.5	15 1.0
12 T	13 19 46.9	21 50.6	12 14.7	6♑35.3	1♈30.6	0♈32.7	3 22.7	17 51.4	18 57.9	4 25.8	26 33.7	15 1.3
13 F	13 23 43.4	22 49.4	12 11.5	18 53.9	3 9.9	1 46.4	4 8.7	18 5.9	18 56.5	4 29.1	26 33.0	15 1.7
14 S	13 27 39.9	23 48.2	12 8.3	1♒32.3	4 50.7	3 0.1	4 54.7	18 20.4	18 55.0	4 32.4	26 32.2	15 2.0
15 S	13 31 36.5	24 46.9	12 5.1	14 35.0	6 33.1	4 13.8	5 40.7	18 34.8	18 53.3	4 35.6	26 31.5	15 2.4
16 M	13 35 33.0	25 45.6	12 1.9	28 5.4	8 17.1	5 27.5	6 26.7	18 49.3	18 51.6	4 38.9	26 30.8	15 2.9
17 T	13 39 29.6	26 44.3	11 58.8	12♓ 4.7	10 2.7	6 41.2	7 12.6	19 3.7	18 49.8	4 42.1	26 30.1	15 3.3
18 W	13 43 26.2	27 43.0	11 55.6	26 31.7	11 49.8	7 54.9	7 58.6	19 18.1	18 47.9	4 45.4	26 29.5	15 3.8
19 T	13 47 22.7	28 41.6	11 52.4	11♈21.8	13 38.6	9 8.6	8 44.6	19 32.5	18 46.0	4 48.6	26 28.9	15 4.3
20 F	13 51 19.3	29 40.2	11 49.2	26 27.4	15 29.0	10 22.2	9 30.5	19 46.9	18 43.9	4 51.8	26 28.3	15 4.8
21 S	13 55 15.8	0♉38.7	11 46.0	11♉39.1	17 21.1	11 35.9	10 16.4	20 1.3	18 41.7	4 54.9	26 27.7	15 5.3
22 S	13 59 12.4	1 37.3	11 42.9	26 46.7	19 14.7	12 49.6	11 2.4	20 15.6	18 39.5	4 58.1	26 27.2	15 5.9
23 M	14 3 8.9	2 35.8	11 39.7	11♊41.3	21 10.0	14 3.3	11 48.3	20 30.0	18 37.2	5 1.2	26 26.8	15 6.5
24 T	14 7 5.5	3 34.2	11 36.5	26 16.4	23 6.9	15 17.0	12 34.2	20 44.3	18 34.7	5 4.4	26 26.3	15 7.1
25 W	14 11 2.0	4 32.7	11 33.3	10♋28.2	25 5.3	16 30.6	13 20.1	20 58.6	18 32.2	5 7.4	26 25.9	15 7.7
26 T	14 14 58.6	5 31.1	11 30.2	24 15.7	27 5.4	17 44.3	14 6.0	21 12.8	18 29.7	5 10.5	26 25.5	15 8.4
27 F	14 18 55.2	6 29.4	11 27.0	7♌39.5	29 6.9	18 57.9	14 51.8	21 27.1	18 27.0	5 13.6	26 25.1	15 9.1
28 S	14 22 51.7	7 27.7	11 23.8	20 42.0	1♉ 9.9	20 11.6	15 37.7	21 41.3	18 24.3	5 16.6	26 24.8	15 9.8
29 S	14 26 48.2	8 26.0	11 20.6	3♍26.0	3 14.3	21 25.2	16 23.5	21 55.4	18 21.5	5 19.6	26 24.5	15 10.5
30 M	14 30 44.8	9 24.3	11 17.5	15 54.5	5 20.0	22 38.8	17 9.3	22 9.6	18 18.6	5 22.6	26 24.3	15 11.2
DECLINATION												
1 S	12 36 24.7	4N22.0	22N20.8	18N10.5	7S55.6	6S22.9	14S22.9	4N59.4	21S22.0	0N52.8	13N 6.6	21N41.6
4 W	12 48 14.4	5 31.1	22 19.5	3 55.5	6 27.7	4 59.3	13 37.4	5 16.2	21 21.6	0 56.9	13 7.7	21 41.8
7 S	13 0 4.1	6 39.4	22 18.3	11S15.2	4 48.6	3 34.4	12 50.9	5 32.9	21 21.1	1 0.9	13 8.7	21 42.0
10 T	13 11 53.7	7 46.7	22 17.1	22 30.4	2 58.9	2 8.4	12 3.2	5 49.6	21 20.6	1 4.9	13 9.6	21 42.2
13 F	13 23 43.4	8 52.8	22 15.8	25 17.3	0 59.3	0 41.8	11 14.6	6 6.2	21 20.0	1 8.8	13 10.4	21 42.3
16 M	13 35 33.0	9 57.5	22 14.6	16 51.7	1N 9.5	0N45.1	10 25.1	6 22.6	21 19.4	1 12.7	13 11.1	21 42.4
19 T	13 47 22.7	11 0.9	22 13.3	0N25.7	3 26.6	2 12.2	9 34.8	6 39.0	21 18.7	1 16.5	13 11.8	21 42.5
22 S	13 59 12.4	12 2.6	22 12.0	18 17.3	5 50.9	3 39.0	8 43.8	6 55.2	21 17.9	1 20.2	13 12.3	21 42.6
25 W	14 11 2.0	13 2.5	22 10.7	25 40.4	8 20.9	5 5.2	7 52.1	7 11.2	21 17.1	1 23.9	13 12.7	21 42.6
28 S	14 22 51.7	14 0.4	22 9.4	19 15.2	10 54.3	6 30.5	6 59.9	7 27.1	21 16.3	1 27.5	13 13.1	21 42.6

MAY 1928

LONGITUDE

DAY	EPHEMERIS SIDEREAL TIME	☉	☊	☽	☿	♀	♂	♃	♄	♅	♆	♇
	h m s	° ′	° ′	° ′	° ′	° ′	° ′	° ′	° ′	° ′	° ′	° ′
1 T	14 34 41.4	10♉22.5	11♓14.3	28♍10.4	7♉26.9	23♈52.5	17♓55.1	22♈23.7	18♐15.6	5♈25.6	26♌24.1	15♋12.0
2 W	14 38 37.9	11 20.7	11 11.1	10♎16.5	9 34.9	25 6.1	18 40.9	22 37.8	18R12.6	5 28.5	26R23.9	15 12.8
3 T	14 42 34.5	12 18.8	11 7.9	22 15.0	11 43.6	26 19.7	19 26.6	22 51.9	18 9.5	5 31.4	26 23.7	15 13.6
4 F	14 46 31.0	13 17.0	11 4.7	4♏ 8.0	13 53.1	27 33.3	20 12.4	23 5.9	18 6.3	5 34.3	26 23.6	15 14.4
5 S	14 50 27.6	14 15.1	11 1.6	15 57.7	16 3.0	28 46.9	20 58.1	23 19.9	18 3.0	5 37.1	26 23.5	15 15.2
6 S	14 54 24.2	15 13.1	10 58.4	27 45.9	18 13.2	0♉ 0.6	21 43.8	23 33.9	17 59.7	5 40.0	26 23.4	15 16.1
7 M	14 58 20.7	16 11.2	10 55.2	9♐34.9	20 23.2	1 14.2	22 29.5	23 47.8	17 56.3	5 42.8	26 23.4	15 17.0
8 T	15 2 17.3	17 9.2	10 52.0	21 27.3	22 33.0	2 27.8	23 15.1	24 1.7	17 52.9	5 45.5	26 23.4	15 17.9
9 W	15 6 13.8	18 7.2	10 48.9	3♑25.9	24 42.1	3 41.4	24 0.8	24 15.5	17 49.4	5 48.3	26D23.4	15 18.8
10 T	15 10 10.4	19 5.2	10 45.7	15 34.2	26 50.3	4 55.0	24 46.4	24 29.3	17 45.8	5 51.0	26 23.5	15 19.7
11 F	15 14 6.9	20 3.1	10 42.5	27 55.9	28 57.4	6 8.6	25 32.0	24 43.1	17 42.2	5 53.7	26 23.6	15 20.7
12 S	15 18 3.5	21 1.0	10 39.3	10♒34.8	1♊ 2.9	7 22.2	26 17.6	24 56.8	17 38.5	5 56.3	26 23.7	15 21.7
13 S	15 22 0.0	21 58.9	10 36.1	23 34.9	3 6.7	8 35.8	27 3.1	25 10.5	17 34.8	5 59.0	26 23.9	15 22.7
14 M	15 25 56.6	22 56.8	10 33.0	6♓59.1	5 8.6	9 49.4	27 48.6	25 24.1	17 31.0	6 1.6	26 24.1	15 23.7
15 T	15 29 53.2	23 54.7	10 29.8	20 49.5	7 8.2	11 3.0	28 34.1	25 37.7	17 27.1	6 4.1	26 24.3	15 24.7
16 W	15 33 49.7	24 52.5	10 26.6	5♈ 6.1	9 5.5	12 16.6	29 19.6	25 51.3	17 23.3	6 6.7	26 24.6	15 25.8
17 T	15 37 46.3	25 50.4	10 23.4	19 46.4	11 0.2	13 30.2	0♈ 5.0	26 4.8	17 19.3	6 9.1	26 24.9	15 26.8
18 F	15 41 42.8	26 48.2	10 20.3	4♉45.1	12 52.2	14 43.9	0 50.4	26 18.2	17 15.3	6 11.6	26 25.2	15 27.9
19 S	15 45 39.4	27 45.9	10 17.1	19 54.6	14 41.4	15 57.5	1 35.8	26 31.6	17 11.3	6 14.0	26 25.6	15 29.0
20 S	15 49 35.9	28 43.7	10 13.9	5♊ 5.4	16 27.7	17 11.1	2 21.1	26 45.0	17 7.2	6 16.4	26 26.0	15 30.2
21 M	15 53 32.5	29 41.4	10 10.7	20 8.2	18 11.1	18 24.7	3 6.4	26 58.3	17 3.1	6 18.8	26 26.4	15 31.3
22 T	15 57 29.0	0♊39.2	10 7.6	4♋54.7	19 51.3	19 38.3	3 51.6	27 11.5	16 59.0	6 21.1	26 26.9	15 32.4
23 W	16 1 25.6	1 36.8	10 4.4	19 18.9	21 28.5	20 51.9	4 36.8	27 24.7	16 54.8	6 23.4	26 27.4	15 33.6
24 T	16 5 22.1	2 34.5	10 1.2	3♌17.3	23 2.4	22 5.5	5 22.0	27 37.8	16 50.6	6 25.7	26 27.9	15 34.8
25 F	16 9 18.7	3 32.1	9 58.0	16 49.3	24 33.2	23 19.1	6 7.1	27 50.9	16 46.3	6 27.9	26 28.5	15 36.0
26 S	16 13 15.2	4 29.8	9 54.9	29 56.1	26 0.8	24 32.7	6 52.2	28 3.9	16 42.0	6 30.0	26 29.1	15 37.2
27 S	16 17 11.8	5 27.3	9 51.7	12♍40.4	27 25.0	25 46.3	7 37.3	28 16.8	16 37.7	6 32.2	26 29.7	15 38.4
28 M	16 21 8.4	6 24.9	9 48.5	25 5.9	28 45.9	26 59.8	8 22.2	28 29.7	16 33.4	6 34.3	26 30.4	15 39.7
29 T	16 25 4.9	7 22.5	9 45.3	7♎16.5	0♋ 3.5	28 13.4	9 7.2	28 42.5	16 29.1	6 36.3	26 31.0	15 40.9
30 W	16 29 1.5	8 20.0	9 42.1	19 16.3	1 17.6	29 27.0	9 52.1	28 55.2	16 24.7	6 38.4	26 31.8	15 42.2
31 T	16 32 58.0	9 17.5	9 39.0	1♏ 8.8	2 28.3	0♊40.6	10 37.0	29 7.9	16 20.3	6 40.3	26 32.5	15 43.5

DECLINATION

DAY	EPHEMERIS SIDEREAL TIME	☉	☊	☽	☿	♀	♂	♃	♄	♅	♆	♇
1 T	14 34 41.4	14N56.3	22N 8.1	5N15.9	13N28.1	7N54.6	6S 7.3	7N42.8	21S15.4	1N31.0	13N13.3	21N42.6
4 F	14 46 31.0	15 50.0	22 6.8	10S 2.4	15 58.0	9 17.2	5 14.3	7 58.3	21 14.4	1 34.4	13 13.5	21 42.6
7 M	14 58 20.7	16 41.2	22 5.5	21 54.1	18 18.9	10 38.0	4 21.0	8 13.7	21 13.4	1 37.7	13 13.5	21 42.5
10 T	15 10 10.4	17 30.0	22 4.1	25 37.2	20 25.2	11 56.6	3 27.4	8 28.8	21 12.4	1 40.9	13 13.4	21 42.4
13 S	15 22 0.0	18 16.2	22 2.8	18 26.6	22 12.3	13 12.7	2 33.8	8 43.7	21 11.4	1 44.0	13 13.3	21 42.3
16 W	15 33 49.7	18 59.7	22 1.4	2 20.6	23 37.1	14 26.0	1 40.0	8 58.3	21 10.3	1 47.0	13 13.0	21 42.2
19 S	15 45 39.4	19 40.2	22 0.0	16N 0.8	24 38.6	15 36.2	0 46.3	9 12.7	21 9.1	1 49.9	13 12.7	21 42.1
22 T	15 57 29.0	20 17.8	21 58.6	25 37.9	25 17.8	16 43.0	0N 7.2	9 26.9	21 8.0	1 52.6	13 12.2	21 41.9
25 F	16 9 18.7	20 52.2	21 57.2	20 27.1	25 36.5	17 45.9	1 0.6	9 40.7	21 6.8	1 55.2	13 11.6	21 41.7
28 M	16 21 8.4	21 23.3	21 55.8	6 37.6	25 37.4	18 44.7	1 53.7	9 54.3	21 5.7	1 57.7	13 11.0	21 41.5
31 T	16 32 58.0	21 51.2	21 54.4	8S47.4	25 23.3	19 39.1	2 46.4	10 7.6	21 4.5	1 60.0	13 10.2	21 41.3

JUNE 1928

LONGITUDE

DAY	EPHEMERIS SIDEREAL TIME	☉	☊	☽	☿	♀	♂	♃	♄	♅	♆	♇
1 F	16 36 54.6	10♊14.9	9♓35.8	12♏57.6	3♋35.4	1♊54.2	11♈21.8	29♈20.5	16♐15.9	6♈42.3	26♌33.3	15♋44.8
2 S	16 40 51.2	11 12.4	9 32.6	24 45.6	4 39.0	3 7.8	12 6.5	29 33.0	16R11.5	6 44.2	26 34.1	15 46.1
3 S	16 44 47.7	12 9.9	9 29.4	6♐35.5	5 38.9	4 21.4	12 51.3	29 45.5	16 7.1	6 46.1	26 34.9	15 47.4
4 M	16 48 44.3	13 7.3	9 26.3	18 29.6	6 35.1	5 35.0	13 35.9	29 57.9	16 2.6	6 47.9	26 35.8	15 48.8
5 T	16 52 40.8	14 4.7	9 23.1	0♑30.1	7 27.5	6 48.5	14 20.5	0♉10.2	15 58.2	6 49.6	26 36.7	15 50.1
6 W	16 56 37.4	15 2.1	9 19.9	12 38.9	8 15.9	8 2.1	15 5.1	0 22.5	15 53.8	6 51.4	26 37.6	15 51.5
7 T	17 0 33.9	15 59.5	9 16.7	24 58.2	9 0.5	9 15.7	15 49.6	0 34.7	15 49.3	6 53.1	26 38.6	15 52.9
8 F	17 4 30.5	16 56.8	9 13.6	7♒30.1	9 41.0	10 29.3	16 34.1	0 46.8	15 44.9	6 54.7	26 39.6	15 54.2
9 S	17 8 27.1	17 54.2	9 10.4	20 16.8	10 17.3	11 43.0	17 18.5	0 58.8	15 40.4	6 56.4	26 40.6	15 55.6
10 S	17 12 23.6	18 51.5	9 7.2	3♓20.7	10 49.4	12 56.6	18 2.9	1 10.7	15 36.0	6 57.9	26 41.7	15 57.0
11 M	17 16 20.1	19 48.9	9 4.0	16 43.5	11 17.2	14 10.2	18 47.2	1 22.6	15 31.6	6 59.4	26 42.7	15 58.5
12 T	17 20 16.7	20 46.2	9 0.8	0♈26.9	11 40.5	15 23.8	19 31.5	1 34.4	15 27.1	7 0.9	26 43.8	15 59.9
13 W	17 24 13.3	21 43.6	8 57.7	14 31.3	11 59.5	16 37.5	20 15.7	1 46.1	15 22.7	7 2.4	26 45.0	16 1.3
14 T	17 28 9.9	22 40.9	8 54.5	28 55.5	12 13.9	17 51.1	20 59.8	1 57.7	15 18.3	7 3.7	26 46.1	16 2.8
15 F	17 32 6.4	23 38.2	8 51.3	13♉36.8	12 23.8	19 4.7	21 43.9	2 9.2	15 13.9	7 5.1	26 47.3	16 4.2
16 S	17 36 2.9	24 35.5	8 48.1	28 30.1	12 29.1	20 18.4	22 27.9	2 20.6	15 9.6	7 6.4	26 48.6	16 5.7
17 S	17 39 59.5	25 32.8	8 45.0	13♊28.6	12 29.8	21 32.1	23 11.8	2 32.0	15 5.2	7 7.6	26 49.8	16 7.1
18 M	17 43 56.1	26 30.1	8 41.8	28 24.3	12R26.1	22 45.7	23 55.7	2 43.2	15 0.9	7 8.9	26 51.1	16 8.6
19 T	17 47 52.7	27 27.4	8 38.6	13♋ 9.2	12 18.0	23 59.4	24 39.5	2 54.4	14 56.6	7 10.0	26 52.4	16 10.1
20 W	17 51 49.2	28 24.7	8 35.4	27 36.1	12 5.6	25 13.1	25 23.2	3 5.4	14 52.3	7 11.1	26 53.7	16 11.6
21 T	17 55 45.8	29 21.9	8 32.3	11♌40.0	11 49.1	26 26.8	26 6.9	3 16.4	14 48.1	7 12.2	26 55.1	16 13.1
22 F	17 59 42.3	0♋19.2	8 29.1	25 18.1	11 28.8	27 40.4	26 50.5	3 27.2	14 43.9	7 13.2	26 56.4	16 14.6
23 S	18 3 38.9	1 16.4	8 25.9	8♍30.1	11 4.9	28 54.1	27 34.0	3 38.0	14 39.7	7 14.2	26 57.8	16 16.1
24 S	18 7 35.4	2 13.7	8 22.7	21 17.9	10 37.8	0♋ 7.8	28 17.4	3 48.6	14 35.6	7 15.1	26 59.3	16 17.6
25 M	18 11 32.0	3 10.9	8 19.5	3♎44.7	10 7.9	1 21.5	29 0.8	3 59.2	14 31.5	7 16.0	27 0.7	16 19.1
26 T	18 15 28.6	4 8.1	8 16.4	15 54.8	9 35.7	2 35.2	29 44.1	4 9.6	14 27.4	7 16.8	27 2.2	16 20.7
27 W	18 19 25.1	5 5.3	8 13.2	27 52.7	9 1.8	3 48.9	0♉27.3	4 20.0	14 23.4	7 17.6	27 3.7	16 22.2
28 T	18 23 21.7	6 2.5	8 10.0	9♏43.4	8 26.5	5 2.6	1 10.4	4 30.2	14 19.4	7 18.4	27 5.2	16 23.7
29 F	18 27 18.2	6 59.7	8 6.8	21 31.2	7 50.6	6 16.3	1 53.4	4 40.3	14 15.5	7 19.1	27 6.8	16 25.3
30 S	18 31 14.8	7 56.9	8 3.7	3♐20.4	7 14.6	7 30.1	2 36.4	4 50.4	14 11.6	7 19.7	27 8.4	16 26.8

DECLINATION

DAY	EPHEMERIS SIDEREAL TIME	☉	☊	☽	☿	♀	♂	♃	♄	♅	♆	♇
1 F	16 36 54.6	21N59.7	21N53.9	13S28.3	25N15.7	19N56.2	3N 3.9	10N11.9	21S 4.1	2N 0.7	13N10.0	21N41.2
4 M	16 48 44.3	22 23.0	21 52.5	23 46.5	24 45.8	20 44.3	3 56.0	10 24.8	21 2.9	2 2.9	13 9.1	21 40.9
7 T	17 0 33.9	22 42.7	21 51.1	24 51.4	24 7.3	21 27.2	4 47.7	10 37.4	21 1.7	2 4.8	13 8.1	21 40.7
10 S	17 12 23.6	22 58.9	21 49.6	15 10.6	23 22.7	22 4.9	5 38.7	10 49.6	21 0.5	2 6.7	13 7.1	21 40.4
13 W	17 24 13.3	23 11.4	21 48.2	1N43.9	22 34.4	22 36.9	6 29.1	11 1.5	20 59.3	2 8.3	13 5.9	21 40.1
16 S	17 36 2.9	23 20.3	21 46.7	18 50.9	21 44.9	23 3.1	7 18.7	11 13.0	20 58.2	2 9.8	13 4.7	21 39.8
19 T	17 47 52.7	23 25.5	21 45.2	25 42.5	20 56.6	23 23.3	8 7.6	11 24.2	20 57.1	2 11.2	13 3.4	21 39.4
22 F	17 59 42.3	23 26.9	21 43.7	17 53.3	20 11.9	23 37.4	8 55.5	11 35.0	20 56.0	2 12.4	13 1.9	21 39.1
25 M	18 11 32.0	23 24.7	21 42.2	2 54.1	19 33.3	23 45.2	9 42.5	11 45.4	20 55.0	2 13.4	13 0.5	21 38.7
28 T	18 23 21.7	23 18.7	21 40.7	12S15.9	19 3.0	23 46.7	10 28.5	11 55.4	20 54.0	2 14.2	12 58.9	21 38.4

JULY 1928

LONGITUDE

DAY	EPHEMERIS SIDEREAL TIME h m s	☉ ° '	☊ ° '	☽ ° '	☿ ° '	♀ ° '	♂ ° '	♃ ° '	♄ ° '	♅ ° '	♆ ° '	♇ ° '
1 S	18 35 11.4	8♋54.1	8♓ 0.5	15♐14.5	6♋39.3	8♋43.8	3♉19.3	5♉ 0.3	14♐ 7.8	7♈20.3	27♌10.0	16♋28.4
2 M	18 39 7.9	9 51.3	7 57.3	27 16.4	6R 5.1	9 57.5	4 2.1	5 10.0	14R 4.0	7 20.9	27 11.6	16 29.9
3 T	18 43 4.5	10 48.5	7 54.1	9♑28.3	5 32.6	11 11.3	4 44.8	5 19.7	14 0.3	7 21.4	27 13.2	16 31.5
4 W	18 47 1.0	11 45.6	7 51.0	21 51.8	5 2.6	12 25.0	5 27.5	5 29.3	13 56.6	7 21.8	27 14.9	16 33.0
5 T	18 50 57.6	12 42.8	7 47.8	4♒28.0	4 35.4	13 38.7	6 10.0	5 38.7	13 53.0	7 22.2	27 16.6	16 34.6
6 F	18 54 54.1	13 40.0	7 44.6	17 17.4	4 11.6	14 52.5	6 52.5	5 48.0	13 49.4	7 22.6	27 18.3	16 36.1
7 S	18 58 50.7	14 37.2	7 41.4	0♓20.3	3 51.6	16 6.3	7 34.9	5 57.2	13 45.9	7 22.9	27 20.0	16 37.7
8 S	19 2 47.3	15 34.4	7 38.3	13 36.9	3 35.8	17 20.1	8 17.2	6 6.3	13 42.5	7 23.1	27 21.7	16 39.2
9 M	19 6 43.8	16 31.5	7 35.1	27 7.1	3 24.5	18 33.8	8 59.4	6 15.2	13 39.1	7 23.3	27 23.5	16 40.8
10 T	19 10 40.3	17 28.8	7 31.9	10♈51.1	3 17.9	19 47.6	9 41.6	6 24.1	13 35.8	7 23.5	27 25.3	16 42.4
11 W	19 14 36.9	18 26.0	7 28.7	24 48.7	3 16.4	21 1.5	10 23.6	6 32.8	13 32.6	7 23.6	27 27.1	16 43.9
12 T	19 18 33.5	19 23.2	7 25.6	8♉59.4	3D20.0	22 15.3	11 5.5	6 41.3	13 29.4	7 23.7	27 28.9	16 45.5
13 F	19 22 30.1	20 20.4	7 22.4	23 21.6	3 28.9	23 29.1	11 47.4	6 49.7	13 26.3	7 23.7	27 30.8	16 47.0
14 S	19 26 26.6	21 17.6	7 19.2	7♊52.9	3 43.2	24 42.9	12 29.1	6 58.0	13 23.2	7R23.6	27 32.6	16 48.6
15 S	19 30 23.1	22 14.9	7 16.0	22 29.3	4 3.0	25 56.8	13 10.7	7 6.2	13 20.3	7 23.6	27 34.5	16 50.1
16 M	19 34 19.7	23 12.2	7 12.9	7♋ 5.3	4 28.2	27 10.7	13 52.3	7 14.2	13 17.4	7 23.4	27 36.4	16 51.7
17 T	19 38 16.3	24 9.4	7 9.7	21 34.8	4 58.8	28 24.5	14 33.7	7 22.1	13 14.6	7 23.3	27 38.3	16 53.2
18 W	19 42 12.8	25 6.7	7 6.5	5♌51.4	5 34.9	29 38.4	15 15.0	7 29.8	13 11.8	7 23.0	27 40.2	16 54.8
19 T	19 46 9.4	26 4.0	7 3.3	19 49.6	6 16.5	0♌52.3	15 56.2	7 37.4	13 9.1	7 22.8	27 42.2	16 56.3
20 F	19 50 5.9	27 1.2	7 0.1	3♍25.8	7 3.4	2 6.2	16 37.3	7 44.9	13 6.6	7 22.4	27 44.1	16 57.9
21 S	19 54 2.5	27 58.5	6 57.0	16 38.2	7 55.6	3 20.1	17 18.3	7 52.2	13 4.1	7 22.1	27 46.1	16 59.4
22 S	19 57 59.0	28 55.8	6 53.8	29 27.2	8 53.1	4 34.0	17 59.2	7 59.3	13 1.6	7 21.6	27 48.1	17 1.0
23 M	20 1 55.6	29 53.1	6 50.6	11♎55.2	9 55.8	5 47.9	18 39.9	8 6.3	12 59.3	7 21.2	27 50.1	17 2.5
24 T	20 5 52.2	0♌50.4	6 47.4	24 5.8	11 3.6	7 1.8	19 20.5	8 13.1	12 57.0	7 20.7	27 52.1	17 4.0
25 W	20 9 48.7	1 47.7	6 44.3	6♏ 3.9	12 16.4	8 15.7	20 1.0	8 19.8	12 54.9	7 20.1	27 54.2	17 5.5
26 T	20 13 45.3	2 45.1	6 41.1	17 54.5	13 34.1	9 29.6	20 41.4	8 26.4	12 52.8	7 19.5	27 56.2	17 7.0
27 F	20 17 41.8	3 42.4	6 37.9	29 42.9	14 56.5	10 43.5	21 21.7	8 32.8	12 50.8	7 18.8	27 58.3	17 8.5
28 S	20 21 38.4	4 39.7	6 34.7	11♐34.1	16 23.6	11 57.5	22 1.8	8 39.0	12 48.9	7 18.1	28 0.3	17 10.0
29 S	20 25 35.0	5 37.1	6 31.5	23 32.7	17 55.1	13 11.4	22 41.9	8 45.0	12 47.1	7 17.4	28 2.4	17 11.5
30 M	20 29 31.5	6 34.4	6 28.4	5♑42.5	19 30.8	14 25.3	23 21.8	8 50.9	12 45.3	7 16.6	28 4.5	17 13.0
31 T	20 33 28.1	7 31.8	6 25.2	18 6.4	21 10.6	15 39.3	24 1.6	8 56.7	12 43.7	7 15.8	28 6.6	17 14.5

DECLINATION

DAY	EPHEMERIS SIDEREAL TIME h m s	☉	☊	☽	☿	♀	♂	♃	♄	♅	♆	♇
1 S	18 35 11.4	23N 9.0	21N39.2	23S 9.7	18N43.1	23N41.9	11N13.5	12N 5.0	20S53.1	2N14.9	12N57.3	21N38.0
4 W	18 47 1.0	22 55.7	21 37.6	25 9.1	18 34.9	23 30.7	11 57.3	12 14.2	20 52.2	2 15.4	12 55.6	21 37.6
7 S	18 58 50.7	22 38.8	21 36.1	16 8.9	18 39.0	23 13.3	12 40.0	12 23.0	20 51.4	2 15.7	12 53.8	21 37.2
10 T	19 10 40.3	22 18.4	21 34.6	0N14.7	18 54.4	22 49.7	13 21.5	12 31.4	20 50.7	2 15.9	12 52.0	21 36.8
13 F	19 22 30.1	21 54.5	21 33.0	17 16.6	19 19.5	22 20.0	14 1.7	12 39.3	20 50.0	2 15.9	12 50.1	21 36.4
16 M	19 34 19.7	21 27.2	21 31.4	25 42.1	19 51.2	21 44.5	14 40.6	12 46.7	20 49.5	2 15.7	12 48.2	21 36.0
19 T	19 46 9.4	20 56.7	21 29.8	19 29.0	20 26.0	21 3.2	15 18.2	12 53.7	20 49.0	2 15.3	12 46.2	21 35.6
22 S	19 57 59.0	20 22.9	21 28.2	4 36.3	20 59.6	20 16.5	15 54.3	13 0.3	20 48.6	2 14.8	12 44.2	21 35.2
25 W	20 9 48.7	19 46.1	21 26.6	10S58.3	21 27.2	19 24.6	16 29.1	13 6.3	20 48.3	2 14.1	12 42.1	21 34.8
28 S	20 21 38.4	19 6.4	21 25.0	22 29.2	21 43.7	18 27.8	17 2.4	13 11.9	20 48.2	2 13.2	12 39.9	21 34.4
31 T	20 33 28.1	18 23.8	21 23.4	25 28.6	21 43.8	17 26.4	17 34.2	13 17.0	20 48.1	2 12.2	12 37.8	21 34.0

AUGUST 1928

LONGITUDE

DAY	EPHEMERIS SIDEREAL TIME h m s	☉ ° '	☊ ° '	☽ ° '	☿ ° '	♀ ° '	♂ ° '	♃ ° '	♄ ° '	♅ ° '	♆ ° '	♇ ° '
1 W	20 37 24.6	8♌29.1	6♓22.0	0♒46.1	22♋54.2	16♌53.2	24♉41.2	9♉ 2.2	12♐42.1	7♈14.9	28♌ 8.7	17♋16.0
2 T	20 41 21.2	9 26.5	6 18.8	13 42.1	24 41.3	18 7.2	25 20.7	9 7.7	12R40.7	7R14.0	28 10.8	17 17.4
3 F	20 45 17.7	10 23.9	6 15.7	26 53.8	26 31.5	19 21.1	26 0.1	9 12.9	12 39.3	7 13.0	28 13.0	17 18.9
4 S	20 49 14.3	11 21.4	6 12.5	10♓19.5	28 24.7	20 35.1	26 39.4	9 18.0	12 38.0	7 12.0	28 15.1	17 20.3
5 S	20 53 10.9	12 18.8	6 9.3	23 57.2	0♌20.3	21 49.1	27 18.5	9 22.9	12 36.8	7 10.9	28 17.3	17 21.8
6 M	20 57 7.4	13 16.3	6 6.1	7♈44.4	2 18.1	23 3.0	27 57.5	9 27.6	12 35.7	7 9.8	28 19.4	17 23.2
7 T	21 1 3.9	14 13.8	6 3.0	21 39.2	4 17.6	24 17.0	28 36.3	9 32.1	12 34.7	7 8.7	28 21.6	17 24.6
8 W	21 5 0.5	15 11.3	5 59.8	5♉39.9	6 18.6	25 31.0	29 15.1	9 36.5	12 33.8	7 7.5	28 23.8	17 26.0
9 T	21 8 57.1	16 8.8	5 56.6	19 45.5	8 20.7	26 45.0	29 53.6	9 40.7	12 33.0	7 6.3	28 25.9	17 27.4
10 F	21 12 53.7	17 6.3	5 53.4	3♊54.9	10 23.4	27 59.0	0♊32.0	9 44.7	12 32.3	7 5.0	28 28.1	17 28.8
11 S	21 16 50.2	18 3.9	5 50.2	18 7.0	12 26.6	29 13.0	1 10.3	9 48.6	12 31.6	7 3.7	28 30.3	17 30.2
12 S	21 20 46.7	19 1.5	5 47.1	2♋20.0	14 29.9	0♍27.0	1 48.4	9 52.2	12 31.1	7 2.4	28 32.5	17 31.6
13 M	21 24 43.3	19 59.1	5 43.9	16 31.1	16 33.0	1 41.0	2 26.4	9 55.7	12 30.7	7 1.0	28 34.7	17 32.9
14 T	21 28 39.9	20 56.8	5 40.7	0♌36.6	18 35.8	2 55.1	3 4.2	9 59.0	12 30.3	6 59.6	28 36.9	17 34.3
15 W	21 32 36.4	21 54.5	5 37.5	14 32.3	20 38.0	4 9.1	3 41.8	10 2.1	12 30.1	6 58.1	28 39.1	17 35.6
16 T	21 36 32.9	22 52.1	5 34.4	28 14.0	22 39.4	5 23.1	4 19.3	10 5.0	12 30.0	6 56.6	28 41.4	17 36.9
17 F	21 40 29.5	23 49.9	5 31.2	11♍38.2	24 40.0	6 37.2	4 56.6	10 7.7	12 29.9	6 55.0	28 43.6	17 38.2
18 S	21 44 26.1	24 47.6	5 28.0	24 42.7	26 39.5	7 51.2	5 33.7	10 10.2	12D30.0	6 53.5	28 45.8	17 39.5
19 S	21 48 22.6	25 45.3	5 24.8	7♎27.1	28 37.9	9 5.2	6 10.6	10 12.6	12 30.1	6 51.8	28 48.0	17 40.8
20 M	21 52 19.2	26 43.1	5 21.7	19 52.6	0♍35.2	10 19.3	6 47.4	10 14.7	12 30.4	6 50.2	28 50.2	17 42.1
21 T	21 56 15.7	27 40.9	5 18.5	2♏ 2.0	2 31.2	11 33.3	7 24.0	10 16.6	12 30.7	6 48.5	28 52.5	17 43.3
22 W	22 0 12.2	28 38.7	5 15.3	13 59.4	4 25.9	12 47.3	8 0.4	10 18.4	12 31.2	6 46.8	28 54.7	17 44.5
23 T	22 4 8.8	29 36.6	5 12.1	25 49.6	6 19.4	14 1.4	8 36.6	10 19.9	12 31.7	6 45.0	28 56.9	17 45.8
24 F	22 8 5.4	0♍34.4	5 8.9	7♐38.0	8 11.5	15 15.4	9 12.6	10 21.3	12 32.4	6 43.2	28 59.1	17 47.0
25 S	22 12 2.0	1 32.3	5 5.8	19 30.1	10 2.3	16 29.4	9 48.5	10 22.5	12 33.1	6 41.4	29 1.4	17 48.2
26 S	22 15 58.5	2 30.2	5 2.6	1♑31.1	11 51.7	17 43.4	10 24.1	10 23.4	12 33.9	6 39.6	29 3.6	17 49.3
27 M	22 19 55.0	3 28.1	4 59.4	13 46.0	13 39.9	18 57.5	10 59.6	10 24.2	12 34.9	6 37.7	29 5.8	17 50.5
28 T	22 23 51.6	4 26.0	4 56.2	26 18.4	15 26.7	20 11.5	11 34.9	10 24.8	12 35.9	6 35.8	29 8.0	17 51.6
29 W	22 27 48.2	5 24.0	4 53.1	9♒10.9	17 12.2	21 25.5	12 9.9	10 25.1	12 37.0	6 33.8	29 10.2	17 52.8
30 T	22 31 44.7	6 22.0	4 49.9	22 24.3	18 56.5	22 39.5	12 44.8	10 25.3	12 38.2	6 31.9	29 12.4	17 53.9
31 F	22 35 41.3	7 20.0	4 46.7	5♓57.6	20 39.4	23 53.5	13 19.4	10R25.3	12 39.6	6 29.9	29 14.7	17 55.0

DECLINATION

DAY	EPHEMERIS SIDEREAL TIME h m s	☉	☊	☽	☿	♀	♂	♃	♄	♅	♆	♇
1 W	20 37 24.6	18N 9.0	21N22.9	23S56.8	21N39.4	17N 4.9	17N44.5	13N18.5	20S48.1	2N11.8	12N37.1	21N33.9
4 S	20 49 14.3	17 22.8	21 21.2	12 22.1	21 11.3	15 57.8	18 14.4	13 22.9	20 48.2	2 10.6	12 34.9	21 33.5
7 T	21 1 3.9	16 34.1	21 19.6	5N 5.7	20 19.3	14 46.7	18 42.8	13 26.8	20 48.4	2 9.2	12 32.6	21 33.1
10 F	21 12 53.7	15 42.9	21 17.9	20 40.7	19 4.4	13 32.1	19 9.7	13 30.2	20 48.7	2 7.7	12 30.4	21 32.7
13 M	21 24 43.3	14 49.5	21 16.2	25 37.8	17 29.2	12 14.1	19 35.0	13 33.0	20 49.1	2 6.0	12 28.1	21 32.3
16 T	21 36 32.9	13 54.0	21 14.6	16 45.0	15 37.9	10 53.2	19 58.9	13 35.4	20 49.7	2 4.2	12 25.8	21 32.0
19 S	21 48 22.6	12 56.4	21 12.9	0 58.7	13 34.8	9 29.7	20 21.3	13 37.1	20 50.3	2 2.3	12 23.5	21 31.6
22 W	22 0 12.2	11 57.0	21 11.2	14S16.0	11 23.8	8 4.0	20 42.1	13 38.3	20 51.1	2 0.2	12 21.2	21 31.3
25 S	22 12 2.0	10 55.9	21 9.5	24 15.1	9 8.0	6 36.3	21 1.6	13 39.0	20 52.0	1 58.1	12 18.9	21 30.9
28 T	22 23 51.6	9 53.3	21 7.8	24 44.0	6 49.8	5 6.9	21 19.6	13 39.1	20 52.9	1 55.8	12 16.6	21 30.6
31 F	22 35 41.3	8 49.3	21 6.0	13 58.6	4 31.3	3 36.3	21 36.2	13 38.7	20 54.0	1 53.4	12 14.4	21 30.3

SEPTEMBER 1928

DAY	EPHEMERIS SIDEREAL TIME	☉	☊	☽	☿	♀	♂	♃	♄	♅	♆	♇
	h m s	° ′	° ′	° ′	° ′	° ′	° ′	° ′	° ′	° ′	° ′	° ′
LONGITUDE												
1 S	22 39 37.8	8♍18.0	4♊43.5	19♓48.0	22♍21.1	25♍ 7.5	13♊53.9	10♉25.1	12♐41.0	6♈27.8	29♌16.9	17♋56.0
2 S	22 43 34.4	9 16.1	4 40.3	3♈51.5	24 1.6	26 21.5	14 28.1	10R24.6	12 42.5	6R25.8	29 19.1	17 57.1
3 M	22 47 31.0	10 14.2	4 37.2	18 3.1	25 40.8	27 35.5	15 2.1	10 24.0	12 44.1	6 23.7	29 21.3	17 58.1
4 T	22 51 27.5	11 12.3	4 34.0	2♉18.3	27 18.8	28 49.5	15 35.9	10 23.2	12 45.8	6 21.6	29 23.4	17 59.2
5 W	22 55 24.0	12 10.5	4 30.8	16 33.3	28 55.6	0♎ 3.5	16 9.5	10 22.1	12 47.6	6 19.5	29 25.6	18 0.2
6 T	22 59 20.6	13 8.7	4 27.6	0♊45.4	0♎31.2	1 17.5	16 42.9	10 20.9	12 49.5	6 17.3	29 27.8	18 1.2
7 F	23 3 17.1	14 6.9	4 24.5	14 52.8	2 5.6	2 31.5	17 16.0	10 19.5	12 51.4	6 15.2	29 30.0	18 2.1
8 S	23 7 13.7	15 5.2	4 21.3	28 54.8	3 38.9	3 45.5	17 48.8	10 17.9	12 53.5	6 13.0	29 32.1	18 3.1
9 S	23 11 10.2	16 3.5	4 18.1	12♋50.8	5 11.0	4 59.5	18 21.5	10 16.0	12 55.7	6 10.8	29 34.3	18 4.0
10 M	23 15 6.8	17 1.8	4 14.9	26 39.8	6 41.9	6 13.5	18 53.8	10 14.0	12 57.9	6 8.5	29 36.4	18 4.9
11 T	23 19 3.3	18 0.2	4 11.7	10♌20.6	8 11.7	7 27.5	19 26.0	10 11.8	13 0.3	6 6.3	29 38.6	18 5.8
12 W	23 22 59.9	18 58.6	4 8.6	23 51.4	9 40.3	8 41.5	19 57.8	10 9.4	13 2.7	6 4.0	29 40.7	18 6.7
13 T	23 26 56.5	19 57.0	4 5.4	7♍10.1	11 7.8	9 55.5	20 29.4	10 6.7	13 5.2	6 1.7	29 42.8	18 7.5
14 F	23 30 53.0	20 55.5	4 2.2	20 14.9	12 34.0	11 9.4	21 0.7	10 3.9	13 7.9	5 59.4	29 44.9	18 8.4
15 S	23 34 49.5	21 54.0	3 59.0	3♎ 4.2	13 59.0	12 23.4	21 31.7	10 0.9	13 10.6	5 57.1	29 47.0	18 9.2
16 S	23 38 46.1	22 52.5	3 55.9	15 37.6	15 22.8	13 37.4	22 2.5	9 57.7	13 13.4	5 54.8	29 49.1	18 10.0
17 M	23 42 42.7	23 51.1	3 52.7	27 55.9	16 45.4	14 51.3	22 32.9	9 54.3	13 16.3	5 52.4	29 51.2	18 10.7
18 T	23 46 39.2	24 49.6	3 49.5	10♏ 0.8	18 6.7	16 5.3	23 3.1	9 50.7	13 19.3	5 50.1	29 53.2	18 11.5
19 W	23 50 35.8	25 48.3	3 46.3	21 55.6	19 26.6	17 19.2	23 32.9	9 46.9	13 22.3	5 47.7	29 55.3	18 12.2
20 T	23 54 32.3	26 46.9	3 43.1	3♐44.3	20 45.2	18 33.2	24 2.5	9 43.0	13 25.5	5 45.3	29 57.3	18 12.9
21 F	23 58 28.9	27 45.6	3 40.0	15 31.6	22 2.3	19 47.1	24 31.7	9 38.8	13 28.7	5 43.0	29 59.4	18 13.6
22 S	0 2 25.5	28 44.3	3 36.8	27 22.7	23 18.0	21 1.0	25 0.6	9 34.5	13 32.0	5 40.6	0♍ 1.4	18 14.2
23 S	0 6 22.0	29 43.0	3 33.6	9♑23.3	24 32.1	22 15.0	25 29.2	9 30.0	13 35.5	5 38.2	0 3.3	18 14.9
24 M	0 10 18.6	0♎41.8	3 30.4	21 38.5	25 44.5	23 28.9	25 57.5	9 25.3	13 39.0	5 35.8	0 5.3	18 15.5
25 T	0 14 15.1	1 40.6	3 27.3	4♒13.1	26 55.3	24 42.8	26 25.5	9 20.5	13 42.5	5 33.4	0 7.3	18 16.1
26 W	0 18 11.7	2 39.4	3 24.1	17 10.6	28 4.1	25 56.6	26 53.1	9 15.5	13 46.2	5 31.0	0 9.2	18 16.6
27 T	0 22 8.2	3 38.2	3 20.9	0♓33.1	29 11.0	27 10.5	27 20.3	9 10.3	13 49.9	5 28.5	0 11.2	18 17.2
28 F	0 26 4.8	4 37.1	3 17.7	14 20.3	0♏15.9	28 24.4	27 47.2	9 4.9	13 53.7	5 26.1	0 13.1	18 17.7
29 S	0 30 1.3	5 36.0	3 14.5	28 29.6	1 18.4	29 38.2	28 13.8	8 59.4	13 57.6	5 23.7	0 15.0	18 18.2
30 S	0 33 57.9	6 35.0	3 11.4	12♈56.1	2 18.6	0♏52.1	28 39.9	8 53.8	14 1.6	5 21.3	0 16.8	18 18.7
DECLINATION												
1 S	22 39 37.8	8N27.7	21N 5.5	8S29.0	3N45.3	3N 5.9	21N41.4	13N38.4	20S54.4	1N52.6	12N13.6	21N30.2
4 T	22 51 27.5	7 22.0	21 3.7	9N46.7	1 28.4	1 34.0	21 56.2	13 37.3	20 55.6	1 50.1	12 11.3	21 29.9
7 F	23 3 17.1	6 15.2	21 2.0	23 31.9	0S45.9	0 1.6	22 9.8	13 35.5	20 57.0	1 47.5	12 9.1	21 29.7
10 M	23 15 6.8	5 7.5	21 0.2	24 45.8	2 56.7	1S31.0	22 22.1	13 33.3	20 58.4	1 44.8	12 6.9	21 29.4
13 T	23 26 56.5	3 58.9	20 58.4	13 31.9	5 3.2	3 3.5	22 33.2	13 30.5	20 59.9	1 42.1	12 4.7	21 29.2
16 S	23 38 46.1	2 49.8	20 56.7	2S43.6	7 4.5	4 35.7	22 43.3	13 27.1	21 1.5	1 39.4	12 2.5	21 29.0
19 W	23 50 35.8	1 40.1	20 54.9	17 20.2	8 59.9	6 7.0	22 52.3	13 23.3	21 3.2	1 36.6	12 0.4	21 28.9
22 S	0 2 25.5	0 30.1	20 53.1	25 33.5	10 48.4	7 37.3	23 0.3	13 18.9	21 4.9	1 33.7	11 58.3	21 28.7
25 T	0 14 15.1	0S40.0	20 51.3	23 33.8	12 29.0	9 6.1	23 7.5	13 14.1	21 6.8	1 30.9	11 56.2	21 28.6
28 F	0 26 4.8	1 50.2	20 49.4	10 45.1	14 0.2	10 33.1	23 14.0	13 8.8	21 8.6	1 28.0	11 54.3	21 28.5

OCTOBER 1928

DAY	EPHEMERIS SIDEREAL TIME	☉	☊	☽	☿	♀	♂	♃	♄	♅	♆	♇
LONGITUDE												
1 M	0 37 54.5	7♎34.0	3♊ 8.2	27♈33.4	3♏16.1	2♏ 5.9	29♊ 5.8	8♉48.0	14♐ 5.7	5♈18.9	0♍18.7	18♋19.1
2 T	0 41 51.0	8 33.0	3 5.0	12♉14.3	4 10.7	3 19.7	29 31.2	8R42.0	14 9.8	5R16.5	0 20.5	18 19.6
3 W	0 45 47.5	9 32.0	3 1.8	26 52.1	5 2.3	4 33.5	29 56.2	8 35.9	14 14.0	5 14.1	0 22.4	18 20.0
4 T	0 49 44.1	10 31.1	2 58.7	11♊21.8	5 50.6	5 47.3	0♋20.9	8 29.6	14 18.3	5 11.7	0 24.2	18 20.3
5 F	0 53 40.7	11 30.2	2 55.5	25 39.7	6 35.2	7 1.1	0 45.1	8 23.2	14 22.7	5 9.3	0 26.0	18 20.7
6 S	0 57 37.2	12 29.4	2 52.3	9♋44.0	7 15.7	8 14.9	1 8.9	8 16.7	14 27.1	5 6.9	0 27.7	18 21.0
7 S	1 1 33.8	13 28.6	2 49.1	23 34.0	7 52.0	9 28.7	1 32.3	8 10.1	14 31.6	5 4.5	0 29.5	18 21.4
8 M	1 5 30.3	14 27.9	2 45.9	7♌ 9.9	8 23.4	10 42.5	1 55.2	8 3.3	14 36.2	5 2.1	0 31.2	18 21.6
9 T	1 9 26.9	15 27.1	2 42.8	20 32.2	8 49.7	11 56.2	2 17.7	7 56.4	14 40.9	4 59.7	0 32.9	18 21.9
10 W	1 13 23.4	16 26.5	2 39.6	3♍41.3	9 10.4	13 10.0	2 39.8	7 49.3	14 45.6	4 57.4	0 34.6	18 22.1
11 T	1 17 20.0	17 25.8	2 36.4	16 37.4	9 24.9	14 23.7	3 1.3	7 42.2	14 50.4	4 55.0	0 36.2	18 22.4
12 F	1 21 16.5	18 25.2	2 33.2	29 20.8	9 32.7	15 37.5	3 22.4	7 35.0	14 55.2	4 52.7	0 37.8	18 22.5
13 S	1 25 13.1	19 24.7	2 30.1	11♎51.7	9 33.4	16 51.2	3 43.0	7 27.6	15 0.2	4 50.4	0 39.5	18 22.7
14 S	1 29 9.7	20 24.1	2 26.9	24 10.5	9R26.6	18 4.9	4 3.1	7 20.2	15 5.2	4 48.1	0 41.0	18 22.9
15 M	1 33 6.2	21 23.6	2 23.7	6♏18.3	9 11.6	19 18.6	4 22.7	7 12.7	15 10.2	4 45.8	0 42.6	18 23.0
16 T	1 37 2.7	22 23.2	2 20.5	18 16.6	8 48.3	20 32.3	4 41.7	7 5.0	15 15.4	4 43.5	0 44.1	18 23.1
17 W	1 40 59.3	23 22.7	2 17.3	0♐ 7.6	8 16.4	21 46.0	5 0.2	6 57.3	15 20.6	4 41.2	0 45.6	18 23.1
18 T	1 44 55.9	24 22.3	2 14.2	11 54.4	7 36.0	22 59.7	5 18.2	6 49.6	15 25.8	4 39.0	0 47.1	18 23.2
19 F	1 48 52.4	25 22.0	2 11.0	23 40.8	6 47.1	24 13.4	5 35.6	6 41.8	15 31.1	4 36.8	0 48.6	18 23.2
20 S	1 52 49.0	26 21.6	2 7.8	5♑31.0	5 50.4	25 27.0	5 52.4	6 33.9	15 36.5	4 34.6	0 50.0	18R23.2
21 S	1 56 45.5	27 21.3	2 4.6	17 29.9	4 46.7	26 40.6	6 8.7	6 25.9	15 42.0	4 32.4	0 51.4	18 23.1
22 M	2 0 42.1	28 21.0	2 1.5	29 42.6	3 37.3	27 54.3	6 24.4	6 17.9	15 47.5	4 30.3	0 52.8	18 23.1
23 T	2 4 38.6	29 20.8	1 58.3	12♒14.0	2 23.8	29 7.9	6 39.5	6 9.9	15 53.0	4 28.1	0 54.2	18 23.0
24 W	2 8 35.2	0♏20.5	1 55.1	25 8.4	1 8.2	0♐21.4	6 54.0	6 1.8	15 58.6	4 26.0	0 55.5	18 22.9
25 T	2 12 31.7	1 20.3	1 51.9	8♓29.0	29♎52.6	1 35.0	7 7.8	5 53.7	16 4.3	4 23.9	0 56.8	18 22.8
26 F	2 16 28.3	2 20.2	1 48.7	22 17.2	28 39.3	2 48.6	7 21.1	5 45.6	16 10.0	4 21.9	0 58.1	18 22.6
27 S	2 20 24.9	3 20.0	1 45.6	6♈32.1	27 30.7	4 2.1	7 33.7	5 37.5	16 15.8	4 19.9	0 59.3	18 22.4
28 S	2 24 21.4	4 19.9	1 42.4	21 9.8	26 28.8	5 15.6	7 45.6	5 29.4	16 21.6	4 17.9	1 0.5	18 22.2
29 M	2 28 18.0	5 19.8	1 39.2	6♉ 4.0	25 35.4	6 29.1	7 56.9	5 21.2	16 27.5	4 15.9	1 1.7	18 22.0
30 T	2 32 14.5	6 19.8	1 36.0	21 6.4	24 52.0	7 42.5	8 7.5	5 13.1	16 33.5	4 14.0	1 2.9	18 21.8
31 W	2 36 11.1	7 19.8	1 32.9	6♊ 8.2	24 19.5	8 56.0	8 17.4	5 4.9	16 39.4	4 12.0	1 4.0	18 21.5
DECLINATION												
1 M	0 37 54.5	3S 0.2	20N47.6	7N55.3	15S20.4	11S58.1	23N19.8	13N 3.1	21S10.6	1N25.1	11N52.3	21N28.5
4 T	0 49 44.1	4 .0.0	20 45.8	23 0.7	16 27.2	13 20.5	23 25.0	12 57.0	21 12.6	1 22.3	11 50.5	21 28.4
7 S	1 1 33.8	5 19.3	20 43.9	25 23.0	17 17.5	14 40.2	23 29.8	12 50.4	21 14.6	1 19.5	11 48.7	21 28.4
10 W	1 13 23.4	6 28.0	20 42.1	14 56.5	17 47.1	15 56.8	23 34.2	12 43.6	21 16.7	1 16.7	11 46.9	21 28.4
13 S	1 25 13.1	7 36.0	20 40.2	1S 5.5	17 50.2	17 9.8	23 38.4	12 36.4	21 18.8	1 13.9	11 45.3	21 28.5
16 T	1 37 2.7	8 43.0	20 38.3	16 11.3	17 20.0	18 19.0	23 42.5	12 29.0	21 21.0	1 11.3	11 43.7	21 28.6
19 F	1 48 52.4	9 48.9	20 36.4	25 19.4	16 10.5	19 24.1	23 46.6	12 21.4	21 23.1	1 8.7	11 42.1	21 28.7
22 M	2 0 42.1	10 53.6	20 34.5	24 35.4	14 22.1	20 24.5	23 50.9	12 13.7	21 25.3	1 6.1	11 40.7	21 28.8
25 T	2 12 31.7	11 56.7	20 32.6	13 11.5	12 8.7	21 20.1	23 55.4	12 5.8	21 27.5	1 3.7	11 39.4	21 29.0
28 S	2 24 21.4	12 58.2	20 30.7	5N10.0	9 58.7	22 10.5	24 0.3	11 57.9	21 29.7	1 1.3	11 38.1	21 29.2
31 W	2 36 11.1	13 57.8	20 28.8	21 50.7	8 22.5	22 55.3	24 5.7	11 50.0	21 31.9	0 59.1	11 37.0	21 29.5

NOVEMBER 1928

LONGITUDE

DAY	EPHEMERIS SIDEREAL TIME h m s	☉ ° ′	☊ ° ′	☽ ° ′	☿ ° ′	♀ ° ′	♂ ° ′	♃ ° ′	♄ ° ′	♅ ° ′	♆ ° ′	♇ ° ′
1 T	2 40 7.6	8♏19.8	1♊29.7	21♊ 1.1	23♎58.5	10♐ 9.4	8♋26.6	4♉56.8	16♐45.5	4♈10.2	1♍ 5.1	18♋21.2
2 F	2 44 4.2	9 19.9	1 26.5	5♋38.8	23R49.1	11 22.9	8 35.1	4R48.7	16 51.6	4R 8.3	1 6.2	18R20.9
3 S	2 48 0.8	10 19.9	1 23.3	19 56.9	23D51.1	12 36.3	8 42.8	4 40.6	16 57.7	4 6.5	1 7.2	18 20.5
4 S	2 51 57.3	11 20.1	1 20.2	3♌53.4	24 4.0	13 49.6	8 49.8	4 32.6	17 3.9	4 4.7	1 8.2	18 20.2
5 M	2 55 53.8	12 20.2	1 17.0	17 28.3	24 27.1	15 3.0	8 56.0	4 24.5	17 10.1	4 3.0	1 9.2	18 19.8
6 T	2 59 50.4	13 20.4	1 13.8	0♍42.7	24 59.7	16 16.3	9 1.5	4 16.6	17 16.3	4 1.3	1 10.1	18 19.4
7 W	3 3 47.0	14 20.7	1 10.6	13 38.7	25 40.9	17 29.7	9 6.2	4 8.7	17 22.6	3 59.6	1 11.1	18 18.9
8 T	3 7 43.5	15 20.9	1 7.4	26 18.5	26 29.7	18 43.0	9 10.1	4 0.8	17 29.0	3 58.0	1 11.9	18 18.5
9 F	3 11 40.1	16 21.2	1 4.3	8♎44.4	27 25.4	19 56.3	9 13.1	3 53.0	17 35.4	3 56.3	1 12.8	18 18.0
10 S	3 15 36.6	17 21.5	1 1.1	20 58.8	28 27.1	21 9.6	9 15.4	3 45.3	17 41.8	3 54.8	1 13.6	18 17.5
11 S	3 19 33.2	18 21.9	0 57.9	3♏ 3.7	29 33.9	22 22.8	9 16.8	3 37.6	17 48.3	3 53.3	1 14.4	18 16.9
12 M	3 23 29.7	19 22.3	0 54.7	15 1.0	0♏45.3	23 36.1	9 17.3	3 30.1	17 54.8	3 51.8	1 15.2	18 16.4
13 T	3 27 26.3	20 22.7	0 51.6	26 52.6	2 0.5	24 49.3	9R17.1	3 22.6	18 1.3	3 50.3	1 15.9	18 15.8
14 W	3 31 22.9	21 23.1	0 48.4	8♐40.6	3 19.0	26 2.5	9 15.9	3 15.2	18 7.9	3 48.9	1 16.6	18 15.2
15 T	3 35 19.4	22 23.6	0 45.2	20 27.2	4 40.3	27 15.6	9 13.9	3 7.9	18 14.5	3 47.6	1 17.2	18 14.6
16 F	3 39 16.0	23 24.1	0 42.0	2♑15.1	6 3.9	28 28.7	9 11.1	3 0.7	18 21.2	3 46.2	1 17.8	18 14.0
17 S	3 43 12.5	24 24.6	0 38.9	14 7.4	7 29.5	29 41.9	9 7.3	2 53.7	18 27.8	3 45.0	1 18.4	18 13.3
18 S	3 47 9.1	25 25.2	0 35.7	26 7.6	8 56.7	0♑54.9	9 2.7	2 46.7	18 34.5	3 43.7	1 19.0	18 12.6
19 M	3 51 5.6	26 25.7	0 32.5	8♒19.6	10 25.2	2 8.0	8 57.3	2 39.9	18 41.3	3 42.5	1 19.5	18 11.9
20 T	3 55 2.2	27 26.3	0 29.3	20 47.6	11 54.9	3 21.0	8 50.9	2 33.2	18 48.0	3 41.4	1 20.0	18 11.2
21 W	3 58 58.8	28 26.9	0 26.1	3♓35.8	13 25.5	4 34.0	8 43.7	2 26.6	18 54.8	3 40.3	1 20.4	18 10.5
22 T	4 2 55.3	29 27.5	0 23.0	16 47.8	14 56.8	5 46.9	8 35.7	2 20.2	19 1.6	3 39.2	1 20.9	18 9.7
23 F	4 6 51.9	0♐28.2	0 19.8	0♈26.3	16 28.8	6 59.8	8 26.8	2 13.9	19 8.5	3 38.2	1 21.2	18 8.9
24 S	4 10 48.4	1 28.8	0 16.6	14 32.2	18 1.1	8 12.7	8 17.0	2 7.7	19 15.3	3 37.3	1 21.6	18 8.1
25 S	4 14 45.0	2 29.5	0 13.4	29 4.2	19 33.9	9 25.5	8 6.3	2 1.7	19 22.2	3 36.3	1 21.9	18 7.3
26 M	4 18 41.6	3 30.2	0 10.3	13♉58.1	21 7.0	10 38.3	7 54.9	1 55.9	19 29.1	3 35.5	1 22.2	18 6.4
27 T	4 22 38.1	4 30.9	0 7.1	29 7.0	22 40.2	11 51.0	7 42.6	1 50.2	19 36.0	3 34.7	1 22.4	18 5.6
28 W	4 26 34.7	5 31.7	0 3.9	14♊21.7	24 13.7	13 3.7	7 29.5	1 44.7	19 43.0	3 33.9	1 22.7	18 4.7
29 T	4 30 31.2	6 32.4	0 0.7	29 32.5	25 47.2	14 16.3	7 15.6	1 39.3	19 49.9	3 33.2	1 22.8	18 3.8
30 F	4 34 27.8	7 33.2	29♉57.6	14♋30.0	27 20.9	15 28.9	7 0.9	1 34.1	19 56.9	3 32.5	1 23.0	18 2.9

DECLINATION

DAY	EPHEMERIS SIDEREAL TIME h m s	☉	☊	☽	☿	♀	♂	♃	♄	♅	♆	♇
1 T	2 40 7.6	14S17.3	20N28.2	24N59.0	8S 1.4	23S 9.0	24N 7.7	11N47.4	21S32.6	0N58.4	11N36.6	21N29.5
4 S	2 51 57.3	15 14.2	20 26.2	23 51.7	7 33.3	23 46.1	24 13.8	11 39.6	21 34.8	0 56.3	11 35.6	21 29.8
7 W	3 3 47.0	16 9.0	20 24.3	11 10.2	7 52.7	24 17.2	24 20.7	11 32.0	21 36.9	0 54.3	11 34.6	21 30.1
10 S	3 15 36.6	17 1.3	20 22.3	5S 4.3	8 47.9	24 41.9	24 28.2	11 24.5	21 39.1	0 52.5	11 33.8	21 30.4
13 T	3 27 26.3	17 51.0	20 20.3	19 8.8	10 6.6	25 0.1	24 36.5	11 17.3	21 41.2	0 50.8	11 33.1	21 30.8
16 F	3 39 16.0	18 37.9	20 18.4	26 13.6	11 38.8	25 11.8	24 45.6	11 10.4	21 43.2	0 49.3	11 32.5	21 31.2
19 M	3 51 5.6	19 21.8	20 16.4	22 55.7	13 17.1	25 16.7	24 55.4	11 3.9	21 45.2	0 47.9	11 32.0	21 31.6
22 T	4 2 55.3	20 2.6	20 14.4	9 53.9	14 56.5	25 14.9	25 5.8	10 57.8	21 47.2	0 46.7	11 31.6	21 32.1
25 S	4 14 45.0	20 40.1	20 12.4	8N33.4	16 33.4	25 6.4	25 16.6	10 52.1	21 49.2	0 45.6	11 31.3	21 32.5
28 W	4 26 34.7	21 14.1	20 10.4	23 47.8	18 5.6	24 51.3	25 27.8	10 46.9	21 51.1	0 44.8	11 31.1	21 33.0

DECEMBER 1928

LONGITUDE

DAY	EPHEMERIS SIDEREAL TIME h m s	☉ ° ′	☊ ° ′	☽ ° ′	☿ ° ′	♀ ° ′	♂ ° ′	♃ ° ′	♄ ° ′	♅ ° ′	♆ ° ′	♇ ° ′
1 S	4 38 24.3	8♐34.0	29♉54.4	29♋ 6.7	28♏54.6	16♑41.5	6♋45.4	1♉29.1	20♐ 3.9	3♈31.9	1♍23.1	18♋ 2.0
2 S	4 42 20.9	9 34.8	29 51.2	13♌18.1	0♐28.3	17 54.0	6R29.2	1R24.2	20 10.9	3R31.3	1 23.2	18R 1.0
3 M	4 46 17.4	10 35.7	29 48.0	27 2.3	2 2.1	19 6.4	6 12.2	1 19.5	20 18.0	3 30.7	1 23.2	18 0.1
4 T	4 50 14.0	11 36.6	29 44.8	10♍20.0	3 35.9	20 18.8	5 54.6	1 15.0	20 25.0	3 30.3	1 23.2	17 59.1
5 W	4 54 10.6	12 37.5	29 41.7	23 13.6	5 9.7	21 31.2	5 36.2	1 10.7	20 32.1	3 29.8	1R23.2	17 58.1
6 T	4 58 7.1	13 38.4	29 38.5	5♎46.6	6 43.6	22 43.5	5 17.2	1 6.6	20 39.1	3 29.5	1 23.1	17 57.1
7 F	5 2 3.7	14 39.3	29 35.3	18 3.0	8 17.4	23 55.8	4 57.6	1 2.6	20 46.2	3 29.1	1 23.0	17 56.1
8 S	5 6 0.2	15 40.3	29 32.1	0♏ 6.9	9 51.3	25 8.0	4 37.4	0 58.8	20 53.3	3 28.8	1 22.9	17 55.0
9 S	5 9 56.8	16 41.3	29 29.0	12 2.0	11 25.2	26 20.1	4 16.6	0 55.3	21 0.3	3 28.6	1 22.7	17 54.0
10 M	5 13 53.4	17 42.3	29 25.8	23 51.7	12 59.1	27 32.2	3 55.4	0 51.9	21 7.4	3 28.4	1 22.5	17 52.9
11 T	5 17 49.9	18 43.3	29 22.6	5♐39.0	14 33.1	28 44.3	3 33.7	0 48.7	21 14.5	3 28.3	1 22.3	17 51.8
12 W	5 21 46.5	19 44.3	29 19.4	17 26.2	16 7.1	29 56.2	3 11.5	0 45.8	21 21.6	3 28.2	1 22.0	17 50.7
13 T	5 25 43.0	20 45.4	29 16.3	29 15.7	17 41.2	1♒ 8.1	2 49.0	0 43.0	21 28.7	3 28.2	1 21.7	17 49.6
14 F	5 29 39.6	21 46.4	29 13.1	11♑ 9.2	19 15.4	2 20.0	2 26.2	0 40.4	21 35.8	3D28.2	1 21.4	17 48.5
15 S	5 33 36.2	22 47.5	29 9.9	23 8.8	20 49.7	3 31.7	2 3.1	0 38.1	21 42.9	3 28.3	1 21.0	17 47.4
16 S	5 37 32.7	23 48.6	29 6.7	5♒16.5	22 24.1	4 43.4	1 39.7	0 35.9	21 50.1	3 28.5	1 20.6	17 46.3
17 M	5 41 29.3	24 49.6	29 3.6	17 34.6	23 58.6	5 55.0	1 16.2	0 33.9	21 57.1	3 28.7	1 20.2	17 45.1
18 T	5 45 25.8	25 50.7	29 0.4	0♓ 5.6	25 33.3	7 6.5	0 52.6	0 32.2	22 4.2	3 28.9	1 19.7	17 43.9
19 W	5 49 22.4	26 51.8	28 57.2	12 52.5	27 8.1	8 18.0	0 28.9	0 30.7	22 11.3	3 29.2	1 19.2	17 42.8
20 T	5 53 18.9	27 52.9	28 54.0	25 58.2	28 43.1	9 29.4	0 5.2	0 29.3	22 18.4	3 29.5	1 18.7	17 41.6
21 F	5 57 15.5	28 54.0	28 50.8	9♈25.4	0♑18.2	10 40.6	29♊41.5	0 28.2	22 25.5	3 29.9	1 18.1	17 40.4
22 S	6 1 12.0	29 55.1	28 47.7	23 16.1	1 53.6	11 51.8	29 17.9	0 27.3	22 32.6	3 30.4	1 17.5	17 39.2
23 S	6 5 8.6	0♑56.3	28 44.5	7♉31.0	3 29.2	13 2.9	28 54.4	0 26.6	22 39.6	3 30.9	1 16.9	17 38.0
24 M	6 9 5.2	1 57.4	28 41.3	22 8.6	5 5.0	14 13.8	28 31.1	0 26.1	22 46.7	3 31.4	1 16.3	17 36.8
25 T	6 13 1.7	2 58.5	28 38.1	7♊ 5.0	6 41.0	15 24.7	28 8.0	0 25.8	22 53.7	3 32.0	1 15.6	17 35.6
26 W	6 16 58.3	3 59.6	28 35.0	22 13.4	8 17.3	16 35.4	27 45.2	0 25.8	23 0.7	3 32.7	1 14.8	17 34.3
27 T	6 20 54.8	5 0.7	28 31.8	7♋24.7	9 53.8	17 46.1	27 22.7	0D25.9	23 7.7	3 33.4	1 14.1	17 33.1
28 F	6 24 51.4	6 1.8	28 28.6	22 29.1	11 30.6	18 56.6	27 0.6	0 26.3	23 14.7	3 34.1	1 13.3	17 31.8
29 S	6 28 48.0	7 3.0	28 25.4	7♌17.1	13 7.6	20 7.0	26 38.8	0 26.8	23 21.7	3 34.9	1 12.5	17 30.6
30 S	6 32 44.5	8 4.1	28 22.3	21 41.4	14 44.9	21 17.3	26 17.5	0 27.6	23 28.6	3 35.8	1 11.7	17 29.3
31 M	6 36 41.1	9 5.2	28 19.1	5♍37.5	16 22.4	22 27.5	25 56.7	0 28.5	23 35.6	3 36.7	1 10.8	17 28.1

DECLINATION

DAY	EPHEMERIS SIDEREAL TIME h m s	☉	☊	☽	☿	♀	♂	♃	♄	♅	♆	♇
1 S	4 38 24.3	21S44.5	20N 8.4	24N46.1	19S31.2	24S29.6	25N39.1	10N42.3	21S52.9	0N44.1	11N31.0	21N33.5
4 T	4 50 14.0	22 11.2	20 6.3	12 31.1	20 49.1	24 1.5	25 50.3	10 38.2	21 54.6	0 43.5	11 31.1	21 34.1
7 F	5 2 3.7	22 34.0	20 4.3	3S46.6	21 58.3	23 27.2	26 1.0	10 34.6	21 56.4	0 43.2	11 31.2	21 34.6
10 M	5 13 53.4	22 52.8	20 2.2	18 9.0	22 57.9	22 47.0	26 11.1	10 31.7	21 58.0	0 43.0	11 31.5	21 35.2
13 T	5 25 43.0	23 7.6	20 0.2	25 59.0	23 47.2	22 1.0	26 20.2	10 29.5	21 59.6	0 43.0	11 31.8	21 35.8
16 S	5 37 32.7	23 18.3	19 58.1	23 33.7	24 25.6	21 9.5	26 28.2	10 27.9	22 1.1	0 43.3	11 32.3	21 36.4
19 W	5 49 22.4	23 24.8	19 56.0	11 26.6	24 52.3	20 13.0	26 34.8	10 26.9	22 2.5	0 43.7	11 32.9	21 37.0
22 S	6 1 12.0	23 27.0	19 54.0	6N 7.1	25 6.9	19 11.7	26 40.1	10 26.6	22 3.9	0 44.2	11 33.6	21 37.7
25 T	6 13 1.7	23 25.0	19 51.9	22 7.2	25 8.8	18 5.9	26 43.8	10 27.0	22 5.1	0 45.0	11 34.4	21 38.3
28 F	6 24 51.4	23 18.7	19 49.8	25 38.1	24 57.4	16 56.0	26 46.2	10 28.0	22 6.4	0 46.0	11 35.2	21 39.0
31 M	6 36 41.1	23 8.3	19 47.6	14 14.5	24 32.3	15 42.4	26 47.2	10 29.7	22 7.5	0 47.1	11 36.2	21 39.6

JANUARY 1929

DAY	EPHEMERIS SIDEREAL TIME	☉	☊	☽	☿	♀	♂	♃	♄	♅	♆	♇
	h m s	° ′	° ′	° ′	° ′	° ′	° ′	° ′	° ′	° ′	° ′	° ′
LONGITUDE												
1 T	6 40 37.6	10♑ 6.4	28♉15.9	19♍ 4.4	18♑ 0.1	23♒37.5	25♊36.3	0♉29.7	23♐42.5	3♈37.6	1♍ 9.9	17♋26.8
2 W	6 44 34.2	11 7.5	28 12.7	2♎ 3.5	19 38.1	24 47.4	25R 16.5	0 31.1	23 49.4	3 38.6	1R 9.0	17R 25.6
3 T	6 48 30.8	12 8.7	28 9.6	14 38.4	21 16.2	25 57.2	24 57.3	0 32.7	23 56.3	3 39.7	1 8.0	17 24.3
4 F	6 52 27.3	13 9.9	28 6.4	26 53.5	22 54.4	27 6.9	24 38.7	0 34.5	24 3.1	3 40.8	1 7.0	17 23.0
5 S	6 56 23.9	14 11.0	28 3.2	8♏54.1	24 32.7	28 16.4	24 20.7	0 36.5	24 10.0	3 42.0	1 6.0	17 21.8
6 S	7 0 20.4	15 12.2	28 0.0	20 45.3	26 11.1	29 25.7	24 3.4	0 38.6	24 16.8	3 43.2	1 5.0	17 20.5
7 M	7 4 17.0	16 13.4	27 56.8	2♐31.8	27 49.4	0♓34.9	23 46.8	0 41.0	24 23.5	3 44.4	1 3.9	17 19.2
8 T	7 8 13.6	17 14.5	27 53.7	14 17.9	29 27.5	1 44.0	23 30.9	0 43.6	24 30.3	3 45.7	1 2.8	17 17.9
9 W	7 12 10.1	18 15.7	27 50.5	26 7.0	1♒ 5.4	2 52.9	23 15.7	0 46.4	24 37.0	3 47.1	1 1.7	17 16.7
10 T	7 16 6.7	19 16.9	27 47.3	8♑ 1.8	2 42.9	4 1.7	23 1.3	0 49.4	24 43.7	3 48.5	1 0.5	17 15.4
11 F	7 20 3.2	20 18.0	27 44.1	20 4.5	4 19.9	5 10.2	22 47.7	0 52.7	24 50.4	3 49.9	0 59.4	17 14.1
12 S	7 23 59.8	21 19.2	27 41.0	2♒16.2	5 56.1	6 18.7	22 34.8	0 56.1	24 57.0	3 51.4	0 58.2	17 12.8
13 S	7 27 56.3	22 20.3	27 37.8	14 38.0	7 31.4	7 26.9	22 22.7	0 59.6	25 3.6	3 53.0	0 57.0	17 11.6
14 M	7 31 52.9	23 21.5	27 34.6	27 10.4	9 5.4	8 34.9	22 11.5	1 3.4	25 10.1	3 54.5	0 55.7	17 10.3
15 T	7 35 49.4	24 22.6	27 31.4	9♓54.2	10 37.8	9 42.8	22 1.0	1 7.4	25 16.7	3 56.2	0 54.5	17 9.0
16 W	7 39 46.0	25 23.7	27 28.3	22 50.2	12 8.4	10 50.4	21 51.4	1 11.6	25 23.1	3 57.9	0 53.2	17 7.8
17 T	7 43 42.6	26 24.8	27 25.1	5♈59.8	13 36.6	11 57.9	21 42.6	1 15.9	25 29.6	3 59.6	0 51.9	17 6.5
18 F	7 47 39.1	27 25.9	27 21.9	19 24.4	15 2.1	13 5.1	21 34.6	1 20.5	25 36.0	4 1.4	0 50.6	17 5.3
19 S	7 51 35.7	28 27.0	27 18.7	3♉ 5.6	16 24.1	14 12.1	21 27.5	1 25.2	25 42.4	4 3.2	0 49.2	17 4.0
20 S	7 55 32.2	29 28.1	27 15.5	17 4.7	17 42.2	15 18.8	21 21.1	1 30.1	25 48.7	4 5.0	0 47.8	17 2.8
21 M	7 59 28.8	0♒29.1	27 12.4	1♊21.8	18 55.8	16 25.4	21 15.6	1 35.2	25 55.0	4 6.9	0 46.5	17 1.5
22 T	8 3 25.4	1 30.2	27 9.2	15 55.4	20 3.9	17 31.7	21 10.9	1 40.5	26 1.2	4 8.9	0 45.0	17 0.3
23 W	8 7 21.9	2 31.2	27 6.0	0♋41.8	21 5.9	18 37.7	21 7.0	1 46.0	26 7.4	4 10.9	0 43.6	16 59.1
24 T	8 11 18.5	3 32.2	27 2.8	15 34.9	22 0.9	19 43.5	21 3.9	1 51.6	26 13.5	4 12.9	0 42.2	16 57.9
25 F	8 15 15.0	4 33.1	26 59.7	0♌26.6	22 48.1	20 49.0	21 1.6	1 57.4	26 19.6	4 15.0	0 40.7	16 56.6
26 S	8 19 11.6	5 34.1	26 56.5	15 8.3	23 26.7	21 54.2	21 0.1	2 3.4	26 25.7	4 17.1	0 39.2	16 55.4
27 S	8 23 8.1	6 35.1	26 53.3	29 31.8	23 55.8	22 59.1	20 59.3	2 9.5	26 31.7	4 19.2	0 37.8	16 54.2
28 M	8 27 4.7	7 36.0	26 50.1	13♍31.3	24 14.7	24 3.7	20D 59.3	2 15.8	26 37.6	4 21.4	0 36.3	16 53.1
29 T	8 31 1.2	8 37.0	26 47.0	27 3.7	24 22.9	25 8.1	21 0.1	2 22.3	26 43.5	4 23.6	0 34.7	16 51.9
30 W	8 34 57.8	9 37.9	26 43.8	10♎ 8.6	24R 19.9	26 12.1	21 1.6	2 28.9	26 49.3	4 25.9	0 33.2	16 50.7
31 T	8 38 54.4	10 38.8	26 40.6	22 48.3	24 5.7	27 15.8	21 3.8	2 35.8	26 55.1	4 28.2	0 31.7	16 49.6
DECLINATION												
1 T	6 40 37.6	23S 3.9	19N46.9	8N49.4	24S20.8	15S17.1	26N47.3	10N30.4	22S 7.8	0N47.5	11N36.6	21N39.8
4 F	6 52 27.3	22 47.9	19 44.8	7S44.7	23 37.0	13 59.1	26 46.8	10 32.9	22 8.9	0 48.9	11 37.7	21 40.5
7 M	7 4 17.0	22 27.8	19 42.7	20 55.5	22 39.2	12 38.2	26 45.3	10 36.1	22 9.8	0 50.4	11 38.8	21 41.2
10 T	7 16 6.7	22 3.8	19 40.5	26 23.5	21 27.6	11 14.8	26 43.2	10 39.8	22 10.7	0 52.1	11 40.1	21 41.9
13 S	7 27 56.3	21 35.8	19 38.4	21 9.7	20 3.3	9 49.1	26 40.6	10 44.2	22 11.5	0 54.0	11 41.4	21 42.5
16 W	7 39 46.0	21 4.1	19 36.2	7 6.6	18 28.5	8 21.6	26 37.8	10 49.2	22 12.3	0 56.1	11 42.9	21 43.2
19 S	7 51 35.7	20 28.8	19 34.1	10N29.2	16 46.7	6 52.7	26 34.8	10 54.8	22 12.9	0 58.3	11 44.3	21 43.9
22 T	8 3 25.4	19 50.0	19 31.9	24 13.3	15 3.9	5 22.6	26 31.9	11 0.9	22 13.5	1 0.6	11 45.9	21 44.5
25 F	8 15 15.0	19 7.9	19 29.7	24 25.7	13 28.8	3 51.8	26 29.0	11 7.5	22 14.0	1 3.1	11 47.5	21 45.2
28 M	8 27 4.7	18 22.7	19 27.5	10 57.5	12 12.5	2 20.6	26 26.4	11 14.6	22 14.5	1 5.8	11 49.1	21 45.8
31 T	8 38 54.4	17 34.4	19 25.3	6S12.2	11 26.1	0 49.2	26 24.1	11 22.2	22 14.9	1 8.6	11 50.8	21 46.5

FEBRUARY 1929

DAY	EPHEMERIS SIDEREAL TIME	☉	☊	☽	☿	♀	♂	♃	♄	♅	♆	♇
LONGITUDE												
1 F	8 42 50.9	11♒39.7	26♉37.4	5♏ 6.9	23♒40.2	28♓19.2	21♊ 6.8	2♉42.7	27♐ 0.9	4♈30.6	0♍30.1	16♋48.4
2 S	8 46 47.5	12 40.6	26 34.3	17 9.4	23R 4.1	29 22.2	21 10.4	2 49.8	27 6.5	4 33.0	0R 28.5	16R 47.3
3 S	8 50 44.0	13 41.4	26 31.1	29 1.3	22 18.2	0♈24.9	21 14.8	2 57.1	27 12.2	4 35.4	0 26.9	16 46.2
4 M	8 54 40.6	14 42.3	26 27.9	10♐48.2	21 23.6	1 27.2	21 19.9	3 4.6	27 17.7	4 37.8	0 25.3	16 45.1
5 T	8 58 37.2	15 43.1	26 24.7	22 35.5	20 21.9	2 29.2	21 25.6	3 12.2	27 23.2	4 40.3	0 23.7	16 44.0
6 W	9 2 33.7	16 43.9	26 21.6	4♑27.6	19 14.9	3 30.8	21 32.0	3 19.9	27 28.7	4 42.9	0 22.1	16 42.9
7 T	9 6 30.3	17 44.7	26 18.4	16 28.4	18 4.4	4 32.0	21 39.1	3 27.8	27 34.1	4 45.4	0 20.5	16 41.8
8 F	9 10 26.8	18 45.5	26 15.2	28 40.6	16 52.6	5 32.7	21 46.8	3 35.8	27 39.4	4 48.0	0 18.8	16 40.7
9 S	9 14 23.4	19 46.3	26 12.0	11♒ 5.8	15 41.4	6 33.1	21 55.1	3 44.0	27 44.6	4 50.6	0 17.2	16 39.7
10 S	9 18 19.9	20 47.0	26 8.8	23 44.7	14 32.5	7 33.0	22 4.1	3 52.4	27 49.8	4 53.3	0 15.6	16 38.7-
11 M	9 22 16.5	21 47.7	26 5.7	6♓36.9	13 27.8	8 32.4	22 13.6	4 0.9	27 55.0	4 56.0	0 13.9	16 37.7
12 T	9 26 13.0	22 48.4	26 2.5	19 41.4	12 28.3	9 31.4	22 23.8	4 9.5	28 0.0	4 58.7	0 12.2	16 36.7
13 W	9 30 9.6	23 49.1	25 59.3	2♈57.2	11 35.3	10 29.9	22 34.6	4 18.2	28 5.0	5 1.5	0 10.6	16 35.7
14 T	9 34 6.1	24 49.8	25 56.1	16 23.1	10 49.4	11 27.9	22 45.9	4 27.1	28 9.9	5 4.3	0 8.9	16 34.7
15 F	9 38 2.7	25 50.4	25 53.0	29 58.7	10 11.0	12 25.4	22 57.8	4 36.1	28 14.8	5 7.1	0 7.2	16 33.8
16 S	9 41 59.3	26 51.0	25 49.8	13♉43.8	9 40.4	13 22.3	23 10.2	4 45.3	28 19.6	5 9.9	0 5.5	16 32.8
17 S	9 45 55.8	27 51.5	25 46.6	27 38.8	9 17.6	14 18.6	23 23.2	4 54.6	28 24.3	5 12.8	0 3.9	16 31.9
18 M	9 49 52.4	28 52.0	25 43.4	11♊43.7	9 2.5	15 14.4	23 36.7	5 4.0	28 28.9	5 15.7	0 2.2	16 31.0
19 T	9 53 48.9	29 52.5	25 40.2	25 58.0	8 54.8	16 9.5	23 50.7	5 13.5	28 33.5	5 18.6	0 0.5	16 30.1
20 W	9 57 45.5	0♓53.0	25 37.1	10♋20.0	8 54.2	17 4.0	24 5.2	5 23.2	28 38.0	5 21.6	29♌58.8	16 29.3
21 T	10 1 42.0	1 53.4	25 33.9	24 46.3	9D 0.4	17 57.9	24 20.2	5 33.0	28 42.4	5 24.5	29 57.1	16 28.4
22 F	10 5 38.6	2 53.8	25 30.7	9♌12.0	9 12.8	18 51.0	24 35.7	5 42.9	28 46.7	5 27.5	29 55.5	16 27.6
23 S	10 9 35.1	3 54.2	25 27.5	23 31.0	9 31.2	19 43.5	24 51.6	5 52.9	28 51.0	5 30.6	29 53.8	16 26.8
24 S	10 13 31.7	4 54.6	25 24.4	7♍37.1	9 55.2	20 35.2	25 8.0	6 3.0	28 55.2	5 33.6	29 52.1	16 26.0
25 M	10 17 28.3	5 54.9	25 21.2	21 25.0	10 24.3	21 26.1	25 24.8	6 13.3	28 59.3	5 36.7	29 50.5	16 25.2
26 T	10 21 24.8	6 55.2	25 18.0	4♎51.0	10 58.1	22 16.3	25 42.0	6 23.6	29 3.3	5 39.8	29 48.8	16 24.5
27 W	10 25 21.3	7 55.4	25 14.8	17 53.8	11 36.4	23 5.7	25 59.6	6 34.1	29 7.2	5 42.9	29 47.1	16 23.7
28 T	10 29 17.9	8 55.7	25 11.6	0♏34.2	12 18.8	23 54.2	26 17.7	6 44.7	29 11.1	5 46.0	29 45.5	16 23.0
DECLINATION												
1 F	8 42 50.9	17S17.7	19N24.6	11S25.4	11S18.7	0S18.8	26N23.4	11N24.8	22S15.0	1N 9.5	11N51.4	21N46.7
4 M	8 54 40.6	16 25.8	19 22.3	23 14.8	11 22.1	1N12.2	26 21.3	11 33.0	22 15.3	1 12.5	11 53.1	21 47.3
7 T	9 6 30.3	15 31.3	19 20.1	26 13.3	11 59.3	2 42.6	26 19.6	11 41.7	22 15.6	1 15.6	11 54.8	21 47.9
10 S	9 18 19.9	14 34.4	19 17.9	18 19.0	12 57.3	4 12.0	26 18.0	11 50.7	22 15.8	1 18.8	11 56.6	21 48.5
13 W	9 30 9.6	13 35.2	19 15.6	2 29.6	14 1.2	5 40.1	26 16.7	12 0.1	22 15.9	1 22.1	11 58.4	21 49.1
16 S	9 41 59.3	12 34.1	19 13.4	14N58.6	14 59.5	7 6.6	26 15.5	12 9.9	22 16.0	1 25.5	12 0.2	21 49.7
19 T	9 53 48.9	11 31.2	19 11.1	25 56.4	15 46.2	8 31.2	26 14.3	12 19.9	22 16.1	1 29.0	12 2.0	21 50.2
22 F	10 5 38.6	10 26.7	19 8.9	22 36.1	16 18.7	9 53.4	26 13.1	12 30.3	22 16.1	1 32.6	12 3.9	21 50.8
25 M	10 17 28.3	9 20.8	19 6.6	7 31.1	16 36.5	11 12.9	26 11.8	12 41.0	22 16.1	1 36.3	12 5.6	21 51.3
28 T	10 29 17.9	8 13.6	19 4.3	9S46.5	16 39.8	12 29.5	26 10.3	12 51.9	22 16.1	1 40.1	12 7.4	21 51.7

MARCH 1929

LONGITUDE

DAY	EPHEMERIS SIDEREAL TIME h m s	☉ ° ′	☊ ° ′	☽ ° ′	☿ ° ′	♀ ° ′	♂ ° ′	♃ ° ′	♄ ° ′	♅ ° ′	♆ ° ′	♇ ° ′
1 F	10 33 14.5	9♓55.9	25♉ 8.5	12♏54.9	13♒ 5.0	24♈41.8	26♊36.2	6♉55.4	29♐14.9	5♈49.2	29♌43.8	16♋22.3
2 S	10 37 11.0	10 56.1	25 5.3	24 59.8	13 54.7	25 28.5	26 55.0	7 6.1	29 18.6	5 52.4	29R42.2	16R21.7
3 S	10 41 7.6	11 56.2	25 2.1	6♐54.0	14 47.7	26 14.3	27 14.2	7 17.0	29 22.2	5 55.5	29 40.5	16 21.0
4 M	10 45 4.1	12 56.4	24 58.9	18 42.8	15 43.8	26 59.1	27 33.8	7 28.0	29 25.7	5 58.8	29 38.9	16 20.4
5 T	10 49 0.7	13 56.5	24 55.8	0♑31.9	16 42.7	27 42.9	27 53.8	7 39.1	29 29.2	6 2.0	29 37.3	16 19.8
6 W	10 52 57.2	14 56.5	24 52.6	12 26.5	17 44.2	28 25.6	28 14.1	7 50.3	29 32.5	6 5.2	29 35.7	16 19.2
7 T	10 56 53.8	15 56.6	24 49.4	24 31.2	18 48.3	29 7.3	28 34.8	8 1.6	29 35.8	6 8.5	29 34.1	16 18.6
8 F	11 0 50.3	16 56.6	24 46.2	6♒50.0	19 54.7	29 47.8	28 55.8	8 13.0	29 39.0	6 11.8	29 32.5	16 18.1
9 S	11 4 46.9	17 56.6	24 43.0	19 25.4	21 3.3	0♉27.1	29 17.1	8 24.4	29 42.1	6 15.1	29 30.9	16 17.6
10 S	11 8 43.5	18 56.6	24 39.9	2♓18.7	22 14.0	1 5.2	29 38.8	8 36.0	29 45.1	6 18.4	29 29.3	16 17.1
11 M	11 12 40.0	19 56.5	24 36.7	15 29.7	23 26.7	1 42.0	0♋ 0.8	8 47.6	29 48.0	6 21.7	29 27.8	16 16.6
12 T	11 16 36.5	20 56.4	24 33.5	28 56.7	24 41.2	2 17.5	0 23.1	8 59.4	29 50.8	6 25.0	29 26.2	16 16.2
13 W	11 20 33.1	21 56.3	24 30.3	12♈37.2	25 57.6	2 51.7	0 45.7	9 11.2	29 53.5	6 28.3	29 24.7	16 15.7
14 T	11 24 29.7	22 56.1	24 27.2	26 28.2	27 15.7	3 24.4	1 8.6	9 23.1	29 56.2	6 31.7	29 23.2	16 15.3
15 F	11 28 26.2	23 56.0	24 24.0	10♉26.4	28 35.4	3 55.6	1 31.8	9 35.1	29 58.7	6 35.1	29 21.7	16 15.0
16 S	11 32 22.8	24 55.7	24 20.8	24 29.3	29 56.8	4 25.2	1 55.3	9 47.2	0♑ 1.2	6 38.4	29 20.2	16 14.6
17 S	11 36 19.3	25 55.4	24 17.6	8♊35.0	1♓19.6	4 53.3	2 19.1	9 59.3	0 3.5	6 41.8	29 18.7	16 14.3
18 M	11 40 15.9	26 55.1	24 14.4	22 42.1	2 44.0	5 19.6	2 43.1	10 11.5	0 5.8	6 45.2	29 17.3	16 14.0
19 T	11 44 12.4	27 54.8	24 11.3	6♋49.6	4 9.9	5 44.2	3 7.4	10 23.8	0 8.0	6 48.6	29 15.8	16 13.7
20 W	11 48 9.0	28 54.4	24 8.1	20 56.0	5 37.3	6 7.1	3 31.9	10 36.2	0 10.0	6 52.0	29 14.4	16 13.4
21 T	11 52 5.5	29 54.0	24 4.9	4♌59.8	7 6.0	6 28.0	3 56.7	10 48.6	0 12.0	6 55.4	29 13.0	16 13.2
22 F	11 56 2.1	0♈53.5	24 1.7	18 58.5	8 36.1	6 47.1	4 21.8	11 1.1	0 13.9	6 58.8	29 11.6	16 13.0
23 S	11 59 58.6	1 53.0	23 58.6	2♍49.2	10 7.7	7 4.1	4 47.1	11 13.7	0 15.7	7 2.2	29 10.3	16 12.8
24 S	12 3 55.2	2 52.5	23 55.4	16 28.5	11 40.6	7 19.1	5 12.6	11 26.4	0 17.4	7 5.6	29 8.9	16 12.6
25 M	12 7 51.8	3 51.9	23 52.2	29 53.4	13 14.8	7 32.0	5 38.3	11 39.1	0 19.0	7 9.1	29 7.6	16 12.5
26 T	12 11 48.3	4 51.3	23 49.0	13♎ 1.8	14 50.4	7 42.7	6 4.2	11 51.8	0 20.5	7 12.5	29 6.3	16 12.4
27 W	12 15 44.8	5 50.7	23 45.8	25 52.4	16 27.4	7 51.1	6 30.4	12 4.7	0 21.9	7 15.9	29 5.0	16 12.3
28 T	12 19 41.4	6 50.0	23 42.7	8♏25.5	18 5.8	7 57.3	6 56.8	12 17.6	0 23.2	7 19.3	29 3.8	16 12.2
29 F	12 23 38.0	7 49.3	23 39.5	20 42.7	19 45.5	8 1.2	7 23.3	12 30.5	0 24.4	7 22.8	29 2.5	16 12.2
30 S	12 27 34.5	8 48.5	23 36.3	2♐46.8	21 26.6	8 2.7	7 50.1	12 43.5	0 25.5	7 26.2	29 1.3	16 12.1
31 S	12 31 31.1	9 47.8	23 33.1	14 41.6	23 9.0	8R 1.8	8 17.1	12 56.6	0 26.5	7 29.6	29 0.1	16 12.1

DECLINATION

DAY	EPHEMERIS SIDEREAL TIME h m s	☉	☊	☽	☿	♀	♂	♃	♄	♅	♆	♇
1 F	10 33 14.5	7S50.9	19N 3.5	14S46.6	16S37.7	12N54.2	26N 9.8	12N55.6	22S16.1	1N41.3	12N 8.0	21N51.9
4 M	10 45 4.1	6 42.3	19 1.2	25 4.3	16 22.4	14 6.2	26 7.9	13 6.8	22 16.0	1 45.2	12 9.8	21 52.4
7 T	10 56 53.8	5 32.8	18 58.9	25 33.5	15 53.6	15 14.3	26 5.7	13 18.2	22 15.9	1 49.1	12 11.5	21 52.8
10 S	11 8 43.5	4 22.6	18 56.6	15 18.3	15 11.9	16 18.0	26 3.1	13 29.8	22 15.8	1 53.0	12 13.1	21 53.2
13 W	11 20 33.1	3 12.0	18 54.3	1N57.5	14 17.7	17 16.9	26 0.0	13 41.5	22 15.7	1 57.0	12 14.8	21 53.6
16 S	11 32 22.8	2 1.0	18 52.0	19 2.6	13 11.4	18 10.5	25 56.4	13 53.4	22 15.5	2 1.0	12 16.4	21 54.0
19 T	11 44 12.4	0 49.8	18 49.6	26 49.4	11 53.4	18 58.0	25 52.1	14 5.4	22 15.4	2 5.1	12 17.9	21 54.3
22 F	11 56 2.1	0N21.3	18 47.3	19 58.7	10 24.0	19 38.7	25 47.1	14 17.5	22 15.2	2 9.1	12 19.4	21 54.6
25 M	12 7 51.8	1 32.2	18 44.9	3 45.8	8 43.5	20 11.7	25 41.3	14 29.7	22 15.0	2 13.2	12 20.8	21 54.9
28 T	12 19 41.4	2 42.8	18 42.6	13S10.4	6 52.3	20 36.0	25 34.8	14 41.9	22 14.9	2 17.3	12 22.1	21 55.1
31 S	12 31 31.1	3 52.9	18 40.2	24 33.8	4 50.7	20 50.4	25 27.4	14 54.1	22 14.7	2 21.4	12 23.4	21 55.4

APRIL 1929

LONGITUDE

DAY	EPHEMERIS SIDEREAL TIME h m s	☉ ° ′	☊ ° ′	☽ ° ′	☿ ° ′	♀ ° ′	♂ ° ′	♃ ° ′	♄ ° ′	♅ ° ′	♆ ° ′	♇ ° ′
1 M	12 35 27.6	10♈47.0	23♉30.0	26♐31.6	24♓52.9	7♉58.4	8♋44.2	13♉ 9.7	0♑27.4	7♈33.1	28♌58.9	16♋12.2
2 T	12 39 24.2	11 46.2	23 26.8	8♑21.8	26 38.1	7R52.6	9 11.6	13 22.9	0 28.2	7 36.5	28R57.8	16D12.2
3 W	12 43 20.7	12 45.3	23 23.6	20 17.3	28 24.8	7 44.4	9 39.1	13 36.1	0 28.9	7 39.9	28 56.7	16 12.3
4 T	12 47 17.3	13 44.4	23 20.4	2♒23.2	0♈12.9	7 33.7	10 6.8	13 49.4	0 29.5	7 43.3	28 55.6	16 12.4
5 F	12 51 13.8	14 43.5	23 17.2	14 43.9	2 2.4	7 20.5	10 34.7	14 2.7	0 30.0	7 46.7	28 54.5	16 12.5
6 S	12 55 10.4	15 42.6	23 14.1	27 23.3	3 53.4	7 4.9	11 2.8	14 16.1	0 30.5	7 50.1	28 53.5	16 12.7
7 S	12 59 6.9	16 41.6	23 10.9	10♓23.7	5 45.8	6 46.8	11 31.1	14 29.5	0 30.8	7 53.5	28 52.5	16 12.9
8 M	13 3 3.5	17 40.6	23 7.7	23 46.2	7 39.6	6 26.5	11 59.5	14 43.0	0 31.0	7 56.9	28 51.5	16 13.1
9 T	13 7 0.1	18 39.6	23 4.5	7♈29.8	9 34.9	6 3.9	12 28.1	14 56.5	0 31.1	8 0.3	28 50.5	16 13.3
10 W	13 10 56.6	19 38.5	23 1.4	21 31.7	11 31.7	5 39.1	12 56.8	15 10.1	0 31.1	8 3.7	28 49.6	16 13.5
11 T	13 14 53.2	20 37.4	22 58.2	5♉47.8	13 29.8	5 12.2	13 25.7	15 23.7	0R31.0	8 7.1	28 48.7	16 13.8
12 F	13 18 49.7	21 36.2	22 55.0	20 13.0	15 29.3	4 43.4	13 54.8	15 37.3	0 30.8	8 10.4	28 47.8	16 14.1
13 S	13 22 46.3	22 35.1	22 51.8	4♊41.9	17 30.2	4 12.8	14 24.0	15 51.0	0 30.6	8 13.8	28 46.9	16 14.4
14 S	13 26 42.8	23 33.9	22 48.6	19 9.6	19 32.3	3 40.5	14 53.3	16 4.7	0 30.2	8 17.1	28 46.1	16 14.8
15 M	13 30 39.4	24 32.6	22 45.5	3♋32.1	21 35.7	3 6.7	15 22.8	16 18.4	0 29.7	8 20.5	28 45.3	16 15.2
16 T	13 34 35.9	25 31.3	22 42.3	17 46.4	23 40.2	2 31.7	15 52.5	16 32.2	0 29.1	8 23.8	28 44.5	16 15.5
17 W	13 38 32.5	26 30.0	22 39.1	1♌50.4	25 45.7	1 55.6	16 22.3	16 46.0	0 28.4	8 27.1	28 43.8	16 16.0
18 T	13 42 29.1	27 28.6	22 35.9	15 42.8	27 52.0	1 18.7	16 52.2	16 59.8	0 27.7	8 30.4	28 43.1	16 16.4
19 F	13 46 25.6	28 27.2	22 32.8	29 22.8	29 59.0	0 41.2	17 22.2	17 13.7	0 26.8	8 33.6	28 42.4	16 16.9
20 S	13 50 22.1	29 25.8	22 29.6	12♍49.9	2♉ 6.5	0 3.3	17 52.4	17 27.6	0 25.8	8 36.9	28 41.8	16 17.4
21 S	13 54 18.7	0♉24.3	22 26.4	26 3.6	4 14.3	29♈25.4	18 22.7	17 41.5	0 24.8	8 40.2	28 41.1	16 17.9
22 M	13 58 15.3	1 22.8	22 23.2	9♎ 3.6	6 22.1	28 47.7	18 53.1	17 55.5	0 23.6	8 43.4	28 40.6	16 18.4
23 T	14 2 11.8	2 21.3	22 20.1	21 49.8	8 29.7	28 10.3	19 23.7	18 9.4	0 22.4	8 46.6	28 40.0	16 19.0
24 W	14 6 8.4	3 19.7	22 16.9	4♏22.6	10 36.7	27 33.7	19 54.3	18 23.4	0 21.0	8 49.8	28 39.5	16 19.5
25 T	14 10 4.9	4 18.1	22 13.7	16 42.7	12 42.8	26 57.9	20 25.1	18 37.4	0 19.6	8 53.0	28 39.0	16 20.1
26 F	14 14 1.5	5 16.5	22 10.5	28 51.6	14 47.8	26 23.3	20 56.0	18 51.5	0 18.1	8 56.1	28 38.5	16 20.8
27 S	14 17 58.0	6 14.8	22 7.3	10♐51.2	16 51.4	25 50.0	21 27.0	19 5.5	0 16.4	8 59.3	28 38.1	16 21.4
28 S	14 21 54.6	7 13.2	22 4.2	22 44.3	18 53.1	25 18.3	21 58.1	19 19.6	0 14.7	9 2.4	28 37.7	16 22.1
29 M	14 25 51.1	8 11.4	22 1.0	4♑34.2	20 52.8	24 48.2	22 29.3	19 33.7	0 12.9	9 5.5	28 37.3	16 22.8
30 T	14 29 47.7	9 9.7	21 57.8	16 24.8	22 50.1	24 20.1	23 0.6	19 47.8	0 11.0	9 8.6	28 37.0	16 23.5

DECLINATION

DAY	EPHEMERIS SIDEREAL TIME h m s	☉	☊	☽	☿	♀	♂	♃	♄	♅	♆	♇
1 M	12 35 27.6	4N16.2	18N39.4	26S20.9	4S 7.9	20N52.9	25N24.7	14N58.2	22S14.7	2N22.7	12N23.8	21N55.4
4 T	12 47 17.3	5 25.4	18 37.0	24 23.5	1 53.2	20 52.7	25 16.1	15 10.5	22 14.5	2 26.8	12 24.9	21 55.6
7 S	12 59 6.9	6 33.8	18 34.6	12 13.1	0N30.5	20 40.2	25 6.6	15 22.7	22 14.4	2 30.8	12 26.0	21 55.8
10 W	13 10 56.6	7 41.2	18 32.2	5N58.7	3 2.3	20 14.9	24 56.1	15 35.0	22 14.2	2 34.8	12 27.0	21 56.0
13 S	13 22 46.3	8 47.5	18 29.8	22 16.0	5 40.7	19 36.6	24 44.5	15 47.2	22 14.1	2 38.8	12 27.9	21 56.1
16 T	13 34 35.9	9 52.4	18 27.4	26 35.4	8 23.4	18 46.0	24 32.0	15 59.3	22 13.9	2 42.7	12 28.7	21 56.2
19 F	13 46 25.6	10 55.8	18 24.9	16 32.9	11 7.2	17 44.9	24 18.4	16 11.4	22 13.8	2 46.6	12 29.5	21 56.2
22 M	13 58 15.3	11 57.6	18 22.5	0S20.6	13 47.5	16 35.9	24 3.7	16 23.4	22 13.7	2 50.4	12 30.1	21 56.3
25 T	14 10 4.9	12 57.6	18 20.1	16 26.3	16 19.2	15 22.7	23 47.9	16 35.3	22 13.6	2 54.1	12 30.6	21 56.3
28 S	14 21 54.6	13 55.7	18 17.6	26 0.4	18 36.5	14 8.9	23 31.0	16 47.1	22 13.5	2 57.8	12 31.0	21 56.2

MAY 1929

DAY	EPHEMERIS SIDEREAL TIME h m s	☉ ° ′	☊ ° ′	☽ ° ′	☿ ° ′	♀ ° ′	♂ ° ′	♃ ° ′	♄ ° ′	♅ ° ′	♆ ° ′	♇ ° ′
						LONGITUDE						
1 W	14 33 44.3	10♉ 7.9	21♉54.6	28♑20.4	24♉44.9	23♈53.9	23♋32.1	20♉ 1.9	0♑ 9.1	9♈11.6	28♌36.7	16♋24.2
2 T	14 37 40.8	11 6.2	21 51.5	10♒25.6	26 36.8	23R29.9	24 3.6	20 16.1	0R 7.0	9 14.7	28R36.4	16 25.0
3 F	14 41 37.4	12 4.3	21 48.3	22 45.0	28 25.6	23 8.1	24 35.2	20 30.2	0 4.8	9 17.7	28 36.2	16 25.7
4 S	14 45 33.9	13 2.5	21 45.1	5♓22.8	0♊11.3	22 48.6	25 6.9	20 44.4	0 2.6	9 20.7	28 35.9	16 26.5
5 S	14 49 30.5	14 0.6	21 41.9	18 22.7	1 53.5	22 31.5	25 38.8	20 58.6	0 0.3	9 23.7	28 35.8	16 27.4
6 M	14 53 27.0	14 58.8	21 38.7	1♈46.9	3 32.3	22 16.7	26 10.7	21 12.8	29♐57.9	9 26.6	28 35.6	16 28.2
7 T	14 57 23.6	15 56.8	21 35.6	15 36.2	5 7.5	22 4.4	26 42.7	21 27.0	29 55.4	9 29.5	28 35.5	16 29.1
8 W	15 1 20.1	16 54.9	21 32.4	29 49.2	6 38.9	21 54.5	27 14.9	21 41.2	29 52.8	9 32.4	28 35.4	16 29.9
9 T	15 5 16.7	17 52.9	21 29.2	14♉22.0	8 6.6	21 47.1	27 47.1	21 55.4	29 50.2	9 35.3	28 35.4	16 30.8
10 F	15 9 13.2	18 51.0	21 26.0	29 8.9	9 30.4	21 42.0	28 19.4	22 9.6	29 47.4	9 38.1	28 35.4	16 31.7
11 S	15 13 9.8	19 48.9	21 22.9	14♊ 2.6	10 50.2	21 39.4	28 51.8	22 23.8	29 44.6	9 40.9	28D35.4	16 32.7
12 S	15 17 6.4	20 46.9	21 19.7	28 55.4	12 6.1	21 39.1	29 24.3	22 38.0	29 41.8	9 43.7	28 35.5	16 33.7
13 M	15 21 2.9	21 44.8	21 16.5	13♋39.9	13 17.9	21D41.1	29 56.9	22 52.2	29 38.8	9 46.5	28 35.5	16 34.6
14 T	15 24 59.5	22 42.7	21 13.3	28 10.5	14 25.6	21 45.4	0♌29.5	23 6.5	29 35.8	9 49.2	28 35.7	16 35.6
15 W	15 28 56.0	23 40.6	21 10.2	12♌23.1	15 29.1	21 51.9	1 2.3	23 20.7	29 32.7	9 51.9	28 35.8	16 36.6
16 T	15 32 52.6	24 38.4	21 7.0	26 15.8	16 28.3	22 0.6	1 35.1	23 34.9	29 29.5	9 54.6	28 36.0	16 37.7
17 F	15 36 49.1	25 36.3	21 3.8	9♍48.3	17 23.3	22 11.5	2 8.0	23 49.1	29 26.3	9 57.2	28 36.2	16 38.7
18 S	15 40 45.7	26 34.0	21 0.6	23 1.7	18 13.8	22 24.4	2 41.0	24 3.3	29 22.9	9 59.8	28 36.5	16 39.8
19 S	15 44 42.3	27 31.8	20 57.4	5♎57.5	18 60.0	22 39.3	3 14.1	24 17.5	29 19.6	10 2.4	28 36.8	16 40.9
20 M	15 48 38.8	28 29.5	20 54.3	18 37.8	19 41.6	22 56.1	3 47.2	24 31.7	29 16.2	10 4.9	28 37.1	16 42.0
21 T	15 52 35.4	29 27.2	20 51.1	1♏ 4.9	20 18.6	23 14.9	4 20.4	24 45.9	29 12.7	10 7.4	28 37.4	16 43.1
22 W	15 56 31.9	0♊24.9	20 47.9	13 20.8	20 51.0	23 35.5	4 53.7	25 0.0	29 9.1	10 9.9	28 37.8	16 44.2
23 T	16 0 28.5	1 22.6	20 44.7	25 27.5	21 18.7	23 57.8	5 27.1	25 14.2	29 5.5	10 12.3	28 38.2	16 45.4
24 F	16 4 25.0	2 20.2	20 41.6	7♐26.9	21 41.8	24 21.9	6 0.5	25 28.3	29 1.8	10 14.7	28 38.7	16 46.5
25 S	16 8 21.6	3 17.8	20 38.4	19 20.9	22 0.0	24 47.6	6 34.0	25 42.5	28 58.1	10 17.1	28 39.2	16 47.7
26 S	16 12 18.2	4 15.4	20 35.2	1♑11.7	22 13.5	25 15.0	7 7.6	25 56.6	28 54.3	10 19.5	28 39.7	16 48.9
27 M	16 16 14.7	5 13.0	20 32.0	13 1.6	22 22.3	25 43.8	7 41.2	26 10.7	28 50.5	10 21.8	28 40.2	16 50.1
28 T	16 20 11.2	6 10.5	20 28.8	24 53.4	22 26.4	26 14.2	8 14.9	26 24.8	28 46.6	10 24.0	28 40.8	16 51.4
29 W	16 24 7.8	7 8.1	20 25.7	6♒50.2	22R25.9	26 45.9	8 48.7	26 38.8	28 42.7	10 26.2	28 41.4	16 52.6
30 T	16 28 4.4	8 5.6	20 22.5	18 55.7	22 20.8	27 19.1	9 22.6	26 52.9	28 38.7	10 28.4	28 42.0	16 53.9
31 F	16 32 1.0	9 3.1	20 19.3	1♓13.7	22 11.5	27 53.5	9 56.5	27 6.9	28 34.7	10 30.6	28 42.7	16 55.2
						DECLINATION						
1 W	14 33 44.3	14N51.7	18N15.2	25S15.9	20N35.1	12N58.4	23N13.0	16N58.7	22S13.5	3N 1.4	12N31.4	21N56.2
4 S	14 45 33.9	15 45.6	18 12.7	14 18.3	22 12.1	11 53.9	22 53.9	17 10.3	22 13.4	3 4.9	12 31.6	21 56.1
7 T	14 57 23.6	16 37.1	18 10.2	3N17.6	23 26.5	10 57.8	22 33.6	17 21.7	22 13.3	3 8.4	12 31.7	21 56.0
10 F	15 9 13.2	17 26.2	18 7.7	20 41.1	24 19.1	10 11.3	22 12.3	17 32.9	22 13.3	3 11.7	12 31.7	21 55.9
13 M	15 21 2.9	18 12.6	18 5.2	26 55.2	24 51.4	9 35.0	21 49.8	17 43.9	22 13.2	3 14.9	12 31.7	21 55.8
16 T	15 32 52.6	18 56.3	18 2.7	17 43.1	25 5.4	9 8.8	21 26.2	17 54.8	22 13.2	3 18.1	12 31.5	21 55.6
19 S	15 44 42.3	19 37.0	18 0.2	1 5.5	25 3.0	8 52.5	21 1.5	18 5.5	22 13.2	3 21.1	12 31.2	21 55.4
22 W	15 56 31.9	20 14.8	17 57.7	15S 9.1	24 46.3	8 45.3	20 35.7	18 16.0	22 13.1	3 24.0	12 30.8	21 55.2
25 S	16 8 21.6	20 49.5	17 55.2	25 29.9	24 17.0	8 46.6	20 8.8	18 26.3	22 13.1	3 26.7	12 30.3	21 55.0
28 T	16 20 11.2	21 20.9	17 52.6	25 48.1	23 37.1	8 55.6	19 40.9	18 36.4	22 13.1	3 29.4	12 29.7	21 54.7
31 F	16 32 1.0	21 49.0	17 50.1	15 52.7	22 48.6	9 11.4	19 11.9	18 46.2	22 13.0	3 31.9	12 29.0	21 54.5

JUNE 1929

						LONGITUDE						
1 S	16 35 57.5	10♊ 0.6	20♉16.1	13♓48.3	21♊57.9	28♈29.3	10♌30.4	27♉20.9	28♐30.7	10♈32.7	28♌43.4	16♋56.4
2 S	16 39 54.0	10 58.1	20 13.0	26 43.4	21R40.5	29 6.2	11 4.5	27 34.9	28R26.6	10 34.8	28 44.1	16 57.7
3 M	16 43 50.6	11 55.6	20 9.8	10♈ 2.5	21 19.5	29 44.3	11 38.6	27 48.9	28 22.4	10 36.8	28 44.9	16 59.1
4 T	16 47 47.2	12 53.1	20 6.6	23 47.7	20 55.3	0♉23.5	12 12.8	28 2.9	28 18.3	10 38.8	28 45.7	17 0.4
5 W	16 51 43.7	13 50.5	20 3.4	7♉59.4	20 28.3	1 3.8	12 47.0	28 16.8	28 14.1	10 40.8	28 46.5	17 1.7
6 T	16 55 40.3	14 48.0	20 0.3	22 35.7	19 58.9	1 45.2	13 21.3	28 30.7	28 9.8	10 42.7	28 47.4	17 3.1
7 F	16 59 36.8	15 45.4	19 57.1	7♊31.6	19 27.7	2 27.5	13 55.7	28 44.5	28 5.6	10 44.6	28 48.3	17 4.4
8 S	17 3 33.4	16 42.8	19 53.9	22 39.7	18 55.1	3 10.8	14 30.2	28 58.4	28 1.3	10 46.4	28 49.2	17 5.8
9 S	17 7 29.9	17 40.2	19 50.7	7♋50.8	18 21.7	3 54.9	15 4.7	29 12.2	27 57.0	10 48.2	28 50.1	17 7.2
10 M	17 11 26.5	18 37.6	19 47.6	22 54.8	17 48.1	4 40.0	15 39.2	29 26.0	27 52.6	10 50.0	28 51.1	17 8.6
11 T	17 15 23.1	19 35.0	19 44.4	7♌43.2	17 14.9	5 25.9	16 13.8	29 39.7	27 48.3	10 51.7	28 52.1	17 10.0
12 W	17 19 19.6	20 32.3	19 41.2	22 9.5	16 42.6	6 12.6	16 48.5	29 53.4	27 43.9	10 53.3	28 53.1	17 11.4
13 T	17 23 16.2	21 29.7	19 38.0	6♍10.2	16 11.8	7 0.1	17 23.3	0♊ 7.1	27 39.5	10 55.0	28 54.2	17 12.9
14 F	17 27 12.7	22 27.0	19 34.9	19 44.6	15 43.0	7 48.3	17 58.1	0 20.8	27 35.1	10 56.6	28 55.3	17 14.3
15 S	17 31 9.3	23 24.3	19 31.7	2♎54.0	15 16.7	8 37.2	18 32.9	0 34.4	27 30.7	10 58.1	28 56.4	17 15.7
16 S	17 35 5.9	24 21.6	19 28.5	15 41.5	14 53.3	9 26.9	19 7.8	0 47.9	27 26.3	10 59.6	28 57.6	17 17.2
17 M	17 39 2.4	25 18.9	19 25.3	28 10.7	14 33.2	10 17.2	19 42.8	1 1.4	27 21.9	11 1.0	28 58.7	17 18.7
18 T	17 42 59.0	26 16.2	19 22.2	10♏25.5	14 16.8	11 8.2	20 17.8	1 14.9	27 17.4	11 2.4	28 60.0	17 20.1
19 W	17 46 55.5	27 13.4	19 19.0	22 29.7	14 4.4	11 59.8	20 52.9	1 28.4	27 13.0	11 3.8	29 1.2	17 21.6
20 T	17 50 52.1	28 10.7	19 15.8	4♐26.5	13 56.2	12 52.0	21 28.0	1 41.8	27 8.6	11 5.1	29 2.4	17 23.1
21 F	17 54 48.6	29 7.9	19 12.6	16 18.8	13 52.3	13 44.8	22 3.2	1 55.1	27 4.1	11 6.4	29 3.7	17 24.6
22 S	17 58 45.2	0♋ 5.1	19 9.4	28 9.0	13D53.0	14 38.1	22 38.5	2 8.4	26 59.7	11 7.6	29 5.0	17 26.1
23 S	18 2 41.8	1 2.3	19 6.3	9♑59.2	13 58.4	15 32.0	23 13.7	2 21.7	26 55.3	11 8.8	29 6.4	17 27.6
24 M	18 6 38.3	1 59.6	19 3.1	21 51.2	14 8.4	16 26.5	23 49.1	2 34.9	26 50.9	11 9.9	29 7.7	17 29.1
25 T	18 10 34.9	2 56.8	18 59.9	3♒46.9	14 23.2	17 21.4	24 24.5	2 48.0	26 46.5	11 11.0	29 9.1	17 30.7
26 W	18 14 31.4	3 54.0	18 56.7	15 48.4	14 42.8	18 16.9	24 59.9	3 1.2	26 42.1	11 12.1	29 10.5	17 32.2
27 T	18 18 28.0	4 51.2	18 53.6	27 57.9	15 7.1	19 12.8	25 35.4	3 14.2	26 37.7	11 13.1	29 12.0	17 33.7
28 F	18 22 24.6	5 48.4	18 50.4	10♓18.2	15 36.2	20 9.2	26 11.0	3 27.2	26 33.4	11 14.0	29 13.5	17 35.3
29 S	18 26 21.1	6 45.6	18 47.2	22 52.5	16 10.0	21 6.0	26 46.6	3 40.2	26 29.0	11 14.9	29 14.9	17 36.8
30 S	18 30 17.6	7 42.8	18 44.0	5♈44.4	16 48.4	22 3.3	27 22.2	3 53.1	26 24.7	11 15.8	29 16.5	17 38.3
						DECLINATION						
1 S	16 35 57.5	21N57.6	17N49.3	10S51.1	22N31.0	9N18.0	19N 2.0	18N49.4	22S13.0	3N32.7	12N28.8	21N54.4
4 T	16 47 47.2	22 21.2	17 46.7	6N59.2	21 35.2	9 41.4	18 31.7	18 59.0	22 13.0	3 35.0	12 27.9	21 54.1
7 F	16 59 36.8	22 41.3	17 44.2	23 2.0	20 38.2	10 9.7	18 0.3	19 8.3	22 13.0	3 37.2	12 27.0	21 53.8
10 M	17 11 26.5	22 57.8	17 41.6	26 2.7	19 44.4	10 42.0	17 28.0	19 17.4	22 12.9	3 39.2	12 26.0	21 53.5
13 T	17 23 16.2	23 10.6	17 39.0	13 55.7	18 58.7	11 17.7	16 54.7	19 26.2	22 12.9	3 41.1	12 24.9	21 53.1
16 S	17 35 5.9	23 19.8	17 36.4	3S23.7	18 25.2	11 56.0	16 20.4	19 34.8	22 12.8	3 42.8	12 23.7	21 52.8
19 W	17 46 55.5	23 25.2	17 33.8	18 32.2	18 6.9	12 36.3	15 45.3	19 43.1	22 12.8	3 44.4	12 22.4	21 52.4
22 S	17 58 45.2	23 27.0	17 31.2	26 34.4	18 4.6	13 18.2	15 9.2	19 51.2	22 12.7	3 45.8	12 21.0	21 52.0
25 T	18 10 34.9	23 25.0	17 28.6	24 6.0	18 17.8	14 1.0	14 32.3	19 59.0	22 12.7	3 47.1	12 19.6	21 51.6
28 F	18 22 24.6	23 19.3	17 26.0	12 10.5	18 44.6	14 44.2	13 54.6	20 6.6	22 12.7	3 48.1	12 18.1	21 51.2

DAY	EPHEMERIS SIDEREAL TIME	☉	☊	☽	☿	♀	♂	♃	♄	♅	♆	♇
	h m s	° ′	° ′	° ′	° ′	° ′	° ′	° ′	° ′	° ′	° ′	° ′
						LONGITUDE						
1 M	18 34 14.2	8♋40.0	18♉40.9	18♈57.3	17♊31.4	23♉ 1.0	27♌58.0	4♊ 5.9	26♐20.4	11♈16.6	29♌18.0	17♋39.9
2 T	18 38 10.8	9 37.2	18 37.7	2♉34.1	18 19.0	23 59.1	28 33.7	4 18.7	26R16.2	11 17.3	29 19.6	17 41.4
3 W	18 42 7.3	10 34.4	18 34.5	16 36.6	19 11.0	24 57.5	29 9.5	4 31.5	26 12.0	11 18.1	29 21.1	17 43.0
4 T	18 46 3.9	11 31.7	18 31.3	1♊ 4.7	20 7.5	25 56.4	29 45.4	4 44.1	26 7.7	11 18.7	29 22.7	17 44.6
5 F	18 50 0.5	12 28.9	18 28.1	15 55.4	21 8.3	26 55.6	0♍21.3	4 56.7	26 3.6	11 19.3	29 24.4	17 46.1
6 S	18 53 57.0	13 26.1	18 25.0	1♋ 2.7	22 13.5	27 55.2	0 57.3	5 9.3	25 59.4	11 19.9	29 26.0	17 47.7
7 S	18 57 53.6	14 23.3	18 21.8	16 17.8	23 22.9	28 55.1	1 33.4	5 21.8	25 55.3	11 20.4	29 27.7	17 49.3
8 M	19 1 50.1	15 20.6	18 18.6	1♌30.1	24 36.5	29 55.3	2 9.5	5 34.2	25 51.3	11 20.9	29 29.4	17 50.8
9 T	19 5 46.7	16 17.8	18 15.4	16 29.0	25 54.2	0♊55.8	2 45.6	5 46.5	25 47.3	11 21.3	29 31.1	17 52.4
10 W	19 9 43.3	17 15.0	18 12.3	1♍ 6.1	27 16.0	1 56.7	3 21.8	5 58.8	25 43.3	11 21.7	29 32.9	17 54.0
11 T	19 13 39.8	18 12.3	18 9.1	15 15.8	28 41.8	2 57.8	3 58.0	6 11.0	25 39.3	11 22.0	29 34.6	17 55.5
12 F	19 17 36.4	19 9.5	18 5.9	28 56.2	0♋11.6	3 59.2	4 34.3	6 23.1	25 35.5	11 22.3	29 36.4	17 57.1
13 S	19 21 32.9	20 6.7	18 2.7	12♎ 8.2	1 45.2	5 0.9	5 10.6	6 35.2	25 31.6	11 22.5	29 38.2	17 58.7
14 S	19 25 29.5	21 4.0	17 59.6	24 54.9	3 22.5	6 2.9	5 47.0	6 47.2	25 27.9	11 22.7	29 40.0	18 0.2
15 M	19 29 26.1	22 1.2	17 56.4	7♏20.7	5 3.4	7 5.2	6 23.5	6 59.1	25 24.1	11 22.8	29 41.8	18 1.8
16 T	19 33 22.6	22 58.4	17 53.2	19 30.5	6 47.9	8 7.7	6 60.0	7 10.9	25 20.5	11 22.9	29 43.7	18 3.4
17 W	19 37 19.2	23 55.7	17 50.0	1♐29.2	8 35.6	9 10.4	7 36.5	7 22.7	25 16.8	11 22.9	29 45.6	18 4.9
18 T	19 41 15.7	24 52.9	17 46.9	13 21.2	10 26.5	10 13.4	8 13.1	7 34.3	25 13.3	11R22.9	29 47.4	18 6.5
19 F	19 45 12.2	25 50.1	17 43.7	25 10.5	12 20.2	11 16.7	8 49.7	7 45.9	25 9.8	11 22.8	29 49.3	18 8.0
20 S	19 49 8.8	26 47.4	17 40.5	7♑ 0.1	14 16.7	12 20.2	9 26.3	7 57.4	25 6.3	11 22.7	29 51.3	18 9.6
21 S	19 53 5.4	27 44.6	17 37.3	18 52.6	16 15.5	13 23.9	10 3.1	8 8.9	25 3.0	11 22.5	29 53.2	18 11.2
22 M	19 57 2.0	28 41.9	17 34.2	0♒49.8	18 16.4	14 27.9	10 39.8	8 20.2	24 59.7	11 22.3	29 55.2	18 12.7
23 T	20 0 58.5	29 39.2	17 31.0	12 53.1	20 19.0	15 32.1	11 16.6	8 31.4	24 56.4	11 22.1	29 57.1	18 14.2
24 W	20 4 55.0	0♌36.4	17 27.8	25 3.7	22 23.1	16 36.5	11 53.5	8 42.6	24 53.2	11 21.8	29 59.1	18 15.8
25 T	20 8 51.6	1 33.7	17 24.6	7♓22.7	24 28.3	17 41.1	12 30.4	8 53.7	24 50.1	11 21.4	0♍ 1.1	18 17.3
26 F	20 12 48.2	2 31.0	17 21.4	19 51.7	26 34.4	18 45.9	13 7.4	9 4.7	24 47.1	11 21.0	0 3.1	18 18.9
27 S	20 16 44.8	3 28.4	17 18.3	2♈32.5	28 40.9	19 51.0	13 44.4	9 15.6	24 44.1	11 20.6	0 5.1	18 20.4
28 S	20 20 41.3	4 25.7	17 15.1	15 27.4	0♌47.5	20 56.2	14 21.4	9 26.3	24 41.2	11 20.1	0 7.2	18 21.9
29 M	20 24 37.8	5 23.1	17 11.9	28 39.1	2 54.1	22 1.6	14 58.5	9 37.0	24 38.4	11 19.5	0 9.2	18 23.4
30 T	20 28 34.4	6 20.4	17 8.7	12♉10.2	5 0.4	23 7.2	15 35.7	9 47.6	24 35.6	11 18.9	0 11.3	18 24.9
31 W	20 32 31.0	7 17.8	17 5.6	26 2.8	7 6.1	24 13.0	16 12.9	9 58.1	24 33.0	11 18.3	0 13.4	18 26.4
						DECLINATION						
1 M	18 34 14.2	23N10.0	17N23.4	4N57.5	19N21.9	15N27.4	13N16.1	20N13.8	22S12.6	3N49.1	12N16.5	21N50.8
4 T	18 46 3.9	22 57.0	17 20.8	21 20.4	20 6.5	16 10.0	12 36.8	20 20.9	22 12.6	3 49.8	12 14.8	21 50.3
7 S	18 57 53.6	22 40.4	17 18.1	26 40.3	20 54.2	16 51.5	11 56.7	20 27.6	22 12.6	3 50.4	12 13.0	21 49.9
10 W	19 9 43.3	22 20.2	17 15.5	15 44.6	21 40.8	17 31.6	11 15.9	20 34.1	22 12.6	3 50.8	12 11.2	21 49.5
13 S	19 21 32.9	21 56.6	17 12.9	1S57.4	22 21.3	18 9.8	10 34.5	20 40.3	22 12.6	3 51.0	12 9.4	21 49.0
16 T	19 33 22.6	21 29.6	17 10.2	17 37.9	22 50.4	18 45.8	9 52.3	20 46.3	22 12.6	3 51.1	12 7.4	21 48.6
19 F	19 45 12.2	20 59.3	17 7.5	26 20.2	23 2.9	19 19.1	9 9.6	20 52.0	22 12.6	3 51.0	12 5.4	21 48.1
22 M	19 57 2.0	20 25.8	17 4.9	24 38.8	22 54.2	19 49.4	8 26.3	20 57.4	22 12.7	3 50.7	12 3.4	21 47.7
25 T	20 8 51.6	19 49.2	17 2.2	13 12.2	22 21.8	20 16.4	7 42.4	21 2.5	22 12.8	3 50.3	12 1.3	21 47.3
28 S	20 20 41.3	19 9.7	16 59.5	3N35.7	21 25.5	20 39.7	6 58.1	21 7.5	22 12.9	3 49.7	11 59.2	21 46.8
31 W	20 32 31.0	18 27.3	16 56.8	19 58.9	20 7.6	20 59.2	6 13.2	21 12.1	22 13.0	3 48.9	11 57.0	21 46.4

AUGUST 1929

DAY	SIDEREAL TIME	☉	☊	☽	☿	♀	♂	♃	♄	♅	♆	♇
						LONGITUDE						
1 T	20 36 27.5	8♌15.2	17♉ 2.4	10♊17.9	9♌11.0	25♊19.0	16♍50.2	10♊ 8.5	24♐30.4	11♈17.6	0♍15.4	18♋27.9
2 F	20 40 24.1	9 12.7	16 59.2	24 54.1	11 15.0	26 25.2	17 27.5	10 18.8	24R27.9	11R16.9	0 17.5	18 29.4
3 S	20 44 20.6	10 10.1	16 56.0	9♋47.5	13 17.9	27 31.5	18 4.8	10 29.0	24 25.4	11 16.1	0 19.7	18 30.9
4 S	20 48 17.2	11 7.6	16 52.9	24 51.0	15 19.6	28 38.0	18 42.3	10 39.1	24 23.1	11 15.3	0 21.8	18 32.4
5 M	20 52 13.7	12 5.1	16 49.7	9♌55.6	17 20.0	29 44.7	19 19.7	10 49.1	24 20.8	11 14.4	0 23.9	18 33.8
6 T	20 56 10.3	13 2.6	16 46.5	24 51.1	19 19.1	0♋51.5	19 57.2	10 58.9	24 18.6	11 13.5	0 26.0	18 35.3
7 W	21 0 6.9	14 0.1	16 43.3	9♍28.5	21 16.8	1 58.5	20 34.8	11 8.7	24 16.5	11 12.6	0 28.2	18 36.7
8 T	21 4 3.4	14 57.6	16 40.1	23 40.9	23 13.0	3 5.6	21 12.4	11 18.3	24 14.5	11 11.6	0 30.3	18 38.1
9 F	21 7 60.0	15 55.2	16 37.0	7♎25.1	25 7.8	4 12.9	21 50.1	11 27.9	24 12.6	11 10.5	0 32.5	18 39.6
10 S	21 11 56.5	16 52.7	16 33.8	20 40.7	27 1.0	5 20.3	22 27.8	11 37.3	24 10.8	11 9.4	0 34.7	18 41.0
11 S	21 15 53.1	17 50.3	16 30.6	3♏30.1	28 52.8	6 27.9	23 5.5	11 46.5	24 9.0	11 8.3	0 36.8	18 42.4
12 M	21 19 49.6	18 47.9	16 27.4	15 57.2	0♍43.0	7 35.6	23 43.3	11 55.7	24 7.4	11 7.1	0 39.0	18 43.8
13 T	21 23 46.2	19 45.5	16 24.3	28 7.2	2 31.8	8 43.5	24 21.2	12 4.8	24 5.8	11 5.9	0 41.2	18 45.2
14 W	21 27 42.8	20 43.1	16 21.1	10♐ 5.3	4 19.0	9 51.5	24 59.1	12 13.7	24 4.4	11 4.7	0 43.4	18 46.5
15 T	21 31 39.3	21 40.8	16 17.9	21 56.7	6 4.8	10 59.6	25 37.0	12 22.5	24 3.0	11 3.4	0 45.6	18 47.9
16 F	21 35 35.9	22 38.4	16 14.7	3♑46.2	7 49.1	12 7.9	26 15.0	12 31.1	24 1.7	11 2.0	0 47.8	18 49.2
17 S	21 39 32.4	23 36.1	16 11.5	15 37.7	9 31.9	13 16.3	26 53.0	12 39.7	24 0.5	11 0.6	0 50.0	18 50.6
18 S	21 43 29.0	24 33.8	16 8.4	27 34.5	11 13.3	14 24.8	27 31.1	12 48.1	23 59.4	10 59.2	0 52.2	18 51.9
19 M	21 47 25.5	25 31.5	16 5.2	9♒39.0	12 53.2	15 33.5	28 9.3	12 56.4	23 58.4	10 57.8	0 54.5	18 53.2
20 T	21 51 22.1	26 29.2	16 2.0	21 52.6	14 31.7	16 42.3	28 47.4	13 4.5	23 57.5	10 56.3	0 56.7	18 54.5
21 W	21 55 18.6	27 27.0	15 58.8	4♓16.2	16 8.8	17 51.2	29 25.7	13 12.5	23 56.7	10 54.7	0 58.9	18 55.8
22 T	21 59 15.2	28 24.8	15 55.7	16 50.1	17 44.5	19 0.2	0♎ 4.0	13 20.4	23 55.9	10 53.2	1 1.1	18 57.0
23 F	22 3 11.8	29 22.6	15 52.5	29 34.7	19 18.8	20 9.4	0 42.3	13 28.1	23 55.3	10 51.6	1 3.3	18 58.3
24 S	22 7 8.3	0♍20.4	15 49.3	12♈30.2	20 51.7	21 18.7	1 20.7	13 35.7	23 54.8	10 49.9	1 5.6	18 59.5
25 S	22 11 4.8	1 18.3	15 46.1	25 37.4	22 23.2	22 28.1	1 59.1	13 43.1	23 54.3	10 48.2	1 7.8	19 0.7
26 M	22 15 1.4	2 16.2	15 42.9	8♉57.2	23 53.4	23 37.7	2 37.6	13 50.4	23 54.0	10 46.5	1 10.0	19 1.9
27 T	22 18 58.0	3 14.1	15 39.8	22 31.1	25 22.1	24 47.3	3 16.1	13 57.6	23 53.8	10 44.8	1 12.2	19 3.1
28 W	22 22 54.6	4 12.0	15 36.6	6♊20.2	26 49.4	25 57.1	3 54.7	14 4.6	23 53.6	10 43.0	1 14.5	19 4.3
29 T	22 26 51.1	5 10.0	15 33.4	20 25.4	28 15.3	27 7.0	4 33.3	14 11.5	23 53.6	10 41.2	1 16.7	19 5.5
30 F	22 30 47.6	6 8.0	15 30.2	4♋46.0	29 39.7	28 17.0	5 12.0	14 18.2	23D53.6	10 39.4	1 18.9	19 6.6
31 S	22 34 44.2	7 6.1	15 27.1	19 19.4	1♎ 2.7	29 27.2	5 50.7	14 24.7	23 53.8	10 37.5	1 21.1	19 7.7
						DECLINATION						
1 T	20 36 27.5	18N12.6	16N55.9	23N55.1	19N37.4	21N 4.7	5N58.1	21N13.6	22S13.1	3N48.6	11N56.2	21N46.2
4 S	20 48 17.2	17 26.6	16 53.2	25 43.1	17 56.4	21 18.5	5 12.7	21 17.9	22 13.3	3 47.6	11 54.0	21 45.8
7 W	21 0 6.9	16 38.0	16 50.5	12 18.3	16 2.9	21 27.8	4 26.8	21 22.0	22 13.5	3 46.4	11 51.8	21 45.4
10 S	21 11 56.5	15 47.1	16 47.8	6S 2.1	14 0.5	21 32.3	3 40.5	21 25.8	22 13.7	3 45.2	11 49.5	21 44.9
13 T	21 23 46.2	14 53.8	16 45.0	20 44.3	11 52.3	21 32.1	2 54.0	21 29.3	22 14.0	3 43.7	11 47.2	21 44.5
16 F	21 35 35.9	13 58.4	16 42.3	27 5.6	9 40.8	21 26.8	2 7.1	21 32.7	22 14.3	3 42.1	11 44.9	21 44.1
19 M	21 47 25.5	13 1.1	16 39.6	22 37.8	7 28.1	21 16.5	1 20.0	21 35.7	22 14.7	3 40.4	11 42.5	21 43.8
22 T	21 59 15.2	12 1.9	16 36.8	9 8.1	5 15.6	21 1.1	0 32.7	21 38.6	22 15.1	3 38.5	11 40.2	21 43.4
25 S	22 11 4.8	11 0.9	16 34.1	8N21.1	3 4.7	20 40.6	0S14.8	21 41.3	22 15.6	3 36.5	11 37.8	21 43.0
28 W	22 22 54.6	9 58.4	16 31.3	23 12.1	0 56.7	20 14.9	1 2.4	21 43.7	22 16.1	3 34.4	11 35.5	21 42.7
31 S	22 34 44.2	8 54.5	16 28.5	26 34.3	1S 7.5	19 44.2	1 50.0	21 45.9	22 16.6	3 32.2	11 33.2	21 42.4

SEPTEMBER 1929

LONGITUDE

DAY	EPHEMERIS SIDEREAL TIME h m s	☉ ° ′	☊ ° ′	☽ ° ′	☿ ° ′	♀ ° ′	♂ ° ′	♃ ° ′	♄ ° ′	♅ ° ′	♆ ° ′	♇ ° ′
1 S	22 38 40.8	8♍ 4.1	15♉23.9	4♌ 1.2	2♎24.1	0♌37.4	6♎29.5	14♊31.1	23♐54.0	10♈35.6	1♍23.3	19♋ 8.9
2 M	22 42 37.3	9 2.3	15 20.7	18 44.6	3 44.1	1 47.7	7 8.4	14 37.4	23 54.3	10R33.6	1 25.6	19 10.0
3 T	22 46 33.9	10 0.4	15 17.5	3♍22.0	5 2.4	2 58.2	7 47.3	14 43.5	23 54.8	10 31.7	1 27.8	19 11.0
4 W	22 50 30.4	10 58.6	15 14.4	17 45.6	6 19.1	4 8.7	8 26.2	14 49.4	23 55.3	10 29.7	1 30.0	19 12.1
5 T	22 54 26.9	11 56.8	15 11.2	1♎49.4	7 34.2	5 19.4	9 5.2	14 55.1	23 56.0	10 27.6	1 32.2	19 13.1
6 F	22 58 23.5	12 55.0	15 8.0	15 29.2	8 47.5	6 30.1	9 44.3	15 0.7	23 56.7	10 25.6	1 34.4	19 14.1
7 S	23 2 20.1	13 53.2	15 4.8	28 43.8	9 58.9	7 41.0	10 23.4	15 6.1	23 57.5	10 23.5	1 36.5	19 15.2
8 S	23 6 16.6	14 51.5	15 1.6	11♏34.1	11 8.5	8 51.9	11 2.5	15 11.4	23 58.5	10 21.4	1 38.7	19 16.1
9 M	23 10 13.1	15 49.8	14 58.5	24 3.1	12 16.0	10 2.9	11 41.7	15 16.5	23 59.5	10 19.3	1 40.9	19 17.1
10 T	23 14 9.7	16 48.1	14 55.3	6♐14.9	13 21.4	11 14.1	12 21.0	15 21.4	24 0.6	10 17.2	1 43.1	19 18.0
11 W	23 18 6.3	17 46.5	14 52.1	18 14.6	14 24.5	12 25.3	13 0.3	15 26.1	24 1.8	10 15.0	1 45.2	19 19.0
12 T	23 22 2.9	18 44.8	14 48.9	0♑ 7.4	15 25.3	13 36.6	13 39.6	15 30.7	24 3.2	10 12.8	1 47.4	19 19.9
13 F	23 25 59.4	19 43.2	14 45.8	11 58.3	16 23.5	14 48.0	14 19.0	15 35.1	24 4.6	10 10.6	1 49.5	19 20.8
14 S	23 29 55.9	20 41.7	14 42.6	23 52.2	17 19.0	15 59.5	14 58.5	15 39.3	24 6.1	10 8.3	1 51.6	19 21.6
15 S	23 33 52.5	21 40.1	14 39.4	5♒53.0	18 11.6	17 11.0	15 38.0	15 43.3	24 7.7	10 6.1	1 53.8	19 22.5
16 M	23 37 49.1	22 38.6	14 36.2	18 4.0	19 1.1	18 22.7	16 17.5	15 47.2	24 9.4	10 3.8	1 55.9	19 23.3
17 T	23 41 45.6	23 37.1	14 33.0	0♓27.4	19 47.2	19 34.5	16 57.1	15 50.8	24 11.2	10 1.6	1 58.0	19 24.1
18 W	23 45 42.1	24 35.7	14 29.9	13 4.6	20 29.7	20 46.3	17 36.8	15 54.3	24 13.1	9 59.3	2 0.1	19 24.9
19 T	23 49 38.7	25 34.2	14 26.7	25 55.8	21 8.3	21 58.2	18 16.5	15 57.6	24 15.1	9 56.9	2 2.1	19 25.6
20 F	23 53 35.3	26 32.9	14 23.5	9♈ 0.5	21 42.8	23 10.2	18 56.2	16 0.7	24 17.1	9 54.6	2 4.2	19 26.4
21 S	23 57 31.8	27 31.5	14 20.3	22 17.7	22 12.7	24 22.3	19 36.0	16 3.7	24 19.3	9 52.3	2 6.3	19 27.1
22 S	0 1 28.4	28 30.2	14 17.2	5♉46.4	22 37.7	25 34.5	20 15.9	16 6.4	24 21.6	9 49.9	2 8.3	19 27.8
23 M	0 5 24.9	29 28.9	14 14.0	19 25.2	22 57.5	26 46.8	20 55.8	16 9.0	24 23.9	9 47.5	2 10.3	19 28.5
24 T	0 9 21.5	0♎27.6	14 10.8	3♊13.5	23 11.6	27 59.1	21 35.7	16 11.3	24 26.4	9 45.2	2 12.4	19 29.1
25 W	0 13 18.1	1 26.4	14 7.6	17 10.4	23 19.8	29 11.6	22 15.7	16 13.5	24 28.9	9 42.8	2 14.4	19 29.8
26 T	0 17 14.6	2 25.2	14 4.4	1♋15.2	23 21.5	0♍24.1	22 55.8	16 15.5	24 31.6	9 40.4	2 16.3	19 30.4
27 F	0 21 11.2	3 24.1	14 1.3	15 26.7	23R16.4	1 36.7	23 35.9	16 17.3	24 34.3	9 38.0	2 18.3	19 31.0
28 S	0 25 7.7	4 23.0	13 58.1	29 43.1	23 4.2	2 49.4	24 16.1	16 18.8	24 37.1	9 35.6	2 20.3	19 31.5
29 S	0 29 4.3	5 21.9	13 54.9	14♌ 1.5	22 44.7	4 2.1	24 56.4	16 20.2	24 40.0	9 33.2	2 22.2	19 32.1
30 M	0 33 0.8	6 20.9	13 51.7	28 18.0	22 17.5	5 14.9	25 36.6	16 21.4	24 43.0	9 30.8	2 24.1	19 32.6

DECLINATION

DAY	EPHEMERIS SIDEREAL TIME h m s	☉ ° ′	☊ ° ′	☽ ° ′	☿ ° ′	♀ ° ′	♂ ° ′	♃ ° ′	♄ ° ′	♅ ° ′	♆ ° ′	♇ ° ′
1 S	22 38 40.8	8N32.9	16N27.6	24N 4.5	1S47.9	19N32.8	2S 6.0	21N46.6	22S16.8	3N31.5	11N32.4	21N42.3
4 W	22 50 30.4	7 27.2	16 24.8	8 43.0	3 45.3	18 55.4	2 53.7	21 48.5	22 17.4	3 29.1	11 30.1	21 42.0
7 S	23 2 20.1	6 20.5	16 22.0	9S46.9	5 36.2	18 13.3	3 41.4	21 50.2	22 18.0	3 26.7	11 27.7	21 41.7
10 T	23 14 9.7	5 12.8	16 19.2	23 17.0	7 19.3	17 26.4	4 29.1	21 51.7	22 18.7	3 24.1	11 25.5	21 41.5
13 F	23 25 59.4	4 4.3	16 16.4	27 14.2	8 52.7	16 35.1	5 16.6	21 53.1	22 19.4	3 21.5	11 23.2	21 41.2
16 M	23 37 49.1	2 55.2	16 13.6	20 15.5	10 14.2	15 39.5	6 4.0	21 54.2	22 20.1	3 18.8	11 21.0	21 41.0
19 T	23 49 38.7	1 45.7	16 10.8	5 3.9	11 21.0	14 39.9	6 51.2	21 55.2	22 20.9	3 16.1	11 18.8	21 40.9
22 S	0 1 28.4	0 35.7	16 8.0	12N51.1	12 9.0	13 36.4	7 38.1	21 55.9	22 21.6	3 13.4	11 16.6	21 40.7
25 W	0 13 18.1	0S34.4	16 5.1	25 44.3	12 33.3	12 29.4	8 24.6	21 56.5	22 22.4	3 10.5	11 14.5	21 40.6
28 S	0 25 7.7	1 44.6	16 2.3	25 8.5	12 27.6	11 19.0	9 10.9	21 56.9	22 23.3	3 7.7	11 12.4	21 40.5

OCTOBER 1929

LONGITUDE

DAY	EPHEMERIS SIDEREAL TIME h m s	☉ ° ′	☊ ° ′	☽ ° ′	☿ ° ′	♀ ° ′	♂ ° ′	♃ ° ′	♄ ° ′	♅ ° ′	♆ ° ′	♇ ° ′
1 T	0 36 57.4	7♎19.9	13♉48.6	12♍28.0	21♎42.7	6♍27.8	26♎17.0	16♊22.4	24♐46.0	9♈28.3	2♍26.0	19♋33.1
2 W	0 40 53.9	8 19.0	13 45.4	26 26.9	21R 0.4	7 40.8	26 57.4	16 23.2	24 49.2	9R25.9	2 27.9	19 33.5
3 T	0 44 50.5	9 18.1	13 42.2	10♎10.4	20 11.0	8 53.8	27 37.8	16 23.8	24 52.5	9 23.5	2 29.8	19 34.0
4 F	0 48 47.0	10 17.2	13 39.0	23 35.6	19 15.0	10 6.9	28 18.3	16 24.1	24 55.8	9 21.1	2 31.6	19 34.4
5 S	0 52 43.6	11 16.3	13 35.8	6♏40.9	18 13.3	11 20.1	28 58.9	16 24.3	24 59.2	9 18.6	2 33.5	19 34.8
6 S	0 56 40.2	12 15.5	13 32.7	19 26.5	17 7.0	12 33.3	29 39.5	16R24.3	25 2.7	9 16.2	2 35.3	19 35.2
7 M	1 0 36.7	13 14.7	13 29.5	1♐53.8	15 57.7	13 46.6	0♏20.2	16 24.1	25 6.3	9 13.8	2 37.1	19 35.5
8 T	1 4 33.2	14 14.0	13 26.3	14 5.9	14 47.0	14 60.0	1 0.9	16 23.6	25 10.0	9 11.4	2 38.9	19 35.8
9 W	1 8 29.8	15 13.3	13 23.1	26 6.7	13 36.7	16 13.4	1 41.7	16 23.0	25 13.7	9 9.0	2 40.6	19 36.1
10 T	1 12 26.4	16 12.6	13 20.0	8♑ 0.5	12 29.0	17 26.9	2 22.5	16 22.2	25 17.6	9 6.6	2 42.3	19 36.4
11 F	1 16 22.9	17 11.9	13 16.8	19 52.2	11 25.6	18 40.4	3 3.4	16 21.2	25 21.5	9 4.2	2 44.0	19 36.7
12 S	1 20 19.5	18 11.3	13 13.6	1♒46.7	10 28.5	19 54.0	3 44.3	16 19.9	25 25.5	9 1.8	2 45.7	19 36.9
13 S	1 24 16.0	19 10.7	13 10.4	13 48.7	9 39.2	21 7.6	4 25.3	16 18.5	25 29.6	8 59.4	2 47.4	19 37.1
14 M	1 28 12.6	20 10.1	13 7.2	26 2.4	8 59.2	22 21.3	5 6.3	16 16.9	25 33.7	8 57.1	2 49.0	19 37.3
15 T	1 32 9.1	21 9.6	13 4.1	8♓31.2	8 29.3	23 35.1	5 47.4	16 15.0	25 37.9	8 54.7	2 50.7	19 37.4
16 W	1 36 5.7	22 9.0	13 0.9	21 17.4	8 10.2	24 48.9	6 28.5	16 13.0	25 42.2	8 52.4	2 52.3	19 37.6
17 T	1 40 2.2	23 8.6	12 57.7	4♈22.4	8 2.3	26 2.7	7 9.7	16 10.8	25 46.6	8 50.0	2 53.8	19 37.7
18 F	1 43 58.8	24 8.1	12 54.5	17 45.9	8D 5.5	27 16.6	7 51.0	16 8.3	25 51.1	8 47.7	2 55.4	19 37.8
19 S	1 47 55.4	25 7.7	12 51.4	1♉26.5	8 19.4	28 30.6	8 32.3	16 5.7	25 55.6	8 45.4	2 56.9	19 37.8
20 S	1 51 51.9	26 7.3	12 48.2	15 21.6	8 43.7	29 44.6	9 13.6	16 2.9	26 0.2	8 43.1	2 58.4	19 37.9
21 M	1 55 48.4	27 7.0	12 45.0	29 27.8	9 17.7	0♎58.7	9 55.0	15 59.9	26 4.9	8 40.9	2 59.9	19 37.9
22 T	1 59 45.0	28 6.6	12 41.8	13♊41.2	10 0.6	2 12.8	10 36.5	15 56.7	26 9.6	8 38.6	3 1.3	19R37.8
23 W	2 3 41.5	29 6.4	12 38.6	27 58.3	10 51.6	3 27.0	11 18.0	15 53.3	26 14.4	8 36.4	3 2.7	19 37.8
24 T	2 7 38.1	0♏ 6.1	12 35.5	12♋15.5	11 49.8	4 41.2	11 59.5	15 49.7	26 19.3	8 34.2	3 4.1	19 37.7
25 F	2 11 34.7	1 5.9	12 32.3	26 29.9	12 54.5	5 55.5	12 41.2	15 45.9	26 24.2	8 32.0	3 5.5	19 37.6
26 S	2 15 31.2	2 5.8	12 29.1	10♌39.2	14 4.8	7 9.8	13 22.8	15 41.9	26 29.3	8 29.8	3 6.8	19 37.5
27 S	2 19 27.8	3 5.6	12 25.9	24 41.3	15 20.0	8 24.2	14 4.6	15 37.8	26 34.3	8 27.7	3 8.2	19 37.4
28 M	2 23 24.3	4 5.6	12 22.8	8♍34.5	16 39.4	9 38.6	14 46.4	15 33.4	26 39.5	8 25.6	3 9.4	19 37.2
29 T	2 27 20.9	5 5.5	12 19.6	22 17.1	18 2.4	10 53.0	15 28.2	15 28.9	26 44.7	8 23.5	3 10.7	19 37.0
30 W	2 31 17.4	6 5.5	12 16.4	5♎47.8	19 28.3	12 7.5	16 10.1	15 24.2	26 50.0	8 21.4	3 11.9	19 36.8
31 T	2 35 14.0	7 5.5	12 13.2	19 5.2	20 56.7	13 22.0	16 52.1	15 19.4	26 55.3	8 19.4	3 13.1	19 36.6

DECLINATION

DAY	EPHEMERIS SIDEREAL TIME h m s	☉ ° ′	☊ ° ′	☽ ° ′	☿ ° ′	♀ ° ′	♂ ° ′	♃ ° ′	♄ ° ′	♅ ° ′	♆ ° ′	♇ ° ′
1 T	0 36 57.4	2S54.7	15N59.5	11N 2.0	11S45.4	10N 5.6	9S56.7	21N57.2	22S24.1	3N 4.9	11N10.4	21N40.4
4 F	0 48 47.0	4 4.5	15 56.6	7S36.2	10 23.3	8 49.5	10 42.0	21 57.2	22 25.0	3 2.0	11 8.5	21 40.4
7 M	1 0 36.7	5 13.9	15 53.8	22 15.9	8 26.3	7 31.0	11 26.7	21 57.1	22 25.8	2 59.2	11 6.6	21 40.4
10 T	1 12 26.4	6 22.7	15 50.9	27 31.4	6 12.3	6 10.3	12 10.9	21 56.8	22 26.7	2 56.4	11 4.7	21 40.4
13 S	1 24 16.0	7 30.7	15 48.0	21 41.8	4 9.2	4 47.8	12 54.4	21 56.3	22 27.6	2 53.6	11 3.0	21 40.5
16 W	1 36 5.7	8 37.8	15 45.1	7 12.1	2 43.0	3 23.8	13 37.2	21 55.7	22 28.4	2 50.8	11 1.3	21 40.6
19 S	1 47 55.4	9 43.7	15 42.3	11N 3.6	2 6.7	1 58.6	14 19.1	21 54.9	22 29.3	2 48.2	10 59.7	21 40.7
22 T	1 59 45.0	10 48.4	15 39.4	25 11.6	2 19.7	0 32.6	15 0.2	21 53.9	22 30.1	2 45.5	10 58.2	21 40.9
25 F	2 11 34.7	11 51.7	15 36.5	25 50.8	3 13.1	0S54.1	15 40.4	21 52.8	22 31.0	2 43.0	10 56.7	21 41.0
28 M	2 23 24.3	12 53.3	15 33.6	12 44.4	4 35.5	2 21.0	16 19.6	21 51.5	22 31.8	2 40.5	10 55.4	21 41.3
31 T	2 35 14.0	13 53.2	15 30.6	5S33.4	6 16.2	3 47.7	16 57.7	21 50.0	22 32.5	2 38.1	10 54.1	21 41.5

NOVEMBER 1929

LONGITUDE

DAY	EPHEMERIS SIDEREAL TIME	☉	☊	☽	☿	♀	♂	♃	♄	♅	♆	♇
	h m s	° ′	° ′	° ′	° ′	° ′	° ′	° ′	° ′	° ′	° ′	° ′
1 F	2 39 10.6	8♏ 5.6	12♉10.1	2♏ 8.5	22♎27.2	14♎36.6	17♏34.1	15♊14.3	27♐ 0.7	8♈17.4	3♍14.3	19♋36.3
2 S	2 43 7.1	9 5.7	12 6.9	14 57.1	23 59.4	15 51.2	18 16.2	15R 9.1	27 6.2	8R15.4	3 15.5	19R36.0
3 S	2 47 3.7	10 5.8	12 3.7	27 31.3	25 32.9	17 5.9	18 58.3	15 3.7	27 11.7	8 13.4	3 16.6	19 35.7
4 M	2 51 0.2	11 5.9	12 0.5	9♐52.0	27 7.5	18 20.5	19 40.5	14 58.2	27 17.3	8 11.5	3 17.6	19 35.4
5 T	2 54 56.8	12 6.1	11 57.3	22 0.8	28 42.9	19 35.2	20 22.7	14 52.5	27 22.9	8 9.6	3 18.7	19 35.0
6 W	2 58 53.3	13 6.3	11 54.2	4♑ 0.3	0♏18.9	20 50.0	21 5.0	14 46.6	27 28.6	8 7.8	3 19.7	19 34.6
7 T	3 2 49.9	14 6.5	11 51.0	15 53.8	1 55.4	22 4.8	21 47.3	14 40.6	27 34.3	8 5.9	3 20.7	19 34.2
8 F	3 6 46.5	15 6.8	11 47.8	27 45.0	3 32.2	23 19.5	22 29.7	14 34.5	27 40.1	8 4.1	3 21.7	19 33.8
9 S	3 10 43.0	16 7.0	11 44.6	9♒38.3	5 9.2	24 34.4	23 12.2	14 28.2	27 46.0	8 2.4	3 22.6	19 33.4
10 S	3 14 39.5	17 7.3	11 41.5	21 38.3	6 46.3	25 49.2	23 54.7	14 21.7	27 51.9	8 0.7	3 23.5	19 32.9
11 M	3 18 36.1	18 7.7	11 38.3	3♓49.8	8 23.4	27 4.1	24 37.2	14 15.2	27 57.8	7 59.0	3 24.4	19 32.4
12 T	3 22 32.7	19 8.0	11 35.1	16 17.1	10 0.5	28 19.0	25 19.8	14 8.5	28 3.9	7 57.3	3 25.2	19 31.9
13 W	3 26 29.2	20 8.4	11 31.9	29 4.2	11 37.5	29 33.9	26 2.5	14 1.7	28 9.9	7 55.7	3 26.0	19 31.3
14 T	3 30 25.8	21 8.8	11 28.8	12♈13.7	13 14.4	0♏48.9	26 45.2	13 54.7	28 16.0	7 54.1	3 26.8	19 30.8
15 F	3 34 22.3	22 9.2	11 25.6	25 47.2	14 51.1	2 3.9	27 27.9	13 47.7	28 22.1	7 52.6	3 27.5	19 30.2
16 S	3 38 18.9	23 9.7	11 22.4	9♉44.1	16 27.7	3 18.9	28 10.7	13 40.5	28 28.3	7 51.1	3 28.2	19 29.6
17 S	3 42 15.5	24 10.1	11 19.2	24 1.6	18 4.0	4 33.9	28 53.6	13 33.2	28 34.6	7 49.7	3 28.9	19 28.9
18 M	3 46 12.0	25 10.6	11 16.0	8♊35.2	19 40.2	5 48.9	29 36.5	13 25.9	28 40.9	7 48.2	3 29.5	19 28.3
19 T	3 50 8.6	26 11.1	11 12.9	23 18.2	21 16.2	7 4.0	0♐19.5	13 18.4	28 47.2	7 46.9	3 30.1	19 27.6
20 W	3 54 5.1	27 11.7	11 9.7	8♋ 3.7	22 51.9	8 19.1	1 2.5	13 10.8	28 53.5	7 45.5	3 30.7	19 26.9
21 T	3 58 1.7	28 12.3	11 6.5	22 44.5	24 27.5	9 34.2	1 45.6	13 3.2	28 59.9	7 44.2	3 31.2	19 26.2
22 F	4 1 58.3	29 12.9	11 3.3	7♌14.7	26 2.8	10 49.4	2 28.7	12 55.5	29 6.4	7 43.0	3 31.7	19 25.5
23 S	4 5 54.8	0♐13.5	11 0.2	21 30.2	27 38.0	12 4.5	3 11.9	12 47.7	29 12.9	7 41.8	3 32.2	19 24.7
24 S	4 9 51.3	1 14.2	10 57.0	5♍28.7	29 13.0	13 19.7	3 55.1	12 39.8	29 19.4	7 40.6	3 32.6	19 23.9
25 M	4 13 47.9	2 14.9	10 53.8	19 9.5	0♐47.9	14 34.9	4 38.4	12 31.9	29 25.9	7 39.5	3 33.0	19 23.1
26 T	4 17 44.5	3 15.6	10 50.6	2♎33.2	2 22.6	15 50.1	5 21.8	12 23.9	29 32.5	7 38.4	3 33.4	19 22.3
27 W	4 21 41.0	4 16.4	10 47.5	15 41.1	3 57.1	17 5.4	6 5.2	12 15.9	29 39.1	7 37.4	3 33.7	19 21.5
28 T	4 25 37.6	5 17.1	10 44.3	28 34.7	5 31.5	18 20.6	6 48.6	12 7.8	29 45.8	7 36.4	3 34.0	19 20.6
29 F	4 29 34.1	6 17.9	10 41.1	11♏15.5	7 5.9	19 35.9	7 32.1	11 59.7	29 52.5	7 35.5	3 34.3	19 19.8
30 S	4 33 30.7	7 18.7	10 37.9	23 44.9	8 40.1	20 51.2	8 15.7	11 51.6	29 59.2	7 34.6	3 34.5	19 18.9

DECLINATION

DAY	EPHEMERIS SIDEREAL TIME	☉	☊	☽	☿	♀	♂	♃	♄	♅	♆	♇
1 F	2 39 10.6	14S12.7	15N29.7	11S21.4	6S52.3	4S16.6	17S10.2	21N49.4	22S32.8	2N37.3	10N53.7	21N41.6
4 M	2 51 0.2	15 9.9	15 26.8	24 22.4	8 45.1	5 42.7	17 46.7	21 47.7	22 33.5	2 35.1	10 52.6	21 41.9
7 T	3 2 49.9	16 4.8	15 23.8	27 12.6	10 40.4	7 7.9	18 22.1	21 45.8	22 34.2	2 33.0	10 51.6	21 42.2
10 S	3 14 39.5	16 57.3	15 20.9	19 13.6	12 34.6	8 31.8	18 56.1	21 43.8	22 34.9	2 31.0	10 50.7	21 42.6
13 W	3 26 29.2	17 47.2	15 18.0	3 41.2	14 25.2	9 54.1	19 28.8	21 41.6	22 35.5	2 29.1	10 49.8	21 43.0
16 S	3 38 18.9	18 34.3	15 15.0	14N31.2	16 10.5	11 14.5	19 60.0	21 39.3	22 36.1	2 27.4	10 49.1	21 43.4
19 T	3 50 8.6	19 18.4	15 12.0	26 44.7	17 49.1	12 32.5	20 29.6	21 36.8	22 36.6	2 25.8	10 48.5	21 43.8
22 F	4 1 58.3	19 59.5	15 9.1	23 31.9	19 20.2	13 47.9	20 57.7	21 34.2	22 37.1	2 24.3	10 48.0	21 44.3
25 M	4 13 47.9	20 37.2	15 6.1	8 9.2	20 42.9	15 0.3	21 24.1	21 31.5	22 37.5	2 23.1	10 47.7	21 44.8
28 T	4 25 37.6	21 11.5	15 3.2	9S49.2	21 56.4	16 9.2	21 48.7	21 28.7	22 37.9	2 21.9	10 47.4	21 45.3

DECEMBER 1929

LONGITUDE

DAY	EPHEMERIS SIDEREAL TIME	☉	☊	☽	☿	♀	♂	♃	♄	♅	♆	♇
1 S	4 37 27.3	8♐19.6	10♉34.8	6♐ 4.3	10♐14.3	22♏ 6.5	8♐59.3	11♊43.4	0♑ 5.9	7♈33.8	3♍34.7	19♋18.0
2 M	4 41 23.8	9 20.4	10 31.6	18 14.6	11 48.4	23 21.8	9 43.0	11R35.2	0 12.7	7R33.0	3 34.9	19R17.1
3 T	4 45 20.4	10 21.3	10 28.4	0♑17.2	13 22.5	24 37.2	10 26.7	11 27.0	0 19.5	7 32.3	3 35.0	19 16.1
4 W	4 49 16.9	11 22.2	10 25.2	12 13.6	14 56.5	25 52.5	11 10.5	11 18.9	0 26.3	7 31.6	3 35.1	19 15.2
5 T	4 53 13.5	12 23.1	10 22.0	24 5.8	16 30.5	27 7.9	11 54.3	11 10.7	0 33.2	7 30.9	3 35.1	19 14.2
6 F	4 57 10.1	13 24.0	10 18.9	5♒56.4	18 4.5	28 23.2	12 38.2	11 2.5	0 40.1	7 30.3	3 35.2	19 13.2
7 S	5 1 6.6	14 25.0	10 15.7	17 48.5	19 38.5	29 38.6	13 22.1	10 54.3	0 47.0	7 29.8	3R35.2	19 12.2
8 S	5 5 3.2	15 25.9	10 12.5	29 46.1	21 12.5	0♐53.9	14 6.0	10 46.2	0 53.9	7 29.3	3 35.1	19 11.2
9 M	5 8 59.7	16 26.9	10 9.3	11♓53.4	22 46.6	2 9.3	14 50.1	10 38.1	1 0.8	7 28.9	3 35.0	19 10.1
10 T	5 12 56.3	17 27.9	10 6.2	24 15.1	24 20.7	3 24.7	15 34.1	10 30.0	1 7.8	7 28.5	3 34.9	19 9.1
11 W	5 16 52.9	18 28.9	10 3.0	6♈55.9	25 54.8	4 40.1	16 18.2	10 21.9	1 14.8	7 28.1	3 34.8	19 8.0
12 T	5 20 49.4	19 29.8	9 59.8	20 0.1	27 28.9	5 55.5	17 2.4	10 14.0	1 21.7	7 27.9	3 34.6	19 6.9
13 F	5 24 45.9	20 30.8	9 56.6	3♉31.0	29 3.1	7 10.9	17 46.6	10 6.0	1 28.7	7 27.6	3 34.4	19 5.8
14 S	5 28 42.5	21 31.9	9 53.5	17 30.1	0♑37.4	8 26.3	18 30.9	9 58.1	1 35.8	7 27.4	3 34.1	19 4.7
15 S	5 32 39.1	22 32.9	9 50.3	1♊56.3	2 11.6	9 41.7	19 15.2	9 50.3	1 42.8	7 27.3	3 33.8	19 3.6
16 M	5 36 35.7	23 33.9	9 47.1	16 45.5	3 45.9	10 57.1	19 59.5	9 42.6	1 49.8	7 27.2	3 33.5	19 2.5
17 T	5 40 32.2	24 34.9	9 43.9	1♋50.6	5 20.2	12 12.5	20 43.9	9 34.9	1 56.9	7 27.2	3 33.2	19 1.4
18 W	5 44 28.7	25 36.0	9 40.7	17 1.8	6 54.4	13 28.0	21 28.3	9 27.3	2 3.9	7D27.2	3 32.8	19 0.2
19 T	5 48 25.3	26 37.1	9 37.6	2♌ 8.8	8 28.6	14 43.4	22 12.8	9 19.9	2 11.0	7 27.3	3 32.3	18 59.0
20 F	5 52 21.9	27 38.1	9 34.4	17 2.1	10 2.6	15 58.8	22 57.4	9 12.5	2 18.1	7 27.4	3 31.9	18 57.9
21 S	5 56 18.4	28 39.2	9 31.2	1♍34.6	11 36.5	17 14.3	23 42.0	9 5.2	2 25.2	7 27.6	3 31.4	18 56.7
22 S	6 0 15.0	29 40.3	9 28.0	15 42.3	13 10.2	18 29.7	24 26.6	8 58.0	2 32.3	7 27.8	3 30.9	18 55.5
23 M	6 4 11.5	0♑41.4	9 24.9	29 24.5	14 43.6	19 45.2	25 11.3	8 50.9	2 39.3	7 28.1	3 30.3	18 54.3
24 T	6 8 8.1	1 42.6	9 21.7	12♎42.4	16 16.5	21 0.7	25 56.1	8 43.9	2 46.4	7 28.4	3 29.8	18 53.1
25 W	6 12 4.7	2 43.7	9 18.5	25 39.0	17 49.0	22 16.1	26 40.9	8 37.0	2 53.5	7 28.8	3 29.2	18 51.9
26 T	6 16 1.2	3 44.8	9 15.3	8♏17.8	19 20.7	23 31.6	27 25.7	8 30.3	3 0.6	7 29.2	3 28.5	18 50.6
27 F	6 19 57.8	4 46.0	9 12.2	20 42.6	20 51.7	24 47.1	28 10.6	8 23.7	3 7.7	7 29.7	3 27.8	18 49.4
28 S	6 23 54.3	5 47.2	9 9.0	2♐56.5	22 21.6	26 2.6	28 55.5	8 17.2	3 14.8	7 30.2	3 27.1	18 48.2
29 S	6 27 50.9	6 48.3	9 5.8	15 2.5	23 50.3	27 18.1	29 40.5	8 10.9	3 21.9	7 30.8	3 26.4	18 46.9
30 M	6 31 47.5	7 49.5	9 2.6	27 2.6	25 17.5	28 33.5	0♑25.5	8 4.7	3 29.0	7 31.5	3 25.6	18 45.7
31 T	6 35 44.0	8 50.7	8 59.5	8♑58.5	26 42.8	29 49.0	1 10.6	7 58.7	3 36.1	7 32.2	3 24.8	18 44.4

DECLINATION

DAY	EPHEMERIS SIDEREAL TIME	☉	☊	☽	☿	♀	♂	♃	♄	♅	♆	♇
1 S	4 37 27.3	21S42.3	15N 0.2	23S25.4	23S 0.2	17S14.5	22S11.5	21N25.8	22S38.2	2N21.0	10N47.2	21N45.9
4 W	4 49 16.9	22 9.3	14 57.2	27 23.4	23 53.5	18 15.6	22 32.5	21 22.8	22 38.4	2 20.2	10 47.2	21 46.5
7 S	5 1 6.6	22 32.4	14 54.2	20 24.7	24 35.7	19 12.2	22 51.5	21 19.8	22 38.6	2 19.6	10 47.2	21 47.1
10 T	5 12 56.3	22 51.5	14 51.2	5 47.6	25 6.3	20 4.0	23 8.5	21 16.8	22 38.7	2 19.2	10 47.4	21 47.7
13 F	5 24 45.9	23 6.6	14 48.2	12N 0.2	25 24.6	20 50.8	23 23.4	21 13.9	22 38.7	2 19.0	10 47.7	21 48.3
16 M	5 36 35.7	23 17.6	14 45.2	25 45.1	25 30.0	21 32.1	23 36.2	21 11.0	22 38.7	2 18.9	10 48.1	21 49.0
19 T	5 48 25.3	23 24.4	14 42.2	24 37.5	25 22.1	22 7.8	23 46.9	21 8.1	22 38.6	2 19.1	10 48.6	21 49.6
22 S	6 0 15.0	23 27.0	14 39.1	9 31.8	25 0.5	22 37.5	23 55.3	21 5.3	22 38.4	2 19.4	10 49.2	21 50.3
25 W	6 12 4.7	23 25.3	14 36.1	8S39.1	24 25.2	23 1.1	24 1.4	21 2.7	22 38.2	2 19.9	10 49.9	21 51.0
28 S	6 23 54.3	23 19.4	14 33.1	22 38.0	23 36.5	23 18.4	24 5.3	21 0.2	22 37.9	2 20.6	10 50.8	21 51.7
31 T	6 35 44.0	23 9.3	14 30.0	27 26.9	22 35.6	23 29.3	24 6.9	20 57.8	22 37.6	2 21.4	10 51.7	21 52.4

JANUARY 1930

DAY	EPHEMERIS SIDEREAL TIME h m s	☉ ° ′	☊ ° ′	☽ ° ′	☿ ° ′	♀ ° ′	♂ ° ′	♃ ° ′	♄ ° ′	♅ ° ′	♆ ° ′	♇ ° ′
						LONGITUDE						
1 W	6 39 40.6	9♑51.9	8♉56.3	20♑51.6	28♑ 6.0	1♑ 4.5	1♑55.7	7♊52.8	3♑43.2	7♈32.9	3♍24.0	18♋43.2
2 T	6 43 37.1	10 53.0	8 53.1	2♒43.2	29 26.5	2 20.0	2 40.8	7R47.1	3 50.2	7 33.7	3R23.1	18R41.9
3 F	6 47 33.7	11 54.2	8 49.9	14 34.9	0♒43.9	3 35.5	3 26.0	7 41.5	3 57.3	7 34.6	3 22.3	18 40.6
4 S	6 51 30.3	12 55.4	8 46.8	26 28.7	1 57.7	4 51.0	4 11.3	7 36.1	4 4.4	7 35.5	3 21.3	18 39.4
5 S	6 55 26.8	13 56.6	8 43.6	8♓27.1	3 7.2	6 6.4	4 56.6	7 30.9	4 11.4	7 36.4	3 20.4	18 38.1
6 M	6 59 23.4	14 57.7	8 40.4	20 33.4	4 11.7	7 21.9	5 41.9	7 25.8	4 18.4	7 37.4	3 19.4	18 36.8
7 T	7 3 19.9	15 58.9	8 37.2	2♈51.6	5 10.5	8 37.4	6 27.2	7 20.9	4 25.4	7 38.4	3 18.4	18 35.5
8 W	7 7 16.5	17 0.0	8 34.1	15 26.1	6 2.8	9 52.8	7 12.6	7 16.2	4 32.4	7 39.5	3 17.4	18 34.3
9 T	7 11 13.1	18 1.2	8 30.9	28 21.7	6 47.6	11 8.3	7 58.1	7 11.7	4 39.4	7 40.7	3 16.3	18 33.0
10 F	7 15 9.6	19 2.3	8 27.7	11♉42.5	7 24.1	12 23.7	8 43.5	7 7.3	4 46.4	7 41.9	3 15.3	18 31.7
11 S	7 19 6.2	20 3.4	8 24.5	25 31.8	7 51.4	13 39.2	9 29.1	7 3.1	4 53.3	7 43.1	3 14.1	18 30.4
12 S	7 23 2.7	21 4.6	8 21.3	9♊50.7	8 8.6	14 54.6	10 14.6	6 59.2	5 0.2	7 44.4	3 13.0	18 29.1
13 M	7 26 59.3	22 5.7	8 18.2	24 37.2	8 15.0	16 10.1	11 0.2	6 55.4	5 7.1	7 45.8	3 11.9	18 27.9
14 T	7 30 55.8	23 6.8	8 15.0	9♋45.6	8R!0.0	17 25.5	11 45.8	6 51.8	5 14.0	7 47.2	3 10.7	18 26.6
15 W	7 34 52.4	24 7.9	8 11.8	25 6.6	7 53.2	18 40.9	12 31.5	6 48.4	5 20.9	7 48.6	3 9.5	18 25.3
16 T	7 38 49.0	25 8.9	8 8.6	10♌28.6	7 24.8	19 56.4	13 17.2	6 45.2	5 27.7	7 50.1	3 8.2	18 24.0
17 F	7 42 45.5	26 10.0	8 5.5	25 39.8	6 44.9	21 11.8	14 2.9	6 42.1	5 34.5	7 51.6	3 7.0	18 22.8
18 S	7 46 42.1	27 11.1	8 2.3	10♍30.1	5 54.5	22 27.2	14 48.7	6 39.3	5 41.3	7 53.2	3 5.7	18 21.5
19 S	7 50 38.6	28 12.1	7 59.1	24 53.1	4 54.8	23 42.6	15 34.5	6 36.7	5 48.0	7 54.8	3 4.4	18 20.2
20 M	7 54 35.2	29 13.2	7 55.9	8♎46.2	3 47.5	24 58.0	16 20.4	6 34.3	5 54.8	7 56.5	3 3.1	18 19.0
21 T	7 58 31.7	0♒14.2	7 52.8	22 10.0	2 34.6	26 13.4	17 6.3	6 32.0	6 1.5	7 58.2	3 1.8	18 17.7
22 W	8 2 28.3	1 15.3	7 49.6	5♏ 7.5	1 18.4	27 28.8	17 52.2	6 30.0	6 8.1	7 60.0	3 0.4	18 16.5
23 T	8 6 24.9	2 16.3	7 46.4	17 43.2	0 1.3	28 44.2	18 38.2	6 28.2	6 14.8	8 1.8	2 59.1	18 15.2
24 F	8 10 21.4	3 17.4	7 43.2	0♐ 1.8	28♑45.5	29 59.6	19 24.2	6 26.6	6 21.4	8 3.6	2 57.7	18 14.0
25 S	8 14 18.0	4 18.4	7 40.0	12 8.1	27 33.1	1♒15.0	20 10.2	6 25.2	6 27.9	8 5.5	2 56.2	18 12.8
26 S	8 18 14.5	5 19.4	7 36.9	24 6.2	26 26.0	2 30.4	20 56.3	6 24.0	6 34.5	8 7.4	2 54.8	18 11.6
27 M	8 22 11.1	6 20.4	7 33.7	5♑59.6	25 25.7	3 45.8	21 42.4	6 23.0	6 41.0	8 9.4	2 53.4	18 10.3
28 T	8 26 7.7	7 21.4	7 30.5	17 51.0	24 33.0	5 1.2	22 28.6	6 22.2	6 47.4	8 11.5	2 51.9	18 9.1
29 W	8 30 4.2	8 22.3	7 27.3	29 42.5	23 48.7	6 16.6	23 14.7	6 21.6	6 53.8	8 13.5	2 50.4	18 7.9
30 T	8 34 0.8	9 23.3	7 24.2	11♒35.4	23 13.2	7 31.9	24 0.9	6 21.2	7 0.2	8 15.6	2 48.9	18 6.8
31 F	8 37 57.3	10 24.2	7 21.0	23 31.2	22 46.4	8 47.3	24 47.2	6 21.0	7 6.6	8 17.8	2 47.4	18 5.6
						DECLINATION						
1 W	6 39 40.6	23S 5.0	14N29.0	26S32.1	22S12.9	23S31.5	24S 6.9	20N57.1	22S37.4	2N21.8	10N52.0	21N52.6
4 S	6 51 30.3	22 49.3	14 26.0	17 14.3	20 59.3	23 33.7	24 5.3	20 55.1	22 37.0	2 22.9	10 53.0	21 53.3
7 T	7 3 19.9	22 29.6	14 22.9	1 38.4	19 41.6	23 29.3	24 1.4	20 53.2	22 36.5	2 24.2	10 54.2	21 54.0
10 F	7 15 9.6	22 5.8	14 19.9	15N32.5	18 26.7	23 18.3	23 55.0	20 51.7	22 35.9	2 25.6	10 55.4	21 54.8
13 M	7 26 59.3	21 38.2	14 16.8	26 55.0	17 24.0	23 0.8	23 46.4	20 50.4	22 35.3	2 27.3	10 56.7	21 55.5
16 T	7 38 49.0	21 6.8	14 13.7	22 26.2	16 42.8	22 37.0	23 35.3	20 49.3	22 34.6	2 29.1	10 58.1	21 56.2
19 S	7 50 38.6	20 31.8	14 10.6	5 12.8	16 29.1	22 7.0	23 21.9	20 48.6	22 33.9	2 31.1	10 59.5	21 56.9
22 W	8 2 28.3	19 53.3	14 7.6	12S58.4	16 41.1	21 30.9	23 6.1	20 48.1	22 33.1	2 33.2	11 1.0	21 57.6
25 S	8 14 18.0	19 11.5	14 4.5	25 2.3	17 10.7	20 49.0	22 48.1	20 48.0	22 32.3	2 35.5	11 2.6	21 58.3
28 T	8 26 7.7	18 26.5	14 1.4	26 54.5	17 48.1	20 1.5	22 27.7	20 48.2	22 31.4	2 37.9	11 4.2	21 59.0
31 F	8 37 57.3	17 38.4	13 58.3	18 11.6	18 26.1	19 8.8	22 5.1	20 48.7	22 30.5	2 40.5	11 5.9	21 59.6

FEBRUARY 1930

DAY	EPHEMERIS SIDEREAL TIME h m s	☉ ° ′	☊ ° ′	☽ ° ′	☿ ° ′	♀ ° ′	♂ ° ′	♃ ° ′	♄ ° ′	♅ ° ′	♆ ° ′	♇ ° ′
						LONGITUDE						
1 S	8 41 53.9	11♒25.2	7♉17.8	5♓30.8	22♑28.4	10♒ 2.6	25♑33.4	6♊21.0	7♑12.8	8♈19.9	2♍45.9	18♋ 4.4
2 S	8 45 50.4	12 26.1	7 14.6	17 35.8	22R18.6	11 18.0	26 19.7	6D21.3	7 19.1	8 22.2	2R44.3	18R 3.3
3 M	8 49 47.0	13 26.9	7 11.5	29 48.2	22 16.8	12 33.3	27 6.1	6 21.7	7 25.3	8 24.4	2 42.8	18 2.1
4 T	8 53 43.5	14 27.8	7 8.3	12♈10.6	22D22.5	13 48.6	27 52.4	6 22.4	7 31.5	8 26.7	2 41.2	18 1.0
5 W	8 57 40.1	15 28.6	7 5.1	24 46.2	22 35.1	15 3.9	28 38.8	6 23.2	7 37.6	8 29.1	2 39.6	17 59.9
6 T	9 1 36.7	16 29.5	7 1.9	7♉39.0	22 54.2	16 19.2	29 25.2	6 24.3	7 43.6	8 31.5	2 38.0	17 58.8
7 F	9 5 33.2	17 30.2	6 58.7	20 52.6	23 19.2	17 34.5	0♒11.6	6 25.5	7 49.7	8 33.9	2 36.4	17 57.7
8 S	9 9 29.7	18 31.0	6 55.6	4♊30.7	23 49.7	18 49.7	0 58.0	6 27.0	7 55.6	8 36.3	2 34.8	17 56.6
9 S	9 13 26.3	19 31.7	6 52.4	18 35.2	24 25.2	20 5.0	1 44.5	6 28.6	8 1.5	8 38.8	2 33.2	17 55.5
10 M	9 17 22.9	20 32.4	6 49.2	3♋ 6.1	25 5.3	21 20.2	2 31.0	6 30.5	8 7.4	8 41.3	2 31.6	17 54.5
11 T	9 21 19.5	21 33.1	6 46.0	17 60.0	25 49.6	22 35.4	3 17.5	6 32.6	8 13.2	8 43.9	2 29.9	17 53.4
12 W	9 25 16.0	22 33.8	6 42.9	3♌!0.0	26 37.8	23 50.6	4 4.0	6 34.8	8 19.0	8 46.5	2 28.3	17 52.4
13 T	9 29 12.5	23 34.4	6 39.7	18 26.3	27 29.5	25 5.8	4 50.6	6 37.3	8 24.7	8 49.1	2 26.6	17 51.4
14 F	9 33 9.1	24 35.0	6 36.5	3♍37.6	28 24.4	26 21.0	5 37.2	6 39.9	8 30.3	8 51.7	2 25.0	17 50.4
15 S	9 37 5.7	25 35.6	6 33.3	18 33.3	29 22.4	27 36.2	6 23.8	6 42.7	8 35.9	8 54.4	2 23.3	17 49.4
16 S	9 41 2.2	26 36.2	6 30.2	3♎ 5.1	0♒23.1	28 51.3	7 10.4	6 45.8	8 41.4	8 57.2	2 21.7	17 48.5
17 M	9 44 58.8	27 36.7	6 27.0	17 8.3	1 26.4	0♓ 6.5	7 57.1	6 49.0	8 46.9	8 59.9	2 20.0	17 47.5
18 T	9 48 55.3	28 37.2	6 23.8	0♏41.7	2 32.0	1 21.6	8 43.7	6 52.4	8 52.3	9 2.7	2 18.3	17 46.6
19 W	9 52 51.9	29 37.7	6 20.6	13 47.0	3 39.9	2 36.7	9 30.4	6 56.0	8 57.6	9 5.5	2 16.6	17 45.7
20 T	9 56 48.4	0♓38.2	6 17.4	26 27.8	4 49.8	3 51.8	10 17.2	6 59.8	9 2.9	9 8.3	2 15.0	17 44.8
21 F	10 0 45.0	1 38.6	6 14.3	8♐48.9	6 1.6	5 6.9	11 3.9	7 3.7	9 8.1	9 11.2	2 13.3	17 43.9
22 S	10 4 41.5	2 39.1	6 11.1	20 55.3	7 15.3	6 22.0	11 50.6	7 7.9	9 13.3	9 14.1	2 11.6	17 43.0
23 S	10 8 38.1	3 39.5	6 7.9	2♑52.1	8 30.7	7 37.0	12 37.4	7 12.2	9 18.4	9 17.0	2 9.9	17 42.2
24 M	10 12 34.7	4 39.9	6 4.7	14 43.7	9 47.6	8 52.1	13 24.2	7 16.7	9 23.4	9 19.9	2 8.2	17 41.4
25 T	10 16 31.2	5 40.2	6 1.6	26 34.0	11 6.2	10 7.1	14 11.0	7 21.4	9 28.4	9 22.9	2 6.6	17 40.6
26 W	10 20 27.8	6 40.6	5 58.4	8♒26.1	12 26.2	11 22.2	14 57.8	7 26.2	9 33.3	9 25.9	2 4.9	17 39.8
27 T	10 24 24.3	7 40.9	5 55.2	20 22.2	13 47.6	12 37.2	15 44.7	7 31.3	9 38.1	9 28.9	2 3.2	17 39.0
28 F	10 28 20.9	8 41.1	5 52.0	2♓24.2	15 10.4	13 52.2	16 31.5	7 36.5	9 42.8	9 32.0	2 1.5	17 38.3
						DECLINATION						
1 S	8 41 53.9	17S21.8	13N57.2	13S33.8	18S38.1	18S50.1	21S57.1	20N48.9	22S30.2	2N41.4	11N 6.5	21N59.8
4 T	8 53 43.5	16 30.0	13 54.1	2N54.9	19 10.1	17 50.8	21 31.5	20 49.8	22 29.3	2 44.1	11 8.2	22 0.5
7 F	9 5 33.2	15 35.7	13 51.0	19 12.5	19 34.7	16 46.9	21 3.9	20 51.0	22 28.3	2 47.0	11 10.0	22 1.1
10 M	9 17 22.9	14 39.0	13 47.9	27 37.7	19 50.4	15 38.8	20 34.1	20 52.5	22 27.3	2 50.1	11 11.8	22 1.8
13 T	9 29 12.5	13 40.1	13 44.7	19 57.6	19 56.1	14 26.8	20 2.4	20 54.3	22 26.3	2 53.2	11 13.6	22 2.4
16 S	9 41 2.2	12 39.2	13 41.6	1 14.6	19 51.2	13 11.3	19 28.7	20 56.4	22 25.3	2 56.4	11 15.4	22 3.0
19 W	9 52 51.9	11 36.5	13 38.5	16S42.6	19 35.1	11 52.5	18 53.1	20 58.8	22 24.3	2 59.8	11 17.3	22 3.5
22 S	10 4 41.5	10 32.1	13 35.3	26 46.3	19 7.7	10 30.9	18 15.7	21 1.4	22 23.2	3 3.2	11 19.1	22 4.1
25 T	10 16 31.2	9 26.2	13 32.2	25 45.8	18 28.6	9 6.8	17 36.5	21 4.2	22 22.2	3 6.8	11 21.0	22 4.6
28 F	10 28 20.9	8 19.0	13 29.0	14 47.6	17 38.0	7 40.6	16 55.7	21 7.3	22 21.2	3 10.4	11 22.8	22 5.1

MARCH 1930

DAY	EPHEMERIS SIDEREAL TIME	☉	☊	☽	☿	♀	♂	♃	♄	♅	♆	♇
	h m s	° ′	° ′	° ′	° ′	° ′	° ′	° ′	° ′	° ′	° ′	° ′
						LONGITUDE						
1 S	10 32 17.4	9♓41.4	5♉48.8	14♓33.1	16♒34.5	15♓ 7.1	17♒18.4	7♊41.9	9♑47.5	9♈35.1	1♍59.9	17♋37.6
2 S	10 36 14.0	10 41.6	5 45.7	26 50.0	17 59.8	16 22.1	18 5.2	7 47.4	9 52.1	9 38.1	1R58.2	17R36.9
3 M	10 40 10.5	11 41.8	5 42.5	9♈15.7	19 26.5	17 37.0	18 52.1	7 53.2	9 56.6	9 41.2	1 56.6	17 36.2
4 T	10 44 7.1	12 42.0	5 39.3	21 51.6	20 54.3	18 52.0	19 39.0	7 59.0	10 1.1	9 44.4	1 54.9	17 35.5
5 W	10 48 3.6	13 42.1	5 36.1	4♉39.2	22 23.3	20 6.9	20 25.9	8 5.1	10 5.5	9 47.5	1 53.3	17 34.9
6 T	10 52 0.2	14 42.2	5 33.0	17 40.6	23 53.6	21 21.7	21 12.8	8 11.3	10 9.8	9 50.7	1 51.7	17 34.3
7 F	10 55 56.8	15 42.2	5 29.8	0♊58.1	25 25.0	22 36.6	21 59.7	8 17.7	10 14.0	9 53.9	1 50.0	17 33.7
8 S	10 59 53.3	16 42.2	5 26.6	14 33.7	26 57.5	23 51.4	22 46.6	8 24.2	10 18.1	9 57.1	1 48.4	17 33.1
9 S	11 3 49.8	17 42.2	5 23.4	28 29.0	28 31.3	25 6.2	23 33.6	8 30.9	10 22.2	10 0.3	1 46.8	17 32.5
10 M	11 7 46.4	18 42.2	5 20.2	12♋44.2	0♓ 6.1	26 21.0	24 20.5	8 37.8	10 26.2	10 3.6	1 45.2	17 32.0
11 T	11 11 43.0	19 42.1	5 17.1	27 17.2	1 42.2	27 35.8	25 7.4	8 44.8	10 30.1	10 6.8	1 43.6	17 31.5
12 W	11 15 39.5	20 42.0	5 13.9	12♌ 3.8	3 19.3	28 50.5	25 54.3	8 51.9	10 33.9	10 10.1	1 42.1	17 31.0
13 T	11 19 36.1	21 41.8	5 10.7	26 57.4	4 57.7	0♈ 5.2	26 41.3	8 59.2	10 37.7	10 13.4	1 40.5	17 30.6
14 F	11 23 32.6	22 41.6	5 7.5	11♍49.6	6 37.2	1 19.9	27 28.2	9 6.7	10 41.3	10 16.7	1 39.0	17 30.1
15 S	11 27 29.2	23 41.4	5 4.4	26 31.8	8 17.9	2 34.6	28 15.2	9 14.2	10 44.9	10 20.0	1 37.4	17 29.7
16 S	11 31 25.7	24 41.1	5 1.2	10♎56.6	9 59.8	3 49.3	29 2.1	9 22.0	10 48.4	10 23.3	1 35.9	17 29.3
17 M	11 35 22.3	25 40.8	4 58.0	24 58.5	11 42.9	5 3.9	29 49.1	9 29.8	10 51.8	10 26.7	1 34.4	17 29.0
18 T	11 39 18.8	26 40.5	4 54.8	8♏34.9	13 27.3	6 18.5	0♓36.0	9 37.8	10 55.1	10 30.0	1 32.9	17 28.6
19 W	11 43 15.4	27 40.1	4 51.6	21 45.5	15 12.8	7 33.1	1 23.0	9 46.0	10 58.4	10 33.4	1 31.4	17 28.3
20 T	11 47 12.0	28 39.7	4 48.5	4♐32.3	16 59.7	8 47.6	2 9.9	9 54.2	11 1.5	10 36.7	1 30.0	17 28.0
21 F	11 51 8.5	29 39.3	4 45.3	16 58.9	18 47.7	10 2.2	2 56.9	10 2.7	11 4.6	10 40.1	1 28.5	17 27.7
22 S	11 55 5.0	0♈38.9	4 42.1	29 9.5	20 37.1	11 16.7	3 43.8	10 11.2	11 7.6	10 43.5	1 27.1	17 27.5
23 S	11 59 1.6	1 38.4	4 38.9	11♑ 9.1	22 27.7	12 31.2	4 30.8	10 19.9	11 10.4	10 46.9	1 25.7	17 27.2
24 M	12 2 58.1	2 37.9	4 35.8	23 2.3	24 19.6	13 45.6	5 17.7	10 28.7	11 13.2	10 50.3	1 24.3	17 27.0
25 T	12 6 54.7	3 37.3	4 32.6	4♒53.9	26 12.7	15 0.1	6 4.7	10 37.6	11 16.0	10 53.7	1 22.9	17 26.9
26 W	12 10 51.3	4 36.8	4 29.4	16 47.8	28 7.2	16 14.5	6 51.6	10 46.6	11 18.6	10 57.1	1 21.6	17 26.7
27 T	12 14 47.8	5 36.2	4 26.2	28 47.6	0♈ 2.9	17 28.9	7 38.5	10 55.8	11 21.1	11 0.5	1 20.3	17 26.6
28 F	12 18 44.4	6 35.6	4 23.0	10♓55.9	1 59.9	18 43.3	8 25.5	11 5.1	11 23.5	11 3.9	1 19.0	17 26.5
29 S	12 22 40.9	7 34.9	4 19.9	23 14.8	3 58.0	19 57.7	9 12.4	11 14.5	11 25.9	11 7.4	1 17.7	17 26.4
30 S	12 26 37.5	8 34.2	4 16.7	5♈45.5	5 57.3	21 12.0	9 59.3	11 24.0	11 28.1	11 10.8	1 16.4	17 26.4
31 M	12 30 34.0	9 33.5	4 13.5	18 28.7	7 57.8	22 26.3	10 46.2	11 33.6	11 30.2	11 14.2	1 15.1	17 26.3
						DECLINATION						
1 S	10 32 17.4	7S56.4	13N28.0	9S39.1	17S18.5	7S11.4	16S41.7	21N 8.4	22S20.9	3N11.6	11N23.4	22N 5.2
4 T	10 44 7.1	6 47.8	13 24.8	7N32.1	16 12.4	5 42.8	15 58.8	21 11.7	22 19.9	3 15.3	11 25.2	22 5.7
7 F	10 55 56.8	5 38.4	13 21.6	22 39.7	14 54.8	4 12.8	15 14.5	21 15.3	22 19.0	3 19.1	11 27.0	22 6.2
10 M	11 7 46.4	4 28.3	13 18.4	27 37.1	13 25.6	2 41.8	14 28.7	21 19.0	22 18.0	3 23.0	11 28.7	22 6.6
13 T	11 19 36.1	3 17.7	13 15.3	16 57.9	11 45.2	1 10.1	13 41.7	21 22.8	22 17.2	3 26.9	11 30.4	22 7.0
16 S	11 31 25.7	2 6.8	13 12.1	2S31.3	9 53.5	0N22.0	12 53.5	21 26.9	22 16.3	3 30.8	11 32.0	22 7.3
19 W	11 43 15.4	0 55.7	13 8.9	19 48.6	7 50.9	1 54.0	12 4.1	21 31.0	22 15.5	3 34.8	11 33.6	22 7.6
22 S	11 55 5.0	0N15.5	13 5.7	27 45.5	5 37.6	3 25.8	11 13.7	21 35.2	22 14.8	3 38.8	11 35.2	22 8.0
25 T	12 6 54.7	1 26.4	13 2.5	24 5.6	3 14.1	4 57.0	10 22.4	21 39.5	22 14.1	3 42.8	11 36.7	22 8.2
28 F	12 18 44.4	2 37.1	12 59.3	11 16.4	0 41.2	6 27.3	9 30.2	21 43.8	22 13.4	3 46.8	11 38.1	22 8.5
31 M	12 30 34.0	3 47.3	12 56.0	6N 2.6	1N59.7	7 56.2	8 37.3	21 48.3	22 12.9	3 50.9	11 39.4	22 8.7

APRIL 1930

DAY	EPHEMERIS SIDEREAL TIME	☉	☊	☽	☿	♀	♂	♃	♄	♅	♆	♇
						LONGITUDE						
1 T	12 34 30.6	10♈32.7	4♉10.3	1♉24.7	9♈59.2	23♈40.6	11♓33.1	11♊43.4	11♑32.3	11♈17.7	1♍13.9	17♋26.3
2 W	12 38 27.1	11 31.9	4 7.2	14 33.5	12 1.6	24 54.9	12 20.0	11 53.3	11 34.2	11 21.1	1R12.7	17D26.3
3 T	12 42 23.7	12 31.1	4 4.0	27 55.0	14 4.8	26 9.1	13 6.8	12 3.2	11 36.1	11 24.5	1 11.6	17 26.4
4 F	12 46 20.3	13 30.2	4 0.8	11♊29.0	16 8.7	27 23.3	13 53.7	12 13.3	11 37.9	11 28.0	1 10.4	17 26.5
5 S	12 50 16.8	14 29.3	3 57.6	25 15.3	18 13.0	28 37.5	14 40.5	12 23.5	11 39.5	11 31.4	1 9.3	17 26.5
6 S	12 54 13.3	15 28.4	3 54.4	9♋13.4	20 17.6	29 51.6	15 27.3	12 33.8	11 41.1	11 34.8	1 8.2	17 26.7
7 M	12 58 9.9	16 27.4	3 51.3	23 22.3	22 22.3	1♉ 5.7	16 14.1	12 44.2	11 42.6	11 38.2	1 7.1	17 26.8
8 T	13 2 6.5	17 26.4	3 48.1	7♌40.2	24 26.8	2 19.8	17 0.9	12 54.7	11 44.0	11 41.6	1 6.0	17 27.0
9 W	13 6 3.0	18 25.3	3 44.9	22 4.1	26 30.8	3 33.9	17 47.7	13 5.2	11 45.2	11 45.1	1 5.0	17 27.2
10 T	13 9 59.6	19 24.2	3 41.7	6♍30.2	28 33.9	4 47.9	18 34.4	13 15.9	11 46.4	11 48.5	1 4.0	17 27.4
11 F	13 13 56.1	20 23.1	3 38.6	20 53.7	0♉36.0	6 1.8	19 21.1	13 26.7	11 47.5	11 51.9	1 3.0	17 27.6
12 S	13 17 52.7	21 21.9	3 35.4	5♎ 9.5	2 36.5	7 15.8	20 7.9	13 37.5	11 48.5	11 55.3	1 2.1	17 27.9
13 S	13 21 49.2	22 20.7	3 32.2	19 12.7	4 35.2	8 29.7	20 54.6	13 48.5	11 49.4	11 58.7	1 1.2	17 28.2
14 M	13 25 45.8	23 19.4	3 29.0	2♏59.2	6 31.8	9 43.6	21 41.2	13 59.5	11 50.2	12 2.0	1 0.3	17 28.5
15 T	13 29 42.3	24 18.2	3 25.8	16 26.4	8 25.8	10 57.5	22 27.9	14 10.7	11 50.9	12 5.4	0 59.4	17 28.8
16 W	13 33 38.9	25 16.9	3 22.7	29 33.3	10 16.9	12 11.3	23 14.5	14 21.9	11 51.5	12 8.8	0 58.6	17 29.2
17 T	13 37 35.4	26 15.5	3 19.5	12♐20.1	12 4.9	13 25.1	24 1.1	14 33.2	11 52.0	12 12.1	0 57.8	17 29.6
18 F	13 41 32.0	27 14.2	3 16.3	24 48.8	13 49.5	14 38.9	24 47.7	14 44.5	11 52.4	12 15.5	0 57.0	17 30.0
19 S	13 45 28.6	28 12.8	3 13.1	7♑ 2.4	15 30.3	15 52.7	25 34.3	14 56.0	11 52.7	12 18.8	0 56.2	17 30.4
20 S	13 49 25.1	29 11.3	3 10.0	19 4.7	17 7.3	17 6.4	26 20.9	15 7.5	11 52.9	12 22.1	0 55.5	17 30.9
21 M	13 53 21.7	0♉ 9.9	3 6.8	1♒ 0.1	18 40.1	18 20.1	27 7.4	15 19.2	11 53.0	12 25.4	0 54.8	17 31.3
22 T	13 57 18.2	1 8.4	3 3.6	12 53.1	20 8.6	19 33.8	27 53.9	15 30.9	11 53.0	12 28.7	0 54.1	17 31.8
23 W	14 1 14.8	2 6.9	3 0.4	24 48.3	21 32.6	20 47.4	28 40.4	15 42.6	11R52.9	12 32.0	0 53.5	17 32.4
24 T	14 5 11.3	3 5.4	2 57.3	6♓50.2	22 52.1	22 1.0	29 26.8	15 54.5	11 52.7	12 35.3	0 52.9	17 32.9
25 F	14 9 7.9	4 3.8	2 54.1	19 2.6	24 6.8	23 14.6	0♈13.2	16 6.4	11 52.4	12 38.5	0 52.3	17 33.5
26 S	14 13 4.4	5 2.2	2 50.9	1♈28.8	25 16.7	24 28.2	0 59.6	16 18.4	11 52.0	12 41.8	0 51.8	17 34.1
27 S	14 17 1.0	6 0.6	2 47.7	14 11.0	26 21.7	25 41.7	1 46.0	16 30.4	11 51.5	12 45.0	0 51.3	17 34.7
28 M	14 20 57.6	6 59.0	2 44.5	27 10.6	27 21.6	26 55.2	2 32.4	16 42.6	11 50.9	12 48.2	0 50.8	17 35.3
29 T	14 24 54.1	7 57.3	2 41.4	10♉27.7	28 16.5	28 8.7	3 18.7	16 54.7	11 50.2	12 51.4	0 50.4	17 36.0
30 W	14 28 50.6	8 55.6	2 38.2	24 1.4	29 6.2	29 22.1	4 4.9	17 7.0	11 49.5	12 54.6	0 49.9	17 36.7
						DECLINATION						
1 T	12 34 30.6	4N10.6	12N55.0	11N51.0	2N54.8	8N25.5	8S19.5	21N49.7	22S12.7	3N52.2	11N39.9	22N 8.8
4 F	12 46 20.3	5 19.9	12 51.8	25 25.4	5 42.9	9 52.3	7 25.7	21 54.2	22 12.2	3 56.3	11 41.1	22 8.9
7 M	12 58 9.9	6 28.4	12 48.5	26 32.1	8 32.4	11 16.9	6 31.4	21 58.6	22 11.8	4 0.3	11 42.3	22 9.1
10 T	13 9 59.6	7 35.8	12 45.3	13 11.8	11 18.6	12 39.2	5 36.6	22 3.1	22 11.5	4 4.3	11 43.4	22 9.2
13 S	13 21 49.2	8 42.1	12 42.1	6S22.6	13 55.6	13 58.7	4 41.4	22 7.5	22 11.2	4 8.3	11 44.3	22 9.3
16 W	13 33 38.9	9 47.1	12 38.8	22 23.5	16 17.9	15 15.1	3 46.0	22 11.8	22 11.0	4 12.2	11 45.2	22 9.4
19 S	13 45 28.6	10 50.6	12 35.6	28 0.8	18 20.9	16 28.1	2 50.3	22 16.1	22 11.0	4 16.1	11 46.1	22 9.4
22 T	13 57 18.2	11 52.6	12 32.3	21 56.0	20 1.8	17 37.4	1 54.6	22 20.4	22 10.9	4 20.0	11 46.8	22 9.4
25 F	14 9 7.9	12 52.8	12 29.0	7 42.1	21 19.5	18 42.6	0 58.8	22 24.5	22 11.0	4 23.8	11 47.4	22 9.4
28 M	14 20 57.6	13 51.1	12 25.8	9N59.2	22 14.0	19 43.4	0 3.0	22 28.6	22 11.2	4 27.5	11 47.9	22 9.4

MAY 1930

DAY	EPHEMERIS SIDEREAL TIME	☉	☊	☽	☿	♀	♂	♃	♄	♅	♆	♇
	h m s	° ′	° ′	° ′	° ′	° ′	° ′	° ′	° ′	° ′	° ′	° ′
							LONGITUDE					
1 T	14 32 47.2	9♉53.9	2♉35.0	7♊49.6	29♉50.7	0♊35.5	4♈51.2	17♊19.3	11♑48.6	12♈57.7	0♍49.6	17♋37.4
2 F	14 36 43.8	10 52.1	2 31.8	21 49.4	0♊30.0	1 48.9	5 37.4	17 31.7	11R47.6	13 0.8	0R49.2	17 38.1
3 S	14 40 40.3	11 50.3	2 28.7	5♋57.7	1 3.9	3 2.2	6 23.6	17 44.1	11 46.6	13 4.0	0 48.9	17 38.9
4 S	14 44 36.9	12 48.5	2 25.5	20 10.9	1 32.5	4 15.5	7 9.7	17 56.6	11 45.4	13 7.0	0 48.6	17 39.6
5 M	14 48 33.4	13 46.7	2 22.3	4♌26.0	1 55.7	5 28.8	7 55.8	18 9.2	11 44.1	13 10.1	0 48.3	17 40.4
6 T	14 52 30.0	14 44.8	2 19.1	18 39.9	2 13.6	6 42.1	8 41.8	18 21.8	11 42.8	13 13.2	0 48.1	17 41.2
7 W	14 56 26.6	15 42.8	2 16.0	2♍50.3	2 26.2	7 55.3	9 27.9	18 34.4	11 41.4	13 16.2	0 47.9	17 42.1
8 T	15 0 23.1	16 40.9	2 12.8	16 54.9	2 33.5	9 8.4	10 13.8	18 47.2	11 39.8	13 19.2	0 47.8	17 42.9
9 F	15 4 19.7	17 38.9	2 9.6	0♎51.8	2 35.7	10 21.5	10 59.8	18 59.9	11 38.2	13 22.2	0 47.7	17 43.8
10 S	15 8 16.2	18 36.9	2 6.4	14 39.1	2R32.8	11 34.6	11 45.7	19 12.7	11 36.5	13 25.1	0 47.6	17 44.7
11 S	15 12 12.8	19 34.8	2 3.2	28 15.1	2 25.1	12 47.7	12 31.5	19 25.6	11 34.7	13 28.0	0 47.5	17 45.6
12 M	15 16 9.3	20 32.7	2 0.1	11♏38.1	2 12.9	14 0.7	13 17.4	19 38.5	11 32.8	13 30.9	0 47.5	17 46.6
13 T	15 20 5.9	21 30.6	1 56.9	24 47.0	1 56.3	15 13.7	14 3.2	19 51.4	11 30.8	13 33.8	0D47.5	17 47.5
14 W	15 24 2.4	22 28.5	1 53.7	7♐40.9	1 35.7	16 26.6	14 48.9	20 4.4	11 28.7	13 36.7	0 47.5	17 48.5
15 T	15 27 59.0	23 26.4	1 50.5	20 19.7	1 11.6	17 39.5	15 34.6	20 17.5	11 26.6	13 39.5	0 47.6	17 49.5
16 F	15 31 55.6	24 24.2	1 47.4	2♑44.4	0 44.3	18 52.4	16 20.3	20 30.5	11 24.4	13 42.3	0 47.7	17 50.5
17 S	15 35 52.1	25 22.0	1 44.2	14 56.5	0 14.4	20 5.3	17 5.9	20 43.7	11 22.1	13 45.1	0 47.8	17 51.5
18 S	15 39 48.7	26 19.8	1 41.0	26 58.7	29♉42.5	21 18.1	17 51.5	20 56.8	11 19.7	13 47.8	0 48.0	17 52.6
19 M	15 43 45.2	27 17.5	1 37.8	8♒54.3	29 9.0	22 30.8	18 37.0	21 10.0	11 17.2	13 50.5	0 48.2	17 53.6
20 T	15 47 41.8	28 15.3	1 34.6	20 47.3	28 34.6	23 43.6	19 22.5	21 23.2	11 14.6	13 53.2	0 48.4	17 54.7
21 W	15 51 38.4	29 13.0	1 31.5	2♓42.2	27 59.9	24 56.3	20 8.0	21 36.5	11 12.0	13 55.8	0 48.7	17 55.8
22 T	15 55 34.9	0♊10.7	1 28.3	14 43.7	27 25.5	26 8.9	20 53.4	21 49.8	11 9.3	13 58.5	0 49.0	17 56.9
23 F	15 59 31.5	1 8.4	1 25.1	26 56.6	26 52.0	27 21.6	21 38.7	22 3.1	11 6.5	14 1.0	0 49.3	17 58.1
24 S	16 3 28.0	2 6.1	1 21.9	9♈25.2	26 19.9	28 34.2	22 24.1	22 16.5	11 3.6	14 3.6	0 49.7	17 59.2
25 S	16 7 24.6	3 3.7	1 18.8	22 13.2	25 49.9	29 46.7	23 9.3	22 29.9	11 0.6	14 6.1	0 50.1	18 0.4
26 M	16 11 21.1	4 1.4	1 15.6	5♉23.3	25 22.3	0♋59.3	23 54.6	22 43.3	10 57.6	14 8.6	0 50.5	18 1.6
27 T	16 15 17.7	4 59.0	1 12.4	18 56.3	24 57.6	2 11.7	24 39.7	22 56.8	10 54.5	14 11.1	0 51.0	18 2.8
28 W	16 19 14.2	5 56.6	1 9.2	2♊51.4	24 36.2	3 24.2	25 24.8	23 10.3	10 51.3	14 13.5	0 51.5	18 4.0
29 T	16 23 10.8	6 54.2	1 6.1	17 5.4	24 18.4	4 36.6	26 9.9	23 23.8	10 48.1	14 15.9	0 52.0	18 5.2
30 F	16 27 7.3	7 51.8	1 2.9	1♋33.3	24 4.5	5 49.0	26 54.9	23 37.3	10 44.8	14 18.2	0 52.6	18 6.5
31 S	16 31 3.9	8 49.3	0 59.7	16 8.8	23 54.6	7 1.3	27 39.9	23 50.9	10 41.5	14 20.5	0 53.2	18 7.7
							DECLINATION					
1 T	14 32 47.2	14N47.3	12N22.5	24N36.9	22N45.9	20N39.5	0N52.6	22N32.5	22S11.4	4N31.2	11N48.3	22N 9.3
4 S	14 44 36.9	15 41.4	12 19.2	27 1.0	22 56.2	21 30.6	1 47.9	22 36.4	22 11.7	4 34.8	11 48.6	22 9.2
7 W	14 56 26.6	16 33.1	12 16.0	14 43.1	22 45.5	22 16.4	2 43.0	22 40.1	22 12.1	4 38.3	11 48.8	22 9.1
10 S	15 8 16.2	17 22.3	12 12.7	4S15.6	22 15.3	22 56.6	3 37.6	22 43.6	22 12.6	4 41.7	11 48.9	22 8.9
13 T	15 20 5.9	18 8.9	12 9.4	20 52.9	21 27.3	23 31.0	4 31.8	22 47.0	22 13.1	4 45.1	11 48.9	22 8.7
16 F	15 31 55.6	18 52.8	12 6.1	27 57.5	20 25.1	23 59.4	5 25.5	22 50.2	22 13.7	4 48.3	11 48.8	22 8.5
19 M	15 43 45.2	19 33.8	12 2.8	23 2.9	19 13.8	24 21.7	6 18.5	22 53.3	22 14.4	4 51.4	11 48.6	22 8.3
22 T	15 55 34.9	20 11.8	11 59.5	9 35.4	18 0.5	24 37.6	7 10.9	22 56.2	22 15.2	4 54.5	11 48.3	22 8.1
25 S	16 7 24.6	20 46.8	11 56.2	7N47.0	16 52.7	24 47.2	8 2.5	22 58.9	22 16.0	4 57.4	11 47.9	22 7.8
28 W	16 19 14.2	21 18.5	11 52.9	23 18.9	15 57.3	24 50.3	8 53.3	23 1.4	22 16.8	5 0.2	11 47.3	22 7.5
31 S	16 31 3.9	21 46.9	11 49.5	27 24.3	15 19.1	24 46.9	9 43.2	23 3.7	22 17.8	5 2.9	11 46.7	22 7.2

JUNE 1930

DAY	EPHEMERIS SIDEREAL TIME	☉	☊	☽	☿	♀	♂	♃	♄	♅	♆	♇
							LONGITUDE					
1 S	16 35 0.5	9♊46.8	0♉56.5	0♌45.3	23♉49.1	8♋13.6	28♈24.8	24♊ 4.4	10♑38.0	14♈22.8	0♍53.8	18♋ 9.0
2 M	16 38 57.0	10 44.3	0 53.3	15 16.5	23R47.9	9 25.8	29 9.6	24 18.0	10R34.5	14 25.1	0 54.4	18 10.3
3 T	16 42 53.5	11 41.8	0 50.2	29 37.8	23D51.1	10 38.1	29 54.4	24 31.7	10 31.0	14 27.3	0 55.1	18 11.6
4 W	16 46 50.1	12 39.3	0 47.0	13♍46.1	23 58.8	11 50.2	0♉39.2	24 45.3	10 27.4	14 29.4	0 55.9	18 12.9
5 T	16 50 46.7	13 36.7	0 43.8	27 40.0	24 11.1	13 2.3	1 23.9	24 59.0	10 23.7	14 31.6	0 56.6	18 14.2
6 F	16 54 43.3	14 34.1	0 40.6	11♎19.4	24 27.7	14 14.4	2 8.5	25 12.6	10 20.0	14 33.6	0 57.4	18 15.6
7 S	16 58 39.8	15 31.5	0 37.5	24 44.7	24 48.8	15 26.4	2 53.1	25 26.3	10 16.2	14 35.7	0 58.2	18 16.9
8 S	17 2 36.3	16 28.9	0 34.3	7♏56.8	25 14.3	16 38.4	3 37.6	25 40.0	10 12.4	14 37.7	0 59.0	18 18.3
9 M	17 6 32.9	17 26.3	0 31.1	20 56.7	25 44.2	17 50.3	4 22.0	25 53.7	10 8.5	14 39.7	0 59.9	18 19.7
10 T	17 10 29.5	18 23.6	0 27.9	3♐44.8	26 18.2	19 2.2	5 6.4	26 7.4	10 4.6	14 41.6	1 0.8	18 21.1
11 W	17 14 26.1	19 21.0	0 24.8	16 21.7	26 56.4	20 14.0	5 50.7	26 21.1	10 0.7	14 43.5	1 1.7	18 22.5
12 T	17 18 22.6	20 18.3	0 21.6	28 47.7	27 38.7	21 25.8	6 35.0	26 34.9	9 56.7	14 45.4	1 2.7	18 23.9
13 F	17 22 19.2	21 15.6	0 18.4	11♑ 3.5	28 25.0	22 37.5	7 19.3	26 48.6	9 52.6	14 47.2	1 3.7	18 25.3
14 S	17 26 15.7	22 12.9	0 15.2	23 10.1	29 15.2	23 49.2	8 3.4	27 2.4	9 48.5	14 49.0	1 4.7	18 26.7
15 S	17 30 12.2	23 10.2	0 12.1	5♒ 9.2	0♊ 9.2	25 0.8	8 47.5	27 16.1	9 44.4	14 50.7	1 5.8	18 28.2
16 M	17 34 8.8	24 7.5	0 8.9	17 2.9	1 7.0	26 12.3	9 31.6	27 29.9	9 40.2	14 52.4	1 6.8	18 29.6
17 T	17 38 5.4	25 4.8	0 5.7	28 54.6	2 8.5	27 23.9	10 15.6	27 43.6	9 36.1	14 54.0	1 7.9	18 31.1
18 W	17 42 2.0	26 2.1	0 2.5	10♓48.0	3 13.7	28 35.3	10 59.5	27 57.4	9 31.8	14 55.6	1 9.1	18 32.6
19 T	17 45 58.5	26 59.3	29♈59.4	22 47.7	4 22.4	29 46.8	11 43.4	28 11.2	9 27.6	14 57.2	1 10.2	18 34.0
20 F	17 49 55.1	27 56.6	29 56.2	4♈58.4	5 34.6	0♌58.1	12 27.2	28 24.9	9 23.3	14 58.7	1 11.4	18 35.5
21 S	17 53 51.6	28 53.9	29 53.0	17 25.3	6 50.3	2 9.4	13 10.9	28 38.7	9 19.0	15 0.2	1 12.6	18 37.0
22 S	17 57 48.2	29 51.1	29 49.8	0♉13.1	8 9.4	3 20.7	13 54.6	28 52.5	9 14.7	15 1.6	1 13.9	18 38.5
23 M	18 1 44.8	0♋48.4	29 46.7	13 25.7	9 32.0	4 31.9	14 38.2	29 6.2	9 10.3	15 3.0	1 15.2	18 40.0
24 T	18 5 41.3	1 45.6	29 43.5	27 5.4	10 57.9	5 43.1	15 21.8	29 20.0	9 6.0	15 4.3	1 16.5	18 41.5
25 W	18 9 37.9	2 42.9	29 40.3	11♊12.2	12 27.1	6 54.2	16 5.3	29 33.7	9 1.6	15 5.6	1 17.8	18 43.1
26 T	18 13 34.4	3 40.1	29 37.1	25 43.5	13 59.6	8 5.2	16 48.7	29 47.5	8 57.2	15 6.8	1 19.1	18 44.6
27 F	18 17 31.0	4 37.4	29 33.9	10♋33.1	15 35.4	9 16.2	17 32.0	0♋ 1.2	8 52.8	15 8.0	1 20.5	18 46.1
28 S	18 21 27.5	5 34.6	29 30.8	25 32.9	17 14.4	10 27.1	18 15.3	0 15.0	8 48.3	15 9.2	1 21.9	18 47.7
29 S	18 25 24.1	6 31.9	29 27.6	10♌33.3	18 56.5	11 38.0	18 58.5	0 28.7	8 43.9	15 10.3	1 23.3	18 49.2
30 M	18 29 20.7	7 29.1	29 24.4	25 25.1	20 41.7	12 48.8	19 41.6	0 42.4	8 39.5	15 11.4	1 24.8	18 50.8
							DECLINATION					
1 S	16 35 0.5	21N55.7	11N48.4	25N 2.4	15N10.6	24N44.3	9N59.6	23N 4.4	22S18.1	5N 3.7	11N46.5	22N 7.1
4 W	16 46 50.1	22 19.5	11 45.1	9 57.3	14 58.4	24 32.4	10 48.1	23 6.4	22 19.0	5 6.2	11 45.7	22 6.7
7 S	16 58 39.8	22 39.8	11 41.8	8S58.1	15 5.6	24 14.1	11 35.6	23 8.2	22 20.0	5 8.6	11 44.8	22 6.4
10 T	17 10 29.5	22 56.6	11 38.4	23 33.6	15 30.4	23 49.6	12 21.9	23 9.9	22 21.1	5 10.8	11 43.9	22 6.0
13 F	17 22 19.2	23 9.7	11 35.1	27 45.0	16 10.4	23 19.1	13 7.1	23 11.3	22 22.1	5 12.9	11 42.8	22 5.6
16 M	17 34 8.8	23 19.2	11 31.8	20 24.3	17 2.6	22 42.8	13 51.0	23 12.4	22 23.2	5 14.8	11 41.7	22 5.2
19 T	17 45 58.5	23 25.0	11♈28.4	5 46.4	18 3.9	22 0.9	14 33.6	23 13.4	22 24.3	5 16.6	11 40.4	22 4.8
22 S	17 57 48.2	23 27.0	11 25.0	11N28.7	19 11.0	21 13.6	15 14.9	23 14.2	22 25.4	5 18.2	11 39.1	22 4.4
25 W	18 9 37.9	23 25.4	11 21.7	25 22.6	20 20.1	20 21.3	15 54.8	23 14.7	22 26.6	5 19.7	11 37.7	22 3.9
28 S	18 21 27.5	23 20.0	11 18.3	25 58.8	21 27.0	19 24.1	16 33.2	23 15.0	22 27.7	5 21.0	11 36.2	22 3.5

JULY 1930

LONGITUDE

DAY	EPHEMERIS SIDEREAL TIME h m s	☉ ° ′	☊ ° ′	☽ ° ′	☿ ° ′	♀ ° ′	♂ ° ′	♃ ° ′	♄ ° ′	♅ ° ′	♆ ° ′	♇ ° ′
1 T	18 33 17.2	8♋26.3	29♈21.2	10♍ 1.1	22♊29.9	13♌59.5	20♉24.7	0♋56.1	8♑35.0	15♈12.4	1♍26.3	18♋52.3
2 W	18 37 13.8	9 23.5	29 18.1	24 17.1	24 20.9	15 10.2	21 7.7	1 9.8	8R30.6	15 13.3	1 27.8	18 53.9
3 T	18 41 10.3	10 20.8	29 14.9	8♎11.2	26 14.7	16 20.8	21 50.6	1 23.4	8 26.2	15 14.3	1 29.3	18 55.4
4 F	18 45 6.9	11 18.0	29 11.7	21 44.0	28 11.2	17 31.3	22 33.4	1 37.1	8 21.7	15 15.1	1 30.9	18 57.0
5 S	18 49 3.5	12 15.2	29 8.5	4♏57.5	0♋10.0	18 41.8	23 16.2	1 50.7	8 17.3	15 15.9	1 32.4	18 58.6
6 S	18 52 60.0	13 12.4	29 5.4	17 54.3	2 11.2	19 52.2	23 58.9	2 4.3	8 12.9	15 16.7	1 34.0	19 0.1
7 M	18 56 56.6	14 9.6	29 2.2	0♐37.0	4 14.3	21 2.5	24 41.5	2 17.9	8 8.5	15 17.5	1 35.6	19 1.7
8 T	19 0 53.1	15 6.7	28 59.0	13 8.1	6 19.1	22 12.7	25 24.1	2 31.5	8 4.1	15 18.1	1 37.3	19 3.3
9 W	19 4 49.7	16 3.9	28 55.8	25 29.4	8 25.5	23 22.9	26 6.6	2 45.1	7 59.8	15 18.8	1 38.9	19 4.9
10 T	19 8 46.2	17 1.1	28 52.6	7♑42.4	10 33.0	24 32.9	26 49.0	2 58.6	7 55.4	15 19.3	1 40.6	19 6.4
11 F	19 12 42.8	17 58.3	28 49.5	19 48.3	12 41.4	25 42.9	27 31.3	3 12.1	7 51.1	15 19.9	1 42.3	19 8.0
12 S	19 16 39.4	18 55.5	28 46.3	1♒48.1	14 50.4	26 52.8	28 13.6	3 25.6	7 46.8	15 20.4	1 44.1	19 9.6
13 S	19 20 36.0	19 52.7	28 43.1	13 43.0	16 59.7	28 2.7	28 55.7	3 39.0	7 42.5	15 20.8	1 45.8	19 11.2
14 M	19 24 32.5	20 49.9	28 39.9	25 34.7	19 8.9	29 12.4	29 37.8	3 52.5	7 38.2	15 21.2	1 47.6	19 12.8
15 T	19 28 29.0	21 47.1	28 36.8	7♓25.5	21 17.9	0♍22.0	0♊19.9	4 5.8	7 34.0	15 21.5	1 49.3	19 14.3
16 W	19 32 25.6	22 44.4	28 33.6	19 18.4	23 26.5	1 31.6	1 1.8	4 19.2	7 29.8	15 21.8	1 51.2	19 15.9
17 T	19 36 22.2	23 41.6	28 30.4	1♈17.2	25 34.2	2 41.1	1 43.7	4 32.6	7 25.6	15 22.1	1 53.0	19 17.5
18 F	19 40 18.7	24 38.9	28 27.2	13 26.3	27 41.1	3 50.5	2 25.5	4 45.9	7 21.5	15 22.3	1 54.8	19 19.1
19 S	19 44 15.3	25 36.1	28 24.1	25 50.5	29 46.8	4 59.8	3 7.2	4 59.2	7 17.4	15 22.4	1 56.7	19 20.6
20 S	19 48 11.8	26 33.4	28 20.9	8♉34.9	1♌51.4	6 9.0	3 48.9	5 12.4	7 13.3	15 22.5	1 58.6	19 22.2
21 M	19 52 8.4	27 30.7	28 17.7	21 44.2	3 54.5	7 18.2	4 30.5	5 25.6	7 9.3	15 22.6	2 0.5	19 23.8
22 T	19 56 4.9	28 28.0	28 14.5	5♊21.7	5 56.2	8 27.2	5 11.9	5 38.8	7 5.3	15 22.6	2 2.4	19 25.3
23 W	20 0 1.5	29 25.3	28 11.4	19 28.8	7 56.4	9 36.2	5 53.3	5 51.9	7 1.4	15R22.5	2 4.3	19 26.9
24 T	20 3 58.0	0♌22.6	28 8.2	4♋ 4.1	9 55.0	10 45.0	6 34.7	6 5.0	6 57.5	15 22.4	2 6.2	19 28.4
25 F	20 7 54.6	1 19.9	28 5.0	19 2.3	11 52.0	11 53.8	7 15.9	6 18.1	6 53.6	15 22.3	2 8.2	19 30.0
26 S	20 11 51.2	2 17.3	28 1.8	4♌14.9	13 47.3	13 2.4	7 57.1	6 31.1	6 49.9	15 22.1	2 10.2	19 31.6
27 S	20 15 47.7	3 14.6	27 58.7	19 31.0	15 41.0	14 11.0	8 38.1	6 44.1	6 46.1	15 21.9	2 12.2	19 33.1
28 M	20 19 44.3	4 12.0	27 55.5	4♍39.7	17 33.0	15 19.4	9 19.1	6 57.0	6 42.4	15 21.6	2 14.2	19 34.6
29 T	20 23 40.8	5 9.4	27 52.3	19 31.4	19 23.3	16 27.7	9 60.0	7 9.9	6 38.8	15 21.2	2 16.2	19 36.2
30 W	20 27 37.4	6 6.8	27 49.1	3♎59.7	21 11.9	17 36.0	10 40.8	7 22.7	6 35.2	15 20.8	2 18.2	19 37.7
31 T	20 31 34.0	7 4.2	27 45.9	18 1.8	22 58.8	18 44.1	11 21.5	7 35.5	6 31.7	15 20.4	2 20.3	19 39.2

DECLINATION

DAY	EPHEMERIS SIDEREAL TIME h m s	☉	☊	☽	☿	♀	♂	♃	♄	♅	♆	♇
1 T	18 33 17.2	23N10.9	11N15.0	11N24.7	22N27.0	18N22.5	17N10.1	23N15.1	22S28.8	5N22.1	11N34.6	22N 3.0
4 F	18 45 6.9	22 58.2	11 11.6	7S47.2	23 14.7	17 16.7	17 45.4	23 15.0	22 29.9	5 23.1	11 33.0	22 2.5
7 M	18 56 56.6	22 41.8	11 8.2	22 47.8	23 45.0	16 7.1	18 19.2	23 14.6	22 31.0	5 23.9	11 31.3	22 2.1
10 T	19 8 46.2	22 22.0	11 4.8	27 51.8	23 53.4	14 54.0	18 51.3	23 14.1	22 32.1	5 24.6	11 29.5	22 1.6
13 S	19 20 36.0	21 58.6	11 1.4	21 20.6	23 37.4	13 37.6	19 21.8	23 13.4	22 33.1	5 25.1	11 27.6	22 1.1
16 W	19 32 25.6	21 31.9	10 58.1	7 9.7	22 56.9	12 18.4	19 50.5	23 12.4	22 34.1	5 25.4	11 25.7	22 0.6
19 S	19 44 15.3	21 1.9	10 54.7	9N46.5	21 54.1	10 56.7	20 17.6	23 11.3	22 35.1	5 25.5	11 23.7	22 0.1
22 T	19 56 4.9	20 28.7	10 51.3	24 11.1	20 32.5	9 32.7	20 43.0	23 10.0	22 36.1	5 25.5	11 21.6	21 59.6
25 F	20 7 54.6	19 52.3	10 47.9	26 59.5	18 56.1	8 6.7	21 6.6	23 8.5	22 37.1	5 25.3	11 19.5	21 59.2
28 M	20 19 44.3	19 13.0	10 44.5	13 31.5	17 8.6	6 39.1	21 28.4	23 6.8	22 38.0	5 24.9	11 17.4	21 58.7
31 T	20 31 34.0	18 30.8	10 41.0	6S19.4	15 13.2	5 10.1	21 48.5	23 4.9	22 38.9	5 24.4	11 15.2	21 58.2

AUGUST 1930

LONGITUDE

DAY	EPHEMERIS SIDEREAL TIME h m s	☉ ° ′	☊ ° ′	☽ ° ′	☿ ° ′	♀ ° ′	♂ ° ′	♃ ° ′	♄ ° ′	♅ ° ′	♆ ° ′	♇ ° ′
1 F	20 35 30.5	8♌ 1.6	27♈42.8	1♏37.6	24♌44.0	19♍52.1	12♊ 2.1	7♋48.2	6♑28.3	15♈19.9	2♍22.3	19♋40.7
2 S	20 39 27.1	8 59.0	27 39.6	14 49.3	26 27.6	20 59.9	12 42.6	8 0.9	6R24.9	15R19.4	2 24.4	19 42.2
3 S	20 43 23.6	9 56.4	27 36.4	27 40.3	28 9.6	22 7.6	13 23.0	8 13.5	6 21.6	15 18.8	2 26.5	19 43.7
4 M	20 47 20.2	10 53.8	27 33.2	10♐14.3	29 49.8	23 15.2	14 3.3	8 26.1	6 18.3	15 18.2	2 28.6	19 45.2
5 T	20 51 16.7	11 51.3	27 30.1	22 35.0	1♍28.5	24 22.7	14 43.6	8 38.6	6 15.1	15 17.5	2 30.7	19 46.7
6 W	20 55 13.3	12 48.8	27 26.9	4♑45.7	3 5.5	25 30.0	15 23.7	8 51.1	6 12.0	15 16.8	2 32.8	19 48.2
7 T	20 59 9.8	13 46.2	27 23.7	16 49.1	4 40.8	26 37.2	16 3.8	9 3.5	6 9.0	15 16.0	2 34.9	19 49.6
8 F	21 3 6.4	14 43.7	27 20.5	28 47.1	6 14.6	27 44.3	16 43.8	9 15.9	6 6.0	15 15.2	2 37.0	19 51.1
9 S	21 7 3.0	15 41.2	27 17.4	10♒41.5	7 46.7	28 51.2	17 23.6	9 28.2	6 3.1	15 14.4	2 39.2	19 52.6
10 S	21 10 59.5	16 38.8	27 14.2	22 33.8	9 17.1	29 57.9	18 3.4	9 40.4	6 0.3	15 13.5	2 41.3	19 54.0
11 M	21 14 56.0	17 36.3	27 11.0	4♓25.4	10 46.0	1♎ 4.5	18 43.1	9 52.5	5 57.5	15 12.6	2 43.5	19 55.4
12 T	21 18 52.6	18 33.9	27 7.8	16 18.0	12 13.1	2 11.0	19 22.7	10 4.7	5 54.9	15 11.6	2 45.6	19 56.8
13 W	21 22 49.2	19 31.4	27 4.6	28 13.9	13 38.6	3 17.2	20 2.2	10 16.7	5 52.3	15 10.5	2 47.8	19 58.2
14 T	21 26 45.8	20 29.1	27 1.5	10♈15.9	15 2.4	4 23.4	20 41.6	10 28.7	5 49.8	15 9.5	2 50.0	19 59.6
15 F	21 30 42.3	21 26.7	26 58.3	22 27.4	16 24.4	5 29.3	21 20.9	10 40.6	5 47.3	15 8.4	2 52.2	20 1.0
16 S	21 34 38.8	22 24.3	26 55.1	4♉52.5	17 44.7	6 35.1	22 0.1	10 52.4	5 45.0	15 7.2	2 54.4	20 2.4
17 S	21 38 35.4	23 22.0	26 51.9	17 35.6	19 3.2	7 40.7	22 39.2	11 4.2	5 42.7	15 6.0	2 56.6	20 3.8
18 M	21 42 32.0	24 19.7	26 48.8	0♊40.9	20 19.8	8 46.2	23 18.2	11 15.9	5 40.5	15 4.7	2 58.8	20 5.1
19 T	21 46 28.5	25 17.5	26 45.6	14 12.2	21 34.5	9 51.5	23 57.1	11 27.5	5 38.4	15 3.5	3 1.0	20 6.5
20 W	21 50 25.1	26 15.2	26 42.4	28 11.7	22 47.3	10 56.6	24 35.9	11 39.1	5 36.4	15 2.1	3 3.2	20 7.8
21 T	21 54 21.6	27 13.0	26 39.2	12♋38.9	23 58.0	12 1.5	25 14.6	11 50.5	5 34.5	15 0.8	3 5.4	20 9.1
22 F	21 58 18.2	28 10.8	26 36.0	27 30.6	25 6.5	13 6.2	25 53.2	12 1.9	5 32.6	14 59.4	3 7.6	20 10.4
23 S	22 2 14.7	29 8.7	26 32.9	12♌39.8	26 12.9	14 10.7	26 31.7	12 13.2	5 30.9	14 57.9	3 9.9	20 11.7
24 S	22 6 11.3	0♍ 6.6	26 29.7	27 56.6	27 17.0	15 15.0	27 10.0	12 24.5	5 29.2	14 56.4	3 12.1	20 12.9
25 M	22 10 7.9	1 4.4	26 26.5	13♍10.2	28 18.6	16 19.1	27 48.3	12 35.6	5 27.7	14 54.9	3 14.3	20 14.2
26 T	22 14 4.4	2 2.4	26 23.3	28 10.0	29 17.6	17 23.0	28 26.4	12 46.7	5 26.2	14 53.3	3 16.5	20 15.4
27 W	22 18 0.9	3 0.3	26 20.2	12♎48.1	0♎14.0	18 26.7	29 4.4	12 57.7	5 24.8	14 51.7	3 18.8	20 16.7
28 T	22 21 57.5	3 58.3	26 17.0	26 59.8	1 7.5	19 30.1	29 42.3	13 8.5	5 23.5	14 50.1	3 21.0	20 17.9
29 F	22 25 54.1	4 56.3	26 13.8	10♏43.5	1 58.0	20 33.3	0♋20.1	13 19.3	5 22.3	14 48.4	3 23.2	20 19.1
30 S	22 29 50.6	5 54.3	26 10.6	24 0.4	2 45.2	21 36.3	0 57.8	13 30.0	5 21.2	14 46.7	3 25.4	20 20.2
31 S	22 33 47.1	6 52.3	26 7.4	6♐53.4	3 29.0	22 39.0	1 35.3	13 40.7	5 20.2	14 45.0	3 27.7	20 21.4

DECLINATION

DAY	EPHEMERIS SIDEREAL TIME h m s	☉	☊	☽	☿	♀	♂	♃	♄	♅	♆	♇
1 F	20 35 30.5	18N16.1	10N39.9	12S24.3	14N33.5	4N40.2	21N54.8	23N 4.3	22S39.2	5N24.2	11N14.5	21N58.0
4 M	20 47 20.2	17 30.4	10 36.5	25 23.8	12 31.8	3 10.0	22 12.5	23 2.2	22 40.0	5 23.5	11 12.2	21 57.6
7 T	20 59 9.8	16 42.0	10 33.1	27 17.6	10 28.0	1 39.0	22 28.4	23 0.0	22 40.8	5 22.6	11 10.0	21 57.1
10 S	21 10 59.5	15 51.3	10 29.6	18 15.1	8 23.8	0 7.8	22 42.6	22 57.7	22 41.6	5 21.5	11 7.7	21 56.7
13 W	21 22 49.2	14 58.2	10 26.2	2 51.2	6 20.8	1S23.6	22 55.1	22 55.2	22 42.3	5 20.3	11 5.3	21 56.2
16 S	21 34 38.8	14 3.0	10 22.8	13N55.2	4 20.4	2 54.7	23 5.8	22 52.7	22 43.0	5 18.9	11 3.0	21 55.8
19 T	21 46 28.5	13 5.8	10 19.3	26 18.5	2 24.1	4 25.4	23 14.8	22 50.0	22 43.7	5 17.4	11 0.6	21 55.4
22 F	21 58 18.2	12 6.7	10 15.9	25 38.7	0 33.5	5 55.4	23 22.1	22 47.2	22 44.3	5 15.8	10 58.2	21 55.0
25 M	22 10 7.9	11 5.9	10 12.4	9 45.6	1S 9.9	7 24.3	23 27.8	22 44.4	22 45.0	5 14.0	10 55.9	21 54.6
28 T	22 21 57.5	10 3.4	10 9.0	10S35.2	2 43.9	8 52.1	23 31.9	22 41.5	22 45.5	5 12.1	10 53.5	21 54.2
31 S	22 33 47.1	8 59.6	10 5.5	24 51.9	4 6.0	10 18.3	23 34.4	22 38.6	22 46.1	5 10.1	10 51.1	21 53.9

SEPTEMBER 1930

DAY	EPHEMERIS SIDEREAL TIME	☉	☊	☽	☿	♀	♂	♃	♄	♅	♆	♇
	h m s	° ′	° ′	° ′	° ′	° ′	° ′	° ′	° ′	° ′	° ′	° ′
LONGITUDE												
1 M	22 37 43.7	7♍50.3	26♈ 4.3	19♐26.5	4♎ 9.2	23♎41.4	2♋12.7	13♋51.2	5♑19.3	14♈43.2	3♍29.9	20♋22.5
2 T	22 41 40.3	8 48.4	26 1.1	1♑43.9	4 45.4	24 43.6	2 50.0	14 1.6	5R18.5	14R41.4	3 32.1	20 23.7
3 W	22 45 36.9	9 46.5	25 57.9	13 49.8	5 17.5	25 45.5	3 27.2	14 11.9	5 17.8	14 39.6	3 34.3	20 24.8
4 T	22 49 33.4	10 44.6	25 54.7	25 48.0	5 45.2	26 47.1	4 4.3	14 22.1	5 17.1	14 37.7	3 36.5	20 25.9
5 F	22 53 29.9	11 42.8	25 51.6	7♒41.7	6 8.2	27 48.3	4 41.2	14 32.3	5 16.6	14 35.8	3 38.7	20 26.9
6 S	22 57 26.5	12 41.0	25 48.4	19 33.5	6 26.2	28 49.3	5 18.0	14 42.3	5 16.2	14 33.9	3 40.9	20 28.0
7 S	23 1 23.1	13 39.2	25 45.2	1♓25.7	6 38.8	29 50.0	5 54.7	14 52.2	5 15.9	14 31.9	3 43.1	20 29.0
8 M	23 5 19.6	14 37.4	25 42.0	13 20.2	6 45.9	0♏50.3	6 31.3	15 2.0	5 15.6	14 29.9	3 45.3	20 30.1
9 T	23 9 16.2	15 35.6	25 38.9	25 18.5	6 47.0	1 50.3	7 7.7	15 11.7	5 15.5	14 27.9	3 47.5	20 31.0
10 W	23 13 12.7	16 33.9	25 35.7	7♈22.4	6R41.9	2 50.0	7 44.0	15 21.3	5 15.4	14 25.9	3 49.7	20 32.0
11 T	23 17 9.3	17 32.3	25 32.5	19 33.7	6 30.4	3 49.2	8 20.1	15 30.8	5D15.5	14 23.8	3 51.9	20 33.0
12 F	23 21 5.8	18 30.6	25 29.3	1♉54.8	6 12.3	4 48.2	8 56.2	15 40.2	5 15.6	14 21.7	3 54.1	20 33.9
13 S	23 25 2.4	19 29.0	25 26.1	14 28.3	5 47.4	5 46.7	9 32.1	15 49.5	5 15.9	14 19.6	3 56.2	20 34.9
14 S	23 28 58.9	20 27.4	25 23.0	27 17.0	5 15.9	6 44.8	10 7.8	15 58.6	5 16.2	14 17.4	3 58.4	20 35.8
15 M	23 32 55.5	21 25.9	25 19.8	10♊24.0	4 37.8	7 42.6	10 43.5	16 7.6	5 16.7	14 15.3	4 0.5	20 36.6
16 T	23 36 52.0	22 24.4	25 16.6	23 52.1	3 53.4	8 39.9	11 19.0	16 16.6	5 17.2	14 13.1	4 2.7	20 37.5
17 W	23 40 48.6	23 22.9	25 13.4	7♋43.0	3 3.2	9 36.8	11 54.3	16 25.3	5 17.9	14 10.9	4 4.8	20 38.4
18 T	23 44 45.1	24 21.5	25 10.3	21 57.0	2 7.9	10 33.2	12 29.5	16 34.0	5 18.6	14 8.6	4 6.9	20 39.2
19 F	23 48 41.7	25 20.1	25 7.1	6♌32.2	1 8.3	11 29.2	13 4.5	16 42.5	5 19.5	14 6.4	4 9.0	20 40.0
20 S	23 52 38.2	26 18.7	25 3.9	21 23.9	0 5.7	12 24.7	13 39.4	16 51.0	5 20.4	14 4.1	4 11.1	20 40.8
21 S	23 56 34.8	27 17.4	25 0.7	6♍25.2	29♍ 1.4	13 19.7	14 14.2	16 59.3	5 21.5	14 1.8	4 13.2	20 41.5
22 M	0 0 31.4	28 16.1	24 57.5	21 27.2	27 56.7	14 14.2	14 48.8	17 7.4	5 22.6	13 59.5	4 15.3	20 42.3
23 T	0 4 27.9	29 14.8	24 54.4	6♎20.9	26 53.3	15 8.1	15 23.2	17 15.4	5 23.8	13 57.2	4 17.3	20 43.0
24 W	0 8 24.5	0♎13.6	24 51.2	20 58.3	25 52.8	16 1.5	15 57.4	17 23.3	5 25.2	13 54.9	4 19.4	20 43.7
25 T	0 12 21.0	1 12.4	24 48.0	5♏13.3	24 56.9	16 54.3	16 31.5	17 31.1	5 26.6	13 52.5	4 21.4	20 44.3
26 F	0 16 17.6	2 11.3	24 44.8	19 2.8	24 6.9	17 46.5	17 5.4	17 38.7	5 28.1	13 50.2	4 23.4	20 45.0
27 S	0 20 14.2	3 10.1	24 41.7	2♐26.1	23 24.3	18 38.1	17 39.2	17 46.1	5 29.7	13 47.8	4 25.5	20 45.6
28 S	0 24 10.7	4 9.0	24 38.5	15 24.7	22 50.1	19 29.0	18 12.8	17 53.5	5 31.5	13 45.4	4 27.4	20 46.2
29 M	0 28 7.3	5 7.9	24 35.3	28 1.5	22 25.2	20 19.3	18 46.2	18 0.7	5 33.3	13 43.0	4 29.4	20 46.8
30 T	0 32 3.8	6 6.9	24 32.1	10♑20.6	22 10.3	21 8.8	19 19.4	18 7.7	5 35.2	13 40.6	4 31.4	20 47.3
DECLINATION												
1 M	22 37 43.7	8N38.0	10N 4.4	27S12.5	4S30.2	10S46.6	23N34.9	22N37.6	22S46.2	5N 9.4	10N50.3	21N53.8
4 T	22 49 33.4	7 32.5	10 0.9	26 2.3	5 31.2	12 10.3	23 35.4	22 34.6	22 46.7	5 7.2	10 47.9	21 53.5
7 S	23 1 23.1	6 25.9	9 57.4	14 48.4	6 11.4	13 31.8	23 34.4	22 31.6	22 47.2	5 4.9	10 45.5	21 53.2
10 W	23 13 12.7	5 18.3	9 54.0	1N33.6	6 25.5	14 50.9	23 32.0	22 28.6	22 47.6	5 2.5	10 43.2	21 52.9
13 S	23 25 2.4	4 9.9	9 50.5	17 55.8	6 7.6	16 7.3	23 28.3	22 25.6	22 48.0	5 0.1	10 40.9	21 52.7
16 T	23 36 52.0	3 0.9	9 47.0	27 48.9	5 13.7	17 20.8	23 23.3	22 22.7	22 48.3	4 57.5	10 38.6	21 52.4
19 F	23 48 41.7	1 51.3	9 43.5	23 34.4	3 44.4	18 31.1	23 17.1	22 19.8	22 48.6	4 54.9	10 36.3	21 52.3
22 M	0 0 31.4	0 41.3	9 40.0	5 57.9	1 49.1	19 38.1	23 9.8	22 17.0	22 48.9	4 52.2	10 34.1	21 52.1
25 T	0 12 21.0	0S28.8	9 36.5	14S15.3	0N13.1	20 41.5	23 1.4	22 14.3	22 49.1	4 49.5	10 31.9	21 52.0
28 S	0 24 10.7	1 39.0	9 33.1	26 45.1	1 58.8	21 41.0	22 52.1	22 11.6	22 49.3	4 46.7	10 29.7	21 51.9

OCTOBER 1930

DAY	EPHEMERIS SIDEREAL TIME	☉	☊	☽	☿	♀	♂	♃	♄	♅	♆	♇
LONGITUDE												
1 W	0 36 0.4	7♎ 5.9	24♈28.9	22♑26.4	22♍ 5.6	21♏57.6	19♋52.4	18♋14.6	5♑37.2	13♈38.2	4♍33.3	20♋47.9
2 T	0 39 56.9	8 4.9	24 25.8	4♒23.3	22D11.3	22 45.6	20 25.3	18 21.3	5 39.3	13R35.8	4 35.3	20 48.4
3 F	0 43 53.5	9 3.9	24 22.6	16 15.6	22 27.4	23 32.8	20 58.0	18 27.9	5 41.5	13 33.4	4 37.2	20 48.9
4 S	0 47 50.0	10 3.0	24 19.4	28 7.1	22 53.3	24 19.2	21 30.5	18 34.4	5 43.8	13 31.0	4 39.1	20 49.3
5 S	0 51 46.6	11 2.1	24 16.2	10♓ 1.1	23 28.8	25 4.7	22 2.8	18 40.6	5 46.2	13 28.6	4 41.0	20 49.8
6 M	0 55 43.2	12 1.2	24 13.1	22 0.3	24 13.2	25 49.3	22 34.9	18 46.8	5 48.6	13 26.1	4 42.8	20 50.2
7 T	0 59 39.7	13 0.4	24 9.9	4♈ 7.0	25 5.9	26 33.0	23 6.8	18 52.7	5 51.2	13 23.7	4 44.6	20 50.6
8 W	1 3 36.2	13 59.6	24 6.7	16 23.0	26 6.1	27 15.7	23 38.5	18 58.6	5 53.8	13 21.3	4 46.5	20 50.9
9 T	1 7 32.8	14 58.8	24 3.5	28 49.5	27 13.1	27 57.4	24 10.1	19 4.2	5 56.6	13 18.8	4 48.3	20 51.3
10 F	1 11 29.4	15 58.1	24 0.3	11♉27.8	28 26.2	28 38.0	24 41.4	19 9.7	5 59.4	13 16.4	4 50.1	20 51.6
11 S	1 15 25.9	16 57.4	23 57.2	24 18.7	29 44.5	29 17.5	25 12.5	19 15.0	6 2.4	13 14.0	4 51.8	20 51.9
12 S	1 19 22.5	17 56.8	23 54.0	7♊23.3	1♎ 7.4	29 55.9	25 43.4	19 20.2	6 5.4	13 11.6	4 53.6	20 52.1
13 M	1 23 19.0	18 56.1	23 50.8	20 42.2	2 34.3	0♐33.0	26 14.1	19 25.2	6 8.5	13 9.2	4 55.3	20 52.4
14 T	1 27 15.6	19 55.6	23 47.6	4♋16.3	4 4.4	1 9.0	26 44.6	19 30.0	6 11.7	13 6.7	4 57.0	20 52.6
15 W	1 31 12.1	20 55.0	23 44.5	18 5.7	5 37.4	1 43.7	27 14.8	19 34.7	6 14.9	13 4.3	4 58.7	20 52.8
16 T	1 35 8.7	21 54.5	23 41.3	2♌10.1	7 12.6	2 17.0	27 44.8	19 39.2	6 18.3	13 2.0	5 0.3	20 53.0
17 F	1 39 5.2	22 54.1	23 38.1	16 28.1	8 49.6	2 49.0	28 14.6	19 43.5	6 21.7	12 59.6	5 1.9	20 53.1
18 S	1 43 1.8	23 53.6	23 34.9	0♍57.0	10 28.1	3 19.5	28 44.2	19 47.6	6 25.3	12 57.2	5 3.6	20 53.2
19 S	1 46 58.3	24 53.2	23 31.7	15 32.7	12 7.6	3 48.5	29 13.5	19 51.5	6 28.9	12 54.8	5 5.1	20 53.3
20 M	1 50 54.9	25 52.9	23 28.6	0♎10.0	13 48.1	4 16.0	29 42.5	19 55.3	6 32.6	12 52.5	5 6.7	20 53.4
21 T	1 54 51.4	26 52.6	23 25.4	14 42.8	15 29.1	4 41.9	0♌11.3	19 58.9	6 36.4	12 50.1	5 8.2	20 53.5
22 W	1 58 48.0	27 52.3	23 22.2	29 4.9	17 10.5	5 6.1	0 39.8	20 2.3	6 40.2	12 47.8	5 9.7	20 53.5
23 T	2 2 44.6	28 52.1	23 19.0	13♏11.1	18 52.1	5 28.6	1 8.1	20 5.5	6 44.2	12 45.5	5 11.2	20R53.5
24 F	2 6 41.1	29 51.8	23 15.9	26 57.4	20 33.8	5 49.2	1 36.1	20 8.5	6 48.2	12 43.2	5 12.7	20 53.4
25 S	2 10 37.7	0♏51.7	23 12.7	10♐21.4	22 15.4	6 8.0	2 3.8	20 11.4	6 52.3	12 40.9	5 14.1	20 53.4
26 S	2 14 34.2	1 51.5	23 9.5	23 23.0	23 56.9	6 24.9	2 31.3	20 14.0	6 56.5	12 38.7	5 15.5	20 53.3
27 M	2 18 30.8	2 51.4	23 6.3	6♑ 3.4	25 38.2	6 39.7	2 58.4	20 16.5	7 0.8	12 36.4	5 16.9	20 53.2
28 T	2 22 27.3	3 51.3	23 3.1	18 25.5	27 19.2	6 52.5	3 25.3	20 18.8	7 5.1	12 34.2	5 18.3	20 53.1
29 W	2 26 23.9	4 51.2	22 60.0	0♒33.1	28 59.9	7 3.2	3 51.8	20 20.8	7 9.5	12 32.0	5 19.6	20 52.9
30 T	2 30 20.5	5 51.2	22 56.8	12 30.5	0♏40.2	7 11.6	4 18.1	20 22.7	7 14.0	12 29.8	5 20.9	20 52.8
31 F	2 34 17.0	6 51.1	22 53.6	24 22.6	2 20.1	7 17.9	4 44.0	20 24.4	7 18.6	12 27.7	5 22.2	20 52.5
DECLINATION												
1 W	0 36 0.4	2S49.1	9N29.6	26S46.0	3N 8.8	22S36.5	22N41.8	22N 9.1	22S49.5	4N44.0	10N27.7	21N51.8
4 S	0 47 50.0	3 58.9	9 26.1	16 12.5	3 33.6	23 27.6	22 30.7	22 6.7	22 49.6	4 41.1	10 25.6	21 51.8
7 T	0 59 39.7	5 8.3	9 22.5	0N 0.9	3 13.4	24 14.3	22 19.0	22 4.5	22 49.6	4 38.3	10 23.7	21 51.8
10 F	1 11 29.4	6 17.1	9 19.0	16 49.1	2 14.5	24 56.3	22 6.5	22 2.5	22 49.6	4 35.5	10 21.7	21 51.8
13 M	1 23 19.0	7 25.2	9 15.5	27 33.1	0 46.3	25 33.3	21 53.6	22 0.6	22 49.6	4 32.7	10 19.9	21 51.9
16 T	1 35 8.7	8 32.4	9 12.0	24 46.6	1S 1.9	26 5.2	21 40.2	21 58.9	22 49.5	4 29.9	10 18.1	21 52.0
19 S	1 46 58.3	9 38.5	9 8.5	8 42.9	3 2.2	26 31.8	21 26.5	21 57.5	22 49.3	4 27.2	10 16.4	21 52.1
22 W	1 58 48.0	10 43.3	9 5.0	11S37.2	5 8.4	26 52.7	21 12.5	21 56.3	22 49.1	4 24.5	10 14.8	21 52.3
25 S	2 10 37.7	11 46.7	9 1.4	25 49.0	7 16.3	27 7.5	20 58.4	21 55.3	22 48.8	4 21.9	10 13.3	21 52.5
28 T	2 22 27.3	12 48.5	8 57.9	27 23.2	9 22.7	27 15.7	20 44.4	21 54.5	22 48.5	4 19.3	10 11.8	21 52.7
31 F	2 34 17.0	13 48.5	8 54.4	17 40.6	11 25.5	27 16.8	20 30.5	21 54.0	22 48.1	4 16.8	10 10.5	21 53.0

NOVEMBER 1930

LONGITUDE

DAY	EPHEMERIS SIDEREAL TIME h m s	☉ ° ′	☊ ° ′	☽ ° ′	☿ ° ′	♀ ° ′	♂ ° ′	♃ ° ′	♄ ° ′	♅ ° ′	♆ ° ′	♇ ° ′
1 S	2 38 13.5	7♏51.1	22♈50.4	6♓14.1	3♏59.7	7♐21.8	5♌ 9.7	20♋25.9	7♑23.2	12♈25.5	5♍23.4	20♋52.3
2 S	2 42 10.1	8 51.2	22 47.3	18 9.5	5 38.8	7 23.3	5 35.0	20 27.2	7 27.9	12R23.4	5 24.6	20R52.1
3 M	2 46 6.7	9 51.3	22 44.1	0♈12.7	7 17.4	7R22.5	6 0.0	20 28.3	7 32.7	12 21.4	5 25.8	20 51.8
4 T	2 50 3.2	10 51.4	22 40.9	12 27.2	8 55.7	7 19.3	6 24.7	20 29.2	7 37.5	12 19.3	5 27.0	20 51.5
5 W	2 53 59.8	11 51.5	22 37.7	24 55.5	10 33.5	7 13.6	6 49.0	20 30.0	7 42.5	12 17.3	5 28.1	20 51.2
6 T	2 57 56.3	12 51.6	22 34.6	7♉39.2	12 11.0	7 5.5	7 13.0	20 30.5	7 47.4	12 15.3	5 29.2	20 50.8
7 F	3 1 52.9	13 51.8	22 31.4	20 38.9	13 48.0	6 54.9	7 36.7	20 30.8	7 52.5	12 13.3	5 30.2	20 50.5
8 S	3 5 49.5	14 52.0	22 28.2	3♊54.2	15 24.6	6 41.9	7 60.0	20 30.9	7 57.6	12 11.4	5 31.3	20 50.1
9 S	3 9 46.0	15 52.3	22 25.0	17 23.8	17 0.9	6 26.4	8 22.9	20R30.8	8 2.8	12 9.5	5 32.3	20 49.6
10 M	3 13 42.6	16 52.5	22 21.8	1♋ 5.9	18 36.8	6 8.6	8 45.5	20 30.6	8 8.0	12 7.6	5 33.3	20 49.2
11 T	3 17 39.1	17 52.8	22 18.7	14 58.1	20 12.4	5 48.5	9 7.6	20 30.1	8 13.3	12 5.8	5 34.2	20 48.7
12 W	3 21 35.7	18 53.2	22 15.5	28 58.2	21 47.6	5 26.2	9 29.4	20 29.4	8 18.7	12 4.0	5 35.1	20 48.3
13 T	3 25 32.2	19 53.6	22 12.3	13♌ 3.9	23 22.5	5 1.8	9 50.8	20 28.5	8 24.1	12 2.2	5 36.0	20 47.8
14 F	3 29 28.8	20 54.0	22 9.1	27 13.3	24 57.1	4 35.3	10 11.8	20 27.4	8 29.6	12 0.5	5 36.8	20 47.2
15 S	3 33 25.3	21 54.4	22 6.0	11♍24.6	26 31.4	4 7.0	10 32.3	20 26.2	8 35.2	11 58.8	5 37.7	20 46.7
16 S	3 37 21.9	22 54.9	22 2.8	25 35.9	28 5.5	3 37.0	10 52.5	20 24.7	8 40.8	11 57.1	5 38.4	20 46.1
17 M	3 41 18.5	23 55.4	21 59.6	9♎44.9	29 39.3	3 5.5	11 12.2	20 23.0	8 46.5	11 55.5	5 39.2	20 45.5
18 T	3 45 15.0	24 55.9	21 56.4	23 49.1	1♐12.9	2 32.6	11 31.4	20 21.1	8 52.2	11 53.9	5 39.9	20 44.9
19 W	3 49 11.6	25 56.5	21 53.3	7♏45.5	2 46.3	1 58.6	11 50.2	20 19.0	8 58.0	11 52.3	5 40.6	20 44.2
20 T	3 53 8.1	26 57.0	21 50.1	21 30.8	4 19.4	1 23.6	12 8.5	20 16.7	9 3.8	11 50.8	5 41.3	20 43.5
21 F	3 57 4.7	27 57.6	21 46.9	5♐ 2.0	5 52.3	0 47.9	12 26.3	20 14.3	9 9.7	11 49.4	5 41.9	20 42.9
22 S	4 1 1.3	28 58.3	21 43.7	18 16.7	7 25.1	0 11.8	12 43.6	20 11.6	9 15.6	11 47.9	5 42.5	20 42.2
23 S	4 4 57.8	29 58.9	21 40.6	1♑13.6	8 57.7	29♏35.4	13 0.5	20 8.7	9 21.6	11 46.5	5 43.0	20 41.4
24 M	4 8 54.4	0♐59.6	21 37.4	13 52.5	10 30.1	28 59.1	13 16.8	20 5.7	9 27.7	11 45.2	5 43.5	20 40.7
25 T	4 12 50.9	2 0.3	21 34.2	26 14.6	12 2.3	28 23.0	13 32.6	20 2.4	9 33.7	11 43.9	5 44.0	20 39.9
26 W	4 16 47.5	3 1.0	21 31.0	8♒22.7	13 34.4	27 47.5	13 47.9	19 59.0	9 39.9	11 42.6	5 44.5	20 39.1
27 T	4 20 44.0	4 1.8	21 27.8	20 20.3	15 6.3	27 12.8	14 2.7	19 55.3	9 46.1	11 41.4	5 44.9	20 38.3
28 F	4 24 40.6	5 2.5	21 24.7	2♓11.7	16 38.0	26 39.0	14 16.9	19 51.5	9 52.3	11 40.2	5 45.3	20 37.5
29 S	4 28 37.1	6 3.3	21 21.5	14 2.1	18 9.5	26 6.4	14 30.5	19 47.5	9 58.6	11 39.1	5 45.6	20 36.6
30 S	4 32 33.7	7 4.1	21 18.3	25 56.6	19 40.8	25 35.3	14 43.6	19 43.3	10 4.9	11 38.0	5 45.9	20 35.8

DECLINATION

DAY	EPHEMERIS SIDEREAL TIME h m s	☉ ° ′	☊ ° ′	☽ ° ′	☿ ° ′	♀ ° ′	♂ ° ′	♃ ° ′	♄ ° ′	♅ ° ′	♆ ° ′	♇ ° ′
1 S	2 38 13.5	14S 8.1	8N53.2	12S50.3	12S 5.4	27S15.5	20N25.9	21N53.9	22S48.0	4N16.0	10N10.1	21N53.1
4 T	2 50 3.2	15 5.4	8 49.6	3N58.5	14 1.4	27 5.9	20 12.3	21 53.8	22 47.5	4 13.6	10 8.8	21 53.4
7 F	3 1 52.9	16 0.4	8 46.1	20 13.2	15 50.9	26 47.5	19 59.1	21 54.0	22 46.9	4 11.4	10 7.7	21 53.7
10 M	3 13 42.6	16 53.1	8 42.6	28 17.0	17 33.2	26 19.6	19 46.5	21 54.4	22 46.3	4 9.2	10 6.7	21 54.1
13 T	3 25 32.2	17 43.2	8 39.0	21 37.2	19 7.7	25 41.9	19 34.5	21 55.1	22 45.6	4 7.2	10 5.8	21 54.5
16 S	3 37 21.9	18 30.6	8 35.4	3 59.7	20 33.6	24 54.4	19 23.3	21 56.1	22 44.9	4 5.3	10 5.0	21 55.0
19 W	3 49 11.6	19 15.0	8 31.9	15S19.3	21 50.5	23 58.2	19 13.0	21 57.3	22 44.0	4 3.5	10 4.3	21 55.5
22 S	4 1 1.3	19 56.3	8 28.3	27 9.7	22 57.6	22 54.8	19 3.9	21 58.8	22 43.1	4 1.9	10 3.7	21 56.0
25 T	4 12 50.9	20 34.4	8 24.8	25 58.5	23 54.4	21 47.0	18 55.9	22 0.6	22 42.1	4 0.4	10 3.2	21 56.5
28 F	4 24 40.6	21 9.0	8 21.2	14 25.7	24 40.2	20 37.8	18 49.4	22 2.6	22 41.0	3 59.0	10 2.8	21 57.1

DECEMBER 1930

LONGITUDE

DAY	EPHEMERIS SIDEREAL TIME h m s	☉ ° ′	☊ ° ′	☽ ° ′	☿ ° ′	♀ ° ′	♂ ° ′	♃ ° ′	♄ ° ′	♅ ° ′	♆ ° ′	♇ ° ′
1 M	4 36 30.3	8♐ 4.9	21♈15.1	8♈ 0.4	21♐12.0	25♏ 5.8	14♌56.1	19♋39.0	10♑11.2	11♈37.0	5♍46.2	20♋34.9
2 T	4 40 26.8	9 5.7	21 12.0	20 18.1	22 42.8	24R38.1	15 8.0	19R34.5	10 17.6	11R36.0	5 46.4	20R34.0
3 W	4 44 23.4	10 6.5	21 8.8	2♉53.7	24 13.4	24 12.3	15 19.3	19 29.7	10 24.1	11 35.1	5 46.7	20 33.1
4 T	4 48 19.9	11 7.4	21 5.6	15 49.9	25 43.6	23 48.6	15 30.0	19 24.9	10 30.5	11 34.2	5 46.8	20 32.1
5 F	4 52 16.5	12 8.2	21 2.4	29 8.1	27 13.5	23 27.1	15 40.0	19 19.8	10 37.0	11 33.3	5 47.0	20 31.2
6 S	4 56 13.1	13 9.1	20 59.3	12♊47.3	28 43.0	23 7.9	15 49.5	19 14.6	10 43.6	11 32.5	5 47.1	20 30.2
7 S	5 0 9.6	14 10.0	20 56.1	26 44.9	0♑12.0	22 51.0	15 58.2	19 9.2	10 50.2	11 31.8	5 47.2	20 29.2
8 M	5 4 6.2	15 10.9	20 52.9	10♋56.6	1 40.4	22 36.6	16 6.4	19 3.7	10 56.8	11 31.1	5 47.2	20 28.2
9 T	5 8 2.7	16 11.9	20 49.7	25 16.6	3 8.0	22 24.7	16 13.8	18 58.0	11 3.4	11 30.4	5 47.2	20 27.2
10 W	5 11 59.3	17 12.8	20 46.6	9♌39.6	4 34.9	22 15.3	16 20.6	18 52.2	11 10.1	11 29.8	5R47.2	20 26.2
11 T	5 15 55.9	18 13.8	20 43.4	24 0.3	6 0.8	22 8.4	16 26.7	18 46.2	11 16.8	11 29.3	5 47.1	20 25.1
12 F	5 19 52.4	19 14.8	20 40.2	8♍15.2	7 25.6	22 4.0	16 32.0	18 40.1	11 23.6	11 28.8	5 47.0	20 24.1
13 S	5 23 49.0	20 15.8	20 37.0	22 22.0	8 49.0	22 2.2	16 36.7	18 33.8	11 30.3	11 28.3	5 46.9	20 23.0
14 S	5 27 45.5	21 16.8	20 33.8	6♎19.6	10 10.9	22D 2.7	16 40.6	18 27.4	11 37.1	11 27.9	5 46.7	20 21.9
15 M	5 31 42.1	22 17.9	20 30.7	20 7.9	11 30.9	22 5.7	16 43.7	18 20.8	11 44.0	11 27.5	5 46.5	20 20.8
16 T	5 35 38.7	23 18.9	20 27.5	3♏46.8	12 48.8	22 11.1	16 46.1	18 14.2	11 50.8	11 27.2	5 46.3	20 19.7
17 W	5 39 35.2	24 20.0	20 24.3	17 16.4	14 4.1	22 18.8	16 47.7	18 7.4	11 57.7	11 27.0	5 46.0	20 18.6
18 T	5 43 31.8	25 21.1	20 21.1	0♐36.0	15 16.4	22 28.8	16 48.6	18 0.4	12 4.6	11 26.8	5 45.7	20 17.4
19 F	5 47 28.3	26 22.2	20 18.0	13 44.8	16 25.3	22 41.1	16 48.6	17 53.4	12 11.5	11 26.6	5 45.3	20 16.3
20 S	5 51 24.9	27 23.3	20 14.8	26 41.6	17 30.2	22 55.4	16R47.9	17 46.3	12 18.5	11 26.6	5 45.0	20 15.1
21 S	5 55 21.5	28 24.5	20 11.6	9♑25.3	18 30.5	23 11.9	16 46.3	17 39.0	12 25.4	11 26.5	5 44.6	20 13.9
22 M	5 59 18.0	29 25.6	20 8.4	21 55.5	19 25.4	23 30.4	16 44.0	17 31.7	12 32.4	11D26.5	5 44.1	20 12.7
23 T	6 3 14.5	0♑26.7	20 5.3	4♒12.5	20 14.2	23 50.8	16 40.8	17 24.3	12 39.4	11 26.6	5 43.7	20 11.5
24 W	6 7 11.1	1 27.9	20 2.1	16 17.6	20 56.1	24 13.2	16 36.8	17 16.7	12 46.4	11 26.7	5 43.2	20 10.3
25 T	6 11 7.7	2 29.0	19 58.9	28 13.3	21 30.2	24 37.4	16 32.0	17 9.1	12 53.4	11 26.9	5 42.6	20 9.1
26 F	6 15 4.3	3 30.2	19 55.7	10♓ 3.2	21 55.5	25 3.3	16 26.3	17 1.5	13 0.5	11 27.1	5 42.1	20 7.9
27 S	6 19 0.8	4 31.3	19 52.6	21 51.5	22 11.2	25 31.0	16 19.9	16 53.7	13 7.5	11 27.3	5 41.5	20 6.7
28 S	6 22 57.3	5 32.5	19 49.4	3♈43.4	22 16.5	26 0.3	16 12.6	16 45.9	13 14.6	11 27.7	5 40.8	20 5.4
29 M	6 26 53.9	6 33.6	19 46.2	15 44.3	22R10.6	26 31.2	16 4.5	16 38.0	13 21.6	11 28.0	5 40.2	20 4.2
30 T	6 30 50.5	7 34.8	19 43.0	27 59.8	21 53.0	27 3.6	15 55.5	16 30.1	13 28.7	11 28.5	5 39.5	20 3.0
31 W	6 34 47.0	8 35.9	19 39.9	10♉35.2	21 23.5	27 37.5	15 45.8	16 22.2	13 35.8	11 28.9	5 38.7	20 1.7

DECLINATION

DAY	EPHEMERIS SIDEREAL TIME h m s	☉ ° ′	☊ ° ′	☽ ° ′	☿ ° ′	♀ ° ′	♂ ° ′	♃ ° ′	♄ ° ′	♅ ° ′	♆ ° ′	♇ ° ′
1 M	4 36 30.3	21S39.9	8N17.6	1N57.6	25S14.4	19S30.6	18N44.4	22N 4.9	22S39.9	3N57.9	10N 2.6	21N57.6
4 T	4 48 19.9	22 7.2	8 14.1	18 30.6	25 36.4	18 28.4	18 41.0	22 7.3	22 38.7	3 56.9	10 2.5	21 58.2
7 S	5 0 9.6	22 30.6	8 10.5	28 0.2	25 45.6	17 33.7	18 39.4	22 10.0	22 37.4	3 56.0	10 2.4	21 58.9
10 W	5 11 59.3	22 50.1	8 6.9	22 30.9	25 41.8	16 48.1	18 39.6	22 12.8	22 36.0	3 55.4	10 2.5	21 59.5
13 S	5 23 49.0	23 5.6	8 3.3	5 20.7	25 24.8	16 12.3	18 41.9	22 15.8	22 34.5	3 54.9	10 2.7	22 0.2
16 T	5 35 38.7	23 16.9	7 59.7	13S46.1	24 55.2	15 46.4	18 46.3	22 18.9	22 33.0	3 54.6	10 3.0	22 0.9
19 F	5 47 28.3	23 24.0	7 56.1	26 24.9	24 14.1	15 30.0	18 52.9	22 22.1	22 31.4	3 54.4	10 3.5	22 1.6
22 M	5 59 18.0	23 27.0	7 52.5	26 37.5	23 24.2	15 22.1	19 1.7	22 25.4	22 29.7	3 54.5	10 4.0	22 2.3
25 T	6 11 7.7	23 25.6	7 49.0	15 50.4	22 29.4	15 21.9	19 12.8	22 28.7	22 27.9	3 54.7	10 4.7	22 3.0
28 S	6 22 57.3	23 20.1	7 45.4	0N 8.8	21 35.4	15 28.4	19 26.0	22 32.1	22 26.1	3 55.2	10 5.4	22 3.8
31 W	6 34 47.0	23 10.3	7 41.8	16 39.8	20 48.8	15 40.4	19 41.3	22 35.4	22 24.2	3 55.8	10 6.3	22 4.5

JANUARY 1931

DAY	EPHEMERIS SIDEREAL TIME	☉	☊	☽	☿	♀	♂	♃	♄	♅	♆	♇
	h m s	° ′	° ′	° ′	° ′	° ′	° ′	° ′	° ′	° ′	° ′	° ′
						LONGITUDE						
1 T	6 38 43.6	9♑37.1	19♈36.7	23♉34.5	20♑42.4	28♏12.8	15♌35.2	16♋14.2	13♑42.9	11♈29.5	5♍38.0	20♋ 0.5
2 F	6 42 40.1	10 38.2	19 33.5	7♊ 0.6	19R50.2	28 49.5	15R23.9	16R 6.1	13 50.0	11 30.0	5R37.2	19R59.2
3 S	6 46 36.7	11 39.3	19 30.3	20 53.8	18 48.1	29 27.5	15 11.7	15 58.1	13 57.1	11 30.7	5 36.4	19 57.9
4 S	6 50 33.3	12 40.5	19 27.1	5♋11.5	17 37.9	0♐ 6.7	14 58.8	15 50.0	14 4.2	11 31.4	5 35.5	19 56.6
5 M	6 54 29.8	13 41.6	19 24.0	19 48.4	16 21.6	0 47.2	14 45.1	15 41.9	14 11.3	11 32.1	5 34.7	19 55.4
6 T	6 58 26.4	14 42.7	19 20.8	4♌36.8	15 1.7	1 28.8	14 30.6	15 33.8	14 18.4	11 32.9	5 33.8	19 54.1
7 W	7 2 22.9	15 43.9	19 17.6	19 27.9	13 40.8	2 11.6	14 15.3	15 25.7	14 25.5	11 33.7	5 32.8	19 52.8
8 T	7 6 19.5	16 45.0	19 14.4	4♍13.4	12 21.6	2 55.5	13 59.4	15 17.6	14 32.6	11 34.6	5 31.9	19 51.5
9 F	7 10 16.1	17 46.2	19 11.3	18 46.7	11 6.4	3 40.4	13 42.7	15 9.5	14 39.7	11 35.5	5 30.9	19 50.2
10 S	7 14 12.6	18 47.3	19 8.1	3♎ 3.8	9 57.3	4 26.3	13 25.3	15 1.4	14 46.8	11 36.5	5 29.9	19 49.0
11 S	7 18 9.2	19 48.4	19 4.9	17 3.1	8 55.8	5 13.2	13 7.2	14 53.3	14 53.9	11 37.6	5 28.8	19 47.7
12 M	7 22 5.7	20 49.6	19 1.7	0♏44.9	8 3.1	6 0.9	12 48.4	14 45.3	15 1.0	11 38.6	5 27.8	19 46.4
13 T	7 26 2.3	21 50.7	18 58.6	14 10.5	7 19.9	6 49.6	12 29.1	14 37.3	15 8.1	11 39.8	5 26.7	19 45.1
14 W	7 29 58.9	22 51.8	18 55.4	27 21.8	6 46.4	7 39.1	12 9.1	14 29.3	15 15.2	11 41.0	5 25.6	19 43.8
15 T	7 33 55.4	23 53.0	18 52.2	10♐20.4	6 22.7	8 29.5	11 48.6	14 21.4	15 22.2	11 42.2	5 24.4	19 42.5
16 F	7 37 52.0	24 54.1	18 49.0	23 7.8	6 8.4	9 20.5	11 27.6	14 13.5	15 29.3	11 43.5	5 23.2	19 41.2
17 S	7 41 48.5	25 55.2	18 45.9	5♑44.6	6 3.1	10 12.4	11 6.0	14 5.7	15 36.3	11 44.8	5 22.1	19 40.0
18 S	7 45 45.1	26 56.4	18 42.7	18 11.4	6D 6.2	11 4.9	10 44.0	13 58.0	15 43.4	11 46.2	5 20.8	19 38.7
19 M	7 49 41.6	27 57.5	18 39.5	0♒28.4	6 17.3	11 58.2	10 21.6	13 50.3	15 50.4	11 47.6	5 19.6	19 37.4
20 T	7 53 38.2	28 58.6	18 36.3	12 36.0	6 35.5	12 52.1	9 58.9	13 42.7	15 57.4	11 49.1	5 18.3	19 36.1
21 W	7 57 34.8	29 59.6	18 33.1	24 35.1	7 0.4	13 46.6	9 35.8	13 35.1	16 4.3	11 50.6	5 17.1	19 34.9
22 T	8 1 31.3	1♒ 0.7	18 30.0	6♓27.5	7 31.3	14 41.7	9 12.4	13 27.7	16 11.3	11 52.2	5 15.7	19 33.6
23 F	8 5 27.9	2 1.8	18 26.8	18 15.4	8 7.6	15 37.5	8 48.8	13 20.4	16 18.3	11 53.8	5 14.4	19 32.4
24 S	8 9 24.4	3 2.8	18 23.6	0♈ 2.4	8 48.9	16 33.7	8 25.0	13 13.1	16 25.2	11 55.5	5 13.1	19 31.1
25 S	8 13 21.0	4 3.8	18 20.4	11 52.6	9 34.7	17 30.5	8 1.1	13 6.0	16 32.1	11 57.2	5 11.7	19 29.9
26 M	8 17 17.5	5 4.9	18 17.3	23 51.0	10 24.5	18 27.9	7 37.0	12 58.9	16 39.0	11 59.0	5 10.3	19 28.6
27 T	8 21 14.1	6 5.9	18 14.1	6♉ 2.7	11 18.0	19 25.7	7 13.0	12 52.0	16 45.8	12 0.8	5 8.9	19 27.4
28 W	8 25 10.7	7 6.8	18 10.9	18 33.4	12 14.8	20 24.0	6 48.9	12 45.2	16 52.6	12 2.6	5 7.5	19 26.2
29 T	8 29 7.2	8 7.8	18 7.7	1♊28.2	13 14.6	21 22.8	6 24.9	12 38.5	16 59.4	12 4.5	5 6.0	19 25.0
30 F	8 33 3.8	9 8.7	18 4.6	14 50.8	14 17.1	22 22.0	6 1.0	12 32.0	17 6.2	12 6.4	5 4.6	19 23.8
31 S	8 37 0.3	10 9.6	18 1.4	28 43.5	15 22.2	23 21.7	5 37.3	12 25.6	17 13.0	12 8.4	5 3.1	19 22.6
						DECLINATION						
1 T	6 38 43.6	23S 6.1	7N40.6	21N21.2	20S35.7	15S45.5	19N46.9	22N36.5	22S23.5	3N56.0	10N 6.6	22N 4.8
4 S	6 50 33.3	22 50.8	7 36.9	28 11.1	20 5.8	16 3.4	20 4.7	22 39.8	22 21.5	3 56.9	10 7.6	22 5.5
7 W	7 2 22.9	22 31.4	7 33.3	19 5.9	19 49.7	16 24.6	20 24.1	22 43.1	22 19.5	3 57.9	10 8.6	22 6.3
10 S	7 14 12.6	22 8.0	7 29.7	0 3.3	19 46.7	16 48.2	20 44.9	22 46.2	22 17.4	3 59.1	10 9.8	22 7.0
13 T	7 26 2.3	21 40.6	7 26.1	18S 8.7	19 55.7	17 13.3	21 6.7	22 49.3	22 15.2	4 0.5	10 11.1	22 7.8
16 F	7 37 52.0	21 9.6	7 22.5	27 46.9	20 14.1	17 39.2	21 29.1	22 52.3	22 13.0	4 2.0	10 12.4	22 8.5
19 M	7 49 41.6	20 34.8	7 18.9	24 49.2	20 38.0	18 5.0	21 51.6	22 55.1	22 10.8	4 3.7	10 13.8	22 9.3
22 T	8 1 31.3	19 56.5	7 15.2	12 12.5	21 3.3	18 30.1	22 13.9	22 57.8	22 8.5	4 5.6	10 15.3	22 10.0
25 S	8 13 21.0	19 14.9	7 11.6	4N15.9	21 26.3	18 53.9	22 35.4	23 0.3	22 6.2	4 7.7	10 16.9	22 10.7
28 W	8 25 10.7	18 30.1	7 8.0	19 53.7	21 44.1	19 15.9	22 55.7	23 2.7	22 3.8	4 9.9	10 18.5	22 11.5
31 S	8 37 0.3	17 42.4	7 4.4	28 14.7	21 54.5	19 35.5	23 14.4	23 4.9	22 1.4	4 12.2	10 20.1	22 12.2

FEBRUARY 1931

DAY	EPHEMERIS SIDEREAL TIME	☉	☊	☽	☿	♀	♂	♃	♄	♅	♆	♇
						LONGITUDE						
1 S	8 40 56.9	11♒10.5	17♈58.2	13♋ 5.4	16♑29.5	24♐21.8	5♌13.7	12♋19.3	17♑19.7	12♈10.4	5♍ 1.6	19♋21.4
2 M	8 44 53.5	12 11.4	17 55.0	27 52.2	17 39.0	25 22.3	4R50.4	12R13.1	17 26.4	12 12.5	5R 0.1	19R20.2
3 T	8 48 50.0	13 12.2	17 51.8	12♌56.4	18 50.4	26 23.2	4 27.3	12 7.1	17 33.0	12 14.6	4 58.6	19 19.1
4 W	8 52 46.5	14 13.1	17 48.7	28 8.0	20 3.5	27 24.5	4 4.6	12 1.3	17 39.6	12 16.7	4 57.1	19 17.9
5 T	8 56 43.1	15 13.9	17 45.5	13♍16.5	21 18.4	28 26.1	3 42.2	11 55.6	17 46.2	12 18.9	4 55.5	19 16.8
6 F	9 0 39.7	16 14.7	17 42.3	28 12.5	22 34.8	29 28.1	3 20.2	11 50.0	17 52.8	12 21.1	4 54.0	19 15.6
7 S	9 4 36.2	17 15.4	17 39.1	12♎49.1	23 52.7	0♑30.4	2 58.6	11 44.6	17 59.3	12 23.3	4 52.4	19 14.5
8 S	9 8 32.8	18 16.2	17 36.0	27 2.5	25 11.9	1 33.1	2 37.5	11 39.4	18 5.8	12 25.6	4 50.8	19 13.4
9 M	9 12 29.3	19 17.0	17 32.8	10♏51.9	26 32.4	2 36.1	2 16.9	11 34.3	18 12.2	12 28.0	4 49.2	19 12.3
10 T	9 16 25.9	20 17.7	17 29.6	24 18.4	27 54.2	3 39.4	1 56.9	11 29.4	18 18.7	12 30.3	4 47.6	19 11.2
11 W	9 20 22.5	21 18.4	17 26.4	7♐24.4	29 17.1	4 43.0	1 37.4	11 24.7	18 25.0	12 32.7	4 46.0	19 10.2
12 T	9 24 19.0	22 19.1	17 23.3	20 12.9	0♒41.2	5 46.9	1 18.5	11 20.1	18 31.3	12 35.2	4 44.4	19 9.1
13 F	9 28 15.5	23 19.8	17 20.1	2♑46.8	2 6.4	6 51.1	1 0.2	11 15.7	18 37.6	12 37.7	4 42.7	19 8.1
14 S	9 32 12.1	24 20.4	17 16.9	15 8.8	3 32.6	7 55.5	0 42.5	11 11.5	18 43.9	12 40.2	4 41.1	19 7.0
15 S	9 36 8.7	25 21.1	17 13.7	27 21.0	4 59.9	9 0.2	0 25.6	11 7.4	18 50.1	12 42.7	4 39.4	19 6.0
16 M	9 40 5.2	26 21.7	17 10.6	9♒25.3	6 28.2	10 5.1	0 9.3	11 3.6	18 56.2	12 45.3	4 37.8	19 5.1
17 T	9 44 1.8	27 22.3	17 7.4	21 23.1	7 57.4	11 10.2	29♋53.8	10 59.9	19 2.3	12 47.9	4 36.1	19 4.1
18 W	9 47 58.3	28 22.8	17 4.2	3♓15.8	9 27.7	12 15.6	29 38.9	10 56.4	19 8.4	12 50.6	4 34.5	19 3.1
19 T	9 51 54.9	29 23.4	17 1.0	15 5.1	10 58.9	13 21.2	29 24.9	10 53.1	19 14.4	12 53.3	4 32.8	19 2.2
20 F	9 55 51.5	0♓23.9	16 57.8	26 52.7	12 31.1	14 27.0	29 11.6	10 50.0	19 20.3	12 56.0	4 31.1	19 1.2
21 S	9 59 48.0	1 24.4	16 54.7	8♈41.3	14 4.2	15 33.0	28 59.0	10 47.1	19 26.2	12 58.7	4 29.5	19 0.3
22 S	10 3 44.6	2 24.8	16 51.5	20 33.7	15 38.3	16 39.2	28 47.3	10 44.4	19 32.1	13 1.5	4 27.8	18 59.5
23 M	10 7 41.1	3 25.3	16 48.3	2♉33.8	17 13.3	17 45.6	28 36.3	10 41.9	19 37.8	13 4.3	4 26.1	18 58.6
24 T	10 11 37.7	4 25.7	16 45.1	14 45.8	18 49.3	18 52.1	28 26.2	10 39.6	19 43.6	13 7.1	4 24.4	18 57.7
25 W	10 15 34.2	5 26.0	16 42.0	27 14.4	20 26.3	19 58.9	28 16.8	10 37.4	19 49.3	13 10.0	4 22.7	18 56.9
26 T	10 19 30.8	6 26.4	16 38.8	10♊ 4.1	22 4.2	21 5.8	28 8.2	10 35.5	19 54.9	13 12.9	4 21.1	18 56.1
27 F	10 23 27.3	7 26.6	16 35.6	23 19.2	23 43.1	22 12.9	28 0.5	10 33.8	20 0.5	13 15.8	4 19.4	18 55.3
28 S	10 27 23.9	8 26.9	16 32.4	7♋ 2.4	25 23.1	23 20.1	27 53.5	10 32.2	20 6.0	13 18.7	4 17.7	18 54.5
						DECLINATION						
1 S	8 40 56.9	17S25.8	7N 3.1	27N49.3	21S56.1	19S41.5	23N20.2	23N 5.6	22S 0.6	4N13.0	10N20.7	22N12.4
4 W	8 52 46.5	16 34.3	6 59.5	15 40.3	21 54.6	19 57.4	23 36.4	23 7.5	21 58.2	4 15.6	10 22.4	22 13.1
7 S	9 4 36.2	15 40.2	6 55.9	4S47.6	21 43.0	20 9.9	23 50.5	23 9.3	21 55.8	4 18.3	10 24.2	22 13.7
10 T	9 16 25.9	14 43.7	6 52.2	21 55.2	21 20.7	20 18.8	24 2.4	23 11.0	21 53.4	4 21.1	10 26.0	22 14.4
13 F	9 28 15.5	13 44.9	6 48.6	28 23.3	20 47.1	20 23.6	24 12.0	23 12.4	21 51.0	4 24.0	10 27.8	22 15.0
16 M	9 40 5.2	12 44.1	6 44.9	22 24.1	20 2.1	20 24.3	24 19.3	23 13.7	21 48.6	4 27.1	10 29.7	22 15.6
19 T	9 51 54.9	11 41.5	6 41.3	8 15.2	19 5.3	20 20.4	24 24.4	23 14.9	21 46.2	4 30.2	10 31.6	22 16.2
22 S	10 3 44.6	10 37.2	6 37.6	8N30.1	17 56.7	20 12.0	24 27.3	23 15.9	21 43.9	4 33.5	10 33.4	22 16.8
25 W	10 15 34.2	9 31.4	6 34.0	22 57.1	16 36.2	19 58.9	24 28.3	23 16.7	21 41.6	4 36.9	10 35.3	22 17.3
28 S	10 27 23.9	8 24.3	6 30.3	28 24.0	15 3.7	19 41.0	24 27.4	23 17.3	21 39.3	4 40.4	10 37.1	22 17.8

MARCH 1931

LONGITUDE

DAY	EPHEMERIS SIDEREAL TIME h m s	☉ ° ′	☊ ° ′	☽ ° ′	☿ ° ′	♀ ° ′	♂ ° ′	♃ ° ′	♄ ° ′	♅ ° ′	♆ ° ′	♇ ° ′
1 S	10 31 20.5	9♓27.1	16♈29.2	21♋14.6	27♒ 4.0	24♑27.5	27♋47.3	10♋30.9	20♑11.4	13♈21.7	4♍16.1	18♋53.8
2 M	10 35 17.0	10 27.3	16 26.1	5♌53.7	28 46.0	25 35.1	27R42.0	10R29.7	20 16.8	13 24.7	4R14.4	18R53.0
3 T	10 39 13.5	11 27.5	16 22.9	20 54.4	0♓29.0	26 42.8	27 37.4	10 28.8	20 22.1	13 27.7	4 12.7	18 52.3
4 W	10 43 10.1	12 27.6	16 19.7	6♍ 8.3	2 13.1	27 50.6	27 33.5	10 28.0	20 27.4	13 30.8	4 11.1	18 51.6
5 T	10 47 6.7	13 27.7	16 16.5	21 25.3	3 58.2	28 58.6	27 30.5	10 27.5	20 32.6	13 33.8	4 9.4	18 50.9
6 F	10 51 3.2	14 27.8	16 13.4	6♎34.7	5 44.5	0♒ 6.8	27 28.2	10 27.1	20 37.7	13 36.9	4 7.8	18 50.3
7 S	10 54 59.8	15 27.8	16 10.2	21 27.6	7 31.8	1 15.0	27 26.7	10 26.9	20 42.8	13 40.0	4 6.1	18 49.7
8 S	10 58 56.3	16 27.8	16 7.0	5♏57.7	9 20.2	2 23.4	27 25.9	10D27.0	20 47.8	13 43.1	4 4.5	18 49.1
9 M	11 2 52.9	17 27.8	16 3.8	20 1.5	11 9.8	3 32.0	27 25.8	10 27.2	20 52.7	13 46.3	4 2.9	18 48.5
10 T	11 6 49.4	18 27.8	16 0.6	3♐38.5	13 0.4	4 40.6	27D26.5	10 27.6	20 57.6	13 49.4	4 1.3	18 47.9
11 W	11 10 46.0	19 27.7	15 57.5	16 50.1	14 52.2	5 49.4	27 27.9	10 28.3	21 2.4	13 52.6	3 59.6	18 47.4
12 T	11 14 42.5	20 27.6	15 54.3	29 39.3	16 45.1	6 58.3	27 30.0	10 29.1	21 7.1	13 55.8	3 58.1	18 46.8
13 F	11 18 39.1	21 27.5	15 51.1	12♑ 9.7	18 39.1	8 7.3	27 32.8	10 30.1	21 11.8	13 59.1	3 56.5	18 46.3
14 S	11 22 35.6	22 27.3	15 47.9	24 25.1	20 34.1	9 16.4	27 36.3	10 31.3	21 16.4	14 2.3	3 54.9	18 45.9
15 S	11 26 32.2	23 27.1	15 44.8	6♒29.2	22 30.1	10 25.7	27 40.5	10 32.7	21 20.9	14 5.6	3 53.3	18 45.4
16 M	11 30 28.8	24 26.9	15 41.6	18 25.3	24 27.2	11 35.0	27 45.4	10 34.3	21 25.3	14 8.8	3 51.8	18 45.0
17 T	11 34 25.3	25 26.7	15 38.4	0♓16.4	26 25.1	12 44.4	27 50.9	10 36.1	21 29.7	14 12.1	3 50.2	18 44.6
18 W	11 38 21.9	26 26.4	15 35.2	12 4.9	28 23.9	13 53.9	27 57.1	10 38.0	21 34.0	14 15.4	3 48.7	18 44.2
19 T	11 42 18.4	27 26.1	15 32.0	23 53.3	0♈23.4	15 3.5	28 3.9	10 40.2	21 38.2	14 18.7	3 47.2	18 43.8
20 F	11 46 15.0	28 25.7	15 28.9	5♈43.4	2 23.4	16 13.2	28 11.3	10 42.5	21 42.3	14 22.1	3 45.7	18 43.5
21 S	11 50 11.5	29 25.4	15 25.7	17 37.5	4 23.9	17 22.9	28 19.4	10 45.1	21 46.4	14 25.4	3 44.2	18 43.2
22 S	11 54 8.1	0♈25.0	15 22.5	29 37.6	6 24.7	18 32.8	28 28.1	10 47.8	21 50.3	14 28.7	3 42.7	18 42.9
23 M	11 58 4.6	1 24.5	15 19.3	11♉46.2	8 25.5	19 42.7	28 37.3	10 50.7	21 54.2	14 32.1	3 41.3	18 42.7
24 T	12 2 1.2	2 24.0	15 16.2	24 6.1	10 26.1	20 52.7	28 47.2	10 53.8	21 58.0	14 35.5	3 39.9	18 42.4
25 W	12 5 57.7	3 23.5	15 13.0	6♊40.3	12 26.2	22 2.7	28 57.6	10 57.1	22 1.8	14 38.8	3 38.5	18 42.2
26 T	12 9 54.3	4 23.0	15 9.8	19 32.0	14 25.5	23 12.9	29 8.6	11 0.6	22 5.4	14 42.2	3 37.1	18 42.0
27 F	12 13 50.8	5 22.4	15 6.6	2♋44.2	16 23.7	24 23.1	29 20.2	11 4.2	22 9.0	14 45.6	3 35.7	18 41.9
28 S	12 17 47.4	6 21.7	15 3.4	16 19.2	18 20.3	25 33.3	29 32.2	11 8.0	22 12.5	14 49.0	3 34.3	18 41.7
29 S	12 21 43.9	7 21.0	15 0.3	0♌18.2	20 15.0	26 43.6	29 44.8	11 12.0	22 15.8	14 52.4	3 33.0	18 41.6
30 M	12 25 40.5	8 20.3	14 57.1	14 40.8	22 7.5	27 54.0	29 57.9	11 16.2	22 19.2	14 55.8	3 31.7	18 41.5
31 T	12 29 37.1	9 19.6	14 53.9	29 24.1	23 57.2	29 4.5	0♌11.5	11 20.5	22 22.4	14 59.3	3 30.4	18 41.5

DECLINATION

DAY	EPHEMERIS SIDEREAL TIME	☉	☊	☽	☿	♀	♂	♃	♄	♅	♆	♇
1 S	10 31 20.5	8S 1.7	6N29.1	26N52.1	14S30.2	19S34.0	24N26.7	23N17.5	21S38.5	4N41.5	10N37.8	22N18.0
4 W	10 43 10.1	6 53.3	6 25.4	12 16.9	12 41.9	19 9.7	24 23.6	23 18.0	21 36.3	4 45.1	10 39.6	22 18.5
7 S	10 54 59.8	5 44.0	6 21.8	8S57.2	10 41.8	18 40.7	24 18.9	23 18.3	21 34.1	4 48.8	10 41.4	22 18.9
10 T	11 6 49.4	4 33.9	6 18.1	24 46.6	8 30.1	18 6.9	24 12.9	23 18.5	21 32.0	4 52.5	10 43.2	22 19.4
13 F	11 18 39.1	3 23.3	6 14.4	28 6.6	6 7.4	17 28.6	24 5.5	23 18.5	21 30.0	4 56.2	10 45.0	22 19.8
16 M	11 30 28.8	2 12.4	6 10.8	19 27.2	3 34.4	16 45.7	23 56.9	23 18.4	21 28.1	5 0.1	10 46.7	22 20.1
19 T	11 42 18.4	1 1.2	6 7.1	4 7.4	0 52.7	15 58.5	23 47.1	23 18.1	21 26.2	5 3.9	10 48.3	22 20.4
22 S	11 54 8.1	0N 9.9	6 3.4	12N39.1	1N55.2	15 7.2	23 36.2	23 17.7	21 24.4	5 7.8	10 50.0	22 20.8
25 W	12 5 57.7	1 21.0	5 59.7	25 33.5	4 45.8	14 12.0	23 24.3	23 17.1	21 22.8	5 11.8	10 51.5	22 21.0
28 S	12 17 47.4	2 31.7	5 56.0	27 42.0	7 33.8	13 13.2	23 11.3	23 16.4	21 21.2	5 15.8	10 53.0	22 21.3
31 T	12 29 37.1	3 41.9	5 52.4	15 11.6	10 13.4	12 10.9	22 57.3	23 15.5	21 19.7	5 19.7	10 54.4	22 21.5

APRIL 1931

LONGITUDE

DAY	EPHEMERIS SIDEREAL TIME	☉	☊	☽	☿	♀	♂	♃	♄	♅	♆	♇
1 W	12 33 33.6	10♈18.8	14♈50.7	14♍22.6	25♈43.8	0♓15.0	0♌25.6	11♋25.0	22♑25.5	15♈ 2.7	3♍29.1	18♋41.4
2 T	12 37 30.2	11 18.0	14 47.6	29 28.8	27 26.9	1 25.6	0 40.2	11 29.7	22 28.6	15 6.1	3R27.8	18R41.4
3 F	12 41 26.7	12 17.1	14 44.4	14♎33.8	29 6.2	2 36.2	0 55.2	11 34.5	22 31.5	15 9.5	3 26.6	18D41.4
4 S	12 45 23.3	13 16.2	14 41.2	29 28.8	0♉41.2	3 46.9	1 10.7	11 39.5	22 34.4	15 13.0	3 25.4	18 41.4
5 S	12 49 19.8	14 15.3	14 38.0	14♏ 5.9	2 11.6	4 57.7	1 26.7	11 44.7	22 37.2	15 16.4	3 24.2	18 41.5
6 M	12 53 16.4	15 14.3	14 34.8	28 19.6	3 37.2	6 8.5	1 43.0	11 50.0	22 39.8	15 19.8	3 23.1	18 41.6
7 T	12 57 12.9	16 13.3	14 31.7	12♐ 7.0	4 57.6	7 19.3	1 59.8	11 55.5	22 42.5	15 23.2	3 21.9	18 41.7
8 W	13 1 9.5	17 12.3	14 28.5	25 27.6	6 12.7	8 30.3	2 17.0	12 1.1	22 45.0	15 26.7	3 20.8	18 41.8
9 T	13 5 6.1	18 11.3	14 25.3	8♑23.2	7 22.1	9 41.2	2 34.6	12 6.9	22 47.4	15 30.1	3 19.7	18 42.0
10 F	13 9 2.6	19 10.2	14 22.1	20 56.8	8 25.8	10 52.3	2 52.6	12 12.9	22 49.7	15 33.5	3 18.7	18 42.1
11 S	13 12 59.1	20 9.1	14 19.0	3♒12.5	9 23.6	12 3.3	3 11.0	12 19.0	22 51.9	15 37.0	3 17.6	18 42.3
12 S	13 16 55.7	21 7.9	14 15.8	15 14.7	10 15.4	13 14.5	3 29.8	12 25.2	22 54.1	15 40.4	3 16.6	18 42.6
13 M	13 20 52.3	22 6.8	14 12.6	27 7.9	11 0.9	14 25.6	3 49.0	12 31.7	22 56.1	15 43.8	3 15.6	18 42.8
14 T	13 24 48.8	23 5.6	14 9.4	8♓56.4	11 40.3	15 36.8	4 8.5	12 38.2	22 58.1	15 47.2	3 14.7	18 43.1
15 W	13 28 45.4	24 4.3	14 6.2	20 44.0	12 13.3	16 48.1	4 28.4	12 44.9	22 59.9	15 50.6	3 13.7	18 43.4
16 T	13 32 41.9	25 3.1	14 3.1	2♈34.0	12 40.0	17 59.4	4 48.7	12 51.8	23 1.7	15 54.0	3 12.8	18 43.7
17 F	13 36 38.5	26 1.8	13 59.9	14 29.3	13 0.5	19 10.7	5 9.3	12 58.8	23 3.3	15 57.4	3 11.9	18 44.1
18 S	13 40 35.0	27 0.5	13 56.7	26 32.2	13 14.6	20 22.1	5 30.2	13 5.9	23 4.9	16 0.8	3 11.1	18 44.5
19 S	13 44 31.6	27 59.1	13 53.5	8♉44.7	13 22.6	21 33.5	5 51.5	13 13.2	23 6.4	16 4.2	3 10.3	18 44.9
20 M	13 48 28.1	28 57.7	13 50.4	21 8.1	13 24.5	22 44.9	6 13.1	13 20.6	23 7.7	16 7.6	3 9.5	18 45.3
21 T	13 52 24.7	29 56.3	13 47.2	3♊43.8	13R20.6	23 56.4	6 35.0	13 28.2	23 9.0	16 10.9	3 8.7	18 45.7
22 W	13 56 21.2	0♉54.9	13 44.0	16 32.9	13 11.0	25 7.8	6 57.3	13 35.8	23 10.2	16 14.3	3 8.0	18 46.2
23 T	14 0 17.8	1 53.4	13 40.8	29 36.6	12 56.1	26 19.4	7 19.8	13 43.7	23 11.3	16 17.6	3 7.3	18 46.7
24 F	14 4 14.4	2 51.9	13 37.6	12♋55.8	12 36.3	27 30.9	7 42.7	13 51.6	23 12.3	16 20.9	3 6.6	18 47.2
25 S	14 8 10.9	3 50.3	13 34.5	26 31.2	12 12.0	28 42.5	8 5.8	13 59.7	23 13.1	16 24.2	3 5.9	18 47.8
26 S	14 12 7.5	4 48.7	13 31.3	10♌23.3	11 43.7	29 54.1	8 29.2	14 7.9	23 13.9	16 27.5	3 5.3	18 48.3
27 M	14 16 4.0	5 47.1	13 28.1	24 31.8	11 12.0	1♈ 5.7	8 52.9	14 16.2	23 14.6	16 30.8	3 4.7	18 48.9
28 T	14 20 0.6	6 45.4	13 24.9	8♍55.3	10 37.4	2 17.4	9 16.8	14 24.6	23 15.2	16 34.1	3 4.2	18 49.5
29 W	14 23 57.1	7 43.7	13 21.8	23 30.9	10 0.6	3 29.1	9 41.1	14 33.2	23 15.7	16 37.4	3 3.7	18 50.2
30 T	14 27 53.7	8 42.0	13 18.6	8♎14.2	9 22.4	4 40.8	10 5.5	14 41.9	23 16.1	16 40.6	3 3.2	18 50.8

DECLINATION

DAY	EPHEMERIS SIDEREAL TIME	☉	☊	☽	☿	♀	♂	♃	♄	♅	♆	♇
1 W	12 33 33.6	4N 5.1	5N51.1	8N35.9	11N 3.5	11S49.4	22N52.4	23N15.2	21S19.3	5N21.1	10N54.9	22N21.5
4 S	12 45 23.3	5 14.5	5 47.4	12S35.3	13 22.0	10 42.9	22 37.1	23 14.1	21 18.0	5 25.0	10 56.2	22 21.7
7 T	12 57 12.9	6 23.0	5 43.8	26 41.7	15 18.8	9 33.5	22 20.8	23 12.8	21 16.8	5 29.0	10 57.5	22 21.8
10 F	13 9 2.6	7 30.5	5 40.1	27 0.7	16 50.5	8 21.6	22 3.6	23 11.4	21 15.8	5 33.0	10 58.6	22 21.9
13 M	13 20 52.3	8 36.9	5 36.4	16 7.5	17 55.1	7 7.3	21 45.4	23 9.8	21 14.8	5 37.0	10 59.7	22 22.0
16 T	13 32 41.9	9 42.1	5 32.7	0N 1.3	18 31.5	5 51.1	21 26.2	23 8.1	21 14.1	5 40.9	11 0.7	22 22.1
19 S	13 44 31.6	10 45.8	5 29.0	16 29.0	18 39.2	4 33.1	21 6.1	23 6.2	21 13.5	5 44.8	11 1.6	22 22.1
22 W	13 56 21.2	11 47.9	5 25.3	27 24.3	18 18.7	3 13.7	20 45.0	23 4.0	21 13.0	5 48.7	11 2.4	22 22.1
25 S	14 8 10.9	12 48.2	5 21.6	25 54.2	17 31.9	1 53.2	20 22.9	23 1.7	21 12.6	5 52.5	11 3.1	22 22.0
28 T	14 20 0.6	13 46.6	5 17.9	11 3.0	16 23.7	0 31.9	19 59.8	22 59.2	21 12.5	5 56.3	11 3.7	22 21.9

MAY 1931

LONGITUDE

DAY	EPHEMERIS SIDEREAL TIME	☉	☊	☽	☿	♀	♂	♃	♄	♅	♆	♇
	h m s	° ′	° ′	° ′	° ′	° ′	° ′	° ′	° ′	° ′	° ′	° ′
1 F	14 31 50.2	9♉40.2	13♈15.4	22♎59.4	8♉43.5	5♈52.5	10♌30.3	14♋50.7	23♑16.4	16♈43.8	3♍ 2.7	18♋51.5
2 S	14 35 46.8	10 38.4	13 12.2	7♏39.7	8R 4.5	7 4.3	10 55.2	14 59.6	23 16.6	16 47.1	3R 2.3	18 52.2
3 S	14 39 43.4	11 36.6	13 9.1	22 8.3	7 26.1	8 16.1	11 20.5	15 8.6	23 16.7	16 50.3	3 1.9	18 52.9
4 M	14 43 39.9	12 34.7	13 5.9	6♐19.2	6 49.0	9 27.9	11 45.9	15 17.8	23 16.7	16 53.4	3 1.5	18 53.7
5 T	14 47 36.5	13 32.9	13 2.7	20 7.9	6 13.9	10 39.8	12 11.6	15 27.0	23R16.6	16 56.6	3 1.2	18 54.4
6 W	14 51 33.0	14 31.0	12 59.5	3♑32.3	5 41.2	11 51.7	12 37.5	15 36.4	23 16.4	16 59.7	3 0.9	18 55.2
7 T	14 55 29.6	15 29.0	12 56.3	16 32.3	5 11.6	13 3.6	13 3.6	15 45.8	23 16.1	17 2.8	3 0.6	18 56.0
8 F	14 59 26.1	16 27.1	12 53.2	29 9.8	4 45.3	14 15.5	13 30.0	15 55.4	23 15.7	17 5.9	3 0.4	18 56.9
9 S	15 3 22.7	17 25.1	12 50.0	11♒28.1	4 22.9	15 27.5	13 56.5	16 5.1	23 15.2	17 9.0	3 0.2	18 57.7
10 S	15 7 19.2	18 23.1	12 46.8	23 31.5	4 4.5	16 39.4	14 23.3	16 14.8	23 14.7	17 12.1	2 60.0	18 58.6
11 M	15 11 15.8	19 21.1	12 43.6	5♓25.1	3 50.4	17 51.5	14 50.3	16 24.7	23 14.0	17 15.1	2 59.9	18 59.5
12 T	15 15 12.4	20 19.0	12 40.5	17 13.7	3 40.7	19 3.5	15 17.5	16 34.7	23 13.2	17 18.1	2 59.7	19 0.4
13 W	15 19 8.9	21 17.0	12 37.3	29 2.3	3 35.6	20 15.5	15 44.9	16 44.8	23 12.3	17 21.1	2 59.7	19 1.3
14 T	15 23 5.5	22 14.9	12 34.1	10♈55.4	3 35.2	21 27.6	16 12.4	16 54.9	23 11.4	17 24.1	2 59.6	19 2.2
15 F	15 27 2.0	23 12.8	12 30.9	22 56.8	3D39.3	22 39.7	16 40.2	17 5.2	23 10.3	17 27.0	2 59.6	19 3.2
16 S	15 30 58.6	24 10.6	12 27.8	5♉ 9.7	3 48.1	23 51.8	17 8.2	17 15.5	23 9.2	17 29.9	2D59.6	19 4.2
17 S	15 34 55.2	25 8.5	12 24.6	17 36.3	4 1.4	25 4.0	17 36.4	17 26.0	23 7.9	17 32.8	2 59.7	19 5.2
18 M	15 38 51.7	26 6.3	12 21.4	0♊17.7	4 19.2	26 16.1	18 4.7	17 36.5	23 6.6	17 35.7	2 59.8	19 6.2
19 T	15 42 48.2	27 4.1	12 18.2	13 14.3	4 41.4	27 28.3	18 33.2	17 47.1	23 5.1	17 38.5	2 59.9	19 7.3
20 W	15 46 44.8	28 1.9	12 15.0	26 25.4	5 7.8	28 40.5	19 2.0	17 57.8	23 3.6	17 41.3	3 0.1	19 8.4
21 T	15 50 41.4	28 59.6	12 11.9	9♋50.0	5 38.5	29 52.7	19 30.9	18 8.6	23 2.0	17 44.1	3 0.2	19 9.4
22 F	15 54 38.0	29 57.4	12 8.7	23 26.4	6 13.2	1♉ 4.9	19 59.9	18 19.5	23 0.3	17 46.9	3 0.5	19 10.5
23 S	15 58 34.5	0♊55.1	12 5.5	7♌13.3	6 51.8	2 17.1	20 29.1	18 30.4	22 58.5	17 49.6	3 0.7	19 11.7
24 S	16 2 31.0	1 52.7	12 2.3	21 9.2	7 34.2	3 29.4	20 58.5	18 41.5	22 56.6	17 52.3	3 1.0	19 12.8
25 M	16 6 27.5	2 50.4	11 59.2	5♍13.0	8 20.3	4 41.7	21 28.1	18 52.6	22 54.6	17 54.9	3 1.3	19 13.9
26 T	16 10 24.1	3 48.0	11 56.0	19 23.6	9 10.0	5 53.9	21 57.8	19 3.8	22 52.5	17 57.6	3 1.7	19 15.1
27 W	16 14 20.7	4 45.6	11 52.8	3♎39.6	10 3.2	7 6.2	22 27.6	19 15.0	22 50.4	18 0.2	3 2.1	19 16.3
28 T	16 18 17.3	5 43.2	11 49.6	17 58.8	10 59.8	8 18.5	22 57.7	19 26.3	22 48.2	18 2.7	3 2.5	19 17.5
29 F	16 22 13.8	6 40.7	11 46.5	2♏18.4	11 59.7	9 30.9	23 27.8	19 37.7	22 45.9	18 5.3	3 2.9	19 18.7
30 S	16 26 10.4	7 38.2	11 43.3	16 34.3	13 2.8	10 43.2	23 58.1	19 49.2	22 43.5	18 7.8	3 3.4	19 19.9
31 S	16 30 6.9	8 35.7	11 40.1	0♐42.1	14 9.0	11 55.6	24 28.6	20 0.7	22 41.0	18 10.2	3 3.9	19 21.2

DECLINATION

DAY	EPHEMERIS SIDEREAL TIME	☉	☊	☽	☿	♀	♂	♃	♄	♅	♆	♇
1 F	14 31 50.2	14N43.0	5N14.2	9S40.8	15N 1.6	0N50.0	19N35.8	22N56.6	21S12.4	5N60.0	11N 4.2	22N21.8
4 M	14 43 39.9	15 37.2	5 10.5	25 26.3	13 35.5	2 12.2	19 10.8	22 53.7	21 12.5	6 3.6	11 4.6	22 21.7
7 T	14 55 29.6	16 29.1	5 6.7	27 35.7	12 15.6	3 34.3	18 44.9	22 50.6	21 12.8	6 7.2	11 4.9	22 21.5
10 S	15 7 19.2	17 18.5	5 3.0	17 28.6	11 10.2	4 56.1	18 18.0	22 47.3	21 13.2	6 10.7	11 5.1	22 21.4
13 W	15 19 8.9	18 5.4	4 59.3	1 36.9	10 24.6	6 17.3	17 50.2	22 43.8	21 13.8	6 14.1	11 5.1	22 21.1
16 S	15 30 58.6	18 49.5	4 55.6	15N 1.1	10 1.0	7 37.6	17 21.4	22 40.1	21 14.5	6 17.5	11 5.1	22 20.9
19 T	15 42 48.2	19 30.8	4 51.9	26 48.1	9 59.4	8 56.5	16 51.7	22 36.1	21 15.4	6 20.7	11 5.0	22 20.6
22 F	15 54 38.0	20 9.1	4 48.2	26 23.7	10 18.2	10 14.0	16 21.1	22 32.0	21 16.4	6 23.8	11 4.7	22 20.3
25 M	16 6 27.5	20 44.2	4 44.4	12 32.9	10 55.2	11 29.5	15 49.5	22 27.6	21 17.5	6 26.9	11 4.4	22 20.0
28 T	16 18 17.3	21 16.2	4 40.7	7S27.1	11 48.0	12 42.9	15 17.0	22 23.0	21 18.8	6 29.8	11 3.9	22 19.7
31 S	16 30 6.9	21 44.8	4 37.0	23 59.7	12 54.0	13 53.7	14 43.7	22 18.1	21 20.2	6 32.6	11 3.4	22 19.3

JUNE 1931

LONGITUDE

DAY	EPHEMERIS SIDEREAL TIME	☉	☊	☽	☿	♀	♂	♃	♄	♅	♆	♇
1 M	16 34 3.5	9♊33.2	11♈36.9	14♐37.0	15♉18.3	13♉ 8.0	24♌59.1	20♋12.3	22♑38.4	18♈12.7	3♍ 4.4	19♋22.4
2 T	16 38 0.0	10 30.7	11 33.7	28 14.9	16 30.6	14 20.4	25 29.9	20 24.0	22R35.8	18 15.1	3 5.0	19 23.7
3 W	16 41 56.6	11 28.2	11 30.6	11♑32.9	17 45.8	15 32.8	26 0.7	20 35.7	22 33.1	18 17.4	3 5.6	19 25.0
4 T	16 45 53.2	12 25.6	11 27.4	24 30.0	19 4.0	16 45.2	26 31.7	20 47.5	22 30.3	18 19.8	3 6.3	19 26.3
5 F	16 49 49.7	13 23.0	11 24.2	7♒ 6.7	20 25.0	17 57.7	27 2.9	20 59.4	22 27.4	18 22.1	3 6.9	19 27.6
6 S	16 53 46.3	14 20.4	11 21.0	19 25.2	21 48.9	19 10.2	27 34.1	21 11.3	22 24.5	18 24.3	3 7.6	19 28.9
7 S	16 57 42.8	15 17.8	11 17.9	1♓29.3	23 15.5	20 22.7	28 5.5	21 23.3	22 21.5	18 26.5	3 8.4	19 30.3
8 M	17 1 39.4	16 15.2	11 14.7	13 23.3	24 45.0	21 35.2	28 37.0	21 35.3	22 18.4	18 28.7	3 9.1	19 31.6
9 T	17 5 36.0	17 12.6	11 11.5	25 12.5	26 17.2	22 47.8	29 8.7	21 47.4	22 15.2	18 30.9	3 9.9	19 33.0
10 W	17 9 32.6	18 10.0	11 8.3	7♈ 2.2	27 52.2	24 0.4	29 40.4	21 59.6	22 12.0	18 33.0	3 10.8	19 34.4
11 T	17 13 29.1	19 7.4	11 5.2	18 57.6	29 29.9	25 12.9	0♍12.3	22 11.8	22 8.7	18 35.1	3 11.6	19 35.8
12 F	17 17 25.6	20 4.7	11 2.0	1♉ 3.7	1♊10.2	26 25.5	0 44.4	22 24.0	22 5.3	18 37.1	3 12.5	19 37.2
13 S	17 21 22.2	21 2.1	10 58.8	13 24.6	2 53.3	27 38.2	1 16.5	22 36.3	22 1.9	18 39.1	3 13.4	19 38.6
14 S	17 25 18.8	21 59.4	10 55.6	26 3.3	4 39.1	28 50.8	1 48.8	22 48.7	21 58.4	18 41.0	3 14.3	19 40.0
15 M	17 29 15.3	22 56.8	10 52.5	9♊ 1.4	6 27.4	0♊ 3.5	2 21.2	23 1.1	21 54.9	18 42.9	3 15.3	19 41.5
16 T	17 33 11.9	23 54.1	10 49.3	22 18.8	8 18.4	1 16.2	2 53.7	23 13.6	21 51.3	18 44.8	3 16.3	19 42.9
17 W	17 37 8.4	24 51.4	10 46.1	5♋54.0	10 11.8	2 28.9	3 26.3	23 26.1	21 47.6	18 46.6	3 17.4	19 44.4
18 T	17 41 5.0	25 48.7	10 42.9	19 43.9	12 7.7	3 41.6	3 59.0	23 38.6	21 43.9	18 48.4	3 18.4	19 45.8
19 F	17 45 1.5	26 46.0	10 39.8	3♌44.6	14 6.0	4 54.4	4 31.9	23 51.2	21 40.1	18 50.2	3 19.5	19 47.3
20 S	17 48 58.1	27 43.3	10 36.6	17 52.0	16 6.5	6 7.1	5 4.8	24 3.8	21 36.3	18 51.9	3 20.6	19 48.8
21 S	17 52 54.7	28 40.5	10 33.4	2♍ 2.4	18 9.0	7 19.9	5 37.9	24 16.5	21 32.5	18 53.5	3 21.8	19 50.3
22 M	17 56 51.2	29 37.8	10 30.2	16 13.0	20 13.5	8 32.7	6 11.1	24 29.2	21 28.5	18 55.2	3 23.0	19 51.8
23 T	18 0 47.8	0♋35.0	10 27.1	0♎21.8	22 19.6	9 45.5	6 44.4	24 41.9	21 24.6	18 56.7	3 24.2	19 53.3
24 W	18 4 44.3	1 32.3	10 23.9	14 27.7	24 27.3	10 58.3	7 17.8	24 54.7	21 20.6	18 58.3	3 25.4	19 54.8
25 T	18 8 40.9	2 29.5	10 20.7	28 29.8	26 36.2	12 11.1	7 51.2	25 7.5	21 16.5	18 59.8	3 26.7	19 56.3
26 F	18 12 37.5	3 26.7	10 17.5	12♏27.1	28 46.0	13 24.0	8 24.8	25 20.4	21 12.4	19 1.2	3 27.9	19 57.9
27 S	18 16 34.0	4 23.9	10 14.3	26 18.2	0♋56.6	14 36.9	8 58.5	25 33.3	21 8.3	19 2.6	3 29.3	19 59.4
28 S	18 20 30.6	5 21.1	10 11.2	10♐ 0.9	3 7.5	15 49.8	9 32.3	25 46.2	21 4.2	19 3.9	3 30.6	20 0.9
29 M	18 24 27.2	6 18.3	10 8.0	23 32.7	5 18.6	17 2.7	10 6.2	25 59.1	20 60.0	19 5.3	3 32.0	20 2.5
30 T	18 28 23.7	7 15.5	10 4.8	6♑51.1	7 29.6	18 15.6	10 40.2	26 12.1	20 55.7	19 6.5	3 33.3	20 4.0

DECLINATION

DAY	EPHEMERIS SIDEREAL TIME	☉	☊	☽	☿	♀	♂	♃	♄	♅	♆	♇
1 M	16 34 3.5	21N53.6	4N35.7	27S 0.9	13N18.4	14N16.8	14N32.4	22N16.5	21S20.7	6N33.5	11N 3.2	22N19.2
4 T	16 45 53.2	22 17.7	4 32.0	26 7.1	14 38.0	15 23.8	13 57.9	22 11.4	21 22.2	6 36.1	11 2.5	22 18.8
7 S	16 57 42.8	22 38.3	4 28.3	14 3.3	16 4.7	16 27.6	13 22.7	22 6.0	21 23.9	6 38.7	11 1.7	22 18.4
10 W	17 9 32.6	22 55.4	4 24.6	2N22.5	17 35.7	17 27.9	12 46.5	22 0.4	21 25.6	6 41.0	11 0.8	22 18.0
13 S	17 21 22.2	23 8.8	4 20.8	18 23.1	19 7.6	18 24.3	12 9.6	21 54.6	21 27.5	6 43.3	10 59.8	22 17.6
16 T	17 33 11.9	23 18.6	4 17.1	27 58.0	20 36.6	19 16.6	11 31.9	21 48.6	21 29.4	6 45.4	10 58.7	22 17.1
19 F	17 45 1.5	23 24.7	4 13.4	23 50.1	21 58.1	20 4.4	10 53.5	21 42.3	21 31.4	6 47.4	10 57.5	22 16.7
22 M	17 56 51.2	23 27.0	4 9.6	7 23.1	23 6.8	20 47.5	10 14.3	21 35.9	21 33.4	6 49.2	10 56.2	22 16.2
25 T	18 8 40.9	23 25.6	4 5.9	12S22.5	23 57.4	21 25.5	9 34.4	21 29.2	21 35.6	6 50.9	10 54.8	22 15.7
28 S	18 20 30.6	23 20.5	4 2.1	26 14.0	24 25.6	21 58.3	8 53.9	21 22.3	21 37.7	6 52.4	10 53.4	22 15.2

JULY 1931

DAY	EPHEMERIS SIDEREAL TIME h m s	☉ ° ′	☊ ° ′	☽ ° ′	☿ ° ′	♀ ° ′	♂ ° ′	♃ ° ′	♄ ° ′	♅ ° ′	♆ ° ′	♇ ° ′
						LONGITUDE						
1 W	18 32 20.2	8♋12.7	10♈ 1.6	19♑53.9	9♋40.1	19♊28.6	11♍14.2	26♋25.1	20♑51.5	19♈ 7.7	3♍34.8	20♋ 5.6
2 T	18 36 16.8	9 9.9	9 58.5	2♒40.1	11 50.0	20 41.6	11 48.4	26 38.1	20R47.2	19 8.9	3 36.2	20 7.2
3 F	18 40 13.4	10 7.0	9 55.3	15 9.5	13 59.0	21 54.6	12 22.7	26 51.2	20 42.9	19 10.0	3 37.7	20 8.7
4 S	18 44 10.0	11 4.2	9 52.1	27 23.8	16 6.9	23 7.7	12 57.0	27 4.3	20 38.6	19 11.1	3 39.2	20 10.3
5 S	18 48 6.5	12 1.4	9 48.9	9♓25.4	18 13.6	24 20.7	13 31.5	27 17.4	20 34.2	19 12.1	3 40.7	20 11.9
6 M	18 52 3.0	12 58.6	9 45.8	21 18.2	20 18.9	25 33.8	14 6.0	27 30.5	20 29.8	19 13.1	3 42.2	20 13.4
7 T	18 55 59.6	13 55.8	9 42.6	3♈ 6.8	22 22.6	26 46.9	14 40.7	27 43.7	20 25.5	19 14.1	3 43.8	20 15.0
8 W	18 59 56.2	14 53.0	9 39.4	14 56.3	24 24.7	28 0.1	15 15.4	27 56.8	20 21.1	19 15.0	3 45.3	20 16.6
9 T	19 3 52.7	15 50.2	9 36.2	26 52.3	26 25.1	29 13.2	15 50.2	28 10.0	20 16.6	19 15.8	3 47.0	20 18.2
10 F	19 7 49.3	16 47.4	9 33.0	9♉ 0.1	28 23.8	0♋26.4	16 25.1	28 23.2	20 12.2	19 16.6	3 48.6	20 19.8
11 S	19 11 45.8	17 44.7	9 29.9	21 24.7	0♌20.6	1 39.6	17 0.1	28 36.5	20 7.8	19 17.4	3 50.2	20 21.4
12 S	19 15 42.4	18 41.9	9 26.7	4♊!0.0	2 15.7	2 52.9	17 35.2	28 49.7	20 3.4	19 18.1	3 51.9	20 22.9
13 M	19 19 38.9	19 39.1	9 23.5	17 18.6	4 8.8	4 6.1	18 10.4	29 3.0	19 58.9	19 18.7	3 53.6	20 24.5
14 T	19 23 35.5	20 36.4	9 20.3	0♋51.2	6 0.1	5 19.4	18 45.7	29 16.2	19 54.5	19 19.3	3 55.3	20 26.1
15 W	19 27 32.1	21 33.6	9 17.2	14 46.0	7 49.4	6 32.7	19 21.0	29 29.5	19 50.0	19 19.9	3 57.0	20 27.7
16 T	19 31 28.6	22 30.9	9 14.0	28 59.2	9 36.9	7 46.1	19 56.5	29 42.8	19 45.6	19 20.4	3 58.8	20 29.3
17 F	19 35 25.2	23 28.1	9 10.8	13♌25.3	11 22.6	8 59.4	20 32.0	29 56.1	19 41.2	19 20.8	4 0.6	20 30.9
18 S	19 39 21.8	24 25.4	9 7.6	27 57.5	13 6.3	10 12.8	21 7.7	0♌ 9.4	19 36.7	19 21.2	4 2.4	20 32.5
19 S	19 43 18.3	25 22.7	9 4.5	12♍29.7	14 48.1	11 26.2	21 43.4	0 22.8	19 32.3	19 21.6	4 4.2	20 34.1
20 M	19 47 14.9	26 19.9	9 1.3	26 56.6	16 28.1	12 39.6	22 19.2	0 36.1	19 27.9	19 21.9	4 6.0	20 35.6
21 T	19 51 11.4	27 17.2	8 58.1	11♎14.8	18 6.2	13 53.1	22 55.1	0 49.4	19 23.5	19 22.2	4 7.9	20 37.2
22 W	19 55 8.0	28 14.5	8 54.9	25 22.1	19 42.4	15 6.6	23 31.0	1 2.8	19 19.2	19 22.4	4 9.7	20 38.8
23 T	19 59 4.5	29 11.8	8 51.8	9♏17.8	21 16.7	16 20.1	24 7.1	1 16.1	19 14.8	19 22.5	4 11.6	20 40.4
24 F	20 3 1.1	0♌ 9.1	8 48.6	23 1.7	22 49.2	17 33.6	24 43.2	1 29.4	19 10.5	19 22.7	4 13.5	20 42.0
25 S	20 6 57.6	1 6.4	8 45.4	6♐34.1	24 19.7	18 47.1	25 19.4	1 42.8	19 6.2	19 22.7	4 15.5	20 43.5
26 S	20 10 54.2	2 3.7	8 42.2	19 54.9	25 48.3	20 0.7	25 55.7	1 56.1	19 1.9	19 22.7	4 17.4	20 45.1
27 M	20 14 50.8	3 1.0	8 39.1	3♑ 3.8	27 15.0	21 14.2	26 32.0	2 9.5	18 57.7	19R22.7	4 19.3	20 46.7
28 T	20 18 47.3	3 58.3	8 35.9	16 0.3	28 39.8	22 27.9	27 8.4	2 22.8	18 53.5	19 22.6	4 21.3	20 48.2
29 W	20 22 43.8	4 55.6	8 32.7	28 44.0	0♍ 2.6	23 41.5	27 44.9	2 36.1	18 49.3	19 22.5	4 23.3	20 49.8
30 T	20 26 40.4	5 53.0	8 29.5	11♒14.6	1 23.3	24 55.1	28 21.5	2 49.5	18 45.1	19 22.3	4 25.3	20 51.3
31 F	20 30 37.0	6 50.3	8 26.3	23 32.4	2 42.0	26 8.8	28 58.2	3 2.8	18 41.0	19 22.1	4 27.3	20 52.8
						DECLINATION						
1 W	18 32 20.2	23N11.8	3N58.4	26S51.1	24N28.8	22N25.6	8N12.7	21N15.2	21S39.9	6N53.7	10N51.9	22N14.7
4 S	18 44 10.0	22 59.3	3 54.7	15 33.0	24 7.1	22 47.3	7 30.9	21 7.9	21 42.1	6 54.9	10 50.2	22 14.2
7 T	18 55 59.6	22 43.3	3 50.9	0N43.9	23 22.6	23 3.1	6 48.5	21 0.4	21 44.3	6 56.0	10 48.5	22 13.7
10 F	19 7 49.3	22 23.7	3 47.2	16 52.5	22 18.5	23 12.9	6 5.6	20 52.7	21 46.6	6 56.9	10 46.8	22 13.1
13 M	19 19 38.9	22 0.6	3 43.4	27 29.6	20 58.6	23 16.7	5 22.1	20 44.8	21 48.8	6 57.6	10 44.9	22 12.6
16 T	19 31 28.6	21 34.2	3 39.7	24 58.5	19 26.5	23 14.4	4 38.2	20 36.7	21 51.0	6 58.1	10 43.0	22 12.1
19 S	19 43 18.3	21 4.4	3 35.9	8 53.8	17 45.6	23 5.9	3 53.8	20 28.4	21 53.2	6 58.5	10 41.0	22 11.5
22 W	19 55 8.0	20 31.4	3 32.2	11S13.4	15 58.5	22 51.3	3 8.9	20 20.0	21 55.3	6 58.7	10 39.0	22 11.0
25 S	20 6 57.6	19 55.3	3 28.4	25 40.4	14 7.9	22 30.7	2 23.7	20 11.4	21 57.4	6 58.8	10 36.9	22 10.5
28 T	20 18 47.3	19 16.2	3 24.6	27 27.2	12 15.7	22 4.1	1 38.1	20 2.6	21 59.4	6 58.7	10 34.8	22 10.0
31 F	20 30 37.0	18 34.3	3 20.9	16 58.8	10 24.0	21 31.6	0 52.3	19 53.8	22 1.4	6 58.4	10 32.6	22 9.4

AUGUST 1931

DAY	EPHEMERIS SIDEREAL TIME h m s	☉ ° ′	☊ ° ′	☽ ° ′	☿ ° ′	♀ ° ′	♂ ° ′	♃ ° ′	♄ ° ′	♅ ° ′	♆ ° ′	♇ ° ′
						LONGITUDE						
1 S	20 34 33.6	7♌47.7	8♈23.2	5♓38.7	3♍58.6	27♋22.5	29♍34.9	3♌16.1	18♑37.0	19♈21.8	4♍29.3	20♋54.4
2 S	20 38 30.1	8 45.1	8 20.0	17 35.4	5 13.1	28 36.3	0♎11.8	3 29.4	18R32.9	19R21.5	4 31.4	20 55.9
3 M	20 42 26.6	9 42.5	8 16.8	29 25.4	6 25.3	29 50.0	0 48.6	3 42.7	18 28.9	19 21.1	4 33.4	20 57.4
4 T	20 46 23.2	10 39.9	8 13.6	11♈12.6	7 35.3	1♌ 3.8	1 25.6	3 56.0	18 25.0	19 20.7	4 35.5	20 58.9
5 W	20 50 19.8	11 37.4	8 10.5	23 1.3	8 42.9	2 17.6	2 2.7	4 9.3	18 21.1	19 20.3	4 37.5	21 0.4
6 T	20 54 16.3	12 34.8	8 7.3	4♉56.6	9 48.0	3 31.5	2 39.8	4 22.5	18 17.2	19 19.8	4 39.6	21 1.9
7 F	20 58 12.9	13 32.3	8 4.1	17 3.7	10 50.6	4 45.3	3 17.0	4 35.8	18 13.4	19 19.2	4 41.7	21 3.4
8 S	21 2 9.4	14 29.8	8 0.9	29 27.8	11 50.5	5 59.2	3 54.3	4 49.0	18 9.7	19 18.6	4 43.8	21 4.9
9 S	21 6 6.0	15 27.4	7 57.8	12♊13.5	12 47.6	7 13.2	4 31.7	5 2.2	18 6.0	19 17.9	4 46.0	21 6.4
10 M	21 10 2.5	16 24.9	7 54.6	25 24.3	13 41.9	8 27.1	5 9.1	5 15.5	18 2.3	19 17.2	4 48.1	21 7.8
11 T	21 13 59.1	17 22.5	7 51.4	9♋ 2.1	14 33.1	9 41.1	5 46.6	5 28.6	17 58.8	19 16.5	4 50.2	21 9.3
12 W	21 17 55.7	18 20.1	7 48.2	23 6.2	15 21.0	10 55.1	6 24.2	5 41.8	17 55.2	19 15.7	4 52.4	21 10.7
13 T	21 21 52.2	19 17.7	7 45.0	7♌33.5	16 5.6	12 9.1	7 1.9	5 55.0	17 51.8	19 14.9	4 54.5	21 12.2
14 F	21 25 48.8	20 15.3	7 41.9	22 17.9	16 46.7	13 23.2	7 39.6	6 8.1	17 48.4	19 14.0	4 56.7	21 13.6
15 S	21 29 45.3	21 13.0	7 38.7	7♍11.8	17 24.0	14 37.2	8 17.5	6 21.2	17 45.0	19 13.1	4 58.9	21 15.0
16 S	21 33 41.9	22 10.7	7 35.5	22 6.7	17 57.3	15 51.3	8 55.3	6 34.3	17 41.8	19 12.1	5 1.0	21 16.4
17 M	21 37 38.5	23 8.4	7 32.3	6♎55.0	18 26.4	17 5.4	9 33.3	6 47.3	17 38.6	19 11.1	5 3.2	21 17.8
18 T	21 41 35.0	24 6.1	7 29.2	21 30.5	18 51.1	18 19.6	10 11.4	7 0.3	17 35.4	19 10.0	5 5.4	21 19.2
19 W	21 45 31.6	25 3.8	7 26.0	5♏49.3	19 11.2	19 33.7	10 49.5	7 13.3	17 32.4	19 8.9	5 7.6	21 20.6
20 T	21 49 28.1	26 1.6	7 22.8	19 49.5	19 26.3	20 47.9	11 27.7	7 26.3	17 29.4	19 7.8	5 9.8	21 21.9
21 F	21 53 24.7	26 59.3	7 19.6	3♐30.8	19 36.4	22 2.1	12 5.9	7 39.2	17 26.5	19 6.6	5 12.0	21 23.2
22 S	21 57 21.2	27 57.1	7 16.4	16 54.1	19 41.1	23 16.3	12 44.3	7 52.1	17 23.7	19 5.3	5 14.2	21 24.6
23 S	22 1 17.8	28 54.9	7 13.3	0♑ 0.7	19R40.2	24 30.5	13 22.7	8 5.0	17 20.9	19 4.0	5 16.4	21 25.9
24 M	22 5 14.3	29 52.7	7 10.1	12 52.3	19 33.7	25 44.8	14 1.2	8 17.8	17 18.2	19 2.7	5 18.7	21 27.2
25 T	22 9 10.9	0♍50.6	7 6.9	25 30.3	19 21.2	26 59.0	14 39.7	8 30.6	17 15.6	19 1.4	5 20.9	21 28.5
26 W	22 13 7.4	1 48.5	7 3.7	7♒56.1	19 2.8	28 13.3	15 18.3	8 43.4	17 13.1	18 60.0	5 23.1	21 29.7
27 T	22 17 4.0	2 46.3	7 0.6	20 11.1	18 38.5	29 27.6	15 57.0	8 56.1	17 10.7	18 58.5	5 25.3	21 31.0
28 F	22 21 0.6	3 44.3	6 57.4	2♓16.5	18 8.3	0♍41.9	16 35.8	9 8.8	17 8.3	18 57.1	5 27.5	21 32.2
29 S	22 24 57.1	4 42.2	6 54.2	14 14.0	17 32.4	1 56.3	17 14.6	9 21.4	17 6.0	18 55.6	5 29.8	21 33.5
30 S	22 28 53.6	5 40.2	6 51.0	26 5.4	16 51.2	3 10.7	17 53.5	9 34.0	17 3.8	18 54.0	5 32.0	21 34.7
31 M	22 32 50.2	6 38.2	6 47.9	7♈53.1	16 5.1	4 25.0	18 32.5	9 46.6	17 1.7	18 52.4	5 34.2	21 35.9
						DECLINATION						
1 S	20 34 33.6	18N19.7	3N19.6	11S54.4	9N47.2	21N19.6	0N36.9	19N50.8	22S 2.1	6N58.3	10N31.8	22N 9.3
4 T	20 46 23.2	17 34.2	3 15.9	4N48.0	7 59.1	20 39.7	0S 9.3	19 41.7	22 4.0	6 57.8	10 29.6	22 8.8
7 F	20 58 12.9	16 46.0	3 12.1	20 7.3	6 15.9	19 54.4	0 55.7	19 32.5	22 5.8	6 57.1	10 27.3	22 8.3
10 M	21 10 2.5	15 55.5	3 8.4	28 23.9	4 39.9	19 3.9	1 42.3	19 23.2	22 7.6	6 56.3	10 25.0	22 7.8
13 T	21 21 52.2	15 2.6	3 4.6	22 38.1	3 13.5	18 8.6	2 29.1	19 13.8	22 9.3	6 55.4	10 22.6	22 7.3
16 S	21 33 41.9	14 7.5	3 0.8	4 16.8	1 59.8	17 8.6	3 15.9	19 4.3	22 10.9	6 54.2	10 20.3	22 6.8
19 W	21 45 31.6	13 10.4	2 57.1	15S53.7	1 2.3	16 4.3	4 2.8	18 54.8	22 12.3	6 53.0	10 17.9	22 6.4
22 S	21 57 21.2	12 11.4	2 53.3	27 40.8	0 25.4	14 56.0	4 49.7	18 45.1	22 13.8	6 51.6	10 15.5	22 6.0
25 T	22 9 10.9	11 10.8	2 49.5	25 51.0	0 13.9	13 44.0	5 36.6	18 35.5	22 15.1	6 50.0	10 13.0	22 5.5
28 F	22 21 0.6	10 8.5	2 45.8	13 20.6	0 31.9	12 28.5	6 23.3	18 25.7	22 16.3	6 48.3	10 10.6	22 5.2
31 M	22 32 50.2	9 4.8	2 42.0	3N19.7	1 21.5	11 10.0	7 9.8	18 16.0	22 17.4	6 46.5	10 8.2	22 4.8

SEPTEMBER 1931

LONGITUDE

DAY	EPHEMERIS SIDEREAL TIME	☉	☊	☽	☿	♀	♂	♃	♄	♅	♆	♇
	h m s	° ′	° ′	° ′	° ′	° ′	° ′	° ′	° ′	° ′	° ′	° ′
1 T	22 36 46.8	7♍36.2	6♈44.7	19♈39.9	15♍14.8	5♍39.4	19♎11.5	9♌59.1	16♑59.7	18♈50.8	5♍36.4	21♋37.0
2 W	22 40 43.3	8 34.2	6 41.5	1♉29.3	14R21.0	6 53.9	19 50.6	10 11.6	16R57.8	18R49.1	5 38.7	21 38.2
3 T	22 44 39.9	9 32.3	6 38.3	13 25.2	13 24.6	8 8.3	20 29.8	10 24.0	16 56.0	18 47.4	5 40.9	21 39.3
4 F	22 48 36.4	10 30.4	6 35.1	25 32.1	12 26.8	9 22.8	21 9.0	10 36.4	16 54.2	18 45.7	5 43.1	21 40.5
5 S	22 52 33.0	11 28.6	6 32.0	7♊54.6	11 28.7	10 37.2	21 48.4	10 48.7	16 52.5	18 43.9	5 45.3	21 41.6
6 S	22 56 29.6	12 26.8	6 28.8	20 37.2	10 31.6	11 51.7	22 27.8	11 1.0	16 51.0	18 42.1	5 47.5	21 42.7
7 M	23 0 26.1	13 25.0	6 25.6	3♋43.8	9 36.8	13 6.3	23 7.2	11 13.2	16 49.5	18 40.3	5 49.8	21 43.7
8 T	23 4 22.7	14 23.3	6 22.4	17 17.2	8 45.5	14 20.8	23 46.8	11 25.4	16 48.1	18 38.4	5 52.0	21 44.8
9 W	23 8 19.2	15 21.5	6 19.3	1♌18.4	7 59.1	15 35.4	24 26.4	11 37.5	16 46.8	18 36.5	5 54.2	21 45.8
10 T	23 12 15.8	16 19.9	6 16.1	15 45.7	7 18.6	16 49.9	25 6.1	11 49.5	16 45.6	18 34.6	5 56.4	21 46.8
11 F	23 16 12.3	17 18.2	6 12.9	0♍34.8	6 45.1	18 4.5	25 45.8	12 1.5	16 44.5	18 32.7	5 58.6	21 47.8
12 S	23 20 8.9	18 16.6	6 9.7	15 38.7	6 19.4	19 19.1	26 25.7	12 13.5	16 43.5	18 30.7	6 0.8	21 48.8
13 S	23 24 5.4	19 15.0	6 6.5	0♎48.5	6 2.1	20 33.8	27 5.6	12 25.4	16 42.6	18 28.7	6 2.9	21 49.8
14 M	23 28 2.0	20 13.5	6 3.4	15 54.7	5 53.8	21 48.4	27 45.6	12 37.2	16 41.8	18 26.6	6 5.1	21 50.7
15 T	23 31 58.5	21 11.9	6 0.2	0♏48.9	5D54.7	23 3.0	28 25.6	12 48.9	16 41.1	18 24.5	6 7.3	21 51.7
16 W	23 35 55.1	22 10.4	5 57.0	15 24.3	6 5.1	24 17.7	29 5.7	13 0.6	16 40.4	18 22.4	6 9.4	21 52.6
17 T	23 39 51.6	23 9.0	5 53.8	29 36.9	6 24.8	25 32.4	29 45.9	13 12.2	16 39.9	18 20.3	6 11.6	21 53.4
18 F	23 43 48.2	24 7.5	5 50.7	13♐25.0	6 53.7	26 47.0	0♏26.2	13 23.8	16 39.5	18 18.2	6 13.7	21 54.3
19 S	23 47 44.7	25 6.1	5 47.5	26 49.1	7 31.6	28 1.7	1 6.5	13 35.2	16 39.2	18 16.0	6 15.9	21 55.1
20 S	23 51 41.3	26 4.7	5 44.3	9♑51.0	8 18.0	29 16.4	1 46.9	13 46.7	16 38.9	18 13.8	6 18.0	21 56.0
21 M	23 55 37.9	27 3.3	5 41.1	22 33.5	9 12.5	0♎31.1	2 27.3	13 58.0	16 38.8	18 11.6	6 20.1	21 56.7
22 T	23 59 34.4	28 2.0	5 37.9	4♒59.7	10 14.5	1 45.8	3 7.9	14 9.2	16 38.8	18 9.4	6 22.2	21 57.5
23 W	0 3 31.0	29 0.7	5 34.8	17 12.8	11 23.3	3 0.6	3 48.4	14 20.4	16D38.9	18 7.1	6 24.3	21 58.3
24 T	0 7 27.5	29 59.4	5 31.6	29 15.8	12 38.5	4 15.3	4 29.1	14 31.5	16 39.0	18 4.9	6 26.4	21 59.0
25 F	0 11 24.1	0♎58.2	5 28.4	11♓11.4	13 59.2	5 30.0	5 9.8	14 42.5	16 39.3	18 2.6	6 28.4	21 59.7
26 S	0 15 20.7	1 57.0	5 25.2	23 2.1	15 24.9	6 44.8	5 50.6	14 53.5	16 39.7	18 0.3	6 30.5	22 0.4
27 S	0 19 17.2	2 55.8	5 22.1	4♈50.2	16 54.9	7 59.5	6 31.5	15 4.4	16 40.1	17 58.0	6 32.5	22 1.1
28 M	0 23 13.8	3 54.6	5 18.9	16 37.9	18 28.6	9 14.3	7 12.4	15 15.1	16 40.7	17 55.6	6 34.6	22 1.7
29 T	0 27 10.3	4 53.5	5 15.7	28 27.5	20 5.4	10 29.1	7 53.4	15 25.8	16 41.4	17 53.3	6 36.6	22 2.3
30 W	0 31 6.8	5 52.5	5 12.5	10♉21.5	21 44.8	11 43.8	8 34.4	15 36.4	16 42.1	17 50.9	6 38.6	22 2.9

DECLINATION

DAY	EPHEMERIS SIDEREAL TIME	☉	☊	☽	☿	♀	♂	♃	♄	♅	♆	♇
1 T	22 36 46.8	8N43.3	2N40.7	8N53.1	1N44.8	10N43.2	7S25.3	18N12.8	22S17.7	6N45.9	10N 7.4	22N 4.7
4 F	22 48 36.4	7 37.9	2 37.0	23 3.7	3 11.4	9 21.1	8 11.6	18 3.0	22 18.7	6 43.9	10 5.0	22 4.3
7 M	23 0 26.1	6 31.3	2 33.2	28 39.0	4 53.1	7 56.7	8 57.6	17 53.3	22 19.5	6 41.8	10 2.5	22 4.0
10 T	23 12 15.8	5 23.8	2 29.4	19 57.1	6 33.6	6 30.2	9 43.3	17 43.6	22 20.3	6 39.6	10 0.1	22 3.7
13 S	23 24 5.4	4 15.4	2 25.6	0 4.0	7 55.9	5 2.1	10 28.6	17 34.0	22 20.9	6 37.3	9 57.8	22 3.5
16 W	23 35 55.1	3 6.4	2 21.9	19S42.8	8 47.5	3 32.6	11 13.4	17 24.4	22 21.4	6 34.9	9 55.4	22 3.2
19 S	23 47 44.7	1 56.8	2 18.1	28 38.3	9 1.8	2 2.2	11 57.7	17 14.9	22 21.9	6 32.4	9 53.1	22 3.0
22 T	23 59 34.4	0 46.9	2 14.3	23 29.3	8 37.6	0 31.0	12 41.5	17 5.5	22 22.2	6 29.9	9 50.8	22 2.9
25 F	0 11 24.1	0S23.2	2 10.5	9 23.0	7 38.2	1S 0.4	13 24.6	16 56.2	22 22.4	6 27.3	9 48.5	22 2.7
28 M	0 23 13.8	1 33.3	2 6.7	7N29.8	6 9.9	2 31.9	14 6.9	16 47.1	22 22.4	6 24.6	9 46.3	22 2.6

OCTOBER 1931

LONGITUDE

DAY	EPHEMERIS SIDEREAL TIME	☉	☊	☽	☿	♀	♂	♃	♄	♅	♆	♇
1 T	0 35 3.4	6♎51.4	5♈ 9.3	22♉22.5	23♍26.3	12♎58.6	9♏15.6	15♌46.9	16♑43.0	17♈48.6	6♍40.6	22♋ 3.5
2 F	0 38 60.0	7 50.4	5 6.2	4♊33.6	25 9.5	14 13.4	9 56.8	15 57.4	16 44.0	17R46.2	6 42.5	22 4.0
3 S	0 42 56.5	8 49.4	5 3.0	16 58.2	26 54.0	15 28.2	10 38.0	16 7.7	16 45.0	17 43.8	6 44.5	22 4.6
4 S	0 46 53.1	9 48.5	4 59.8	29 39.7	28 39.4	16 43.0	11 19.4	16 17.9	16 46.2	17 41.4	6 46.4	22 5.1
5 M	0 50 49.6	10 47.6	4 56.6	12♋41.4	0♎25.4	17 57.9	12 0.8	16 28.1	16 47.4	17 39.0	6 48.4	22 5.5
6 T	0 54 46.2	11 46.8	4 53.5	26 6.4	2 11.9	19 12.7	12 42.3	16 38.1	16 48.8	17 36.5	6 50.3	22 6.0
7 W	0 58 42.7	12 46.0	4 50.3	9♌56.5	3 58.6	20 27.5	13 23.8	16 48.1	16 50.2	17 34.1	6 52.1	22 6.4
8 T	1 2 39.3	13 45.2	4 47.1	24 12.0	5 45.2	21 42.4	14 5.4	16 58.0	16 51.8	17 31.7	6 54.0	22 6.8
9 F	1 6 35.8	14 44.5	4 43.9	8♍50.8	7 31.7	22 57.3	14 47.1	17 7.7	16 53.4	17 29.3	6 55.9	22 7.2
10 S	1 10 32.4	15 43.8	4 40.7	23 48.2	9 18.0	24 12.1	15 28.8	17 17.4	16 55.2	17 26.8	6 57.7	22 7.6
11 S	1 14 29.0	16 43.1	4 37.6	8♎57.2	11 3.9	25 27.0	16 10.7	17 26.9	16 57.0	17 24.4	6 59.5	22 7.9
12 M	1 18 25.5	17 42.5	4 34.4	24 8.6	12 49.4	26 41.9	16 52.6	17 36.3	16 59.0	17 22.0	7 1.3	22 8.2
13 T	1 22 22.0	18 41.9	4 31.2	9♏13.0	14 34.4	27 56.8	17 34.5	17 45.6	17 1.0	17 19.5	7 3.1	22 8.5
14 W	1 26 18.6	19 41.3	4 28.0	24 1.4	16 18.8	29 11.6	18 16.5	17 54.9	17 3.1	17 17.1	7 4.8	22 8.8
15 T	1 30 15.2	20 40.8	4 24.9	8♐27.3	18 2.6	0♏26.5	18 58.6	18 4.0	17 5.3	17 14.7	7 6.6	22 9.0
16 F	1 34 11.7	21 40.3	4 21.7	22 26.6	19 45.9	1 41.4	19 40.8	18 12.9	17 7.7	17 12.2	7 8.3	22 9.2
17 S	1 38 8.3	22 39.8	4 18.5	5♑58.1	21 28.5	2 56.3	20 23.0	18 21.8	17 10.1	17 9.8	7 10.0	22 9.4
18 S	1 42 4.8	23 39.4	4 15.3	19 3.2	23 10.5	4 11.2	21 5.3	18 30.5	17 12.6	17 7.4	7 11.6	22 9.6
19 M	1 46 1.4	24 39.0	4 12.1	1♒44.8	24 51.8	5 26.1	21 47.6	18 39.2	17 15.2	17 5.0	7 13.3	22 9.7
20 T	1 49 57.9	25 38.6	4 9.0	14 6.9	26 32.5	6 41.0	22 30.1	18 47.7	17 17.9	17 2.6	7 14.9	22 9.8
21 W	1 53 54.5	26 38.2	4 5.8	26 13.8	28 12.6	7 55.9	23 12.5	18 56.0	17 20.7	17 0.2	7 16.5	22 9.9
22 T	1 57 51.1	27 37.9	4 2.6	8♓10.2	29 52.1	9 10.8	23 55.1	19 4.3	17 23.5	16 57.8	7 18.1	22 10.0
23 F	2 1 47.6	28 37.6	3 59.4	20 0.1	1♏30.9	10 25.7	24 37.7	19 12.4	17 26.5	16 55.4	7 19.6	22 10.0
24 S	2 5 44.2	29 37.3	3 56.3	1♈47.3	3 9.2	11 40.5	25 20.3	19 20.4	17 29.6	16 53.1	7 21.1	22 10.0
25 S	2 9 40.7	0♏37.1	3 53.1	13 35.1	4 46.9	12 55.4	26 3.1	19 28.3	17 32.7	16 50.7	7 22.6	22R10.0
26 M	2 13 37.3	1 36.9	3 49.9	25 26.1	6 24.0	14 10.3	26 45.9	19 36.0	17 35.9	16 48.4	7 24.1	22 9.9
27 T	2 17 33.8	2 36.7	3 46.7	7♉22.4	8 0.5	15 25.2	27 28.7	19 43.6	17 39.2	16 46.0	7 25.5	22 9.9
28 W	2 21 30.4	3 36.6	3 43.6	19 25.9	9 36.6	16 40.1	28 11.6	19 51.1	17 42.6	16 43.7	7 27.0	22 9.8
29 T	2 25 26.9	4 36.5	3 40.4	1♊38.2	11 12.1	17 55.0	28 54.6	19 58.4	17 46.1	16 41.5	7 28.4	22 9.7
30 F	2 29 23.5	5 36.4	3 37.2	14 0.8	12 47.2	19 9.9	29 37.7	20 5.6	17 49.7	16 39.2	7 29.7	22 9.5
31 S	2 33 20.0	6 36.4	3 34.0	26 35.1	14 21.7	20 24.8	0♐20.8	20 12.6	17 53.4	16 36.9	7 31.1	22 9.4

DECLINATION

DAY	EPHEMERIS SIDEREAL TIME	☉	☊	☽	☿	♀	♂	♃	♄	♅	♆	♇
1 T	0 35 3.4	2S43.4	2N 3.0	22N 7.1	4N20.1	4S 3.1	14S48.5	16N38.1	22S22.4	6N21.9	9N44.1	22N 2.5
4 S	0 46 53.1	3 53.2	1 59.2	28 43.1	2 16.1	5 33.6	15 29.2	16 29.3	22 22.3	6 19.2	9 42.0	22 2.5
7 W	0 58 42.7	5 2.7	1 55.4	21 57.9	0 3.8	7 3.1	16 9.1	16 20.7	22 22.0	6 16.4	9 40.0	22 2.5
10 S	1 10 32.4	6 11.6	1 51.6	3 26.5	2S12.2	8 31.3	16 47.9	16 12.3	22 21.6	6 13.6	9 38.0	22 2.5
13 T	1 22 22.0	7 19.8	1 47.8	17S21.7	4 28.5	9 57.8	17 25.6	16 4.1	22 21.1	6 10.9	9 36.1	22 2.6
16 F	1 34 11.7	8 27.1	1 44.1	28 22.1	6 42.9	11 22.3	18 2.2	15 56.2	22 20.5	6 8.1	9 34.2	22 2.7
19 M	1 46 1.4	9 33.2	1 40.3	24 22.8	8 53.6	12 44.4	18 37.6	15 48.6	22 19.8	6 5.3	9 32.4	22 2.8
22 T	1 57 51.1	10 38.2	1 36.5	10 44.6	10 59.5	14 3.8	19 11.7	15 41.3	22 19.0	6 2.6	9 30.7	22 3.0
25 S	2 9 40.7	11 41.7	1 32.7	6N 3.4	12 59.7	15 20.0	19 44.3	15 34.4	22 18.0	5 60.0	9 29.1	22 3.2
28 W	2 21 30.4	12 43.5	1 28.9	21 6.0	14 53.5	16 32.7	20 15.5	15 27.7	22 16.9	5 57.3	9 27.6	22 3.5
31 S	2 33 20.0	13 43.7	1 25.1	28 33.2	16 40.3	17 41.7	20 45.2	15 21.5	22 15.8	5 54.8	9 26.1	22 3.8

NOVEMBER 1931

DAY	EPHEMERIS SIDEREAL TIME	☉	☊	☽	☿	♀	♂	♃	♄	♅	♆	♇
	h m s	° ′	° ′	° ′	° ′	° ′	° ′	° ′	° ′	° ′	° ′	° ′
						LONGITUDE						
1 S	2 37 16.6	7♏36.4	3♈30.8	9♋23.0	15♏55.8	21♏39.7	1♐ 3.9	20♌19.5	17♑57.1	16♈34.7	7♍32.4	22♋ 9.2
2 M	2 41 13.1	8 36.4	3 27.7	22 26.4	17 29.5	22 54.6	1 47.2	20 26.3	18 0.9	16R32.5	7 33.7	22R 9.0
3 T	2 45 9.7	9 36.5	3 24.5	5♌47.2	19 2.7	24 9.5	2 30.5	20 32.9	18 4.8	16 30.3	7 34.9	22 8.7
4 W	2 49 6.3	10 36.6	3 21.3	19 27.1	20 35.5	25 24.4	3 13.9	20 39.3	18 8.8	16 28.2	7 36.1	22 8.5
5 T	2 53 2.8	11 36.7	3 18.1	3♍27.2	22 7.9	26 39.3	3 57.3	20 45.6	18 12.9	16 26.0	7 37.3	22 8.2
6 F	2 56 59.4	12 36.9	3 15.0	17 47.3	23 39.9	27 54.2	4 40.8	20 51.8	18 17.0	16 23.9	7 38.5	22 7.9
7 S	3 0 55.9	13 37.1	3 11.8	2♎25.5	25 11.5	29 9.1	5 24.4	20 57.8	18 21.3	16 21.8	7 39.7	22 7.5
8 S	3 4 52.5	14 37.4	3 8.6	17 17.5	26 42.7	0♐24.0	6 8.0	21 3.6	18 25.6	16 19.7	7 40.8	22 7.2
9 M	3 8 49.1	15 37.7	3 5.4	2♏16.7	28 13.6	1 39.0	6 51.7	21 9.3	18 30.0	16 17.7	7 41.8	22 6.8
10 T	3 12 45.6	16 38.0	3 2.3	17 14.8	29 44.1	2 53.9	7 35.4	21 14.8	18 34.4	16 15.7	7 42.9	22 6.4
11 W	3 16 42.2	17 38.3	2 59.1	2♐ 3.0	1♐14.2	4 8.8	8 19.2	21 20.2	18 39.0	16 13.7	7 43.9	22 6.0
12 T	3 20 38.7	18 38.7	2 55.9	16 33.1	2 43.9	5 23.7	9 3.1	21 25.4	18 43.6	16 11.8	7 44.9	22 5.5
13 F	3 24 35.3	19 39.1	2 52.7	0♑39.2	4 13.2	6 38.6	9 47.1	21 30.4	18 48.3	16 9.8	7 45.9	22 5.0
14 S	3 28 31.8	20 39.5	2 49.5	14 17.9	5 42.0	7 53.5	10 31.1	21 35.3	18 53.0	16 8.0	7 46.8	22 4.5
15 S	3 32 28.4	21 39.9	2 46.4	27 29.0	7 10.5	9 8.4	11 15.1	21 39.9	18 57.8	16 6.1	7 47.7	22 4.0
16 M	3 36 24.9	22 40.4	2 43.2	10♒14.4	8 38.5	10 23.3	11 59.2	21 44.5	19 2.7	16 4.3	7 48.5	22 3.5
17 T	3 40 21.5	23 40.9	2 40.0	22 38.0	10 5.9	11 38.2	12 43.4	21 48.8	19 7.7	16 2.5	7 49.4	22 2.9
18 W	3 44 18.1	24 41.4	2 36.8	4♓44.4	11 32.9	12 53.1	13 27.6	21 53.0	19 12.7	16 0.8	7 50.2	22 2.3
19 T	3 48 14.6	25 41.9	2 33.7	16 39.1	12 59.3	14 8.0	14 11.9	21 57.0	19 17.8	15 59.0	7 50.9	22 1.7
20 F	3 52 11.2	26 42.4	2 30.5	28 27.3	14 25.0	15 22.9	14 56.2	22 0.8	19 23.0	15 57.4	7 51.7	22 1.0
21 S	3 56 7.7	27 43.0	2 27.3	10♈14.0	15 50.0	16 37.8	15 40.6	22 4.4	19 28.2	15 55.7	7 52.4	22 0.4
22 S	4 0 4.3	28 43.6	2 24.1	22 3.5	17 14.2	17 52.6	16 25.1	22 7.9	19 33.5	15 54.1	7 53.0	21 59.7
23 M	4 4 0.9	29 44.2	2 21.0	3♉59.5	18 37.6	19 7.5	17 9.6	22 11.2	19 38.9	15 52.6	7 53.7	21 59.0
24 T	4 7 57.4	0♐44.8	2 17.8	16 4.7	19 59.9	20 22.3	17 54.1	22 14.3	19 44.3	15 51.0	7 54.3	21 58.3
25 W	4 11 53.9	1 45.5	2 14.6	28 20.9	21 21.1	21 37.2	18 38.8	22 17.2	19 49.8	15 49.5	7 54.8	21 57.6
26 T	4 15 50.5	2 46.2	2 11.4	10♊49.3	22 40.9	22 52.0	19 23.4	22 19.9	19 55.3	15 48.1	7 55.4	21 56.8
27 F	4 19 47.1	3 46.9	2 8.2	23 29.9	23 59.4	24 6.9	20 8.2	22 22.5	20 0.9	15 46.7	7 55.9	21 56.0
28 S	4 23 43.7	4 47.6	2 5.1	6♋22.8	25 16.1	25 21.7	20 52.9	22 24.8	20 6.6	15 45.4	7 56.3	21 55.2
29 S	4 27 40.2	5 48.3	2 1.9	19 27.3	26 30.8	26 36.6	21 37.8	22 27.0	20 12.3	15 44.0	7 56.8	21 54.4
30 M	4 31 36.8	6 49.1	1 58.7	2♌43.4	27 43.4	27 51.4	22 22.7	22 29.0	20 18.1	15 42.8	7 57.2	21 53.6
						DECLINATION						
1 S	2 37 16.6	14S 3.3	1N23.9	28N17.6	17S14.2	18S 3.7	20S54.7	15N19.5	22S15.3	5N53.9	9N25.7	22N 3.9
4 W	2 49 6.3	15 0.8	1 20.1	18 30.8	18 50.7	19 7.0	21 22.2	15 13.8	22 14.0	5 51.5	9 24.3	22 4.2
7 S	3 0 55.9	15 56.1	1 16.3	0S45.6	20 18.9	20 5.7	21 48.0	15 8.5	22 12.6	5 49.1	9 23.1	22 4.6
10 T	3 12 45.6	16 49.0	1 12.5	20 20.2	21 38.1	20 59.3	22 12.0	15 3.6	22 11.0	5 46.8	9 22.0	22 5.0
13 F	3 24 35.3	17 39.3	1 8.7	28 35.1	22 47.7	21 47.7	22 34.1	14 59.2	22 9.3	5 44.6	9 21.0	22 5.4
16 M	3 36 24.9	18 26.9	1 4.9	21 41.7	23 47.2	22 30.4	22 54.3	14 55.3	22 7.5	5 42.6	9 20.1	22 5.9
19 T	3 48 14.6	19 11.6	1 1.1	6 42.3	24 35.7	23 7.3	23 12.4	14 51.9	22 5.6	5 40.6	9 19.3	22 6.4
22 S	4 0 4.3	19 53.1	0 57.3	10N 3.3	25 12.7	23 38.0	23 28.5	14 49.0	22 3.6	5 38.8	9 18.6	22 7.0
25 W	4 11 53.9	20 31.4	0 53.6	23 49.9	25 37.6	24 2.3	23 42.4	14 46.6	22 1.4	5 37.1	9 18.0	22 7.5
28 S	4 23 43.7	21 6.2	0 49.8	28 20.6	25 49.9	24 20.2	23 54.2	14 44.8	21 59.2	5 35.6	9 17.6	22 8.1

DECEMBER 1931

DAY	EPHEMERIS SIDEREAL TIME	☉	☊	☽	☿	♀	♂	♃	♄	♅	♆	♇
						LONGITUDE						
1 T	4 35 33.3	7♐49.9	1♈55.5	16♌10.9	28♐53.4	29♐ 6.2	23♐ 7.6	22♌30.8	20♑23.9	15♈41.5	7♍57.5	21♋52.7
2 W	4 39 29.9	8 50.7	1 52.4	29 50.4	0♑ 0.4	0♑21.0	23 52.6	22 32.4	20 29.8	15R40.3	7 57.9	21R51.8
3 T	4 43 26.4	9 51.6	1 49.2	13♍42.4	1 4.1	1 35.8	24 37.7	22 33.8	20 35.7	15 39.2	7 58.2	21 50.9
4 F	4 47 23.0	10 52.4	1 46.0	27 47.1	2 4.0	2 50.6	25 22.8	22 35.0	20 41.7	15 38.1	7 58.4	21 50.0
5 S	4 51 19.5	11 53.3	1 42.8	12♎ 4.2	2 59.4	4 5.4	26 8.0	22 36.1	20 47.7	15 37.1	7 58.6	21 49.1
6 S	4 55 16.1	12 54.3	1 39.7	26 31.8	3 49.9	5 20.2	26 53.2	22 36.9	20 53.8	15 36.1	7 58.8	21 48.1
7 M	4 59 12.7	13 55.2	1 36.5	11♏ 6.4	4 34.6	6 35.0	27 38.5	22 37.5	20 60.0	15 35.1	7 59.0	21 47.2
8 T	5 3 9.2	14 56.2	1 33.3	25 42.5	5 12.8	7 49.8	28 23.8	22 37.9	21 6.1	15 34.2	7 59.1	21 46.2
9 W	5 7 5.8	15 57.1	1 30.1	10♐13.4	5 43.7	9 4.6	29 9.2	22 38.2	21 12.4	15 33.3	7 59.2	21 45.2
10 T	5 11 2.3	16 58.1	1 27.0	24 32.1	6 6.5	10 19.4	29 54.6	22 38.2	21 18.7	15 32.5	7 59.2	21 44.2
11 F	5 14 58.9	17 59.1	1 23.8	8♑32.1	6 20.2	11 34.2	0♑40.1	22R38.1	21 25.0	15 31.7	7 59.3	21 43.1
12 S	5 18 55.5	19 0.1	1 20.6	22 9.3	6 24.1	12 48.9	1 25.7	22 37.7	21 31.3	15 31.0	7R59.3	21 42.1
13 S	5 22 52.0	20 1.2	1 17.4	5♒21.6	6R17.4	14 3.7	2 11.2	22 37.1	21 37.7	15 30.4	7 59.2	21 41.0
14 M	5 26 48.6	21 2.2	1 14.2	18 9.5	5 59.4	15 18.4	2 56.8	22 36.4	21 44.2	15 29.7	7 59.1	21 39.9
15 T	5 30 45.1	22 3.3	1 11.1	0♓35.5	5 30.0	16 33.1	3 42.5	22 35.4	21 50.7	15 29.2	7 59.0	21 38.9
16 W	5 34 41.7	23 4.3	1 7.9	12 43.9	4 49.0	17 47.8	4 28.2	22 34.3	21 57.2	15 28.7	7 58.8	21 37.8
17 T	5 38 38.3	24 5.4	1 4.7	24 39.7	3 56.9	19 2.5	5 14.0	22 32.9	22 3.7	15 28.2	7 58.7	21 36.6
18 F	5 42 34.8	25 6.4	1 1.5	6♈28.4	2 54.6	20 17.2	5 59.8	22 31.4	22 10.3	15 27.8	7 58.4	21 35.5
19 S	5 46 31.4	26 7.5	0 58.4	18 15.8	1 43.8	21 31.8	6 45.7	22 29.7	22 17.0	15 27.4	7 58.2	21 34.4
20 S	5 50 27.9	27 8.6	0 55.2	0♉ 7.1	0 26.4	22 46.5	7 31.6	22 27.7	22 23.6	15 27.1	7 57.9	21 33.2
21 M	5 54 24.5	28 9.7	0 52.0	12 7.1	29♐ 5.0	24 1.1	8 17.5	22 25.6	22 30.3	15 26.9	7 57.6	21 32.1
22 T	5 58 21.0	29 10.8	0 48.8	24 19.5	27 42.2	25 15.7	9 3.5	22 23.3	22 37.0	15 26.7	7 57.2	21 30.9
23 W	6 2 17.6	0♑11.9	0 45.7	6♊47.2	26 20.8	26 30.3	9 49.5	22 20.8	22 43.8	15 26.5	7 56.8	21 29.7
24 T	6 6 14.2	1 13.0	0 42.5	19 31.3	25 3.5	27 44.9	10 35.6	22 18.1	22 50.6	15 26.4	7 56.4	21 28.5
25 F	6 10 10.7	2 14.1	0 39.3	2♋32.0	23 52.6	28 59.4	11 21.7	22 15.2	22 57.4	15 26.3	7 55.9	21 27.3
26 S	6 14 7.3	3 15.2	0 36.1	15 47.8	22 49.9	0♒13.9	12 7.8	22 12.2	23 4.2	15 26.3	7 55.5	21 26.1
27 S	6 18 3.8	4 16.3	0 33.0	29 16.7	21 56.7	1 28.4	12 54.0	22 8.9	23 11.1	15D26.4	7 54.9	21 24.9
28 M	6 22 0.4	5 17.4	0 29.8	12♌56.0	21 13.7	2 42.9	13 40.2	22 5.4	23 18.0	15 26.5	7 54.4	21 23.6
29 T	6 25 57.0	6 18.6	0 26.6	26 43.2	20 41.4	3 57.4	14 26.5	22 1.8	23 24.9	15 26.6	7 53.8	21 22.4
30 W	6 29 53.5	7 19.7	0 23.4	10♍36.4	20 19.6	5 11.8	15 12.8	21 58.0	23 31.8	15 26.8	7 53.2	21 21.2
31 T	6 33 50.1	8 20.9	0 20.3	24 34.3	20 8.0	6 26.2	15 59.2	21 54.0	23 38.8	15 27.1	7 52.5	21 19.9
						DECLINATION						
1 T	4 35 33.3	21S37.5	0N46.0	19N31.2	25S49.3	24S31.4	24S 3.6	14N43.5	21S56.8	5N34.2	9N17.2	22N 8.7
4 F	4 47 23.0	22 5.1	0 42.2	1 17.9	25 36.1	24 35.8	24 10.8	14 42.8	21 54.3	5 33.0	9 17.0	22 9.4
7 M	4 59 12.7	22 28.9	0 38.4	18S 8.6	25 10.8	24 33.5	24 15.7	14 42.7	21 51.8	5 31.9	9 16.9	22 10.0
10 T	5 11 2.3	22 48.7	0 34.6	28 18.5	24 34.9	24 24.3	24 18.2	14 43.1	21 49.1	5 31.0	9 16.9	22 10.7
13 S	5 22 52.0	23 4.5	0 30.8	23 0.1	23 50.3	24 8.5	24 18.2	14 44.2	21 46.3	5 30.3	9 17.0	22 11.5
16 W	5 34 41.7	23 16.2	0 27.0	8 17.5	22 59.0	23 46.0	24 15.9	14 45.8	21 43.4	5 29.8	9 17.2	22 12.2
19 S	5 46 31.4	23 23.6	0 23.2	8N30.7	22 3.7	23 17.0	24 11.1	14 48.0	21 40.4	5 29.4	9 17.6	22 12.9
22 T	5 58 21.0	23 26.9	0 19.4	22 44.9	21 9.9	22 41.8	24 3.8	14 50.8	21 37.3	5 29.2	9 18.0	22 13.7
25 F	6 10 10.7	23 25.9	0 15.6	28 25.1	20 27.0	22 0.5	23 54.2	14 54.1	21 34.2	5 29.2	9 18.6	22 14.5
28 M	6 22 0.4	23 20.7	0 11.9	20 27.9	20 4.0	21 13.4	23 42.0	14 57.9	21 30.9	5 29.3	9 19.3	22 15.2
31 T	6 33 50.1	23 11.2	0 8.1	2 35.1	20 3.3	20 20.8	23 27.5	15 2.3	21 27.6	5 29.7	9 20.1	22 16.0

JANUARY 1932

LONGITUDE

DAY	EPHEMERIS SIDEREAL TIME h m s	☉ ° ′	☊ ° ′	☽ ° ′	☿ ° ′	♀ ° ′	♂ ° ′	♃ ° ′	♄ ° ′	♅ ° ′	♆ ° ′	♇ ° ′
1 F	6 37 46.6	9♑22.0	0♈17.1	8♎36.3	20♐ 6.1	7♒40.6	16♑45.6	21♌49.9	23♑45.7	15♈27.4	7♍51.9	21♋18.7
2 S	6 41 43.2	10 23.2	0 13.9	22 41.9	20 D 13.3	8 55.0	17 32.0	21 R 45.5	23 52.7	15 27.7	7 R 51.1	21 R 17.4
3 S	6 45 39.7	11 24.3	0 10.7	6♏50.4	20 28.7	10 9.4	18 18.5	21 41.0	23 59.7	15 28.2	7 50.4	21 16.1
4 M	6 49 36.3	12 25.5	0 7.5	21 0.1	20 51.8	11 23.7	19 5.0	21 36.3	24 6.8	15 28.6	7 49.6	21 14.9
5 T	6 53 32.9	13 26.7	0 4.4	5♐ 8.5	21 21.7	12 38.0	19 51.5	21 31.5	24 13.8	15 29.1	7 48.8	21 13.6
6 W	6 57 29.4	14 27.9	0 1.2	19 11.9	21 57.8	13 52.3	20 38.1	21 26.5	24 20.9	15 29.7	7 48.0	21 12.3
7 T	7 1 26.0	15 29.1	29♓58.0	3♑ 5.8	22 39.5	15 6.5	21 24.7	21 21.3	24 27.9	15 30.3	7 47.1	21 11.0
8 F	7 5 22.6	16 30.2	29 54.8	16 46.0	23 26.1	16 20.8	22 11.4	21 15.9	24 35.0	15 31.0	7 46.2	21 9.7
9 S	7 9 19.1	17 31.4	29 51.7	0♒ 8.8	24 17.1	17 35.0	22 58.1	21 10.4	24 42.1	15 31.7	7 45.3	21 8.4
10 S	7 13 15.7	18 32.6	29 48.5	13 12.1	25 12.1	18 49.1	23 44.8	21 4.8	24 49.2	15 32.5	7 44.4	21 7.1
11 M	7 17 12.2	19 33.8	29 45.3	25 55.3	26 10.6	20 3.2	24 31.5	20 59.0	24 56.3	15 33.3	7 43.4	21 5.8
12 T	7 21 8.8	20 34.9	29 42.1	8♓19.7	27 12.3	21 17.3	25 18.3	20 53.1	25 3.5	15 34.2	7 42.4	21 4.6
13 W	7 25 5.4	21 36.1	29 39.0	20 28.2	28 16.8	22 31.4	26 5.1	20 47.0	25 10.6	15 35.1	7 41.4	21 3.3
14 T	7 29 1.9	22 37.2	29 35.8	2♈24.7	29 23.8	23 45.4	26 51.9	20 40.8	25 17.7	15 36.1	7 40.3	21 2.0
15 F	7 32 58.5	23 38.3	29 32.6	14 14.2	0♑33.2	24 59.4	27 38.8	20 34.4	25 24.8	15 37.1	7 39.2	21 0.7
16 S	7 36 55.0	24 39.4	29 29.4	26 2.1	1 44.6	26 13.3	28 25.7	20 28.0	25 32.0	15 38.2	7 38.1	20 59.4
17 S	7 40 51.6	25 40.6	29 26.3	7♉53.9	2 57.8	27 27.2	29 12.6	20 21.4	25 39.1	15 39.3	7 37.0	20 58.1
18 M	7 44 48.1	26 41.7	29 23.1	19 54.9	4 12.8	28 41.1	29 59.5	20 14.7	25 46.2	15 40.5	7 35.8	20 56.8
19 T	7 48 44.7	27 42.7	29 19.9	2♊10.0	5 29.3	29 54.9	0♒46.5	20 7.9	25 53.4	15 41.8	7 34.7	20 55.5
20 W	7 52 41.3	28 43.8	29 16.7	14 43.0	6 47.2	1♓ 8.6	1 33.5	20 0.9	26 0.5	15 43.0	7 33.5	20 54.2
21 T	7 56 37.8	29 44.8	29 13.5	27 36.5	8 6.4	2 22.3	2 20.5	19 53.9	26 7.6	15 44.4	7 32.2	20 53.0
22 F	8 0 34.4	0♒45.9	29 10.4	10♋51.3	9 26.8	3 36.0	3 7.5	19 46.8	26 14.7	15 45.7	7 31.0	20 51.7
23 S	8 4 30.9	1 46.9	29 7.2	24 26.5	10 48.4	4 49.6	3 54.6	19 39.6	26 21.9	15 47.2	7 29.7	20 50.4
24 S	8 8 27.5	2 47.9	29 4.0	8♌19.3	12 11.0	6 3.2	4 41.7	19 32.2	26 29.0	15 48.6	7 28.4	20 49.2
25 M	8 12 24.0	3 48.9	29 0.8	22 25.5	13 34.7	7 16.7	5 28.8	19 24.8	26 36.1	15 50.1	7 27.1	20 47.9
26 T	8 16 20.6	4 49.9	28 57.7	6♍40.3	14 59.2	8 30.1	6 15.9	19 17.4	26 43.2	15 51.7	7 25.7	20 46.7
27 W	8 20 17.2	5 50.9	28 54.5	20 58.9	16 24.7	9 43.5	7 3.0	19 9.8	26 50.2	15 53.3	7 24.4	20 45.4
28 T	8 24 13.7	6 51.8	28 51.3	5♎17.1	17 51.1	10 56.8	7 50.2	19 2.2	26 57.3	15 55.0	7 23.0	20 44.2
29 F	8 28 10.3	7 52.8	28 48.1	19 32.1	19 18.3	12 10.1	8 37.3	18 54.5	27 4.4	15 56.7	7 21.6	20 42.9
30 S	8 32 6.8	8 53.7	28 45.0	3♏41.6	20 46.3	13 23.3	9 24.5	18 46.8	27 11.4	15 58.4	7 20.2	20 41.7
31 S	8 36 3.4	9 54.7	28 41.8	17 44.5	22 15.1	14 36.5	10 11.8	18 39.0	27 18.4	16 0.2	7 18.8	20 40.5

DECLINATION

DAY	EPHEMERIS SIDEREAL TIME h m s	☉	☊	☽	☿	♀	♂	♃	♄	♅	♆	♇
1 F	6 37 46.6	23S 7.2	0N 6.8	4S 7.2	20S 7.3	20S 2.0	23S22.1	15N 3.9	21S26.5	5N29.8	9N20.4	22N16.3
4 M	6 49 36.3	22 52.2	0 3.0	21 48.1	20 29.1	19 2.5	23 4.3	15 8.9	21 23.0	5 30.4	9 21.3	22 17.1
7 T	7 1 26.0	22 33.1	0S 0.8	28 25.2	20 59.8	17 58.2	22 44.2	15 14.4	21 19.5	5 31.2	9 22.3	22 17.9
10 S	7 13 15.7	22 .0.0	0 4.6	20 18.5	21 33.5	16 49.4	22 21.7	15 20.3	21 15.9	5 32.1	9 23.4	22 18.7
13 W	7 25 5.4	21 43.0	0 8.4	4 25.6	22 5.8	15 36.6	21 57.0	15 26.6	21 12.3	5 33.2	9 24.6	22 19.5
16 S	7 36 55.0	21 12.2	0 12.2	12N15.7	22 33.2	14 20.0	21 30.0	15 33.2	21 8.6	5 34.5	9 25.9	22 20.3
19 T	7 48 44.7	20 37.7	0 16.0	25 4.7	22 53.7	13 0.0	21 0.8	15 40.1	21 4.8	5 36.0	9 27.3	22 21.0
22 F	8 0 34.4	19 59.8	0 19.8	27 56.4	23 5.6	11 37.1	20 29.5	15 47.3	21 1.0	5 37.6	9 28.7	22 21.8
25 M	8 12 24.0	19 18.4	0 23.5	16 48.9	23 7.7	10 11.5	19 56.2	15 54.7	20 57.2	5 39.4	9 30.3	22 22.6
28 T	8 24 13.7	18 33.9	0 27.3	2S45.5	22 59.2	8 43.6	19 20.9	16 2.3	20 53.4	5 41.4	9 31.9	22 23.3
31 S	8 36 3.4	17 46.4	0 31.1	20 56.3	22 39.6	7 13.7	18 43.7	16 9.9	20 49.5	5 43.5	9 33.5	22 24.1

FEBRUARY 1932

LONGITUDE

DAY	EPHEMERIS SIDEREAL TIME h m s	☉ ° ′	☊ ° ′	☽ ° ′	☿ ° ′	♀ ° ′	♂ ° ′	♃ ° ′	♄ ° ′	♅ ° ′	♆ ° ′	♇ ° ′
1 M	8 39 59.9	10♒55.6	28♓38.6	1♐39.9	23♑44.7	15♓49.6	10♒59.0	18♌31.2	27♑25.4	16♈ 2.0	7♍17.3	20♋39.3
2 T	8 43 56.5	11 56.5	28 35.4	15 26.8	25 15.0	17 2.7	11 46.3	18 R 23.3	27 32.4	16 3.9	7 R 15.9	20 R 38.1
3 W	8 47 53.0	12 57.4	28 32.3	29 4.2	26 46.2	18 15.6	12 33.5	18 15.4	27 39.4	16 5.8	7 14.4	20 36.9
4 T	8 51 49.6	13 58.3	28 29.1	12♑30.6	28 18.0	19 28.6	13 20.8	18 7.5	27 46.4	16 7.8	7 12.9	20 35.7
5 F	8 55 46.1	14 59.1	28 25.9	25 44.5	29 50.7	20 41.4	14 8.1	17 59.5	27 53.3	16 9.8	7 11.4	20 34.6
6 S	8 59 42.7	15 60.0	28 22.7	8♒44.6	1♒24.1	21 54.2	14 55.4	17 51.6	28 0.2	16 11.8	7 9.8	20 33.4
7 S	9 3 39.3	17 0.8	28 19.5	21 30.0	2 58.3	23 6.9	15 42.8	17 43.6	28 7.1	16 13.9	7 8.3	20 32.3
8 M	9 7 35.8	18 1.6	28 16.4	4♓ 0.6	4 33.2	24 19.6	16 30.1	17 35.6	28 14.0	16 16.1	7 6.7	20 31.1
9 T	9 11 32.4	19 2.4	28 13.2	16 17.1	6 8.9	25 32.2	17 17.4	17 27.6	28 20.8	16 18.2	7 5.2	20 30.0
10 W	9 15 28.9	20 3.2	28 10.0	28 21.4	7 45.4	26 44.7	18 4.8	17 19.7	28 27.7	16 20.4	7 3.6	20 28.9
11 T	9 19 25.5	21 3.9	28 6.8	10♈16.4	9 22.7	27 57.1	18 52.2	17 11.7	28 34.4	16 22.7	7 2.0	20 27.8
12 F	9 23 22.1	22 4.6	28 3.7	22 5.6	11 0.8	29 9.4	19 39.5	17 3.8	28 41.2	16 25.0	7 0.4	20 26.7
13 S	9 27 18.6	23 5.3	28 0.5	3♉53.5	12 39.7	0♈21.7	20 26.9	16 55.9	28 47.9	16 27.3	6 58.8	20 25.7
14 S	9 31 15.2	24 5.9	27 57.3	15 44.8	14 19.5	1 33.9	21 14.3	16 48.0	28 54.6	16 29.7	6 57.2	20 24.6
15 M	9 35 11.7	25 6.6	27 54.1	27 44.7	16 0.1	2 45.9	22 1.7	16 40.2	29 1.3	16 32.1	6 55.5	20 23.6
16 T	9 39 8.3	26 7.2	27 51.0	9♊58.3	17 41.6	3 57.9	22 49.1	16 32.4	29 7.9	16 34.5	6 53.9	20 22.6
17 W	9 43 4.8	27 7.7	27 47.8	22 30.0	19 23.9	5 9.8	23 36.4	16 24.6	29 14.5	16 37.0	6 52.3	20 21.6
18 T	9 47 1.4	28 8.3	27 44.6	5♋23.8	21 7.1	6 21.6	24 23.8	16 16.9	29 21.1	16 39.5	6 50.6	20 20.6
19 F	9 50 57.9	29 8.8	27 41.4	18 42.0	22 51.3	7 33.3	25 11.2	16 9.3	29 27.6	16 42.0	6 49.0	20 19.6
20 S	9 54 54.5	0♓ 9.3	27 38.2	2♌25.1	24 36.4	8 44.9	25 58.6	16 1.8	29 34.1	16 44.6	6 47.3	20 18.7
21 S	9 58 51.1	1 9.7	27 35.1	16 31.6	26 22.4	9 56.4	26 46.0	15 54.3	29 40.6	16 47.2	6 45.6	20 17.7
22 M	10 2 47.6	2 10.1	27 31.9	0♍57.5	28 9.3	11 7.8	27 33.4	15 46.9	29 47.0	16 49.9	6 44.0	20 16.8
23 T	10 6 44.1	3 10.5	27 28.7	15 37.1	29 57.2	12 19.1	28 20.8	15 39.6	29 53.3	16 52.5	6 42.3	20 15.9
24 W	10 10 40.7	4 10.9	27 25.5	0♎23.2	1♓46.0	13 30.3	29 8.1	15 32.3	29 59.7	16 55.3	6 40.6	20 15.0
25 T	10 14 37.3	5 11.3	27 22.4	15 8.9	3 35.7	14 41.3	29 55.5	15 25.2	0♒ 5.9	16 58.0	6 39.0	20 14.2
26 F	10 18 33.8	6 11.6	27 19.2	29 47.8	5 26.4	15 52.3	0♓42.9	15 18.1	0 12.2	17 0.8	6 37.3	20 13.3
27 S	10 22 30.4	7 11.9	27 16.0	14♏14.9	7 18.0	17 3.1	1 30.3	15 11.2	0 18.4	17 3.6	6 35.6	20 12.5
28 S	10 26 26.9	8 12.1	27 12.8	28 27.0	9 10.4	18 13.8	2 17.7	15 4.3	0 24.5	17 6.4	6 33.9	20 11.7
29 M	10 30 23.5	9 12.4	27 9.6	12♐22.4	11 3.7	19 24.5	3 5.0	14 57.6	0 30.6	17 9.2	6 32.3	20 10.9

DECLINATION

DAY	EPHEMERIS SIDEREAL TIME h m s	☉	☊	☽	☿	♀	♂	♃	♄	♅	♆	♇
1 M	8 39 59.9	17S29.9	0S32.4	25S 2.8	22S30.5	6S43.3	18S30.8	16N12.5	20S48.2	5N44.2	9N34.1	22N24.3
4 T	8 51 49.6	16 38.6	0 36.2	27 47.8	21 55.2	5 11.4	17 51.2	16 20.2	20 44.3	5 46.5	9 35.8	22 25.0
7 S	9 3 39.3	15 44.6	0 40.0	17 9.8	21 7.8	3 38.2	17 9.8	16 27.9	20 40.4	5 49.0	9 37.5	22 25.7
10 W	9 15 28.9	14 48.3	0 43.8	0 30.1	20 8.1	2 4.2	16 26.8	16 35.5	20 36.4	5 51.6	9 39.3	22 26.4
13 S	9 27 18.6	13 49.7	0 47.6	15N48.1	18 55.9	0 29.8	15 42.3	16 43.0	20 32.5	5 54.3	9 41.2	22 27.1
16 T	9 39 8.3	12 49.0	0 51.3	26 54.4	17 31.1	1N 4.9	14 56.3	16 50.3	20 28.7	5 57.1	9 43.0	22 27.7
19 F	9 50 57.9	11 46.6	0 55.1	26 56.2	15 53.6	2 39.4	14 8.9	16 57.4	20 24.8	6 0.1	9 44.9	22 28.3
22 M	10 2 47.6	10 42.4	0 58.9	13 14.2	14 3.4	4 13.3	13 20.3	17 4.3	20 21.0	6 3.2	9 46.8	22 28.9
25 T	10 14 37.3	9 36.8	1 2.7	7S32.7	12 0.7	5 46.5	12 30.5	17 10.8	20 17.2	6 6.4	9 48.7	22 29.5
28 S	10 26 26.9	8 29.9	1 6.5	24 22.0	9 46.0	7 18.6	11 39.6	17 17.1	20 13.5	6 9.6	9 50.6	22 30.0

MARCH 1932

DAY	EPHEMERIS SIDEREAL TIME	☉	☊	☽	☿	♀	♂	♃	♄	♅	♆	♇
	h m s	° ′	° ′	° ′	° ′	° ′	° ′	° ′	° ′	° ′	° ′	° ′
LONGITUDE												
1 T	10 34 20.0	10♓12.6	27♓ 6.5	26♐ 0.7	12♓57.7	20♈34.9	3♓52.4	14♌51.0	0♒36.7	17♈12.1	6♍30.6	20♋10.1
2 W	10 38 16.6	11 12.8	27 3.3	9♑22.3	14 52.4	21 45.3	4 39.8	14R44.5	0 42.7	17 15.0	6R28.9	20R 9.4
3 T	10 42 13.2	12 13.0	27 0.1	22 28.1	16 47.7	22 55.6	5 27.1	14 38.1	0 48.7	17 18.0	6 27.3	20 8.6
4 F	10 46 9.7	13 13.1	26 56.9	5♒19.4	18 43.5	24 5.7	6 14.5	14 31.9	0 54.6	17 20.9	6 25.6	20 7.9
5 S	10 50 6.3	14 13.3	26 53.8	17 57.2	20 39.6	25 15.7	7 1.8	14 25.8	1 0.4	17 23.9	6 23.9	20 7.2
6 S	10 54 2.8	15 13.3	26 50.6	0♓22.8	22 35.9	26 25.6	7 49.1	14 19.8	1 6.2	17 26.9	6 22.3	20 6.6
7 M	10 57 59.4	16 13.4	26 47.4	12 37.5	24 32.2	27 35.3	8 36.5	14 13.9	1 11.9	17 30.0	6 20.6	20 5.9
8 T	11 1 55.9	17 13.4	26 44.2	24 42.6	26 28.2	28 44.9	9 23.8	14 8.2	1 17.6	17 33.0	6 19.0	20 5.3
9 W	11 5 52.5	18 13.4	26 41.0	6♈39.9	28 23.7	29 54.3	10 11.1	14 2.7	1 23.3	17 36.1	6 17.3	20 4.7
10 T	11 9 49.0	19 13.4	26 37.9	18 31.4	0♈18.3	1♉ 3.6	10 58.4	13 57.3	1 28.8	17 39.2	6 15.7	20 4.1
11 F	11 13 45.6	20 13.3	26 34.7	0♉19.8	2 11.7	2 12.8	11 45.6	13 52.1	1 34.4	17 42.4	6 14.1	20 3.6
12 S	11 17 42.1	21 13.2	26 31.5	12 8.1	4 3.6	3 21.8	12 32.9	13 47.0	1 39.8	17 45.5	6 12.5	20 3.0
13 S	11 21 38.7	22 13.1	26 28.3	23 60.0	5 53.4	4 30.6	13 20.1	13 42.0	1 45.2	17 48.7	6 10.9	20 2.5
14 M	11 25 35.2	23 12.9	26 25.2	5♊59.4	7 40.9	5 39.3	14 7.3	13 37.3	1 50.5	17 51.8	6 9.3	20 2.0
15 T	11 29 31.8	24 12.7	26 22.0	18 10.8	9 25.4	6 47.8	14 54.5	13 32.7	1 55.8	17 55.1	6 7.7	20 1.6
16 W	11 33 28.4	25 12.4	26 18.8	0♋38.7	11 6.6	7 56.2	15 41.7	13 28.3	2 1.0	17 58.3	6 6.2	20 1.1
17 T	11 37 24.9	26 12.1	26 15.6	13 27.2	12 43.9	9 4.3	16 28.8	13 24.0	2 6.1	18 1.5	6 4.6	20 0.7
18 F	11 41 21.5	27 11.8	26 12.4	26 39.9	14 16.8	10 12.3	17 16.0	13 19.9	2 11.2	18 4.8	6 3.1	20 0.3
19 S	11 45 18.0	28 11.4	26 9.3	10♌19.0	15 45.0	11 20.1	18 3.1	13 16.0	2 16.2	18 8.0	6 1.5	19 60.0
20 S	11 49 14.6	29 11.0	26 6.1	24 25.0	17 7.9	12 27.7	18 50.2	13 12.3	2 21.1	18 11.3	6 0.0	19 59.6
21 M	11 53 11.1	0♈10.6	26 2.9	8♍55.7	18 25.1	13 35.1	19 37.2	13 8.7	2 26.0	18 14.6	5 58.5	19 59.3
22 T	11 57 7.7	1 10.1	25 59.7	23 46.5	19 36.3	14 42.3	20 24.3	13 5.3	2 30.8	18 17.9	5 57.0	19 59.0
23 W	12 1 4.2	2 9.6	25 56.6	8♎50.3	20 41.0	15 49.3	21 11.3	13 2.1	2 35.5	18 21.2	5 55.6	19 58.7
24 T	12 5 0.8	3 9.0	25 53.4	23 58.2	21 39.1	16 56.1	21 58.3	12 59.1	2 40.2	18 24.6	5 54.1	19 58.5
25 F	12 8 57.3	4 8.5	25 50.2	9♏ 1.1	22 30.2	18 2.6	22 45.3	12 56.3	2 44.8	18 27.9	5 52.7	19 58.3
26 S	12 12 53.9	5 7.9	25 47.0	23 50.7	23 14.1	19 9.0	23 32.2	12 53.6	2 49.3	18 31.3	5 51.2	19 58.0
27 S	12 16 50.4	6 7.2	25 43.8	8♐20.6	23 50.6	20 15.1	24 19.2	12 51.1	2 53.7	18 34.6	5 49.8	19 57.9
28 M	12 20 47.0	7 6.5	25 40.7	22 27.1	24 19.7	21 21.0	25 6.1	12 48.9	2 58.1	18 38.0	5 48.5	19 57.7
29 T	12 24 43.6	8 5.9	25 37.5	6♑ 9.1	24 41.4	22 26.7	25 53.0	12 46.8	3 2.4	18 41.4	5 47.1	19 57.6
30 W	12 28 40.1	9 5.1	25 34.3	19 27.2	24 55.5	23 32.1	26 39.8	12 44.9	3 6.6	18 44.8	5 45.8	19 57.5
31 T	12 32 36.7	10 4.4	25 31.1	2♒23.8	25 2.2	24 37.3	27 26.6	12 43.1	3 10.7	18 48.2	5 44.4	19 57.4
DECLINATION												
1 T	10 34 20.0	7S44.6	1S 9.0	28S39.4	8S 9.9	8N19.2	11S 5.1	17N21.0	20S11.0	6N11.9	9N51.9	22N30.3
4 F	10 46 9.7	6 35.9	1 12.8	22 55.0	5 37.3	9 48.7	10 12.6	17 26.6	20 7.4	6 15.3	9 53.7	22 30.8
7 M	10 57 59.4	5 26.3	1 16.6	7 58.2	2 56.6	11 16.3	9 19.2	17 31.9	20 3.8	6 18.8	9 55.6	22 31.3
10 T	11 9 49.0	4 16.0	1 20.4	9N 7.8	0 11.2	12 41.7	8 25.1	17 36.6	20 0.4	6 22.4	9 57.4	22 31.7
13 S	11 21 38.7	3 5.3	1 24.2	23 7.4	2N33.8	14 4.6	7 30.4	17 41.0	19 57.0	6 26.1	9 59.2	22 32.1
16 W	11 33 28.4	1 54.3	1 28.0	28 43.7	5 11.8	15 24.6	6 35.1	17 44.8	19 53.7	6 29.8	10 1.0	22 32.4
19 S	11 45 18.0	0 43.2	1 31.8	21 19.5	7 35.6	16 41.5	5 39.4	17 48.2	19 50.5	6 33.5	10 2.7	22 32.8
22 T	11 57 7.7	0N27.9	1 35.6	2 40.8	9 38.0	17 54.9	4 43.2	17 51.1	19 47.5	6 37.3	10 4.3	22 33.1
25 F	12 8 57.3	1 38.8	1 39.3	17S55.1	11 13.0	19 4.7	3 46.8	17 53.5	19 44.6	6 41.2	10 5.9	22 33.3
28 M	12 20 47.0	2 49.4	1 43.1	28 30.1	12 16.2	20 10.5	2 50.2	17 55.4	19 41.8	6 45.0	10 7.5	22 33.5
31 T	12 32 36.7	3 59.5	1 46.9	23 47.2	12 44.6	21 12.2	1 53.5	17 56.8	19 39.1	6 48.9	10 9.0	22 33.7

APRIL 1932

DAY	EPHEMERIS SIDEREAL TIME	☉	☊	☽	☿	♀	♂	♃	♄	♅	♆	♇
LONGITUDE												
1 F	12 36 33.2	11♈ 3.6	25♓28.0	15♒ 1.7	25♈ 1.7	25♉42.3	28♓13.4	12♌41.6	3♒14.8	18♈51.6	5♍43.1	19♋57.3
2 S	12 40 29.8	12 2.8	25 24.8	27 24.3	24R54.3	26 47.0	29 0.2	12R40.3	3 18.8	18 55.0	5R41.8	19R57.3
3 S	12 44 26.3	13 1.9	25 21.6	9♓34.9	24 40.1	27 51.4	29 47.0	12 39.1	3 22.7	18 58.4	5 40.6	19D57.3
4 M	12 48 22.9	14 1.0	25 18.4	21 36.3	24 19.8	28 55.6	0♈33.7	12 38.1	3 26.5	19 1.9	5 39.3	19 57.3
5 T	12 52 19.4	15 0.1	25 15.2	3♈31.3	23 53.6	29 59.5	1 20.4	12 37.4	3 30.2	19 5.3	5 38.1	19 57.4
6 W	12 56 16.0	15 59.2	25 12.1	15 22.1	23 22.4	1♊ 3.1	2 7.0	12 36.8	3 33.9	19 8.7	5 36.9	19 57.5
7 T	13 0 12.5	16 58.2	25 8.9	27 10.8	22 46.7	2 6.4	2 53.6	12 36.4	3 37.4	19 12.2	5 35.7	19 57.6
8 F	13 4 9.1	17 57.2	25 5.7	8♉59.5	22 7.4	3 9.5	3 40.2	12 36.2	3 40.9	19 15.6	5 34.6	19 57.7
9 S	13 8 5.7	18 56.1	25 2.5	20 50.4	21 25.1	4 12.2	4 26.8	12 36.2	3 44.3	19 19.0	5 33.5	19 57.8
10 S	13 12 2.2	19 55.1	24 59.4	2♊45.8	20 40.9	5 14.5	5 13.3	12D36.4	3 47.6	19 22.5	5 32.4	19 58.0
11 M	13 15 58.7	20 53.9	24 56.2	14 48.4	19 55.5	6 16.6	5 59.8	12 36.7	3 50.9	19 25.9	5 31.3	19 58.2
12 T	13 19 55.3	21 52.8	24 53.0	27 1.4	19 9.9	7 18.3	6 46.2	12 37.3	3 54.0	19 29.3	5 30.2	19 58.4
13 W	13 23 51.9	22 51.6	24 49.8	9♋28.2	18 24.9	8 19.7	7 32.6	12 38.0	3 57.1	19 32.8	5 29.2	19 58.7
14 T	13 27 48.4	23 50.4	24 46.6	22 12.5	17 41.3	9 20.7	8 19.0	12 39.0	4 0.0	19 36.2	5 28.2	19 58.9
15 F	13 31 45.0	24 49.1	24 43.5	5♌17.9	16 59.9	10 21.3	9 5.3	12 40.1	4 2.9	19 39.6	5 27.2	19 59.2
16 S	13 35 41.5	25 47.8	24 40.3	18 47.6	16 21.3	11 21.5	9 51.6	12 41.4	4 5.7	19 43.0	5 26.3	19 59.5
17 S	13 39 38.1	26 46.4	24 37.1	2♍43.5	15 46.1	12 21.3	10 37.8	12 42.9	4 8.4	19 46.4	5 25.4	19 59.9
18 M	13 43 34.7	27 45.1	24 33.9	17 5.7	15 14.8	13 20.8	11 24.0	12 44.5	4 11.0	19 49.9	5 24.5	20 0.2
19 T	13 47 31.2	28 43.6	24 30.8	1♎51.8	14 47.7	14 19.7	12 10.2	12 46.4	4 13.5	19 53.3	5 23.6	20 0.6
20 W	13 51 27.7	29 42.2	24 27.6	16 56.4	14 25.3	15 18.3	12 56.3	12 48.4	4 15.9	19 56.7	5 22.8	20 1.0
21 T	13 55 24.3	0♉40.7	24 24.4	2♏11.3	14 7.6	16 16.3	13 42.4	12 50.6	4 18.3	20 0.0	5 22.0	20 1.5
22 F	13 59 20.9	1 39.2	24 21.2	17 26.4	13 54.9	17 13.9	14 28.4	12 53.0	4 20.5	20 3.4	5 21.2	20 1.9
23 S	14 3 17.4	2 37.6	24 18.1	2♐31.3	13 47.2	18 11.1	15 14.4	12 55.6	4 22.7	20 6.8	5 20.5	20 2.4
24 S	14 7 14.0	3 36.1	24 14.9	17 16.9	13 44.6	19 7.7	16 0.4	12 58.3	4 24.7	20 10.2	5 19.8	20 2.9
25 M	14 11 10.5	4 34.4	24 11.7	1♑37.1	13D46.9	20 3.8	16 46.3	13 1.3	4 26.7	20 13.5	5 19.1	20 3.5
26 T	14 15 7.1	5 32.8	24 8.5	15 28.7	13 54.2	20 59.4	17 32.2	13 4.4	4 28.5	20 16.9	5 18.4	20 4.0
27 W	14 19 3.6	6 31.2	24 5.3	28 51.8	14 6.4	21 54.4	18 18.0	13 7.6	4 30.3	20 20.2	5 17.8	20 4.6
28 T	14 23 0.2	7 29.5	24 2.2	11♒48.6	14 23.2	22 48.9	19 3.8	13 11.1	4 32.0	20 23.5	5 17.2	20 5.2
29 F	14 26 56.7	8 27.8	23 59.0	24 22.8	14 44.5	23 42.7	19 49.6	13 14.7	4 33.6	20 26.8	5 16.6	20 5.8
30 S	14 30 53.3	9 26.0	23 55.8	6♓39.1	15 10.3	24 36.0	20 35.3	13 18.4	4 35.0	20 30.1	5 16.1	20 6.5
DECLINATION												
1 F	12 36 33.2	4N22.7	1S48.2	19S39.6	12N46.0	21N31.8	1S34.6	17N57.2	19S38.3	6N50.2	10N 9.4	22N33.8
4 M	12 48 22.9	5 31.9	1 51.9	3 43.3	12 26.8	22 27.6	0 37.9	17 58.0	19 35.9	6 54.1	10 10.8	22 33.9
7 T	13 0 12.5	6 40.2	1 55.7	13N 0.0	11 34.9	23 18.7	0N18.8	17 58.2	19 33.6	6 58.1	10 12.1	22 34.0
10 S	13 12 2.2	7 47.5	1 59.5	25 26.3	10 17.8	24 5.0	1 15.3	17 58.0	19 31.5	7 2.0	10 13.3	22 34.1
13 W	13 23 51.9	8 53.6	2 3.3	28 11.0	8 46.6	24 46.4	2 11.5	17 57.3	19 29.5	7 5.9	10 14.5	22 34.2
16 S	13 35 41.5	9 58.4	2 7.1	18 11.8	7 14.1	25 22.7	3 7.3	17 56.0	19 27.8	7 9.8	10 15.5	22 34.2
19 T	13 47 31.2	11 1.6	2 10.9	1S14.4	5 51.9	25 53.9	4 2.7	17 54.4	19 26.2	7 13.6	10 16.5	22 34.2
22 F	13 59 20.9	12 3.3	2 14.6	20 57.1	4 47.9	26 20.0	4 57.7	17 52.2	19 24.9	7 17.5	10 17.3	22 34.1
25 M	14 11 10.5	13 3.1	2 18.4	28 35.5	4 6.3	26 40.9	5 52.0	17 49.6	19 23.7	7 21.3	10 18.1	22 34.0
28 T	14 23 0.2	14 1.0	2 22.2	20 41.4	3 48.2	26 56.8	6 45.7	17 46.5	19 22.7	7 25.0	10 18.7	22 33.9

MAY 1932

DAY	EPHEMERIS SIDEREAL TIME	☉	☊	☽	☿	♀	♂	♃	♄	♅	♆	♇
	h m s	° ′	° ′	° ′	° ′	° ′	° ′	° ′	° ′	° ′	° ′	° ′
						LONGITUDE						
1 S	14 34 49.9	10♉24.3	23♓52.6	18♓42.1	15♈40.4	25♊28.7	21♈20.9	13♌22.4	4♒36.4	20♈33.4	5♍15.6	20♋ 7.2
2 M	14 38 46.4	11 22.5	23 49.5	0♈36.2	16 14.5	26 20.7	22 6.6	13 26.5	4 37.7	20 36.7	5R15.1	20 7.8
3 T	14 42 43.0	12 20.7	23 46.3	12 25.4	16 52.6	27 12.1	22 52.1	13 30.8	4 38.9	20 39.9	5 14.6	20 8.6
4 W	14 46 39.5	13 18.9	23 43.1	24 12.9	17 34.4	28 2.7	23 37.7	13 35.2	4 40.0	20 43.2	5 14.2	20 9.3
5 T	14 50 36.1	14 17.0	23 39.9	6♉ 1.4	18 19.9	28 52.6	24 23.2	13 39.8	4 41.0	20 46.4	5 13.8	20 10.1
6 F	14 54 32.6	15 15.1	23 36.8	17 53.2	19 8.8	29 41.8	25 8.6	13 44.6	4 41.9	20 49.6	5 13.5	20 10.8
7 S	14 58 29.2	16 13.2	23 33.6	29 49.8	20 1.1	0♋30.3	25 54.0	13 49.5	4 42.7	20 52.8	5 13.2	20 11.6
8 S	15 2 25.7	17 11.2	23 30.4	11♊52.9	20 56.7	1 17.9	26 39.3	13 54.6	4 43.4	20 56.0	5 12.9	20 12.5
9 M	15 6 22.3	18 9.3	23 27.2	24 4.0	21 55.3	2 4.6	27 24.6	13 59.8	4 44.0	20 59.1	5 12.6	20 13.3
10 T	15 10 18.8	19 7.3	23 24.0	6♋24.7	22 56.9	2 50.5	28 9.8	14 5.2	4 44.5	21 2.2	5 12.4	20 14.2
11 W	15 14 15.4	20 5.2	23 20.9	18 57.1	24 1.4	3 35.5	28 55.0	14 10.8	4 44.9	21 5.4	5 12.2	20 15.1
12 T	15 18 12.0	21 3.2	23 17.7	1♌43.7	25 8.7	4 19.6	29 40.2	14 16.5	4 45.2	21 8.4	5 12.1	20 16.0
13 F	15 22 8.5	22 1.1	23 14.5	14 47.2	26 18.7	5 2.7	0♉25.2	14 22.3	4 45.4	21 11.5	5 11.9	20 16.9
14 S	15 26 5.1	22 58.9	23 11.3	28 10.4	27 31.4	5 44.8	1 10.3	14 28.3	4 45.6	21 14.6	5 11.9	20 17.8
15 S	15 30 1.6	23 56.8	23 8.2	11♍55.7	28 46.6	6 25.8	1 55.2	14 34.4	4 45.6	21 17.6	5 11.8	20 18.8
16 M	15 33 58.2	24 54.6	23 5.0	26 4.5	0♉ 4.4	7 5.7	2 40.2	14 40.7	4R45.5	21 20.6	5 11.8	20 19.8
17 T	15 37 54.8	25 52.4	23 1.8	10♎36.2	1 24.6	7 44.4	3 25.0	14 47.1	4 45.3	21 23.5	5D11.8	20 20.8
18 W	15 41 51.3	26 50.2	22 58.6	25 27.6	2 47.3	8 22.0	4 9.9	14 53.7	4 45.0	21 26.5	5 11.8	20 21.8
19 T	15 45 47.9	27 47.9	22 55.5	10♏32.7	4 12.3	8 58.3	4 54.6	15 0.4	4 44.7	21 29.4	5 11.9	20 22.9
20 F	15 49 44.4	28 45.6	22 52.3	25 42.7	5 39.8	9 33.4	5 39.3	15 7.2	4 44.2	21 32.3	5 12.0	20 23.9
21 S	15 53 41.0	29 43.3	22 49.1	10♐47.4	7 9.6	10 7.1	6 24.0	15 14.2	4 43.6	21 35.2	5 12.1	20 25.0
22 S	15 57 37.5	0♊41.0	22 45.9	25 37.0	8 41.7	10 39.5	7 8.6	15 21.3	4 43.0	21 38.0	5 12.3	20 26.1
23 M	16 1 34.0	1 38.6	22 42.7	10♑ 3.4	10 16.1	11 10.4	7 53.2	15 28.5	4 42.2	21 40.9	5 12.5	20 27.2
24 T	16 5 30.6	2 36.2	22 39.6	24 1.9	11 52.9	11 39.8	8 37.7	15 35.9	4 41.4	21 43.7	5 12.7	20 28.3
25 W	16 9 27.2	3 33.9	22 36.4	7♒30.9	13 32.0	12 7.8	9 22.1	15 43.4	4 40.4	21 46.4	5 13.0	20 29.5
26 T	16 13 23.8	4 31.5	22 33.2	20 31.9	15 13.3	12 34.1	10 6.5	15 51.0	4 39.4	21 49.2	5 13.3	20 30.7
27 F	16 17 20.3	5 29.0	22 30.0	3♓ 8.2	16 57.0	12 58.8	10 50.9	15 58.7	4 38.2	21 51.9	5 13.6	20 31.8
28 S	16 21 16.8	6 26.6	22 26.9	15 24.7	18 42.9	13 21.8	11 35.2	16 6.6	4 37.0	21 54.5	5 14.0	20 33.0
29 S	16 25 13.4	7 24.2	22 23.7	27 26.5	20 31.1	13 43.0	12 19.4	16 14.6	4 35.7	21 57.2	5 14.4	20 34.2
30 M	16 29 10.0	8 21.7	22 20.5	9♈18.9	22 21.6	14 2.5	13 3.6	16 22.7	4 34.3	21 59.8	5 14.8	20 35.5
31 T	16 33 6.5	9 19.2	22 17.3	21 6.9	24 14.3	14 20.0	13 47.7	16 30.9	4 32.8	22 2.4	5 15.3	20 36.7
						DECLINATION						
1 S	14 34 49.9	14N56.9	2S26.0	5S 1.9	3N52.5	27N 7.8	7N38.7	17N43.0	19S22.0	7N28.7	10N19.3	22N33.8
4 W	14 46 39.5	15 50.6	2 29.7	11N42.0	4 17.3	27 14.0	8 30.9	17 39.1	19 21.4	7 32.4	10 19.7	22 33.6
7 S	14 58 29.2	16 41.9	2 33.5	24 38.0	5 0.4	27 15.6	9 22.2	17 34.7	19 21.1	7 36.0	10 20.1	22 33.4
10 T	15 10 18.8	17 30.7	2 37.3	28 16.5	5 59.6	27 12.8	10 12.6	17 29.9	19 21.0	7 39.5	10 20.3	22 33.2
13 F	15 22 8.5	18 16.9	2 41.1	19 30.9	7 12.7	27 5.9	11 1.9	17 24.7	19 21.1	7 42.9	10 20.4	22 32.9
16 M	15 33 58.2	19 0.2	2 44.8	1 25.1	8 37.7	26 55.3	11 50.2	17 19.1	19 21.4	7 46.3	10 20.5	22 32.6
19 T	15 45 47.9	19 40.7	2 48.6	18S28.6	10 12.7	26 41.2	12 37.3	17 13.0	19 21.9	7 49.6	10 20.4	22 32.3
22 S	15 57 37.5	20 18.2	2 52.4	28 25.4	11 55.7	26 24.0	13 23.2	17 6.6	19 22.6	7 52.8	10 20.2	22 32.0
25 W	16 9 27.2	20 52.5	2 56.1	21 54.8	13 44.6	26 4.0	14 7.9	16 59.9	19 23.6	7 55.9	10 19.9	22 31.6
28 S	16 21 16.8	21 23.7	2 59.9	6 23.8	15 37.2	25 41.6	14 51.2	16 52.7	19 24.7	7 58.8	10 19.5	22 31.2
31 T	16 33 6.5	21 51.5	3 3.7	10N26.0	17 30.3	25 17.1	15 33.2	16 45.2	19 26.0	8 1.7	10 18.9	22 30.8

JUNE 1932

DAY	EPHEMERIS SIDEREAL TIME	☉	☊	☽	☿	♀	♂	♃	♄	♅	♆	♇
						LONGITUDE						
1 W	16 37 3.1	10♊16.7	22♓14.2	2♉54.7	26♉ 9.3	14♋35.7	14♉31.8	16♌39.3	4♒31.1	22♈ 4.9	5♍15.8	20♋38.0
2 T	16 40 59.7	11 14.2	22 11.0	14 45.9	28 6.4	14 49.3	15 15.8	16 47.7	4R29.5	22 7.5	5 16.3	20 39.3
3 F	16 44 56.2	12 11.7	22 7.8	26 43.2	0♊ 5.6	15 0.9	15 59.8	16 56.3	4 27.7	22 9.9	5 16.9	20 40.5
4 S	16 48 52.8	13 9.2	22 4.6	8♊48.4	2 6.8	15 10.4	16 43.7	17 5.0	4 25.8	22 12.4	5 17.5	20 41.9
5 S	16 52 49.3	14 6.6	22 1.5	21 2.8	4 9.9	15 17.7	17 27.6	17 13.8	4 23.8	22 14.8	5 18.1	20 43.2
6 M	16 56 45.9	15 4.1	21 58.3	3♋27.2	6 14.9	15 22.8	18 11.4	17 22.7	4 21.8	22 17.2	5 18.7	20 44.5
7 T	17 0 42.5	16 1.5	21 55.1	16 2.0	8 21.5	15 25.7	18 55.1	17 31.7	4 19.7	22 19.5	5 19.4	20 45.8
8 W	17 4 39.0	16 58.9	21 51.9	28 47.8	10 29.5	15 26.2	19 38.8	17 40.8	4 17.4	22 21.9	5 20.1	20 47.2
9 T	17 8 35.6	17 56.3	21 48.7	11♌45.4	12 38.9	15R24.4	20 22.4	17 50.1	4 15.1	22 24.1	5 20.9	20 48.6
10 F	17 12 32.1	18 53.6	21 45.6	24 56.1	14 49.2	15 20.2	21 5.9	17 59.4	4 12.7	22 26.4	5 21.7	20 50.0
11 S	17 16 28.7	19 51.0	21 42.4	8♍21.4	17 0.4	15 13.6	21 49.4	18 8.8	4 10.3	22 28.6	5 22.5	20 51.3
12 S	17 20 25.3	20 48.3	21 39.2	22 3.2	19 12.1	15 4.6	22 32.9	18 18.3	4 7.7	22 30.7	5 23.3	20 52.8
13 M	17 24 21.8	21 45.6	21 36.0	6♎ 2.5	21 24.1	14 53.2	23 16.3	18 28.0	4 5.1	22 32.9	5 24.2	20 54.2
14 T	17 28 18.4	22 42.9	21 32.9	20 19.5	23 36.1	14 39.3	23 59.6	18 37.7	4 2.4	22 35.0	5 25.1	20 55.6
15 W	17 32 14.9	23 40.2	21 29.7	4♏52.6	25 47.8	14 23.0	24 42.8	18 47.5	3 59.6	22 37.0	5 26.0	20 57.0
16 T	17 36 11.4	24 37.5	21 26.5	19 37.8	27 58.9	14 4.4	25 26.0	18 57.4	3 56.7	22 39.0	5 27.0	20 58.5
17 F	17 40 8.0	25 34.8	21 23.3	4♐28.8	0♋ 9.2	13 43.5	26 9.1	19 7.4	3 53.8	22 41.0	5 28.0	20 60.0
18 S	17 44 4.6	26 32.0	21 20.2	19 17.5	2 18.5	13 20.4	26 52.2	19 17.5	3 50.8	22 42.9	5 29.0	21 1.4
19 S	17 48 1.2	27 29.3	21 17.0	3♑55.4	4 26.6	12 55.2	27 35.2	19 27.6	3 47.7	22 44.8	5 30.0	21 2.9
20 M	17 51 57.7	28 26.5	21 13.8	18 14.9	6 33.2	12 27.9	28 18.2	19 37.9	3 44.6	22 46.6	5 31.1	21 4.4
21 T	17 55 54.3	29 23.7	21 10.6	2♒10.5	8 38.3	11 58.8	29 1.1	19 48.2	3 41.4	22 48.4	5 32.2	21 5.9
22 W	17 59 50.8	0♋20.9	21 7.5	15 39.5	10 41.6	11 27.9	29 43.9	19 58.7	3 38.1	22 50.2	5 33.3	21 7.4
23 T	18 3 47.4	1 18.2	21 4.3	28 42.1	12 43.1	10 55.5	0♊26.7	20 9.2	3 34.7	22 51.9	5 34.5	21 8.9
24 F	18 7 44.0	2 15.4	21 1.1	11♓20.8	14 42.8	10 21.7	1 9.5	20 19.7	3 31.3	22 53.6	5 35.7	21 10.4
25 S	18 11 40.5	3 12.6	20 57.9	23 39.4	16 40.4	9 46.8	1 52.1	20 30.4	3 27.8	22 55.3	5 36.9	21 11.9
26 S	18 15 37.1	4 9.8	20 54.7	5♈43.0	18 36.0	9 10.8	2 34.7	20 41.2	3 24.3	22 56.9	5 38.2	21 13.5
27 M	18 19 33.6	5 7.0	20 51.6	17 36.9	20 29.6	8 34.2	3 17.3	20 52.0	3 20.7	22 58.4	5 39.4	21 15.0
28 T	18 23 30.2	6 4.2	20 48.4	29 26.5	22 21.1	7 57.0	3 59.8	21 2.9	3 17.1	22 59.9	5 40.7	21 16.6
29 W	18 27 26.7	7 1.5	20 45.2	11♉16.6	24 10.4	7 19.5	4 42.2	21 13.8	3 13.3	23 1.4	5 42.0	21 18.1
30 T	18 31 23.3	7 58.7	20 42.0	23 11.6	25 57.7	6 42.0	5 24.6	21 24.9	3 9.6	23 2.8	5 43.4	21 19.7
						DECLINATION						
1 W	16 37 3.1	22N 0.0	3S 4.9	15N30.9	18N 7.6	25N 8.5	15N46.8	16N42.6	19S26.5	8N 2.7	10N18.7	22N30.7
4 S	16 48 52.8	22 23.3	3 8.7	26 34.7	19 55.7	24 41.6	16 26.9	16 34.6	19 28.1	8 5.4	10 18.1	22 30.2
7 T	17 0 42.5	22 43.0	3 12.4	27 1.7	21 34.6	24 13.3	17 5.4	16 26.3	19 29.9	8 8.0	10 17.3	22 29.8
10 F	17 12 32.1	22 59.2	3 16.2	15 21.1	22 58.7	23 43.5	17 42.3	16 17.6	19 31.9	8 10.5	10 16.4	22 29.3
13 M	17 24 21.8	23 11.7	3 19.9	3S33.2	24 3.1	23 12.6	18 17.7	16 8.7	19 34.0	8 12.8	10 15.5	22 28.8
16 T	17 36 11.4	23 20.5	3 23.7	21 45.1	24 43.8	22 40.5	18 51.4	15 59.4	19 36.3	8 15.1	10 14.4	22 28.3
19 S	17 48 1.2	23 25.6	3 27.5	28 16.2	24 59.3	22 7.3	19 23.4	15 49.7	19 38.7	8 17.1	10 13.2	22 27.8
22 W	17 59 50.8	23 27.0	3 31.2	18 53.9	24 50.3	21 33.3	19 53.7	15 39.8	19 41.3	8 19.1	10 12.0	22 27.3
25 S	18 11 40.5	23 24.7	3 35.0	2 15.4	24 19.0	20 58.8	20 22.2	15 29.6	19 44.0	8 20.9	10 10.6	22 26.7
28 T	18 23 30.2	23 18.7	3 38.7	14N15.7	23 29.0	20 24.5	20 49.0	15 19.2	19 46.8	8 22.6	10 9.2	22 26.2

JULY 1932

DAY	EPHEMERIS SIDEREAL TIME	☉	☊	☽	☿	♀	♂	♃	♄	♅	♆	♇
	h m s	° ′	° ′	° ′	° ′	° ′	° ′	° ′	° ′	° ′	° ′	° ′
						LONGITUDE						
1 F	18 35 19.9	8♋55.9	20♓38.9	5♊15.1	27♋42.8	6♋ 4.7	6♊ 6.9	21♌36.0	3♒ 5.7	23♈ 4.2	5♍44.8	21♋21.2
2 S	18 39 16.5	9 53.1	20 35.7	17 29.5	29 25.7	5R27.8	6 49.1	21 47.2	3R 1.9	23 5.5	5 46.2	21 22.8
3 S	18 43 13.0	10 50.3	20 32.5	29 56.4	1♌ 6.6	4 51.6	7 31.3	21 58.5	2 58.0	23 6.8	5 47.6	21 24.4
4 M	18 47 9.5	11 47.6	20 29.3	12♋36.4	2 45.3	4 16.3	8 13.4	22 9.8	2 54.0	23 8.0	5 49.1	21 26.0
5 T	18 51 6.1	12 44.8	20 26.2	25 29.4	4 21.8	3 42.1	8 55.5	22 21.2	2 50.0	23 9.2	5 50.5	21 27.5
6 W	18 55 2.7	13 42.0	20 23.0	8♌34.7	5 56.2	3 9.2	9 37.5	22 32.6	2 45.9	23 10.4	5 52.0	21 29.1
7 T	18 58 59.2	14 39.2	20 19.8	21 51.5	7 28.4	2 37.7	10 19.4	22 44.1	2 41.8	23 11.5	5 53.6	21 30.7
8 F	19 2 55.8	15 36.4	20 16.6	5♍19.2	8 58.4	2 7.9	11 1.3	22 55.7	2 37.7	23 12.5	5 55.1	21 32.3
9 S	19 6 52.3	16 33.7	20 13.5	18 57.4	10 26.2	1 39.9	11 43.1	23 7.3	2 33.5	23 13.5	5 56.7	21 33.9
10 S	19 10 48.9	17 30.9	20 10.3	2♎46.1	11 51.8	1 13.8	12 24.8	23 19.0	2 29.3	23 14.5	5 58.3	21 35.5
11 M	19 14 45.4	18 28.1	20 7.1	16 45.3	13 15.2	0 49.7	13 6.5	23 30.8	2 25.1	23 15.4	5 59.9	21 37.1
12 T	19 18 42.0	19 25.3	20 3.9	0♏54.7	14 36.2	0 27.8	13 48.1	23 42.6	2 20.8	23 16.2	6 1.5	21 38.7
13 W	19 22 38.6	20 22.5	20 0.8	15 12.8	15 54.9	0 8.0	14 29.6	23 54.5	2 16.5	23 17.1	6 3.2	21 40.3
14 T	19 26 35.1	21 19.7	19 57.6	29 37.1	17 11.3	29♊50.6	15 11.1	24 6.4	2 12.2	23 17.8	6 4.9	21 41.9
15 F	19 30 31.7	22 16.9	19 54.4	14♐ 3.6	18 25.2	29 35.5	15 52.5	24 18.3	2 7.9	23 18.5	6 6.6	21 43.5
16 S	19 34 28.2	23 14.2	19 51.2	28 27.1	19 36.6	29 22.8	16 33.9	24 30.3	2 3.5	23 19.2	6 8.3	21 45.1
17 S	19 38 24.8	24 11.4	19 48.0	12♑41.5	20 45.4	29 12.4	17 15.1	24 42.4	1 59.1	23 19.8	6 10.0	21 46.7
18 M	19 42 21.4	25 8.6	19 44.9	26 41.5	21 51.6	29 4.4	17 56.4	24 54.5	1 54.7	23 20.4	6 11.8	21 48.3
19 T	19 46 17.9	26 5.8	19 41.7	10♒22.6	22 55.1	28 58.9	18 37.5	25 6.7	1 50.3	23 20.9	6 13.6	21 49.9
20 W	19 50 14.5	27 3.1	19 38.5	23 42.3	23 55.7	28 55.7	19 18.6	25 18.9	1 45.9	23 21.4	6 15.4	21 51.5
21 T	19 54 11.0	28 0.3	19 35.3	6♓39.8	24 53.5	28 54.9	19 59.6	25 31.1	1 41.5	23 21.9	6 17.2	21 53.1
22 F	19 58 7.6	28 57.6	19 32.2	19 16.6	25 48.1	28D56.4	20 40.6	25 43.4	1 37.0	23 22.2	6 19.1	21 54.7
23 S	20 2 4.1	29 54.9	19 29.0	1♈35.4	26 39.6	29 0.2	21 21.5	25 55.7	1 32.6	23 22.6	6 20.9	21 56.3
24 S	20 6 0.7	0♌52.2	19 25.8	13 40.2	27 27.8	29 6.3	22 2.3	26 8.1	1 28.1	23 22.8	6 22.8	21 57.8
25 M	20 9 57.3	1 49.5	19 22.6	25 35.7	28 12.6	29 14.5	22 43.1	26 20.5	1 23.6	23 23.1	6 24.7	21 59.4
26 T	20 13 53.8	2 46.8	19 19.5	7♉27.0	28 53.8	29 24.9	23 23.8	26 33.0	1 19.2	23 23.3	6 26.6	22 1.0
27 W	20 17 50.4	3 44.2	19 16.3	19 19.1	29 31.2	29 37.3	24 4.5	26 45.5	1 14.7	23 23.4	6 28.5	22 2.6
28 T	20 21 46.9	4 41.5	19 13.1	1♊16.9	0♍ 4.6	29 51.7	24 45.1	26 58.0	1 10.3	23 23.5	6 30.5	22 4.1
29 F	20 25 43.5	5 38.9	19 9.9	13 24.6	0 34.0	0♋ 8.2	25 25.6	27 10.6	1 5.8	23 23.5	6 32.4	22 5.7
30 S	20 29 40.1	6 36.3	19 6.7	25 45.6	0 59.1	0 26.5	26 6.1	27 23.2	1 1.4	23R23.5	6 34.4	22 7.3
31 S	20 33 36.6	7 33.7	19 3.6	8♋22.4	1 19.8	0 46.6	26 46.5	27 35.8	0 57.0	23 23.5	6 36.4	22 8.8
						DECLINATION						
1 F	18 35 19.9	23N 9.0	3S42.5	25N58.3	22N23.7	19N51.2	21N13.9	15N 8.4	19S49.8	8N24.1	10N 7.7	22N25.6
4 M	18 47 9.5	22 55.6	3 46.2	27 27.7	21 6.5	19 20.0	21 37.0	14 57.4	19 52.8	8 25.4	10 6.1	22 25.1
7 T	18 58 59.2	22 38.7	3 50.0	16 25.2	19 40.6	18 51.9	21 58.3	14 46.1	19 55.8	8 26.6	10 4.4	22 24.5
10 S	19 10 48.9	22 18.2	3 53.7	2S13.1	18 8.8	18 28.0	22 17.6	14 34.6	19 59.0	8 27.7	10 2.6	22 23.9
13 W	19 22 38.6	21 54.3	3 57.5	20 27.2	16 33.6	18 8.9	22 35.1	14 22.8	20 2.2	8 28.5	10 0.8	22 23.3
16 S	19 34 28.2	21 26.9	4 1.2	28 27.1	14 57.6	17 54.8	22 50.7	14 10.8	20 5.4	8 29.3	9 58.9	22 22.8
19 T	19 46 17.9	20 56.4	4 4.9	20 40.0	13 23.0	17 45.6	23 4.4	13 58.7	20 8.6	8 29.8	9 56.9	22 22.2
22 F	19 58 7.6	20 22.6	4 8.7	4 8.9	11 52.2	17 41.1	23 16.2	13 46.2	20 11.9	8 30.2	9 54.8	22 21.6
25 M	20 9 57.3	19 45.8	4 12.4	12N49.4	10 28.0	17 40.7	23 26.1	13 33.6	20 15.1	8 30.5	9 52.8	22 21.0
28 T	20 21 46.9	19 6.0	4 16.2	25 15.2	9 13.2	17 43.5	23 34.2	13 20.9	20 18.3	8 30.6	9 50.6	22 20.5
31 S	20 33 36.6	18 23.3	4 19.9	28 0.2	8 11.1	17 48.9	23 40.4	13 7.9	20 21.4	8 30.5	9 48.4	22 19.9

AUGUST 1932

DAY	EPHEMERIS SIDEREAL TIME	☉	☊	☽	☿	♀	♂	♃	♄	♅	♆	♇
						LONGITUDE						
1 M	20 37 33.1	8♌31.1	19♓ 0.4	21♋16.2	1♍35.8	1♋ 8.5	27♊26.8	27♌48.5	0♒52.6	23♈23.4	6♍38.4	22♋10.4
2 T	20 41 29.7	9 28.5	18 57.2	4♌27.0	1 46.9	1 32.1	28 7.0	28 1.2	0R48.2	23R23.2	6 40.4	22 11.9
3 W	20 45 26.3	10 26.0	18 54.0	17 53.8	1 53.2	1 57.4	28 47.2	28 13.9	0 43.8	23 23.0	6 42.4	22 13.4
4 T	20 49 22.8	11 23.5	18 50.9	1♍34.5	1 54.3	2 24.3	29 27.3	28 26.6	0 39.5	23 22.7	6 44.5	22 15.0
5 F	20 53 19.4	12 21.0	18 47.7	15 26.4	1R50.1	2 52.7	0♋ 7.4	28 39.4	0 35.1	23 22.4	6 46.5	22 16.5
6 S	20 57 15.9	13 18.5	18 44.5	29 27.0	1 40.7	3 22.5	0 47.4	28 52.2	0 30.8	23 22.1	6 48.6	22 18.0
7 S	21 1 12.5	14 16.0	18 41.3	13♎33.7	1 25.9	3 53.8	1 27.3	29 5.0	0 26.6	23 21.7	6 50.7	22 19.5
8 M	21 5 9.0	15 13.5	18 38.2	27 44.2	1 5.9	4 26.5	2 7.1	29 17.9	0 22.3	23 21.2	6 52.8	22 21.0
9 T	21 9 5.6	16 11.0	18 35.0	11♏56.4	0 40.6	5 0.4	2 46.9	29 30.8	0 18.1	23 20.7	6 54.9	22 22.5
10 W	21 13 2.2	17 8.6	18 31.8	26 8.3	0 10.4	5 35.7	3 26.6	29 43.7	0 14.0	23 20.2	6 57.0	22 24.0
11 T	21 16 58.7	18 6.2	18 28.6	10♐17.8	29♌35.4	6 12.2	4 6.2	29 56.6	0 9.8	23 19.6	6 59.1	22 25.4
12 F	21 20 55.2	19 3.7	18 25.4	24 22.6	28 56.1	6 49.8	4 45.7	0♍ 9.5	0 5.7	23 19.0	7 1.3	22 26.9
13 S	21 24 51.8	20 1.3	18 22.3	8♑19.8	28 12.9	7 28.6	5 25.2	0 22.4	0 1.7	23 18.3	7 3.4	22 28.3
14 S	21 28 48.4	20 58.9	18 19.1	22 6.8	27 26.6	8 8.6	6 4.6	0 35.4	29♑57.6	23 17.5	7 5.6	22 29.8
15 M	21 32 45.0	21 56.6	18 15.9	5♒40.8	26 37.8	8 49.5	6 44.0	0 48.4	29 53.7	23 16.8	7 7.7	22 31.2
16 T	21 36 41.5	22 54.2	18 12.7	18 59.6	25 47.3	9 31.6	7 23.2	1 1.4	29 49.8	23 15.9	7 9.9	22 32.6
17 W	21 40 38.0	23 51.9	18 9.6	2♓ 1.8	24 56.1	10 14.6	8 2.4	1 14.3	29 45.9	23 15.1	7 12.0	22 34.0
18 T	21 44 34.6	24 49.6	18 6.4	14 47.2	24 5.1	10 58.5	8 41.6	1 27.4	29 42.1	23 14.2	7 14.2	22 35.4
19 F	21 48 31.2	25 47.3	18 3.2	27 16.4	23 15.5	11 43.4	9 20.7	1 40.4	29 38.3	23 13.2	7 16.4	22 36.8
20 S	21 52 27.7	26 45.1	18 0.0	9♈31.2	22 28.1	12 29.2	9 59.6	1 53.4	29 34.6	23 12.2	7 18.6	22 38.2
21 S	21 56 24.3	27 42.8	17 56.9	21 34.6	21 44.0	13 15.8	10 38.6	2 6.4	29 30.9	23 11.1	7 20.8	22 39.5
22 M	22 0 20.8	28 40.6	17 53.7	3♉30.0	21 4.2	14 3.3	11 17.4	2 19.5	29 27.3	23 10.1	7 23.0	22 40.9
23 T	22 4 17.4	29 38.4	17 50.5	15 21.7	20 29.6	14 51.6	11 56.2	2 32.5	29 23.8	23 8.9	7 25.2	22 42.2
24 W	22 8 13.9	0♍36.3	17 47.3	27 14.3	20 0.9	15 40.7	12 34.9	2 45.6	29 20.3	23 7.8	7 27.4	22 43.5
25 T	22 12 10.5	1 34.2	17 44.1	9♊12.3	19 38.8	16 30.4	13 13.6	2 58.7	29 16.9	23 6.5	7 29.6	22 44.8
26 F	22 16 7.0	2 32.1	17 41.0	21 20.6	19 23.9	17 20.9	13 52.1	3 11.7	29 13.5	23 5.3	7 31.9	22 46.1
27 S	22 20 3.6	3 30.0	17 37.8	3♋43.3	19 16.6	18 12.1	14 30.6	3 24.8	29 10.2	23 4.0	7 34.1	22 47.4
28 S	22 24 0.1	4 28.0	17 34.6	16 24.0	19D17.4	19 4.0	15 9.1	3 37.9	29 7.0	23 2.6	7 36.3	22 48.6
29 M	22 27 56.7	5 26.0	17 31.4	29 25.1	19 26.2	19 56.5	15 47.4	3 50.9	29 3.8	23 1.2	7 38.5	22 49.9
30 T	22 31 53.3	6 24.0	17 28.3	12♌47.9	19 43.4	20 49.6	16 25.7	4 4.0	29 0.7	22 59.8	7 40.8	22 51.1
31 W	22 35 49.8	7 22.1	17 25.1	26 31.8	20 8.9	21 43.4	17 3.9	4 17.0	28 57.7	22 58.3	7 43.0	22 52.3
						DECLINATION						
1 M	20 37 33.1	18N 8.5	4S21.1	26N 0.9	7N53.9	17N51.1	23N42.0	13N 3.5	20S22.5	8N30.4	9N47.7	22N19.7
4 T	20 49 22.8	17 22.2	4 24.9	12 14.8	7 14.4	17 58.7	23 45.8	12 50.3	20 25.6	8 30.1	9 45.4	22 19.2
7 S	21 1 12.5	16 33.5	4 28.6	7S28.3	6 56.3	18 7.0	23 47.7	12 37.0	20 28.6	8 29.7	9 43.1	22 18.7
10 W	21 13 2.2	15 42.3	4 32.3	24 0.9	7 2.7	18 15.3	23 47.8	12 23.5	20 31.5	8 29.0	9 40.7	22 18.1
13 S	21 24 51.8	14 48.8	4 36.1	28 3.0	7 34.6	18 23.1	23 46.2	12 9.9	20 34.3	8 28.3	9 38.4	22 17.6
16 T	21 36 41.5	13 53.3	4 39.8	17 29.2	8 29.8	18 29.6	23 42.8	11 56.2	20 37.1	8 27.3	9 36.0	22 17.1
19 F	21 48 31.2	12 55.8	4 43.5	0 14.1	9 41.5	18 34.4	23 37.8	11 42.4	20 39.7	8 26.3	9 33.6	22 16.7
22 M	22 0 20.8	11 56.4	4 47.2	16N16.1	10 59.9	18 37.0	23 31.1	11 28.5	20 42.2	8 25.0	9 31.1	22 16.2
25 T	22 12 10.5	10 55.3	4 51.0	26 59.5	12 13.6	18 36.8	23 22.8	11 14.5	20 44.5	8 23.7	9 28.7	22 15.8
28 S	22 24 0.1	9 52.6	4 54.7	27 0.4	13 12.3	18 33.6	23 13.0	11 0.5	20 46.7	8 22.2	9 26.2	22 15.3
31 W	22 35 49.8	8 48.5	4 58.4	14 25.4	13 48.2	18 27.0	23 1.7	10 46.4	20 48.8	8 20.5	9 23.7	22 15.0

SEPTEMBER 1932

LONGITUDE

DAY	EPHEMERIS SIDEREAL TIME h m s	☉ ° ′	☊ ° ′	☽ ° ′	☿ ° ′	♀ ° ′	♂ ° ′	♃ ° ′	♄ ° ′	♅ ° ′	♆ ° ′	♇ ° ′
1 T	22 39 46.3	8♍20.2	17♓21.9	10♍34.5	20♌42.6	22♋37.7	17♋42.0	4♍30.1	28♑54.8	22♈56.8	7♍45.2	22♋53.5
2 F	22 43 42.9	9 18.3	17 18.7	24 52.3	21 24.3	23 32.5	18 20.0	4 43.1	28R51.9	22R55.3	7 47.4	22 54.7
3 S	22 47 39.5	10 16.5	17 15.5	9♎20.1	22 13.8	24 27.9	18 58.0	4 56.2	28 49.2	22 53.7	7 49.7	22 55.9
4 S	22 51 36.1	11 14.6	17 12.4	23 52.6	23 10.8	25 23.8	19 35.8	5 9.2	28 46.5	22 52.1	7 51.9	22 57.0
5 M	22 55 32.6	12 12.8	17 9.2	8♏24.2	24 14.8	26 20.2	20 13.6	5 22.2	28 43.8	22 50.4	7 54.1	22 58.1
6 T	22 59 29.1	13 11.0	17 6.0	22 50.3	25 25.6	27 17.2	20 51.3	5 35.3	28 41.3	22 48.7	7 56.3	22 59.2
7 W	23 3 25.7	14 9.3	17 2.8	7♐ 7.1	26 42.5	28 14.5	21 28.9	5 48.3	28 38.9	22 47.0	7 58.6	23 0.3
8 T	23 7 22.3	15 7.6	16 59.7	21 12.0	28 5.1	29 12.4	22 6.5	6 1.2	28 36.5	22 45.3	8 0.8	23 1.4
9 F	23 11 18.8	16 5.8	16 56.5	5♑ 3.5	29 32.9	0♌10.7	22 43.9	6 14.2	28 34.2	22 43.5	8 3.0	23 2.5
10 S	23 15 15.4	17 4.2	16 53.3	18 40.8	1♍ 5.2	1 9.4	23 21.3	6 27.1	28 32.0	22 41.6	8 5.2	23 3.5
11 S	23 19 11.9	18 2.5	16 50.1	2♒ 3.8	2 41.6	2 8.5	23 58.6	6 40.1	28 29.9	22 39.8	8 7.4	23 4.5
12 M	23 23 8.5	19 0.9	16 47.0	15 12.6	4 21.5	3 8.1	24 35.8	6 53.0	28 27.9	22 37.9	8 9.6	23 5.5
13 T	23 27 5.0	19 59.3	16 43.8	28 7.5	6 4.3	4 8.0	25 12.9	7 5.9	28 25.9	22 36.0	8 11.8	23 6.5
14 W	23 31 1.6	20 57.7	16 40.6	10♓49.2	7 49.6	5 8.4	25 50.0	7 18.8	28 24.1	22 34.0	8 13.9	23 7.4
15 T	23 34 58.1	21 56.2	16 37.4	23 18.4	9 37.0	6 9.1	26 26.9	7 31.6	28 22.3	22 32.0	8 16.1	23 8.4
16 F	23 38 54.7	22 54.7	16 34.2	5♈36.1	11 25.8	7 10.3	27 3.8	7 44.5	28 20.6	22 30.0	8 18.3	23 9.3
17 S	23 42 51.2	23 53.2	16 31.1	17 43.7	13 15.9	8 11.7	27 40.6	7 57.3	28 19.1	22 28.0	8 20.5	23 10.2
18 S	23 46 47.8	24 51.7	16 27.9	29 43.1	15 6.8	9 13.6	28 17.3	8 10.0	28 17.6	22 25.9	8 22.6	23 11.1
19 M	23 50 44.3	25 50.3	16 24.7	11♉36.8	16 58.2	10 15.7	28 53.9	8 22.8	28 16.2	22 23.8	8 24.8	23 11.9
20 T	23 54 40.9	26 48.9	16 21.5	23 27.9	18 49.9	11 18.3	29 30.4	8 35.5	28 14.9	22 21.7	8 26.9	23 12.8
21 W	23 58 37.4	27 47.6	16 18.3	5♊19.7	20 41.6	12 21.1	0♌ 6.9	8 48.2	28 13.7	22 19.6	8 29.0	23 13.6
22 T	0 2 34.0	28 46.3	16 15.2	17 16.5	22 33.2	13 24.3	0 43.2	9 0.9	28 12.6	22 17.4	8 31.2	23 14.4
23 F	0 6 30.6	29 45.0	16 12.0	29 22.6	24 24.5	14 27.7	1 19.5	9 13.5	28 11.6	22 15.2	8 33.3	23 15.2
24 S	0 10 27.1	0♎43.8	16 8.8	11♋42.5	26 15.3	15 31.5	1 55.7	9 26.1	28 10.7	22 13.0	8 35.4	23 15.9
25 S	0 14 23.7	1 42.6	16 5.6	24 20.5	28 5.6	16 35.5	2 31.8	9 38.7	28 9.9	22 10.8	8 37.5	23 16.6
26 M	0 18 20.3	2 41.5	16 2.5	7♌20.4	29 55.3	17 39.9	3 7.7	9 51.2	28 9.2	22 8.5	8 39.5	23 17.3
27 T	0 22 16.8	3 40.4	15 59.3	20 45.1	1♎44.2	18 44.5	3 43.6	10 3.7	28 8.5	22 6.3	8 41.6	23 18.0
28 W	0 26 13.3	4 39.3	15 56.1	4♍35.5	3 32.4	19 49.4	4 19.4	10 16.2	28 8.0	22 4.0	8 43.6	23 18.7
29 T	0 30 9.9	5 38.3	15 52.9	18 50.7	5 19.9	20 54.5	4 55.1	10 28.6	28 7.6	22 1.7	8 45.7	23 19.3
30 F	0 34 6.5	6 37.3	15 49.8	3♎27.1	7 6.5	21 60.0	5 30.7	10 41.0	28 7.3	21 59.3	8 47.7	23 19.9

DECLINATION

DAY	SIDEREAL TIME	☉	☊	☽	☿	♀	♂	♃	♄	♅	♆	♇
1 T	22 39 46.3	8N26.9	4S59.6	8N 9.7	13N54.1	18N24.0	22N57.5	10N41.7	20S49.5	8N20.0	9N22.9	22N14.8
4 S	22 51 36.1	7 21.1	5 3.3	12S12.7	13 51.8	18 12.5	22 44.3	10 27.5	20 51.3	8 18.2	9 20.4	22 14.5
7 W	23 3 25.7	6 14.3	5 7.1	26 38.3	13 18.5	17 57.1	22 29.7	10 13.4	20 53.1	8 16.2	9 18.0	22 14.1
10 S	23 15 15.4	5 6.5	5 10.8	26 36.5	12 15.2	17 37.6	22 13.7	9 59.2	20 54.6	8 14.2	9 15.5	22 13.8
13 T	23 27 5.0	3 58.0	5 14.5	13 44.9	10 45.7	17 13.9	21 56.5	9 45.1	20 56.0	8 12.1	9 13.1	22 13.6
16 F	23 38 54.7	2 48.9	5 18.2	3N45.9	8 55.4	16 46.0	21 38.1	9 30.9	20 57.2	8 9.8	9 10.7	22 13.3
19 M	23 50 44.3	1 39.3	5 21.9	19 24.5	6 50.2	16 13.8	21 18.6	9 16.8	20 58.2	8 7.5	9 8.3	22 13.1
22 T	0 2 34.0	0 29.3	5 25.6	28 5.2	4 35.6	15 37.4	20 58.0	9 2.8	20 59.0	8 5.1	9 6.0	22 13.0
25 S	0 14 23.7	0S40.8	5 29.3	25 23.3	2 15.9	14 56.7	20 36.3	8 48.8	20 59.7	8 2.6	9 3.7	22 12.8
28 W	0 26 13.3	1 51.0	5 33.0	10 53.7	0S 5.4	14 11.9	20 13.8	8 35.0	21 0.2	8 0.0	9 1.4	22 12.7

OCTOBER 1932

LONGITUDE

DAY	SIDEREAL TIME	☉	☊	☽	☿	♀	♂	♃	♄	♅	♆	♇
1 S	0 38 3.0	7♎36.3	15♓46.6	18♎18.6	8♎52.3	23♌ 5.6	6♌ 6.2	10♍53.3	28♑ 7.1	21♈57.0	8♍49.7	23♋20.5
2 S	0 41 59.6	8 35.3	15 43.4	3♏17.3	10 37.3	24 11.5	6 41.6	11 5.6	28R 6.9	21R54.6	8 51.7	23 21.1
3 M	0 45 56.1	9 34.4	15 40.2	18 14.5	12 21.4	25 17.6	7 16.8	11 17.8	28 6.9	21 52.3	8 53.7	23 21.6
4 T	0 49 52.7	10 33.6	15 37.0	3♐ 2.1	14 4.6	26 23.9	7 52.0	11 30.0	28D 7.0	21 49.9	8 55.6	23 22.1
5 W	0 53 49.2	11 32.7	15 33.9	17 33.7	15 47.1	27 30.5	8 27.0	11 42.2	28 7.2	21 47.5	8 57.6	23 22.6
6 T	0 57 45.8	12 31.9	15 30.7	1♑45.0	17 28.7	28 37.3	9 2.0	11 54.3	28 7.5	21 45.1	8 59.5	23 23.1
7 F	1 1 42.3	13 31.1	15 27.5	15 34.5	19 9.5	29 44.3	9 36.8	12 6.3	28 7.9	21 42.7	9 1.4	23 23.6
8 S	1 5 38.9	14 30.4	15 24.3	29 2.5	20 49.5	0♍51.5	10 11.6	12 18.3	28 8.3	21 40.3	9 3.3	23 24.0
9 S	1 9 35.4	15 29.6	15 21.1	12♒10.4	22 28.8	1 58.9	10 46.2	12 30.2	28 8.9	21 37.9	9 5.2	23 24.4
10 M	1 13 32.0	16 28.9	15 18.0	25 1.0	24 7.3	3 6.5	11 20.7	12 42.1	28 9.6	21 35.4	9 7.1	23 24.8
11 T	1 17 28.6	17 28.3	15 14.8	7♓36.7	25 45.0	4 14.3	11 55.1	12 53.9	28 10.4	21 33.0	9 8.9	23 25.1
12 W	1 21 25.1	18 27.6	15 11.6	20 0.2	27 22.0	5 22.3	12 29.3	13 5.7	28 11.3	21 30.6	9 10.7	23 25.4
13 T	1 25 21.7	19 27.0	15 8.4	2♈13.8	28 58.3	6 30.5	13 3.5	13 17.4	28 12.3	21 28.1	9 12.5	23 25.7
14 F	1 29 18.2	20 26.4	15 5.3	14 19.6	0♏33.9	7 38.9	13 37.6	13 29.0	28 13.4	21 25.7	9 14.3	23 26.0
15 S	1 33 14.8	21 25.9	15 2.1	26 19.1	2 8.8	8 47.4	14 11.5	13 40.6	28 14.5	21 23.3	9 16.1	23 26.3
16 S	1 37 11.3	22 25.4	14 58.9	8♉14.0	3 43.1	9 56.2	14 45.3	13 52.1	28 15.8	21 20.8	9 17.8	23 26.5
17 M	1 41 7.9	23 24.9	14 55.7	20 6.0	5 16.7	11 5.1	15 19.0	14 3.6	28 17.2	21 18.4	9 19.5	23 26.7
18 T	1 45 4.4	24 24.5	14 52.6	1♊57.0	6 49.7	12 14.1	15 52.5	14 14.9	28 18.7	21 15.9	9 21.2	23 26.9
19 W	1 49 1.0	25 24.1	14 49.4	13 49.5	8 22.0	13 23.4	16 26.0	14 26.2	28 20.3	21 13.5	9 22.9	23 27.0
20 T	1 52 57.6	26 23.7	14 46.2	25 46.2	9 53.8	14 32.8	16 59.3	14 37.5	28 21.9	21 11.1	9 24.6	23 27.1
21 F	1 56 54.1	27 23.4	14 43.0	7♋50.8	11 24.9	15 42.4	17 32.5	14 48.7	28 23.7	21 8.6	9 26.2	23 27.2
22 S	2 0 50.6	28 23.1	14 39.8	20 7.1	12 55.5	16 52.1	18 5.5	14 59.7	28 25.6	21 6.2	9 27.8	23 27.3
23 S	2 4 47.2	29 22.9	14 36.7	2♌39.7	14 25.5	18 2.0	18 38.5	15 10.8	28 27.6	21 3.8	9 29.4	23 27.4
24 M	2 8 43.8	0♏22.7	14 33.5	15 32.8	15 54.8	19 12.1	19 11.2	15 21.7	28 29.6	21 1.4	9 31.0	23 27.4
25 T	2 12 40.3	1 22.5	14 30.3	28 50.5	17 23.6	20 22.3	19 43.9	15 32.6	28 31.8	20 59.0	9 32.5	23 27.4
26 W	2 16 36.9	2 22.3	14 27.1	12♍35.6	18 51.8	21 32.6	20 16.4	15 43.4	28 34.1	20 56.6	9 34.0	23R27.4
27 T	2 20 33.4	3 22.2	14 24.0	26 49.1	20 19.3	22 43.1	20 48.8	15 54.1	28 36.4	20 54.2	9 35.5	23 27.3
28 F	2 24 30.0	4 22.2	14 20.8	11♎29.2	21 46.2	23 53.7	21 21.0	16 4.7	28 38.9	20 51.9	9 36.9	23 27.2
29 S	2 28 26.5	5 22.1	14 17.6	26 30.7	23 12.5	25 4.4	21 53.0	16 15.2	28 41.4	20 49.5	9 38.4	23 27.1
30 S	2 32 23.1	6 22.1	14 14.4	11♏45.2	24 38.0	26 15.3	22 24.9	16 25.7	28 44.0	20 47.2	9 39.8	23 27.0
31 M	2 36 19.6	7 22.2	14 11.2	27 2.2	26 2.9	27 26.2	22 56.7	16 36.0	28 46.8	20 44.9	9 41.2	23 26.9

DECLINATION

DAY	SIDEREAL TIME	☉	☊	☽	☿	♀	♂	♃	♄	♅	♆	♇
1 S	0 38 3.0	3S 1.1	5S36.7	9S42.1	2S26.0	13N23.1	19N50.3	8N21.2	21S 0.5	7N57.4	8N59.2	22N12.6
4 T	0 49 52.7	4 10.9	5 40.4	25 45.5	4 44.2	12 30.5	19 26.1	8 7.6	21 0.6	7 54.8	8 57.0	22 12.6
7 F	1 1 42.3	5 20.3	5 44.1	27 6.2	6 58.6	11 34.2	19 1.1	7 54.1	21 0.5	7 52.1	8 54.9	22 12.6
10 M	1 13 32.0	6 29.0	5 47.8	15 1.7	9 8.4	10 34.4	18 35.5	7 40.7	21 0.3	7 49.4	8 52.9	22 12.7
13 T	1 25 21.7	7 36.9	5 51.5	2N 9.0	11 12.9	9 31.4	18 9.3	7 27.6	20 59.8	7 46.7	8 50.9	22 12.7
16 S	1 37 11.3	8 43.9	5 55.1	18 5.4	13 11.3	8 25.3	17 42.6	7 14.6	20 59.2	7 44.0	8 49.0	22 12.9
19 W	1 49 1.0	9 49.7	5 58.8	27 35.1	15 3.2	7 16.4	17 15.4	7 1.8	20 58.4	7 41.2	8 47.1	22 13.0
22 S	2 0 50.6	10 54.3	6 2.5	26 10.7	16 48.0	6 5.0	16 47.8	6 49.3	20 57.4	7 38.5	8 45.4	22 13.2
25 T	2 12 40.3	11 57.5	6 6.2	13 19.6	18 25.1	4 51.3	16 20.0	6 37.0	20 56.2	7 35.9	8 43.7	22 13.4
28 F	2 24 30.0	12 59.0	6 9.9	6S34.1	19 54.0	3 35.6	15 51.9	6 25.0	20 54.9	7 33.2	8 42.1	22 13.7
31 M	2 36 19.6	13 58.7	6 13.5	24 12.2	21 14.1	2 18.3	15 23.6	6 13.3	20 53.3	7 30.7	8 40.6	22 14.0

NOVEMBER 1932

LONGITUDE

DAY	EPHEMERIS SIDEREAL TIME h m s	☉ ° ′	☊ ° ′	☽ ° ′	☿ ° ′	♀ ° ′	♂ ° ′	♃ ° ′	♄ ° ′	♅ ° ′	♆ ° ′	♇ ° ′
1 T	2 40 16.2	8 ♏ 22.2	14 ♓ 8.1	12 ♐ 10.5	27 ♏ 27.0	28 ♍ 37.3	23 ♌ 28.3	16 ♍ 46.3	28 ♑ 49.6	20 ♈ 42.6	9 ♍ 42.5	23 ♋ 26.7
2 W	2 44 12.8	9 22.3	14 4.9	27 0.7	28 50.3	29 48.6	23 59.7	16 56.5	28 52.5	20 R 40.3	9 43.8	23 R 26.5
3 T	2 48 9.3	10 22.5	14 1.7	11 ♑ 26.1	0 ♐ 12.7	0 ≏ 59.9	24 31.0	17 6.6	28 55.5	20 38.0	9 45.1	23 26.3
4 F	2 52 5.9	11 22.6	13 58.5	25 23.7	1 34.2	2 11.3	25 2.1	17 16.5	28 58.6	20 35.8	9 46.4	23 26.0
5 S	2 56 2.4	12 22.8	13 55.4	8 ♒ 53.4	2 54.7	3 22.8	25 33.0	17 26.4	29 1.8	20 33.6	9 47.6	23 25.7
6 S	2 59 59.0	13 23.0	13 52.2	21 57.6	4 14.1	4 34.5	26 3.8	17 36.2	29 5.1	20 31.4	9 48.9	23 25.4
7 M	3 3 55.6	14 23.2	13 49.0	4 ♓ 40.1	5 32.2	5 46.3	26 34.4	17 45.9	29 8.5	20 29.2	9 50.0	23 25.1
8 T	3 7 52.1	15 23.4	13 45.8	17 5.2	6 49.1	6 58.1	27 4.8	17 55.5	29 11.9	20 27.1	9 51.2	23 24.8
9 W	3 11 48.7	16 23.7	13 42.7	29 17.2	8 4.4	8 10.1	27 35.0	18 4.9	29 15.5	20 24.9	9 52.3	23 24.4
10 T	3 15 45.2	17 24.0	13 39.5	11 ♈ 19.9	9 18.0	9 22.1	28 5.0	18 14.3	29 19.1	20 22.8	9 53.4	23 24.0
11 F	3 19 41.8	18 24.3	13 36.3	23 16.6	10 29.8	10 34.3	28 34.9	18 23.6	29 22.8	20 20.7	9 54.5	23 23.6
12 S	3 23 38.3	19 24.6	13 33.1	5 ♉ 9.9	11 39.5	11 46.5	29 4.6	18 32.7	29 26.6	20 18.7	9 55.5	23 23.1
13 S	3 27 34.9	20 25.0	13 30.0	17 1.8	12 46.9	12 58.8	29 34.1	18 41.8	29 30.5	20 16.7	9 56.5	23 22.7
14 M	3 31 31.4	21 25.4	13 26.8	28 53.8	13 51.6	14 11.3	0 ♍ 3.4	18 50.7	29 34.4	20 14.7	9 57.5	23 22.2
15 T	3 35 28.0	22 25.8	13 23.6	10 ♊ 47.4	14 53.4	15 23.8	0 32.5	18 59.5	29 38.5	20 12.7	9 58.4	23 21.7
16 W	3 39 24.5	23 26.3	13 20.4	22 43.9	15 51.7	16 36.4	1 1.4	19 8.2	29 42.6	20 10.8	9 59.3	23 21.1
17 T	3 43 21.1	24 26.8	13 17.2	4 ♋ 45.0	16 46.3	17 49.1	1 30.1	19 16.8	29 46.8	20 8.9	10 0.2	23 20.6
18 F	3 47 17.7	25 27.3	13 14.1	16 52.9	17 36.6	19 1.9	1 58.6	19 25.3	29 51.1	20 7.0	10 1.0	23 20.0
19 S	3 51 14.2	26 27.8	13 10.9	29 10.5	18 22.0	20 14.7	2 26.9	19 33.6	29 55.4	20 5.2	10 1.9	23 19.4
20 S	3 55 10.8	27 28.4	13 7.7	11 ♌ 41.3	19 2.0	21 27.6	2 54.9	19 41.8	29 59.9	20 3.4	10 2.6	23 18.8
21 M	3 59 7.4	28 29.0	13 4.5	24 29.3	19 35.8	22 40.7	3 22.8	19 49.9	0 ♒ 4.4	20 1.6	10 3.4	23 18.1
22 T	4 3 3.9	29 29.6	13 1.4	7 ♍ 38.4	20 2.8	23 53.8	3 50.4	19 57.9	0 9.0	19 59.9	10 4.1	23 17.5
23 W	4 7 0.5	0 ♐ 30.3	12 58.2	21 12.5	20 22.2	25 6.9	4 17.8	20 5.7	0 13.6	19 58.2	10 4.8	23 16.8
24 T	4 10 57.0	1 31.0	12 55.0	5 ≏ 13.9	20 33.2	26 20.1	4 44.9	20 13.4	0 18.4	19 56.5	10 5.4	23 16.0
25 F	4 14 53.6	2 31.7	12 51.8	19 42.8	20 34.9	27 33.5	5 11.8	20 21.0	0 23.2	19 54.9	10 6.1	23 15.3
26 S	4 18 50.1	3 32.4	12 48.7	4 ♏ 36.3	20 R 26.8	28 46.8	5 38.5	20 28.4	0 28.1	19 53.4	10 6.6	23 14.6
27 S	4 22 46.7	4 33.2	12 45.5	19 47.9	20 8.3	0 ♏ 0.3	6 4.8	20 35.7	0 33.0	19 51.8	10 7.2	23 13.8
28 M	4 26 43.3	5 34.0	12 42.3	5 ♐ 7.6	19 38.8	1 13.7	6 31.0	20 42.8	0 38.0	19 50.3	10 7.7	23 13.0
29 T	4 30 39.8	6 34.8	12 39.1	20 23.9	18 58.3	2 27.3	6 56.8	20 49.9	0 43.1	19 48.9	10 8.2	23 12.2
30 W	4 34 36.4	7 35.6	12 35.9	5 ♑ 25.5	18 7.2	3 40.9	7 22.4	20 56.7	0 48.3	19 47.4	10 8.6	23 11.3

DECLINATION

DAY	EPHEMERIS SIDEREAL TIME h m s	☉	☊	☽	☿	♀	♂	♃	♄	♅	♆	♇
1 T	2 40 16.2	14 S 18.1	6 S 14.7	27 S 18.4	21 S 38.6	1 N 52.2	15 N 14.2	6 N 9.5	20 S 52.8	7 N 29.8	8 N 40.1	22 N 14.2
4 F	2 52 5.9	15 15.1	6 18.4	24 55.2	22 45.7	0 33.1	14 45.9	5 58.2	20 51.0	7 27.3	8 38.7	22 14.5
7 M	3 3 55.6	16 9.8	6 22.1	10 41.5	23 42.0	0 S 47.0	14 17.7	5 47.3	20 49.1	7 24.9	8 37.5	22 14.9
10 T	3 15 45.2	17 2.0	6 25.7	6 N 31.9	24 26.8	2 7.6	13 49.5	5 36.7	20 46.9	7 22.5	8 36.3	22 15.4
13 S	3 27 34.9	17 51.6	6 29.4	21 11.5	24 59.2	3 28.6	13 21.6	5 26.5	20 44.7	7 20.3	8 35.2	22 15.8
16 W	3 39 24.5	18 38.5	6 33.1	28 12.6	25 18.2	4 49.6	12 53.9	5 16.7	20 42.2	7 18.1	8 34.2	22 16.4
19 S	3 51 14.2	19 22.4	6 36.7	23 48.1	25 22.5	6 10.3	12 26.6	5 7.3	20 39.6	7 16.1	8 33.4	22 16.9
22 T	4 3 3.9	20 3.1	6 40.4	9 12.6	25 11.0	7 30.2	11 59.7	4 58.4	20 36.8	7 14.2	8 32.6	22 17.5
25 F	4 14 53.6	20 40.6	6 44.0	10 S 27.2	24 41.8	8 49.2	11 33.4	4 49.9	20 33.8	7 12.4	8 32.0	22 18.1
28 M	4 26 43.3	21 14.6	6 47.7	26 2.0	23 52.9	10 6.7	11 7.7	4 41.9	20 30.7	7 10.7	8 31.5	22 18.7

DECEMBER 1932

LONGITUDE

DAY	SIDEREAL TIME	☉	☊	☽	☿	♀	♂	♃	♄	♅	♆	♇
1 T	4 38 32.9	8 ♐ 36.5	12 ♓ 32.8	20 ♑ 3.4	17 ♐ 6.1	4 ♏ 54.5	7 ♍ 47.7	21 ♍ 3.5	0 ♒ 53.5	19 ♈ 46.1	10 ♍ 9.0	23 ♋ 10.5
2 F	4 42 29.5	9 37.3	12 29.6	4 ♒ 12.3	15 R 56.4	6 8.3	8 12.8	21 10.0	0 58.8	19 R 44.7	10 9.4	23 R 9.6
3 S	4 46 26.0	10 38.2	12 26.4	17 50.7	14 39.9	7 22.0	8 37.5	21 16.5	1 4.2	19 43.5	10 9.8	23 8.7
4 S	4 50 22.6	11 39.1	12 23.2	1 ♓ 0.2	13 18.8	8 35.8	9 2.0	21 22.7	1 9.6	19 42.2	10 10.1	23 7.8
5 M	4 54 19.2	12 40.0	12 20.1	13 44.5	11 55.9	9 49.6	9 26.1	21 28.9	1 15.1	19 41.0	10 10.3	23 6.9
6 T	4 58 15.7	13 40.9	12 16.9	26 8.3	10 34.0	11 3.5	9 50.0	21 34.8	1 20.6	19 39.9	10 10.6	23 5.9
7 W	5 2 12.3	14 41.8	12 13.7	8 ♈ 16.8	9 15.8	12 17.5	10 13.5	21 40.7	1 26.2	19 38.8	10 10.8	23 5.0
8 T	5 6 8.8	15 42.8	12 10.5	20 15.1	8 3.8	13 31.4	10 36.7	21 46.3	1 31.9	19 37.7	10 11.0	23 4.0
9 F	5 10 5.4	16 43.7	12 7.4	2 ♉ 7.5	7 0.0	14 45.5	10 59.6	21 51.8	1 37.6	19 36.7	10 11.1	23 3.0
10 S	5 14 2.0	17 44.7	12 4.2	13 58.0	6 6.1	15 59.5	11 22.2	21 57.2	1 43.4	19 35.7	10 11.2	23 2.0
11 S	5 17 58.5	18 45.7	12 1.0	25 49.2	5 22.8	17 13.6	11 44.5	22 2.4	1 49.2	19 34.8	10 11.3	23 1.0
12 M	5 21 55.1	19 46.7	11 57.8	7 ♊ 43.5	4 50.8	18 27.8	12 6.4	22 7.4	1 55.1	19 33.9	10 11.3	22 59.9
13 T	5 25 51.6	20 47.7	11 54.6	19 42.4	4 30.0	19 41.9	12 27.9	22 12.2	2 1.0	19 33.1	10 R 11.3	22 58.9
14 W	5 29 48.2	21 48.7	11 51.5	1 ♋ 46.8	4 20.1	20 56.2	12 49.1	22 16.9	2 7.0	19 32.3	10 11.3	22 57.8
15 T	5 33 44.8	22 49.7	11 48.3	13 57.8	4 D 20.6	22 10.4	13 10.0	22 21.5	2 13.1	19 31.6	10 11.2	22 56.7
16 F	5 37 41.3	23 50.7	11 45.1	26 16.3	4 30.7	23 24.7	13 30.4	22 25.8	2 19.2	19 30.9	10 11.1	22 55.6
17 S	5 41 37.9	24 51.8	11 41.9	8 ♌ 43.8	4 49.7	24 39.0	13 50.5	22 30.0	2 25.3	19 30.3	10 11.0	22 54.5
18 S	5 45 34.4	25 52.8	11 38.8	21 22.1	5 16.7	25 53.4	14 10.2	22 34.0	2 31.5	19 29.7	10 10.8	22 53.4
19 M	5 49 31.0	26 53.9	11 35.6	4 ♍ 14.0	5 51.0	27 7.8	14 29.5	22 37.8	2 37.7	19 29.2	10 10.6	22 52.2
20 T	5 53 27.5	27 55.0	11 32.4	17 22.3	6 31.7	28 22.2	14 48.4	22 41.5	2 44.0	19 28.7	10 10.3	22 51.1
21 W	5 57 24.1	28 56.1	11 29.2	0 ≏ 50.0	7 18.1	29 36.7	15 6.9	22 45.0	2 50.3	19 28.3	10 10.1	22 49.9
22 T	6 1 20.7	29 57.2	11 26.1	14 39.5	8 9.7	0 ♐ 51.2	15 25.0	22 48.3	2 56.7	19 27.9	10 9.8	22 48.7
23 F	6 5 17.2	0 ♑ 58.4	11 22.9	28 52.1	9 5.7	2 5.7	15 42.6	22 51.4	3 3.1	19 27.6	10 9.4	22 47.6
24 S	6 9 13.8	1 59.5	11 19.7	13 ♏ 26.4	10 5.6	3 20.3	15 59.7	22 54.4	3 9.6	19 27.3	10 9.0	22 46.4
25 S	6 13 10.3	3 0.7	11 16.5	28 18.5	11 9.0	4 34.8	16 16.4	22 57.1	3 16.1	19 27.1	10 8.6	22 45.2
26 M	6 17 6.9	4 1.8	11 13.4	13 ♐ 21.3	12 15.5	5 49.4	16 32.7	22 59.7	3 22.6	19 26.9	10 8.2	22 43.9
27 T	6 21 3.4	5 3.0	11 10.2	28 25.4	13 24.7	7 4.1	16 48.4	23 2.1	3 29.2	19 26.8	10 7.7	22 42.7
28 W	6 25 0.0	6 4.2	11 7.0	13 ♑ 20.7	14 36.3	8 18.7	17 3.7	23 4.3	3 35.8	19 26.7	10 7.2	22 41.5
29 T	6 28 56.6	7 5.4	11 3.8	27 58.1	15 50.0	9 33.4	17 18.5	23 6.3	3 42.4	19 26.7	10 6.7	22 40.2
30 F	6 32 53.1	8 6.5	11 0.7	12 ♒ 10.9	17 5.6	10 48.0	17 32.7	23 8.1	3 49.1	19 D 26.7	10 6.1	22 39.0
31 S	6 36 49.7	9 7.7	10 57.5	25 55.7	18 22.8	12 2.7	17 46.5	23 9.8	3 55.8	19 26.8	10 5.5	22 37.7

DECLINATION

DAY	SIDEREAL TIME	☉	☊	☽	☿	♀	♂	♃	♄	♅	♆	♇
1 T	4 38 32.9	21 S 44.9	6 S 51.3	25 S 53.7	22 S 43.3	11 S 22.6	10 N 42.8	4 N 34.5	20 S 27.5	7 N 9.2	8 N 31.1	22 N 19.4
4 S	4 50 22.6	22 11.6	6 55.0	12 3.9	21 18.1	12 36.2	10 18.6	4 27.5	20 24.1	7 7.8	8 30.8	22 20.1
7 W	5 2 12.3	22 34.3	6 58.6	5 N 18.0	19 52.6	13 47.5	9 55.4	4 21.1	20 20.5	7 6.6	8 30.6	22 20.8
10 S	5 14 2.0	22 53.1	7 2.2	20 14.5	18 47.6	14 55.9	9 33.2	4 15.3	20 16.8	7 5.6	8 30.6	22 21.5
13 T	5 25 51.6	23 7.8	7 5.9	27 58.4	18 16.0	16 1.1	9 12.1	4 10.1	20 13.0	7 4.7	8 30.7	22 22.3
16 F	5 37 41.3	23 18.4	7 9.5	24 22.0	18 17.4	17 2.8	8 52.2	4 5.5	20 9.0	7 4.0	8 30.8	22 23.1
19 M	5 49 31.0	23 24.8	7 13.1	10 29.3	18 43.6	18 0.7	8 33.7	4 1.4	20 4.9	7 3.4	8 31.1	22 23.8
22 T	6 1 20.7	23 27.0	7 16.8	8 S 23.5	19 25.2	18 54.3	8 16.6	3 58.0	20 0.7	7 3.0	8 31.5	22 24.7
25 S	6 13 10.3	23 25.0	7 20.4	24 35.6	20 14.0	19 43.3	8 1.0	3 55.3	19 56.3	7 2.8	8 32.1	22 25.5
28 W	6 25 0.0	23 18.7	7 24.0	26 58.3	21 4.2	20 27.5	7 47.1	3 53.2	19 51.9	7 2.8	8 32.7	22 26.3
31 S	6 36 49.7	23 8.2	7 27.6	14 0.7	21 51.8	21 6.6	7 35.1	3 51.8	19 47.3	7 2.9	8 33.5	22 27.1

JANUARY 1933

DAY	EPHEMERIS SIDEREAL TIME h m s	☉ ° ′	☊ ° ′	☽ ° ′	☿ ° ′	♀ ° ′	♂ ° ′	♃ ° ′	♄ ° ′	♅ ° ′	♆ ° ′	♇ ° ′
						LONGITUDE						
1 S	6 40 46.2	10♑ 8.9	10♓54.3	9♓12.2	19♐41.5	13♐17.4	17♍59.7	23♍11.2	4♒ 2.6	19♈26.9	10♍ 4.9	22♋36.5
2 M	6 44 42.8	11 10.1	10 51.1	22 2.8	21 1.5	14 32.1	18 12.3	23 12.5	4 9.4	19 27.1	10R 4.2	22R35.2
3 T	6 48 39.4	12 11.2	10 48.0	4♈31.3	22 22.7	15 46.9	18 24.5	23 13.6	4 16.2	19 27.4	10 3.5	22 33.9
4 W	6 52 35.9	13 12.4	10 44.8	16 42.7	23 45.0	17 1.6	18 36.0	23 14.4	4 23.0	19 27.7	10 2.8	22 32.7
5 T	6 56 32.5	14 13.5	10 41.6	28 42.2	25 8.3	18 16.4	18 47.0	23 15.1	4 29.9	19 28.0	10 2.0	22 31.4
6 F	7 0 29.0	15 14.7	10 38.4	10♉34.8	26 32.5	19 31.1	18 57.5	23 15.6	4 36.8	19 28.4	10 1.2	22 30.1
7 S	7 4 25.6	16 15.8	10 35.2	22 25.4	27 57.5	20 45.9	19 7.3	23 15.9	4 43.7	19 28.9	10 0.4	22 28.8
8 S	7 8 22.2	17 17.0	10 32.1	4♊17.8	29 23.3	22 0.7	19 16.5	23 16.0	4 50.6	19 29.4	9 59.6	22 27.5
9 M	7 12 18.7	18 18.1	10 28.9	16 15.3	0♑49.8	23 15.5	19 25.2	23R15.9	4 57.6	19 30.0	9 58.7	22 26.2
10 T	7 16 15.3	19 19.2	10 25.7	28 20.3	2 16.9	24 30.3	19 33.2	23 15.7	5 4.6	19 30.6	9 57.8	22 24.9
11 W	7 20 11.8	20 20.3	10 22.5	10♋34.4	3 44.8	25 45.1	19 40.5	23 15.2	5 11.6	19 31.2	9 56.8	22 23.6
12 T	7 24 8.4	21 21.5	10 19.4	22 58.5	5 13.2	26 60.0	19 47.3	23 14.5	5 18.6	19 32.0	9 55.9	22 22.3
13 F	7 28 5.0	22 22.6	10 16.2	5♌33.1	6 42.2	28 14.8	19 53.3	23 13.7	5 25.6	19 32.7	9 54.9	22 21.0
14 S	7 32 1.5	23 23.7	10 13.0	18 18.4	8 11.8	29 29.7	19 58.8	23 12.6	5 32.7	19 33.5	9 53.9	22 19.7
15 S	7 35 58.1	24 24.8	10 9.8	1♍14.9	9 42.0	0♑44.6	20 3.5	23 11.4	5 39.7	19 34.4	9 52.8	22 18.4
16 M	7 39 54.6	25 25.9	10 6.7	14 23.0	11 12.8	1 59.4	20 7.5	23 10.0	5 46.8	19 35.3	9 51.8	22 17.1
17 T	7 43 51.2	26 26.9	10 3.5	27 43.5	12 44.1	3 14.3	20 10.9	23 8.3	5 53.9	19 36.3	9 50.7	22 15.8
18 W	7 47 47.8	27 28.0	10 0.3	11♎17.6	14 16.0	4 29.2	20 13.5	23 6.5	6 1.1	19 37.3	9 49.5	22 14.5
19 T	7 51 44.3	28 29.1	9 57.1	25 6.1	15 48.4	5 44.1	20 15.4	23 4.5	6 8.2	19 38.4	9 48.4	22 13.2
20 F	7 55 40.8	29 30.2	9 53.9	9♏ 9.2	17 21.3	6 59.0	20 16.5	23 2.3	6 15.3	19 39.5	9 47.2	22 11.9
21 S	7 59 37.4	0♒31.2	9 50.8	23 26.2	18 54.9	8 14.0	20 17.0	22 60.0	6 22.4	19 40.7	9 46.0	22 10.7
22 S	8 3 34.0	1 32.3	9 47.6	7♐54.7	20 29.0	9 28.9	20R16.6	22 57.4	6 29.6	19 41.9	9 44.8	22 9.4
23 M	8 7 30.5	2 33.4	9 44.4	22 30.3	22 3.7	10 43.8	20 15.5	22 54.6	6 36.8	19 43.1	9 43.6	22 8.1
24 T	8 11 27.1	3 34.4	9 41.2	7♑ 7.3	23 39.0	11 58.8	20 13.6	22 51.7	6 43.9	19 44.5	9 42.3	22 6.8
25 W	8 15 23.6	4 35.4	9 38.1	21 38.7	25 14.9	13 13.7	20 11.0	22 48.6	6 51.1	19 45.8	9 41.0	22 5.6
26 T	8 19 20.2	5 36.4	9 34.9	5♒58.0	26 51.4	14 28.7	20 7.5	22 45.2	6 58.3	19 47.2	9 39.7	22 4.3
27 F	8 23 16.8	6 37.5	9 31.7	19 59.4	28 28.6	15 43.6	20 3.3	22 41.8	7 5.4	19 48.7	9 38.4	22 3.0
28 S	8 27 13.3	7 38.4	9 28.5	3♓39.0	0♒ 6.4	16 58.6	19 58.3	22 38.1	7 12.6	19 50.2	9 37.0	22 1.8
29 S	8 31 9.9	8 39.4	9 25.4	16 55.3	1 44.8	18 13.5	19 52.5	22 34.2	7 19.8	19 51.8	9 35.7	22 0.6
30 M	8 35 6.4	9 40.4	9 22.2	29 48.7	3 23.9	19 28.5	19 45.8	22 30.2	7 27.0	19 53.4	9 34.3	21 59.3
31 T	8 39 3.0	10 41.3	9 19.0	12♈21.5	5 3.8	20 43.4	19 38.4	22 26.0	7 34.1	19 55.0	9 32.9	21 58.1
						DECLINATION						
1 S	6 40 46.2	23S 3.7	7S28.8	8S 9.0	22S 6.6	21S18.4	7N31.5	3N51.5	19S45.8	7N 3.0	8N33.7	22N27.4
4 W	6 52 35.9	22 47.7	7 32.4	9N25.3	22 46.4	21 50.1	7 22.1	3 51.0	19 41.1	7 3.4	8 34.6	22 28.3
7 S	7 4 25.6	22 27.6	7 36.0	23 5.6	23 18.1	22 16.1	7 14.7	3 51.2	19 36.3	7 3.9	8 35.6	22 29.1
10 T	7 16 15.3	22 3.5	7 39.6	28 15.0	23 40.6	22 36.2	7 9.5	3 52.1	19 31.4	7 4.7	8 36.7	22 29.9
13 F	7 28 5.0	21 35.5	7 43.2	21 36.0	23 52.7	22 50.2	7 6.5	3 53.7	19 26.4	7 5.6	8 37.9	22 30.8
16 M	7 39 54.6	21 3.8	7 46.8	5 39.2	23 53.8	22 57.9	7 5.9	3 55.9	19 21.4	7 6.7	8 39.2	22 31.6
19 T	7 51 44.3	20 28.4	7 50.4	13S13.4	23 43.3	22 59.4	7 7.9	3 58.8	19 16.3	7 7.9	8 40.5	22 32.4
22 S	8 3 34.0	19 49.6	7 54.0	26 44.5	23 20.7	22 54.6	7 12.4	4 2.4	19 11.1	7 9.3	8 41.9	22 33.2
25 W	8 15 23.6	19 7.4	7 57.6	25 25.4	22 45.6	22 43.5	7 19.5	4 6.6	19 5.9	7 10.9	8 43.5	22 34.0
28 S	8 27 13.3	18 22.1	8 1.2	10 32.3	21 57.7	22 26.1	7 29.3	4 11.4	19 0.7	7 12.7	8 45.0	22 34.8
31 T	8 39 3.0	17 33.8	8 4.8	7N36.5	20 56.6	22 2.6	7 41.7	4 16.9	18 55.4	7 14.6	8 46.7	22 35.6

FEBRUARY 1933

DAY	EPHEMERIS SIDEREAL TIME h m s	☉ ° ′	☊ ° ′	☽ ° ′	☿ ° ′	♀ ° ′	♂ ° ′	♃ ° ′	♄ ° ′	♅ ° ′	♆ ° ′	♇ ° ′
						LONGITUDE						
1 W	8 42 59.5	11♒42.2	9♓15.8	24♈37.2	6♒44.3	21♑58.4	19♍30.2	22♍21.7	7♒41.3	19♈56.7	9♍31.4	21♋56.9
2 T	8 46 56.1	12 43.1	9 12.7	6♉40.1	8 25.5	23 13.3	19R21.2	22R17.1	7 48.5	19 58.4	9R30.0	21R55.7
3 F	8 50 52.6	13 44.0	9 9.5	18 35.1	10 7.4	24 28.2	19 11.5	22 12.5	7 55.6	20 0.2	9 28.5	21 54.5
4 S	8 54 49.2	14 44.8	9 6.3	0♊27.1	11 50.1	25 43.2	19 0.9	22 7.6	8 2.8	20 2.0	9 27.1	21 53.3
5 S	8 58 45.8	15 45.6	9 3.1	12 20.7	13 33.6	26 58.1	18 49.6	22 2.6	8 9.9	20 3.9	9 25.6	21 52.1
6 M	9 2 42.3	16 46.4	8 59.9	24 20.3	15 17.7	28 13.0	18 37.5	21 57.5	8 17.0	20 5.8	9 24.1	21 50.9
7 T	9 6 38.9	17 47.2	8 56.8	6♋29.4	17 2.7	29 28.0	18 24.6	21 52.1	8 24.1	20 7.8	9 22.6	21 49.8
8 W	9 10 35.4	18 47.9	8 53.6	18 50.8	18 48.4	0♒42.9	18 11.0	21 46.7	8 31.2	20 9.8	9 21.0	21 48.6
9 T	9 14 32.0	19 48.6	8 50.4	1♌26.5	20 34.8	1 57.8	17 56.7	21 41.1	8 38.3	20 11.8	9 19.5	21 47.5
10 F	9 18 28.6	20 49.3	8 47.2	14 17.4	22 22.0	3 12.7	17 41.6	21 35.3	8 45.4	20 13.9	9 17.9	21 46.4
11 S	9 22 25.1	21 50.0	8 44.1	27 23.6	24 9.9	4 27.6	17 25.8	21 29.5	8 52.5	20 16.0	9 16.3	21 45.3
12 S	9 26 21.7	22 50.7	8 40.9	10♍44.1	25 58.5	5 42.5	17 9.4	21 23.5	8 59.5	20 18.2	9 14.8	21 44.2
13 M	9 30 18.2	23 51.3	8 37.7	24 17.8	27 47.7	6 57.4	16 52.2	21 17.3	9 6.5	20 20.4	9 13.2	21 43.1
14 T	9 34 14.8	24 51.9	8 34.5	8♎ 2.9	29 37.5	8 12.4	16 34.4	21 11.0	9 13.5	20 22.6	9 11.6	21 42.1
15 W	9 38 11.3	25 52.5	8 31.4	21 57.4	1♓27.8	9 27.3	16 16.0	21 4.7	9 20.5	20 24.9	9 10.0	21 41.0
16 T	9 42 7.9	26 53.1	8 28.2	5♏59.5	3 18.6	10 42.2	15 57.0	20 58.1	9 27.5	20 27.2	9 8.3	21 40.0
17 F	9 46 4.4	27 53.6	8 25.0	20 7.3	5 9.7	11 57.1	15 37.4	20 51.5	9 34.4	20 29.6	9 6.7	21 39.0
18 S	9 50 1.0	28 54.2	8 21.8	4♐18.8	7 1.0	13 12.0	15 17.2	20 44.8	9 41.3	20 32.0	9 5.1	21 38.0
19 S	9 53 57.5	29 54.7	8 18.6	18 31.8	8 52.4	14 26.9	14 56.5	20 38.0	9 48.2	20 34.4	9 3.4	21 37.0
20 M	9 57 54.1	0♓55.2	8 15.5	2♑43.8	10 43.6	15 41.8	14 35.4	20 31.0	9 55.1	20 36.9	9 1.8	21 36.0
21 T	10 1 50.7	1 55.6	8 12.3	16 51.9	12 34.4	16 56.7	14 13.7	20 24.0	10 2.0	20 39.4	9 0.1	21 35.1
22 W	10 5 47.2	2 56.1	8 9.1	0♒52.8	14 24.6	18 11.6	13 51.7	20 16.9	10 8.8	20 41.9	8 58.4	21 34.1
23 T	10 9 43.8	3 56.5	8 5.9	14 43.5	16 13.8	19 26.4	13 29.3	20 9.7	10 15.6	20 44.5	8 56.8	21 33.2
24 F	10 13 40.3	4 56.9	8 2.8	28 20.9	18 1.8	20 41.3	13 6.6	20 2.4	10 22.3	20 47.1	8 55.1	21 32.3
25 S	10 17 36.9	5 57.2	7 59.6	11♓42.7	19 48.0	21 56.2	12 43.6	19 55.0	10 29.1	20 49.8	8 53.5	21 31.4
26 S	10 21 33.4	6 57.6	7 56.4	24 47.5	21 32.2	23 11.0	12 20.3	19 47.6	10 35.7	20 52.4	8 51.8	21 30.6
27 M	10 25 30.0	7 57.9	7 53.2	7♈34.9	23 13.8	24 25.9	11 56.8	19 40.1	10 42.4	20 55.1	8 50.1	21 29.7
28 T	10 29 26.5	8 58.1	7 50.0	20 5.7	24 52.3	25 40.7	11 33.2	19 32.5	10 49.0	20 57.9	8 48.4	21 28.9
						DECLINATION						
1 W	8 42 59.5	17S17.0	8S 6.0	13N 4.9	20S33.4	21S53.4	7N46.4	4N18.8	18S53.6	7N15.3	8N47.2	22N35.9
4 S	8 54 49.2	16 25.1	8 9.6	25 19.6	19 14.6	21 21.9	8 2.1	4 25.1	18 48.3	7 17.4	8 49.0	22 36.6
7 T	9 6 38.9	15 30.5	8 13.2	27 53.3	17 42.4	20 44.6	8 20.2	4 31.8	18 43.0	7 19.6	8 50.7	22 37.3
10 F	9 18 28.6	14 33.6	8 16.7	18 33.4	15 56.9	20 1.9	8 40.5	4 39.0	18 37.6	7 22.0	8 52.5	22 38.0
13 M	9 30 18.2	13 34.5	8 20.3	0 53.1	13 58.4	19 13.8	9 2.7	4 46.7	18 32.3	7 24.5	8 54.4	22 38.7
16 T	9 42 7.9	12 33.4	8 23.9	17S45.2	11 47.5	18 20.7	9 26.5	4 54.8	18 27.0	7 27.2	8 56.2	22 39.4
19 S	9 53 57.5	11 30.5	8 27.4	28 7.1	9 25.7	17 22.8	9 51.6	5 3.2	18 21.7	7 30.0	8 58.1	22 40.0
22 W	10 5 47.2	10 25.9	8 31.0	23 4.0	6 55.4	16 20.5	10 17.6	5 11.9	18 16.4	7 32.9	9 0.0	22 40.6
25 S	10 17 36.9	9 19.9	8 34.6	6 50.1	4 20.5	15 14.1	10 43.9	5 20.9	18 11.2	7 35.9	9 2.0	22 41.2
28 T	10 29 26.5	8 12.6	8 38.1	11N 9.4	1 46.8	14 3.8	11 10.2	5 30.1	18 6.0	7 39.0	9 3.9	22 41.7

MARCH 1933

LONGITUDE

DAY	EPHEMERIS SIDEREAL TIME h m s	☉ ° ′	☊ ° ′	☽ ° ′	☿ ° ′	♀ ° ′	♂ ° ′	♃ ° ′	♄ ° ′	♅ ° ′	♆ ° ′	♇ ° ′
1 W	10 33 23.1	9♓58.4	7♓46.9	2♉22.0	26♓27.1	26♒55.6	11♍ 9.5	19♍24.9	10♒55.6	21♈ 0.6	8♍46.8	21♋28.1
2 T	10 37 19.7	10 58.6	7 43.7	14 26.5	27 57.7	28 10.4	10R45.7	19R17.3	11 2.2	21 3.4	8R45.1	21R27.3
3 F	10 41 16.2	11 58.8	7 40.5	26 23.1	29 23.6	29 25.2	10 21.9	19 9.6	11 8.7	21 6.2	8 43.4	21 26.6
4 S	10 45 12.7	12 58.9	7 37.3	8♊15.9	0♈44.0	0♓40.0	9 58.1	19 1.8	11 15.2	21 9.1	8 41.7	21 25.8
5 S	10 49 9.3	13 59.0	7 34.2	20 9.5	1 58.5	1 54.8	9 34.4	18 54.1	11 21.6	21 12.0	8 40.1	21 25.1
6 M	10 53 5.9	14 59.1	7 31.0	2♋ 8.8	3 6.5	3 9.6	9 10.9	18 46.3	11 28.0	21 14.9	8 38.4	21 24.4
7 T	10 57 2.4	15 59.1	7 27.8	14 18.2	4 7.5	4 24.3	8 47.5	18 38.5	11 34.3	21 17.8	8 36.8	21 23.7
8 W	11 0 59.0	16 59.1	7 24.6	26 41.9	5 1.0	5 39.1	8 24.3	18 30.7	11 40.7	21 20.8	8 35.1	21 23.1
9 T	11 4 55.5	17 59.1	7 21.4	9♌23.2	5 46.6	6 53.8	8 1.4	18 22.9	11 46.9	21 23.8	8 33.4	21 22.4
10 F	11 8 52.1	18 59.0	7 18.3	22 24.5	6 23.9	8 8.5	7 38.8	18 15.0	11 53.1	21 26.8	8 31.8	21 21.8
11 S	11 12 48.6	19 58.9	7 15.1	5♍46.7	6 52.8	9 23.3	7 16.5	18 7.2	11 59.3	21 29.8	8 30.2	21 21.2
12 S	11 16 45.2	20 58.8	7 11.9	19 29.2	7 12.9	10 38.0	6 54.5	17 59.4	12 5.4	21 32.9	8 28.5	21 20.7
13 M	11 20 41.7	21 58.6	7 8.7	3♎29.6	7 24.3	11 52.7	6 33.0	17 51.6	12 11.5	21 35.9	8 26.9	21 20.1
14 T	11 24 38.3	22 58.4	7 5.6	17 44.1	7 27.1	13 7.4	6 11.9	17 43.8	12 17.5	21 39.0	8 25.3	21 19.6
15 W	11 28 34.9	23 58.1	7 2.4	2♏ 7.7	7R21.3	14 22.0	5 51.3	17 36.1	12 23.5	21 42.2	8 23.7	21 19.1
16 T	11 32 31.4	24 57.9	6 59.2	16 35.0	7 7.3	15 36.7	5 31.2	17 28.4	12 29.5	21 45.3	8 22.1	21 18.6
17 F	11 36 28.0	25 57.6	6 56.0	1♐ 0.9	6 45.5	16 51.4	5 11.7	17 20.7	12 35.3	21 48.5	8 20.5	21 18.1
18 S	11 40 24.5	26 57.3	6 52.8	15 21.0	6 16.6	18 6.0	4 52.7	17 13.0	12 41.1	21 51.6	8 19.0	21 17.7
19 S	11 44 21.0	27 56.9	6 49.7	29 32.3	5 41.2	19 20.7	4 34.3	17 5.4	12 46.9	21 54.8	8 17.4	21 17.3
20 M	11 48 17.6	28 56.5	6 46.5	13♑32.5	5 0.2	20 35.3	4 16.5	16 57.9	12 52.6	21 58.1	8 15.9	21 16.9
21 T	11 52 14.2	29 56.1	6 43.3	27 20.8	4 14.6	21 49.9	3 59.3	16 50.4	12 58.3	22 1.3	8 14.3	21 16.6
22 W	11 56 10.7	0♈55.7	6 40.1	10♒56.7	3 25.4	23 4.5	3 42.9	16 43.0	13 3.9	22 4.5	8 12.8	21 16.2
23 T	12 0 7.3	1 55.2	6 37.0	24 20.1	2 33.7	24 19.1	3 27.1	16 35.6	13 9.4	22 7.8	8 11.3	21 15.9
24 F	12 4 3.8	2 54.7	6 33.8	7♓31.1	1 40.7	25 33.7	3 12.0	16 28.4	13 14.9	22 11.1	8 9.8	21 15.6
25 S	12 8 0.4	3 54.2	6 30.6	20 29.7	0 47.5	26 48.3	2 57.6	16 21.2	13 20.3	22 14.4	8 8.3	21 15.4
26 S	12 11 56.9	4 53.6	6 27.4	3♈15.8	29♓55.1	28 2.9	2 44.0	16 14.0	13 25.7	22 17.7	8 6.9	21 15.1
27 M	12 15 53.5	5 53.0	6 24.2	15 49.6	29 4.6	29 17.4	2 31.1	16 7.0	13 31.0	22 21.0	8 5.4	21 14.9
28 T	12 19 50.0	6 52.4	6 21.1	28 11.7	28 16.8	0♈31.9	2 19.0	16 0.1	13 36.2	22 24.4	8 4.0	21 14.7
29 W	12 23 46.6	7 51.7	6 17.9	10♉23.1	27 32.5	1 46.5	2 7.7	15 53.2	13 41.4	22 27.7	8 2.6	21 14.6
30 T	12 27 43.2	8 51.0	6 14.7	22 25.4	26 52.4	3 1.0	1 57.2	15 46.5	13 46.5	22 31.1	8 1.2	21 14.4
31 F	12 31 39.7	9 50.3	6 11.5	4♊21.1	26 17.0	4 15.5	1 47.4	15 39.8	13 51.5	22 34.4	7 59.8	21 14.3

DECLINATION

DAY	EPHEMERIS SIDEREAL TIME h m s	☉ ° ′	☊ ° ′	☽ ° ′	☿ ° ′	♀ ° ′	♂ ° ′	♃ ° ′	♄ ° ′	♅ ° ′	♆ ° ′	♇ ° ′
1 W	10 33 23.1	7S50.0	8S39.3	16N20.5	0S57.1	13S39.6	11N18.8	5N33.2	18S 4.3	7N40.1	9N 4.5	22N41.9
4 S	10 45 12.7	6 41.3	8 42.9	26 54.3	1N22.9	12 24.9	11 44.0	5 42.5	17 59.2	7 43.3	9 6.4	22 42.4
7 T	10 57 2.4	5 31.8	8 46.4	26 54.2	3 22.3	11 7.1	12 8.0	5 51.9	17 54.2	7 46.6	9 8.3	22 42.8
10 F	11 8 52.1	4 21.7	8 49.9	15 22.5	4 52.3	9 46.7	12 30.3	6 1.2	17 49.2	7 50.0	9 10.2	22 43.3
13 M	11 20 41.7	3 11.1	8 53.5	3S29.3	5 46.0	8 23.9	12 50.6	6 10.5	17 44.4	7 53.5	9 12.0	22 43.7
16 T	11 32 31.4	2 0.1	8 57.0	21 29.6	5 58.9	6 59.1	13 8.6	6 19.6	17 39.7	7 57.1	9 13.8	22 44.0
19 S	11 44 21.0	0 49.0	9 0.6	28 19.4	5 31.1	5 32.6	13 24.1	6 28.6	17 35.1	8 0.7	9 15.6	22 44.4
22 W	11 56 10.7	0N22.2	9 4.1	19 46.0	4 28.1	4 4.8	13 36.9	6 37.3	17 30.6	8 4.3	9 17.3	22 44.7
25 S	12 8 0.4	1 33.1	9 7.6	2 42.1	3 1.6	2 35.9	13 46.9	6 45.7	17 26.2	8 8.0	9 19.0	22 44.9
28 T	12 19 50.0	2 43.8	9 11.1	14N35.7	1 26.5	1 6.3	13 54.2	6 53.7	17 22.0	8 11.8	9 20.6	22 45.1
31 F	12 31 39.7	3 53.9	9 14.7	26 6.9	0S 2.8	0N23.7	13 58.6	7 1.4	17 17.9	8 15.6	9 22.2	22 45.3

APRIL 1933

LONGITUDE

DAY	EPHEMERIS SIDEREAL TIME h m s	☉ ° ′	☊ ° ′	☽ ° ′	☿ ° ′	♀ ° ′	♂ ° ′	♃ ° ′	♄ ° ′	♅ ° ′	♆ ° ′	♇ ° ′
1 S	12 35 36.2	10♈49.5	6♓ 8.4	16♊13.2	25♓46.7	5♈29.9	1♍38.5	15♍33.3	13♒56.5	22♈37.8	7♍58.5	21♋14.2
2 S	12 39 32.8	11 48.7	6 5.2	28 5.8	25R21.8	6 44.4	1R30.3	15R26.9	14 1.4	22 41.2	7R57.1	21R14.1
3 M	12 43 29.4	12 47.8	6 2.0	10♋ 3.1	25 2.4	7 58.8	1 22.9	15 20.6	14 6.2	22 44.6	7 55.8	21 14.1
4 T	12 47 25.9	13 47.0	5 58.8	22 10.0	24 48.6	9 13.3	1 16.3	15 14.5	14 10.9	22 48.0	7 54.5	21 14.1
5 W	12 51 22.5	14 46.0	5 55.6	4♌31.3	24 40.4	10 27.7	1 10.5	15 8.5	14 15.6	22 51.4	7 53.2	21D14.1
6 T	12 55 19.0	15 45.0	5 52.5	17 11.5	24 37.8	11 42.1	1 5.5	15 2.6	14 20.2	22 54.8	7 52.0	21 14.1
7 F	12 59 15.6	16 44.0	5 49.3	0♍14.7	24D40.6	12 56.4	1 1.3	14 56.8	14 24.8	22 58.2	7 50.8	21 14.2
8 S	13 3 12.1	17 43.0	5 46.1	13 43.3	24 48.7	14 10.8	0 57.8	14 51.2	14 29.2	23 1.7	7 49.6	21 14.3
9 S	13 7 8.7	18 41.9	5 42.9	27 38.0	25 2.0	15 25.2	0 55.2	14 45.7	14 33.6	23 5.1	7 48.4	21 14.4
10 M	13 11 5.2	19 40.8	5 39.8	11♎56.8	25 20.1	16 39.5	0 53.2	14 40.3	14 37.9	23 8.5	7 47.2	21 14.5
11 T	13 15 1.8	20 39.6	5 36.6	26 35.3	25 43.0	17 53.8	0 52.0	14 35.1	14 42.2	23 11.9	7 46.1	21 14.7
12 W	13 18 58.3	21 38.4	5 33.4	11♏26.3	26 10.4	19 8.1	0 51.6	14 30.1	14 46.3	23 15.4	7 45.0	21 14.9
13 T	13 22 54.9	22 37.2	5 30.2	26 21.4	26 42.1	20 22.4	0D51.9	14 25.2	14 50.4	23 18.8	7 43.9	21 15.1
14 F	13 26 51.5	23 36.0	5 27.1	11♐11.9	27 18.0	21 36.7	0 52.9	14 20.5	14 54.4	23 22.3	7 42.8	21 15.3
15 S	13 30 48.0	24 34.7	5 23.9	25 50.5	27 57.7	22 50.9	0 54.7	14 15.9	14 58.4	23 25.7	7 41.8	21 15.6
16 S	13 34 44.6	25 33.4	5 20.7	10♑12.0	28 41.2	24 5.2	0 57.1	14 11.4	15 2.2	23 29.1	7 40.8	21 15.8
17 M	13 38 41.1	26 32.1	5 17.5	24 13.7	29 28.2	25 19.4	1 0.3	14 7.2	15 6.0	23 32.6	7 39.8	21 16.1
18 T	13 42 37.7	27 30.7	5 14.3	7♒55.2	0♈18.6	26 33.6	1 4.1	14 3.1	15 9.7	23 36.0	7 38.8	21 16.5
19 W	13 46 34.2	28 29.3	5 11.2	21 17.6	1 12.2	27 47.8	1 8.6	13 59.1	15 13.3	23 39.4	7 37.9	21 16.8
20 T	13 50 30.8	29 27.9	5 8.0	4♓23.1	2 8.9	29 2.0	1 13.8	13 55.4	15 16.8	23 42.9	7 37.0	21 17.2
21 F	13 54 27.3	0♉26.5	5 4.8	17 14.0	3 8.6	0♉16.2	1 19.7	13 51.8	15 20.2	23 46.3	7 36.1	21 17.6
22 S	13 58 23.9	1 25.0	5 1.6	29 52.4	4 11.0	1 30.4	1 26.2	13 48.3	15 23.6	23 49.7	7 35.3	21 18.1
23 S	14 2 20.5	2 23.5	4 58.5	12♈20.2	5 16.1	2 44.6	1 33.3	13 45.1	15 26.8	23 53.1	7 34.5	21 18.5
24 M	14 6 17.0	3 22.0	4 55.3	24 38.9	6 23.9	3 58.7	1 41.1	13 42.0	15 30.0	23 56.5	7 33.7	21 19.0
25 T	14 10 13.5	4 20.4	4 52.1	6♉49.4	7 34.1	5 12.8	1 49.5	13 39.1	15 33.1	23 59.9	7 32.9	21 19.5
26 W	14 14 10.1	5 18.8	4 48.9	18 52.9	8 46.7	6 26.9	1 58.5	13 36.4	15 36.1	24 3.3	7 32.2	21 20.0
27 T	14 18 6.7	6 17.2	4 45.7	0♊50.5	10 1.7	7 41.1	2 8.2	13 33.9	15 39.0	24 6.7	7 31.5	21 20.6
28 F	14 22 3.2	7 15.6	4 42.6	12 43.7	11 18.9	8 55.1	2 18.4	13 31.5	15 41.8	24 10.1	7 30.8	21 21.1
29 S	14 25 59.8	8 13.9	4 39.4	24 34.8	12 38.3	10 9.2	2 29.2	13 29.3	15 44.6	24 13.4	7 30.2	21 21.7
30 S	14 29 56.3	9 12.1	4 36.2	6♋26.5	13 59.9	11 23.3	2 40.5	13 27.3	15 47.2	24 16.8	7 29.5	21 22.3

DECLINATION

DAY	EPHEMERIS SIDEREAL TIME h m s	☉ ° ′	☊ ° ′	☽ ° ′	☿ ° ′	♀ ° ′	♂ ° ′	♃ ° ′	♄ ° ′	♅ ° ′	♆ ° ′	♇ ° ′
1 S	12 35 36.2	4N17.2	9S15.8	27N50.2	0S29.4	0N53.7	13N59.5	7N 3.8	17S16.6	8N16.8	9N22.7	22N45.4
4 T	12 47 25.9	5 26.4	9 19.3	25 15.1	1 36.0	2 23.7	14 0.3	7 10.9	17 12.8	8 20.6	9 24.1	22 45.5
7 F	12 59 15.6	6 34.8	9 22.8	11 58.8	2 20.2	3 53.2	13 58.5	7 17.4	17 9.1	8 24.5	9 25.5	22 45.6
10 M	13 11 5.2	7 42.1	9 26.4	7S26.1	2 41.2	5 22.1	13 54.2	7 23.5	17 5.7	8 28.3	9 26.8	22 45.7
13 T	13 22 54.9	8 48.3	9 29.9	24 14.9	2 40.1	6 50.0	13 47.6	7 28.9	17 2.4	8 32.1	9 28.0	22 45.7
16 S	13 34 44.6	9 53.1	9 33.4	27 19.3	2 18.6	8 16.5	13 38.7	7 33.8	16 59.3	8 35.9	9 29.1	22 45.7
19 W	13 46 34.2	10 56.5	9 36.8	15 41.5	1 38.9	9 41.3	13 27.7	7 38.2	16 56.5	8 39.8	9 30.2	22 45.7
22 S	13 58 23.9	11 58.3	9 40.3	1N48.4	0 42.8	11 4.2	13 14.7	7 41.8	16 53.8	8 43.5	9 31.1	22 45.6
25 T	14 10 13.5	12 58.4	9 43.8	17 58.0	0N27.7	12 24.7	12 59.8	7 44.9	16 51.4	8 47.3	9 32.0	22 45.5
28 F	14 22 3.2	13 56.5	9 47.3	27 18.3	1 51.2	13 42.5	12 43.0	7 47.3	16 49.2	8 51.0	9 32.7	22 45.3

MAY 1933

DAY	EPHEMERIS SIDEREAL TIME h m s	☉ ° ′	☊ ° ′	☽ ° ′	☿ ° ′	♀ ° ′	♂ ° ′	♃ ° ′	♄ ° ′	♅ ° ′	♆ ° ′	♇ ° ′
						LONGITUDE						
1 M	14 33 52.9	10♉10.4	4♓33.0	18♋22.5	15♈23.6	12♉37.3	2♍52.4	13♍25.5	15♒49.7	24♈20.1	7♍29.0	21♋23.0
2 T	14 37 49.5	11 8.6	4 29.9	0♌27.1	16 49.4	13 51.3	3 4.9	13R23.9	15 52.2	24 23.5	7R28.4	21 23.6
3 W	14 41 46.0	12 6.8	4 26.7	12 44.9	18 17.2	15 5.3	3 17.9	13 22.4	15 54.6	24 26.8	7 27.9	21 24.3
4 T	14 45 42.6	13 4.9	4 23.5	25 21.0	19 47.1	16 19.3	3 31.4	13 21.1	15 56.8	24 30.1	7 27.4	21 25.0
5 F	14 49 39.1	14 3.0	4 20.3	8♍20.1	21 18.9	17 33.3	3 45.4	13 20.1	15 59.0	24 33.4	7 26.9	21 25.8
6 S	14 53 35.7	15 1.1	4 17.2	21 46.2	22 52.7	18 47.2	3 60.0	13 19.2	16 1.1	24 36.6	7 26.5	21 26.5
7 S	14 57 32.2	15 59.2	4 14.0	5♎41.4	24 28.5	20 1.2	4 15.0	13 18.5	16 3.1	24 39.9	7 26.1	21 27.3
8 M	15 1 28.8	16 57.2	4 10.8	20 5.4	26 6.3	21 15.1	4 30.5	13 17.9	16 5.0	24 43.1	7 25.8	21 28.1
9 T	15 5 25.3	17 55.2	4 7.6	4♏54.4	27 46.0	22 29.0	4 46.4	13 17.6	16 6.8	24 46.4	7 25.4	21 28.9
10 W	15 9 21.9	18 53.1	4 4.4	20 1.2	29 27.7	23 42.9	5 2.9	13 17.4	16 8.5	24 49.6	7 25.1	21 29.7
11 T	15 13 18.5	19 51.1	4 1.3	5♐15.8	1♉11.4	24 56.8	5 19.7	13D17.4	16 10.1	24 52.8	7 24.9	21 30.6
12 F	15 17 15.0	20 49.0	3 58.1	20 27.2	2 57.0	26 10.7	5 37.0	13 17.6	16 11.6	24 56.0	7 24.6	21 31.5
13 S	15 21 11.6	21 46.9	3 54.9	5♑25.2	4 44.6	27 24.5	5 54.7	13 18.0	16 13.1	24 59.1	7 24.4	21 32.4
14 S	15 25 8.1	22 44.7	3 51.7	20 2.2	6 34.2	28 38.4	6 12.9	13 18.6	16 14.4	25 2.3	7 24.2	21 33.3
15 M	15 29 4.7	23 42.6	3 48.6	4♒14.0	8 25.8	29 52.2	6 31.4	13 19.3	16 15.6	25 5.4	7 24.1	21 34.2
16 T	15 33 1.2	24 40.4	3 45.4	17 59.5	10 19.4	1♊ 6.0	6 50.4	13 20.2	16 16.8	25 8.5	7 24.0	21 35.2
17 W	15 36 57.8	25 38.2	3 42.2	1♓20.2	12 14.9	2 19.8	7 9.7	13 21.3	16 17.8	25 11.6	7 23.9	21 36.2
18 T	15 40 54.4	26 36.0	3 39.0	14 19.0	14 12.3	3 33.6	7 29.5	13 22.6	16 18.7	25 14.6	7 23.9	21 37.2
19 F	15 44 50.9	27 33.8	3 35.8	26 59.7	16 11.6	4 47.4	7 49.6	13 24.1	16 19.6	25 17.7	7 23.9	21 38.2
20 S	15 48 47.5	28 31.5	3 32.7	9♈26.0	18 12.7	6 1.2	8 10.1	13 25.7	16 20.3	25 20.7	7D23.9	21 39.2
21 S	15 52 44.0	29 29.3	3 29.5	21 41.2	20 15.7	7 15.0	8 31.0	13 27.5	16 21.0	25 23.7	7 23.9	21 40.3
22 M	15 56 40.6	0♊27.0	3 26.3	3♉48.1	22 20.3	8 28.8	8 52.2	13 29.5	16 21.5	25 26.6	7 24.0	21 41.4
23 T	16 0 37.1	1 24.7	3 23.1	15 48.8	24 26.5	9 42.5	9 13.8	13 31.7	16 22.0	25 29.6	7 24.1	21 42.5
24 W	16 4 33.7	2 22.3	3 20.0	27 45.2	26 34.1	10 56.3	9 35.8	13 34.0	16 22.3	25 32.5	7 24.3	21 43.6
25 T	16 8 30.3	3 20.0	3 16.8	9♊38.4	28 43.0	12 10.0	9 58.1	13 36.5	16 22.6	25 35.4	7 24.5	21 44.7
26 F	16 12 26.8	4 17.6	3 13.6	21 30.0	0♊52.9	13 23.7	10 20.7	13 39.2	16 22.7	25 38.2	7 24.7	21 45.9
27 S	16 16 23.3	5 15.2	3 10.4	3♋21.5	3 3.8	14 37.4	10 43.7	13 42.1	16 22.8	25 41.1	7 25.0	21 47.0
28 S	16 20 19.9	6 12.8	3 7.3	15 14.8	5 15.3	15 51.1	11 6.9	13 45.1	16R22.7	25 43.9	7 25.2	21 48.2
29 M	16 24 16.5	7 10.4	3 4.1	27 12.7	7 27.2	17 4.8	11 30.5	13 48.3	16 22.6	25 46.7	7 25.5	21 49.4
30 T	16 28 13.0	8 7.9	3 0.9	9♌18.5	9 39.2	18 18.5	11 54.4	13 51.7	16 22.3	25 49.4	7 25.9	21 50.6
31 W	16 32 9.6	9 5.4	2 57.7	21 36.1	11 51.1	19 32.1	12 18.7	13 55.2	16 22.0	25 52.1	7 26.3	21 51.8
						DECLINATION						
1 M	14 33 52.9	14N52.5	9S50.8	25N51.3	3N26.2	14N57.3	12N24.5	7N49.1	16S47.3	8N54.7	9N33.4	22N45.2
4 T	14 45 42.6	15 46.4	9 54.3	13 53.8	5 11.3	16 8.8	12 4.3	7 50.3	16 45.6	8 58.4	9 33.9	22 45.0
7 S	14 57 32.2	16 37.8	9 57.7	4S37.2	7 5.2	17 16.6	11 42.6	7 50.7	16 44.2	9 2.0	9 34.3	22 44.7
10 W	15 9 21.9	17 26.8	10 1.2	22 25.6	9 6.5	18 20.4	11 19.4	7 50.6	16 43.0	9 5.5	9 34.6	22 44.5
13 S	15 21 11.6	18 13.1	10 4.7	27 38.3	11 13.5	19 19.8	10 54.9	7 49.8	16 42.0	9 9.0	9 34.9	22 44.2
16 T	15 33 1.2	18 56.8	10 8.1	16 46.8	13 24.2	20 14.7	10 29.0	7 48.3	16 41.4	9 12.4	9 35.0	22 43.8
19 F	15 44 50.9	19 37.5	10 11.6	0N36.4	15 35.8	21 4.6	10 1.8	7 46.3	16 41.0	9 15.7	9 35.0	22 43.5
22 M	15 56 40.6	20 15.3	10 15.0	16 51.8	17 44.7	21 49.2	9 33.4	7 43.6	16 40.8	9 18.9	9 34.9	22 43.1
25 T	16 8 30.3	20 49.9	10 18.5	26 48.2	19 46.4	22 28.4	9 3.8	7 40.3	16 41.0	9 22.1	9 34.6	22 42.7
28 S	16 20 19.9	21 21.3	10 21.9	26 14.2	21 35.6	23 1.8	8 33.1	7 36.5	16 41.4	9 25.1	9 34.3	22 42.3
31 W	16 32 9.6	21 49.4	10 25.3	15 11.9	23 7.0	23 29.3	8 1.3	7 32.0	16 42.0	9 28.1	9 33.8	22 41.8

JUNE 1933

DAY	h m s	☉	☊	☽	☿	♀	♂	♃	♄	♅	♆	♇
						LONGITUDE						
1 T	16 36 6.1	10♊ 2.9	2♓54.6	4♍10.1	14♊ 2.5	20♊45.8	12♍43.2	13♍58.9	16♒21.5	25♈54.8	7♍26.7	21♋53.1
2 F	16 40 2.7	11 0.4	2 51.4	17 5.1	16 13.2	21 59.4	13 7.9	14 2.8	16R21.0	25 57.5	7 27.1	21 54.3
3 S	16 43 59.2	11 57.9	2 48.2	0♎25.4	18 23.0	23 13.0	13 33.0	14 6.8	16 20.4	26 0.1	7 27.6	21 55.6
4 S	16 47 55.8	12 55.3	2 45.0	14 14.0	20 31.6	24 26.6	13 58.4	14 11.0	16 19.6	26 2.7	7 28.1	21 56.9
5 M	16 51 52.4	13 52.7	2 41.9	28 31.9	22 38.8	25 40.2	14 24.0	14 15.4	16 18.8	26 5.3	7 28.7	21 58.2
6 T	16 55 48.9	14 50.1	2 38.7	13♏16.9	24 44.3	26 53.8	14 49.9	14 19.9	16 17.9	26 7.8	7 29.3	21 59.5
7 W	16 59 45.5	15 47.5	2 35.5	28 23.2	26 48.0	28 7.3	15 16.0	14 24.5	16 16.9	26 10.3	7 29.9	22 0.9
8 T	17 3 42.0	16 44.9	2 32.3	13♐41.6	28 49.8	29 20.9	15 42.4	14 29.3	16 15.8	26 12.8	7 30.5	22 2.2
9 F	17 7 38.6	17 42.2	2 29.1	29 0.8	0♋49.6	0♋34.4	16 9.1	14 34.3	16 14.6	26 15.2	7 31.2	22 3.6
10 S	17 11 35.2	18 39.6	2 26.0	14♑ 9.5	2 47.2	1 47.9	16 36.0	14 39.4	16 13.3	26 17.6	7 31.9	22 4.9
11 S	17 15 31.7	19 36.9	2 22.8	28 58.4	4 42.6	3 1.4	17 3.1	14 44.7	16 11.9	26 20.0	7 32.6	22 6.3
12 M	17 19 28.3	20 34.2	2 19.6	13♒21.2	6 35.6	4 14.9	17 30.5	14 50.1	16 10.4	26 22.3	7 33.4	22 7.7
13 T	17 23 24.8	21 31.5	2 16.4	27 15.5	8 26.3	5 28.4	17 58.1	14 55.7	16 8.9	26 24.6	7 34.1	22 9.1
14 W	17 27 21.4	22 28.8	2 13.3	10♓41.8	10 14.6	6 41.9	18 26.0	15 1.4	16 7.2	26 26.9	7 35.0	22 10.6
15 T	17 31 17.9	23 26.1	2 10.1	23 42.7	12 0.6	7 55.4	18 54.0	15 7.2	16 5.4	26 29.1	7 35.8	22 12.0
16 F	17 35 14.5	24 23.4	2 6.9	6♈22.2	13 44.0	9 8.8	19 22.3	15 13.2	16 3.6	26 31.3	7 36.7	22 13.4
17 S	17 39 11.1	25 20.7	2 3.7	18 44.6	15 25.1	10 22.3	19 50.8	15 19.3	16 1.7	26 33.4	7 37.6	22 14.9
18 S	17 43 7.7	26 18.0	2 0.6	0♉54.2	17 3.6	11 35.8	20 19.6	15 25.6	15 59.7	26 35.5	7 38.6	22 16.3
19 M	17 47 4.2	27 15.3	1 57.4	12 55.0	18 39.7	12 49.2	20 48.5	15 32.0	15 57.6	26 37.6	7 39.5	22 17.8
20 T	17 51 0.7	28 12.5	1 54.2	24 50.2	20 13.3	14 2.6	21 17.7	15 38.6	15 55.4	26 39.6	7 40.5	22 19.3
21 W	17 54 57.3	29 9.8	1 51.0	6♊42.5	21 44.4	15 16.0	21 47.1	15 45.3	15 53.1	26 41.6	7 41.6	22 20.8
22 T	17 58 53.9	0♋ 7.1	1 47.8	18 33.9	23 13.0	16 29.5	22 16.6	15 52.1	15 50.7	26 43.6	7 42.6	22 22.3
23 F	18 2 50.5	1 4.3	1 44.7	0♋26.3	24 39.0	17 42.9	22 46.4	15 59.1	15 48.3	26 45.5	7 43.7	22 23.8
24 S	18 6 47.0	2 1.6	1 41.5	12 21.1	26 2.4	18 56.3	23 16.4	16 6.1	15 45.7	26 47.3	7 44.8	22 25.3
25 S	18 10 43.5	2 58.8	1 38.3	24 20.0	27 23.2	20 9.6	23 46.6	16 13.4	15 43.1	26 49.2	7 46.0	22 26.9
26 M	18 14 40.1	3 56.1	1 35.1	6♌24.8	28 41.3	21 23.0	24 17.0	16 20.7	15 40.4	26 50.9	7 47.2	22 28.4
27 T	18 18 36.7	4 53.3	1 32.0	18 37.8	29 56.8	22 36.4	24 47.5	16 28.2	15 37.7	26 52.7	7 48.4	22 29.9
28 W	18 22 33.2	5 50.5	1 28.8	1♍ 1.8	1♌ 9.5	23 49.7	25 18.3	16 35.8	15 34.8	26 54.4	7 49.6	22 31.5
29 T	18 26 29.8	6 47.7	1 25.6	13 40.2	2 19.3	25 3.0	25 49.2	16 43.5	15 31.9	26 56.1	7 50.9	22 33.0
30 F	18 30 26.3	7 44.9	1 22.4	26 36.6	3 26.3	26 16.3	26 20.3	16 51.3	15 28.9	26 57.7	7 52.1	22 34.6
						DECLINATION						
1 T	16 36 6.1	21N58.0	10S26.5	9N49.9	23N32.7	23N37.1	7N50.4	7N30.4	16S42.3	9N29.1	9N33.7	22N41.7
4 S	16 47 55.8	22 21.5	10 29.9	8S43.3	24 33.8	23 56.4	7 17.2	7 25.2	16 43.3	9 31.9	9 33.1	22 41.2
7 W	16 59 45.5	22 41.5	10 33.3	24 41.4	25 10.2	24 9.3	6 43.1	7 19.4	16 44.6	9 34.6	9 32.4	22 40.7
10 S	17 11 35.2	22 57.9	10 36.8	26 22.5	25 22.4	24 15.9	6 8.1	7 13.1	16 46.1	9 37.2	9 31.6	22 40.2
13 T	17 23 24.8	23 10.7	10 40.2	12 45.5	25 12.7	24 16.0	5 32.2	7 6.3	16 47.9	9 39.7	9 30.7	22 39.6
16 F	17 35 14.5	23 19.9	10 43.6	5N12.8	24 44.1	24 9.7	4 55.4	6 59.0	16 49.9	9 42.0	9 29.7	22 39.1
19 M	17 47 4.2	23 25.3	10 47.0	20 17.8	23 59.9	23 56.9	4 17.9	6 51.2	16 52.2	9 44.3	9 28.6	22 38.5
22 T	17 58 53.9	23 27.0	10 50.4	27 44.5	23 3.4	23 37.8	3 39.6	6 42.9	16 54.6	9 46.4	9 27.4	22 37.9
25 S	18 10 43.5	23 25.0	10 53.8	24 10.7	21 57.7	23 12.4	3 0.6	6 34.1	16 57.3	9 48.3	9 26.1	22 37.4
28 W	18 22 33.2	23 19.3	10 57.2	11 0.7	20 45.7	22 41.0	2 20.9	6 24.9	17 0.2	9 50.2	9 24.7	22 36.8

JULY 1933

LONGITUDE

DAY	EPHEMERIS SIDEREAL TIME (h m s)	☉ (° ′)	☊ (° ′)	☽ (° ′)	☿ (° ′)	♀ (° ′)	♂ (° ′)	♃ (° ′)	♄ (° ′)	♅ (° ′)	♆ (° ′)	♇ (° ′)
1 S	18 34 22.9	8♋42.2	1♓19.3	9♎54.4	4♌30.3	27♋29.6	26♍51.6	16♍59.3	15♒25.8	26♈59.2	7♍53.4	22♋36.2
2 S	18 38 19.4	9 39.4	1 16.1	23 36.4	5 31.2	28 42.9	27 23.1	17 7.4	15R 22.7	27 0.8	7 54.8	22 37.7
3 M	18 42 16.0	10 36.5	1 12.9	7♏44.0	6 29.0	29 56.2	27 54.7	17 15.5	15 19.5	27 2.3	7 56.2	22 39.3
4 T	18 46 12.6	11 33.7	1 9.7	22 16.0	7 23.5	1♌ 9.4	28 26.5	17 23.8	15 16.2	27 3.7	7 57.5	22 40.9
5 W	18 50 9.1	12 30.9	1 6.6	7♐ 8.6	8 14.6	2 22.6	28 58.5	17 32.3	15 12.9	27 5.1	7 58.9	22 42.5
6 T	18 54 5.7	13 28.1	1 3.4	22 14.8	9 2.3	3 35.9	29 30.6	17 40.8	15 9.5	27 6.4	8 0.4	22 44.1
7 F	18 58 2.3	14 25.3	1 0.2	7♑25.2	9 46.4	4 49.1	0♎ 2.9	17 49.4	15 6.0	27 7.7	8 1.9	22 45.7
8 S	19 1 58.8	15 22.4	0 57.0	22 29.7	10 26.7	6 2.2	0 35.4	17 58.2	15 2.5	27 9.0	8 3.3	22 47.3
9 S	19 5 55.4	16 19.6	0 53.9	7♒18.8	11 3.2	7 15.4	1 8.0	18 7.0	14 58.9	27 10.2	8 4.8	22 48.8
10 M	19 9 51.9	17 16.8	0 50.7	21 45.5	11 35.7	8 28.5	1 40.7	18 16.0	14 55.2	27 11.4	8 6.4	22 50.4
11 T	19 13 48.5	18 14.0	0 47.5	5♓45.7	12 4.0	9 41.7	2 13.6	18 25.0	14 51.5	27 12.5	8 7.9	22 52.1
12 W	19 17 45.1	19 11.2	0 44.3	19 18.4	12 28.1	10 54.8	2 46.7	18 34.2	14 47.7	27 13.6	8 9.5	22 53.7
13 T	19 21 41.6	20 8.4	0 41.2	2♈24.9	12 47.8	12 7.9	3 19.9	18 43.4	14 43.9	27 14.6	8 11.1	22 55.3
14 F	19 25 38.1	21 5.6	0 38.0	15 8.2	13 2.9	13 21.0	3 53.3	18 52.8	14 40.0	27 15.6	8 12.8	22 56.9
15 S	19 29 34.7	22 2.9	0 34.8	27 32.5	13 13.3	14 34.1	4 26.8	19 2.3	14 36.1	27 16.5	8 14.4	22 58.5
16 S	19 33 31.3	23 0.1	0 31.6	9♉42.2	13 19.1	15 47.1	5 0.4	19 11.8	14 32.2	27 17.4	8 16.1	23 0.1
17 M	19 37 27.9	23 57.3	0 28.4	21 41.7	13 20.0	17 0.2	5 34.2	19 21.5	14 28.1	27 18.2	8 17.8	23 1.7
18 T	19 41 24.4	24 54.6	0 25.3	3♊35.4	13R 16.0	18 13.2	6 8.2	19 31.2	14 24.1	27 19.0	8 19.5	23 3.3
19 W	19 45 20.9	25 51.9	0 22.1	15 26.7	13 7.2	19 26.3	6 42.2	19 41.0	14 20.0	27 19.8	8 21.2	23 4.9
20 T	19 49 17.5	26 49.2	0 18.9	27 18.9	12 53.6	20 39.3	7 16.5	19 51.0	14 15.8	27 20.5	8 23.0	23 6.5
21 F	19 53 14.1	27 46.4	0 15.7	9♋14.4	12 35.2	21 52.3	7 50.9	20 1.0	14 11.7	27 21.1	8 24.7	23 8.1
22 S	19 57 10.6	28 43.8	0 12.6	21 15.4	12 12.3	23 5.2	8 25.4	20 11.1	14 7.4	27 21.7	8 26.5	23 9.8
23 S	20 1 7.2	29 41.1	0 9.4	3♌23.5	11 45.1	24 18.2	9 0.0	20 21.3	14 3.2	27 22.2	8 28.3	23 11.4
24 M	20 5 3.7	0♌38.4	0 6.2	15 40.3	11 13.8	25 31.1	9 34.8	20 31.5	13 58.9	27 22.7	8 30.2	23 12.9
25 T	20 9 0.3	1 35.7	0 3.0	28 7.1	10 38.9	26 44.0	10 9.7	20 41.9	13 54.6	27 23.2	8 32.0	23 14.5
26 W	20 12 56.8	2 33.1	29♒59.9	10♍45.5	10 0.9	27 56.9	10 44.8	20 52.3	13 50.3	27 23.6	8 33.9	23 16.1
27 T	20 16 53.4	3 30.4	29 56.7	23 37.1	9 20.3	29 9.8	11 19.9	21 2.9	13 45.9	27 24.0	8 35.8	23 17.7
28 F	20 20 50.0	4 27.8	29 53.5	6♎43.8	8 37.6	0♍22.7	11 55.2	21 13.5	13 41.5	27 24.3	8 37.7	23 19.3
29 S	20 24 46.5	5 25.1	29 50.3	20 7.4	7 53.8	1 35.5	12 30.7	21 24.1	13 37.1	27 24.5	8 39.6	23 20.9
30 S	20 28 43.0	6 22.5	29 47.1	3♏49.2	7 9.4	2 48.3	13 6.2	21 34.9	13 32.7	27 24.7	8 41.5	23 22.5
31 M	20 32 39.6	7 19.9	29 44.0	17 49.7	6 25.2	4 1.1	13 41.9	21 45.7	13 28.2	27 24.9	8 43.5	23 24.1

DECLINATION

DAY	EPHEMERIS SIDEREAL TIME (h m s)	☉ (° ′)	☊ (° ′)	☽ (° ′)	☿ (° ′)	♀ (° ′)	♂ (° ′)	♃ (° ′)	♄ (° ′)	♅ (° ′)	♆ (° ′)	♇ (° ′)
1 S	18 34 22.9	23N 9.9	11S 0.6	6S57.9	19N30.2	22N 3.6	1N40.5	6N15.3	17S 3.3	9N51.8	9N23.2	22N36.1
4 T	18 46 12.6	22 56.8	11 4.0	23 15.1	18 14.0	21 20.7	0 59.6	6 5.3	17 6.5	9 53.4	9 21.7	22 35.5
7 F	18 58 2.3	22 40.1	11 7.4	27 17.1	16 59.8	20 32.3	0 18.2	5 54.9	17 9.9	9 54.8	9 20.0	22 34.9
10 M	19 9 51.9	22 20.0	11 10.7	14 53.8	15 50.5	19 38.8	0S 23.7	5 44.1	17 13.5	9 56.0	9 18.3	22 34.3
13 T	19 21 41.6	21 56.3	11 14.1	3N33.9	14 49.2	18 40.4	1 6.1	5 32.9	17 17.2	9 57.1	9 16.5	22 33.7
16 S	19 33 31.3	21 29.3	11 17.5	19 21.3	13 58.9	17 37.4	1 48.8	5 21.4	17 21.0	9 58.0	9 14.6	22 33.0
19 W	19 45 20.9	20 59.0	11 20.8	27 35.9	13 22.9	16 30.2	2 32.0	5 9.6	17 24.9	9 58.8	9 12.7	22 32.4
22 S	19 57 10.6	20 25.4	11 24.2	24 54.2	13 3.7	15 19.1	3 15.4	4 57.4	17 28.8	9 59.5	9 10.6	22 31.8
25 T	20 9 0.3	19 48.8	11 27.6	12 10.8	13 3.0	14 4.4	3 59.2	4 45.0	17 32.9	9 59.9	9 8.6	22 31.2
28 F	20 20 50.0	19 9.2	11 30.9	5S38.6	13 20.8	12 46.4	4 43.1	4 32.2	17 36.9	10 0.2	9 6.4	22 30.6
31 M	20 32 39.6	18 26.8	11 34.3	22 5.6	13 54.8	11 25.4	5 27.2	4 19.2	17 41.0	10 0.4	9 4.2	22 30.0

AUGUST 1933

LONGITUDE

DAY	EPHEMERIS SIDEREAL TIME (h m s)	☉ (° ′)	☊ (° ′)	☽ (° ′)	☿ (° ′)	♀ (° ′)	♂ (° ′)	♃ (° ′)	♄ (° ′)	♅ (° ′)	♆ (° ′)	♇ (° ′)
1 T	20 36 36.2	8♌17.3	29♒40.8	2♐ 8.0	5♌42.2	5♍13.8	14♎17.7	21♍56.6	13♒23.8	27♈25.0	8♍45.5	23♋25.6
2 W	20 40 32.8	9 14.7	29 37.6	16 41.6	5R 1.0	6 26.6	14 53.7	22 7.6	13R 19.3	27 25.0	8 47.4	23 27.2
3 T	20 44 29.3	10 12.1	29 34.4	1♑25.9	4 22.6	7 39.3	15 29.7	22 18.6	13 14.9	27 25.0	8 49.4	23 28.7
4 F	20 48 25.9	11 9.5	29 31.3	16 14.4	3 47.6	8 51.9	16 5.9	22 29.7	13 10.4	27R 25.0	8 51.4	23 30.3
5 S	20 52 22.4	12 6.9	29 28.1	0♒60.0	3 16.7	10 4.6	16 42.1	22 40.9	13 5.9	27 24.9	8 53.5	23 31.8
6 S	20 56 19.0	13 4.4	29 24.9	15 35.2	2 50.6	11 17.2	17 18.5	22 52.2	13 1.4	27 24.8	8 55.5	23 33.4
7 M	21 0 15.5	14 1.9	29 21.7	29 53.6	2 29.9	12 29.8	17 55.0	23 3.5	12 56.9	27 24.6	8 57.6	23 34.9
8 T	21 4 12.1	14 59.4	29 18.6	13♓50.7	2 15.1	13 42.4	18 31.7	23 14.8	12 52.5	27 24.3	8 59.6	23 36.4
9 W	21 8 8.7	15 56.9	29 15.4	27 24.2	2 6.4	14 54.9	19 8.4	23 26.3	12 48.0	27 24.1	9 1.7	23 37.9
10 T	21 12 5.2	16 54.4	29 12.2	10♈33.6	2 4.3	16 7.4	19 45.2	23 37.8	12 43.5	27 23.7	9 3.8	23 39.4
11 F	21 16 1.7	17 52.0	29 9.0	23 20.7	2D 9.1	17 19.9	20 22.2	23 49.3	12 39.1	27 23.3	9 5.9	23 40.9
12 S	21 19 58.3	18 49.5	29 5.8	5♉48.3	2 20.8	18 32.4	20 59.3	24 0.9	12 34.6	27 22.9	9 8.0	23 42.4
13 S	21 23 54.9	19 47.1	29 2.7	18 0.3	2 39.6	19 44.8	21 36.5	24 12.6	12 30.2	27 22.4	9 10.1	23 43.9
14 M	21 27 51.4	20 44.8	28 59.5	0♊ 1.2	3 5.6	20 57.2	22 13.8	24 24.3	12 25.7	27 21.9	9 12.2	23 45.3
15 T	21 31 48.0	21 42.4	28 56.3	11 55.4	3 38.7	22 9.6	22 51.2	24 36.1	12 21.3	27 21.3	9 14.4	23 46.8
16 W	21 35 44.5	22 40.1	28 53.1	23 47.3	4 18.8	23 22.0	23 28.7	24 48.0	12 17.0	27 20.7	9 16.5	23 48.2
17 T	21 39 41.1	23 37.8	28 50.0	5♋41.1	5 5.9	24 34.3	24 6.3	24 59.8	12 12.6	27 20.0	9 18.7	23 49.7
18 F	21 43 37.6	24 35.5	28 46.8	17 40.5	5 59.9	25 46.6	24 44.0	25 11.8	12 8.3	27 19.3	9 20.8	23 51.1
19 S	21 47 34.2	25 33.3	28 43.6	29 48.4	7 0.5	26 58.9	25 21.9	25 23.8	12 4.0	27 18.6	9 23.0	23 52.5
20 S	21 51 30.8	26 31.1	28 40.4	12♌ 7.2	8 7.5	28 11.1	25 59.9	25 35.8	11 59.7	27 17.8	9 25.2	23 53.9
21 M	21 55 27.3	27 28.9	28 37.3	24 38.7	9 20.5	29 23.3	26 37.9	25 47.9	11 55.4	27 16.9	9 27.4	23 55.3
22 T	21 59 23.9	28 26.7	28 34.1	7♍23.8	10 39.4	0♎35.5	27 16.1	26 0.1	11 51.2	27 16.0	9 29.6	23 56.7
23 W	22 3 20.4	29 24.5	28 30.9	20 23.1	12 3.8	1 47.7	27 54.4	26 12.2	11 47.0	27 15.1	9 31.7	23 58.0
24 T	22 7 17.0	0♍22.4	28 27.7	3♎36.4	13 33.2	2 59.8	28 32.8	26 24.5	11 42.9	27 14.1	9 34.0	23 59.4
25 F	22 11 13.5	1 20.3	28 24.5	17 3.3	15 7.3	4 11.9	29 11.3	26 36.7	11 38.8	27 13.0	9 36.2	24 0.7
26 S	22 15 10.1	2 18.2	28 21.4	0♏43.1	16 45.6	5 23.9	29 49.8	26 49.0	11 34.7	27 12.0	9 38.4	24 2.0
27 S	22 19 6.6	3 16.1	28 18.2	14 34.6	18 27.6	6 36.0	0♏28.5	27 1.4	11 30.7	27 10.8	9 40.6	24 3.3
28 M	22 23 3.2	4 14.1	28 15.0	28 36.8	20 13.0	7 47.9	1 7.3	27 13.8	11 26.8	27 9.7	9 42.8	24 4.6
29 T	22 26 59.8	5 12.1	28 11.8	12♐47.8	22 1.1	8 59.9	1 46.2	27 26.2	11 22.9	27 8.5	9 45.0	24 5.9
30 W	22 30 56.3	6 10.1	28 8.7	27 5.5	23 51.7	10 11.8	2 25.2	27 38.7	11 19.0	27 7.2	9 47.2	24 7.1
31 T	22 34 52.8	7 8.1	28 5.5	11♑27.1	25 44.2	11 23.6	3 4.3	27 51.2	11 15.2	27 5.9	9 49.5	24 8.4

DECLINATION

DAY	EPHEMERIS SIDEREAL TIME (h m s)	☉ (° ′)	☊ (° ′)	☽ (° ′)	☿ (° ′)	♀ (° ′)	♂ (° ′)	♃ (° ′)	♄ (° ′)	♅ (° ′)	♆ (° ′)	♇ (° ′)
1 T	20 36 36.2	18N12.1	11S35.4	25S43.6	14N 9.0	10N57.8	5S41.9	4N14.8	17S42.4	10N 0.4	9N 3.5	22N29.8
4 F	20 48 25.9	17 26.1	11 38.7	25 58.8	14 57.3	9 33.5	6 26.2	4 1.4	17 46.5	10 0.4	9 1.2	22 29.2
7 M	21 0 15.5	16 37.5	11 42.0	11 24.1	15 49.2	8 7.0	7 10.4	3 47.8	17 50.6	10 0.1	8 58.9	22 28.6
10 T	21 12 5.2	15 46.6	11 45.4	7N25.7	16 38.6	6 38.5	7 54.7	3 34.0	17 54.6	9 59.8	8 56.6	22 28.0
13 S	21 23 54.9	14 53.3	11 48.7	22 10.6	17 19.5	5 8.6	8 38.8	3 20.0	17 58.6	9 59.2	8 54.2	22 27.5
16 W	21 35 44.5	13 57.9	11 52.0	28 4.6	17 46.4	3 37.4	9 22.8	3 5.7	18 2.5	9 58.6	8 51.8	22 26.9
19 S	21 47 34.2	13 0.5	11 55.3	22 41.4	17 54.5	2 5.2	10 6.7	2 51.3	18 6.4	9 57.7	8 49.3	22 26.4
22 T	21 59 23.9	12 1.2	11 58.6	8 2.7	17 39.6	0 32.4	10 50.3	2 36.7	18 10.1	9 56.8	8 46.9	22 25.9
25 F	22 11 13.5	11 0.2	12 2.0	10S21.3	16 59.2	1S 0.7	11 33.6	2 22.0	18 13.7	9 55.6	8 44.4	22 25.5
28 M	22 23 3.2	9 57.7	12 5.3	25 0.2	15 53.0	2 33.8	12 16.5	2 7.1	18 17.2	9 54.4	8 41.9	22 25.0
31 T	22 34 52.8	8 53.7	12 8.6	26 48.9	14 23.0	4 6.5	12 58.9	1 52.1	18 20.5	9 53.0	8 39.4	22 24.6

SEPTEMBER 1933

LONGITUDE

DAY	EPHEMERIS SIDEREAL TIME h m s	☉ ° ′	☊ ° ′	☽ ° ′	☿ ° ′	♀ ° ′	♂ ° ′	♃ ° ′	♄ ° ′	♅ ° ′	♆ ° ′	♇ ° ′
1 F	22 38 49.4	8♍ 6.1	28♒ 2.3	25♑49.1	27♌38.1	12♎35.4	3♏43.5	28♍ 3.7	11♒11.4	27♈ 4.6	9♍51.7	24♋ 9.6
2 S	22 42 46.0	9 4.2	27 59.1	10♒ 7.6	29 33.3	13 47.2	4 22.8	28 16.2	11R 7.8	27R 3.2	9 53.9	24 10.8
3 S	22 46 42.6	10 2.3	27 55.9	24 18.2	1♍29.2	14 59.0	5 2.1	28 28.8	11 4.1	27 1.8	9 56.1	24 12.0
4 M	22 50 39.1	11 0.4	27 52.8	8♓16.8	3 25.6	16 10.6	5 41.6	28 41.5	11 0.5	27 0.3	9 58.4	24 13.2
5 T	22 54 35.6	11 58.6	27 49.6	21 59.8	5 22.2	17 22.3	6 21.1	28 54.1	10 57.0	26 58.8	10 0.6	24 14.4
6 W	22 58 32.2	12 56.8	27 46.4	5♈24.7	7 18.7	18 33.9	7 0.8	29 6.8	10 53.6	26 57.3	10 2.8	24 15.5
7 T	23 2 28.8	13 55.0	27 43.2	18 30.1	9 15.0	19 45.4	7 40.5	29 19.5	10 50.2	26 55.7	10 5.0	24 16.6
8 F	23 6 25.3	14 53.2	27 40.1	1♉16.3	11 10.8	20 57.0	8 20.4	29 32.2	10 46.9	26 54.1	10 7.3	24 17.8
9 S	23 10 21.8	15 51.5	27 36.9	13 44.6	13 6.0	22 8.4	9 0.3	29 44.9	10 43.6	26 52.5	10 9.5	24 18.8
10 S	23 14 18.4	16 49.8	27 33.7	25 57.8	15 0.6	23 19.8	9 40.3	29 57.7	10 40.4	26 50.8	10 11.7	24 19.9
11 M	23 18 15.0	17 48.1	27 30.5	7♊59.6	16 54.4	24 31.2	10 20.5	0♎10.5	10 37.3	26 49.1	10 13.9	24 21.0
12 T	23 22 11.5	18 46.5	27 27.3	19 54.1	18 47.3	25 42.6	11 0.7	0 23.3	10 34.3	26 47.3	10 16.1	24 22.0
13 W	23 26 8.1	19 44.9	27 24.2	1♋46.1	20 39.2	26 53.9	11 41.0	0 36.2	10 31.3	26 45.5	10 18.3	24 23.0
14 T	23 30 4.6	20 43.4	27 21.0	13 40.4	22 30.2	28 5.1	12 21.4	0 49.0	10 28.4	26 43.7	10 20.5	24 24.0
15 F	23 34 1.1	21 41.9	27 17.8	25 41.6	24 20.2	29 16.3	13 1.9	1 1.9	10 25.6	26 41.9	10 22.7	24 25.0
16 S	23 37 57.7	22 40.4	27 14.6	7♌54.0	26 9.2	0♏27.5	13 42.5	1 14.8	10 22.9	26 40.0	10 24.9	24 26.0
17 S	23 41 54.3	23 38.9	27 11.5	20 21.1	27 57.2	1 38.6	14 23.2	1 27.7	10 20.2	26 38.1	10 27.1	24 26.9
18 M	23 45 50.8	24 37.5	27 8.3	3♍ 5.6	29 44.1	2 49.7	15 3.9	1 40.6	10 17.6	26 36.1	10 29.3	24 27.8
19 T	23 49 47.3	25 36.1	27 5.1	16 8.8	1♎30.0	4 0.7	15 44.8	1 53.5	10 15.2	26 34.1	10 31.4	24 28.7
20 W	23 53 43.9	26 34.8	27 1.9	29 30.9	3 14.9	5 11.7	16 25.7	2 6.5	10 12.8	26 32.1	10 33.6	24 29.6
21 T	23 57 40.5	27 33.5	26 58.7	13♎10.4	4 58.7	6 22.6	17 6.8	2 19.5	10 10.5	26 30.1	10 35.8	24 30.4
22 F	0 1 37.1	28 32.2	26 55.6	27 4.5	6 41.5	7 33.5	17 47.9	2 32.4	10 8.2	26 28.0	10 37.9	24 31.3
23 S	0 5 33.6	29 31.0	26 52.4	11♏ 9.7	8 23.4	8 44.3	18 29.1	2 45.4	10 6.1	26 25.9	10 40.0	24 32.1
24 S	0 9 30.2	0♎29.7	26 49.2	25 21.7	10 4.3	9 55.0	19 10.4	2 58.3	10 4.0	26 23.8	10 42.1	24 32.9
25 M	0 13 26.7	1 28.5	26 46.0	9♐36.6	11 44.2	11 5.7	19 51.8	3 11.3	10 2.1	26 21.7	10 44.3	24 33.6
26 T	0 17 23.3	2 27.4	26 42.9	23 51.1	13 23.2	12 16.4	20 33.3	3 24.3	10 0.2	26 19.5	10 46.4	24 34.4
27 W	0 21 19.8	3 26.3	26 39.7	8♑ 2.3	15 1.2	13 26.9	21 14.9	3 37.3	9 58.4	26 17.3	10 48.5	24 35.1
28 T	0 25 16.4	4 25.1	26 36.5	22 8.5	16 38.3	14 37.4	21 56.5	3 50.3	9 56.8	26 15.1	10 50.5	24 35.8
29 F	0 29 12.9	5 24.1	26 33.3	6♒ 8.3	18 14.6	15 47.9	22 38.3	4 3.3	9 55.2	26 12.9	10 52.6	24 36.5
30 S	0 33 9.5	6 23.0	26 30.1	20 0.4	19 49.9	16 58.2	23 20.1	4 16.2	9 53.7	26 10.6	10 54.7	24 37.1

DECLINATION

DAY	SIDEREAL TIME	☉	☊	☽	☿	♀	♂	♃	♄	♅	♆	♇
1 F	22 38 49.4	8N32.1	12S 9.7	23S48.2	13N48.5	4S37.3	13S12.9	1N47.1	18S21.6	9N52.5	8N38.6	22N24.5
4 M	22 50 39.1	7 26.5	12 12.9	7 38.8	11 53.5	6 9.2	13 54.6	1 32.0	18 24.6	9 50.9	8 36.1	22 24.1
7 T	23 2 28.8	6 19.8	12 16.2	10N58.7	9 45.6	7 40.0	14 35.7	1 16.8	18 27.6	9 49.2	8 33.6	22 23.7
10 S	23 14 18.4	5 12.1	12 19.5	24 21.0	7 29.4	9 9.5	15 16.1	1 1.5	18 30.3	9 47.4	8 31.1	22 23.4
13 W	23 26 8.1	4 3.7	12 22.8	27 49.7	5 8.6	10 37.4	15 55.8	0 46.1	18 32.8	9 45.4	8 28.6	22 23.1
16 S	23 37 57.7	2 54.5	12 26.0	20 5.2	2 46.0	12 3.3	16 34.6	0 30.7	18 35.2	9 43.4	8 26.2	22 22.8
19 T	23 49 47.3	1 44.9	12 29.3	4 0.3	0 23.8	13 26.9	17 12.5	0 15.3	18 37.3	9 41.3	8 23.8	22 22.6
22 F	0 1 37.1	0 34.9	12 32.6	14S34.8	1S56.4	14 48.0	17 49.4	0S 0.2	18 39.2	9 39.0	8 21.4	22 22.4
25 M	0 13 26.7	0S35.2	12 35.8	26 56.0	4 13.4	16 6.1	18 25.2	0 15.6	18 40.8	9 36.7	8 19.0	22 22.3
28 T	0 25 16.4	1 45.4	12 39.1	24 38.6	6 26.5	17 20.9	18 59.8	0 31.1	18 42.2	9 34.3	8 16.7	22 22.2

OCTOBER 1933

LONGITUDE

DAY	SIDEREAL TIME	☉	☊	☽	☿	♀	♂	♃	♄	♅	♆	♇
1 S	0 37 6.0	7♎22.0	26♒27.0	3♓43.7	21♎24.5	18♏ 8.5	24♏ 2.0	4♎29.2	9♒52.3	26♈ 8.4	10♍56.7	24♋37.8
2 M	0 41 2.6	8 21.0	26 23.8	17 16.7	22 58.1	19 18.7	24 43.9	4 42.2	9R51.0	26R 6.1	10 58.7	24 38.4
3 T	0 44 59.1	9 20.1	26 20.6	0♈37.9	24 30.9	20 28.9	25 26.0	4 55.2	9 49.8	26 3.8	11 0.7	24 39.0
4 W	0 48 55.7	10 19.1	26 17.4	13 45.9	26 2.9	21 39.0	26 8.1	5 8.1	9 48.6	26 1.5	11 2.8	24 39.5
5 T	0 52 52.3	11 18.2	26 14.3	26 39.4	27 34.1	22 49.0	26 50.3	5 21.1	9 47.6	25 59.1	11 4.7	24 40.1
6 F	0 56 48.8	12 17.4	26 11.1	9♉18.0	29 4.4	23 58.9	27 32.6	5 34.0	9 46.7	25 56.8	11 6.7	24 40.6
7 S	1 0 45.4	13 16.6	26 7.9	21 42.0	0♏34.0	25 8.7	28 15.0	5 46.9	9 45.9	25 54.4	11 8.7	24 41.1
8 S	1 4 41.9	14 15.8	26 4.7	3♊53.1	2 2.7	26 18.5	28 57.4	5 59.9	9 45.2	25 52.0	11 10.6	24 41.5
9 M	1 8 38.5	15 15.0	26 1.5	15 53.5	3 30.6	27 28.2	29 40.0	6 12.8	9 44.6	25 49.6	11 12.5	24 42.0
10 T	1 12 35.0	16 14.3	25 58.4	27 46.9	4 57.6	28 37.8	0♐22.6	6 25.7	9 44.1	25 47.2	11 14.4	24 42.4
11 W	1 16 31.6	17 13.7	25 55.2	9♋37.5	6 23.9	29 47.3	1 5.3	6 38.6	9 43.6	25 44.8	11 16.3	24 42.8
12 T	1 20 28.1	18 13.1	25 52.0	21 30.1	7 49.2	0♐56.8	1 48.0	6 51.4	9 43.3	25 42.4	11 18.2	24 43.1
13 F	1 24 24.7	19 12.5	25 48.8	3♌30.0	9 13.7	2 6.1	2 30.9	7 4.3	9 43.1	25 40.0	11 20.0	24 43.5
14 S	1 28 21.2	20 11.9	25 45.7	15 42.2	10 37.3	3 15.4	3 13.8	7 17.1	9 43.0	25 37.5	11 21.9	24 43.8
15 S	1 32 17.8	21 11.4	25 42.5	28 11.7	11 59.9	4 24.6	3 56.8	7 29.9	9 43.0	25 35.1	11 23.7	24 44.1
16 M	1 36 14.4	22 10.9	25 39.3	11♍ 2.5	13 21.5	5 33.6	4 39.9	7 42.7	9D43.0	25 32.7	11 25.5	24 44.4
17 T	1 40 10.9	23 10.5	25 36.1	24 17.2	14 42.1	6 42.6	5 23.1	7 55.5	9 43.2	25 30.2	11 27.3	24 44.6
18 W	1 44 7.5	24 10.1	25 32.9	7♎56.5	16 1.6	7 51.5	6 6.3	8 8.2	9 43.5	25 27.8	11 29.0	24 44.8
19 T	1 48 4.0	25 9.7	25 29.8	21 58.8	17 20.0	9 0.3	6 49.7	8 21.0	9 43.9	25 25.3	11 30.7	24 45.0
20 F	1 52 0.6	26 9.4	25 26.6	6♏20.0	18 37.1	10 9.0	7 33.1	8 33.7	9 44.4	25 22.9	11 32.4	24 45.2
21 S	1 55 57.1	27 9.1	25 23.4	20 54.0	19 52.8	11 17.6	8 16.5	8 46.3	9 45.0	25 20.4	11 34.1	24 45.3
22 S	1 59 53.7	28 8.8	25 20.2	5♐33.4	21 7.2	12 26.0	9 0.1	8 59.0	9 45.7	25 18.0	11 35.8	24 45.4
23 M	2 3 50.2	29 8.6	25 17.1	20 10.9	22 19.9	13 34.4	9 43.7	9 11.6	9 46.5	25 15.5	11 37.4	24 45.5
24 T	2 7 46.8	0♏ 8.4	25 13.9	4♑40.4	23 31.0	14 42.6	10 27.4	9 24.1	9 47.4	25 13.1	11 39.1	24 45.6
25 W	2 11 43.4	1 8.2	25 10.7	18 57.9	24 40.1	15 50.7	11 11.2	9 36.7	9 48.4	25 10.6	11 40.7	24 45.7
26 T	2 15 39.9	2 8.0	25 7.5	3♒ 1.0	25 47.2	16 58.7	11 55.0	9 49.2	9 49.5	25 8.2	11 42.2	24 45.7
27 F	2 19 36.4	3 7.9	25 4.3	16 49.4	26 52.0	18 6.5	12 38.9	10 1.6	9 50.7	25 5.8	11 43.8	24R45.6
28 S	2 23 33.0	4 7.8	25 1.2	0♓23.8	27 54.3	19 14.2	13 22.9	10 14.1	9 52.0	25 3.4	11 45.3	24 45.6
29 S	2 27 29.6	5 7.7	24 58.0	13 45.2	28 53.9	20 21.8	14 6.9	10 26.4	9 53.5	25 1.0	11 46.8	24 45.6
30 M	2 31 26.1	6 7.7	24 54.8	26 54.8	29 50.3	21 29.2	14 51.0	10 38.8	9 55.0	24 58.6	11 48.3	24 45.5
31 T	2 35 22.7	7 7.7	24 51.6	9♈53.2	0♐43.2	22 36.4	15 35.2	10 51.1	9 56.6	24 56.2	11 49.7	24 45.4

DECLINATION

DAY	SIDEREAL TIME	☉	☊	☽	☿	♀	♂	♃	♄	♅	♆	♇
1 S	0 37 6.0	2S55.5	12S42.3	9S40.5	8S34.7	18S32.2	19S33.2	0S46.5	18S43.4	9N31.9	8N14.4	22N22.1
4 W	0 48 55.7	4 5.3	12 45.6	8N50.0	10 37.6	19 39.6	20 5.3	1 1.8	18 44.4	9 29.4	8 12.2	22 22.0
7 S	1 0 45.4	5 14.6	12 48.8	23 7.1	12 34.6	20 42.8	20 36.0	1 17.1	18 45.1	9 26.8	8 10.0	22 22.0
10 T	1 12 35.0	6 23.4	12 52.0	27 51.3	14 25.0	21 41.5	21 5.1	1 32.4	18 45.5	9 24.2	8 7.8	22 22.1
13 F	1 24 24.7	7 31.4	12 55.2	21 23.7	16 8.2	22 35.4	21 32.7	1 47.5	18 45.7	9 21.6	8 5.8	22 22.2
16 M	1 36 14.4	8 38.5	12 58.5	6 18.0	17 43.6	23 24.3	21 58.6	2 2.6	18 45.7	9 18.9	8 3.8	22 22.3
19 T	1 48 4.0	9 44.5	13 1.7	12S25.1	19 10.4	24 7.9	22 22.8	2 17.5	18 45.4	9 16.2	8 1.9	22 22.4
22 S	1 59 53.7	10 49.2	13 4.9	26 9.5	20 27.6	24 46.0	22 45.1	2 32.3	18 44.8	9 13.6	8 0.0	22 22.7
25 W	2 11 43.4	11 52.5	13 8.1	25 9.4	21 34.2	25 18.4	23 5.6	2 46.9	18 44.0	9 10.9	7 58.2	22 22.9
28 S	2 23 33.0	12 54.1	13 11.3	10 59.7	22 28.7	25 44.9	23 24.0	3 1.4	18 43.0	9 8.3	7 56.6	22 23.2
31 T	2 35 22.7	13 53.9	13 14.5	7N 7.4	23 9.4	26 5.4	23 40.5	3 15.7	18 41.7	9 5.7	7 55.0	22 23.5

NOVEMBER 1933

DAY	EPHEMERIS SIDEREAL TIME h m s	☉ ° ′	☊ ° ′	☽ ° ′	☿ ° ′	♀ ° ′	♂ ° ′	♃ ° ′	♄ ° ′	♅ ° ′	♆ ° ′	♇ ° ′
						LONGITUDE						
1 W	2 39 19.2	8♏ 7.7	24♒48.5	22♈40.9	1♐32.4	23♐43.5	16♐19.4	11♎ 3.3	9♒58.3	24♈53.8	11♍51.1	24♋45.2
2 T	2 43 15.8	9 7.7	24 45.3	5♉17.7	2 17.2	24 50.4	17 3.7	11 15.6	10 0.1	24R51.5	11 52.5	24R45.1
3 F	2 47 12.3	10 7.8	24 42.1	17 43.6	2 57.3	25 57.1	17 48.1	11 27.7	10 2.0	24 49.1	11 53.9	24 44.9
4 S	2 51 8.9	11 7.9	24 38.9	29 58.9	3 32.0	27 3.7	18 32.5	11 39.8	10 4.0	24 46.8	11 55.2	24 44.7
5 S	2 55 5.5	12 8.0	24 35.8	12♊ 4.3	4 0.9	28 10.0	19 17.0	11 51.9	10 6.1	24 44.5	11 56.5	24 44.4
6 M	2 59 2.0	13 8.2	24 32.6	24 1.3	4 23.2	29 16.2	20 1.6	12 3.9	10 8.3	24 42.2	11 57.8	24 44.2
7 T	3 2 58.6	14 8.4	24 29.4	5♋52.4	4 38.4	0♑22.2	20 46.2	12 15.9	10 10.6	24 39.9	11 59.1	24 43.9
8 W	3 6 55.1	15 8.6	24 26.2	17 40.9	4 45.7	1 28.1	21 30.9	12 27.8	10 13.0	24 37.7	12 0.3	24 43.6
9 T	3 10 51.7	16 8.9	24 23.1	29 31.2	4R44.4	2 33.7	22 15.7	12 39.7	10 15.5	24 35.4	12 1.5	24 43.2
10 F	3 14 48.2	17 9.2	24 19.9	11♌28.0	4 34.0	3 39.0	23 0.5	12 51.5	10 18.1	24 33.2	12 2.6	24 42.9
11 S	3 18 44.8	18 9.5	24 16.7	23 36.8	4 13.9	4 44.2	23 45.4	13 3.2	10 20.7	24 31.0	12 3.8	24 42.5
12 S	3 22 41.4	19 9.9	24 13.5	6♍ 3.1	3 43.8	5 49.2	24 30.4	13 14.9	10 23.5	24 28.9	12 4.9	24 42.1
13 M	3 26 37.9	20 10.3	24 10.3	18 51.9	3 3.5	6 53.9	25 15.4	13 26.5	10 26.4	24 26.7	12 6.0	24 41.7
14 T	3 30 34.5	21 10.7	24 7.2	2♎ 7.4	2 13.3	7 58.4	26 0.4	13 38.1	10 29.3	24 24.6	12 7.0	24 41.2
15 W	3 34 31.0	22 11.2	24 4.0	15 51.8	1 13.8	9 2.7	26 45.6	13 49.6	10 32.4	24 22.5	12 8.0	24 40.7
16 T	3 38 27.6	23 11.7	24 0.8	0♏ 4.7	0 6.0	10 6.7	27 30.8	14 1.0	10 35.5	24 20.4	12 9.0	24 40.2
17 F	3 42 24.1	24 12.2	23 57.6	14 42.5	28♏51.6	11 10.4	28 16.1	14 12.4	10 38.8	24 18.4	12 10.0	24 39.7
18 S	3 46 20.7	25 12.8	23 54.5	29 38.2	27 32.5	12 13.9	29 1.4	14 23.7	10 42.1	24 16.4	12 10.9	24 39.1
19 S	3 50 17.3	26 13.3	23 51.3	14♐42.4	26 11.3	13 17.0	29 46.8	14 34.9	10 45.5	24 14.4	12 11.8	24 38.6
20 M	3 54 13.8	27 13.9	23 48.1	29 45.1	24 50.6	14 19.9	0♑32.2	14 46.0	10 49.0	24 12.5	12 12.6	24 38.0
21 T	3 58 10.4	28 14.5	23 44.9	14♑37.0	23 33.1	15 22.5	1 17.7	14 57.1	10 52.6	24 10.6	12 13.5	24 37.4
22 W	4 2 6.9	29 15.2	23 41.8	29 11.3	22 21.2	16 24.8	2 3.2	15 8.1	10 56.3	24 8.7	12 14.3	24 36.7
23 T	4 6 3.5	0♐15.8	23 38.6	13♒24.4	21 17.3	17 26.7	2 48.8	15 19.0	11 0.0	24 6.8	12 15.0	24 36.1
24 F	4 10 0.0	1 16.5	23 35.4	27 15.3	20 23.0	18 28.2	3 34.5	15 29.9	11 3.9	24 5.0	12 15.8	24 35.4
25 S	4 13 56.6	2 17.2	23 32.2	10♓45.0	19 39.5	19 29.4	4 20.2	15 40.6	11 7.8	24 3.3	12 16.5	24 34.7
26 S	4 17 53.2	3 17.9	23 29.0	23 56.0	19 7.4	20 30.3	5 6.0	15 51.3	11 11.8	24 1.5	12 17.1	24 33.9
27 M	4 21 49.7	4 18.6	23 25.9	6♈50.9	18 47.0	21 30.7	5 51.8	16 1.9	11 15.9	23 59.8	12 17.7	24 33.2
28 T	4 25 46.3	5 19.4	23 22.7	19 32.4	18 38.0	22 30.7	6 37.6	16 12.4	11 20.1	23 58.1	12 18.3	24 32.4
29 W	4 29 42.8	6 20.1	23 19.5	2♉ 2.6	18D39.9	23 30.3	7 23.5	16 22.8	11 24.4	23 56.5	12 18.9	24 31.6
30 T	4 33 39.4	7 20.9	23 16.3	14 23.2	18 52.1	24 29.5	8 9.5	16 33.1	11 28.7	23 54.9	12 19.4	24 30.8
						DECLINATION						
1 W	2 39 19.2	14S13.4	13S15.5	12N43.4	23S19.6	26S10.8	23S45.5	3S20.4	18S41.2	9N 4.9	7N54.5	22N23.6
4 S	2 51 8.9	15 10.5	13 18.7	25 1.7	23 38.1	26 23.2	23 59.1	3 34.4	18 39.6	9 2.4	7 53.0	22 24.0
7 T	3 2 58.6	16 5.4	13 21.9	27 6.3	23 36.1	26 29.5	24 10.5	3 48.2	18 37.8	8 59.9	7 51.6	22 24.4
10 F	3 14 48.2	16 57.8	13 25.0	18 27.1	23 8.9	26 29.7	24 19.6	4 1.7	18 35.7	8 57.5	7 50.4	22 24.9
13 M	3 26 37.9	17 47.7	13 28.2	2 29.8	22 11.4	26 23.8	24 26.4	4 15.1	18 33.3	8 55.2	7 49.2	22 25.4
16 T	3 38 27.6	18 34.8	13 31.4	15S46.7	20 42.0	26 12.1	24 30.9	4 28.1	18 30.8	8 52.9	7 48.1	22 25.9
19 S	3 50 17.3	19 19.0	13 34.5	27 12.7	18 49.9	25 54.7	24 33.0	4 40.9	18 28.0	8 50.8	7 47.2	22 26.5
22 W	4 2 6.9	19 60.0	13 37.7	22 20.6	16 58.9	25 31.7	24 32.7	4 53.3	18 25.0	8 48.7	7 46.3	22 27.1
25 S	4 13 56.6	20 37.7	13 40.8	6 8.0	15 36.8	25 3.5	24 29.9	5 5.5	18 21.8	8 46.8	7 45.6	22 27.8
28 T	4 25 46.3	21 11.9	13 43.9	11N31.3	14 58.4	24 30.4	24 24.6	5 17.3	18 18.3	8 45.0	7 45.0	22 28.4

DECEMBER 1933

DAY	SID. TIME	☉	☊	☽	☿	♀	♂	♃	♄	♅	♆	♇
						LONGITUDE						
1 F	4 37 36.0	8♐21.7	23♒13.2	26♉35.5	19♏13.7	25♑28.2	8♑55.5	16♎43.4	11♒33.1	23♈53.4	12♍19.9	24♋30.0
2 S	4 41 32.5	9 22.5	23 10.0	8♊40.3	19 43.9	26 26.4	9 41.5	16 53.5	11 37.6	23R51.9	12 20.4	24R29.2
3 S	4 45 29.1	10 23.4	23 6.8	20 38.6	20 21.8	27 24.2	10 27.6	17 3.6	11 42.2	23 50.4	12 20.8	24 28.3
4 M	4 49 25.6	11 24.2	23 3.6	2♋31.5	21 6.5	28 21.4	11 13.8	17 13.5	11 46.8	23 49.0	12 21.2	24 27.4
5 T	4 53 22.2	12 25.1	23 0.5	14 20.9	21 57.3	29 18.1	11 59.9	17 23.4	11 51.6	23 47.6	12 21.6	24 26.5
6 W	4 57 18.7	13 26.0	22 57.3	26 9.1	22 53.3	0♒14.2	12 46.2	17 33.2	11 56.4	23 46.2	12 21.9	24 25.6
7 T	5 1 15.3	14 26.9	22 54.1	7♌59.2	23 54.0	1 9.8	13 32.5	17 42.8	12 1.2	23 44.9	12 22.2	24 24.6
8 F	5 5 11.9	15 27.9	22 50.9	19 55.3	24 58.8	2 4.8	14 18.8	17 52.4	12 6.2	23 43.7	12 22.4	24 23.7
9 S	5 9 8.4	16 28.8	22 47.7	2♍ 2.0	26 7.0	2 59.2	15 5.1	18 1.8	12 11.2	23 42.5	12 22.7	24 22.7
10 S	5 13 5.0	17 29.8	22 44.6	14 24.4	27 18.4	3 52.9	15 51.5	18 11.2	12 16.3	23 41.3	12 22.8	24 21.7
11 M	5 17 1.5	18 30.8	22 41.4	27 7.6	28 32.3	4 46.0	16 38.0	18 20.4	12 21.4	23 40.2	12 23.0	24 20.7
12 T	5 20 58.1	19 31.8	22 38.2	10♎16.5	29 48.6	5 38.4	17 24.5	18 29.6	12 26.6	23 39.1	12 23.1	24 19.7
13 W	5 24 54.6	20 32.8	22 35.0	23 54.3	1♐ 6.8	6 30.0	18 11.0	18 38.6	12 31.9	23 38.1	12 23.1	24 18.6
14 T	5 28 51.2	21 33.9	22 31.9	8♏ 2.5	2 26.7	7 21.0	18 57.6	18 47.5	12 37.3	23 37.1	12 23.2	24 17.6
15 F	5 32 47.8	22 34.9	22 28.7	22 39.3	3 48.2	8 11.2	19 44.2	18 56.3	12 42.7	23 36.1	12 23.3	24 16.5
16 S	5 36 44.3	23 36.0	22 25.5	7♐39.3	5 10.9	9 0.5	20 30.9	19 4.9	12 48.2	23 35.3	12R23.2	24 15.4
17 S	5 40 40.9	24 37.1	22 22.3	22 53.7	6 34.8	9 49.0	21 17.6	19 13.5	12 53.7	23 34.4	12 23.2	24 14.3
18 M	5 44 37.4	25 38.2	22 19.2	8♑11.6	7 59.7	10 36.7	22 4.3	19 21.9	12 59.3	23 33.6	12 23.1	24 13.2
19 T	5 48 34.0	26 39.3	22 16.0	23 22.0	9 25.4	11 23.4	22 51.1	19 30.2	13 5.0	23 32.9	12 23.0	24 12.1
20 W	5 52 30.6	27 40.4	22 12.8	8♒15.4	10 51.9	12 9.2	23 37.9	19 38.4	13 10.7	23 32.2	12 22.8	24 10.9
21 T	5 56 27.1	28 41.6	22 9.6	22 45.7	12 19.1	12 54.0	24 24.7	19 46.5	13 16.5	23 31.5	12 22.6	24 9.8
22 F	6 0 23.7	29 42.7	22 6.5	6♓49.6	13 46.9	13 37.8	25 11.6	19 54.4	13 22.3	23 31.0	12 22.4	24 8.6
23 S	6 4 20.2	0♑43.8	22 3.3	20 27.2	15 15.2	14 20.5	25 58.5	20 2.2	13 28.2	23 30.4	12 22.1	24 7.5
24 S	6 8 16.8	1 44.9	22 0.1	3♈40.4	16 44.1	15 2.0	26 45.4	20 9.8	13 34.2	23 29.9	12 21.8	24 6.3
25 M	6 12 13.4	2 46.1	21 56.9	16 32.3	18 13.3	15 42.4	27 32.3	20 17.4	13 40.2	23 29.5	12 21.5	24 5.1
26 T	6 16 9.9	3 47.2	21 53.8	29 6.7	19 43.1	16 21.5	28 19.3	20 24.8	13 46.3	23 29.1	12 21.2	24 3.9
27 W	6 20 6.5	4 48.3	21 50.6	11♉27.0	21 13.2	16 59.4	29 6.3	20 32.0	13 52.4	23 28.8	12 20.8	24 2.7
28 T	6 24 3.0	5 49.5	21 47.4	23 36.7	22 43.6	17 35.9	29 53.4	20 39.1	13 58.5	23 28.5	12 20.3	24 1.4
29 F	6 27 59.6	6 50.6	21 44.2	5♊38.4	24 14.5	18 11.0	0♒40.4	20 46.1	14 4.7	23 28.2	12 19.9	24 0.2
30 S	6 31 56.1	7 51.7	21 41.1	17 34.6	25 45.7	18 44.7	1 27.5	20 52.9	14 11.0	23 28.1	12 19.4	23 59.0
31 S	6 35 52.7	8 52.9	21 37.9	29 26.9	27 17.2	19 16.9	2 14.6	20 59.6	14 17.3	23 27.9	12 18.9	23 57.7
						DECLINATION						
1 F	4 37 36.0	21S42.6	13S47.1	24N15.3	15S 2.0	23S52.6	24S16.9	5S28.7	18S14.7	8N43.3	7N44.5	22N29.1
4 M	4 49 25.6	22 9.5	13 50.2	27 14.6	15 37.1	23 10.6	24 6.8	5 39.8	18 10.8	8 41.8	7 44.1	22 29.9
7 T	5 1 15.3	22 32.6	13 53.3	19 25.7	16 32.3	22 24.8	23 54.1	5 50.6	18 6.8	8 40.4	7 43.8	22 30.6
10 S	5 13 5.0	22 51.7	13 56.4	4 18.6	17 38.1	21 35.6	23 39.0	6 0.9	18 2.5	8 39.1	7 43.7	22 31.4
13 W	5 24 54.6	23 6.8	13 59.5	13S28.1	18 47.7	20 43.4	23 21.5	6 10.8	17 58.1	8 38.0	7 43.7	22 32.2
16 S	5 36 44.3	23 17.7	14 2.6	26 23.9	19 56.3	19 48.7	23 1.5	6 20.3	17 53.5	8 37.1	7 43.8	22 33.0
19 T	5 48 34.0	23 24.5	14 5.7	23 44.2	21 0.9	18 52.0	22 39.2	6 29.3	17 48.7	8 36.3	7 44.0	22 33.8
22 F	6 0 23.7	23 27.0	14 8.8	7 40.3	21 59.0	17 53.8	22 14.6	6 37.9	17 43.8	8 35.7	7 44.3	22 34.7
25 M	6 12 13.4	23 25.2	14 11.9	10N26.2	22 49.0	16 54.8	21 47.6	6 45.9	17 38.6	8 35.2	7 44.7	22 35.5
28 T	6 24 3.0	23 19.3	14 15.0	23 38.6	23 29.9	15 55.6	21 18.5	6 53.5	17 33.4	8 35.0	7 45.3	22 36.4
31 S	6 35 52.7	23 9.1	14 18.0	27 25.5	24 0.6	14 57.0	20 47.2	7 0.6	17 28.0	8 34.9	7 46.0	22 37.3

JANUARY 1934

LONGITUDE

DAY	EPHEMERIS SIDEREAL TIME h m s	☉ ° ′	☊ ° ′	☾ ° ′	☿ ° ′	♀ ° ′	♂ ° ′	♃ ° ′	♄ ° ′	♅ ° ′	♆ ° ′	♇ ° ′
1 M	6 39 49.3	9♑54.0	21♒34.7	11♋17.2	28♐49.1	19♒47.5	3♒ 1.7	21♎ 6.2	14♒23.6	23♈27.8	12♍18.3	23♋56.4
2 T	6 43 45.8	10 55.1	21 31.5	23 7.1	0♑21.4	20 16.6	3 48.9	21 12.6	14 30.0	23R27.8	12R17.7	23R55.2
3 W	6 47 42.4	11 56.3	21 28.3	4♌58.4	1 53.9	20 43.9	4 36.0	21 18.8	14 36.5	23D27.8	12 17.1	23 53.9
4 T	6 51 38.9	12 57.4	21 25.2	16 53.4	3 26.9	21 9.5	5 23.2	21 24.9	14 42.9	23 27.9	12 16.4	23 52.6
5 F	6 55 35.5	13 58.6	21 22.0	28 54.8	5 0.2	21 33.3	6 10.4	21 30.9	14 49.4	23 28.0	12 15.8	23 51.4
6 S	6 59 32.0	14 59.7	21 18.8	11♍ 5.9	6 33.9	21 55.2	6 57.7	21 36.6	14 56.0	23 28.2	12 15.0	23 50.1
7 S	7 3 28.6	16 0.8	21 15.6	23 30.4	8 7.9	22 15.2	7 44.9	21 42.3	15 2.6	23 28.5	12 14.3	23 48.8
8 M	7 7 25.2	17 2.0	21 12.5	6♎12.4	9 42.4	22 33.2	8 32.2	21 47.8	15 9.2	23 28.7	12 13.5	23 47.5
9 T	7 11 21.7	18 3.1	21 9.3	19 16.0	11 17.3	22 49.1	9 19.5	21 53.1	15 15.9	23 29.1	12 12.7	23 46.2
10 W	7 15 18.3	19 4.3	21 6.1	2♏44.4	12 52.5	23 3.0	10 6.8	21 58.3	15 22.6	23 29.5	12 11.9	23 44.9
11 T	7 19 14.8	20 5.4	21 2.9	16 39.7	14 28.3	23 14.6	10 54.1	22 3.2	15 29.3	23 29.9	12 11.0	23 43.6
12 F	7 23 11.4	21 6.6	20 59.8	1♐ 1.9	16 4.4	23 24.0	11 41.5	22 8.1	15 36.1	23 30.4	12 10.1	23 42.3
13 S	7 27 8.0	22 7.7	20 56.6	15 48.1	17 41.1	23 31.2	12 28.8	22 12.8	15 42.9	23 31.0	12 9.2	23 41.0
14 S	7 31 4.5	23 8.9	20 53.4	0♑52.2	19 18.2	23 36.0	13 16.2	22 17.3	15 49.8	23 31.6	12 8.3	23 39.7
15 M	7 35 1.1	24 10.0	20 50.2	16 5.6	20 55.8	23 38.4	14 3.6	22 21.6	15 56.6	23 32.2	12 7.3	23 38.4
16 T	7 38 57.6	25 11.1	20 47.0	1♒18.0	22 33.9	23R38.4	14 51.0	22 25.7	16 3.5	23 32.9	12 6.3	23 37.0
17 W	7 42 54.2	26 12.3	20 43.9	16 19.6	24 12.5	23 35.9	15 38.4	22 29.7	16 10.5	23 33.7	12 5.2	23 35.7
18 T	7 46 50.8	27 13.4	20 40.7	1♓ 2.0	25 51.7	23 30.8	16 25.8	22 33.5	16 17.4	23 34.5	12 4.2	23 34.4
19 F	7 50 47.3	28 14.5	20 37.5	15 19.7	27 31.4	23 23.3	17 13.3	22 37.2	16 24.4	23 35.3	12 3.1	23 33.1
20 S	7 54 43.9	29 15.6	20 34.3	29 10.1	29 11.7	23 13.3	18 0.7	22 40.6	16 31.4	23 36.2	12 2.0	23 31.8
21 S	7 58 40.4	0♒16.6	20 31.2	12♈33.3	0♒52.5	23 0.7	18 48.1	22 43.9	16 38.4	23 37.2	12 0.8	23 30.5
22 M	8 2 37.0	1 17.7	20 28.0	25 31.6	2 33.9	22 45.6	19 35.6	22 47.0	16 45.4	23 38.2	11 59.7	23 29.2
23 T	8 6 33.5	2 18.7	20 24.8	8♉ 8.2	4 15.8	22 28.0	20 23.0	22 49.9	16 52.5	23 39.3	11 58.5	23 27.9
24 W	8 10 30.1	3 19.8	20 21.6	20 27.3	5 58.3	22 8.0	21 10.5	22 52.7	16 59.6	23 40.4	11 57.3	23 26.7
25 T	8 14 26.6	4 20.8	20 18.5	2♊33.1	7 41.3	21 45.7	21 57.9	22 55.2	17 6.7	23 41.5	11 56.1	23 25.4
26 F	8 18 23.2	5 21.7	20 15.3	14 29.8	9 24.9	21 21.2	22 45.4	22 57.6	17 13.8	23 42.7	11 54.8	23 24.1
27 S	8 22 19.8	6 22.7	20 12.1	26 21.1	11 9.1	20 54.5	23 32.8	22 59.8	17 20.9	23 44.0	11 53.5	23 22.8
28 S	8 26 16.3	7 23.7	20 8.9	8♋10.3	12 53.7	20 25.9	24 20.3	23 1.8	17 28.1	23 45.3	11 52.2	23 21.6
29 M	8 30 12.9	8 24.6	20 5.8	20 0.2	14 38.7	19 55.4	25 7.7	23 3.7	17 35.2	23 46.7	11 50.9	23 20.3
30 T	8 34 9.4	9 25.5	20 2.6	1♌53.2	16 24.1	19 23.3	25 55.1	23 5.3	17 42.4	23 48.1	11 49.6	23 19.0
31 W	8 38 6.0	10 26.4	19 59.4	13 51.2	18 9.9	18 49.7	26 42.6	23 6.8	17 49.6	23 49.5	11 48.2	23 17.8

DECLINATION

DAY	EPHEMERIS SIDEREAL TIME h m s	☉	☊	☾	☿	♀	♂	♃	♄	♅	♆	♇
1 M	6 39 49.3	23S 4.8	14S19.1	26N10.6	24S 8.5	14S37.6	20S36.4	7S 2.9	17S26.1	8N34.9	7N46.2	22N37.6
4 T	6 51 38.9	22 49.1	14 22.1	16 1.1	24 24.5	13 40.7	20 2.3	7 9.3	17 20.5	8 35.0	7 47.0	22 38.5
7 S	7 3 28.6	22 29.3	14 25.2	0S 5.6	24 28.7	12 46.0	19 26.3	7 15.1	17 14.8	8 35.3	7 48.0	22 39.4
10 W	7 15 18.3	22 5.6	14 28.2	17 7.0	24 20.7	11 54.3	18 48.3	7 20.4	17 9.0	8 35.8	7 49.0	22 40.2
13 S	7 27 8.0	21 37.9	14 31.3	27 21.3	23 59.8	11 6.6	18 8.5	7 25.1	17 3.0	8 36.4	7 50.1	22 41.1
16 T	7 38 57.6	21 6.4	14 34.3	21 28.3	23 25.8	10 23.7	17 27.0	7 29.3	16 57.0	8 37.2	7 51.3	22 42.0
19 F	7 50 47.3	20 31.3	14 37.4	3 39.5	22 38.3	9 46.7	16 43.8	7 32.9	16 50.8	8 38.2	7 52.6	22 42.9
22 M	8 2 37.0	19 52.8	14 40.4	14N21.2	21 37.1	9 16.5	15 59.0	7 35.8	16 44.6	8 39.4	7 54.0	22 43.7
25 T	8 14 26.6	19 10.9	14 43.4	25 42.5	20 21.9	8 54.0	15 12.7	7 38.2	16 38.2	8 40.7	7 55.5	22 44.6
28 S	8 26 16.3	18 25.8	14 46.4	26 40.1	18 52.8	8 39.6	14 25.1	7 39.9	16 31.8	8 42.2	7 57.0	22 45.4
31 W	8 38 6.0	17 37.8	14 49.4	17 9.3	17 10.2	8 33.6	13 36.2	7 41.1	16 25.4	8 43.8	7 58.6	22 46.2

FEBRUARY 1934

LONGITUDE

DAY	EPHEMERIS SIDEREAL TIME h m s	☉ ° ′	☊ ° ′	☾ ° ′	☿ ° ′	♀ ° ′	♂ ° ′	♃ ° ′	♄ ° ′	♅ ° ′	♆ ° ′	♇ ° ′
1 T	8 42 2.6	11♒27.3	19♒56.2	25♌56.2	19♒55.9	18♒15.0	27♒30.0	23♎ 8.0	17♒56.7	23♈51.0	11♍46.8	23♋16.6
2 F	8 45 59.1	12 28.2	19 53.0	8♍ 9.8	21 42.0	17R39.2	28 17.5	23 9.1	18 3.9	23 52.6	11R45.5	23R15.3
3 S	8 49 55.7	13 29.0	19 49.9	20 33.9	23 28.2	17 2.6	29 4.9	23 10.0	18 11.1	23 54.1	11 44.0	23 14.1
4 S	8 53 52.2	14 29.8	19 46.7	3♎10.5	25 14.2	16 25.6	29 52.3	23 10.7	18 18.4	23 55.8	11 42.6	23 12.9
5 M	8 57 48.8	15 30.6	19 43.5	16 1.6	26 59.9	15 48.3	0♓39.7	23 11.3	18 25.6	23 57.5	11 41.1	23 11.7
6 T	9 1 45.3	16 31.5	19 40.3	29 9.3	28 45.1	15 11.0	1 27.1	23 11.6	18 32.8	23 59.2	11 39.7	23 10.5
7 W	9 5 41.9	17 32.2	19 37.2	12♏35.6	0♓29.4	14 34.1	2 14.6	23 11.7	18 40.0	24 1.0	11 38.2	23 9.3
8 T	9 9 38.4	18 33.0	19 34.0	26 21.8	2 12.7	13 57.6	3 1.9	23R11.7	18 47.2	24 2.8	11 36.7	23 8.2
9 F	9 13 35.0	19 33.8	19 30.8	10♐28.1	3 54.5	13 22.0	3 49.3	23 11.4	18 54.5	24 4.6	11 35.2	23 7.0
10 S	9 17 31.6	20 34.5	19 27.6	24 53.4	5 34.6	12 47.3	4 36.7	23 11.0	19 1.7	24 6.5	11 33.7	23 5.9
11 S	9 21 28.1	21 35.2	19 24.5	9♑34.5	7 12.3	12 13.9	5 24.1	23 10.4	19 8.9	24 8.5	11 32.1	23 4.8
12 M	9 25 24.7	22 35.9	19 21.3	24 26.0	8 47.2	11 42.0	6 11.5	23 9.6	19 16.1	24 10.5	11 30.6	23 3.6
13 T	9 29 21.2	23 36.6	19 18.1	9♒21.0	10 18.8	11 11.7	6 58.8	23 8.5	19 23.3	24 12.5	11 29.0	23 2.5
14 W	9 33 17.8	24 37.3	19 14.9	24 11.8	11 46.6	10 43.2	7 46.2	23 7.3	19 30.5	24 14.6	11 27.4	23 1.4
15 T	9 37 14.3	25 37.9	19 11.7	8♓50.5	13 9.7	10 16.6	8 33.5	23 6.0	19 37.8	24 16.7	11 25.8	23 0.4
16 F	9 41 10.9	26 38.5	19 8.6	23 10.5	14 27.6	9 52.1	9 20.8	23 4.4	19 45.0	24 18.9	11 24.2	22 59.3
17 S	9 45 7.4	27 39.1	19 5.4	7♈ 7.3	15 39.6	9 29.8	10 8.1	23 2.6	19 52.1	24 21.1	11 22.6	22 58.3
18 S	9 49 4.0	28 39.6	19 2.2	20 38.7	16 45.0	9 9.7	10 55.4	23 0.7	19 59.3	24 23.3	11 21.0	22 57.2
19 M	9 53 0.5	29 40.2	18 59.0	3♉44.7	17 43.1	8 52.0	11 42.6	22 58.5	20 6.5	24 25.6	11 19.4	22 56.2
20 T	9 56 57.1	0♓40.7	18 55.9	16 27.5	18 33.2	8 36.7	12 29.9	22 56.2	20 13.6	24 27.9	11 17.7	22 55.2
21 W	10 0 53.7	1 41.1	18 52.7	28 50.4	19 14.8	8 23.9	13 17.1	22 53.7	20 20.8	24 30.3	11 16.1	22 54.2
22 T	10 4 50.2	2 41.5	18 49.5	10♊57.6	19 47.3	8 13.4	14 4.3	22 51.0	20 27.9	24 32.6	11 14.5	22 53.3
23 F	10 8 46.8	3 41.9	18 46.3	22 54.0	20 10.3	8 5.5	14 51.5	22 48.1	20 35.0	24 35.1	11 12.8	22 52.3
24 S	10 12 43.3	4 42.3	18 43.1	4♋44.2	20 23.6	8 0.0	15 38.6	22 45.1	20 42.1	24 37.5	11 11.1	22 51.4
25 S	10 16 39.9	5 42.6	18 40.0	16 32.8	20 26.9	7 57.0	16 25.7	22 41.9	20 49.2	24 40.0	11 9.5	22 50.5
26 M	10 20 36.4	6 42.9	18 36.8	28 23.9	20R20.4	7 56.4	17 12.9	22 38.5	20 56.2	24 42.6	11 7.8	22 49.6
27 T	10 24 33.0	7 43.2	18 33.6	10♌21.2	20 4.3	7D58.3	17 59.9	22 34.9	21 3.2	24 45.1	11 6.2	22 48.7
28 W	10 28 29.5	8 43.5	18 30.4	22 27.5	19 39.0	8 2.5	18 47.0	22 31.2	21 10.3	24 47.7	11 4.5	22 47.9

DECLINATION

DAY	EPHEMERIS SIDEREAL TIME h m s	☉	☊	☾	☿	♀	♂	♃	♄	♅	♆	♇
1 T	8 42 2.6	17S21.2	14S50.4	12N18.0	16S33.1	8S33.4	13S19.6	7S41.3	16S23.2	8N44.4	7N59.2	22N46.5
4 S	8 53 52.2	16 29.4	14 53.4	4S38.0	14 33.8	8 38.0	12 29.1	7 41.6	16 16.7	8 46.3	8 0.9	22 47.3
7 W	9 5 41.9	15 35.1	14 56.4	20 37.6	12 24.1	8 49.5	11 37.6	7 41.3	16 10.2	8 48.3	8 2.6	22 48.0
10 S	9 17 31.6	14 38.3	14 59.4	27 39.5	10 7.2	9 6.6	10 45.0	7 40.3	16 3.6	8 50.4	8 4.4	22 48.8
13 T	9 29 21.2	13 39.4	15 2.4	18 48.5	7 48.6	9 27.8	9 51.6	7 38.7	15 57.0	8 52.7	8 6.2	22 49.5
16 F	9 41 10.9	12 38.4	15 5.4	0N 0.1	5 35.9	9 51.6	8 57.4	7 36.5	15 50.4	8 55.1	8 8.1	22 50.2
19 M	9 53 0.5	11 35.6	15 8.3	17 33.3	3 38.7	10 16.5	8 2.5	7 33.7	15 43.9	8 57.6	8 10.0	22 50.8
22 T	10 4 50.2	10 31.1	15 11.3	26 57.4	2 7.8	10 41.3	7 7.0	7 30.3	15 37.3	9 0.3	8 11.9	22 51.4
25 S	10 16 39.9	9 25.3	15 14.3	25 15.8	1 13.1	11 4.7	6 11.0	7 26.3	15 30.7	9 3.1	8 13.9	22 52.0
28 W	10 28 29.5	8 18.1	15 17.2	13 45.7	1 1.2	11 25.9	5 14.6	7 21.8	15 24.2	9 6.0	8 15.8	22 52.6

MARCH 1934

LONGITUDE

DAY	EPHEMERIS SIDEREAL TIME h m s	☉ ° ′	☊ ° ′	☽ ° ′	☿ ° ′	♀ ° ′	♂ ° ′	♃ ° ′	♄ ° ′	♅ ° ′	♆ ° ′	♇ ° ′
1 T	10 32 26.1	9♓43.7	18♒27.3	4♍45.0	19♓ 5.2	8♒ 9.0	19♓34.0	22♎27.3	21♒17.2	24♈50.4	11♍ 2.8	22♋47.0
2 F	10 36 22.7	10 43.9	18 24.1	17 15.1	18R23.8	8 17.8	20 21.0	22R23.2	21 24.2	24 53.0	11R 1.1	22R46.2
3 S	10 40 19.2	11 44.0	18 20.9	29 58.8	17 35.7	8 28.8	21 8.0	22 18.9	21 31.2	24 55.7	10 59.5	22 45.4
4 S	10 44 15.7	12 44.1	18 17.7	12♎56.1	16 42.3	8 41.9	21 54.9	22 14.5	21 38.1	24 58.4	10 57.8	22 44.6
5 M	10 48 12.3	13 44.2	18 14.5	26 7.1	15 44.9	8 57.2	22 41.9	22 10.0	21 45.0	25 1.2	10 56.1	22 43.9
6 T	10 52 8.9	14 44.3	18 11.4	9♏31.2	14 45.0	9 14.4	23 28.8	22 5.2	21 51.8	25 4.0	10 54.5	22 43.1
7 W	10 56 5.4	15 44.3	18 8.2	23 7.9	13 43.9	9 33.7	24 15.6	22 0.4	21 58.7	25 6.8	10 52.8	22 42.4
8 T	11 0 2.0	16 44.3	18 5.0	6♐56.6	12 43.1	9 54.8	25 2.5	21 55.3	22 5.5	25 9.7	10 51.1	22 41.7
9 F	11 3 58.5	17 44.3	18 1.8	20 56.6	11 44.0	10 17.8	25 49.3	21 50.1	22 12.2	25 12.5	10 49.5	22 41.0
10 S	11 7 55.1	18 44.3	17 58.7	5♑ 6.9	10 47.7	10 42.6	26 36.0	21 44.8	22 19.0	25 15.4	10 47.8	22 40.4
11 S	11 11 51.6	19 44.2	17 55.5	19 25.9	9 55.3	11 9.0	27 22.8	21 39.3	22 25.7	25 18.4	10 46.2	22 39.8
12 M	11 15 48.2	20 44.1	17 52.3	3♒51.0	9 7.6	11 37.1	28 9.5	21 33.7	22 32.4	25 21.3	10 44.5	22 39.2
13 T	11 19 44.7	21 44.0	17 49.1	18 18.8	8 25.2	12 6.7	28 56.2	21 28.0	22 39.0	25 24.3	10 42.9	22 38.6
14 W	11 23 41.3	22 43.9	17 45.9	2♓44.6	7 48.7	12 37.9	29 42.9	21 22.1	22 45.6	25 27.3	10 41.2	22 38.0
15 T	11 27 37.8	23 43.7	17 42.8	17 3.4	7 18.3	13 10.5	0♈29.5	21 16.1	22 52.2	25 30.3	10 39.6	22 37.5
16 F	11 31 34.4	24 43.5	17 39.6	1♈ 9.8	6 54.2	13 44.5	1 16.1	21 9.9	22 58.7	25 33.4	10 38.0	22 37.0
17 S	11 35 31.0	25 43.2	17 36.4	14 59.1	6 36.6	14 19.9	2 2.7	21 3.7	23 5.2	25 36.5	10 36.4	22 36.5
18 S	11 39 27.5	26 42.9	17 33.2	28 28.0	6 25.3	14 56.5	2 49.2	20 57.3	23 11.6	25 39.6	10 34.8	22 36.0
19 M	11 43 24.1	27 42.6	17 30.1	11♉34.9	6 20.1	15 34.3	3 35.7	20 50.8	23 18.0	25 42.7	10 33.2	22 35.6
20 T	11 47 20.6	28 42.3	17 26.9	24 20.3	6D21.0	16 13.3	4 22.1	20 44.2	23 24.4	25 45.8	10 31.6	22 35.1
21 W	11 51 17.2	29 41.9	17 23.7	6♊46.0	6 27.7	16 53.5	5 8.6	20 37.5	23 30.7	25 49.0	10 30.1	22 34.7
22 T	11 55 13.7	0♈41.4	17 20.5	18 55.4	6 40.0	17 34.7	5 54.9	20 30.7	23 37.0	25 52.2	10 28.5	22 34.4
23 F	11 59 10.3	1 41.0	17 17.3	0♋53.0	6 57.5	18 17.0	6 41.3	20 23.8	23 43.2	25 55.4	10 27.0	22 34.0
24 S	12 3 6.8	2 40.5	17 14.2	12 43.6	7 20.1	19 0.3	7 27.5	20 16.8	23 49.4	25 58.6	10 25.5	22 33.7
25 S	12 7 3.4	3 39.9	17 11.0	24 32.6	7 47.4	19 44.6	8 13.8	20 9.8	23 55.5	26 1.8	10 23.9	22 33.4
26 M	12 10 60.0	4 39.3	17 7.8	6♌25.0	8 19.2	20 29.8	9 0.0	20 2.7	24 1.6	26 5.1	10 22.5	22 33.1
27 T	12 14 56.5	5 38.7	17 4.6	18 25.6	8 55.2	21 15.9	9 46.2	19 55.4	24 7.6	26 8.3	10 21.0	22 32.9
28 W	12 18 53.0	6 38.0	17 1.5	0♍38.6	9 35.2	22 2.8	10 32.3	19 48.2	24 13.6	26 11.6	10 19.5	22 32.6
29 T	12 22 49.6	7 37.3	16 58.3	13 7.0	10 19.0	22 50.6	11 18.4	19 40.8	24 19.5	26 14.9	10 18.0	22 32.4
30 F	12 26 46.2	8 36.6	16 55.1	25 53.1	11 6.3	23 39.2	12 4.4	19 33.4	24 25.3	26 18.2	10 16.6	22 32.2
31. S	12 30 42.7	9 35.9	16 51.9	8♎57.2	11 57.0	24 28.5	12 50.4	19 26.0	24 31.2	26 21.5	10 15.2	22 32.1

DECLINATION

DAY	EPHEMERIS SIDEREAL TIME h m s	☉	☊	☽	☿	♀	♂	♃	♄	♅	♆	♇
1 T	10 32 26.1	7S55.5	15S18.2	8N28.1	1S 7.0	11S32.4	4S55.7	7S20.1	15S22.1	9N 7.0	8N16.4	22N52.8
4 S	10 44 15.7	6 47.0	15 21.1	9S 0.1	1 50.9	11 49.4	3 58.9	7 14.8	15 15.6	9 10.0	8 18.4	22 53.3
7 W	10 56 5.4	5 37.6	15 24.1	23 36.4	3 5.3	12 2.7	3 2.0	7 9.1	15 9.3	9 13.1	8 20.3	22 53.8
10 S	11 7 55.1	4 27.5	15 27.0	26 58.7	4 34.0	12 11.8	2 4.8	7 2.8	15 2.9	9 16.3	8 22.2	22 54.2
13 T	11 19 44.7	3 16.8	15 29.9	15 24.7	6 0.9	12 16.4	1 7.7	6 56.1	14 56.7	9 19.6	8 24.1	22 54.6
16 F	11 31 34.4	2 5.8	15 32.8	3N39.9	7 14.3	12 16.4	0 10.6	6 48.9	14 50.6	9 23.0	8 26.0	22 55.0
19 M	11 43 24.1	0 54.7	15 35.7	20 11.4	8 8.2	12 11.7	0N46.4	6 41.4	14 44.5	9 26.4	8 27.8	22 55.3
22 T	11 55 13.7	0N16.5	15 38.6	27 26.0	8 40.8	12 2.2	1 43.1	6 33.6	14 38.6	9 29.9	8 29.6	22 55.6
25 S	12 7 3.4	1 27.5	15 41.5	23 17.3	8 52.3	11 47.9	2 39.5	6 25.5	14 32.9	9 33.5	8 31.3	22 55.9
28 W	12 18 53.0	2 38.1	15 44.4	10 13.9	8 44.3	11 28.9	3 35.5	6 17.1	14 27.2	9 37.1	8 33.0	22 56.1
31 S	12 30 42.7	3 48.2	15 47.3	7S11.3	8 18.2	11 5.1	4 31.0	6 8.6	14 21.7	9 40.7	8 34.6	22 56.3

APRIL 1934

LONGITUDE

DAY	EPHEMERIS SIDEREAL TIME h m s	☉ ° ′	☊ ° ′	☽ ° ′	☿ ° ′	♀ ° ′	♂ ° ′	♃ ° ′	♄ ° ′	♅ ° ′	♆ ° ′	♇ ° ′
1 S	12 34 39.3	10♈35.1	16♒48.8	22♎18.9	12♓50.9	25♒18.6	13♈36.4	19♎18.5	24♒36.9	26♈24.9	10♍13.8	22♋32.0
2 M	12 38 35.8	11 34.2	16 45.6	5♏55.8	13 47.7	26 9.4	14 22.3	19R10.9	24 42.6	26 28.2	10R12.4	22R31.9
3 T	12 42 32.4	12 33.4	16 42.4	19 45.2	14 47.4	27 0.9	15 8.2	19 3.3	24 48.3	26 31.6	10 11.1	22 31.8
4 W	12 46 28.9	13 32.5	16 39.2	3♐43.5	15 49.8	27 53.0	15 54.0	18 55.7	24 53.9	26 34.9	10 9.7	22 31.7
5 T	12 50 25.5	14 31.5	16 36.0	17 47.5	16 54.8	28 45.8	16 39.8	18 48.1	24 59.4	26 38.3	10 8.4	22 31.7
6 F	12 54 22.0	15 30.6	16 32.9	1♑54.5	18 2.2	29 39.2	17 25.5	18 40.4	25 4.9	26 41.7	10 7.1	22 31.7
7 S	12 58 18.6	16 29.6	16 29.7	16 2.5	19 12.0	0♓33.2	18 11.2	18 32.7	25 10.3	26 45.1	10 5.8	22D31.7
8 S	13 2 15.1	17 28.6	16 26.5	0♒10.0	20 24.1	1 27.8	18 56.9	18 25.0	25 15.6	26 48.5	10 4.6	22 31.8
9 M	13 6 11.7	18 27.5	16 23.3	14 16.0	21 38.3	2 22.9	19 42.5	18 17.3	25 20.9	26 51.9	10 3.3	22 31.8
10 T	13 10 8.2	19 26.5	16 20.2	28 19.2	22 54.6	3 18.5	20 28.1	18 9.6	25 26.1	26 55.3	10 2.1	22 31.9
11 W	13 14 4.8	20 25.4	16 17.0	12♓18.1	24 12.9	4 14.6	21 13.6	18 1.9	25 31.3	26 58.8	10 0.9	22 32.0
12 T	13 18 1.3	21 24.2	16 13.8	26 10.3	25 33.2	5 11.2	21 59.1	17 54.2	25 36.4	27 2.2	9 59.7	22 32.2
13 F	13 21 57.9	22 23.1	16 10.6	9♈52.9	26 55.4	6 8.2	22 44.5	17 46.5	25 41.4	27 5.6	9 58.6	22 32.4
14 S	13 25 54.5	23 21.9	16 7.4	23 22.9	28 19.4	7 5.7	23 29.9	17 38.8	25 46.3	27 9.1	9 57.5	22 32.6
15 S	13 29 51.0	24 20.7	16 4.3	6♉37.6	29 45.3	8 3.6	24 15.3	17 31.2	25 51.2	27 12.5	9 56.4	22 32.8
16 M	13 33 47.6	25 19.4	16 1.1	19 35.2	1♈13.0	9 2.0	25 0.6	17 23.6	25 56.0	27 15.9	9 55.3	22 33.0
17 T	13 37 44.1	26 18.1	15 57.9	2♊15.1	2 42.4	10 0.7	25 45.8	17 16.0	26 0.8	27 19.4	9 54.2	22 33.3
18 W	13 41 40.7	27 16.8	15 54.7	14 38.1	4 13.6	10 59.8	26 31.0	17 8.5	26 5.4	27 22.8	9 53.2	22 33.6
19 T	13 45 37.2	28 15.4	15 51.6	26 46.4	5 46.4	11 59.3	27 16.2	17 1.0	26 10.0	27 26.3	9 52.2	22 33.9
20 F	13 49 33.8	29 14.0	15 48.4	8♋43.6	7 21.1	12 59.1	28 1.3	16 53.6	26 14.6	27 29.7	9 51.3	22 34.3
21 S	13 53 30.3	0♉12.6	15 45.2	20 33.9	8 57.4	13 59.2	28 46.3	16 46.3	26 19.0	27 33.1	9 50.3	22 34.6
22 S	13 57 26.9	1 11.1	15 42.0	2♌22.7	10 35.4	14 59.7	29 31.3	16 39.0	26 23.4	27 36.6	9 49.4	22 35.0
23 M	14 1 23.5	2 9.6	15 38.8	14 15.1	12 15.1	16 0.6	0♉16.2	16 31.8	26 27.7	27 40.0	9 48.5	22 35.5
24 T	14 5 20.0	3 8.1	15 35.7	26 16.8	13 56.5	17 1.7	1 1.1	16 24.6	26 31.9	27 43.5	9 47.7	22 35.9
25 W	14 9 16.5	4 6.5	15 32.5	8♍32.7	15 39.6	18 3.1	1 46.0	16 17.5	26 36.0	27 46.9	9 46.8	22 36.4
26 T	14 13 13.1	5 4.9	15 29.3	21 7.3	17 24.4	19 4.9	2 30.8	16 10.6	26 40.1	27 50.3	9 46.0	22 36.9
27 F	14 17 9.7	6 3.2	15 26.1	4♎ 3.7	19 11.0	20 6.9	3 15.5	16 3.7	26 44.1	27 53.7	9 45.3	22 37.4
28 S	14 21 6.2	7 1.5	15 23.0	17 23.2	20 59.3	21 9.2	4 0.2	15 56.9	26 48.0	27 57.1	9 44.5	22 37.9
29 S	14 25 2.8	7 59.8	15 19.8	1♏ 5.1	22 49.3	22 11.7	4 44.8	15 50.1	26 51.8	28 0.5	9 43.8	22 38.5
30 M	14 28 59.3	8 58.1	15 16.6	15 6.5	24 41.0	23 14.5	5 29.4	15 43.5	26 55.5	28 3.9	9 43.1	22 39.0

DECLINATION

DAY	EPHEMERIS SIDEREAL TIME h m s	☉	☊	☽	☿	♀	♂	♃	♄	♅	♆	♇
1 S	12 34 39.3	4N11.5	15S48.2	12S57.0	8S 5.9	10S56.1	4N49.4	6S 5.7	14S19.9	9N41.9	8N35.1	22N56.4
4 W	12 46 28.9	5 20.8	15 51.1	25 42.7	7 18.4	10 26.1	5 44.2	5 57.0	14 14.6	9 45.6	8 36.6	22 56.5
7 S	12 58 18.6	6 29.2	15 54.0	25 8.1	6 16.4	9 51.7	6 38.3	5 48.3	14 9.5	9 49.3	8 38.1	22 56.6
10 T	13 10 8.2	7 36.7	15 56.8	11 9.9	5 1.1	9 13.0	7 31.8	5 39.6	14 4.6	9 53.0	8 39.5	22 56.6
13 F	13 21 57.9	8 43.0	15 59.7	7N36.6	3 33.6	8 30.3	8 24.4	5 30.9	13 59.9	9 56.7	8 40.8	22 56.6
16 M	13 33 47.6	9 48.0	16 2.5	22 28.6	1 54.8	7 43.8	9 16.2	5 22.3	13 55.4	10 0.5	8 42.0	22 56.6
19 T	13 45 37.2	10 51.6	16 5.4	27 15.3	0 5.7	6 53.7	10 7.1	5 13.9	13 51.1	10 4.2	8 43.1	22 56.6
22 S	13 57 26.9	11 53.5	16 8.2	20 48.9	1N53.0	6 0.2	10 56.9	5 5.7	13 47.0	10 7.9	8 44.1	22 56.5
25 W	14 9 16.5	12 53.6	16 11.0	6 34.7	4 0.2	5 3.8	11 45.7	4 57.8	13 43.1	10 11.6	8 45.1	22 56.3
28 S	14 21 6.2	13 51.9	16 13.8	10S54.4	6 15.0	4 4.5	12 33.4	4 50.2	13 39.5	10 15.3	8 45.9	22 56.1

MAY 1934

LONGITUDE

DAY	EPHEMERIS SIDEREAL TIME h m s	☉ ° ′	☊ ° ′	☽ ° ′	☿ ° ′	♀ ° ′	♂ ° ′	♃ ° ′	♄ ° ′	♅ ° ′	♆ ° ′	♇ ° ′
1 T	14 32 55.9	9♉56.3	15♒13.4	29♏22.7	26♈34.5	24♓17.6	6♉13.9	15♎37.0	26♒59.2	28♈ 7.3	9♍42.4	22♋39.7
2 W	14 36 52.5	10 54.5	15 10.2	13♐47.7	28 29.8	25 20.9	6 58.4	15R30.6	27 2.8	28 10.7	9R41.8	22 40.3
3 T	14 40 49.0	11 52.7	15 7.1	28 15.4	0♉26.7	26 24.5	7 42.9	15 24.3	27 6.3	28 14.1	9 41.2	22 41.0
4 F	14 44 45.6	12 50.8	15 3.9	12♑40.3	2 25.4	27 28.3	8 27.2	15 18.2	27 9.7	28 17.4	9 40.7	22 41.6
5 S	14 48 42.1	13 48.9	15 0.7	26 58.6	4 25.7	28 32.3	9 11.6	15 12.1	27 13.0	28 20.8	9 40.1	22 42.3
6 S	14 52 38.7	14 47.0	14 57.5	11♒ 7.9	6 27.6	29 36.5	9 55.8	15 6.2	27 16.3	28 24.1	9 39.6	22 43.0
7 M	14 56 35.2	15 45.1	14 54.4	25 7.2	8 31.1	0♈40.9	10 40.1	15 0.4	27 19.4	28 27.5	9 39.1	22 43.8
8 T	15 0 31.8	16 43.2	14 51.2	8♓56.4	10 36.1	1 45.6	11 24.3	14 54.7	27 22.5	28 30.8	9 38.7	22 44.6
9 W	15 4 28.3	17 41.2	14 48.0	22 35.5	12 42.5	2 50.4	12 8.4	14 49.1	27 25.5	28 34.1	9 38.3	22 45.3
10 T	15 8 24.9	18 39.2	14 44.8	6♈ 4.5	14 50.1	3 55.4	12 52.5	14 43.7	27 28.3	28 37.4	9 37.9	22 46.2
11 F	15 12 21.4	19 37.2	14 41.7	19 22.9	16 58.9	5 0.6	13 36.5	14 38.5	27 31.1	28 40.6	9 37.5	22 47.0
12 S	15 16 18.0	20 35.2	14 38.5	2♉29.9	19 8.5	6 6.0	14 20.5	14 33.3	27 33.8	28 43.9	9 37.2	22 47.8
13 S	15 20 14.6	21 33.1	14 35.3	15 24.5	21 18.9	7 11.6	15 4.4	14 28.4	27 36.5	28 47.1	9 36.9	22 48.7
14 M	15 24 11.1	22 31.0	14 32.1	28 5.8	23 29.7	8 17.3	15 48.3	14 23.5	27 39.0	28 50.4	9 36.7	22 49.6
15 T	15 28 7.7	23 28.9	14 28.9	10♊33.5	25 40.8	9 23.1	16 32.1	14 18.9	27 41.4	28 53.6	9 36.5	22 50.5
16 W	15 32 4.2	24 26.8	14 25.8	22 48.1	27 51.9	10 29.2	17 15.8	14 14.4	27 43.8	28 56.8	9 36.3	22 51.5
17 T	15 36 0.8	25 24.6	14 22.6	4♋51.2	0♊ 2.6	11 35.3	17 59.6	14 10.0	27 46.0	28 59.9	9 36.1	22 52.4
18 F	15 39 57.3	26 22.4	14 19.4	16 45.3	2 12.8	12 41.7	18 43.2	14 5.8	27 48.1	29 3.1	9 36.0	22 53.4
19 S	15 43 53.9	27 20.2	14 16.2	28 33.9	4 22.1	13 48.1	19 26.8	14 1.7	27 50.2	29 6.2	9 35.9	22 54.4
20 S	15 47 50.4	28 18.0	14 13.1	10♌21.5	6 30.2	14 54.7	20 10.3	13 57.9	27 52.2	29 9.3	9 35.9	22 55.4
21 M	15 51 47.0	29 15.7	14 9.9	22 13.0	8 37.0	16 1.4	20 53.8	13 54.2	27 54.0	29 12.4	9 35.8	22 56.5
22 T	15 55 43.6	0♊13.4	14 6.7	4♍13.8	10 42.1	17 8.3	21 37.3	13 50.6	27 55.8	29 15.5	9D35.8	22 57.5
23 W	15 59 40.1	1 11.1	14 3.5	16 29.4	12 45.3	18 15.3	22 20.7	13 47.3	27 57.5	29 18.5	9 35.9	22 58.6
24 T	16 3 36.7	2 8.7	14 0.4	29 4.8	14 46.5	19 22.4	23 4.0	13 44.0	27 59.1	29 21.6	9 35.9	22 59.7
25 F	16 7 33.2	3 6.4	13 57.2	12♎ 4.2	16 45.4	20 29.6	23 47.2	13 41.0	28 0.5	29 24.6	9 36.0	23 0.8
26 S	16 11 29.8	4 4.0	13 54.0	25 29.9	18 42.0	21 36.9	24 30.5	13 38.2	28 1.9	29 27.5	9 36.2	23 1.9
27 S	16 15 26.4	5 1.6	13 50.8	9♏22.5	20 36.1	22 44.4	25 13.6	13 35.5	28 3.2	29 30.5	9 36.4	23 3.1
28 M	16 19 22.9	5 59.1	13 47.6	23 39.4	22 27.6	23 52.0	25 56.7	13 33.0	28 4.4	29 33.4	9 36.6	23 4.2
29 T	16 23 19.4	6 56.6	13 44.5	8♐15.5	24 16.4	24 59.6	26 39.8	13 30.6	28 5.5	29 36.3	9 36.8	23 5.4
30 W	16 27 16.0	7 54.2	13 41.3	23 3.6	26 2.5	26 7.5	27 22.8	13 28.5	28 6.5	29 39.2	9 37.1	23 6.6
31 T	16 31 12.6	8 51.7	13 38.1	7♑55.3	27 45.8	27 15.4	28 5.7	13 26.5	28 7.4	29 42.1	9 37.4	23 7.8

DECLINATION

DAY	EPHEMERIS SIDEREAL TIME h m s	☉ ° ′	☊ ° ′	☽ ° ′	☿ ° ′	♀ ° ′	♂ ° ′	♃ ° ′	♄ ° ′	♅ ° ′	♆ ° ′	♇ ° ′
1 T	14 32 55.9	14N48.1	16S16.6	24S46.0	8N35.9	3S 2.6	13N19.8	4S43.0	13S36.2	10N18.9	8N46.6	22N55.9
4 F	14 44 45.6	15 42.1	16 19.4	25 31.0	11 1.0	1 58.5	14 5.0	4 36.1	13 33.1	10 22.5	8 47.3	22 55.7
7 M	14 56 35.2	16 33.7	16 22.2	12 18.0	13 27.8	0 52.5	14 48.9	4 29.8	13 30.2	10 26.1	8 47.8	22 55.4
10 T	15 8 24.9	17 22.9	16 25.0	6N 1.2	15 52.6	0N15.3	15 31.5	4 23.9	13 27.7	10 29.6	8 48.2	22 55.1
13 S	15 20 14.6	18 9.6	16 27.8	21 14.5	18 10.9	1 24.4	16 12.6	4 18.5	13 25.4	10 33.0	8 48.5	22 54.8
16 W	15 32 4.2	18 53.4	16 30.6	27 8.3	20 17.1	2 34.5	16 52.2	4 13.7	13 23.4	10 36.4	8 48.7	22 54.4
19 S	15 43 53.9	19 34.4	16 33.3	21 42.8	22 6.1	3 45.4	17 30.3	4 9.4	13 21.7	10 39.8	8 48.8	22 54.1
22 T	15 55 43.6	20 12.4	16 36.1	8 15.8	23 33.6	4 56.7	18 6.9	4 5.8	13 20.3	10 43.0	8 48.7	22 53.6
25 F	16 7 33.2	20 47.2	16 38.8	8S45.9	24 37.5	6 8.2	18 41.8	4 2.7	13 19.2	10 46.2	8 48.6	22 53.2
28 M	16 19 22.9	21 18.9	16 41.6	23 29.5	25 17.8	7 19.5	19 15.0	4 0.3	13 18.5	10 49.3	8 48.4	22 52.7
31 T	16 31 12.6	21 47.2	16 44.3	26 4.2	25 36.0	8 30.3	19 46.6	3 58.4	13 18.0	10 52.3	8 48.0	22 52.2

JUNE 1934

LONGITUDE

DAY	EPHEMERIS SIDEREAL TIME h m s	☉ ° ′	☊ ° ′	☽ ° ′	☿ ° ′	♀ ° ′	♂ ° ′	♃ ° ′	♄ ° ′	♅ ° ′	♆ ° ′	♇ ° ′
1 F	16 35 9.1	9♊49.2	13♒34.9	22♑42.8	29♊26.3	28♈23.4	28♉48.6	13♎24.7	28♒ 8.2	29♈44.9	9♍37.7	23♋ 9.0
2 S	16 39 5.7	10 46.6	13 31.8	7♒19.5	1♋ 3.9	29 31.5	29 31.5	13R23.0	28 8.9	29 47.7	9 38.1	23 10.3
3 S	16 43 2.2	11 44.1	13 28.6	21 41.2	2 38.7	0♉39.7	0♊14.3	13 21.6	28 9.5	29 50.4	9 38.5	23 11.5
4 M	16 46 58.8	12 41.5	13 25.4	5♓45.8	4 10.5	1 48.1	0 57.0	13 20.3	28 10.1	29 53.2	9 38.9	23 12.8
5 T	16 50 55.4	13 39.0	13 22.2	19 33.0	5 39.4	2 56.5	1 39.7	13 19.2	28 10.5	29 55.9	9 39.4	23 14.1
6 W	16 54 51.9	14 36.4	13 19.1	3♈ 3.3	7 5.3	4 5.0	2 22.3	13 18.3	28 10.8	29 58.6	9 39.8	23 15.4
7 T	16 58 48.5	15 33.8	13 15.9	16 18.0	8 28.2	5 13.6	3 4.9	13 17.6	28 11.0	0♉ 1.2	9 40.4	23 16.7
8 F	17 2 45.0	16 31.2	13 12.7	29 18.6	9 48.1	6 22.4	3 47.4	13 17.0	28 11.1	0 3.8	9 40.9	23 18.0
9 S	17 6 41.6	17 28.6	13 9.5	12♉ 6.1	11 4.9	7 31.2	4 29.9	13 16.7	28 11.1	0 6.4	9 41.5	23 19.4
10 S	17 10 38.1	18 26.0	13 6.4	24 41.5	12 18.6	8 40.0	5 12.4	13 16.5	28R11.0	0 9.0	9 42.1	23 20.8
11 M	17 14 34.7	19 23.4	13 3.2	7♊ 5.5	13 29.1	9 49.0	5 54.7	13 16.5	28 10.9	0 11.5	9 42.8	23 22.1
12 T	17 18 31.3	20 20.8	12 60.0	19 18.9	14 36.3	10 58.0	6 37.1	13D16.6	28 10.6	0 14.0	9 43.5	23 23.5
13 W	17 22 27.8	21 18.1	12 56.8	1♋22.9	15 40.2	12 7.1	7 19.3	13 17.0	28 10.2	0 16.4	9 44.2	23 24.9
14 T	17 26 24.4	22 15.4	12 53.6	13 18.8	16 40.8	13 16.3	8 1.6	13 17.5	28 9.7	0 18.9	9 44.9	23 26.3
15 F	17 30 20.9	23 12.8	12 50.5	25 8.7	17 37.8	14 25.6	8 43.7	13 18.2	28 9.1	0 21.2	9 45.7	23 27.8
16 S	17 34 17.5	24 10.1	12 47.3	6♌55.5	18 31.4	15 35.0	9 25.8	13 19.1	28 8.5	0 23.6	9 46.5	23 29.2
17 S	17 38 14.1	25 7.4	12 44.1	18 42.5	19 21.2	16 44.4	10 7.9	13 20.2	28 7.7	0 25.9	9 47.3	23 30.6
18 M	17 42 10.6	26 4.7	12 40.9	0♍33.9	20 7.4	17 53.9	10 49.9	13 21.5	28 6.8	0 28.2	9 48.2	23 32.1
19 T	17 46 7.2	27 2.0	12 37.8	12 34.4	20 49.7	19 3.4	11 31.8	13 22.9	28 5.9	0 30.4	9 49.1	23 33.6
20 W	17 50 3.7	27 59.2	12 34.6	24 48.9	21 28.0	20 13.0	12 13.7	13 24.5	28 4.8	0 32.6	9 50.0	23 35.0
21 T	17 54 0.3	28 56.5	12 31.4	7♎22.5	22 2.2	21 22.7	12 55.5	13 26.3	28 3.7	0 34.8	9 51.0	23 36.5
22 F	17 57 56.8	29 53.7	12 28.2	20 19.4	22 32.3	22 32.5	13 37.3	13 28.2	28 2.4	0 36.9	9 52.0	23 38.0
23 S	18 1 53.4	0♋50.9	12 25.1	3♏43.3	22 58.1	23 42.3	14 19.1	13 30.4	28 1.1	0 39.0	9 53.0	23 39.5
24 S	18 5 50.0	1 48.2	12 21.9	17 35.4	23 19.5	24 52.2	15 0.7	13 32.7	27 59.6	0 41.1	9 54.1	23 41.1
25 M	18 9 46.5	2 45.4	12 18.7	1♐55.0	23 36.5	26 2.1	15 42.4	13 35.1	27 58.1	0 43.1	9 55.1	23 42.6
26 T	18 13 43.0	3 42.6	12 15.5	16 38.0	23 48.9	27 12.1	16 23.9	13 37.8	27 56.5	0 45.0	9 56.2	23 44.1
27 W	18 17 39.6	4 39.8	12 12.4	1♑37.7	23 56.8	28 22.2	17 5.4	13 40.6	27 54.8	0 47.0	9 57.4	23 45.6
28 T	18 21 36.2	5 37.0	12 9.2	16 45.3	24 0.0	29 32.4	17 46.9	13 43.6	27 53.0	0 48.9	9 58.5	23 47.2
29 F	18 25 32.8	6 34.2	12 6.0	1♒51.3	23R58.7	0♊42.6	18 28.3	13 46.7	27 51.1	0 50.7	9 59.7	23 48.7
30 S	18 29 29.3	7 31.3	12 2.8	16 47.0	23 52.7	1 52.9	19 9.7	13 50.0	27 49.1	0 52.5	10 0.9	23 50.3

DECLINATION

DAY	EPHEMERIS SIDEREAL TIME h m s	☉ ° ′	☊ ° ′	☽ ° ′	☿ ° ′	♀ ° ′	♂ ° ′	♃ ° ′	♄ ° ′	♅ ° ′	♆ ° ′	♇ ° ′
1 F	16 35 9.1	21N55.9	16S45.2	23S12.4	25N37.6	8N53.8	19N56.7	3S58.0	13S17.9	10N53.3	8N47.9	22N52.1
4 M	16 46 58.8	22 19.7	16 48.0	7 29.6	25 30.4	10 3.6	20 25.9	3 57.0	13 17.8	10 56.2	8 47.3	22 51.5
7 T	16 58 48.5	22 40.0	16 50.7	10N39.0	25 7.7	11 12.1	20 53.3	3 56.7	13 18.0	10 59.0	8 46.7	22 51.0
10 S	17 10 38.1	22 56.8	16 53.4	23 45.6	24 32.5	12 19.2	21 18.9	3 57.0	13 18.6	11 1.7	8 46.0	22 50.4
13 W	17 22 27.8	23 9.8	16 56.1	26 43.6	23 47.8	13 24.4	21 42.7	3 57.9	13 19.4	11 4.2	8 45.2	22 49.8
16 S	17 34 17.5	23 19.3	16 58.8	18 54.5	22 56.3	14 27.5	22 4.6	3 59.5	13 20.6	11 6.7	8 44.2	22 49.2
19 T	17 46 7.2	23 25.0	17 1.5	4 20.3	22 1.0	15 28.1	22 24.6	4 1.7	13 22.0	11 9.1	8 43.2	22 48.6
22 F	17 57 56.8	23 27.0	17 4.2	12S25.7	21 4.5	16 25.9	22 42.6	4 4.5	13 23.8	11 11.3	8 42.1	22 48.0
25 M	18 9 46.5	23 25.2	17 6.8	25 17.3	20 9.5	17 20.6	22 58.8	4 7.9	13 25.8	11 13.4	8 40.8	22 47.4
28 T	18 21 36.2	23 19.8	17 9.5	24 29.4	19 18.9	18 12.0	23 13.1	4 11.9	13 28.1	11 15.3	8 39.5	22 46.7

JULY 1934

DAY	EPHEMERIS SIDEREAL TIME	☉	☊	☽	☿	♀	♂	♃	♄	♅	♆	♇
	h m s	° ′	° ′	° ′	° ′	° ′	° ′	° ′	° ′	° ′	° ′	° ′
LONGITUDE												
1 S	18 33 25.9	8♋28.5	11♒59.6	1♓25.7	23♋42.3	3♊ 3.2	19♊51.0	13♎53.5	27♒47.0	0♉54.3	10♍ 2.2	23♋51.9
2 M	18 37 22.4	9 25.7	11 56.5	15 43.2	23R 27.5	4 13.6	20 32.3	13 57.1	27R 44.9	0 56.0	10 3.4	23 53.4
3 T	18 41 19.0	10 22.9	11 53.3	29 37.6	23 8.5	5 24.1	21 13.5	14 1.0	27 42.7	0 57.7	10 4.7	23 55.0
4 W	18 45 15.5	11 20.1	11 50.1	13♈ 9.3	22 45.7	6 34.7	21 54.6	14 4.9	27 40.3	0 59.3	10 6.1	23 56.6
5 T	18 49 12.1	12 17.3	11 46.9	26 19.7	22 19.1	7 45.3	22 35.8	14 9.0	27 37.9	1 0.9	10 7.4	23 58.2
6 F	18 53 8.7	13 14.5	11 43.8	9♉11.2	21 49.4	8 55.9	23 16.8	14 13.3	27 35.4	1 2.5	10 8.8	23 59.8
7 S	18 57 5.2	14 11.7	11 40.6	21 46.5	21 16.8	10 6.7	23 57.8	14 17.8	27 32.8	1 4.0	10 10.2	24 1.4
8 S	19 1 1.8	15 9.0	11 37.4	4♊ 8.1	20 41.8	11 17.5	24 38.8	14 22.4	27 30.2	1 5.4	10 11.6	24 3.0
9 M	19 4 58.3	16 6.2	11 34.2	16 18.5	20 5.1	12 28.3	25 19.7	14 27.1	27 27.4	1 6.8	10 13.0	24 4.6
10 T	19 8 54.9	17 3.4	11 31.1	28 20.0	19 27.2	13 39.2	26 0.6	14 32.0	27 24.6	1 8.2	10 14.5	24 6.2
11 W	19 12 51.5	18 0.6	11 27.9	10♋14.7	18 48.7	14 50.2	26 41.4	14 37.1	27 21.7	1 9.5	10 16.0	24 7.8
12 T	19 16 48.1	18 57.9	11 24.7	22 4.6	18 10.4	16 1.2	27 22.2	14 42.3	27 18.8	1 10.8	10 17.6	24 9.4
13 F	19 20 44.6	19 55.1	11 21.5	3♌51.8	17 32.8	17 12.3	28 2.9	14 47.7	27 15.7	1 12.1	10 19.1	24 11.0
14 S	19 24 41.1	20 52.4	11 18.4	15 38.7	16 56.6	18 23.4	28 43.6	14 53.2	27 12.6	1 13.3	10 20.7	24 12.7
15 S	19 28 37.7	21 49.6	11 15.2	27 28.0	16 22.5	19 34.5	29 24.2	14 58.8	27 9.4	1 14.4	10 22.3	24 14.3
16 M	19 32 34.2	22 46.8	11 12.0	9♍22.7	15 51.1	20 45.8	0♋ 4.7	15 4.6	27 6.1	1 15.5	10 23.9	24 15.9
17 T	19 36 30.8	23 44.1	11 8.8	21 26.3	15 22.9	21 57.1	0 45.2	15 10.6	27 2.8	1 16.5	10 25.5	24 17.5
18 W	19 40 27.4	24 41.4	11 5.7	3♎42.7	14 58.5	23 8.4	1 25.7	15 16.7	26 59.4	1 17.5	10 27.2	24 19.1
19 T	19 44 23.9	25 38.6	11 2.5	16 16.0	14 38.4	24 19.8	2 6.1	15 22.9	26 55.9	1 18.5	10 28.9	24 20.8
20 F	19 48 20.5	26 35.9	10 59.3	29 10.1	14 23.0	25 31.2	2 46.4	15 29.3	26 52.4	1 19.4	10 30.6	24 22.4
21 S	19 52 17.0	27 33.1	10 56.1	12♏28.4	14 12.5	26 42.7	3 26.7	15 35.8	26 48.8	1 20.3	10 32.3	24 24.0
22 S	19 56 13.6	28 30.4	10 52.9	26 13.1	14 7.4	27 54.2	4 7.0	15 42.5	26 45.2	1 21.1	10 34.0	24 25.6
23 M	20 0 10.2	29 27.7	10 49.8	10♐24.6	14D 7.8	29 5.8	4 47.2	15 49.2	26 41.5	1 21.8	10 35.8	24 27.2
24 T	20 4 6.7	0♌25.0	10 46.6	25 0.9	14 14.0	0♋17.5	5 27.3	15 56.1	26 37.7	1 22.5	10 37.6	24 28.9
25 W	20 8 3.3	1 22.3	10 43.4	9♑57.1	14 26.0	1 29.1	6 7.4	16 3.2	26 33.9	1 23.2	10 39.4	24 30.5
26 T	20 11 59.8	2 19.5	10 40.2	25 6.1	14 43.9	2 40.9	6 47.5	16 10.4	26 30.0	1 23.8	10 41.2	24 32.1
27 F	20 15 56.4	3 16.9	10 37.1	10♒18.7	15 7.9	3 52.7	7 27.5	16 17.7	26 26.1	1 24.4	10 43.0	24 33.7
28 S	20 19 53.0	4 14.2	10 33.9	25 25.3	15 37.9	5 4.6	8 7.4	16 25.1	26 22.1	1 24.9	10 44.9	24 35.3
29 S	20 23 49.5	5 11.5	10 30.7	10♓17.3	16 14.0	6 16.5	8 47.3	16 32.6	26 18.1	1 25.4	10 46.8	24 36.9
30 M	20 27 46.0	6 8.9	10 27.5	24 48.1	16 56.0	7 28.4	9 27.2	16 40.3	26 14.0	1 25.8	10 48.7	24 38.5
31 T	20 31 42.6	7 6.2	10 24.4	8♈53.9	17 44.0	8 40.5	10 7.0	16 48.1	26 9.9	1 26.2	10 50.6	24 40.1
DECLINATION												
1 S	18 33 25.9	23N10.7	17S12.2	9S13.8	18N35.1	18N59.6	23N25.4	4S16.5	13S30.7	11N17.2	8N38.1	22N46.1
4 W	18 45 15.5	22 57.9	17 14.8	9N28.1	18 0.5	19 43.2	23 35.8	4 21.6	13 33.6	11 18.9	8 36.6	22 45.4
7 S	18 57 5.2	22 41.6	17 17.5	23 9.9	17 37.0	20 22.6	23 44.2	4 27.3	13 36.7	11 20.4	8 35.0	22 44.7
10 T	19 8 54.9	22 21.6	17 20.1	26 57.1	17 25.8	20 57.4	23 50.8	4 33.5	13 40.0	11 21.9	8 33.3	22 44.0
13 F	19 20 44.6	21 58.2	17 22.7	19 51.8	17 27.1	21 27.4	23 55.4	4 40.2	13 43.5	11 23.1	8 31.5	22 43.4
16 M	19 32 34.2	21 31.5	17 25.3	5 40.3	17 40.2	21 52.3	23 58.1	4 47.4	13 47.3	11 24.3	8 29.7	22 42.7
19 T	19 44 23.9	21 1.4	17 28.0	10S51.1	18 3.2	22 12.1	23 58.9	4 55.1	13 51.3	11 25.3	8 27.7	22 42.0
22 S	19 56 13.6	20 28.1	17 30.6	24 15.0	18 33.7	22 26.4	23 57.9	5 3.3	13 55.4	11 26.1	8 25.7	22 41.3
25 W	20 8 3.3	19 51.8	17 33.2	25 44.5	19 8.1	22 35.2	23 55.0	5 11.8	13 59.7	11 26.8	8 23.7	22 40.7
28 S	20 19 53.0	19 12.4	17 35.8	11 44.6	19 42.6	22 38.3	23 50.4	5 20.9	14 4.1	11 27.3	8 21.6	22 40.0
31 T	20 31 42.6	18 30.3	17 38.3	7N41.2	20 12.7	22 35.7	23 43.9	5 30.3	14 8.6	11 27.7	8 19.4	22 39.4

AUGUST 1934

DAY	EPHEMERIS SIDEREAL TIME	☉	☊	☽	☿	♀	♂	♃	♄	♅	♆	♇
LONGITUDE												
1 W	20 35 39.2	8♌ 3.6	10♒21.2	22♈33.1	18♋37.8	9♋52.5	10♋46.8	16♎56.0	26♒ 5.8	1♉26.5	10♍52.5	24♋41.7
2 T	20 39 35.7	9 1.0	10 18.0	5♉46.8	19 37.4	11 4.7	11 26.5	17 4.1	26R 1.6	1 26.8	10 54.4	24 43.2
3 F	20 43 32.3	9 58.4	10 14.8	18 37.2	20 42.7	12 16.9	12 6.1	17 12.2	25 57.4	1 27.0	10 56.4	24 44.8
4 S	20 47 28.8	10 55.9	10 11.6	1♊ 7.7	21 53.5	13 29.1	12 45.8	17 20.5	25 53.1	1 27.2	10 58.4	24 46.4
5 S	20 51 25.4	11 53.3	10 8.5	13 22.3	23 9.7	14 41.4	13 25.3	17 28.9	25 48.8	1 27.3	11 0.4	24 47.9
6 M	20 55 22.0	12 50.8	10 5.3	25 24.8	24 31.0	15 53.8	14 4.9	17 37.4	25 44.5	1 27.4	11 2.4	24 49.5
7 T	20 59 18.5	13 48.3	10 2.1	7♋18.9	25 57.3	17 6.2	14 44.3	17 46.0	25 40.1	1 27.4	11 4.4	24 51.1
8 W	21 3 15.1	14 45.9	9 58.9	19 7.9	27 28.4	18 18.6	15 23.8	17 54.7	25 35.7	1R 27.4	11 6.4	24 52.6
9 T	21 7 11.6	15 43.4	9 55.8	0♌54.9	29 3.8	19 31.1	16 3.1	18 3.5	25 31.3	1 27.3	11 8.4	24 54.1
10 F	21 11 8.2	16 41.0	9 52.6	12 42.5	0♌43.5	20 43.7	16 42.5	18 12.5	25 26.9	1 27.2	11 10.5	24 55.7
11 S	21 15 4.7	17 38.5	9 49.4	24 33.1	2 26.9	21 56.3	17 21.8	18 21.5	25 22.5	1 27.1	11 12.6	24 57.2
12 S	21 19 1.3	18 36.1	9 46.2	6♍28.8	4 13.8	23 8.9	18 1.0	18 30.7	25 18.0	1 26.8	11 14.7	24 58.7
13 M	21 22 57.9	19 33.8	9 43.1	18 31.9	6 3.8	24 21.6	18 40.2	18 40.0	25 13.5	1 26.6	11 16.7	25 0.2
14 T	21 26 54.4	20 31.4	9 39.9	0♎44.5	7 56.5	25 34.3	19 19.3	18 49.3	25 9.0	1 26.3	11 18.9	25 1.7
15 W	21 30 51.0	21 29.1	9 36.7	13 9.0	9 51.5	26 47.1	19 58.4	18 58.8	25 4.5	1 25.9	11 21.0	25 3.2
16 T	21 34 47.5	22 26.7	9 33.5	25 48.0	11 48.4	27 60.0	20 37.4	19 8.3	24 60.0	1 25.5	11 23.1	25 4.6
17 F	21 38 44.0	23 24.4	9 30.3	8♏43.9	13 46.8	29 12.8	21 16.4	19 18.0	24 55.5	1 25.0	11 25.2	25 6.1
18 S	21 42 40.6	24 22.1	9 27.2	21 59.4	15 46.4	0♌25.8	21 55.3	19 27.7	24 51.0	1 24.5	11 27.4	25 7.5
19 S	21 46 37.2	25 19.8	9 24.0	5♐36.3	17 46.8	1 38.7	22 34.2	19 37.6	24 46.4	1 23.9	11 29.5	25 9.0
20 M	21 50 33.8	26 17.6	9 20.8	19 35.6	19 47.6	2 51.8	23 13.0	19 47.5	24 41.9	1 23.3	11 31.7	25 10.4
21 T	21 54 30.3	27 15.3	9 17.6	3♑56.9	21 48.6	4 4.8	23 51.8	19 57.6	24 37.4	1 22.7	11 33.8	25 11.8
22 W	21 58 26.8	28 13.1	9 14.5	18 37.7	23 49.5	5 17.9	24 30.5	20 7.7	24 32.9	1 22.0	11 36.0	25 13.2
23 T	22 2 23.4	29 10.9	9 11.3	3♒33.4	25 50.1	6 31.1	25 9.2	20 17.9	24 28.4	1 21.2	11 38.2	25 14.6
24 F	22 6 20.0	0♍ 8.7	9 8.1	18 37.0	27 50.2	7 44.3	25 47.8	20 28.2	24 23.9	1 20.5	11 40.4	25 16.0
25 S	22 10 16.5	1 6.6	9 4.9	3♓40.1	29 49.6	8 57.5	26 26.4	20 38.5	24 19.4	1 19.6	11 42.6	25 17.4
26 S	22 14 13.0	2 4.4	9 1.7	18 33.9	1♍48.2	10 10.8	27 5.0	20 49.0	24 15.0	1 18.7	11 44.8	25 18.7
27 M	22 18 9.6	3 2.3	8 58.6	3♈10.5	3 45.9	11 24.2	27 43.4	20 59.5	24 10.5	1 17.8	11 47.0	25 20.0
28 T	22 22 6.2	4 0.3	8 55.4	17 23.9	5 42.6	12 37.6	28 21.9	21 10.2	24 6.1	1 16.8	11 49.2	25 21.4
29 W	22 26 2.7	4 58.2	8 52.2	1♉10.7	7 38.2	13 51.0	29 0.3	21 20.9	24 1.7	1 15.8	11 51.4	25 22.7
30 T	22 29 59.3	5 56.2	8 49.0	14 30.3	9 32.7	15 4.5	29 38.6	21 31.6	23 57.3	1 14.8	11 53.6	25 24.0
31 F	22 33 55.8	6 54.2	8 45.9	27 24.1	11 26.0	16 18.0	0♌16.9	21 42.5	23 53.0	1 13.6	11 55.8	25 25.2
DECLINATION												
1 W	20 35 39.2	18N15.6	17S39.2	13N27.5	20N20.9	22N33.6	23N41.4	5S33.5	14S10.1	11N27.8	8N18.7	22N39.2
4 S	20 47 28.8	17 29.8	17 41.8	25 14.2	20 37.6	22 23.2	23 32.6	5 43.4	14 14.8	11 27.9	8 16.4	22 38.5
7 T	20 59 18.5	16 41.4	17 44.3	26 7.8	20 38.4	22 7.1	23 22.2	5 53.7	14 19.5	11 28.0	8 14.1	22 37.9
10 F	21 11 8.2	15 50.6	17 46.9	16 47.2	20 18.9	21 45.3	23 10.1	6 4.3	14 24.3	11 27.8	8 11.8	22 37.3
13 M	21 22 57.9	14 57.5	17 49.5	1 31.2	19 36.0	21 17.8	22 56.4	6 15.3	14 29.1	11 27.5	8 9.4	22 36.7
16 T	21 34 47.5	14 2.2	17 52.0	14S43.8	18 29.1	20 44.7	22 41.1	6 26.5	14 33.9	11 27.1	8 7.0	22 36.1
19 S	21 46 37.2	13 5.0	17 54.5	25 56.4	17 0.1	20 6.3	22 24.3	6 38.1	14 38.7	11 26.5	8 4.5	22 35.6
22 W	21 58 26.8	12 5.9	17 57.1	24 4.8	15 12.8	19 22.7	22 6.1	6 49.9	14 43.4	11 25.8	8 2.1	22 35.0
25 S	22 10 16.5	11 5.1	17 59.6	8 12.7	13 11.4	18 34.1	21 46.4	7 1.9	14 48.1	11 24.9	7 59.6	22 34.5
28 T	22 22 6.2	10 2.7	18 2.1	11N18.1	11 0.5	17 40.7	21 25.4	7 14.2	14 52.7	11 23.9	7 57.1	22 34.1
31 F	22 33 55.8	8 58.9	18 4.6	24 27.3	8 43.6	16 42.8	21 3.0	7 26.7	14 57.2	11 22.7	7 54.5	22 33.6

SEPTEMBER 1934

DAY	EPHEMERIS SIDEREAL TIME	☉	☊	☽	☿	♀	♂	♃	♄	♅	♆	♇
	h m s	° ′	° ′	° ′	° ′	° ′	° ′	° ′	° ′	° ′	° ′	° ′
						LONGITUDE						
1 S	22 37 52.4	7♍52.3	8♒42.7	9♓55.4	13♍18.1	17♌31.6	0♌55.2	21♎53.4	23♒48.6	1♉12.5	11♍58.0	25♋26.5
2 S	22 41 48.9	8 50.3	8 39.5	22 8.6	15 9.0	18 45.2	1 33.4	22 4.4	23R44.3	1R11.3	12 0.3	25 27.8
3 M	22 45 45.5	9 48.5	8 36.3	4♋ 8.3	16 58.7	19 58.9	2 11.5	22 15.5	23 40.1	1 10.1	12 2.5	25 29.0
4 T	22 49 42.0	10 46.6	8 33.1	15 59.4	18 47.1	21 12.6	2 49.6	22 26.7	23 35.8	1 8.8	12 4.7	25 30.2
5 W	22 53 38.6	11 44.8	8 30.0	27 46.5	20 34.4	22 26.4	3 27.7	22 37.9	23 31.7	1 7.5	12 6.9	25 31.4
6 T	22 57 35.1	12 43.0	8 26.8	9♌33.6	22 20.4	23 40.2	4 5.7	22 49.2	23 27.5	1 6.1	12 9.2	25 32.6
7 F	23 1 31.7	13 41.2	8 23.6	21 24.4	24 5.3	24 54.0	4 43.7	23 0.6	23 23.4	1 4.7	12 11.4	25 33.7
8 S	23 5 28.3	14 39.5	8 20.4	3♍21.8	25 48.9	26 7.9	5 21.6	23 12.0	23 19.3	1 3.3	12 13.6	25 34.9
9 S	23 9 24.8	15 37.8	8 17.3	15 27.8	27 31.4	27 21.9	5 59.4	23 23.5	23 15.3	1 1.8	12 15.9	25 36.0
10 M	23 13 21.3	16 36.1	8 14.1	27 44.2	29 12.7	28 35.8	6 37.2	23 35.1	23 11.4	1 0.2	12 18.1	25 37.1
11 T	23 17 17.9	17 34.5	8 10.9	10♎12.1	0♎53.0	29 49.8	7 15.0	23 46.7	23 7.4	0 58.7	12 20.3	25 38.2
12 W	23 21 14.5	18 32.9	8 7.7	22 52.3	2 32.0	1♍ 3.9	7 52.7	23 58.4	23 3.6	0 57.1	12 22.5	25 39.3
13 T	23 25 11.1	19 31.3	8 4.6	5♏45.3	4 10.0	2 18.0	8 30.3	24 10.1	22 59.8	0 55.4	12 24.7	25 40.4
14 F	23 29 7.6	20 29.7	8 1.4	18 51.8	5 46.9	3 32.1	9 7.9	24 21.9	22 56.0	0 53.8	12 26.9	25 41.4
15 S	23 33 4.1	21 28.2	7 58.2	2♐12.4	7 22.7	4 46.2	9 45.5	24 33.8	22 52.3	0 52.0	12 29.1	25 42.4
16 S	23 37 0.7	22 26.7	7 55.0	15 47.9	8 57.5	6 0.4	10 22.9	24 45.7	22 48.7	0 50.3	12 31.4	25 43.4
17 M	23 40 57.3	23 25.2	7 51.8	29 39.0	10 31.1	7 14.6	11 0.4	24 57.7	22 45.1	0 48.5	12 33.6	25 44.4
18 T	23 44 53.8	24 23.8	7 48.7	13♑45.8	12 3.8	8 28.9	11 37.7	25 9.7	22 41.6	0 46.7	12 35.7	25 45.3
19 W	23 48 50.3	25 22.4	7 45.5	28 7.3	13 35.4	9 43.1	12 15.1	25 21.7	22 38.2	0 44.9	12 37.9	25 46.3
20 T	23 52 46.9	26 21.0	7 42.3	12♒41.4	15 5.9	10 57.4	12 52.3	25 33.9	22 34.8	0 43.0	12 40.1	25 47.2
21 F	23 56 43.5	27 19.6	7 39.1	27 23.8	16 35.4	12 11.8	13 29.5	25 46.0	22 31.5	0 41.1	12 42.3	25 48.1
22 S	0 0 40.0	28 18.3	7 36.0	12♓ 9.0	18 3.9	13 26.2	14 6.7	25 58.3	22 28.3	0 39.1	12 44.4	25 48.9
23 S	0 4 36.6	29 17.0	7 32.8	26 49.7	19 31.3	14 40.6	14 43.8	26 10.5	22 25.1	0 37.1	12 46.6	25 49.8
24 M	0 8 33.1	0♎15.7	7 29.6	11♈18.5	20 57.6	15 55.0	15 20.9	26 22.8	22 22.1	0 35.1	12 48.7	25 50.6
25 T	0 12 29.7	1 14.4	7 26.4	25 29.0	22 22.9	17 9.5	15 57.9	26 35.2	22 19.1	0 33.1	12 50.9	25 51.4
26 W	0 16 26.3	2 13.2	7 23.2	9♉16.4	23 47.1	18 24.0	16 34.8	26 47.6	22 16.1	0 31.1	12 53.0	25 52.2
27 T	0 20 22.8	3 12.1	7 20.1	22 38.3	25 10.2	19 38.6	17 11.7	27 0.0	22 13.3	0 29.0	12 55.1	25 53.0
28 F	0 24 19.4	4 10.9	7 16.9	5♊34.9	26 32.1	20 53.1	17 48.6	27 12.5	22 10.5	0 26.9	12 57.2	25 53.7
29 S	0 28 15.9	5 9.8	7 13.7	18 8.5	27 52.8	22 7.7	18 25.3	27 25.0	22 7.8	0 24.7	12 59.3	25 54.4
30 S	0 32 12.4	6 8.8	7 10.5	0♋22.9	29 12.3	23 22.4	19 2.1	27 37.6	22 5.2	0 22.6	13 1.4	25 55.1
						DECLINATION						
1 S	22 37 52.4	8N37.3	18S 5.4	26N26.5	7N57.1	16N22.5	20N55.3	7S30.9	14S58.7	11N22.3	7N53.7	22N33.5
4 T	22 49 42.0	7 31.7	18 7.9	24 36.8	5 36.6	15 18.9	20 31.2	7 43.7	15 3.0	11 21.0	7 51.2	22 33.0
7 F	23 1 31.7	6 25.1	18 10.4	13 23.8	3 15.8	14 11.4	20 6.0	7 56.6	15 7.2	11 19.5	7 48.6	22 32.7
10 M	23 13 21.3	5 17.4	18 12.9	2S37.7	0 56.3	13 0.4	19 39.6	8 9.7	15 11.2	11 17.9	7 46.1	22 32.3
13 T	23 25 11.1	4 9.0	18 15.3	18 18.0	1S20.7	11 46.0	19 12.2	8 22.9	15 15.0	11 16.2	7 43.6	22 32.0
16 S	23 37 0.7	2 59.9	18 17.8	26 49.7	3 34.4	10 28.6	18 43.7	8 36.3	15 18.7	11 14.4	7 41.1	22 31.7
19 W	23 48 50.3	1 50.4	18 20.3	21 32.1	5 43.9	9 8.6	18 14.3	8 49.7	15 22.1	11 12.5	7 38.6	22 31.5
22 S	0 0 40.0	0 40.5	18 22.7	4 25.7	7 48.5	7 46.2	17 44.0	9 3.3	15 25.3	11 10.4	7 36.2	22 31.2
25 T	0 12 29.7	0S29.6	18 25.1	14N28.8	9 47.4	6 21.8	17 12.8	9 16.9	15 28.2	11 8.3	7 33.8	22 31.1
28 F	0 24 19.4	1 39.8	18 27.6	25 43.7	11 40.1	4 55.7	16 40.8	9 30.6	15 30.9	11 6.1	7 31.4	22 30.9

OCTOBER 1934

DAY	EPHEMERIS SIDEREAL TIME	☉	☊	☽	☿	♀	♂	♃	♄	♅	♆	♇
						LONGITUDE						
1 M	0 36 9.0	7♎ 7.8	7♒ 7.3	12♋22.9	0♏30.5	24♍37.1	19♌38.8	27♎50.1	22♒ 2.7	0♉20.4	13♍ 3.5	25♋55.8
2 T	0 40 5.6	8 6.8	7 4.2	24 13.8	1 47.4	25 51.8	20 15.4	28 2.8	22R 0.2	0R18.2	13 5.6	25 56.5
3 W	0 44 2.1	9 5.9	7 1.0	6♌ 1.0	3 2.9	27 6.5	20 51.9	28 15.4	21 57.9	0 15.9	13 7.6	25 57.1
4 T	0 47 58.7	10 5.0	6 57.8	17 49.7	4 16.8	28 21.3	21 28.5	28 28.1	21 55.6	0 13.7	13 9.6	25 57.7
5 F	0 51 55.2	11 4.1	6 54.6	29 44.5	5 29.2	29 36.0	22 4.9	28 40.9	21 53.4	0 11.4	13 11.7	25 58.3
6 S	0 55 51.8	12 3.3	6 51.5	11♍49.1	6 39.9	0♎50.9	22 41.3	28 53.6	21 51.4	0 9.1	13 13.7	25 58.8
7 S	0 59 48.3	13 2.5	6 48.3	24 6.5	7 48.8	2 5.7	23 17.6	29 6.4	21 49.4	0 6.8	13 15.7	25 59.4
8 M	1 3 44.9	14 1.7	6 45.1	6♎38.3	8 55.7	3 20.6	23 53.9	29 19.2	21 47.5	0 4.5	13 17.7	25 59.9
9 T	1 7 41.4	15 1.0	6 41.9	19 25.1	10 0.5	4 35.4	24 30.1	29 32.1	21 45.7	0 2.2	13 19.6	26 0.4
10 W	1 11 38.0	16 0.3	6 38.8	2♏26.6	11 3.0	5 50.4	25 6.3	29 44.9	21 43.9	29♈59.8	13 21.6	26 0.8
11 T	1 15 34.6	16 59.7	6 35.6	15 41.4	12 3.1	7 5.3	25 42.3	29 57.8	21 42.3	29 57.4	13 23.5	26 1.3
12 F	1 19 31.1	17 59.1	6 32.4	29 7.9	13 0.4	8 20.2	26 18.3	0♏10.8	21 40.8	29 55.0	13 25.4	26 1.7
13 S	1 23 27.6	18 58.5	6 29.2	12♐44.5	13 54.7	9 35.2	26 54.3	0 23.7	21 39.4	29 52.6	13 27.3	26 2.0
14 S	1 27 24.2	19 57.9	6 26.0	26 29.9	14 45.7	10 50.2	27 30.2	0 36.6	21 38.0	29 50.2	13 29.2	26 2.4
15 M	1 31 20.8	20 57.4	6 22.9	10♑23.2	15 33.2	12 5.2	28 6.0	0 49.6	21 36.8	29 47.8	13 31.0	26 2.7
16 T	1 35 17.3	21 56.9	6 19.7	24 23.9	16 16.7	13 20.2	28 41.7	1 2.6	21 35.7	29 45.4	13 32.9	26 3.0
17 W	1 39 13.9	22 56.4	6 16.5	8♒31.6	16 55.8	14 35.3	29 17.4	1 15.6	21 34.7	29 43.0	13 34.7	26 3.3
18 T	1 43 10.4	23 55.9	6 13.3	22 45.4	17 30.2	15 50.3	29 53.0	1 28.6	21 33.7	29 40.5	13 36.5	26 3.6
19 F	1 47 7.0	24 55.5	6 10.1	7♓ 3.5	17 59.3	17 5.4	0♍28.6	1 41.7	21 32.9	29 38.1	13 38.3	26 3.8
20 S	1 51 3.5	25 55.1	6 7.0	21 22.9	18 22.7	18 20.5	1 4.1	1 54.7	21 32.2	29 35.6	13 40.0	26 4.0
21 S	1 55 0.1	26 54.8	6 3.8	5♈39.2	18 39.8	19 35.6	1 39.5	2 7.8	21 31.5	29 33.2	13 41.8	26 4.2
22 M	1 58 56.6	27 54.5	6 0.6	19 47.2	18 50.0	20 50.7	2 14.8	2 20.9	21 31.0	29 30.7	13 43.5	26 4.4
23 T	2 2 53.2	28 54.2	5 57.4	3♉41.7	18 52.8	22 5.8	2 50.1	2 33.9	21 30.6	29 28.3	13 45.2	26 4.5
24 W	2 6 49.7	29 53.9	5 54.3	17 18.2	18R47.6	23 20.9	3 25.3	2 47.0	21 30.2	29 25.8	13 46.9	26 4.6
25 T	2 10 46.3	0♏53.7	5 51.1	0♊33.8	18 33.9	24 36.1	4 0.4	3 0.1	21 30.0	29 23.4	13 48.5	26 4.7
26 F	2 14 42.9	1 53.5	5 47.9	13 27.5	18 11.4	25 51.3	4 35.5	3 13.2	21 29.9	29 20.9	13 50.2	26 4.8
27 S	2 18 39.4	2 53.3	5 44.7	26 0.3	17 39.7	27 6.5	5 10.5	3 26.3	21 29.9	29 18.4	13 51.8	26 4.8
28 S	2 22 36.0	3 53.2	5 41.6	8♋14.9	16 58.8	28 21.7	5 45.4	3 39.4	21D30.0	29 16.0	13 53.3	26 4.8
29 M	2 26 32.5	4 53.1	5 38.4	20 15.4	16 9.0	29 36.9	6 20.3	3 52.5	21 30.2	29 13.6	13 54.9	26R 4.8
30 T	2 30 29.1	5 53.1	5 35.2	2♌ 6.7	15 10.8	0♏52.1	6 55.0	4 5.6	21 30.5	29 11.1	13 56.4	26 4.7
31 W	2 34 25.6	6 53.1	5 32.0	13 54.4	14 5.2	2 7.4	7 29.7	4 18.7	21 30.8	29 8.7	13 57.9	26 4.7
						DECLINATION						
1 M	0 36 9.0	2S49.9	18S30.0	25N 7.2	13S25.7	3N28.2	16N 8.1	9S44.3	15S33.4	11N 3.8	7N29.0	22N30.8
4 T	0 47 58.7	3 59.7	18 32.4	14 42.4	15 3.3	1 59.6	15 34.6	9 58.1	15 35.5	11 1.5	7 26.7	22 30.8
7 S	0 59 48.3	5 9.1	18 34.8	0S59.7	16 31.7	0 30.2	15 0.6	10 11.9	15 37.4	10 59.1	7 24.5	22 30.8
10 W	1 11 38.0	6 18.0	18 37.2	17 1.7	17 49.5	0S59.5	14 25.9	10 25.6	15 39.0	10 56.6	7 22.3	22 30.8
13 S	1 23 27.6	7 26.1	18 39.6	26 24.7	18 54.8	2 29.3	13 50.8	10 39.4	15 40.4	10 54.1	7 20.2	22 30.9
16 T	1 35 17.3	8 33.2	18 41.9	22 20.8	19 45.0	3 58.9	13 15.2	10 53.1	15 41.4	10 51.6	7 18.1	22 31.0
19 F	1 47 7.0	9 39.3	18 44.3	6 34.7	20 16.6	5 27.8	12 39.2	11 6.8	15 42.1	10 49.0	7 16.1	22 31.2
22 M	1 58 56.6	10 44.0	18 46.7	12N10.7	20 24.7	6 55.7	12 2.8	11 20.4	15 42.5	10 46.4	7 14.2	22 31.4
25 T	2 10 46.3	11 47.4	18 49.0	24 44.3	20 3.1	8 22.4	11 26.2	11 33.9	15 42.6	10 43.8	7 12.3	22 31.7
28 S	2 22 36.0	12 49.1	18 51.4	25 31.0	19 5.4	9 47.4	10 49.2	11 47.3	15 42.4	10 41.3	7 10.6	22 31.9
31 W	2 34 25.6	13 49.1	18 53.7	15 57.9	17 29.2	11 10.5	10 12.1	12 0.7	15 41.9	10 38.7	7 8.9	22 32.3

NOVEMBER 1934

LONGITUDE

DAY	EPHEMERIS SIDEREAL TIME h m s	☉ ° ′	☊ ° ′	☽ ° ′	☿ ° ′	♀ ° ′	♂ ° ′	♃ ° ′	♄ ° ′	♅ ° ′	♆ ° ′	♇ ° ′
1 T	2 38 22.2	7♏53.1	5♒28.8	25♌44.0	12♏53.5	3♏22.6	8♍ 4.3	4♏31.8	21♒31.3	29♈ 6.3	13♍59.4	26♋ 4.6
2 F	2 42 18.7	8 53.2	5 25.7	7♍40.9	11R37.5	4 37.9	8 38.9	4 44.9	21 31.9	29R 3.8	14 0.9	26R 4.4
3 S	2 46 15.3	9 53.3	5 22.5	19 50.0	10 19.4	5 53.2	9 13.4	4 58.0	21 32.6	29 1.4	14 2.3	26 4.3
4 S	2 50 11.9	10 53.4	5 19.3	2♎15.2	9 1.6	7 8.5	9 47.7	5 11.1	21 33.5	28 59.1	14 3.7	26 4.1
5 M	2 54 8.4	11 53.6	5 16.1	14 59.0	7 46.6	8 23.8	10 22.0	5 24.2	21 34.4	28 56.7	14 5.1	26 3.9
6 T	2 58 5.0	12 53.8	5 13.0	28 2.5	6 36.7	9 39.2	10 56.2	5 37.3	21 35.4	28 54.3	14 6.4	26 3.7
7 W	3 2 1.5	13 54.0	5 9.8	11♏25.1	5 34.1	10 54.5	11 30.3	5 50.3	21 36.5	28 51.9	14 7.8	26 3.4
8 T	3 5 58.1	14 54.3	5 6.6	25 4.5	4 40.6	12 9.8	12 4.4	6 3.4	21 37.7	28 49.6	14 9.1	26 3.2
9 F	3 9 54.6	15 54.6	5 3.4	8♐57.1	3 57.5	13 25.2	12 38.3	6 16.4	21 39.0	28 47.3	14 10.3	26 2.9
10 S	3 13 51.2	16 54.9	5 0.3	22 58.8	3 25.8	14 40.5	13 12.2	6 29.4	21 40.5	28 45.0	14 11.6	26 2.6
11 S	3 17 47.7	17 55.2	4 57.1	7♑ 5.7	3 5.6	15 55.9	13 45.9	6 42.4	21 42.0	28 42.7	14 12.8	26 2.2
12 M	3 21 44.3	18 55.6	4 53.9	21 14.3	2 57.2	17 11.3	14 19.6	6 55.4	21 43.6	28 40.4	14 14.0	26 1.8
13 T	3 25 40.9	19 56.0	4 50.7	5♒22.6	2D60.0	18 26.6	14 53.2	7 8.4	21 45.4	28 38.2	14 15.1	26 1.4
14 W	3 29 37.4	20 56.4	4 47.5	19 28.9	3 13.5	19 42.0	15 26.6	7 21.3	21 47.2	28 35.9	14 16.2	26 1.0
15 T	3 33 34.0	21 56.8	4 44.4	3♓32.7	3 37.0	20 57.4	15 60.0	7 34.3	21 49.1	28 33.7	14 17.3	26 0.6
16 F	3 37 30.5	22 57.2	4 41.2	17 33.0	4 9.5	22 12.8	16 33.3	7 47.2	21 51.2	28 31.6	14 18.4	26 0.1
17 S	3 41 27.1	23 57.7	4 38.0	1♈28.8	4 50.3	23 28.2	17 6.4	8 0.1	21 53.3	28 29.4	14 19.4	25 59.6
18 S	3 45 23.7	24 58.2	4 34.8	15 18.5	5 38.4	24 43.5	17 39.5	8 12.9	21 55.5	28 27.3	14 20.4	25 59.1
19 M	3 49 20.2	25 58.7	4 31.7	28 59.5	6 32.9	25 58.9	18 12.5	8 25.7	21 57.8	28 25.2	14 21.4	25 58.6
20 T	3 53 16.7	26 59.3	4 28.5	12♉29.3	7 33.0	27 14.3	18 45.3	8 38.5	22 0.3	28 23.1	14 22.3	25 58.0
21 W	3 57 13.3	27 59.8	4 25.3	25 45.0	8 38.1	28 29.7	19 18.1	8 51.3	22 2.8	28 21.1	14 23.2	25 57.4
22 T	4 1 9.9	29 0.4	4 22.1	8♊44.8	9 47.4	29 45.1	19 50.8	9 4.0	22 5.4	28 19.0	14 24.1	25 56.8
23 F	4 5 6.4	0♐ 1.1	4 19.0	21 27.6	11 0.4	1♐ 0.5	20 23.3	9 16.7	22 8.1	28 17.1	14 24.9	25 56.2
24 S	4 9 3.0	1 1.7	4 15.8	3♋53.8	12 16.5	2 15.9	20 55.8	9 29.4	22 10.9	28 15.1	14 25.7	25 55.5
25 S	4 12 59.5	2 2.4	4 12.6	16 4.8	13 35.2	3 31.3	21 28.1	9 42.0	22 13.8	28 13.2	14 26.5	25 54.8
26 M	4 16 56.1	3 3.1	4 9.4	28 3.8	14 56.3	4 46.8	22 0.3	9 54.6	22 16.8	28 11.3	14 27.3	25 54.2
27 T	4 20 52.7	4 3.8	4 6.2	9♌54.7	16 19.2	6 2.2	22 32.4	10 7.2	22 19.9	28 9.4	14 28.0	25 53.4
28 W	4 24 49.2	5 4.5	4 3.1	21 42.0	17 43.8	7 17.6	23 4.4	10 19.7	22 23.1	28 7.6	14 28.6	25 52.7
29 T	4 28 45.8	6 5.3	3 59.9	3♍31.2	19 9.8	8 33.0	23 36.3	10 32.2	22 26.4	28 5.8	14 29.3	25 51.9
30 F	4 32 42.3	7 6.1	3 56.7	15 27.7	20 36.9	9 48.5	24 8.0	10 44.6	22 29.7	28 4.0	14 29.9	25 51.2

DECLINATION

DAY	EPHEMERIS SIDEREAL TIME h m s	☉	☊	☽	☿	♀	♂	♃	♄	♅	♆	♇
1 T	2 38 22.2	14S 8.7	18S54.5	11N18.7	16S49.7	11S37.7	9N59.7	12S 5.1	15S41.7	10N37.8	7N 8.3	22N32.4
4 S	2 50 11.9	15 6.0	18 56.8	4S45.3	14 39.4	12 57.5	9 22.4	12 18.3	15 40.8	10 35.3	7 6.8	22 32.8
7 W	3 2 1.5	16 1.1	18 59.1	19 59.3	12 35.9	14 14.5	8 45.0	12 31.3	15 39.6	10 32.9	7 5.3	22 33.2
10 S	3 13 51.2	16 53.7	19 1.4	26 35.0	11 8.7	15 28.2	8 7.7	12 44.2	15 38.0	10 30.4	7 3.9	22 33.7
13 T	3 25 40.9	17 43.8	19 3.7	18 49.6	10 31.7	16 38.4	7 30.4	12 57.0	15 36.2	10 28.1	7 2.7	22 34.2
16 F	3 37 30.5	18 31.1	19 6.0	1 42.8	10 41.8	17 44.7	6 53.1	13 9.5	15 34.1	10 25.8	7 1.5	22 34.8
19 M	3 49 20.2	19 15.5	19 8.3	15N48.7	11 27.7	18 46.7	6 16.1	13 21.9	15 31.7	10 23.6	7 0.5	22 35.4
22 T	4 1 9.9	19 56.7	19 10.5	25 49.9	12 37.0	19 44.1	5 39.2	13 34.1	15 29.0	10 21.4	6 59.5	22 36.0
25 S	4 12 59.5	20 34.7	19 12.8	23 56.4	13 59.4	20 36.5	5 2.5	13 46.1	15 26.1	10 19.4	6 58.7	22 36.7
28 W	4 24 49.2	21 9.2	19 15.0	12 42.1	15 27.5	21 23.6	4 26.1	13 57.8	15 22.9	10 17.5	6 58.0	22 37.4

DECEMBER 1934

LONGITUDE

DAY	EPHEMERIS SIDEREAL TIME h m s	☉ ° ′	☊ ° ′	☽ ° ′	☿ ° ′	♀ ° ′	♂ ° ′	♃ ° ′	♄ ° ′	♅ ° ′	♆ ° ′	♇ ° ′
1 S	4 36 38.9	8♐ 6.9	3♒53.5	27♍36.7	22♏ 5.0	11♐ 3.9	24♍39.6	10♏57.0	22♒33.2	28♈ 2.3	14♍30.5	25♋50.4
2 S	4 40 35.5	9 7.7	3 50.4	10♎ 3.2	23 33.9	12 19.3	25 11.1	11 9.4	22 36.7	28R 0.6	14 31.0	25R49.5
3 M	4 44 32.0	10 8.6	3 47.2	22 51.0	25 3.5	13 34.8	25 42.5	11 21.7	22 40.4	27 59.0	14 31.5	25 48.7
4 T	4 48 28.6	11 9.5	3 44.0	6♏ 2.4	26 33.7	14 50.2	26 13.7	11 34.0	22 44.1	27 57.4	14 32.0	25 47.8
5 W	4 52 25.1	12 10.4	3 40.8	19 37.8	28 4.3	16 5.7	26 44.8	11 46.2	22 47.9	27 55.8	14 32.4	25 47.0
6 T	4 56 21.7	13 11.3	3 37.7	3♐35.4	29 35.3	17 21.1	27 15.8	11 58.3	22 51.8	27 54.3	14 32.9	25 46.1
7 F	5 0 18.3	14 12.3	3 34.5	17 51.3	1♐ 6.7	18 36.6	27 46.6	12 10.4	22 55.8	27 52.8	14 33.2	25 45.1
8 S	5 4 14.8	15 13.2	3 31.3	2♑19.7	2 38.3	19 52.1	28 17.2	12 22.5	22 59.8	27 51.4	14 33.6	25 44.2
9 S	5 8 11.3	16 14.2	3 28.1	16 54.1	4 10.2	21 7.5	28 47.7	12 34.5	23 4.0	27 50.0	14 33.9	25 43.2
10 M	5 12 7.9	17 15.2	3 24.9	1♒28.4	5 42.3	22 23.0	29 18.1	12 46.4	23 8.2	27 48.6	14 34.1	25 42.3
11 T	5 16 4.5	18 16.2	3 21.8	15 57.4	7 14.6	23 38.4	29 48.3	12 58.3	23 12.5	27 47.3	14 34.4	25 41.3
12 W	5 20 1.0	19 17.2	3 18.6	0♓17.1	8 47.0	24 53.9	0♎18.4	13 10.1	23 16.9	27 46.0	14 34.6	25 40.3
13 T	5 23 57.6	20 18.2	3 15.4	14 25.5	10 19.5	26 9.3	0 48.3	13 21.9	23 21.4	27 44.8	14 34.7	25 39.3
14 F	5 27 54.1	21 19.3	3 12.2	28 21.3	11 52.2	27 24.7	1 18.0	13 33.5	23 26.0	27 43.6	14 34.9	25 38.2
15 S	5 31 50.7	22 20.3	3 9.1	12♈ 4.3	13 25.1	28 40.2	1 47.6	13 45.2	23 30.6	27 42.5	14 35.0	25 37.2
16 S	5 35 47.3	23 21.3	3 5.9	25 34.6	14 58.1	29 55.6	2 17.0	13 56.7	23 35.3	27 41.4	14 35.0	25 36.1
17 M	5 39 43.8	24 22.4	3 2.7	8♉52.1	16 31.2	1♑11.0	2 46.2	14 8.2	23 40.1	27 40.4	14 35.1	25 35.0
18 T	5 43 40.4	25 23.5	2 59.5	21 56.8	18 4.4	2 26.4	3 15.3	14 19.6	23 44.9	27 39.4	14R35.1	25 33.9
19 W	5 47 36.9	26 24.5	2 56.4	4♊48.8	19 37.8	3 41.9	3 44.2	14 30.9	23 49.9	27 38.4	14 35.0	25 32.8
20 T	5 51 33.5	27 25.6	2 53.2	17 27.8	21 11.3	4 57.3	4 12.9	14 42.2	23 54.9	27 37.5	14 34.9	25 31.7
21 F	5 55 30.1	28 26.7	2 50.0	29 54.3	22 45.0	6 12.7	4 41.4	14 53.4	23 59.9	27 36.7	14 34.8	25 30.5
22 S	5 59 26.6	29 27.8	2 46.8	12♋ 8.7	24 18.9	7 28.1	5 9.8	15 4.5	24 5.1	27 35.8	14 34.7	25 29.4
23 S	6 3 23.2	0♑28.8	2 43.7	24 12.5	25 53.0	8 43.5	5 37.9	15 15.6	24 10.3	27 35.1	14 34.5	25 28.2
24 M	6 7 19.7	1 30.0	2 40.5	6♌ 7.7	27 27.2	9 58.9	6 5.9	15 26.5	24 15.6	27 34.4	14 34.3	25 27.1
25 T	6 11 16.3	2 31.1	2 37.3	17 57.0	29 1.7	11 14.3	6 33.7	15 37.4	24 20.9	27 33.7	14 34.1	25 25.9
26 W	6 15 12.9	3 32.2	2 34.1	29 44.1	0♑36.5	12 29.7	7 1.3	15 48.2	24 26.3	27 33.1	14 33.8	25 24.7
27 T	6 19 9.4	4 33.3	2 31.0	11♍33.0	2 11.5	13 45.1	7 28.6	15 58.9	24 31.8	27 32.6	14 33.5	25 23.5
28 F	6 23 6.0	5 34.5	2 27.8	23 28.3	3 46.7	15 0.4	7 55.8	16 9.5	24 37.3	27 32.1	14 33.1	25 22.2
29 S	6 27 2.5	6 35.6	2 24.6	5♎35.1	5 22.2	16 15.8	8 22.8	16 20.1	24 42.9	27 31.6	14 32.7	25 21.0
30 S	6 30 59.1	7 36.8	2 21.4	17 58.2	6 58.0	17 31.2	8 49.5	16 30.5	24 48.6	27 31.2	14 32.3	25 19.8
31 M	6 34 55.7	8 37.9	2 18.3	0♏42.2	8 34.2	18 46.6	9 16.0	16 40.9	24 54.3	27 30.9	14 31.9	25 18.5

DECLINATION

DAY	EPHEMERIS SIDEREAL TIME h m s	☉	☊	☽	☿	♀	♂	♃	♄	♅	♆	♇
1 S	4 36 38.9	21S40.2	19S17.3	2S53.7	16S56.3	22S 5.1	3N50.1	14S 9.4	15S19.4	10N15.7	6N57.4	22N38.1
4 T	4 48 28.6	22 7.4	19 19.5	18 21.0	18 22.2	22 40.8	3 14.5	14 20.7	15 15.6	10 14.0	6 56.9	22 38.9
7 F	5 0 18.3	22 30.8	19 21.8	26 27.6	19 42.8	23 10.4	2 39.4	14 31.7	15 11.6	10 12.4	6 56.6	22 39.7
10 M	5 12 7.9	22 50.3	19 24.0	19 52.5	20 56.5	23 33.7	2 4.8	14 42.5	15 7.3	10 11.0	6 56.3	22 40.5
13 T	5 23 57.6	23 5.7	19 26.2	2 53.9	22 1.8	23 50.5	1 30.7	14 53.0	15 2.8	10 9.7	6 56.2	22 41.4
16 S	5 35 47.3	23 16.9	19 28.4	14N40.8	22 58.0	24 0.7	0 57.3	15 3.2	14 58.0	10 8.6	6 56.2	22 42.2
19 W	5 47 36.9	23 24.0	19 30.6	25 22.2	23 44.0	24 4.2	0 24.6	15 13.1	14 53.0	10 7.6	6 56.3	22 43.1
22 S	5 59 26.6	23 26.9	19 32.8	24 36.1	24 19.2	24 1.1	0S 7.5	15 22.8	14 47.8	10 6.8	6 56.6	22 44.0
25 T	6 11 16.3	23 25.5	19 34.9	14 1.3	24 43.0	23 51.2	0 38.7	15 32.1	14 42.4	10 6.1	6 56.9	22 44.9
28 F	6 23 6.0	23 19.9	19 37.1	1S13.3	24 54.7	23 34.6	1 9.2	15 41.1	14 36.8	10 5.6	6 57.4	22 45.8
31 M	6 34 55.7	23 10.1	19 39.2	16 38.4	24 53.8	23 11.5	1 38.7	15 49.8	14 31.0	10 5.3	6 58.0	22 46.7

JANUARY 1935

DAY	EPHEMERIS SIDEREAL TIME	☉	☊	☽	☿	♀	♂	♃	♄	♅	♆	♇
	h m s	° ′	° ′	° ′	° ′	° ′	° ′	° ′	° ′	° ′	° ′	° ′
						LONGITUDE						
1 T	6 38 52.2	9♑39.1	2♒15.1	13♏50.7	10♑10.6	20♑ 2.0	9♎42.3	16♏51.2	25♒ 0.1	27♈30.5	14♍31.4	25♋17.3
2 W	6 42 48.8	10 40.3	2 11.9	27 25.8	11 47.4	21 17.3	10 8.3	17 1.3	25 5.9	27R30.3	14R30.9	25R16.0
3 T	6 46 45.3	11 41.4	2 8.7	11♐27.5	13 24.5	22 32.7	10 34.1	17 11.4	25 11.9	27 30.1	14 30.3	25 14.8
4 F	6 50 41.9	12 42.6	2 5.5	25 53.4	15 2.0	23 48.1	10 59.7	17 21.4	25 17.8	27 30.0	14 29.8	25 13.5
5 S	6 54 38.4	13 43.8	2 2.4	10♑38.2	16 39.8	25 3.4	11 25.0	17 31.3	25 23.8	27 29.9	14 29.2	25 12.2
6 S	6 58 35.0	14 45.0	1 59.2	25 34.9	18 18.0	26 18.8	11 50.0	17 41.1	25 29.9	27 29.8	14 28.5	25 10.9
7 M	7 2 31.5	15 46.2	1 56.0	10♒34.9	19 56.6	27 34.1	12 14.8	17 50.7	25 36.0	27D29.8	14 27.9	25 9.6
8 T	7 6 28.1	16 47.4	1 52.8	25 30.0	21 35.5	28 49.4	12 39.3	18 0.3	25 42.2	27 29.9	14 27.2	25 8.3
9 W	7 10 24.7	17 48.5	1 49.7	10♓13.0	23 14.8	0♒ 4.8	13 3.5	18 9.7	25 48.4	27 30.0	14 26.4	25 7.0
10 T	7 14 21.2	18 49.7	1 46.5	24 38.7	24 54.5	1 20.1	13 27.5	18 19.1	25 54.7	27 30.2	14 25.7	25 5.7
11 F	7 18 17.8	19 50.8	1 43.3	8♈44.2	26 34.5	2 35.4	13 51.1	18 28.3	26 1.0	27 30.4	14 24.9	25 4.4
12 S	7 22 14.3	20 52.0	1 40.1	22 28.4	28 14.7	3 50.6	14 14.5	18 37.4	26 7.4	27 30.7	14 24.0	25 3.1
13 S	7 26 10.9	21 53.1	1 37.0	5♉52.0	29 55.3	5 5.9	14 37.6	18 46.4	26 13.8	27 31.0	14 23.2	25 1.8
14 M	7 30 7.5	22 54.2	1 33.8	18 56.5	1♒36.1	6 21.2	15 0.4	18 55.3	26 20.3	27 31.4	14 22.3	25 0.5
15 T	7 34 4.0	23 55.3	1 30.6	1♊44.0	3 17.0	7 36.4	15 22.8	19 4.1	26 26.8	27 31.8	14 21.4	24 59.2
16 W	7 38 0.6	24 56.4	1 27.4	14 16.9	4 58.1	8 51.6	15 45.0	19 12.8	26 33.3	27 32.3	14 20.5	24 57.9
17 T	7 41 57.1	25 57.5	1 24.2	26 37.4	6 39.2	10 6.8	16 6.8	19 21.3	26 39.9	27 32.8	14 19.5	24 56.5
18 F	7 45 53.7	26 58.6	1 21.1	8♋47.6	8 20.2	11 22.1	16 28.4	19 29.7	26 46.5	27 33.4	14 18.5	24 55.2
19 S	7 49 50.3	27 59.6	1 17.9	20 49.4	10 1.0	12 37.2	16 49.5	19 38.0	26 53.2	27 34.1	14 17.5	24 53.9
20 S	7 53 46.8	29 0.7	1 14.7	2♌44.8	11 41.4	13 52.4	17 10.4	19 46.2	26 59.9	27 34.8	14 16.4	24 52.6
21 M	7 57 43.4	0♒ 1.7	1 11.5	14 35.5	13 21.3	15 7.6	17 30.9	19 54.2	27 6.6	27 35.5	14 15.4	24 51.3
22 T	8 1 39.9	1 2.8	1 8.4	26 23.8	15 0.4	16 22.7	17 51.0	20 2.1	27 13.4	27 36.3	14 14.3	24 50.0
23 W	8 5 36.5	2 3.8	1 5.2	8♍12.1	16 38.5	17 37.8	18 10.8	20 9.9	27 20.2	27 37.2	14 13.1	24 48.7
24 T	8 9 33.0	3 4.8	1 2.0	20 3.1	18 15.4	18 52.9	18 30.2	20 17.5	27 27.0	27 38.0	14 12.0	24 47.4
25 F	8 13 29.6	4 5.8	0 58.8	2♎ 0.3	19 50.6	20 8.0	18 49.2	20 25.0	27 33.9	27 39.0	14 10.8	24 46.1
26 S	8 17 26.1	5 6.8	0 55.7	14 7.2	21 23.7	21 23.1	19 7.8	20 32.4	27 40.8	27 40.0	14 9.6	24 44.8
27 S	8 21 22.7	6 7.8	0 52.5	26 27.9	22 54.3	22 38.2	19 26.0	20 39.6	27 47.7	27 41.0	14 8.4	24 43.5
28 M	8 25 19.3	7 8.8	0 49.3	9♏ 6.6	24 22.0	23 53.2	19 43.8	20 46.7	27 54.7	27 42.1	14 7.2	24 42.2
29 T	8 29 15.8	8 9.7	0 46.1	22 7.1	25 46.0	25 8.2	20 1.2	20 53.7	28 1.6	27 43.3	14 5.9	24 40.9
30 W	8 33 12.4	9 10.7	0 42.9	5♐32.7	27 5.8	26 23.3	20 18.2	21 0.5	28 8.7	27 44.5	14 4.6	24 39.7
31 T	8 37 8.9	10 11.6	0 39.8	19 25.3	28 20.8	27 38.3	20 34.7	21 7.1	28 15.7	27 45.7	14 3.3	24 38.4
						DECLINATION						
1 T	6 38 52.2	23S 5.9	19S40.0	20S53.5	24S50.7	23S 2.4	1S48.4	15S52.6	14S29.0	10N 5.2	6N58.2	22N47.0
4 F	6 50 41.9	22 50.5	19 42.1	26 25.8	24 32.2	22 30.8	2 16.6	16 0.9	14 23.0	10 5.1	6 59.0	22 48.0
7 M	7 2 31.5	22 31.0	19 44.2	16 45.2	24 0.1	21 53.1	2 43.9	16 8.8	14 16.7	10 5.1	6 59.8	22 48.9
10 T	7 14 21.2	22 7.5	19 46.4	1N46.7	23 14.0	21 9.5	3 10.0	16 16.3	14 10.3	10 5.4	7 0.8	22 49.8
13 S	7 26 10.9	21 40.2	19 48.5	18 26.9	22 13.8	20 20.3	3 35.0	16 23.5	14 3.8	10 5.7	7 1.8	22 50.8
16 W	7 38 0.6	21 9.0	19 50.6	26 21.7	20 59.6	19 25.7	3 58.8	16 30.4	13 57.1	10 6.3	7 3.0	22 51.7
19 S	7 49 50.3	20 34.3	19 52.7	22 46.3	19 31.8	18 26.1	4 21.4	16 36.9	13 50.3	10 7.0	7 4.2	22 52.6
22 T	8 1 39.9	19 56.0	19 54.8	10 35.3	17 51.6	17 21.8	4 42.6	16 43.0	13 43.3	10 7.9	7 5.5	22 53.5
25 F	8 13 29.6	19 14.4	19 56.9	5S 2.8	16 1.4	16 13.2	5 2.5	16 48.7	13 36.3	10 9.0	7 7.0	22 54.4
28 M	8 25 19.3	18 29.6	19 58.9	19 30.1	14 5.0	15 0.5	5 20.9	16 54.0	13 29.1	10 10.2	7 8.5	22 55.3
31 T	8 37 8.9	17 41.8	20 1.0	26 32.6	12 8.6	13 44.1	5 37.8	16 59.0	13 21.9	10 11.6	7 10.0	22 56.1

FEBRUARY 1935

DAY	EPHEMERIS SIDEREAL TIME	☉	☊	☽	☿	♀	♂	♃	♄	♅	♆	♇
						LONGITUDE						
1 F	8 41 5.5	11♒12.5	0♒36.6	3♑44.7	29♒30.1	28♒53.2	20♎50.8	21♏13.7	28♒22.8	27♈47.0	14♍ 2.0	24♋37.2
2 S	8 45 2.1	12 13.5	0 33.4	18 28.3	0♓32.9	0♓ 8.2	21 6.4	21 20.0	28 29.8	27 48.4	14R 0.6	24R35.9
3 S	8 48 58.6	13 14.3	0 30.2	3♒30.4	1 28.5	1 23.2	21 21.5	21 26.2	28 36.9	27 49.8	13 59.2	24 34.7
4 M	8 52 55.1	14 15.2	0 27.1	18 42.9	2 16.1	2 38.1	21 36.2	21 32.3	28 44.1	27 51.2	13 57.9	24 33.4
5 T	8 56 51.7	15 16.1	0 23.9	3♓56.0	2 54.9	3 53.0	21 50.3	21 38.2	28 51.2	27 52.7	13 56.4	24 32.2
6 W	9 0 48.3	16 16.9	0 20.7	18 59.9	3 24.3	5 7.9	22 4.0	21 43.9	28 58.4	27 54.2	13 55.0	24 31.0
7 T	9 4 44.8	17 17.7	0 17.5	3♈46.2	3 43.5	6 22.7	22 17.1	21 49.5	29 5.6	27 55.8	13 53.6	24 29.8
8 F	9 8 41.4	18 18.5	0 14.4	18 8.7	3 52.2	7 37.5	22 29.7	21 55.0	29 12.8	27 57.4	13 52.1	24 28.6
9 S	9 12 37.9	19 19.3	0 11.2	2♉ 4.5	3R50.0	8 52.3	22 41.8	22 0.2	29 20.0	27 59.1	13 50.6	24 27.4
10 S	9 16 34.5	20 20.0	0 8.0	15 33.2	3 37.0	10 7.1	22 53.3	22 5.4	29 27.2	28 0.8	13 49.1	24 26.3
11 M	9 20 31.0	21 20.7	0 4.8	28 36.7	3 13.4	11 21.9	23 4.3	22 10.3	29 34.4	28 2.6	13 47.6	24 25.1
12 T	9 24 27.6	22 21.4	0 1.6	11♊18.1	2 39.7	12 36.6	23 14.8	22 15.1	29 41.7	28 4.4	13 46.1	24 24.0
13 W	9 28 24.2	23 22.1	29♑58.5	23 41.5	1 56.6	13 51.3	23 24.7	22 19.7	29 48.9	28 6.3	13 44.6	24 22.8
14 T	9 32 20.7	24 22.7	29 55.3	5♋50.7	1 5.4	15 5.9	23 33.9	22 24.1	29 56.2	28 8.2	13 43.0	24 21.7
15 F	9 36 17.3	25 23.3	29 52.1	17 49.9	0 7.4	16 20.5	23 42.6	22 28.4	0♓ 3.4	28 10.1	13 41.5	24 20.6
16 S	9 40 13.8	26 23.9	29 48.9	29 42.5	29♒ 4.3	17 35.1	23 50.7	22 32.5	0 10.7	28 12.1	13 39.9	24 19.5
17 S	9 44 10.4	27 24.4	29 45.8	11♌31.5	27 57.7	18 49.7	23 58.2	22 36.5	0 18.0	28 14.1	13 38.3	24 18.5
18 M	9 48 6.9	28 25.0	29 42.6	23 19.6	26 49.6	20 4.2	24 5.1	22 40.3	0 25.3	28 16.2	13 36.7	24 17.4
19 T	9 52 3.5	29 25.5	29 39.4	5♍ 8.9	25 41.6	21 18.7	24 11.3	22 43.9	0 32.5	28 18.3	13 35.1	24 16.3
20 W	9 56 0.0	0♓25.9	29 36.2	17 1.2	24 35.4	22 33.1	24 16.9	22 47.3	0 39.8	28 20.4	13 33.5	24 15.3
21 T	9 59 56.6	1 26.4	29 33.1	28 58.5	23 32.6	23 47.6	24 21.8	22 50.5	0 47.1	28 22.6	13 31.9	24 14.3
22 F	10 3 53.2	2 26.8	29 29.9	11♎ 2.7	22 34.4	25 1.9	24 26.1	22 53.6	0 54.4	28 24.9	13 30.3	24 13.3
23 S	10 7 49.7	3 27.2	29 26.7	23 15.9	21 41.8	26 16.3	24 29.6	22 56.5	1 1.7	28 27.1	13 28.6	24 12.3
24 S	10 11 46.2	4 27.6	29 23.5	5♏40.6	20 55.6	27 30.6	24 32.5	22 59.2	1 8.9	28 29.4	13 27.0	24 11.4
25 M	10 15 42.8	5 27.9	29 20.3	18 19.6	20 16.3	28 44.9	24 34.7	23 1.7	1 16.2	28 31.8	13 25.3	24 10.4
26 T	10 19 39.4	6 28.2	29 17.2	1♐16.1	19 44.1	29 59.2	24 36.1	23 4.1	1 23.5	28 34.2	13 23.7	24 9.5
27 W	10 23 35.9	7 28.5	29 14.0	14 33.0	19 19.2	1♈13.4	24 36.9	23 6.3	1 30.8	28 36.6	13 22.0	24 8.6
28 T	10 27 32.5	8 28.8	29 10.8	28 12.9	19 1.5	2 27.6	24R36.9	23 8.2	1 38.0	28 39.0	13 20.4	24 7.7
						DECLINATION						
1 F	8 41 5.5	17S25.2	20S 1.7	25S50.1	11S31.3	13S17.9	5S43.1	17S 0.6	13S19.4	10N12.1	7N10.6	22N56.4
4 M	8 52 55.1	16 33.6	20 3.7	13 42.0	9 49.2	11 57.2	5 57.8	17 5.0	13 12.1	10 13.7	7 12.2	22 57.2
7 T	9 4 44.8	15 39.4	20 5.8	5N48.1	8 31.1	10 33.7	6 10.8	17 9.0	13 4.6	10 15.4	7 14.0	22 58.0
10 S	9 16 34.5	14 42.9	20 7.8	21 22.8	7 47.9	9 7.6	6 22.1	17 12.7	12 57.1	10 17.3	7 15.7	22 58.8
13 W	9 28 24.2	13 44.1	20 9.8	26 29.7	7 46.0	7 39.5	6 31.6	17 15.9	12 49.6	10 19.3	7 17.6	22 59.6
16 S	9 40 13.8	12 43.3	20 11.9	20 20.6	8 23.2	6 9.6	6 39.2	17 18.7	12 42.0	10 21.5	7 19.4	23 0.3
19 T	9 52 3.5	11 40.7	20 13.9	6 53.5	9 27.9	4 38.2	6 44.8	17 21.2	12 34.4	10 23.8	7 21.3	23 1.0
22 F	10 3 53.2	10 36.4	20 15.9	8S52.7	10 43.6	3 5.7	6 48.4	17 23.2	12 26.8	10 26.2	7 23.2	23 1.6
25 M	10 15 42.8	9 30.7	20 17.8	22 2.7	11 55.6	1 32.5	6 50.0	17 24.8	12 19.2	10 28.7	7 25.2	23 2.2
28 T	10 27 32.5	8 23.6	20 19.8	26 13.1	12 54.7	0N 1.2	6 49.3	17 26.0	12 11.6	10 31.4	7 27.1	23 2.8

MARCH 1935

LONGITUDE

DAY	EPHEMERIS SIDEREAL TIME	☉	☊	☽	☿	♀	♂	♃	♄	♅	♆	♇
	h m s	° ′	° ′	° ′	° ′	° ′	° ′	° ′	° ′	° ′	° ′	° ′
1 F	10 31 29.0	9 ♓ 29.1	29 ♑ 7.6	12 ♑ 17.4	18 ♒ 50.9	3 ♈ 41.7	24 ♎ 36.1	23 ♏ 10.0	1 ♓ 45.3	28 ♈ 41.5	13 ♍ 18.7	24 ♋ 6.8
2 S	10 35 25.6	10 29.3	29 4.5	26 46.0	18 R 47.2	4 55.8	24 R 34.6	23 11.7	1 52.5	28 44.0	13 R 17.0	24 R 6.0
3 S	10 39 22.1	11 29.5	29 1.3	11 ♒ 36.0	18 D 50.0	6 9.9	24 32.4	23 13.1	1 59.7	28 46.6	13 15.4	24 5.1
4 M	10 43 18.7	12 29.7	28 58.1	26 41.6	18 59.0	7 23.9	24 29.3	23 14.3	2 7.0	28 49.2	13 13.7	24 4.3
5 T	10 47 15.2	13 29.8	28 54.9	11 ♓ 54.2	19 13.9	8 37.9	24 25.5	23 15.4	2 14.2	28 51.8	13 12.0	24 3.5
6 W	10 51 11.8	14 29.9	28 51.7	27 3.9	19 34.4	9 51.9	24 21.0	23 16.2	2 21.3	28 54.5	13 10.3	24 2.8
7 T	10 55 8.4	15 30.0	28 48.6	12 ♈ 0.4	19 60.0	11 5.8	24 15.6	23 16.9	2 28.5	28 57.2	13 8.7	24 2.0
8 F	10 59 4.9	16 30.1	28 45.4	26 35.3	20 30.4	12 19.7	24 9.5	23 17.4	2 35.7	28 59.9	13 7.0	24 1.3
9 S	11 3 1.4	17 30.1	28 42.2	10 ♉ 43.0	21 5.3	13 33.5	24 2.6	23 17.7	2 42.8	29 2.7	13 5.3	24 0.6
10 S	11 6 58.0	18 30.0	28 39.0	24 21.3	21 44.5	14 47.3	23 54.9	23 17.8	2 49.9	29 5.4	13 3.7	23 59.9
11 M	11 10 54.6	19 30.0	28 35.9	7 ♊ 30.9	22 27.6	16 1.0	23 46.4	23 R 17.7	2 57.0	29 8.3	13 2.0	23 59.2
12 T	11 14 51.1	20 29.9	28 32.7	20 14.8	23 14.3	17 14.7	23 37.2	23 17.5	3 4.1	29 11.1	13 0.4	23 58.6
13 W	11 18 47.7	21 29.8	28 29.5	2 ♋ 37.3	24 4.5	18 28.4	23 27.2	23 17.0	3 11.2	29 14.0	12 58.7	23 58.0
14 T	11 22 44.2	22 29.6	28 26.3	14 43.5	24 57.9	19 41.9	23 16.5	23 16.4	3 18.2	29 16.9	12 57.0	23 57.4
15 F	11 26 40.8	23 29.4	28 23.1	26 38.6	25 54.3	20 65.5	23 5.0	23 15.5	3 25.2	29 19.8	12 55.4	23 56.8
16 S	11 30 37.3	24 29.1	28 20.0	8 ♌ 27.3	26 53.5	22 8.9	22 52.7	23 14.5	3 32.2	29 22.8	12 53.8	23 56.2
17 S	11 34 33.9	25 28.9	28 16.8	20 14.1	27 55.3	23 22.4	22 39.8	23 13.3	3 39.1	29 25.7	12 52.2	23 55.7
18 M	11 38 30.4	26 28.6	28 13.6	2 ♍ 2.3	28 59.7	24 35.7	22 26.0	23 11.9	3 46.1	29 28.7	12 50.5	23 55.2
19 T	11 42 27.0	27 28.2	28 10.4	13 55.1	0 ♓ 6.4	25 49.1	22 11.6	23 10.4	3 53.0	29 31.8	12 48.9	23 54.7
20 W	11 46 23.5	28 27.8	28 7.3	25 54.3	1 15.4	27 2.3	21 56.5	23 8.6	3 59.8	29 34.8	12 47.3	23 54.2
21 T	11 50 20.1	29 27.4	28 4.1	8 ♎ 1.7	2 26.5	28 15.5	21 40.7	23 6.7	4 6.7	29 37.9	12 45.7	23 53.8
22 F	11 54 16.7	0 ♈ 27.0	28 0.9	20 18.0	3 39.6	29 28.7	21 24.3	23 4.5	4 13.5	29 41.0	12 44.2	23 53.4
23 S	11 58 13.2	1 26.5	27 57.7	2 ♏ 44.3	4 54.8	0 ♉ 41.8	21 7.2	23 2.2	4 20.2	29 44.1	12 42.6	23 53.0
24 S	12 2 9.8	2 26.0	27 54.5	15 21.3	6 11.7	1 54.8	20 49.5	22 59.8	4 27.0	29 47.2	12 41.0	23 52.6
25 M	12 6 6.3	3 25.4	27 51.4	28 10.1	7 30.5	3 7.8	20 31.2	22 57.1	4 33.7	29 50.4	12 39.5	23 52.3
26 T	12 10 2.9	4 24.8	27 48.2	11 ♐ 12.1	8 51.1	4 20.7	20 12.3	22 54.2	4 40.4	29 53.6	12 38.0	23 52.0
27 W	12 13 59.4	5 24.2	27 45.0	24 29.2	10 13.3	5 33.6	19 52.9	22 51.2	4 47.0	29 56.8	12 36.4	23 51.7
28 T	12 17 56.0	6 23.6	27 41.8	8 ♑ 3.3	11 37.2	6 46.4	19 32.9	22 48.0	4 53.6	29 60.0	12 34.9	23 51.4
29 F	12 21 52.5	7 22.9	27 38.6	21 56.1	13 2.8	7 59.2	19 12.5	22 44.7	5 0.1	0 ♉ 3.2	12 33.4	23 51.2
30 S	12 25 49.1	8 22.3	27 35.5	6 ♒ 8.2	14 29.9	9 11.9	18 51.6	22 41.1	5 6.7	0 6.5	12 32.0	23 51.0
31 S	12 29 45.6	9 21.5	27 32.3	20 38.7	15 58.5	10 24.5	18 30.3	22 37.4	5 13.1	0 9.7	12 30.5	23 50.8

DECLINATION

DAY	EPHEMERIS SIDEREAL TIME	☉	☊	☽	☿	♀	♂	♃	♄	♅	♆	♇
1 F	10 31 29.0	8 S 1.0	20 S 20.5	24 S 30.2	13 S 10.8	0 N 32.5	6 S 48.6	17 S 26.3	12 S 9.1	10 N 32.3	7 N 27.8	23 N 3.0
4 M	10 43 18.7	6 52.5	20 22.4	10 28.3	13 47.2	2 6.2	6 45.0	17 26.9	12 1.5	10 35.1	7 29.7	23 3.6
7 T	10 55 8.4	5 43.1	20 24.4	9 N 14.8	14 5.9	3 39.6	6 39.2	17 27.1	11 54.0	10 38.0	7 31.7	23 4.1
10 S	11 6 58.0	4 33.0	20 26.3	23 24.3	14 7.6	5 12.4	6 31.1	17 26.9	11 46.5	10 41.0	7 33.6	23 4.5
13 W	11 18 47.7	3 22.4	20 28.3	25 46.9	13 53.4	6 44.1	6 20.9	17 26.3	11 39.1	10 44.0	7 35.5	23 4.9
16 S	11 30 37.3	2 11.5	20 30.2	17 25.0	13 24.2	8 14.5	6 8.5	17 25.2	11 31.8	10 47.2	7 37.4	23 5.3
19 T	11 42 27.0	1 0.4	20 32.1	3 2.8	12 41.0	9 43.2	5 54.1	17 23.8	11 24.5	10 50.4	7 39.3	23 5.7
22 F	11 54 16.7	0 N 10.7	20 34.0	12 S 33.7	11 44.4	11 9.9	5 37.9	17 21.9	11 17.3	10 53.7	7 41.1	23 6.0
25 M	12 6 6.3	1 21.7	20 35.9	24 3.2	10 35.3	12 34.3	5 20.0	17 19.7	11 10.3	10 57.1	7 42.9	23 6.2
28 T	12 17 56.0	2 32.4	20 37.8	24 58.6	9 14.2	13 56.0	5 0.6	17 17.1	11 3.3	11 0.5	7 44.7	23 6.4
31 S	12 29 45.6	3 42.6	20 39.7	12 48.1	7 41.6	15 14.8	4 40.1	17 14.1	10 56.5	11 4.0	7 46.3	23 6.6

APRIL 1935

LONGITUDE

DAY	EPHEMERIS SIDEREAL TIME	☉	☊	☽	☿	♀	♂	♃	♄	♅	♆	♇
1 M	12 33 42.2	10 ♈ 20.8	27 ♑ 29.1	5 ♓ 24.4	17 ♓ 28.7	11 ♉ 37.1	18 ♎ 8.6	22 ♏ 33.5	5 ♓ 19.6	0 ♉ 13.0	12 ♍ 29.1	23 ♋ 50.6
2 T	12 37 38.7	11 20.0	27 25.9	20 19.6	19 0.3	12 49.6	17 R 46.6	22 R 29.5	5 25.9	0 16.3	12 R 27.6	23 R 50.5
3 W	12 41 35.3	12 19.2	27 22.8	5 ♈ 16.1	20 33.5	14 2.1	17 24.3	22 25.2	5 32.3	0 19.6	12 26.2	23 50.3
4 T	12 45 31.8	13 18.3	27 19.6	20 5.0	22 8.2	15 14.5	17 1.7	22 20.9	5 38.6	0 22.9	12 24.9	23 50.3
5 F	12 49 28.4	14 17.5	27 16.4	4 ♉ 37.4	23 44.3	16 26.9	16 39.0	22 16.3	5 44.8	0 26.3	12 23.5	23 50.2
6 S	12 53 25.0	15 16.5	27 13.2	18 46.7	25 21.9	17 39.1	16 16.0	22 11.6	5 51.0	0 29.6	12 22.1	23 50.1
7 S	12 57 21.5	16 15.6	27 10.1	2 ♊ 28.9	27 1.0	18 51.3	15 53.0	22 6.8	5 57.2	0 33.0	12 20.8	23 50.1
8 M	13 1 18.1	17 14.6	27 6.9	15 43.2	28 41.6	20 3.5	15 29.9	22 1.8	6 3.3	0 36.4	12 19.5	23 D 50.1
9 T	13 5 14.6	18 13.6	27 3.7	28 31.4	0 ♈ 23.6	21 15.5	15 6.8	21 56.6	6 9.3	0 39.7	12 18.2	23 50.2
10 W	13 9 11.2	19 12.5	27 0.5	10 ♋ 57.0	2 7.2	22 27.5	14 43.7	21 51.4	6 15.3	0 43.1	12 16.9	23 50.2
11 T	13 13 7.7	20 11.4	26 57.3	23 5.0	3 52.2	23 39.4	14 20.7	21 45.9	6 21.3	0 46.5	12 15.7	23 50.3
12 F	13 17 4.3	21 10.3	26 54.2	5 ♌ 0.9	5 38.8	24 51.3	13 57.8	21 40.4	6 27.2	0 49.9	12 14.5	23 50.4
13 S	13 21 0.8	22 9.1	26 51.0	16 50.1	7 26.8	26 3.1	13 35.0	21 34.7	6 33.0	0 53.4	12 13.3	23 50.6
14 S	13 24 57.4	23 7.9	26 47.8	28 37.8	9 16.5	27 14.7	13 12.5	21 28.8	6 38.8	0 56.8	12 12.1	23 50.7
15 M	13 28 53.9	24 6.6	26 44.6	10 ♍ 28.5	11 7.6	28 26.4	12 50.2	21 22.9	6 44.5	1 0.2	12 10.9	23 50.9
16 T	13 32 50.5	25 5.3	26 41.4	22 26.1	13 0.3	29 37.9	12 28.2	21 16.8	6 50.2	1 3.6	12 9.8	23 51.1
17 W	13 36 47.0	26 4.0	26 38.3	4 ♎ 33.3	14 54.5	0 ♊ 49.3	12 6.6	21 10.6	6 55.8	1 7.1	12 8.7	23 51.3
18 T	13 40 43.6	27 2.6	26 35.1	16 52.1	16 50.3	2 0.7	11 45.3	21 4.3	7 1.3	1 10.5	12 7.6	23 51.6
19 F	13 44 40.2	28 1.2	26 31.9	29 23.3	18 47.6	3 12.0	11 24.4	20 57.9	7 6.8	1 13.9	12 6.6	23 51.9
20 S	13 48 36.7	28 59.8	26 28.7	12 ♏ 6.9	20 46.4	4 23.2	11 3.9	20 51.4	7 12.2	1 17.4	12 5.5	23 52.2
21 S	13 52 33.2	29 58.4	26 25.6	25 2.7	22 46.7	5 34.3	10 43.9	20 44.8	7 17.6	1 20.8	12 4.5	23 52.5
22 M	13 56 29.8	0 ♉ 56.9	26 22.4	8 ♐ 9.8	24 48.4	6 45.3	10 24.4	20 38.1	7 22.9	1 24.3	12 3.5	23 52.9
23 T	14 0 26.4	1 55.4	26 19.2	21 28.0	26 51.5	7 56.2	10 5.5	20 31.2	7 28.1	1 27.7	12 2.6	23 53.3
24 W	14 4 22.9	2 53.8	26 16.0	4 ♑ 57.0	28 55.9	9 7.1	9 47.1	20 24.3	7 33.3	1 31.2	12 1.6	23 53.7
25 T	14 8 19.5	3 52.3	26 12.9	18 37.1	1 ♉ 1.5	10 17.9	9 29.3	20 17.4	7 38.4	1 34.6	12 0.7	23 54.1
26 F	14 12 16.0	4 50.7	26 9.7	2 ♒ 28.9	3 8.1	11 28.5	9 12.1	20 10.3	7 43.4	1 38.1	11 59.9	23 54.6
27 S	14 16 12.6	5 49.0	26 6.5	16 32.6	5 15.7	12 39.1	8 55.5	20 3.1	7 48.4	1 41.5	11 59.0	23 55.1
28 S	14 20 9.1	6 47.4	26 3.3	0 ♓ 47.8	7 24.1	13 49.6	8 39.7	19 55.9	7 53.3	1 44.9	11 58.2	23 55.6
29 M	14 24 5.7	7 45.7	26 0.1	15 12.7	9 33.0	15 0.0	8 24.5	19 48.7	7 58.1	1 48.4	11 57.4	23 56.1
30 T	14 28 2.2	8 44.0	25 57.0	29 43.8	11 42.2	16 10.4	8 10.0	19 41.3	8 2.9	1 51.8	11 56.7	23 56.6

DECLINATION

DAY	EPHEMERIS SIDEREAL TIME	☉	☊	☽	☿	♀	♂	♃	♄	♅	♆	♇
1 M	12 33 42.2	4 N 5.9	20 S 40.3	6 S 42.0	7 S 8.3	15 N 40.3	4 S 33.1	17 S 13.0	10 S 54.3	11 N 5.1	7 N 46.9	23 N 6.7
4 T	12 45 31.8	5 15.3	20 42.2	12 N 27.5	5 21.3	16 54.6	4 11.6	17 9.5	10 47.7	11 8.7	7 48.5	23 6.8
7 S	12 57 21.5	6 23.8	20 44.0	24 42.5	3 24.1	18 5.1	3 49.9	17 5.6	10 41.2	11 12.2	7 50.0	23 6.9
10 W	13 9 11.2	7 31.4	20 45.9	24 24.9	1 17.2	19 11.6	3 28.4	17 1.5	10 34.9	11 15.8	7 51.5	23 6.9
13 S	13 21 0.8	8 37.8	20 47.7	14 10.8	0 N 58.7	20 13.7	3 7.6	16 57.0	10 28.8	11 19.4	7 52.8	23 6.9
16 T	13 32 50.5	9 42.8	20 49.6	0 S 47.7	3 22.8	21 11.1	2 47.8	16 52.2	10 22.8	11 23.0	7 54.1	23 6.9
19 F	13 44 40.2	10 46.5	20 51.4	15 55.3	5 53.7	22 3.6	2 29.5	16 47.1	10 17.1	11 26.6	7 55.3	23 6.8
22 M	13 56 29.8	11 48.5	20 53.2	25 20.3	8 29.7	22 50.8	2 12.9	16 41.8	10 11.6	11 30.2	7 56.5	23 6.7
25 T	14 8 19.5	12 48.8	20 55.0	22 45.7	11 8.2	23 32.7	1 58.4	16 36.3	10 6.3	11 33.8	7 57.5	23 6.5
28 S	14 20 9.1	13 47.2	20 56.8	8 28.1	13 45.5	24 8.8	1 46.1	16 30.6	10 1.2	11 37.4	7 58.4	23 6.3

MAY 1935

DAY	EPHEMERIS SIDEREAL TIME h m s	☉ ° ′	☊ ° ′	☽ ° ′	☿ ° ′	♀ ° ′	♂ ° ′	♃ ° ′	♄ ° ′	♅ ° ′	♆ ° ′	♇ ° ′
						LONGITUDE						
1 W	14 31 58.8	9♉42.3	25♑53.8	14♈15.9	13♉51.5	17♊20.6	7♎56.3	19♏33.9	8♓ 7.6	1♉55.2	11♍55.9	23♋57.2
2 T	14 35 55.4	10 40.6	25 50.6	28 42.5	16 0.5	18 30.7	7R43.3	19R26.5	8 12.2	1 58.7	11R55.2	23 57.8
3 F	14 39 51.9	11 38.8	25 47.4	12♉56.9	18 9.1	19 40.7	7 31.0	19 19.0	8 16.7	2 2.1	11 54.6	23 58.4
4 S	14 43 48.5	12 37.0	25 44.3	26 53.4	20 16.9	20 50.7	7 19.6	19 11.5	8 21.2	2 5.5	11 53.9	23 59.1
5 S	14 47 45.0	13 35.1	25 41.1	10♊27.8	22 23.6	22 0.5	7 8.9	19 3.9	8 25.6	2 8.9	11 53.3	23 59.8
6 M	14 51 41.6	14 33.3	25 37.9	23 38.6	24 29.0	23 10.2	6 59.0	18 56.3	8 29.9	2 12.3	11 52.7	24 0.4
7 T	14 55 38.1	15 31.4	25 34.7	6♋26.1	26 32.6	24 19.8	6 49.9	18 48.7	8 34.1	2 15.6	11 52.2	24 1.2
8 W	14 59 34.7	16 29.4	25 31.6	18 52.8	28 34.4	25 29.3	6 41.7	18 41.1	8 38.3	2 19.0	11 51.6	24 1.9
9 T	15 3 31.3	17 27.5	25 28.4	1♌ 2.7	0♊33.9	26 38.7	6 34.2	18 33.4	8 42.4	2 22.4	11 51.2	24 2.7
10 F	15 7 27.8	18 25.5	25 25.2	13 0.5	2 31.0	27 48.0	6 27.5	18 25.8	8 46.3	2 25.7	11 50.7	24 3.4
11 S	15 11 24.3	19 23.5	25 22.0	24 51.6	4 25.5	28 57.1	6 21.7	18 18.1	8 50.3	2 29.1	11 50.3	24 4.2
12 S	15 15 20.9	20 21.4	25 18.8	6♍41.3	6 17.2	0♋ 6.2	6 16.7	18 10.5	8 54.1	2 32.4	11 49.9	24 5.1
13 M	15 19 17.5	21 19.3	25 15.7	18 34.6	8 6.0	1 15.1	6 12.4	18 2.9	8 57.8	2 35.7	11 49.5	24 5.9
14 T	15 23 14.0	22 17.2	25 12.5	0♎36.2	9 51.7	2 23.8	6 9.0	17 55.2	9 1.5	2 39.0	11 49.2	24 6.8
15 W	15 27 10.6	23 15.1	25 9.3	12 49.9	11 34.2	3 32.5	6 6.3	17 47.6	9 5.1	2 42.3	11 48.9	24 7.7
16 T	15 31 7.1	24 12.9	25 6.1	25 18.2	13 13.5	4 41.0	6 4.5	17 40.1	9 8.6	2 45.5	11 48.6	24 8.6
17 F	15 35 3.7	25 10.7	25 3.0	8♏ 2.6	14 49.5	5 49.3	6 3.4	17 32.5	9 12.0	2 48.8	11 48.4	24 9.5
18 S	15 39 0.3	26 8.5	24 59.8	21 3.5	16 22.0	6 57.6	6 3.1	17 25.0	9 15.3	2 52.0	11 48.2	24 10.5
19 S	15 42 56.8	27 6.3	24 56.6	4♐19.8	17 51.1	8 5.6	6D 3.6	17 17.6	9 18.6	2 55.3	11 48.0	24 11.4
20 M	15 46 53.4	28 4.0	24 53.4	17 49.9	19 16.8	9 13.6	6 4.8	17 10.2	9 21.7	2 58.5	11 47.9	24 12.4
21 T	15 50 49.9	29 1.7	24 50.3	1♑31.4	20 38.8	10 21.4	6 6.7	17 2.8	9 24.8	3 1.6	11 47.8	24 13.5
22 W	15 54 46.5	29 59.4	24 47.1	15 22.1	21 57.3	11 29.0	6 9.4	16 55.5	9 27.8	3 4.8	11 47.7	24 14.5
23 T	15 58 43.0	0♊57.1	24 43.9	29 19.8	23 12.1	12 36.5	6 12.9	16 48.2	9 30.7	3 8.0	11 47.6	24 15.5
24 F	16 2 39.6	1 54.7	24 40.7	13♒23.1	24 23.2	13 43.9	6 17.0	16 41.0	9 33.5	3 11.1	11 47.6	24 16.6
25 S	16 6 36.1	2 52.4	24 37.5	27 30.5	25 30.6	14 51.1	6 21.9	16 33.9	9 36.2	3 14.2	11D47.6	24 17.7
26 S	16 10 32.7	3 50.0	24 34.4	11♓40.7	26 34.1	15 58.1	6 27.5	16 26.9	9 38.8	3 17.3	11 47.7	24 18.8
27 M	16 14 29.2	4 47.6	24 31.2	25 52.3	27 33.8	17 5.0	6 33.7	16 19.9	9 41.3	3 20.3	11 47.8	24 19.9
28 T	16 18 25.8	5 45.2	24 28.0	10♈ 2.9	28 29.6	18 11.7	6 40.7	16 13.0	9 43.8	3 23.4	11 47.9	24 21.1
29 W	16 22 22.4	6 42.8	24 24.8	24 9.7	29 21.3	19 18.2	6 48.3	16 6.2	9 46.1	3 26.4	11 48.0	24 22.2
30 T	16 26 18.9	7 40.3	24 21.7	8♉ 9.0	0♋ 9.0	20 24.6	6 56.6	15 59.5	9 48.4	3 29.4	11 48.2	24 23.4
31 F	16 30 15.5	8 37.9	24 18.5	21 57.2	0 52.5	21 30.8	7 5.5	15 53.0	9 50.5	3 32.4	11 48.5	24 24.6
						DECLINATION						
1 W	14 31 58.8	14N43.6	20S58.5	10N10.2	16N16.7	24N39.1	1S36.4	16S24.8	9S56.4	11N40.9	7N59.2	23N 6.1
4 S	14 43 48.5	15 37.8	21 0.3	23 36.8	18 36.5	25 3.5	1 29.2	16 18.8	9 51.8	11 44.5	7 59.9	23 5.8
7 T	14 55 38.1	16 29.7	21 2.1	24 51.2	20 39.5	25 21.7	1 24.9	16 12.8	9 47.5	11 48.0	8 0.5	23 5.5
10 F	15 7 27.8	17 19.1	21 3.8	15 21.2	22 21.8	25 33.7	1 23.2	16 6.7	9 43.5	11 51.4	8 1.1	23 5.2
13 M	15 19 17.5	18 5.9	21 5.6	0 43.1	23 41.5	25 39.6	1 24.4	16 0.7	9 39.7	11 54.9	8 1.4	23 4.8
16 T	15 31 7.1	18 50.0	21 7.3	14S30.2	24 38.6	25 39.2	1 28.1	15 54.6	9 36.3	11 58.2	8 1.7	23 4.4
19 S	15 42 56.8	19 31.2	21 9.0	24 47.7	25 14.4	25 32.8	1 34.5	15 48.7	9 33.1	12 1.5	8 1.9	23 4.0
22 W	15 54 46.5	20 9.4	21 10.7	23 15.4	25 31.1	25 20.3	1 43.3	15 42.8	9 30.2	12 4.8	8 2.0	23 3.5
25 S	16 6 36.1	20 44.5	21 12.4	9 37.1	25 31.1	25 1.9	1 54.5	15 37.1	9 27.7	12 8.0	8 1.9	23 3.1
28 T	16 18 25.8	21 16.4	21 14.1	8N34.6	25 17.1	24 37.9	2 8.0	15 31.6	9 25.4	12 11.1	8 1.7	23 2.6
31 F	16 30 15.5	21 45.1	21 15.8	22 35.6	24 51.4	24 8.3	2 23.7	15 26.4	9 23.5	12 14.1	8 1.5	23 2.0

JUNE 1935

DAY	EPHEMERIS SIDEREAL TIME h m s	☉ ° ′	☊ ° ′	☽ ° ′	☿ ° ′	♀ ° ′	♂ ° ′	♃ ° ′	♄ ° ′	♅ ° ′	♆ ° ′	♇ ° ′
						LONGITUDE						
1 S	16 34 12.0	9♊35.4	24♑15.3	5♊30.7	1♋31.8	22♋36.8	7♎15.1	15♏46.5	9♓52.6	3♉35.3	11♍48.7	24♋25.8
2 S	16 38 8.6	10 32.9	24 12.1	18 47.0	2 6.7	23 42.6	7 25.4	15R40.1	9 54.6	3 38.2	11 49.0	24 27.0
3 M	16 42 5.2	11 30.4	24 9.0	1♋44.8	2 37.3	24 48.2	7 36.3	15 33.8	9 56.4	3 41.1	11 49.3	24 28.3
4 T	16 46 1.7	12 27.9	24 5.8	14 24.2	3 3.4	25 53.7	7 47.7	15 27.6	9 58.2	3 44.0	11 49.7	24 29.5
5 W	16 49 58.3	13 25.4	24 2.6	26 46.7	3 24.9	26 58.9	7 59.8	15 21.6	9 59.9	3 46.8	11 50.0	24 30.8
6 T	16 53 54.8	14 22.8	23 59.4	8♌55.1	3 42.0	28 3.9	8 12.5	15 15.6	10 1.5	3 49.7	11 50.4	24 32.1
7 F	16 57 51.4	15 20.3	23 56.2	20 53.0	3 54.4	29 8.7	8 25.8	15 9.8	10 2.9	3 52.4	11 50.9	24 33.4
8 S	17 1 47.9	16 17.7	23 53.1	2♍44.9	4 2.2	0♌13.3	8 39.7	15 4.2	10 4.3	3 55.2	11 51.4	24 34.7
9 S	17 5 44.5	17 15.1	23 49.9	14 35.7	4 5.4	1 17.7	8 54.1	14 58.6	10 5.6	3 57.9	11 51.9	24 36.1
10 M	17 9 41.1	18 12.4	23 46.7	26 30.2	4R 4.1	2 21.8	9 9.0	14 53.2	10 6.8	4 0.6	11 52.4	24 37.4
11 T	17 13 37.6	19 9.8	23 43.5	8♎33.5	3 58.3	3 25.6	9 24.5	14 48.0	10 7.9	4 3.3	11 53.0	24 38.8
12 W	17 17 34.1	20 7.1	23 40.4	20 49.8	3 48.3	4 29.3	9 40.5	14 42.8	10 8.9	4 5.9	11 53.6	24 40.1
13 T	17 21 30.7	21 4.4	23 37.2	3♏22.8	3 34.1	5 32.6	9 57.1	14 37.9	10 9.8	4 8.5	11 54.2	24 41.5
14 F	17 25 27.3	22 1.7	23 34.0	16 15.2	3 16.0	6 35.7	10 14.1	14 33.1	10 10.6	4 11.1	11 54.9	24 42.9
15 S	17 29 23.9	22 59.0	23 30.8	29 28.1	2 54.3	7 38.6	10 31.7	14 28.4	10 11.3	4 13.6	11 55.6	24 44.4
16 S	17 33 20.4	23 56.3	23 27.7	13♐ 1.1	2 29.4	8 41.1	10 49.7	14 23.9	10 11.9	4 16.1	11 56.3	24 45.8
17 M	17 37 16.9	24 53.6	23 24.5	26 52.3	2 1.5	9 43.3	11 8.1	14 19.5	10 12.4	4 18.6	11 57.1	24 47.2
18 T	17 41 13.5	25 50.8	23 21.3	10♑58.4	1 31.3	10 45.3	11 27.1	14 15.3	10 12.8	4 21.0	11 57.9	24 48.7
19 W	17 45 10.1	26 48.1	23 18.1	25 15.2	0 59.1	11 47.0	11 46.5	14 11.2	10 13.1	4 23.5	11 58.7	24 50.1
20 T	17 49 6.6	27 45.3	23 15.0	9♒38.1	0 25.6	12 48.3	12 6.4	14 7.3	10 13.3	4 25.8	11 59.6	24 51.6
21 F	17 53 3.2	28 42.6	23 11.8	24 2.6	29♊51.2	13 49.3	12 26.7	14 3.6	10 13.4	4 28.2	12 0.4	24 53.1
22 S	17 56 59.8	29 39.8	23 8.6	8♓24.9	29 16.6	14 50.0	12 47.4	14 0.0	10 13.4	4 30.5	12 1.3	24 54.6
23 S	18 0 56.3	0♋37.0	23 5.4	22 41.8	28 42.3	15 50.4	13 8.5	13 56.6	10R13.3	4 32.7	12 2.3	24 56.1
24 M	18 4 52.9	1 34.3	23 2.3	6♈50.8	28 9.0	16 50.4	13 30.1	13 53.4	10 13.1	4 34.9	12 3.3	24 57.6
25 T	18 8 49.4	2 31.5	22 59.1	20 50.0	27 37.2	17 50.1	13 52.0	13 50.3	10 12.8	4 37.1	12 4.3	24 59.1
26 W	18 12 46.0	3 28.7	22 55.9	4♉38.0	27 7.4	18 49.4	14 14.4	13 47.4	10 12.4	4 39.3	12 5.3	25 0.6
27 T	18 16 42.6	4 26.0	22 52.7	18 13.6	26 40.3	19 48.4	14 37.2	13 44.7	10 11.9	4 41.4	12 6.3	25 2.2
28 F	18 20 39.1	5 23.2	22 49.5	1♊35.9	26 16.1	20 46.9	15 0.3	13 42.2	10 11.3	4 43.5	12 7.4	25 3.7
29 S	18 24 35.7	6 20.4	22 46.4	14 44.3	25 55.5	21 45.1	15 23.8	13 39.8	10 10.7	4 45.5	12 8.6	25 5.3
30 S	18 28 32.2	7 17.7	22 43.2	27 38.3	25 38.7	22 42.8	15 47.8	13 37.6	10 9.9	4 47.5	12 9.7	25 6.8
						DECLINATION						
1 S	16 34 12.0	21N53.9	21S16.3	24N56.8	24N40.7	23N57.3	2S29.4	15S24.7	9S22.9	12N15.1	8N 1.4	23N 1.8
4 T	16 46 1.7	22 17.9	21 18.0	23 23.6	24 3.1	23 20.7	2 47.8	15 19.8	9 21.4	12 18.0	8 0.9	23 1.3
7 F	16 57 51.4	22 38.5	21 19.7	12 11.5	23 19.3	22 39.3	3 8.1	15 15.2	9 20.3	12 20.8	8 0.4	23 0.7
10 M	17 9 41.1	22 55.5	21 21.3	2S54.2	22 31.3	21 53.3	3 30.2	15 11.0	9 19.5	12 23.6	7 59.7	23 0.1
13 T	17 21 30.7	23 8.9	21 22.9	17 26.6	21 41.5	21 3.0	3 53.9	15 7.1	9 19.0	12 26.2	7 59.0	22 59.4
16 S	17 33 20.4	23 18.6	21 24.6	25 38.5	20 52.7	20 8.7	4 19.2	15 3.6	9 18.9	12 28.8	7 58.1	22 58.8
19 W	17 45 10.1	23 24.6	21 26.2	20 48.6	20 7.6	19 10.9	4 45.9	15 0.6	9 19.1	12 31.2	7 57.2	22 58.1
22 S	17 56 59.8	23 26.9	21 27.8	4 53.5	19 29.5	18 9.8	5 13.9	14 57.9	9 19.6	12 33.5	7 56.1	22 57.4
25 T	18 8 49.4	23 25.5	21 29.4	12N59.7	19 1.5	17 5.8	5 43.1	14 55.8	9 20.5	12 35.7	7 54.9	22 56.7
28 F	18 20 39.1	23 20.3	21 31.0	24 27.6	18 46.0	15 59.2	6 13.5	14 54.1	9 21.7	12 37.8	7 53.7	22 56.0

JULY 1935

DAY	EPHEMERIS SIDEREAL TIME	☉	☊	☽	☿	♀	♂	♃	♄	♅	♆	♇
	h m s	° ′	° ′	° ′	° ′	° ′	° ′	° ′	° ′	° ′	° ′	° ′
						LONGITUDE						
1 M	18 32 28.8	8♋14.9	22♑40.0	10♋17.9	25♊26.0	23♌40.1	16♎12.0	13♏35.6	10♓ 9.0	4♉49.4	12♍10.9	25♋ 8.4
2 T	18 36 25.3	9 12.1	22 36.8	22 43.9	25R17.7	24 37.0	16 36.7	13R33.7	10R 8.0	4 51.4	12 12.1	25 10.0
3 W	18 40 21.9	10 9.3	22 33.7	4♌57.6	25 14.1	25 33.4	17 1.7	13 32.1	10 6.9	4 53.2	12 13.3	25 11.5
4 T	18 44 18.5	11 6.6	22 30.5	17 0.8	25D15.2	26 29.3	17 27.0	13 30.6	10 5.8	4 55.1	12 14.6	25 13.1
5 F	18 48 15.0	12 3.8	22 27.3	28 56.3	25 21.3	27 24.8	17 52.7	13 29.3	10 4.5	4 56.9	12 15.8	25 14.7
6 S	18 52 11.5	13 1.0	22 24.1	10♍47.4	25 32.4	28 19.7	18 18.7	13 28.2	10 3.1	4 58.6	12 17.1	25 16.3
7 S	18 56 8.1	13 58.2	22 21.0	22 37.9	25 48.6	29 14.1	18 45.1	13 27.3	10 1.7	5 0.3	12 18.5	25 17.9
8 M	19 0 4.7	14 55.4	22 17.8	4♎32.2	26 9.8	0♍ 8.0	19 11.8	13 26.5	10 0.1	5 2.0	12 19.8	25 19.5
9 T	19 4 1.3	15 52.6	22 14.6	16 34.8	26 36.2	1 1.3	19 38.8	13 26.0	9 58.5	5 3.6	12 21.2	25 21.1
10 W	19 7 57.8	16 49.8	22 11.4	28 50.1	27 7.7	1 54.0	20 6.1	13 25.6	9 56.7	5 5.1	12 22.6	25 22.8
11 T	19 11 54.3	17 47.0	22 8.2	11♏22.6	27 44.3	2 46.0	20 33.7	13 25.4	9 54.9	5 6.7	12 24.1	25 24.4
12 F	19 15 50.9	18 44.2	22 5.1	24 15.8	28 25.8	3 37.5	21 1.6	13 25.3	9 53.0	5 8.2	12 25.5	25 26.0
13 S	19 19 47.5	19 41.4	22 1.9	7♐32.3	29 12.4	4 28.3	21 29.8	13D25.5	9 51.0	5 9.6	12 27.0	25 27.6
14 S	19 23 44.0	20 38.6	21 58.7	21 13.1	0♋ 4.0	5 18.4	21 58.3	13 25.8	9 48.9	5 11.0	12 28.5	25 29.2
15 M	19 27 40.6	21 35.8	21 55.5	5♑17.3	1 0.4	6 7.8	22 27.0	13 26.3	9 46.7	5 12.3	12 30.1	25 30.9
16 T	19 31 37.1	22 33.0	21 52.4	19 41.9	2 1.7	6 56.5	22 56.0	13 27.0	9 44.4	5 13.6	12 31.6	25 32.5
17 W	19 35 33.7	23 30.2	21 49.2	4♒21.8	3 7.8	7 44.4	23 25.3	13 27.9	9 42.0	5 14.9	12 33.2	25 34.1
18 T	19 39 30.3	24 27.5	21 46.0	19 10.3	4 18.5	8 31.5	23 54.9	13 29.0	9 39.6	5 16.1	12 34.8	25 35.8
19 F	19 43 26.8	25 24.7	21 42.8	4♓ 0.2	5 33.9	9 17.8	24 24.7	13 30.2	9 37.1	5 17.3	12 36.4	25 37.4
20 S	19 47 23.4	26 21.9	21 39.7	18 44.4	6 53.8	10 3.3	24 54.8	13 31.6	9 34.5	5 18.4	12 38.1	25 39.0
21 S	19 51 19.9	27 19.2	21 36.5	3♈16.9	8 18.1	10 47.9	25 25.1	13 33.2	9 31.8	5 19.5	12 39.8	25 40.6
22 M	19 55 16.5	28 16.4	21 33.3	17 33.4	9 46.8	11 31.6	25 55.7	13 35.0	9 29.0	5 20.5	12 41.4	25 42.3
23 T	19 59 13.1	29 13.7	21 30.1	1♉31.6	11 19.7	12 14.3	26 26.5	13 36.9	9 26.1	5 21.5	12 43.2	25 43.9
24 W	20 3 9.6	0♌11.0	21 27.0	15 10.6	12 56.5	12 56.1	26 57.6	13 39.0	9 23.2	5 22.4	12 44.9	25 45.5
25 T	20 7 6.2	1 8.3	21 23.8	28 31.0	14 37.3	13 36.9	27 28.9	13 41.3	9 20.2	5 23.3	12 46.6	25 47.2
26 F	20 11 2.7	2 5.7	21 20.6	11♊34.1	16 21.7	14 16.6	28 0.5	13 43.8	9 17.1	5 24.1	12 48.4	25 48.8
27 S	20 14 59.3	3 3.0	21 17.4	24 21.5	18 9.5	14 55.3	28 32.3	13 46.4	9 14.0	5 24.9	12 50.2	25 50.4
28 S	20 18 55.8	4 0.4	21 14.2	6♋55.3	20 0.4	15 32.8	29 4.3	13 49.3	9 10.7	5 25.7	12 52.0	25 52.0
29 M	20 22 52.4	4 57.7	21 11.1	19 17.2	21 54.3	16 9.1	29 36.5	13 52.2	9 7.4	5 26.4	12 53.8	25 53.7
30 T	20 26 48.9	5 55.1	21 7.9	1♌28.9	23 50.7	16 44.2	0♏ 9.0	13 55.4	9 4.0	5 27.0	12 55.7	25 55.3
31 W	20 30 45.5	6 52.5	21 4.7	13 32.3	25 49.3	17 18.1	0 41.7	13 58.7	9 0.6	5 27.6	12 57.6	25 56.9
						DECLINATION						
1 M	18 32 28.8	23N11.5	21S32.5	24N 6.8	18N43.9	14N50.4	6S44.9	14S52.8	9S23.2	12N39.7	7N52.3	22N55.3
4 T	18 44 18.5	22 59.0	21 34.1	13 36.4	18 55.1	13 39.8	7 17.3	14 52.1	9 25.1	12 41.6	7 50.8	22 54.6
7 S	18 56 8.1	22 42.9	21 35.7	1S18.5	19 18.0	12 27.8	7 50.5	14 51.8	9 27.2	12 43.3	7 49.3	22 53.9
10 W	19 7 57.8	22 23.3	21 37.2	15 57.8	19 49.8	11 14.7	8 24.5	14 52.1	9 29.7	12 44.8	7 47.6	22 53.2
13 S	19 19 47.5	22 0.2	21 38.7	25 14.0	20 27.1	10 1.0	8 59.1	14 52.8	9 32.5	12 46.3	7 45.9	22 52.4
16 T	19 31 37.1	21 33.7	21 40.3	22 12.8	21 5.8	8 47.1	9 34.3	14 54.0	9 35.6	12 47.6	7 44.1	22 51.7
19 F	19 43 26.8	21 3.9	21 41.8	6 44.5	21 41.3	7 33.4	10 10.0	14 55.7	9 38.9	12 48.7	7 42.2	22 51.0
22 M	19 55 16.5	20 30.9	21 43.3	11N45.5	22 8.4	6 20.4	10 46.1	14 57.9	9 42.5	12 49.8	7 40.3	22 50.3
25 T	20 7 6.2	19 54.8	21 44.8	23 58.8	22 21.9	5 8.5	11 22.5	15 0.5	9 46.4	12 50.6	7 38.3	22 49.5
28 S	20 18 55.8	19 15.7	21 46.3	24 38.8	22 16.7	3 58.2	11 59.2	15 3.6	9 50.5	12 51.4	7 36.2	22 48.8
31 W	20 30 45.5	18 33.7	21 47.7	14 54.7	21 49.3	2 50.2	12 36.0	15 7.1	9 54.8	12 52.0	7 34.0	22 48.1

AUGUST 1935

DAY	EPHEMERIS SIDEREAL TIME	☉	☊	☽	☿	♀	♂	♃	♄	♅	♆	♇
						LONGITUDE						
1 T	20 34 42.1	7♌49.9	21♑ 1.5	25♌29.1	27♋49.8	17♍50.6	1♏14.6	14♏ 2.2	8♓57.1	5♉28.1	12♍59.5	25♋58.5
2 F	20 38 38.6	8 47.3	20 58.4	7♍21.3	29 51.8	18 21.8	1 47.7	14 5.9	8R53.5	5 28.6	13 1.4	26 0.1
3 S	20 42 35.1	9 44.8	20 55.2	19 11.2	1♌55.0	18 51.5	2 21.1	14 9.7	8 49.9	5 29.1	13 3.3	26 1.7
4 S	20 46 31.7	10 42.2	20 52.0	1♎ 1.7	3 59.1	19 19.7	2 54.6	14 13.7	8 46.2	5 29.5	13 5.2	26 3.3
5 M	20 50 28.3	11 39.7	20 48.8	12 56.0	6 3.7	19 46.5	3 28.4	14 17.9	8 42.4	5 29.8	13 7.2	26 4.9
6 T	20 54 24.9	12 37.1	20 45.7	24 57.6	8 8.5	20 11.6	4 2.4	14 22.2	8 38.6	5 30.1	13 9.1	26 6.4
7 W	20 58 21.4	13 34.6	20 42.5	7♏10.8	10 13.3	20 35.0	4 36.5	14 26.7	8 34.8	5 30.4	13 11.1	26 8.0
8 T	21 2 17.9	14 32.1	20 39.3	19 39.7	12 17.7	20 56.7	5 10.9	14 31.3	8 30.8	5 30.5	13 13.1	26 9.6
9 F	21 6 14.5	15 29.6	20 36.1	2♐28.5	14 21.6	21 16.7	5 45.4	14 36.1	8 26.9	5 30.7	13 15.1	26 11.1
10 S	21 10 11.1	16 27.2	20 32.9	15 40.9	16 24.8	21 34.8	6 20.1	14 41.1	8 22.8	5 30.8	13 17.1	26 12.7
11 S	21 14 7.7	17 24.7	20 29.8	29 19.4	18 27.2	21 51.0	6 55.1	14 46.2	8 18.8	5 30.9	13 19.2	26 14.2
12 M	21 18 4.2	18 22.3	20 26.6	13♑25.0	20 28.5	22 5.2	7 30.2	14 51.5	8 14.7	5R30.8	13 21.2	26 15.8
13 T	21 22 0.7	19 19.8	20 23.4	27 56.0	22 28.7	22 17.4	8 5.4	14 56.9	8 10.5	5 30.8	13 23.3	26 17.3
14 W	21 25 57.3	20 17.4	20 20.2	12♒48.1	24 27.7	22 27.6	8 40.9	15 2.4	8 6.3	5 30.7	13 25.3	26 18.8
15 T	21 29 53.8	21 15.0	20 17.1	27 54.2	26 25.5	22 35.6	9 16.5	15 8.2	8 2.1	5 30.6	13 27.4	26 20.3
16 F	21 33 50.4	22 12.6	20 13.9	13♓ 5.0	28 21.9	22 41.4	9 52.3	15 14.0	7 57.8	5 30.4	13 29.5	26 21.8
17 S	21 37 47.0	23 10.3	20 10.7	28 10.6	0♍17.0	22 44.9	10 28.3	15 20.0	7 53.5	5 30.1	13 31.6	26 23.3
18 S	21 41 43.5	24 8.0	20 7.5	13♈ 2.1	2 10.7	22 46.2	11 4.4	15 26.2	7 49.1	5 29.8	13 33.8	26 24.8
19 M	21 45 40.0	25 5.7	20 4.3	27 32.7	4 3.0	22R45.3	11 40.7	15 32.5	7 44.8	5 29.5	13 35.9	26 26.2
20 T	21 49 36.6	26 3.4	20 1.2	11♉38.4	5 53.9	22 41.9	12 17.2	15 38.9	7 40.4	5 29.1	13 38.0	26 27.7
21 W	21 53 33.2	27 1.2	19 58.0	25 18.1	7 43.4	22 36.2	12 53.8	15 45.5	7 35.9	5 28.6	13 40.2	26 29.1
22 T	21 57 29.7	27 58.9	19 54.8	8♊33.2	9 31.5	22 28.2	13 30.6	15 52.2	7 31.5	5 28.2	13 42.3	26 30.6
23 F	22 1 26.2	28 56.8	19 51.6	21 26.2	11 18.2	22 17.8	14 7.5	15 59.1	7 27.0	5 27.6	13 44.5	26 32.0
24 S	22 5 22.8	29 54.6	19 48.5	4♋ 0.8	13 3.5	22 5.0	14 44.7	16 6.1	7 22.5	5 27.0	13 46.7	26 33.4
25 S	22 9 19.4	0♍52.5	19 45.3	16 20.6	14 47.5	21 49.9	15 21.9	16 13.2	7 18.0	5 26.4	13 48.8	26 34.8
26 M	22 13 16.0	1 50.4	19 42.1	28 29.2	16 30.2	21 32.5	15 59.4	16 20.5	7 13.5	5 25.7	13 51.0	26 36.2
27 T	22 17 12.5	2 48.3	19 38.9	10♌29.7	18 11.5	21 12.8	16 36.9	16 27.9	7 8.9	5 25.0	13 53.2	26 37.5
28 W	22 21 9.0	3 46.2	19 35.7	22 24.7	19 51.5	20 50.9	17 14.7	16 35.5	7 4.4	5 24.2	13 55.4	26 38.9
29 T	22 25 5.6	4 44.2	19 32.6	4♍16.4	21 30.2	20 26.9	17 52.6	16 43.1	6 59.8	5 23.4	13 57.6	26 40.2
30 F	22 29 2.2	5 42.2	19 29.4	16 6.7	23 7.6	20 0.9	18 30.6	16 50.9	6 55.2	5 22.5	13 59.8	26 41.6
31 S	22 32 58.7	6 40.3	19 26.2	27 57.3	24 43.7	19 32.9	19 8.8	16 58.9	6 50.7	5 21.6	14 2.0	26 42.9
						DECLINATION						
1 T	20 34 42.1	18N19.1	21S48.2	10N17.5	21N34.8	2N28.1	12S48.3	15S 8.4	9S56.3	12N52.1	7N33.3	22N47.9
4 S	20 46 31.7	17 33.5	21 49.7	4S54.6	20 35.7	1 24.0	13 25.3	15 12.5	10 0.9	12 52.5	7 31.0	22 47.2
7 W	20 58 21.4	16 45.3	21 51.2	18 41.4	19 14.6	0 23.9	14 2.2	15 17.0	10 5.6	12 52.8	7 28.8	22 46.6
10 S	21 10 11.1	15 54.7	21 52.6	25 45.5	17 35.0	0S31.5	14 38.9	15 22.0	10 10.5	12 52.8	7 26.4	22 45.9
13 T	21 22 0.7	15 1.8	21 54.0	20 2.4	15 41.3	1 21.1	15 15.4	15 27.3	10 15.5	12 52.8	7 24.1	22 45.3
16 F	21 33 50.4	14 6.8	21 55.4	2 53.2	13 37.4	2 3.9	15 51.7	15 32.9	10 20.7	12 52.6	7 21.6	22 44.7
19 M	21 45 40.0	13 9.7	21 56.8	15N25.5	11 26.7	2 38.9	16 27.5	15 38.9	10 25.9	12 52.2	7 19.2	22 44.1
22 T	21 57 29.7	12 10.8	21 58.2	25 14.5	9 12.2	3 4.8	17 2.8	15 45.3	10 31.1	12 51.8	7 16.7	22 43.5
25 S	22 9 19.4	11 10.1	21 59.6	22 55.0	6 55.8	3 20.6	17 37.6	15 52.0	10 36.4	12 51.1	7 14.2	22 42.9
28 W	22 21 9.0	10 7.8	22 1.0	11 32.1	4 39.5	3 25.5	18 11.7	15 58.9	10 41.8	12 50.4	7 11.7	22 42.4
31 S	22 32 58.7	9 4.0	22 2.4	3S30.6	2 24.5	3 18.8	18 45.1	16 6.1	10 47.1	12 49.4	7 9.2	22 41.9

SEPTEMBER 1935

DAY	EPHEMERIS SIDEREAL TIME h m s	☉ ° ′	☊ ° ′	☽ ° ′	☿ ° ′	♀ ° ′	♂ ° ′	♃ ° ′	♄ ° ′	♅ ° ′	♆ ° ′	♇ ° ′
						LONGITUDE						
1 S	22 36 55.2	7♍38.3	19♑23.0	9♎50.0	26♍18.5	19♍ 3.2	19♏47.2	17♏ 6.9	6♓46.1	5♉20.7	14♍ 4.2	26♋44.2
2 M	22 40 51.8	8 36.4	19 19.9	21 47.1	27 52.1	18R31.8	20 25.7	17 15.1	6R41.5	5R19.7	14 6.4	26 45.4
3 T	22 44 48.4	9 34.5	19 16.7	3♏50.9	29 24.4	17 59.0	21 4.3	17 23.3	6 37.0	5 18.6	14 8.7	26 46.7
4 W	22 48 44.9	10 32.7	19 13.5	16 4.5	0♎55.4	17 25.0	21 43.1	17 31.8	6 32.4	5 17.5	14 10.9	26 48.0
5 T	22 52 41.5	11 30.8	19 10.3	28 31.5	2 25.2	16 49.8	22 22.0	17 40.3	6 27.9	5 16.4	14 13.1	26 49.2
6 F	22 56 38.0	12 29.0	19 7.1	11♐15.7	3 53.7	16 13.8	23 1.0	17 48.9	6 23.3	5 15.2	14 15.3	26 50.4
7 S	23 0 34.6	13 27.2	19 4.0	24 21.1	5 20.9	15 37.2	23 40.2	17 57.7	6 18.8	5 14.0	14 17.6	26 51.6
8 S	23 4 31.1	14 25.4	19 0.8	7♑51.2	6 46.8	15 0.1	24 19.5	18 6.6	6 14.3	5 12.7	14 19.8	26 52.8
9 M	23 8 27.7	15 23.7	18 57.6	21 48.3	8 11.4	14 22.9	24 59.0	18 15.6	6 9.8	5 11.4	14 22.0	26 54.0
10 T	23 12 24.2	16 22.0	18 54.4	6♒12.8	9 34.7	13 45.8	25 38.5	18 24.7	6 5.4	5 10.0	14 24.2	26 55.1
11 W	23 16 20.8	17 20.3	18 51.3	21 2.2	10 56.6	13 9.1	26 18.2	18 33.9	6 0.9	5 8.6	14 26.5	26 56.2
12 T	23 20 17.3	18 18.6	18 48.1	6♓10.6	12 17.1	12 32.9	26 58.0	18 43.2	5 56.5	5 7.2	14 28.7	26 57.4
13 F	23 24 13.9	19 17.0	18 44.9	21 29.0	13 36.2	11 57.5	27 38.0	18 52.6	5 52.2	5 5.7	14 30.9	26 58.4
14 S	23 28 10.5	20 15.4	18 41.7	6♈46.4	14 53.7	11 23.2	28 18.0	19 2.1	5 47.8	5 4.2	14 33.1	26 59.5
15 S	23 32 7.0	21 13.8	18 38.5	21 51.7	16 9.8	10 50.1	28 58.2	19 11.8	5 43.5	5 2.7	14 35.3	27 0.6
16 M	23 36 3.5	22 12.3	18 35.4	6♉35.6	17 24.2	10 18.5	29 38.5	19 21.5	5 39.2	5 1.1	14 37.6	27 1.6
17 T	23 40 0.1	23 10.8	18 32.2	20 52.2	18 36.9	9 48.5	0♐18.9	19 31.3	5 34.9	4 59.5	14 39.8	27 2.6
18 W	23 43 56.7	24 9.3	18 29.0	4♊39.1	19 47.9	9 20.3	0 59.5	19 41.3	5 30.7	4 57.8	14 42.0	27 3.6
19 T	23 47 53.3	25 7.9	18 25.8	17 57.0	20 57.1	8 54.1	1 40.1	19 51.3	5 26.6	4 56.1	14 44.2	27 4.6
20 F	23 51 49.8	26 6.5	18 22.7	0♋49.0	22 4.2	8 29.9	2 20.9	20 1.4	5 22.4	4 54.4	14 46.4	27 5.5
21 S	23 55 46.3	27 5.1	18 19.5	13 19.4	23 9.3	8 7.9	3 1.8	20 11.6	5 18.4	4 52.6	14 48.6	27 6.5
22 S	23 59 42.9	28 3.8	18 16.3	25 33.1	24 12.1	7 48.2	3 42.8	20 21.9	5 14.3	4 50.8	14 50.7	27 7.4
23 M	0 3 39.5	29 2.5	18 13.1	7♌34.8	25 12.6	7 30.8	4 24.0	20 32.3	5 10.3	4 48.9	14 52.9	27 8.3
24 T	0 7 36.0	0♎ 1.3	18 9.9	19 29.0	26 10.5	7 15.7	5 5.2	20 42.8	5 6.4	4 47.1	14 55.1	27 9.2
25 W	0 11 32.6	1 0.1	18 6.8	1♍19.4	27 5.6	7 3.1	5 46.6	20 53.4	5 2.5	4 45.2	14 57.3	27 10.0
26 T	0 15 29.1	1 58.9	18 3.6	13 9.0	27 57.8	6 52.9	6 28.0	21 4.1	4 58.7	4 43.2	14 59.4	27 10.8
27 F	0 19 25.7	2 57.8	18 0.4	24 60.0	28 46.8	6 45.1	7 9.6	21 14.9	4 55.0	4 41.3	15 1.6	27 11.7
28 S	0 23 22.2	3 56.7	17 57.2	6♎54.2	29 32.3	6 39.7	7 51.3	21 25.7	4 51.3	4 39.3	15 3.7	27 12.4
29 S	0 27 18.8	4 55.6	17 54.1	18 52.9	0♏13.9	6 36.7	8 33.1	21 36.6	4 47.6	4 37.2	15 5.8	27 13.2
30 M	0 31 15.3	5 54.5	17 50.9	0♏57.4	0 51.5	6 36.2	9 15.0	21 47.6	4 44.0	4 35.2	15 7.9	27 13.9

DAY	EPHEMERIS SIDEREAL TIME	☉	☊	☽	☿	♀	♂	♃	♄	♅	♆	♇
						DECLINATION						
1 S	22 36 55.2	8N42.4	22S 2.8	8S30.8	1N40.0	3S14.0	18S56.0	16S 8.6	10S48.8	12N49.1	7N 8.3	22N41.8
4 W	22 48 44.9	7 37.0	22 4.2	21 4.8	0S31.5	2 52.1	19 28.3	16 16.2	10 54.1	12 48.0	7 5.8	22 41.3
7 S	23 0 34.6	6 30.4	22 5.5	25 35.6	2 39.2	2 19.8	19 59.6	16 24.0	10 59.2	12 46.8	7 3.2	22 40.9
10 T	23 12 24.2	5 22.9	22 6.9	17 23.3	4 42.2	1 38.9	20 29.8	16 32.0	11 4.3	12 45.4	7 0.7	22 40.5
13 F	23 24 13.9	4 14.6	22 8.2	0N42.7	6 39.5	0 51.7	20 58.8	16 40.2	11 9.3	12 44.0	6 58.1	22 40.2
16 M	23 36 3.5	3 5.7	22 9.5	18 18.1	8 30.3	0 1.0	21 26.6	16 48.6	11 14.1	12 42.4	6 55.6	22 39.9
19 T	23 47 53.3	1 56.1	22 10.8	25 34.0	10 13.3	0N50.3	21 53.0	16 57.1	11 18.7	12 40.7	6 53.1	22 39.6
22 S	23 59 42.9	0 46.2	22 12.1	20 31.6	11 47.1	1 39.7	22 18.1	17 5.8	11 23.2	12 38.9	6 50.6	22 39.4
25 W	0 11 32.6	0S23.9	22 13.4	7 51.7	13 9.8	2 25.2	22 41.6	17 14.6	11 27.4	12 37.0	6 48.1	22 39.2
28 S	0 23 22.2	1 34.1	22 14.6	7S14.2	14 19.0	3 5.4	23 3.5	17 23.5	11 31.5	12 35.0	6 45.7	22 39.0

OCTOBER 1935

DAY	EPHEMERIS SIDEREAL TIME	☉	☊	☽	☿	♀	♂	♃	♄	♅	♆	♇
						LONGITUDE						
1 T	0 35 11.9	6♎53.5	17♑47.7	13♏ 9.0	1♏24.6	6♍38.0	9♐57.0	21♏58.7	4♓40.5	4♉33.1	15♍10.0	27♋14.7
2 W	0 39 8.5	7 52.6	17 44.5	25 29.4	1 52.9	6D42.1	10 39.2	22 9.9	4R37.1	4R31.0	15 12.1	27 15.3
3 T	0 43 5.0	8 51.6	17 41.4	8♐ 0.9	2 15.9	6 48.4	11 21.4	22 21.1	4 33.7	4 28.8	15 14.2	27 16.0
4 F	0 47 1.5	9 50.7	17 38.2	20 46.2	2 33.2	6 57.0	12 3.7	22 32.5	4 30.4	4 26.7	15 16.3	27 16.7
5 S	0 50 58.1	10 49.8	17 35.0	3♑48.7	2 44.4	7 7.8	12 46.1	22 43.9	4 27.2	4 24.5	15 18.3	27 17.3
6 S	0 54 54.7	11 49.0	17 31.8	17 11.6	2 48.9	7 20.7	13 28.6	22 55.3	4 24.1	4 22.3	15 20.4	27 17.9
7 M	0 58 51.2	12 48.1	17 28.6	0♒57.7	2R46.5	7 35.7	14 11.3	23 6.9	4 21.0	4 20.1	15 22.4	27 18.5
8 T	1 2 47.8	13 47.3	17 25.5	15 8.5	2 36.5	7 52.6	14 54.0	23 18.5	4 18.0	4 17.8	15 24.4	27 19.0
9 W	1 6 44.3	14 46.6	17 22.3	29 43.4	2 18.7	8 11.6	15 36.8	23 30.2	4 15.1	4 15.5	15 26.4	27 19.5
10 T	1 10 40.9	15 45.8	17 19.1	14♓38.6	1 52.9	8 32.4	16 19.7	23 41.9	4 12.3	4 13.3	15 28.4	27 20.0
11 F	1 14 37.4	16 45.1	17 15.9	29 47.0	1 18.9	8 55.1	17 2.6	23 53.7	4 9.5	4 10.9	15 30.4	27 20.5
12 S	1 18 34.0	17 44.5	17 12.8	14♈59.1	0 36.7	9 19.5	17 45.7	24 5.6	4 6.9	4 8.6	15 32.3	27 21.0
13 S	1 22 30.5	18 43.8	17 9.6	0♉ 4.0	29♎46.7	9 45.7	18 28.9	24 17.5	4 4.3	4 6.3	15 34.3	27 21.4
14 M	1 26 27.1	19 43.2	17 6.4	14 51.6	28 49.4	10 13.5	19 12.1	24 29.5	4 1.8	4 3.9	15 36.2	27 21.8
15 T	1 30 23.6	20 42.7	17 3.2	29 14.3	27 45.9	10 43.0	19 55.4	24 41.6	3 59.4	4 1.6	15 38.1	27 22.2
16 W	1 34 20.2	21 42.1	17 0.0	13♊ 8.0	26 37.2	11 14.0	20 38.9	24 53.7	3 57.1	3 59.2	15 40.0	27 22.5
17 T	1 38 16.7	22 41.6	16 56.9	26 32.0	25 25.0	11 46.5	21 22.4	25 5.9	3 54.8	3 56.8	15 41.8	27 22.8
18 F	1 42 13.3	23 41.2	16 53.7	9♋28.4	24 11.2	12 20.4	22 6.0	25 18.1	3 52.7	3 54.4	15 43.7	27 23.1
19 S	1 46 9.8	24 40.8	16 50.5	22 1.2	22 57.9	12 55.8	22 49.6	25 30.4	3 50.7	3 51.9	15 45.5	27 23.4
20 S	1 50 6.4	25 40.4	16 47.3	4♌15.4	21 47.2	13 32.5	23 33.4	25 42.7	3 48.7	3 49.5	15 47.3	27 23.7
21 M	1 54 3.0	26 40.1	16 44.2	16 16.4	20 41.3	14 10.5	24 17.2	25 55.1	3 46.9	3 47.1	15 49.1	27 23.9
22 T	1 57 59.5	27 39.7	16 41.0	28 9.3	19 42.0	14 49.7	25 1.2	26 7.6	3 45.1	3 44.6	15 50.9	27 24.1
23 W	2 1 56.0	28 39.5	16 37.8	9♍58.8	18 51.2	15 30.1	25 45.2	26 20.1	3 43.4	3 42.2	15 52.6	27 24.3
24 T	2 5 52.6	29 39.2	16 34.6	21 48.9	18 10.2	16 11.7	26 29.3	26 32.6	3 41.8	3 39.7	15 54.4	27 24.4
25 F	2 9 49.2	0♏39.1	16 31.4	3♎42.8	17 39.9	16 54.4	27 13.4	26 45.2	3 40.4	3 37.3	15 56.1	27 24.6
26 S	2 13 45.7	1 38.9	16 28.3	15 42.7	17 20.9	17 38.1	27 57.7	26 57.9	3 39.0	3 34.8	15 57.8	27 24.7
27 S	2 17 42.3	2 38.8	16 25.1	27 50.3	17 13.3	18 22.8	28 42.0	27 10.5	3 37.7	3 32.3	15 59.4	27 24.7
28 M	2 21 38.8	3 38.7	16 21.9	10♏ 6.4	17D17.0	19 8.5	29 26.4	27 23.3	3 36.6	3 29.9	16 1.1	27 24.8
29 T	2 25 35.4	4 38.6	16 18.7	22 31.6	17 31.5	19 55.2	0♑10.9	27 36.0	3 35.5	3 27.4	16 2.7	27 24.8
30 W	2 29 32.0	5 38.6	16 15.6	5♐ 6.4	17 56.3	20 42.8	0 55.5	27 48.9	3 34.5	3 24.9	16 4.3	27R24.8
31 T	2 33 28.5	6 38.6	16 12.4	17 51.5	18 30.6	21 31.3	1 40.1	28 1.7	3 33.6	3 22.5	16 5.8	27 24.8

DAY	EPHEMERIS SIDEREAL TIME	☉	☊	☽	☿	♀	♂	♃	♄	♅	♆	♇
						DECLINATION						
1 T	0 35 11.9	2S44.2	22S15.9	20S 7.4	15S11.1	3N39.1	23S23.7	17S32.5	11S35.3	12N32.9	6N43.3	22N38.9
4 F	0 47 1.5	3 54.1	22 17.1	25 25.5	15 41.8	4 5.8	23 42.1	17 41.6	11 38.8	12 30.7	6 40.9	22 38.9
7 M	0 58 51.2	5 3.5	22 18.4	18 50.4	15 45.0	4 25.2	23 58.6	17 50.7	11 42.1	12 28.5	6 38.6	22 38.8
10 T	1 10 40.9	6 12.4	22 19.6	2 10.3	15 13.9	4 37.1	24 13.2	17 59.8	11 45.1	12 26.2	6 36.3	22 38.9
13 S	1 22 30.5	7 20.5	22 20.8	16N 3.6	14 2.9	4 41.7	24 25.8	18 9.0	11 47.8	12 23.8	6 34.1	22 38.9
16 W	1 34 20.2	8 27.7	22 22.0	25 9.0	12 13.1	4 39.1	24 36.2	18 18.2	11 50.2	12 21.4	6 32.0	22 39.0
19 S	1 46 9.8	9 33.8	22 23.2	21 11.0	9 59.0	4 29.6	24 44.6	18 27.3	11 52.2	12 19.0	6 29.9	22 39.2
22 T	1 57 59.5	10 38.8	22 24.4	8 58.9	7 48.5	4 13.6	24 50.7	18 36.4	11 54.0	12 16.5	6 27.9	22 39.4
25 F	2 9 49.2	11♏42.3	22 25.6	5S57.9	6 10.9	3 51.5	24 54.6	18 45.5	11 55.4	12 14.0	6 26.0	22 39.7
28 M	2 21 38.8	12 44.2	22 26.7	19 10.7	5 23.4	3 23.7	24 56.1	18 54.6	11 56.4	12 11.6	6 24.1	22 40.0
31 T	2 33 28.5	13 44.3	22 27.9	25 11.8	5 26.8	2 50.5	24 55.4	19 3.5	11 57.2	12 9.1	6 22.4	22 40.3

NOVEMBER 1935

DAY	EPHEMERIS SIDEREAL TIME h m s	☉ ° ′	☊ ° ′	☽ ° ′	☿ ° ′	♀ ° ′	♂ ° ′	♃ ° ′	♄ ° ′	♅ ° ′	♆ ° ′	♇ ° ′
						LONGITUDE						
1 F	2 37 25.1	7♏38.6	16♑ 9.2	0♑48.1	19♎13.5	22♍20.5	2♑24.8	28♏14.6	3♓32.9	3♉20.0	16♍ 7.4	27♋24.7
2 S	2 41 21.6	8 38.7	16 6.0	13 57.8	20 4.2	23 10.6	3 9.6	28 27.5	3R32.2	3R17.6	16 8.9	27R24.6
3 S	2 45 18.2	9 38.8	16 2.8	27 22.5	21 1.8	24 1.5	3 54.4	28 40.5	3 31.7	3 15.1	16 10.4	27 24.5
4 M	2 49 14.7	10 38.9	15 59.7	11♒ 4.0	22 5.5	24 53.2	4 39.3	28 53.5	3 31.2	3 12.7	16 11.9	27 24.4
5 T	2 53 11.3	11 39.0	15 56.5	25 3.8	23 14.4	25 45.6	5 24.3	29 6.5	3 30.9	3 10.2	16 13.3	27 24.2
6 W	2 57 7.8	12 39.2	15 53.3	9♓21.6	24 27.9	26 38.6	6 9.3	29 19.5	3 30.6	3 7.8	16 14.7	27 24.0
7 T	3 1 4.4	13 39.4	15 50.1	23 55.6	25 45.4	27 32.4	6 54.4	29 32.6	3 30.5	3 5.4	16 16.1	27 23.8
8 F	3 5 1.0	14 39.6	15 47.0	8♈41.2	27 6.1	28 26.8	7 39.6	29 45.7	3 30.4	3 3.0	16 17.5	27 23.6
9 S	3 8 57.5	15 39.8	15 43.8	23 31.6	28 29.7	29 21.9	8 24.8	29 58.9	3D30.5	3 0.6	16 18.8	27 23.4
10 S	3 12 54.1	16 40.1	15 40.6	8♉18.6	29 55.6	0♎17.6	9 10.0	0♐12.0	3 30.7	2 58.2	16 20.1	27 23.1
11 M	3 16 50.6	17 40.4	15 37.4	22 53.7	1♏23.4	1 13.8	9 55.4	0 25.2	3 31.0	2 55.9	16 21.4	27 22.7
12 T	3 20 47.2	18 40.7	15 34.2	7♊ 9.7	2 52.9	2 10.7	10 40.8	0 38.4	3 31.3	2 53.5	16 22.6	27 22.4
13 W	3 24 43.7	19 41.1	15 31.1	21 1.7	4 23.7	3 8.1	11 26.2	0 51.7	3 31.8	2 51.2	16 23.9	27 22.1
14 T	3 28 40.3	20 41.5	15 27.9	4♋27.5	5 55.5	4 6.1	12 11.7	1 4.9	3 32.4	2 48.9	16 25.1	27 21.7
15 F	3 32 36.8	21 41.9	15 24.7	17 27.6	7 28.2	5 4.6	12 57.2	1 18.2	3 33.1	2 46.6	16 26.2	27 21.3
16 S	3 36 33.4	22 42.3	15 21.5	0♌ 4.7	9 1.5	6 3.6	13 42.8	1 31.5	3 33.9	2 44.3	16 27.4	27 20.8
17 S	3 40 29.9	23 42.8	15 18.4	12 22.6	10 35.4	7 3.1	14 28.5	1 44.8	3 34.8	2 42.0	16 28.5	27 20.4
18 M	3 44 26.5	24 43.3	15 15.2	24 26.4	12 9.7	8 3.0	15 14.2	1 58.1	3 35.8	2 39.8	16 29.5	27 19.9
19 T	3 48 23.1	25 43.8	15 12.0	6♍21.1	13 44.2	9 3.4	15 60.0	2 11.5	3 36.9	2 37.6	16 30.6	27 19.4
20 W	3 52 19.6	26 44.4	15 8.8	18 12.0	15 19.0	10 4.3	16 45.8	2 24.8	3 38.2	2 35.4	16 31.6	27 18.9
21 T	3 56 16.2	27 45.0	15 5.7	0♎ 3.7	16 53.9	11 5.6	17 31.7	2 38.2	3 39.5	2 33.2	16 32.6	27 18.3
22 F	4 0 12.7	28 45.6	15 2.5	12 0.4	18 28.8	12 7.3	18 17.6	2 51.6	3 40.9	2 31.1	16 33.5	27 17.8
23 S	4 4 9.3	29 46.3	14 59.3	24 5.6	20 3.8	13 9.3	19 3.6	3 5.0	3 42.4	2 29.0	16 34.5	27 17.2
24 S	4 8 5.8	0♐47.0	14 56.1	6♏21.5	21 38.8	14 11.8	19 49.6	3 18.4	3 44.1	2 26.9	16 35.3	27 16.5
25 M	4 12 2.4	1 47.7	14 52.9	18 49.8	23 13.8	15 14.6	20 35.7	3 31.8	3 45.8	2 24.8	16 36.2	27 15.9
26 T	4 15 58.9	2 48.4	14 49.8	1♐31.1	24 48.7	16 17.8	21 21.8	3 45.2	3 47.6	2 22.8	16 37.0	27 15.2
27 W	4 19 55.5	3 49.1	14 46.6	14 25.4	26 23.5	17 21.3	22 8.0	3 58.6	3 49.6	2 20.8	16 37.8	27 14.5
28 T	4 23 52.1	4 49.9	14 43.4	27 32.0	27 58.2	18 25.2	22 54.2	4 12.0	3 51.6	2 18.8	16 38.6	27 13.8
29 F	4 27 48.6	5 50.7	14 40.2	10♑50.3	29 32.9	19 29.4	23 40.4	4 25.4	3 53.8	2 16.9	16 39.3	27 13.1
30 S	4 31 45.2	6 51.5	14 37.1	24 19.5	1♐ 7.5	20 33.8	24 26.7	4 38.8	3 56.0	2 14.9	16 40.0	27 12.3
						DECLINATION						
1 F	2 37 25.1	14S 3.9	22S28.3	24S41.4	5S37.8	2N38.3	24S54.6	19S 6.5	11S57.3	12N 8.2	6N21.8	22N40.5
4 M	2 49 14.7	15 1.4	22 29.4	15 18.3	6 34.0	1 58.7	24 50.6	19 15.3	11 57.6	12 5.8	6 20.2	22 40.9
7 T	3 1 4.4	15 56.6	22 30.5	1N56.3	7 55.6	1 14.8	24 44.2	19 24.1	11 57.5	12 3.3	6 18.6	22 41.3
10 S	3 12 54.1	16 49.5	22 31.6	18 40.1	9 32.5	0 26.8	24 35.5	19 32.7	11 57.1	12 0.9	6 17.2	22 41.8
13 W	3 24 43.7	17 39.8	22 32.7	25 8.5	11 16.9	0S24.8	24 24.3	19 41.2	11 56.3	11 58.5	6 15.8	22 42.4
16 S	3 36 33.4	18 27.3	22 33.8	18 45.0	13 3.3	1 19.6	24 10.7	19 49.6	11 55.1	11 56.2	6 14.5	22 42.9
19 T	3 48 23.1	19 11.9	22 34.9	5 23.9	14 48.3	2 17.2	23 54.7	19 57.8	11 53.7	11 54.0	6 13.4	22 43.6
22 F	4 0 12.7	19 53.4	22 36.0	9S28.0	16 29.1	3 17.1	23 36.3	20 5.9	11 51.8	11 51.8	6 12.4	22 44.2
25 M	4 12 2.4	20 31.7	22 37.0	21 27.6	18 4.0	4 19.0	23 15.5	20 13.8	11 49.7	11 49.7	6 11.4	22 44.9
28 T	4 23 52.1	21 6.5	22 38.1	24 49.3	19 31.8	5 22.4	22 52.4	20 21.5	11 47.2	11 47.7	6 10.6	22 45.7

DECEMBER 1935

DAY	EPHEMERIS SIDEREAL TIME h m s	☉ ° ′	☊ ° ′	☽ ° ′	☿ ° ′	♀ ° ′	♂ ° ′	♃ ° ′	♄ ° ′	♅ ° ′	♆ ° ′	♇ ° ′
						LONGITUDE						
1 S	4 35 41.7	7♐52.3	14♑33.9	7♒59.4	2♐42.0	21♎38.6	25♑13.0	4♐52.2	3♓58.4	2♉13.1	16♍40.6	27♋11.6
2 M	4 39 38.3	8 53.2	14 30.7	21 49.5	4 16.4	22 43.7	25 59.4	5 5.6	4 0.8	2R11.2	16 41.3	27R10.8
3 T	4 43 34.9	9 54.0	14 27.5	5♓49.3	5 50.8	23 49.0	26 45.8	5 19.0	4 3.4	2 9.4	16 41.8	27 10.0
4 W	4 47 31.4	10 54.9	14 24.4	19 58.2	7 25.1	24 54.7	27 32.2	5 32.4	4 6.0	2 7.7	16 42.4	27 9.1
5 T	4 51 28.0	11 55.8	14 21.2	4♈14.4	8 59.4	26 0.5	28 18.7	5 45.8	4 8.7	2 5.9	16 42.9	27 8.3
6 F	4 55 24.5	12 56.7	14 18.0	18 35.4	10 33.6	27 6.7	29 5.2	5 59.2	4 11.6	2 4.2	16 43.4	27 7.4
7 S	4 59 21.1	13 57.6	14 14.8	2♉57.2	12 7.8	28 13.1	29 51.7	6 12.6	4 14.5	2 2.6	16 43.9	27 6.5
8 S	5 3 17.7	14 58.5	14 11.7	17 15.0	13 42.0	29 19.7	0♒38.2	6 25.9	4 17.5	2 0.9	16 44.3	27 5.6
9 M	5 7 14.2	15 59.4	14 8.5	1♊23.8	15 16.2	0♏26.6	1 24.8	6 39.2	4 20.6	1 59.4	16 44.7	27 4.7
10 T	5 11 10.8	17 0.4	14 5.3	15 18.8	16 50.5	1 33.7	2 11.4	6 52.6	4 23.8	1 57.8	16 45.0	27 3.7
11 W	5 15 7.3	18 1.4	14 2.1	28 56.1	18 24.8	2 41.1	2 58.1	7 5.9	4 27.2	1 56.3	16 45.4	27 2.7
12 T	5 19 3.9	19 2.3	13 59.0	12♋13.4	19 59.1	3 48.6	3 44.7	7 19.2	4 30.6	1 54.9	16 45.6	27 1.8
13 F	5 23 0.4	20 3.3	13 55.8	25 10.2	21 33.5	4 56.4	4 31.4	7 32.5	4 34.0	1 53.5	16 45.9	27 0.8
14 S	5 26 57.0	21 4.3	13 52.6	7♌47.4	23 8.1	6 4.4	5 18.1	7 45.7	4 37.6	1 52.1	16 46.1	26 59.7
15 S	5 30 53.5	22 5.4	13 49.4	20 7.4	24 42.7	7 12.5	6 4.8	7 59.0	4 41.3	1 50.7	16 46.3	26 58.7
16 M	5 34 50.1	23 6.4	13 46.2	2♍13.9	26 17.4	8 20.9	6 51.6	8 12.2	4 45.0	1 49.5	16 46.4	26 57.7
17 T	5 38 46.7	24 7.5	13 43.1	14 11.0	27 52.3	9 29.5	7 38.4	8 25.4	4 48.9	1 48.2	16 46.5	26 56.6
18 W	5 42 43.2	25 8.5	13 39.9	26 3.4	29 27.3	10 38.2	8 25.2	8 38.5	4 52.8	1 47.0	16 46.6	26 55.5
19 T	5 46 39.8	26 9.6	13 36.7	7♎56.0	1♑ 2.4	11 47.2	9 12.0	8 51.7	4 56.8	1 45.9	16 46.7	26 54.4
20 F	5 50 36.3	27 10.7	13 33.5	19 53.6	2 37.8	12 56.2	9 58.8	9 4.8	5 0.9	1 44.8	16 46.7	26 53.3
21 S	5 54 32.9	28 11.8	13 30.4	2♏ 0.5	4 13.2	14 5.5	10 45.7	9 17.9	5 5.1	1 43.7	16R46.6	26 52.2
22 S	5 58 29.5	29 13.0	13 27.2	14 20.5	5 48.9	15 14.9	11 32.6	9 30.9	5 9.4	1 42.7	16 46.6	26 51.0
23 M	6 2 26.0	0♑14.1	13 24.0	26 56.4	7 24.7	16 24.5	12 19.5	9 44.0	5 13.7	1 41.7	16 46.5	26 49.9
24 T	6 6 22.6	1 15.3	13 20.8	9♐50.0	9 0.6	17 34.2	13 6.4	9 57.0	5 18.2	1 40.8	16 46.4	26 48.7
25 W	6 10 19.1	2 16.4	13 17.7	23 1.8	10 36.8	18 44.0	13 53.3	10 9.9	5 22.7	1 39.9	16 46.2	26 47.6
26 T	6 14 15.7	3 17.6	13 14.5	6♑31.1	12 13.0	19 54.0	14 40.3	10 22.8	5 27.3	1 39.1	16 46.0	26 46.4
27 F	6 18 12.3	4 18.8	13 11.3	20 16.0	13 49.4	21 4.1	15 27.2	10 35.7	5 32.0	1 38.4	16 45.8	26 45.2
28 S	6 22 8.8	5 19.9	13 8.1	4♒13.5	15 25.8	22 14.4	16 14.2	10 48.6	5 36.7	1 37.6	16 45.5	26 44.0
29 S	6 26 5.4	6 21.1	13 4.9	18 20.3	17 2.3	23 24.7	17 1.2	11 1.4	5 41.5	1 37.0	16 45.2	26 42.7
30 M	6 30 1.9	7 22.3	13 1.8	2♓32.8	18 38.8	24 35.2	17 48.2	11 14.1	5 46.5	1 36.3	16 44.9	26 41.5
31 T	6 33 58.5	8 23.5	12 58.6	16 47.7	20 15.2	25 45.8	18 35.2	11 26.8	5 51.4	1 35.8	16 44.5	26 40.3
						DECLINATION						
1 S	4 35 41.7	21S37.8	22S39.1	16S 9.6	20S51.4	6S27.0	22S27.0	20S29.1	11S44.4	11N45.8	6N 9.9	22N46.4
4 W	4 47 31.4	22 5.3	22 40.1	0N25.8	22 1.9	7 32.3	21 59.4	20 36.5	11 41.2	11 44.0	6 9.4	22 47.2
7 S	4 59 21.1	22 29.0	22 41.2	17 5.9	23 2.7	8 38.0	21 29.7	20 43.6	11 37.8	11 42.3	6 8.9	22 48.1
10 T	5 11 10.8	22 48.8	22 42.2	25 2.7	23 53.1	9 43.6	20 57.8	20 50.6	11 34.0	11 40.8	6 8.6	22 48.9
13 F	5 23 0.4	23 4.5	22 43.2	20 0.1	24 32.4	10 48.9	20 23.8	20 57.3	11 29.9	11 39.4	6 8.4	22 49.8
16 M	5 34 50.1	23 16.1	22 44.1	6 57.0	25 0.0	11 53.3	19 47.9	21 3.8	11 25.5	11 38.1	6 8.3	22 50.7
19 T	5 46 39.8	23 23.5	22 45.1	7S57.7	25 15.3	12 56.5	19 10.1	21 10.1	11 20.9	11 36.9	6 8.3	22 51.6
22 S	5 58 29.5	23 26.8	22 46.1	20 25.9	25 17.8	13 58.0	18 30.5	21 16.2	11 16.0	11 35.9	6 8.5	22 52.5
25 W	6 10 19.1	23 25.7	22 47.0	25 2.7	25 7.0	14 57.6	17 49.1	21 22.1	11 10.8	11 35.0	6 8.7	22 53.5
28 S	6 22 8.8	23 20.4	22 48.0	17 19.4	24 42.3	15 54.7	17 6.1	21 27.7	11 5.3	11 34.3	6 9.1	22 54.5
31 T	6 33 58.5	23 10.9	22 48.9	0 50.0	24 3.7	16 49.1	16 21.5	21 33.1	10 59.6	11 33.8	6 9.6	22 55.4

JANUARY 1936

DAY	EPHEMERIS SIDEREAL TIME h m s	☉ ° ′	☊ ° ′	☽ ° ′	☿ ° ′	♀ ° ′	♂ ° ′	♃ ° ′	♄ ° ′	♅ ° ′	♆ ° ′	♇ ° ′
						LONGITUDE						
1 W	6 37 55.1	9♑24.6	12♑55.4	1♈ 1.9	21♑51.5	26♏56.5	19♒22.2	11♐39.5	5♓56.5	1♉35.3	16♍44.1	26♋39.0
2 T	6 41 51.6	10 25.8	12 52.2	15 12.8	23 27.5	28 7.3	20 9.2	11 52.1	6 1.6	1R34.8	16R43.7	26R37.8
3 F	6 45 48.2	11 26.9	12 49.1	29 18.3	25 3.2	29 18.2	20 56.2	12 4.7	6 6.8	1 34.4	16 43.2	26 36.5
4 S	6 49 44.7	12 28.1	12 45.9	13♉16.7	26 38.5	0♐29.3	21 43.2	12 17.2	6 12.1	1 34.0	16 42.7	26 35.2
5 S	6 53 41.3	13 29.3	12 42.7	27 6.1	28 13.2	1 40.4	22 30.2	12 29.7	6 17.4	1 33.7	16 42.2	26 34.0
6 M	6 57 37.9	14 30.4	12 39.5	10♊44.9	29 47.0	2 51.6	23 17.2	12 42.1	6 22.8	1 33.4	16 41.6	26 32.7
7 T	7 1 34.4	15 31.5	12 36.4	24 11.6	1♒19.8	4 2.9	24 4.2	12 54.5	6 28.3	1 33.2	16 41.0	26 31.4
8 W	7 5 30.9	16 32.7	12 33.2	7♋25.0	2 51.4	5 14.3	24 51.2	13 6.8	6 33.8	1 33.1	16 40.4	26 30.1
9 T	7 9 27.5	17 33.8	12 30.0	20 24.1	4 21.4	6 25.8	25 38.2	13 19.0	6 39.4	1 33.0	16 39.7	26 28.8
10 F	7 13 24.1	18 34.9	12 26.8	3♌ 8.5	5 49.5	7 37.4	26 25.2	13 31.2	6 45.1	1 32.9	16 39.0	26 27.5
11 S	7 17 20.6	19 36.1	12 23.7	15 38.6	7 15.3	8 49.0	27 12.2	13 43.3	6 50.8	1 32.9	16 38.3	26 26.2
12 S	7 21 17.2	20 37.2	12 20.5	27 55.6	8 38.3	10 0.8	27 59.2	13 55.4	6 56.6	1D33.0	16 37.6	26 24.9
13 M	7 25 13.7	21 38.3	12 17.3	10♍ 1.5	9 58.0	11 12.6	28 46.2	14 7.4	7 2.4	1 33.1	16 36.8	26 23.5
14 T	7 29 10.3	22 39.4	12 14.1	21 59.1	11 13.9	12 24.5	29 33.2	14 19.4	7 8.3	1 33.2	16 36.0	26 22.2
15 W	7 33 6.9	23 40.5	12 10.9	3♎52.0	12 25.2	13 36.5	0♓20.2	14 31.2	7 14.3	1 33.4	16 35.1	26 20.9
16 T	7 37 3.4	24 41.7	12 7.8	15 44.3	13 31.2	14 48.6	1 7.1	14 43.1	7 20.3	1 33.7	16 34.3	26 19.6
17 F	7 40 60.0	25 42.8	12 4.6	27 40.5	14 31.2	16 0.7	1 54.1	14 54.8	7 26.3	1 34.0	16 33.4	26 18.3
18 S	7 44 56.5	26 43.9	12 1.4	9♏45.5	15 24.3	17 12.9	2 41.1	15 6.5	7 32.5	1 34.4	16 32.5	26 16.9
19 S	7 48 53.1	27 45.0	11 58.2	22 3.8	16 9.6	18 25.2	3 28.0	15 18.1	7 38.6	1 34.8	16 31.5	26 15.6
20 M	7 52 49.7	28 46.1	11 55.1	4♐39.7	16 46.3	19 37.5	4 14.9	15 29.6	7 44.9	1 35.3	16 30.5	26 14.3
21 T	7 56 46.2	29 47.2	11 51.9	17 36.7	17 13.5	20 49.9	5 1.9	15 41.0	7 51.2	1 35.8	16 29.5	26 13.0
22 W	8 0 42.7	0♒48.2	11 48.7	0♑57.0	17 30.5	22 2.3	5 48.8	15 52.4	7 57.5	1 36.4	16 28.5	26 11.7
23 T	8 4 39.3	1 49.3	11 45.5	14 41.0	17 36.6	23 14.9	6 35.7	16 3.7	8 3.9	1 37.0	16 27.4	26 10.3
24 F	8 8 35.9	2 50.4	11 42.4	28 47.1	17R31.3	24 27.4	7 22.6	16 14.9	8 10.3	1 37.7	16 26.3	26 9.0
25 S	8 12 32.4	3 51.4	11 39.2	13♒11.5	17 14.5	25 40.0	8 9.5	16 26.1	8 16.8	1 38.4	16 25.2	26 7.7
26 S	8 16 29.0	4 52.4	11 36.0	27 48.4	16 46.2	26 52.7	8 56.3	16 37.1	8 23.3	1 39.2	16 24.1	26 6.4
27 M	8 20 25.5	5 53.5	11 32.8	12♓30.9	16 7.1	28 5.3	9 43.2	16 48.1	8 29.9	1 40.0	16 22.9	26 5.1
28 T	8 24 22.1	6 54.5	11 29.6	27 11.9	15 17.9	29 18.1	10 30.0	16 58.9	8 36.5	1 40.9	16 21.7	26 3.8
29 W	8 28 18.7	7 55.4	11 26.5	11♈44.9	14 19.9	0♑30.9	11 16.8	17 9.7	8 43.1	1 41.8	16 20.5	26 2.5
30 T	8 32 15.2	8 56.4	11 23.3	26 5.2	13 14.8	1 43.7	12 3.6	17 20.4	8 49.8	1 42.8	16 19.3	26 1.2
31 F	8 36 11.8	9 57.3	11 20.1	10♉ 9.9	12 4.4	2 56.5	12 50.4	17 31.0	8 56.5	1 43.9	16 18.0	25 59.9
						DECLINATION						
1 W	6 37 55.1	23S 6.8	22S49.2	5N 9.4	23S47.8	17S 6.6	16S 6.3	21S34.9	10S57.7	11N33.6	6N 9.8	22N55.8
4 S	6 49 44.7	22 51.8	22 50.1	20 10.2	22 50.7	17 56.7	15 19.7	21 40.0	10 51.7	11 33.3	6 10.5	22 56.7
7 T	7 1 34.4	22 32.7	22 51.0	25 0.4	21 40.7	18 43.1	14 31.8	21 44.8	10 45.4	11 33.1	6 11.3	22 57.7
10 F	7 13 24.1	22 9.5	22 51.9	17 40.1	20 19.3	19 25.7	13 42.7	21 49.5	10 39.0	11 33.1	6 12.1	22 58.7
13 M	7 25 13.7	21 42.5	22 52.8	3 41.7	18 49.7	20 4.0	12 52.4	21 53.8	10 32.3	11 33.2	6 13.1	22 59.7
16 T	7 37 3.4	21 11.7	22 53.7	11S 3.0	17 17.2	20 37.6	12 1.0	21 58.0	10 25.5	11 33.5	6 14.2	23 0.6
19 S	7 48 53.1	20 37.2	22 54.5	22 13.8	15 49.4	21 6.5	11 8.7	22 1.9	10 18.4	11 34.0	6 15.4	23 1.6
22 W	8 0 42.7	19 59.1	22 55.4	24 31.4	14 36.8	21 30.2	10 15.4	22 5.7	10 11.2	11 34.6	6 16.7	23 2.6
25 S	8 12 32.4	19 17.7	22 56.2	14 18.5	13 50.1	21 48.6	9 21.4	22 9.2	10 3.9	11 35.4	6 18.0	23 3.5
28 T	8 24 22.1	18 33.2	22 57.0	3N30.9	13 36.8	22 1.5	8 26.6	22 12.4	9 56.4	11 36.4	6 19.5	23 4.4
31 F	8 36 11.8	17 45.6	22 57.9	19 15.9	13 56.4	22 8.8	7 31.3	22 15.5	9 48.7	11 37.5	6 21.0	23 5.3

FEBRUARY 1936

DAY	EPHEMERIS SIDEREAL TIME h m s	☉ ° ′	☊ ° ′	☽ ° ′	☿ ° ′	♀ ° ′	♂ ° ′	♃ ° ′	♄ ° ′	♅ ° ′	♆ ° ′	♇ ° ′
						LONGITUDE						
1 S	8 40 8.3	10♒58.3	11♑16.9	23♉57.9	10♒51.0	4♑ 9.4	13♓37.1	17♐41.5	9♓ 3.3	1♉45.0	16♍16.7	25♋58.7
2 S	8 44 4.9	11 59.1	11 13.8	7♊29.5	9R36.7	5 22.4	14 23.9	17 51.9	9 10.1	1 46.1	16R15.4	25R57.4
3 M	8 48 1.4	13 0.0	11 10.6	20 45.6	8 23.6	6 35.3	15 10.6	18 2.2	9 16.9	1 47.3	16 14.1	25 56.1
4 T	8 51 58.0	14 0.9	11 7.4	3♋47.6	7 13.5	7 48.3	15 57.2	18 12.4	9 23.8	1 48.5	16 12.8	25 54.9
5 W	8 55 54.5	15 1.7	11 4.2	16 37.0	6 8.2	9 1.4	16 43.9	18 22.5	9 30.7	1 49.8	16 11.4	25 53.7
6 T	8 59 51.1	16 2.5	11 1.1	29 14.9	5 9.1	10 14.4	17 30.5	18 32.5	9 37.6	1 51.1	16 10.0	25 52.4
7 F	9 3 47.7	17 3.3	10 57.9	11♌42.4	4 17.0	11 27.5	18 17.1	18 42.4	9 44.6	1 52.5	16 8.6	25 51.2
8 S	9 7 44.2	18 4.0	10 54.7	24 0.2	3 32.7	12 40.7	19 3.7	18 52.2	9 51.6	1 54.0	16 7.2	25 50.0
9 S	9 11 40.8	19 4.8	10 51.5	6♍ 9.4	2 56.4	13 53.8	19 50.2	19 1.9	9 58.6	1 55.4	16 5.8	25 48.8
10 M	9 15 37.3	20 5.5	10 48.3	18 11.1	2 28.5	15 7.0	20 36.7	19 11.5	10 5.7	1 57.0	16 4.3	25 47.6
11 T	9 19 33.9	21 6.2	10 45.2	0♎ 7.0	2 8.7	16 20.3	21 23.2	19 21.0	10 12.7	1 58.5	16 2.9	25 46.4
12 W	9 23 30.5	22 6.9	10 42.0	11 59.4	1 56.8	17 33.6	22 9.7	19 30.3	10 19.8	2 0.2	16 1.4	25 45.2
13 T	9 27 27.0	23 7.5	10 38.8	23 51.1	1 52.6	18 46.8	22 56.1	19 39.6	10 27.0	2 1.8	15 59.9	25 44.1
14 F	9 31 23.5	24 8.2	10 35.6	5♏45.8	1D55.6	20 0.2	23 42.5	19 48.7	10 34.1	2 3.5	15 58.4	25 42.9
15 S	9 35 20.1	25 8.8	10 32.5	17 47.8	2 5.4	21 13.5	24 28.9	19 57.7	10 41.3	2 5.3	15 56.8	25 41.8
16 S	9 39 16.7	26 9.4	10 29.3	0♐ 1.8	2 21.5	22 26.9	25 15.2	20 6.6	10 48.5	2 7.1	15 55.3	25 40.7
17 M	9 43 13.2	27 10.0	10 26.1	12 32.7	2 43.5	23 40.3	26 1.5	20 15.4	10 55.7	2 8.9	15 53.8	25 39.6
18 T	9 47 9.8	28 10.6	10 22.9	25 25.2	3 11.0	24 53.7	26 47.8	20 24.1	11 2.9	2 10.8	15 52.2	25 38.5
19 W	9 51 6.3	29 11.1	10 19.7	8♑43.1	3 43.5	26 7.2	27 34.1	20 32.6	11 10.1	2 12.7	15 50.6	25 37.4
20 T	9 55 2.9	0♓11.6	10 16.6	22 28.8	4 20.7	27 20.6	28 20.3	20 41.0	11 17.4	2 14.7	15 49.0	25 36.4
21 F	9 58 59.4	1 12.1	10 13.4	6♒42.3	5 2.1	28 34.1	29 6.5	20 49.3	11 24.7	2 16.7	15 47.4	25 35.3
22 S	10 2 56.0	2 12.6	10 10.2	21 20.9	5 47.5	29 47.6	29 52.6	20 57.4	11 32.0	2 18.8	15 45.8	25 34.3
23 S	10 6 52.5	3 13.0	10 7.0	6♓18.4	6 36.6	1♒ 1.1	0♈38.7	21 5.5	11 39.3	2 20.9	15 44.2	25 33.3
24 M	10 10 49.1	4 13.4	10 3.9	21 25.9	7 29.0	2 14.7	1 24.8	21 13.3	11 46.6	2 23.0	15 42.6	25 32.3
25 T	10 14 45.7	5 13.8	10 0.7	6♈33.1	8 24.6	3 28.2	2 10.9	21 21.1	11 53.9	2 25.2	15 40.9	25 31.3
26 W	10 18 42.2	6 14.2	9 57.5	21 30.1	9 23.0	4 41.8	2 56.9	21 28.7	12 1.2	2 27.5	15 39.3	25 30.4
27 T	10 22 38.8	7 14.5	9 54.3	6♉ 9.2	10 24.1	5 55.3	3 42.9	21 36.2	12 8.6	2 29.7	15 37.6	25 29.4
28 F	10 26 35.3	8 14.8	9 51.1	20 25.4	11 27.7	7 8.9	4 28.8	21 43.5	12 15.9	2 32.0	15 36.0	25 28.5
29 S	10 30 31.8	9 15.0	9 48.0	4♊17.0	12 33.7	8 22.5	5 14.7	21 50.7	12 23.3	2 34.3	15 34.3	25 27.6
						DECLINATION						
1 S	8 40 8.3	17S29.1	22S58.1	22N34.1	14S 8.7	22S 9.9	7S12.7	22S16.5	9S46.1	11N37.9	6N21.5	23N 5.6
4 T	8 51 58.0	16 37.7	22 58.9	24 11.4	14 56.5	22 9.5	6 16.8	22 19.3	9 38.3	11 39.2	6 23.1	23 6.5
7 F	9 3 47.7	15 43.8	22 59.7	14 50.6	15 50.2	22 3.3	5 20.4	22 21.8	9 30.4	11 40.7	6 24.8	23 7.3
10 M	9 15 37.3	14 47.5	23 0.5	0 19.8	16 40.1	21 51.2	4 23.7	22 24.2	9 22.4	11 42.3	6 26.6	23 8.1
13 T	9 27 27.0	13 48.9	23 1.3	13S56.5	17 20.9	21 33.4	3 26.8	22 26.5	9 14.3	11 44.1	6 28.4	23 8.9
16 S	9 39 16.7	12 48.2	23 2.0	23 31.4	17 50.3	21 9.8	2 29.8	22 28.5	9 6.2	11 46.0	6 30.2	23 9.7
19 W	9 51 6.3	11 45.7	23 2.8	23 26.3	18 7.3	20 40.6	1 32.8	22 30.4	8 57.9	11 48.0	6 32.1	23 10.4
22 S	10 2 56.0	10 41.5	23 3.5	11 17.5	18 11.9	20 5.9	0 35.7	22 32.1	8 49.7	11 50.1	6 34.0	23 11.1
25 T	10 14 45.7	9 35.8	23 4.2	7N15.7	18 3.8	19 26.0	0N21.2	22 33.6	8 41.3	11 52.4	6 36.0	23 11.7
28 F	10 26 35.3	8 28.8	23 4.9	21 39.5	17 43.3	18 41.0	1 17.9	22 35.0	8 33.0	11 54.8	6 37.9	23 12.3

MARCH 1936

LONGITUDE

DAY	EPHEMERIS SIDEREAL TIME h m s	☉ ° ′	☊ ° ′	☽ ° ′	☿ ° ′	♀ ° ′	♂ ° ′	♃ ° ′	♄ ° ′	♅ ° ′	♆ ° ′	♇ ° ′
1 S	10 34 28.4	10♓15.3	9♑44.8	17♊44.7	13♒41.9	9♒36.1	6♈ 0.6	21♐57.7	12♓30.6	2♉36.7	15♍32.7	25♋26.7
2 M	10 38 25.0	11 15.5	9 41.6	0♋50.9	14 52.1	10 49.7	6 46.4	22 4.6	12 38.0	2 39.1	15R31.0	25R25.8
3 T	10 42 21.5	12 15.6	9 38.4	13 38.8	16 4.3	12 3.3	7 32.2	22 11.4	12 45.3	2 41.6	15 29.3	25 25.0
4 W	10 46 18.1	13 15.7	9 35.3	26 11.9	17 18.3	13 17.0	8 17.9	22 18.0	12 52.7	2 44.1	15 27.7	25 24.2
5 T	10 50 14.6	14 15.8	9 32.1	8♌33.5	18 34.1	14 30.6	9 3.6	22 24.5	13 0.0	2 46.6	15 26.0	25 23.3
6 F	10 54 11.2	15 15.9	9 28.9	20 46.0	19 51.6	15 44.2	9 49.3	22 30.8	13 7.4	2 49.2	15 24.3	25 22.6
7 S	10 58 7.7	16 15.9	9 25.7	2♍51.7	21 10.7	16 57.9	10 34.9	22 36.9	13 14.8	2 51.7	15 22.7	25 21.8
8 S	11 2 4.3	17 15.9	9 22.6	14 52.0	22 31.3	18 11.5	11 20.4	22 42.9	13 22.1	2 54.4	15 21.0	25 21.1
9 M	11 6 0.8	18 15.8	9 19.4	26 48.4	23 53.4	19 25.2	12 5.9	22 48.8	13 29.4	2 57.0	15 19.3	25 20.3
10 T	11 9 57.4	19 15.7	9 16.2	8♎41.9	25 17.0	20 38.9	12 51.4	22 54.5	13 36.8	2 59.7	15 17.7	25 19.6
11 W	11 13 54.0	20 15.6	9 13.0	20 34.1	26 42.0	21 52.6	13 36.9	23 0.0	13 44.1	3 2.4	15 16.0	25 18.9
12 T	11 17 50.5	21 15.5	9 9.8	2♏26.8	28 8.4	23 6.3	14 22.2	23 5.4	13 51.4	3 5.2	15 14.3	25 18.3
13 F	11 21 47.0	22 15.3	9 6.7	14 22.5	29 36.1	24 20.0	15 7.6	23 10.6	13 58.7	3 7.9	15 12.7	25 17.6
14 S	11 25 43.6	23 15.1	9 3.5	26 24.5	1♓ 5.1	25 33.7	15 52.9	23 15.7	14 6.0	3 10.8	15 11.0	25 17.0
15 S	11 29 40.2	24 14.9	9 0.3	8♐36.8	2 35.5	26 47.4	16 38.2	23 20.5	14 13.3	3 13.6	15 9.4	25 16.4
16 M	11 33 36.7	25 14.6	8 57.1	21 3.8	4 7.2	28 1.2	17 23.4	23 25.3	14 20.6	3 16.5	15 7.7	25 15.9
17 T	11 37 33.3	26 14.3	8 54.0	3♑50.2	5 40.1	29 14.9	18 8.6	23 29.8	14 27.9	3 19.4	15 6.1	25 15.3
18 W	11 41 29.8	27 14.0	8 50.8	17 0.8	7 14.3	0♓28.7	18 53.7	23 34.2	14 35.1	3 22.3	15 4.5	25 14.8
19 T	11 45 26.4	28 13.7	8 47.6	0♒39.1	8 49.8	1 42.4	19 38.8	23 38.4	14 42.3	3 25.2	15 2.8	25 14.3
20 F	11 49 22.9	29 13.3	8 44.4	14 46.9	10 26.6	2 56.2	20 23.8	23 42.5	14 49.6	3 28.2	15 1.2	25 13.8
21 S	11 53 19.5	0♈12.9	8 41.2	29 23.4	12 4.7	4 9.9	21 8.9	23 46.4	14 56.8	3 31.2	14 59.6	25 13.4
22 S	11 57 16.0	1 12.5	8 38.1	14♓23.8	13 44.0	5 23.7	21 53.8	23 50.0	15 3.9	3 34.2	14 58.0	25 12.9
23 M	12 1 12.6	2 12.0	8 34.9	29 39.8	15 24.6	6 37.5	22 38.7	23 53.6	15 11.1	3 37.3	14 56.5	25 12.5
24 T	12 5 9.1	3 11.5	8 31.7	15♈ 0.5	17 6.5	7 51.2	23 23.6	23 56.9	15 18.2	3 40.3	14 54.9	25 12.2
25 W	12 9 5.7	4 11.0	8 28.5	0♉14.1	18 49.7	9 5.0	24 8.4	24 0.1	15 25.4	3 43.4	14 53.3	25 11.8
26 T	12 13 2.2	5 10.4	8 25.4	15 10.1	20 34.2	10 18.8	24 53.2	24 3.1	15 32.5	3 46.6	14 51.8	25 11.5
27 F	12 16 58.8	6 9.8	8 22.2	29 41.3	22 20.1	11 32.5	25 37.9	24 5.9	15 39.5	3 49.7	14 50.2	25 11.2
28 S	12 20 55.3	7 9.1	8 19.0	13♊44.0	24 7.3	12 46.3	26 22.6	24 8.5	15 46.6	3 52.9	14 48.7	25 10.9
29 S	12 24 51.9	8 8.5	8 15.8	27 18.1	25 55.8	14 0.0	27 7.2	24 10.9	15 53.6	3 56.0	14 47.2	25 10.6
30 M	12 28 48.5	9 7.7	8 12.6	10♋25.9	27 45.7	15 13.8	27 51.8	24 13.2	16 0.6	3 59.2	14 45.7	25 10.4
31 T	12 32 45.0	10 7.0	8 9.5	23 11.2	29 37.0	16 27.5	28 36.3	24 15.3	16 7.5	4 2.4	14 44.2	25 10.2

DECLINATION

DAY	EPHEMERIS SIDEREAL TIME h m s	☉ ° ′	☊ ° ′	☽ ° ′	☿ ° ′	♀ ° ′	♂ ° ′	♃ ° ′	♄ ° ′	♅ ° ′	♆ ° ′	♇ ° ′
1 S	10 34 28.4	7S43.6	23S 5.4	24N53.4	17S22.8	18S 8.3	1N55.5	22S35.8	8S27.4	11N56.5	6N39.2	23N12.7
4 W	10 46 18.1	6 34.8	23 6.1	19 36.2	16 41.9	17 15.4	2 51.7	22 37.0	8 19.1	11 59.1	6 41.2	23 13.3
7 S	10 58 7.7	5 25.3	23 6.8	6 44.1	15 48.9	16 18.0	3 47.5	22 38.0	8 10.8	12 1.8	6 43.2	23 13.8
10 T	11 9 57.4	4 15.1	23 7.4	8S 3.6	14 44.2	15 16.6	4 42.8	22 38.9	8 2.4	12 4.6	6 45.1	23 14.3
13 F	11 21 47.0	3 4.4	23 8.1	20 6.0	13 27.8	14 11.3	5 37.5	22 39.8	7 54.2	12 7.4	6 47.1	23 14.7
16 M	11 33 36.7	1 53.5	23 8.7	24 43.7	11 60.0	13 2.4	6 31.6	22 40.4	7 45.9	12 10.4	6 49.0	23 15.1
19 T	11 45 26.4	0 42.3	23 9.4	18 13.4	10 21.0	11 50.3	7 25.0	22 41.0	7 37.7	12 13.4	6 50.9	23 15.4
22 S	11 57 16.0	0N28.8	23 10.0	1 56.2	8 31.1	10 35.3	8 17.6	22 41.6	7 29.6	12 16.6	6 52.8	23 15.7
25 W	12 9 5.7	1 39.8	23 10.6	15N54.5	6 30.6	9 17.7	9 9.4	22 42.0	7 21.6	12 19.7	6 54.6	23 16.0
28 S	12 20 55.3	2 50.4	23 11.2	24 31.4	4 19.8	7 57.8	10 0.3	22 42.3	7 13.6	12 23.0	6 56.4	23 16.2
31 T	12 32 45.0	4 0.5	23 11.8	20 9.6	1 59.3	6 35.9	10 50.2	22 42.6	7 5.8	12 26.3	6 58.1	23 16.3

APRIL 1936

LONGITUDE

DAY	EPHEMERIS SIDEREAL TIME h m s	☉ ° ′	☊ ° ′	☽ ° ′	☿ ° ′	♀ ° ′	♂ ° ′	♃ ° ′	♄ ° ′	♅ ° ′	♆ ° ′	♇ ° ′
1 W	12 36 41.5	11♈ 6.2	8♑ 6.3	5♌38.5	1♈29.6	17♓41.3	29♈20.8	24♐17.2	16♓14.4	4♉ 5.7	14♍42.8	25♋10.0
2 T	12 40 38.1	12 5.3	8 3.1	17 52.1	3 23.6	18 55.0	0♉ 5.3	24 18.9	16 21.3	4 8.9	14R41.3	25R 9.8
3 F	12 44 34.7	13 4.4	7 59.9	29 56.2	5 19.0	20 8.8	0 49.6	24 20.4	16 28.2	4 12.2	14 39.9	25 9.7
4 S	12 48 31.2	14 3.5	7 56.8	11♍53.9	7 15.7	21 22.5	1 34.0	24 21.8	16 35.0	4 15.5	14 38.5	25 9.6
5 S	12 52 27.8	15 2.6	7 53.6	23 48.1	9 13.7	22 36.2	2 18.2	24 22.9	16 41.8	4 18.8	14 37.1	25 9.5
6 M	12 56 24.3	16 1.6	7 50.4	5♎40.8	11 13.1	23 50.0	3 2.5	24 23.9	16 48.5	4 22.1	14 35.7	25 9.5
7 T	13 0 20.9	17 0.6	7 47.2	17 33.4	13 13.7	25 3.7	3 46.6	24 24.7	16 55.3	4 25.4	14 34.3	25 9.4
8 W	13 4 17.4	17 59.5	7 44.0	29 27.5	15 15.5	26 17.4	4 30.8	24 25.3	17 1.9	4 28.7	14 33.0	25 9.4
9 T	13 8 14.0	18 58.4	7 40.9	11♏24.2	17 18.4	27 31.2	5 14.9	24 25.7	17 8.6	4 32.1	14 31.7	25D 9.5
10 F	13 12 10.5	19 57.3	7 37.7	23 25.3	19 22.3	28 44.9	5 58.9	24 25.9	17 15.2	4 35.4	14 30.4	25 9.5
11 S	13 16 7.1	20 56.1	7 34.5	5♐32.9	21 27.1	29 58.6	6 42.9	24 26.0	17 21.7	4 38.8	14 29.1	25 9.6
12 S	13 20 3.6	21 55.0	7 31.3	17 49.8	23 32.6	1♈12.4	7 26.8	24R25.8	17 28.3	4 42.2	14 27.9	25 9.7
13 M	13 24 0.2	22 53.8	7 28.1	0♑19.3	25 38.8	2 26.1	8 10.7	24 25.5	17 34.8	4 45.6	14 26.6	25 9.8
14 T	13 27 56.8	23 52.5	7 25.0	13 5.4	27 45.2	3 39.8	8 54.5	24 25.0	17 41.2	4 49.0	14 25.4	25 9.9
15 W	13 31 53.3	24 51.2	7 21.8	26 12.1	29 51.8	4 53.6	9 38.3	24 24.2	17 47.6	4 52.4	14 24.2	25 10.1
16 T	13 35 49.9	25 50.0	7 18.6	9♒42.9	1♉58.3	6 7.3	10 22.1	24 23.3	17 53.9	4 55.8	14 23.0	25 10.3
17 F	13 39 46.4	26 48.6	7 15.4	23 40.3	4 4.3	7 21.0	11 5.7	24 22.3	18 0.2	4 59.2	14 21.9	25 10.5
18 S	13 43 43.0	27 47.3	7 12.3	8♓ 4.7	6 9.6	8 34.7	11 49.4	24 21.0	18 6.5	5 2.7	14 20.8	25 10.8
19 S	13 47 39.5	28 45.9	7 9.1	22 53.2	8 13.9	9 48.5	12 33.0	24 19.5	18 12.7	5 6.1	14 19.7	25 11.0
20 M	13 51 36.1	29 44.5	7 5.9	7♈59.7	10 16.8	11 2.2	13 16.5	24 17.9	18 18.8	5 9.5	14 18.6	25 11.3
21 T	13 55 32.6	0♉43.0	7 2.7	23 14.9	12 18.0	12 15.9	14 0.0	24 16.0	18 24.9	5 13.0	14 17.6	25 11.7
22 W	13 59 29.2	1 41.6	6 59.6	8♉28.0	14 17.2	13 29.6	14 43.5	24 14.0	18 31.0	5 16.4	14 16.6	25 12.0
23 T	14 3 25.8	2 40.1	6 56.4	23 28.0	16 14.1	14 43.3	15 26.9	24 11.8	18 37.0	5 19.9	14 15.6	25 12.4
24 F	14 7 22.3	3 38.5	6 53.2	8♊ 6.4	18 8.3	15 57.0	16 10.2	24 9.4	18 42.9	5 23.3	14 14.6	25 12.8
25 S	14 11 18.8	4 37.0	6 50.0	22 17.9	19 59.6	17 10.7	16 53.5	24 6.8	18 48.8	5 26.8	14 13.6	25 13.2
26 S	14 15 15.4	5 35.4	6 46.8	6♋ 0.4	21 47.8	18 24.4	17 36.8	24 4.1	18 54.6	5 30.2	14 12.7	25 13.6
27 M	14 19 12.0	6 33.7	6 43.7	19 15.1	23 32.7	19 38.1	18 20.0	24 1.2	19 0.4	5 33.7	14 11.9	25 14.1
28 T	14 23 8.5	7 32.1	6 40.5	2♌ 4.9	25 14.0	20 51.8	19 3.1	23 58.1	19 6.1	5 37.2	14 11.0	25 14.6
29 W	14 27 5.1	8 30.4	6 37.3	14 34.0	26 51.6	22 5.5	19 46.2	23 54.8	19 11.8	5 40.6	14 10.2	25 15.1
30 T	14 31 1.6	9 28.6	6 34.1	26 47.3	28 25.4	23 19.1	20 29.3	23 51.4	19 17.4	5 44.0	14 9.4	25 15.7

DECLINATION

DAY	EPHEMERIS SIDEREAL TIME h m s	☉ ° ′	☊ ° ′	☽ ° ′	☿ ° ′	♀ ° ′	♂ ° ′	♃ ° ′	♄ ° ′	♅ ° ′	♆ ° ′	♇ ° ′
1 W	12 36 41.5	4N23.7	23S12.0	16N36.3	1S10.4	6S 8.3	11N 6.6	22S42.7	7S 3.2	12N27.4	6N58.7	23N16.4
4 S	12 48 31.2	5 32.8	23 12.6	2 56.1	1N21.9	4 44.3	11 55.1	22 42.8	6 55.5	12 30.7	7 0.3	23 16.5
7 T	13 0 20.9	6 41.1	23 13.1	11S25.7	3 45.1	3 19.0	12 42.5	22 42.9	6 48.0	12 34.1	7 1.9	23 16.5
10 F	13 12 10.5	7 48.3	23 13.7	21 57.4	6 46.2	1 52.9	13 28.7	22 43.0	6 40.5	12 37.5	7 3.4	23 16.6
13 M	13 24 0.2	8 54.4	23 14.2	23 58.5	9 32.9	0 26.1	14 13.7	22 43.0	6 33.3	12 40.9	7 4.8	23 16.5
16 T	13 35 49.9	9 59.1	23 14.8	15 7.9	12 17.3	1N 1.1	14 57.4	22 42.9	6 26.2	12 44.4	7 6.1	23 16.5
19 S	13 47 39.5	11 2.4	23 15.3	1N41.4	14 54.0	2 28.2	15 39.7	22 42.7	6 19.3	12 47.9	7 7.4	23 16.4
22 W	13 59 29.2	12 4.0	23 15.8	18 20.8	17 17.4	3 55.0	16 20.7	22 42.5	6 12.6	12 51.3	7 8.6	23 16.2
25 S	14 11 18.8	13 3.9	23 16.3	24 22.1	19 22.7	5 21.1	17 0.1	22 42.3	6 6.0	12 54.8	7 9.6	23 16.0
28 T	14 23 8.5	14 1.8	23 16.8	17 27.5	21 6.7	6 46.3	17 38.1	22 41.9	5 59.7	12 58.3	7 10.6	23 15.8

MAY 1936

DAY	EPHEMERIS SIDEREAL TIME h m s	☉ ° ′	☊ ° ′	☽ ° ′	☿ ° ′	♀ ° ′	♂ ° ′	♃ ° ′	♄ ° ′	♅ ° ′	♆ ° ′	♇ ° ′
						LONGITUDE						
1 F	14 34 58.2	10♉26.8	6♑31.0	8♍49.4	29♉55.1	24♈32.8	21♉12.3	23♐47.8	19♓22.9	5♉47.5	14♍ 8.6	25♋16.2
2 S	14 38 54.7	11 25.0	6 27.8	20 44.6	1♊20.8	25 46.4	21 55.2	23R44.0	19 28.4	5 50.9	14R 7.8	25 16.8
3 S	14 42 51.3	12 23.2	6 24.6	2♎36.6	2 42.3	27 0.1	22 38.1	23 40.0	19 33.8	5 54.4	14 7.1	25 17.5
4 M	14 46 47.8	13 21.3	6 21.4	14 28.4	3 59.5	28 13.7	23 20.9	23 35.9	19 39.1	5 57.8	14 6.4	25 18.1
5 T	14 50 44.4	14 19.4	6 18.2	26 22.6	5 12.4	29 27.4	24 3.7	23 31.6	19 44.4	6 1.2	14 5.8	25 18.8
6 W	14 54 40.9	15 17.5	6 15.1	8♏20.9	6 20.8	0♉41.0	24 46.5	23 27.2	19 49.6	6 4.7	14 5.2	25 19.4
7 T	14 58 37.5	16 15.5	6 11.9	20 24.8	7 24.8	1 54.6	25 29.1	23 22.6	19 54.8	6 8.1	14 4.6	25 20.2
8 F	15 2 34.1	17 13.5	6 8.7	2♐35.7	8 24.2	3 8.3	26 11.8	23 17.9	19 59.8	6 11.5	14 4.0	25 20.9
9 S	15 6 30.6	18 11.5	6 5.5	14 54.9	9 19.0	4 21.9	26 54.4	23 13.0	20 4.8	6 14.9	14 3.5	25 21.6
10 S	15 10 27.2	19 9.5	6 2.4	27 24.1	10 9.1	5 35.5	27 36.9	23 7.9	20 9.8	6 18.3	14 3.0	25 22.4
11 M	15 14 23.7	20 7.4	5 59.2	10♑ 5.0	10 54.5	6 49.1	28 19.4	23 2.8	20 14.7	6 21.6	14 2.5	25 23.2
12 T	15 18 20.3	21 5.3	5 56.0	23 0.2	11 35.0	8 2.8	29 1.9	22 57.4	20 19.5	6 25.0	14 2.1	25 24.0
13 W	15 22 16.8	22 3.2	5 52.8	6♒11.9	12 10.8	9 16.4	29 44.2	22 52.0	20 24.2	6 28.4	14 1.6	25 24.9
14 T	15 26 13.4	23 1.1	5 49.6	19 42.7	12 41.6	10 30.0	0♊26.6	22 46.3	20 28.8	6 31.7	14 1.3	25 25.7
15 F	15 30 9.9	23 58.9	5 46.5	3♓34.1	13 7.5	11 43.6	1 8.9	22 40.6	20 33.4	6 35.1	14 0.9	25 26.6
16 S	15 34 6.5	24 56.8	5 43.3	17 46.3	13 28.5	12 57.3	1 51.2	22 34.7	20 37.9	6 38.4	14 0.6	25 27.5
17 S	15 38 3.1	25 54.6	5 40.1	2♈17.8	13 44.5	14 10.9	2 33.4	22 28.7	20 42.4	6 41.7	14 0.3	25 28.4
18 M	15 41 59.6	26 52.4	5 36.9	17 4.5	13 55.7	15 24.5	3 15.5	22 22.6	20 46.7	6 45.0	14 0.1	25 29.4
19 T	15 45 56.2	27 50.2	5 33.8	1♉59.7	14 1.9	16 38.2	3 57.7	22 16.4	20 51.0	6 48.3	13 59.8	25 30.3
20 W	15 49 52.7	28 47.9	5 30.6	16 55.3	14 3.3	17 51.8	4 39.7	22 10.0	20 55.2	6 51.5	13 59.6	25 31.3
21 T	15 53 49.3	29 45.7	5 27.4	1♊42.7	14R 0.1	19 5.4	5 21.8	22 3.6	20 59.3	6 54.8	13 59.5	25 32.3
22 F	15 57 45.8	0♊43.4	5 24.2	16 14.0	13 52.4	20 19.0	6 3.7	21 57.0	21 3.4	6 58.0	13 59.4	25 33.4
23 S	16 1 42.4	1 41.1	5 21.1	0♋23.5	13 40.3	21 32.7	6 45.7	21 50.3	21 7.3	7 1.3	13 59.3	25 34.4
24 S	16 5 38.9	2 38.7	5 17.9	14 8.0	13 24.1	22 46.3	7 27.5	21 43.5	21 11.2	7 4.4	13 59.2	25 35.5
25 M	16 9 35.5	3 36.4	5 14.7	27 26.7	13 4.2	23 59.9	8 9.4	21 36.7	21 15.0	7 7.6	13 59.2	25 36.6
26 T	16 13 32.1	4 34.0	5 11.5	10♌21.3	12 40.9	25 13.5	8 51.2	21 29.7	21 18.7	7 10.8	13D59.2	25 37.7
27 W	16 17 28.6	5 31.6	5 8.4	22 54.8	12 14.6	26 27.1	9 32.9	21 22.7	21 22.3	7 13.9	13 59.2	25 38.8
28 T	16 21 25.1	6 29.2	5 5.2	5♍11.2	11 45.8	27 40.7	10 14.6	21 15.6	21 25.9	7 17.1	13 59.3	25 39.9
29 F	16 25 21.7	7 26.7	5 2.0	17 15.1	11 14.9	28 54.3	10 56.2	21 8.4	21 29.3	7 20.2	13 59.4	25 41.1
30 S	16 29 18.3	8 24.2	4 58.8	29 11.2	10 42.5	0♊ 8.0	11 37.8	21 1.2	21 32.7	7 23.2	13 59.5	25 42.3
31 S	16 33 14.8	9 21.7	4 55.6	11♎ 3.7	10 9.2	1 21.6	12 19.4	20 53.9	21 36.0	7 26.3	13 59.7	25 43.5
						DECLINATION						
1 F	14 34 58.2	14N57.6	23S17.2	4N 1.6	22N28.3	8N10.3	18N14.6	22S41.5	5S53.6	13N 1.7	7N11.5	23N15.5
4 M	14 46 47.8	15 51.2	23 17.7	10S20.0	23 27.6	9 32.6	18 49.4	22 41.1	5 47.8	13 5.1	7 12.2	23 15.2
7 T	14 58 37.5	16 42.4	23 18.2	21 16.9	24 5.8	10 53.1	19 22.6	22 40.5	5 42.2	13 8.5	7 12.9	23 14.9
10 S	15 10 27.2	17 31.2	23 18.6	24 1.9	24 24.4	12 11.3	19 54.1	22 39.9	5 36.8	13 11.9	7 13.5	23 14.5
13 W	15 22 16.8	18 17.3	23 19.0	16 4.2	24 25.0	13 27.0	20 23.9	22 39.2	5 31.7	13 15.2	7 13.9	23 14.1
16 S	15 34 6.5	19 0.6	23 19.4	0 15.8	24 9.0	14 39.8	20 52.0	22 38.4	5 26.9	13 18.5	7 14.3	23 13.6
19 T	15 45 56.2	19 41.1	23 19.8	16N27.3	23 38.1	15 49.5	21 18.2	22 37.6	5 22.3	13 21.7	7 14.5	23 13.2
22 F	15 57 45.8	20 18.6	23 20.2	24 17.8	22 53.9	16 55.6	21 42.7	22 36.7	5 18.1	13 24.9	7 14.6	23 12.6
25 M	16 9 35.5	20 52.9	23 20.6	18 37.1	21 59.0	17 57.8	22 5.3	22 35.6	5 14.1	13 28.1	7 14.6	23 12.1
28 T	16 21 25.1	21 24.0	23 21.0	5 20.3	20 57.0	18 55.9	22 26.1	22 34.6	5 10.5	13 31.1	7 14.5	23 11.5
31 S	16 33 14.8	21 51.7	23 21.4	9S 8.7	19 52.8	19 49.4	22 45.0	22 33.4	5 7.1	13 34.1	7 14.3	23 10.9

JUNE 1936

DAY	SIDEREAL TIME	☉	☊	☽	☿	♀	♂	♃	♄	♅	♆	♇
						LONGITUDE						
1 M	16 37 11.4	10♊19.2	4♑52.5	22♎56.7	9♊35.5	2♊35.2	13♊ 0.9	20♐46.5	21♓39.2	7♉29.3	13♍59.9	25♋44.7
2 T	16 41 7.9	11 16.7	4 49.3	4♏53.6	9R 2.0	3 48.8	13 42.3	20R39.1	21 42.3	7 32.3	14 0.1	25 45.9
3 W	16 45 4.5	12 14.1	4 46.1	16 57.3	8 29.4	5 2.4	14 23.7	20 31.7	21 45.3	7 35.3	14 0.4	25 47.1
4 T	16 49 1.0	13 11.5	4 42.9	29 10.0	7 58.1	6 16.0	15 5.1	20 24.2	21 48.2	7 38.3	14 0.7	25 48.4
5 F	16 52 57.6	14 9.0	4 39.8	11♐33.3	7 28.7	7 29.6	15 46.4	20 16.6	21 51.1	7 41.2	14 1.1	25 49.7
6 S	16 56 54.2	15 6.3	4 36.6	24 8.3	7 1.6	8 43.2	16 27.7	20 9.1	21 53.8	7 44.1	14 1.4	25 51.0
7 S	17 0 50.8	16 3.7	4 33.4	6♑55.7	6 37.4	9 56.8	17 8.9	20 1.5	21 56.5	7 47.0	14 1.8	25 52.3
8 M	17 4 47.3	17 1.1	4 30.2	19 56.1	6 16.4	11 10.4	17 50.1	19 53.9	21 59.0	7 49.9	14 2.2	25 53.6
9 T	17 8 43.8	17 58.4	4 27.1	3♒10.0	5 59.0	12 24.0	18 31.2	19 46.2	22 1.5	7 52.7	14 2.7	25 54.9
10 W	17 12 40.4	18 55.8	4 23.9	16 37.5	5 45.4	13 37.7	19 12.3	19 38.6	22 3.9	7 55.5	14 3.2	25 56.3
11 T	17 16 37.0	19 53.1	4 20.7	0♓18.7	5 35.9	14 51.3	19 53.4	19 30.9	22 6.2	7 58.3	14 3.7	25 57.6
12 F	17 20 33.5	20 50.4	4 17.5	14 13.6	5 30.6	16 4.9	20 34.4	19 23.3	22 8.4	8 1.0	14 4.3	25 59.0
13 S	17 24 30.1	21 47.8	4 14.3	28 21.0	5 29.8	17 18.6	21 15.3	19 15.6	22 10.5	8 3.8	14 4.9	26 0.4
14 S	17 28 26.7	22 45.1	4 11.2	12♈39.4	5D33.5	18 32.2	21 56.3	19 8.0	22 12.5	8 6.4	14 5.5	26 1.8
15 M	17 32 23.2	23 42.4	4 8.0	27 5.8	5 41.7	19 45.9	22 37.2	19 0.4	22 14.4	8 9.1	14 6.1	26 3.2
16 T	17 36 19.7	24 39.7	4 4.8	11♉36.2	5 54.6	20 59.6	23 18.0	18 52.8	22 16.2	8 11.7	14 6.8	26 4.6
17 W	17 40 16.3	25 37.0	4 1.6	26 5.5	6 12.0	22 13.2	23 58.8	18 45.2	22 17.9	8 14.3	14 7.5	26 6.1
18 T	17 44 12.9	26 34.3	3 58.5	10♊28.4	6 34.0	23 26.9	24 39.6	18 37.6	22 19.5	8 16.9	14 8.3	26 7.5
19 F	17 48 9.5	27 31.6	3 55.3	24 39.6	7 0.5	24 40.6	25 20.3	18 30.1	22 21.0	8 19.4	14 9.0	26 9.0
20 S	17 52 6.0	28 28.9	3 52.1	8♋34.7	7 31.6	25 54.3	26 1.0	18 22.7	22 22.4	8 21.9	14 9.8	26 10.5
21 S	17 56 2.5	29 26.1	3 48.9	22 10.3	8 7.0	27 8.0	26 41.6	18 15.3	22 23.8	8 24.4	14 10.7	26 12.0
22 M	17 59 59.1	0♋23.4	3 45.8	5♌25.2	8 46.9	28 21.7	27 22.2	18 7.9	22 25.0	8 26.8	14 11.5	26 13.4
23 T	18 3 55.7	1 20.6	3 42.6	18 19.2	9 31.0	29 35.4	28 2.8	18 0.6	22 26.1	8 29.2	14 12.4	26 15.0
24 W	18 7 52.2	2 17.9	3 39.4	0♍54.1	10 19.4	0♋49.1	28 43.3	17 53.4	22 27.1	8 31.5	14 13.4	26 16.5
25 T	18 11 48.8	3 15.1	3 36.2	13 12.6	11 11.9	2 2.8	29 23.8	17 46.2	22 28.0	8 33.9	14 14.3	26 18.0
26 F	18 15 45.3	4 12.3	3 33.1	25 18.4	12 8.6	3 16.5	0♋ 4.2	17 39.1	22 28.9	8 36.1	14 15.3	26 19.5
27 S	18 19 41.9	5 9.5	3 29.9	7♎15.7	13 9.3	4 30.2	0 44.6	17 32.1	22 29.6	8 38.4	14 16.3	26 21.1
28 S	18 23 38.4	6 6.8	3 26.7	19 9.1	14 14.1	5 43.9	1 24.9	17 25.1	22 30.2	8 40.6	14 17.4	26 22.6
29 M	18 27 35.0	7 3.9	3 23.5	1♏ 3.2	15 22.7	6 57.6	2 5.2	17 18.3	22 30.7	8 42.8	14 18.4	26 24.2
30 T	18 31 31.6	8 1.1	3 20.3	13 2.1	16 35.3	8 11.4	2 45.5	17 11.5	22 31.1	8 44.9	14 19.5	26 25.8
						DECLINATION						
1 M	16 37 11.4	22N 0.2	23S21.5	13S30.2	19N32.0	20N 6.3	22N50.9	22S33.0	5S 6.1	13N35.1	7N14.2	23N10.7
4 T	16 49 1.0	22 23.4	23 21.8	22 52.2	18 34.1	20 53.4	23 7.2	22 31.7	5 3.2	13 38.0	7 13.8	23 10.1
7 S	17 0 50.8	22 43.1	23 22.1	22 56.9	17 47.6	21 35.4	23 21.7	22 30.4	5 0.6	13 40.8	7 13.3	23 9.5
10 W	17 12 40.4	22 59.2	23 22.5	12 25.1	17 16.5	22 12.0	23 34.2	22 29.0	4 58.3	13 43.5	7 12.7	23 8.8
13 S	17 24 30.1	23 11.6	23 22.8	4N 9.5	17 3.0	22 43.0	23 44.8	22 27.6	4 56.4	13 46.2	7 12.0	23 8.1
16 T	17 36 19.7	23 20.4	23 23.1	19 15.9	17 7.2	23 8.1	23 53.5	22 26.1	4 54.9	13 48.7	7 11.2	23 7.4
19 F	17 48 9.5	23 25.5	23 23.4	24 9.0	17 27.5	23 27.1	24 0.3	22 24.6	4 53.7	13 51.1	7 10.2	23 6.7
22 M	17 59 59.1	23 26.8	23 23.6	16 12.3	18 1.7	23 40.0	24 5.2	22 23.1	4 52.8	13 53.5	7 9.2	23 6.0
25 T	18 11 48.8	23 24.4	23 23.9	2 1.2	18 46.7	23 46.7	24 8.1	22 21.7	4 52.4	13 55.7	7 8.1	23 5.2
28 S	18 23 38.4	23 18.4	23 24.2	12S12.2	19 39.1	23 47.0	24 9.2	22 20.2	4 52.2	13 57.8	7 6.8	23 4.5

JULY 1936

LONGITUDE

DAY	EPHEMERIS SIDEREAL TIME h m s	☉ ° ′	☊ ° ′	☽ ° ′	☿ ° ′	♀ ° ′	♂ ° ′	♃ ° ′	♄ ° ′	♅ ° ′	♆ ° ′	♇ ° ′
1 W	18 35 28.1	8♋58.3	3♑17.2	25♏10.0	17♊51.7	9♋25.1	3♋25.7	17♐ 4.9	22♓31.5	8♉47.0	14♍20.7	26♋27.3
2 T	18 39 24.7	9 55.5	3 14.0	7♐30.0	19 11.9	10 38.8	4 5.9	16R58.3	22 31.7	8 49.1	14 21.8	26 28.9
3 F	18 43 21.2	10 52.7	3 10.8	20 4.8	20 35.9	11 52.6	4 46.0	16 51.9	22 31.8	8 51.1	14 23.0	26 30.5
4 S	18 47 17.8	11 49.9	3 7.6	2♑55.8	22 3.5	13 6.3	5 26.1	16 45.6	22 31.8	8 53.0	14 24.2	26 32.1
5 S	18 51 14.4	12 47.0	3 4.5	16 3.7	23 34.8	14 20.1	6 6.2	16 39.3	22R31.7	8 55.0	14 25.5	26 33.7
6 M	18 55 10.9	13 44.2	3 1.3	29 28.0	25 9.7	15 33.8	6 46.2	16 33.2	22 31.6	8 56.9	14 26.7	26 35.3
7 T	18 59 7.5	14 41.4	2 58.1	13♒ 7.2	26 48.1	16 47.6	7 26.2	16 27.2	22 31.3	8 58.7	14 28.0	26 36.9
8 W	19 3 4.1	15 38.6	2 54.9	26 59.2	28 29.9	18 1.4	8 6.1	16 21.4	22 30.9	9 0.5	14 29.4	26 38.5
9 T	19 7 0.6	16 35.8	2 51.8	11♓ 1.0	0♋15.0	19 15.2	8 46.0	16 15.6	22 30.4	9 2.3	14 30.7	26 40.1
10 F	19 10 57.1	17 33.0	2 48.6	25 9.9	2 3.3	20 29.0	9 25.9	16 10.0	22 29.9	9 4.0	14 32.1	26 41.8
11 S	19 14 53.7	18 30.2	2 45.4	9♈22.8	3 54.6	21 42.8	10 5.8	16 4.5	22 29.2	9 5.7	14 33.5	26 43.4
12 S	19 18 50.3	19 27.4	2 42.2	23 37.0	5 48.8	22 56.6	10 45.6	15 59.2	22 28.4	9 7.4	14 34.9	26 45.0
13 M	19 22 46.8	20 24.6	2 39.1	7♉50.0	7 45.6	24 10.4	11 25.3	15 54.0	22 27.5	9 9.0	14 36.3	26 46.7
14 T	19 26 43.4	21 21.8	2 35.9	21 59.5	9 44.8	25 24.3	12 5.1	15 49.0	22 26.6	9 10.5	14 37.8	26 48.3
15 W	19 30 39.9	22 19.1	2 32.7	6♊ 3.0	11 46.2	26 38.1	12 44.8	15 44.0	22 25.5	9 12.0	14 39.3	26 49.9
16 T	19 34 36.5	23 16.3	2 29.5	19 58.5	13 49.4	27 52.0	13 24.4	15 39.3	22 24.3	9 13.5	14 40.8	26 51.6
17 F	19 38 33.1	24 13.6	2 26.3	3♋43.5	15 54.2	29 5.8	14 4.1	15 34.7	22 23.1	9 14.9	14 42.4	26 53.2
18 S	19 42 29.6	25 10.8	2 23.2	17 15.9	18 0.2	0♌19.7	14 43.7	15 30.3	22 21.7	9 16.3	14 43.9	26 54.9
19 S	19 46 26.1	26 8.1	2 20.0	0♌34.0	20 7.1	1 33.6	15 23.2	15 26.0	22 20.2	9 17.6	14 45.5	26 56.5
20 M	19 50 22.7	27 5.4	2 16.8	13 36.4	22 14.7	2 47.5	16 2.8	15 21.8	22 18.7	9 18.9	14 47.2	26 58.1
21 T	19 54 19.3	28 2.7	2 13.6	26 22.7	24 22.5	4 1.4	16 42.3	15 17.9	22 17.0	9 20.2	14 48.8	26 59.8
22 W	19 58 15.8	28 60.0	2 10.5	8♍53.3	26 30.4	5 15.3	17 21.7	15 14.1	22 15.3	9 21.4	14 50.5	27 1.4
23 T	20 2 12.4	29 57.3	2 7.3	21 9.9	28 38.1	6 29.2	18 1.1	15 10.5	22 13.5	9 22.5	14 52.1	27 3.1
24 F	20 6 8.9	0♌54.6	2 4.1	3♎15.0	0♌45.2	7 43.1	18 40.5	15 7.0	22 11.5	9 23.6	14 53.8	27 4.7
25 S	20 10 5.5	1 51.9	2 0.9	15 11.9	2 51.7	8 57.0	19 19.9	15 3.7	22 9.5	9 24.6	14 55.5	27 6.3
26 S	20 14 2.0	2 49.2	1 57.8	27 4.7	4 57.3	10 10.9	19 59.2	15 0.6	22 7.4	9 25.6	14 57.3	27 8.0
27 M	20 17 58.6	3 46.6	1 54.6	8♏58.1	7 1.8	11 24.8	20 38.5	14 57.7	22 5.2	9 26.6	14 59.1	27 9.6
28 T	20 21 55.2	4 43.9	1 51.4	20 56.7	9 5.2	12 38.7	21 17.7	14 54.9	22 2.9	9 27.5	15 0.8	27 11.3
29 W	20 25 51.7	5 41.3	1 48.2	3♐ 5.4	11 7.2	13 52.7	21 56.9	14 52.4	22 0.5	9 28.4	15 2.6	27 12.9
30 T	20 29 48.3	6 38.6	1 45.0	15 28.7	13 7.9	15 6.6	22 36.1	14 50.0	21 58.1	9 29.2	15 4.5	27 14.5
31 F	20 33 44.8	7 36.0	1 41.9	28 10.3	15 7.2	16 20.5	23 15.2	14 47.7	21 55.5	9 29.9	15 6.3	27 16.1

DECLINATION

DAY	EPHEMERIS SIDEREAL TIME h m s	☉ ° ′	☊ ° ′	☽ ° ′	☿ ° ′	♀ ° ′	♂ ° ′	♃ ° ′	♄ ° ′	♅ ° ′	♆ ° ′	♇ ° ′
1 W	18 35 28.1	23N 8.6	23S24.4	22S14.8	20N35.0	23N41.0	24N 8.3	22S18.8	4S52.4	13N59.9	7N 5.5	23N 3.7
4 S	18 47 17.8	22 55.2	23 24.6	23 28.2	21 30.3	23 28.6	24 5.7	22 17.4	4 53.0	14 1.8	7 4.1	23 2.9
7 T	18 59 7.5	22 38.3	23 24.9	13 39.4	22 20.0	23 10.0	24 1.2	22 16.1	4 53.9	14 3.5	7 2.5	23 2.1
10 F	19 10 57.1	22 17.8	23 25.1	2N51.5	22 59.1	22 45.2	23 54.8	22 14.8	4 55.2	14 5.2	7 0.9	23 1.4
13 M	19 22 46.8	21 53.8	23 25.3	18 13.9	23 22.1	22 14.4	23 46.7	22 13.7	4 56.9	14 6.7	6 59.2	23 0.6
16 T	19 34 36.5	21 26.4	23 25.4	24 17.7	23 24.4	21 37.7	23 36.9	22 12.7	4 58.8	14 8.1	6 57.4	22 59.8
19 S	19 46 26.1	20 55.8	23 25.6	17 42.0	23 3.0	20 55.4	23 25.3	22 11.8	5 1.1	14 9.4	6 55.6	22 59.0
22 W	19 58 15.8	20 22.0	23 25.8	3 49.7	22 17.3	20 7.7	23 12.1	22 11.1	5 3.8	14 10.5	6 53.6	22 58.3
25 S	20 10 5.5	19 45.1	23 25.9	10S41.4	21 9.1	19 14.8	22 57.2	22 10.5	5 6.7	14 11.5	6 51.6	22 57.5
28 T	20 21 55.2	19 5.2	23 26.1	21 22.7	19 41.9	18 17.1	22 40.8	22 10.1	5 10.0	14 12.4	6 49.5	22 56.7
31 F	20 33 44.8	18 22.6	23 26.2	23 53.4	17 59.7	17 14.8	22 22.7	22 9.9	5 13.5	14 13.1	6 47.4	22 56.0

AUGUST 1936

LONGITUDE

DAY	EPHEMERIS SIDEREAL TIME h m s	☉ ° ′	☊ ° ′	☽ ° ′	☿ ° ′	♀ ° ′	♂ ° ′	♃ ° ′	♄ ° ′	♅ ° ′	♆ ° ′	♇ ° ′
1 S	20 37 41.4	8♌33.4	1♑38.7	11♑12.9	17♌ 4.9	17♌34.5	23♋54.3	14♐45.7	21♓52.9	9♉30.7	15♍ 8.2	27♋17.8
2 S	20 41 38.0	9 30.8	1 35.5	24 37.8	19 1.1	18 48.4	24 33.4	14R43.8	21R50.2	9 31.3	15 10.0	27 19.4
3 M	20 45 34.5	10 28.2	1 32.3	8♒24.4	20 55.8	20 2.3	25 12.5	14 42.2	21 47.4	9 31.9	15 11.9	27 21.0
4 T	20 49 31.1	11 25.6	1 29.2	22 29.8	22 48.8	21 16.3	25 51.5	14 40.7	21 44.5	9 32.5	15 13.8	27 22.6
5 W	20 53 27.6	12 23.0	1 26.0	6♓49.8	24 40.3	22 30.2	26 30.4	14 39.4	21 41.6	9 33.0	15 15.8	27 24.2
6 T	20 57 24.2	13 20.5	1 22.8	21 18.6	26 30.2	23 44.2	27 9.4	14 38.2	21 38.5	9 33.5	15 17.7	27 25.8
7 F	21 1 20.7	14 17.9	1 19.6	5♈49.9	28 18.6	24 58.1	27 48.3	14 37.3	21 35.4	9 33.9	15 19.7	27 27.4
8 S	21 5 17.3	15 15.4	1 16.4	20 18.2	0♍ 5.3	26 12.1	28 27.2	14 36.5	21 32.2	9 34.3	15 21.6	27 28.9
9 S	21 9 13.9	16 13.0	1 13.3	4♉38.8	1 50.6	27 26.1	29 6.1	14 36.0	21 29.0	9 34.6	15 23.6	27 30.5
10 M	21 13 10.4	17 10.5	1 10.1	18 48.7	3 34.2	28 40.0	29 44.9	14 35.6	21 25.7	9 34.9	15 25.6	27 32.1
11 T	21 17 6.9	18 8.1	1 6.9	2♊46.5	5 16.4	29 54.0	0♌23.7	14 35.4	21 22.3	9 35.1	15 27.6	27 33.6
12 W	21 21 3.5	19 5.7	1 3.7	16 31.6	6 57.0	1♍ 8.0	1 2.5	14 35.3	21 18.8	9 35.3	15 29.7	27 35.2
13 T	21 25 0.1	20 3.3	1 0.6	0♋ 4.3	8 36.1	2 22.0	1 41.2	14D35.5	21 15.2	9 35.4	15 31.7	27 36.7
14 F	21 28 56.6	21 0.9	0 57.4	13 24.9	10 13.7	3 36.0	2 19.9	14 35.9	21 11.6	9 35.5	15 33.8	27 38.3
15 S	21 32 53.2	21 58.6	0 54.2	26 33.6	11 49.8	4 50.0	2 58.6	14 36.4	21 8.0	9 35.5	15 35.8	27 39.8
16 S	21 36 49.7	22 56.3	0 51.0	9♌30.6	13 24.4	6 4.0	3 37.3	14 37.1	21 4.2	9R35.5	15 37.9	27 41.3
17 M	21 40 46.3	23 54.0	0 47.9	22 15.7	14 57.6	7 18.0	4 15.9	14 38.0	21 0.4	9 35.4	15 40.0	27 42.8
18 T	21 44 42.8	24 51.7	0 44.7	4♍49.0	16 29.2	8 32.0	4 54.5	14 39.1	20 56.6	9 35.3	15 42.1	27 44.3
19 W	21 48 39.4	25 49.5	0 41.5	17 10.5	17 59.3	9 46.0	5 33.0	14 40.4	20 52.7	9 35.1	15 44.2	27 45.8
20 T	21 52 35.9	26 47.2	0 38.3	29 21.2	19 28.0	11 0.0	6 11.6	14 41.9	20 48.7	9 34.9	15 46.3	27 47.3
21 F	21 56 32.5	27 45.0	0 35.1	11♎22.5	20 55.1	12 14.1	6 50.1	14 43.5	20 44.7	9 34.6	15 48.5	27 48.7
22 S	22 0 29.1	28 42.9	0 32.0	23 16.9	22 20.7	13 28.1	7 28.6	14 45.4	20 40.6	9 34.3	15 50.6	27 50.2
23 S	22 4 25.6	29 40.7	0 28.8	5♏ 7.6	23 44.7	14 42.1	8 7.0	14 47.4	20 36.5	9 33.9	15 52.8	27 51.6
24 M	22 8 22.2	0♍38.5	0 25.6	16 58.8	25 7.1	15 56.1	8 45.4	14 49.6	20 32.4	9 33.5	15 54.9	27 53.0
25 T	22 12 18.7	1 36.4	0 22.4	28 55.0	26 27.9	17 10.1	9 23.8	14 52.0	20 28.2	9 33.0	15 57.1	27 54.5
26 W	22 16 15.3	2 34.3	0 19.3	11♐ 1.4	27 47.1	18 24.1	10 2.1	14 54.5	20 23.9	9 32.5	15 59.3	27 55.9
27 T	22 20 11.8	3 32.2	0 16.1	23 23.1	29 4.5	19 38.1	10 40.5	14 57.3	20 19.6	9 31.9	16 1.4	27 57.2
28 F	22 24 8.4	4 30.2	0 12.9	6♑ 5.1	0♎20.2	20 52.0	11 18.8	15 0.2	20 15.3	9 31.3	16 3.6	27 58.6
29 S	22 28 5.0	5 28.2	0 9.7	19 11.4	1 34.1	22 6.0	11 57.0	15 3.3	20 10.9	9 30.7	16 5.8	27 60.0
30 S	22 32 1.5	6 26.1	0 6.5	2♒44.5	2 46.0	23 20.0	12 35.2	15 6.5	20 6.5	9 29.9	16 8.0	28 1.3
31 M	22 35 58.0	7 24.1	0 3.4	16 44.6	3 56.1	24 34.0	13 13.4	15 10.0	20 2.1	9 29.2	16 10.2	28 2.6

DECLINATION

DAY	EPHEMERIS SIDEREAL TIME h m s	☉ ° ′	☊ ° ′	☽ ° ′	☿ ° ′	♀ ° ′	♂ ° ′	♃ ° ′	♄ ° ′	♅ ° ′	♆ ° ′	♇ ° ′
1 S	20 37 41.4	18N 7.8	23S26.2	22S14.9	17N23.0	16N53.1	22N16.4	22S 9.8	5S14.7	14N13.3	6N46.7	22N55.7
4 T	20 49 31.1	17 21.5	23 26.4	10 18.0	15 26.7	15 45.1	21 56.4	22 9.8	5 18.6	14 13.8	6 44.4	22 55.0
7 F	21 1 20.7	16 32.8	23 26.5	7N 2.4	13 23.7	14 33.4	21 34.9	22 10.0	5 22.8	14 14.2	6 42.2	22 54.3
10 M	21 13 10.4	15 41.6	23 26.5	20 51.5	11 16.5	13 18.0	21 12.0	22 10.4	5 27.2	14 14.5	6 39.8	22 53.6
13 T	21 25 0.1	14 48.1	23 26.6	23 40.8	9 7.3	11 59.5	20 47.7	22 10.9	5 31.8	14 14.6	6 37.5	22 52.9
16 S	21 36 49.7	13 52.5	23 26.7	14 54.5	6 57.7	10 38.1	20 22.2	22 11.6	5 36.7	14 14.6	6 35.0	22 52.3
19 W	21 48 39.4	12 54.9	23 26.7	0 32.3	4 49.3	9 14.1	19 55.3	22 12.6	5 41.7	14 14.4	6 32.6	22 51.6
22 S	22 0 29.1	11 55.5	23 26.8	13S26.3	2 43.3	7 48.0	19 27.3	22 13.7	5 46.9	14 14.1	6 30.1	22 51.0
25 T	22 12 18.7	10 54.4	23 26.8	22 36.4	0 41.1	6 19.9	18 58.1	22 14.9	5 52.2	14 13.7	6 27.6	22 50.5
28 F	22 24 8.4	9 51.8	23 26.8	22 54.1	1S16.3	4 50.3	18 27.7	22 16.4	5 57.6	14 13.1	6 25.0	22 49.9
31 M	22 35 58.0	8 47.7	23 26.9	12 23.2	3 7.4	3 19.5	17 56.4	22 18.0	6 3.1	14 12.4	6 22.5	22 49.4

SEPTEMBER 1936

LONGITUDE

DAY	EPHEMERIS SIDEREAL TIME h m s	☉ ° ′	☊ ° ′	☽ ° ′	☿ ° ′	♀ ° ′	♂ ° ′	♃ ° ′	♄ ° ′	♅ ° ′	♆ ° ′	♇ ° ′
1 T	22 39 54.6	8♍22.2	0♑ 0.2	1♓ 9.3	5♎ 4.0	25♍47.9	13♌51.6	15♐13.6	19♓57.7	9♉28.4	16♍12.4	28♋ 4.0
2 W	22 43 51.2	9 20.2	29♐57.0	15 53.0	6 9.8	27 1.9	14 29.8	15 17.4	19R53.2	9R27.5	16 14.6	28 5.3
3 T	22 47 47.7	10 18.3	29 53.8	0♈47.7	7 13.3	28 15.9	15 7.9	15 21.3	19 48.7	9 26.6	16 16.9	28 6.6
4 F	22 51 44.2	11 16.5	29 50.7	15 44.4	8 14.5	29 29.8	15 46.0	15 25.5	19 44.2	9 25.7	16 19.1	28 7.8
5 S	22 55 40.8	12 14.6	29 47.5	0♉34.2	9 13.1	0♎43.8	16 24.1	15 29.8	19 39.6	9 24.7	16 21.3	28 9.1
6 S	22 59 37.4	13 12.8	29 44.3	15 10.1	10 9.0	1 57.7	17 2.1	15 34.2	19 35.0	9 23.7	16 23.5	28 10.3
7 M	23 3 33.9	14 11.0	29 41.1	29 27.8	11 2.0	3 11.7	17 40.1	15 38.9	19 30.5	9 22.6	16 25.7	28 11.5
8 T	23 7 30.5	15 9.3	29 37.9	13♊25.3	11 52.0	4 25.6	18 18.1	15 43.6	19 25.9	9 21.5	16 28.0	28 12.7
9 W	23 11 27.0	16 7.6	29 34.8	27 3.1	12 38.7	5 39.6	18 56.1	15 48.6	19 21.3	9 20.3	16 30.2	28 13.9
10 T	23 15 23.6	17 5.9	29 31.6	10♋22.6	13 22.0	6 53.5	19 34.0	15 53.7	19 16.7	9 19.1	16 32.4	28 15.1
11 F	23 19 20.1	18 4.2	29 28.4	23 26.3	14 1.5	8 7.5	20 11.9	15 59.0	19 12.1	9 17.9	16 34.7	28 16.2
12 S	23 23 16.7	19 2.6	29 25.2	6♌16.3	14 37.0	9 21.4	20 49.8	16 4.4	19 7.4	9 16.6	16 36.9	28 17.4
13 S	23 27 13.2	20 1.1	29 22.1	18 54.6	15 8.1	10 35.3	21 27.7	16 10.0	19 2.8	9 15.2	16 39.1	28 18.5
14 M	23 31 9.8	20 59.5	29 18.9	1♍22.6	15 34.6	11 49.2	22 5.5	16 15.8	18 58.2	9 13.8	16 41.3	28 19.6
15 T	23 35 6.3	21 58.0	29 15.7	13 41.5	15 56.2	13 3.2	22 43.3	16 21.7	18 53.6	9 12.4	16 43.5	28 20.6
16 W	23 39 2.9	22 56.6	29 12.5	25 51.9	16 12.5	14 17.1	23 21.1	16 27.8	18 49.0	9 11.0	16 45.8	28 21.7
17 T	23 42 59.5	23 55.1	29 9.3	7♎54.7	16 23.1	15 31.0	23 58.9	16 34.0	18 44.4	9 9.5	16 48.0	28 22.7
18 F	23 46 56.0	24 53.7	29 6.2	19 50.9	16 27.6	16 44.9	24 36.6	16 40.4	18 39.8	9 7.9	16 50.2	28 23.8
19 S	23 50 52.6	25 52.3	29 3.0	1♏42.3	16R25.9	17 58.8	25 14.3	16 46.9	18 35.2	9 6.3	16 52.4	28 24.8
20 S	23 54 49.1	26 51.0	28 59.8	13 31.2	16 17.4	19 12.7	25 52.0	16 53.6	18 30.7	9 4.7	16 54.6	28 25.7
21 M	23 58 45.7	27 49.7	28 56.6	25 20.7	16 2.0	20 26.6	26 29.6	17 0.4	18 26.1	9 3.1	16 56.8	28 26.7
22 T	0 2 42.2	28 48.4	28 53.5	7♐15.0	15 39.4	21 40.5	27 7.2	17 7.4	18 21.6	9 1.4	16 59.0	28 27.6
23 W	0 6 38.8	29 47.1	28 50.3	19 18.6	15 9.6	22 54.3	27 44.8	17 14.5	18 17.1	8 59.6	17 1.2	28 28.5
24 T	0 10 35.3	0♎45.9	28 47.1	1♑36.7	14 32.6	24 8.2	28 22.3	17 21.7	18 12.7	8 57.9	17 3.4	28 29.4
25 F	0 14 31.9	1 44.7	28 43.9	14 14.5	13 48.6	25 22.0	28 59.8	17 29.1	18 8.3	8 56.1	17 5.5	28 30.3
26 S	0 18 28.4	2 43.5	28 40.7	27 17.1	12 58.1	26 35.9	29 37.3	17 36.7	18 3.9	8 54.2	17 7.7	28 31.1
27 S	0 22 25.0	3 42.3	28 37.6	10♒48.1	12 1.7	27 49.7	0♍14.8	17 44.3	17 59.5	8 52.4	17 9.9	28 32.0
28 M	0 26 21.5	4 41.2	28 34.4	24 49.3	11 0.2	29 3.5	0 52.2	17 52.1	17 55.2	8 50.5	17 12.0	28 32.8
29 T	0 30 18.1	5 40.1	28 31.2	9♓19.3	9 55.0	0♏17.3	1 29.6	18 0.1	17 50.9	8 48.6	17 14.1	28 33.5
30 W	0 34 14.7	6 39.1	28 28.0	24 13.6	8 47.4	1 31.1	2 7.0	18 8.1	17 46.6	8 46.6	17 16.3	28 34.3

DECLINATION

DAY	EPHEMERIS SIDEREAL TIME h m s	☉	☊	☽	☿	♀	♂	♃	♄	♅	♆	♇
1 T	22 39 54.6	8N26.1	23S26.9	6S58.9	3S42.8	2N49.0	17N45.7	22S18.5	6S 5.0	14N12.1	6N21.6	22N49.2
4 F	22 51 44.2	7 20.4	23 26.9	10N40.9	5 23.2	1 17.0	17 13.0	22 20.3	6 10.5	14 11.2	6 19.1	22 48.7
7 M	23 3 33.9	6 13.6	23 26.8	22 35.2	6 53.3	0S15.5	16 39.3	22 22.3	6 16.1	14 10.2	6 16.5	22 48.3
10 T	23 15 23.6	5 5.8	23 26.8	22 10.3	8 10.4	1 48.1	16 4.7	22 24.3	6 21.8	14 9.1	6 13.9	22 47.9
13 S	23 27 13.2	3 57.3	23 26.8	11 34.4	9 11.3	3 20.6	15 29.3	22 26.5	6 27.3	14 7.8	6 11.3	22 47.5
16 W	23 39 2.9	2 48.1	23 26.7	2S55.8	9 51.4	4 52.6	14 53.1	22 28.8	6 32.9	14 6.4	6 8.8	22 47.2
19 S	23 50 52.6	1 38.5	23 26.7	16 1.3	10 5.2	6 23.8	14 16.1	22 31.2	6 38.3	14 4.9	6 6.2	22 46.9
22 T	0 2 42.2	0 28.5	23 26.6	23 20.8	9 46.5	7 53.8	13 38.4	22 33.6	6 43.7	14 3.3	6 3.7	22 46.7
25 F	0 14 31.9	0S41.6	23 26.5	21 20.1	8 50.1	9 22.4	13 0.1	22 36.1	6 48.9	14 1.6	6 1.2	22 46.5
28 M	0 26 21.5	1 51.8	23 26.4	9 18.4	7 15.6	10 49.1	12 21.2	22 38.7	6 54.0	13 59.8	5 58.7	22 46.3

OCTOBER 1936

LONGITUDE

DAY	EPHEMERIS SIDEREAL TIME h m s	☉ ° ′	☊ ° ′	☽ ° ′	☿ ° ′	♀ ° ′	♂ ° ′	♃ ° ′	♄ ° ′	♅ ° ′	♆ ° ′	♇ ° ′
1 T	0 38 11.2	7♎38.0	28♐24.9	9♈23.8	7♎39.0	2♏44.8	2♍44.4	18♐16.3	17♓42.4	8♉44.6	17♍18.4	28♋35.0
2 F	0 42 7.8	8 37.1	28 21.7	24 39.4	6R31.6	3 58.6	3 21.7	18 24.6	17R38.3	8R42.6	17 20.5	28 35.8
3 S	0 46 4.3	9 36.1	28 18.5	9♉49.3	5 27.1	5 12.3	3 59.0	18 33.1	17 34.2	8 40.5	17 22.6	28 36.4
4 S	0 50 0.9	10 35.2	28 15.3	24 43.9	4 27.2	6 26.1	4 36.3	18 41.7	17 30.1	8 38.5	17 24.7	28 37.1
5 M	0 53 57.4	11 34.3	28 12.1	9♊16.5	3 33.6	7 39.8	5 13.5	18 50.4	17 26.1	8 36.4	17 26.8	28 37.8
6 T	0 57 54.0	12 33.5	28 9.0	23 23.7	2 47.9	8 53.5	5 50.8	18 59.2	17 22.2	8 34.2	17 28.8	28 38.4
7 W	1 1 50.5	13 32.7	28 5.8	7♋ 5.4	2 11.1	10 7.3	6 28.0	19 8.2	17 18.3	8 32.1	17 30.9	28 39.0
8 T	1 5 47.1	14 31.9	28 2.6	20 23.3	1 44.2	11 21.0	7 5.1	19 17.2	17 14.4	8 29.9	17 32.9	28 39.5
9 F	1 9 43.6	15 31.2	27 59.4	3♌20.5	1 27.9	12 34.7	7 42.3	19 26.4	17 10.6	8 27.7	17 34.9	28 40.1
10 S	1 13 40.2	16 30.5	27 56.3	16 0.5	1 22.4	13 48.3	8 19.4	19 35.7	17 6.9	8 25.5	17 36.9	28 40.6
11 S	1 17 36.8	17 29.8	27 53.1	28 26.7	1D27.8	15 2.0	8 56.5	19 45.1	17 3.2	8 23.2	17 38.9	28 41.1
12 M	1 21 33.3	18 29.2	27 49.9	10♍42.2	1 43.7	16 15.7	9 33.5	19 54.7	16 59.7	8 20.9	17 40.9	28 41.6
13 T	1 25 29.8	19 28.7	27 46.7	22 49.2	2 9.8	17 29.4	10 10.6	20 4.3	16 56.1	8 18.6	17 42.9	28 42.0
14 W	1 29 26.4	20 28.1	27 43.5	4♎49.9	2 45.5	18 43.0	10 47.6	20 14.1	16 52.7	8 16.3	17 44.8	28 42.4
15 T	1 33 22.9	21 27.6	27 40.4	16 45.5	3 30.0	19 56.6	11 24.5	20 23.9	16 49.3	8 14.0	17 46.7	28 42.8
16 F	1 37 19.5	22 27.2	27 37.2	28 37.6	4 22.7	21 10.3	12 1.5	20 33.9	16 46.0	8 11.7	17 48.7	28 43.2
17 S	1 41 16.1	23 26.7	27 34.0	10♏27.5	5 22.7	22 23.9	12 38.4	20 44.0	16 42.8	8 9.3	17 50.6	28 43.6
18 S	1 45 12.6	24 26.3	27 30.8	22 17.0	6 29.1	23 37.5	13 15.2	20 54.2	16 39.6	8 6.9	17 52.4	28 43.9
19 M	1 49 9.2	25 26.0	27 27.7	4♐ 8.4	7 41.3	24 51.1	13 52.1	21 4.5	16 36.5	8 4.5	17 54.3	28 44.2
20 T	1 53 5.7	26 25.6	27 24.5	16 4.7	8 58.5	26 4.7	14 28.9	21 14.9	16 33.5	8 2.1	17 56.1	28 44.5
21 W	1 57 2.3	27 25.3	27 21.3	28 9.4	10 20.0	27 18.2	15 5.7	21 25.4	16 30.6	7 59.7	17 57.9	28 44.7
22 T	2 0 58.8	28 25.0	27 18.1	10♑26.9	11 45.0	28 31.8	15 42.4	21 35.9	16 27.8	7 57.3	17 59.7	28 44.9
23 F	2 4 55.4	29 24.8	27 14.9	23 1.9	13 13.1	29 45.3	16 19.1	21 46.6	16 25.0	7 54.9	18 1.5	28 45.1
24 S	2 8 51.9	0♏24.6	27 11.8	5♒59.0	14 43.8	0♐58.8	16 55.8	21 57.4	16 22.4	7 52.4	18 3.3	28 45.3
25 S	2 12 48.5	1 24.4	27 8.6	19 22.2	16 16.5	2 12.3	17 32.5	22 8.3	16 19.8	7 50.0	18 5.0	28 45.4
26 M	2 16 45.0	2 24.2	27 5.4	3♓14.3	17 50.9	3 25.8	18 9.1	22 19.2	16 17.3	7 47.5	18 6.7	28 45.5
27 T	2 20 41.6	3 24.1	27 2.2	17 35.7	19 26.6	4 39.2	18 45.6	22 30.3	16 14.9	7 45.0	18 8.4	28 45.6
28 W	2 24 38.1	4 23.9	26 59.0	2♈23.4	21 3.4	5 52.7	19 22.2	22 41.4	16 12.6	7 42.6	18 10.1	28 45.7
29 T	2 28 34.7	5 23.9	26 55.9	17 31.2	22 41.0	7 6.1	19 58.7	22 52.7	16 10.4	7 40.1	18 11.8	28 45.7
30 F	2 32 31.3	6 23.8	26 52.7	2♉49.6	24 19.2	8 19.5	20 35.2	23 4.0	16 8.3	7 37.7	18 13.4	28 45.7
31 S	2 36 27.8	7 23.8	26 49.5	18 7.5	25 57.7	9 32.8	21 11.6	23 15.4	16 6.3	7 35.2	18 15.0	28R45.7

DECLINATION

DAY	EPHEMERIS SIDEREAL TIME h m s	☉	☊	☽	☿	♀	♂	♃	♄	♅	♆	♇
1 T	0 38 11.2	3S 1.8	23S26.3	8N14.3	5S12.8	12S13.6	11N41.8	22S41.3	6S58.9	13N57.9	5N56.3	22N46.2
4 S	0 50 0.9	4 11.5	23 26.2	21 36.5	3 3.1	13 35.6	11 1.8	22 43.9	7 3.6	13 55.9	5 53.9	22 46.2
7 W	1 1 50.5	5 20.8	23 26.0	22 24.7	1 13.1	14 54.8	10 21.3	22 46.5	7 8.0	13 53.8	5 51.5	22 46.1
10 S	1 13 40.2	6 29.5	23 25.9	12 25.3	0 3.9	16 10.7	9 40.5	22 49.1	7 12.3	13 51.7	5 49.2	22 46.2
13 T	1 25 29.8	7 37.5	23 25.7	1S45.7	0N16.1	17 23.2	8 59.2	22 51.7	7 16.2	13 49.5	5 47.0	22 46.2
16 F	1 37 19.5	8 44.5	23 25.6	14 58.5	0S10.4	18 31.7	8 17.7	22 54.2	7 19.9	13 47.3	5 44.8	22 46.4
19 M	1 49 9.2	9 50.3	23 25.4	22 50.4	1 14.3	19 35.9	7 35.8	22 56.7	7 23.3	13 45.0	5 42.7	22 46.6
22 T	2 0 58.8	10 54.9	23 25.2	21 45.0	2 44.9	20 35.5	6 53.8	22 59.1	7 26.4	13 42.7	5 40.6	22 46.8
25 S	2 12 48.5	11 58.0	23 25.0	11 6.1	4 32.6	21 30.3	6 11.5	23 1.5	7 29.1	13 40.3	5 38.7	22 47.1
28 W	2 24 38.1	12 59.5	23 24.8	5N36.5	6 29.5	22 19.7	5 29.1	23 3.7	7 31.5	13 37.9	5 36.8	22 47.4
31 S	2 36 27.8	13 59.1	23 24.6	20 12.7	8 30.1	23 3.7	4 46.6	23 5.9	7 33.6	13 35.5	5 34.9	22 47.8

NOVEMBER 1936

DAY	EPHEMERIS SIDEREAL TIME	☉	☊	☽	☿	♀	♂	♃	♄	♅	♆	♇
	h m s	° ′	° ′	° ′	° ′	° ′	° ′	° ′	° ′	° ′	° ′	° ′
						LONGITUDE						
1 S	2 40 24.4	8♏23.8	26♐46.3	3♓14.1	27♎36.6	10♐46.2	21♍48.0	23♐26.8	16♓ 4.4	7♉32.7	18♍16.6	28♋45.7
2 M	2 44 20.9	9 23.9	26 43.2	18 0.5	29 15.5	11 59.5	22 24.4	23 38.4	16R 2.5	7R30.2	18 18.1	28R45.6
3 T	2 48 17.5	10 24.0	26 40.0	2♋21.2	0♏54.5	13 12.8	23 0.7	23 50.0	16 0.8	7 27.8	18 19.6	28 45.5
4 W	2 52 14.0	11 24.1	26 36.8	16 14.1	2 33.4	14 26.1	23 37.1	24 1.7	15 59.2	7 25.3	18 21.2	28 45.4
5 T	2 56 10.6	12 24.2	26 33.6	29 39.6	4 12.2	15 39.4	24 13.3	24 13.5	15 57.6	7 22.8	18 22.6	28 45.3
6 F	3 0 7.1	13 24.4	26 30.5	12♌40.3	5 50.8	16 52.6	24 49.6	24 25.4	15 56.2	7 20.4	18 24.1	28 45.1
7 S	3 4 3.7	14 24.6	26 27.3	25 19.8	7 29.3	18 5.9	25 25.8	24 37.3	15 54.9	7 17.9	18 25.5	28 44.9
8 S	3 8 0.3	15 24.9	26 24.1	7♍42.2	9 7.4	19 19.1	26 2.0	24 49.4	15 53.6	7 15.5	18 26.9	28 44.7
9 M	3 11 56.8	16 25.2	26 20.9	19 51.7	10 45.3	20 32.3	26 38.1	25 1.4	15 52.5	7 13.1	18 28.3	28 44.5
10 T	3 15 53.3	17 25.5	26 17.7	1♎52.0	12 23.0	21 45.5	27 14.2	25 13.6	15 51.5	7 10.6	18 29.6	28 44.2
11 W	3 19 49.9	18 25.9	26 14.6	13 46.4	14 0.3	22 58.6	27 50.3	25 25.8	15 50.5	7 8.2	18 31.0	28 43.9
12 T	3 23 46.5	19 26.3	26 11.4	25 37.6	15 37.3	24 11.7	28 26.3	25 38.1	15 49.7	7 5.8	18 32.3	28 43.6
13 F	3 27 43.1	20 26.7	26 8.2	7♏27.7	17 14.1	25 24.9	29 2.3	25 50.5	15 49.0	7 3.4	18 33.5	28 43.2
14 S	3 31 39.6	21 27.1	26 5.0	19 18.9	18 50.5	26 37.9	29 38.2	26 2.9	15 48.4	7 1.0	18 34.8	28 42.9
15 S	3 35 36.1	22 27.6	26 1.9	1♐12.7	20 26.7	27 51.0	0♎14.1	26 15.4	15 47.9	6 58.7	18 36.0	28 42.5
16 M	3 39 32.7	23 28.1	25 58.7	13 10.9	22 2.6	29 4.0	0 49.9	26 27.9	15 47.5	6 56.3	18 37.1	28 42.0
17 T	3 43 29.3	24 28.6	25 55.5	25 15.6	23 38.2	0♑17.0	1 25.8	26 40.5	15 47.2	6 54.0	18 38.3	28 41.6
18 W	3 47 25.8	25 29.2	25 52.3	7♑29.1	25 13.6	1 30.0	2 1.5	26 53.2	15 47.0	6 51.7	18 39.4	28 41.1
19 T	3 51 22.4	26 29.7	25 49.2	19 54.1	26 48.7	2 42.9	2 37.2	27 5.9	15 46.9	6 49.4	18 40.5	28 40.6
20 F	3 55 18.9	27 30.3	25 46.0	2♒33.7	28 23.6	3 55.8	3 12.9	27 18.7	15D46.9	6 47.1	18 41.5	28 40.1
21 S	3 59 15.5	28 30.9	25 42.8	15 31.3	29 58.3	5 8.7	3 48.5	27 31.5	15 47.1	6 44.9	18 42.6	28 39.6
22 S	4 3 12.0	29 31.6	25 39.6	28 49.9	1♐32.8	6 21.5	4 24.1	27 44.4	15 47.3	6 42.6	18 43.6	28 39.0
23 M	4 7 8.6	0♐32.2	25 36.4	12♓32.0	3 7.1	7 34.3	4 59.7	27 57.3	15 47.7	6 40.4	18 44.5	28 38.4
24 T	4 11 5.2	1 32.9	25 33.3	26 38.4	4 41.3	8 47.0	5 35.1	28 10.3	15 48.1	6 38.3	18 45.4	28 37.8
25 W	4 15 1.7	2 33.6	25 30.1	11♈ 8.0	6 15.2	9 59.7	6 10.6	28 23.3	15 48.7	6 36.1	18 46.3	28 37.2
26 T	4 18 58.3	3 34.3	25 26.9	25 57.2	7 49.1	11 12.4	6 46.0	28 36.4	15 49.3	6 34.0	18 47.2	28 36.5
27 F	4 22 54.8	4 35.0	25 23.7	10♉59.4	9 22.9	12 25.0	7 21.3	28 49.5	15 50.1	6 31.9	18 48.1	28 35.8
28 S	4 26 51.4	5 35.7	25 20.6	26 6.3	10 56.5	13 37.5	7 56.6	29 2.6	15 51.0	6 29.8	18 48.9	28 35.1
29 S	4 30 47.9	6 36.5	25 17.4	11♊ 8.3	12 30.0	14 50.0	8 31.8	29 15.8	15 52.0	6 27.7	18 49.6	28 34.4
30 M	4 34 44.5	7 37.3	25 14.2	25 56.5	14 3.5	16 2.5	9 7.0	29 29.1	15 53.1	6 25.7	18 50.4	28 33.7
						DECLINATION						
1 S	2 40 24.4	14S18.5	23S24.5	22N42.0	9S10.5	23S17.0	4N32.4	23S 6.6	7S34.2	13N34.7	5N34.4	22N47.9
4 W	2 52 14.0	15 15.4	23 24.2	20 36.6	11 10.3	23 53.1	3 49.8	23 8.6	7 35.8	13 32.4	5 32.7	22 48.3
7 S	3 4 3.7	16 10.1	23 24.0	8 50.9	13 6.7	24 23.1	3 7.2	23 10.5	7 37.0	13 30.0	5 31.1	22 48.8
10 T	3 15 53.3	17 2.3	23 23.7	5S27.1	14 57.8	24 46.8	2 24.7	23 12.2	7 37.9	13 27.6	5 29.5	22 49.3
13 F	3 27 43.1	17 52.0	23 23.5	17 36.2	16 42.6	25 3.9	1 42.2	23 13.8	7 38.4	13 25.3	5 28.1	22 49.9
16 M	3 39 32.7	18 38.8	23 23.2	23 24.1	18 20.1	25 14.5	0 59.8	23 15.2	7 38.5	13 23.1	5 26.8	22 50.5
19 T	3 51 22.4	19 22.6	23 22.9	19 44.3	19 49.5	25 18.3	0 17.7	23 16.4	7 38.2	13 20.8	5 25.6	22 51.2
22 S	4 3 12.0	20 3.3	23 22.6	7 26.5	21 10.1	25 15.4	0S24.3	23 17.5	7 37.5	13 18.7	5 24.5	22 51.9
25 W	4 15 1.7	20 40.7	23 22.2	9N 1.9	22 21.4	25 5.9	1 6.0	23 18.4	7 36.5	13 16.6	5 23.6	22 52.6
28 S	4 26 51.4	21 14.7	23 21.9	21 42.4	23 22.6	24 49.7	1 47.5	23 19.1	7 35.1	13 14.6	5 22.7	22 53.4

DECEMBER 1936

DAY	EPHEMERIS SIDEREAL TIME	☉	☊	☽	☿	♀	♂	♃	♄	♅	♆	♇
						LONGITUDE						
1 T	4 38 41.1	8♐38.1	25♐11.0	10♋24.0	15♐36.9	17♑14.9	9♎42.2	29♐42.4	15♓54.3	6♉23.8	18♍51.1	28♋32.9
2 W	4 42 37.6	9 38.9	25 7.9	24 26.3	17 10.2	18 27.3	10 17.3	29 55.7	15 55.6	6R21.8	18 51.7	28R32.1
3 T	4 46 34.2	10 39.8	25 4.7	8♌ 1.7	18 43.5	19 39.6	10 52.3	0♑ 9.0	15 57.0	6 19.9	18 52.4	28 31.3
4 F	4 50 30.7	11 40.6	25 1.5	21 10.9	20 16.7	20 51.8	11 27.3	0 22.4	15 58.5	6 18.0	18 53.0	28 30.5
5 S	4 54 27.3	12 41.5	24 58.3	3♍56.4	21 49.9	22 4.0	12 2.3	0 35.8	16 0.1	6 16.1	18 53.6	28 29.6
6 S	4 58 23.8	13 42.4	24 55.2	16 21.9	23 23.1	23 16.2	12 37.2	0 49.3	16 1.8	6 14.3	18 54.1	28 28.8
7 M	5 2 20.4	14 43.4	24 52.0	28 31.8	24 56.2	24 28.3	13 12.0	1 2.8	16 3.7	6 12.5	18 54.6	28 27.9
8 T	5 6 17.0	15 44.3	24 48.8	10♎30.6	26 29.2	25 40.3	13 46.8	1 16.3	16 5.6	6 10.8	18 55.1	28 27.0
9 W	5 10 13.5	16 45.3	24 45.6	22 22.6	28 2.2	26 52.3	14 21.5	1 29.8	16 7.6	6 9.1	18 55.5	28 26.1
10 T	5 14 10.1	17 46.3	24 42.4	4♏12.1	29 35.1	28 4.2	14 56.2	1 43.4	16 9.7	6 7.4	18 55.9	28 25.1
11 F	5 18 6.6	18 47.3	24 39.3	16 2.4	1♑ 7.8	29 16.1	15 30.8	1 57.0	16 12.0	6 5.7	18 56.3	28 24.2
12 S	5 22 3.2	19 48.4	24 36.1	27 56.7	2 40.4	0♒27.8	16 5.3	2 10.6	16 14.3	6 4.1	18 56.6	28 23.2
13 S	5 25 59.7	20 49.4	24 32.9	9♐57.3	4 12.8	1 39.5	16 39.8	2 24.3	16 16.8	6 2.6	18 56.9	28 22.2
14 M	5 29 56.3	21 50.5	24 29.7	22 6.3	5 44.9	2 51.2	17 14.2	2 38.0	16 19.3	6 1.1	18 57.2	28 21.2
15 T	5 33 52.9	22 51.5	24 26.6	4♑25.1	7 16.8	4 2.8	17 48.5	2 51.7	16 21.9	5 59.6	18 57.4	28 20.1
16 W	5 37 49.4	23 52.6	24 23.4	16 55.1	8 48.2	5 14.2	18 22.8	3 5.4	16 24.7	5 58.2	18 57.6	28 19.1
17 T	5 41 46.0	24 53.7	24 20.2	29 37.3	10 19.1	6 25.6	18 57.0	3 19.1	16 27.5	5 56.8	18 57.8	28 18.0
18 F	5 45 42.5	25 54.8	24 17.0	12♒32.7	11 49.5	7 37.0	19 31.1	3 32.8	16 30.4	5 55.4	18 57.9	28 16.9
19 S	5 49 39.1	26 55.9	24 13.9	25 42.4	13 19.1	8 48.2	20 5.2	3 46.6	16 33.5	5 54.1	18 58.0	28 15.9
20 S	5 53 35.7	27 57.0	24 10.7	9♓ 7.3	14 47.7	9 59.3	20 39.2	4 0.4	16 36.6	5 52.9	18 58.0	28 14.8
21 M	5 57 32.2	28 58.2	24 7.5	22 48.0	16 15.3	11 10.4	21 13.1	4 14.2	16 39.8	5 51.7	18 58.1	28 13.6
22 T	6 1 28.8	29 59.3	24 4.3	6♈44.8	17 41.6	12 21.3	21 46.9	4 28.0	16 43.2	5 50.5	18R58.0	28 12.5
23 W	6 5 25.3	1♑ 0.4	24 1.1	20 56.9	19 6.3	13 32.2	22 20.7	4 41.7	16 46.6	5 49.4	18 58.0	28 11.3
24 T	6 9 21.9	2 1.5	23 58.0	5♉22.4	20 29.2	14 42.9	22 54.3	4 55.6	16 50.1	5 48.3	18 57.9	28 10.2
25 F	6 13 18.4	3 2.6	23 54.8	19 58.0	21 49.8	15 53.5	23 28.0	5 9.4	16 53.7	5 47.3	18 57.8	28 9.0
26 S	6 17 15.0	4 3.8	23 51.6	4♊38.8	23 7.8	17 4.0	24 1.5	5 23.2	16 57.4	5 46.3	18 57.7	28 7.8
27 S	6 21 11.6	5 4.9	23 48.4	19 18.7	24 22.7	18 14.4	24 34.9	5 37.0	17 1.1	5 45.4	18 57.5	28 6.6
28 M	6 25 8.1	6 6.0	23 45.3	3♋51.3	25 34.0	19 24.7	25 8.3	5 50.8	17 5.0	5 44.5	18 57.2	28 5.4
29 T	6 29 4.7	7 7.2	23 42.1	18 10.2	26 41.0	20 34.8	25 41.6	6 4.7	17 8.9	5 43.7	18 57.0	28 4.2
30 W	6 33 1.2	8 8.3	23 38.9	2♌10.4	27 43.1	21 44.8	26 14.8	6 18.5	17 13.0	5 42.9	18 56.7	28 3.0
31 T	6 36 57.8	9 9.4	23 35.7	15 48.3	28 39.7	22 54.7	26 47.9	6 32.3	17 17.1	5 42.1	18 56.4	28 1.7
						DECLINATION						
1 T	4 38 41.1	21S45.0	23S21.6	21N34.6	24S13.1	24S27.0	2S28.6	23S19.6	7S33.3	13N12.6	5N22.0	22N54.2
4 F	4 50 30.7	22 11.6	23 21.2	10 14.8	24 52.3	23 57.9	3 9.4	23 19.8	7 31.2	13 10.8	5 21.3	22 55.1
7 M	5 2 20.4	22 34.3	23 20.9	4S15.0	25 19.7	23 22.7	3 49.8	23 19.9	7 28.6	13 9.1	5 20.8	22 55.9
10 T	5 14 10.1	22 53.1	23 20.5	16 44.5	25 34.5	22 41.5	4 29.7	23 19.8	7 25.8	13 7.4	5 20.4	22 56.8
13 S	5 25 59.7	23 7.8	23 20.1	23 14.9	25 36.3	21 54.7	5 9.2	23 19.5	7 22.5	13 5.9	5 20.2	22 57.8
16 W	5 37 49.4	23 18.3	23 19.7	20 21.0	25 24.8	21 2.5	5 48.1	23 18.9	7 19.0	13 4.5	5 20.0	22 58.7
19 S	5 49 39.1	23 24.7	23 19.3	8 34.4	24 59.7	20 5.3	6 26.5	23 18.1	7 15.0	13 3.3	5 20.0	22 59.7
22 T	6 1 28.8	23 26.8	23 18.9	7N25.3	24 21.5	19 3.3	7 4.3	23 17.1	7 10.8	13 2.2	5 20.1	23 0.7
25 F	6 13 18.4	23 24.7	23 18.4	20 36.9	23 31.1	17 56.9	7 41.5	23 15.9	7 6.2	13 1.2	5 20.3	23 1.7
28 M	6 25 8.1	23 18.4	23 18.0	22 30.8	22 30.7	16 46.6	8 18.1	23 14.5	7 1.4	13 0.3	5 20.6	23 2.7
31 T	6 36 57.8	23 7.9	23 17.5	12 9.2	21 24.2	15 32.6	8 53.9	23 12.8	6 56.2	12 59.6	5 21.1	23 3.7

JANUARY 1937

DAY	EPHEMERIS SIDEREAL TIME	☉	☊	☽	☿	♀	♂	♃	♄	♅	♆	♇
	h m s	° ′	° ′	° ′	° ′	° ′	° ′	° ′	° ′	° ′	° ′	° ′
						LONGITUDE						
1 F	6 40 54.3	10♑10.6	23♐32.6	29♌ 2.6	29♑29.7	24♒ 4.4	27♎21.0	6♑46.1	17♓21.3	5♉41.5	18♍56.0	28♋ 0.5
2 S	6 44 50.9	11 11.7	23 29.4	11♍53.9	0♒12.5	25 14.0	27 53.9	6 60.0	17 25.6	5R40.8	18R55.7	27R59.2
3 S	6 48 47.5	12 12.9	23 26.2	24 24.4	0 47.0	26 23.5	28 26.8	7 13.8	17 30.0	5 40.2	18 55.2	27 58.0
4 M	6 52 44.0	13 14.1	23 23.0	6♎37.7	1 12.4	27 32.8	28 59.6	7 27.6	17 34.4	5 39.7	18 54.8	27 56.7
5 T	6 56 40.6	14 15.2	23 19.9	18 38.1	1 27.8	28 41.9	29 32.3	7 41.4	17 39.0	5 39.2	18 54.3	27 55.4
6 W	7 0 37.1	15 16.4	23 16.7	0♏30.5	1 32.4	29 50.9	0♏ 4.8	7 55.2	17 43.6	5 38.8	18 53.8	27 54.1
7 T	7 4 33.7	16 17.6	23 13.5	12 19.8	1R25.6	0♓59.8	0 37.3	8 9.0	17 48.3	5 38.4	18 53.2	27 52.8
8 F	7 8 30.3	17 18.7	23 10.3	24 10.8	1 7.1	2 8.5	1 9.7	8 22.7	17 53.1	5 38.1	18 52.7	27 51.5
9 S	7 12 26.8	18 19.9	23 7.2	6♐ 7.9	0 36.7	3 17.0	1 42.0	8 36.5	17 58.0	5 37.8	18 52.0	27 50.2
10 S	7 16 23.4	19 21.1	23 4.0	18 14.8	29♑54.9	4 25.4	2 14.2	8 50.2	18 2.9	5 37.6	18 51.4	27 48.9
11 M	7 20 19.9	20 22.2	23 0.8	0♑34.4	29 2.3	5 33.5	2 46.3	9 4.0	18 7.9	5 37.4	18 50.7	27 47.6
12 T	7 24 16.5	21 23.4	22 57.6	13 8.8	28 0.4	6 41.5	3 18.2	9 17.7	18 13.0	5 37.3	18 50.0	27 46.3
13 W	7 28 13.0	22 24.6	22 54.4	25 58.8	26 50.8	7 49.3	3 50.1	9 31.4	18 18.1	5 37.2	18 49.3	27 44.9
14 T	7 32 9.6	23 25.7	22 51.3	9♒ 4.5	25 35.7	8 56.9	4 21.8	9 45.0	18 23.4	5 37.2	18 48.5	27 43.6
15 F	7 36 6.2	24 26.8	22 48.1	22 24.8	24 17.5	10 4.3	4 53.4	9 58.7	18 28.7	5D37.2	18 47.7	27 42.3
16 S	7 40 2.7	25 28.0	22 44.9	5♓58.1	22 58.7	11 11.5	5 24.9	10 12.3	18 34.0	5 37.3	18 46.9	27 41.0
17 S	7 43 59.3	26 29.1	22 41.7	19 42.4	21 41.6	12 18.5	5 56.3	10 25.9	18 39.5	5 37.5	18 46.0	27 39.6
18 M	7 47 55.8	27 30.2	22 38.6	3♈35.7	20 28.6	13 25.2	6 27.5	10 39.5	18 45.0	5 37.7	18 45.1	27 38.3
19 T	7 51 52.4	28 31.3	22 35.4	17 36.0	19 21.3	14 31.7	6 58.6	10 53.0	18 50.6	5 37.9	18 44.2	27 37.0
20 W	7 55 48.9	29 32.4	22 32.2	1♉41.7	18 21.4	15 37.9	7 29.6	11 6.5	18 56.2	5 38.2	18 43.3	27 35.6
21 T	7 59 45.5	0♒33.4	22 29.0	15 51.5	17 29.7	16 43.9	8 0.5	11 20.0	19 1.9	5 38.6	18 42.3	27 34.3
22 F	8 3 42.1	1 34.5	22 25.9	0♊ 3.6	16 46.9	17 49.7	8 31.2	11 33.5	19 7.7	5 39.0	18 41.3	27 33.0
23 S	8 7 38.6	2 35.5	22 22.7	14 16.2	16 13.4	18 55.1	9 1.8	11 46.9	19 13.5	5 39.4	18 40.3	27 31.7
24 S	8 11 35.2	3 36.5	22 19.5	28 26.7	15 49.0	20 0.3	9 32.3	12 0.3	19 19.4	5 39.9	18 39.2	27 30.3
25 M	8 15 31.7	4 37.5	22 16.3	12♋31.9	15 33.6	21 5.2	10 2.6	12 13.6	19 25.3	5 40.5	18 38.2	27 29.0
26 T	8 19 28.3	5 38.5	22 13.1	26 28.2	15 26.8	22 9.8	10 32.8	12 26.9	19 31.3	5 41.1	18 37.1	27 27.7
27 W	8 23 24.8	6 39.5	22 10.0	10♌11.7	15D28.1	23 14.1	11 2.8	12 40.2	19 37.4	5 41.8	18 35.9	27 26.4
28 T	8 27 21.4	7 40.4	22 6.8	23 39.2	15 36.9	24 18.1	11 32.7	12 53.4	19 43.5	5 42.5	18 34.8	27 25.1
29 F	8 31 17.9	8 41.3	22 3.6	6♍48.3	15 52.8	25 21.7	12 2.5	13 6.6	19 49.7	5 43.3	18 33.6	27 23.8
30 S	8 35 14.5	9 42.3	22 0.4	19 38.2	16 15.1	26 25.0	12 32.0	13 19.7	19 55.9	5 44.1	18 32.4	27 22.5
31 S	8 39 11.0	10 43.2	21 57.3	2♎ 9.5	16 43.3	27 28.0	13 1.5	13 32.9	20 2.2	5 45.0	18 31.2	27 21.2
						DECLINATION						
1 F	6 40 54.3	23S 3.4	23S17.4	7N20.1	21S 1.6	15S 7.2	9S 5.7	23S12.2	6S54.4	12N59.4	5N21.3	23N 4.0
4 M	6 52 44.0	22 47.3	23 16.9	7S21.2	19 56.5	13 48.8	9 40.6	23 10.3	6 48.9	12 58.9	5 21.9	23 5.1
7 T	7 4 33.7	22 27.2	23 16.4	18 53.3	19 2.0	12 27.7	10 14.8	23 8.1	6 43.0	12 58.6	5 22.6	23 6.1
10 S	7 16 23.4	22 3.0	23 15.9	23 28.4	18 25.8	11 4.0	10 48.2	23 5.7	6 36.9	12 58.4	5 23.4	23 7.1
13 W	7 28 13.0	21 35.0	23 15.4	18 14.9	18 11.6	9 38.3	11 20.7	23 3.2	6 30.6	12 58.4	5 24.4	23 8.1
16 S	7 40 2.7	21 3.2	23 14.9	4 43.2	18 17.2	8 10.7	11 51.8	23 0.4	6 24.0	12 58.5	5 25.4	23 9.2
19 T	7 51 52.4	20 27.8	23 14.4	11N18.2	18 36.4	6 41.8	12 23.3	22 57.5	6 17.2	12 58.8	5 26.6	23 10.2
22 F	8 3 42.1	19 48.9	23 13.8	22 13.0	19 3.0	5 11.9	12 53.3	22 54.4	6 10.2	12 59.2	5 27.8	23 11.2
25 M	8 15 31.7	19 6.8	23 13.3	21 11.8	19 32.3	3 41.3	13 22.3	22 51.1	6 2.9	12 59.8	5 29.2	23 12.1
28 T	8 27 21.4	18 21.5	23 12.7	9 25.4	20 0.6	2 10.3	13 50.5	22 47.6	5 55.5	13 0.6	5 30.6	23 13.1
31 S	8 39 11.0	17 33.1	23 12.2	5S30.6	20 24.9	0 39.3	14 17.7	22 44.0	5 47.9	13 1.5	5 32.1	23 14.0

FEBRUARY 1937

DAY	EPHEMERIS SIDEREAL TIME	☉	☊	☽	☿	♀	♂	♃	♄	♅	♆	♇
						LONGITUDE						
1 M	8 43 7.6	11♒44.1	21♐54.1	14♎24.3	17♑17.0	28♓30.6	13♏30.8	13♑45.9	20♓ 8.5	5♉45.9	18♍29.9	27♋19.9
2 T	8 47 4.2	12 44.9	21 50.9	26 26.1	17 55.6	29 32.8	13 59.9	13 58.9	20 14.9	5 46.9	18R28.7	27R18.6
3 W	8 51 0.7	13 45.8	21 47.7	8♏19.1	18 38.7	0♈34.7	14 28.8	14 11.9	20 21.3	5 47.9	18 27.4	27 17.4
4 T	8 54 57.3	14 46.6	21 44.5	20 8.4	19 25.9	1 36.1	14 57.6	14 24.8	20 27.8	5 49.0	18 26.1	27 16.1
5 F	8 58 53.8	15 47.5	21 41.4	1♐59.2	20 16.8	2 37.2	15 26.2	14 37.7	20 34.3	5 50.1	18 24.7	27 14.8
6 S	9 2 50.4	16 48.3	21 38.2	13 57.0	21 11.1	3 37.9	15 54.6	14 50.5	20 40.9	5 51.3	18 23.4	27 13.6
7 S	9 6 46.9	17 49.1	21 35.0	26 6.7	22 8.6	4 38.1	16 22.9	15 3.2	20 47.5	5 52.5	18 22.0	27 12.4
8 M	9 10 43.5	18 49.9	21 31.8	8♑32.5	23 8.9	5 37.9	16 50.9	15 15.9	20 54.2	5 53.8	18 20.6	27 11.1
9 T	9 14 40.0	19 50.7	21 28.7	21 17.8	24 11.8	6 37.2	17 18.7	15 28.6	21 0.9	5 55.1	18 19.2	27 9.9
10 W	9 18 36.6	20 51.4	21 25.5	4♒24.3	25 17.1	7 36.1	17 46.4	15 41.2	21 7.6	5 56.5	18 17.8	27 8.7
11 T	9 22 33.2	21 52.1	21 22.3	17 51.8	26 24.7	8 34.4	18 13.8	15 53.7	21 14.4	5 57.9	18 16.3	27 7.5
12 F	9 26 29.7	22 52.8	21 19.1	1♓38.4	27 34.3	9 32.3	18 41.1	16 6.2	21 21.2	5 59.4	18 14.9	27 6.3
13 S	9 30 26.3	23 53.5	21 15.9	15 40.4	28 45.9	10 29.6	19 8.1	16 18.6	21 28.1	6 0.9	18 13.4	27 5.2
14 S	9 34 22.8	24 54.2	21 12.8	29 52.7	29 59.2	11 26.4	19 34.9	16 30.9	21 35.0	6 2.4	18 11.9	27 4.0
15 M	9 38 19.4	25 54.8	21 9.6	14♈10.2	1♒14.2	12 22.6	20 1.5	16 43.2	21 41.9	6 4.0	18 10.4	27 2.9
16 T	9 42 15.9	26 55.4	21 6.4	28 27.9	2 30.8	13 18.2	20 27.8	16 55.4	21 48.9	6 5.7	18 8.9	27 1.7
17 W	9 46 12.5	27 56.0	21 3.2	12♉42.3	3 48.9	14 13.2	20 54.0	17 7.5	21 55.9	6 7.4	18 7.3	27 0.6
18 T	9 50 9.0	28 56.5	21 0.1	26 50.9	5 8.5	15 7.6	21 19.8	17 19.6	22 2.9	6 9.1	18 5.8	26 59.5
19 F	9 54 5.6	29 57.0	20 56.9	10♊52.5	6 29.4	16 1.3	21 45.5	17 31.5	22 10.0	6 10.9	18 4.2	26 58.4
20 S	9 58 2.1	0♓57.5	20 53.7	24 46.7	7 51.6	16 54.3	22 10.9	17 43.5	22 17.0	6 12.8	18 2.7	26 57.3
21 S	10 1 58.7	1 57.9	20 50.5	8♋33.2	9 15.0	17 46.6	22 36.1	17 55.3	22 24.2	6 14.7	18 1.1	26 56.3
22 M	10 5 55.3	2 58.3	20 47.4	22 11.6	10 39.7	18 38.2	23 1.0	18 7.0	22 31.3	6 16.6	17 59.5	26 55.2
23 T	10 9 51.8	3 58.7	20 44.2	5♌41.2	12 5.5	19 28.9	23 25.6	18 18.7	22 38.5	6 18.5	17 57.9	26 54.2
24 W	10 13 48.4	4 59.1	20 41.0	19 0.4	13 32.5	20 18.9	23 50.0	18 30.3	22 45.6	6 20.6	17 56.3	26 53.2
25 T	10 17 44.9	5 59.4	20 37.8	2♍ 7.8	15 0.6	21 8.1	24 14.1	18 41.8	22 52.9	6 22.6	17 54.6	26 52.2
26 F	10 21 41.5	6 59.7	20 34.6	15 1.6	16 29.9	21 56.3	24 38.0	18 53.3	23 0.1	6 24.7	17 53.0	26 51.2
27 S	10 25 38.0	7 60.0	20 31.5	27 41.0	18 0.2	22 43.7	25 1.5	19 4.6	23 7.3	6 26.8	17 51.4	26 50.3
28 S	10 29 34.6	9 0.2	20 28.3	10♎ 5.9	19 31.6	23 30.2	25 24.8	19 15.9	23 14.6	6 29.0	17 49.7	26 49.3
						DECLINATION						
1 M	8 43 7.6	17S16.4	23S12.0	10S 5.3	20S31.7	0S 9.0	14S26.6	22S42.8	5S45.3	13N 1.8	5N32.6	23N14.3
4 T	8 54 57.3	16 24.4	23 11.4	20 28.1	20 47.1	1N21.5	14 52.6	22 39.0	5 37.5	13 2.9	5 34.2	23 15.2
7 S	9 6 46.9	15 29.8	23 10.8	23 6.4	20 54.0	2 51.4	15 17.6	22 35.1	5 29.5	13 4.2	5 35.9	23 16.1
10 W	9 18 36.6	14 32.8	23 10.2	15 52.7	20 51.2	4 20.1	15 41.6	22 31.0	5 21.4	13 5.5	5 37.6	23 17.0
13 S	9 30 26.3	13 33.7	23 9.6	1 0.8	20 38.1	5 47.5	16 4.6	22 26.9	5 13.2	13 7.1	5 39.4	23 17.8
16 T	9 42 15.9	12 32.5	23 8.9	14N44.1	20 14.0	7 13.2	16 26.7	22 22.6	5 4.9	13 8.8	5 41.2	23 18.6
19 F	9 54 5.6	11 29.6	23 8.3	23 2.3	19 38.7	8 36.7	16 47.8	22 18.3	4 56.4	13 10.6	5 43.1	23 19.3
22 M	10 5 55.3	10 25.0	23 7.6	19 5.3	18 52.0	9 57.8	17 7.9	22 14.0	4 47.9	13 12.5	5 45.0	23 20.0
25 T	10 17 44.9	9 19.1	23 7.0	6 17.4	17 53.6	11 16.1	17 27.0	22 9.6	4 39.3	13 14.6	5 47.0	23 20.7
28 S	10 29 34.6	8 11.8	23 6.3	8S21.0	16 43.7	12 31.3	17 45.2	22 5.1	4 30.6	13 16.7	5 48.9	23 21.3

MARCH 1937

LONGITUDE

DAY	EPHEMERIS SIDEREAL TIME h m s	☉ ° ′	☊ ° ′	☽ ° ′	☿ ° ′	♀ ° ′	♂ ° ′	♃ ° ′	♄ ° ′	♅ ° ′	♆ ° ′	♇ ° ′
1 M	10 33 31.1	10♓ 0.4	20♐25.1	22♎17.3	21♒ 4.1	24♈15.7	25♏47.8	19♑27.1	23♓21.9	6♉31.2	17♍48.1	26♋48.4
2 T	10 37 27.7	11 0.6	20 21.9	4♏17.3	22 37.7	25 0.2	26 10.5	19 38.2	23 29.2	6 33.5	17R46.4	26R47.5
3 W	10 41 24.2	12 0.7	20 18.8	16 9.4	24 12.4	25 43.7	26 32.8	19 49.2	23 36.5	6 35.8	17 44.8	26 46.6
4 T	10 45 20.8	13 0.9	20 15.6	27 57.9	25 48.1	26 26.1	26 54.9	20 0.1	23 43.9	6 38.1	17 43.1	26 45.8
5 F	10 49 17.3	14 1.0	20 12.4	9♐47.6	27 24.9	27 7.4	27 16.6	20 10.9	23 51.2	6 40.5	17 41.5	26 44.9
6 S	10 53 13.9	15 1.0	20 9.2	21 44.1	29 2.8	27 47.5	27 38.0	20 21.6	23 58.6	6 42.9	17 39.8	26 44.1
7 S	10 57 10.5	16 1.1	20 6.0	3♑52.9	0♓41.8	28 26.4	27 59.0	20 32.2	24 6.0	6 45.3	17 38.1	26 43.3
8 M	11 1 7.0	17 1.1	20 2.9	16 19.4	2 21.9	29 4.1	28 19.7	20 42.8	24 13.4	6 47.8	17 36.5	26 42.5
9 T	11 5 3.5	18 1.1	19 59.7	29 7.9	4 3.1	29 40.5	28 40.0	20 53.2	24 20.8	6 50.3	17 34.8	26 41.8
10 W	11 9 0.1	19 1.1	19 56.5	12♒21.7	5 45.5	0♉15.6	28 60.0	21 3.5	24 28.2	6 52.8	17 33.1	26 41.0
11 T	11 12 56.7	20 1.0	19 53.3	26 1.7	7 29.0	0 49.3	29 19.6	21 13.7	24 35.6	6 55.4	17 31.4	26 40.3
12 F	11 16 53.2	21 0.9	19 50.2	10♓ 6.4	9 13.6	1 21.5	29 38.8	21 23.8	24 43.0	6 58.0	17 29.8	26 39.6
13 S	11 20 49.8	22 0.8	19 47.0	24 31.5	10 59.4	1 52.2	29 57.6	21 33.8	24 50.5	7 0.7	17 28.1	26 38.9
14 S	11 24 46.3	23 0.6	19 43.8	9♈10.4	12 46.4	2 21.4	0♐15.9	21 43.7	24 57.9	7 3.4	17 26.4	26 38.3
15 M	11 28 42.9	24 0.5	19 40.6	23 55.2	14 34.5	2 48.9	0 33.9	21 53.5	25 5.3	7 6.1	17 24.8	26 37.6
16 T	11 32 39.4	25 0.2	19 37.4	8♉37.9	16 23.9	3 14.8	0 51.4	22 3.2	25 12.8	7 8.8	17 23.1	26 37.0
17 W	11 36 36.0	25 60.0	19 34.3	23 12.1	18 14.5	3 38.8	1 8.6	22 12.7	25 20.2	7 11.6	17 21.5	26 36.5
18 T	11 40 32.5	26 59.7	19 31.1	7♊33.3	20 6.2	4 1.1	1 25.2	22 22.2	25 27.6	7 14.4	17 19.8	26 35.9
19 F	11 44 29.1	27 59.3	19 27.9	21 39.2	21 59.2	4 21.5	1 41.4	22 31.5	25 35.1	7 17.3	17 18.2	26 35.3
20 S	11 48 25.6	28 59.0	19 24.7	5♋29.4	23 53.4	4 40.0	1 57.2	22 40.7	25 42.5	7 20.1	17 16.6	26 34.8
21 S	11 52 22.2	29 58.5	19 21.6	19 4.6	25 48.7	4 56.4	2 12.5	22 49.8	25 49.9	7 23.0	17 14.9	26 34.3
22 M	11 56 18.7	0♈58.1	19 18.4	2♌26.0	27 45.2	5 10.8	2 27.3	22 58.8	25 57.3	7 25.9	17 13.3	26 33.9
23 T	12 0 15.3	1 57.6	19 15.2	15 34.9	29 42.9	5 23.0	2 41.7	23 7.6	26 4.7	7 28.9	17 11.7	26 33.4
24 W	12 4 11.8	2 57.0	19 12.0	28 32.2	1♈41.5	5 33.0	2 55.5	23 16.3	26 12.1	7 31.8	17 10.1	26 33.0
25 T	12 8 8.4	3 56.5	19 8.8	11♍18.2	3 41.2	5 40.8	3 8.9	23 24.9	26 19.5	7 34.8	17 8.5	26 32.6
26 F	12 12 5.0	4 55.9	19 5.7	23 53.2	5 41.9	5 46.3	3 21.7	23 33.4	26 26.9	7 37.9	17 7.0	26 32.3
27 S	12 16 1.5	5 55.2	19 2.5	6♎17.2	7 43.3	5 49.4	3 34.0	23 41.7	26 34.3	7 40.9	17 5.4	26 31.9
28 S	12 19 58.0	6 54.6	18 59.3	18 30.6	9 45.4	5 50.1	3 45.8	23 49.9	26 41.7	7 44.0	17 3.8	26 31.6
29 M	12 23 54.6	7 53.9	18 56.1	0♏34.4	11 48.0	5R48.4	3 57.0	23 58.0	26 49.0	7 47.1	17 2.3	26 31.3
30 T	12 27 51.2	8 53.1	18 52.9	12 29.9	13 51.0	5 44.2	4 7.6	24 5.9	26 56.3	7 50.2	17 0.8	26 31.0
31 W	12 31 47.7	9 52.3	18 49.8	24 19.7	15 54.1	5 37.5	4 17.7	24 13.7	27 3.7	7 53.3	16 59.3	26 30.8

DECLINATION

DAY	SIDEREAL TIME	☉	☊	☽	☿	♀	♂	♃	♄	♅	♆	♇
1 M	10 33 31.1	7S49.2	23S 6.1	12S38.4	16S17.8	12N55.5	17S51.1	22S 3.6	4S27.7	13N17.5	5N49.6	23N21.5
4 T	10 45 20.8	6 40.5	23 5.4	21 34.8	14 52.3	14 5.8	18 8.0	21 59.2	4 19.0	13 19.8	5 51.6	23 22.1
7 S	10 57 10.5	5 31.0	23 4.7	22 11.6	13 15.3	15 11.9	18 24.0	21 54.7	4 10.2	13 22.3	5 53.6	23 22.6
10 W	11 9 0.1	4 20.8	23 3.9	13 16.5	11 26.7	16 13.4	18 39.1	21 50.3	4 1.5	13 24.8	5 55.6	23 23.1
13 S	11 20 49.8	3 10.1	23 3.2	2N24.2	9 26.9	17 9.7	18 53.3	21 45.9	3 52.7	13 27.4	5 57.5	23 23.6
16 T	11 32 39.4	1 59.1	23 2.5	17 27.9	7 15.9	18 0.1	19 6.7	21 41.5	3 43.9	13 30.1	5 59.5	23 24.0
19 F	11 44 29.1	0 48.0	23 1.7	22 56.2	4 54.3	18 43.9	19 19.1	21 37.3	3 35.1	13 33.0	6 1.4	23 24.3
22 M	11 56 18.7	0N23.1	23 1.0	16 13.7	2 22.8	19 20.3	19 30.8	21 33.1	3 26.4	13 35.8	6 3.3	23 24.6
25 T	12 8 8.4	1 34.0	23 0.2	2 43.0	0N17.4	19 48.1	19 41.7	21 29.0	3 17.7	13 38.8	6 5.2	23 24.9
28 S	12 19 58.0	2 44.6	22 59.4	11S15.1	3 4.1	20 6.4	19 51.8	21 25.1	3 9.1	13 41.8	6 7.0	23 25.1
31 W	12 31 47.7	3 54.7	22 58.6	20 46.8	5 54.4	20 13.9	20 1.1	21 21.3	3 0.6	13 44.9	6 8.8	23 25.3

APRIL 1937

LONGITUDE

DAY	SIDEREAL TIME	☉	☊	☽	☿	♀	♂	♃	♄	♅	♆	♇
1 T	12 35 44.3	10♈51.5	18♐46.6	6♐ 7.1	17♈57.1	5♉28.4	4♐27.2	24♑21.3	27♓11.0	7♉56.5	16♍57.8	26♋30.5
2 F	12 39 40.8	11 50.7	18 43.4	17 56.1	19 59.7	5R16.8	4 36.1	24 28.9	27 18.2	7 59.6	16R56.3	26R30.3
3 S	12 43 37.4	12 49.8	18 40.2	29 51.6	22 1.6	5 2.7	4 44.4	24 36.2	27 25.5	8 2.8	16 54.8	26 30.2
4 S	12 47 33.9	13 49.0	18 37.1	11♑58.8	24 2.4	4 46.3	4 52.1	24 43.5	27 32.8	8 6.0	16 53.4	26 30.0
5 M	12 51 30.5	14 48.0	18 33.9	24 23.0	26 1.9	4 27.4	4 59.1	24 50.6	27 40.0	8 9.3	16 51.9	26 29.9
6 T	12 55 27.0	15 47.1	18 30.7	7♒ 9.2	27 59.7	4 6.2	5 5.5	24 57.5	27 47.2	8 12.5	16 50.5	26 29.8
7 W	12 59 23.6	16 46.1	18 27.5	20 21.6	29 55.4	3 42.8	5 11.2	25 4.3	27 54.4	8 15.8	16 49.1	26 29.7
8 T	13 3 20.1	17 45.1	18 24.3	4♓ 2.5	1♉48.5	3 17.2	5 16.2	25 11.0	28 1.6	8 19.1	16 47.7	26 29.7
9 F	13 7 16.7	18 44.1	18 21.2	18 11.9	3 38.9	2 49.6	5 20.6	25 17.5	28 8.7	8 22.4	16 46.3	26 29.7
10 S	13 11 13.2	19 43.0	18 18.0	2♈46.4	5 26.0	2 20.1	5 24.3	25 23.8	28 15.8	8 25.7	16 45.0	26D29.7
11 S	13 15 9.8	20 41.9	18 14.8	17 40.0	7 9.6	1 48.9	5 27.2	25 30.0	28 22.9	8 29.0	16 43.6	26 29.7
12 M	13 19 6.3	21 40.7	18 11.6	2♉43.8	8 49.4	1 16.1	5 29.5	25 36.0	28 29.9	8 32.3	16 42.3	26 29.8
13 T	13 23 2.9	22 39.6	18 8.5	17 48.2	10 25.1	0 41.9	5 31.0	25 41.9	28 37.0	8 35.7	16 41.1	26 29.8
14 W	13 26 59.5	23 38.4	18 5.3	2♊44.1	11 56.4	0 6.6	5 31.8	25 47.6	28 44.0	8 39.1	16 39.8	26 30.0
15 T	13 30 56.0	24 37.1	18 2.1	17 24.4	13 23.2	29♈30.2	5 31.9	25 53.2	28 50.9	8 42.4	16 38.5	26 30.1
16 F	13 34 52.5	25 35.8	17 58.9	1♋44.7	14 45.1	28 53.2	5R31.2	25 58.6	28 57.9	8 45.8	16 37.3	26 30.2
17 S	13 38 49.1	26 34.5	17 55.7	15 43.1	16 2.1	28 15.6	5 29.8	26 3.8	29 4.8	8 49.2	16 36.1	26 30.4
18 S	13 42 45.7	27 33.2	17 52.6	29 19.8	17 14.0	27 37.8	5 27.7	26 8.9	29 11.6	8 52.6	16 34.9	26 30.6
19 M	13 46 42.2	28 31.8	17 49.4	12♌36.5	18 20.7	26 59.9	5 24.8	26 13.7	29 18.5	8 56.0	16 33.8	26 30.9
20 T	13 50 38.8	29 30.3	17 46.2	25 35.3	19 22.0	26 22.3	5 21.1	26 18.5	29 25.3	8 59.5	16 32.7	26 31.1
21 W	13 54 35.3	0♉28.9	17 43.0	8♍18.8	20 17.8	25 45.2	5 16.7	26 23.0	29 32.0	9 2.9	16 31.6	26 31.4
22 T	13 58 31.9	1 27.4	17 39.9	20 49.1	21 8.1	25 8.9	5 11.6	26 27.4	29 38.7	9 6.3	16 30.5	26 31.7
23 F	14 2 28.4	2 25.8	17 36.7	3♎ 8.4	21 52.8	24 33.5	5 5.7	26 31.6	29 45.4	9 9.8	16 29.4	26 32.1
24 S	14 6 25.0	3 24.3	17 33.5	15 18.1	22 31.8	23 59.3	4 59.0	26 35.7	29 52.0	9 13.2	16 28.4	26 32.4
25 S	14 10 21.5	4 22.7	17 30.3	27 20.0	23 5.1	23 26.5	4 51.6	26 39.6	29 58.6	9 16.6	16 27.4	26 32.8
26 M	14 14 18.1	5 21.0	17 27.1	9♏15.5	23 32.7	22 55.3	4 43.4	26 43.3	0♈ 5.2	9 20.1	16 26.4	26 33.2
27 T	14 18 14.7	6 19.4	17 24.0	21 6.2	23 54.5	22 25.9	4 34.5	26 46.8	0 11.7	9 23.6	16 25.5	26 33.7
28 W	14 22 11.2	7 17.7	17 20.8	2♐54.3	24 10.7	21 58.4	4 24.8	26 50.1	0 18.1	9 27.0	16 24.5	26 34.1
29 T	14 26 7.8	8 16.0	17 17.6	14 42.2	24 21.2	21 32.9	4 14.4	26 53.3	0 24.5	9 30.5	16 23.6	26 34.6
30 F	14 30 4.3	9 14.2	17 14.4	26 33.2	24 26.1	21 9.6	4 3.2	26 56.3	0 30.9	9 33.9	16 22.8	26 35.1

DECLINATION

DAY	SIDEREAL TIME	☉	☊	☽	☿	♀	♂	♃	♄	♅	♆	♇
1 T	12 35 44.3	4N17.9	22S58.4	22S18.3	6N51.3	20N13.8	20S 4.1	21S20.1	2S57.7	13N45.9	6N 9.4	23N25.3
4 S	12 47 33.9	5 27.2	22 57.6	20 46.7	9 39.2	20 5.3	20 12.5	21 16.6	2 49.3	13 49.0	6 11.1	23 25.4
7 W	12 59 23.6	6 35.5	22 56.7	10 23.3	12 18.7	19 43.9	20 20.1	21 13.2	2 40.9	13 52.2	6 12.7	23 25.5
10 S	13 11 13.2	7 42.9	22 55.9	5N35.4	14 43.9	19 9.3	20 27.0	21 10.0	2 32.7	13 55.4	6 14.3	23 25.5
13 T	13 23 2.9	8 49.1	22 55.1	19 29.8	16 49.9	18 22.1	20 33.2	21 7.1	2 24.5	13 58.7	6 15.8	23 25.4
16 F	13 34 52.5	9 53.9	22 54.2	22 4.0	18 33.4	17 23.8	20 38.7	21 4.4	2 16.5	14 2.0	6 17.2	23 25.4
19 M	13 46 42.2	10 57.3	22 53.3	12 55.0	19 52.7	16 16.8	20 43.4	21 2.0	2 8.7	14 5.3	6 18.5	23 25.2
22 T	13 58 31.9	11 59.0	22 52.5	1S 4.2	20 47.2	15 4.6	20 47.3	20 59.8	2 1.0	14 8.6	6 19.8	23 25.1
25 S	14 10 21.5	12 59.0	22 51.6	14 7.4	21 16.9	13 50.9	20 50.4	20 57.9	1 53.5	14 11.9	6 20.9	23 24.9
28 W	14 22 11.2	13 57.1	22 50.7	21 51.4	21 22.3	12 39.4	20 52.6	20 56.3	1 46.1	14 15.2	6 22.0	23 24.6

MAY 1937

DAY	EPHEMERIS SIDEREAL TIME	☉	☊	☽	☿	♀	♂	♃	♄	♅	♆	♇
	h m s	° ′	° ′	° ′	° ′	° ′	° ′	° ′	° ′	° ′	° ′	° ′
						LONGITUDE						
1 S	14 34 0.9	10♉12.4	17♐11.3	8♑30.8	24♉25.7	20♈48.5	3♐51.3	26♑59.1	0♈37.2	9♉37.4	16♍21.9	26♋35.6
2 S	14 37 57.4	11 10.6	17 8.1	20 39.2	24R20.0	20R29.8	3R38.7	27 1.7	0 43.5	9 40.8	16R21.1	26 36.2
3 M	14 41 54.0	12 8.8	17 4.9	3♒ 3.1	24 9.4	20 13.5	3 25.4	27 4.2	0 49.7	9 44.3	16 20.3	26 36.8
4 T	14 45 50.5	13 7.0	17 1.7	15 46.8	23 54.0	19 59.6	3 11.4	27 6.5	0 55.9	9 47.8	16 19.6	26 37.4
5 W	14 49 47.1	14 5.1	16 58.5	28 54.6	23 34.3	19 48.1	2 56.7	27 8.5	1 2.0	9 51.2	16 18.8	26 38.0
6 T	14 53 43.6	15 3.2	16 55.4	12♓29.4	23 10.6	19 39.1	2 41.4	27 10.4	1 8.1	9 54.7	16 18.1	26 38.7
7 F	14 57 40.2	16 1.3	16 52.2	26 32.3	22 43.5	19 32.5	2 25.5	27 12.1	1 14.1	9 58.1	16 17.5	26 39.3
8 S	15 1 36.8	16 59.3	16 49.0	11♈ 2.1	22 13.4	19 28.3	2 8.9	27 13.7	1 20.1	10 1.6	16 16.8	26 40.0
9 S	15 5 33.3	17 57.4	16 45.8	25 54.2	21 40.8	19 26.5	1 51.8	27 15.0	1 26.0	10 5.0	16 16.2	26 40.8
10 M	15 9 29.9	18 55.4	16 42.7	11♉ 1.3	21 6.5	19D27.1	1 34.2	27 16.1	1 31.8	10 8.4	16 15.6	26 41.5
11 T	15 13 26.4	19 53.4	16 39.5	26 14.3	20 31.0	19 30.0	1 16.0	27 17.1	1 37.6	10 11.9	16 15.1	26 42.3
12 W	15 17 23.0	20 51.3	16 36.3	11♊23.1	19 54.9	19 35.2	0 57.3	27 17.8	1 43.4	10 15.3	16 14.6	26 43.1
13 T	15 21 19.5	21 49.2	16 33.1	26 18.7	19 18.8	19 42.6	0 38.2	27 18.4	1 49.0	10 18.7	16 14.1	26 43.9
14 F	15 25 16.1	22 47.1	16 30.0	10♋54.4	18 43.5	19 52.1	0 18.7	27 18.8	1 54.6	10 22.1	16 13.6	26 44.7
15 S	15 29 12.6	23 45.0	16 26.8	25 6.0	18 9.5	20 3.8	29♏58.9	27 19.0	2 0.2	10 25.5	16 13.2	26 45.6
16 S	15 33 9.2	24 42.9	16 23.6	8♌52.0	17 37.3	20 17.5	29 38.7	27 19.0	2 5.7	10 28.9	16 12.8	26 46.5
17 M	15 37 5.8	25 40.7	16 20.4	22 13.1	17 7.6	20 33.2	29 18.3	27R18.8	2 11.1	10 32.2	16 12.4	26 47.4
18 T	15 41 2.3	26 38.5	16 17.2	5♍11.5	16 40.6	20 50.7	28 57.6	27 18.4	2 16.4	10 35.6	16 12.1	26 48.3
19 W	15 44 58.8	27 36.2	16 14.1	17 50.2	16 17.0	21 10.2	28 36.7	27 17.9	2 21.7	10 38.9	16 11.8	26 49.2
20 T	15 48 55.4	28 34.0	16 10.9	0♎12.8	15 56.9	21 31.4	28 15.7	27 17.1	2 26.9	10 42.3	16 11.5	26 50.2
21 F	15 52 52.0	29 31.7	16 7.7	12 22.7	15 40.7	21 54.4	27 54.6	27 16.2	2 32.1	10 45.6	16 11.3	26 51.2
22 S	15 56 48.5	0♊29.3	16 4.5	24 23.0	15 28.7	22 19.1	27 33.4	27 15.0	2 37.2	10 48.9	16 11.1	26 52.2
23 S	16 0 45.1	1 27.0	16 1.4	6♏16.8	15 20.9	22 45.4	27 12.2	27 13.7	2 42.2	10 52.2	16 10.9	26 53.2
24 M	16 4 41.6	2 24.6	15 58.2	18 6.6	15 17.5	23 13.3	26 51.0	27 12.2	2 47.1	10 55.5	16 10.8	26 54.2
25 T	16 8 38.2	3 22.2	15 55.0	29 54.8	15D18.6	23 42.7	26 30.0	27 10.5	2 52.0	10 58.7	16 10.7	26 55.3
26 W	16 12 34.8	4 19.8	15 51.8	11♐43.7	15 24.2	24 13.6	26 9.0	27 8.7	2 56.8	11 2.0	16 10.6	26 56.4
27 T	16 16 31.3	5 17.4	15 48.7	23 35.6	15 34.3	24 45.8	25 48.2	27 6.6	3 1.6	11 5.2	16 10.5	26 57.5
28 F	16 20 27.8	6 15.0	15 45.5	5♑32.6	15 48.9	25 19.4	25 27.6	27 4.3	3 6.2	11 8.4	16 10.5	26 58.6
29 S	16 24 24.4	7 12.5	15 42.3	17 37.5	16 7.9	25 54.3	25 7.2	27 1.9	3 10.8	11 11.6	16D10.6	26 59.7
30 S	16 28 21.0	8 10.0	15 39.1	29 53.1	16 31.4	26 30.5	24 47.1	26 59.3	3 15.3	11 14.8	16 10.6	27 0.9
31 M	16 32 17.5	9 7.5	15 36.0	12♒22.4	16 59.0	27 7.9	24 27.4	26 56.5	3 19.7	11 18.0	16 10.7	27 2.0
						DECLINATION						
1 S	14 34 0.9	14N53.1	22S49.8	21S 8.0	21N 3.9	11N33.3	20S53.9	20S55.0	1S38.9	14N18.5	6N22.9	23N24.3
4 T	14 45 50.5	15 46.8	22 48.9	11 46.4	20 23.3	10 35.0	20 54.2	20 54.0	1 32.0	14 21.8	6 23.8	23 24.0
7 F	14 57 40.2	16 38.3	22 47.9	3N19.7	19 23.6	9 46.1	20 53.6	20 53.4	1 25.2	14 25.1	6 24.6	23 23.6
10 M	15 9 29.9	17 27.3	22 47.0	17 56.5	18 10.4	9 7.2	20 51.8	20 53.1	1 18.6	14 28.3	6 25.2	23 23.2
13 T	15 21 19.5	18 13.6	22 46.0	22 22.9	16 51.2	8 38.5	20 49.1	20 53.1	1 12.3	14 31.6	6 25.7	23 22.8
16 S	15 33 9.2	18 57.2	22 45.1	13 57.1	15 34.6	8 19.8	20 45.4	20 53.4	1 6.2	14 34.8	6 26.2	23 22.3
19 W	15 44 58.8	19 37.9	22 44.1	0S 2.1	14 28.9	8 10.4	20 40.8	20 54.1	1 0.4	14 37.9	6 26.5	23 21.8
22 S	15 56 48.5	20 15.6	22 43.1	13 15.1	13 40.1	8 9.7	20 35.5	20 55.2	0 54.8	14 41.0	6 26.7	23 21.2
25 T	16 8 38.2	20 50.1	22 42.1	21 29.5	13 11.4	8 16.9	20 29.6	20 56.5	0 49.5	14 44.1	6 26.8	23 20.6
28 F	16 20 27.8	21 21.5	22 41.1	21 28.6	13 3.7	8 31.1	20 23.4	20 58.2	0 44.5	14 47.1	6 26.8	23 20.0
31 M	16 32 17.5	21 49.5	22 40.1	12 48.7	13 16.0	8 51.5	20 17.0	21 0.2	0 39.7	14 50.0	6 26.6	23 19.4

JUNE 1937

DAY	EPHEMERIS SIDEREAL TIME	☉	☊	☽	☿	♀	♂	♃	♄	♅	♆	♇
						LONGITUDE						
1 T	16 36 14.1	10♊ 5.0	15♐32.8	25♒ 8.7	17♉30.9	27♈46.4	24♏ 8.0	26♑53.6	3♈24.1	11♉21.1	16♍10.8	27♋ 3.2
2 W	16 40 10.6	11 2.5	15 29.6	8♓15.1	18 6.9	28 26.0	23R49.0	26R50.4	3 28.4	11 24.2	16 11.0	27 4.4
3 T	16 44 7.2	11 60.0	15 26.4	21 44.1	18 46.9	29 6.7	23 30.5	26 47.1	3 32.6	11 27.3	16 11.2	27 5.7
4 F	16 48 3.7	12 57.4	15 23.2	5♈37.1	19 30.8	29 48.4	23 12.5	26 43.6	3 36.7	11 30.4	16 11.4	27 6.9
5 S	16 52 0.3	13 54.9	15 20.1	19 54.1	20 18.5	0♉31.1	22 55.0	26 39.9	3 40.7	11 33.5	16 11.6	27 8.2
6 S	16 55 56.9	14 52.3	15 16.9	4♉32.7	21 10.0	1 14.8	22 38.0	26 36.1	3 44.7	11 36.5	16 11.9	27 9.4
7 M	16 59 53.4	15 49.7	15 13.7	19 28.2	22 5.0	1 59.3	22 21.7	26 32.1	3 48.5	11 39.5	16 12.2	27 10.7
8 T	17 3 49.9	16 47.1	15 10.5	4♊33.4	23 3.6	2 44.7	22 5.9	26 27.9	3 52.3	11 42.5	16 12.6	27 12.0
9 W	17 7 46.5	17 44.5	15 7.4	19 39.8	24 5.6	3 31.0	21 50.9	26 23.5	3 56.0	11 45.4	16 12.9	27 13.3
10 T	17 11 43.1	18 41.9	15 4.2	4♋38.5	25 11.1	4 18.0	21 36.5	26 19.0	3 59.7	11 48.4	16 13.4	27 14.7
11 F	17 15 39.7	19 39.3	15 1.0	19 21.3	26 19.9	5 5.8	21 22.8	26 14.3	4 3.2	11 51.3	16 13.8	27 16.0
12 S	17 19 36.2	20 36.7	14 57.8	3♌42.0	27 31.9	5 54.4	21 9.8	26 9.5	4 6.6	11 54.2	16 14.3	27 17.4
13 S	17 23 32.7	21 34.0	14 54.6	17 37.2	28 47.2	6 43.6	20 57.6	26 4.5	4 10.0	11 57.0	16 14.8	27 18.8
14 M	17 27 29.3	22 31.3	14 51.5	1♍ 5.6	0♊ 5.6	7 33.5	20 46.2	25 59.4	4 13.3	11 59.8	16 15.3	27 20.2
15 T	17 31 25.9	23 28.6	14 48.3	14 8.6	1 27.3	8 24.1	20 35.6	25 54.1	4 16.5	12 2.6	16 15.9	27 21.6
16 W	17 35 22.4	24 25.9	14 45.1	26 48.7	2 52.0	9 15.4	20 25.7	25 48.7	4 19.5	12 5.4	16 16.5	27 23.0
17 T	17 39 19.0	25 23.2	14 41.9	9♎ 9.9	4 19.8	10 7.2	20 16.7	25 43.1	4 22.5	12 8.1	16 17.1	27 24.4
18 F	17 43 15.6	26 20.5	14 38.8	21 16.4	5 50.7	10 59.7	20 8.5	25 37.5	4 25.5	12 10.8	16 17.8	27 25.9
19 S	17 47 12.1	27 17.8	14 35.6	3♏12.6	7 24.6	11 52.7	20 1.1	25 31.6	4 28.3	12 13.5	16 18.5	27 27.3
20 S	17 51 8.6	28 15.0	14 32.4	15 2.6	9 1.5	12 46.3	19 54.5	25 25.7	4 31.0	12 16.2	16 19.2	27 28.8
21 M	17 55 5.2	29 12.2	14 29.2	26 50.3	10 41.4	13 40.4	19 48.8	25 19.6	4 33.6	12 18.8	16 20.0	27 30.3
22 T	17 59 1.8	0♋ 9.4	14 26.1	8♐39.2	12 24.3	14 35.0	19 43.9	25 13.4	4 36.2	12 21.4	16 20.8	27 31.8
23 W	18 2 58.4	1 6.7	14 22.9	20 32.0	14 10.0	15 30.1	19 39.9	25 7.0	4 38.6	12 23.9	16 21.6	27 33.3
24 T	18 6 54.9	2 3.9	14 19.7	2♑31.2	15 58.6	16 25.7	19 36.6	25 0.6	4 41.0	12 26.4	16 22.5	27 34.8
25 F	18 10 51.5	3 1.1	14 16.5	14 38.9	17 49.9	17 21.8	19 34.2	24 54.1	4 43.2	12 28.9	16 23.3	27 36.3
26 S	18 14 48.0	3 58.3	14 13.4	26 56.7	19 43.9	18 18.3	19 32.6	24 47.4	4 45.4	12 31.4	16 24.2	27 37.8
27 S	18 18 44.6	4 55.5	14 10.2	9♒26.2	21 40.4	19 15.3	19 31.9	24 40.7	4 47.5	12 33.8	16 25.2	27 39.4
28 M	18 22 41.2	5 52.7	14 7.0	22 8.7	23 39.3	20 12.7	19D32.0	24 33.8	4 49.4	12 36.2	16 26.1	27 40.9
29 T	18 26 37.7	6 49.9	14 3.8	5♓ 5.5	25 40.5	21 10.6	19 32.8	24 26.9	4 51.3	12 38.5	16 27.2	27 42.5
30 W	18 30 34.3	7 47.1	14 0.7	18 18.1	27 43.7	22 8.8	19 34.5	24 19.8	4 53.1	12 40.8	16 28.2	27 44.0
						DECLINATION						
1 T	16 36 14.1	21N58.1	22S39.8	8S26.9	13N24.3	8N59.5	20S14.8	21S 1.0	0S38.2	14N51.0	6N26.5	23N19.2
4 F	16 48 3.7	22 21.6	22 38.7	6N47.2	14 0.1	9 26.9	20 8.7	21 3.4	0 33.9	14 53.9	6 26.3	23 18.5
7 M	16 59 53.4	22 41.6	22 37.7	19 48.8	14 50.4	9 58.7	20 3.0	21 6.1	0 29.8	14 56.6	6 25.9	23 17.8
10 T	17 11 43.1	22 57.9	22 36.6	21 35.5	15 52.5	10 34.0	19 58.1	21 9.1	0 26.1	14 59.4	6 25.3	23 17.1
13 S	17 23 32.7	23 10.7	22 35.6	11 4.7	17 3.3	11 12.3	19 54.1	21 12.3	0 22.7	15 2.0	6 24.7	23 16.3
16 W	17 35 22.4	23 19.8	22 34.5	3S29.2	18 19.7	11 52.9	19 51.4	21 15.8	0 19.6	15 4.5	6 24.0	23 15.6
19 S	17 47 12.1	23 25.1	22 33.4	15 54.6	19 38.4	12 35.3	19 50.0	21 19.4	0 16.9	15 7.0	6 23.1	23 14.8
22 T	17 59 1.8	23 26.8	22 32.3	22 20.7	20 55.3	13 18.9	19 50.2	21 23.2	0 14.5	15 9.4	6 22.2	23 14.0
25 F	18 10 51.5	23 24.7	22 31.2	20 3.4	22 5.9	14 3.1	19 51.8	21 27.2	0 12.4	15 11.6	6 21.1	23 13.2
28 M	18 22 41.2	23 19.0	22 30.1	9 32.9	23 5.1	14 47.5	19 55.1	21 31.3	0 10.7	15 13.8	6 19.9	23 12.4

JULY 1937

DAY	EPHEMERIS SIDEREAL TIME	☉	☊	☽	☿	♀	♂	♃	♄	♅	♆	♇
	h m s	° ′	° ′	° ′	° ′	° ′	° ′	° ′	° ′	° ′	° ′	° ′
						LONGITUDE						
1 T	18 34 30.8	8♋44.3	13♐57.5	1♈47.5	29♊48.7	23♉ 7.4	19♏37.0	24♑12.7	4♈54.8	12♉43.1	16♍29.2	27♋45.6
2 F	18 38 27.3	9 41.5	13 54.3	15 34.6	1♋55.3	24 6.4	19 40.3	24R 5.5	4 56.4	12 45.3	16 30.3	27 47.2
3 S	18 42 23.9	10 38.7	13 51.1	29 39.5	4 3.2	25 5.7	19 44.4	23 58.2	4 57.9	12 47.5	16 31.4	27 48.8
4 S	18 46 20.5	11 35.9	13 47.9	14♉ 1.1	6 12.1	26 5.4	19 49.3	23 50.9	4 59.2	12 49.7	16 32.6	27 50.4
5 M	18 50 17.0	12 33.1	13 44.8	28 37.0	8 21.7	27 5.4	19 54.9	23 43.5	5 0.5	12 51.8	16 33.7	27 52.0
6 T	18 54 13.6	13 30.3	13 41.6	13♊22.9	10 31.7	28 5.8	20 1.3	23 36.0	5 1.7	12 53.9	16 34.9	27 53.6
7 W	18 58 10.1	14 27.6	13 38.4	28 12.8	12 41.9	29 6.5	20 8.5	23 28.5	5 2.8	12 55.9	16 36.2	27 55.2
8 T	19 2 6.7	15 24.8	13 35.2	12♋59.6	14 52.0	0♊ 7.4	20 16.5	23 21.0	5 3.8	12 57.9	16 37.4	27 56.8
9 F	19 6 3.3	16 22.0	13 32.1	27 35.8	17 1.7	1 8.7	20 25.2	23 13.4	5 4.6	12 59.9	16 38.7	27 58.4
10 S	19 9 59.8	17 19.2	13 28.9	11♌54.9	19 10.7	2 10.3	20 34.6	23 5.7	5 5.4	13 1.8	16 40.0	28 0.1
11 S	19 13 56.4	18 16.5	13 25.7	25 51.7	21 18.9	3 12.1	20 44.7	22 58.0	5 6.1	13 3.7	16 41.3	28 1.7
12 M	19 17 52.9	19 13.7	13 22.5	9♍23.5	23 26.1	4 14.2	20 55.6	22 50.3	5 6.7	13 5.5	16 42.7	28 3.3
13 T	19 21 49.5	20 11.0	13 19.4	22 30.0	25 32.0	5 16.5	21 7.2	22 42.6	5 7.2	13 7.3	16 44.1	28 5.0
14 W	19 25 46.1	21 8.2	13 16.2	5♎12.8	27 36.6	6 19.1	21 19.4	22 34.9	5 7.5	13 9.1	16 45.5	28 6.6
15 T	19 29 42.6	22 5.4	13 13.0	17 35.3	29 39.7	7 22.0	21 32.4	22 27.2	5 7.8	13 10.8	16 46.9	28 8.3
16 F	19 33 39.1	23 2.6	13 9.8	29 41.8	1♌41.3	8 25.1	21 46.0	22 19.4	5 8.0	13 12.5	16 48.4	28 9.9
17 S	19 37 35.7	23 59.9	13 6.6	11♏37.2	3 41.3	9 28.4	22 0.3	22 11.7	5 8.0	13 14.1	16 49.9	28 11.6
18 S	19 41 32.3	24 57.1	13 3.5	23 26.5	5 39.6	10 32.0	22 15.2	22 4.0	5R 8.0	13 15.7	16 51.4	28 13.2
19 M	19 45 28.8	25 54.4	13 0.3	5♐14.6	7 36.1	11 35.8	22 30.7	21 56.3	5 7.9	13 17.2	16 52.9	28 14.9
20 T	19 49 25.4	26 51.6	12 57.1	17 6.0	9 31.0	12 39.8	22 46.9	21 48.6	5 7.6	13 18.7	16 54.5	28 16.5
21 W	19 53 22.0	27 48.9	12 53.9	29 4.4	11 24.0	13 44.1	23 3.6	21 40.9	5 7.3	13 20.1	16 56.1	28 18.2
22 T	19 57 18.5	28 46.1	12 50.8	11♑13.0	13 15.3	14 48.5	23 20.9	21 33.3	5 6.9	13 21.5	16 57.7	28 19.8
23 F	20 1 15.1	29 43.4	12 47.6	23 33.9	15 4.9	15 53.2	23 38.9	21 25.7	5 6.3	13 22.9	16 59.3	28 21.5
24 S	20 5 11.6	0♌40.7	12 44.4	6♒ 8.4	16 52.6	16 58.0	23 57.3	21 18.1	5 5.7	13 24.2	17 0.9	28 23.1
25 S	20 9 8.2	1 38.0	12 41.2	18 57.1	18 38.7	18 3.1	24 16.4	21 10.6	5 4.9	13 25.5	17 2.6	28 24.8
26 M	20 13 4.8	2 35.3	12 38.1	1♓59.7	20 22.9	19 8.4	24 36.0	21 3.2	5 4.1	13 26.7	17 4.3	28 26.5
27 T	20 17 1.3	3 32.6	12 34.9	15 15.4	22 5.4	20 13.8	24 56.1	20 55.8	5 3.2	13 27.9	17 6.0	28 28.1
28 W	20 20 57.8	4 29.9	12 31.7	28 43.4	23 46.2	21 19.5	25 16.7	20 48.4	5 2.1	13 29.0	17 7.7	28 29.8
29 T	20 24 54.4	5 27.3	12 28.5	12♈22.7	25 25.2	22 25.3	25 37.8	20 41.1	5 1.0	13 30.1	17 9.5	28 31.4
30 F	20 28 51.0	6 24.6	12 25.3	26 12.6	27 2.5	23 31.3	25 59.5	20 33.9	4 59.8	13 31.1	17 11.2	28 33.0
31 S	20 32 47.5	7 22.0	12 22.2	10♉12.5	28 38.1	24 37.5	26 21.7	20 26.8	4 58.4	13 32.1	17 13.0	28 34.7
						DECLINATION						
1 T	18 34 30.8	23N 9.5	22S28.9	5N19.2	23N47.5	15N31.7	19S59.9	21S35.5	0S 9.3	15N15.9	6N18.7	23N11.6
4 S	18 46 20.5	22 56.4	22 27.8	18 37.6	24 8.4	16 15.0	20 6.3	21 39.8	0 8.3	15 17.9	6 17.3	23 10.8
7 W	18 58 10.1	22 39.7	22 26.7	22 13.9	24 4.9	16 57.2	20 14.2	21 44.1	0 7.7	15 19.7	6 15.8	23 9.9
10 S	19 9 59.8	22 19.5	22 25.5	13 0.9	23 36.5	17 37.7	20 23.5	21 48.4	0 7.4	15 21.5	6 14.3	23 9.1
13 T	19 21 49.5	21 55.7	22 24.3	1S45.4	22 45.0	18 16.1	20 34.2	21 52.7	0 7.5	15 23.1	6 12.6	23 8.3
16 F	19 33 39.1	21 28.7	22 23.1	14 48.0	21 33.8	18 52.2	20 46.1	21 56.9	0 7.9	15 24.6	6 10.9	23 7.4
19 M	19 45 28.8	20 58.3	22 21.9	22 0.6	20 6.5	19 25.5	20 59.2	22 1.1	0 8.7	15 26.0	6 9.1	23 6.6
22 T	19 57 18.5	20 24.8	22 20.7	20 39.4	18 27.0	19 55.6	21 13.2	22 5.1	0 9.9	15 27.3	6 7.2	23 5.8
25 S	20 9 8.2	19 48.2	22 19.5	10 43.9	16 38.7	20 22.3	21 28.0	22 9.0	0 11.4	15 28.4	6 5.2	23 5.0
28 W	20 20 57.8	19 8.6	22 18.3	4N 2.0	14 44.3	20 45.3	21 43.6	22 12.8	0 13.2	15 29.4	6 3.2	23 4.2
31 S	20 32 47.5	18 26.1	22 17.1	17 34.3	12 46.3	21 4.2	21 59.6	22 16.4	0 15.4	15 30.3	6 1.1	23 3.4

AUGUST 1937

DAY	EPHEMERIS SIDEREAL TIME	☉	☊	☽	☿	♀	♂	♃	♄	♅	♆	♇
						LONGITUDE						
1 S	20 36 44.1	8♌19.4	12♐19.0	24♉21.8	0♍11.9	25♊43.9	26♏44.3	20♑19.8	4♈57.0	13♉33.0	17♍14.9	28♋36.3
2 M	20 40 40.6	9 16.8	12 15.8	8♊39.2	1 44.0	26 50.4	27 7.4	20R12.8	4R55.5	13 33.9	17 16.7	28 38.0
3 T	20 44 37.1	10 14.3	12 12.6	23 2.5	3 14.4	27 57.1	27 31.0	20 6.0	4 53.8	13 34.7	17 18.5	28 39.6
4 W	20 48 33.7	11 11.7	12 9.5	7♋28.6	4 43.0	29 4.0	27 55.1	19 59.2	4 52.1	13 35.5	17 20.4	28 41.2
5 T	20 52 30.3	12 9.2	12 6.3	21 53.1	6 9.8	0♋11.0	28 19.6	19 52.5	4 50.3	13 36.3	17 22.3	28 42.8
6 F	20 56 26.9	13 6.7	12 3.1	6♌10.5	7 34.9	1 18.1	28 44.5	19 46.0	4 48.4	13 37.0	17 24.2	28 44.4
7 S	21 0 23.4	14 4.2	11 59.9	20 15.2	8 58.1	2 25.5	29 10.0	19 39.5	4 46.4	13 37.6	17 26.1	28 46.1
8 S	21 4 19.9	15 1.8	11 56.7	4♍ 2.6	10 19.5	3 32.9	29 35.8	19 33.2	4 44.3	13 38.2	17 28.0	28 47.7
9 M	21 8 16.5	15 59.3	11 53.6	17 29.0	11 39.0	4 40.5	0♐ 2.1	19 26.9	4 42.1	13 38.8	17 30.0	28 49.3
10 T	21 12 13.1	16 56.9	11 50.4	0♎33.0	12 56.6	5 48.3	0 28.7	19 20.9	4 39.8	13 39.2	17 32.0	28 50.8
11 W	21 16 9.6	17 54.5	11 47.2	13 15.1	14 12.2	6 56.1	0 55.8	19 14.9	4 37.5	13 39.7	17 33.9	28 52.4
12 T	21 20 6.2	18 52.1	11 44.0	25 37.6	15 25.7	8 4.1	1 23.3	19 9.1	4 35.0	13 40.1	17 35.9	28 54.0
13 F	21 24 2.7	19 49.7	11 40.9	7♏44.1	16 37.1	9 12.3	1 51.2	19 3.4	4 32.5	13 40.4	17 37.9	28 55.6
14 S	21 27 59.3	20 47.3	11 37.7	19 39.5	17 46.4	10 20.6	2 19.4	18 57.8	4 29.8	13 40.7	17 40.0	28 57.1
15 S	21 31 55.9	21 44.9	11 34.5	1♐28.9	18 53.3	11 29.0	2 48.1	18 52.4	4 27.1	13 41.0	17 42.0	28 58.7
16 M	21 35 52.4	22 42.6	11 31.3	13 17.7	19 57.9	12 37.5	3 17.1	18 47.2	4 24.3	13 41.2	17 44.0	29 0.2
17 T	21 39 48.9	23 40.3	11 28.1	25 11.3	20 60.0	13 46.2	3 46.4	18 42.0	4 21.4	13 41.3	17 46.1	29 1.7
18 W	21 43 45.5	24 38.0	11 25.0	7♑14.3	21 59.5	14 55.0	4 16.1	18 37.1	4 18.5	13 41.4	17 48.2	29 3.3
19 T	21 47 42.0	25 35.7	11 21.8	19 30.9	22 56.3	16 3.9	4 46.1	18 32.3	4 15.4	13 41.5	17 50.3	29 4.8
20 F	21 51 38.6	26 33.4	11 18.6	2♒ 3.9	23 50.2	17 12.9	5 16.5	18 27.6	4 12.3	13 41.5	17 52.4	29 6.3
21 S	21 55 35.2	27 31.2	11 15.4	14 55.0	24 41.1	18 22.1	5 47.2	18 23.1	4 9.1	13R41.4	17 54.5	29 7.8
22 S	21 59 31.7	28 28.9	11 12.3	28 4.2	25 28.7	19 31.4	6 18.2	18 18.8	4 5.8	13 41.3	17 56.6	29 9.3
23 M	22 3 28.2	29 26.7	11 9.1	11♓30.2	26 13.0	20 40.8	6 49.5	18 14.7	4 2.5	13 41.1	17 58.7	29 10.7
24 T	22 7 24.8	0♍24.6	11 5.9	25 10.4	26 53.7	21 50.3	7 21.2	18 10.7	3 59.1	13 41.0	18 0.8	29 12.2
25 W	22 11 21.4	1 22.4	11 2.7	9♈ 1.6	27 30.6	22 59.9	7 53.1	18 6.9	3 55.6	13 40.7	18 3.0	29 13.6
26 T	22 15 17.9	2 20.3	10 59.6	23 0.4	28 3.4	24 9.7	8 25.3	18 3.2	3 52.0	13 40.4	18 5.2	29 15.1
27 F	22 19 14.5	3 18.2	10 56.4	7♉ 3.9	28 32.0	25 19.5	8 57.8	17 59.7	3 48.4	13 40.1	18 7.3	29 16.5
28 S	22 23 11.0	4 16.2	10 53.2	21 9.7	28 56.0	26 29.5	9 30.6	17 56.4	3 44.7	13 39.7	18 9.5	29 17.9
29 S	22 27 7.6	5 14.1	10 50.0	5♊16.6	29 15.2	27 39.6	10 3.7	17 53.3	3 41.0	13 39.2	18 11.7	29 19.3
30 M	22 31 4.2	6 12.1	10 46.8	19 23.4	29 29.3	28 49.8	10 37.1	17 50.4	3 37.1	13 38.7	18 13.8	29 20.7
31 T	22 35 0.7	7 10.2	10 43.7	3♋29.2	29 38.1	0♌ 0.2	11 10.7	17 47.6	3 33.3	13 38.2	18 16.0	29 22.0
						DECLINATION						
1 S	20 36 44.1	18N11.4	22S16.7	20N30.9	12N 6.5	21N 9.6	22S 5.1	22S17.6	0S16.2	15N30.6	6N 0.4	23N 3.1
4 W	20 48 33.7	17 25.3	22 15.4	21 10.4	10 6.8	21 22.7	22 21.7	22 21.0	0 18.9	15 31.3	5 58.2	23 2.3
7 S	21 0 23.4	16 36.7	22 14.1	10 18.3	8 7.9	21 31.3	22 38.5	22 24.2	0 21.9	15 31.9	5 55.9	23 1.5
10 T	21 12 13.1	15 45.7	22 12.9	4S39.0	6 11.4	21 35.1	22 55.5	22 27.1	0 25.1	15 32.3	5 53.6	23 0.8
13 F	21 24 2.7	14 52.4	22 11.6	16 50.8	4 19.0	21 34.1	23 12.3	22 29.9	0 28.7	15 32.6	5 51.2	23 0.1
16 M	21 35 52.4	13 57.0	22 10.3	22 20.4	2 32.4	21 28.0	23 29.0	22 32.4	0 32.5	15 32.8	5 48.8	22 59.4
19 T	21 47 42.0	12 59.6	22 9.0	19 0.6	0 53.5	21 16.7	23 45.3	22 34.7	0 36.6	15 32.9	5 46.4	22 58.7
22 S	21 59 31.7	12 0.3	22 7.7	7 34.2	0S35.2	21 0.4	24 1.2	22 36.8	0 41.0	15 32.8	5 43.9	22 58.0
25 W	22 11 21.4	10 59.4	22 6.4	7N40.4	1 50.9	20 38.9	24 16.4	22 38.6	0 45.6	15 32.6	5 41.4	22 57.4
28 S	22 23 11.0	9 56.8	22 5.0	19 43.6	2 50.0	20 12.2	24 30.9	22 40.2	0 50.4	15 32.2	5 38.9	22 56.8
31 T	22 35 0.7	8 52.9	22 3.7	21 29.0	3 28.1	19 40.5	24 44.5	22 41.5	0 55.4	15 31.7	5 36.3	22 56.3

SEPTEMBER 1937

DAY	EPHEMERIS SIDEREAL TIME	☉	☊	☽	☿	♀	♂	♃	♄	♅	♆	♇
	h m s	° ′	° ′	° ′	° ′	° ′	° ′	° ′	° ′	° ′	° ′	° ′
						LONGITUDE						
1 W	22 38 57.2	8♍ 8.2	10♐40.5	17♋32.8	29♍41.2	1♌10.6	11♐44.6	17♑45.0	3♈29.3	13♉37.6	18♍18.2	29♋23.4
2 T	22 42 53.8	9 6.3	10 37.3	1♌32.1	29R38.5	2 21.1	12 18.8	17R42.7	3R25.3	13R36.9	18 20.4	29 24.7
3 F	22 46 50.4	10 4.5	10 34.1	15 24.4	29 29.7	3 31.7	12 53.2	17 40.5	3 21.3	13 36.3	18 22.6	29 26.0
4 S	22 50 46.9	11 2.6	10 31.0	29 6.3	29 14.6	4 42.5	13 27.9	17 38.4	3 17.2	13 35.5	18 24.8	29 27.3
5 S	22 54 43.4	12 0.8	10 27.8	12♍34.5	28 53.2	5 53.3	14 2.8	17 36.6	3 13.0	13 34.7	18 27.1	29 28.6
6 M	22 58 40.0	12 59.0	10 24.6	25 46.3	28 25.4	7 4.2	14 38.0	17 35.0	3 8.8	13 33.9	18 29.3	29 29.9
7 T	23 2 36.6	13 57.3	10 21.4	8♎40.0	27 51.4	8 15.2	15 13.4	17 33.5	3 4.6	13 33.0	18 31.5	29 31.2
8 W	23 6 33.1	14 55.6	10 18.2	21 15.5	27 11.3	9 26.3	15 49.1	17 32.3	3 0.3	13 32.1	18 33.7	29 32.4
9 T	23 10 29.7	15 53.9	10 15.1	3♏34.0	26 25.5	10 37.5	16 25.0	17 31.2	2 56.0	13 31.1	18 36.0	29 33.6
10 F	23 14 26.2	16 52.2	10 11.9	15 38.3	25 34.6	11 48.8	17 1.1	17 30.4	2 51.6	13 30.1	18 38.2	29 34.8
11 S	23 18 22.8	17 50.5	10 8.7	27 32.4	24 39.3	13 0.2	17 37.5	17 29.7	2 47.2	13 29.1	18 40.4	29 36.0
12 S	23 22 19.3	18 48.9	10 5.5	9♐21.1	23 40.7	14 11.7	18 14.1	17 29.2	2 42.7	13 27.9	18 42.6	29 37.2
13 M	23 26 15.9	19 47.3	10 2.4	21 9.5	22 39.7	15 23.2	18 50.9	17 28.9	2 38.3	13 26.8	18 44.9	29 38.3
14 T	23 30 12.4	20 45.8	9 59.2	3♑ 3.3	21 37.7	16 34.9	19 27.9	17 28.9	2 33.8	13 25.6	18 47.1	29 39.5
15 W	23 34 9.0	21 44.2	9 56.0	15 7.8	20 36.1	17 46.6	20 5.1	17D29.0	2 29.2	13 24.4	18 49.3	29 40.6
16 T	23 38 5.5	22 42.7	9 52.8	27 27.9	19 36.4	18 58.4	20 42.5	17 29.3	2 24.7	13 23.1	18 51.5	29 41.7
17 F	23 42 2.1	23 41.2	9 49.6	10♒ 7.7	18 40.0	20 10.3	21 20.1	17 29.8	2 20.1	13 21.8	18 53.8	29 42.8
18 S	23 45 58.7	24 39.8	9 46.5	23 9.5	17 48.4	21 22.3	21 57.9	17 30.4	2 15.5	13 20.4	18 56.0	29 43.8
19 S	23 49 55.2	25 38.3	9 43.3	6♓34.3	17 2.8	22 34.3	22 35.9	17 31.3	2 10.9	13 19.0	18 58.2	29 44.8
20 M	23 53 51.7	26 36.9	9 40.1	20 20.5	16 24.6	23 46.4	23 14.0	17 32.4	2 6.3	13 17.5	19 0.4	29 45.9
21 T	23 57 48.3	27 35.6	9 36.9	4♈24.8	15 54.6	24 58.7	23 52.4	17 33.7	2 1.6	13 16.1	19 2.6	29 46.9
22 W	0 1 44.9	28 34.3	9 33.8	18 42.2	15 33.7	26 11.0	24 30.9	17 35.1	1 57.0	13 14.5	19 4.8	29 47.8
23 T	0 5 41.4	29 33.0	9 30.6	3♉ 6.7	15 22.3	27 23.4	25 9.6	17 36.8	1 52.3	13 13.0	19 7.0	29 48.8
24 F	0 9 38.0	0♎31.7	9 27.4	17 32.8	15 20.8	28 35.8	25 48.4	17 38.6	1 47.6	13 11.4	19 9.2	29 49.7
25 S	0 13 34.5	1 30.5	9 24.2	1♊55.8	15D29.4	29 48.4	26 27.5	17 40.6	1 43.0	13 9.7	19 11.4	29 50.6
26 S	0 17 31.1	2 29.3	9 21.0	16 12.5	15 47.9	1♍ 1.0	27 6.7	17 42.8	1 38.3	13 8.0	19 13.6	29 51.5
27 M	0 21 27.7	3 28.1	9 17.9	0♋20.7	16 16.0	2 13.7	27 46.0	17 45.2	1 33.6	13 6.3	19 15.8	29 52.4
28 T	0 25 24.2	4 27.0	9 14.7	14 19.6	16 53.4	3 26.5	28 25.5	17 47.8	1 29.0	13 4.6	19 17.9	29 53.2
29 W	0 29 20.7	5 26.0	9 11.5	28 8.8	17 39.6	4 39.3	29 5.2	17 50.6	1 24.3	13 2.8	19 20.1	29 54.1
30 T	0 33 17.3	6 24.9	9 8.3	11♌48.1	18 33.9	5 52.3	29 45.0	17 53.5	1 19.6	13 0.9	19 22.2	29 54.9
						DECLINATION						
1 W	22 38 57.2	8N31.2	22S 3.2	19N19.7	3S35.3	19N28.8	24S48.8	22S41.9	0S57.1	15N31.5	5N35.4	22N56.1
4 S	22 50 46.9	7 25.6	22 1.9	7 11.1	3 37.4	18 50.5	25 1.1	22 43.0	1 2.4	15 30.9	5 32.9	22 55.6
7 T	23 2 36.6	6 18.8	22 0.5	7S29.1	3 6.8	18 7.3	25 12.2	22 43.8	1 7.8	15 30.1	5 30.3	22 55.1
10 F	23 14 26.2	5 11.2	21 59.1	18 30.1	2 1.5	17 19.5	25 22.1	22 44.3	1 13.3	15 29.2	5 27.7	22 54.7
13 M	23 26 15.9	4 2.7	21 57.7	22 8.7	0 25.7	16 27.3	25 30.6	22 44.6	1 18.8	15 28.2	5 25.1	22 54.3
16 T	23 38 5.5	2 53.6	21 56.3	16 59.7	1N27.8	15 30.8	25 37.7	22 44.7	1 24.5	15 27.0	5 22.5	22 53.9
19 S	23 49 55.2	1 44.0	21 54.9	4 25.6	3 19.6	14 30.3	25 43.2	22 44.6	1 30.2	15 25.8	5 19.9	22 53.6
22 W	0 1 44.9	0 34.1	21 53.5	10N54.1	4 49.2	13 26.1	25 47.0	22 44.2	1 35.9	15 24.4	5 17.3	22 53.3
25 S	0 13 34.5	0S36.0	21 52.1	21 6.9	5 42.1	12 18.3	25 49.2	22 43.6	1 41.5	15 22.9	5 14.8	22 53.1
28 T	0 25 24.2	1 46.2	21 50.6	19 42.1	5 52.1	11 7.2	25 49.5	22 42.7	1 47.2	15 21.4	5 12.3	22 52.9

OCTOBER 1937

DAY	EPHEMERIS SIDEREAL TIME	☉	☊	☽	☿	♀	♂	♃	♄	♅	♆	♇
						LONGITUDE						
1 F	0 37 13.8	7♎23.9	9♐ 5.1	25♌16.8	19♍35.8	7♍ 5.3	0♑25.0	17♑56.7	1♈15.0	12♉59.1	19♍24.4	29♋55.7
2 S	0 41 10.4	8 23.0	9 2.0	8♍34.2	20 44.4	8 18.3	1 5.2	18 0.0	1R10.4	12R57.2	19 26.5	29 56.4
3 S	0 45 7.0	9 22.1	8 58.8	21 39.1	21 59.1	9 31.5	1 45.5	18 3.5	1 5.8	12 55.3	19 28.6	29 57.1
4 M	0 49 3.5	10 21.2	8 55.6	4♎30.7	23 19.1	10 44.7	2 25.9	18 7.2	1 1.2	12 53.3	19 30.8	29 57.9
5 T	0 53 0.1	11 20.3	8 52.4	17 8.2	24 43.8	11 57.9	3 6.5	18 11.1	0 56.6	12 51.3	19 32.9	29 58.5
6 W	0 56 56.6	12 19.5	8 49.3	29 31.8	26 12.6	13 11.2	3 47.3	18 15.2	0 52.1	12 49.3	19 35.0	29 59.2
7 T	1 0 53.2	13 18.7	8 46.1	11♏42.3	27 44.7	14 24.6	4 28.2	18 19.4	0 47.5	12 47.3	19 37.0	29 59.8
8 F	1 4 49.7	14 18.0	8 42.9	23 41.8	29 19.7	15 38.1	5 9.2	18 23.8	0 43.1	12 45.2	19 39.1	0♌ 0.5
9 S	1 8 46.3	15 17.2	8 39.7	5♐33.1	0♎57.0	16 51.6	5 50.3	18 28.4	0 38.6	12 43.1	19 41.2	0 1.0
10 S	1 12 42.8	16 16.6	8 36.5	17 20.1	2 36.2	18 5.1	6 31.6	18 33.2	0 34.2	12 41.0	19 43.2	0 1.6
11 M	1 16 39.4	17 15.9	8 33.4	29 7.3	4 16.9	19 18.8	7 13.0	18 38.1	0 29.8	12 38.8	19 45.2	0 2.2
12 T	1 20 35.9	18 15.3	8 30.2	10♑59.8	5 58.7	20 32.4	7 54.5	18 43.2	0 25.5	12 36.6	19 47.2	0 2.7
13 W	1 24 32.5	19 14.7	8 27.0	23 2.8	7 41.3	21 46.1	8 36.2	18 48.5	0 21.2	12 34.4	19 49.2	0 3.2
14 T	1 28 29.0	20 14.1	8 23.8	5♒21.5	9 24.5	22 59.9	9 18.0	18 53.9	0 16.9	12 32.2	19 51.2	0 3.6
15 F	1 32 25.6	21 13.6	8 20.7	18 0.8	11 8.1	24 13.8	9 59.8	18 59.6	0 12.7	12 30.0	19 53.2	0 4.1
16 S	1 36 22.2	22 13.0	8 17.5	1♓ 4.3	12 51.8	25 27.6	10 41.8	19 5.4	0 8.6	12 27.7	19 55.2	0 4.5
17 S	1 40 18.7	23 12.6	8 14.3	14 34.0	14 35.6	26 41.6	11 23.9	19 11.3	0 4.5	12 25.4	19 57.1	0 4.9
18 M	1 44 15.2	24 12.1	8 11.1	28 29.8	16 19.2	27 55.5	12 6.1	19 17.4	0 0.4	12 23.1	19 59.0	0 5.2
19 T	1 48 11.8	25 11.7	8 7.9	12♈49.1	18 2.6	29 9.6	12 48.5	19 23.7	29♓56.4	12 20.8	20 0.9	0 5.6
20 W	1 52 8.4	26 11.3	8 4.8	27 26.5	19 45.8	0♎23.7	13 30.9	19 30.1	29 52.5	12 18.4	20 2.8	0 5.9
21 T	1 56 4.9	27 10.9	8 1.6	12♉15.1	21 28.6	1 37.8	14 13.4	19 36.7	29 48.6	12 16.1	20 4.7	0 6.2
22 F	2 0 1.5	28 10.6	7 58.4	27 6.8	23 10.9	2 52.0	14 56.0	19 43.4	29 44.8	12 13.7	20 6.5	0 6.5
23 S	2 3 58.0	29 10.3	7 55.2	11♊54.1	24 52.9	4 6.2	15 38.7	19 50.3	29 41.0	12 11.3	20 8.3	0 6.7
24 S	2 7 54.6	0♏10.1	7 52.1	26 30.9	26 34.3	5 20.5	16 21.5	19 57.4	29 37.3	12 8.9	20 10.1	0 6.9
25 M	2 11 51.1	1 9.9	7 48.9	10♋52.9	28 15.3	6 34.8	17 4.4	20 4.6	29 33.7	12 6.5	20 11.9	0 7.1
26 T	2 15 47.7	2 9.7	7 45.7	24 57.7	29 55.8	7 49.2	17 47.3	20 11.9	29 30.1	12 4.1	20 13.7	0 7.3
27 W	2 19 44.2	3 9.6	7 42.5	8♌44.8	1♏35.7	9 3.6	18 30.4	20 19.4	29 26.7	12 1.6	20 15.5	0 7.4
28 T	2 23 40.8	4 9.5	7 39.3	22 14.3	3 15.2	10 18.0	19 13.6	20 27.1	29 23.2	11 59.2	20 17.2	0 7.5
29 F	2 27 37.3	5 9.4	7 36.2	5♍27.6	4 54.2	11 32.6	19 56.8	20 34.9	29 19.9	11 56.7	20 18.9	0 7.6
30 S	2 31 33.9	6 9.4	7 33.0	18 25.6	6 32.6	12 47.1	20 40.1	20 42.8	29 16.6	11 54.3	20 20.6	0 7.6
31 S	2 35 30.5	7 9.4	7 29.8	1♎ 9.9	8 10.6	14 1.7	21 23.6	20 50.9	29 13.5	11 51.8	20 22.2	0 7.7
						DECLINATION						
1 F	0 37 13.8	2S56.2	21S49.2	8N25.9	5N20.4	9N53.2	25S47.9	22S41.6	1S52.7	15N19.7	5N 9.8	22N52.8
4 M	0 49 3.5	4 6.0	21 47.7	5S57.3	4 13.1	8 36.5	25 44.4	22 40.3	1 58.2	15 17.9	5 7.4	22 52.7
7 T	1 0 53.2	5 15.4	21 46.2	17 27.2	2 38.6	7 17.4	25 38.9	22 38.8	2 3.6	15 16.1	5 5.0	22 52.7
10 S	1 12 42.8	6 24.2	21 44.7	21 56.3	0 45.3	5 56.2	25 31.3	22 37.0	2 8.7	15 14.2	5 2.6	22 52.7
13 W	1 24 32.5	7 32.1	21 43.2	17 49.3	1S19.4	4 33.3	25 21.7	22 34.9	2 13.8	15 12.2	5 0.3	22 52.8
16 S	1 36 22.2	8 39.2	21 41.7	6 17.8	3 29.7	3 9.0	25 10.0	22 32.6	2 18.6	15 10.1	4 58.0	22 52.9
19 T	1 48 11.8	9 45.1	21 40.2	8N54.7	5 41.6	1 43.5	24 56.1	22 30.1	2 23.2	15 8.0	4 55.9	22 53.0
22 F	2 0 1.5	10 49.8	21 38.7	20 21.0	7 52.2	0 17.2	24 40.2	22 27.3	2 27.5	15 5.9	4 53.7	22 53.3
25 M	2 11 51.1	11 53.0	21 37.1	20 4.0	9 59.5	1S 9.6	24 22.1	22 24.3	2 31.6	15 3.7	4 51.7	22 53.5
28 T	2 23 40.8	12 54.6	21 35.6	9 19.0	12 2.1	2 36.6	24 1.9	22 21.0	2 35.4	15 1.5	4 49.7	22 53.9
31 S	2 35 30.5	13 54.4	21 34.0	4S48.6	13 58.8	4 3.4	23 39.5	22 17.5	2 38.9	14 59.2	4 47.8	22 54.2

NOVEMBER 1937

LONGITUDE

DAY	EPHEMERIS SIDEREAL TIME	☉	☊	☽	☿	♀	♂	♃	♄	♅	♆	♇
	h m s	° ′	° ′	° ′	° ′	° ′	° ′	° ′	° ′	° ′	° ′	° ′
1 M	2 39 27.0	8♏ 9.5	7♐26.6	13♎41.4	9♏48.1	15♎16.3	22♑ 7.1	20♑59.1	29♓10.4	11♉49.3	20♍23.9	0♌ 7.7
2 T	2 43 23.5	9 9.5	7 23.5	26 1.4	11 25.1	16 30.9	22 50.6	21 7.4	29R 7.3	11R46.8	20 25.5	0R 7.6
3 W	2 47 20.1	10 9.6	7 20.8	8♏11.1	13 1.6	17 45.6	23 34.3	21 15.9	29 4.4	11 44.4	20 27.1	0 7.6
4 T	2 51 16.7	11 9.8	7 17.1	20 11.8	14 37.8	19 0.4	24 18.1	21 24.6	29 1.6	11 41.9	20 28.6	0 7.5
5 F	2 55 13.2	12 10.0	7 13.9	2♐ 5.3	16 13.5	20 15.1	25 1.9	21 33.3	28 58.8	11 39.4	20 30.2	0 7.4
6 S	2 59 9.8	13 10.2	7 10.7	13 53.7	17 48.8	21 29.9	25 45.8	21 42.2	28 56.1	11 36.9	20 31.7	0 7.3
7 S	3 3 6.3	14 10.4	7 7.6	25 39.8	19 23.7	22 44.7	26 29.7	21 51.2	28 53.5	11 34.4	20 33.2	0 7.1
8 M	3 7 2.9	15 10.6	7 4.4	7♑27.1	20 58.2	23 59.5	27 13.7	22 0.4	28 51.0	11 32.0	20 34.7	0 7.0
9 T	3 10 59.5	16 10.9	7 1.2	19 19.5	22 32.4	25 14.4	27 57.8	22 9.7	28 48.6	11 29.5	20 36.1	0 6.8
10 W	3 14 56.0	17 11.2	6 58.0	1♒21.2	24 6.3	26 29.3	28 42.0	22 19.1	28 46.3	11 27.0	20 37.5	0 6.5
11 T	3 18 52.5	18 11.6	6 54.9	13 37.1	25 39.8	27 44.2	29 26.2	22 28.6	28 44.1	11 24.6	20 38.9	0 6.3
12 F	3 22 49.1	19 11.9	6 51.7	26 11.7	27 13.0	28 59.2	0♒10.5	22 38.3	28 42.0	11 22.1	20 40.3	0 6.0
13 S	3 26 45.7	20 12.3	6 48.5	9♓ 9.3	28 45.9	0♏14.1	0 54.8	22 48.0	28 40.0	11 19.7	20 41.6	0 5.7
14 S	3 30 42.2	21 12.7	6 45.3	22 33.1	0♐18.5	1 29.1	1 39.2	22 57.9	28 38.1	11 17.2	20 42.9	0 5.4
15 M	3 34 38.8	22 13.1	6 42.2	6♈24.7	1 50.8	2 44.1	2 23.6	23 7.9	28 36.2	11 14.8	20 44.2	0 5.0
16 T	3 38 35.3	23 13.6	6 39.0	20 43.5	3 22.9	3 59.2	3 8.1	23 18.0	28 34.5	11 12.4	20 45.4	0 4.6
17 W	3 42 31.9	24 14.0	6 35.8	5♉26.0	4 54.6	5 14.2	3 52.7	23 28.3	28 32.9	11 10.0	20 46.6	0 4.2
18 T	3 46 28.5	25 14.5	6 32.6	20 26.0	6 26.2	6 29.3	4 37.3	23 38.6	28 31.4	11 7.6	20 47.8	0 3.8
19 F	3 50 25.0	26 15.0	6 29.4	5♊35.1	7 57.4	7 44.4	5 21.9	23 49.0	28 29.9	11 5.2	20 49.0	0 3.3
20 S	3 54 21.5	27 15.6	6 26.3	20 44.0	9 28.4	8 59.5	6 6.6	23 59.6	28 28.6	11 2.9	20 50.1	0 2.9
21 S	3 58 18.1	28 16.2	6 23.1	5♋43.5	10 59.2	10 14.6	6 51.3	24 10.3	28 27.4	11 0.5	20 51.2	0 2.4
22 M	4 2 14.7	29 16.8	6 19.9	20 26.3	12 29.6	11 29.8	7 36.0	24 21.0	28 26.3	10 58.2	20 52.3	0 1.8
23 T	4 6 11.2	0♐17.4	6 16.7	4♌47.3	13 59.8	12 45.0	8 20.8	24 31.9	28 25.3	10 55.9	20 53.3	0 1.3
24 W	4 10 7.8	1 18.1	6 13.6	18 43.9	15 29.7	14 0.2	9 5.7	24 42.8	28 24.4	10 53.6	20 54.3	0 0.7
25 T	4 14 4.3	2 18.7	6 10.4	2♍16.0	16 59.2	15 15.4	9 50.5	24 53.9	28 23.6	10 51.4	20 55.3	0 0.1
26 F	4 18 0.9	3 19.4	6 7.2	15 25.1	18 28.4	16 30.7	10 35.4	25 5.1	28 22.9	10 49.1	20 56.2	29♋59.5
27 S	4 21 57.4	4 20.2	6 4.0	28 13.7	19 57.1	17 45.9	11 20.4	25 16.3	28 22.3	10 46.9	20 57.1	29 58.8
28 S	4 25 54.0	5 21.0	6 0.9	10♎45.0	21 25.4	19 1.2	12 5.4	25 27.7	28 21.8	10 44.7	20 58.0	29 58.2
29 M	4 29 50.6	6 21.7	5 57.7	23 2.1	22 53.2	20 16.5	12 50.4	25 39.1	28 21.5	10 42.5	20 58.9	29 57.5
30 T	4 33 47.1	7 22.6	5 54.5	5♏ 8.2	24 20.4	21 31.8	13 35.5	25 50.7	28 21.2	10 40.4	20 59.7	29 56.8

DECLINATION

DAY	EPHEMERIS SIDEREAL TIME	☉	☊	☽	☿	♀	♂	♃	♄	♅	♆	♇
1 M	2 39 27.0	14S 13.9	21S 33.5	9S 13.7	14S 36.3	4S 32.3	23S 31.6	22S 16.2	2S 40.0	14N 58.5	4N 47.2	22N 54.4
4 T	2 51 16.7	15 11.0	21 32.0	19 11.3	16 24.1	5 58.3	23 6.5	22 12.4	2 43.0	14 56.2	4 45.4	22 54.8
7 S	3 3 6.3	16 5.8	21 30.4	21 36.5	18 4.4	7 23.4	22 39.3	22 8.2	2 45.7	14 53.9	4 43.8	22 55.3
10 W	3 14 56.0	16 58.2	21 28.8	15 37.8	19 36.6	8 47.1	22 10.1	22 3.8	2 48.1	14 51.7	4 42.2	22 55.9
13 S	3 26 45.7	17 48.1	21 27.2	3 14.9	21 0.1	10 9.2	21 39.0	21 59.1	2 50.1	14 49.4	4 40.7	22 56.5
16 T	3 38 35.3	18 35.1	21 25.6	11N 35.0	22 14.3	11 29.2	21 5.9	21 54.2	2 51.7	14 47.2	4 39.3	22 57.1
19 F	3 50 25.0	19 19.2	21 24.0	21 17.2	23 18.6	12 46.8	20 31.0	21 48.9	2 53.0	14 45.1	4 38.0	22 57.8
22 M	4 2 14.7	20 0.1	21 22.3	18 13.3	24 12.4	14 1.8	19 54.3	21 43.4	2 53.9	14 42.9	4 36.8	22 58.5
25 T	4 14 4.3	20 37.8	21 20.7	5 43.6	24 55.0	15 13.6	19 15.9	21 37.7	2 54.4	14 40.8	4 35.7	22 59.3
28 S	4 25 54.0	21 12.0	21 19.0	8S 16.2	25 25.8	16 21.9	18 35.8	21 31.6	2 54.4	14 38.8	4 34.8	23 0.1

DECEMBER 1937

LONGITUDE

DAY	EPHEMERIS SIDEREAL TIME	☉	☊	☽	☿	♀	♂	♃	♄	♅	♆	♇
1 W	4 37 43.7	8♐23.4	5♐51.3	17♏ 6.0	25♐46.9	22♏47.1	14♒20.6	26♑ 2.3	28♓21.1	10♉38.3	21♍ 0.5	29♋56.0
2 T	4 41 40.2	9 24.3	5 48.1	28 58.1	27 12.6	24 2.5	15 5.7	26 14.0	28R21.0	10R36.2	21 1.2	29R55.3
3 F	4 45 36.8	10 25.1	5 45.0	10♐46.7	28 37.4	25 17.8	15 50.8	26 25.8	28D21.1	10 34.1	21 2.0	29 54.5
4 S	4 49 33.3	11 26.0	5 41.8	22 33.9	0♑ 1.2	26 33.2	16 36.0	26 37.7	28 21.2	10 32.1	21 2.6	29 53.7
5 S	4 53 29.9	12 26.9	5 38.6	4♑21.9	1 23.7	27 48.5	17 21.2	26 49.7	28 21.5	10 30.1	21 3.3	29 52.9
6 M	4 57 26.5	13 27.9	5 35.4	16 12.9	2 44.8	29 3.9	18 6.5	27 1.8	28 21.9	10 28.1	21 3.9	29 52.0
7 T	5 1 23.0	14 28.8	5 32.3	28 9.6	4 4.3	0♐19.3	18 51.7	27 13.9	28 22.4	10 26.2	21 4.5	29 51.2
8 W	5 5 19.6	15 29.8	5 29.1	10♒14.8	5 21.9	1 34.7	19 37.0	27 26.1	28 23.0	10 24.3	21 5.0	29 50.3
9 T	5 9 16.1	16 30.7	5 25.9	22 31.8	6 37.2	2 50.1	20 22.3	27 38.4	28 23.7	10 22.4	21 5.6	29 49.4
10 F	5 13 12.7	17 31.7	5 22.7	5♓ 4.3	7 50.0	4 5.5	21 7.6	27 50.8	28 24.6	10 20.6	21 6.0	29 48.5
11 S	5 17 9.3	18 32.7	5 19.6	17 55.8	8 59.7	5 20.9	21 53.0	28 3.2	28 25.5	10 18.8	21 6.5	29 47.5
12 S	5 21 5.8	19 33.7	5 16.4	1♈ 9.8	10 6.0	6 36.3	22 38.3	28 15.7	28 26.6	10 17.0	21 6.9	29 46.6
13 M	5 25 2.4	20 34.7	5 13.2	14 48.9	11 8.3	7 51.7	23 23.7	28 28.3	28 27.7	10 15.3	21 7.3	29 45.6
14 T	5 28 58.9	21 35.7	5 10.0	28 54.3	12 6.0	9 7.2	24 9.0	28 41.0	28 29.0	10 13.6	21 7.6	29 44.6
15 W	5 32 55.5	22 36.8	5 6.8	13♉25.2	12 58.4	10 22.6	24 54.4	28 53.7	28 30.3	10 11.9	21 7.9	29 43.6
16 T	5 36 52.0	23 37.8	5 3.7	28 18.1	13 44.8	11 38.0	25 39.8	29 6.5	28 31.8	10 10.3	21 8.2	29 42.6
17 F	5 40 48.6	24 38.8	5 0.5	13♊26.5	14 24.4	12 53.4	26 25.2	29 19.3	28 33.4	10 8.8	21 8.5	29 41.5
18 S	5 44 45.2	25 39.9	4 57.3	28 41.8	14 56.2	14 8.9	27 10.6	29 32.2	28 35.1	10 7.2	21 8.7	29 40.5
19 S	5 48 41.7	26 41.0	4 54.1	13♋53.9	15 19.5	15 24.3	27 56.0	29 45.2	28 36.8	10 5.7	21 8.9	29 39.4
20 M	5 52 38.3	27 42.0	4 51.0	28 53.0	15 33.3	16 39.8	28 41.4	29 58.2	28 38.7	10 4.3	21 9.0	29 38.3
21 T	5 56 34.8	28 43.1	4 47.8	13♌30.9	15 36.8	17 55.2	29 26.8	0♒11.3	28 40.7	10 2.9	21 9.1	29 37.2
22 W	6 0 31.4	29 44.2	4 44.6	27 42.4	15R29.2	19 10.7	0♓12.2	0 24.5	28 42.8	10 1.5	21 9.2	29 36.1
23 T	6 4 27.9	0♑45.3	4 41.4	11♍25.3	15 10.1	20 26.1	0 57.6	0 37.6	28 45.0	10 0.2	21 9.2	29 35.0
24 F	6 8 24.5	1 46.4	4 38.3	24 40.1	14 39.2	21 41.6	1 43.1	0 50.9	28 47.3	9 58.9	21 9.2	29 33.8
25 S	6 12 21.1	2 47.6	4 35.1	7♎29.5	13 56.7	22 57.1	2 28.5	1 4.2	28 49.7	9 57.7	21R 9.2	29 32.7
26 S	6 16 17.6	3 48.7	4 31.9	19 57.5	13 3.2	24 12.6	3 13.9	1 17.6	28 52.3	9 56.5	21 9.1	29 31.5
27 M	6 20 14.2	4 49.9	4 28.7	2♏ 8.5	11 59.8	25 28.1	3 59.3	1 31.0	28 54.9	9 55.4	21 9.0	29 30.3
28 T	6 24 10.7	5 51.0	4 25.5	14 7.2	10 48.3	26 43.5	4 44.7	1 44.4	28 57.6	9 54.3	21 8.9	29 29.1
29 W	6 28 7.3	6 52.2	4 22.4	25 58.2	9 30.7	27 59.0	5 30.2	1 57.9	29 0.4	9 53.2	21 8.7	29 27.9
30 T	6 32 3.8	7 53.4	4 19.2	7♐45.2	8 9.7	29 14.5	6 15.6	2 11.5	29 3.3	9 52.3	21 8.5	29 26.7
31 F	6 36 0.4	8 54.5	4 16.0	19 31.7	6 47.9	0♑30.0	7 1.0	2 25.1	29 6.3	9 51.3	21 8.3	29 25.4

DECLINATION

DAY	EPHEMERIS SIDEREAL TIME	☉	☊	☽	☿	♀	♂	♃	♄	♅	♆	♇
1 W	4 37 43.7	21S 42.6	21S 17.4	18S 36.3	25S 44.3	17S 26.4	17S 54.1	21S 25.3	2S 54.1	14N 36.9	4N 33.9	23N 0.9
4 S	4 49 33.3	22 9.5	21 15.7	21 44.1	25 49.9	18 26.8	17 10.8	21 18.7	2 53.4	14 35.0	4 33.2	23 1.8
7 T	5 1 23.0	22 32.6	21 14.0	16 26.3	25 42.7	19 22.6	16 26.2	21 11.8	2 52.3	14 33.2	4 32.6	23 2.7
10 F	5 13 12.7	22 51.7	21 12.3	4 43.7	25 22.8	20 13.6	15 40.2	21 4.6	2 50.8	14 31.5	4 32.1	23 3.6
13 M	5 25 2.4	23 6.7	21 10.6	9N 38.5	24 51.3	20 59.4	14 52.9	20 57.2	2 49.0	14 29.9	4 31.7	23 4.6
16 T	5 36 52.0	23 17.6	21 8.9	20 29.1	24 10.3	21 39.7	14 4.5	20 49.5	2 46.7	14 28.4	4 31.5	23 5.6
19 S	5 48 41.7	23 24.3	21 7.2	19 30.1	23 22.9	22 14.3	13 14.9	20 41.6	2 44.1	14 27.0	4 31.4	23 6.6
22 W	6 0 31.4	23 26.8	21 5.5	7 23.1	22 33.6	22 42.9	12 24.4	20 33.3	2 41.1	14 25.8	4 31.4	23 7.6
25 S	6 12 21.1	23 25.0	21 3.7	7S 4.9	21 46.9	23 5.4	11 32.9	20 24.9	2 37.7	14 24.6	4 31.5	23 8.7
28 T	6 24 10.7	23 19.0	21 2.0	17 56.5	21 6.3	23 21.6	10 40.6	20 16.1	2 34.0	14 23.6	4 31.8	23 9.7
31 F	6 36 0.4	23 8.8	21 0.2	21 48.2	20 34.7	23 31.2	9 47.5	20 7.1	2 29.9	14 22.8	4 32.1	23 10.8

JANUARY 1938

DAY	EPHEMERIS SIDEREAL TIME	☉	☊	☽	☿	♀	♂	♃	♄	♅	♆	♇
	h m s	° ′	° ′	° ′	° ′	° ′	° ′	° ′	° ′	° ′	° ′	° ′
						LONGITUDE						
1 S	6 39 57.0	9♑55.7	4♐12.8	1♑20.3	5♑28.0	1♑45.5	7♓46.4	2♒38.7	29♓ 9.4	9♉50.4	21♍ 8.0	29♋24.2
2 S	6 43 53.5	10 56.9	4 9.7	13 13.4	4R12.5	3 1.0	8 31.8	2 52.4	29 12.6	9R49.5	21R 7.7	29R22.9
3 M	6 47 50.1	11 58.1	4 6.5	25 12.5	3 3.5	4 16.5	9 17.2	3 6.1	29 15.9	9 48.7	21 7.4	29 21.7
4 T	6 51 46.6	12 59.3	4 3.3	7♒19.3	2 2.5	5 32.0	10 2.6	3 19.9	29 19.3	9 48.0	21 7.0	29 20.4
5 W	6 55 43.2	14 0.5	4 0.1	19 35.2	1 10.8	6 47.5	10 48.0	3 33.7	29 22.8	9 47.3	21 6.6	29 19.1
6 T	6 59 39.7	15 1.6	3 57.0	2♓ 1.6	0 28.9	8 2.9	11 33.4	3 47.5	29 26.4	9 46.6	21 6.1	29 17.9
7 F	7 3 36.3	16 2.8	3 53.8	14 40.4	29♐57.2	9 18.4	12 18.8	4 1.4	29 30.1	9 46.0	21 5.7	29 16.6
8 S	7 7 32.9	17 4.0	3 50.6	27 33.7	29 35.5	10 33.9	13 4.1	4 15.3	29 33.8	9 45.5	21 5.2	29 15.3
9 S	7 11 29.4	18 5.1	3 47.4	10♈43.9	29 23.5	11 49.4	13 49.4	4 29.2	29 37.7	9 45.0	21 4.6	29 14.0
10 M	7 15 26.0	19 6.3	3 44.3	24 13.1	29 20.8	13 4.8	14 34.8	4 43.1	29 41.7	9 44.6	21 4.1	29 12.6
11 T	7 19 22.5	20 7.4	3 41.1	8♉ 3.4	29D26.7	14 20.3	15 20.1	4 57.1	29 45.7	9 44.2	21 3.4	29 11.3
12 W	7 23 19.1	21 8.5	3 37.9	22 15.4	29 40.5	15 35.7	16 5.3	5 11.1	29 49.8	9 43.8	21 2.8	29 10.0
13 T	7 27 15.7	22 9.7	3 34.7	6♊48.3	0♑ 1.7	16 51.2	16 50.6	5 25.1	29 54.0	9 43.5	21 2.2	29 8.7
14 F	7 31 12.2	23 10.8	3 31.6	21 38.8	0 29.4	18 6.6	17 35.9	5 39.2	29 58.3	9 43.3	21 1.5	29 7.4
15 S	7 35 8.8	24 11.9	3 28.4	6♋40.7	1 3.2	19 22.1	18 21.1	5 53.3	0♈ 2.7	9 43.1	21 0.7	29 6.0
16 S	7 39 5.3	25 12.9	3 25.2	21 45.8	1 42.4	20 37.5	19 6.3	6 7.4	0 7.2	9 43.0	20 60.0	29 4.7
17 M	7 43 1.9	26 14.0	3 22.0	6♌44.6	2 26.5	21 52.9	19 51.5	6 21.5	0 11.7	9 42.9	20 59.2	29 3.4
18 T	7 46 58.4	27 15.1	3 18.8	21 27.6	3 15.0	23 8.4	20 36.6	6 35.6	0 16.4	9 42.9	20 58.4	29 2.0
19 W	7 50 55.0	28 16.2	3 15.7	5♍47.5	4 7.5	24 23.8	21 21.8	6 49.8	0 21.1	9D42.9	20 57.5	29 0.7
20 T	7 54 51.6	29 17.2	3 12.5	19 39.8	5 3.5	25 39.2	22 6.9	7 3.9	0 25.8	9 43.0	20 56.7	28 59.4
21 F	7 58 48.1	0♒18.3	3 9.3	3♎ 3.0	6 2.7	26 54.6	22 52.0	7 18.1	0 30.7	9 43.1	20 55.8	28 58.0
22 S	8 2 44.6	1 19.3	3 6.1	15 58.6	7 4.9	28 10.0	23 37.0	7 32.3	0 35.7	9 43.3	20 54.8	28 56.7
23 S	8 6 41.2	2 20.3	3 3.0	28 30.0	8 9.6	29 25.4	24 22.1	7 46.5	0 40.7	9 43.5	20 53.9	28 55.4
24 M	8 10 37.8	3 21.4	2 59.8	10♏42.1	9 16.8	0♒40.8	25 7.1	8 0.7	0 45.8	9 43.8	20 52.9	28 54.0
25 T	8 14 34.3	4 22.4	2 56.6	22 40.1	10 26.1	1 56.2	25 52.1	8 15.0	0 50.9	9 44.1	20 51.9	28 52.7
26 W	8 18 30.9	5 23.4	2 53.4	4♐29.5	11 37.4	3 11.6	26 37.1	8 29.2	0 56.2	9 44.5	20 50.8	28 51.4
27 T	8 22 27.4	6 24.4	2 50.2	16 15.5	12 50.6	4 27.0	27 22.0	8 43.4	1 1.5	9 44.9	20 49.8	28 50.0
28 F	8 26 24.0	7 25.4	2 47.1	28 2.6	14 5.4	5 42.4	28 6.9	8 57.7	1 6.9	9 45.4	20 48.7	28 48.7
29 S	8 30 20.6	8 26.4	2 43.9	9♑54.6	15 21.7	6 57.7	28 51.8	9 11.9	1 12.3	9 46.0	20 47.6	28 47.4
30 S	8 34 17.1	9 27.3	2 40.7	21 54.5	16 39.5	8 13.1	29 36.7	9 26.2	1 17.9	9 46.6	20 46.4	28 46.1
31 M	8 38 13.6	10 28.3	2 37.5	4♒ 4.3	17 58.6	9 28.5	0♈21.5	9 40.4	1 23.5	9 47.2	20 45.3	28 44.8
						DECLINATION						
1 S	6 39 57.0	23S 4.5	20S59.6	21S11.7	20S26.7	23S33.0	9S29.6	20S 4.1	2S28.5	14N22.5	4N32.3	23N11.2
4 T	6 51 46.6	22 48.7	20 57.9	14 1.8	20 12.6	23 34.0	8 35.6	19 54.8	2 23.9	14 21.8	4 32.8	23 12.3
7 F	7 3 36.3	22 28.9	20 56.1	1 19.8	20 14.0	23 28.3	7 41.1	19 45.2	2 19.1	14 21.3	4 33.4	23 13.3
10 M	7 15 26.0	22 5.1	20 54.3	12N32.7	20 28.9	23 16.2	6 46.1	19 35.4	2 13.9	14 20.9	4 34.2	23 14.4
13 T	7 27 15.7	21 37.4	20 52.5	21 18.4	20 52.5	22 57.5	5 50.7	19 25.5	2 8.5	14 20.7	4 35.1	23 15.5
16 S	7 39 5.3	21 5.9	20 50.7	17 59.7	21 19.6	22 32.5	4 55.0	19 15.3	2 2.7	14 20.6	4 36.0	23 16.6
19 W	7 50 55.0	20 30.8	20 48.9	4 38.1	21 45.9	22 1.4	3 59.1	19 4.8	1 56.7	14 20.6	4 37.1	23 17.6
22 S	8 2 44.6	19 52.3	20 47.0	9S49.0	22 7.9	21 24.2	3 3.0	18 54.2	1 50.4	14 20.8	4 38.3	23 18.6
25 T	8 14 34.3	19 10.3	20 45.2	19 26.6	22 23.2	20 41.2	2 6.8	18 43.5	1 43.8	14 21.2	4 39.6	23 19.7
28 F	8 26 24.0	18 25.2	20 43.3	21 22.5	22 30.2	19 52.7	1 10.7	18 32.5	1 37.0	14 21.7	4 40.9	23 20.7
31 M	8 38 13.6	17 37.1	20 41.5	14 59.0	22 27.6	18 59.0	0 14.6	18 21.4	1 30.0	14 22.3	4 42.4	23 21.7

FEBRUARY 1938

DAY	EPHEMERIS SIDEREAL TIME	☉	☊	☽	☿	♀	♂	♃	♄	♅	♆	♇
						LONGITUDE						
1 T	8 42 10.2	11♒29.2	2♐34.4	16♒25.1	19♑19.0	10♒43.8	1♈ 6.4	9♒54.7	1♈29.1	9♉48.0	20♍44.1	28♋43.5
2 W	8 46 6.8	12 30.1	2 31.2	28 57.5	20 40.5	11 59.2	1 51.2	10 9.0	1 34.9	9 48.7	20R42.9	28R42.2
3 T	8 50 3.3	13 31.0	2 28.0	11♓41.3	22 3.2	13 14.5	2 35.9	10 23.2	1 40.6	9 49.5	20 41.6	28 40.9
4 F	8 53 59.9	14 31.9	2 24.8	24 36.5	23 26.9	14 29.8	3 20.6	10 37.5	1 46.5	9 50.4	20 40.4	28 39.6
5 S	8 57 56.4	15 32.7	2 21.6	7♈43.2	24 51.7	15 45.1	4 5.3	10 51.7	1 52.4	9 51.3	20 39.1	28 38.3
6 S	9 1 53.0	16 33.6	2 18.5	21 1.6	26 17.5	17 0.4	4 50.0	11 5.9	1 58.4	9 52.3	20 37.8	28 37.0
7 M	9 5 49.6	17 34.4	2 15.3	4♉32.5	27 44.2	18 15.7	5 34.6	11 20.2	2 4.4	9 53.3	20 36.5	28 35.8
8 T	9 9 46.1	18 35.1	2 12.1	18 17.1	29 11.8	19 31.0	6 19.2	11 34.4	2 10.5	9 54.3	20 35.1	28 34.5
9 W	9 13 42.6	19 35.9	2 8.9	2♊16.2	0♒40.4	20 46.2	7 3.8	11 48.6	2 16.7	9 55.4	20 33.7	28 33.3
10 T	9 17 39.2	20 36.6	2 5.8	16 29.9	2 9.8	22 1.5	7 48.3	12 2.7	2 22.9	9 56.6	20 32.4	28 32.1
11 F	9 21 35.8	21 37.3	2 2.6	0♋57.0	3 40.2	23 16.7	8 32.8	12 16.9	2 29.1	9 57.8	20 31.0	28 30.9
12 S	9 25 32.3	22 38.0	1 59.4	15 34.1	5 11.4	24 31.9	9 17.3	12 31.1	2 35.5	9 59.1	20 29.5	28 29.7
13 S	9 29 28.9	23 38.6	1 56.2	0♌16.1	6 43.5	25 47.1	10 1.7	12 45.2	2 41.8	10 0.4	20 28.1	28 28.5
14 M	9 33 25.4	24 39.2	1 53.1	14 55.9	8 16.4	27 2.3	10 46.1	12 59.3	2 48.2	10 1.8	20 26.6	28 27.3
15 T	9 37 22.0	25 39.8	1 49.9	29 25.7	9 50.3	28 17.4	11 30.4	13 13.4	2 54.7	10 3.2	20 25.2	28 26.1
16 W	9 41 18.5	26 40.4	1 46.7	13♍38.3	11 25.0	29 32.6	12 14.7	13 27.5	3 1.2	10 4.6	20 23.7	28 24.9
17 T	9 45 15.1	27 40.9	1 43.5	27 28.3	13 0.6	0♓47.7	12 59.0	13 41.6	3 7.8	10 6.1	20 22.2	28 23.8
18 F	9 49 11.6	28 41.4	1 40.3	10♎52.8	14 37.1	2 2.9	13 43.2	13 55.6	3 14.4	10 7.7	20 20.7	28 22.7
19 S	9 53 8.2	29 41.9	1 37.2	23 51.6	16 14.5	3 18.0	14 27.4	14 9.6	3 21.0	10 9.3	20 19.1	28 21.5
20 S	9 57 4.8	0♓42.4	1 34.0	6♏26.8	17 52.8	4 33.1	15 11.5	14 23.6	3 27.7	10 10.9	20 17.6	28 20.4
21 M	10 1 1.3	1 42.9	1 30.8	18 42.2	19 32.0	5 48.2	15 55.6	14 37.6	3 34.5	10 12.6	20 16.1	28 19.4
22 T	10 4 57.9	2 43.3	1 27.6	0♐42.8	21 12.2	7 3.2	16 39.7	14 51.5	3 41.2	10 14.4	20 14.5	28 18.3
23 W	10 8 54.4	3 43.7	1 24.5	12 34.0	22 53.3	8 18.3	17 23.8	15 5.4	3 48.1	10 16.1	20 12.9	28 17.2
24 T	10 12 50.9	4 44.1	1 21.3	24 21.5	24 35.4	9 33.3	18 7.8	15 19.3	3 54.9	10 17.9	20 11.3	28 16.2
25 F	10 16 47.5	5 44.5	1 18.1	6♑10.6	26 18.5	10 48.4	18 51.7	15 33.2	4 1.8	10 19.8	20 9.7	28 15.2
26 S	10 20 44.1	6 44.8	1 14.9	18 6.2	28 2.6	12 3.4	19 35.7	15 47.0	4 8.8	10 21.7	20 8.1	28 14.2
27 S	10 24 40.6	7 45.1	1 11.7	0♒12.1	29 47.7	13 18.4	20 19.5	16 0.8	4 15.8	10 23.7	20 6.5	28 13.2
28 M	10 28 37.2	8 45.4	1 8.6	12 31.4	1♓33.8	14 33.4	21 3.4	16 14.5	4 22.8	10 25.7	20 4.9	28 12.2
						DECLINATION						
1 T	8 42 10.2	17S20.5	20S40.9	11S19.5	22S24.5	18S39.9	0N 4.1	18S17.6	1S27.6	14N22.6	4N42.9	23N22.0
4 F	8 53 59.9	16 28.7	20 39.0	2N 9.5	22 8.0	17 39.7	0 59.9	18 6.3	1 20.3	14 23.4	4 44.4	23 22.9
7 M	9 5 49.6	15 34.3	20 37.1	15 17.4	21 40.3	16 35.0	1 55.5	17 54.9	1 12.8	14 24.4	4 46.0	23 23.9
10 T	9 17 39.2	14 37.5	20 35.2	21 33.7	21 1.1	15 26.1	2 50.8	17 43.3	1 5.1	14 25.6	4 47.7	23 24.8
13 S	9 29 28.9	13 38.6	20 33.3	15 56.7	20 10.2	14 13.4	3 45.7	17 31.7	0 57.3	14 26.8	4 49.5	23 25.6
16 W	9 41 18.5	12 37.6	20 31.4	1 54.2	19 7.2	12 57.2	4 40.1	17 19.9	0 49.3	14 28.2	4 51.3	23 26.4
19 S	9 53 8.2	11 34.9	20 29.5	12S 7.1	17 52.1	11 37.9	5 34.0	17 8.1	0 41.1	14 29.8	4 53.2	23 27.2
22 T	10 4 57.9	10 30.4	20 27.6	20 21.6	16 24.8	10 15.7	6 27.2	16 56.2	0 32.8	14 31.5	4 55.1	23 28.0
25 F	10 16 47.5	9 24.5	20 25.6	20 25.0	14 45.2	8 51.2	7 19.9	16 44.2	0 24.4	14 33.2	4 57.0	23 28.7
28 M	10 28 37.2	8 17.3	20 23.7	12 28.9	12 53.4	7 24.5	8 11.8	16 32.2	0 15.9	14 35.2	4 59.0	23 29.3

MARCH 1938

LONGITUDE

DAY	EPHEMERIS SIDEREAL TIME h m s	☉ ° ′	☊ ° ′	☽ ° ′	☿ ° ′	♀ ° ′	♂ ° ′	♃ ° ′	♄ ° ′	♅ ° ′	♆ ° ′	♇ ° ′
1 T	10 32 33.7	9♓45.6	1♐ 5.4	25♒ 5.7	3♓20.9	15♓48.4	21♈47.2	16♒28.2	4♈29.8	10♉27.7	20♍ 3.2	28♋11.2
2 W	10 36 30.3	10 45.9	1 2.2	7♓55.6	5 9.1	17 3.3	22 31.0	16 41.9	4 36.9	10 29.8	20R 1.6	28R10.3
3 T	10 40 26.8	11 46.1	0 59.0	21 0.2	6 58.3	18 18.2	23 14.7	16 55.5	4 44.0	10 31.9	19 60.0	28 9.4
4 F	10 44 23.4	12 46.2	0 55.9	4♈18.1	8 48.5	19 33.2	23 58.4	17 9.1	4 51.1	10 34.1	19 58.3	28 8.5
5 S	10 48 19.9	13 46.4	0 52.7	17 47.3	10 39.8	20 48.1	24 42.1	17 22.6	4 58.3	10 36.3	19 56.6	28 7.6
6 S	10 52 16.5	14 46.5	0 49.5	1♉25.9	12 32.1	22 2.9	25 25.7	17 36.1	5 5.5	10 38.6	19 55.0	28 6.7
7 M	10 56 13.1	15 46.5	0 46.3	15 12.3	14 25.4	23 17.8	26 9.3	17 49.6	5 12.7	10 40.8	19 53.3	28 5.9
8 T	11 0 9.6	16 46.6	0 43.1	29 5.7	16 19.6	24 32.6	26 52.8	18 3.0	5 20.0	10 43.2	19 51.7	28 5.1
9 W	11 4 6.1	17 46.6	0 40.0	13♊ 5.4	18 14.8	25 47.4	27 36.3	18 16.3	5 27.2	10 45.5	19 50.0	28 4.3
10 T	11 8 2.7	18 46.5	0 36.8	27 11.2	20 10.8	27 2.2	28 19.7	18 29.6	5 34.5	10 47.9	19 48.3	28 3.5
11 F	11 11 59.3	19 46.5	0 33.6	11♋22.2	22 7.7	28 17.0	29 3.1	18 42.9	5 41.8	10 50.4	19 46.7	28 2.7
12 S	11 15 55.8	20 46.3	0 30.4	25 36.7	24 5.2	29 31.7	29 46.5	18 56.1	5 49.2	10 52.8	19 45.0	28 2.0
13 S	11 19 52.4	21 46.2	0 27.3	9♌51.9	26 3.4	0♈46.4	0♉29.8	19 9.2	5 56.5	10 55.3	19 43.3	28 1.3
14 M	11 23 48.9	22 46.0	0 24.1	24 3.8	28 1.9	2 1.1	1 13.0	19 22.3	6 3.9	10 57.9	19 41.7	28 0.6
15 T	11 27 45.4	23 45.8	0 20.9	8♍ 7.6	0♈ 0.8	3 15.8	1 56.3	19 35.3	6 11.3	11 0.5	19 40.0	27 59.9
16 W	11 31 42.0	24 45.5	0 17.7	21 58.3	1 59.7	4 30.4	2 39.4	19 48.3	6 18.7	11 3.1	19 38.3	27 59.3
17 T	11 35 38.6	25 45.2	0 14.5	5♎32.0	3 58.5	5 45.0	3 22.6	20 1.2	6 26.1	11 5.7	19 36.7	27 58.7
18 F	11 39 35.1	26 44.9	0 11.4	18 45.8	5 56.9	6 59.6	4 5.7	20 14.1	6 33.5	11 8.4	19 35.0	27 58.1
19 S	11 43 31.7	27 44.5	0 8.2	1♏38.8	7 54.5	8 14.2	4 48.7	20 26.9	6 41.0	11 11.1	19 33.4	27 57.5
20 S	11 47 28.2	28 44.1	0 5.0	14 11.9	9 51.1	9 28.7	5 31.7	20 39.6	6 48.4	11 13.8	19 31.7	27 56.9
21 M	11 51 24.8	29 43.7	0 1.8	26 27.6	11 46.4	10 43.2	6 14.7	20 52.3	6 55.9	11 16.6	19 30.1	27 56.4
22 T	11 55 21.3	0♈43.3	29♏58.7	8♐29.6	13 39.7	11 57.7	6 57.6	21 4.8	7 3.4	11 19.4	19 28.4	27 55.9
23 W	11 59 17.9	1 42.8	29 55.5	20 22.7	15 30.9	13 12.2	7 40.4	21 17.4	7 10.9	11 22.2	19 26.8	27 55.4
24 T	12 3 14.4	2 42.3	29 52.3	2♑11.9	17 19.5	14 26.7	8 23.3	21 29.8	7 18.4	11 25.1	19 25.2	27 54.9
25 F	12 7 11.0	3 41.8	29 49.1	14 2.7	19 4.9	15 41.1	9 6.1	21 42.2	7 25.9	11 28.0	19 23.6	27 54.5
26 S	12 11 7.6	4 41.2	29 45.9	26 0.3	20 46.9	16 55.5	9 48.8	21 54.6	7 33.4	11 30.9	19 22.0	27 54.1
27 S	12 15 4.1	5 40.6	29 42.8	8♒ 9.3	22 24.9	18 9.9	10 31.5	22 6.8	7 40.9	11 33.8	19 20.4	27 53.7
28 M	12 19 0.6	6 40.0	29 39.6	20 33.9	23 58.5	19 24.2	11 14.2	22 19.0	7 48.4	11 36.8	19 18.8	27 53.3
29 T	12 22 57.2	7 39.3	29 36.4	3♓16.7	25 27.5	20 38.6	11 56.8	22 31.1	7 55.9	11 39.8	19 17.2	27 53.0
30 W	12 26 53.8	8 38.6	29 33.2	16 19.2	26 51.3	21 52.9	12 39.4	22 43.1	8 3.4	11 42.8	19 15.7	27 52.7
31 T	12 30 50.3	9 37.9	29 30.1	29 41.0	28 9.7	23 7.2	13 21.9	22 55.0	8 10.9	11 45.8	19 14.1	27 52.4

DECLINATION

DAY	EPHEMERIS SIDEREAL TIME h m s	☉ ° ′	☊ ° ′	☽ ° ′	☿ ° ′	♀ ° ′	♂ ° ′	♃ ° ′	♄ ° ′	♅ ° ′	♆ ° ′	♇ ° ′
1 T	10 32 33.7	7S54.7	20S23.0	8S27.6	12S13.5	6S55.2	8N28.9	16S28.2	0S13.1	14N35.8	4N59.6	23N29.5
4 F	10 44 23.4	6 46.1	20 21.1	5N31.1	10 5.7	5 26.2	9 19.7	16 16.2	0 4.4	14 37.9	5 1.6	23 30.2
7 M	10 56 13.1	5 36.6	20 19.1	17 36.8	7 46.4	3 56.0	10 9.7	16 4.2	0N 4.3	14 40.0	5 3.6	23 30.7
10 T	11 8 2.7	4 26.5	20 17.1	21 4.5	5 16.5	2 24.8	10 58.7	15 52.2	0 13.0	14 42.3	5 5.6	23 31.2
13 S	11 19 52.4	3 15.9	20 15.1	13 11.6	2 37.3	0 53.0	11 46.7	15 40.3	0 21.8	14 44.7	5 7.6	23 31.7
16 W	11 31 42.0	2 5.0	20 13.1	1S 5.4	0N 8.7	0N39.1	12 33.7	15 28.4	0 30.7	14 47.2	5 9.6	23 32.1
19 S	11 43 31.7	0 53.9	20 11.1	14 12.8	2 57.9	2 11.2	13 19.5	15 16.6	0 39.5	14 49.7	5 11.5	23 32.5
22 T	11 55 21.3	0N17.2	20 9.1	20 50.9	5 45.0	3 43.0	14 4.2	15 4.9	0 48.4	14 52.3	5 13.5	23 32.8
25 F	12 7 11.0	1 28.2	20 7.1	19 3.9	8 23.8	5 14.1	14 47.7	14 53.3	0 57.3	14 55.0	5 15.4	23 33.1
28 M	12 19 0.6	2 38.9	20 5.0	9 49.7	10 47.6	6 44.1	15 29.9	14 41.9	1 6.1	14 57.8	5 17.2	23 33.3
31 T	12 30 50.3	3 49.0	20 3.0	3N52.2	12 50.3	8 12.8	16 10.8	14 30.6	1 15.0	15 0.6	5 19.1	23 33.5

APRIL 1938

LONGITUDE

DAY	EPHEMERIS SIDEREAL TIME h m s	☉ ° ′	☊ ° ′	☽ ° ′	☿ ° ′	♀ ° ′	♂ ° ′	♃ ° ′	♄ ° ′	♅ ° ′	♆ ° ′	♇ ° ′
1 F	12 34 46.9	10♈37.2	29♏26.9	13♈20.6	29♈22.4	24♈21.4	14♉ 4.4	23♒ 6.9	8♈18.4	11♉48.9	19♍12.6	27♋52.1
2 S	12 38 43.4	11 36.4	29 23.7	27 14.7	0♉29.2	25 35.7	14 46.9	23 18.7	8 25.9	11 52.0	19R11.1	27R51.9
3 S	12 42 39.9	12 35.5	29 20.5	11♉19.5	1 29.7	26 49.9	15 29.3	23 30.3	8 33.4	11 55.1	19 9.6	27 51.7
4 M	12 46 36.5	13 34.7	29 17.3	25 31.0	2 23.8	28 4.1	16 11.7	23 41.9	8 41.0	11 58.2	19 8.1	27 51.5
5 T	12 50 33.1	14 33.8	29 14.2	9♊45.4	3 11.4	29 18.2	16 54.0	23 53.5	8 48.4	12 1.4	19 6.6	27 51.3
6 W	12 54 29.6	15 32.9	29 11.0	23 59.9	3 52.3	0♉32.3	17 36.3	24 4.9	8 55.9	12 4.6	19 5.2	27 51.2
7 T	12 58 26.2	16 31.9	29 7.8	8♋12.1	4 26.5	1 46.4	18 18.5	24 16.2	9 3.4	12 7.8	19 3.7	27 51.1
8 F	13 2 22.7	17 30.9	29 4.6	22 20.2	4 53.8	3 0.5	19 0.7	24 27.5	9 10.9	12 11.0	19 2.3	27 51.0
9 S	13 6 19.3	18 29.8	29 1.4	6♌22.8	5 14.4	4 14.5	19 42.9	24 38.6	9 18.3	12 14.2	19 0.9	27 51.0
10 S	13 10 15.8	19 28.7	28 58.3	20 18.3	5 28.1	5 28.5	20 25.0	24 49.7	9 25.8	12 17.5	18 59.5	27 50.9
11 M	13 14 12.4	20 27.6	28 55.1	4♍ 5.2	5 35.2	6 42.5	21 7.0	25 0.6	9 33.2	12 20.7	18 58.1	27 50.9
12 T	13 18 8.9	21 26.4	28 51.9	17 41.5	5 35.8	7 56.4	21 49.0	25 11.5	9 40.6	12 24.0	18 56.7	27D50.9
13 W	13 22 5.5	22 25.2	28 48.7	1♎ 5.3	5R30.0	9 10.3	22 31.0	25 22.2	9 48.0	12 27.3	18 55.4	27 51.0
14 T	13 26 2.1	23 24.0	28 45.6	14 14.9	5 18.3	10 24.2	23 12.9	25 32.9	9 55.4	12 30.6	18 54.1	27 51.0
15 F	13 29 58.6	24 22.7	28 42.4	27 9.3	5 0.9	11 38.0	23 54.8	25 43.5	10 2.8	12 34.0	18 52.8	27 51.1
16 S	13 33 55.1	25 21.4	28 39.2	9♏48.1	4 38.2	12 51.8	24 36.6	25 53.9	10 10.1	12 37.3	18 51.5	27 51.3
17 S	13 37 51.7	26 20.1	28 36.0	22 12.0	4 10.8	14 5.6	25 18.4	26 4.3	10 17.4	12 40.6	18 50.3	27 51.4
18 M	13 41 48.3	27 18.7	28 32.8	4♐22.7	3 39.3	15 19.3	26 0.2	26 14.5	10 24.8	12 44.0	18 49.0	27 51.6
19 T	13 45 44.8	28 17.3	28 29.7	16 22.7	3 4.3	16 33.0	26 41.9	26 24.6	10 32.1	12 47.4	18 47.8	27 51.8
20 W	13 49 41.4	29 15.9	28 26.5	28 15.7	2 26.5	17 46.7	27 23.6	26 34.7	10 39.3	12 50.8	18 46.6	27 52.0
21 T	13 53 37.9	0♉14.4	28 23.3	10♑ 5.5	1 46.7	19 0.4	28 5.2	26 44.6	10 46.6	12 54.2	18 45.5	27 52.2
22 F	13 57 34.4	1 12.9	28 20.1	21 57.0	1 5.6	20 14.0	28 46.8	26 54.4	10 53.8	12 57.6	18 44.3	27 52.5
23 S	14 1 31.0	2 11.4	28 17.0	3♒54.8	0 23.9	21 27.6	29 28.3	27 4.1	11 1.0	13 1.0	18 43.2	27 52.8
24 S	14 5 27.6	3 9.9	28 13.8	16 4.0	29♈42.6	22 41.2	0♊ 9.8	27 13.7	11 8.1	13 4.4	18 42.1	27 53.1
25 M	14 9 24.1	4 8.3	28 10.6	28 28.9	29 2.2	23 54.7	0 51.3	27 23.1	11 15.3	13 7.8	18 41.1	27 53.5
26 T	14 13 20.7	5 6.8	28 7.4	11♓13.5	28 23.5	25 8.2	1 32.7	27 32.4	11 22.4	13 11.3	18 40.0	27 53.9
27 W	14 17 17.2	6 5.1	28 4.2	24 20.3	27 47.1	26 21.7	2 14.1	27 41.7	11 29.5	13 14.7	18 39.0	27 54.3
28 T	14 21 13.8	7 3.5	28 1.1	7♈50.6	27 13.6	27 35.1	2 55.5	27 50.7	11 36.5	13 18.2	18 38.0	27 54.7
29 F	14 25 10.3	8 1.8	27 57.9	21 43.5	26 43.4	28 48.6	3 36.8	27 59.7	11 43.6	13 21.6	18 37.0	27 55.1
30 S	14 29 6.9	9 0.1	27 54.7	5♉56.4	26 17.0	0♊ 2.0	4 18.0	28 8.5	11 50.5	13 25.1	18 36.1	27 55.6

DECLINATION

DAY	EPHEMERIS SIDEREAL TIME h m s	☉ ° ′	☊ ° ′	☽ ° ′	☿ ° ′	♀ ° ′	♂ ° ′	♃ ° ′	♄ ° ′	♅ ° ′	♆ ° ′	♇ ° ′
1 F	12 34 46.9	4N12.3	20S 2.3	8N34.7	13N25.8	8N42.0	16N24.2	14S26.8	1N17.9	15N 1.6	5N19.7	23N33.5
4 M	12 46 36.5	5 21.6	20 0.2	19 19.6	14 53.6	10 8.4	17 3.2	14 15.7	1 26.7	15 4.5	5 21.4	23 33.6
7 T	12 58 26.2	6 30.0	19 58.2	19 49.4	15 51.9	11 32.7	17 40.9	14 4.9	1 35.4	15 7.5	5 23.1	23 33.7
10 S	13 10 15.8	7 37.5	19 56.1	9 50.6	16 18.8	12 54.5	18 17.0	13 54.2	1 44.0	15 10.5	5 24.7	23 33.7
13 W	13 22 5.5	8 43.7	19 54.0	4S23.3	16 13.9	14 13.5	18 51.7	13 43.8	1 52.6	15 13.5	5 26.3	23 33.6
16 S	13 33 55.1	9 48.6	19 51.9	16 13.6	15 38.4	15 29.4	19 24.7	13 33.6	2 1.1	15 16.6	5 27.8	23 33.5
19 T	13 45 44.8	10 52.1	19 49.8	21 1.3	14 36.3	16 41.7	19 56.2	13 23.7	2 9.5	15 19.7	5 29.2	23 33.4
22 F	13 57 34.4	11 54.0	19 47.7	17 25.1	13 15.2	17 50.3	20 26.0	13 14.1	2 17.7	15 22.8	5 30.5	23 33.2
25 M	14 9 24.1	12 54.2	19 45.6	7 4.8	11 45.7	18 54.7	20 54.1	13 4.8	2 25.9	15 25.9	5 31.8	23 33.0
28 T	14 21 13.8	13 52.4	19 43.4	6N45.9	10 19.0	19 54.7	21 20.6	12 55.9	2 33.9	15 29.1	5 32.9	23 32.7

MAY 1938

LONGITUDE

DAY	EPHEMERIS SIDEREAL TIME h m s	☉ ° ′	☊ ° ′	☾ ° ′	☿ ° ′	♀ ° ′	♂ ° ′	♃ ° ′	♄ ° ′	♅ ° ′	♆ ° ′	♇ ° ′
1 S	14 33 3.4	9♉58.4	27♏51.5	20♉24.6	25♈54.8	1♊15.3	4♊59.3	28♒17.2	11♈57.5	13♉28.6	18♍35.2	27♋56.1
2 M	14 37 0.0	10 56.6	27 48.4	5♊ 2.3	25R36.9	2 28.6	5 40.5	28 25.8	12 4.4	13 32.0	18R34.3	27 56.6
3 T	14 40 56.6	11 54.9	27 45.2	19 43.1	25 23.6	3 41.9	6 21.6	28 34.3	12 11.3	13 35.5	18 33.5	27 57.2
4 W	14 44 53.1	12 53.0	27 42.0	4♋20.9	25 14.9	4 55.2	7 2.7	28 42.6	12 18.1	13 39.0	18 32.6	27 57.7
5 T	14 48 49.6	13 51.2	27 38.8	18 50.6	25 11.0	6 8.4	7 43.8	28 50.8	12 24.9	13 42.4	18 31.8	27 58.3
6 F	14 52 46.2	14 49.3	27 35.6	3♌ 8.1	25D11.8	7 21.6	8 24.8	28 58.8	12 31.7	13 45.9	18 31.0	27 59.0
7 S	14 56 42.8	15 47.4	27 32.5	17 11.2	25 17.4	8 34.8	9 5.8	29 6.7	12 38.4	13 49.4	18 30.3	27 59.6
8 S	15 0 39.3	16 45.4	27 29.3	0♍58.6	25 27.6	9 47.9	9 46.8	29 14.5	12 45.1	13 52.8	18 29.6	28 0.3
9 M	15 4 35.9	17 43.4	27 26.1	14 29.9	25 42.5	11 1.0	10 27.7	29 22.1	12 51.8	13 56.3	18 28.9	28 1.0
10 T	15 8 32.4	18 41.4	27 22.9	27 45.6	26 1.8	12 14.0	11 8.6	29 29.5	12 58.4	13 59.7	18 28.3	28 1.7
11 W	15 12 29.0	19 39.4	27 19.8	10♎46.4	26 25.6	13 27.0	11 49.4	29 36.9	13 4.9	14 3.2	18 27.6	28 2.4
12 T	15 16 25.5	20 37.3	27 16.6	23 33.1	26 53.6	14 39.9	12 30.2	29 44.1	13 11.4	14 6.7	18 27.0	28 3.2
13 F	15 20 22.1	21 35.2	27 13.4	6♏ 6.8	27 25.7	15 52.9	13 10.9	29 51.1	13 17.9	14 10.1	18 26.5	28 4.0
14 S	15 24 18.7	22 33.1	27 10.2	18 28.6	28 1.8	17 5.8	13 51.6	29 58.0	13 24.3	14 13.5	18 25.9	28 4.8
15 S	15 28 15.2	23 30.9	27 7.1	0♐39.9	28 41.8	18 18.6	14 32.3	0♓ 4.7	13 30.7	14 17.0	18 25.4	28 5.6
16 M	15 32 11.8	24 28.7	27 3.9	12 42.4	29 25.6	19 31.4	15 12.9	0 11.3	13 37.0	14 20.4	18 25.0	28 6.4
17 T	15 36 8.3	25 26.5	27 0.7	24 38.0	0♉12.9	20 44.2	15 53.5	0 17.8	13 43.3	14 23.8	18 24.5	28 7.3
18 W	15 40 4.9	26 24.3	26 57.5	6♑29.2	1 3.7	21 56.9	16 34.1	0 24.1	13 49.5	14 27.2	18 24.1	28 8.2
19 T	15 44 1.4	27 22.1	26 54.3	18 21.6	1 57.9	23 9.6	17 14.6	0 30.2	13 55.6	14 30.6	18 23.7	28 9.1
20 F	15 47 58.0	28 19.8	26 51.2	0♒11.0	2 55.4	24 22.3	17 55.1	0 36.1	14 1.7	14 34.0	18 23.4	28 10.0
21 S	15 51 54.6	29 17.5	26 48.0	12 9.0	3 56.0	25 34.9	18 35.6	0 42.0	14 7.8	14 37.4	18 23.1	28 11.0
22 S	15 55 51.1	0♊15.2	26 44.8	24 17.2	4 59.7	26 47.5	19 16.0	0 47.6	14 13.8	14 40.8	18 22.8	28 12.0
23 M	15 59 47.7	1 12.9	26 41.6	6♓40.0	6 6.3	28 0.0	19 56.4	0 53.1	14 19.8	14 44.2	18 22.5	28 13.0
24 T	16 3 44.2	2 10.6	26 38.5	19 21.6	7 15.9	29 12.5	20 36.7	0 58.4	14 25.6	14 47.5	18 22.3	28 14.0
25 W	16 7 40.7	3 8.2	26 35.3	2♈25.7	8 28.3	0♋25.0	21 17.0	1 3.6	14 31.5	14 50.9	18 22.1	28 15.0
26 T	16 11 37.3	4 5.8	26 32.1	15 54.8	9 43.5	1 37.5	21 57.3	1 8.5	14 37.2	14 54.2	18 22.0	28 16.1
27 F	16 15 33.9	5 3.5	26 28.9	29 49.9	11 1.4	2 49.9	22 37.6	1 13.4	14 43.0	14 57.5	18 21.8	28 17.2
28 S	16 19 30.4	6 1.1	26 25.8	14♉ 9.7	12 22.0	4 2.2	23 17.8	1 18.0	14 48.6	15 0.8	18 21.8	28 18.3
29 S	16 23 27.0	6 58.6	26 22.6	28 50.6	13 45.3	5 14.6	23 58.0	1 22.5	14 54.2	15 4.1	18 21.7	28 19.4
30 M	16 27 23.5	7 56.2	26 19.4	13♊46.5	15 11.1	6 26.8	24 38.1	1 26.8	14 59.7	15 7.3	18 21.7	28 20.5
31 T	16 31 20.1	8 53.7	26 16.2	28 49.3	16 39.6	7 39.1	25 18.3	1 30.9	15 5.2	15 10.6	18D21.7	28 21.6

DECLINATION

DAY	EPHEMERIS SIDEREAL TIME h m s	☉ ° ′	☊ ° ′	☾ ° ′	☿ ° ′	♀ ° ′	♂ ° ′	♃ ° ′	♄ ° ′	♅ ° ′	♆ ° ′	♇ ° ′
1 S	14 33 3.4	14N48.6	19S41.3	18N25.8	9N 5.0	20N49.9	21N45.3	12S47.3	2N41.7	15N32.2	5N33.9	23N32.4
4 W	14 44 53.1	15 42.6	19 39.2	20 9.7	8 10.1	21 40.1	22 8.2	12 39.1	2 49.4	15 35.3	5 34.9	23 32.0
7 S	14 56 42.8	16 34.2	19 37.0	10 43.4	7 37.5	22 24.9	22 29.4	12 31.3	2 57.0	15 38.5	5 35.7	23 31.6
10 T	15 8 32.4	17 23.4	19 34.8	3S16.4	7 27.6	23 4.1	22 48.7	12 24.0	3 4.3	15 41.6	5 36.5	23 31.2
13 F	15 20 22.1	18 9.9	19 32.7	15 20.1	7 39.3	23 37.4	23 6.2	12 17.1	3 11.5	15 44.7	5 37.1	23 30.7
16 M	15 32 11.8	18 53.7	19 30.5	20 53.4	8 10.5	24 4.8	23 21.9	12 10.6	3 18.5	15 47.7	5 37.6	23 30.2
19 T	15 44 1.4	19 34.6	19 28.3	18 5.2	8 58.9	24 25.9	23 35.7	12 4.6	3 25.2	15 50.8	5 38.0	23 29.6
22 S	15 55 51.1	20 12.6	19 26.1	8 26.3	10 2.1	24 40.7	23 47.7	11 59.2	3 31.8	15 53.8	5 38.3	23 29.1
25 W	16 7 40.7	20 47.4	19 23.9	4N55.1	11 17.6	24 49.1	23 57.7	11 54.2	3 38.1	15 56.7	5 38.5	23 28.4
28 S	16 19 30.4	21 19.0	19 21.7	17 12.5	12 43.3	24 51.0	24 5.9	11 49.8	3 44.2	15 59.6	5 38.6	23 27.8
31 T	16 31 20.1	21 47.4	19 19.4	20 38.6	14 16.7	24 46.5	24 12.3	11 45.9	3 50.0	16 2.5	5 38.5	23 27.1

JUNE 1938

LONGITUDE

DAY	EPHEMERIS SIDEREAL TIME h m s	☉ ° ′	☊ ° ′	☾ ° ′	☿ ° ′	♀ ° ′	♂ ° ′	♃ ° ′	♄ ° ′	♅ ° ′	♆ ° ′	♇ ° ′
1 W	16 35 16.6	9♊51.3	26♏13.0	13♋50.2	18♉10.6	8♋51.3	25♊58.4	1♓34.8	15♈10.6	15♉13.8	18♍21.7	28♋22.8
2 T	16 39 13.2	10 48.8	26 9.9	28 41.0	19 44.2	10 3.5	26 38.4	1 38.6	15 15.9	15 17.0	18 21.8	28 24.0
3 F	16 43 9.8	11 46.3	26 6.7	13♌14.9	21 20.3	11 15.6	27 18.4	1 42.2	15 21.2	15 20.2	18 21.9	28 25.2
4 S	16 47 6.3	12 43.7	26 3.5	27 27.7	22 58.9	12 27.6	27 58.4	1 45.6	15 26.3	15 23.4	18 22.0	28 26.4
5 S	16 51 2.9	13 41.2	26 0.3	11♍17.2	24 40.0	13 39.7	28 38.4	1 48.8	15 31.5	15 26.6	18 22.2	28 27.7
6 M	16 54 59.4	14 38.6	25 57.2	24 43.7	26 23.7	14 51.6	29 18.3	1 51.9	15 36.5	15 29.7	18 22.4	28 28.9
7 T	16 58 55.9	15 36.0	25 54.0	7♎48.8	28 9.8	16 3.5	29 58.2	1 54.7	15 41.5	15 32.8	18 22.6	28 30.2
8 W	17 2 52.5	16 33.4	25 50.8	20 35.1	29 58.4	17 15.4	0♋38.0	1 57.4	15 46.4	15 35.9	18 22.9	28 31.5
9 T	17 6 49.1	17 30.8	25 47.6	3♏ 5.5	1♊49.4	18 27.2	1 17.8	1 59.9	15 51.2	15 39.0	18 23.2	28 32.8
10 F	17 10 45.7	18 28.1	25 44.5	15 23.1	3 42.9	19 39.0	1 57.6	2 2.2	15 56.0	15 42.0	18 23.5	28 34.1
11 S	17 14 42.2	19 25.4	25 41.3	27 30.7	5 38.6	20 50.7	2 37.4	2 4.3	16 0.7	15 45.1	18 23.9	28 35.5
12 S	17 18 38.7	20 22.8	25 38.1	9♐30.7	7 36.7	22 2.4	3 17.1	2 6.2	16 5.3	15 48.1	18 24.3	28 36.8
13 M	17 22 35.3	21 20.1	25 34.9	21 25.4	9 36.9	23 14.0	3 56.8	2 8.0	16 9.8	15 51.0	18 24.7	28 38.2
14 T	17 26 31.9	22 17.4	25 31.7	3♑16.8	11 39.2	24 25.5	4 36.4	2 9.5	16 14.3	15 54.0	18 25.2	28 39.6
15 W	17 30 28.5	23 14.7	25 28.6	15 7.0	13 43.3	25 37.0	5 16.1	2 10.9	16 18.7	15 56.9	18 25.7	28 41.0
16 T	17 34 25.0	24 11.9	25 25.4	26 58.0	15 49.3	26 48.5	5 55.7	2 12.1	16 23.0	15 59.8	18 26.2	28 42.4
17 F	17 38 21.5	25 9.2	25 22.2	8♒52.3	17 56.7	27 59.9	6 35.2	2 13.1	16 27.2	16 2.7	18 26.7	28 43.8
18 S	17 42 18.1	26 6.5	25 19.0	20 52.6	20 5.5	29 11.2	7 14.8	2 13.9	16 31.3	16 5.5	18 27.3	28 45.2
19 S	17 46 14.7	27 3.7	25 15.9	3♓ 1.9	22 15.4	0♌22.5	7 54.3	2 14.5	16 35.4	16 8.4	18 27.9	28 46.7
20 M	17 50 11.2	28 1.0	25 12.7	15 24.0	24 26.2	1 33.7	8 33.8	2 14.9	16 39.4	16 11.1	18 28.6	28 48.1
21 T	17 54 7.8	28 58.2	25 9.5	28 2.5	26 37.5	2 44.9	9 13.3	2 15.1	16 43.3	16 13.9	18 29.3	28 49.6
22 W	17 58 4.3	29 55.5	25 6.3	11♈ 1.3	28 49.0	3 56.0	9 52.7	2 15.1	16 47.1	16 16.6	18 30.0	28 51.1
23 T	18 2 0.9	0♋52.7	25 3.2	24 23.8	1♋ 0.6	5 7.1	10 32.1	2R15.0	16 50.8	16 19.3	18 30.7	28 52.6
24 F	18 5 57.5	1 50.0	24 60.0	8♉12.3	3 11.9	6 18.1	11 11.5	2 14.6	16 54.5	16 22.0	18 31.5	28 54.1
25 S	18 9 54.0	2 47.2	24 56.8	22 27.5	5 22.7	7 29.0	11 50.9	2 14.0	16 58.0	16 24.7	18 32.3	28 55.6
26 S	18 13 50.6	3 44.5	24 53.6	7♊ 7.4	7 32.7	8 39.9	12 30.2	2 13.3	17 1.5	16 27.3	18 33.1	28 57.1
27 M	18 17 47.1	4 41.7	24 50.4	22 7.4	9 41.7	9 50.8	13 9.5	2 12.3	17 4.9	16 29.8	18 34.0	28 58.6
28 T	18 21 43.7	5 38.9	24 47.3	7♋19.6	11 49.5	11 1.5	13 48.8	2 11.2	17 8.2	16 32.4	18 34.9	29 0.2
29 W	18 25 40.3	6 36.2	24 44.1	22 34.2	13 55.9	12 12.2	14 28.1	2 9.9	17 11.4	16 34.9	18 35.8	29 1.7
30 T	18 29 36.8	7 33.4	24 40.9	7♌40.7	16 0.8	13 22.9	15 7.3	2 8.3	17 14.5	16 37.4	18 36.8	29 3.3

DECLINATION

DAY	EPHEMERIS SIDEREAL TIME h m s	☉ ° ′	☊ ° ′	☾ ° ′	☿ ° ′	♀ ° ′	♂ ° ′	♃ ° ′	♄ ° ′	♅ ° ′	♆ ° ′	♇ ° ′
1 W	16 35 16.6	21N56.0	19S18.7	18N53.1	14N49.2	24N43.6	24N13.9	11S44.8	3N51.9	16N 3.4	5N38.5	23N26.9
4 S	16 47 6.3	22 19.8	19 16.4	7 24.1	16 29.0	24 30.5	24 17.8	11 41.7	3 57.4	16 6.2	5 38.3	23 26.2
7 T	16 58 55.9	22 40.0	19 14.2	6S45.5	18 10.1	24 11.1	24 19.7	11 39.2	4 2.6	16 9.0	5 38.0	23 25.4
10 F	17 10 45.7	22 56.7	19 11.9	17 27.4	19 49.0	23 45.6	24 19.9	11 37.3	4 7.6	16 11.6	5 37.5	23 24.6
13 M	17 22 35.3	23 9.7	19 9.7	20 59.3	21 21.2	23 14.1	24 18.1	11 36.0	4 12.3	16 14.2	5 37.0	23 23.9
16 T	17 34 25.0	23 19.1	19 7.4	16 19.0	22 41.6	22 36.8	24 14.6	11 35.3	4 16.6	16 16.7	5 36.3	23 23.1
19 S	17 46 14.7	23 24.8	19 5.1	5 33.6	23 44.9	21 54.0	24 9.3	11 35.2	4 20.7	16 19.2	5 35.6	23 22.2
22 W	17 58 4.3	23 26.7	19 2.8	7N46.7	24 26.2	21 5.8	24 2.2	11 35.7	4 24.5	16 21.6	5 34.7	23 21.4
25 S	18 9 54.0	23 25.0	19 0.5	18 44.5	24 42.8	20 12.7	23 53.3	11 36.9	4 28.0	16 23.8	5 33.7	23 20.5
28 T	18 21 43.7	23 19.5	18 58.2	19 51.0	24 34.2	19 14.8	23 42.7	11 38.7	4 31.2	16 26.0	5 32.6	23 19.7

JULY 1938

LONGITUDE

DAY	EPHEMERIS SIDEREAL TIME (h m s)	☉ (° ′)	☊ (° ′)	☽ (° ′)	☿ (° ′)	♀ (° ′)	♂ (° ′)	♃ (° ′)	♄ (° ′)	♅ (° ′)	♆ (° ′)	♇ (° ′)
1 F	18 33 33.4	8♋30.6	24♏37.7	22♌29.8	18♋ 4.1	14♌33.4	15♋46.5	2♓ 6.6	17♈17.5	16♉39.8	18♍37.8	29♋ 4.9
2 S	18 37 29.9	9 27.8	24 34.6	6♍54.9	20 5.7	15 43.9	16 25.7	2R 4.7	17 20.4	16 42.2	18 38.8	29 6.4
3 S	18 41 26.5	10 25.1	24 31.4	20 52.3	22 5.4	16 54.4	17 4.9	2 2.6	17 23.2	16 44.6	18 39.8	29 8.0
4 M	18 45 23.1	11 22.3	24 28.2	4♎21.7	24 3.3	18 4.7	17 44.0	2 0.3	17 26.0	16 46.9	18 40.9	29 9.6
5 T	18 49 19.6	12 19.5	24 25.0	17 25.0	25 59.3	19 15.0	18 23.1	1 57.8	17 28.6	16 49.2	18 42.0	29 11.2
6 W	18 53 16.1	13 16.7	24 21.9	0♏ 5.8	27 53.3	20 25.2	19 2.2	1 55.2	17 31.2	16 51.5	18 43.1	29 12.8
7 T	18 57 12.7	14 13.9	24 18.7	12 28.2	29 45.4	21 35.4	19 41.2	1 52.3	17 33.6	16 53.7	18 44.3	29 14.5
8 F	19 1 9.3	15 11.1	24 15.5	24 36.7	1♌35.5	22 45.4	20 20.3	1 49.3	17 36.0	16 55.9	18 45.5	29 16.1
9 S	19 5 5.8	16 8.3	24 12.3	6♐35.6	3 23.6	23 55.4	20 59.3	1 46.1	17 38.3	16 58.0	18 46.7	29 17.7
10 S	19 9 2.4	17 5.4	24 9.2	18 28.5	5 9.7	25 5.2	21 38.3	1 42.7	17 40.4	17 0.1	18 47.9	29 19.3
11 M	19 12 58.9	18 2.6	24 6.0	0♑18.6	6 53.8	26 15.0	22 17.2	1 39.2	17 42.5	17 2.2	18 49.2	29 21.0
12 T	19 16 55.5	18 59.8	24 2.8	12 8.5	8 36.0	27 24.7	22 56.2	1 35.4	17 44.5	17 4.2	18 50.5	29 22.6
13 W	19 20 52.1	19 57.0	23 59.6	24 0.1	10 16.1	28 34.4	23 35.1	1 31.5	17 46.3	17 6.2	18 51.8	29 24.3
14 T	19 24 48.6	20 54.2	23 56.4	5♒55.2	11 54.3	29 43.9	24 14.0	1 27.4	17 48.1	17 8.2	18 53.1	29 25.9
15 F	19 28 45.1	21 51.4	23 53.3	17 55.3	13 30.4	0♍53.3	24 52.8	1 23.2	17 49.8	17 10.1	18 54.5	29 27.6
16 S	19 32 41.7	22 48.6	23 50.1	0♓ 2.1	15 4.6	2 2.7	25 31.7	1 18.7	17 51.4	17 11.9	18 55.9	29 29.2
17 S	19 36 38.3	23 45.9	23 46.9	12 17.5	16 36.8	3 11.9	26 10.5	1 14.1	17 52.9	17 13.8	18 57.3	29 30.9
18 M	19 40 34.8	24 43.1	23 43.7	24 43.7	18 7.0	4 21.1	26 49.3	1 9.4	17 54.2	17 15.5	18 58.8	29 32.6
19 T	19 44 31.4	25 40.4	23 40.6	7♈23.6	19 35.1	5 30.1	27 28.1	1 4.5	17 55.5	17 17.3	19 0.3	29 34.2
20 W	19 48 27.9	26 37.6	23 37.4	20 20.4	21 1.2	6 39.1	28 6.9	0 59.4	17 56.7	17 19.0	19 1.7	29 35.9
21 T	19 52 24.5	27 34.9	23 34.2	3♉37.2	22 25.2	7 48.0	28 45.7	0 54.2	17 57.8	17 20.6	19 3.3	29 37.5
22 F	19 56 21.0	28 32.2	23 31.0	17 17.0	23 47.1	8 56.8	29 24.4	0 48.8	17 58.8	17 22.2	19 4.8	29 39.2
23 S	20 0 17.6	29 29.5	23 27.9	1♊21.3	25 6.9	10 5.4	0♌ 3.1	0 43.3	17 59.6	17 23.8	19 6.4	29 40.9
24 S	20 4 14.2	0♌26.8	23 24.7	15 50.2	26 24.5	11 14.0	0 41.9	0 37.6	18 0.4	17 25.3	19 8.0	29 42.6
25 M	20 8 10.7	1 24.1	23 21.5	0♋40.7	27 39.8	12 22.5	1 20.5	0 31.8	18 1.1	17 26.8	19 9.6	29 44.2
26 T	20 12 7.3	2 21.4	23 18.3	15 46.7	28 52.9	13 30.8	1 59.2	0 25.8	18 1.6	17 28.2	19 11.2	29 45.9
27 W	20 16 3.8	3 18.8	23 15.1	0♌59.5	0♍ 3.6	14 39.1	2 37.9	0 19.7	18 2.1	17 29.6	19 12.9	29 47.6
28 T	20 20 0.4	4 16.2	23 12.0	16 8.5	1 11.9	15 47.3	3 16.5	0 13.5	18 2.4	17 31.0	19 14.6	29 49.2
29 F	20 23 57.0	5 13.5	23 8.8	1♍ 3.3	2 17.6	16 55.3	3 55.1	0 7.1	18 2.7	17 32.3	19 16.3	29 50.9
30 S	20 27 53.5	6 10.9	23 5.6	15 35.5	3 20.7	18 3.2	4 33.7	0 0.7	18 2.8	17 33.5	19 18.0	29 52.5
31 S	20 31 50.1	7 8.3	23 2.4	29 39.8	4 21.2	19 11.0	5 12.3	29♒54.1	18 2.9	17 34.7	19 19.7	29 54.2

DECLINATION

DAY	EPHEMERIS SIDEREAL TIME (h m s)	☉	☊	☽	☿	♀	♂	♃	♄	♅	♆	♇
1 F	18 33 33.4	23N10.3	18S55.9	9N 8.6	24N 2.1	18N12.5	23N30.4	11S41.1	4N34.0	16N28.1	5N31.4	23N18.8
4 M	18 45 23.1	22 57.5	18 53.6	5S26.9	23 9.5	17 6.1	23 16.5	11 44.2	4 36.5	16 30.1	5 30.1	23 17.9
7 T	18 57 12.7	22 41.1	18 51.2	16 43.8	22 0.2	15 56.0	23 0.9	11 47.8	4 38.6	16 32.0	5 28.7	23 17.0
10 S	19 9 2.4	22 21.2	18 48.9	20 58.9	20 37.7	14 42.4	22 43.8	11 52.0	4 40.5	16 33.8	5 27.2	23 16.1
13 W	19 20 52.1	21 57.8	18 46.5	17 2.3	19 5.3	13 25.6	22 25.1	11 56.7	4 42.0	16 35.5	5 25.6	23 15.2
16 S	19 32 41.7	21 31.0	18 44.2	6 43.3	17 26.0	12 6.1	22 4.9	12 2.0	4 43.1	16 37.1	5 24.0	23 14.3
19 T	19 44 31.4	21 0.9	18 41.8	6N22.5	15 42.3	10 44.0	21 43.2	12 7.8	4 43.9	16 38.6	5 22.2	23 13.5
22 F	19 56 21.0	20 27.6	18 39.4	17 37.9	13 56.6	9 19.8	21 20.1	12 14.1	4 44.4	16 40.0	5 20.4	23 12.6
25 M	20 8 10.7	19 51.2	18 37.1	20 27.7	12 10.9	7 53.7	20 55.6	12 20.8	4 44.5	16 41.2	5 18.4	23 11.7
28 T	20 20 0.4	19 11.8	18 34.7	11 14.1	10 27.4	6 26.0	20 29.7	12 27.9	4 44.2	16 42.4	5 16.4	23 10.8
31 S	20 31 50.1	18 29.5	18 32.3	3S37.3	8 48.3	4 57.0	20 2.6	12 35.3	4 43.6	16 43.4	5 14.4	23 10.0

AUGUST 1938

LONGITUDE

DAY	EPHEMERIS SIDEREAL TIME (h m s)	☉ (° ′)	☊ (° ′)	☽ (° ′)	☿ (° ′)	♀ (° ′)	♂ (° ′)	♃ (° ′)	♄ (° ′)	♅ (° ′)	♆ (° ′)	♇ (° ′)
1 M	20 35 46.6	8♌ 5.7	22♏59.3	13♎14.6	5♍18.7	20♍18.6	5♌50.9	29♒47.4	18♈ 2.8	17♉35.9	19♍21.5	29♋55.9
2 T	20 39 43.2	9 3.2	22 56.1	26 21.0	6 13.4	21 26.2	6 29.4	29R40.6	18R 2.7	17 37.0	19 23.3	29 57.5
3 W	20 43 39.7	10 0.6	22 52.9	9♏ 2.4	7 4.9	22 33.6	7 8.0	29 33.6	18 2.4	17 38.0	19 25.1	29 59.2
4 T	20 47 36.3	10 58.0	22 49.7	21 23.5	7 53.2	23 40.8	7 46.5	29 26.6	18 2.0	17 39.0	19 26.9	0♌ 0.8
5 F	20 51 32.8	11 55.5	22 46.5	3♐29.4	8 38.0	24 48.0	8 25.0	29 19.5	18 1.6	17 40.0	19 28.7	0 2.4
6 S	20 55 29.4	12 52.9	22 43.4	15 25.3	9 19.4	25 54.9	9 3.5	29 12.4	18 1.0	17 40.9	19 30.6	0 4.1
7 S	20 59 25.9	13 50.4	22 40.2	27 15.7	9 56.9	27 1.7	9 41.9	29 5.1	18 0.3	17 41.8	19 32.5	0 5.7
8 M	21 3 22.5	14 47.9	22 37.0	9♑ 4.9	10 30.6	28 8.4	10 20.4	28 57.7	17 59.5	17 42.6	19 34.3	0 7.3
9 T	21 7 19.0	15 45.4	22 33.8	20 56.1	11 0.1	29 14.9	10 58.8	28 50.3	17 58.7	17 43.4	19 36.2	0 8.9
10 W	21 11 15.6	16 42.9	22 30.7	2♒51.9	11 25.2	0♎21.3	11 37.2	28 42.8	17 57.7	17 44.1	19 38.2	0 10.6
11 T	21 15 12.2	17 40.5	22 27.5	14 54.1	11 45.8	1 27.5	12 15.6	28 35.3	17 56.6	17 44.8	19 40.1	0 12.2
12 F	21 19 8.7	18 38.0	22 24.3	27 3.8	12 1.7	2 33.5	12 54.0	28 27.7	17 55.4	17 45.4	19 42.1	0 13.8
13 S	21 23 5.3	19 35.6	22 21.1	9♓22.0	12 12.5	3 39.4	13 32.4	28 20.0	17 54.1	17 45.9	19 44.0	0 15.4
14 S	21 27 1.8	20 33.2	22 17.9	21 49.5	12 18.3	4 45.0	14 10.8	28 12.3	17 52.8	17 46.5	19 46.0	0 16.9
15 M	21 30 58.4	21 30.8	22 14.8	4♈27.2	12 18.6	5 50.5	14 49.1	28 4.5	17 51.3	17 46.9	19 48.0	0 18.5
16 T	21 34 54.9	22 28.5	22 11.6	17 16.4	12R13.6	6 55.9	15 27.5	27 56.7	17 49.7	17 47.4	19 50.1	0 20.1
17 W	21 38 51.5	23 26.1	22 8.4	0♉18.9	12 2.9	8 1.0	16 5.8	27 48.9	17 48.1	17 47.7	19 52.1	0 21.7
18 T	21 42 48.1	24 23.8	22 5.2	13 36.9	11 46.5	9 6.0	16 44.1	27 41.1	17 46.3	17 48.1	19 54.1	0 23.2
19 F	21 46 44.6	25 21.6	22 2.1	27 12.6	11 24.5	10 10.7	17 22.4	27 33.2	17 44.4	17 48.3	19 56.2	0 24.7
20 S	21 50 41.2	26 19.3	21 58.9	11♊ 7.7	10 57.0	11 15.3	18 0.7	27 25.3	17 42.5	17 48.6	19 58.2	0 26.3
21 S	21 54 37.7	27 17.1	21 55.7	25 22.9	10 24.1	12 19.6	18 39.0	27 17.5	17 40.4	17 48.7	20 0.3	0 27.8
22 M	21 58 34.3	28 14.9	21 52.5	9♋56.6	9 46.0	13 23.8	19 17.3	27 9.6	17 38.3	17 48.9	20 2.4	0 29.3
23 T	22 2 30.8	29 12.7	21 49.3	24 44.9	9 3.3	14 27.7	19 55.5	27 1.7	17 36.0	17 48.9	20 4.5	0 30.8
24 W	22 6 27.4	0♍10.6	21 46.2	9♌41.1	8 16.6	15 31.5	20 33.8	26 53.8	17 33.7	17 49.0	20 6.6	0 32.3
25 T	22 10 23.9	1 8.5	21 43.0	24 36.8	7 26.3	16 35.0	21 12.0	26 46.0	17 31.3	17R48.9	20 8.8	0 33.8
26 F	22 14 20.5	2 6.4	21 39.8	9♍22.5	6 33.5	17 38.3	21 50.3	26 38.2	17 28.7	17 48.9	20 10.9	0 35.2
27 S	22 18 17.0	3 4.3	21 36.6	23 50.0	5 38.9	18 41.3	22 28.5	26 30.3	17 26.1	17 48.7	20 13.0	0 36.7
28 S	22 22 13.6	4 2.3	21 33.5	7♎53.4	4 43.8	19 44.1	23 6.7	26 22.6	17 23.4	17 48.5	20 15.2	0 38.1
29 M	22 26 10.1	5 0.3	21 30.3	21 29.6	3 49.2	20 46.6	23 44.9	26 14.9	17 20.6	17 48.3	20 17.3	0 39.6
30 T	22 30 6.7	5 58.3	21 27.1	4♏38.5	2 56.2	21 48.9	24 23.1	26 7.2	17 17.8	17 48.1	20 19.5	0 41.0
31 W	22 34 3.2	6 56.3	21 23.9	17 22.5	2 6.0	22 50.9	25 1.3	25 59.6	17 14.8	17 47.7	20 21.7	0 42.4

DECLINATION

DAY	EPHEMERIS SIDEREAL TIME (h m s)	☉	☊	☽	☿	♀	♂	♃	♄	♅	♆	♇
1 M	20 35 46.6	18N14.9	18S31.5	8S15.3	8N16.6	4N27.1	19N53.2	12S37.9	4N43.3	16N43.7	5N13.7	23N 9.7
4 T	20 47 36.3	17 29.0	18 29.1	18 18.5	6 47.0	2 56.9	19 24.4	12 45.7	4 42.3	16 44.5	5 11.5	23 8.9
7 S	20 59 25.9	16 40.6	18 26.6	20 37.2	5 27.8	1 26.0	18 54.4	12 53.8	4 40.9	16 45.3	5 9.3	23 8.0
10 W	21 11 15.6	15 49.9	18 24.2	14 57.0	4 22.2	0S 5.1	18 23.3	13 2.0	4 39.1	16 45.9	5 7.0	23 7.2
13 S	21 23 5.3	14 56.8	18 21.8	3 37.3	3 34.1	1 36.2	17 51.1	13 10.4	4 37.0	16 46.4	5 4.7	23 6.5
16 T	21 34 54.9	14 1.5	18 19.3	9N26.1	3 7.6	3 7.1	17 17.8	13 18.8	4 34.6	16 46.7	5 2.3	23 5.7
19 F	21 46 44.6	13 4.3	18 16.9	19 5.4	3 7.0	4 37.5	16 43.4	13 27.3	4 31.9	16 47.0	4 59.8	23 5.0
22 M	21 58 34.3	12 5.2	18 14.4	19 20.3	3 35.1	6 7.1	16 8.1	13 35.8	4 28.9	16 47.1	4 57.4	23 4.3
25 T	22 10 23.9	11 4.3	18 11.9	8 35.8	4 31.7	7 35.7	15 31.9	13 44.1	4 25.6	16 47.1	4 54.9	23 3.6
28 S	22 22 13.6	10 1.8	18 9.5	6S17.3	5 51.5	9 2.9	14 54.8	13 52.3	4 22.0	16 46.9	4 52.3	23 3.0
31 W	22 34 3.2	8 58.0	18 7.0	17 18.6	7 23.8	10 28.6	14 16.9	14 0.3	4 18.1	16 46.7	4 49.8	23 2.4

SEPTEMBER 1938

DAY	EPHEMERIS SIDEREAL TIME	☉	☊	☽	☿	♀	♂	♃	♄	♅	♆	♇
	h m s	° ′	° ′	° ′	° ′	° ′	° ′	° ′	° ′	° ′	° ′	° ′
						LONGITUDE						
1 T	22 37 59.8	7♍54.4	21♏20.7	29♏45.6	1♍19.9	23♎52.6	25♌39.5	25♒52.0	17♈11.8	17♉47.3	20♍23.9	0♌43.7
2 F	22 41 56.3	8 52.5	21 17.6	11♐52.7	0R38.8	24 54.0	26 17.6	25R44.5	17R 8.7	17R46.9	20 26.1	0 45.1
3 S	22 45 52.9	9 50.6	21 14.4	23 49.2	0 3.7	25 55.1	26 55.8	25 37.1	17 5.5	17 46.4	20 28.2	0 46.5
4 S	22 49 49.4	10 48.7	21 11.2	5♑40.3	29♌35.6	26 55.9	27 33.9	25 29.7	17 2.2	17 45.9	20 30.4	0 47.8
5 M	22 53 46.0	11 46.9	21 8.0	17 30.7	29 15.0	27 56.4	28 12.0	25 22.4	16 58.9	17 45.4	20 32.6	0 49.1
6 T	22 57 42.6	12 45.0	21 4.9	29 24.8	29 2.6	28 56.5	28 50.1	25 15.3	16 55.5	17 44.7	20 34.9	0 50.4
7 W	23 1 39.1	13 43.2	21 1.7	11♒25.7	28 58.8	29 56.3	29 28.3	25 8.2	16 52.0	17 44.1	20 37.1	0 51.7
8 T	23 5 35.7	14 41.5	20 58.5	23 36.0	29D 3.7	0♏55.8	0♍ 6.4	25 1.2	16 48.4	17 43.4	20 39.3	0 53.0
9 F	23 9 32.2	15 39.7	20 55.3	5♓57.2	29 17.7	1 54.8	0 44.4	24 54.3	16 44.8	17 42.6	20 41.5	0 54.3
10 S	23 13 28.8	16 38.0	20 52.1	18 30.0	29 40.5	2 53.5	1 22.5	24 47.5	16 41.1	17 41.8	20 43.7	0 55.5
11 S	23 17 25.3	17 36.3	20 49.0	1♈14.5	0♍12.2	3 51.8	2 0.6	24 40.8	16 37.3	17 40.9	20 45.9	0 56.7
12 M	23 21 21.9	18 34.7	20 45.8	14 10.5	0 52.5	4 49.7	2 38.7	24 34.2	16 33.5	17 40.0	20 48.2	0 58.0
13 T	23 25 18.4	19 33.0	20 42.6	27 17.7	1 40.9	5 47.1	3 16.7	24 27.8	16 29.6	17 39.1	20 50.4	0 59.2
14 W	23 29 15.0	20 31.5	20 39.4	10♉36.1	2 37.2	6 44.2	3 54.8	24 21.4	16 25.6	17 38.1	20 52.6	1 0.3
15 T	23 33 11.5	21 29.9	20 36.3	24 5.9	3 40.8	7 40.7	4 32.8	24 15.2	16 21.6	17 37.0	20 54.8	1 1.5
16 F	23 37 8.1	22 28.4	20 33.1	7♊47.7	4 51.2	8 36.9	5 10.9	24 9.1	16 17.6	17 35.9	20 57.1	1 2.6
17 S	23 41 4.6	23 26.9	20 29.9	21 41.9	6 7.8	9 32.5	5 48.9	24 3.2	16 13.4	17 34.8	20 59.3	1 3.7
18 S	23 45 1.2	24 25.5	20 26.7	5♋48.6	7 30.0	10 27.7	6 27.0	23 57.4	16 9.3	17 33.6	21 1.5	1 4.8
19 M	23 48 57.7	25 24.1	20 23.5	20 6.8	8 57.2	11 22.3	7 5.0	23 51.8	16 5.0	17 32.4	21 3.8	1 5.9
20 T	23 52 54.3	26 22.7	20 20.4	4♌33.9	10 28.8	12 16.5	7 43.0	23 46.2	16 0.8	17 31.2	21 6.0	1 7.0
21 W	23 56 50.8	27 21.3	20 17.2	19 5.7	12 4.1	13 10.0	8 21.0	23 40.9	15 56.4	17 29.8	21 8.2	1 8.0
22 T	0 0 47.4	28 20.1	20 14.0	3♍36.5	13 42.7	14 3.0	8 59.1	23 35.7	15 52.1	17 28.5	21 10.4	1 9.0
23 F	0 4 44.0	29 18.8	20 10.8	17 59.7	15 24.0	14 55.5	9 37.1	23 30.7	15 47.7	17 27.1	21 12.6	1 10.0
24 S	0 8 40.5	0♎17.6	20 7.7	2♎ 9.3	17 7.5	15 47.3	10 15.1	23 25.8	15 43.2	17 25.7	21 14.8	1 11.0
25 S	0 12 37.1	1 16.4	20 4.5	15 59.9	18 52.7	16 38.5	10 53.1	23 21.1	15 38.7	17 24.2	21 17.0	1 12.0
26 M	0 16 33.6	2 15.2	20 1.3	29 28.5	20 39.3	17 29.0	11 31.1	23 16.5	15 34.2	17 22.7	21 19.2	1 12.9
27 T	0 20 30.2	3 14.1	19 58.1	12♏34.1	22 26.9	18 18.8	12 9.1	23 12.2	15 29.7	17 21.1	21 21.4	1 13.8
28 W	0 24 26.7	4 13.0	19 54.9	25 17.7	24 15.1	19 7.9	12 47.0	23 8.0	15 25.1	17 19.5	21 23.6	1 14.7
29 T	0 28 23.3	5 11.9	19 51.8	7♐41.9	26 3.8	19 56.3	13 25.0	23 3.9	15 20.5	17 17.9	21 25.8	1 15.6
30 F	0 32 19.8	6 10.9	19 48.6	19 50.8	27 52.6	20 43.9	14 3.0	23 0.1	15 15.9	17 16.2	21 28.0	1 16.4
						DECLINATION						
1 T	22 37 59.8	8N36.4	18S 6.1	19S19.6	7N54.8	10S56.8	14N 4.1	14S 2.9	4N16.8	16N46.6	4N48.9	23N 2.2
4 S	22 49 49.4	7 30.9	18 3.7	19 44.8	9 21.3	12 19.9	13 25.2	14 10.5	4 12.6	16 46.1	4 46.3	23 1.6
7 W	23 1 39.1	6 24.2	18 1.1	12 33.7	10 27.8	13 40.8	12 45.5	14 17.8	4 8.1	16 45.6	4 43.7	23 1.1
10 S	23 13 28.8	5 16.7	17 58.6	0 28.2	11 4.9	14 59.3	12 5.2	14 24.8	4 3.5	16 44.9	4 41.1	23 0.6
13 T	23 25 18.4	4 8.3	17 56.1	12N18.0	11 7.7	16 15.0	11 24.2	14 31.3	3 58.6	16 44.1	4 38.5	23 0.2
16 F	23 37 8.1	2 59.3	17 53.6	20 0.9	10 35.3	17 27.8	10 42.7	14 37.5	3 53.6	16 43.2	4 35.9	22 59.8
19 M	23 48 57.7	1 49.7	17 51.0	17 31.3	9 30.4	18 37.4	10 0.6	14 43.1	3 48.5	16 42.2	4 33.3	22 59.5
22 T	0 0 47.4	0 39.8	17 48.5	5 34.5	7 58.4	19 43.5	9 17.9	14 48.3	3 43.2	16 41.1	4 30.7	22 59.2
25 S	0 12 37.1	0S30.4	17 45.9	8S51.2	6 5.9	20 46.0	8 34.8	14 52.9	3 37.8	16 39.9	4 28.1	22 58.9
28 W	0 24 26.7	1 40.6	17 43.4	18 30.1	3 59.6	21 44.6	7 51.3	14 57.0	3 32.3	16 38.6	4 25.6	22 58.7

OCTOBER 1938

DAY	EPHEMERIS SIDEREAL TIME	☉	☊	☽	☿	♀	♂	♃	♄	♅	♆	♇
						LONGITUDE						
1 S	0 36 16.4	7♎ 9.8	19♏45.4	1♑49.0	29♍41.4	21♏30.6	14♍40.9	22♒56.5	15♈11.2	17♉14.5	21♍30.1	1♌17.2
2 S	0 40 13.0	8 8.9	19 42.2	13 41.4	1♎30.0	22 16.6	15 18.9	22R53.0	15R 6.6	17R12.8	21 32.3	1 18.0
3 M	0 44 9.5	9 7.9	19 39.1	25 33.2	3 18.4	23 1.6	15 56.8	22 49.7	15 1.9	17 11.0	21 34.4	1 18.8
4 T	0 48 6.0	10 7.0	19 35.9	7♒29.2	5 6.3	23 45.7	16 34.8	22 46.6	14 57.2	17 9.2	21 36.6	1 19.6
5 W	0 52 2.6	11 6.1	19 32.7	19 33.5	6 53.7	24 28.9	17 12.7	22 43.7	14 52.5	17 7.3	21 38.7	1 20.3
6 T	0 55 59.1	12 5.2	19 29.5	1♓49.6	8 40.5	25 11.0	17 50.6	22 41.0	14 47.7	17 5.5	21 40.8	1 21.0
7 F	0 59 55.7	13 4.4	19 26.3	14 20.0	10 26.7	25 52.1	18 28.5	22 38.5	14 43.0	17 3.5	21 42.9	1 21.7
8 S	1 3 52.3	14 3.6	19 23.2	27 6.1	12 12.3	26 32.2	19 6.5	22 36.1	14 38.3	17 1.6	21 45.0	1 22.4
9 S	1 7 48.8	15 2.8	19 20.0	10♈ 8.2	13 57.1	27 11.1	19 44.4	22 34.0	14 33.6	16 59.6	21 47.1	1 23.0
10 M	1 11 45.3	16 2.1	19 16.8	23 25.6	15 41.3	27 48.8	20 22.3	22 32.1	14 28.8	16 57.6	21 49.2	1 23.6
11 T	1 15 41.9	17 1.4	19 13.6	6♉56.8	17 24.7	28 25.3	21 0.2	22 30.3	14 24.1	16 55.6	21 51.2	1 24.2
12 W	1 19 38.5	18 0.7	19 10.5	20 39.8	19 7.4	29 0.6	21 38.1	22 28.8	14 19.4	16 53.5	21 53.3	1 24.8
13 T	1 23 35.0	19 0.1	19 7.3	4♊32.4	20 49.4	29 34.5	22 16.0	22 27.4	14 14.7	16 51.4	21 55.3	1 25.3
14 F	1 27 31.6	19 59.5	19 4.1	18 32.5	22 30.7	0♐ 7.1	22 53.9	22 26.3	14 10.0	16 49.3	21 57.3	1 25.8
15 S	1 31 28.1	20 58.9	19 0.9	2♋38.2	24 11.3	0 38.2	23 31.8	22 25.3	14 5.3	16 47.1	21 59.4	1 26.3
16 S	1 35 24.7	21 58.4	18 57.7	16 47.8	25 51.2	1 7.9	24 9.7	22 24.6	14 0.6	16 45.0	22 1.4	1 26.8
17 M	1 39 21.2	22 58.0	18 54.6	0♌59.2	27 30.4	1 36.1	24 47.6	22 24.1	13 56.0	16 42.8	22 3.3	1 27.2
18 T	1 43 17.8	23 57.5	18 51.4	15 10.6	29 8.9	2 2.7	25 25.4	22 23.7	13 51.3	16 40.5	22 5.3	1 27.6
19 W	1 47 14.3	24 57.1	18 48.2	29 19.3	0♏46.8	2 27.6	26 3.3	22 23.6	13 46.7	16 38.3	22 7.2	1 28.0
20 T	1 51 10.9	25 56.8	18 45.0	13♍22.6	2 24.1	2 50.9	26 41.2	22D23.6	13 42.2	16 36.0	22 9.2	1 28.4
21 F	1 55 7.5	26 56.4	18 41.9	27 17.2	4 0.7	3 12.4	27 19.1	22 23.9	13 37.6	16 33.7	22 11.1	1 28.7
22 S	1 59 4.0	27 56.2	18 38.7	10♎59.9	5 36.8	3 32.1	27 57.0	22 24.4	13 33.1	16 31.4	22 13.0	1 29.0
23 S	2 3 0.5	28 55.9	18 35.5	24 28.0	7 12.3	3 49.8	28 34.8	22 25.0	13 28.6	16 29.1	22 14.8	1 29.3
24 M	2 6 57.1	29 55.7	18 32.3	7♏39.5	8 47.2	4 5.6	29 12.7	22 25.9	13 24.2	16 26.7	22 16.7	1 29.5
25 T	2 10 53.6	0♏55.5	18 29.1	20 33.7	10 21.5	4 19.4	29 50.6	22 27.0	13 19.8	16 24.4	22 18.5	1 29.8
26 W	2 14 50.2	1 55.3	18 26.0	3♐10.7	11 55.3	4 31.2	0♎28.4	22 28.2	13 15.4	16 22.0	22 20.4	1 30.0
27 T	2 18 46.8	2 55.2	18 22.8	15 32.0	13 28.6	4 40.7	1 6.3	22 29.7	13 11.1	16 19.6	22 22.2	1 30.2
28 F	2 22 43.3	3 55.1	18 19.6	27 40.2	15 1.4	4 48.1	1 44.1	22 31.4	13 6.8	16 17.2	22 23.9	1 30.3
29 S	2 26 39.9	4 55.1	18 16.4	9♑38.7	16 33.7	4 53.2	2 22.0	22 33.3	13 2.6	16 14.8	22 25.7	1 30.4
30 S	2 30 36.4	5 55.0	18 13.3	21 31.6	18 5.5	4 56.0	2 59.8	22 35.4	12 58.4	16 12.4	22 27.4	1 30.5
31 M	2 34 33.0	6 55.0	18 10.1	3♒23.5	19 36.8	4 56.4	3 37.6	22 37.6	12 54.3	16 9.9	22 29.1	1 30.6
						DECLINATION						
1 S	0 36 16.4	2S50.6	17S40.8	19S52.9	1N45.1	22S39.1	7N 7.5	15S 0.5	3N26.8	16N37.1	4N23.1	22N58.5
4 T	0 48 6.0	4 0.4	17 38.2	13 29.2	0S33.1	23 29.2	6 23.3	15 3.5	3 21.3	16 35.6	4 20.6	22 58.4
7 F	0 59 55.7	5 9.8	17 35.7	1 52.2	2 52.0	24 14.7	5 38.8	15 5.8	3 15.8	16 34.0	4 18.1	22 58.4
10 M	1 11 45.3	6 18.6	17 33.1	11N 6.9	5 9.2	24 55.4	4 54.0	15 7.6	3 10.3	16 32.3	4 15.7	22 58.4
13 T	1 23 35.0	7 26.6	17 30.5	19 35.0	7 23.1	25 31.0	4 9.1	15 8.8	3 4.8	16 30.6	4 13.4	22 58.4
16 S	1 35 24.7	8 33.7	17 27.9	17 56.5	9 32.6	26 1.2	3 23.9	15 9.3	2 59.5	16 28.7	4 11.1	22 58.6
19 W	1 47 14.3	9 39.8	17 25.2	6 53.7	11 36.7	26 25.7	2 38.7	15 9.3	2 54.3	16 26.8	4 8.8	22 58.7
22 S	1 59 4.0	10 44.6	17 22.6	7S15.0	13 34.8	26 44.1	1 53.3	15 8.6	2 49.2	16 24.9	4 6.6	22 58.9
25 T	2 10 53.6	11 47.9	17 20.0	17 38.8	15 26.2	26 55.9	1 7.9	15 7.4	2 44.2	16 22.9	4 4.5	22 59.2
28 F	2 22 43.3	12 49.7	17 17.4	20 2.2	17 10.5	27 0.5	0 22.6	15 5.5	2 39.5	16 20.8	4 2.5	22 59.5
31 M	2 34 33.0	13 49.6	17 14.7	14 25.4	18 46.9	26 57.1	0S22.8	15 3.1	2 34.9	16 18.7	4 0.5	22 59.9

NOVEMBER 1938

LONGITUDE

DAY	EPHEMERIS SIDEREAL TIME h m s	☉ ° ′	☊ ° ′	☽ ° ′	☿ ° ′	♀ ° ′	♂ ° ′	♃ ° ′	♄ ° ′	♅ ° ′	♆ ° ′	♇ ° ′
1 T	2 38 29.5	7♏55.0	18♏ 6.9	15♒19.0	21♏ 7.6	4♐54.4	4♎15.4	22♒40.1	12♈50.3	16♉ 7.5	22♍30.8	1♌30.7
2 W	2 42 26.1	8 55.1	18 3.7	27 22.9	22 37.9	4R50.0	4 53.2	22 42.8	12R46.3	16R 5.0	22 32.5	1 30.7
3 T	2 46 22.6	9 55.1	18 0.5	9♓39.6	24 7.8	4 43.2	5 31.1	22 45.6	12 42.3	16 2.5	22 34.2	1R30.7
4 F	2 50 19.2	10 55.2	17 57.4	22 12.9	25 37.2	4 33.9	6 8.9	22 48.7	12 38.5	16 0.1	22 35.8	1 30.7
5 S	2 54 15.7	11 55.3	17 54.2	5♈ 5.5	27 6.1	4 22.1	6 46.7	22 51.9	12 34.6	15 57.6	22 37.4	1 30.6
6 S	2 58 12.3	12 55.5	17 51.0	18 19.1	28 34.5	4 8.0	7 24.4	22 55.4	12 30.9	15 55.1	22 38.9	1 30.5
7 M	3 2 8.8	13 55.7	17 47.8	1♉53.8	0♐ 2.4	3 51.4	8 2.2	22 59.0	12 27.2	15 52.6	22 40.5	1 30.4
8 T	3 6 5.4	14 55.9	17 44.7	15 47.7	1 29.8	3 32.4	8 40.0	23 2.8	12 23.6	15 50.2	22 42.0	1 30.3
9 W	3 10 2.0	15 56.1	17 41.5	29 57.8	2 56.6	3 11.2	9 17.8	23 6.8	12 20.1	15 47.7	22 43.5	1 30.1
10 T	3 13 58.5	16 56.4	17 38.3	14♊19.6	4 22.8	2 47.8	9 55.6	23 11.0	12 16.6	15 45.2	22 45.0	1 29.9
11 F	3 17 55.1	17 56.7	17 35.1	28 47.7	5 48.4	2 22.3	10 33.4	23 15.4	12 13.2	15 42.7	22 46.5	1 29.7
12 S	3 21 51.6	18 57.0	17 31.9	13♋16.9	7 13.3	1 54.9	11 11.1	23 20.0	12 9.9	15 40.2	22 47.9	1 29.5
13 S	3 25 48.2	19 57.4	17 28.8	27 42.4	8 37.4	1 25.7	11 48.9	23 24.7	12 6.7	15 37.7	22 49.3	1 29.2
14 M	3 29 44.7	20 57.8	17 25.6	12♌ 0.3	10 0.8	0 54.8	12 26.7	23 29.6	12 3.6	15 35.3	22 50.7	1 28.9
15 T	3 33 41.3	21 58.2	17 22.4	26 7.8	11 23.2	0 22.5	13 4.4	23 34.7	12 0.5	15 32.8	22 52.0	1 28.6
16 W	3 37 37.8	22 58.6	17 19.2	10♍ 3.2	12 44.7	29♏49.0	13 42.2	23 40.0	11 57.5	15 30.3	22 53.3	1 28.3
17 T	3 41 34.4	23 59.1	17 16.1	23 45.6	14 5.1	29 14.4	14 19.9	23 45.5	11 54.7	15 27.9	22 54.6	1 27.9
18 F	3 45 31.0	24 59.7	17 12.9	7♎14.6	15 24.2	28 39.0	14 57.7	23 51.1	11 51.9	15 25.4	22 55.9	1 27.5
19 S	3 49 27.5	26 0.2	17 9.7	20 30.3	16 42.0	28 3.0	15 35.4	23 56.9	11 49.1	15 23.0	22 57.1	1 27.1
20 S	3 53 24.1	27 0.8	17 6.5	3♏32.8	17 58.2	27 26.7	16 13.2	24 2.9	11 46.5	15 20.6	22 58.3	1 26.7
21 M	3 57 20.6	28 1.4	17 3.3	16 22.3	19 12.6	26 50.4	16 50.9	24 9.1	11 44.0	15 18.1	22 59.5	1 26.2
22 T	4 1 17.2	29 2.0	17 0.2	28 59.2	20 25.0	26 14.1	17 28.6	24 15.4	11 41.6	15 15.7	23 0.6	1 25.7
23 W	4 5 13.8	0♐ 2.7	16 57.0	11♐24.0	21 35.0	25 38.3	18 6.4	24 21.9	11 39.2	15 13.4	23 1.7	1 25.2
24 T	4 9 10.3	1 3.4	16 53.8	23 37.8	22 42.5	25 3.2	18 44.1	24 28.5	11 37.0	15 11.0	23 2.8	1 24.6
25 F	4 13 6.8	2 4.1	16 50.6	5♑42.0	23 47.0	24 28.9	19 21.8	24 35.3	11 34.8	15 8.6	23 3.8	1 24.1
26 S	4 17 3.4	3 4.8	16 47.5	17 38.8	24 48.0	23 55.8	19 59.5	24 42.3	11 32.8	15 6.3	23 4.9	1 23.5
27 S	4 20 60.0	4 5.5	16 44.3	29 31.0	25 45.2	23 23.9	20 37.2	24 49.5	11 30.8	15 4.0	23 5.9	1 22.9
28 M	4 24 56.5	5 6.3	16 41.1	11♒21.9	26 38.0	22 53.6	21 14.8	24 56.8	11 29.0	15 1.7	23 6.8	1 22.3
29 T	4 28 53.1	6 7.0	16 37.9	23 15.6	27 25.8	22 25.0	21 52.5	25 4.2	11 27.2	14 59.4	23 7.7	1 21.6
30 W	4 32 49.6	7 7.8	16 34.8	5♓16.5	28 7.9	21 58.2	22 30.2	25 11.8	11 25.6	14 57.1	23 8.6	1 20.9

DECLINATION

DAY	EPHEMERIS SIDEREAL TIME h m s	☉ ° ′	☊ ° ′	☽ ° ′	☿ ° ′	♀ ° ′	♂ ° ′	♃ ° ′	♄ ° ′	♅ ° ′	♆ ° ′	♇ ° ′
1 T	2 38 29.5	14S 9.1	17S13.8	11S12.0	19S17.3	26S54.1	0S37.9	15S 2.1	2N33.5	16N18.0	3N59.9	23N 0.1
4 F	2 50 19.2	15 6.4	17 11.2	0N55.2	20 42.5	26 38.8	1 23.1	14 58.9	2 29.3	16 15.9	3 58.0	23 0.5
7 M	3 2 8.8	16 1.4	17 8.5	13 29.8	21 58.6	26 13.9	2 8.2	14 55.1	2 25.3	16 13.8	3 56.2	23 1.0
10 T	3 13 58.5	16 54.0	17 5.8	20 10.3	23 4.9	25 38.7	2 53.1	14 50.7	2 21.7	16 11.7	3 54.6	23 1.6
13 S	3 25 48.2	17 44.0	17 3.2	15 45.1	24 0.7	24 53.2	3 37.8	14 45.8	2 18.3	16 9.6	3 53.0	23 2.2
16 W	3 37 37.8	18 31.3	17 0.5	3 15.9	24 45.3	23 58.2	4 22.3	14 40.3	2 15.3	16 7.4	3 51.5	23 2.8
19 S	3 49 27.5	19 15.6	16 57.8	10S15.7	25 18.1	22 55.4	5 6.4	14 34.3	2 12.5	16 5.3	3 50.1	23 3.5
22 T	4 1 17.2	19 56.9	16 55.1	18 56.3	25 38.3	21 47.3	5 50.2	14 27.8	2 10.2	16 3.3	3 48.9	23 4.3
25 F	4 13 6.8	20 34.8	16 52.4	19 24.8	25 45.6	20 37.0	6 33.7	14 20.7	2 8.2	16 1.2	3 47.7	23 5.1
28 M	4 24 56.5	21 9.3	16 49.7	12 20.7	25 39.5	19 27.9	7 16.7	14 13.2	2 6.5	15 59.2	3 46.6	23 5.9

DECEMBER 1938

LONGITUDE

DAY	EPHEMERIS SIDEREAL TIME h m s	☉ ° ′	☊ ° ′	☽ ° ′	☿ ° ′	♀ ° ′	♂ ° ′	♃ ° ′	♄ ° ′	♅ ° ′	♆ ° ′	♇ ° ′
1 T	4 36 46.2	8♐ 8.6	16♏31.6	17♓29.3	28♐43.5	21♏33.4	23♎ 7.8	25♒19.6	11♈24.1	14♉54.9	23♍ 9.5	1♌20.2
2 F	4 40 42.7	9 9.5	16 28.4	29 58.6	29 12.0	21R10.8	23 45.4	25 27.5	11R22.6	14R52.7	23 10.3	1R19.5
3 S	4 44 39.3	10 10.3	16 25.2	12♈48.7	29 32.5	20 50.3	24 23.1	25 35.6	11 21.3	14 50.5	23 11.1	1 18.7
4 S	4 48 35.9	11 11.2	16 22.1	26 2.9	29 44.1	20 32.2	25 0.7	25 43.8	11 20.1	14 48.4	23 11.9	1 18.0
5 M	4 52 32.4	12 12.0	16 18.9	9♉43.1	29 46.0	20 16.5	25 38.3	25 52.2	11 19.0	14 46.2	23 12.6	1 17.2
6 T	4 56 29.0	13 12.9	16 15.7	23 49.1	29R37.5	20 3.2	26 15.9	26 0.7	11 18.0	14 44.1	23 13.3	1 16.4
7 W	5 0 25.5	14 13.8	16 12.5	8♊18.2	29 18.0	19 52.4	26 53.5	26 9.3	11 17.0	14 42.1	23 14.0	1 15.5
8 T	5 4 22.1	15 14.7	16 9.3	23 4.8	28 47.3	19 44.1	27 31.1	26 18.1	11 16.3	14 40.0	23 14.6	1 14.7
9 F	5 8 18.6	16 15.6	16 6.2	8♋ 1.5	28 5.1	19 38.3	28 8.7	26 27.0	11 15.6	14 38.0	23 15.2	1 13.8
10 S	5 12 15.2	17 16.6	16 3.0	22 59.5	27 12.1	19 35.0	28 46.2	26 36.1	11 15.0	14 36.0	23 15.8	1 12.9
11 S	5 16 11.8	18 17.5	15 59.8	7♌50.2	26 9.2	19 34.2	29 23.8	26 45.2	11 14.5	14 34.1	23 16.3	1 12.0
12 M	5 20 8.3	19 18.5	15 56.6	22 26.5	24 57.7	19D35.9	0♏ 1.4	26 54.6	11 14.1	14 32.1	23 16.8	1 11.1
13 T	5 24 4.9	20 19.5	15 53.5	6♍43.6	23 39.9	19 39.9	0 38.9	27 4.0	11 13.9	14 30.2	23 17.3	1 10.1
14 W	5 28 1.4	21 20.5	15 50.3	20 39.3	22 18.0	19 46.4	1 16.5	27 13.6	11 13.7	14 28.4	23 17.7	1 9.2
15 T	5 31 58.0	22 21.6	15 47.1	4♎13.7	20 55.0	19 55.1	1 54.0	27 23.3	11 13.7	14 26.6	23 18.1	1 8.2
16 F	5 35 54.5	23 22.6	15 43.9	17 28.1	19 33.5	20 6.2	2 31.5	27 33.1	11D13.8	14 24.8	23 18.5	1 7.2
17 S	5 39 51.1	24 23.7	15 40.8	0♏24.9	18 16.4	20 19.4	3 9.0	27 43.1	11 14.0	14 23.1	23 18.8	1 6.2
18 S	5 43 47.7	25 24.8	15 37.6	13 6.9	17 5.8	20 34.7	3 46.5	27 53.2	11 14.3	14 21.3	23 19.1	1 5.1
19 M	5 47 44.2	26 25.9	15 34.4	25 36.4	16 3.7	20 52.2	4 24.0	28 3.3	11 14.7	14 19.7	23 19.3	1 4.1
20 T	5 51 40.8	27 27.0	15 31.2	7♐55.8	15 11.3	21 11.6	5 1.5	28 13.7	11 15.2	14 18.0	23 19.6	1 3.0
21 W	5 55 37.3	28 28.1	15 28.0	20 6.8	14 29.6	21 33.0	5 39.0	28 24.1	11 15.8	14 16.5	23 19.8	1 1.9
22 T	5 59 33.9	29 29.3	15 24.9	2♑10.7	13 58.8	21 56.2	6 16.4	28 34.7	11 16.5	14 14.9	23 19.9	1 0.8
23 F	6 3 30.5	0♑30.4	15 21.7	14 9.1	13 38.8	22 21.3	6 53.8	28 45.3	11 17.4	14 13.4	23 20.0	0 59.7
24 S	6 7 27.0	1 31.6	15 18.5	26 3.1	13 29.3	22 48.1	7 31.3	28 56.1	11 18.3	14 11.9	23 20.1	0 58.6
25 S	6 11 23.6	2 32.7	15 15.3	7♒54.5	13D29.6	23 16.6	8 8.7	29 7.0	11 19.4	14 10.5	23 20.2	0 57.4
26 M	6 15 20.1	3 33.9	15 12.2	19 45.4	13 39.2	23 46.7	8 46.0	29 18.0	11 20.6	14 9.1	23 20.2	0 56.3
27 T	6 19 16.7	4 35.0	15 9.0	1♓38.7	13 57.2	24 18.3	9 23.4	29 29.1	11 21.9	14 7.8	23R20.2	0 55.1
28 W	6 23 13.2	5 36.2	15 5.8	13 37.7	14 22.8	24 51.5	10 0.7	29 40.3	11 23.3	14 6.5	23 20.1	0 53.9
29 T	6 27 9.8	6 37.3	15 2.6	25 46.6	14 55.4	25 26.0	10 38.1	29 51.6	11 24.8	14 5.3	23 20.0	0 52.7
30 F	6 31 6.4	7 38.5	14 59.5	8♈ 9.9	15 34.2	26 2.0	11 15.4	0♓ 3.0	11 26.4	14 4.1	23 19.9	0 51.5
31 S	6 35 2.9	8 39.6	14 56.3	20 52.4	16 18.5	26 39.3	11 52.7	0 14.5	11 28.1	14 2.9	23 19.8	0 50.3

DECLINATION

DAY	EPHEMERIS SIDEREAL TIME h m s	☉ ° ′	☊ ° ′	☽ ° ′	☿ ° ′	♀ ° ′	♂ ° ′	♃ ° ′	♄ ° ′	♅ ° ′	♆ ° ′	♇ ° ′
1 T	4 36 46.2	21S40.2	16S46.9	0S44.5	25S20.1	18S23.3	7S59.2	14S 5.1	2N 5.3	15N57.3	3N45.7	23N 6.8
4 S	4 48 35.9	22 7.5	16 44.2	11N52.1	24 47.4	17 25.7	8 41.2	13 56.6	2 4.4	15 55.4	3 44.9	23 7.7
7 W	5 0 25.5	22 30.8	16 41.5	19 52.3	24 1.8	16 37.0	9 22.7	13 47.6	2 3.9	15 53.6	3 44.2	23 8.6
10 S	5 12 15.2	22 50.2	16 38.7	16 48.4	23 3.7	15 58.1	10 3.6	13 38.1	2 3.8	15 51.9	3 43.6	23 9.6
13 T	5 24 4.9	23 5.6	16 36.0	4 28.6	21 56.3	15 29.3	10 43.9	13 28.2	2 4.1	15 50.3	3 43.1	23 10.6
16 F	5 35 54.5	23 16.8	16 33.2	9S15.5	20 49.1	15 10.2	11 23.6	13 17.9	2 4.8	15 48.7	3 42.8	23 11.6
19 M	5 47 44.2	23 23.8	16 30.4	18 26.7	19 57.0	15 0.1	12 2.5	13 7.2	2 5.9	15 47.3	3 42.6	23 12.7
22 T	5 59 33.9	23 26.6	16 27.7	19 47.1	19 30.7	14 58.2	12 40.7	12 56.0	2 7.3	15 45.9	3 42.5	23 13.8
25 S	6 11 23.6	23 25.2	16 24.9	13 24.0	19 31.3	15 3.3	13 18.0	12 44.5	2 9.2	15 44.7	3 42.5	23 14.8
28 W	6 23 13.2	23 19.6	16 22.1	2 13.6	19 52.5	15 14.4	13 54.6	12 32.5	2 11.4	15 43.6	3 42.7	23 16.0
31 S	6 35 2.9	23 9.7	16 19.3	10N11.8	20 26.4	15 30.6	14 30.3	12 20.3	2 14.0	15 42.6	3 43.0	23 17.1

JANUARY 1939

LONGITUDE

DAY	EPHEMERIS SIDEREAL TIME h m s	☉ ° ′	☊ ° ′	☽ ° ′	☿ ° ′	♀ ° ′	♂ ° ′	♃ ° ′	♄ ° ′	♅ ° ′	♆ ° ′	♇ ° ′
1 S	6 38 59.5	9♑40.8	14♏53.1	3♉58.7	17♐ 7.7	27♏17.9	12♏30.0	0♓26.1	11♈29.9	14♉ 1.8	23♍19.6	0♌49.0
2 M	6 42 56.0	10 41.9	14 49.9	17 32.3	18 1.3	27 57.8	13 7.2	0 37.7	11 31.8	14R 0.7	23R19.3	0R47.8
3 T	6 46 52.6	11 43.1	14 46.7	1♊35.3	18 58.8	28 38.8	13 44.5	0 49.5	11 33.9	13 59.7	23 19.1	0 46.5
4 W	6 50 49.1	12 44.2	14 43.6	16 6.7	19 59.8	29 20.9	14 21.7	1 1.4	11 36.0	13 58.8	23 18.8	0 45.3
5 T	6 54 45.7	13 45.4	14 40.4	1♋ 2.6	21 3.8	0♐ 4.2	14 58.9	1 13.4	11 38.3	13 57.9	23 18.5	0 44.0
6 F	6 58 42.3	14 46.5	14 37.2	16 15.2	22 10.6	0 48.5	15 36.1	1 25.4	11 40.6	13 57.0	23 18.1	0 42.7
7 S	7 2 38.8	15 47.6	14 34.0	1♌34.1	23 19.8	1 33.9	16 13.3	1 37.5	11 43.1	13 56.2	23 17.7	0 41.4
8 S	7 6 35.3	16 48.7	14 30.9	16 47.9	24 31.2	2 20.2	16 50.4	1 49.7	11 45.6	13 55.4	23 17.3	0 40.1
9 M	7 10 31.9	17 49.9	14 27.7	1♍46.1	25 44.5	3 7.5	17 27.6	2 2.0	11 48.3	13 54.7	23 16.8	0 38.8
10 T	7 14 28.5	18 51.0	14 24.5	16 21.0	26 59.6	3 55.7	18 4.7	2 14.4	11 51.0	13 54.0	23 16.3	0 37.5
11 W	7 18 25.0	19 52.1	14 21.3	0♎28.5	28 16.3	4 44.8	18 41.8	2 26.9	11 53.9	13 53.4	23 15.8	0 36.2
12 T	7 22 21.6	20 53.3	14 18.2	14 7.8	29 34.4	5 34.7	19 18.9	2 39.4	11 56.8	13 52.8	23 15.3	0 34.9
13 F	7 26 18.1	21 54.4	14 15.0	27 20.9	0♑53.9	6 25.4	19 55.9	2 52.0	11 59.9	13 52.3	23 14.7	0 33.6
14 S	7 30 14.7	22 55.5	14 11.8	10♏11.3	2 14.5	7 16.8	20 33.0	3 4.7	12 3.1	13 51.9	23 14.1	0 32.3
15 S	7 34 11.3	23 56.7	14 8.6	22 43.2	3 36.3	8 9.0	21 10.0	3 17.5	12 6.3	13 51.4	23 13.4	0 30.9
16 M	7 38 7.8	24 57.8	14 5.4	5♐ 0.8	4 59.1	9 1.9	21 47.0	3 30.3	12 9.7	13 51.1	23 12.7	0 29.6
17 T	7 42 4.4	25 58.9	14 2.3	17 8.0	6 22.8	9 55.5	22 24.0	3 43.2	12 13.1	13 50.8	23 12.0	0 28.2
18 W	7 46 0.9	27 0.0	13 59.1	29 8.2	7 47.4	10 49.8	23 0.9	3 56.2	12 16.6	13 50.5	23 11.3	0 26.9
19 T	7 49 57.5	28 1.2	13 55.9	11♑ 3.9	9 12.9	11 44.7	23 37.9	4 9.2	12 20.3	13 50.3	23 10.5	0 25.6
20 F	7 53 54.1	29 2.3	13 52.7	22 57.0	10 39.2	12 40.1	24 14.7	4 22.3	12 24.0	13 50.2	23 9.7	0 24.2
21 S	7 57 50.6	0♒ 3.3	13 49.6	4♒49.0	12 6.2	13 36.2	24 51.6	4 35.5	12 27.8	13 50.0	23 8.9	0 22.9
22 S	8 1 47.1	1 4.4	13 46.4	16 41.2	13 34.0	14 32.8	25 28.4	4 48.7	12 31.7	13 50.0	23 8.0	0 21.5
23 M	8 5 43.7	2 5.5	13 43.2	28 34.9	15 2.5	15 29.9	26 5.2	5 2.0	12 35.7	13D50.0	23 7.1	0 20.2
24 T	8 9 40.3	3 6.5	13 40.0	10♓31.6	16 31.7	16 27.5	26 42.0	5 15.4	12 39.8	13 50.1	23 6.2	0 18.8
25 W	8 13 36.8	4 7.6	13 36.9	22 33.7	18 1.6	17 25.7	27 18.8	5 28.8	12 44.0	13 50.2	23 5.3	0 17.5
26 T	8 17 33.4	5 8.6	13 33.7	4♈44.1	19 32.2	18 24.3	27 55.5	5 42.3	12 48.3	13 50.3	23 4.3	0 16.2
27 F	8 21 29.9	6 9.6	13 30.5	17 6.2	21 3.4	19 23.3	28 32.1	5 55.8	12 52.6	13 50.6	23 3.3	0 14.8
28 S	8 25 26.5	7 10.6	13 27.3	29 44.4	22 35.3	20 22.8	29 8.8	6 9.4	12 57.1	13 50.8	23 2.2	0 13.5
29 S	8 29 23.1	8 11.5	13 24.1	12♉42.9	24 7.9	21 22.7	29 45.4	6 23.0	13 1.6	13 51.2	23 1.2	0 12.2
30 M	8 33 19.6	9 12.5	13 21.0	26 6.1	25 41.1	22 23.1	0♐22.0	6 36.6	13 6.2	13 51.5	23 0.1	0 10.8
31 T	8 37 16.1	10 13.4	13 17.8	9♊56.9	27 15.0	23 23.8	0 58.5	6 50.4	13 10.9	13 52.0	22 59.0	0 9.5

DECLINATION

DAY	SIDEREAL TIME	☉	☊	☽	☿	♀	♂	♃	♄	♅	♆	♇
1 S	6 38 59.5	23S 5.5	16S18.4	13N53.0	20S39.2	15S36.9	14S42.0	12S16.1	2N15.0	15N42.3	3N43.1	23N17.4
4 W	6 50 49.1	22 50.1	16 15.6	20 11.8	21 19.2	15 58.1	15 16.5	12 3.3	2 18.1	15 41.4	3 43.5	23 18.6
7 S	7 2 38.8	22 30.6	16 12.8	15 1.4	21 58.1	16 22.1	15 50.0	11 50.2	2 21.6	15 40.7	3 44.1	23 19.7
10 T	7 14 28.5	22 7.2	16 .0	1 22.3	22 32.4	16 48.0	16 22.6	11 36.8	2 25.4	15 40.2	3 44.7	23 20.8
13 F	7 26 18.1	21 39.8	16 7.1	12S 0.2	22 60.0	17 15.0	16 54.1	11 23.1	2 29.5	15 39.7	3 45.5	23 22.0
16 M	7 38 7.8	21 8.6	16 4.3	19 27.8	23 19.0	17 42.3	17 24.6	11 9.1	2 34.0	15 39.4	3 46.4	23 23.1
19 T	7 49 57.5	20 33.8	16 1.5	18 50.0	23 28.4	18 9.3	17 54.0	10 54.8	2 38.8	15 39.3	3 47.4	23 24.2
22 S	8 1 47.1	19 55.5	15 58.6	11 4.2	23 27.3	18 35.4	18 22.3	10 40.2	2 43.9	15 39.3	3 48.5	23 25.3
25 W	8 13 36.8	19 13.8	15 55.8	0N38.5	23 15.0	18 59.8	18 49.5	10 25.4	2 49.3	15 39.4	3 49.7	23 26.4
28 S	8 25 26.5	18 29.0	15 52.9	12 30.6	22 51.0	19 22.2	19 15.5	10 10.4	2 55.0	15 39.7	3 51.0	23 27.4
31 T	8 37 16.1	17 41.1	15 50.0	19 43.7	22 14.9	19 42.1	19 40.3	9 55.1	3 0.9	15 40.1	3 52.4	23 28.4

FEBRUARY 1939

LONGITUDE

DAY	SIDEREAL TIME	☉	☊	☽	☿	♀	♂	♃	♄	♅	♆	♇
1 W	8 41 12.7	11♒14.3	13♏14.6	24♊16.7	28♑49.6	24♐24.9	1♐35.0	7♓ 4.1	13♈15.7	13♉52.5	22♍57.9	0♌ 8.2
2 T	8 45 9.3	12 15.2	13 11.4	9♋ 3.5	0♒24.9	25 26.4	2 11.5	7 17.9	13 20.5	13 53.0	22R56.7	0R 6.9
3 F	8 49 5.8	13 16.0	13 8.3	24 11.7	2 0.9	26 28.2	2 48.0	7 31.8	13 25.5	13 53.6	22 55.5	0 5.6
4 S	8 53 2.4	14 16.9	13 5.1	9♌32.2	3 37.6	27 30.4	3 24.4	7 45.7	13 30.5	13 54.2	22 54.3	0 4.3
5 S	8 56 58.9	15 17.7	13 1.9	24 53.2	5 15.1	28 32.9	4 0.8	7 59.6	13 35.5	13 54.9	22 53.1	0 3.0
6 M	9 0 55.5	16 18.5	12 58.7	10♍ 3.1	6 53.3	29 35.8	4 37.1	8 13.6	13 40.7	13 55.6	22 51.9	0 1.7
7 T	9 4 52.1	17 19.3	12 55.6	24 51.8	8 32.3	0♑39.0	5 13.4	8 27.6	13 45.9	13 56.4	22 50.6	0 0.4
8 W	9 8 48.6	18 20.0	12 52.4	9♎12.9	10 12.0	1 42.4	5 49.7	8 41.6	13 51.2	13 57.3	22 49.3	29♋59.1
9 T	9 12 45.1	19 20.8	12 49.2	23 3.6	11 52.5	2 46.2	6 25.9	8 55.7	13 56.6	13 58.2	22 48.0	29 57.9
10 F	9 16 41.7	20 21.5	12 46.0	6♏24.7	13 33.8	3 50.2	7 2.1	9 9.8	14 2.0	13 59.1	22 46.6	29 56.6
11 S	9 20 38.3	21 22.2	12 42.8	19 19.2	15 16.0	4 54.6	7 38.3	9 24.0	14 7.6	14 0.1	22 45.3	29 55.4
12 S	9 24 34.8	22 22.9	12 39.7	1♐51.6	16 58.9	5 59.2	8 14.4	9 38.1	14 13.2	14 1.2	22 43.9	29 54.2
13 M	9 28 31.4	23 23.6	12 36.5	14 6.9	18 42.8	7 4.0	8 50.5	9 52.3	14 18.8	14 2.3	22 42.5	29 52.9
14 T	9 32 27.9	24 24.3	12 33.3	26 10.0	20 27.4	8 9.1	9 26.5	10 6.6	14 24.5	14 3.4	22 41.1	29 51.7
15 W	9 36 24.5	25 24.9	12 30.1	8♑ 5.4	22 13.0	9 14.4	10 2.5	10 20.8	14 30.3	14 4.6	22 39.7	29 50.5
16 T	9 40 21.0	26 25.5	12 27.0	19 56.9	23 59.4	10 20.0	10 38.4	10 35.1	14 36.2	14 5.9	22 38.2	29 49.3
17 F	9 44 17.6	27 26.1	12 23.8	1♒47.5	25 46.6	11 25.7	11 14.3	10 49.5	14 42.1	14 7.2	22 36.8	29 48.2
18 S	9 48 14.1	28 26.7	12 20.6	13 39.6	27 34.8	12 31.7	11 50.2	11 3.8	14 48.1	14 8.5	22 35.3	29 47.0
19 S	9 52 10.7	29 27.2	12 17.4	25 34.7	29 23.7	13 37.9	12 25.9	11 18.2	14 54.1	14 9.9	22 33.8	29 45.8
20 M	9 56 7.2	0♓27.7	12 14.2	7♓34.1	1♓13.5	14 44.2	13 1.7	11 32.5	15 0.2	14 11.4	22 32.3	29 44.7
21 T	10 0 3.8	1 28.2	12 11.1	19 39.0	3 4.1	15 50.8	13 37.4	11 46.9	15 6.4	14 12.9	22 30.8	29 43.6
22 W	10 4 0.3	2 28.7	12 7.9	1♈50.5	4 55.5	16 57.5	14 13.0	12 1.3	15 12.6	14 14.4	22 29.2	29 42.5
23 T	10 7 56.9	3 29.1	12 4.7	14 10.2	6 47.6	18 4.4	14 48.5	12 15.8	15 18.8	14 16.0	22 27.7	29 41.4
24 F	10 11 53.4	4 29.5	12 1.5	26 40.4	8 40.3	19 11.5	15 24.0	12 30.2	15 25.2	14 17.6	22 26.1	29 40.3
25 S	10 15 50.0	5 29.9	11 58.4	9♉23.7	10 33.6	20 18.7	15 59.5	12 44.7	15 31.5	14 19.3	22 24.6	29 39.3
26 S	10 19 46.6	6 30.3	11 55.2	22 23.3	12 27.3	21 26.1	16 34.9	12 59.2	15 38.0	14 21.0	22 23.0	29 38.2
27 M	10 23 43.1	7 30.6	11 52.0	5♊42.5	14 21.4	22 33.7	17 10.2	13 13.6	15 44.5	14 22.8	22 21.4	29 37.2
28 T	10 27 39.7	8 30.8	11 48.8	19 24.1	16 15.6	23 41.4	17 45.4	13 28.1	15 51.0	14 24.6	22 19.8	29 36.2

DECLINATION

DAY	SIDEREAL TIME	☉	☊	☽	☿	♀	♂	♃	♄	♅	♆	♇
1 W	8 41 12.7	17S24.5	15S49.1	20N 2.2	22S 0.2	19S48.1	19S48.3	9S50.0	3N 3.0	15N40.3	3N52.9	23N28.8
4 S	8 53 2.4	16 33.0	15 46.2	13 3.2	21 7.5	20 3.9	20 11.5	9 34.4	3 9.3	15 40.9	3 54.4	23 29.8
7 T	9 4 52.1	15 38.8	15 43.3	1S21.7	20 2.1	20 16.2	20 33.5	9 18.7	3 15.8	15 41.6	3 56.0	23 30.7
10 F	9 16 41.7	14 42.3	15 40.4	14 8.9	18 43.8	20 24.6	20 54.2	9 2.8	3 22.6	15 42.5	3 57.6	23 31.7
13 M	9 28 31.4	13 43.5	15 37.5	19 51.2	17 12.6	20 29.0	21 13.7	8 46.8	3 29.6	15 43.5	3 59.3	23 32.6
16 T	9 40 21.0	12 42.7	15 34.6	17 21.5	15 28.3	20 29.0	21 31.8	8 30.6	3 36.7	15 44.6	4 1.1	23 33.5
19 S	9 52 10.7	11 40.0	15 31.7	8 25.3	13 31.2	20 24.5	21 48.7	8 14.2	3 44.1	15 45.9	4 2.9	23 34.3
22 W	10 4 0.3	10 35.6	15 28.8	3N38.2	11 21.6	20 15.3	22 4.4	7 57.8	3 51.7	15 47.3	4 4.8	23 35.1
25 S	10 15 50.0	9 29.8	15 25.9	14 43.2	9 0.5	20 1.4	22 18.7	7 41.3	3 59.4	15 48.8	4 6.7	23 35.8
28 T	10 27 39.7	8 22.8	15 23.0	19 50.0	6 29.3	19 42.6	22 31.8	7 24.7	4 7.2	15 50.5	4 8.7	23 36.5

MARCH 1939

DAY	EPHEMERIS SIDEREAL TIME h m s	☉ ° ′	☊ ° ′	☽ ° ′	☿ ° ′	♀ ° ′	♂ ° ′	♃ ° ′	♄ ° ′	♅ ° ′	♆ ° ′	♇ ° ′
LONGITUDE												
1 W	10 31 36.2	9 ♓ 31.1	11 ♏ 45.6	3 ♋ 29.6	18 ♓ 9.8	24 ♑ 49.2	18 ♐ 20.6	13 ♓ 42.6	15 ♈ 57.6	14 ♉ 26.5	22 ♍ 18.2	29 ♋ 35.2
2 T	10 35 32.8	10 31.3	11 42.5	17 58.6	20 3.8	25 57.2	18 55.8	13 57.1	16 4.2	14 28.4	22 R 16.5	29 R 34.2
3 F	10 39 29.3	11 31.5	11 39.3	2 ♌ 47.8	21 57.3	27 5.3	19 30.9	14 11.6	16 10.9	14 30.3	22 14.9	29 33.3
4 S	10 43 25.9	12 31.6	11 36.1	17 50.7	23 50.0	28 13.6	20 5.9	14 26.1	16 17.6	14 32.3	22 13.3	29 32.4
5 S	10 47 22.4	13 31.7	11 32.9	2 ♍ 58.3	25 41.5	29 22.0	20 40.8	14 40.6	16 24.3	14 34.3	22 11.6	29 31.4
6 M	10 51 19.0	14 31.8	11 29.7	18 0.4	27 31.6	0 ♒ 30.5	21 15.7	14 55.1	16 31.2	14 36.4	22 10.0	29 30.6
7 T	10 55 15.5	15 31.8	11 26.6	2 ♎ 47.3	29 19.8	1 39.1	21 50.5	15 9.7	16 38.0	14 38.5	22 8.3	29 29.7
8 W	10 59 12.1	16 31.8	11 23.4	17 11.6	1 ♈ 5.7	2 47.9	22 25.3	15 24.2	16 44.9	14 40.7	22 6.7	29 28.8
9 T	11 3 8.6	17 31.8	11 20.2	1 ♏ 8.8	2 48.7	3 56.7	22 60.0	15 38.7	16 51.8	14 42.9	22 5.0	29 28.0
10 F	11 7 5.2	18 31.8	11 17.0	14 37.6	4 28.4	5 5.7	23 34.6	15 53.2	16 58.8	14 45.1	22 3.4	29 27.2
11 S	11 11 1.7	19 31.7	11 13.9	27 39.7	6 4.2	6 14.9	24 9.1	16 7.7	17 5.8	14 47.4	22 1.7	29 26.4
12 S	11 14 58.3	20 31.6	11 10.7	10 ♐ 18.1	7 35.7	7 24.1	24 43.6	16 22.2	17 12.8	14 49.7	22 0.0	29 25.6
13 M	11 18 54.8	21 31.5	11 7.5	22 37.5	9 2.3	8 33.4	25 18.0	16 36.7	17 19.9	14 52.0	21 58.4	29 24.9
14 T	11 22 51.4	22 31.3	11 4.3	4 ♑ 42.8	10 23.5	9 42.8	25 52.3	16 51.2	17 27.0	14 54.4	21 56.7	29 24.1
15 W	11 26 47.9	23 31.1	11 1.1	16 38.9	11 38.9	10 52.3	26 26.5	17 5.6	17 34.1	14 56.9	21 55.0	29 23.4
16 T	11 30 44.5	24 30.9	10 58.0	28 30.4	12 47.9	12 2.0	27 0.6	17 20.1	17 41.3	14 59.3	21 53.4	29 22.7
17 F	11 34 41.1	25 30.7	10 54.8	10 ♒ 21.4	13 50.2	13 11.7	27 34.6	17 34.6	17 48.5	15 1.8	21 51.7	29 22.1
18 S	11 38 37.6	26 30.4	10 51.6	22 15.3	14 45.3	14 21.4	28 8.6	17 49.0	17 55.8	15 4.4	21 50.0	29 21.4
19 S	11 42 34.1	27 30.1	10 48.4	4 ♓ 14.6	15 33.1	15 31.3	28 42.4	18 3.4	18 3.0	15 6.9	21 48.4	29 20.8
20 M	11 46 30.7	28 29.8	10 45.3	16 21.5	16 13.2	16 41.3	29 16.2	18 17.8	18 10.3	15 9.5	21 46.7	29 20.2
21 T	11 50 27.3	29 29.4	10 42.1	28 37.1	16 45.4	17 51.3	29 49.8	18 32.2	18 17.6	15 12.2	21 45.1	29 19.6
22 W	11 54 23.8	0 ♈ 29.0	10 38.9	11 ♈ 2.6	17 9.7	19 1.4	0 ♑ 23.4	18 46.6	18 25.0	15 14.8	21 43.4	29 19.1
23 T	11 58 20.4	1 28.6	10 35.7	23 38.5	17 25.9	20 11.6	0 56.8	19 0.9	18 32.3	15 17.5	21 41.8	29 18.6
24 F	12 2 16.9	2 28.1	10 32.5	6 ♉ 25.8	17 34.1	21 21.8	1 30.2	19 15.3	18 39.7	15 20.3	21 40.1	29 18.1
25 S	12 6 13.5	3 27.6	10 29.4	19 25.2	17 34.5	22 32.1	2 3.4	19 29.6	18 47.1	15 23.0	21 38.5	29 17.6
26 S	12 10 10.0	4 27.1	10 26.2	2 ♊ 38.1	17 R 27.3	23 42.5	2 36.5	19 43.9	18 54.5	15 25.8	21 36.9	29 17.1
27 M	12 14 6.6	5 26.5	10 23.0	16 5.6	17 12.7	24 52.9	3 9.5	19 58.1	19 2.0	15 28.7	21 35.3	29 16.7
28 T	12 18 3.1	6 25.9	10 19.8	29 48.7	16 51.3	26 3.4	3 42.4	20 12.4	19 9.4	15 31.5	21 33.7	29 16.3
29 W	12 21 59.7	7 25.2	10 16.7	13 ♋ 48.1	16 23.7	27 14.0	4 15.2	20 26.6	19 16.9	15 34.4	21 32.1	29 15.9
30 T	12 25 56.2	8 24.5	10 13.5	28 3.1	15 50.3	28 24.6	4 47.9	20 40.7	19 24.4	15 37.3	21 30.5	29 15.6
31 F	12 29 52.8	9 23.8	10 10.3	12 ♌ 31.5	15 12.2	29 35.3	5 20.4	20 54.9	19 31.9	15 40.2	21 28.9	29 15.2
DECLINATION												
1 W	10 31 36.2	8 S 0.2	15 S 22.0	19 N 20.2	5 S 37.0	19 S 35.2	22 S 35.8	7 S 19.1	4 N 9.9	15 N 51.0	4 N 9.3	23 N 36.7
4 S	10 43 25.9	6 51.7	15 19.1	10 41.7	2 56.7	19 10.0	22 47.2	7 2.4	4 17.9	15 52.8	4 11.3	23 37.4
7 T	10 55 15.5	5 42.3	15 16.1	3 S 55.4	0 14.8	18 40.0	22 57.3	6 45.7	4 26.0	15 54.7	4 13.3	23 38.0
10 F	11 7 5.2	4 32.3	15 13.2	15 48.0	2 N 22.4	18 5.3	23 6.2	6 29.0	4 34.2	15 56.7	4 15.3	23 38.5
13 M	11 18 54.8	3 21.7	15 10.2	19 44.1	4 47.3	17 25.9	23 13.8	6 12.2	4 42.6	15 58.8	4 17.3	23 39.0
16 T	11 30 44.5	2 10.7	15 7.2	15 31.5	6 51.9	16 42.1	23 20.3	5 55.4	4 51.0	16 1.0	4 19.3	23 39.4
19 S	11 42 34.1	0 59.6	15 4.3	5 36.8	8 28.9	15 53.9	23 25.6	5 38.7	4 59.4	16 3.3	4 21.3	23 39.8
22 W	11 54 23.8	0 N 11.6	15 1.3	6 N 35.4	9 32.6	15 1.7	23 29.7	5 21.9	5 8.0	16 5.7	4 23.2	23 40.2
25 S	12 6 13.5	1 22.6	14 58.3	16 39.6	9 58.9	14 5.6	23 32.8	5 5.3	5 16.5	16 8.1	4 25.2	23 40.4
28 T	12 18 3.1	2 33.2	14 55.3	19 23.4	9 46.8	13 5.9	23 34.9	4 48.7	5 25.1	16 10.6	4 27.1	23 40.7
31 F	12 29 52.8	3 43.5	14 52.3	12 3.3	8 58.8	12 2.7	23 35.9	4 32.2	5 33.7	16 13.2	4 29.0	23 40.8

APRIL 1939

DAY	EPHEMERIS SIDEREAL TIME h m s	☉ ° ′	☊ ° ′	☽ ° ′	☿ ° ′	♀ ° ′	♂ ° ′	♃ ° ′	♄ ° ′	♅ ° ′	♆ ° ′	♇ ° ′
LONGITUDE												
1 S	12 33 49.3	10 ♈ 23.0	10 ♏ 7.1	27 ♌ 9.2	14 ♈ 29.9	0 ♓ 46.0	5 ♑ 52.8	21 ♓ 9.0	19 ♈ 39.4	15 ♉ 43.2	21 ♍ 27.4	29 ♋ 14.9
2 S	12 37 45.9	11 22.2	10 3.9	11 ♍ 50.5	13 R 44.6	1 56.7	6 25.1	21 23.1	19 47.0	15 46.2	21 R 25.8	29 R 14.6
3 M	12 41 42.4	12 21.3	10 0.8	26 28.6	12 57.1	3 7.6	6 57.3	21 37.1	19 54.5	15 49.2	21 24.3	29 14.4
4 T	12 45 39.0	13 20.4	9 57.6	10 ♎ 56.5	12 8.4	4 18.5	7 29.3	21 51.1	20 2.1	15 52.2	21 22.8	29 14.2
5 W	12 49 35.6	14 19.5	9 54.4	25 8.0	11 19.6	5 29.4	8 1.2	22 5.1	20 9.6	15 55.3	21 21.2	29 14.0
6 T	12 53 32.1	15 18.5	9 51.2	8 ♏ 58.8	10 31.5	6 40.4	8 33.0	22 19.0	20 17.2	15 58.4	21 19.7	29 13.8
7 F	12 57 28.6	16 17.6	9 48.0	22 26.5	9 45.0	7 51.4	9 4.6	22 32.9	20 24.7	16 1.5	21 18.3	29 13.6
8 S	13 1 25.2	17 16.5	9 44.9	5 ♐ 30.8	9 1.0	9 2.5	9 36.1	22 46.8	20 32.3	16 4.6	21 16.8	29 13.5
9 S	13 5 21.7	18 15.5	9 41.7	18 13.4	8 20.1	10 13.7	10 7.5	23 0.6	20 39.9	16 7.8	21 15.3	29 13.4
10 M	13 9 18.3	19 14.4	9 38.5	0 ♑ 37.3	7 43.0	11 24.9	10 38.7	23 14.4	20 47.5	16 11.0	21 13.9	29 13.3
11 T	13 13 14.9	20 13.3	9 35.3	12 46.6	7 10.2	12 36.1	11 9.7	23 28.1	20 55.1	16 14.1	21 12.5	29 13.3
12 W	13 17 11.4	21 12.2	9 32.2	24 45.5	6 41.9	13 47.4	11 40.6	23 41.8	21 2.7	16 17.4	21 11.1	29 13.3
13 T	13 21 8.0	22 11.0	9 29.0	6 ♒ 39.0	6 18.6	14 58.7	12 11.3	23 55.5	21 10.3	16 20.6	21 9.7	29 D 13.3
14 F	13 25 4.5	23 9.8	9 25.8	18 31.6	6 0.4	16 10.1	12 41.9	24 9.1	21 17.9	16 23.8	21 8.3	29 13.3
15 S	13 29 1.1	24 8.6	9 22.6	0 ♓ 27.5	5 47.5	17 21.5	13 12.2	24 22.6	21 25.4	16 27.1	21 7.0	29 13.3
16 S	13 32 57.6	25 7.3	9 19.4	12 30.6	5 39.7	18 32.9	13 42.4	24 36.1	21 33.0	16 30.4	21 5.7	29 13.4
17 M	13 36 54.2	26 6.0	9 16.3	24 43.9	5 37.3	19 44.4	14 12.4	24 49.6	21 40.6	16 33.7	21 4.4	29 13.5
18 T	13 40 50.7	27 4.7	9 13.1	7 ♈ 9.7	5 D 40.0	20 55.9	14 42.2	25 3.0	21 48.2	16 37.0	21 3.1	29 13.7
19 W	13 44 47.3	28 3.4	9 9.9	19 49.6	5 47.8	22 7.5	15 11.9	25 16.3	21 55.7	16 40.3	21 1.8	29 13.8
20 T	13 48 43.8	29 2.0	9 6.7	2 ♉ 44.3	6 0.5	23 19.0	15 41.3	25 29.6	22 3.3	16 43.7	21 0.6	29 14.0
21 F	13 52 40.4	0 ♉ 0.6	9 3.6	15 53.6	6 18.0	24 30.6	16 10.5	25 42.8	22 10.9	16 47.0	20 59.4	29 14.2
22 S	13 56 36.9	0 59.2	9 0.4	29 16.9	6 40.2	25 42.3	16 39.5	25 56.0	22 18.4	16 50.4	20 58.2	29 14.4
23 S	14 0 33.5	1 57.7	8 57.2	12 ♊ 53.2	7 6.7	26 53.9	17 8.2	26 9.1	22 25.9	16 53.8	20 57.0	29 14.7
24 M	14 4 30.1	2 56.2	8 54.0	26 40.9	7 37.6	28 5.6	17 36.8	26 22.2	22 33.4	16 57.2	20 55.8	29 15.0
25 T	14 8 26.6	3 54.6	8 50.9	10 ♋ 38.5	8 12.5	29 17.3	18 5.2	26 35.2	22 40.9	17 0.6	20 54.7	29 15.3
26 W	14 12 23.1	4 53.0	8 47.7	24 44.2	8 51.3	0 ♈ 29.1	18 33.3	26 48.1	22 48.4	17 4.0	20 53.6	29 15.6
27 T	14 16 19.7	5 51.4	8 44.5	8 ♌ 55.9	9 33.8	1 40.8	19 1.1	27 1.0	22 55.9	17 7.4	20 52.5	29 16.0
28 F	14 20 16.3	6 49.8	8 41.3	23 11.4	10 20.0	2 52.6	19 28.8	27 13.8	23 3.4	17 10.8	20 51.5	29 16.4
29 S	14 24 12.8	7 48.1	8 38.1	7 ♍ 28.0	11 9.5	4 4.4	19 56.2	27 26.5	23 10.8	17 14.3	20 50.5	29 16.8
30 S	14 28 9.4	8 46.4	8 35.0	21 42.6	12 2.4	5 16.3	20 23.3	27 39.1	23 18.2	17 17.7	20 49.4	29 17.3
DECLINATION												
1 S	12 33 49.3	4 N 6.7	14 S 51.3	7 N 48.7	8 N 36.0	11 S 41.0	23 S 36.1	4 S 26.7	5 N 36.6	16 N 14.1	4 N 29.6	23 N 40.9
4 T	12 45 39.0	5 16.0	14 48.3	6 S 33.7	7 13.1	10 33.7	23 35.9	4 10.3	5 45.1	16 16.7	4 31.4	23 41.0
7 F	12 57 28.6	6 24.5	14 45.3	17 9.4	5 38.7	9 23.6	23 34.8	3 54.1	5 53.7	16 19.5	4 33.1	23 41.1
10 M	13 9 18.3	7 32.0	14 42.3	19 17.5	4 6.8	8 11.0	23 32.9	3 38.0	6 2.3	16 22.2	4 34.8	23 41.1
13 T	13 21 8.0	8 38.4	14 39.3	13 31.3	2 48.3	6 56.2	23 30.4	3 22.0	6 10.8	16 25.0	4 36.4	23 41.0
16 S	13 32 57.6	9 43.5	14 36.2	2 50.0	1 50.2	5 39.3	23 27.2	3 6.2	6 19.2	16 27.9	4 38.0	23 40.9
19 W	13 44 47.3	10 47.1	14 33.2	9 N 18.8	1 15.1	4 20.9	23 23.4	2 50.6	6 27.6	16 30.7	4 39.5	23 40.8
22 S	13 56 36.9	11 49.2	14 30.2	18 9.5	1 3.4	3 1.0	23 19.2	2 35.2	6 35.9	16 33.6	4 40.9	23 40.6
25 T	14 8 26.6	12 49.5	14 27.1	18 21.3	1 13.5	1 40.1	23 14.6	2 20.0	6 44.2	16 36.6	4 42.2	23 40.3
28 F	14 20 16.3	13 47.9	14 24.1	8 57.5	1 43.4	0 18.5	23 9.7	2 5.1	6 52.3	16 39.5	4 43.4	23 40.0

MAY 1939

DAY	EPHEMERIS SIDEREAL TIME h m s	☉ ° ′	☊ ° ′	☽ ° ′	☿ ° ′	♀ ° ′	♂ ° ′	♃ ° ′	♄ ° ′	♅ ° ′	♆ ° ′	♇ ° ′
						LONGITUDE						
1 M	14 32 5.9	9♉44.6	8♏31.8	5♎51.6	12♈58.4	6♈28.1	20♑50.2	27♓51.7	23♈25.6	17♉21.2	20♍48.5	29♋17.7
2 T	14 36 2.5	10 42.8	8 28.6	19 51.5	13 57.4	7 40.0	21 16.9	28 4.2	23 33.0	17 24.6	20R47.5	29 18.2
3 W	14 39 59.0	11 41.0	8 25.4	3♏39.1	14 59.3	8 51.9	21 43.3	28 16.7	23 40.4	17 28.1	20 46.6	29 18.7
4 T	14 43 55.6	12 39.1	8 22.2	17 11.5	16 4.1	10 3.8	22 9.4	28 29.1	23 47.7	17 31.5	20 45.7	29 19.2
5 F	14 47 52.1	13 37.3	8 19.1	0♐26.7	17 11.5	11 15.8	22 35.2	28 41.3	23 55.0	17 35.0	20 44.8	29 19.8
6 S	14 51 48.7	14 35.3	8 15.9	13 24.1	18 21.6	12 27.8	23 0.8	28 53.6	24 2.3	17 38.5	20 44.0	29 20.4
7 S	14 55 45.2	15 33.4	8 12.7	26 3.9	19 34.2	13 39.8	23 26.0	29 5.7	24 9.5	17 42.0	20 43.2	29 21.0
8 M	14 59 41.8	16 31.5	8 9.5	8♑27.8	20 49.3	14 51.8	23 51.0	29 17.8	24 16.8	17 45.4	20 42.4	29 21.6
9 T	15 3 38.4	17 29.5	8 6.4	20 38.3	22 6.8	16 3.8	24 15.6	29 29.7	24 24.0	17 48.9	20 41.6	29 22.3
10 W	15 7 34.9	18 27.5	8 3.2	2♒38.8	23 26.7	17 15.9	24 39.9	29 41.6	24 31.2	17 52.4	20 40.9	29 23.0
11 T	15 11 31.4	19 25.4	8 0.0	14 33.5	24 48.9	18 28.0	25 3.9	29 53.5	24 38.3	17 55.8	20 40.2	29 23.7
12 F	15 15 28.0	20 23.4	7 56.8	26 26.8	26 13.3	19 40.1	25 27.6	0♈ 5.2	24 45.4	17 59.3	20 39.5	29 24.4
13 S	15 19 24.6	21 21.3	7 53.7	8♓23.4	27 40.0	20 52.3	25 50.9	0 16.8	24 52.5	18 2.8	20 38.9	29 25.2
14 S	15 23 21.1	22 19.2	7 50.5	20 27.8	29 8.9	22 4.4	26 13.8	0 28.4	24 59.6	18 6.3	20 38.3	29 25.9
15 M	15 27 17.7	23 17.1	7 47.3	2♈44.3	0♉39.9	23 16.6	26 36.4	0 39.9	25 6.6	18 9.7	20 37.7	29 26.7
16 T	15 31 14.2	24 15.0	7 44.1	15 16.4	2 13.2	24 28.8	26 58.6	0 51.2	25 13.6	18 13.2	20 37.2	29 27.5
17 W	15 35 10.8	25 12.8	7 40.9	28 6.9	3 48.6	25 41.1	27 20.4	1 2.5	25 20.5	18 16.7	20 36.6	29 28.4
18 T	15 39 7.4	26 10.7	7 37.8	11♉17.2	5 26.2	26 53.3	27 41.8	1 13.7	25 27.4	18 20.1	20 36.2	29 29.3
19 F	15 43 3.9	27 8.5	7 34.6	24 47.4	7 5.9	28 5.6	28 2.8	1 24.8	25 34.3	18 23.6	20 35.7	29 30.1
20 S	15 47 0.5	28 6.2	7 31.4	8♊36.0	8 47.7	29 17.8	28 23.4	1 35.8	25 41.1	18 27.0	20 35.3	29 31.0
21 S	15 50 57.0	29 4.0	7 28.2	22 39.9	10 31.7	0♉30.1	28 43.6	1 46.7	25 47.9	18 30.4	20 34.9	29 32.0
22 M	15 54 53.6	0♊ 1.7	7 25.1	6♋55.0	12 17.9	1 42.4	29 3.3	1 57.5	25 54.7	18 33.9	20 34.5	29 32.9
23 T	15 58 50.1	0 59.4	7 21.9	21 16.4	14 6.2	2 54.7	29 22.6	2 8.2	26 1.4	18 37.3	20 34.2	29 33.9
24 W	16 2 46.7	1 57.1	7 18.7	5♌39.4	15 56.6	4 7.1	29 41.4	2 18.7	26 8.0	18 40.7	20 33.9	29 34.9
25 T	16 6 43.2	2 54.8	7 15.5	19 59.6	17 49.1	5 19.4	29 59.8	2 29.2	26 14.7	18 44.1	20 33.6	29 35.9
26 F	16 10 39.8	3 52.4	7 12.3	4♍13.7	19 43.7	6 31.8	0♒17.7	2 39.6	26 21.2	18 47.5	20 33.4	29 36.9
27 S	16 14 36.3	4 50.0	7 9.2	18 19.4	21 40.4	7 44.2	0 35.1	2 49.9	26 27.8	18 50.9	20 33.2	29 38.0
28 S	16 18 32.9	5 47.6	7 6.0	2♎15.1	23 39.1	8 56.5	0 52.0	2 60.0	26 34.2	18 54.2	20 33.0	29 39.1
29 M	16 22 29.5	6 45.1	7 2.8	15 59.9	25 39.8	10 8.9	1 8.4	3 10.0	26 40.7	18 57.6	20 32.9	29 40.1
30 T	16 26 26.0	7 42.7	6 59.6	29 33.3	27 42.3	11 21.4	1 24.4	3 20.0	26 47.0	19 0.9	20 32.8	29 41.3
31 W	16 30 22.6	8 40.2	6 56.5	12♏54.8	29 46.7	12 33.8	1 39.8	3 29.8	26 53.4	19 4.3	20 32.7	29 42.4
						DECLINATION						
1 M	14 32 5.9	14N44.2	14S21.0	4S56.6	2N31.0	1N 3.7	23S 4.7	1S50.4	7N 0.3	16N42.4	4N44.5	23N39.7
4 T	14 43 55.6	15 38.3	14 17.9	16 11.8	3 34.2	2 26.1	22 59.6	1 36.0	7 8.3	16 45.4	4 45.6	23 39.3
7 S	14 55 45.2	16 30.2	14 14.9	19 28.9	4 51.1	3 48.4	22 54.5	1 21.8	7 16.1	16 48.3	4 46.5	23 38.9
10 W	15 7 34.9	17 19.5	14 11.8	14 27.5	6 19.9	5 10.2	22 49.6	1 8.0	7 23.7	16 51.2	4 47.3	23 38.4
13 S	15 19 24.6	18 6.3	14 8.7	4 11.1	7 58.9	6 31.4	22 45.0	0 54.5	7 31.3	16 54.2	4 48.0	23 37.9
16 T	15 31 14.2	18 50.3	14 5.6	7N55.7	9 46.4	7 51.6	22 40.9	0 41.3	7 38.6	16 57.1	4 48.6	23 37.3
19 F	15 43 3.9	19 31.5	14 2.5	17 31.8	11 40.7	9 10.5	22 37.4	0 28.5	7 45.8	16 60.0	4 49.1	23 36.8
22 M	15 54 53.6	20 9.7	13 59.4	18 47.8	13 39.7	10 27.7	22 34.6	0 16.0	7 52.9	17 2.8	4 49.5	23 36.1
25 T	16 6 43.2	20 44.8	13 56.3	9 57.1	15 40.9	11 43.0	22 32.7	0 3.9	7 59.7	17 5.6	4 49.8	23 35.5
28 S	16 18 32.9	21 16.6	13 53.2	3S43.2	17 41.2	12 56.1	22 31.8	0N 7.7	8 6.4	17 8.4	4 49.9	23 34.8
31 W	16 30 22.6	21 45.2	13 50.1	15 18.8	19 36.5	14 6.6	22 32.0	0 19.0	8 12.8	17 11.2	4 50.0	23 34.0

JUNE 1939

DAY	EPHEMERIS SIDEREAL TIME h m s	☉ ° ′	☊ ° ′	☽ ° ′	☿ ° ′	♀ ° ′	♂ ° ′	♃ ° ′	♄ ° ′	♅ ° ′	♆ ° ′	♇ ° ′
						LONGITUDE						
1 T	16 34 19.1	9♊37.7	6♏53.3	26♏ 3.9	1♊52.7	13♉46.3	1♒54.6	3♈39.5	26♈59.7	19♉ 7.6	20♍32.7	29♋43.5
2 F	16 38 15.7	10 35.1	6 50.1	9♐ 0.2	4 0.2	14 58.7	2 9.0	3 49.0	27 5.9	19 10.9	20R32.6	29 44.7
3 S	16 42 12.2	11 32.6	6 46.9	21 43.4	6 9.0	16 11.2	2 22.7	3 58.5	27 12.1	19 14.1	20D32.7	29 45.9
4 S	16 46 8.8	12 30.0	6 43.8	4♑13.7	8 19.0	17 23.7	2 35.9	4 7.8	27 18.2	19 17.4	20 32.7	29 47.1
5 M	16 50 5.3	13 27.4	6 40.6	16 31.9	10 29.9	18 36.2	2 48.5	4 17.1	27 24.2	19 20.7	20 32.8	29 48.3
6 T	16 54 1.9	14 24.9	6 37.4	28 39.4	12 41.5	19 48.8	3 0.6	4 26.2	27 30.2	19 23.9	20 32.9	29 49.6
7 W	16 57 58.4	15 22.2	6 34.2	10♒38.5	14 53.5	21 1.3	3 12.0	4 35.1	27 36.2	19 27.1	20 33.1	29 50.8
8 T	17 1 55.0	16 19.6	6 31.0	22 32.4	17 5.6	22 13.9	3 22.8	4 44.0	27 42.1	19 30.3	20 33.3	29 52.1
9 F	17 5 51.6	17 17.0	6 27.9	4♓24.9	19 17.5	23 26.5	3 32.9	4 52.7	27 47.9	19 33.5	20 33.5	29 53.4
10 S	17 9 48.1	18 14.4	6 24.7	16 20.3	21 29.1	24 39.2	3 42.4	5 1.3	27 53.7	19 36.6	20 33.7	29 54.7
11 S	17 13 44.7	19 11.7	6 21.5	28 23.5	23 40.0	25 51.8	3 51.3	5 9.7	27 59.4	19 39.8	20 34.0	29 56.0
12 M	17 17 41.2	20 9.1	6 18.3	10♈39.3	25 50.0	27 4.5	3 59.5	5 18.0	28 5.0	19 42.9	20 34.3	29 57.3
13 T	17 21 37.8	21 6.4	6 15.2	23 12.5	27 58.8	28 17.1	4 7.0	5 26.2	28 10.6	19 46.0	20 34.7	29 58.7
14 W	17 25 34.4	22 3.8	6 12.0	6♉ 7.0	0♋ 6.2	29 29.9	4 13.8	5 34.2	28 16.2	19 49.1	20 35.1	0♌ 0.0
15 T	17 29 30.9	23 1.1	6 8.8	19 25.7	2 12.1	0♊42.6	4 19.8	5 42.2	28 21.6	19 52.1	20 35.5	0 1.4
16 F	17 33 27.5	23 58.4	6 5.6	3♊ 9.6	4 16.4	1 55.3	4 25.2	5 49.9	28 27.0	19 55.1	20 35.9	0 2.8
17 S	17 37 24.0	24 55.7	6 2.5	17 17.4	6 18.7	3 8.1	4 29.9	5 57.5	28 32.3	19 58.1	20 36.4	0 4.2
18 S	17 41 20.5	25 53.0	5 59.3	1♋45.4	8 19.2	4 20.8	4 33.8	6 5.0	28 37.6	20 1.1	20 36.9	0 5.6
19 M	17 45 17.1	26 50.3	5 56.1	16 27.2	10 17.6	5 33.6	4 37.0	6 12.3	28 42.7	20 4.1	20 37.4	0 7.1
20 T	17 49 13.7	27 47.6	5 52.9	1♌15.2	12 13.9	6 46.5	4 39.4	6 19.5	28 47.9	20 7.0	20 38.0	0 8.5
21 W	17 53 10.3	28 44.9	5 49.8	16 1.3	14 8.1	7 59.3	4 41.1	6 26.5	28 52.9	20 9.9	20 38.6	0 10.0
22 T	17 57 6.8	29 42.1	5 46.6	0♍38.4	16 0.1	9 12.1	4 42.0	6 33.4	28 57.9	20 12.7	20 39.2	0 11.5
23 F	18 1 3.3	0♋39.4	5 43.4	15 1.4	17 49.9	10 25.0	4 42.2	6 40.1	29 2.8	20 15.6	20 39.9	0 13.0
24 S	18 4 59.9	1 36.6	5 40.2	29 7.3	19 37.4	11 37.9	4R41.7	6 46.7	29 7.6	20 18.4	20 40.6	0 14.5
25 S	18 8 56.5	2 33.8	5 37.0	12♎55.2	21 22.7	12 50.8	4 40.4	6 53.1	29 12.3	20 21.2	20 41.3	0 16.0
26 M	18 12 53.1	3 31.1	5 33.9	26 25.8	23 5.7	14 3.7	4 38.4	6 59.3	29 17.0	20 23.9	20 42.1	0 17.5
27 T	18 16 49.6	4 28.3	5 30.7	9♏40.6	24 46.4	15 16.6	4 35.6	7 5.4	29 21.6	20 26.7	20 42.9	0 19.0
28 W	18 20 46.1	5 25.5	5 27.5	22 41.3	26 24.9	16 29.5	4 32.1	7 11.3	29 26.1	20 29.4	20 43.7	0 20.6
29 T	18 24 42.7	6 22.6	5 24.3	5♐29.7	28 1.0	17 42.5	4 27.8	7 17.1	29 30.5	20 32.0	20 44.5	0 22.1
30 F	18 28 39.3	7 19.8	5 21.2	18 7.0	29 34.9	18 55.5	4 22.8	7 22.7	29 34.9	20 34.7	20 45.4	0 23.7
						DECLINATION						
1 T	16 34 19.1	21N54.0	13S49.0	17S43.3	20N13.0	14N29.4	22S32.3	0N22.6	8N15.0	17N12.1	4N50.0	23N33.8
4 S	16 46 8.8	22 18.0	13 45.9	19 4.2	21 53.8	15 36.0	22 34.2	0 33.3	8 21.1	17 14.8	4 49.9	23 33.0
7 W	16 57 58.4	22 38.5	13 42.8	12 35.7	23 17.6	16 39.3	22 37.5	0 43.4	8 27.1	17 17.4	4 49.6	23 32.3
10 S	17 9 48.1	22 55.5	13 39.6	1 39.9	24 19.6	17 39.0	22 42.5	0 53.2	8 32.8	17 20.0	4 49.3	23 31.4
13 T	17 21 37.8	23 8.8	13 36.5	10N13.2	24 57.0	18 34.7	22 49.1	1 2.4	8 38.4	17 22.5	4 48.8	23 30.6
16 F	17 33 27.5	23 18.5	13 33.3	18 36.8	25 9.4	19 26.2	22 57.4	1 11.1	8 43.6	17 25.0	4 48.3	23 29.7
19 M	17 45 17.1	23 24.4	13 30.2	17 41.2	24 58.3	20 13.2	23 7.5	1 19.2	8 48.6	17 27.3	4 47.6	23 28.9
22 T	17 57 6.8	23 26.7	13 27.0	6 51.7	24 26.6	20 55.4	23 19.4	1 26.8	8 53.4	17 29.7	4 46.8	23 28.0
25 S	18 8 56.5	23 25.2	13 23.9	7S 1.5	23 37.6	21 32.5	23 32.9	1 33.9	8 57.9	17 31.9	4 45.9	23 27.1
28 W	18 20 46.1	23 20.0	13 20.7	17 6.4	22 34.7	22 4.4	23 48.1	1 40.4	9 2.1	17 34.1	4 44.9	23 26.1

JULY 1939

DAY	EPHEMERIS SIDEREAL TIME	☉	☊	☽	☿	♀	♂	♃	♄	♅	♆	♇
	h m s	° ′	° ′	° ′	° ′	° ′	° ′	° ′	° ′	° ′	° ′	° ′
LONGITUDE												
1 S	18 32 35.8	8♋17.0	5♏18.0	0♑34.1	1♌ 6.5	20♊ 8.5	4♒17.1	7♈28.1	29♈39.1	20♉37.2	20♍46.3	0♌25.2
2 S	18 36 32.4	9 14.2	5 14.8	12 52.0	2 35.7	21 21.5	4R 10.6	7 33.4	29 43.3	20 39.8	20 47.3	0 26.8
3 M	18 40 28.9	10 11.4	5 11.6	25 1.2	4 2.6	22 34.6	4 3.5	7 38.5	29 47.5	20 42.4	20 48.2	0 28.4
4 T	18 44 25.5	11 8.6	5 8.5	7♒ 3.0	5 27.1	23 47.7	3 55.6	7 43.4	29 51.5	20 44.9	20 49.2	0 30.0
5 W	18 48 22.0	12 5.7	5 5.3	18 58.7	6 49.2	25 0.7	3 47.0	7 48.2	29 55.4	20 47.3	20 50.3	0 31.6
6 T	18 52 18.6	13 2.9	5 2.1	0♓50.6	8 8.9	26 13.9	3 37.8	7 52.8	29 59.3	20 49.7	20 51.3	0 33.2
7 F	18 56 15.2	14 0.1	4 58.9	12 41.7	9 26.1	27 27.0	3 27.8	7 57.2	0♉ 3.1	20 52.1	20 52.4	0 34.8
8 S	19 0 11.7	14 57.3	4 55.7	24 35.6	10 40.7	28 40.2	3 17.3	8 1.4	0 6.8	20 54.5	20 53.5	0 36.4
9 S	19 4 8.3	15 54.5	4 52.6	6♈36.8	11 52.8	29 53.4	3 6.1	8 5.5	0 10.4	20 56.8	20 54.7	0 38.1
10 M	19 8 4.8	16 51.7	4 49.4	18 50.1	13 2.2	1♋ 6.6	2 54.3	8 9.4	0 13.9	20 59.1	20 55.8	0 39.7
11 T	19 12 1.4	17 48.9	4 46.2	1♉20.7	14 8.9	2 19.8	2 41.9	8 13.1	0 17.3	21 1.4	20 57.0	0 41.4
12 W	19 15 58.0	18 46.1	4 43.0	14 13.4	15 12.7	3 33.1	2 28.9	8 16.6	0 20.6	21 3.6	20 58.3	0 43.0
13 T	19 19 54.5	19 43.3	4 39.9	27 32.3	16 13.7	4 46.4	2 15.5	8 20.0	0 23.9	21 5.8	20 59.5	0 44.7
14 F	19 23 51.1	20 40.6	4 36.7	11♊19.7	17 11.6	5 59.7	2 1.5	8 23.1	0 27.0	21 7.9	21 0.8	0 46.3
15 S	19 27 47.6	21 37.8	4 33.5	25 35.6	18 6.5	7 13.1	1 47.1	8 26.1	0 30.1	21 10.0	21 2.1	0 48.0
16 S	19 31 44.2	22 35.1	4 30.3	10♋16.6	18 58.1	8 26.5	1 32.2	8 28.8	0 33.1	21 12.1	21 3.4	0 49.6
17 M	19 35 40.7	23 32.3	4 27.2	25 16.2	19 46.4	9 39.8	1 17.0	8 31.4	0 35.9	21 14.1	21 4.8	0 51.3
18 T	19 39 37.3	24 29.6	4 24.0	10♌24.9	20 31.2	10 53.3	1 1.4	8 33.8	0 38.7	21 16.1	21 6.2	0 53.0
19 W	19 43 33.9	25 26.9	4 20.8	25 32.3	21 12.3	12 6.7	0 45.6	8 36.0	0 41.4	21 18.0	21 7.6	0 54.6
20 T	19 47 30.4	26 24.1	4 17.6	10♍28.5	21 49.6	13 20.2	0 29.5	8 38.0	0 44.0	21 19.9	21 9.0	0 56.3
21 F	19 51 26.9	27 21.4	4 14.4	25 6.2	22 23.1	14 33.6	0 13.2	8 39.9	0 46.5	21 21.7	21 10.5	0 58.0
22 S	19 55 23.5	28 18.7	4 11.3	9♎20.9	22 52.4	15 47.1	29♑56.7	8 41.5	0 48.9	21 23.6	21 12.0	0 59.7
23 S	19 59 20.1	29 16.0	4 8.1	23 11.3	23 17.4	17 0.7	29 40.2	8 42.9	0 51.2	21 25.3	21 13.5	1 1.4
24 M	20 3 16.7	0♌13.3	4 4.9	6♏38.4	23 38.0	18 14.2	29 23.6	8 44.2	0 53.4	21 27.1	21 15.0	1 3.0
25 T	20 7 13.1	1 10.6	4 1.7	19 44.8	23 54.0	19 27.8	29 7.0	8 45.2	0 55.5	21 28.7	21 16.6	1 4.7
26 W	20 11 9.7	2 7.9	3 58.6	2♐33.6	24 5.3	20 41.4	28 50.4	8 46.1	0 57.5	21 30.4	21 18.1	1 6.4
27 T	20 15 6.3	3 5.2	3 55.4	15 8.0	24 11.7	21 55.0	28 33.9	8 46.7	0 59.4	21 32.0	21 19.7	1 8.1
28 F	20 19 2.9	4 2.5	3 52.2	27 31.0	24 13.1	23 8.6	28 17.5	8 47.2	1 1.2	21 33.5	21 21.4	1 9.8
29 S	20 22 59.4	4 59.8	3 49.0	9♑44.9	24R 9.5	24 22.3	28 1.3	8 47.4	1 2.9	21 35.0	21 23.0	1 11.4
30 S	20 26 55.9	5 57.2	3 45.8	21 51.5	24 0.7	25 36.0	27 45.3	8 47.5	1 4.5	21 36.5	21 24.7	1 13.1
31 M	20 30 52.5	6 54.5	3 42.7	3♒52.1	23 46.8	26 49.7	27 29.5	8R 47.4	1 6.0	21 37.9	21 26.4	1 14.8
DECLINATION												
1 S	18 32 35.8	23N 11.2	13S 17.5	19S 21.1	21N 21.3	22N 30.7	24S 4.6	1N 46.2	9N 6.1	17N 36.2	4N 43.7	23N 25.2
4 T	18 44 25.5	22 58.7	13 14.3	13 37.9	20 0.4	22 51.3	24 22.4	1 51.5	9 9.7	17 38.2	4 42.5	23 24.3
7 F	18 56 15.2	22 42.5	13 11.1	3 3.8	18 34.6	23 6.0	24 41.2	1 56.2	9 13.1	17 40.1	4 41.2	23 23.3
10 M	19 8 4.8	22 22.9	13 7.9	8N 43.8	17 6.7	23 14.7	25 0.6	2 0.2	9 16.2	17 41.9	4 39.8	23 22.4
13 T	19 19 54.5	21 59.7	13 4.7	17 45.9	15 39.1	23 17.3	25 20.3	2 3.5	9 19.0	17 43.6	4 38.3	23 21.4
16 S	19 31 44.2	21 33.2	13 1.5	18 30.3	14 14.5	23 13.8	25 39.8	2 6.2	9 21.5	17 45.2	4 36.6	23 20.5
19 W	19 43 33.9	21 3.3	12 58.3	8 35.4	12 55.5	23 4.2	25 58.7	2 8.2	9 23.7	17 46.8	4 34.9	23 19.5
22 S	19 55 23.5	20 30.2	12 55.1	5S 40.3	11 45.3	22 48.5	26 16.4	2 9.6	9 25.5	17 48.2	4 33.1	23 18.6
25 T	20 7 13.1	19 54.1	12 51.9	16 23.4	10 47.0	22 26.7	26 32.6	2 10.2	9 27.1	17 49.5	4 31.3	23 17.7
28 F	20 19 2.9	19 15.0	12 48.7	19 23.9	10 4.1	21 59.0	26 46.9	2 10.2	9 28.3	17 50.8	4 29.3	23 16.7
31 M	20 30 52.5	18 33.0	12 45.4	14 25.9	9 40.1	21 25.4	26 59.1	2 9.4	9 29.2	17 51.9	4 27.3	23 15.8

AUGUST 1939

DAY	EPHEMERIS SIDEREAL TIME	☉	☊	☽	☿	♀	♂	♃	♄	♅	♆	♇
LONGITUDE												
1 T	20 34 49.1	7♌51.9	3♏39.5	15♒48.1	23♌27.9	28♋ 3.4	27♑14.0	8♈47.1	1♉ 7.4	21♉39.3	21♍28.1	1♌16.5
2 W	20 38 45.6	8 49.3	3 36.3	27 40.8	23R 4.1	29 17.1	26R 58.9	8R 46.5	1 8.7	21 40.6	21 29.8	1 18.1
3 T	20 42 42.2	9 46.6	3 33.1	9♓31.7	22 35.5	0♌30.9	26 44.1	8 45.8	1 9.9	21 41.9	21 31.6	1 19.8
4 F	20 46 38.7	10 44.1	3 30.0	21 23.1	22 2.5	1 44.7	26 29.8	8 44.9	1 11.0	21 43.1	21 33.3	1 21.5
5 S	20 50 35.3	11 41.5	3 26.8	3♈17.8	21 25.4	2 58.6	26 15.9	8 43.8	1 12.0	21 44.3	21 35.1	1 23.1
6 S	20 54 31.8	12 38.9	3 23.6	15 19.3	20 44.8	4 12.4	26 2.4	8 42.5	1 12.9	21 45.4	21 36.9	1 24.8
7 M	20 58 28.4	13 36.4	3 20.4	27 32.0	20 1.2	5 26.3	25 49.5	8 41.0	1 13.7	21 46.5	21 38.8	1 26.4
8 T	21 2 25.0	14 33.9	3 17.3	10♉ 0.4	19 15.2	6 40.2	25 37.1	8 39.3	1 14.4	21 47.5	21 40.6	1 28.1
9 W	21 6 21.5	15 31.4	3 14.1	22 49.6	18 27.7	7 54.1	25 25.4	8 37.4	1 14.9	21 48.5	21 42.5	1 29.7
10 T	21 10 18.0	16 29.0	3 10.9	6♊ 3.9	17 39.6	9 8.1	25 14.2	8 35.3	1 15.4	21 49.5	21 44.4	1 31.4
11 F	21 14 14.6	17 26.5	3 7.7	19 46.6	16 51.5	10 22.1	25 3.6	8 33.0	1 15.8	21 50.4	21 46.3	1 33.0
12 S	21 18 11.2	18 24.1	3 4.5	3♋58.9	16 4.6	11 36.1	24 53.8	8 30.5	1 16.0	21 51.2	21 48.2	1 34.6
13 S	21 22 7.7	19 21.7	3 1.4	18 38.9	15 19.7	12 50.1	24 44.6	8 27.8	1 16.2	21 52.0	21 50.1	1 36.2
14 M	21 26 4.2	20 19.3	2 58.2	3♌41.2	14 37.7	14 4.2	24 36.1	8 24.9	1 16.2	21 52.8	21 52.1	1 37.8
15 T	21 30 0.8	21 17.0	2 55.0	18 56.9	13 59.5	15 18.3	24 28.4	8 21.9	1R 16.2	21 53.5	21 54.0	1 39.4
16 W	21 33 57.4	22 14.7	2 51.8	4♍15.0	13 25.9	16 32.4	24 21.5	8 18.6	1 16.0	21 54.1	21 56.0	1 41.0
17 T	21 37 54.0	23 12.4	2 48.7	19 24.3	12 57.6	17 46.5	24 15.3	8 15.2	1 15.8	21 54.7	21 58.0	1 42.6
18 F	21 41 50.5	24 10.1	2 45.5	4♎15.3	12 35.2	19 0.7	24 9.9	8 11.6	1 15.4	21 55.3	22 0.0	1 44.2
19 S	21 45 47.0	25 7.8	2 42.3	18 41.8	12 19.4	20 14.8	24 5.4	8 7.8	1 14.9	21 55.8	22 2.0	1 45.8
20 S	21 49 43.6	26 5.6	2 39.1	2♏40.9	12 10.6	21 29.0	24 1.6	8 3.8	1 14.3	21 56.2	22 4.1	1 47.3
21 M	21 53 40.1	27 3.3	2 35.9	16 13.0	12 9.0	22 43.2	23 58.7	7 59.6	1 13.7	21 56.6	22 6.1	1 48.9
22 T	21 57 36.7	28 1.1	2 32.8	29 20.2	12D 15.1	23 57.4	23 56.6	7 55.3	1 12.9	21 57.0	22 8.2	1 50.4
23 W	22 1 33.3	28 58.9	2 29.6	12♐ 6.1	12 28.8	25 11.7	23 55.4	7 50.8	1 12.0	21 57.3	22 10.3	1 51.9
24 T	22 5 29.8	29 56.7	2 26.4	24 34.9	12 50.3	26 25.9	23 55.0	7 46.1	1 11.0	21 57.5	22 12.3	1 53.5
25 F	22 9 26.3	0♍54.6	2 23.2	6♑50.3	13 19.6	27 40.2	23D 55.4	7 41.2	1 9.9	21 57.7	22 14.4	1 55.0
26 S	22 13 22.9	1 52.4	2 20.1	18 56.0	13 56.7	28 54.5	23 56.7	7 36.2	1 8.7	21 57.9	22 16.6	1 56.5
27 S	22 17 19.5	2 50.3	2 16.9	0♒55.1	14 41.3	0♍ 8.8	23 58.7	7 31.1	1 7.4	21 58.0	22 18.7	1 57.9
28 M	22 21 16.0	3 48.2	2 13.7	12 49.8	15 33.3	1 23.2	24 1.6	7 25.7	1 6.0	21 58.0	22 20.8	1 59.4
29 T	22 25 12.6	4 46.2	2 10.5	24 42.3	16 32.4	2 37.5	24 5.3	7 20.2	1 4.5	21 58.0	22 22.9	2 0.9
30 W	22 29 9.1	5 44.1	2 7.4	6♓34.1	17 38.3	3 51.9	24 9.9	7 14.6	1 2.9	21R 58.0	22 25.1	2 2.3
31 T	22 33 5.7	6 42.1	2 4.2	18 26.9	18 50.6	5 6.3	24 15.2	7 8.8	1 1.2	21 57.9	22 27.2	2 3.8
DECLINATION												
1 T	20 34 49.1	18N 18.4	12S 44.4	11S 26.4	9N 36.9	21N 13.0	27S 2.6	2N 9.0	9N 29.5	17N 52.2	4N 26.6	23N 15.5
4 F	20 46 38.7	17 32.8	12 41.1	0 21.4	9 42.1	20 32.1	27 11.7	2 7.4	9 30.0	17 53.2	4 24.5	23 14.6
7 M	20 58 28.4	16 44.6	12 37.9	11N 1.1	10 9.9	19 45.8	27 18.1	2 5.0	9 30.1	17 54.1	4 22.3	23 13.8
10 T	21 10 18.0	15 54.0	12 34.6	18 34.6	10 57.5	18 54.3	27 22.0	2 2.0	9 30.0	17 54.8	4 20.1	23 12.9
13 S	21 22 7.7	15 1.1	12 31.4	17 17.9	11 58.9	17 58.1	27 23.4	1 58.3	9 29.5	17 55.4	4 17.8	23 12.1
16 W	21 33 57.4	14 6.0	12 28.1	5 58.9	13 5.8	16 57.2	27 22.3	1 54.0	9 28.7	17 56.0	4 15.4	23 11.3
19 S	21 45 47.0	13 8.9	12 24.8	8S 22.6	14 9.3	15 52.2	27 18.7	1 49.0	9 27.6	17 56.4	4 13.0	23 10.5
22 T	21 57 36.7	12 9.9	12 21.6	17 41.8	15 1.0	14 43.1	27 12.9	1 43.4	9 26.2	17 56.6	4 10.5	23 9.7
25 F	22 9 26.3	11 9.2	12 18.3	18 39.4	15 34.3	13 30.4	27 5.0	1 37.2	9 24.4	17 56.8	4 8.0	23 9.0
28 M	22 21 16.0	10 7.0	12 15.0	12 11.9	15 43.9	12 14.3	26 55.1	1 30.5	9 22.4	17 56.9	4 5.5	23 8.3
31 T	22 33 5.7	9 3.2	12 11.7	1 25.3	15 26.4	10 55.2	26 43.5	1 23.2	9 20.0	17 56.8	4 3.0	23 7.7

SEPTEMBER 1939

LONGITUDE

DAY	EPHEMERIS SIDEREAL TIME	☉	☊	☽	☿	♀	♂	♃	♄	♅	♆	♇
	h m s	° '	° '	° '	° '	° '	° '	° '	° '	° '	° '	° '
1 F	22 37 2.2	7♍40.1	2♏ 1.0	0♈22.3	20♌ 8.9	6♍20.7	24♑21.3	7♈ 2.9	0♉59.4	21♉57.7	22♍29.4	2♌ 5.2
2 S	22 40 58.7	8 38.2	1 57.8	12 22.4	21 32.8	7 35.1	24 28.2	6R56.8	0R57.5	21R57.5	22 31.6	2 6.6
3 S	22 44 55.3	9 36.3	1 54.6	24 29.8	23 1.9	8 49.5	24 35.8	6 50.6	0 55.5	21 57.3	22 33.7	2 8.0
4 M	22 48 51.9	10 34.4	1 51.5	6♉47.4	24 35.5	10 4.0	24 44.3	6 44.2	0 53.4	21 57.0	22 35.9	2 9.4
5 T	22 52 48.5	11 32.5	1 48.3	19 19.0	26 13.2	11 18.5	24 53.5	6 37.7	0 51.3	21 56.6	22 38.1	2 10.7
6 W	22 56 45.0	12 30.7	1 45.1	2♊ 8.5	27 54.5	12 33.0	25 3.4	6 31.1	0 49.0	21 56.2	22 40.3	2 12.1
7 T	23 0 41.5	13 28.9	1 41.9	15 19.5	29 38.9	13 47.5	25 14.1	6 24.4	0 46.6	21 55.8	22 42.5	2 13.4
8 F	23 4 38.1	14 27.1	1 38.7	28 55.3	1♍25.8	15 2.0	25 25.5	6 17.6	0 44.1	21 55.3	22 44.7	2 14.7
9 S	23 8 34.7	15 25.4	1 35.6	12♋57.6	3 14.8	16 16.6	25 37.6	6 10.6	0 41.6	21 54.8	22 46.9	2 16.0
10 S	23 12 31.2	16 23.7	1 32.4	27 25.7	5 5.6	17 31.1	25 50.4	6 3.5	0 38.9	21 54.2	22 49.1	2 17.3
11 M	23 16 27.7	17 22.1	1 29.2	12♌16.1	6 57.5	18 45.7	26 4.0	5 56.4	0 36.2	21 53.5	22 51.4	2 18.6
12 T	23 20 24.3	18 20.4	1 26.0	27 22.1	8 50.4	20 0.3	26 18.2	5 49.1	0 33.4	21 52.8	22 53.6	2 19.8
13 W	23 24 20.9	19 18.8	1 22.9	12♍34.5	10 43.9	21 14.9	26 33.1	5 41.7	0 30.5	21 52.1	22 55.8	2 21.0
14 T	23 28 17.4	20 17.3	1 19.7	27 42.9	12 37.7	22 29.6	26 48.7	5 34.3	0 27.5	21 51.3	22 58.0	2 22.3
15 F	23 32 13.9	21 15.8	1 16.5	12♎37.6	14 31.6	23 44.2	27 5.0	5 26.7	0 24.4	21 50.5	23 0.3	2 23.5
16 S	23 36 10.5	22 14.3	1 13.3	27 11.0	16 25.3	24 58.8	27 21.9	5 19.1	0 21.2	21 49.6	23 2.5	2 24.6
17 S	23 40 7.0	23 12.8	1 10.1	11♏18.4	18 18.7	26 13.5	27 39.4	5 11.5	0 18.0	21 48.6	23 4.7	2 25.8
18 M	23 44 3.6	24 11.4	1 7.0	24 58.3	20 11.6	27 28.2	27 57.6	5 3.7	0 14.7	21 47.7	23 7.0	2 26.9
19 T	23 48 0.2	25 9.9	1 3.8	8♐11.8	22 3.9	28 42.9	28 16.3	4 55.9	0 11.3	21 46.6	23 9.2	2 28.1
20 W	23 51 56.7	26 8.5	1 0.6	21 1.4	23 55.5	29 57.6	28 35.7	4 48.1	0 7.8	21 45.6	23 11.4	2 29.1
21 T	23 55 53.2	27 7.2	0 57.4	3♑31.2	25 46.4	1♎12.3	28 55.7	4 40.2	0 4.2	21 44.5	23 13.6	2 30.2
22 F	23 59 49.8	28 5.9	0 54.2	15 45.3	27 36.5	2 27.0	29 16.2	4 32.3	0 0.6	21 43.3	23 15.9	2 31.3
23 S	0 3 46.4	29 4.6	0 51.1	27 48.2	29 25.7	3 41.7	29 37.3	4 24.3	29♈56.9	21 42.1	23 18.1	2 32.3
24 S	0 7 43.0	0♎ 3.3	0 47.9	9♒43.9	1♎14.0	4 56.4	29 58.9	4 16.3	29 53.2	21 40.8	23 20.3	2 33.4
25 M	0 11 39.5	1 2.0	0 44.7	21 36.0	3 1.4	6 11.1	0♒21.1	4 8.3	29 49.3	21 39.6	23 22.5	2 34.4
26 T	0 15 36.0	2 0.8	0 41.5	3♓27.5	4 47.9	7 25.9	0 43.7	4 0.3	29 45.4	21 38.2	23 24.7	2 35.3
27 W	0 19 32.6	2 59.6	0 38.4	15 21.0	6 33.4	8 40.6	1 6.9	3 52.2	29 41.5	21 36.8	23 26.9	2 36.3
28 T	0 23 29.2	3 58.5	0 35.2	27 18.6	8 18.1	9 55.4	1 30.5	3 44.2	29 37.5	21 35.4	23 29.1	2 37.2
29 F	0 27 25.7	4 57.4	0 32.0	9♈22.0	10 1.8	11 10.1	1 54.7	3 36.2	29 33.4	21 34.0	23 31.3	2 38.1
30 S	0 31 22.3	5 56.3	0 28.8	21 32.9	11 44.6	12 24.9	2 19.2	3 28.1	29 29.3	21 32.5	23 33.5	2 39.0

DECLINATION

DAY	EPHEMERIS SIDEREAL TIME	☉	☊	☽	☿	♀	♂	♃	♄	♅	♆	♇
1 F	22 37 2.2	8N41.7	12S10.6	2N29.9	15N14.3	10N28.3	26S39.2	1N20.7	9N19.2	17N56.8	4N 2.1	23N 7.5
4 M	22 48 51.9	7 36.3	12 7.3	13 14.0	14 18.9	9 5.7	26 25.3	1 12.8	9 16.5	17 56.5	3 59.5	23 6.9
7 T	23 0 41.5	6 29.7	12 4.0	19 0.4	12 57.1	7 40.8	26 9.9	1 4.5	9 13.5	17 56.2	3 56.9	23 6.3
10 S	23 12 31.2	5 22.2	12 0.7	15 37.8	11 13.2	6 14.0	25 53.0	0 55.8	9 10.2	17 55.8	3 54.3	23 5.8
13 W	23 24 20.9	4 13.8	11 57.4	3 19.7	9 12.7	4 45.6	25 34.5	0 46.8	9 6.7	17 55.2	3 51.7	23 5.3
16 S	23 36 10.5	3 4.8	11 54.1	10S41.4	7 0.8	3 15.9	25 14.7	0 37.6	9 3.0	17 54.5	3 49.1	23 4.9
19 T	23 48 0.2	1 55.3	11 50.8	18 28.8	4 42.2	1 45.3	24 53.5	0 28.2	8 59.0	17 53.8	3 46.4	23 4.5
22 F	23 59 49.8	0 45.4	11 47.5	17 29.6	2 20.5	0 14.1	24 30.9	0 18.6	8 54.8	17 52.9	3 43.8	23 4.2
25 M	0 11 39.5	0S24.7	11 44.1	9 43.6	0S 1.7	1S17.5	24 6.9	0 9.0	8 50.5	17 51.9	3 41.2	23 3.9
28 T	0 23 29.2	1 34.8	11 40.8	1N28.9	2 22.3	2 48.9	23 41.7	0S 0.6	8 46.0	17 50.8	3 38.7	23 3.6

OCTOBER 1939

LONGITUDE

DAY	EPHEMERIS SIDEREAL TIME	☉	☊	☽	☿	♀	♂	♃	♄	♅	♆	♇
1 S	0 35 18.8	6♎55.2	0♏25.6	3♉52.9	13♎26.5	13♎39.7	2♒44.3	3♈20.1	29♈25.1	21♉30.9	23♍35.7	2♌39.9
2 M	0 39 15.4	7 54.2	0 22.5	16 23.7	15 7.6	14 54.4	3 9.8	3R12.1	29R20.8	21R29.4	23 37.9	2 40.7
3 T	0 43 11.9	8 53.2	0 19.3	29 7.3	16 47.7	16 9.2	3 35.7	3 4.2	29 16.6	21 27.7	23 40.0	2 41.6
4 W	0 47 8.5	9 52.3	0 16.1	12♊ 5.8	18 27.1	17 24.0	4 2.0	2 56.2	29 12.2	21 26.1	23 42.2	2 42.4
5 T	0 51 5.0	10 51.4	0 12.9	25 21.3	20 5.6	18 38.8	4 28.8	2 48.3	29 7.8	21 24.4	23 44.3	2 43.1
6 F	0 55 1.6	11 50.5	0 9.8	8♋55.5	21 43.2	19 53.6	4 55.9	2 40.5	29 3.4	21 22.7	23 46.5	2 43.9
7 S	0 58 58.1	12 49.7	0 6.6	22 49.5	23 20.1	21 8.5	5 23.5	2 32.7	28 58.9	21 20.9	23 48.6	2 44.6
8 S	1 2 54.7	13 48.9	0 3.4	7♌ 3.1	24 56.3	22 23.3	5 51.4	2 24.9	28 54.4	21 19.1	23 50.7	2 45.3
9 M	1 6 51.2	14 48.2	0 0.2	21 34.0	26 31.6	23 38.1	6 19.7	2 17.2	28 49.9	21 17.2	23 52.9	2 46.0
10 T	1 10 47.8	15 47.5	29♎57.0	6♍18.3	28 6.2	24 53.0	6 48.4	2 9.6	28 45.3	21 15.4	23 55.0	2 46.7
11 W	1 14 44.3	16 46.8	29 53.9	21 9.9	29 40.1	26 7.8	7 17.5	2 2.0	28 40.7	21 13.5	23 57.1	2 47.3
12 T	1 18 40.9	17 46.2	29 50.7	6♎ 1.1	1♏13.2	27 22.7	7 46.9	1 54.6	28 36.0	21 11.5	23 59.1	2 47.9
13 F	1 22 37.5	18 45.6	29 47.5	20 44.3	2 45.7	28 37.5	8 16.7	1 47.2	28 31.4	21 9.6	24 1.2	2 48.5
14 S	1 26 34.0	19 45.0	29 44.3	5♏12.2	4 17.4	29 52.4	8 46.8	1 39.9	28 26.7	21 7.5	24 3.3	2 49.1
15 S	1 30 30.5	20 44.5	29 41.1	19 19.5	5 48.5	1♏ 7.3	9 17.2	1 32.7	28 22.0	21 5.5	24 5.3	2 49.6
16 M	1 34 27.1	21 44.0	29 38.0	3♐ 2.9	7 18.8	2 22.1	9 48.0	1 25.6	28 17.2	21 3.4	24 7.3	2 50.1
17 T	1 38 23.7	22 43.5	29 34.8	16 21.6	8 48.5	3 37.0	10 19.1	1 18.7	28 12.5	21 1.4	24 9.3	2 50.6
18 W	1 42 20.2	23 43.1	29 31.6	29 16.5	10 17.5	4 51.9	10 50.4	1 11.8	28 7.7	20 59.2	24 11.3	2 51.1
19 T	1 46 16.8	24 42.7	29 28.4	11♑50.3	11 45.7	6 6.8	11 22.1	1 5.1	28 2.9	20 57.1	24 13.3	2 51.5
20 F	1 50 13.3	25 42.3	29 25.3	24 6.9	13 13.3	7 21.6	11 54.1	0 58.4	27 58.2	20 54.9	24 15.3	2 51.9
21 S	1 54 9.9	26 42.0	29 22.1	6♒10.5	14 40.1	8 36.5	12 26.4	0 52.0	27 53.4	20 52.7	24 17.3	2 52.3
22 S	1 58 6.4	27 41.6	29 18.9	18 5.8	16 6.2	9 51.4	12 58.9	0 45.6	27 48.6	20 50.5	24 19.2	2 52.6
23 M	2 2 3.0	28 41.3	29 15.7	29 57.3	17 31.6	11 6.2	13 31.7	0 39.4	27 43.8	20 48.3	24 21.1	2 53.0
24 T	2 5 59.5	29 41.1	29 12.5	11♓49.1	18 56.1	12 21.1	14 4.8	0 33.3	27 39.0	20 46.0	24 23.0	2 53.3
25 W	2 9 56.1	0♏40.8	29 9.4	23 45.1	20 19.9	13 36.0	14 38.1	0 27.4	27 34.2	20 43.7	24 24.9	2 53.6
26 T	2 13 52.7	1 40.6	29 6.2	5♈48.4	21 42.8	14 50.9	15 11.6	0 21.6	27 29.5	20 41.4	24 26.8	2 53.8
27 F	2 17 49.2	2 40.5	29 3.0	18 1.6	23 4.7	16 5.7	15 45.4	0 16.0	27 24.7	20 39.1	24 28.6	2 54.0
28 S	2 21 45.7	3 40.3	28 59.8	0♉26.4	24 25.7	17 20.6	16 19.4	0 10.5	27 19.9	20 36.7	24 30.4	2 54.2
29 S	2 25 42.3	4 40.2	28 56.7	13 4.2	25 45.7	18 35.4	16 53.6	0 5.2	27 15.2	20 34.4	24 32.2	2 54.4
30 M	2 29 38.8	5 40.1	28 53.5	25 55.4	27 4.5	19 50.3	17 28.1	0 0.0	27 10.5	20 32.0	24 34.0	2 54.6
31 T	2 33 35.4	6 40.1	28 50.3	9♊ 0.3	28 22.1	21 5.2	18 2.7	29♓55.1	27 5.8	20 29.6	24 35.8	2 54.7

DECLINATION

DAY	EPHEMERIS SIDEREAL TIME	☉	☊	☽	☿	♀	♂	♃	♄	♅	♆	♇
1 S	0 35 18.8	2S44.9	11S37.5	12N25.2	4S40.1	4S20.0	23S15.2	0S10.2	8N41.3	17N49.6	3N36.1	23N 3.5
4 W	0 47 8.5	3 54.7	11 34.1	18 41.9	6 53.9	5 50.4	22 47.4	0 19.6	8 36.5	17 48.4	3 33.6	23 3.3
7 S	0 58 58.1	5 4.1	11 30.8	16 20.9	9 3.0	7 19.7	22 18.2	0 28.8	8 31.6	17 47.0	3 31.1	23 3.2
10 T	1 10 47.8	6 13.0	11♎27.4	5 16.8	11 6.7	8 47.6	21 47.8	0 37.8	8 26.6	17 45.6	3 28.6	23 3.2
13 F	1 22 37.5	7 21.1	11 24.1	8S49.6	13 4.3	10 13.8	21 16.0	0 46.4	8 21.5	17 44.0	3 26.2	23 3.3
16 M	1 34 27.1	8 28.3	11 20.7	17 52.9	14 55.5	11 37.9	20 43.0	0 54.7	8 16.4	17 42.4	3 23.9	23 3.4
19 T	1 46 16.8	9 34.5	11 17.4	17 53.3	16 39.5	12 59.5	20 8.7	1 2.5	8 11.3	17 40.8	3 21.6	23 3.5
22 S	1 58 6.4	10 39.3	11 14.0	10 38.2	18 15.8	14 18.3	19 33.1	1 9.8	8 6.2	17 39.0	3 19.3	23 3.7
25 W	2 9 56.1	11 42.8	11 10.6	0N21.0	19 43.7	15 33.9	18 56.3	1 16.6	8 1.2	17 37.2	3 17.1	23 4.0
28 S	2 21 45.7	12 44.6	11 7.2	11 31.9	21 2.6	16 46.0	18 18.3	1 22.8	7 56.2	17 35.4	3 15.0	23 4.3
31 T	2 33 35.4	13 44.7	11 3.8	18 27.8	22 11.6	17 54.2	17 39.2	1 28.4	7 51.3	17 33.5	3 13.0	23 4.7

NOVEMBER 1939

LONGITUDE

DAY	EPHEMERIS SIDEREAL TIME h m s	☉ ° ′	☊ ° ′	☽ ° ′	☿ ° ′	♀ ° ′	♂ ° ′	♃ ° ′	♄ ° ′	♅ ° ′	♆ ° ′	♇ ° ′
1 W	2 37 32.0	7♏40.1	28♎47.1	22♊18.7	29♏38.4	22♏20.0	18♒37.6	29♓50.2	27♈ 1.1	20♉27.2	24♍37.5	2♌54.8
2 T	2 41 28.5	8 40.1	28 44.0	5♋50.1	0♐53.3	23 34.9	19 12.6	29R45.6	26R56.5	20R24.8	24 39.3	2 54.8
3 F	2 45 25.1	9 40.2	28 40.8	19 33.8	2 6.5	24 49.8	19 47.8	29 41.1	26 51.9	20 22.3	24 41.0	2 54.9
4 S	2 49 21.6	10 40.3	28 37.6	3♌29.0	3 18.0	26 4.7	20 23.3	29 36.9	26 47.3	20 19.9	24 42.6	2 54.9
5 S	2 53 18.2	11 40.4	28 34.4	17 34.6	4 27.5	27 19.5	20 58.9	29 32.8	26 42.7	20 17.5	24 44.3	2R54.9
6 M	2 57 14.7	12 40.6	28 31.2	1♍48.9	5 34.9	28 34.4	21 34.7	29 28.9	26 38.2	20 15.0	24 45.9	2 54.9
7 T	3 1 11.3	13 40.8	28 28.1	16 9.8	6 39.8	29 49.3	22 10.7	29 25.1	26 33.8	20 12.5	24 47.5	2 54.8
8 W	3 5 7.8	14 41.0	28 24.9	0♎34.0	7 41.9	1♐ 4.2	22 46.8	29 21.6	26 29.3	20 10.0	24 49.1	2 54.7
9 T	3 9 4.4	15 41.3	28 21.7	14 57.6	8 41.1	2 19.0	23 23.2	29 18.3	26 24.9	20 7.6	24 50.7	2 54.6
10 F	3 13 0.9	16 41.6	28 18.5	29 16.1	9 36.8	3 33.9	23 59.7	29 15.1	26 20.6	20 5.1	24 52.2	2 54.4
11 S	3 16 57.5	17 41.9	28 15.4	13♏24.6	10 28.6	4 48.8	24 36.3	29 12.2	26 16.3	20 2.6	24 53.8	2 54.3
12 S	3 20 54.0	18 42.3	28 12.2	27 18.8	11 16.1	6 3.7	25 13.2	29 9.4	26 12.0	20 0.1	24 55.2	2 54.1
13 M	3 24 50.6	19 42.7	28 9.0	10♐55.2	11 58.8	7 18.6	25 50.1	29 6.9	26 7.9	19 57.6	24 56.7	2 53.9
14 T	3 28 47.2	20 43.1	28 5.8	24 11.5	12 36.0	8 33.5	26 27.3	29 4.5	26 3.7	19 55.1	24 58.1	2 53.6
15 W	3 32 43.7	21 43.5	28 2.6	7♑ 7.1	13 7.1	9 48.3	27 4.6	29 2.4	25 59.7	19 52.6	24 59.6	2 53.3
16 T	3 36 40.3	22 44.0	27 59.5	19 43.1	13 31.4	11 3.2	27 42.0	29 0.4	25 55.6	19 50.1	25 0.9	2 53.0
17 F	3 40 36.8	23 44.5	27 56.3	2♒ 1.8	13 48.2	12 18.1	28 19.5	28 58.7	25 51.7	19 47.6	25 2.3	2 52.7
18 S	3 44 33.4	24 45.0	27 53.1	14 6.9	13 56.7	13 32.9	28 57.2	28 57.2	25 47.8	19 45.1	25 3.6	2 52.4
19 S	3 48 30.0	25 45.5	27 49.9	26 2.5	13R56.3	14 47.8	29 35.0	28 55.8	25 44.0	19 42.6	25 4.9	2 52.0
20 M	3 52 26.5	26 46.1	27 46.8	7♓53.6	13 46.2	16 2.6	0♓13.0	28 54.7	25 40.3	19 40.2	25 6.2	2 51.6
21 T	3 56 23.0	27 46.6	27 43.6	19 45.2	13 25.9	17 17.5	0 51.0	28 53.8	25 36.6	19 37.7	25 7.4	2 51.2
22 W	4 0 19.6	28 47.2	27 40.4	1♈42.1	12 55.0	18 32.3	1 29.2	28 53.1	25 33.0	19 35.2	25 8.6	2 50.7
23 T	4 4 16.2	29 47.8	27 37.2	13 48.7	12 13.5	19 47.1	2 7.5	28 52.6	25 29.5	19 32.8	25 9.8	2 50.2
24 F	4 8 12.7	0♐48.5	27 34.1	26 9.0	11 21.5	21 2.0	2 45.9	28 52.3	25 26.0	19 30.4	25 11.0	2 49.7
25 S	4 12 9.3	1 49.1	27 30.9	8♉45.8	10 20.0	22 16.8	3 24.3	28 52.3	25 22.6	19 27.9	25 12.1	2 49.2
26 S	4 16 5.8	2 49.8	27 27.7	21 40.9	9 10.1	23 31.6	4 2.9	28D52.4	25 19.3	19 25.5	25 13.2	2 48.6
27 M	4 20 2.4	3 50.5	27 24.5	4♊54.6	7 53.6	24 46.4	4 41.6	28 52.7	25 16.1	19 23.1	25 14.3	2 48.1
28 T	4 23 59.0	4 51.2	27 21.3	18 25.7	6 32.8	26 1.2	5 20.4	28 53.3	25 13.0	19 20.8	25 15.3	2 47.5
29 W	4 27 55.5	5 52.0	27 18.2	2♋11.8	5 10.3	27 16.0	5 59.2	28 54.0	25 10.0	19 18.4	25 16.3	2 46.9
30 T	4 31 52.0	6 52.7	27 15.0	16 9.6	3 48.9	28 30.8	6 38.2	28 55.0	25 7.0	19 16.0	25 17.3	2 46.2

DECLINATION

DAY	EPHEMERIS SIDEREAL TIME h m s	☉	☊	☽	☿	♀	♂	♃	♄	♅	♆	♇
1 W	2 37 32.0	14S 4.3	11S 2.7	19N 0.3	22S32.2	18S16.1	17S25.9	1S30.1	7N49.7	17N32.9	3N12.3	23N 4.8
4 S	2 49 21.6	15 1.7	10 59.3	14 15.4	23 26.5	19 18.5	16 45.3	1 34.8	7 45.0	17 31.0	3 10.4	23 5.3
7 T	3 1 11.3	15 56.9	10 55.9	2 7.8	24 8.5	20 16.3	16 3.6	1 38.8	7 40.5	17 29.0	3 8.6	23 5.8
10 F	3 13 0.9	16 49.8	10 52.5	11S13.1	24 36.9	21 9.0	15 20.9	1 42.1	7 36.1	17 27.0	3 6.8	23 6.4
13 M	3 24 50.6	17 40.0	10 49.1	18 37.4	24 49.9	21 56.4	14 37.1	1 44.7	7 31.9	17 25.1	3 5.1	23 7.0
16 T	3 36 40.3	18 27.5	10 45.7	16 52.6	24 45.4	22 38.1	13 52.4	1 46.6	7 27.9	17 23.1	3 3.6	23 7.6
19 S	3 48 30.0	19 12.1	10 42.3	8 26.5	24 20.3	23 13.9	13 6.7	1 47.6	7 24.2	17 21.1	3 2.1	23 8.4
22 W	4 0 19.6	19 53.6	10 38.9	2N53.2	23 31.2	23 43.5	12 20.3	1 48.0	7 20.7	17 19.1	3 0.8	23 9.1
25 S	4 12 9.3	20 31.8	10 35.5	13 35.5	22 16.0	24 6.7	11 33.0	1 47.5	7 17.5	17 17.2	2 59.5	23 9.9
28 T	4 23 59.0	21 6.6	10 32.1	19 0.6	20 40.1	24 23.4	10 45.0	1 46.4	7 14.6	17 15.3	2 58.4	23 10.8

DECEMBER 1939

LONGITUDE

DAY	EPHEMERIS SIDEREAL TIME h m s	☉ ° ′	☊ ° ′	☽ ° ′	☿ ° ′	♀ ° ′	♂ ° ′	♃ ° ′	♄ ° ′	♅ ° ′	♆ ° ′	♇ ° ′
1 F	4 35 48.6	7♐53.5	27♎11.8	0♌15.2	2♐31.3	29♐45.5	7♓17.2	28♓56.2	25♈ 4.2	19♉13.7	25♍18.2	2♌45.5
2 S	4 39 45.2	8 54.3	27 8.6	14 24.9	1R20.0	1♑ 0.3	7 56.3	28 57.5	25R 1.4	19R11.4	25 19.1	2R44.9
3 S	4 43 41.7	9 55.2	27 5.5	28 35.5	0 17.1	2 15.1	8 35.5	28 59.1	24 58.7	19 9.1	25 20.0	2 44.2
4 M	4 47 38.3	10 56.0	27 2.3	12♍44.8	29♏24.1	3 29.9	9 14.8	29 0.9	24 56.2	19 6.8	25 20.8	2 43.4
5 T	4 51 34.8	11 56.9	26 59.1	26 50.9	28 42.0	4 44.6	9 54.1	29 2.9	24 53.7	19 4.6	25 21.6	2 42.7
6 W	4 55 31.4	12 57.8	26 55.9	10♎52.9	28 11.4	5 59.4	10 33.5	29 5.1	24 51.3	19 2.4	25 22.4	2 41.9
7 T	4 59 27.9	13 58.7	26 52.7	24 49.5	27 52.1	7 14.1	11 13.0	29 7.5	24 49.0	19 0.2	25 23.2	2 41.1
8 F	5 3 24.5	14 59.7	26 49.6	8♏39.4	27 44.0	8 28.9	11 52.6	29 10.1	24 46.8	18 58.0	25 23.9	2 40.3
9 S	5 7 21.1	16 0.7	26 46.4	22 20.9	27D46.4	9 43.6	12 32.3	29 12.9	24 44.7	18 55.8	25 24.6	2 39.4
10 S	5 11 17.6	17 1.6	26 43.2	5♐52.0	27 58.7	10 58.3	13 12.0	29 15.8	24 42.7	18 53.7	25 25.2	2 38.5
11 M	5 15 14.2	18 2.6	26 40.0	19 10.4	28 20.0	12 13.1	13 51.7	29 19.0	24 40.8	18 51.6	25 25.8	2 37.7
12 T	5 19 10.7	19 3.7	26 36.9	2♑14.2	28 49.4	13 27.8	14 31.6	29 22.4	24 39.0	18 49.6	25 26.4	2 36.8
13 W	5 23 7.3	20 4.7	26 33.7	15 2.2	29 26.1	14 42.5	15 11.5	29 26.0	24 37.3	18 47.5	25 27.0	2 35.8
14 T	5 27 3.8	21 5.7	26 30.5	27 34.2	0♐ 9.3	15 57.2	15 51.5	29 29.8	24 35.7	18 45.5	25 27.5	2 34.9
15 F	5 31 0.4	22 6.8	26 27.3	9♒51.2	0 58.3	17 11.8	16 31.5	29 33.8	24 34.2	18 43.5	25 27.9	2 33.9
16 S	5 34 57.0	23 7.8	26 24.2	21 55.5	1 52.3	18 26.5	17 11.6	29 38.0	24 32.9	18 41.6	25 28.4	2 33.0
17 S	5 38 53.5	24 8.9	26 21.0	3♓50.4	2 50.8	19 41.1	17 51.7	29 42.3	24 31.6	18 39.7	25 28.8	2 32.0
18 M	5 42 50.1	25 10.0	26 17.8	15 40.3	3 53.2	20 55.8	18 31.9	29 46.9	24 30.5	18 37.8	25 29.2	2 30.9
19 T	5 46 46.6	26 11.1	26 14.6	27 30.1	4 59.1	22 10.4	19 12.1	29 51.6	24 29.4	18 36.0	25 29.5	2 29.9
20 W	5 50 43.2	27 12.1	26 11.4	9♈25.2	6 7.9	23 25.0	19 52.3	29 56.5	24 28.5	18 34.2	25 29.8	2 28.9
21 T	5 54 39.8	28 13.2	26 8.3	21 31.0	7 19.4	24 39.5	20 32.7	0♈ 1.6	24 27.6	18 32.4	25 30.1	2 27.8
22 F	5 58 36.3	29 14.3	26 5.1	3♉52.5	8 33.1	25 54.1	21 13.0	0 6.9	24 26.9	18 30.7	25 30.3	2 26.7
23 S	6 2 32.9	0♑15.4	26 1.9	16 34.3	9 48.9	27 8.6	21 53.4	0 12.4	24 26.3	18 29.0	25 30.5	2 25.6
24 S	6 6 29.4	1 16.5	25 58.7	29 39.2	11 6.5	28 23.1	22 33.8	0 18.0	24 25.8	18 27.4	25 30.7	2 24.5
25 M	6 10 26.0	2 17.6	25 55.6	13♊ 8.7	12 25.6	29 37.6	23 14.2	0 23.9	24 25.4	18 25.8	25 30.8	2 23.4
26 T	6 14 22.5	3 18.8	25 52.4	27 1.7	13 46.1	0♒52.1	23 54.7	0 29.9	24 25.1	18 24.2	25 30.9	2 22.2
27 W	6 18 19.1	4 19.9	25 49.2	11♋14.7	15 7.8	2 6.6	24 35.2	0 36.0	24 25.0	18 22.7	25 31.0	2 21.1
28 T	6 22 15.7	5 21.0	25 46.0	25 42.1	16 30.7	3 21.0	25 15.8	0 42.4	24 24.9	18 21.2	25 31.0	2 19.9
29 F	6 26 12.2	6 22.1	25 42.9	10♌16.9	17 54.5	4 35.4	25 56.3	0 48.9	24D25.0	18 19.8	25R31.0	2 18.7
30 S	6 30 8.8	7 23.2	25 39.7	24 51.9	19 19.1	5 49.8	26 36.9	0 55.6	24 25.1	18 18.4	25 31.0	2 17.5
31 S	6 34 5.3	8 24.4	25 36.5	9♍21.0	20 44.6	7 4.1	27 17.5	1 2.4	24 25.4	18 17.0	25 30.9	2 16.3

DECLINATION

DAY	EPHEMERIS SIDEREAL TIME h m s	☉	☊	☽	☿	♀	♂	♃	♄	♅	♆	♇
1 F	4 35 48.6	21S37.8	10S28.6	15N 3.0	19S 1.4	24S33.4	9S56.4	1S44.4	7N12.0	17N13.4	2N57.3	23N11.7
4 M	4 47 38.3	22 5.3	10 25.2	3 21.0	17 44.4	24 36.6	9 7.1	1 41.8	7 9.8	17 11.6	2 56.4	23 12.6
7 T	4 59 27.9	22 29.0	10 21.8	9S55.6	17 4.7	24 33.0	8 17.2	1 38.4	7 7.8	17 9.8	2 55.6	23 13.6
10 S	5 11 17.6	22 48.7	10 18.3	18 12.9	17 2.9	24 22.7	7 26.9	1 34.3	7 6.3	17 8.1	2 54.9	23 14.6
13 W	5 23 7.3	23 4.4	10 14.9	17 39.4	17 30.1	24 5.7	6 36.0	1 29.4	7 5.0	17 6.4	2 54.4	23 15.7
16 S	5 34 57.0	23 16.0	10 11.4	9 48.0	18 15.8	23 42.1	5 44.8	1 23.9	7 4.2	17 4.9	2 54.0	23 16.7
19 T	5 46 46.6	23 23.4	10 8.0	1N20.9	19 11.0	23 12.0	4 53.2	1 17.7	7 3.7	17 3.4	2 53.7	23 17.8
22 F	5 58 36.3	23 26.5	10 4.5	12 16.3	20 9.3	22 35.7	4 1.4	1 10.9	7 3.5	17 2.0	2 53.5	23 18.9
25 M	6 10 26.0	23 25.5	10 1.1	18 46.3	21 6.0	21 53.3	3 9.4	1 3.4	7 3.8	17 0.7	2 53.4	23 20.1
28 T	6 22 15.7	23 20.2	9 57.6	16 3.4	21 58.1	21 5.3	2 17.3	0 55.4	7 4.4	16 59.5	2 53.5	23 21.2
31 S	6 34 5.3	23 10.7	9 54.1	4 38.6	22 43.4	20 11.7	1 25.0	0 46.7	7 5.4	16 58.4	2 53.6	23 22.4

JANUARY 1940

DAY	EPHEMERIS SIDEREAL TIME	☉	☊	☽	☿	♀	♂	♃	♄	♅	♆	♇
	h m s	° ′	° ′	° ′	° ′	° ′	° ′	° ′	° ′	° ′	° ′	° ′
						LONGITUDE						
1 M	6 38 1.9	9♑25.5	25♎33.3	23♍40.0	22♐10.9	8♒18.4	27♓58.1	1♈ 9.4	24♈25.8	18♉15.7	25♍30.8	2♌15.1
2 T	6 41 58.4	10 26.7	25 30.2	7♎46.3	23 37.7	9 32.7	28 38.8	1 16.6	24 26.3	18R14.4	25R30.7	2R13.9
3 W	6 45 55.0	11 27.8	25 27.0	21 39.4	25 5.3	10 47.0	29 19.5	1 23.9	24 26.9	18 13.2	25 30.5	2 12.6
4 T	6 49 51.6	12 29.0	25 23.8	5♏19.7	26 33.4	12 1.3	0♈ 0.2	1 31.4	24 27.6	18 12.1	25 30.3	2 11.4
5 F	6 53 48.1	13 30.2	25 20.6	18 48.0	28 2.0	13 15.5	0 40.9	1 39.0	24 28.5	18 10.9	25 30.0	2 10.1
6 S	6 57 44.7	14 31.4	25 17.4	2♐ 5.2	29 31.2	14 29.7	1 21.6	1 46.8	24 29.4	18 9.8	25 29.8	2 8.8
7 S	7 1 41.2	15 32.5	25 14.3	15 11.8	1♑ 0.9	15 43.9	2 2.4	1 54.8	24 30.5	18 8.8	25 29.5	2 7.5
8 M	7 5 37.8	16 33.7	25 11.1	28 7.8	2 31.0	16 58.1	2 43.2	2 2.9	24 31.6	18 7.8	25 29.1	2 6.3
9 T	7 9 34.3	17 34.9	25 7.9	10♑52.7	4 1.7	18 12.2	3 24.0	2 11.1	24 32.9	18 6.9	25 28.7	2 5.0
10 W	7 13 30.9	18 36.1	25 4.7	23 26.0	5 32.8	19 26.3	4 4.8	2 19.5	24 34.3	18 6.0	25 28.3	2 3.7
11 T	7 17 27.5	19 37.2	25 1.6	5♒47.7	7 4.4	20 40.3	4 45.7	2 28.1	24 35.8	18 5.2	25 27.9	2 2.4
12 F	7 21 24.0	20 38.4	24 58.4	17 58.0	8 36.4	21 54.3	5 26.5	2 36.8	24 37.4	18 4.4	25 27.4	2 1.0
13 S	7 25 20.5	21 39.5	24 55.2	29 58.3	10 8.9	23 8.3	6 7.4	2 45.6	24 39.1	18 3.6	25 26.9	1 59.7
14 S	7 29 17.1	22 40.7	24 52.0	11♓50.8	11 41.9	24 22.3	6 48.2	2 54.6	24 40.9	18 3.0	25 26.3	1 58.4
15 M	7 33 13.7	23 41.8	24 48.9	23 38.9	13 15.4	25 36.2	7 29.1	3 3.7	24 42.9	18 2.3	25 25.8	1 57.0
16 T	7 37 10.2	24 42.9	24 45.7	5♈26.7	14 49.3	26 50.0	8 10.0	3 12.9	24 44.9	18 1.7	25 25.2	1 55.7
17 W	7 41 6.8	25 44.1	24 42.5	17 19.1	16 23.7	28 3.8	8 50.9	3 22.3	24 47.1	18 1.2	25 24.5	1 54.4
18 T	7 45 3.3	26 45.2	24 39.3	29 21.6	17 58.7	29 17.6	9 31.8	3 31.8	24 49.3	18 0.7	25 23.9	1 53.0
19 F	7 48 59.9	27 46.2	24 36.1	11♉39.7	19 34.1	0♓31.3	10 12.7	3 41.4	24 51.7	18 0.3	25 23.2	1 51.7
20 S	7 52 56.5	28 47.3	24 33.0	24 18.9	21 10.1	1 45.0	10 53.7	3 51.2	24 54.1	17 59.9	25 22.4	1 50.3
21 S	7 56 53.0	29 48.4	24 29.8	7♊23.5	22 46.6	2 58.6	11 34.6	4 1.1	24 56.7	17 59.6	25 21.7	1 49.0
22 M	8 0 49.6	0♒49.4	24 26.6	20 56.4	24 23.7	4 12.2	12 15.5	4 11.1	24 59.3	17 59.3	25 20.9	1 47.6
23 T	8 4 46.1	1 50.4	24 23.4	4♋58.1	26 1.4	5 25.7	12 56.4	4 21.2	25 2.1	17 59.1	25 20.1	1 46.3
24 W	8 8 42.7	2 51.4	24 20.3	19 25.9	27 39.7	6 39.2	13 37.3	4 31.5	25 5.0	17 58.9	25 19.2	1 44.9
25 T	8 12 39.2	3 52.4	24 17.1	4♌13.9	29 18.5	7 52.5	14 18.2	4 41.8	25 8.0	17 58.8	25 18.3	1 43.6
26 F	8 16 35.8	4 53.4	24 13.9	19 13.4	0♒58.0	9 5.9	14 59.1	4 52.3	25 11.0	17 58.7	25 17.4	1 42.2
27 S	8 20 32.3	5 54.4	24 10.7	4♍14.9	2 38.1	10 19.2	15 40.0	5 2.9	25 14.2	17 58.7	25 16.5	1 40.9
28 S	8 24 28.9	6 55.4	24 7.6	19 9.0	4 18.9	11 32.4	16 20.8	5 13.6	25 17.5	17D58.8	25 15.5	1 39.5
29 M	8 28 25.5	7 56.3	24 4.4	3♎48.5	6 0.4	12 45.6	17 1.7	5 24.4	25 20.8	17 58.9	25 14.6	1 38.2
30 T	8 32 22.0	8 57.2	24 1.2	18 8.8	7 42.5	13 58.7	17 42.6	5 35.3	25 24.3	17 59.0	25 13.5	1 36.8
31 W	8 36 18.6	9 58.2	23 58.0	2♏ 8.2	9 25.2	15 11.7	18 23.5	5 46.4	25 27.8	17 59.2	25 12.5	1 35.5
						DECLINATION						
1 M	6 38 1.9	23S 6.6	9S53.0	0N 0.8	22S56.7	19S52.7	1S 7.6	0S43.7	7N 5.8	16N58.0	2N53.7	23N22.8
4 T	6 49 51.6	22 51.5	9 49.5	12S32.6	23 30.4	18 52.3	0 15.4	0 34.2	7 7.3	16 57.1	2 54.1	23 24.0
7 S	7 1 41.2	22 32.3	9 46.0	18 50.5	23 54.2	17 47.2	0N36.8	0 24.3	7 9.1	16 56.3	2 54.5	23 25.2
10 W	7 13 30.9	22 9.2	9 42.5	16 29.2	24 7.3	16 37.7	1 28.9	0 13.8	7 11.3	16 55.6	2 55.1	23 26.3
13 S	7 25 20.5	21 42.1	9 39.0	7 38.8	24 9.0	15 24.2	2 20.8	0 2.8	7 13.9	16 55.0	2 55.8	23 27.5
16 T	7 37 10.2	21 11.2	9 35.6	3N40.3	23 58.7	14 7.0	3 12.5	0N 8.7	7 16.8	16 54.5	2 56.6	23 28.7
19 F	7 48 59.9	20 36.7	9 32.1	13 54.4	23 36.0	12 46.5	4 3.9	0 20.6	7 20.0	16 54.2	2 57.5	23 29.8
22 M	8 0 49.6	19 58.7	9 28.6	18 56.4	23 0.5	11 23.1	4 54.9	0 32.9	7 23.6	16 54.0	2 58.6	23 31.0
25 T	8 12 39.2	19 17.3	9 25.1	14 24.8	22 11.9	9 57.1	5 45.5	0 45.7	7 27.5	16 53.9	2 59.7	23 32.1
28 S	8 24 28.9	18 32.8	9 21.6	1 41.8	21 9.9	8 28.8	6 35.6	0 58.8	7 31.7	16 54.0	3 0.9	23 33.2
31 W	8 36 18.6	17 45.2	9 18.0	11S28.2	19 54.3	6 58.6	7 25.2	1 12.3	7 36.2	16 54.2	3 2.2	23 34.3

FEBRUARY 1940

DAY	EPHEMERIS SIDEREAL TIME	☉	☊	☽	☿	♀	♂	♃	♄	♅	♆	♇
						LONGITUDE						
1 T	8 40 15.1	10♒59.1	23♎54.8	15♏47.1	11♒ 8.7	16♓24.7	19♈ 4.3	5♈57.5	25♈31.5	17♉59.5	25♍11.4	1♌34.2
2 F	8 44 11.7	11 60.0	23 51.7	29 7.2	12 52.9	17 37.6	19 45.2	6 8.7	25 35.2	17 59.8	25R10.3	1R32.8
3 S	8 48 8.2	13 0.9	23 48.5	12♐10.8	14 37.7	18 50.5	20 26.0	6 20.1	25 39.1	18 0.1	25 9.2	1 31.5
4 S	8 52 4.8	14 1.8	23 45.3	25 0.3	16 23.2	20 3.3	21 6.9	6 31.5	25 43.0	18 0.5	25 8.1	1 30.2
5 M	8 56 1.3	15 2.6	23 42.1	7♑37.7	18 9.3	21 16.0	21 47.7	6 43.0	25 47.0	18 1.0	25 6.9	1 28.9
6 T	8 59 57.9	16 3.5	23 39.0	20 4.5	19 56.0	22 28.6	22 28.6	6 54.7	25 51.1	18 1.5	25 5.7	1 27.6
7 W	9 3 54.5	17 4.3	23 35.8	2♒21.8	21 43.3	23 41.2	23 9.4	7 6.4	25 55.3	18 2.1	25 4.5	1 26.3
8 T	9 7 51.0	18 5.1	23 32.6	14 30.6	23 31.2	24 53.7	23 50.2	7 18.2	25 59.6	18 2.7	25 3.3	1 25.0
9 F	9 11 47.5	19 5.9	23 29.4	26 31.6	25 19.5	26 6.2	24 31.0	7 30.1	26 4.0	18 3.4	25 2.0	1 23.7
10 S	9 15 44.1	20 6.6	23 26.2	8♓26.2	27 8.2	27 18.5	25 11.9	7 42.1	26 8.4	18 4.1	25 0.7	1 22.4
11 S	9 19 40.7	21 7.4	23 23.1	20 15.8	28 57.2	28 30.8	25 52.7	7 54.2	26 13.0	18 4.9	24 59.4	1 21.2
12 M	9 23 37.2	22 8.1	23 19.9	2♈ 2.9	0♓46.4	29 43.0	26 33.5	8 6.4	26 17.6	18 5.7	24 58.1	1 19.9
13 T	9 27 33.8	23 8.8	23 16.7	13 50.6	2 35.5	0♈55.1	27 14.2	8 18.6	26 22.4	18 6.6	24 56.7	1 18.7
14 W	9 31 30.3	24 9.5	23 13.5	25 42.7	4 24.5	2 7.1	27 55.0	8 30.9	26 27.1	18 7.5	24 55.4	1 17.4
15 T	9 35 26.9	25 10.1	23 10.4	7♉43.9	6 13.2	3 19.0	28 35.7	8 43.4	26 32.0	18 8.5	24 54.0	1 16.2
16 F	9 39 23.4	26 10.7	23 7.2	19 59.2	8 1.2	4 30.8	29 16.5	8 55.8	26 37.0	18 9.6	24 52.6	1 15.0
17 S	9 43 20.0	27 11.3	23 4.0	2♊33.7	9 48.3	5 42.6	29 57.2	9 8.4	26 42.0	18 10.6	24 51.2	1 13.8
18 S	9 47 16.6	28 11.8	23 0.8	15 32.4	11 34.2	6 54.2	0♉37.9	9 21.0	26 47.1	18 11.8	24 49.7	1 12.6
19 M	9 51 13.1	29 12.4	22 57.6	28 59.0	13 18.4	8 5.7	1 18.6	9 33.8	26 52.3	18 13.0	24 48.3	1 11.4
20 T	9 55 9.6	0♓12.8	22 54.5	12♋55.5	15 0.7	9 17.1	1 59.3	9 46.5	26 57.6	18 14.2	24 46.8	1 10.3
21 W	9 59 6.2	1 13.3	22 51.3	27 21.2	16 40.4	10 28.4	2 39.9	9 59.4	27 2.9	18 15.5	24 45.3	1 9.1
22 T	10 3 2.8	2 13.7	22 48.1	12♌11.9	18 17.1	11 39.7	3 20.5	10 12.3	27 8.3	18 16.8	24 43.8	1 8.0
23 F	10 6 59.3	3 14.1	22 44.9	27 20.1	19 50.2	12 50.7	4 1.1	10 25.3	27 13.8	18 18.2	24 42.3	1 6.9
24 S	10 10 55.9	4 14.5	22 41.8	12♍35.8	21 19.1	14 1.7	4 41.7	10 38.3	27 19.3	18 19.6	24 40.8	1 5.8
25 S	10 14 52.4	5 14.9	22 38.6	27 48.4	22 43.2	15 12.6	5 22.3	10 51.4	27 25.0	18 21.1	24 39.2	1 4.7
26 M	10 18 49.0	6 15.2	22 35.4	12♎48.0	24 1.9	16 23.3	6 2.9	11 4.6	27 30.6	18 22.6	24 37.7	1 3.6
27 T	10 22 45.5	7 15.5	22 32.2	27 27.5	25 14.6	17 33.9	6 43.4	11 17.8	27 36.4	18 24.2	24 36.1	1 2.6
28 W	10 26 42.1	8 15.7	22 29.0	11♏42.6	26 20.6	18 44.4	7 23.9	11 31.1	27 42.2	18 25.8	24 34.5	1 1.5
29 T	10 30 38.6	9 16.0	22 25.9	25 32.0	27 19.4	19 54.8	8 4.4	11 44.5	27 48.1	18 27.5	24 32.9	1 0.5
						DECLINATION						
1 T	8 40 15.1	17S28.7	9S16.9	14S41.7	19S26.0	6S28.2	7N41.6	1N16.9	7N37.8	16N54.2	3N 2.7	23N34.7
4 S	8 52 4.8	16 37.3	9 13.4	18 53.5	17 52.2	4 56.0	8 30.5	1 30.8	7 42.7	16 54.6	3 4.1	23 35.7
7 W	9 3 54.5	15 43.3	9 9.8	14 47.9	16 5.0	3 22.8	9 18.6	1 45.1	7 47.8	16 55.1	3 5.7	23 36.7
10 S	9 15 44.1	14 47.0	9 6.3	5 10.6	14 4.9	1 48.7	10 6.1	1 59.6	7 53.2	16 55.7	3 7.3	23 37.7
13 T	9 27 33.8	13 48.3	9 2.8	6N 5.6	11 53.0	0 14.2	10 52.8	2 14.4	7 58.9	16 56.5	3 8.9	23 38.7
16 F	9 39 23.4	12 47.7	8 59.3	15 22.9	9 31.5	1N20.4	11 38.7	2 29.5	8 4.8	16 57.4	3 10.7	23 39.6
19 M	9 51 13.1	11 45.2	8 55.7	18 42.2	7 3.8	2 54.8	12 23.8	2 44.8	8 10.9	16 58.4	3 12.4	23 40.5
22 T	10 3 2.8	10 41.0	8 52.2	12 32.6	4 35.3	4 28.7	13 7.9	3 0.3	8 17.3	16 59.6	3 14.3	23 41.3
25 S	10 14 52.4	9 35.4	8 48.7	0S58.8	2 13.6	6 1.6	13 51.0	3 16.0	8 23.8	17 0.8	3 16.2	23 42.1
28 W	10 26 42.1	8 28.4	8 45.1	13 35.2	0 7.7	7 33.5	14 33.1	3 31.8	8 30.5	17 2.2	3 18.1	23 42.8

MARCH 1940

LONGITUDE

DAY	EPHEMERIS SIDEREAL TIME h m s	☉ ° ′	☊ ° ′	☽ ° ′	☿ ° ′	♀ ° ′	♂ ° ′	♃ ° ′	♄ ° ′	♅ ° ′	♆ ° ′	♇ ° ′
1 F	10 34 35.2	10♓16.2	22♎22.7	8♐56.8	28♓10.4	21♈ 5.1	8♉44.9	11♈57.9	27♈54.0	18♉29.2	24♍31.3	0♌59.5
2 S	10 38 31.7	11 16.4	22 19.5	21 59.3	28 53.1	22 15.2	9 25.3	12 11.3	28 0.1	18 31.0	24R29.7	0R58.5
3 S	10 42 28.3	12 16.6	22 16.3	4♑42.8	29 27.2	23 25.2	10 5.8	12 24.8	28 6.1	18 32.8	24 28.1	0 57.5
4 M	10 46 24.8	13 16.7	22 13.2	17 10.5	29 52.2	24 35.0	10 46.2	12 38.4	28 12.3	18 34.6	24 26.5	0 56.6
5 T	10 50 21.4	14 16.8	22 10.0	29 25.7	0♈ 8.1	25 44.8	11 26.6	12 52.0	28 18.4	18 36.5	24 24.9	0 55.6
6 W	10 54 17.9	15 16.9	22 6.8	11♒31.3	0 14.8	26 54.4	12 7.0	13 5.7	28 24.7	18 38.4	24 23.2	0 54.7
7 T	10 58 14.5	16 17.0	22 3.6	23 29.5	0R12.3	28 3.8	12 47.4	13 19.4	28 31.0	18 40.4	24 21.6	0 53.9
8 F	11 2 11.1	17 17.0	22 0.4	5♓22.5	0 0.9	29 13.1	13 27.7	13 33.1	28 37.4	18 42.4	24 19.9	0 53.0
9 S	11 6 7.6	18 17.0	21 57.3	17 12.2	29♓40.9	0♉22.3	14 8.0	13 46.9	28 43.8	18 44.5	24 18.3	0 52.1
10 S	11 10 4.1	19 17.0	21 54.1	29 0.4	29 12.8	1 31.3	14 48.4	14 0.8	28 50.2	18 46.6	24 16.6	0 51.3
11 M	11 14 0.7	20 16.9	21 50.9	10♈49.0	28 37.5	2 40.1	15 28.7	14 14.7	28 56.8	18 48.7	24 15.0	0 50.5
12 T	11 17 57.3	21 16.8	21 47.7	22 40.4	27 55.8	3 48.8	16 8.9	14 28.6	29 3.3	18 50.9	24 13.3	0 49.7
13 W	11 21 53.8	22 16.7	21 44.6	4♉37.4	27 8.7	4 57.3	16 49.2	14 42.5	29 10.0	18 53.1	24 11.6	0 48.9
14 T	11 25 50.3	23 16.5	21 41.4	16 43.1	26 17.4	6 5.7	17 29.4	14 56.5	29 16.6	18 55.4	24 10.0	0 48.2
15 F	11 29 46.9	24 16.3	21 38.2	29 1.4	25 23.0	7 13.8	18 9.6	15 10.6	29 23.3	18 57.7	24 8.3	0 47.4
16 S	11 33 43.5	25 16.1	21 35.0	11♊36.2	24 26.9	8 21.8	18 49.8	15 24.6	29 30.1	19 0.1	24 6.6	0 46.7
17 S	11 37 40.0	26 15.8	21 31.8	24 31.5	23 30.2	9 29.6	19 30.0	15 38.7	29 36.9	19 2.4	24 5.0	0 46.1
18 M	11 41 36.5	27 15.5	21 28.7	7♋50.8	22 34.2	10 37.3	20 10.1	15 52.8	29 43.8	19 4.9	24 3.3	0 45.4
19 T	11 45 33.1	28 15.1	21 25.5	21 36.7	21 40.1	11 44.7	20 50.2	16 7.0	29 50.7	19 7.3	24 1.6	0 44.8
20 W	11 49 29.7	29 14.7	21 22.3	5♌49.5	20 48.7	12 51.9	21 30.3	16 21.2	29 57.6	19 9.8	23 60.0	0 44.2
21 T	11 53 26.2	0♈14.3	21 19.1	20 27.5	20 1.1	13 58.9	22 10.4	16 35.4	0♉ 4.6	19 12.3	23 58.3	0 43.6
22 F	11 57 22.8	1 13.8	21 16.0	5♍25.7	19 17.9	15 5.7	22 50.4	16 49.6	0 11.6	19 14.9	23 56.7	0 43.0
23 S	12 1 19.3	2 13.3	21 12.8	20 36.4	18 39.6	16 12.3	23 30.5	17 3.9	0 18.6	19 17.5	23 55.0	0 42.5
24 S	12 5 15.9	3 12.8	21 9.6	5♎50.2	18 6.8	17 18.6	24 10.4	17 18.2	0 25.7	19 20.1	23 53.4	0 41.9
25 M	12 9 12.4	4 12.2	21 6.4	20 57.1	17 39.7	18 24.8	24 50.4	17 32.5	0 32.8	19 22.8	23 51.8	0 41.4
26 T	12 13 9.0	5 11.6	21 3.2	5♏48.2	17 18.5	19 30.7	25 30.4	17 46.8	0 40.0	19 25.5	23 50.1	0 41.0
27 W	12 17 5.5	6 11.0	21 0.1	20 17.0	17 3.2	20 36.3	26 10.3	18 1.1	0 47.2	19 28.2	23 48.5	0 40.5
28 T	12 21 2.1	7 10.3	20 56.9	4♐19.8	16 53.8	21 41.7	26 50.2	18 15.5	0 54.4	19 30.9	23 46.9	0 40.1
29 F	12 24 58.6	8 9.6	20 53.7	17 55.3	16 50.3	22 46.9	27 30.0	18 29.9	1 1.6	19 33.7	23 45.3	0 39.7
30 S	12 28 55.2	9 8.9	20 50.5	1♑ 5.0	16D52.4	23 51.8	28 9.9	18 44.3	1 8.9	19 36.6	23 43.7	0 39.3
31 S	12 32 51.7	10 8.1	20 47.3	13 51.4	17 0.1	24 56.5	28 49.7	18 58.7	1 16.2	19 39.4	23 42.1	0 39.0

DECLINATION

DAY	EPHEMERIS SIDEREAL TIME h m s	☉	☊	☽	☿	♀	♂	♃	♄	♅	♆	♇
1 F	10 34 35.2	7S43.1	8S42.7	17S58.7	1N 2.6	8N33.9	15N 0.5	3N42.5	8N35.1	17N 3.1	3N19.4	23N43.3
4 M	10 46 24.8	6 34.4	8 39.2	17 12.7	2 20.6	10 3.1	15 40.8	3 58.6	8 42.0	17 4.7	3 21.4	23 43.9
7 T	10 58 14.5	5 24.8	8 35.6	9 34.8	2 59.5	11 30.4	16 19.9	4 14.8	8 49.2	17 6.4	3 23.4	23 44.5
10 S	11 10 4.1	4 14.6	8 32.1	1N20.1	2 55.5	12 55.3	16 57.8	4 31.1	8 56.4	17 8.1	3 25.4	23 45.1
13 W	11 21 53.8	3 3.9	8 28.5	11 49.5	2 11.2	14 17.7	17 34.5	4 47.5	9 3.8	17 10.0	3 27.4	23 45.6
16 S	11 33 43.5	1 52.9	8 25.0	18 6.2	0 55.7	15 37.2	18 9.9	5 3.9	9 11.3	17 11.9	3 29.4	23 46.0
19 T	11 45 33.1	0 41.7	8 21.4	16 30.9	0S36.1	16 53.6	18 44.0	5 20.4	9 18.9	17 14.0	3 31.4	23 46.4
22 F	11 57 22.8	0N29.4	8 17.8	6 4.5	2 8.2	18 6.5	19 16.6	5 37.0	9 26.5	17 16.1	3 33.4	23 46.8
25 M	12 9 12.4	1 40.3	8 14.2	8S 5.9	3 28.3	19 15.7	19 47.9	5 53.5	9 34.3	17 18.3	3 35.3	23 47.0
28 T	12 21 2.1	2 50.8	8 10.7	17 22.7	4 28.7	20 20.9	20 17.6	6 10.0	9 42.1	17 20.5	3 37.3	23 47.3
31 S	12 32 51.7	4 0.9	8 7.1	17 29.6	5 6.7	21 21.9	20 45.9	6 26.6	9 49.9	17 22.9	3 39.1	23 47.4

APRIL 1940

LONGITUDE

DAY	EPHEMERIS SIDEREAL TIME h m s	☉	☊	☽	☿	♀	♂	♃	♄	♅	♆	♇
1 M	12 36 48.3	11♈ 7.3	20♎44.2	26♑18.3	17♓13.0	26♉ 0.9	29♉29.5	19♈13.1	1♉23.6	19♉42.3	23♍40.5	0♌38.7
2 T	12 40 44.8	12 6.5	20 41.0	8♒29.7	17 31.0	27 5.0	0♊ 9.3	19 27.5	1 30.9	19 45.2	23R39.0	0R38.4
3 W	12 44 41.4	13 5.7	20 37.8	20 29.8	17 53.9	28 8.9	0 49.1	19 42.0	1 38.3	19 48.1	23 37.4	0 38.1
4 T	12 48 37.9	14 4.8	20 34.6	2♓22.5	18 21.4	29 12.4	1 28.8	19 56.4	1 45.7	19 51.1	23 35.9	0 37.9
5 F	12 52 34.5	15 3.9	20 31.5	14 11.1	18 53.2	0♊15.7	2 8.5	20 10.9	1 53.2	19 54.1	23 34.3	0 37.6
6 S	12 56 31.0	16 3.0	20 28.3	25 58.8	19 29.2	1 18.7	2 48.2	20 25.4	2 0.6	19 57.1	23 32.8	0 37.4
7 S	13 0 27.6	17 2.0	20 25.1	7♈48.1	20 9.2	2 21.3	3 27.9	20 39.8	2 8.1	20 0.1	23 31.3	0 37.3
8 M	13 4 24.1	18 1.0	20 21.9	19 41.5	20 52.8	3 23.7	4 7.6	20 54.3	2 15.6	20 3.2	23 29.8	0 37.1
9 T	13 8 20.7	18 60.0	20 18.7	1♉40.9	21 40.0	4 25.7	4 47.2	21 8.8	2 23.1	20 6.3	23 28.4	0 37.0
10 W	13 12 17.3	19 58.9	20 15.6	13 48.4	22 30.6	5 27.3	5 26.8	21 23.3	2 30.7	20 9.4	23 26.9	0 36.9
11 T	13 16 13.8	20 57.8	20 12.4	26 5.8	23 24.3	6 28.6	6 6.4	21 37.8	2 38.2	20 12.5	23 25.4	0 36.9
12 F	13 20 10.3	21 56.6	20 9.2	8♊35.4	24 21.1	7 29.6	6 46.0	21 52.3	2 45.8	20 15.6	23 24.0	0 36.8
13 S	13 24 6.9	22 55.4	20 6.0	21 19.3	25 20.8	8 30.1	7 25.5	22 6.7	2 53.4	20 18.8	23 22.6	0 36.8
14 S	13 28 3.5	23 54.2	20 2.9	4♋19.8	26 23.2	9 30.3	8 5.0	22 21.2	3 1.0	20 22.0	23 21.2	0D36.8
15 M	13 32 0.0	24 53.0	19 59.7	17 38.9	27 28.2	10 30.1	8 44.5	22 35.7	3 8.6	20 25.2	23 19.9	0 36.9
16 T	13 35 56.6	25 51.7	19 56.5	1♌18.2	28 35.8	11 29.4	9 24.0	22 50.2	3 16.2	20 28.4	23 18.5	0 36.9
17 W	13 39 53.1	26 50.3	19 53.3	15 18.5	29 45.8	12 28.4	10 3.4	23 4.6	3 23.8	20 31.7	23 17.2	0 37.0
18 T	13 43 49.7	27 49.0	19 50.1	29 39.0	0♈58.1	13 26.8	10 42.9	23 19.1	3 31.4	20 35.0	23 15.9	0 37.1
19 F	13 47 46.2	28 47.6	19 47.0	14♍17.1	2 12.7	14 24.9	11 22.3	23 33.5	3 39.1	20 38.3	23 14.6	0 37.3
20 S	13 51 42.8	29 46.1	19 43.8	29 8.2	3 29.4	15 22.4	12 1.6	23 48.0	3 46.7	20 41.5	23 13.3	0 37.5
21 S	13 55 39.3	0♉44.7	19 40.6	14♎ 5.9	4 48.3	16 19.4	12 41.0	24 2.4	3 54.4	20 44.9	23 12.1	0 37.7
22 M	13 59 35.9	1 43.1	19 37.4	29 2.3	6 9.3	17 16.0	13 20.3	24 16.8	4 2.0	20 48.2	23 10.8	0 37.9
23 T	14 3 32.4	2 41.6	19 34.3	13♏49.3	7 32.3	18 12.0	13 59.6	24 31.2	4 9.7	20 51.5	23 9.6	0 38.1
24 W	14 7 29.0	3 40.0	19 31.1	28 19.6	8 57.3	19 7.4	14 38.9	24 45.6	4 17.3	20 54.9	23 8.4	0 38.4
25 T	14 11 25.5	4 38.4	19 27.9	12♐27.7	10 24.2	20 2.3	15 18.1	24 59.9	4 25.0	20 58.3	23 7.3	0 38.7
26 F	14 15 22.1	5 36.8	19 24.7	26 10.6	11 53.0	20 56.7	15 57.4	25 14.3	4 32.6	21 1.6	23 6.1	0 39.0
27 S	14 19 18.7	6 35.2	19 21.5	9♑27.4	13 23.8	21 50.4	16 36.6	25 28.6	4 40.3	21 5.0	23 5.0	0 39.4
28 S	14 23 15.2	7 33.5	19 18.4	22 19.5	14 56.4	22 43.5	17 15.8	25 42.9	4 48.0	21 8.4	23 3.9	0 39.7
29 M	14 27 11.8	8 31.8	19 15.2	4♒49.9	16 30.9	23 36.0	17 54.9	25 57.2	4 55.6	21 11.9	23 2.9	0 40.1
30 T	14 31 8.3	9 30.0	19 12.0	17 2.6	18 7.2	24 27.9	18 34.1	26 11.5	5 3.2	21 15.3	23 1.8	0 40.6

DECLINATION

DAY	EPHEMERIS SIDEREAL TIME h m s	☉	☊	☽	☿	♀	♂	♃	♄	♅	♆	♇
1 M	12 36 48.3	4N24.1	8S 5.9	15S43.7	5S14.3	21N41.3	20N55.0	6N32.1	9N52.5	17N23.7	3N39.8	23N47.5
4 T	12 48 37.9	5 33.3	8 2.3	6 58.4	5 22.6	22 36.4	21 21.3	6 48.5	10 0.4	17 26.1	3 41.6	23 47.6
7 S	13 0 27.6	6 41.6	7 58.7	4N 7.6	5 10.4	23 26.9	21 45.9	7 5.0	10 8.3	17 28.6	3 43.4	23 47.6
10 W	13 12 17.3	7 48.8	7 55.1	13 56.4	4 39.5	24 12.6	22 9.0	7 21.3	10 16.2	17 31.1	3 45.1	23 47.6
13 S	13 24 6.9	8 54.9	7 51.5	18 31.2	3 51.8	24 53.4	22 30.4	7 37.6	10 24.1	17 33.6	3 46.8	23 47.5
16 T	13 35 56.6	9 59.6	7 47.9	14 48.2	2 49.1	25 29.1	22 50.2	7 53.7	10 31.9	17 36.3	3 48.4	23 47.4
19 F	13 47 46.2	11 2.9	7 44.3	3 19.6	1 32.7	25 59.8	23 8.3	8 9.8	10 39.8	17 38.9	3 49.9	23 47.2
22 M	13 59 35.9	12 4.5	7 40.7	10S21.5	0 4.0	26 25.4	23 24.6	8 25.7	10 47.6	17 41.6	3 51.3	23 47.0
25 T	14 11 25.5	13 4.3	7 37.1	18 8.3	1N35.7	26 45.9	23 39.3	8 41.5	10 55.3	17 44.2	3 52.7	23 46.7
28 S	14 23 15.2	14 2.1	7 33.5	16 23.6	3 25.5	27 1.5	23 52.2	8 57.1	11 3.0	17 47.0	3 53.9	23 46.4

MAY 1940

LONGITUDE

DAY	EPHEMERIS SIDEREAL TIME h m s	☉ ° ′	☊ ° ′	☽ ° ′	☿ ° ′	♀ ° ′	♂ ° ′	♃ ° ′	♄ ° ′	♅ ° ′	♆ ° ′	♇ ° ′
1 W	14 35 4.8	10♉28.3	19♎ 8.8	29♒ 2.3	19♈45.4	25♊19.0	19♊13.2	26♈25.7	5♉10.9	21♉18.7	23♍ 0.8	0♌41.0
2 T	14 39 1.4	11 26.5	19 5.6	10♓53.7	21 25.5	26 9.5	19 52.3	26 40.0	5 18.5	21 22.2	22R59.8	0 41.5
3 F	14 42 58.0	12 24.7	19 2.5	22 41.5	23 7.4	26 59.2	20 31.4	26 54.2	5 26.2	21 25.6	22 58.9	0 42.0
4 S	14 46 54.5	13 22.9	18 59.3	4♈29.8	24 51.2	27 48.2	21 10.5	27 8.3	5 33.8	21 29.1	22 57.9	0 42.5
5 S	14 50 51.1	14 21.0	18 56.1	16 22.6	26 36.8	28 36.4	21 49.6	27 22.5	5 41.4	21 32.5	22 57.0	0 43.1
6 M	14 54 47.6	15 19.1	18 52.9	28 22.9	28 24.2	29 23.7	22 28.6	27 36.6	5 49.0	21 36.0	22 56.1	0 43.6
7 T	14 58 44.2	16 17.2	18 49.8	10♉33.1	0♉13.6	0♋10.3	23 7.6	27 50.7	5 56.6	21 39.5	22 55.3	0 44.2
8 W	15 2 40.8	17 15.3	18 46.6	22 55.0	2 4.8	0 55.9	23 46.6	28 4.8	6 4.2	21 42.9	22 54.5	0 44.9
9 T	15 6 37.3	18 13.3	18 43.4	5♊29.8	3 57.9	1 40.7	24 25.6	28 18.8	6 11.7	21 46.4	22 53.7	0 45.5
10 F	15 10 33.8	19 11.3	18 40.2	18 18.0	5 52.8	2 24.5	25 4.5	28 32.8	6 19.3	21 49.9	22 52.9	0 46.2
11 S	15 14 30.4	20 9.3	18 37.1	1♋20.0	7 49.5	3 7.3	25 43.5	28 46.7	6 26.8	21 53.4	22 52.2	0 46.9
12 S	15 18 27.0	21 7.2	18 33.9	14 35.7	9 48.1	3 49.1	26 22.4	29 0.7	6 34.3	21 56.9	22 51.4	0 47.6
13 M	15 22 23.5	22 5.2	18 30.7	28 4.9	11 48.5	4 29.9	27 1.3	29 14.5	6 41.8	22 0.4	22 50.8	0 48.3
14 T	15 26 20.1	23 3.0	18 27.5	11♌47.6	13 50.5	5 9.5	27 40.2	29 28.4	6 49.3	22 3.8	22 50.1	0 49.1
15 W	15 30 16.6	24 0.9	18 24.3	25 43.4	15 54.3	5 47.9	28 19.0	29 42.2	6 56.7	22 7.3	22 49.5	0 49.9
16 T	15 34 13.2	24 58.7	18 21.2	9♍51.5	17 59.6	6 25.2	28 57.9	29 55.9	7 4.1	22 10.8	22 48.9	0 50.7
17 F	15 38 9.8	25 56.5	18 18.0	24 10.8	20 6.3	7 1.3	29 36.7	0♉ 9.7	7 11.6	22 14.3	22 48.3	0 51.5
18 S	15 42 6.3	26 54.3	18 14.8	8♎38.8	22 14.4	7 36.0	0♋15.5	0 23.3	7 18.9	22 17.8	22 47.8	0 52.4
19 S	15 46 2.8	27 52.0	18 11.6	23 11.9	24 23.6	8 9.3	0 54.3	0 37.0	7 26.3	22 21.2	22 47.3	0 53.3
20 M	15 49 59.4	28 49.8	18 8.5	7♏45.5	26 33.7	8 41.3	1 33.0	0 50.5	7 33.6	22 24.7	22 46.8	0 54.2
21 T	15 53 56.0	29 47.5	18 5.3	22 13.9	28 44.6	9 11.9	2 11.7	1 4.1	7 40.9	22 28.2	22 46.4	0 55.1
22 W	15 57 52.5	0♊45.1	18 2.1	6♐30.9	0♊56.1	9 40.9	2 50.5	1 17.6	7 48.2	22 31.6	22 46.0	0 56.0
23 T	16 1 49.0	1 42.8	17 58.9	20 31.3	3 7.8	10 8.4	3 29.2	1 31.0	7 55.4	22 35.1	22 45.6	0 57.0
24 F	16 5 45.6	2 40.4	17 55.7	4♑11.0	5 19.4	10 34.2	4 7.8	1 44.4	8 2.7	22 38.5	22 45.3	0 58.0
25 S	16 9 42.2	3 38.0	17 52.6	17 27.8	7 30.8	10 58.4	4 46.5	1 57.7	8 9.9	22 42.0	22 44.9	0 59.0
26 S	16 13 38.7	4 35.6	17 49.4	0♒21.6	9 41.7	11 20.9	5 25.2	2 11.0	8 17.0	22 45.4	22 44.7	1 0.0
27 M	16 17 35.3	5 33.2	17 46.2	12 54.1	11 51.7	11 41.5	6 3.8	2 24.3	8 24.1	22 48.8	22 44.4	1 1.1
28 T	16 21 31.8	6 30.8	17 43.0	25 8.6	14 0.6	12 0.4	6 42.4	2 37.4	8 31.2	22 52.2	22 44.2	1 2.1
29 W	16 25 28.4	7 28.3	17 39.9	7♓ 9.4	16 8.1	12 17.3	7 21.0	2 50.6	8 38.3	22 55.6	22 44.0	1 3.2
30 T	16 29 25.0	8 25.8	17 36.7	19 1.4	18 14.1	12 32.3	7 59.6	3 3.6	8 45.3	22 59.0	22 43.8	1 4.3
31 F	16 33 21.5	9 23.4	17 33.5	0♈49.8	20 18.4	12 45.3	8 38.2	3 16.6	8 52.3	23 2.4	22 43.7	1 5.5

DECLINATION

DAY	h m s	☉	☊	☽	☿	♀	♂	♃	♄	♅	♆	♇
1 W	14 35 4.8	14N57.9	7S29.9	7S58.3	5N24.1	27N12.2	24N 3.4	9N12.6	11N10.7	17N49.7	3N55.1	23N46.0
4 S	14 46 54.5	15 51.5	7 26.3	3N 4.7	7 30.3	27 18.2	24 12.8	9 27.9	11 18.2	17 52.4	3 56.2	23 45.6
7 T	14 58 44.2	16 42.8	7 22.7	13 14.1	9 42.6	27 19.7	24 20.4	9 43.0	11 25.7	17 55.1	3 57.2	23 45.1
10 F	15 10 33.8	17 31.5	7 19.0	18 29.6	11 59.2	27 16.9	24 26.3	9 57.9	11 33.1	17 57.9	3 58.0	23 44.6
13 M	15 22 23.5	18 17.6	7 15.4	15 29.9	14 17.5	27 10.2	24 30.4	10 12.5	11 40.3	18 0.6	3 58.8	23 44.1
16 T	15 34 13.2	19 0.9	7 11.8	4 47.2	16 34.2	26 59.8	24 32.7	10 27.0	11 47.5	18 3.3	3 59.5	23 43.5
19 S	15 46 2.8	19 41.3	7 8.2	8S42.6	18 44.8	26 46.0	24 33.3	10 41.2	11 54.5	18 6.0	4 0.0	23 42.8
22 W	15 57 52.5	20 18.8	7 4.5	17 40.0	20 44.2	26 29.2	24 32.1	10 55.2	12 1.4	18 8.7	4 0.4	23 42.2
25 S	16 9 42.2	20 53.0	7 0.9	17 11.6	22 27.0	26 9.7	24 29.1	11 8.9	12 8.1	18 11.3	4 0.8	23 41.4
28 T	16 21 31.8	21 24.1	6 57.3	9 13.1	23 48.5	25 47.8	24 24.5	11 22.3	12 14.7	18 13.9	4 1.0	23 40.7
31 F	16 33 21.5	21 51.8	6 53.6	1N47.9	24 46.1	25 23.6	24 18.1	11 35.5	12 21.2	18 16.5	4 1.1	23 39.9

JUNE 1940

LONGITUDE

DAY	h m s	☉	☊	☽	☿	♀	♂	♃	♄	♅	♆	♇
1 S	16 37 18.1	10♊20.9	17♎30.3	12♈39.9	22♊20.7	12♋56.2	9♋16.7	3♉29.6	8♉59.2	23♉ 5.8	22♍43.6	1♌ 6.6
2 S	16 41 14.6	11 18.4	17 27.2	24 36.4	24 20.9	13 5.0	9 55.3	3 42.5	9 6.1	23 9.2	22R43.6	1 7.8
3 M	16 45 11.2	12 15.8	17 24.0	6♉43.4	26 19.0	13 11.7	10 33.8	3 55.3	9 13.0	23 12.5	22 43.5	1 8.9
4 T	16 49 7.7	13 13.3	17 20.8	19 4.2	28 14.7	13 16.1	11 12.3	4 8.0	9 19.8	23 15.8	22D43.6	1 10.2
5 W	16 53 4.3	14 10.8	17 17.6	1♊41.1	0♋ 8.0	13 18.2	11 50.8	4 20.7	9 26.6	23 19.2	22 43.6	1 11.4
6 T	16 57 0.9	15 8.2	17 14.5	14 34.9	1 58.9	13R18.0	12 29.3	4 33.4	9 33.4	23 22.5	22 43.7	1 12.6
7 F	17 0 57.4	16 5.6	17 11.3	27 45.4	3 47.2	13 15.4	13 7.8	4 45.9	9 40.1	23 25.7	22 43.8	1 13.9
8 S	17 4 53.9	17 3.0	17 8.1	11♋11.1	5 33.0	13 10.5	13 46.2	4 58.4	9 46.7	23 29.0	22 43.9	1 15.1
9 S	17 8 50.5	18 0.4	17 4.9	24 49.8	7 16.3	13 3.2	14 24.7	5 10.8	9 53.3	23 32.3	22 44.1	1 16.4
10 M	17 12 47.1	18 57.8	17 1.7	8♌38.7	8 56.9	12 53.5	15 3.1	5 23.1	9 59.9	23 35.5	22 44.3	1 17.7
11 T	17 16 43.6	19 55.2	16 58.6	22 35.4	10 34.9	12 41.3	15 41.6	5 35.4	10 6.4	23 38.7	22 44.5	1 19.1
12 W	17 20 40.2	20 52.5	16 55.4	6♍37.7	12 10.2	12 26.8	16 20.0	5 47.6	10 12.8	23 41.9	22 44.8	1 20.4
13 T	17 24 36.7	21 49.8	16 52.2	20 43.9	13 42.9	12 9.8	16 58.4	5 59.7	10 19.2	23 45.1	22 45.1	1 21.7
14 F	17 28 33.3	22 47.2	16 49.0	4♎52.8	15 12.9	11 50.6	17 36.8	6 11.7	10 25.6	23 48.2	22 45.4	1 23.1
15 S	17 32 29.9	23 44.5	16 45.9	19 3.3	16 40.2	11 29.0	18 15.1	6 23.7	10 31.9	23 51.4	22 45.8	1 24.5
16 S	17 36 26.4	24 41.7	16 42.7	3♏13.7	18 4.7	11 5.3	18 53.5	6 35.5	10 38.1	23 54.5	22 46.2	1 25.9
17 M	17 40 22.9	25 39.0	16 39.5	17 22.0	19 26.5	10 39.4	19 31.8	6 47.3	10 44.3	23 57.6	22 46.6	1 27.3
18 T	17 44 19.5	26 36.2	16 36.3	1♐25.0	20 45.4	10 11.6	20 10.1	6 59.0	10 50.5	24 0.7	22 47.1	1 28.7
19 W	17 48 16.1	27 33.5	16 33.2	15 19.3	22 1.5	9 41.9	20 48.5	7 10.6	10 56.6	24 3.7	22 47.6	1 30.2
20 T	17 52 12.6	28 30.7	16 30.0	29 0.9	23 14.7	9 10.5	21 26.8	7 22.1	11 2.6	24 6.7	22 48.1	1 31.6
21 F	17 56 9.2	29 27.9	16 26.8	12♑26.4	24 24.9	8 37.6	22 5.0	7 33.6	11 8.5	24 9.7	22 48.6	1 33.1
22 S	18 0 5.7	0♋25.2	16 23.6	25 33.7	25 32.1	8 3.4	22 43.3	7 44.9	11 14.5	24 12.7	22 49.2	1 34.5
23 S	18 4 2.3	1 22.4	16 20.4	8♒21.6	26 36.2	7 28.1	23 21.6	7 56.2	11 20.3	24 15.6	22 49.8	1 36.0
24 M	18 7 58.9	2 19.6	16 17.3	20 51.0	27 37.1	6 51.8	23 59.9	8 7.4	11 26.1	24 18.6	22 50.5	1 37.5
25 T	18 11 55.4	3 16.8	16 14.1	3♓ 4.1	28 34.8	6 14.9	24 38.1	8 18.4	11 31.8	24 21.5	22 51.2	1 39.1
26 W	18 15 52.0	4 14.0	16 10.9	15 4.3	29 29.1	5 37.5	25 16.3	8 29.4	11 37.5	24 24.3	22 51.9	1 40.6
27 T	18 19 48.5	5 11.2	16 7.7	26 56.2	0♌19.9	4 59.9	25 54.6	8 40.3	11 43.1	24 27.2	22 52.6	1 42.1
28 F	18 23 45.1	6 8.4	16 4.6	8♈44.9	1 7.2	4 22.4	26 32.8	8 51.1	11 48.6	24 30.0	22 53.4	1 43.7
29 S	18 27 41.7	7 5.6	16 1.4	20 35.8	1 50.8	3 45.1	27 11.0	9 1.8	11 54.1	24 32.8	22 54.2	1 45.2
30 S	18 31 38.2	8 2.9	15 58.2	2♉34.3	2 30.6	3 8.4	27 49.2	9 12.3	11 59.5	24 35.5	22 55.0	1 46.8

DECLINATION

DAY	h m s	☉	☊	☽	☿	♀	♂	♃	♄	♅	♆	♇
1 S	16 37 18.1	22N 0.3	6S52.4	5N31.2	24N59.9	25N15.1	24N15.6	11N39.8	12N23.3	18N17.4	4N 1.1	23N39.7
4 T	16 49 7.7	22 23.4	6 48.8	15 0.5	25 25.3	24 48.4	24 6.9	11 52.5	12 29.5	18 19.9	4 1.0	23 38.8
7 F	17 0 57.4	22 43.1	6 45.1	18 40.1	25 28.5	24 20.0	23 56.6	12 5.0	12 35.6	18 22.4	4 0.8	23 38.0
10 M	17 12 47.1	22 59.1	6 41.5	13 30.6	25 12.3	23 49.9	23 44.7	12 17.2	12 41.4	18 24.8	4 0.6	23 37.1
13 T	17 24 36.7	23 11.5	6 37.8	1 32.3	24 40.0	23 18.1	23 31.1	12 29.0	12 47.1	18 27.2	4 0.1	23 36.2
16 S	17 36 26.4	23 20.3	6 34.2	11S19.3	23 54.6	22 44.7	23 15.9	12 40.5	12 52.6	18 29.5	3 59.6	23 35.3
19 W	17 48 16.1	23 25.3	6 30.5	18 23.4	22 59.4	22 9.9	22 59.2	12 51.6	12 57.9	18 31.8	3 59.0	23 34.4
22 S	18 0 5.7	23 26.6	6 26.8	16 8.2	21 57.2	21 34.0	22 40.9	13 2.5	13 3.0	18 34.0	3 58.2	23 33.4
25 T	18 11 55.4	23 24.2	6 23.2	7 7.8	20 51.0	20 57.6	22 21.2	13 12.9	13 7.9	18 36.2	3 57.4	23 32.4
28 F	18 23 45.1	23 18.1	6 19.5	4N 5.9	19 43.4	20 21.6	21 60.0	13 23.0	13 12.6	18 38.2	3 56.4	23 31.5

JULY 1940

LONGITUDE

DAY	EPHEMERIS SIDEREAL TIME h m s	☉ ° ′	☊ ° ′	☽ ° ′	☿ ° ′	♀ ° ′	♂ ° ′	♃ ° ′	♄ ° ′	♅ ° ′	♆ ° ′	♇ ° ′
1 M	18 35 34.8	9♋ 0.1	15♎55.0	14♉45.4	3♌ 6.4	2♋32.4	28♋27.4	9♉22.8	12♉ 4.8	24♉38.2	22♍55.9	1♌48.3
2 T	18 39 31.3	9 57.3	15 51.8	27 13.5	3 38.3	1R57.4	29 5.6	9 33.2	12 10.1	24 40.9	22 56.8	1 49.9
3 W	18 43 27.9	10 54.5	15 48.7	10♊ 1.5	4 5.9	1 23.5	29 43.8	9 43.4	12 15.3	24 43.6	22 57.7	1 51.5
4 T	18 47 24.4	11 51.7	15 45.5	23 11.1	4 29.3	0 51.0	0♌22.0	9 53.6	12 20.4	24 46.2	22 58.7	1 53.1
5 F	18 51 21.0	12 48.9	15 42.3	6♋41.7	4 48.2	0 20.1	1 0.2	10 3.6	12 25.4	24 48.8	22 59.6	1 54.7
6 S	18 55 17.5	13 46.2	15 39.1	20 31.2	5 2.7	29♊50.9	1 38.4	10 13.6	12 30.4	24 51.4	23 0.7	1 56.4
7 S	18 59 14.1	14 43.4	15 36.0	4♌35.4	5 12.5	29 23.5	2 16.6	10 23.4	12 35.3	24 53.9	23 1.7	1 58.0
8 M	19 3 10.7	15 40.6	15 32.8	18 49.5	5 17.7	28 58.1	2 54.7	10 33.1	12 40.1	24 56.4	23 2.8	1 59.6
9 T	19 7 7.2	16 37.8	15 29.6	3♍ 8.3	5 18.1	28 34.7	3 32.9	10 42.7	12 44.9	24 58.9	23 3.9	2 1.3
10 W	19 11 3.7	17 35.0	15 26.4	17 27.1	5R13.8	28 13.5	4 11.0	10 52.1	12 49.5	25 1.3	23 5.0	2 2.9
11 T	19 15 0.3	18 32.3	15 23.3	1♎42.5	5 4.8	27 54.6	4 49.2	11 1.5	12 54.1	25 3.7	23 6.2	2 4.5
12 F	19 18 56.9	19 29.5	15 20.1	15 52.5	4 51.1	27 37.9	5 27.3	11 10.7	12 58.6	25 6.0	23 7.3	2 6.2
13 S	19 22 53.5	20 26.7	15 16.9	29 55.8	4 32.9	27 23.6	6 5.5	11 19.8	13 3.1	25 8.3	23 8.6	2 7.9
14 S	19 26 50.0	21 23.9	15 13.7	13♏51.7	4 10.4	27 11.6	6 43.6	11 28.7	13 7.4	25 10.6	23 9.8	2 9.5
15 M	19 30 46.5	22 21.1	15 10.5	27 39.9	3 43.9	27 2.1	7 21.7	11 37.6	13 11.7	25 12.9	23 11.1	2 11.2
16 T	19 34 43.1	23 18.3	15 7.4	11♐19.6	3 13.6	26 54.8	7 59.8	11 46.3	13 15.8	25 15.1	23 12.4	2 12.9
17 W	19 38 39.7	24 15.6	15 4.2	24 49.3	2 39.9	26 50.0	8 37.9	11 54.9	13 19.9	25 17.2	23 13.7	2 14.6
18 T	19 42 36.2	25 12.8	15 1.0	8♑ 7.6	2 3.5	26 47.6	9 16.0	12 3.3	13 24.0	25 19.4	23 15.0	2 16.2
19 F	19 46 32.8	26 10.0	14 57.8	21 12.7	1 24.7	26 47.5	9 54.1	12 11.6	13 27.9	25 21.5	23 16.4	2 17.9
20 S	19 50 29.3	27 7.3	14 54.7	4♒ 3.3	0 44.2	26D49.7	10 32.2	12 19.8	13 31.7	25 23.5	23 17.8	2 19.6
21 S	19 54 25.9	28 4.5	14 51.5	16 38.8	0 2.7	26 54.1	11 10.3	12 27.9	13 35.5	25 25.5	23 19.2	2 21.3
22 M	19 58 22.4	29 1.8	14 48.3	28 59.6	29♋20.9	27 0.8	11 48.4	12 35.8	13 39.2	25 27.5	23 20.7	2 23.0
23 T	20 2 19.0	29 59.0	14 45.1	11♓ 7.2	28 39.5	27 9.6	12 26.5	12 43.5	13 42.8	25 29.4	23 22.1	2 24.7
24 W	20 6 15.6	0♌56.3	14 42.0	23 4.3	27 59.3	27 20.6	13 4.6	12 51.2	13 46.2	25 31.3	23 23.6	2 26.4
25 T	20 10 12.1	1 53.6	14 38.8	4♈54.4	27 21.0	27 33.6	13 42.7	12 58.7	13 49.7	25 33.1	23 25.1	2 28.1
26 F	20 14 8.7	2 50.9	14 35.6	16 42.1	26 45.4	27 48.7	14 20.7	13 6.0	13 53.0	25 34.9	23 26.7	2 29.8
27 S	20 18 5.2	3 48.3	14 32.4	28 32.5	26 13.0	28 5.7	14 58.8	13 13.2	13 56.2	25 36.7	23 28.3	2 31.5
28 S	20 22 1.8	4 45.6	14 29.3	10♉30.9	25 44.6	28 24.5	15 36.9	13 20.2	13 59.3	25 38.4	23 29.8	2 33.2
29 M	20 25 58.3	5 43.0	14 26.1	22 42.7	25 20.6	28 45.2	16 15.0	13 27.1	14 2.4	25 40.1	23 31.5	2 34.8
30 T	20 29 54.9	6 40.3	14 22.9	5♊12.9	25 1.6	29 7.6	16 53.1	13 33.8	14 5.3	25 41.7	23 33.1	2 36.5
31 W	20 33 51.4	7 37.7	14 19.7	18 5.4	24 48.1	29 31.8	17 31.2	13 40.4	14 8.1	25 43.3	23 34.7	2 38.2

DECLINATION

DAY	EPHEMERIS SIDEREAL TIME h m s	☉	☊	☽	☿	♀	♂	♃	♄	♅	♆	♇
1 M	18 35 34.8	23N 8.3	6S15.8	13N58.5	18N37.4	19N47.3	21N37.3	13N32.7	13N17.0	18N40.3	3N55.3	23N30.5
4 T	18 47 24.4	22 54.9	6 12.2	18 39.1	17 35.9	19 15.8	21 13.3	13 42.0	13 21.2	18 42.2	3 54.2	23 29.5
7 S	18 59 14.1	22 37.9	6 8.5	14 30.8	16 41.7	18 48.3	20 47.9	13 51.0	13 25.2	18 44.0	3 52.9	23 28.5
10 W	19 11 3.7	22 17.3	6 4.8	2 47.9	15 57.8	18 25.5	20 21.2	13 59.5	13 28.9	18 45.8	3 51.5	23 27.5
13 S	19 22 53.5	21 53.3	6 1.2	10S14.3	15 26.9	18 8.0	19 53.3	14 7.6	13 32.4	18 47.5	3 50.0	23 26.4
16 T	19 34 43.1	21 25.9	5 57.5	17 59.4	15 11.0	17 55.8	19 24.1	14 15.3	13 35.7	18 49.1	3 48.4	23 25.4
19 F	19 46 32.8	20 55.3	5 53.8	16 50.8	15 11.1	17 48.7	18 53.7	14 22.6	13 38.7	18 50.6	3 46.8	23 24.4
22 M	19 58 22.4	20 21.5	5 50.1	8 29.2	15 26.3	17 46.1	18 22.2	14 29.5	13 41.4	18 52.1	3 45.0	23 23.4
25 T	20 10 12.1	19 44.6	5 46.4	2N39.6	15 54.4	17 47.3	17 49.6	14 35.9	13 43.9	18 53.4	3 43.2	23 22.4
28 S	20 22 1.8	19 4.7	5 42.7	12 47.4	16 31.7	17 51.6	17 15.9	14 41.9	13 46.1	18 54.6	3 41.2	23 21.5
31 W	20 33 51.4	18 22.0	5 39.0	18 20.6	17 13.7	17 58.2	16 41.2	14 47.4	13 48.0	18 55.8	3 39.2	23 20.5

AUGUST 1940

LONGITUDE

DAY	EPHEMERIS SIDEREAL TIME h m s	☉ ° ′	☊ ° ′	☽ ° ′	☿ ° ′	♀ ° ′	♂ ° ′	♃ ° ′	♄ ° ′	♅ ° ′	♆ ° ′	♇ ° ′
1 T	20 37 48.0	8♌35.2	14♎16.5	1♋22.9	24♋40.3	29♊57.6	18♌ 9.3	13♉46.9	14♉10.9	25♉44.8	23♍36.4	2♌39.9
2 F	20 41 44.6	9 32.6	14 13.4	15 5.8	24R38.6	0♋24.9	18 47.4	13 53.1	14 13.6	25 46.3	23 38.1	2 41.6
3 S	20 45 41.1	10 30.0	14 10.2	29 12.1	24D43.2	0 53.8	19 25.5	13 59.2	14 16.1	25 47.8	23 39.8	2 43.3
4 S	20 49 37.6	11 27.5	14 7.0	13♌37.5	24 54.3	1 24.1	20 3.6	14 5.2	14 18.6	25 49.2	23 41.6	2 45.0
5 M	20 53 34.2	12 25.0	14 3.8	28 15.4	25 11.9	1 55.9	20 41.7	14 10.9	14 20.9	25 50.5	23 43.4	2 46.6
6 T	20 57 30.8	13 22.5	14 0.7	12♍58.6	25 36.1	2 29.0	21 19.8	14 16.6	14 23.2	25 51.8	23 45.1	2 48.3
7 W	21 1 27.3	14 20.0	13 57.5	27 39.9	26 7.0	3 3.4	21 57.9	14 22.0	14 25.3	25 53.1	23 46.9	2 50.0
8 T	21 5 23.9	15 17.5	13 54.3	12♎13.4	26 44.5	3 39.0	22 36.0	14 27.3	14 27.4	25 54.3	23 48.8	2 51.6
9 F	21 9 20.4	16 15.1	13 51.1	26 35.0	27 28.6	4 15.9	23 14.1	14 32.4	14 29.4	25 55.5	23 50.6	2 53.3
10 S	21 13 17.0	17 12.6	13 47.9	10♏42.5	28 19.2	4 53.9	23 52.2	14 37.3	14 31.2	25 56.6	23 52.5	2 55.0
11 S	21 17 13.5	18 10.2	13 44.8	24 35.0	29 16.1	5 33.1	24 30.3	14 42.1	14 33.0	25 57.7	23 54.3	2 56.6
12 M	21 21 10.1	19 7.7	13 41.6	8♐12.7	0♌19.2	6 13.3	25 8.4	14 46.6	14 34.6	25 58.7	23 56.2	2 58.2
13 T	21 25 6.7	20 5.3	13 38.4	21 36.2	1 28.3	6 54.6	25 46.5	14 51.0	14 36.2	25 59.7	23 58.1	2 59.9
14 W	21 29 3.2	21 3.0	13 35.2	4♑46.2	2 43.2	7 36.9	26 24.6	14 55.3	14 37.6	26 0.6	24 0.1	3 1.5
15 T	21 32 59.8	22 0.6	13 32.1	17 43.3	4 3.6	8 20.1	27 2.8	14 59.3	14 39.0	26 1.5	24 2.0	3 3.1
16 F	21 36 56.3	22 58.2	13 28.9	0♒27.7	5 29.3	9 4.3	27 40.9	15 3.2	14 40.2	26 2.3	24 4.0	3 4.7
17 S	21 40 52.9	23 55.9	13 25.7	12 59.7	6 59.9	9 49.4	28 19.0	15 6.9	14 41.3	26 3.1	24 5.9	3 6.3
18 S	21 44 49.4	24 53.6	13 22.5	25 20.1	8 35.0	10 35.4	28 57.1	15 10.4	14 42.4	26 3.8	24 7.9	3 7.9
19 M	21 48 46.0	25 51.3	13 19.3	7♓29.4	10 14.4	11 22.3	29 35.2	15 13.7	14 43.3	26 4.5	24 9.9	3 9.5
20 T	21 52 42.5	26 49.0	13 16.2	19 29.3	11 57.5	12 9.9	0♍13.4	15 16.9	14 44.1	26 5.1	24 11.9	3 11.1
21 W	21 56 39.1	27 46.8	13 13.0	1♈21.7	13 43.9	12 58.4	0 51.5	15 19.8	14 44.8	26 5.7	24 14.0	3 12.7
22 T	22 0 35.7	28 44.6	13 9.8	13 9.5	15 33.3	13 47.6	1 29.7	15 22.6	14 45.5	26 6.2	24 16.0	3 14.2
23 F	22 4 32.2	29 42.4	13 6.6	24 56.3	17 25.1	14 37.5	2 7.8	15 25.1	14 46.0	26 6.7	24 18.1	3 15.8
24 S	22 8 28.7	0♍40.2	13 3.5	6♉46.3	19 19.0	15 28.2	2 46.0	15 27.5	14 46.4	26 7.2	24 20.1	3 17.3
25 S	22 12 25.3	1 38.1	13 0.3	18 44.1	21 14.5	16 19.5	3 24.1	15 29.7	14 46.7	26 7.5	24 22.2	3 18.9
26 M	22 16 21.8	2 36.0	12 57.1	0♊54.7	23 11.3	17 11.5	4 2.3	15 31.7	14 46.8	26 7.9	24 24.3	3 20.4
27 T	22 20 18.4	3 33.9	12 53.9	13 23.1	25 9.0	18 4.2	4 40.5	15 33.5	14 46.9	26 8.2	24 26.4	3 21.9
28 W	22 24 14.9	4 31.9	12 50.7	26 13.9	27 7.3	18 57.4	5 18.7	15 35.1	14R46.9	26 8.4	24 28.5	3 23.4
29 T	22 28 11.5	5 29.9	12 47.6	9♋30.4	29 5.8	19 51.3	5 56.9	15 36.5	14 46.8	26 8.6	24 30.6	3 24.9
30 F	22 32 8.0	6 27.9	12 44.4	23 14.5	1♍ 4.3	20 45.7	6 35.1	15 37.7	14 46.5	26 8.7	24 32.8	3 26.3
31 S	22 36 4.6	7 25.9	12 41.2	7♌25.5	3 2.6	21 40.7	7 13.3	15 38.7	14 46.2	26 8.8	24 34.9	3 27.8

DECLINATION

DAY	EPHEMERIS SIDEREAL TIME h m s	☉	☊	☽	☿	♀	♂	♃	♄	♅	♆	♇
1 T	20 37 48.0	18N 7.1	5S37.8	18N28.7	17N27.9	18N 0.8	16N29.4	14N49.2	13N48.6	18N56.1	3N38.5	23N20.2
4 S	20 49 37.6	17 20.9	5 34.1	12 33.1	18 8.7	18 9.2	15 53.4	14 54.1	13 50.2	18 57.2	3 36.5	23 19.2
7 W	21 1 27.3	16 32.0	5 30.4	0S16.9	18 43.0	18 18.1	15 16.5	14 58.5	13 51.5	18 58.1	3 34.3	23 18.3
10 S	21 13 17.0	15 40.8	5 26.7	12 44.4	19 5.8	18 26.8	14 38.6	15 2.5	13 52.6	18 58.9	3 32.1	23 17.4
13 T	21 25 6.7	14 47.4	5 23.0	18 24.2	19 12.3	18 34.7	13 60.0	15 6.0	13 53.4	18 59.6	3 29.8	23 16.5
16 F	21 36 56.3	13 51.8	5 19.3	15 18.3	18 58.0	18 41.1	13 20.5	15 9.0	13 53.8	19 0.2	3 27.4	23 15.7
19 M	21 48 46.0	12 54.2	5 15.6	6 3.9	18 19.8	18 45.6	12 40.3	15 11.5	13 54.1	19 0.7	3 25.0	23 14.8
22 T	22 0 35.7	11 54.8	5 11.9	5N 4.2	17 16.7	18 47.6	11 59.4	15 13.5	13 54.0	19 1.1	3 22.6	23 14.1
25 S	22 12 25.3	10 53.7	5 8.2	14 22.8	15 50.2	18 46.8	11 17.8	15 15.0	13 53.7	19 1.4	3 20.1	23 13.3
28 W	22 24 14.9	9 51.1	5 4.5	18 22.6	14 4.0	18 42.9	10 35.5	15 16.0	13 53.1	19 1.6	3 17.6	23 12.6
31 S	22 36 4.6	8 47.0	5 0.8	13 53.3	12 2.7	18 35.4	9 52.7	15 16.5	13 52.2	19 1.6	3 15.0	23 11.9

SEPTEMBER 1940

DAY	EPHEMERIS SIDEREAL TIME	☉	☊	☽	☿	♀	♂	♃	♄	♅	♆	♇
	h m s	° ′	° ′	° ′	° ′	° ′	° ′	° ′	° ′	° ′	° ′	° ′
						LONGITUDE						
1 S	22 40 1.2	8♍24.0	12♎38.0	22♌ 0.2	5♍ 0.5	22♋36.2	7♍51.6	15♉39.5	14♉45.7	26♉ 8.8	24♍37.1	3♌29.2
2 M	22 43 57.7	9 22.1	12 34.9	6♍52.5	6 57.8	23 32.3	8 29.8	15 40.1	14R45.2	26R 8.8	24 39.2	3 30.6
3 T	22 47 54.3	10 20.3	12 31.7	21 54.3	8 54.4	24 28.8	9 8.1	15 40.6	14 44.5	26 8.7	24 41.4	3 32.1
4 W	22 51 50.8	11 18.4	12 28.5	6♎56.6	10 50.1	25 25.8	9 46.3	15 40.8	14 43.7	26 8.6	24 43.6	3 33.5
5 T	22 55 47.4	12 16.6	12 25.3	21 51.0	12 45.0	26 23.3	10 24.6	15R40.8	14 42.8	26 8.4	24 45.8	3 34.8
6 F	22 59 43.9	13 14.8	12 22.1	6♏30.9	14 38.8	27 21.3	11 2.9	15 40.6	14 41.9	26 8.2	24 47.9	3 36.2
7 S	23 3 40.4	14 13.1	12 19.0	20 51.7	16 31.7	28 19.6	11 41.1	15 40.2	14 40.8	26 7.9	24 50.1	3 37.6
8 S	23 7 37.0	15 11.4	12 15.8	4♐51.1	18 23.4	29 18.5	12 19.4	15 39.6	14 39.6	26 7.6	24 52.4	3 38.9
9 M	23 11 33.6	16 9.7	12 12.6	18 29.0	20 14.1	0♌17.7	12 57.7	15 38.8	14 38.3	26 7.2	24 54.6	3 40.2
10 T	23 15 30.1	17 8.0	12 9.4	1♑46.4	22 3.6	1 17.3	13 36.0	15 37.8	14 36.9	26 6.8	24 56.8	3 41.5
11 W	23 19 26.6	18 6.3	12 6.2	14 45.1	23 52.1	2 17.3	14 14.3	15 36.6	14 35.4	26 6.3	24 59.0	3 42.8
12 T	23 23 23.2	19 4.7	12 3.1	27 27.4	25 39.4	3 17.7	14 52.7	15 35.2	14 33.8	26 5.8	25 1.2	3 44.1
13 F	23 27 19.8	20 3.1	11 59.9	9♒55.6	27 25.6	4 18.5	15 31.0	15 33.6	14 32.1	26 5.2	25 3.4	3 45.3
14 S	23 31 16.4	21 1.5	11 56.7	22 12.0	29 10.7	5 19.6	16 9.3	15 31.8	14 30.3	26 4.6	25 5.6	3 46.6
15 S	23 35 12.9	21 60.0	11 53.5	4♓18.5	0♎54.7	6 21.1	16 47.7	15 29.8	14 28.4	26 3.9	25 7.9	3 47.8
16 M	23 39 9.4	22 58.4	11 50.4	16 17.2	2 37.6	7 23.0	17 26.0	15 27.6	14 26.4	26 3.2	25 10.1	3 49.0
17 T	23 43 6.0	23 57.0	11 47.2	28 9.8	4 19.5	8 25.2	18 4.4	15 25.2	14 24.3	26 2.4	25 12.3	3 50.2
18 W	23 47 2.6	24 55.5	11 44.0	9♈58.6	6 0.3	9 27.7	18 42.8	15 22.6	14 22.1	26 1.6	25 14.5	3 51.3
19 T	23 50 59.1	25 54.1	11 40.8	21 45.6	7 40.1	10 30.5	19 21.2	15 19.8	14 19.8	26 0.8	25 16.8	3 52.5
20 F	23 54 55.6	26 52.7	11 37.6	3♉33.8	9 18.9	11 33.7	19 59.6	15 16.8	14 17.4	25 59.9	25 19.0	3 53.6
21 S	23 58 52.2	27 51.3	11 34.5	15 26.0	10 56.6	12 37.2	20 38.0	15 13.7	14 14.9	25 58.9	25 21.2	3 54.7
22 S	0 2 48.8	28 50.0	11 31.3	27 25.9	12 33.5	13 40.9	21 16.5	15 10.3	14 12.3	25 57.9	25 23.5	3 55.8
23 M	0 6 45.3	29 48.8	11 28.1	9♊37.3	14 9.3	14 45.0	21 54.9	15 6.8	14 9.7	25 56.9	25 25.7	3 56.9
24 T	0 10 41.9	0♎47.5	11 24.9	22 4.4	15 44.2	15 49.3	22 33.4	15 3.0	14 6.9	25 55.8	25 27.9	3 57.9
25 W	0 14 38.4	1 46.3	11 21.7	4♋51.3	17 18.1	16 53.9	23 11.9	14 59.1	14 4.1	25 54.6	25 30.1	3 58.9
26 T	0 18 35.0	2 45.1	11 18.6	18 1.7	18 51.2	17 58.8	23 50.4	14 55.0	14 1.1	25 53.4	25 32.3	3 59.9
27 F	0 22 31.5	3 44.0	11 15.4	1♌38.2	20 23.3	19 4.0	24 28.9	14 50.7	13 58.1	25 52.2	25 34.6	4 0.9
28 S	0 26 28.1	4 42.9	11 12.2	15 41.8	21 54.5	20 9.4	25 7.4	14 46.2	13 55.0	25 50.9	25 36.8	4 1.9
29 S	0 30 24.6	5 41.9	11 9.0	0♍11.1	23 24.8	21 15.0	25 46.0	14 41.6	13 51.8	25 49.6	25 39.0	4 2.8
30 M	0 34 21.2	6 40.9	11 5.9	15 2.2	24 54.2	22 20.9	26 24.5	14 36.8	13 48.5	25 48.3	25 41.2	4 3.7

DAY	EPHEMERIS SIDEREAL TIME	☉	☊	☽	☿	♀	♂	♃	♄	♅	♆	♇
						DECLINATION						
1 S	22 40 1.2	8N25.3	4S59.5	10N25.7	11N19.8	18N32.1	9N38.3	15N16.6	13N51.8	19N 1.6	3N14.2	23N11.7
4 W	22 51 50.8	7 19.5	4 55.8	3S 7.0	9 5.5	18 19.7	8 54.7	15 16.4	13 50.6	19 1.6	3 11.6	23 11.0
7 S	23 3 40.4	6 12.7	4 52.1	14 44.5	6 46.0	18 3.3	8 10.6	15 15.7	13 49.1	19 1.4	3 9.0	23 10.4
10 T	23 15 30.1	5 5.0	4 48.4	18 15.3	4 24.1	17 42.7	7 26.1	15 14.5	13 47.3	19 1.1	3 6.4	23 9.9
13 F	23 27 19.8	3 56.5	4 44.7	13 19.3	2 2.0	17 17.9	6 41.2	15 12.7	13 45.3	19 0.7	3 3.7	23 9.4
16 M	23 39 9.4	2 47.4	4 40.9	3 22.6	0S18.6	16 48.9	5 55.9	15 10.5	13 43.1	19 0.3	3 1.1	23 8.9
19 T	23 50 59.1	1 37.8	4 37.2	7N33.8	2 36.5	16 15.6	5 10.2	15 7.8	13 40.6	18 59.7	2 58.5	23 8.5
22 S	0 2 48.8	0 27.8	4 33.5	15 51.0	4 50.9	15 37.9	4 24.3	15 4.6	13 37.9	18 59.0	2 55.8	23 8.2
25 W	0 14 38.4	0S42.3	4 29.7	18 5.6	7 0.9	14 56.1	3 38.1	15 0.9	13 34.9	18 58.2	2 53.2	23 7.9
28 S	0 26 28.1	1 52.5	4 26.0	11 57.9	9 5.9	14 10.2	2 51.7	14 56.8	13 31.8	18 57.3	2 50.6	23 7.6

OCTOBER 1940

DAY	EPHEMERIS SIDEREAL TIME	☉	☊	☽	☿	♀	♂	♃	♄	♅	♆	♇
						LONGITUDE						
1 T	0 38 17.7	7♎39.9	11♎ 2.7	0♎ 8.4	26♎22.7	23♌27.1	27♍ 3.1	14♉31.8	13♉45.2	25♉46.9	25♍43.4	4♌ 4.6
2 W	0 42 14.3	8 39.0	10 59.5	15 20.8	27 50.3	24 33.4	27 41.7	14R26.6	13R41.7	25R45.4	25 45.5	4 5.5
3 T	0 46 10.8	9 38.0	10 56.3	0♏29.9	29 16.9	25 40.0	28 20.3	14 21.3	13 38.2	25 43.9	25 47.7	4 6.3
4 F	0 50 7.4	10 37.2	10 53.1	15 26.5	0♏42.6	26 46.8	28 58.9	14 15.8	13 34.6	25 42.4	25 49.9	4 7.2
5 S	0 54 3.9	11 36.3	10 50.0	0♐ 3.5	2 7.4	27 53.8	29 37.5	14 10.1	13 31.0	25 40.8	25 52.1	4 8.0
6 S	0 58 0.5	12 35.5	10 46.8	14 16.1	3 31.1	29 1.0	0♎16.1	14 4.3	13 27.2	25 39.2	25 54.2	4 8.7
7 M	1 1 57.1	13 34.7	10 43.6	28 2.4	4 53.8	0♍ 8.4	0 54.8	13 58.3	13 23.4	25 37.6	25 56.4	4 9.5
8 T	1 5 53.6	14 34.0	10 40.4	11♑22.8	6 15.5	1 16.0	1 33.5	13 52.2	13 19.5	25 35.9	25 58.5	4 10.2
9 W	1 9 50.1	15 33.2	10 37.3	24 19.5	7 36.1	2 23.8	2 12.1	13 46.0	13 15.6	25 34.2	26 0.6	4 10.9
10 T	1 13 46.7	16 32.5	10 34.1	6♒55.6	8 55.5	3 31.8	2 50.8	13 39.6	13 11.6	25 32.4	26 2.8	4 11.6
11 F	1 17 43.3	17 31.9	10 30.9	19 14.9	10 13.7	4 40.0	3 29.5	13 33.1	13 7.5	25 30.6	26 4.9	4 12.3
12 S	1 21 39.8	18 31.2	10 27.7	1♓21.2	11 30.6	5 48.3	4 8.3	13 26.4	13 3.4	25 28.8	26 7.0	4 12.9
13 S	1 25 36.4	19 30.6	10 24.5	13 18.3	12 46.2	6 56.8	4 47.0	13 19.6	12 59.2	25 26.9	26 9.0	4 13.5
14 M	1 29 32.9	20 30.0	10 21.4	25 9.4	14 0.3	8 5.5	5 25.7	13 12.8	12 55.0	25 25.0	26 11.1	4 14.1
15 T	1 33 29.5	21 29.5	10 18.2	6♈57.6	15 12.8	9 14.4	6 4.5	13 5.7	12 50.7	25 23.1	26 13.2	4 14.7
16 W	1 37 26.0	22 29.0	10 15.0	18 45.3	16 23.7	10 23.5	6 43.3	12 58.6	12 46.3	25 21.2	26 15.2	4 15.2
17 T	1 41 22.6	23 28.5	10 11.8	0♉34.8	17 32.7	11 32.7	7 22.1	12 51.4	12 42.0	25 19.2	26 17.3	4 15.7
18 F	1 45 19.1	24 28.1	10 8.7	12 28.3	18 39.7	12 42.1	8 0.9	12 44.1	12 37.5	25 17.1	26 19.3	4 16.2
19 S	1 49 15.7	25 27.7	10 5.5	24 27.8	19 44.6	13 51.6	8 39.8	12 36.6	12 33.0	25 15.1	26 21.3	4 16.6
20 S	1 53 12.2	26 27.3	10 2.3	6♊35.4	20 47.0	15 1.3	9 18.6	12 29.1	12 28.5	25 13.0	26 23.3	4 17.1
21 M	1 57 8.8	27 27.0	9 59.1	18 53.7	21 46.8	16 11.2	9 57.5	12 21.5	12 23.9	25 10.9	26 25.3	4 17.5
22 T	2 1 5.3	28 26.7	9 55.9	1♋25.1	22 43.8	17 21.2	10 36.4	12 13.9	12 19.3	25 8.7	26 27.2	4 17.9
23 W	2 5 1.9	29 26.4	9 52.8	14 12.5	23 37.5	18 31.3	11 15.3	12 6.1	12 14.7	25 6.6	26 29.2	4 18.2
24 T	2 8 58.4	0♏26.2	9 49.6	27 18.6	24 27.7	19 41.6	11 54.2	11 58.3	12 10.0	25 4.4	26 31.1	4 18.5
25 F	2 12 55.0	1 26.0	9 46.4	10♌46.1	25 14.0	20 52.1	12 33.2	11 50.4	12 5.3	25 2.2	26 33.0	4 18.8
26 S	2 16 51.6	2 25.8	9 43.2	24 36.6	25 55.9	22 2.6	13 12.1	11 42.4	12 0.6	24 59.9	26 34.9	4 19.1
27 S	2 20 48.1	3 25.7	9 40.1	8♍50.6	26 33.1	23 13.3	13 51.1	11 34.4	11 55.9	24 57.7	26 36.8	4 19.4
28 M	2 24 44.6	4 25.7	9 36.9	23 26.5	27 4.9	24 24.2	14 30.1	11 26.4	11 51.1	24 55.4	26 38.6	4 19.6
29 T	2 28 41.2	5 25.6	9 33.7	8♎20.3	27 30.8	25 35.2	15 9.2	11 18.3	11 46.3	24 53.1	26 40.5	4 19.8
30 W	2 32 37.8	6 25.6	9 30.5	23 25.6	27 50.2	26 46.2	15 48.2	11 10.2	11 41.5	24 50.8	26 42.3	4 20.0
31 T	2 36 34.3	7 25.6	9 27.3	8♏33.8	28 2.6	27 57.4	16 27.3	11 2.1	11 36.7	24 48.4	26 44.1	4 20.1

DAY	EPHEMERIS SIDEREAL TIME	☉	☊	☽	☿	♀	♂	♃	♄	♅	♆	♇
						DECLINATION						
1 T	0 38 17.7	3S 2.5	4S22.3	0S58.6	11S 5.2	13N20.3	2N 5.1	14N52.2	13N28.4	18N56.4	2N48.1	23N 7.4
4 F	0 50 7.4	4 12.3	4 18.5	13 35.6	12 58.2	12 26.6	1 18.3	14 47.2	13 24.9	18 55.3	2 45.5	23 7.3
7 M	1 1 57.1	5 21.6	4 14.8	18 15.8	14 44.3	11 29.3	0 31.5	14 41.8	13 21.2	18 54.1	2 43.0	23 7.2
10 T	1 13 46.7	6 30.3	4 11.1	13 55.4	16 22.8	10 28.5	0S15.3	14 36.0	13 17.4	18 52.9	2 40.5	23 7.2
13 S	1 25 36.4	7 38.1	4 7.3	4 16.7	17 52.6	9 24.6	1 2.2	14 29.9	13 13.4	18 51.6	2 38.1	23 7.2
16 W	1 37 26.0	8 45.1	4 3.6	6N41.6	19 12.9	8 17.6	1 49.0	14 23.5	13 9.3	18 50.2	2 35.7	23 7.3
19 S	1 49 15.7	9 50.9	3 59.8	15 21.9	20 22.3	7 7.9	2 35.7	14 16.8	13 5.1	18 48.8	2 33.4	23 7.5
22 T	2 1 5.3	10 55.4	3 56.1	18 14.4	21 19.1	5 55.7	3 22.3	14 9.8	13 0.9	18 47.3	2 31.1	23 7.7
25 F	2 12 55.0	11 58.5	3 52.4	13 8.2	22 1.0	4 41.3	4 8.8	14 2.7	12 56.6	18 45.7	2 28.9	23 7.9
28 M	2 24 44.6	12 59.9	3 48.6	1 8.9	22 25.1	3 25.0	4 55.1	13 55.5	12 52.2	18 44.1	2 26.7	23 8.3
31 T	2 36 34.3	13 59.6	3 44.9	12S 3.0	22 27.1	2 7.1	5 41.1	13 48.1	12 47.8	18 42.4	2 24.6	23 8.7

NOVEMBER 1940

DAY	EPHEMERIS SIDEREAL TIME	☉	☊	☽	☿	♀	♂	♃	♄	♅	♆	♇
	h m s	° ′	° ′	° ′	° ′	° ′	° ′	° ′	° ′	° ′	° ′	° ′
LONGITUDE												
1 F	2 40 30.9	8♏25.7	9♎24.2	23♏35.4	28♏ 7.2	29♍ 8.8	17♎ 6.3	10♉53.9	11♉31.8	24♉46.0	26♍45.9	4♌20.2
2 S	2 44 27.4	9 25.8	9 21.0	8♐21.5	28R 3.4	0♎20.2	17 45.4	10R45.8	11R27.0	24R43.7	26 47.6	4 20.3
3 S	2 48 24.0	10 25.9	9 17.8	22 45.0	27 50.8	1 31.7	18 24.6	10 37.6	11 22.2	24 41.3	26 49.3	4 20.4
4 M	2 52 20.6	11 26.1	9 14.6	6♑41.6	27 28.7	2 43.4	19 3.7	10 29.4	11 17.3	24 38.9	26 51.1	4 20.4
5 T	2 56 17.1	12 26.2	9 11.5	20 9.9	26 57.0	3 55.1	19 42.8	10 21.3	11 12.5	24 36.4	26 52.8	4 20.4
6 W	3 0 13.6	13 26.4	9 8.3	3♒11.0	26 15.5	5 6.9	20 22.0	10 13.1	11 7.6	24 34.0	26 54.4	4R20.4
7 T	3 4 10.2	14 26.6	9 5.1	15 48.2	25 24.5	6 18.9	21 1.2	10 5.0	11 2.8	24 31.5	26 56.1	4 20.3
8 F	3 8 6.7	15 26.9	9 1.9	28 5.7	24 24.6	7 30.9	21 40.4	9 56.9	10 58.0	24 29.1	26 57.7	4 20.3
9 S	3 12 3.3	16 27.2	8 58.7	10♓ 8.4	23 16.9	8 43.1	22 19.6	9 48.8	10 53.2	24 26.6	26 59.3	4 20.2
10 S	3 15 59.9	17 27.5	8 55.6	22 1.3	22 2.9	9 55.3	22 58.8	9 40.8	10 48.4	24 24.1	27 0.9	4 20.0
11 M	3 19 56.4	18 27.8	8 52.4	3♈49.0	20 44.6	11 7.6	23 38.1	9 32.8	10 43.6	24 21.7	27 2.4	4 19.9
12 T	3 23 53.0	19 28.1	8 49.2	15 35.8	19 24.5	12 20.0	24 17.3	9 24.9	10 38.8	24 19.2	27 3.9	4 19.7
13 W	3 27 49.5	20 28.5	8 46.0	27 25.1	18 4.9	13 32.5	24 56.6	9 17.0	10 34.1	24 16.7	27 5.4	4 19.5
14 T	3 31 46.1	21 28.9	8 42.9	9♉19.9	16 48.6	14 45.1	25 35.9	9 9.2	10 29.4	24 14.2	27 6.9	4 19.3
15 F	3 35 42.6	22 29.3	8 39.7	21 22.4	15 38.1	15 57.7	26 15.3	9 1.5	10 24.7	24 11.7	27 8.3	4 19.0
16 S	3 39 39.2	23 29.8	8 36.5	3♊34.1	14 35.4	17 10.5	26 54.6	8 53.8	10 20.0	24 9.2	27 9.8	4 18.7
17 S	3 43 35.7	24 30.3	8 33.3	15 56.0	13 42.4	18 23.3	27 34.0	8 46.2	10 15.4	24 6.7	27 11.2	4 18.4
18 M	3 47 32.3	25 30.8	8 30.2	28 28.9	13 0.2	19 36.2	28 13.4	8 38.8	10 10.8	24 4.2	27 12.5	4 18.1
19 T	3 51 28.9	26 31.3	8 27.0	11♋13.7	12 29.5	20 49.2	28 52.8	8 31.4	10 6.3	24 1.7	27 13.9	4 17.7
20 W	3 55 25.4	27 31.9	8 23.8	24 10.9	12 10.4	22 2.3	29 32.2	8 24.0	10 1.8	23 59.2	27 15.2	4 17.4
21 T	3 59 21.9	28 32.5	8 20.6	7♌21.8	12 3.0	23 15.4	0♏11.6	8 16.8	9 57.3	23 56.7	27 16.5	4 16.9
22 F	4 3 18.5	29 33.1	8 17.4	20 47.6	12D 6.6	24 28.7	0 51.1	8 9.8	9 52.9	23 54.2	27 17.7	4 16.5
23 S	4 7 15.1	0♐33.7	8 14.3	4♍29.6	12 20.6	25 41.9	1 30.6	8 2.8	9 48.5	23 51.7	27 19.0	4 16.1
24 S	4 11 11.6	1 34.4	8 11.1	18 28.6	12 44.2	26 55.3	2 10.1	7 55.9	9 44.2	23 49.2	27 20.2	4 15.6
25 M	4 15 8.2	2 35.1	8 7.9	2♎44.8	13 16.5	28 8.7	2 49.7	7 49.2	9 39.9	23 46.8	27 21.3	4 15.1
26 T	4 19 4.7	3 35.8	8 4.7	17 16.5	13 56.6	29 22.2	3 29.2	7 42.6	9 35.7	23 44.3	27 22.5	4 14.5
27 W	4 23 1.3	4 36.6	8 1.6	2♏ 0.3	14 43.6	0♏35.7	4 8.8	7 36.1	9 31.5	23 41.8	27 23.6	4 14.0
28 T	4 26 57.9	5 37.4	7 58.4	16 50.4	15 36.8	1 49.3	4 48.4	7 29.8	9 27.4	23 39.4	27 24.6	4 13.4
29 F	4 30 54.4	6 38.2	7 55.2	1♐39.3	16 35.2	3 3.0	5 28.0	7 23.6	9 23.4	23 37.0	27 25.7	4 12.8
30 S	4 34 51.0	7 39.0	7 52.0	16 18.8	17 38.4	4 16.7	6 7.7	7 17.5	9 19.4	23 34.6	27 26.7	4 12.1
DECLINATION												
1 F	2 40 30.9	14S19.0	3S43.6	15S13.6	22S21.9	1N40.8	5S56.3	13N45.7	12N46.4	18N41.8	2N24.0	23N 8.8
4 M	2 52 20.6	15 15.9	3 39.9	18 4.2	21 45.8	0 21.3	6 41.9	13 38.3	12 42.0	18 40.1	2 22.0	23 9.3
7 T	3 4 10.2	16 10.5	3 36.1	12 1.2	20 34.8	0S59.2	7 27.1	13 31.0	12 37.7	18 38.3	2 20.1	23 9.8
10 S	3 15 59.9	17 2.7	3 32.4	1 38.1	18 50.3	2 20.2	8 11.9	13 23.7	12 33.4	18 36.5	2 18.3	23 10.4
13 W	3 27 49.5	17 52.3	3 28.6	9N 9.2	16 47.1	3 41.5	8 56.3	13 16.6	12 29.3	18 34.7	2 16.6	23 11.1
16 S	3 39 39.2	18 39.1	3 24.8	16 48.9	14 54.4	5 2.6	9 40.1	13 9.7	12 25.2	18 32.9	2 15.0	23 11.8
19 T	3 51 28.9	19 22.9	3 21.1	17 51.2	13 38.9	6 23.4	10 23.4	13 3.1	12 21.3	18 31.1	2 13.5	23 12.5
22 F	4 3 18.5	20 3.5	3 17.3	10 53.1	13 11.2	7 43.4	11 6.1	12 56.7	12 17.5	18 29.3	2 12.1	23 13.3
25 M	4 15 8.2	20 40.9	3 13.6	1S40.0	13 26.1	9 2.3	11 48.1	12 50.7	12 13.9	18 27.5	2 10.8	23 14.2
28 T	4 26 57.9	21 14.8	3 9.8	13 54.3	14 11.6	10 19.8	12 29.5	12 45.1	12 10.4	18 25.7	2 9.6	23 15.0

DECEMBER 1940

DAY	EPHEMERIS SIDEREAL TIME	☉	☊	☽	☿	♀	♂	♃	♄	♅	♆	♇
LONGITUDE												
1 S	4 38 47.5	8♐39.9	7♎48.9	0♑41.2	18♏45.6	5♏30.5	6♏47.3	7♉11.6	9♉15.5	23♉32.2	27♍27.7	4♌11.5
2 M	4 42 44.1	9 40.7	7 45.7	14 40.4	19 56.2	6 44.3	7 27.0	7R 5.9	9R11.7	23R29.8	27 28.6	4R10.8
3 T	4 46 40.6	10 41.6	7 42.5	28 13.3	21 9.9	7 58.1	8 6.7	7 0.4	9 7.9	23 27.4	27 29.6	4 10.1
4 W	4 50 37.2	11 42.5	7 39.3	11♒19.3	22 26.2	9 12.0	8 46.4	6 54.9	9 4.2	23 25.1	27 30.5	4 9.4
5 T	4 54 33.7	12 43.4	7 36.1	24 0.3	23 44.7	10 26.0	9 26.1	6 49.7	9 0.6	23 22.7	27 31.3	4 8.6
6 F	4 58 30.3	13 44.3	7 33.0	6♓20.2	25 5.1	11 40.0	10 5.9	6 44.6	8 57.1	23 20.4	27 32.1	4 7.9
7 S	5 2 26.9	14 45.3	7 29.8	18 23.8	26 27.2	12 54.0	10 45.7	6 39.8	8 53.7	23 18.2	27 32.9	4 7.1
8 S	5 6 23.4	15 46.2	7 26.6	0♈16.5	27 50.6	14 8.1	11 25.5	6 35.1	8 50.3	23 15.9	27 33.7	4 6.3
9 M	5 10 20.0	16 47.2	7 23.4	12 3.9	29 15.3	15 22.2	12 5.3	6 30.5	8 47.0	23 13.7	27 34.4	4 5.4
10 T	5 14 16.5	17 48.1	7 20.3	23 51.2	0♐41.0	16 36.3	12 45.1	6 26.2	8 43.8	23 11.4	27 35.1	4 4.6
11 W	5 18 13.1	18 49.1	7 17.1	5♉43.2	2 7.6	17 50.5	13 24.9	6 22.0	8 40.7	23 9.3	27 35.8	4 3.7
12 T	5 22 9.7	19 50.1	7 13.9	17 43.8	3 35.0	19 4.8	14 4.8	6 18.1	8 37.7	23 7.1	27 36.4	4 2.8
13 F	5 26 6.2	20 51.1	7 10.7	29 55.9	5 3.0	20 19.0	14 44.7	6 14.3	8 34.7	23 5.0	27 37.0	4 1.9
14 S	5 30 2.8	21 52.1	7 7.6	12♊21.4	6 31.7	21 33.3	15 24.6	6 10.7	8 31.9	23 2.8	27 37.5	4 1.0
15 S	5 33 59.3	22 53.1	7 4.4	25 0.9	8 0.8	22 47.6	16 4.5	6 7.3	8 29.1	23 0.8	27 38.1	3 60.0
16 M	5 37 55.9	23 54.2	7 1.2	7♋54.2	9 30.4	24 2.0	16 44.4	6 4.1	8 26.5	22 58.7	27 38.6	3 59.0
17 T	5 41 52.4	24 55.2	6 58.0	21 0.3	11 0.4	25 16.4	17 24.4	6 1.1	8 23.9	22 56.7	27 39.0	3 58.0
18 W	5 45 49.0	25 56.3	6 54.8	4♌17.9	12 30.7	26 30.8	18 4.4	5 58.3	8 21.4	22 54.7	27 39.5	3 57.0
19 T	5 49 45.5	26 57.3	6 51.7	17 45.6	14 1.4	27 45.3	18 44.4	5 55.7	8 19.1	22 52.7	27 39.8	3 56.0
20 F	5 53 42.1	27 58.4	6 48.5	1♍22.6	15 32.4	28 59.8	19 24.4	5 53.3	8 16.8	22 50.8	27 40.2	3 55.0
21 S	5 57 38.7	28 59.5	6 45.3	15 8.5	17 3.7	0♐14.3	20 4.5	5 51.1	8 14.6	22 48.9	27 40.5	3 53.9
22 S	6 1 35.2	0♑ 0.6	6 42.1	29 3.3	18 35.2	1 28.9	20 44.6	5 49.1	8 12.6	22 47.1	27 40.8	3 52.8
23 M	6 5 31.8	1 1.8	6 39.0	13♎ 7.0	20 7.0	2 43.4	21 24.7	5 47.3	8 10.6	22 45.3	27 41.1	3 51.7
24 T	6 9 28.3	2 2.9	6 35.8	27 19.2	21 39.1	3 58.0	22 4.8	5 45.7	8 8.7	22 43.5	27 41.3	3 50.6
25 W	6 13 24.9	3 4.0	6 32.6	11♏38.5	23 11.5	5 12.7	22 44.9	5 44.4	8 7.0	22 41.7	27 41.5	3 49.5
26 T	6 17 21.5	4 5.2	6 29.4	26 2.0	24 44.1	6 27.3	23 25.1	5 43.2	8 5.3	22 40.0	27 41.6	3 48.4
27 F	6 21 18.0	5 6.4	6 26.3	10♐25.1	26 16.9	7 42.0	24 5.3	5 42.3	8 3.8	22 38.4	27 41.7	3 47.2
28 S	6 25 14.6	6 7.5	6 23.1	24 42.3	27 50.1	8 56.7	24 45.5	5 41.5	8 2.3	22 36.7	27 41.8	3 46.0
29 S	6 29 11.1	7 8.7	6 19.9	8♑47.4	29 23.5	10 11.4	25 25.7	5 41.0	8 1.0	22 35.1	27 41.8	3 44.8
30 M	6 33 7.7	8 9.9	6 16.7	22 35.3	0♑57.2	11 26.1	26 5.9	5 40.7	7 59.8	22 33.6	27 41.9	3 43.7
31 T	6 37 4.3	9 11.1	6 13.5	6♒ 1.9	2 31.1	12 40.9	26 46.2	5 40.5	7 58.6	22 32.1	27R41.8	3 42.5
DECLINATION												
1 S	4 38 47.5	21S45.1	3S 6.0	18S25.1	15S16.3	11S35.4	13S10.1	12N39.9	12N 7.2	18N23.9	2N 8.5	23N16.0
4 W	4 50 37.2	22 11.7	3 2.3	13 15.5	16 30.8	12 48.9	13 49.9	12 35.1	12 4.2	18 22.2	2 7.5	23 17.0
7 S	5 2 26.9	22 34.4	2 58.5	2 57.7	17 48.6	13 59.8	14 28.8	12 30.9	12 1.5	18 20.5	2 6.7	23 18.0
10 T	5 14 16.5	22 53.1	2 54.8	8N 1.1	19 5.3	15 7.8	15 6.8	12 27.3	11 59.0	18 18.9	2 5.9	23 19.0
13 F	5 26 6.2	23 7.7	2 51.0	16 16.8	20 17.8	16 12.5	15 43.9	12 24.2	11 56.8	18 17.3	2 5.3	23 20.1
16 M	5 37 55.9	23 18.2	2 47.2	18 12.1	21 23.9	17 13.7	16 19.9	12 21.6	11 54.8	18 15.7	2 4.8	23 21.3
19 T	5 49 45.5	23 24.6	2 43.5	11 52.1	22 22.1	18 10.9	16 54.9	12 19.7	11 53.2	18 14.3	2 4.5	23 22.4
22 S	6 1 35.2	23 26.7	2 39.7	0S16.2	23 11.2	19 3.8	17 28.8	12 18.4	11 51.9	18 12.9	2 4.2	23 23.6
25 W	6 13 24.9	23 24.5	2 35.9	12 36.1	23 50.3	19 52.1	18 1.5	12 17.7	11 50.9	18 11.6	2 4.1	23 24.8
28 S	6 25 14.6	23 18.1	2 32.1	18 26.5	24 18.6	20 35.4	18 33.0	12 17.6	11 50.2	18 10.4	2 4.1	23 26.0
31 T	6 37 4.3	23 7.6	2 28.4	14 33.6	24 35.5	21 13.6	19 3.2	12 18.1	11 49.8	18 9.3	2 4.2	23 27.2

JANUARY 1941

DAY	EPHEMERIS SIDEREAL TIME h m s	☉	☊	☽	☿	♀	♂	♃	♄	♅	♆	♇
		LONGITUDE										
1 W	6 41 0.8	10♉12.2	6☋10.4	19≏ 5.7	4♉ 5.4	13♐55.7	27♏26.5	5♈40.6	7♈57.6	22♉30.6	27♍41.8	3♌41.2
2 T	6 44 57.3	11 13.4	6 7.2	1♏47.1	5 40.0	15 10.4	28 6.8	5D40.9	7R56.7	22R29.2	27R41.7	3R40.0
3 F	6 48 53.9	12 14.6	6 4.0	14 8.4	7 15.0	16 25.2	28 47.1	5 41.5	7 56.0	22 27.9	27 41.6	3 38.8
4 S	6 52 50.5	13 15.8	6 0.8	26 13.6	8 50.3	17 40.0	29 27.4	5 42.2	7 55.3	22 26.5	27 41.4	3 37.5
5 S	6 56 47.0	14 16.9	5 57.7	8♏ 7.6	10 25.9	18 54.8	0♐ 7.7	5 43.1	7 54.7	22 25.2	27 41.2	3 36.2
6 M	7 0 43.6	15 18.1	5 54.5	19 55.9	12 1.9	20 9.6	0 48.1	5 44.3	7 54.3	22 24.0	27 41.0	3 35.0
7 T	7 4 40.1	16 19.2	5 51.3	1♐44.2	13 38.3	21 24.5	1 28.5	5 45.6	7 54.0	22 22.8	27 40.7	3 33.7
8 W	7 8 36.7	17 20.4	5 48.1	13 37.8	15 15.2	22 39.3	2 8.9	5 47.2	7 53.7	22 21.7	27 40.4	3 32.4
9 T	7 12 33.3	18 21.5	5 45.0	25 41.7	16 52.4	23 54.2	2 49.3	5 48.9	7 53.6	22 20.6	27 40.1	3 31.1
10 F	7 16 29.8	19 22.6	5 41.8	7♑60.0	18 30.1	25 9.0	3 29.7	5 50.9	7D53.6	22 19.5	27 39.7	3 29.8
11 S	7 20 26.3	20 23.8	5 38.6	20 35.4	20 8.2	26 23.9	4 10.2	5 53.1	7 53.7	22 18.5	27 39.3	3 28.5
12 S	7 24 22.9	21 24.9	5 35.4	3≈29.6	21 46.8	27 38.8	4 50.7	5 55.4	7 54.0	22 17.6	27 38.9	3 27.2
13 M	7 28 19.5	22 26.0	5 32.2	16 42.2	23 25.8	28 53.6	5 31.2	5 58.0	7 54.3	22 16.7	27 38.4	3 25.8
14 T	7 32 16.0	23 27.1	5 29.1	0♓11.6	25 5.3	0♑ 8.5	6 11.7	6 0.8	7 54.8	22 15.8	27 37.9	3 24.5
15 W	7 36 12.6	24 28.2	5 25.9	13 54.9	26 45.3	1 23.4	6 52.2	6 3.8	7 55.3	22 15.0	27 37.4	3 23.2
16 T	7 40 9.1	25 29.3	5 22.7	27 48.6	28 25.8	2 38.4	7 32.8	6 6.9	7 56.0	22 14.2	27 36.8	3 21.8
17 F	7 44 5.7	26 30.3	5 19.5	11♈49.0	0≈ 6.8	3 53.3	8 13.3	6 10.3	7 56.8	22 13.5	27 36.2	3 20.5
18 S	7 48 2.2	27 31.4	5 16.4	25 53.3	1 48.2	5 8.2	8 53.9	6 13.8	7 57.7	22 12.9	27 35.6	3 19.1
19 S	7 51 58.8	28 32.5	5 13.2	9♉59.2	3 30.2	6 23.1	9 34.6	6 17.6	7 58.7	22 12.3	27 35.0	3 17.8
20 M	7 55 55.4	29 33.5	5 10.0	24 5.2	5 12.5	7 38.1	10 15.2	6 21.5	7 59.8	22 11.7	27 34.3	3 16.4
21 T	7 59 51.9	0≈34.6	5 6.8	8♊15.5	6 55.3	8 53.0	10 55.9	6 25.6	8 1.1	22 11.2	27 33.6	3 15.1
22 W	8 3 48.5	1 35.7	5 3.7	22 14.2	8 38.4	10 8.0	11 36.6	6 29.9	8 2.4	22 10.8	27 32.8	3 13.7
23 T	8 7 45.0	2 36.7	5 0.5	6♋15.1	10 21.9	11 23.0	12 17.3	6 34.4	8 3.9	22 10.4	27 32.1	3 12.3
24 F	8 11 41.6	3 37.7	4 57.3	20 11.3	12 5.6	12 37.9	12 58.0	6 39.1	8 5.4	22 10.0	27 31.3	3 11.0
25 S	8 15 38.1	4 38.8	4 54.1	4♌ 0.0	13 49.5	13 52.9	13 38.7	6 44.0	8 7.1	22 9.7	27 30.4	3 9.6
26 S	8 19 34.7	5 39.8	4 50.9	17 38.3	15 33.5	15 7.9	14 19.5	6 49.0	8 8.9	22 9.5	27 29.5	3 8.3
27 M	8 23 31.3	6 40.8	4 47.8	1≏ 3.1	17 17.5	16 22.9	15 0.2	6 54.2	8 10.8	22 9.3	27 28.7	3 6.9
28 T	8 27 27.8	7 41.8	4 44.6	14 12.0	19 1.3	17 37.9	15 41.0	6 59.6	8 12.8	22 9.1	27 27.7	3 5.6
29 W	8 31 24.4	8 42.7	4 41.4	27 3.3	20 44.7	18 52.9	16 21.8	7 5.2	8 14.9	22 9.1	27 26.8	3 4.2
30 T	8 35 20.9	9 43.7	4 38.2	9♏37.2	22 27.6	20 7.8	17 2.6	7 11.0	8 17.1	22 9.0	27 25.8	3 2.8
31 F	8 39 17.5	10 44.6	4 35.1	21 54.8	24 9.7	21 22.8	17 43.5	7 16.9	8 19.4	22D 9.0	27 24.8	3 1.5
		DECLINATION										
1 W	6 41 0.8	23S 3.1	2S27.1	11S37.3	24S38.5	21S25.1	19S13.0	12N18.5	11N49.8	18N 8.9	2N 4.3	23N27.6
4 S	6 52 50.5	22 47.0	2 23.3	0 44.8	24 39.2	21 55.9	19 41.4	12 19.8	11 49.8	18 7.9	2 4.6	23 28.8
7 T	7 4 40.1	22 26.8	2 19.6	9N58.8	24 27.3	22 20.9	20 8.5	12 21.9	11 50.2	18 7.0	2 5.0	23 30.0
10 F	7 16 29.8	22 2.7	2 15.8	17 13.6	24 2.2	22 39.9	20 34.2	12 24.5	11 51.0	18 6.3	2 5.5	23 31.3
13 M	7 28 19.5	21 34.6	2 12.0	17 31.2	23 23.6	22 52.8	20 58.3	12 27.7	11 52.0	18 5.6	2 6.2	23 32.5
16 T	7 40 9.1	21 2.8	2 8.2	9 25.0	22 31.1	22 59.5	21 20.9	12 31.4	11 53.4	18 5.0	2 7.0	23 33.7
19 S	7 51 58.8	20 27.4	2 4.5	3S28.3	21 24.6	22 59.8	21 42.0	12 35.8	11 55.2	18 4.6	2 7.8	23 34.9
22 W	8 3 48.5	19 48.5	2 0.7	14 39.7	20 4.1	22 53.8	22 1.5	12 40.7	11 57.2	18 4.3	2 8.8	23 36.1
25 S	8 15 38.1	19 6.3	1 56.9	18 18.7	18 29.8	22 41.6	22 19.3	12 46.1	11 59.5	18 4.1	2 9.9	23 37.3
28 T	8 27 27.8	18 21.0	1 53.1	12 53.3	16 42.7	22 23.1	22 35.4	12 52.0	12 2.2	18 4.0	2 11.1	23 38.5
31 F	8 39 17.5	17 32.6	1 49.3	2 18.3	14 44.3	21 58.4	22 49.8	12 58.4	12 5.1	18 4.0	2 12.4	23 39.6

FEBRUARY 1941

DAY	EPHEMERIS SIDEREAL TIME	☉	☊	☽	☿	♀	♂	♃	♄	♅	♆	♇
		LONGITUDE										
1 S	8 43 14.0	11≈45.6	4☋31.9	3♈58.9	25≈50.7	22♑37.8	18♐24.3	7♈23.0	8♈21.8	22♉ 9.1	27♍23.8	3♌ 0.1
2 S	8 47 10.6	12 46.5	4 28.7	15 53.0	27 30.3	23 52.8	19 5.2	7 29.3	8 24.4	22 9.3	27R22.7	2R58.8
3 M	8 51 7.2	13 47.3	4 25.5	27 41.8	29 8.1	25 7.7	19 46.1	7 35.7	8 27.0	22 9.4	27 21.6	2 57.5
4 T	8 55 3.7	14 48.2	4 22.3	9♉30.2	0♓43.7	26 22.7	20 27.0	7 42.3	8 29.8	22 9.7	27 20.5	2 56.1
5 W	8 59 0.2	15 49.0	4 19.2	21 23.8	2 16.6	27 37.7	21 7.9	7 49.1	8 32.6	22 10.0	27 19.4	2 54.8
6 T	9 2 56.8	16 49.8	4 16.0	3♊27.6	3 46.2	28 52.6	21 48.8	7 56.0	8 35.6	22 10.3	27 18.2	2 53.5
7 F	9 6 53.4	17 50.6	4 12.8	15 46.7	5 11.9	0≈ 7.6	22 29.8	8 3.1	8 38.6	22 10.7	27 17.1	2 52.2
8 S	9 10 49.9	18 51.3	4 9.6	28 25.0	6 33.2	1 22.5	23 10.7	8 10.4	8 41.7	22 11.2	27 15.8	2 50.9
9 S	9 14 46.5	19 52.0	4 6.5	11♋25.2	7 49.2	2 37.5	23 51.7	8 17.8	8 45.0	22 11.6	27 14.6	2 49.6
10 M	9 18 43.0	20 52.7	4 3.3	24 48.6	8 59.4	3 52.4	24 32.7	8 25.3	8 48.3	22 12.2	27 13.4	2 48.3
11 T	9 22 39.6	21 53.4	4 0.1	8♌34.1	10 2.9	5 7.3	25 13.7	8 33.0	8 51.8	22 12.8	27 12.1	2 47.0
12 W	9 26 36.1	22 54.1	3 56.9	22 38.9	11 0.0	6 22.3	25 54.7	8 40.9	8 55.3	22 13.5	27 10.8	2 45.8
13 T	9 30 32.7	23 54.7	3 53.7	6♍58.4	11 46.9	7 37.2	26 35.7	8 48.9	8 58.9	22 14.2	27 9.5	2 44.5
14 F	9 34 29.2	24 55.3	3 50.6	21 26.9	12 26.1	8 52.1	27 16.8	8 57.0	9 2.7	22 14.9	27 8.1	2 43.3
15 S	9 38 25.8	25 55.9	3 47.4	5≏58.5	12 55.9	10 7.1	27 57.9	9 5.3	9 6.5	22 15.7	27 6.8	2 42.0
16 S	9 42 22.4	26 56.5	3 44.2	20 28.0	13 15.9	11 22.0	28 39.0	9 13.7	9 10.4	22 16.6	27 5.4	2 40.8
17 M	9 46 18.9	27 57.0	3 41.0	4♏51.2	13 25.7	12 36.9	29 20.1	9 22.3	9 14.4	22 17.5	27 4.0	2 39.6
18 T	9 50 15.4	28 57.5	3 37.9	19 5.2	13R25.2	13 51.8	0♑ 1.2	9 31.0	9 18.5	22 18.5	27 2.6	2 38.4
19 W	9 54 12.0	29 58.0	3 34.7	3♐ 8.0	13 14.4	15 6.7	0 42.4	9 39.8	9 22.7	22 19.5	27 1.2	2 37.2
20 T	9 58 8.6	0♓58.5	3 31.5	16 58.9	12 53.7	16 21.7	1 23.6	9 48.8	9 26.9	22 20.6	26 59.7	2 36.0
21 F	10 2 5.1	1 59.0	3 28.3	0♑37.3	12 23.4	17 36.6	2 4.7	9 57.9	9 31.3	22 21.7	26 58.3	2 34.9
22 S	10 6 1.7	2 59.4	3 25.2	14 2.9	11 44.3	18 51.5	2 45.9	10 7.1	9 35.7	22 22.9	26 56.8	2 33.7
23 S	10 9 58.2	3 59.8	3 22.0	27 15.5	10 57.6	20 6.4	3 27.1	10 16.4	9 40.3	22 24.1	26 55.3	2 32.6
24 M	10 13 54.7	5 0.2	3 18.8	10≈14.9	10 4.7	21 21.3	4 8.4	10 25.9	9 44.9	22 25.3	26 53.8	2 31.5
25 T	10 17 51.3	6 0.6	3 15.6	23 0.9	9 6.0	22 36.1	4 49.6	10 35.5	9 49.6	22 26.6	26 52.3	2 30.3
26 W	10 21 47.9	7 0.9	3 12.4	5♓33.4	8 4.2	23 51.0	5 30.8	10 45.3	9 54.4	22 27.8	26 50.8	2 29.3
27 T	10 25 44.4	8 1.2	3 9.3	17 54.0	7 0.4	25 5.9	6 12.1	10 55.1	9 59.3	22 29.4	26 49.2	2 28.2
28 F	10 29 41.0	9 1.5	3 6.1	0♈ 2.7	5 56.2	26 20.8	6 53.4	11 5.1	10 4.2	22 30.9	26 47.6	2 27.1
		DECLINATION										
1 S	8 43 14.0	17S15.9	1S48.1	1N29.6	14S 2.8	21S48.9	22S54.3	13N 0.7	12N 6.2	18N 4.1	2N12.8	23N40.0
4 T	8 55 3.7	16 23.8	1 44.3	11 44.3	16 4.1	21 16.3	23 6.4	13 7.7	12 9.5	18 4.3	2 14.2	23 41.1
7 F	9 6 53.4	15 29.3	1 40.5	17 46.8	9 44.3	20 38.0	23 16.7	13 15.2	12 13.1	18 4.6	2 15.7	23 42.1
10 M	9 18 43.0	14 32.3	1 36.7	16 28.1	7 41.0	19 54.2	23 25.1	13 23.0	12 17.0	18 5.0	2 17.3	23 43.1
13 T	9 30 32.7	13 33.2	1 32.9	6 53.5	5 54.7	19 5.1	23 31.8	13 31.3	12 21.1	18 5.6	2 18.9	23 44.1
16 T	9 42 22.4	12 32.1	1 29.1	5N 2.9	4 36.5	18 11.1	23 36.6	13 39.9	12 25.5	18 6.3	2 20.6	23 45.1
19 W	9 54 12.0	11 29.1	1 25.4	16 18.6	3 59.9	17 12.4	23 39.6	13 48.8	12 30.1	18 7.1	2 22.4	23 46.0
22 S	10 6 1.7	10 24.6	1 21.6	17 37.4	3 59.9	16 9.2	23 40.7	13 58.1	12 35.0	18 8.0	2 24.2	23 47.0
25 T	10 17 51.3	9 18.5	1 17.8	10 44.2	4 43.6	15 2.0	23 40.0	14 7.6	12 40.0	18 9.0	2 26.1	23 47.6
28 F	10 29 41.0	8 11.3	1 14.0	0N10.1	5 56.1	13 51.1	23 37.4	14 17.4	12 45.2	18 10.2	2 28.0	23 48.4

MARCH 1941

LONGITUDE

DAY	EPHEMERIS SIDEREAL TIME h m s	☉ ° ′	☊ ° ′	☽ ° ′	☿ ° ′	♀ ° ′	♂ ° ′	♃ ° ′	♄ ° ′	♅ ° ′	♆ ° ′	♇ ° ′
1 S	10 33 37.5	10♓ 1.8	3♎ 2.9	12♈ 1.8	4♓53.2	27♒35.6	7♑34.6	11♉15.2	10♉ 9.2	22♉32.4	26♍46.1	2♌26.1
2 S	10 37 34.1	11 2.0	2 59.7	23 53.9	3R52.7	28 50.5	8 15.9	11 25.4	10 14.3	22 34.0	26R44.5	2R25.1
3 M	10 41 30.6	12 2.2	2 56.5	5♉42.3	2 56.0	0♓ 5.3	8 57.2	11 35.7	10 19.5	22 35.6	26 42.9	2 24.1
4 T	10 45 27.2	13 2.3	2 53.4	17 30.9	2 3.9	1 20.1	9 38.5	11 46.1	10 24.8	22 37.2	26 41.3	2 23.1
5 W	10 49 23.7	14 2.4	2 50.2	29 24.0	1 17.3	2 34.9	10 19.8	11 56.6	10 30.1	22 38.9	26 39.7	2 22.1
6 T	10 53 20.3	15 2.5	2 47.0	11♊26.4	0 36.9	3 49.7	11 1.2	12 7.2	10 35.5	22 40.7	26 38.1	2 21.2
7 F	10 57 16.9	16 2.5	2 43.8	23 42.9	0 2.9	5 4.5	11 42.5	12 18.0	10 41.0	22 42.5	26 36.4	2 20.2
8 S	11 1 13.4	17 2.5	2 40.7	6♋18.1	29♒35.5	6 19.3	12 23.8	12 28.8	10 46.5	22 44.3	26 34.8	2 19.3
9 S	11 5 9.9	18 2.5	2 37.5	19 15.8	29 14.9	7 34.0	13 5.2	12 39.8	10 52.1	22 46.2	26 33.2	2 18.4
10 M	11 9 6.5	19 2.4	2 34.3	2♌38.6	29 1.0	8 48.8	13 46.5	12 50.8	10 57.8	22 48.1	26 31.5	2 17.6
11 T	11 13 3.0	20 2.3	2 31.1	16 27.5	28 53.7	10 3.5	14 27.9	13 1.9	11 3.6	22 50.1	26 29.9	2 16.7
12 W	11 16 59.6	21 2.2	2 27.9	0♍41.1	28 52.7	11 18.2	15 9.3	13 13.2	11 9.4	22 52.1	26 28.2	2 15.9
13 T	11 20 56.2	22 2.0	2 24.8	15 15.6	28D57.9	12 32.9	15 50.7	13 24.5	11 15.3	22 54.1	26 26.6	2 15.1
14 F	11 24 52.7	23 1.8	2 21.6	0♎ 5.1	29 8.8	13 47.6	16 32.1	13 35.9	11 21.2	22 56.2	26 24.9	2 14.3
15 S	11 28 49.2	24 1.6	2 18.4	15 2.0	29 25.3	15 2.3	17 13.5	13 47.4	11 27.3	22 58.3	26 23.2	2 13.5
16 S	11 32 45.8	25 1.3	2 15.2	29 58.1	29 47.0	16 17.0	17 54.9	13 59.0	11 33.3	23 0.5	26 21.6	2 12.8
17 M	11 36 42.4	26 1.0	2 12.1	14♏45.8	0♓13.6	17 31.7	18 36.4	14 10.6	11 39.5	23 2.7	26 19.9	2 12.1
18 T	11 40 38.9	27 0.7	2 8.9	29 19.2	0 44.8	18 46.3	19 17.8	14 22.4	11 45.7	23 5.0	26 18.3	2 11.4
19 W	11 44 35.5	28 0.4	2 5.7	13♐34.1	1 20.4	20 1.0	19 59.3	14 34.2	11 51.9	23 7.3	26 16.6	2 10.7
20 T	11 48 32.0	28 60.0	2 2.5	27 28.6	2 0.1	21 15.6	20 40.7	14 46.2	11 58.2	23 9.6	26 14.9	2 10.0
21 F	11 52 28.6	29 59.6	1 59.3	11♑ 2.2	2 43.6	22 30.2	21 22.2	14 58.2	12 4.6	23 12.0	26 13.3	2 9.4
22 S	11 56 25.1	0♈59.1	1 56.2	24 16.1	3 30.7	23 44.9	22 3.7	15 10.2	12 11.0	23 14.4	26 11.6	2 8.8
23 S	12 0 21.7	1 58.6	1 53.0	7♒12.1	4 21.2	24 59.5	22 45.2	15 22.4	12 17.5	23 16.8	26 10.0	2 8.2
24 M	12 4 18.2	2 58.1	1 49.8	19 52.2	5 14.8	26 14.1	23 26.7	15 34.6	12 24.0	23 19.3	26 8.3	2 7.7
25 T	12 8 14.8	3 57.6	1 46.6	2♓18.9	6 11.5	27 28.7	24 8.1	15 46.9	12 30.6	23 21.8	26 6.7	2 7.1
26 W	12 12 11.3	4 57.1	1 43.5	14 34.1	7 11.0	28 43.2	24 49.6	15 59.3	12 37.2	23 24.4	26 5.0	2 6.6
27 T	12 16 7.9	5 56.5	1 40.3	26 40.0	8 13.1	29 57.8	25 31.1	16 11.8	12 43.9	23 27.0	26 3.4	2 6.1
28 F	12 20 4.4	6 55.8	1 37.1	8♈38.4	9 17.8	1♈12.3	26 12.6	16 24.3	12 50.6	23 29.6	26 1.7	2 5.7
29 S	12 24 1.0	7 55.2	1 33.9	20 31.3	10 24.9	2 26.9	26 54.1	16 36.9	12 57.4	23 32.2	26 0.1	2 5.2
30 S	12 27 57.5	8 54.5	1 30.7	2♉20.8	11 34.3	3 41.4	27 35.6	16 49.5	13 4.2	23 34.9	25 58.5	2 4.8
31 M	12 31 54.1	9 53.8	1 27.6	14 9.2	12 45.9	4 55.9	28 17.1	17 2.3	13 11.1	23 37.6	25 56.9	2 4.4

DECLINATION

DAY	EPHEMERIS SIDEREAL TIME h m s	☉	☊	☽	☿	♀	♂	♃	♄	♅	♆	♇
1 S	10 33 37.5	7S48.6	1S12.7	3N53.8	6S23.8	13S26.7	23S36.1	14N20.7	12N47.0	18N10.6	2N28.6	23N48.7
4 T	10 45 27.2	6 39.9	1 9.0	13 26.0	7 48.7	12 11.3	23 31.0	14 30.8	12 52.5	18 11.9	2 30.6	23 49.3
7 F	10 57 16.9	5 30.4	1 5.2	18 4.5	9 5.9	10 53.0	23 24.1	14 41.2	12 58.2	18 13.3	2 32.5	23 50.0
10 M	11 9 6.5	4 20.3	1 1.4	15 8.9	10 6.9	9 32.1	23 15.4	14 51.7	13 4.0	18 14.8	2 34.5	23 50.6
13 T	11 20 56.2	3 9.6	0 57.6	4 25.0	10 48.2	8 8.8	23 4.8	15 2.4	13 10.0	18 16.3	2 36.5	23 51.1
16 S	11 32 45.8	1 58.7	0 53.8	9S 7.0	11 9.5	6 43.6	22 52.4	15 13.2	13 16.1	18 18.0	2 38.6	23 51.6
19 W	11 44 35.5	0 47.6	0 50.0	17 26.2	11 11.5	5 16.8	22 38.3	15 24.1	13 22.3	18 19.8	2 40.6	23 52.0
22 S	11 56 25.1	0N23.5	0 46.2	16 26.5	10 55.8	3 48.7	22 22.4	15 35.2	13 28.6	18 21.6	2 42.6	23 52.3
25 T	12 8 14.8	1 34.5	0 42.4	8 12.5	10 23.7	2 19.6	22 4.9	15 46.3	13 35.0	18 23.5	2 44.5	23 52.6
28 F	12 20 4.4	2 45.1	0 38.6	2N51.0	9 36.6	0 49.9	21 45.6	15 57.5	13 41.5	18 25.5	2 46.5	23 52.9
31 M	12 31 54.1	3 55.2	0 34.8	12 40.9	8 35.6	0N40.2	21 24.8	16 8.7	13 48.1	18 27.6	2 48.4	23 53.1

APRIL 1941

LONGITUDE

DAY	EPHEMERIS SIDEREAL TIME h m s	☉ ° ′	☊ ° ′	☽ ° ′	☿ ° ′	♀ ° ′	♂ ° ′	♃ ° ′	♄ ° ′	♅ ° ′	♆ ° ′	♇ ° ′
1 T	12 35 50.6	10♈53.0	1♎24.4	25♉59.1	13♓59.6	6♈10.4	28♑58.6	17♉15.0	13♉18.0	23♉40.4	25♍55.3	2♌ 4.1
2 W	12 39 47.2	11 52.2	1 21.2	7♊53.8	15 15.4	7 24.9	29 40.0	17 27.9	13 25.0	23 43.2	25R53.7	2R 3.7
3 T	12 43 43.7	12 51.3	1 18.0	19 56.7	16 33.0	8 39.3	0♒21.5	17 40.8	13 32.0	23 46.0	25 52.1	2 3.4
4 F	12 47 40.3	13 50.5	1 14.8	2♋11.8	17 52.6	9 53.7	1 3.0	17 53.7	13 39.0	23 48.8	25 50.6	2 3.1
5 S	12 51 36.8	14 49.5	1 11.7	14 43.2	19 14.0	11 8.2	1 44.4	18 6.7	13 46.1	23 51.7	25 49.0	2 2.9
6 S	12 55 33.4	15 48.6	1 8.5	27 34.9	20 37.2	12 22.6	2 25.9	18 19.8	13 53.2	23 54.6	25 47.5	2 2.6
7 M	12 59 29.9	16 47.6	1 5.3	10♌50.4	22 2.2	13 37.0	3 7.4	18 32.9	14 0.3	23 57.5	25 45.9	2 2.4
8 T	13 3 26.5	17 46.5	1 2.1	24 32.2	23 28.8	14 51.3	3 48.8	18 46.1	14 7.5	24 0.5	25 44.4	2 2.2
9 W	13 7 23.1	18 45.5	0 59.0	8♍41.0	24 57.1	16 5.7	4 30.3	18 59.3	14 14.7	24 3.5	25 42.9	2 2.1
10 T	13 11 19.6	19 44.4	0 55.8	23 15.2	26 27.1	17 20.0	5 11.7	19 12.6	14 22.0	24 6.5	25 41.4	2 1.9
11 F	13 15 16.1	20 43.2	0 52.6	8♎10.3	27 58.7	18 34.3	5 53.1	19 25.9	14 29.2	24 9.5	25 39.9	2 1.8
12 S	13 19 12.7	21 42.0	0 49.4	23 19.2	29 32.0	19 48.6	6 34.6	19 39.2	14 36.5	24 12.5	25 38.5	2 1.7
13 S	13 23 9.3	22 40.8	0 46.2	8♏32.6	1♈ 6.8	21 2.9	7 16.0	19 52.6	14 43.9	24 15.6	25 37.0	2 1.7
14 M	13 27 5.8	23 39.6	0 43.1	23 40.7	2 43.3	22 17.2	7 57.4	20 6.1	14 51.2	24 18.7	25 35.6	2 1.7
15 T	13 31 2.4	24 38.3	0 39.9	8♐34.2	4 21.4	23 31.5	8 38.9	20 19.6	14 58.6	24 21.9	25 34.2	2 1.7
16 W	13 34 58.9	25 37.0	0 36.7	23 6.0	6 1.1	24 45.7	9 20.3	20 33.1	15 6.0	24 25.0	25 32.8	2D 1.7
17 T	13 38 55.4	26 35.7	0 33.5	7♑12.2	7 42.4	25 59.9	10 1.7	20 46.7	15 13.5	24 28.2	25 31.4	2 1.7
18 F	13 42 52.0	27 34.3	0 30.4	20 51.4	9 25.3	27 14.2	10 43.1	21 0.3	15 21.0	24 31.4	25 30.0	2 1.8
19 S	13 46 48.6	28 32.9	0 27.2	4♒ 4.6	11 9.8	28 28.4	11 24.4	21 13.9	15 28.5	24 34.6	25 28.7	2 1.9
20 S	13 50 45.1	29 31.5	0 24.0	16 54.7	12 56.0	29 42.6	12 5.8	21 27.6	15 36.0	24 37.8	25 27.4	2 2.0
21 M	13 54 41.7	0♉30.1	0 20.8	29 25.3	14 43.8	0♉56.8	12 47.2	21 41.3	15 43.5	24 41.0	25 26.1	2 2.2
22 T	13 58 38.2	1 28.6	0 17.6	11♓40.5	16 33.2	2 10.9	13 28.5	21 55.0	15 51.1	24 44.3	25 24.8	2 2.4
23 W	14 2 34.8	2 27.1	0 14.5	23 44.1	18 24.3	3 25.1	14 9.8	22 8.8	15 58.6	24 47.6	25 23.5	2 2.6
24 T	14 6 31.3	3 25.6	0 11.3	5♈39.8	20 17.1	4 39.2	14 51.1	22 22.6	16 6.2	24 50.9	25 22.3	2 2.8
25 F	14 10 27.9	4 24.0	0 8.1	17 30.6	22 11.5	5 53.4	15 32.4	22 36.5	16 13.8	24 54.2	25 21.1	2 3.1
26 S	14 14 24.4	5 22.4	0 4.9	29 19.2	24 7.5	7 7.5	16 13.6	22 50.3	16 21.5	24 57.5	25 19.9	2 3.4
27 S	14 18 21.0	6 20.8	0 1.8	11♉ 7.8	26 5.2	8 21.6	16 54.8	23 4.2	16 29.1	25 0.9	25 18.7	2 3.7
28 M	14 22 17.6	7 19.2	29♍58.6	22 58.3	28 4.5	9 35.7	17 36.0	23 18.1	16 36.8	25 4.3	25 17.6	2 4.0
29 T	14 26 14.1	8 17.5	29 55.4	4♊52.6	0♉ 5.3	10 49.8	18 17.2	23 32.1	16 44.4	25 7.6	25 16.5	2 4.4
30 W	14 30 10.7	9 15.8	29 52.2	16 52.7	2 7.7	12 3.8	18 58.3	23 46.0	16 52.1	25 11.0	25 15.3	2 4.8

DECLINATION

DAY	EPHEMERIS SIDEREAL TIME h m s	☉	☊	☽	☿	♀	♂	♃	♄	♅	♆	♇
1 T	12 35 50.6	4N18.5	0S33.6	15N 5.0	8S12.4	1N10.2	21S17.5	16N12.4	13N50.3	18N28.3	2N49.1	23N53.1
4 F	12 47 40.3	5 27.7	0 29.8	18 8.6	6 54.4	2 40.2	20 54.6	16 23.7	13 56.9	18 30.4	2 50.9	23 53.2
7 M	12 59 29.9	6 36.0	0 26.0	13 33.9	5 24.6	4 9.7	20 30.2	16 34.9	14 3.6	18 32.6	2 52.7	23 53.3
10 T	13 11 19.6	7 43.3	0 22.2	1 57.4	3 43.7	5 38.5	20 4.3	16 46.2	14 10.4	18 34.8	2 54.5	23 53.3
13 S	13 23 9.3	8 49.5	0 18.4	11S21.9	1 52.4	7 6.1	19 37.0	16 57.4	14 17.1	18 37.1	2 56.2	23 53.2
16 W	13 34 58.9	9 54.3	0 14.6	18 4.8	0N 8.5	8 32.4	19 8.4	17 8.5	14 23.9	18 39.5	2 57.9	23 53.1
19 S	13 46 48.6	10 57.7	0 10.8	14 56.0	2 18.3	9 57.0	18 38.5	17 19.6	14 30.6	18 41.8	2 59.5	23 52.9
22 T	13 58 38.2	11 59.4	0 7.0	5 31.7	4 36.0	11 19.4	18 7.3	17 30.6	14 37.4	18 44.3	3 1.0	23 52.6
25 F	14 10 27.9	12 59.4	0 3.2	5N33.2	7 0.5	12 39.5	17 35.0	17 41.5	14 44.1	18 46.7	3 2.4	23 52.4
28 M	14 22 17.6	13 57.5	0N 0.6	14 35.1	9 29.9	13 56.8	17 1.7	17 52.4	14 50.8	18 49.1	3 3.7	23 52.0

MAY 1941

DAY	EPHEMERIS SIDEREAL TIME h m s	☉ ° ′	☊ ° ′	☽ ° ′	☿ ° ′	♀ ° ′	♂ ° ′	♃ ° ′	♄ ° ′	♅ ° ′	♆ ° ′	♇ ° ′
LONGITUDE												
1 T	14 34 7.2	10♉14.0	29♍49.0	29♊ 0.8	4♉11.5	13♉17.9	19♒39.4	24♉ 0.0	16♉59.8	25♉14.4	25♍14.3	2♌ 5.2
2 F	14 38 3.8	11 12.3	29 45.9	11♋19.4	6 16.8	14 31.9	20 20.5	24 14.0	17 7.5	25 17.8	25R13.2	2 5.6
3 S	14 42 0.3	12 10.5	29 42.7	23 51.6	8 23.2	15 45.9	21 1.5	24 28.1	17 15.2	25 21.2	25 12.2	2 6.1
4 S	14 45 56.9	13 8.6	29 39.5	6♌40.6	10 30.9	16 59.9	21 42.5	24 42.1	17 22.9	25 24.7	25 11.2	2 6.6
5 M	14 49 53.4	14 6.7	29 36.3	19 49.7	12 39.4	18 13.9	22 23.5	24 56.2	17 30.6	25 28.1	25 10.2	2 7.1
6 T	14 53 50.0	15 4.8	29 33.1	3♍22.0	14 48.8	19 27.8	23 4.4	25 10.2	17 38.3	25 31.5	25 9.3	2 7.6
7 W	14 57 46.5	16 2.9	29 30.0	17 19.3	16 58.8	20 41.8	23 45.3	25 24.3	17 46.0	25 35.0	25 8.4	2 8.2
8 T	15 1 43.1	17 0.9	29 26.8	1♎42.1	19 9.1	21 55.7	24 26.2	25 38.4	17 53.7	25 38.5	25 7.5	2 8.8
9 F	15 5 39.7	17 58.9	29 23.6	16 28.2	21 19.5	23 9.6	25 7.0	25 52.5	18 1.5	25 41.9	25 6.6	2 9.4
10 S	15 9 36.2	18 56.9	29 20.4	1♏32.3	23 29.8	24 23.5	25 47.8	26 6.6	18 9.2	25 45.4	25 5.8	2 10.0
11 S	15 13 32.7	19 54.8	29 17.3	16 46.4	25 39.5	25 37.4	26 28.5	26 20.7	18 16.9	25 48.9	25 5.0	2 10.7
12 M	15 17 29.3	20 52.8	29 14.1	2♐ 0.3	27 48.6	26 51.2	27 9.3	26 34.9	18 24.6	25 52.4	25 4.2	2 11.4
13 T	15 21 25.9	21 50.6	29 10.9	17 3.5	29 56.6	28 5.1	27 49.9	26 49.0	18 32.3	25 55.9	25 3.4	2 12.1
14 W	15 25 22.4	22 48.5	29 7.7	1♑46.8	2♊ 3.3	29 18.9	28 30.6	27 3.2	18 40.0	25 59.3	25 2.7	2 12.8
15 T	15 29 19.0	23 46.4	29 4.6	16 3.7	4 8.4	0♊32.8	29 11.1	27 17.3	18 47.7	26 2.8	25 2.0	2 13.6
16 F	15 33 15.5	24 44.2	29 1.4	29 51.4	6 11.7	1 46.6	29 51.7	27 31.5	18 55.4	26 6.3	25 1.3	2 14.3
17 S	15 37 12.1	25 42.0	28 58.2	13♒ 9.9	8 13.0	3 0.4	0♓32.2	27 45.6	19 3.1	26 9.8	25 0.7	2 15.1
18 S	15 41 8.6	26 39.8	28 55.0	26 1.7	10 12.0	4 14.2	1 12.6	27 59.8	19 10.8	26 13.3	25 0.1	2 16.0
19 M	15 45 5.2	27 37.5	28 51.8	8♓31.0	12 8.6	5 27.9	1 53.0	28 13.9	19 18.5	26 16.8	24 59.5	2 16.8
20 T	15 49 1.7	28 35.3	28 48.7	20 42.6	14 2.7	6 41.7	2 33.3	28 28.1	19 26.1	26 20.3	24 59.0	2 17.7
21 W	15 52 58.3	29 33.0	28 45.5	2♈41.7	15 54.0	7 55.5	3 13.6	28 42.2	19 33.8	26 23.8	24 58.5	2 18.6
22 T	15 56 54.9	0♊30.7	28 42.3	14 33.0	17 42.6	9 9.2	3 53.8	28 56.4	19 41.4	26 27.3	24 58.0	2 19.5
23 F	16 0 51.4	1 28.4	28 39.1	26 20.7	19 28.3	10 23.0	4 33.9	29 10.6	19 49.1	26 30.8	24 57.5	2 20.4
24 S	16 4 48.0	2 26.1	28 36.0	8♉ 8.4	21 11.0	11 36.7	5 13.9	29 24.7	19 56.7	26 34.3	24 57.1	2 21.4
25 S	16 8 44.5	3 23.8	28 32.8	19 58.9	22 50.8	12 50.4	5 53.9	29 38.8	20 4.3	26 37.7	24 56.7	2 22.4
26 M	16 12 41.1	4 21.4	28 29.6	1♊54.5	24 27.5	14 4.1	6 33.8	29 53.0	20 11.8	26 41.2	24 56.3	2 23.4
27 T	16 16 37.6	5 19.0	28 26.4	13 56.6	26 1.0	15 17.8	7 13.7	0♊ 7.1	20 19.4	26 44.7	24 56.0	2 24.4
28 W	16 20 34.2	6 16.6	28 23.3	26 6.6	27 31.5	16 31.5	7 53.4	0 21.2	20 27.0	26 48.2	24 55.7	2 25.4
29 T	16 24 30.7	7 14.2	28 20.1	8♋25.5	28 58.8	17 45.2	8 33.1	0 35.3	20 34.5	26 51.6	24 55.5	2 26.5
30 F	16 28 27.3	8 11.8	28 16.9	20 54.4	0♋22.9	18 58.8	9 12.6	0 49.4	20 42.0	26 55.0	24 55.2	2 27.6
31 S	16 32 23.9	9 9.3	28 13.7	3♌34.9	1 43.7	20 12.5	9 52.1	1 3.5	20 49.5	26 58.5	24 55.0	2 28.7
DECLINATION												
1 T	14 34 7.2	14N53.5	0N 4.4	18N16.4	12N 1.8	15N11.1	16S27.3	18N 3.0	14N57.5	18N51.6	3N 5.0	23N51.6
4 S	14 45 56.9	15 47.2	0 8.2	14 32.3	14 32.9	16 22.0	15 52.0	18 13.6	15 4.1	18 54.1	3 6.1	23 51.2
7 W	14 57 46.5	16 38.7	0 11.9	3 53.2	16 58.6	17 29.1	15 15.9	18 24.0	15 10.7	18 56.6	3 7.2	23 50.7
10 S	15 9 36.2	17 27.6	0 15.7	9S32.8	19 13.6	18 32.1	14 38.9	18 34.3	15 17.2	18 59.1	3 8.1	23 50.1
13 T	15 21 25.9	18 13.9	0 19.5	17 51.6	21 12.5	19 30.8	14 1.2	18 44.4	15 23.6	19 1.6	3 9.0	23 49.6
16 F	15 33 15.5	18 57.4	0 23.3	15 49.6	22 50.9	20 24.7	13 22.8	18 54.3	15 30.0	19 4.1	3 9.7	23 48.9
19 M	15 45 5.2	19 38.1	0 27.1	6 37.1	24 6.5	21 13.7	12 43.9	19 4.0	15 36.3	19 6.6	3 10.4	23 48.3
22 T	15 56 54.9	20 15.7	0 30.9	4N34.0	24 58.7	21 57.4	12 4.5	19 13.6	15 42.4	19 9.0	3 10.9	23 47.5
25 S	16 8 44.5	20 50.3	0 34.7	13 59.7	25 28.9	22 35.5	11 24.7	19 22.9	15 48.5	19 11.5	3 11.3	23 46.8
28 W	16 20 34.2	21 21.6	0 38.5	18 21.4	25 39.3	23 7.9	10 44.6	19 32.0	15 54.5	19 13.9	3 11.6	23 46.0
31 S	16 32 23.9	21 49.6	0 42.3	15 18.9	25 32.6	23 34.2	10 4.2	19 41.0	16 0.3	19 16.3	3 11.8	23 45.2

JUNE 1941

DAY	EPHEMERIS SIDEREAL TIME h m s	☉ ° ′	☊ ° ′	☽ ° ′	☿ ° ′	♀ ° ′	♂ ° ′	♃ ° ′	♄ ° ′	♅ ° ′	♆ ° ′	♇ ° ′
LONGITUDE												
1 S	16 36 20.4	10♊ 6.8	28♍10.5	16♌28.9	3♋ 1.3	21♊26.1	10♓31.5	1♊17.5	20♉56.9	27♉ 1.9	24♍54.8	2♌29.8
2 M	16 40 16.9	11 4.3	28 7.4	29 38.6	4 15.5	22 39.7	11 10.8	1 31.6	21 4.3	27 5.3	24R54.7	2 30.9
3 T	16 44 13.5	12 1.8	28 4.2	13♍ 6.5	5 26.3	23 53.3	11 50.1	1 45.6	21 11.7	27 8.8	24 54.6	2 32.1
4 W	16 48 10.1	12 59.2	28 1.0	26 54.6	6 33.7	25 6.9	12 29.2	1 59.6	21 19.1	27 12.2	24 54.5	2 33.3
5 T	16 52 6.7	13 56.6	27 57.8	11♎ 4.0	7 37.6	26 20.5	13 8.2	2 13.6	21 26.5	27 15.5	24 54.5	2 34.5
6 F	16 56 3.2	14 54.1	27 54.7	25 34.2	8 37.9	27 34.1	13 47.1	2 27.5	21 33.8	27 18.9	24 54.5	2 35.7
7 S	16 59 59.7	15 51.4	27 51.5	10♏22.0	9 34.5	28 47.6	14 25.9	2 41.5	21 41.1	27 22.3	24D54.5	2 36.9
8 S	17 3 56.3	16 48.8	27 48.3	25 21.6	10 27.4	0♋ 1.1	15 4.7	2 55.4	21 48.4	27 25.6	24 54.6	2 38.2
9 M	17 7 52.9	17 46.2	27 45.1	10♐24.6	11 16.5	1 14.6	15 43.3	3 9.3	21 55.6	27 29.0	24 54.7	2 39.5
10 T	17 11 49.4	18 43.5	27 42.0	25 21.4	12 1.7	2 28.2	16 21.8	3 23.1	22 2.8	27 32.3	24 54.8	2 40.8
11 W	17 15 46.0	19 40.8	27 38.8	10♑ 2.7	12 42.9	3 41.6	17 0.2	3 37.0	22 10.0	27 35.6	24 54.9	2 42.1
12 T	17 19 42.5	20 38.2	27 35.6	24 21.0	13 20.1	4 55.1	17 38.5	3 50.8	22 17.1	27 38.9	24 55.1	2 43.4
13 F	17 23 39.0	21 35.5	27 32.4	8♒12.0	13 53.0	6 8.6	18 16.6	4 4.6	22 24.2	27 42.1	24 55.3	2 44.7
14 S	17 27 35.6	22 32.8	27 29.2	21 34.4	14 21.6	7 22.0	18 54.7	4 18.3	22 31.2	27 45.4	24 55.6	2 46.1
15 S	17 31 32.2	23 30.1	27 26.1	4♓29.7	14 46.0	8 35.5	19 32.6	4 32.1	22 38.3	27 48.6	24 55.9	2 47.4
16 M	17 35 28.8	24 27.4	27 22.9	17 1.5	15 5.8	9 48.9	20 10.3	4 45.8	22 45.3	27 51.9	24 56.2	2 48.8
17 T	17 39 25.3	25 24.6	27 19.7	29 14.4	15 21.2	11 2.3	20 48.0	4 59.4	22 52.2	27 55.0	24 56.5	2 50.2
18 W	17 43 21.8	26 21.9	27 16.5	11♈13.9	15 32.1	12 15.8	21 25.5	5 13.1	22 59.1	27 58.2	24 56.9	2 51.6
19 T	17 47 18.4	27 19.2	27 13.4	23 5.2	15 38.4	13 29.2	22 2.8	5 26.7	23 6.0	28 1.4	24 57.3	2 53.0
20 F	17 51 15.0	28 16.5	27 10.2	4♉53.5	15 40.1	14 42.6	22 40.0	5 40.2	23 12.8	28 4.5	24 57.8	2 54.5
21 S	17 55 11.6	29 13.7	27 7.0	16 43.2	15R37.3	15 56.0	23 17.0	5 53.7	23 19.6	28 7.6	24 58.2	2 55.9
22 S	17 59 8.1	0♋11.0	27 3.8	28 37.8	15 30.1	17 9.3	23 53.9	6 7.2	23 26.3	28 10.7	24 58.7	2 57.4
23 M	18 3 4.6	1 8.3	27 0.7	10♊40.2	15 18.5	18 22.7	24 30.6	6 20.7	23 33.0	28 13.8	24 59.3	2 58.9
24 T	18 7 1.2	2 5.5	26 57.5	22 52.4	15 2.8	19 36.1	25 7.1	6 34.1	23 39.6	28 16.9	24 59.9	3 0.4
25 W	18 10 57.8	3 2.8	26 54.3	5♋15.3	14 43.2	20 49.4	25 43.5	6 47.4	23 46.2	28 19.9	25 0.5	3 1.9
26 T	18 14 54.3	4 0.0	26 51.1	17 49.4	14 19.8	22 2.7	26 19.6	7 0.7	23 52.8	28 22.9	25 1.1	3 3.4
27 F	18 18 50.9	4 57.2	26 47.9	0♌34.7	13 53.2	23 16.1	26 55.6	7 14.0	23 59.3	28 25.8	25 1.7	3 4.9
28 S	18 22 47.4	5 54.5	26 44.8	13 31.3	13 23.6	24 29.4	27 31.4	7 27.2	24 5.7	28 28.8	25 2.4	3 6.5
29 S	18 26 44.0	6 51.7	26 41.6	26 39.4	12 51.5	25 42.7	28 7.0	7 40.4	24 12.1	28 31.7	25 3.2	3 8.0
30 M	18 30 40.5	7 48.9	26 38.4	9♍59.6	12 17.4	26 55.9	28 42.4	7 53.5	24 18.4	28 34.6	25 3.9	3 9.6
DECLINATION												
1 S	16 36 20.4	21N58.2	0N43.5	12N38.8	25N27.1	23N41.7	9S50.8	19N43.9	16N 2.3	19N17.1	3N11.8	23N44.9
4 W	16 48 10.1	22 21.7	0 47.3	1 4.8	25 2.2	23 59.8	9 10.2	19 52.5	16 7.9	19 19.4	3 11.9	23 44.0
7 S	16 59 59.7	22 41.6	0 51.1	11S44.5	24 27.0	24 11.6	8 29.7	20 0.9	16 13.5	19 21.8	3 11.8	23 43.1
10 T	17 11 49.4	22 57.9	0 54.9	18 21.2	23 44.1	24 16.9	7 49.2	20 9.1	16 18.9	19 24.0	3 11.6	23 42.2
13 F	17 23 39.0	23 10.6	0 58.7	14 31.0	22 56.1	24 15.9	7 8.7	20 17.0	16 24.2	19 26.3	3 11.3	23 41.3
16 M	17 35 28.8	23 19.7	1 2.5	4 16.3	22 5.7	24 8.3	6 28.5	20 24.7	16 29.3	19 28.5	3 10.8	23 40.3
19 T	17 47 18.4	23 25.0	1 6.3	6N57.0	21 15.3	23 54.4	5 48.6	20 32.1	16 34.3	19 30.6	3 10.3	23 39.3
22 S	17 59 8.1	23 26.6	1 10.1	15 33.6	20 27.4	23 34.1	5 9.1	20 39.3	16 39.1	19 32.7	3 9.6	23 38.3
25 W	18 10 57.8	23 24.5	1 13.9	18 23.8	19 44.4	23 7.6	4 30.1	20 46.2	16 43.8	19 34.8	3 8.8	23 37.3
28 S	18 22 47.4	23 18.7	1 17.6	13 30.3	19 8.5	22 35.1	3 51.7	20 52.9	16 48.3	19 36.7	3 8.0	23 36.2

JULY 1941

DAY	EPHEMERIS SIDEREAL TIME	☉	☊	☽	☿	♀	♂	♃	♄	♅	♆	♇
	h m s	° ′	° ′	° ′	° ′	° ′	° ′	° ′	° ′	° ′	° ′	° ′
						LONGITUDE						
1 T	18 34 37.1	8♋46.1	26♍35.2	23♍32.8	11♋41.9	28♋ 9.2	29♓17.5	8♊ 6.6	24♉24.7	28♉37.5	25♍ 4.7	3♌11.1
2 W	18 38 33.7	9 43.3	26 32.1	7♎20.0	11R 5.6	29 22.4	29 52.5	8 19.6	24 30.9	28 40.3	25 5.5	3 12.7
3 T	18 42 30.2	10 40.5	26 28.9	21 21.9	10 29.0	0♌35.7	0♈27.2	8 32.6	24 37.1	28 43.1	25 6.4	3 14.3
4 F	18 46 26.8	11 37.7	26 25.7	5♏38.3	9 52.9	1 48.9	1 1.8	8 45.5	24 43.2	28 45.9	25 7.3	3 15.9
5 S	18 50 23.3	12 34.9	26 22.5	20 7.2	9 17.7	3 2.1	1 36.1	8 58.4	24 49.3	28 48.7	25 8.2	3 17.5
6 S	18 54 19.9	13 32.1	26 19.4	4♐44.9	8 44.2	4 15.2	2 10.1	9 11.2	24 55.3	28 51.4	25 9.1	3 19.1
7 M	18 58 16.5	14 29.3	26 16.2	19 25.6	8 12.9	5 28.4	2 44.0	9 23.9	25 1.2	28 54.1	25 10.1	3 20.8
8 T	19 2 13.0	15 26.5	26 13.0	4♑ 2.0	7 44.5	6 41.5	3 17.6	9 36.6	25 7.1	28 56.7	25 11.1	3 22.4
9 W	19 6 9.6	16 23.7	26 9.8	18 26.9	7 19.3	7 54.6	3 51.0	9 49.2	25 12.9	28 59.3	25 12.1	3 24.0
10 T	19 10 6.1	17 20.8	26 6.6	2♒33.6	6 57.9	9 7.7	4 24.1	10 1.8	25 18.6	29 1.9	25 13.2	3 25.7
11 F	19 14 2.7	18 18.0	26 3.5	16 17.6	6 40.6	10 20.8	4 56.9	10 14.3	25 24.3	29 4.5	25 14.3	3 27.3
12 S	19 17 59.2	19 15.2	26 0.3	29 36.9	6 27.9	11 33.9	5 29.5	10 26.7	25 29.9	29 7.0	25 15.4	3 29.0
13 S	19 21 55.8	20 12.4	25 57.1	12♓31.9	6 20.0	12 46.9	6 1.8	10 39.1	25 35.5	29 9.5	25 16.5	3 30.7
14 M	19 25 52.4	21 9.6	25 53.9	25 4.7	6 17.1	13 60.0	6 33.9	10 51.4	25 41.0	29 12.0	25 17.7	3 32.3
15 T	19 29 48.9	22 6.9	25 50.8	7♈19.5	6D19.5	15 13.0	7 5.6	11 3.7	25 46.4	29 14.4	25 18.9	3 34.0
16 W	19 33 45.4	23 4.1	25 47.6	19 20.8	6 27.3	16 26.0	7 37.0	11 15.8	25 51.7	29 16.8	25 20.1	3 35.7
17 T	19 37 42.0	24 1.3	25 44.4	1♉14.0	6 40.6	17 39.0	8 8.2	11 27.9	25 57.0	29 19.1	25 21.4	3 37.4
18 F	19 41 38.6	24 58.6	25 41.2	13 4.3	6 59.5	18 52.0	8 39.0	11 40.0	26 2.2	29 21.4	25 22.7	3 39.1
19 S	19 45 35.2	25 55.9	25 38.1	24 56.6	7 23.9	20 4.9	9 9.4	11 51.9	26 7.4	29 23.7	25 24.0	3 40.8
20 S	19 49 31.7	26 53.1	25 34.9	6♊55.3	7 54.0	21 17.8	9 39.6	12 3.8	26 12.4	29 25.9	25 25.3	3 42.5
21 M	19 53 28.2	27 50.4	25 31.7	19 4.0	8 29.6	22 30.8	10 9.4	12 15.6	26 17.4	29 28.1	25 26.6	3 44.2
22 T	19 57 24.8	28 47.7	25 28.5	1♋25.4	9 10.8	23 43.7	10 38.8	12 27.3	26 22.3	29 30.3	25 28.0	3 45.9
23 W	20 1 21.4	29 45.0	25 25.4	14 1.1	9 57.6	24 56.6	11 7.9	12 39.0	26 27.2	29 32.4	25 29.4	3 47.6
24 T	20 5 17.9	0♌42.3	25 22.2	26 51.5	10 49.8	26 9.4	11 36.6	12 50.5	26 31.9	29 34.5	25 30.9	3 49.3
25 F	20 9 14.5	1 39.7	25 19.0	9♌56.3	11 47.4	27 22.3	12 4.9	13 2.0	26 36.6	29 36.5	25 32.3	3 51.0
26 S	20 13 11.0	2 37.0	25 15.8	23 14.4	12 50.3	28 35.1	12 32.8	13 13.4	26 41.2	29 38.5	25 33.8	3 52.7
27 S	20 17 7.6	3 34.4	25 12.6	6♍44.2	13 58.5	29 47.9	13 0.3	13 24.7	26 45.7	29 40.5	25 35.3	3 54.4
28 M	20 21 4.1	4 31.7	25 9.5	20 24.5	15 11.8	1♍ 0.7	13 27.4	13 35.9	26 50.2	29 42.4	25 36.9	3 56.1
29 T	20 25 0.7	5 29.1	25 6.3	4♎13.8	16 30.0	2 13.5	13 54.0	13 47.1	26 54.5	29 44.3	25 38.4	3 57.8
30 W	20 28 57.2	6 26.5	25 3.1	18 11.2	17 53.1	3 26.2	14 20.3	13 58.1	26 58.8	29 46.1	25 40.0	3 59.5
31 T	20 32 53.8	7 23.9	24 59.9	2♏15.8	19 20.9	4 38.9	14 46.1	14 9.1	27 3.0	29 47.9	25 41.6	4 1.2
						DECLINATION						
1 T	18 34 37.1	23N 9.2	1N21.4	2N22.3	18N42.0	21N56.7	3S 13.9	20N59.3	16N52.6	19N38.7	3N 7.0	23N35.2
4 F	18 46 26.8	22 56.1	1 25.2	10S21.0	18 26.4	21 12.7	2 36.9	21 5.5	16 56.7	19 40.5	3 5.9	23 34.1
7 M	18 58 16.5	22 39.4	1 29.0	18 1.8	18 22.5	20 23.4	2 0.7	21 11.4	17 0.7	19 42.3	3 4.7	23 33.1
10 T	19 10 6.1	22 19.1	1 32.8	15 41.2	18 30.4	19 28.9	1 25.4	21 17.1	17 4.5	19 44.0	3 3.3	23 32.0
13 S	19 21 55.8	21 55.4	1 36.6	5 51.5	18 49.0	18 29.7	0 51.1	21 22.5	17 8.1	19 45.7	3 1.9	23 30.9
16 W	19 33 45.4	21 28.3	1 40.4	5N36.5	19 16.0	17 26.0	0 17.9	21 27.7	17 11.5	19 47.2	3 0.4	23 29.9
19 S	19 45 35.2	20 57.9	1 44.1	14 42.6	19 48.4	16 18.1	0N14.1	21 32.6	17 14.8	19 48.7	2 58.8	23 28.8
22 T	19 57 24.8	20 24.3	1 47.9	18 23.3	20 22.5	15 6.3	0 44.9	21 37.2	17 17.8	19 50.1	2 57.1	23 27.7
25 F	20 9 14.5	19 47.6	1 51.7	14 20.5	20 54.0	13 51.0	1 14.3	21 41.7	17 20.6	19 51.5	2 55.3	23 26.7
28 M	20 21 4.1	19 8.0	1 55.5	3 31.8	21 17.8	12 32.4	1 42.2	21 45.8	17 23.3	19 52.7	2 53.5	23 25.6
31 T	20 32 53.8	18 25.5	1 59.3	9S14.3	21 28.9	11 11.0	2 8.6	21 49.8	17 25.7	19 53.9	2 51.5	23 24.6

AUGUST 1941

DAY	EPHEMERIS SIDEREAL TIME	☉	☊	☽	☿	♀	♂	♃	♄	♅	♆	♇
						LONGITUDE						
1 F	20 36 50.3	8♌21.3	24♍56.8	16♏26.6	20♋53.1	5♍51.6	15♈11.4	14♊19.9	27♉ 7.1	29♉49.7	25♍43.2	4♌ 2.9
2 S	20 40 46.9	9 18.7	24 53.6	0♐41.8	22 29.7	7 4.2	15 36.3	14 30.7	27 11.1	29 51.4	25 44.9	4 4.6
3 S	20 44 43.5	10 16.1	24 50.4	14 58.8	24 10.2	8 16.9	16 0.7	14 41.3	27 15.1	29 53.0	25 46.5	4 6.3
4 M	20 48 40.0	11 13.5	24 47.2	29 14.2	25 54.4	9 29.4	16 24.7	14 51.9	27 18.9	29 54.6	25 48.2	4 8.0
5 T	20 52 36.5	12 10.9	24 44.0	13♑23.7	27 42.1	10 42.0	16 48.2	15 2.3	27 22.7	29 56.2	25 49.9	4 9.7
6 W	20 56 33.1	13 8.4	24 40.9	27 22.9	29 33.0	11 54.6	17 11.1	15 12.7	27 26.3	29 57.7	25 51.7	4 11.4
7 T	21 0 29.7	14 5.9	24 37.7	11♒ 7.5	1♌26.5	13 7.1	17 33.6	15 23.0	27 29.9	29 59.2	25 53.4	4 13.1
8 F	21 4 26.2	15 3.3	24 34.5	24 34.4	3 22.5	14 19.5	17 55.5	15 33.1	27 33.4	0♊ 0.6	25 55.2	4 14.8
9 S	21 8 22.7	16 0.9	24 31.3	7♓41.8	5 20.4	15 32.0	18 16.9	15 43.2	27 36.8	0 2.0	25 57.0	4 16.5
10 S	21 12 19.3	16 58.4	24 28.2	20 29.5	7 20.0	16 44.4	18 37.8	15 53.1	27 40.1	0 3.4	25 58.8	4 18.2
11 M	21 16 15.9	17 55.9	24 25.0	2♈59.0	9 20.9	17 56.8	18 58.1	16 3.0	27 43.3	0 4.7	26 0.6	4 19.8
12 T	21 20 12.5	18 53.5	24 21.8	15 12.8	11 22.7	19 9.2	19 17.8	16 12.7	27 46.4	0 5.9	26 2.5	4 21.5
13 W	21 24 9.0	19 51.1	24 18.6	27 14.6	13 25.1	20 21.5	19 36.9	16 22.3	27 49.5	0 7.1	26 4.3	4 23.1
14 T	21 28 5.5	20 48.7	24 15.4	9♉ 8.9	15 27.8	21 33.8	19 55.4	16 31.8	27 52.4	0 8.3	26 6.2	4 24.8
15 F	21 32 2.1	21 46.3	24 12.3	21 0.4	17 30.5	22 46.1	20 13.3	16 41.2	27 55.2	0 9.4	26 8.1	4 26.4
16 S	21 35 58.6	22 44.0	24 9.1	2♊54.0	19 32.9	23 58.3	20 30.6	16 50.4	27 58.0	0 10.4	26 10.0	4 28.1
17 S	21 39 55.2	23 41.7	24 5.9	14 54.5	21 34.9	25 10.6	20 47.2	16 59.6	28 0.6	0 11.5	26 12.0	4 29.7
18 M	21 43 51.8	24 39.4	24 2.7	27 6.3	23 36.2	26 22.7	21 3.1	17 8.6	28 3.1	0 12.4	26 13.9	4 31.3
19 T	21 47 48.3	25 37.1	23 59.6	9♋32.9	25 36.8	27 34.9	21 18.4	17 17.5	28 5.6	0 13.3	26 15.9	4 33.0
20 W	21 51 44.9	26 34.9	23 56.4	22 17.0	27 36.4	28 47.0	21 32.9	17 26.3	28 7.9	0 14.2	26 17.9	4 34.6
21 T	21 55 41.4	27 32.7	23 53.2	5♌20.1	29 35.0	29 59.1	21 46.8	17 34.9	28 10.1	0 15.0	26 19.9	4 36.2
22 F	21 59 38.0	28 30.5	23 50.0	18 42.1	1♍32.5	1♎11.2	21 59.9	17 43.4	28 12.3	0 15.8	26 21.9	4 37.8
23 S	22 3 34.5	29 28.4	23 46.8	2♍21.7	3 28.8	2 23.2	22 12.3	17 51.8	28 14.3	0 16.5	26 23.9	4 39.3
24 S	22 7 31.1	0♍26.2	23 43.7	16 16.4	5 23.9	3 35.2	22 23.9	18 0.1	28 16.2	0 17.2	26 25.9	4 40.9
25 M	22 11 27.6	1 24.1	23 40.5	0♎22.7	7 17.7	4 47.2	22 34.8	18 8.2	28 18.1	0 17.8	26 28.0	4 42.5
26 T	22 15 24.2	2 22.1	23 37.3	14 36.9	9 10.2	5 59.2	22 44.9	18 16.2	28 19.8	0 18.3	26 30.1	4 44.0
27 W	22 19 20.8	3 20.0	23 34.1	28 55.0	11 1.5	7 11.0	22 54.2	18 24.0	28 21.4	0 18.8	26 32.1	4 45.6
28 T	22 23 17.3	4 17.9	23 30.9	13♏13.7	12 51.4	8 22.9	23 2.7	18 31.7	28 22.9	0 19.3	26 34.2	4 47.1
29 F	22 27 13.8	5 15.9	23 27.8	27 29.9	14 40.0	9 34.7	23 10.5	18 39.3	28 24.3	0 19.7	26 36.3	4 48.6
30 S	22 31 10.4	6 13.9	23 24.6	11♐41.1	16 27.4	10 46.5	23 17.4	18 46.7	28 25.6	0 20.1	26 38.4	4 50.1
31 S	22 35 7.0	7 11.9	23 21.4	25 45.0	18 13.4	11 58.2	23 23.6	18 54.0	28 26.8	0 20.4	26 40.6	4 51.6
						DECLINATION						
1 F	20 36 50.3	18N10.8	2N 0.5	12S49.2	21N28.8	10N43.3	2N17.1	21N51.1	17N26.5	19N54.3	2N50.9	23N24.3
4 M	20 48 40.0	17 24.7	2 4.3	18 18.9	21 15.3	9 18.6	2 41.4	21 54.7	17 28.7	19 55.3	2 48.8	23 23.3
7 T	21 0 29.7	16 36.1	2 8.1	14 6.0	20 39.1	7 51.7	3 4.0	21 58.1	17 30.6	19 56.3	2 46.7	23 22.3
10 S	21 12 19.3	15 45.1	2 11.9	3 33.0	19 39.1	6 23.0	3 24.8	22 1.3	17 32.4	19 57.2	2 44.5	23 21.3
13 W	21 24 9.0	14 51.8	2 15.6	7N45.5	18 16.6	4 52.8	3 43.8	22 4.3	17 33.9	19 58.0	2 42.3	23 20.4
16 S	21 35 58.6	13 56.4	2 19.4	15 56.1	16 35.0	3 21.5	4 0.8	22 7.0	17 35.3	19 58.6	2 40.0	23 19.5
19 T	21 47 48.3	12 59.0	2 23.2	18 6.3	14 38.7	1 49.2	4 15.9	22 9.6	17 36.4	19 59.2	2 37.6	23 18.6
22 F	21 59 38.0	11 59.7	2 27.0	12 25.4	12 31.7	0 16.4	4 28.9	22 11.9	17 37.3	19 59.8	2 35.2	23 17.7
25 M	22 11 27.6	10 58.7	2 30.7	0 29.3	10 18.0	1S16.7	4 39.7	22 14.1	17 38.0	20 0.2	2 32.7	23 16.9
28 T	22 23 17.3	9 56.1	2 34.5	11S56.3	8 0.3	2 49.7	4 48.4	22 16.1	17 38.5	20 0.5	2 30.2	23 16.1
31 S	22 35 7.0	8 52.2	2 38.3	18 7.2	5 41.1	4 22.4	4 54.9	22 17.9	17 38.8	20 0.7	2 27.7	23 15.4

SEPTEMBER 1941

DAY	EPHEMERIS SIDEREAL TIME h m s	☉ ° '	☊ ° '	☽ ° '	☿ ° '	♀ ° '	♂ ° '	♃ ° '	♄ ° '	♅ ° '	♆ ° '	♇ ° '
						LONGITUDE						
1 M	22 39 3.5	8♍10.0	23♍18.2	9♑40.0	19♍58.2	13♎ 9.9	23♈28.9	19♊ 1.1	28♉27.9	0♊20.6	26♍42.7	4♌53.1
2 T	22 43 0.0	9 8.1	23 15.1	23 24.2	21 41.7	14 21.5	23 33.3	19 8.1	28 28.9	0 20.9	26 44.8	4 54.5
3 W	22 46 56.6	10 6.1	23 11.9	6♒56.3	23 24.0	15 33.1	23 37.0	19 14.9	28 29.8	0 21.0	26 47.0	4 56.0
4 T	22 50 53.2	11 4.3	23 8.7	20 14.8	25 5.0	16 44.7	23 39.8	19 21.6	28 30.6	0 21.1	26 49.1	4 57.4
5 F	22 54 49.7	12 2.4	23 5.5	3♓18.9	26 44.9	17 56.2	23 41.7	19 28.1	28 31.2	0 21.2	26 51.3	4 58.8
6 S	22 58 46.3	13 0.6	23 2.3	16 8.2	28 23.5	19 7.6	23 42.8	19 34.4	28 31.8	0 21.2	26 53.5	5 0.2
7 S	23 2 42.8	13 58.8	22 59.2	28 42.8	0♎ 1.0	20 19.1	23 43.1	19 40.7	28 32.2	0R21.1	26 55.6	5 1.6
8 M	23 6 39.4	14 57.0	22 56.0	11♈ 3.9	1 37.3	21 30.4	23R42.4	19 46.7	28 32.6	0 21.1	26 57.8	5 3.0
9 T	23 10 35.9	15 55.3	22 52.8	23 13.0	3 12.4	22 41.7	23 40.9	19 52.6	28 32.8	0 20.9	27 0.0	5 4.4
10 W	23 14 32.5	16 53.6	22 49.6	5♉12.8	4 46.4	23 53.0	23 38.6	19 58.3	28 32.9	0 20.7	27 2.2	5 5.7
11 T	23 18 29.0	17 51.9	22 46.5	17 6.5	6 19.2	25 4.2	23 35.3	20 3.9	28 33.0	0 20.5	27 4.4	5 7.0
12 F	23 22 25.6	18 50.3	22 43.3	28 57.7	7 51.0	26 15.4	23 31.2	20 9.3	28R32.9	0 20.2	27 6.6	5 8.4
13 S	23 26 22.1	19 48.7	22 40.1	10♊51.0	9 21.6	27 26.5	23 26.2	20 14.5	28 32.7	0 19.8	27 8.8	5 9.7
14 S	23 30 18.7	20 47.1	22 36.9	22 50.6	10 51.0	28 37.6	23 20.3	20 19.6	28 32.4	0 19.4	27 11.1	5 10.9
15 M	23 34 15.2	21 45.6	22 33.7	5♋ 1.3	12 19.3	29 48.6	23 13.6	20 24.5	28 32.0	0 19.0	27 13.3	5 12.2
16 T	23 38 11.7	22 44.1	22 30.6	17 27.4	13 46.5	0♏59.6	23 6.0	20 29.2	28 31.4	0 18.5	27 15.5	5 13.4
17 W	23 42 8.3	23 42.6	22 27.4	0♌12.8	15 12.5	2 10.5	22 57.6	20 33.8	28 30.8	0 17.9	27 17.7	5 14.7
18 T	23 46 4.9	24 41.2	22 24.2	13 20.3	16 37.4	3 21.4	22 48.4	20 38.1	28 30.1	0 17.4	27 20.0	5 15.9
19 F	23 50 1.5	25 39.8	22 21.0	26 51.3	18 1.0	4 32.3	22 38.4	20 42.3	28 29.2	0 16.7	27 22.2	5 17.1
20 S	23 53 58.0	26 38.4	22 17.9	10♍45.5	19 23.5	5 43.0	22 27.5	20 46.3	28 28.3	0 16.0	27 24.4	5 18.2
21 S	23 57 54.5	27 37.1	22 14.7	25 0.4	20 44.7	6 53.8	22 15.9	20 50.2	28 27.2	0 15.3	27 26.6	5 19.4
22 M	0 1 51.1	28 35.8	22 11.5	9♎31.8	22 4.5	8 4.4	22 3.6	20 53.8	28 26.1	0 14.5	27 28.9	5 20.5
23 T	0 5 47.7	29 34.6	22 8.3	24 13.4	23 23.1	9 15.0	21 50.6	20 57.3	28 24.8	0 13.6	27 31.1	5 21.6
24 W	0 9 44.2	0♎33.4	22 5.1	8♏58.5	24 40.2	10 25.6	21 36.9	21 0.5	28 23.4	0 12.8	27 33.3	5 22.7
25 T	0 13 40.8	1 32.2	22 2.0	23 40.1	25 55.9	11 36.1	21 22.5	21 3.6	28 21.9	0 11.8	27 35.6	5 23.8
26 F	0 17 37.3	2 31.0	21 58.8	8♐12.4	27 10.1	12 46.5	21 7.6	21 6.5	28 20.3	0 10.8	27 37.8	5 24.8
27 S	0 21 33.9	3 29.9	21 55.6	22 30.8	28 22.6	13 56.9	20 52.1	21 9.2	28 18.6	0 9.8	27 40.0	5 25.8
28 S	0 25 30.4	4 28.8	21 52.4	6♑32.7	29 33.4	15 7.2	20 36.1	21 11.7	28 16.9	0 8.7	27 42.2	5 26.8
29 M	0 29 27.0	5 27.7	21 49.3	20 17.1	0♏42.4	16 17.4	20 19.6	21 14.1	28 15.0	0 7.6	27 44.4	5 27.8
30 T	0 33 23.5	6 26.6	21 46.1	3♒44.1	1 49.4	17 27.5	20 2.6	21 16.2	28 13.0	0 6.4	27 46.6	5 28.8
						DECLINATION						
1 M	22 39 3.5	8N30.6	2N39.5	18S 3.8	4N54.6	4S53.1	4N56.6	22N18.5	17N38.9	20N 0.8	2N26.8	23N15.1
4 T	22 50 53.2	7 24.9	2 43.3	12 2.7	2 36.0	6 24.8	5 0.2	22 20.1	17 38.9	20 0.8	2 24.3	23 14.5
7 S	23 2 42.8	6 18.2	2 47.1	1 1.2	0 19.3	7 55.4	5 1.6	22 21.5	17 38.7	20 0.8	2 21.7	23 13.8
10 W	23 14 32.5	5 10.6	2 50.8	9N53.4	1S54.4	9 24.6	5 0.9	22 22.8	17 38.3	20 0.7	2 19.1	23 13.2
13 S	23 26 22.1	4 2.1	2 54.6	16 57.0	4 4.3	10 52.2	4 58.1	22 23.9	17 37.6	20 0.6	2 16.4	23 12.7
16 T	23 38 11.7	2 53.0	2 58.4	17 32.1	6 9.6	12 17.7	4 53.4	22 24.9	17 36.8	20 0.3	2 13.8	23 12.2
19 F	23 50 1.5	1 43.4	3 2.1	10 23.1	8 9.5	13 40.9	4 46.7	22 25.7	17 35.8	19 59.9	2 11.2	23 11.7
22 M	0 1 51.1	0 33.5	3 5.9	2S22.3	10 3.3	15 1.4	4 38.4	22 26.4	17 34.6	19 59.4	2 8.5	23 11.3
25 T	0 13 40.8	0S36.7	3 9.7	14 13.1	11 49.9	16 19.0	4 28.7	22 27.0	17 33.2	19 58.9	2 5.9	23 11.0
28 S	0 25 30.4	1 46.8	3 13.4	18 9.7	13 28.4	17 33.3	4 18.0	22 27.5	17 31.6	19 58.2	2 3.3	23 10.7

OCTOBER 1941

DAY	EPHEMERIS SIDEREAL TIME h m s	☉ ° '	☊ ° '	☽ ° '	☿ ° '	♀ ° '	♂ ° '	♃ ° '	♄ ° '	♅ ° '	♆ ° '	♇ ° '
						LONGITUDE						
1 W	0 37 20.1	7♎25.6	21♍42.9	16♒54.7	2♏54.3	18♏37.6	19♈45.3	21♊18.1	28♉10.9	0♊ 5.2	27♍48.9	5♌29.7
2 T	0 41 16.7	8 24.6	21 39.7	29 50.3	3 57.0	19 47.6	19R27.6	21 19.9	28R 8.7	0R 4.0	27 51.1	5 30.7
3 F	0 45 13.2	9 23.7	21 36.5	12♓32.3	4 57.3	20 57.5	19 9.6	21 21.4	28 6.4	0 2.7	27 53.3	5 31.5
4 S	0 49 9.7	10 22.7	21 33.4	25 2.3	5 54.9	22 7.3	18 51.4	21 22.8	28 4.0	0 1.3	27 55.4	5 32.4
5 S	0 53 6.3	11 21.8	21 30.2	7♈21.6	6 49.6	23 17.1	18 32.9	21 23.9	28 1.5	29♉60.0	27 57.6	5 33.3
6 M	0 57 2.8	12 21.0	21 27.0	19 31.6	7 41.3	24 26.8	18 14.2	21 24.9	27 58.9	29 58.5	27 59.8	5 34.1
7 T	1 0 59.4	13 20.1	21 23.8	1♉33.8	8 29.6	25 36.4	17 55.5	21 25.7	27 56.3	29 57.1	28 2.0	5 34.9
8 W	1 4 56.0	14 19.3	21 20.7	13 30.0	9 14.1	26 45.9	17 36.6	21 26.2	27 53.5	29 55.6	28 4.1	5 35.7
9 T	1 8 52.5	15 18.6	21 17.5	25 22.1	9 54.6	27 55.3	17 17.7	21 26.6	27 50.7	29 54.0	28 6.3	5 36.4
10 F	1 12 49.0	16 17.9	21 14.3	7♊12.9	10 30.7	29 4.6	16 58.9	21 26.7	27 47.7	29 52.4	28 8.4	5 37.2
11 S	1 16 45.6	17 17.2	21 11.1	19 5.5	11 1.9	0♐13.8	16 40.1	21R26.7	27 44.7	29 50.8	28 10.6	5 37.9
12 S	1 20 42.2	18 16.5	21 7.9	1♋ 3.7	11 27.8	1 23.0	16 21.4	21 26.5	27 41.6	29 49.1	28 12.7	5 38.5
13 M	1 24 38.7	19 15.9	21 4.8	13 11.4	11 48.0	2 32.0	16 2.9	21 26.0	27 38.4	29 47.4	28 14.8	5 39.2
14 T	1 28 35.3	20 15.4	21 1.6	25 33.3	12 1.8	3 41.0	15 44.6	21 25.4	27 35.1	29 45.7	28 16.9	5 39.8
15 W	1 32 31.8	21 14.8	20 58.4	8♌13.8	12 8.9	4 49.8	15 26.6	21 24.5	27 31.7	29 43.9	28 19.0	5 40.4
16 T	1 36 28.4	22 14.4	20 55.2	21 17.0	12R 8.7	5 58.6	15 8.9	21 23.5	27 28.2	29 42.1	28 21.1	5 41.0
17 F	1 40 24.9	23 13.9	20 52.0	4♍46.0	12 0.7	7 7.3	14 51.5	21 22.2	27 24.7	29 40.2	28 23.2	5 41.6
18 S	1 44 21.5	24 13.5	20 48.9	18 42.3	11 44.5	8 15.8	14 34.5	21 20.8	27 21.1	29 38.3	28 25.2	5 42.1
19 S	1 48 18.0	25 13.1	20 45.7	3♎ 5.1	11 19.7	9 24.2	14 18.0	21 19.1	27 17.4	29 36.4	28 27.2	5 42.6
20 M	1 52 14.6	26 12.8	20 42.5	17 50.8	10 46.2	10 32.6	14 2.0	21 17.2	27 13.6	29 34.5	28 29.3	5 43.1
21 T	1 56 11.1	27 12.5	20 39.3	2♏52.6	10 3.9	11 40.8	13 46.5	21 15.2	27 9.8	29 32.5	28 31.3	5 43.6
22 W	2 0 7.7	28 12.2	20 36.2	18 1.5	9 13.3	12 48.9	13 31.5	21 12.9	27 5.9	29 30.4	28 33.3	5 44.0
23 T	2 4 4.2	29 11.9	20 33.0	3♐ 7.7	8 14.7	13 56.9	13 17.1	21 10.5	27 1.9	29 28.4	28 35.3	5 44.4
24 F	2 8 0.8	0♏11.7	20 29.8	18 1.6	7 9.3	15 4.7	13 3.4	21 7.8	26 57.9	29 26.3	28 37.2	5 44.8
25 S	2 11 57.3	1 11.6	20 26.6	2♑36.1	5 58.3	16 12.4	12 50.4	21 4.9	26 53.8	29 24.2	28 39.2	5 45.1
26 S	2 15 53.9	2 11.4	20 23.4	16 46.8	4 43.6	17 20.0	12 38.0	21 1.9	26 49.6	29 22.1	28 41.1	5 45.4
27 M	2 19 50.5	3 11.3	20 20.3	0♒32.3	3 27.2	18 27.4	12 26.3	20 58.7	26 45.4	29 19.9	28 43.1	5 45.7
28 T	2 23 47.0	4 11.2	20 17.1	13 53.5	2 11.2	19 34.7	12 15.4	20 55.2	26 41.1	29 17.7	28 45.0	5 46.0
29 W	2 27 43.6	5 11.1	20 13.9	26 52.9	0 58.2	20 41.8	12 5.2	20 51.6	26 36.8	29 15.5	28 46.8	5 46.2
30 T	2 31 40.1	6 11.1	20 10.7	9♓33.9	29♎50.4	21 48.7	11 55.8	20 47.8	26 32.4	29 13.3	28 48.7	5 46.5
31 F	2 35 36.7	7 11.0	20 7.6	22 0.1	28 49.8	22 55.5	11 47.2	20 43.8	26 28.0	29 11.0	28 50.5	5 46.7
						DECLINATION						
1 W	0 37 20.1	2S56.9	3N17.2	12S49.1	14S57.4	18S44.0	4N 6.5	22N27.9	17N29.8	19N57.5	2N 0.7	23N10.5
4 S	0 49 9.7	4 6.6	3 21.0	2 9.7	16 15.2	19 50.8	3 54.7	22 28.1	17 27.8	19 56.6	1 58.1	23 10.3
7 T	1 0 59.4	5 15.9	3 24.7	8N55.6	17 19.5	20 53.3	3 43.0	22 28.2	17 25.7	19 55.7	1 55.5	23 10.2
10 F	1 12 49.0	6 24.6	3 28.5	16 32.4	18 7.2	21 51.4	3 31.6	22 28.3	17 23.4	19 54.8	1 53.0	23 10.1
13 M	1 24 38.7	7 32.6	3 32.2	17 55.2	18 33.9	22 44.6	3 21.1	22 28.2	17 21.0	19 53.7	1 50.6	23 10.2
16 T	1 36 28.4	8 39.6	3 36.0	11 50.4	18 34.0	23 32.8	3 11.7	22 28.0	17 18.4	19 52.6	1 48.1	23 10.2
19 S	1 48 18.0	9 45.6	3 39.7	0S20.7	18 0.7	24 15.6	3 3.8	22 27.7	17 15.7	19 51.4	1 45.7	23 10.4
22 W	2 0 7.7	10 50.3	3 43.5	13 5.1	16 48.3	24 53.0	2 57.8	22 27.3	17 12.8	19 50.1	1 43.4	23 10.6
25 S	2 11 57.3	11 53.5	3 47.2	18 19.8	14 57.7	25 24.6	2 53.9	22 26.8	17 9.9	19 48.8	1 41.1	23 10.8
28 T	2 23 47.0	12 55.1	3 51.0	13 35.7	12 44.1	25 50.4	2 52.3	22 26.2	17 6.8	19 47.4	1 38.9	23 11.2
31 F	2 35 36.7	13 54.8	3 54.7	3 10.2	10 37.0	26 10.2	2 53.2	22 25.5	17 3.7	19 45.9	1 36.8	23 11.5

NOVEMBER 1941

DAY	EPHEMERIS SIDEREAL TIME	☉	☊	☾	☿	♀	♂	♃	♄	♅	♆	♇
	h m s	° ′	° ′	° ′	° ′	° ′	° ′	° ′	° ′	° ′	° ′	° ′
						LONGITUDE						
1 S	2 39 33.2	8♏11.0	20♍ 4.4	4♈14.8	27♎58.3	24♐ 2.1	11♈39.3	20♊39.6	26♉23.5	29♉ 8.7	28♍52.4	5♌46.8
2 S	2 43 29.8	9 11.1	20 1.2	16 20.8	27R17.0	25 8.5	11R32.2	20R35.3	26R19.0	29R 6.4	28 54.2	5 47.0
3 M	2 47 26.3	10 11.2	19 58.0	28 20.7	26 46.9	26 14.8	11 25.9	20 30.7	26 14.4	29 4.1	28 56.0	5 47.1
4 T	2 51 22.9	11 11.3	19 54.9	10♉16.3	26 28.3	27 20.8	11 20.5	20 26.0	26 9.8	29 1.8	28 57.7	5 47.2
5 W	2 55 19.4	12 11.4	19 51.7	22 9.2	26 21.4	28 26.7	11 15.8	20 21.1	26 5.1	28 59.4	28 59.5	5 47.2
6 T	2 59 16.0	13 11.5	19 48.5	4♊ 0.9	26D25.8	29 32.3	11 11.9	20 16.1	26 0.5	28 57.0	29 1.2	5 47.2
7 F	3 3 12.5	14 11.7	19 45.3	15 53.0	26 40.9	0♑37.7	11 8.8	20 10.8	25 55.7	28 54.6	29 2.9	5 47.2
8 S	3 7 9.1	15 12.0	19 42.1	27 47.6	27 6.1	1 43.0	11 6.6	20 5.5	25 51.0	28 52.2	29 4.6	5R47.2
9 S	3 11 5.7	16 12.2	19 39.0	9♋47.0	27 40.4	2 48.0	11 5.1	19 59.9	25 46.2	28 49.8	29 6.2	5 47.2
10 M	3 15 2.2	17 12.5	19 35.8	21 54.4	28 23.1	3 52.8	11 4.4	19 54.2	25 41.5	28 47.4	29 7.9	5 47.1
11 T	3 18 58.8	18 12.8	19 32.6	4♌13.6	29 13.2	4 57.3	11D 4.5	19 48.3	25 36.6	28 44.9	29 9.5	5 47.0
12 W	3 22 55.3	19 13.2	19 29.4	16 48.6	0♏ 9.8	6 1.6	11 5.4	19 42.3	25 31.8	28 42.4	29 11.1	5 46.8
13 T	3 26 51.9	20 13.6	19 26.2	29 44.0	1 12.2	7 5.6	11 7.1	19 36.2	25 26.9	28 40.0	29 12.6	5 46.7
14 F	3 30 48.4	21 14.0	19 23.1	13♍ 3.8	2 19.6	8 9.4	11 9.6	19 29.9	25 22.1	28 37.5	29 14.2	5 46.5
15 S	3 34 45.0	22 14.4	19 19.9	26 51.1	3 31.2	9 12.9	11 12.8	19 23.4	25 17.2	28 35.0	29 15.7	5 46.3
16 S	3 38 41.5	23 14.9	19 16.7	11♎ 7.1	4 46.6	10 16.2	11 16.8	19 16.8	25 12.3	28 32.5	29 17.2	5 46.1
17 M	3 42 38.1	24 15.4	19 13.5	25 50.3	6 5.0	11 19.1	11 21.6	19 10.1	25 7.4	28 30.0	29 18.6	5 45.8
18 T	3 46 34.7	25 16.0	19 10.4	10♏55.4	7 26.2	12 21.8	11 27.1	19 3.3	25 2.5	28 27.5	29 20.0	5 45.5
19 W	3 50 31.2	26 16.5	19 7.2	26 13.7	8 49.6	13 24.2	11 33.4	18 56.3	24 57.6	28 25.0	29 21.5	5 45.2
20 T	3 54 27.8	27 17.1	19 4.0	11♐34.2	10 14.8	14 26.2	11 40.3	18 49.2	24 52.8	28 22.5	29 22.8	5 44.8
21 F	3 58 24.3	28 17.7	19 0.8	26 45.1	11 41.6	15 27.9	11 48.1	18 42.1	24 47.9	28 19.9	29 24.2	5 44.5
22 S	4 2 20.9	29 18.4	18 57.7	11♑36.4	13 9.8	16 29.3	11 56.5	18 34.8	24 43.0	28 17.4	29 25.5	5 44.1
23 S	4 6 17.4	0♐19.0	18 54.5	26 1.2	14 39.0	17 30.3	12 5.6	18 27.4	24 38.1	28 14.9	29 26.8	5 43.7
24 M	4 10 14.0	1 19.7	18 51.3	9♒56.4	16 9.1	18 30.9	12 15.4	18 19.9	24 33.3	28 12.4	29 28.1	5 43.2
25 T	4 14 10.5	2 20.4	18 48.1	23 22.3	17 39.9	19 31.1	12 25.9	18 12.3	24 28.5	28 9.9	29 29.3	5 42.8
26 W	4 18 7.1	3 21.1	18 44.9	6♓21.6	19 11.3	20 30.9	12 37.0	18 4.7	24 23.7	28 7.4	29 30.5	5 42.3
27 T	4 22 3.6	4 21.9	18 41.8	18 58.6	20 43.2	21 30.3	12 48.8	17 56.9	24 18.9	28 4.9	29 31.7	5 41.7
28 F	4 26 0.2	5 22.6	18 38.6	1♈18.0	22 15.4	22 29.2	13 1.3	17 49.1	24 14.1	28 2.4	29 32.9	5 41.2
29 S	4 29 56.8	6 23.4	18 35.4	13 24.7	23 48.0	23 27.7	13 14.3	17 41.3	24 9.4	27 59.9	29 34.0	5 40.6
30 S	4 33 53.3	7 24.1	18 32.2	25 22.8	25 20.8	24 25.7	13 27.9	17 33.4	24 4.7	27 57.5	29 35.1	5 40.0
						DECLINATION						
1 S	2 39 33.2	14S14.3	3N56.0	0N41.2	10S 1.5	26S15.5	2N54.0	22N25.2	17N 2.6	19N45.4	1N36.1	23N11.7
4 T	2 51 22.9	15 11.3	3 59.7	11 15.8	8 46.8	26 27.2	2 58.1	22 24.3	16 59.4	19 43.9	1 34.1	23 12.2
7 F	3 3 12.5	16 6.1	4 3.5	17 39.4	8 24.0	26 32.9	3 4.6	22 23.3	16 56.1	19 42.4	1 32.1	23 12.7
10 M	3 15 2.2	16 58.5	4 7.2	17 20.8	8 47.2	26 32.5	3 13.5	22 22.2	16 52.8	19 40.8	1 30.3	23 13.3
13 T	3 26 51.9	17 48.3	4 10.9	9 50.7	9 44.3	26 26.2	3 24.8	22 21.0	16 49.4	19 39.2	1 28.5	23 13.9
16 S	3 38 41.5	18 35.3	4 14.7	2S46.4	11 3.1	26 14.1	3 38.3	22 19.6	16 46.1	19 37.6	1 26.8	23 14.6
19 W	3 50 31.2	19 19.4	4 18.4	14 50.0	12 34.0	25 56.4	3 53.9	22 18.2	16 42.8	19 36.0	1 25.2	23 15.4
22 S	4 2 20.9	20 0.4	4 22.1	18 15.8	14 10.0	25 33.2	4 11.6	22 16.6	16 39.5	19 34.3	1 23.7	23 16.2
25 T	4 14 10.5	20 38.0	4 25.9	11 36.1	15 46.3	25 4.9	4 31.3	22 14.9	16 36.3	19 32.7	1 22.3	23 17.1
28 F	4 26 0.2	21 12.2	4 29.6	0 24.8	17 19.6	24 31.8	4 52.7	22 13.2	16 33.1	19 31.1	1 21.0	23 18.0

DECEMBER 1941

DAY	EPHEMERIS SIDEREAL TIME	☉	☊	☾	☿	♀	♂	♃	♄	♅	♆	♇
						LONGITUDE						
1 M	4 37 49.9	8♐24.9	18♍29.1	7♉16.2	26♏53.8	25♑23.1	13♈42.1	17♊25.4	24♉ 0.0	27♉55.0	29♍36.1	5♌39.4
2 T	4 41 46.4	9 25.8	18 25.9	19 7.6	28 26.9	26 20.1	13 56.9	17R17.4	23R55.4	27R52.6	29 37.1	5R38.8
3 W	4 45 43.0	10 26.6	18 22.7	0♊59.2	0♐ 0.1	27 16.5	14 12.3	17 9.3	23 50.8	27 50.1	29 38.1	5 38.1
4 T	4 49 39.5	11 27.5	18 19.5	12 52.7	1 33.5	28 12.4	14 28.2	17 1.2	23 46.3	27 47.7	29 39.1	5 37.4
5 F	4 53 36.1	12 28.3	18 16.4	24 49.3	3 6.8	29 7.7	14 44.6	16 53.1	23 41.8	27 45.3	29 40.0	5 36.7
6 S	4 57 32.7	13 29.2	18 13.2	6♋50.1	4 40.3	0♒ 2.4	15 1.5	16 44.9	23 37.3	27 42.9	29 41.0	5 36.0
7 S	5 1 29.2	14 30.1	18 10.0	18 56.4	6 13.8	0 56.4	15 19.0	16 36.8	23 32.9	27 40.5	29 41.8	5 35.2
8 M	5 5 25.8	15 31.0	18 6.8	1♌10.1	7 47.3	1 49.8	15 36.9	16 28.6	23 28.6	27 38.2	29 42.7	5 34.4
9 T	5 9 22.3	16 32.0	18 3.6	13 33.6	9 20.9	2 42.5	15 55.4	16 20.4	23 24.3	27 35.8	29 43.5	5 33.6
10 W	5 13 18.9	17 32.9	18 0.5	26 9.7	10 54.5	3 34.6	16 14.3	16 12.2	23 20.0	27 33.5	29 44.2	5 32.8
11 T	5 17 15.4	18 33.9	17 57.3	9♍ 2.3	12 28.2	4 25.9	16 33.6	16 4.1	23 15.9	27 31.2	29 45.0	5 32.0
12 F	5 21 12.0	19 34.9	17 54.1	22 14.9	14 2.0	5 16.4	16 53.4	15 55.9	23 11.7	27 28.9	29 45.7	5 31.1
13 S	5 25 8.6	20 36.0	17 50.9	5♎51.0	15 35.8	6 6.1	17 13.7	15 47.8	23 7.7	27 26.7	29 46.4	5 30.2
14 S	5 29 5.1	21 37.0	17 47.8	19 52.8	17 9.7	6 55.1	17 34.4	15 39.7	23 3.7	27 24.4	29 47.0	5 29.3
15 M	5 33 1.6	22 38.1	17 44.6	4♏20.6	18 43.7	7 43.1	17 55.5	15 31.6	22 59.7	27 22.2	29 47.6	5 28.4
16 T	5 36 58.2	23 39.1	17 41.4	19 11.6	20 17.8	8 30.3	18 17.0	15 23.5	22 55.9	27 20.0	29 48.2	5 27.4
17 W	5 40 54.8	24 40.2	17 38.2	4♐19.4	21 52.0	9 16.6	18 39.0	15 15.6	22 52.1	27 17.9	29 48.7	5 26.5
18 T	5 44 51.4	25 41.3	17 35.1	19 34.5	23 26.4	10 1.9	19 1.3	15 7.6	22 48.4	27 15.7	29 49.3	5 25.5
19 F	5 48 47.9	26 42.4	17 31.9	4♑45.9	25 0.9	10 46.2	19 24.0	14 59.7	22 44.8	27 13.6	29 49.7	5 24.5
20 S	5 52 44.4	27 43.5	17 28.7	19 42.5	26 35.6	11 29.5	19 47.1	14 51.9	22 41.2	27 11.6	29 50.2	5 23.5
21 S	5 56 41.0	28 44.7	17 25.5	4♒15.8	28 10.4	12 11.6	20 10.6	14 44.2	22 37.8	27 9.5	29 50.6	5 22.4
22 M	6 0 37.6	29 45.8	17 22.4	18 20.6	29 45.4	12 52.7	20 34.4	14 36.5	22 34.4	27 7.5	29 50.9	5 21.4
23 T	6 4 34.1	0♑46.9	17 19.2	1♓55.3	1♑20.7	13 32.5	20 58.6	14 29.0	22 31.1	27 5.5	29 51.3	5 20.3
24 W	6 8 30.7	1 48.1	17 16.0	15 1.4	2 56.1	14 11.1	21 23.1	14 21.5	22 27.9	27 3.6	29 51.6	5 19.2
25 T	6 12 27.2	2 49.2	17 12.8	27 42.6	4 31.8	14 48.4	21 48.0	14 14.1	22 24.7	27 1.7	29 51.8	5 18.1
26 F	6 16 23.8	3 50.3	17 9.6	10♈ 3.7	6 7.7	15 24.4	22 13.1	14 6.8	22 21.7	26 59.8	29 52.1	5 17.0
27 S	6 20 20.4	4 51.5	17 6.5	22 9.8	7 43.9	15 58.9	22 38.6	13 59.6	22 18.8	26 58.0	29 52.3	5 15.9
28 S	6 24 16.9	5 52.6	17 3.3	4♉ 6.2	9 20.4	16 32.0	23 4.4	13 52.5	22 15.9	26 56.2	29 52.4	5 14.7
29 M	6 28 13.5	6 53.8	17 0.1	15 57.6	10 57.1	17 3.5	23 30.5	13 45.6	22 13.2	26 54.4	29 52.6	5 13.5
30 T	6 32 10.0	7 54.9	16 56.9	27 47.9	12 34.1	17 33.5	23 56.8	13 38.8	22 10.5	26 52.7	29 52.7	5 12.4
31 W	6 36 6.6	8 56.0	16 53.8	9♊40.4	14 11.4	18 1.8	24 23.5	13 32.1	22 7.9	26 51.0	29 52.7	5 11.2
						DECLINATION						
1 M	4 37 49.9	21S42.8	4N33.3	10N25.4	18S47.7	23S54.3	5N15.8	22N11.3	16N30.1	19N29.4	1N19.9	23N19.0
4 T	4 49 39.5	22 9.6	4 37.1	17 25.4	20 8.8	23 12.6	5 40.4	22 9.3	16 27.1	19 27.8	1 18.8	23 20.0
7 S	5 1 29.2	22 32.6	4 40.8	17 50.7	21 21.9	22 27.2	6 6.4	22 7.3	16 24.3	19 26.2	1 17.9	23 21.0
10 W	5 13 18.9	22 51.7	4 44.5	11 2.7	22 26.0	21 38.6	6 33.6	22 5.3	16 21.6	19 24.7	1 17.0	23 22.1
13 S	5 25 8.6	23 6.7	4 48.2	0S53.4	23 20.2	20 47.2	7 1.9	22 3.2	16 19.0	19 23.2	1 16.3	23 23.2
16 T	5 36 58.2	23 17.5	4 51.9	13 16.7	24 3.9	19 53.5	7 31.3	22 1.0	16 16.7	19 21.7	1 15.7	23 24.4
19 F	5 48 47.9	23 24.2	4 55.7	18 35.3	24 36.4	18 58.1	8 1.5	21 58.9	16 14.5	19 20.3	1 15.3	23 25.6
22 M	6 0 37.6	23 26.6	4 59.4	13 3.4	24 57.1	18 1.4	8 32.6	21 56.8	16 12.5	19 18.9	1 14.9	23 26.8
25 T	6 12 27.2	23 24.8	5 3.1	1 48.5	25 5.4	17 4.2	9 4.3	21 54.7	16 10.8	19 17.7	1 14.7	23 28.0
28 S	6 24 16.9	23 18.8	5 6.8	9N22.4	25 0.7	16 7.1	9 36.7	21 52.8	16 9.2	19 16.4	1 14.6	23 29.3
31 W	6 36 6.6	23 8.6	5 10.5	16 57.5	24 42.7	15 10.7	10 9.6	21 50.9	16 7.9	19 15.3	1 14.7	23 30.5

JANUARY 1942

LONGITUDE

DAY	EPHEMERIS SIDEREAL TIME (h m s)	☉ (° ′)	☊ (° ′)	☽ (° ′)	☿ (° ′)	♀ (° ′)	♂ (° ′)	♃ (° ′)	♄ (° ′)	♅ (° ′)	♆ (° ′)	♇ (° ′)
1 T	6 40 3.2	9♑57.2	16♍50.6	21♊37.5	15♑48.9	18♒28.4	24♈50.4	13♊25.5	22♉ 5.5	26♉49.4	29♍52.7	5♌10.0
2 F	6 43 59.7	10 58.3	16 47.4	3♋40.8	17 26.7	18 53.2	25 17.6	13R19.0	22R 3.1	26R47.8	29R52.7	5R 8.8
3 S	6 47 56.2	11 59.4	16 44.2	15 51.4	19 4.8	19 16.2	25 45.0	13 12.7	22 0.8	26 46.2	29 52.7	5 7.5
4 S	6 51 52.8	13 0.6	16 41.0	28 10.1	20 43.1	19 37.3	26 12.7	13 6.6	21 58.7	26 44.7	29 52.6	5 6.3
5 M	6 55 49.4	14 1.7	16 37.9	10♌37.5	22 21.7	19 56.4	26 40.6	13 0.6	21 56.6	26 43.2	29 52.5	5 5.0
6 T	6 59 45.9	15 2.9	16 34.7	23 14.7	24 0.4	20 13.5	27 8.7	12 54.7	21 54.7	26 41.8	29 52.4	5 3.8
7 W	7 3 42.5	16 4.0	16 31.5	6♍ 2.9	25 39.3	20 28.5	27 37.1	12 49.0	21 52.8	26 40.4	29 52.2	5 2.5
8 T	7 7 39.0	17 5.1	16 28.3	19 4.0	27 18.3	20 41.3	28 5.7	12 43.4	21 51.1	26 39.0	29 52.0	5 1.2
9 F	7 11 35.6	18 6.3	16 25.2	2♎20.1	28 57.3	20 52.0	28 34.5	12 38.0	21 49.4	26 37.7	29 51.7	4 59.9
10 S	7 15 32.2	19 7.4	16 22.0	15 53.4	0♒36.3	21 0.3	29 3.5	12 32.8	21 47.9	26 36.4	29 51.4	4 58.6
11 S	7 19 28.7	20 8.6	16 18.8	29 45.7	2 15.2	21 6.4	29 32.8	12 27.8	21 46.5	26 35.2	29 51.1	4 57.3
12 M	7 23 25.3	21 9.7	16 15.6	13♏57.5	3 53.7	21 10.1	0♉ 2.2	12 22.9	21 45.1	26 34.1	29 50.8	4 56.0
13 T	7 27 21.8	22 10.8	16 12.5	28 27.4	5 31.9	21 11.4	0 31.8	12 18.2	21 43.9	26 32.9	29 50.4	4 54.7
14 W	7 31 18.4	23 12.0	16 9.3	13♐11.6	7 9.5	21R10.2	1 1.7	12 13.6	21 42.8	26 31.9	29 50.0	4 53.3
15 T	7 35 14.9	24 13.1	16 6.1	28 3.7	8 46.3	21 6.6	1 31.7	12 9.3	21 41.8	26 30.8	29 49.5	4 52.0
16 F	7 39 11.5	25 14.3	16 2.9	12♑55.7	10 22.1	21 0.4	2 1.9	12 5.1	21 41.0	26 29.9	29 49.0	4 50.7
17 S	7 43 8.0	26 15.4	15 59.7	27 38.8	11 56.5	20 51.8	2 32.3	12 1.1	21 40.2	26 28.9	29 48.5	4 49.3
18 S	7 47 4.6	27 16.5	15 56.6	12♒ 4.9	13 29.4	20 40.7	3 2.9	11 57.4	21 39.5	26 28.0	29 48.0	4 48.0
19 M	7 51 1.2	28 17.6	15 53.4	26 8.3	15 0.2	20 27.0	3 33.7	11 53.8	21 39.0	26 27.2	29 47.4	4 46.6
20 T	7 54 57.7	29 18.7	15 50.2	9♓45.9	16 28.5	20 10.9	4 4.6	11 50.4	21 38.6	26 26.4	29 46.8	4 45.3
21 W	7 58 54.3	0♒19.8	15 47.0	22 57.2	17 53.9	19 52.3	4 35.7	11 47.2	21 38.3	26 25.7	29 46.2	4 43.9
22 T	8 2 50.8	1 20.8	15 43.9	5♈44.3	19 15.8	19 31.4	5 6.9	11 44.1	21 38.1	26 25.0	29 45.5	4 42.5
23 F	8 6 47.4	2 21.9	15 40.7	18 10.6	20 33.5	19 8.2	5 38.4	11 41.3	21 38.0	26 24.4	29 44.8	4 41.2
24 S	8 10 43.9	3 22.9	15 37.5	0♉20.7	21 46.4	18 42.8	6 9.9	11 38.7	21D38.0	26 23.8	29 44.0	4 39.8
25 S	8 14 40.5	4 23.9	15 34.3	12 19.6	22 53.7	18 15.3	6 41.6	11 36.3	21 38.2	26 23.3	29 43.3	4 38.4
26 M	8 18 37.0	5 24.9	15 31.2	24 12.3	23 54.6	17 45.9	7 13.5	11 34.1	21 38.4	26 22.8	29 42.5	4 37.1
27 T	8 22 33.6	6 25.9	15 28.0	6♊ 3.6	24 48.3	17 14.8	7 45.4	11 32.1	21 38.8	26 22.4	29 41.7	4 35.7
28 W	8 26 30.2	7 26.8	15 24.8	17 57.7	25 34.0	16 42.1	8 17.5	11 30.3	21 39.3	26 22.0	29 40.8	4 34.3
29 T	8 30 26.7	8 27.8	15 21.6	29 58.2	26 10.8	16 8.0	8 49.8	11 28.7	21 39.9	26 21.7	29 39.9	4 33.0
30 F	8 34 23.3	9 28.7	15 18.4	12♋ 7.8	26 38.0	15 32.8	9 22.1	11 27.3	21 40.6	26 21.5	29 39.0	4 31.6
31 S	8 38 19.8	10 29.6	15 15.3	24 28.5	26 54.8	14 56.7	9 54.6	11 26.1	21 41.4	26 21.3	29 38.1	4 30.2

DECLINATION

DAY	EPHEMERIS SIDEREAL TIME (h m s)	☉	☊	☽	☿	♀	♂	♃	♄	♅	♆	♇
1 T	6 40 3.2	23S 4.3	5N11.7	18N11.0	24S33.6	14S52.2	10N20.6	21N50.2	16N 7.6	19N14.9	1N14.7	23N31.0
4 S	6 51 52.8	22 48.5	5 15.5	16 54.0	23 57.1	13 58.1	10 53.9	21 48.5	16 6.6	19 13.9	1 14.9	23 32.2
7 W	7 3 42.5	22 28.6	5 19.2	8 33.5	23 6.5	13 6.6	11 27.5	21 46.9	16 5.9	19 13.0	1 15.2	23 33.5
10 S	7 15 32.2	22 4.8	5 22.9	3S49.5	22 1.8	12 18.5	12 1.3	21 45.4	16 5.4	19 12.1	1 15.6	23 34.8
13 T	7 27 21.8	21 37.1	5 26.6	15 2.3	20 43.7	11 34.8	12 35.1	21 44.2	16 5.2	19 11.3	1 16.2	23 36.1
16 F	7 39 11.5	21 5.6	5 30.3	18 20.3	19 13.1	10 56.4	13 9.0	21 43.1	16 5.2	19 10.7	1 16.9	23 37.4
19 M	7 51 1.2	20 30.4	5 34.0	11 18.2	17 32.6	10 24.1	13 42.8	21 42.2	16 5.6	19 10.1	1 17.7	23 38.6
22 T	8 2 50.8	19 51.8	5 37.7	0N31.9	15 46.2	9 58.8	14 16.4	21 41.6	16 6.2	19 9.7	1 18.6	23 39.9
25 S	8 14 40.5	19 9.9	5 41.3	11 20.8	14 0.3	9 41.0	14 49.9	21 41.2	16 7.0	19 9.3	1 19.6	23 41.1
28 W	8 26 30.2	18 24.8	5 45.0	17 45.4	12 24.0	9 31.2	15 23.1	21 41.0	16 8.2	19 9.1	1 20.7	23 42.3
31 S	8 38 19.8	17 36.7	5 48.7	17 21.4	11 8.8	9 29.0	15 55.9	21 41.0	16 9.5	19 9.0	1 21.9	23 43.5

FEBRUARY 1942

LONGITUDE

DAY	EPHEMERIS SIDEREAL TIME (h m s)	☉ (° ′)	☊ (° ′)	☽ (° ′)	☿ (° ′)	♀ (° ′)	♂ (° ′)	♃ (° ′)	♄ (° ′)	♅ (° ′)	♆ (° ′)	♇ (° ′)
1 S	8 42 16.4	11♒30.5	15♍12.1	7♌ 1.2	27♒ 0.9	14♒19.9	10♉27.2	11♊25.1	21♉42.3	26♉21.1	29♍37.1	4♌28.9
2 M	8 46 12.9	12 31.3	15 8.9	19 46.5	26R55.8	13R42.8	10 59.9	11R24.3	21 43.4	26R21.0	29R36.1	4R27.5
3 T	8 50 9.5	13 32.2	15 5.7	2♍44.3	26 39.5	13 5.4	11 32.7	11 23.7	21 44.6	26 21.0	29 35.1	4 26.2
4 W	8 54 6.0	14 33.0	15 2.6	15 54.3	26 12.3	12 28.3	12 5.7	11 23.3	21 45.8	26 20.9	29 34.1	4 24.8
5 T	8 58 2.6	15 33.8	14 59.4	29 16.1	25 34.7	11 51.5	12 38.7	11 23.2	21 47.2	26D21.0	29 33.0	4 23.5
6 F	9 1 59.1	16 34.6	14 56.2	12♎49.5	24 47.6	11 15.3	13 11.8	11D23.2	21 48.7	26 21.1	29 31.9	4 22.2
7 S	9 5 55.7	17 35.4	14 53.0	26 34.3	23 52.2	10 40.1	13 45.1	11 23.4	21 50.3	26 21.3	29 30.8	4 20.8
8 S	9 9 52.3	18 36.2	14 49.9	10♏30.1	22 50.2	10 5.9	14 18.4	11 23.8	21 52.0	26 21.5	29 29.6	4 19.5
9 M	9 13 48.8	19 36.9	14 46.7	24 36.2	21 43.2	9 33.2	14 51.8	11 24.5	21 53.8	26 21.7	29 28.5	4 18.2
10 T	9 17 45.3	20 37.6	14 43.5	8♐51.2	20 33.2	9 1.9	15 25.4	11 25.3	21 55.7	26 22.1	29 27.3	4 16.9
11 W	9 21 41.9	21 38.4	14 40.3	23 12.6	19 22.3	8 32.4	15 59.0	11 26.3	21 57.8	26 22.4	29 26.1	4 15.6
12 T	9 25 38.5	22 39.1	14 37.1	7♑36.7	18 12.2	8 4.8	16 32.7	11 27.6	21 59.9	26 22.9	29 24.8	4 14.3
13 F	9 29 35.0	23 39.7	14 34.0	21 59.0	17 4.7	7 39.2	17 6.5	11 29.0	22 2.2	26 23.3	29 23.6	4 13.0
14 S	9 33 31.6	24 40.4	14 30.8	6♒14.3	16 1.4	7 15.7	17 40.4	11 30.6	22 4.5	26 23.9	29 22.3	4 11.7
15 S	9 37 28.1	25 41.0	14 27.6	20 17.6	15 3.4	6 54.5	18 14.4	11 32.5	22 7.0	26 24.5	29 21.0	4 10.5
16 M	9 41 24.7	26 41.6	14 24.4	4♓ 4.6	14 11.9	6 35.6	18 48.4	11 34.5	22 9.6	26 25.1	29 19.6	4 9.2
17 T	9 45 21.2	27 42.2	14 21.3	17 32.3	13 27.3	6 19.1	19 22.6	11 36.8	22 12.2	26 25.8	29 18.3	4 8.0
18 W	9 49 17.8	28 42.8	14 18.1	0♈39.5	12 50.2	6 5.0	19 56.8	11 39.2	22 15.0	26 26.5	29 16.9	4 6.8
19 T	9 53 14.3	29 43.3	14 14.9	13 26.5	12 20.8	5 53.3	20 31.1	11 41.8	22 17.9	26 27.3	29 15.5	4 5.5
20 F	9 57 10.9	0♓43.8	14 11.7	25 55.2	11 59.0	5 44.1	21 5.5	11 44.6	22 20.9	26 28.2	29 14.1	4 4.3
21 S	10 1 7.5	1 44.3	14 8.5	8♉ 8.4	11 44.8	5 37.4	21 39.9	11 47.6	22 24.0	26 29.1	29 12.7	4 3.1
22 S	10 5 4.0	2 44.7	14 5.4	20 10.3	11 37.8	5 33.2	22 14.4	11 50.8	22 27.1	26 30.0	29 11.3	4 2.0
23 M	10 9 0.6	3 45.1	14 2.2	2♊ 5.0	11 37.8	5 31.4	22 49.0	11 54.2	22 30.4	26 31.0	29 9.8	4 0.8
24 T	10 12 57.1	4 45.5	13 59.0	13 57.5	11D44.3	5D31.9	23 23.7	11 57.8	22 33.8	26 32.1	29 8.4	3 59.6
25 W	10 16 53.7	5 45.8	13 55.8	25 52.4	11 57.2	5 34.9	23 58.4	12 1.6	22 37.3	26 33.2	29 6.9	3 58.5
26 T	10 20 50.2	6 46.2	13 52.7	7♋54.2	12 15.8	5 40.2	24 33.2	12 5.5	22 40.9	26 34.3	29 5.4	3 57.4
27 F	10 24 46.8	7 46.4	13 49.5	20 6.9	12 39.9	5 47.8	25 8.0	12 9.6	22 44.5	26 35.5	29 3.9	3 56.3
28 S	10 28 43.3	8 46.7	13 46.3	2♌33.7	13 9.1	5 57.6	25 42.9	12 13.9	22 48.3	26 36.8	29 2.3	3 55.2

DECLINATION

DAY	EPHEMERIS SIDEREAL TIME (h m s)	☉	☊	☽	☿	♀	♂	♃	♄	♅	♆	♇
1 S	8 42 16.4	17S20.0	5N50.0	15N30.9	10S50.4	9S29.9	16N 6.7	21N41.1	16N10.1	19N 8.9	1N22.3	23N43.9
4 W	8 54 6.0	16 28.3	5 53.6	5 45.6	10 19.7	9 37.2	16 38.9	21 41.5	16 11.8	19 9.0	1 23.6	23 45.0
7 S	9 5 55.7	15 33.9	5 57.3	6S54.9	10 28.2	9 50.2	17 10.5	21 42.1	16 13.8	19 9.1	1 25.0	23 46.2
10 T	9 17 45.3	14 37.1	6 1.0	16 37.1	11 10.6	10 7.7	17 41.6	21 43.0	16 16.0	19 9.3	1 26.5	23 47.2
13 F	9 29 35.0	13 38.1	6 4.7	17 35.5	12 13.1	10 28.2	18 12.0	21 44.2	16 18.5	19 9.7	1 28.1	23 48.3
16 M	9 41 24.7	12 37.1	6 8.4	9 13.3	13 20.4	10 50.4	18 41.6	21 45.5	16 21.2	19 10.2	1 29.8	23 49.3
19 T	9 53 14.3	11 34.3	6 12.0	2N52.1	14 21.0	11 13.0	19 10.6	21 47.1	16 24.1	19 10.7	1 31.5	23 50.2
22 S	10 5 4.0	10 29.9	6 15.7	13 6.7	15 8.6	11 34.8	19 38.6	21 48.9	16 27.2	19 11.4	1 33.3	23 51.1
25 W	10 16 53.7	9 24.0	6 19.4	18 13.5	15 41.0	11 55.0	20 5.8	21 50.9	16 30.5	19 12.2	1 35.1	23 52.0
28 S	10 28 43.3	8 16.8	6 23.0	16 13.2	15 57.8	12 12.8	20 32.1	21 53.1	16 34.1	19 13.1	1 37.0	23 52.8

MARCH 1942

DAY	EPHEMERIS SIDEREAL TIME h m s	☉ ° ′	☊ ° ′	☽ ° ′	☿ ° ′	♀ ° ′	♂ ° ′	♃ ° ′	♄ ° ′	♅ ° ′	♆ ° ′	♇ ° ′
						LONGITUDE						
1 S	10 32 39.9	9♓46.9	13♍43.1	15♌16.9	13♒43.0	6♒ 9.7	26♉17.8	12♊18.4	22♉52.1	26♉38.1	29♍ 0.8	3♌54.1
2 M	10 36 36.4	10 47.1	13 39.9	28 17.7	14 21.3	6 23.8	26 52.8	12 23.1	22 56.1	26 39.4	28R59.2	3R53.1
3 T	10 40 33.0	11 47.2	13 36.8	11♍36.3	15 3.6	6 40.0	27 27.8	12 27.9	23 0.1	26 40.8	28 57.7	3 52.0
4 W	10 44 29.5	12 47.4	13 33.6	25 11.5	15 49.7	6 58.2	28 2.9	12 32.9	23 4.3	26 42.3	28 56.1	3 51.0
5 T	10 48 26.1	13 47.4	13 30.4	9♎ 1.0	16 39.4	7 18.3	28 38.1	12 38.1	23 8.5	26 43.8	28 54.5	3 50.0
6 F	10 52 22.6	14 47.5	13 27.2	23 2.0	17 32.3	7 40.3	29 13.2	12 43.5	23 12.8	26 45.3	28 52.9	3 49.0
7 S	10 56 19.2	15 47.5	13 24.0	7♏10.9	18 28.2	8 4.1	29 48.5	12 49.0	23 17.2	26 46.9	28 51.3	3 48.1
8 S	11 0 15.7	16 47.6	13 20.9	21 24.5	19 27.0	8 29.6	0♊23.7	12 54.7	23 21.7	26 48.5	28 49.7	3 47.1
9 M	11 4 12.3	17 47.5	13 17.7	5♐39.3	20 28.5	8 56.8	0 59.1	13 0.5	23 26.2	26 50.2	28 48.1	3 46.2
10 T	11 8 8.8	18 47.5	13 14.5	19 52.7	21 32.5	9 25.7	1 34.4	13 6.5	23 30.9	26 51.9	28 46.5	3 45.3
11 W	11 12 5.4	19 47.4	13 11.3	4♑ 2.0	22 38.9	9 56.1	2 9.8	13 12.7	23 35.6	26 53.7	28 44.8	3 44.4
12 T	11 16 2.0	20 47.3	13 8.2	18 5.4	23 47.4	10 28.0	2 45.3	13 19.0	23 40.4	26 55.5	28 43.2	3 43.5
13 F	11 19 58.5	21 47.2	13 5.0	2♒ 0.9	24 58.1	11 1.3	3 20.8	13 25.5	23 45.3	26 57.4	28 41.6	3 42.7
14 S	11 23 55.0	22 47.0	13 1.8	15 46.7	26 10.8	11 36.0	3 56.3	13 32.1	23 50.3	26 59.3	28 39.9	3 41.9
15 S	11 27 51.6	23 46.9	12 58.6	29 21.3	27 25.4	12 12.0	4 31.9	13 38.9	23 55.4	27 1.2	28 38.2	3 41.0
16 M	11 31 48.2	24 46.6	12 55.4	12♓43.1	28 41.8	12 49.2	5 7.5	13 45.9	24 0.5	27 3.2	28 36.6	3 40.3
17 T	11 35 44.7	25 46.4	12 52.3	25 50.9	0♓ 0.0	13 27.7	5 43.2	13 53.0	24 5.7	27 5.3	28 34.9	3 39.5
18 W	11 39 41.3	26 46.1	12 49.1	8♈43.9	1 19.9	14 7.4	6 18.9	14 0.3	24 11.0	27 7.3	28 33.3	3 38.8
19 T	11 43 37.8	27 45.8	12 45.9	21 22.2	2 41.3	14 48.1	6 54.6	14 7.6	24 16.4	27 9.5	28 31.6	3 38.0
20 F	11 47 34.3	28 45.5	12 42.7	3♉46.5	4 4.4	15 29.9	7 30.4	14 15.2	24 21.8	27 11.6	28 29.9	3 37.3
21 S	11 51 30.9	29 45.1	12 39.6	15 58.3	5 29.0	16 12.8	8 6.2	14 22.9	24 27.3	27 13.8	28 28.3	3 36.7
22 S	11 55 27.5	0♈44.7	12 36.4	28 0.2	6 55.1	16 56.6	8 42.0	14 30.7	24 32.9	27 16.1	28 26.6	3 36.0
23 M	11 59 24.0	1 44.2	12 33.2	9♊55.4	8 22.7	17 41.4	9 17.9	14 38.7	24 38.6	27 18.3	28 25.0	3 35.4
24 T	12 3 20.6	2 43.7	12 30.0	21 47.9	9 51.7	18 27.1	9 53.8	14 46.8	24 44.3	27 20.7	28 23.3	3 34.8
25 W	12 7 17.1	3 43.2	12 26.8	3♋42.0	11 22.1	19 13.6	10 29.7	14 55.0	24 50.1	27 23.0	28 21.6	3 34.2
26 T	12 11 13.7	4 42.6	12 23.7	15 42.6	12 54.0	20 1.0	11 5.7	15 3.3	24 55.9	27 25.4	28 20.0	3 33.7
27 F	12 15 10.2	5 42.0	12 20.5	27 54.3	14 27.2	20 49.3	11 41.7	15 11.8	25 1.8	27 27.9	28 18.4	3 33.1
28 S	12 19 6.8	6 41.3	12 17.3	10♌21.5	16 1.9	21 38.2	12 17.7	15 20.5	25 7.8	27 30.3	28 16.7	3 32.6
29 S	12 23 3.3	7 40.6	12 14.1	23 8.2	17 37.9	22 28.0	12 53.7	15 29.2	25 13.9	27 32.8	28 15.1	3 32.2
30 M	12 26 59.9	8 39.9	12 10.9	6♍17.1	19 15.3	23 18.4	13 29.8	15 38.1	25 20.0	27 35.4	28 13.4	3 31.7
31 T	12 30 56.4	9 39.1	12 7.8	19 49.3	20 54.2	24 9.6	14 5.9	15 47.1	25 26.1	27 38.0	28 11.8	3 31.3
						DECLINATION						
1 S	10 32 39.9	7S54.2	6N24.3	13N52.2	15S60.0	12S18.0	20N40.6	21N53.9	16N35.3	19N13.4	1N37.6	23N53.1
4 W	10 44 29.5	6 45.6	6 27.9	2 54.3	15 56.7	12 31.6	21 5.5	21 56.3	16 39.0	19 14.4	1 39.5	23 53.8
7 S	10 56 19.2	5 36.2	6 31.6	9S52.5	15 39.0	12 41.4	21 29.3	21 58.9	16 43.0	19 15.6	1 41.5	23 54.5
10 T	11 8 8.8	4 26.1	6 35.2	17 49.3	15 7.7	12 47.2	21 52.0	22 1.6	16 47.1	19 16.8	1 43.5	23 55.1
13 F	11 19 58.5	3 15.5	6 38.9	16 18.2	14 23.3	12 48.6	22 13.5	22 4.5	16 51.3	19 18.1	1 45.5	23 55.7
16 M	11 31 48.2	2 4.5	6 42.5	6 43.5	13 26.2	12 45.6	22 33.8	22 7.5	16 55.7	19 19.5	1 47.5	23 56.2
19 T	11 43 37.8	0 53.4	6 46.2	5N19.6	12 17.0	12 37.9	22 52.9	22 10.6	17 0.2	19 21.0	1 49.5	23 56.6
22 S	11 55 27.5	0N17.8	6 49.8	14 46.5	10 56.1	12 25.5	23 10.7	22 13.8	17 4.9	19 22.5	1 51.5	23 57.0
25 W	12 7 17.1	1 28.7	6 53.5	18 28.3	9 23.9	12 8.5	23 27.2	22 17.0	17 9.6	19 24.2	1 53.5	23 57.3
28 S	12 19 6.8	2 39.4	6 57.1	14 53.7	7 40.7	11 46.8	23 42.3	22 20.3	17 14.4	19 25.9	1 55.5	23 57.6
31 T	12 30 56.4	3 49.5	7 0.8	4 34.7	5 47.0	11 20.6	23 56.0	22 23.6	17 19.3	19 27.6	1 57.4	23 57.8

APRIL 1942

DAY	EPHEMERIS SIDEREAL TIME h m s	☉ ° ′	☊ ° ′	☽ ° ′	☿ ° ′	♀ ° ′	♂ ° ′	♃ ° ′	♄ ° ′	♅ ° ′	♆ ° ′	♇ ° ′
						LONGITUDE						
1 W	12 34 53.0	10♈38.4	12♍ 4.6	3♎44.3	22♓34.4	25♒ 1.4	14♊42.0	15♊56.2	25♉32.4	27♉40.6	28♍10.2	3♌30.9
2 T	12 38 49.5	11 37.5	12 1.4	17 59.1	24 16.0	25 53.9	15 18.1	16 5.4	25 38.6	27 43.2	28R 8.6	3R30.5
3 F	12 42 46.1	12 36.6	11 58.2	2♏28.8	25 59.0	26 47.0	15 54.2	16 14.8	25 45.0	27 45.9	28 7.0	3 30.1
4 S	12 46 42.6	13 35.8	11 55.1	17 7.2	27 43.4	27 40.7	16 30.4	16 24.2	25 51.4	27 48.6	28 5.4	3 29.8
5 S	12 50 39.2	14 34.8	11 51.9	1♐47.1	29 29.3	28 35.0	17 6.6	16 33.8	25 57.8	27 51.3	28 3.8	3 29.5
6 M	12 54 35.8	15 33.9	11 48.7	16 22.0	1♈16.6	29 29.8	17 42.8	16 43.5	26 4.4	27 54.1	28 2.2	3 29.2
7 T	12 58 32.3	16 32.9	11 45.5	0♑46.6	3 5.4	0♓25.2	18 19.0	16 53.3	26 10.9	27 56.9	28 0.7	3 29.0
8 W	13 2 28.8	17 31.9	11 42.3	14 57.5	4 55.6	1 21.0	18 55.2	17 3.2	26 17.5	27 59.7	27 59.1	3 28.7
9 T	13 6 25.4	18 30.8	11 39.2	28 52.9	6 47.3	2 17.4	19 31.5	17 13.2	26 24.2	28 2.6	27 57.6	3 28.5
10 F	13 10 22.0	19 29.7	11 36.0	12♒32.6	8 40.5	3 14.3	20 7.8	17 23.3	26 30.9	28 5.5	27 56.1	3 28.4
11 S	13 14 18.5	20 28.6	11 32.8	25 57.2	10 35.1	4 11.6	20 44.1	17 33.5	26 37.6	28 8.4	27 54.6	3 28.2
12 S	13 18 15.1	21 27.5	11 29.6	9♓ 7.8	12 31.2	5 9.4	21 20.4	17 43.8	26 44.5	28 11.4	27 53.1	3 28.1
13 M	13 22 11.6	22 26.3	11 26.5	22 5.6	14 28.8	6 7.6	21 56.8	17 54.2	26 51.3	28 14.3	27 51.6	3 28.0
14 T	13 26 8.2	23 25.2	11 23.3	4♈51.5	16 27.8	7 6.1	22 33.1	18 4.8	26 58.2	28 17.3	27 50.1	3 27.9
15 W	13 30 4.7	24 23.9	11 20.1	17 26.3	18 28.2	8 5.1	23 9.5	18 15.4	27 5.1	28 20.4	27 48.7	3 27.9
16 T	13 34 1.3	25 22.7	11 16.9	29 50.7	20 29.9	9 4.5	23 45.9	18 26.1	27 12.1	28 23.4	27 47.2	3 27.8
17 F	13 37 57.8	26 21.4	11 13.7	12♉ 5.4	22 32.9	10 4.2	24 22.3	18 36.9	27 19.2	28 26.5	27 45.8	3D27.8
18 S	13 41 54.4	27 20.1	11 10.6	24 11.4	24 37.1	11 4.3	24 58.8	18 47.8	27 26.2	28 29.6	27 44.4	3 27.9
19 S	13 45 50.9	28 18.7	11 7.4	6♊10.1	26 42.4	12 4.7	25 35.2	18 58.8	27 33.3	28 32.7	27 43.0	3 27.9
20 M	13 49 47.5	29 17.3	11 4.2	18 3.7	28 48.6	13 5.4	26 11.7	19 9.8	27 40.5	28 35.9	27 41.7	3 28.0
21 T	13 53 44.0	0♉15.9	11 1.0	29 55.1	0♉55.7	14 6.4	26 48.2	19 21.0	27 47.6	28 39.0	27 40.3	3 28.1
22 W	13 57 40.6	1 14.4	10 57.8	11♋47.8	3 3.3	15 7.8	27 24.7	19 32.2	27 54.9	28 42.2	27 39.0	3 28.3
23 T	14 1 37.1	2 12.9	10 54.7	23 46.2	5 11.4	16 9.4	28 1.2	19 43.5	28 2.1	28 45.4	27 37.7	3 28.4
24 F	14 5 33.7	3 11.4	10 51.5	5♌54.9	7 19.6	17 11.3	28 37.8	19 54.9	28 9.4	28 48.7	27 36.4	3 28.6
25 S	14 9 30.3	4 9.8	10 48.3	18 18.9	9 27.8	18 13.5	29 14.3	20 6.4	28 16.7	28 51.9	27 35.1	3 28.9
26 S	14 13 26.8	5 8.2	10 45.1	1♍ 3.0	11 35.6	19 16.0	29 50.8	20 18.0	28 24.1	28 55.2	27 33.9	3 29.1
27 M	14 17 23.3	6 6.6	10 42.0	14 11.4	13 42.7	20 18.7	0♋27.4	20 29.6	28 31.4	28 58.5	27 32.6	3 29.4
28 T	14 21 19.9	7 4.9	10 38.8	27 46.9	15 48.8	21 21.7	1 4.0	20 41.3	28 38.8	29 1.8	27 31.4	3 29.7
29 W	14 25 16.5	8 3.2	10 35.6	11♎50.3	17 53.7	22 24.9	1 40.6	20 53.1	28 46.3	29 5.1	27 30.3	3 30.0
30 T	14 29 13.0	9 1.5	10 32.4	26 19.5	19 56.9	23 28.4	2 17.2	21 4.9	28 53.7	29 8.4	27 29.1	3 30.3
						DECLINATION						
1 W	12 34 53.0	4N12.7	7N 2.0	0N11.6	5S 6.8	11S10.8	24N 0.2	22N24.7	17N21.0	19N28.2	1N58.1	23N57.8
4 S	12 46 42.6	5 22.0	7 5.6	12S27.4	2 59.7	10 38.6	24 12.0	22 28.1	17 26.0	19 30.1	1 60.0	23 57.9
7 T	12 58 32.3	6 30.4	7 9.2	18 29.3	0 43.2	10 2.0	24 22.3	22 31.4	17 31.1	19 32.0	2 1.8	23 58.0
10 F	13 10 22.0	7 37.8	7 12.9	14 30.9	1N42.1	9 21.3	24 31.2	22 34.7	17 36.2	19 34.0	2 3.6	23 58.0
13 M	13 22 11.6	8 44.1	7 16.5	3 53.6	4 14.8	8 36.7	24 38.5	22 38.0	17 41.3	19 36.0	2 5.4	23 57.9
16 T	13 34 1.3	9 49.1	7 20.1	7N53.3	6 53.4	7 48.4	24 44.4	22 41.2	17 46.5	19 38.0	2 7.1	23 57.8
19 S	13 45 50.9	10 52.6	7 23.7	16 19.2	9 35.4	6 56.6	24 48.6	22 44.4	17 51.7	19 40.1	2 8.7	23 57.6
22 W	13 57 40.6	11 54.5	7 27.4	18 28.8	12 17.3	6 1.6	24 51.4	22 47.5	17 56.9	19 42.2	2 10.3	23 57.4
25 S	14 9 30.3	12 54.6	7 31.0	13 22.4	14 54.2	5 3.6	24 52.6	22 50.5	18 2.1	19 44.4	2 11.8	23 57.1
28 T	14 21 19.9	13 52.8	7 34.6	2 9.4	17 20.8	4 2.9	24 52.2	22 53.4	18 7.3	19 46.6	2 13.2	23 56.7

MAY 1942

DAY	EPHEMERIS SIDEREAL TIME	☉	☊	☽	☿	♀	♂	♃	♄	♅	♆	♇
	h m s	° ′	° ′	° ′	° ′	° ′	° ′	° ′	° ′	° ′	° ′	° ′
						LONGITUDE						
1 F	14 33 9.6	9♉59.7	10♍29.3	11♏ 9.2	21♉58.3	24♓32.1	2♋53.7	21♊16.8	29♉ 1.2	29♉11.8	27♍28.0	3♌30.7
2 S	14 37 6.1	10 57.9	10 26.1	26 11.5	23 57.5	25 36.0	3 30.4	21 28.8	29 8.7	29 15.1	27R26.9	3 31.1
3 S	14 41 2.7	11 56.1	10 22.9	11♐16.6	25 54.3	26 40.1	4 7.0	21 40.9	29 16.2	29 18.5	27 25.8	3 31.5
4 M	14 44 59.2	12 54.2	10 19.7	26 14.7	27 48.5	27 44.5	4 43.6	21 53.0	29 23.8	29 21.9	27 24.7	3 32.0
5 T	14 48 55.8	13 52.3	10 16.5	10♑57.6	29 39.7	28 49.0	5 20.2	22 5.2	29 31.3	29 25.3	27 23.7	3 32.5
6 W	14 52 52.3	14 50.4	10 13.4	25 20.0	1♊28.0	29 53.8	5 56.9	22 17.4	29 38.9	29 28.7	27 22.7	3 33.0
7 T	14 56 48.9	15 48.5	10 10.2	9♒19.4	3 13.0	0♈58.8	6 33.6	22 29.7	29 46.5	29 32.1	27 21.7	3 33.5
8 F	15 0 45.5	16 46.6	10 7.0	22 55.7	4 54.7	2 3.9	7 10.2	22 42.1	29 54.2	29 35.5	27 20.7	3 34.0
9 S	15 4 42.0	17 44.6	10 3.8	6♓10.9	6 32.9	3 9.3	7 46.9	22 54.5	0♊ 1.8	29 39.0	27 19.8	3 34.6
10 S	15 8 38.5	18 42.6	10 0.7	19 7.7	8 7.5	4 14.8	8 23.6	23 6.9	0 9.5	29 42.4	27 18.9	3 35.2
11 M	15 12 35.1	19 40.6	9 57.5	1♈49.3	9 38.5	5 20.4	9 0.3	23 19.5	0 17.2	29 45.9	27 18.0	3 35.8
12 T	15 16 31.7	20 38.6	9 54.3	14 18.5	11 5.9	6 26.3	9 37.1	23 32.1	0 24.9	29 49.4	27 17.2	3 36.5
13 W	15 20 28.2	21 36.5	9 51.1	26 37.6	12 29.4	7 32.3	10 13.8	23 44.7	0 32.6	29 52.8	27 16.4	3 37.2
14 T	15 24 24.8	22 34.4	9 48.0	8♉48.6	13 49.1	8 38.5	10 50.6	23 57.4	0 40.3	29 56.3	27 15.6	3 37.9
15 F	15 28 21.3	23 32.3	9 44.8	20 52.9	15 4.9	9 44.7	11 27.3	24 10.1	0 48.0	29 59.8	27 14.8	3 38.6
16 S	15 32 17.9	24 30.2	9 41.6	2♊51.7	16 16.7	10 51.2	12 4.1	24 22.9	0 55.7	0♊ 3.3	27 14.0	3 39.3
17 S	15 36 14.4	25 28.0	9 38.4	14 46.2	17 24.5	11 57.8	12 40.9	24 35.8	1 3.5	0 6.8	27 13.3	3 40.1
18 M	15 40 11.0	26 25.9	9 35.2	26 37.9	18 28.3	13 4.5	13 17.7	24 48.7	1 11.2	0 10.3	27 12.7	3 40.9
19 T	15 44 7.6	27 23.7	9 32.1	8♋28.8	19 27.9	14 11.3	13 54.5	25 1.6	1 19.0	0 13.8	27 12.0	3 41.7
20 W	15 48 4.1	28 21.4	9 28.9	20 21.5	20 23.3	15 18.3	14 31.3	25 14.5	1 26.8	0 17.3	27 11.4	3 42.6
21 T	15 52 0.7	29 19.2	9 25.7	2♌19.5	21 14.4	16 25.4	15 8.1	25 27.6	1 34.5	0 20.8	27 10.8	3 43.4
22 F	15 55 57.2	0♊16.9	9 22.5	14 26.7	22 1.3	17 32.6	15 45.0	25 40.6	1 42.3	0 24.3	27 10.2	3 44.3
23 S	15 59 53.8	1 14.6	9 19.4	26 47.9	22 43.6	18 39.9	16 21.8	25 53.7	1 50.1	0 27.8	27 9.7	3 45.2
24 S	16 3 50.3	2 12.2	9 16.2	9♍27.9	23 21.6	19 47.4	16 58.6	26 6.8	1 57.8	0 31.3	27 9.2	3 46.1
25 M	16 7 46.9	3 9.9	9 13.0	22 31.6	23 54.9	20 54.9	17 35.5	26 20.0	2 5.6	0 34.8	27 8.7	3 47.1
26 T	16 11 43.4	4 7.5	9 9.8	6♎ 2.8	24 23.7	22 2.6	18 12.4	26 33.2	2 13.4	0 38.3	27 8.3	3 48.1
27 W	16 15 40.0	5 5.1	9 6.6	20 3.6	24 47.9	23 10.4	18 49.2	26 46.4	2 21.1	0 41.8	27 7.9	3 49.1
28 T	16 19 36.5	6 2.6	9 3.5	4♏33.4	25 7.3	24 18.3	19 26.1	26 59.7	2 28.9	0 45.3	27 7.5	3 50.1
29 F	16 23 33.1	7 0.2	9 0.3	19 28.3	25 22.0	25 26.3	20 3.0	27 13.0	2 36.6	0 48.8	27 7.2	3 51.1
30 S	16 27 29.6	7 57.7	8 57.1	4♐40.5	25 32.1	26 34.3	20 39.9	27 26.3	2 44.4	0 52.3	27 6.9	3 52.2
31 S	16 31 26.2	8 55.2	8 53.9	19 59.5	25 37.4	27 42.5	21 16.8	27 39.6	2 52.1	0 55.8	27 6.6	3 53.2
						DECLINATION						
1 F	14 33 9.6	14N49.0	7N38.2	11S 1.1	19N31.7	2S59.8	24N50.3	22N56.2	18N12.5	19N48.8	2N14.5	23N56.3
4 M	14 44 59.2	15 42.9	7 41.8	18 29.5	21 22.8	1 54.6	24 46.8	22 58.8	18 17.7	19 51.0	2 15.7	23 55.8
7 T	14 56 48.9	16 34.5	7 45.4	15 20.1	22 51.7	0 47.5	24 41.7	23 1.3	18 22.8	19 53.2	2 16.9	23 55.3
10 S	15 8 38.5	17 23.6	7 49.0	4 57.1	23 58.2	0N21.2	24 35.1	23 3.7	18 27.9	19 55.5	2 17.9	23 54.8
13 W	15 20 28.2	18 10.2	7 52.6	6N54.3	24 43.1	1 31.1	24 26.9	23 5.9	18 32.9	19 57.7	2 18.8	23 54.1
16 S	15 32 17.9	18 54.0	7 56.2	15 51.5	25 8.5	2 42.0	24 17.1	23 8.0	18 37.9	19 60.0	2 19.7	23 53.5
19 T	15 44 7.6	19 34.9	7 59.8	18 46.6	25 16.3	3 53.6	24 5.9	23 9.8	18 42.9	20 2.2	2 20.4	23 52.8
22 F	15 55 57.2	20 12.8	8 3.4	14 27.2	25 8.9	5 5.5	23 53.1	23 11.5	18 47.7	20 4.4	2 21.0	23 52.0
25 M	16 7 46.9	20 47.6	8 6.9	4 0.9	24 48.2	6 17.5	23 38.9	23 13.1	18 52.5	20 6.7	2 21.5	23 51.2
28 T	16 19 36.5	21 19.2	8 10.5	9S 9.2	24 16.3	7 29.2	23 23.1	23 14.4	18 57.2	20 8.9	2 21.9	23 50.4
31 S	16 31 26.2	21 47.5	8 14.1	18 10.2	23 35.0	8 40.4	23 5.9	23 15.5	19 1.8	20 11.0	2 22.2	23 49.5

JUNE 1942

DAY	EPHEMERIS SIDEREAL TIME	☉	☊	☽	☿	♀	♂	♃	♄	♅	♆	♇
						LONGITUDE						
1 M	16 35 22.8	9♊52.7	8♍50.8	5♑13.8	25♊38.2	28♈50.8	21♋53.7	27♊53.0	2♊59.9	0♊59.3	27♍ 6.4	3♌54.4
2 T	16 39 19.3	10 50.2	8 47.6	20 13.1	25R34.4	29 59.2	22 30.6	28 6.4	3 7.6	1 2.7	27R 6.1	3 55.5
3 W	16 43 15.8	11 47.6	8 44.4	4♒49.5	25 26.3	1♉ 7.7	23 7.5	28 19.8	3 15.3	1 6.2	27 5.9	3 56.6
4 T	16 47 12.4	12 45.1	8 41.2	18 59.1	25 13.9	2 16.3	23 44.5	28 33.3	3 23.0	1 9.6	27 5.8	3 57.8
5 F	16 51 9.0	13 42.5	8 38.0	2♓41.0	24 57.7	3 25.0	24 21.4	28 46.8	3 30.7	1 13.1	27 5.7	3 58.9
6 S	16 55 5.6	14 40.0	8 34.9	15 57.1	24 37.7	4 33.8	24 58.4	29 0.3	3 38.4	1 16.5	27 5.6	4 0.1
7 S	16 59 2.1	15 37.4	8 31.7	28 50.6	24 14.4	5 42.6	25 35.3	29 13.8	3 46.1	1 20.0	27 5.5	4 1.3
8 M	17 2 58.6	16 34.8	8 28.5	11♈25.5	23 48.1	6 51.6	26 12.3	29 27.3	3 53.7	1 23.4	27 5.5	4 2.6
9 T	17 6 55.2	17 32.2	8 25.3	23 45.9	23 19.3	8 0.6	26 49.3	29 40.9	4 1.4	1 26.8	27D 5.5	4 3.8
10 W	17 10 51.8	18 29.6	8 22.2	5♉55.5	22 48.5	9 9.7	27 26.3	29 54.5	4 9.0	1 30.2	27 5.5	4 5.1
11 T	17 14 48.3	19 26.9	8 19.0	17 57.4	22 16.1	10 18.9	28 3.3	0♋ 8.1	4 16.6	1 33.6	27 5.6	4 6.4
12 F	17 18 44.9	20 24.3	8 15.8	29 54.1	21 42.8	11 28.1	28 40.4	0 21.7	4 24.2	1 36.9	27 5.7	4 7.7
13 S	17 22 41.4	21 21.7	8 12.6	11♊47.6	21 9.1	12 37.5	29 17.4	0 35.3	4 31.7	1 40.3	27 5.9	4 9.0
14 S	17 26 38.0	22 19.0	8 9.5	23 39.4	20 35.5	13 46.9	29 54.5	0 49.0	4 39.3	1 43.6	27 6.0	4 10.3
15 M	17 30 34.6	23 16.4	8 6.3	5♋31.0	20 2.7	14 56.4	0♌31.5	1 2.6	4 46.8	1 47.0	27 6.2	4 11.7
16 T	17 34 31.1	24 13.7	8 3.1	17 24.0	19 31.2	16 5.9	1 8.6	1 16.3	4 54.3	1 50.3	27 6.5	4 13.1
17 W	17 38 27.6	25 11.0	7 59.9	29 20.2	19 1.6	17 15.5	1 45.7	1 29.9	5 1.8	1 53.6	27 6.7	4 14.4
18 T	17 42 24.2	26 8.3	7 56.7	11♌22.1	18 34.2	18 25.2	2 22.8	1 43.6	5 9.2	1 56.8	27 7.0	4 15.8
19 F	17 46 20.7	27 5.6	7 53.6	23 32.8	18 9.7	19 35.0	2 59.9	1 57.3	5 16.6	2 0.1	27 7.4	4 17.2
20 S	17 50 17.3	28 2.9	7 50.4	5♍55.9	17 48.5	20 44.8	3 37.0	2 11.0	5 24.0	2 3.3	27 7.7	4 18.7
21 S	17 54 13.9	29 0.1	7 47.2	18 35.7	17 30.8	21 54.7	4 14.1	2 24.7	5 31.4	2 6.6	27 8.1	4 20.1
22 M	17 58 10.5	29 57.4	7 44.0	1♎36.4	17 17.0	23 4.6	4 51.3	2 38.4	5 38.7	2 9.8	27 8.6	4 21.6
23 T	18 2 7.0	0♋54.6	7 40.9	15 1.9	17 7.3	24 14.6	5 28.4	2 52.1	5 46.0	2 12.9	27 9.0	4 23.0
24 W	18 6 3.5	1 51.8	7 37.7	28 54.8	17 2.1	25 24.7	6 5.6	3 5.8	5 53.3	2 16.1	27 9.5	4 24.5
25 T	18 10 0.1	2 49.1	7 34.5	13♏15.6	17 1.4	26 34.8	6 42.7	3 19.5	6 0.6	2 19.2	27 10.0	4 26.0
26 F	18 13 56.7	3 46.3	7 31.3	28 2.0	17D 5.3	27 45.0	7 19.9	3 33.2	6 7.8	2 22.4	27 10.6	4 27.5
27 S	18 17 53.3	4 43.5	7 28.2	13♐ 7.9	17 14.0	28 55.2	7 57.1	3 46.8	6 14.9	2 25.4	27 11.2	4 29.1
28 S	18 21 49.8	5 40.7	7 25.0	28 24.3	17 27.5	0♊ 5.5	8 34.3	4 0.5	6 22.1	2 28.5	27 11.8	4 30.6
29 M	18 25 46.3	6 37.9	7 21.8	13♑40.3	17 45.8	1 15.9	9 11.5	4 14.2	6 29.2	2 31.6	27 12.5	4 32.1
30 T	18 29 42.9	7 35.0	7 18.6	28 45.0	18 9.0	2 26.3	9 48.7	4 27.9	6 36.2	2 34.6	27 13.1	4 33.7
						DECLINATION						
1 M	16 35 22.8	21N56.2	8N15.3	18S51.8	23N19.6	9N 3.9	22N59.9	23N15.8	19N 3.3	20N11.8	2N22.2	23N49.2
4 T	16 47 12.4	22 19.9	8 18.9	13 32.7	22 29.2	10 13.9	22 40.8	23 16.7	19 7.8	20 13.9	2 22.4	23 48.3
7 S	16 59 2.1	22 40.1	8 22.4	2 5.1	21 35.2	11 22.6	22 20.3	23 17.3	19 12.2	20 16.0	2 22.4	23 47.4
10 W	17 10 51.8	22 56.7	8 26.0	9N29.1	20 40.8	12 29.7	21 58.4	23 17.8	19 16.5	20 18.1	2 22.3	23 46.4
13 S	17 22 41.4	23 9.7	8 29.6	17 15.4	19 50.2	13 34.9	21 35.2	23 18.0	19 20.7	20 20.2	2 22.0	23 45.4
16 T	17 34 31.1	23 19.1	8 33.1	18 30.9	19 7.9	14 37.8	21 10.7	23 18.0	19 24.7	20 22.2	2 21.7	23 44.4
19 F	17 46 20.7	23 24.7	8 36.7	12 35.3	18 37.6	15 38.2	20 44.9	23 17.8	19 28.7	20 24.2	2 21.2	23 43.4
22 M	17 58 10.5	23 26.7	8 40.2	1 20.0	18 21.8	16 35.7	20 17.8	23 17.4	19 32.5	20 26.1	2 20.7	23 42.3
25 T	18 10 0.1	23 24.9	8 43.8	11S22.5	18 21.4	17 30.1	19 49.5	23 16.8	19 36.3	20 28.0	2 20.0	23 41.2
28 S	18 21 49.8	23 19.3	8 47.3	18 44.6	18 35.7	18 21.0	19 20.1	23 15.9	19 39.9	20 29.9	2 19.2	23 40.1

JULY 1942

LONGITUDE

DAY	EPHEMERIS SIDEREAL TIME h m s	☉ ° ′	☊ ° ′	☽ ° ′	☿ ° ′	♀ ° ′	♂ ° ′	♃ ° ′	♄ ° ′	♅ ° ′	♆ ° ′	♇ ° ′
1 W	18 33 39.5	8♋32.2	7♍15.5	13♒29.4	18♊37.0	3♊36.8	10♌25.9	4♋41.6	6♊43.2	2♊37.6	27♍13.8	4♌35.2
2 T	18 37 36.0	9 29.4	7 12.3	27 47.8	19 9.8	4 47.4	11 3.2	4 55.2	6 50.2	2 40.6	27 14.6	4 36.8
3 F	18 41 32.6	10 26.6	7 9.1	11♓37.8	19 47.4	5 58.0	11 40.4	5 8.9	6 57.2	2 43.5	27 15.4	4 38.4
4 S	18 45 29.2	11 23.8	7 5.9	25 0.0	20 29.7	7 8.7	12 17.7	5 22.5	7 4.1	2 46.4	27 16.2	4 40.0
5 S	18 49 25.7	12 21.0	7 2.8	7♈57.1	21 16.7	8 19.4	12 55.0	5 36.2	7 10.9	2 49.3	27 17.0	4 41.6
6 M	18 53 22.2	13 18.2	6 59.6	20 32.8	22 8.2	9 30.2	13 32.2	5 49.8	7 17.7	2 52.2	27 17.9	4 43.2
7 T	18 57 18.8	14 15.4	6 56.4	2♉51.7	23 4.3	10 41.1	14 9.6	6 3.4	7 24.5	2 55.0	27 18.8	4 44.8
8 W	19 1 15.4	15 12.6	6 53.2	14 58.1	24 4.9	11 52.0	14 46.9	6 17.0	7 31.2	2 57.8	27 19.7	4 46.5
9 T	19 5 11.9	16 9.9	6 50.0	26 56.2	25 9.9	13 3.0	15 24.2	6 30.6	7 37.9	3 0.6	27 20.6	4 48.1
10 F	19 9 8.5	17 7.1	6 46.9	8♊49.4	26 19.3	14 14.0	16 1.6	6 44.2	7 44.6	3 3.4	27 21.6	4 49.8
11 S	19 13 5.0	18 4.3	6 43.7	20 40.7	27 33.0	15 25.1	16 39.0	6 57.7	7 51.1	3 6.1	27 22.6	4 51.4
12 S	19 17 1.6	19 1.6	6 40.5	2♋32.5	28 51.0	16 36.3	17 16.3	7 11.2	7 57.7	3 8.8	27 23.7	4 53.1
13 M	19 20 58.2	19 58.8	6 37.3	14 26.8	0♋13.1	17 47.5	17 53.8	7 24.8	8 4.1	3 11.4	27 24.8	4 54.8
14 T	19 24 54.7	20 56.1	6 34.2	26 25.2	1 39.4	18 58.7	18 31.2	7 38.2	8 10.6	3 14.1	27 25.9	4 56.4
15 W	19 28 51.3	21 53.3	6 31.0	8♌29.3	3 9.6	20 10.0	19 8.6	7 51.7	8 16.9	3 16.6	27 27.0	4 58.1
16 T	19 32 47.8	22 50.6	6 27.8	20 40.8	4 43.8	21 21.4	19 46.1	8 5.2	8 23.2	3 19.2	27 28.1	4 59.8
17 F	19 36 44.4	23 47.8	6 24.6	3♍1.8	6 21.8	22 32.8	20 23.5	8 18.6	8 29.5	3 21.7	27 29.3	5 1.5
18 S	19 40 40.9	24 45.1	6 21.4	15 34.5	8 3.4	23 44.2	21 1.0	8 32.0	8 35.7	3 24.2	27 30.5	5 3.2
19 S	19 44 37.5	25 42.4	6 18.3	28 21.7	9 48.5	24 55.7	21 38.5	8 45.3	8 41.9	3 26.7	27 31.8	5 4.9
20 M	19 48 34.0	26 39.6	6 15.1	11♎26.4	11 36.9	26 7.3	22 16.0	8 58.7	8 47.9	3 29.1	27 33.0	5 6.6
21 T	19 52 30.5	27 36.9	6 11.9	24 51.2	13 28.4	27 18.9	22 53.5	9 12.0	8 54.0	3 31.5	27 34.3	5 8.3
22 W	19 56 27.1	28 34.2	6 8.7	8♏38.1	15 22.8	28 30.5	23 31.1	9 25.2	8 59.9	3 33.8	27 35.7	5 10.0
23 T	20 0 23.7	29 31.5	6 5.6	22 47.9	17 19.7	29 42.2	24 8.6	9 38.5	9 5.8	3 36.1	27 37.0	5 11.7
24 F	20 4 20.3	0♌28.8	6 2.4	7♐18.9	19 18.9	0♋54.0	24 46.2	9 51.7	9 11.7	3 38.4	27 38.4	5 13.5
25 S	20 8 16.8	1 26.0	5 59.2	22 7.3	21 20.1	2 5.7	25 23.8	10 4.9	9 17.4	3 40.6	27 39.8	5 15.2
26 S	20 12 13.3	2 23.3	5 56.0	7♑6.5	23 22.9	3 17.6	26 1.4	10 18.0	9 23.2	3 42.8	27 41.2	5 16.9
27 M	20 16 9.9	3 20.7	5 52.9	22 8.1	25 27.1	4 29.5	26 39.0	10 31.1	9 28.8	3 44.9	27 42.6	5 18.6
28 T	20 20 6.5	4 18.0	5 49.7	7♒3.0	27 32.2	5 41.4	27 16.6	10 44.2	9 34.4	3 47.1	27 44.1	5 20.3
29 W	20 24 3.1	5 15.3	5 46.5	21 42.9	29 38.0	6 53.5	27 54.3	10 57.2	9 39.9	3 49.1	27 45.6	5 22.1
30 T	20 27 59.6	6 12.7	5 43.3	6♓1.4	1♌44.1	8 5.5	28 31.9	11 10.2	9 45.3	3 51.2	27 47.1	5 23.8
31 F	20 31 56.1	7 10.0	5 40.1	19 54.7	3 50.3	9 17.6	29 9.6	11 23.1	9 50.7	3 53.2	27 48.7	5 25.5

DECLINATION

DAY	EPHEMERIS SIDEREAL TIME	☉	☊	☽	☿	♀	♂	♃	♄	♅	♆	♇
1 W	18 33 39.5	23N10.2	8N50.9	14S55.2	19N 2.7	19N 8.1	18N49.5	23N14.9	19N43.3	20N31.6	2N18.3	23N39.0
4 S	18 45 29.2	22 57.3	8 54.4	3 32.4	19 39.3	19 51.1	18 17.8	23 13.6	19 46.7	20 33.4	2 17.2	23 37.9
7 T	18 57 18.8	22 40.9	8 57.9	8N25.1	20 22.2	20 29.8	17 45.0	23 12.1	19 49.9	20 35.1	2 16.1	23 36.8
10 F	19 9 8.5	22 20.9	9 1.5	16 43.8	21 7.2	21 3.9	17 11.1	23 10.4	19 53.0	20 36.7	2 14.9	23 35.6
13 M	19 20 58.2	21 57.4	9 5.0	18 43.0	21 49.7	21 33.1	16 36.3	23 8.5	19 55.9	20 38.2	2 13.5	23 34.5
16 T	19 32 47.8	21 30.6	9 8.5	13 24.4	22 24.8	21 57.2	16 0.5	23 6.5	19 58.8	20 39.7	2 12.1	23 33.4
19 S	19 44 37.5	21 0.4	9 12.0	2 33.7	22 47.0	22 16.0	15 23.7	23 4.2	20 1.4	20 41.2	2 10.6	23 32.2
22 W	19 56 27.1	20 27.1	9 15.5	9S57.6	22 51.3	22 29.4	14 46.1	23 1.8	20 4.0	20 42.5	2 9.0	23 31.1
25 S	20 8 16.8	19 50.7	9 19.1	18 15.7	22 33.6	22 37.2	14 7.6	22 59.1	20 6.4	20 43.8	2 7.2	23 30.0
28 T	20 20 6.5	19 11.3	9 22.6	16 11.2	21 51.9	22 39.3	13 28.3	22 56.3	20 8.7	20 45.0	2 5.4	23 28.9
31 F	20 31 56.1	18 29.1	9 26.1	5 17.1	20 47.0	22 35.7	12 48.2	22 53.4	20 10.8	20 46.2	2 3.6	23 27.8

AUGUST 1942

LONGITUDE

DAY	EPHEMERIS SIDEREAL TIME h m s	☉ ° ′	☊ ° ′	☽ ° ′	☿ ° ′	♀ ° ′	♂ ° ′	♃ ° ′	♄ ° ′	♅ ° ′	♆ ° ′	♇ ° ′
1 S	20 35 52.7	8♌ 7.4	5♍37.0	3♈21.9	5♌56.4	10♋29.8	29♌47.3	11♋36.0	9♊56.0	3♊55.1	27♍50.2	5♌27.2
2 S	20 39 49.3	9 4.8	5 33.8	16 24.0	8 1.9	11 42.0	0♍25.0	11 48.9	10 1.2	3 57.0	27 51.8	5 28.9
3 M	20 43 45.8	10 2.2	5 30.6	29 3.9	10 6.8	12 54.3	1 2.8	12 1.7	10 6.4	3 58.9	27 53.4	5 30.7
4 T	20 47 42.4	10 59.6	5 27.4	11♉25.4	12 10.9	14 6.6	1 40.5	12 14.4	10 11.5	4 0.7	27 55.1	5 32.4
5 W	20 51 38.9	11 57.1	5 24.3	23 32.9	14 14.0	15 19.0	2 18.3	12 27.2	10 16.5	4 2.5	27 56.7	5 34.1
6 T	20 55 35.5	12 54.6	5 21.1	5♊30.8	16 16.0	16 31.4	2 56.1	12 39.8	10 21.4	4 4.2	27 58.4	5 35.8
7 F	20 59 32.0	13 52.1	5 17.9	17 23.6	18 16.8	17 43.9	3 33.9	12 52.4	10 26.3	4 5.9	28 0.1	5 37.5
8 S	21 3 28.6	14 49.6	5 14.7	29 15.1	20 16.3	18 56.4	4 11.8	13 5.0	10 31.1	4 7.6	28 1.8	5 39.2
9 S	21 7 25.1	15 47.1	5 11.5	11♋ 8.9	22 14.4	20 9.0	4 49.6	13 17.5	10 35.8	4 9.2	28 3.6	5 40.9
10 M	21 11 21.7	16 44.7	5 8.4	23 7.7	24 11.2	21 21.6	5 27.5	13 30.0	10 40.4	4 10.8	28 5.3	5 42.6
11 T	21 15 18.2	17 42.3	5 5.2	5♌13.8	26 6.5	22 34.3	6 5.4	13 42.4	10 44.9	4 12.3	28 7.1	5 44.3
12 W	21 19 14.8	18 39.9	5 2.0	17 29.2	28 0.3	23 47.0	6 43.4	13 54.7	10 49.4	4 13.7	28 8.9	5 46.0
13 T	21 23 11.4	19 37.5	4 58.8	29 55.2	29 52.6	24 59.8	7 21.3	14 7.0	10 53.7	4 15.2	28 10.8	5 47.7
14 F	21 27 7.9	20 35.1	4 55.7	12♍32.9	1♍43.5	26 12.6	7 59.3	14 19.3	10 58.0	4 16.5	28 12.6	5 49.4
15 S	21 31 4.4	21 32.8	4 52.5	25 23.3	3 32.9	27 25.5	8 37.3	14 31.4	11 2.2	4 17.9	28 14.5	5 51.0
16 S	21 35 1.0	22 30.5	4 49.3	8♎27.4	5 20.9	28 38.4	9 15.3	14 43.5	11 6.4	4 19.2	28 16.3	5 52.7
17 M	21 38 57.6	23 28.2	4 46.1	21 45.8	7 7.3	29 51.4	9 53.3	14 55.6	11 10.4	4 20.4	28 18.2	5 54.4
18 T	21 42 54.1	24 25.9	4 42.9	5♏19.2	8 52.3	1♌ 4.4	10 31.4	15 7.5	11 14.3	4 21.6	28 20.1	5 56.0
19 W	21 46 50.7	25 23.6	4 39.8	19 7.9	10 35.9	2 17.4	11 9.5	15 19.4	11 18.2	4 22.7	28 22.1	5 57.7
20 T	21 50 47.2	26 21.3	4 36.6	3♐11.6	12 18.1	3 30.5	11 47.6	15 31.3	11 21.9	4 23.8	28 24.0	5 59.3
21 F	21 54 43.8	27 19.1	4 33.4	17 28.9	13 58.8	4 43.6	12 25.7	15 43.0	11 25.6	4 24.8	28 26.0	6 0.9
22 S	21 58 40.3	28 16.9	4 30.2	1♑57.0	15 38.2	5 56.8	13 3.8	15 54.7	11 29.2	4 25.8	28 27.9	6 2.5
23 S	22 2 36.9	29 14.7	4 27.1	16 31.9	17 16.1	7 10.0	13 42.0	16 6.4	11 32.7	4 26.8	28 29.9	6 4.1
24 M	22 6 33.4	0♍12.5	4 23.9	1♒ 8.5	18 52.7	8 23.3	14 20.2	16 17.9	11 36.1	4 27.7	28 31.9	6 5.7
25 T	22 10 30.0	1 10.4	4 20.7	15 40.8	20 27.9	9 36.6	14 58.4	16 29.4	11 39.4	4 28.5	28 34.0	6 7.3
26 W	22 14 26.5	2 8.2	4 17.5	0♓ 2.7	22 1.7	10 49.9	15 36.6	16 40.8	11 42.6	4 29.3	28 36.0	6 8.9
27 T	22 18 23.1	3 6.1	4 14.3	14 9.1	23 34.2	12 3.3	16 14.8	16 52.1	11 45.7	4 30.1	28 38.0	6 10.5
28 F	22 22 19.6	4 4.0	4 11.2	27 56.0	25 5.3	13 16.8	16 53.1	17 3.3	11 48.7	4 30.8	28 40.1	6 12.0
29 S	22 26 16.2	5 2.0	4 8.0	11♈21.2	26 35.0	14 30.3	17 31.4	17 14.5	11 51.6	4 31.4	28 42.2	6 13.6
30 S	22 30 12.8	5 60.0	4 4.8	24 24.4	28 3.4	15 43.8	18 9.7	17 25.6	11 54.4	4 32.0	28 44.2	6 15.1
31 M	22 34 9.3	6 58.0	4 1.6	7♉ 6.7	29 30.4	16 57.4	18 48.1	17 36.5	11 57.2	4 32.6	28 46.3	6 16.7

DECLINATION

DAY	EPHEMERIS SIDEREAL TIME	☉	☊	☽	☿	♀	♂	♃	♄	♅	♆	♇
1 S	20 35 52.7	18N14.4	9N27.2	0S59.5	20N20.5	22N33.2	12N34.7	22N52.4	20N11.5	20N46.5	2N 2.9	23N27.4
4 T	20 47 42.4	17 28.5	9 30.7	10N40.0	18 48.9	22 21.8	11 53.6	22 49.2	20 13.4	20 47.6	2 0.9	23 26.4
7 F	20 59 32.0	16 40.1	9 34.2	17 45.5	17 2.0	22 4.6	11 11.8	22 46.0	20 15.2	20 48.6	1 58.8	23 25.3
10 M	21 11 21.7	15 49.2	9 37.7	18 2.9	15 3.8	21 41.7	10 29.4	22 42.5	20 16.9	20 49.5	1 56.7	23 24.3
13 T	21 23 11.4	14 56.1	9 41.2	11 8.0	12 57.8	21 13.1	9 46.4	22 39.0	20 18.5	20 50.3	1 54.5	23 23.3
16 S	21 35 1.0	14 0.8	9 44.7	0S37.2	10 47.1	20 39.1	9 2.7	22 35.4	20 19.9	20 51.0	1 52.2	23 22.3
19 W	21 46 50.7	13 3.6	9 48.2	12 36.0	8 33.8	19 59.6	8 18.6	22 31.7	20 21.1	20 51.7	1 49.9	23 21.4
22 S	21 58 40.3	12 4.4	9 51.7	18 45.0	6 19.8	19 15.0	7 33.9	22 27.9	20 22.2	20 52.3	1 47.5	23 20.5
25 T	22 10 30.0	11 3.6	9 55.1	14 31.7	4 6.7	18 25.5	6 48.8	22 24.0	20 23.2	20 52.8	1 45.1	23 19.6
28 F	22 22 19.6	10 1.2	9 58.6	2 46.5	1 55.6	17 31.2	6 3.2	22 20.1	20 24.1	20 53.2	1 42.6	23 18.8
31 M	22 34 9.3	8 57.3	10 2.1	9N26.2	0S12.3	16 32.4	5 17.3	22 16.1	20 24.8	20 53.5	1 40.1	23 18.0

SEPTEMBER 1942

DAY	EPHEMERIS SIDEREAL TIME	☉	☊	☽	☿	♀	♂	♃	♄	♅	♆	♇
	h m s	° ′	° ′	° ′	° ′	° ′	° ′	° ′	° ′	° ′	° ′	° ′
						LONGITUDE						
1 T	22 38 5.9	7♍56.0	3♍58.5	19♉30.8	0♎56.0	18♌11.0	19♍26.4	17♋47.4	11♊59.8	4♊33.1	28♍48.4	6♌18.2
2 W	22 42 2.4	8 54.1	3 55.3	1♊40.3	2 20.1	19 24.7	20 4.8	17 58.3	12 2.3	4 33.5	28 50.5	6 19.7
3 T	22 45 58.9	9 52.2	3 52.1	13 39.4	3 42.9	20 38.4	20 43.3	18 9.0	12 4.7	4 33.9	28 52.7	6 21.2
4 F	22 49 55.5	10 50.3	3 48.9	25 32.7	5 4.2	21 52.2	21 21.7	18 19.6	12 7.1	4 34.2	28 54.8	6 22.6
5 S	22 53 52.1	11 48.5	3 45.7	7♋24.9	6 23.9	23 6.0	22 0.2	18 30.2	12 9.3	4 34.5	28 57.0	6 24.1
6 S	22 57 48.6	12 46.7	3 42.6	19 20.3	7 42.1	24 19.8	22 38.7	18 40.6	12 11.4	4 34.8	28 59.1	6 25.5
7 M	23 1 45.2	13 44.9	3 39.4	1♌23.0	8 58.8	25 33.7	23 17.3	18 51.0	12 13.4	4 35.0	29 1.3	6 27.0
8 T	23 5 41.7	14 43.2	3 36.2	13 36.3	10 13.7	26 47.6	23 55.8	19 1.2	12 15.3	4 35.1	29 3.4	6 28.4
9 W	23 9 38.3	15 41.4	3 33.0	26 3.1	11 26.9	28 1.6	24 34.4	19 11.4	12 17.1	4 35.2	29 5.6	6 29.8
10 T	23 13 34.9	16 39.8	3 29.9	8♍44.9	12 38.4	29 15.6	25 13.0	19 21.4	12 18.8	4 35.2	29 7.8	6 31.2
11 F	23 17 31.4	17 38.1	3 26.7	21 42.8	13 47.9	0♍29.6	25 51.7	19 31.4	12 20.4	4R35.2	29 10.0	6 32.5
12 S	23 21 27.9	18 36.5	3 23.5	4♎56.6	14 55.5	1 43.7	26 30.4	19 41.2	12 21.9	4 35.2	29 12.2	6 33.9
13 S	23 25 24.5	19 34.9	3 20.3	18 25.2	16 0.9	2 57.9	27 9.1	19 51.0	12 23.3	4 35.0	29 14.4	6 35.2
14 M	23 29 21.1	20 33.4	3 17.1	2♏6.9	17 4.1	4 12.0	27 47.8	20 0.6	12 24.6	4 34.9	29 16.6	6 36.5
15 T	23 33 17.6	21 31.8	3 14.0	15 59.7	18 4.9	5 26.2	28 26.6	20 10.1	12 25.7	4 34.7	29 18.8	6 37.8
16 W	23 37 14.1	22 30.3	3 10.8	0♐1.1	19 3.2	6 40.4	29 5.3	20 19.5	12 26.8	4 34.4	29 21.0	6 39.1
17 T	23 41 10.7	23 28.9	3 7.6	14 8.7	19 58.8	7 54.7	29 44.2	20 28.8	12 27.7	4 34.1	29 23.3	6 40.4
18 F	23 45 7.3	24 27.4	3 4.4	28 20.3	20 51.5	9 9.0	0♎23.0	20 38.0	12 28.6	4 33.7	29 25.5	6 41.7
19 S	23 49 3.8	25 26.0	3 1.3	12♑33.6	21 41.1	10 23.3	1 1.9	20 47.1	12 29.3	4 33.3	29 27.7	6 42.9
20 S	23 53 0.3	26 24.6	2 58.1	26 46.4	22 27.3	11 37.6	1 40.7	20 56.0	12 29.9	4 32.8	29 29.9	6 44.1
21 M	23 56 56.9	27 23.2	2 54.9	10♒56.3	23 9.8	12 52.0	2 19.7	21 4.8	12 30.4	4 32.3	29 32.1	6 45.3
22 T	0 0 53.5	28 21.9	2 51.7	25 0.6	23 48.4	14 6.4	2 58.6	21 13.5	12 30.8	4 31.7	29 34.4	6 46.5
23 W	0 4 50.0	29 20.6	2 48.5	8♓56.3	24 22.8	15 20.8	3 37.6	21 22.1	12 31.1	4 31.1	29 36.6	6 47.6
24 T	0 8 46.6	0♎19.3	2 45.4	22 40.7	24 52.7	16 35.3	4 16.6	21 30.6	12 31.3	4 30.4	29 38.8	6 48.7
25 F	0 12 43.1	1 18.1	2 42.2	6♈11.0	25 17.5	17 49.8	4 55.6	21 38.9	12 31.4	4 29.7	29 41.1	6 49.9
26 S	0 16 39.7	2 16.8	2 39.0	19 25.0	25 37.1	19 4.3	5 34.7	21 47.1	12R31.3	4 28.9	29 43.3	6 50.9
27 S	0 20 36.2	3 15.7	2 35.8	2♉21.7	25 50.9	20 18.9	6 13.8	21 55.2	12 31.2	4 28.1	29 45.5	6 52.0
28 M	0 24 32.8	4 14.5	2 32.6	15 1.1	25 58.6	21 33.5	6 52.9	22 3.1	12 31.0	4 27.3	29 47.8	6 53.1
29 T	0 28 29.3	5 13.4	2 29.5	27 24.3	25 59.7	22 48.1	7 32.0	22 10.9	12 30.6	4 26.4	29 50.0	6 54.1
30 W	0 32 25.9	6 12.4	2 26.3	9♊33.8	25R53.9	24 2.8	8 11.2	22 18.6	12 30.1	4 25.4	29 52.2	6 55.1
						DECLINATION						
1 T	22 38 5.9	8N35.8	10N 3.2	12N41.2	0S54.1	16N11.8	5N 1.9	22N14.8	20N25.0	20N53.6	1N39.3	23N17.7
4 F	22 49 55.5	7 30.2	10 6.7	18 26.8	2 56.2	15 7.5	4 15.5	22 10.8	20 25.6	20 53.8	1 36.7	23 17.0
7 M	23 1 45.2	6 23.6	10 10.1	17 3.1	4 52.8	13 59.2	3 28.9	22 6.8	20 26.0	20 54.0	1 34.2	23 16.3
10 T	23 13 34.9	5 16.0	10 13.6	8 40.4	6 42.6	12 47.5	2 41.9	22 2.9	20 26.3	20 54.0	1 31.5	23 15.6
13 S	23 25 24.5	4 7.5	10 17.0	3S49.5	8 24.4	11 32.5	1 54.8	21 58.9	20 26.5	20 54.0	1 28.9	23 15.0
16 W	23 37 14.1	2 58.5	10 20.5	15 2.0	9 56.4	10 14.6	1 7.4	21 55.0	20 26.5	20 53.9	1 26.3	23 14.5
19 S	23 49 3.8	1 48.9	10 23.9	18 45.0	11 16.4	8 54.0	0 20.0	21 51.2	20 26.4	20 53.7	1 23.6	23 14.0
22 T	0 0 53.5	0 39.0	10 27.4	12 24.0	12 21.4	7 31.2	0S27.6	21 47.5	20 26.2	20 53.4	1 21.0	23 13.5
25 F	0 12 43.1	0S31.1	10 30.8	0 5.6	13 7.5	6 6.4	1 15.1	21 43.8	20 25.9	20 53.0	1 18.4	23 13.1
28 M	0 24 32.8	1 41.2	10 34.2	11N37.8	13 29.6	4 39.9	2 2.7	21 40.3	20 25.5	20 52.6	1 15.7	23 12.8

OCTOBER 1942

DAY	EPHEMERIS SIDEREAL TIME	☉	☊	☽	☿	♀	♂	♃	♄	♅	♆	♇
						LONGITUDE						
1 T	0 36 22.4	7♎11.3	2♍23.1	21♊32.9	25♎40.8	25♍17.5	8♎50.5	22♋26.1	12♊29.5	4♊24.4	29♍54.4	6♌56.1
2 F	0 40 19.0	8 10.3	2 19.9	3♋25.9	25R20.2	26 32.2	9 29.7	22 33.5	12R28.9	4R23.4	29 56.6	6 57.1
3 S	0 44 15.6	9 9.4	2 16.8	15 17.4	24 51.9	27 46.9	10 9.0	22 40.7	12 28.1	4 22.3	29 58.8	6 58.0
4 S	0 48 12.1	10 8.5	2 13.6	27 12.3	24 15.8	29 1.7	10 48.3	22 47.8	12 27.1	4 21.1	0♎1.0	6 58.9
5 M	0 52 8.6	11 7.6	2 10.4	9♌15.8	23 32.0	0♎16.5	11 27.7	22 54.8	12 26.1	4 19.9	0 3.2	6 59.8
6 T	0 56 5.2	12 6.7	2 7.2	21 32.4	22 41.1	1 31.3	12 7.1	23 1.6	12 25.0	4 18.7	0 5.4	7 0.7
7 W	1 0 1.8	13 6.0	2 4.0	4♍6.1	21 43.5	2 46.2	12 46.5	23 8.3	12 23.8	4 17.4	0 7.6	7 1.6
8 T	1 3 58.3	14 5.2	2 0.9	16 59.9	20 40.3	4 1.0	13 25.9	23 14.8	12 22.4	4 16.1	0 9.8	7 2.4
9 F	1 7 54.9	15 4.5	1 57.7	0♎15.1	19 32.7	5 15.9	14 5.4	23 21.1	12 21.0	4 14.7	0 12.0	7 3.2
10 S	1 11 51.4	16 3.8	1 54.5	13 51.6	18 22.2	6 30.8	14 44.9	23 27.3	12 19.4	4 13.3	0 14.1	7 4.0
11 S	1 15 48.0	17 3.1	1 51.3	27 47.0	17 10.6	7 45.8	15 24.5	23 33.4	12 17.8	4 11.9	0 16.3	7 4.7
12 M	1 19 44.5	18 2.5	1 48.2	11♏57.5	15 59.9	9 0.8	16 4.1	23 39.3	12 16.0	4 10.4	0 18.5	7 5.5
13 T	1 23 41.1	19 1.9	1 45.0	26 17.7	14 52.1	10 15.7	16 43.7	23 45.0	12 14.2	4 8.8	0 20.6	7 6.2
14 W	1 27 37.6	20 1.3	1 41.8	10♐42.0	13 49.1	11 30.7	17 23.3	23 50.5	12 12.2	4 7.2	0 22.7	7 6.8
15 T	1 31 34.2	21 0.8	1 38.6	25 5.1	12 52.8	12 45.7	18 3.0	23 55.9	12 10.1	4 5.6	0 24.9	7 7.5
16 F	1 35 30.7	22 0.3	1 35.4	9♑23.0	12 4.9	14 0.8	18 42.7	24 1.2	12 7.9	4 4.0	0 27.0	7 8.1
17 S	1 39 27.3	22 59.8	1 32.3	23 32.8	11 26.5	15 15.8	19 22.5	24 6.2	12 5.7	4 2.3	0 29.1	7 8.7
18 S	1 43 23.8	23 59.4	1 29.1	7♒33.1	10 58.5	16 30.9	20 2.2	24 11.1	12 3.3	4 0.5	0 31.1	7 9.3
19 M	1 47 20.4	24 58.9	1 25.9	21 23.3	10 41.6	17 46.0	20 42.1	24 15.8	12 0.8	3 58.8	0 33.2	7 9.9
20 T	1 51 16.9	25 58.5	1 22.7	5♓3.2	10 35.9	19 1.0	21 21.9	24 20.4	11 58.2	3 57.0	0 35.3	7 10.4
21 W	1 55 13.5	26 58.2	1 19.6	18 32.9	10D41.3	20 16.2	22 1.8	24 24.8	11 55.6	3 55.1	0 37.3	7 10.9
22 T	1 59 10.1	27 57.9	1 16.4	1♈52.0	10 57.5	21 31.3	22 41.7	24 29.0	11 52.8	3 53.3	0 39.4	7 11.4
23 F	2 3 6.6	28 57.6	1 13.2	14 60.0	11 23.8	22 46.4	23 21.6	24 33.0	11 50.0	3 51.3	0 41.4	7 11.8
24 S	2 7 3.1	29 57.3	1 10.0	27 55.9	11 59.7	24 1.5	24 1.6	24 36.8	11 47.0	3 49.4	0 43.4	7 12.3
25 S	2 10 59.7	0♏57.1	1 6.8	10♉39.2	12 44.2	25 16.7	24 41.6	24 40.5	11 44.0	3 47.4	0 45.4	7 12.7
26 M	2 14 56.3	1 56.9	1 3.7	23 9.4	13 36.6	26 31.9	25 21.6	24 44.0	11 40.9	3 45.4	0 47.4	7 13.0
27 T	2 18 52.8	2 56.7	1 0.5	5♊26.9	14 36.0	27 47.1	26 1.7	24 47.3	11 37.7	3 43.4	0 49.3	7 13.4
28 W	2 22 49.4	3 56.6	0 57.3	17 33.1	15 41.6	29 2.3	26 41.8	24 50.4	11 34.4	3 41.3	0 51.3	7 13.7
29 T	2 26 45.9	4 56.5	0 54.1	29 30.1	16 52.6	0♏17.5	27 22.0	24 53.3	11 31.0	3 39.2	0 53.2	7 14.0
30 F	2 30 42.5	5 56.4	0 51.0	11♋21.2	18 8.3	1 32.7	28 2.2	24 56.1	11 27.6	3 37.1	0 55.1	7 14.3
31 S	2 34 39.0	6 56.4	0 47.8	23 10.7	19 27.9	2 48.0	28 42.4	24 58.7	11 24.0	3 34.9	0 57.0	7 14.5
						DECLINATION						
1 T	0 36 22.4	2S51.2	10N37.6	18N13.8	13S21.2	3N12.1	2S50.3	21N36.9	20N24.9	20N52.1	1N13.1	23N12.6
4 S	0 48 12.1	4 1.0	10 41.1	17 40.9	12 36.0	1 43.4	3 37.7	21 33.7	20 24.2	20 51.5	1 10.5	23 12.4
7 W	1 0 1.8	5 10.4	10 44.5	10 2.1	11 10.6	0 13.9	4 25.1	21 30.7	20 23.4	20 50.8	1 7.9	23 12.2
10 S	1 11 51.4	6 19.2	10 47.9	2S23.9	9 10.7	1S15.9	5 12.2	21 27.8	20 22.5	20 50.0	1 5.4	23 12.1
13 T	1 23 41.1	7 27.3	10 51.3	14 22.3	6 55.7	2 45.8	5 59.2	21 25.2	20 21.5	20 49.2	1 2.9	23 12.1
16 F	1 35 30.7	8 34.4	10 54.7	18 58.9	4 54.3	4 15.2	6 45.8	21 22.7	20 20.4	20 48.3	1 0.4	23 12.2
19 M	1 47 20.4	9 40.4	10 58.1	13 23.4	3 32.0	5 44.1	7 32.2	21 20.6	20 19.2	20 47.4	0 58.0	23 12.3
22 T	1 59 10.1	10 45.2	11 1.5	1 31.2	3 0.6	7 11.8	8 18.1	21 18.6	20 17.9	20 46.3	0 55.6	23 12.5
25 S	2 10 59.7	11 48.4	11 4.9	10N33.1	3 18.1	8 38.3	9 3.7	21 17.0	20 16.4	20 45.2	0 53.3	23 12.7
28 W	2 22 49.4	12 50.1	11 8.2	18 0.1	4 14.6	10 3.0	9 48.7	21 15.6	20 15.0	20 44.1	0 51.1	23 13.0
31 S	2 34 39.0	13 50.0	11 11.6	18 19.5	5 38.3	11 25.6	10 33.2	21 14.5	20 13.4	20 42.9	0 48.9	23 13.4

NOVEMBER 1942

LONGITUDE

DAY	EPHEMERIS SIDEREAL TIME h m s	☉ ° ′	☊ ° ′	☽ ° ′	☿ ° ′	♀ ° ′	♂ ° ′	♃ ° ′	♄ ° ′	♅ ° ′	♆ ° ′	♇ ° ′
1 S	2 38 35.6	7♏56.4	0♍44.6	5♌ 3.3	20♎50.9	4♏ 3.2	29♎22.7	25♋ 1.0	11♊20.4	3♊32.7	0♎58.9	7♌14.7
2 M	2 42 32.1	8 56.4	0 41.4	17 4.3	22 16.7	5 18.5	0♏ 3.0	25 3.2	11R16.7	3R30.5	1 0.7	7 14.9
3 T	2 46 28.7	9 56.5	0 38.2	29 19.1	23 44.9	6 33.8	0 43.3	25 5.2	11 13.0	3 28.3	1 2.6	7 15.1
4 W	2 50 25.3	10 56.6	0 35.1	11♍52.8	25 15.1	7 49.1	1 23.7	25 7.0	11 9.1	3 26.0	1 4.4	7 15.2
5 T	2 54 21.8	11 56.8	0 31.9	24 49.9	26 46.9	9 4.4	2 4.1	25 8.6	11 5.2	3 23.8	1 6.2	7 15.3
6 F	2 58 18.4	12 57.0	0 28.7	8♎13.2	28 19.9	10 19.7	2 44.6	25 10.0	11 1.2	3 21.5	1 7.9	7 15.4
7 S	3 2 14.9	13 57.2	0 25.5	22 3.4	29 53.9	11 35.0	3 25.1	25 11.2	10 57.2	3 19.1	1 9.7	7 15.4
8 S	3 6 11.5	14 57.4	0 22.4	6♏18.6	1♏28.8	12 50.3	4 5.6	25 12.2	10 53.0	3 16.8	1 11.4	7 15.5
9 M	3 10 8.0	15 57.7	0 19.2	20 53.8	3 4.2	14 5.7	4 46.2	25 13.0	10 48.9	3 14.4	1 13.2	7 15.5
10 T	3 14 4.6	16 58.0	0 16.0	5♐41.7	4 40.1	15 21.0	5 26.8	25 13.6	10 44.6	3 12.0	1 14.8	7R15.4
11 W	3 18 1.1	17 58.4	0 12.8	20 33.5	6 16.3	16 36.4	6 7.4	25 14.0	10 40.3	3 9.6	1 16.5	7 15.4
12 T	3 21 57.7	18 58.7	0 9.6	5♑20.6	7 52.7	17 51.8	6 48.1	25 14.3	10 35.9	3 7.2	1 18.1	7 15.3
13 F	3 25 54.2	19 59.1	0 6.5	19 56.1	9 29.2	19 7.1	7 28.8	25 14.3	10 31.5	3 4.8	1 19.8	7 15.2
14 S	3 29 50.8	20 59.5	0 3.3	4♒15.6	11 5.7	20 22.5	8 9.5	25R14.1	10 27.1	3 2.4	1 21.4	7 15.1
15 S	3 33 47.4	21 60.0	0 0.1	18 16.9	12 42.2	21 37.9	8 50.3	25 13.7	10 22.6	2 59.9	1 22.9	7 14.9
16 M	3 37 43.9	23 0.4	29♌56.9	2♓ 0.0	14 18.7	22 53.2	9 31.1	25 13.1	10 18.0	2 57.4	1 24.5	7 14.7
17 T	3 41 40.4	24 0.9	29 53.8	15 26.4	15 55.0	24 8.6	10 11.9	25 12.3	10 13.4	2 54.9	1 26.0	7 14.5
18 W	3 45 37.0	25 1.4	29 50.6	28 37.9	17 31.2	25 24.0	10 52.8	25 11.3	10 8.8	2 52.5	1 27.5	7 14.2
19 T	3 49 33.6	26 1.9	29 47.4	11♈36.5	19 7.3	26 39.4	11 33.7	25 10.2	10 4.1	2 50.0	1 29.0	7 14.0
20 F	3 53 30.1	27 2.4	29 44.2	24 23.5	20 43.2	27 54.8	12 14.7	25 8.8	9 59.4	2 47.5	1 30.4	7 13.7
21 S	3 57 26.7	28 3.0	29 41.0	7♉ 0.2	22 18.9	29 10.2	12 55.7	25 7.2	9 54.7	2 45.0	1 31.8	7 13.3
22 S	4 1 23.2	29 3.6	29 37.9	19 27.0	23 54.5	0♐25.5	13 36.7	25 5.4	9 49.9	2 42.5	1 33.2	7 13.0
23 M	4 5 19.8	0♐ 4.2	29 34.7	1♊44.4	25 29.8	1 40.9	14 17.8	25 3.4	9 45.1	2 39.9	1 34.6	7 12.6
24 T	4 9 16.4	1 4.8	29 31.5	13 52.8	27 5.1	2 56.3	14 58.9	25 1.3	9 40.3	2 37.4	1 35.9	7 12.2
25 W	4 13 12.9	2 5.5	29 28.3	25 53.1	28 40.1	4 11.7	15 40.0	24 58.9	9 35.4	2 34.9	1 37.2	7 11.8
26 T	4 17 9.5	3 6.2	29 25.2	7♋46.6	0♐15.0	5 27.1	16 21.2	24 56.3	9 30.5	2 32.4	1 38.5	7 11.3
27 F	4 21 6.0	4 6.9	29 22.0	19 35.8	1 49.8	6 42.5	17 2.4	24 53.6	9 25.7	2 29.9	1 39.8	7 10.8
28 S	4 25 2.6	5 7.6	29 18.8	1♌23.8	3 24.4	7 58.0	17 43.7	24 50.7	9 20.8	2 27.3	1 41.0	7 10.3
29 S	4 28 59.1	6 8.4	29 15.6	13 14.5	4 58.9	9 13.4	18 25.0	24 47.5	9 15.9	2 24.8	1 42.2	7 9.8
30 M	4 32 55.7	7 9.1	29 12.5	25 12.7	6 33.3	10 28.8	19 6.3	24 44.2	9 10.9	2 22.3	1 43.3	7 9.3

DECLINATION

DAY	EPHEMERIS SIDEREAL TIME	☉	☊	☽	☿	♀	♂	♃	♄	♅	♆	♇
1 S	2 38 35.6	14S 9.6	11N12.7	16N47.2	6S10.4	11S52.7	10S48.0	21N14.2	20N12.8	20N42.5	0N48.1	23N13.5
4 W	2 50 25.3	15 6.8	11 16.1	7 56.0	7 54.9	13 12.0	11 31.7	21 13.6	20 11.1	20 41.3	0 46.1	23 14.0
7 S	3 2 14.9	16 1.8	11 19.5	4S58.8	9 46.1	14 28.5	12 14.8	21 13.3	20 9.4	20 40.0	0 44.0	23 14.5
10 T	3 14 4.6	16 54.4	11 22.8	16 20.1	11 39.1	15 41.6	12 57.2	21 13.2	20 7.6	20 38.6	0 42.1	23 15.1
13 F	3 25 54.2	17 44.4	11 26.2	18 42.9	13 30.3	16 51.2	13 38.8	21 13.6	20 5.7	20 37.3	0 40.2	23 15.8
16 M	3 37 43.9	18 31.7	11 29.5	10 53.3	15 17.6	17 56.7	14 19.6	21 14.2	20 3.8	20 35.9	0 38.5	23 16.5
19 T	3 49 33.6	19 16.0	11 32.9	1N32.5	16 59.0	18 57.9	14 59.4	21 15.2	20 1.8	20 34.4	0 36.8	23 17.3
22 S	4 1 23.2	19 57.2	11 36.2	12 51.9	18 33.6	19 54.4	15 38.4	21 16.5	19 59.8	20 33.0	0 35.2	23 18.1
25 W	4 13 12.9	20 35.1	11 39.6	18 54.9	20 0.2	20 45.9	16 16.3	21 18.2	19 57.8	20 31.6	0 33.8	23 19.0
28 S	4 25 2.6	21 9.5	11 42.9	17 35.6	21 18.1	21 32.0	16 53.1	21 20.1	19 55.8	20 30.1	0 32.4	23 19.9

DECEMBER 1942

LONGITUDE

DAY	EPHEMERIS SIDEREAL TIME h m s	☉ ° ′	☊ ° ′	☽ ° ′	☿ ° ′	♀ ° ′	♂ ° ′	♃ ° ′	♄ ° ′	♅ ° ′	♆ ° ′	♇ ° ′
1 T	4 36 52.2	8♐ 9.9	29♌ 9.3	7♍23.7	8♐ 7.7	11♐44.2	19♏47.7	24♋40.7	9♊ 6.0	2♊19.8	1♎44.5	7♌ 8.7
2 W	4 40 48.8	9 10.8	29 6.1	19 52.9	9 41.9	12 59.6	20 29.2	24R37.0	9R 1.1	2R17.3	1 45.6	7R 8.1
3 T	4 44 45.4	10 11.6	29 2.9	2♎45.5	11 16.2	14 15.1	21 10.6	24 33.1	8 56.2	2 14.8	1 46.7	7 7.5
4 F	4 48 41.9	11 12.5	28 59.8	16 5.8	12 50.3	15 30.5	21 52.1	24 29.0	8 51.2	2 12.3	1 47.7	7 6.8
5 S	4 52 38.5	12 13.4	28 56.6	29 56.0	14 24.5	16 45.9	22 33.7	24 24.7	8 46.3	2 9.8	1 48.7	7 6.1
6 S	4 56 35.0	13 14.3	28 53.4	14♏15.8	15 58.6	18 1.4	23 15.2	24 20.3	8 41.4	2 7.4	1 49.7	7 5.4
7 M	5 0 31.6	14 15.3	28 50.2	29 1.3	17 32.7	19 16.8	23 56.9	24 15.7	8 36.5	2 4.9	1 50.6	7 4.7
8 T	5 4 28.2	15 16.2	28 47.0	14♐ 5.2	19 6.9	20 32.3	24 38.5	24 10.9	8 31.6	2 2.5	1 51.6	7 4.0
9 W	5 8 24.7	16 17.2	28 43.9	29 17.5	20 41.1	21 47.7	25 20.2	24 6.0	8 26.8	2 0.1	1 52.5	7 3.2
10 T	5 12 21.3	17 18.2	28 40.7	14♑27.3	22 15.3	23 3.1	26 2.0	24 0.8	8 21.9	1 57.6	1 53.3	7 2.4
11 F	5 16 17.8	18 19.2	28 37.5	29 24.9	23 49.6	24 18.6	26 43.7	23 55.5	8 17.1	1 55.3	1 54.1	7 1.6
12 S	5 20 14.4	19 20.2	28 34.3	14♒ 2.8	25 23.9	25 34.0	27 25.5	23 50.1	8 12.3	1 52.9	1 54.9	7 0.8
13 S	5 24 10.9	20 21.2	28 31.2	28 17.2	26 58.3	26 49.5	28 7.4	23 44.5	8 7.5	1 50.5	1 55.7	6 59.9
14 M	5 28 7.5	21 22.2	28 28.0	12♓ 7.0	28 32.8	28 4.9	28 49.2	23 38.7	8 2.8	1 48.2	1 56.4	6 59.0
15 T	5 32 4.0	22 23.3	28 24.8	25 33.5	0♑ 7.3	29 20.3	29 31.2	23 32.8	7 58.1	1 45.9	1 57.1	6 58.1
16 W	5 36 0.6	23 24.3	28 21.6	8♈39.2	1 42.0	0♑35.7	0♐13.1	23 26.8	7 53.4	1 43.6	1 57.7	6 57.2
17 T	5 39 57.2	24 25.4	28 18.5	21 27.3	3 16.6	1 51.2	0 55.1	23 20.6	7 48.8	1 41.3	1 58.4	6 56.3
18 F	5 43 53.7	25 26.4	28 15.3	4♉ 1.0	4 51.4	3 6.6	1 37.1	23 14.3	7 44.2	1 39.0	1 58.9	6 55.3
19 S	5 47 50.3	26 27.5	28 12.1	16 23.1	6 26.1	4 22.0	2 19.2	23 7.8	7 39.7	1 36.8	1 59.5	6 54.3
20 S	5 51 46.8	27 28.6	28 8.9	28 35.8	8 0.9	5 37.4	3 1.3	23 1.2	7 35.2	1 34.6	2 0.0	6 53.4
21 M	5 55 43.4	28 29.6	28 5.7	10♊41.0	9 35.7	6 52.8	3 43.4	22 54.5	7 30.8	1 32.4	2 0.5	6 52.3
22 T	5 59 40.0	29 30.7	28 2.6	22 40.0	11 10.4	8 8.2	4 25.6	22 47.7	7 26.4	1 30.3	2 1.0	6 51.3
23 W	6 3 36.5	0♑31.8	27 59.4	4♋34.2	12 45.0	9 23.6	5 7.8	22 40.7	7 22.1	1 28.2	2 1.4	6 50.3
24 T	6 7 33.1	1 32.9	27 56.2	16 24.9	14 19.5	10 38.9	5 50.1	22 33.7	7 17.8	1 26.1	2 1.8	6 49.2
25 F	6 11 29.6	2 34.0	27 53.0	28 13.6	15 53.8	11 54.3	6 32.4	22 26.5	7 13.6	1 24.0	2 2.1	6 48.1
26 S	6 15 26.2	3 35.1	27 49.9	10♌ 3.2	17 27.8	13 9.7	7 14.7	22 19.2	7 9.5	1 22.0	2 2.4	6 47.0
27 S	6 19 22.7	4 36.3	27 46.7	21 55.9	19 1.3	14 25.1	7 57.1	22 11.9	7 5.4	1 20.0	2 2.7	6 45.9
28 M	6 23 19.3	5 37.4	27 43.5	3♍55.7	20 34.4	15 40.4	8 39.5	22 4.4	7 1.4	1 18.0	2 3.0	6 44.8
29 T	6 27 15.8	6 38.5	27 40.3	16 6.5	22 6.7	16 55.8	9 21.9	21 56.9	6 57.4	1 16.1	2 3.2	6 43.6
30 W	6 31 12.4	7 39.7	27 37.2	28 33.3	23 38.2	18 11.2	10 4.4	21 49.3	6 53.5	1 14.2	2 3.4	6 42.5
31 T	6 35 9.0	8 40.8	27 34.0	11♎20.6	25 8.7	19 26.5	10 47.0	21 41.6	6 49.7	1 12.4	2 3.5	6 41.3

DECLINATION

DAY	EPHEMERIS SIDEREAL TIME	☉	☊	☽	☿	♀	♂	♃	♄	♅	♆	♇
1 T	4 36 52.2	21S40.4	11N46.2	9N30.7	22S26.6	22S12.5	17S28.8	21N22.4	19N53.8	20N28.6	0N31.2	23N20.9
4 F	4 48 41.9	22 7.6	11 49.5	2S53.7	23 25.0	22 47.2	18 3.3	21 24.9	19 51.8	20 27.2	0 30.0	23 21.9
7 M	5 0 31.6	22 30.9	11 52.9	15 2.2	24 12.8	23 15.6	18 36.5	21 27.7	19 49.9	20 25.8	0 29.0	23 23.0
10 T	5 12 21.3	22 50.3	11 56.2	19 13.5	24 49.2	23 37.8	19 8.4	21 30.8	19 47.9	20 24.4	0 28.1	23 24.1
13 S	5 24 10.9	23 5.6	11 59.5	12 8.5	25 13.6	23 53.4	19 39.0	21 34.1	19 46.0	20 23.0	0 27.3	23 25.3
16 W	5 36 0.6	23 16.8	12 2.8	0N21.1	25 25.5	24 2.5	20 8.0	21 37.6	19 44.2	20 21.6	0 26.6	23 26.5
19 S	5 47 50.3	23 23.8	12 6.1	11 58.1	25 24.3	24 4.8	20 35.6	21 41.3	19 42.5	20 20.3	0 26.0	23 27.7
22 T	5 59 40.0	23 26.6	12 9.4	18 41.4	25 9.6	24 0.4	21 1.5	21 45.1	19 40.8	20 19.0	0 25.6	23 29.0
25 F	6 11 29.6	23 25.2	12 12.7	18 10.4	24 41.2	23 49.3	21 25.9	21 49.1	19 39.2	20 17.8	0 25.3	23 30.2
28 M	6 23 19.3	23 19.5	12 16.0	10 43.9	23 59.0	23 31.6	21 48.5	21 53.1	19 37.8	20 16.6	0 25.1	23 31.5
31 T	6 35 9.0	23 9.6	12 19.2	1S 6.6	23 3.5	23 7.3	22 9.4	21 57.2	19 36.4	20 15.5	0 25.0	23 32.8

JANUARY 1943

DAY	EPHEMERIS SIDEREAL TIME (h m s)	☉ (° ′)	☊ (° ′)	☽ (° ′)	☿ (° ′)	♀ (° ′)	♂ (° ′)	♃ (° ′)	♄ (° ′)	♅ (° ′)	♆ (° ′)	♇ (° ′)
LONGITUDE												
1 F	6 39 5.5	9♑42.0	27♌30.8	24♎33.0	26♑37.8	20♑41.9	11♐29.5	21♋33.9	6♊46.0	1♊10.5	2♎ 3.6	6♌40.1
2 S	6 43 2.1	10 43.2	27 27.6	8♏13.6	28 5.4	21 57.2	12 12.2	21R26.0	6R42.3	1R 8.7	2 3.7	6R38.9
3 S	6 46 58.6	11 44.3	27 24.4	22 23.6	29 31.0	23 12.6	12 54.8	21 18.2	6 38.8	1 7.0	2 3.7	6 37.7
4 M	6 50 55.2	12 45.5	27 21.3	7♐ 1.3	0♒54.3	24 27.9	13 37.5	21 10.2	6 35.3	1 5.3	2 3.7	6 36.5
5 T	6 54 51.8	13 46.7	27 18.1	22 1.6	2 15.0	25 43.3	14 20.2	21 2.3	6 31.9	1 3.6	2R 3.7	6 35.2
6 W	6 58 48.3	14 47.9	27 14.9	7♑16.1	3 32.3	26 58.6	15 3.0	20 54.3	6 28.6	1 2.0	2 3.6	6 34.0
7 T	7 2 44.8	15 49.1	27 11.7	22 34.3	4 45.8	28 13.9	15 45.8	20 46.2	6 25.3	1 0.4	2 3.5	6 32.7
8 F	7 6 41.4	16 50.2	27 8.6	7♒45.2	5 54.9	29 29.2	16 28.6	20 38.2	6 22.2	0 58.8	2 3.4	6 31.4
9 S	7 10 38.0	17 51.4	27 5.4	22 39.5	6 58.7	0♒44.5	17 11.5	20 30.1	6 19.1	0 57.3	2 3.2	6 30.1
10 S	7 14 34.5	18 52.6	27 2.2	7♓10.4	7 56.6	1 59.8	17 54.4	20 22.0	6 16.2	0 55.9	2 3.1	6 28.8
11 M	7 18 31.1	19 53.7	26 59.0	21 14.5	8 47.7	3 15.1	18 37.4	20 13.9	6 13.3	0 54.5	2 2.8	6 27.5
12 T	7 22 27.6	20 54.9	26 55.9	4♈51.4	9 31.1	4 30.4	19 20.4	20 5.8	6 10.5	0 53.1	2 2.5	6 26.2
13 W	7 26 24.2	21 56.0	26 52.7	18 2.8	10 5.9	5 45.6	20 3.4	19 57.7	6 7.8	0 51.8	2 2.2	6 24.9
14 T	7 30 20.7	22 57.1	26 49.5	0♉51.7	10 31.3	7 0.9	20 46.4	19 49.6	6 5.3	0 50.5	2 1.9	6 23.6
15 F	7 34 17.3	23 58.3	26 46.3	13 22.1	10 46.3	8 16.1	21 29.5	19 41.6	6 2.8	0 49.3	2 1.5	6 22.3
16 S	7 38 13.9	24 59.4	26 43.1	25 37.7	10 50.4	9 31.3	22 12.6	19 33.5	6 0.4	0 48.1	2 1.1	6 20.9
17 S	7 42 10.4	26 0.4	26 40.0	7♊42.4	10R43.0	10 46.5	22 55.8	19 25.5	5 58.1	0 46.9	2 0.7	6 19.6
18 M	7 46 7.0	27 1.5	26 36.8	19 39.5	10 23.8	12 1.7	23 39.0	19 17.5	5 55.9	0 45.8	2 0.2	6 18.2
19 T	7 50 3.5	28 2.6	26 33.6	1♋31.9	9 53.1	13 16.9	24 22.2	19 9.6	5 53.9	0 44.8	1 59.7	6 16.9
20 W	7 54 0.1	29 3.7	26 30.4	13 21.9	9 11.1	14 32.0	25 5.5	19 1.8	5 51.9	0 43.8	1 59.2	6 15.5
21 T	7 57 56.6	0♒ 4.7	26 27.3	25 11.8	8 19.0	15 47.2	25 48.8	18 53.9	5 50.0	0 42.8	1 58.6	6 14.1
22 F	8 1 53.2	1 5.7	26 24.1	7♌ 3.3	7 18.0	17 2.3	26 32.1	18 46.2	5 48.3	0 41.9	1 58.0	6 12.8
23 S	8 5 49.8	2 6.7	26 20.9	18 58.3	6 9.9	18 17.4	27 15.5	18 38.5	5 46.6	0 41.1	1 57.4	6 11.4
24 S	8 9 46.3	3 7.8	26 17.7	0♍58.8	4 56.7	19 32.5	27 58.9	18 30.9	5 45.1	0 40.3	1 56.8	6 10.0
25 M	8 13 42.9	4 8.8	26 14.6	13 7.2	3 40.8	20 47.5	28 42.3	18 23.3	5 43.7	0 39.5	1 56.1	6 8.7
26 T	8 17 39.4	5 9.7	26 11.4	25 26.1	2 24.4	22 2.6	29 25.8	18 15.8	5 42.4	0 38.8	1 55.4	6 7.3
27 W	8 21 36.0	6 10.7	26 8.2	7♎58.7	1 9.7	23 17.6	0♑ 9.3	18 8.4	5 41.1	0 38.2	1 54.6	6 5.9
28 T	8 25 32.5	7 11.7	26 5.0	20 48.1	29♑58.8	24 32.6	0 52.9	18 1.2	5 40.0	0 37.6	1 53.8	6 4.5
29 F	8 29 29.1	8 12.6	26 1.8	3♏57.5	28 53.4	25 47.7	1 36.5	17 54.0	5 39.0	0 37.0	1 53.0	6 3.2
30 S	8 33 25.7	9 13.6	25 58.7	17 29.5	27 54.8	27 2.6	2 20.1	17 46.9	5 38.2	0 36.5	1 52.2	6 1.8
31 S	8 37 22.2	10 14.5	25 55.5	1♐25.8	27 3.9	28 17.6	3 3.8	17 39.9	5 37.4	0 36.1	1 51.3	6 0.4
DECLINATION												
1 F	6 39 5.5	23S 5.4	12N20.3	5S25.1	22S42.3	22S57.8	22S16.0	21N58.6	19N36.0	20N15.1	0N25.0	23N33.3
4 M	6 50 55.2	22 49.9	12 23.6	16 29.8	21 31.5	22 25.1	22 34.5	22 2.7	19 34.8	20 14.1	0 25.1	23 34.6
7 T	7 2 44.8	22 30.4	12 26.9	18 46.3	20 12.6	21 46.3	22 51.1	22 6.8	19 33.8	20 13.1	0 25.3	23 35.9
10 S	7 14 34.5	22 6.9	12 30.1	9 51.8	18 50.8	21 1.7	23 5.8	22 10.9	19 32.9	20 12.3	0 25.7	23 37.3
13 W	7 26 24.2	21 39.5	12 33.4	3N14.9	17 33.8	20 11.4	23 18.5	22 14.9	19 32.2	20 11.4	0 26.2	23 38.6
16 S	7 38 13.9	21 8.3	12 36.6	14 6.2	16 31.6	19 15.9	23 29.2	22 18.8	19 31.6	20 10.7	0 26.7	23 40.0
19 T	7 50 3.5	20 33.5	12 39.9	19 13.6	15 53.6	18 15.4	23 37.9	22 22.6	19 31.2	20 10.1	0 27.4	23 41.3
22 F	8 1 53.2	19 55.1	12 43.1	16 56.7	15 45.2	17 10.3	23 44.5	22 26.2	19 31.0	20 9.6	0 28.2	23 42.6
25 M	8 13 42.9	19 13.5	12 46.4	8 9.1	16 3.5	16 0.9	23 49.0	22 29.7	19 30.9	20 9.1	0 29.2	23 43.9
28 T	8 25 32.5	18 28.6	12 49.6	4S 4.4	16 39.2	14 47.5	23 51.3	22 33.1	19 31.0	20 8.7	0 30.2	23 45.1
31 S	8 37 22.2	17 40.8	12 52.8	15 18.7	17 21.5	13 30.5	23 51.6	22 36.2	19 31.4	20 8.5	0 31.3	23 46.4

FEBRUARY 1943

DAY	EPHEMERIS SIDEREAL TIME (h m s)	☉ (° ′)	☊ (° ′)	☽ (° ′)	☿ (° ′)	♀ (° ′)	♂ (° ′)	♃ (° ′)	♄ (° ′)	♅ (° ′)	♆ (° ′)	♇ (° ′)
LONGITUDE												
1 M	8 41 18.7	11♒15.4	25♌52.3	15♐46.0	26♑21.3	29♒32.6	3♑47.5	17♋33.0	5♊36.7	0♊35.7	1♎50.4	5♌59.0
2 T	8 45 15.3	12 16.4	25 49.1	0♑27.5	25R47.4	0♓47.5	4 31.3	17R26.3	5R36.2	0R35.3	1R49.5	5R57.7
3 W	8 49 11.9	13 17.3	25 46.0	15 25.1	25 22.1	2 2.4	5 15.0	17 19.7	5 35.8	0 35.1	1 48.6	5 56.3
4 T	8 53 8.4	14 18.1	25 42.8	0♒31.1	25 5.3	3 17.3	5 58.9	17 13.2	5 35.4	0 34.8	1 47.6	5 54.9
5 F	8 57 5.0	15 19.0	25 39.6	15 36.5	24 56.6	4 32.2	6 42.7	17 6.8	5 35.2	0 34.6	1 46.6	5 53.6
6 S	9 1 1.5	16 19.8	25 36.4	0♓32.1	24 55.8	5 47.0	7 26.6	17 0.6	5 35.2	0 34.5	1 45.5	5 52.2
7 S	9 4 58.1	17 20.7	25 33.3	15 10.1	25D 2.2	7 1.8	8 10.5	16 54.5	5D35.2	0 34.4	1 44.5	5 50.9
8 M	9 8 54.6	18 21.5	25 30.1	29 24.6	25 15.4	8 16.6	8 54.4	16 48.5	5 35.3	0 34.4	1 43.4	5 49.5
9 T	9 12 51.2	19 22.2	25 26.9	13♈12.8	25 35.0	9 31.4	9 38.4	16 42.7	5 35.6	0D34.4	1 42.3	5 48.2
10 W	9 16 47.7	20 23.0	25 23.7	26 34.2	26 0.4	10 46.1	10 22.4	16 37.1	5 35.9	0 34.5	1 41.1	5 46.9
11 T	9 20 44.3	21 23.7	25 20.5	9♉30.5	26 31.2	12 0.9	11 6.4	16 31.6	5 36.4	0 34.7	1 40.0	5 45.6
12 F	9 24 40.9	22 24.4	25 17.4	22 4.9	27 6.9	13 15.5	11 50.5	16 26.3	5 37.0	0 34.9	1 38.8	5 44.3
13 S	9 28 37.4	23 25.1	25 14.2	4♊21.5	27 47.1	14 30.2	12 34.6	16 21.1	5 37.7	0 35.1	1 37.6	5 42.9
14 S	9 32 34.0	24 25.7	25 11.0	16 24.6	28 31.5	15 44.8	13 18.7	16 16.1	5 38.6	0 35.4	1 36.4	5 41.6
15 M	9 36 30.5	25 26.3	25 7.8	28 18.9	29 19.7	16 59.4	14 2.8	16 11.2	5 39.5	0 35.8	1 35.1	5 40.4
16 T	9 40 27.1	26 26.9	25 4.6	10♋ 8.4	0♒11.4	18 13.9	14 47.0	16 6.6	5 40.5	0 36.2	1 33.8	5 39.1
17 W	9 44 23.6	27 27.5	25 1.5	21 57.1	1 6.3	19 28.5	15 31.2	16 2.1	5 41.7	0 36.6	1 32.6	5 37.8
18 T	9 48 20.2	28 28.0	24 58.3	3♌48.2	2 4.2	20 43.0	16 15.4	15 57.8	5 43.0	0 37.1	1 31.2	5 36.6
19 F	9 52 16.7	29 28.5	24 55.1	15 44.5	3 4.9	21 57.4	16 59.7	15 53.6	5 44.4	0 37.7	1 29.9	5 35.3
20 S	9 56 13.3	0♓28.9	24 51.9	27 48.3	4 8.1	23 11.8	17 44.0	15 49.7	5 45.8	0 38.3	1 28.5	5 34.1
21 S	10 0 9.8	1 29.4	24 48.8	10♍ 1.2	5 13.7	24 26.2	18 28.3	15 45.9	5 47.4	0 39.0	1 27.2	5 32.9
22 M	10 4 6.4	2 29.8	24 45.6	22 24.9	6 21.5	25 40.5	19 12.7	15 42.3	5 49.2	0 39.7	1 25.8	5 31.7
23 T	10 8 2.9	3 30.2	24 42.4	5♎ 0.5	7 31.3	26 54.9	19 57.1	15 38.9	5 51.0	0 40.5	1 24.4	5 30.5
24 W	10 11 59.5	4 30.6	24 39.2	17 49.2	8 43.1	28 9.1	20 41.5	15 35.7	5 52.9	0 41.3	1 22.9	5 29.3
25 T	10 15 56.0	5 30.9	24 36.0	0♏51.9	9 56.7	29 23.4	21 26.0	15 32.6	5 54.9	0 42.2	1 21.5	5 28.1
26 F	10 19 52.6	6 31.2	24 32.9	14 9.6	11 12.1	0♈37.6	22 10.5	15 29.8	5 57.1	0 43.1	1 20.0	5 27.0
27 S	10 23 49.2	7 31.5	24 29.7	27 43.2	12 29.1	1 51.7	22 55.0	15 27.1	5 59.3	0 44.1	1 18.6	5 25.8
28 S	10 27 45.7	8 31.8	24 26.5	11♐33.1	13 47.7	3 5.9	23 39.5	15 24.7	6 1.7	0 45.1	1 17.1	5 24.7
DECLINATION												
1 M	8 41 18.7	17S24.2	12N53.9	17S46.3	17S35.5	13S 4.1	23S51.2	22N37.2	19N31.5	20N 8.4	0N31.7	23N46.8
4 T	8 53 8.4	16 32.6	12 57.1	17 54.1	18 15.1	11 42.8	23 48.5	22 40.0	19 32.0	20 8.3	0 33.0	23 48.0
7 S	9 4 58.1	15 38.4	13 0.3	7 32.2	18 47.9	10 18.8	23 43.7	22 42.7	19 32.8	20 8.3	0 34.3	23 49.2
10 W	9 16 47.7	14 41.8	13 3.5	5N54.0	19 11.9	8 52.4	23 36.7	22 45.1	19 33.7	20 8.3	0 35.7	23 50.3
13 S	9 28 37.4	13 43.0	13 6.7	15 52.7	19 26.0	7 23.8	23 27.5	22 47.4	19 34.8	20 8.5	0 37.3	23 51.4
16 T	9 40 27.1	12 42.2	13 9.9	19 19.5	19 29.3	5 53.6	23 16.2	22 49.3	19 36.1	20 8.8	0 38.9	23 52.4
19 F	9 52 16.7	11 39.5	13 13.1	15 18.3	19 21.4	4 22.0	23 2.7	22 51.1	19 37.5	20 9.1	0 40.5	23 53.4
22 M	10 4 6.4	10 35.2	13 16.3	5 15.2	19 2.0	2 49.3	22 47.1	22 52.7	19 39.1	20 9.6	0 42.2	23 54.4
25 T	10 15 56.0	9 29.5	13 19.5	7S15.0	18 30.9	1 15.9	22 29.4	22 54.0	19 40.9	20 10.2	0 44.0	23 55.3
28 S	10 27 45.7	8 22.4	13 22.7	17 9.5	17 48.2	0N17.8	22 9.7	22 55.1	19 42.8	20 10.8	0 45.9	23 56.2

MARCH 1943

LONGITUDE

DAY	EPHEMERIS SIDEREAL TIME h m s	☉ ° ′	☊ ° ′	☽ ° ′	☿ ° ′	♀ ° ′	♂ ° ′	♃ ° ′	♄ ° ′	♅ ° ′	♆ ° ′	♇ ° ′
1 M	10 31 42.2	9 ♓ 32.1	24 ♌ 23.3	25 ♐ 39.0	15 ♒ 7.7	4 ♈ 19.9	24 ♑ 24.1	15 ♋ 22.4	6 ♊ 4.1	0 ♊ 46.2	1 ♎ 15.6	5 ♌ 23.6
2 T	10 35 38.8	10 32.3	24 20.2	9 ♑ 59.7	16 29.2	5 34.0	25 8.7	15 R 20.3	6 6.7	0 47.3	1 R 14.0	5 R 22.5
3 W	10 39 35.4	11 32.5	24 17.0	24 32.5	17 52.1	6 48.0	25 53.3	15 18.4	6 9.4	0 48.5	1 12.5	5 21.5
4 T	10 43 31.9	12 32.7	24 13.8	9 ♒ 13.2	19 16.4	8 2.0	26 38.0	15 16.7	6 12.2	0 49.7	1 11.0	5 20.4
5 F	10 47 28.5	13 32.8	24 10.6	23 56.3	20 41.9	9 15.9	27 22.7	15 15.2	6 15.0	0 51.0	1 9.4	5 19.4
6 S	10 51 25.0	14 32.9	24 7.4	8 ♓ 35.1	22 8.8	10 29.8	28 7.4	15 13.9	6 18.0	0 52.3	1 7.8	5 18.3
7 S	10 55 21.6	15 33.0	24 4.3	23 3.0	23 36.8	11 43.7	28 52.1	15 12.8	6 21.1	0 53.7	1 6.3	5 17.3
8 M	10 59 18.1	16 33.1	24 1.1	7 ♈ 14.0	25 6.2	12 57.5	29 36.8	15 11.9	6 24.3	0 55.1	1 4.7	5 16.3
9 T	11 3 14.7	17 33.1	23 57.9	21 3.6	26 36.7	14 11.3	0 ♒ 21.6	15 11.2	6 27.6	0 56.6	1 3.1	5 15.4
10 W	11 7 11.2	18 33.1	23 54.7	4 ♉ 29.5	28 8.4	15 25.0	1 6.4	15 10.7	6 30.9	0 58.1	1 1.5	5 14.4
11 T	11 11 7.8	19 33.0	23 51.6	17 31.3	29 41.3	16 38.6	1 51.2	15 10.4	6 34.4	0 59.7	0 59.9	5 13.5
12 F	11 15 4.3	20 32.9	23 48.4	0 ♊ 10.7	1 ♓ 15.4	17 52.3	2 36.1	15 10.3	6 38.0	1 1.3	0 58.2	5 12.6
13 S	11 19 0.9	21 32.8	23 45.2	12 30.9	2 50.7	19 5.8	3 20.9	15 D 10.4	6 41.7	1 3.0	0 56.6	5 11.7
14 S	11 22 57.4	22 32.7	23 42.0	24 35.9	4 27.1	20 19.3	4 5.8	15 10.7	6 45.4	1 4.7	0 55.0	5 10.8
15 M	11 26 54.0	23 32.5	23 38.8	6 ♋ 30.7	6 4.8	21 32.8	4 50.7	15 11.1	6 49.3	1 6.5	0 53.3	5 10.0
16 T	11 30 50.5	24 32.2	23 35.7	18 20.1	7 43.6	22 46.2	5 35.6	15 11.8	6 53.2	1 8.3	0 51.7	5 9.2
17 W	11 34 47.1	25 32.0	23 32.5	0 ♌ 9.2	9 23.7	23 59.6	6 20.5	15 12.7	6 57.3	1 10.1	0 50.0	5 8.4
18 T	11 38 43.7	26 31.7	23 29.3	12 2.4	11 4.9	25 12.9	7 5.5	15 13.7	7 1.4	1 12.0	0 48.4	5 7.6
19 F	11 42 40.2	27 31.3	23 26.1	24 3.7	12 47.4	26 26.1	7 50.4	15 15.0	7 5.6	1 13.9	0 46.7	5 6.8
20 S	11 46 36.7	28 30.9	23 22.9	6 ♍ 16.5	14 31.1	27 39.3	8 35.4	15 16.4	7 9.9	1 15.9	0 45.1	5 6.1
21 S	11 50 33.3	29 30.5	23 19.8	18 43.0	16 16.1	28 52.4	9 20.4	15 18.1	7 14.3	1 17.9	0 43.4	5 5.4
22 M	11 54 29.9	0 ♈ 30.1	23 16.6	1 ♎ 24.6	18 2.3	0 ♉ 5.5	10 5.5	15 19.9	7 18.8	1 20.0	0 41.8	5 4.7
23 T	11 58 26.4	1 29.6	23 13.4	14 21.8	19 49.8	1 18.5	10 50.5	15 21.9	7 23.4	1 22.1	0 40.1	5 4.0
24 W	12 2 23.0	2 29.1	23 10.2	27 33.8	21 38.6	2 31.5	11 35.6	15 24.1	7 28.0	1 24.3	0 38.4	5 3.4
25 T	12 6 19.5	3 28.5	23 7.1	10 ♏ 59.5	23 28.7	3 44.3	12 20.7	15 26.5	7 32.7	1 26.4	0 36.8	5 2.8
26 F	12 10 16.1	4 27.9	23 3.9	24 37.1	25 20.1	4 57.2	13 5.8	15 29.0	7 37.6	1 28.7	0 35.1	5 2.2
27 S	12 14 12.6	5 27.3	23 0.7	8 ♐ 24.9	27 12.8	6 10.0	13 50.9	15 31.8	7 42.5	1 30.9	0 33.5	5 1.6
28 S	12 18 9.2	6 26.7	22 57.5	22 21.0	29 6.8	7 22.7	14 36.0	15 34.7	7 47.4	1 33.2	0 31.8	5 1.0
29 M	12 22 5.7	7 26.0	22 54.4	6 ♑ 24.2	1 ♈ 2.1	8 35.3	15 21.2	15 37.8	7 52.5	1 35.6	0 30.2	5 0.5
30 T	12 26 2.3	8 25.3	22 51.2	20 33.1	2 58.6	9 47.9	16 6.4	15 41.1	7 57.6	1 38.0	0 28.5	5 0.0
31 W	12 29 58.8	9 24.6	22 48.0	4 ♒ 46.3	4 56.5	11 0.5	16 51.5	15 44.6	8 2.8	1 40.4	0 26.9	4 59.5

DECLINATION

DAY	EPHEMERIS SIDEREAL TIME h m s	☉ ° ′	☊ ° ′	☽ ° ′	☿ ° ′	♀ ° ′	♂ ° ′	♃ ° ′	♄ ° ′	♅ ° ′	♆ ° ′	♇ ° ′
1 M	10 31 42.2	7 S 59.8	13 N 23.7	18 S 50.0	17 S 31.3	0 N 49.1	22 S 2.6	22 N 55.5	19 N 43.4	20 N 11.1	0 N 46.5	23 N 56.4
4 T	10 43 31.9	6 51.3	13 26.9	16 34.1	16 33.0	2 22.8	21 40.2	22 56.3	19 45.6	20 11.8	0 48.4	23 57.2
7 S	10 55 21.6	5 41.9	13 30.0	5 2.4	15 23.1	3 56.1	21 15.7	22 56.9	19 47.8	20 12.7	0 50.3	23 57.9
10 W	11 7 11.2	4 31.8	13 33.2	8 N 22.9	14 1.7	5 28.7	20 49.3	22 57.3	19 50.2	20 13.7	0 52.3	23 58.6
13 S	11 19 0.9	3 21.2	13 36.4	17 21.0	12 29.0	7 0.3	20 21.1	22 57.5	19 52.7	20 14.7	0 54.3	23 59.2
16 T	11 30 50.5	2 10.2	13 39.5	19 6.3	10 45.0	8 30.4	19 51.0	22 57.5	19 55.3	20 15.8	0 56.3	23 59.7
19 F	11 42 40.2	0 59.1	13 42.6	13 26.7	8 50.0	9 58.8	19 19.2	22 57.2	19 58.1	20 17.1	0 58.3	24 0.2
22 M	11 54 29.9	0 N 12.0	13 45.8	2 17.6	6 44.3	11 25.2	18 45.6	22 56.8	20 0.9	20 18.3	1 0.3	24 0.6
25 T	12 6 19.5	1 22.9	13 48.9	10 S 20.5	4 28.2	12 49.2	18 10.4	22 56.2	20 3.8	20 19.7	1 2.3	24 1.0
28 S	12 18 9.2	2 33.6	13 52.0	18 40.4	2 2.2	14 10.4	17 33.6	22 55.4	20 6.8	20 21.1	1 4.3	24 1.2
31 W	12 29 58.8	3 43.8	13 55.1	17 24.6	0 N 32.6	15 28.7	16 55.3	22 54.3	20 9.9	20 22.6	1 6.2	24 1.5

APRIL 1943

LONGITUDE

DAY	EPHEMERIS SIDEREAL TIME h m s	☉ ° ′	☊ ° ′	☽ ° ′	☿ ° ′	♀ ° ′	♂ ° ′	♃ ° ′	♄ ° ′	♅ ° ′	♆ ° ′	♇ ° ′
1 T	12 33 55.4	10 ♈ 23.9	22 ♌ 44.8	19 ♒ 2.0	6 ♈ 55.5	12 ♉ 13.0	17 ♒ 36.7	15 ♋ 48.2	8 ♊ 8.1	1 ♊ 42.9	0 ♎ 25.3	4 ♌ 59.1
2 F	12 37 51.9	11 23.1	22 41.6	3 ♓ 17.6	8 55.7	13 25.4	18 22.0	15 52.0	8 13.5	1 45.3	0 R 23.6	4 R 58.7
3 S	12 41 48.5	12 22.3	22 38.5	17 29.8	10 57.0	14 37.7	19 7.2	15 56.0	8 18.9	1 47.9	0 22.0	4 58.3
4 S	12 45 45.0	13 21.4	22 35.3	1 ♈ 34.6	12 59.3	15 50.0	19 52.4	16 0.2	8 24.4	1 50.4	0 20.4	4 57.9
5 M	12 49 41.6	14 20.6	22 32.1	15 27.7	15 2.5	17 2.2	20 37.6	16 4.5	8 30.0	1 53.0	0 18.8	4 57.5
6 T	12 53 38.1	15 19.6	22 28.9	29 5.2	17 6.5	18 14.4	21 22.9	16 9.1	8 35.6	1 55.7	0 17.2	4 57.2
7 W	12 57 34.7	16 18.7	22 25.7	12 ♉ 24.0	19 11.1	19 26.5	22 8.1	16 13.7	8 41.3	1 58.3	0 15.6	4 56.9
8 T	13 1 31.2	17 17.7	22 22.6	25 22.8	21 16.1	20 38.5	22 53.4	16 18.6	8 47.1	2 1.0	0 14.0	4 56.6
9 F	13 5 27.8	18 16.7	22 19.4	8 ♊ 1.7	23 21.3	21 50.4	23 38.6	16 23.6	8 53.0	2 3.8	0 12.5	4 56.4
10 S	13 9 24.4	19 15.6	22 16.2	20 22.6	25 26.5	23 2.3	24 23.9	16 28.8	8 58.9	2 6.6	0 10.9	4 56.2
11 S	13 13 20.9	20 14.5	22 13.0	2 ♋ 28.6	27 31.3	24 14.1	25 9.2	16 34.1	9 4.9	2 9.4	0 9.4	4 56.0
12 M	13 17 17.4	21 13.4	22 9.9	14 23.9	29 35.5	25 25.8	25 54.4	16 39.6	9 10.9	2 12.2	0 7.8	4 55.8
13 T	13 21 14.0	22 12.2	22 6.7	26 13.7	1 ♉ 38.8	26 37.4	26 39.7	16 45.2	9 17.0	2 15.0	0 6.3	4 55.7
14 W	13 25 10.5	23 11.0	22 3.5	8 ♌ 3.1	3 40.9	27 49.0	27 25.0	16 51.1	9 23.2	2 17.9	0 4.8	4 55.6
15 T	13 29 7.1	24 9.8	22 0.3	19 57.5	5 41.3	29 0.5	28 10.3	16 57.0	9 29.4	2 20.8	0 3.3	4 55.5
16 F	13 33 3.7	25 8.5	21 57.1	2 ♍ 2.0	7 39.8	0 ♊ 11.9	28 55.5	17 3.1	9 35.7	2 23.8	0 1.9	4 55.4
17 S	13 37 0.2	26 7.2	21 54.0	14 20.9	9 36.0	1 23.2	29 40.8	17 9.4	9 42.1	2 26.7	0 0.4	4 55.4
18 S	13 40 56.8	27 5.8	21 50.8	26 57.7	11 29.5	2 34.4	0 ♓ 26.1	17 15.8	9 48.5	2 29.7	29 ♍ 59.0	4 55.4
19 M	13 44 53.3	28 4.4	21 47.6	9 ♎ 54.6	13 20.1	3 45.5	1 11.3	17 22.4	9 54.9	2 32.8	29 57.5	4 D 55.4
20 T	13 48 49.9	29 3.0	21 44.4	23 11.8	15 7.6	4 56.6	1 56.6	17 29.1	10 1.4	2 35.8	29 56.1	4 55.4
21 W	13 52 46.4	0 ♉ 1.6	21 41.3	6 ♏ 48.0	16 51.5	6 7.5	2 41.9	17 35.9	10 8.0	2 38.9	29 54.7	4 55.5
22 T	13 56 43.0	1 0.1	21 38.1	20 40.3	18 31.7	7 18.4	3 27.2	17 42.9	10 14.6	2 42.0	29 53.4	4 55.6
23 F	14 0 39.5	1 58.6	21 34.9	4 ♐ 44.5	20 8.0	8 29.2	4 12.5	17 50.0	10 21.2	2 45.1	29 52.0	4 55.7
24 S	14 4 36.1	2 57.0	21 31.7	18 55.8	21 40.3	9 39.8	4 57.7	17 57.3	10 28.0	2 48.2	29 50.7	4 55.9
25 S	14 8 32.6	3 55.4	21 28.5	3 ♑ 9.9	23 8.2	10 50.4	5 43.0	18 4.7	10 34.7	2 51.4	29 49.4	4 56.0
26 M	14 12 29.2	4 53.8	21 25.4	17 23.3	24 31.8	12 0.9	6 28.3	18 12.2	10 41.5	2 54.6	29 48.1	4 56.2
27 T	14 16 25.7	5 52.2	21 22.2	1 ♒ 33.4	25 50.9	13 11.3	7 13.5	18 19.8	10 48.4	2 57.8	29 46.8	4 56.5
28 W	14 20 22.3	6 50.6	21 19.0	15 38.9	27 5.3	14 21.6	7 58.8	18 27.6	10 55.3	3 1.0	29 45.5	4 56.7
29 T	14 24 18.9	7 48.9	21 15.8	29 39.0	28 15.0	15 31.9	8 44.0	18 35.6	11 2.2	3 4.3	29 44.3	4 57.0
30 F	14 28 15.4	8 47.2	21 12.7	13 ♓ 33.1	29 20.0	16 42.0	9 29.3	18 43.6	11 9.2	3 7.5	29 43.1	4 57.3

DECLINATION

DAY	EPHEMERIS SIDEREAL TIME h m s	☉ ° ′	☊ ° ′	☽ ° ′	☿ ° ′	♀ ° ′	♂ ° ′	♃ ° ′	♄ ° ′	♅ ° ′	♆ ° ′	♇ ° ′
1 T	12 33 55.4	4 N 7.1	13 N 56.2	14 S 41.0	1 N 25.9	15 N 54.0	16 S 42.2	22 N 53.9	20 N 10.9	20 N 23.1	1 N 6.9	24 N 1.5
4 S	12 45 45.0	5 16.4	13 59.3	2 14.7	4 10.1	17 7.7	16 2.0	22 52.6	20 14.1	20 24.7	1 8.8	24 1.7
7 W	12 57 34.7	6 24.9	14 2.4	10 N 47.2	6 58.4	18 17.6	15 20.5	22 51.1	20 17.3	20 26.3	1 10.7	24 1.7
10 S	13 9 24.4	7 32.5	14 5.5	18 33.5	9 46.8	19 23.4	14 37.6	22 49.4	20 20.5	20 28.0	1 12.5	24 1.7
13 T	13 21 14.0	8 38.8	14 8.6	18 37.9	12 30.3	20 24.7	13 53.7	22 47.5	20 23.8	20 29.7	1 14.3	24 1.7
16 F	13 33 3.7	9 43.9	14 11.7	11 29.4	15 3.1	21 21.4	13 8.6	22 45.3	20 27.1	20 31.4	1 16.1	24 1.5
19 M	13 44 53.3	10 47.5	14 14.7	0 S 31.1	17 20.0	22 13.0	12 22.4	22 43.0	20 30.5	20 33.2	1 17.8	24 1.4
22 T	13 56 43.0	11 49.5	14 17.8	13 3.7	19 16.8	22 59.4	11 35.3	22 40.4	20 33.8	20 35.1	1 19.4	24 1.1
25 S	14 8 32.6	12 49.8	14 20.9	19 36.0	20 51.2	23 40.3	10 47.4	22 37.6	20 37.1	20 36.9	1 20.9	24 0.8
28 W	14 20 22.3	13 48.1	14 23.9	15 37.1	22 2.6	24 15.6	9 58.6	22 34.6	20 40.5	20 38.8	1 22.4	24 0.4

MAY 1943

LONGITUDE

DAY	EPHEMERIS SIDEREAL TIME h m s	☉ ° ′	☊ ° ′	☽ ° ′	☿ ° ′	♀ ° ′	♂ ° ′	♃ ° ′	♄ ° ′	♅ ° ′	♆ ° ′	♇ ° ′
1 S	14 32 12.0	9♉45.5	21♌ 9.5	27♓20.3	0♊20.0	17♊52.0	10♓14.5	18♋51.8	11♊16.2	3♊10.8	29♍41.9	4♌57.6
2 S	14 36 8.5	10 43.7	21 6.3	10♈59.3	1 15.1	19 1.9	10 59.7	19 0.1	11 23.3	3 14.1	29R40.7	4 58.0
3 M	14 40 5.1	11 41.9	21 3.1	24 28.0	2 5.2	20 11.7	11 44.9	19 8.5	11 30.4	3 17.4	29 39.6	4 58.4
4 T	14 44 1.6	12 40.2	20 59.9	7♉44.5	2 50.2	21 21.4	12 30.1	19 17.0	11 37.5	3 20.8	29 38.5	4 58.8
5 W	14 47 58.2	13 38.3	20 56.8	20 46.8	3 30.0	22 31.0	13 15.3	19 25.7	11 44.7	3 24.1	29 37.4	4 59.2
6 T	14 51 54.7	14 36.5	20 53.6	3♊33.5	4 4.7	23 40.5	14 0.4	19 34.5	11 51.9	3 27.5	29 36.3	4 59.7
7 F	14 55 51.3	15 34.6	20 50.4	16 4.4	4 34.2	24 49.9	14 45.6	19 43.3	11 59.2	3 30.8	29 35.3	5 0.2
8 S	14 59 47.8	16 32.6	20 47.2	28 20.4	4 58.5	25 59.2	15 30.7	19 52.3	12 6.5	3 34.2	29 34.3	5 0.7
9 S	15 3 44.4	17 30.7	20 44.1	10♋23.6	5 17.5	27 8.3	16 15.8	20 1.5	12 13.8	3 37.6	29 33.3	5 1.2
10 M	15 7 40.9	18 28.7	20 40.9	22 17.6	5 31.3	28 17.3	17 0.8	20 10.7	12 21.2	3 41.1	29 32.3	5 1.8
11 T	15 11 37.5	19 26.7	20 37.7	4♌ 6.4	5 39.9	29 26.2	17 45.9	20 20.0	12 28.5	3 44.5	29 31.3	5 2.4
12 W	15 15 34.1	20 24.7	20 34.5	15 55.1	5 43.5	0♋35.0	18 30.9	20 29.5	12 36.0	3 47.9	29 30.4	5 3.0
13 T	15 19 30.6	21 22.6	20 31.4	27 49.2	5R42.1	1 43.7	19 15.9	20 39.0	12 43.4	3 51.4	29 29.5	5 3.6
14 F	15 23 27.2	22 20.5	20 28.2	9♍54.0	5 35.9	2 52.2	20 0.8	20 48.6	12 50.9	3 54.8	29 28.7	5 4.3
15 S	15 27 23.7	23 18.3	20 25.0	22 14.9	5 25.1	4 0.5	20 45.8	20 58.4	12 58.4	3 58.3	29 27.8	5 5.0
16 S	15 31 20.3	24 16.2	20 21.8	4♎56.3	5 9.9	5 8.8	21 30.7	21 8.2	13 5.9	4 1.8	29 27.0	5 5.7
17 M	15 35 16.8	25 14.0	20 18.6	18 1.4	4 50.8	6 16.8	22 15.6	21 18.2	13 13.4	4 5.2	29 26.3	5 6.4
18 T	15 39 13.4	26 11.8	20 15.5	1♏31.5	4 28.0	7 24.8	23 0.5	21 28.2	13 21.0	4 8.7	29 25.5	5 7.2
19 W	15 43 10.0	27 9.6	20 12.3	15 25.5	4 2.0	8 32.6	23 45.3	21 38.3	13 28.6	4 12.2	29 24.8	5 8.0
20 T	15 47 6.5	28 7.3	20 9.1	29 40.1	3 33.2	9 40.2	24 30.1	21 48.5	13 36.2	4 15.7	29 24.1	5 8.8
21 F	15 51 3.0	29 5.0	20 5.9	14♐ 9.5	3 2.2	10 47.7	25 14.9	21 58.8	13 43.8	4 19.2	29 23.4	5 9.6
22 S	15 54 59.6	0♊ 2.7	20 2.8	28 46.7	2 29.5	11 55.0	25 59.6	22 9.2	13 51.4	4 22.7	29 22.8	5 10.5
23 S	15 58 56.2	1 0.4	19 59.6	13♑24.8	1 55.7	13 2.1	26 44.4	22 19.7	13 59.1	4 26.2	29 22.2	5 11.4
24 M	16 2 52.7	1 58.0	19 56.4	27 57.5	1 21.4	14 9.1	27 29.0	22 30.3	14 6.8	4 29.8	29 21.6	5 12.3
25 T	16 6 49.2	2 55.7	19 53.2	12♒20.3	0 47.1	15 16.0	28 13.7	22 40.9	14 14.5	4 33.3	29 21.1	5 13.2
26 W	16 10 45.8	3 53.3	19 50.0	26 30.7	0 13.6	16 22.6	28 58.3	22 51.7	14 22.2	4 36.8	29 20.6	5 14.1
27 T	16 14 42.4	4 50.9	19 46.9	10♓27.7	29♉41.3	17 29.1	29 42.9	23 2.5	14 29.9	4 40.3	29 20.1	5 15.1
28 F	16 18 38.9	5 48.5	19 43.7	24 11.3	29 10.9	18 35.4	0♈27.5	23 13.4	14 37.6	4 43.8	29 19.6	5 16.1
29 S	16 22 35.5	6 46.1	19 40.5	7♈42.1	28 42.7	19 41.6	1 12.0	23 24.4	14 45.4	4 47.3	29 19.2	5 17.1
30 S	16 26 32.0	7 43.6	19 37.3	21 0.6	28 17.3	20 47.5	1 56.4	23 35.4	14 53.1	4 50.9	29 18.8	5 18.1
31 M	16 30 28.6	8 41.2	19 34.2	4♉ 7.2	27 55.0	21 53.3	2 40.8	23 46.6	15 0.9	4 54.4	29 18.5	5 19.2

DECLINATION

DAY	SIDEREAL TIME	☉	☊	☽	☿	♀	♂	♃	♄	♅	♆	♇
1 S	14 32 12.0	14N44.5	14N27.0	3S44.8	22N51.5	24N44.9	9S 9.2	22N31.4	20N43.8	20N40.7	1N23.8	24N 0.0
4 T	14 44 1.6	15 38.6	14 30.0	9N29.0	23 18.6	25 8.3	8 19.1	22 27.9	20 47.1	20 42.7	1 25.1	23 59.5
7 F	14 55 51.3	16 30.5	14 33.1	18 12.2	23 25.2	25 25.6	7 28.5	22 24.2	20 50.4	20 44.6	1 26.3	23 59.0
10 M	15 7 40.9	17 19.8	14 36.1	19 15.0	23 12.2	25 36.8	6 37.4	22 20.3	20 53.6	20 46.6	1 27.4	23 58.4
13 T	15 19 30.6	18 6.6	14 39.1	12 51.0	22 41.0	25 41.7	5 45.9	22 16.2	20 56.8	20 48.6	1 28.4	23 57.8
16 S	15 31 20.3	18 50.6	14 42.2	1 17.5	21 53.3	25 40.5	4 54.2	22 11.8	21 0.0	20 50.5	1 29.3	23 57.1
19 W	15 43 10.0	19 31.7	14 45.2	11S40.5	20 52.5	25 33.2	4 2.3	22 7.2	21 3.1	20 52.5	1 30.1	23 56.3
22 S	15 54 59.6	20 9.9	14 48.2	19 33.3	19 43.4	25 20.0	3 10.2	22 2.4	21 6.2	20 54.5	1 30.8	23 55.6
25 T	16 6 49.2	20 44.9	14 51.2	16 31.9	18 32.5	25 0.8	2 18.0	21 57.3	21 9.2	20 56.4	1 31.4	23 54.7
28 F	16 18 38.9	21 16.8	14 54.2	4 59.1	17 26.9	24 36.1	1 25.9	21 52.0	21 12.1	20 58.4	1 31.9	23 53.9
31 M	16 30 28.6	21 45.3	14 57.2	8N18.0	16 33.4	24 5.9	0 33.8	21 46.5	21 15.0	21 0.3	1 32.3	23 53.0

JUNE 1943

LONGITUDE

DAY	SIDEREAL TIME	☉	☊	☽	☿	♀	♂	♃	♄	♅	♆	♇
1 T	16 34 25.2	9♊38.7	19♌31.0	17♉ 1.9	27♉36.2	22♋58.9	3♈25.2	23♋57.8	15♊ 8.7	4♊57.9	29♍18.1	5♌20.2
2 W	16 38 21.7	10 36.2	19 27.8	29 44.3	27R21.2	24 4.2	4 9.5	24 9.1	15 16.5	5 1.4	29R17.8	5 21.3
3 T	16 42 18.3	11 33.7	19 24.6	12♊14.5	27 10.2	25 9.4	4 53.8	24 20.4	15 24.2	5 4.9	29 17.6	5 22.4
4 F	16 46 14.8	12 31.2	19 21.4	24 32.7	27 3.4	26 14.4	5 38.0	24 31.9	15 32.0	5 8.4	29 17.3	5 23.6
5 S	16 50 11.4	13 28.7	19 18.3	6♋39.7	27 1.0	27 19.1	6 22.2	24 43.4	15 39.8	5 11.9	29 17.1	5 24.7
6 S	16 54 7.9	14 26.1	19 15.1	18 37.3	27D 2.9	28 23.6	7 6.3	24 54.9	15 47.6	5 15.4	29 17.0	5 25.9
7 M	16 58 4.5	15 23.6	19 11.9	0♌27.8	27 9.4	29 27.9	7 50.4	25 6.6	15 55.4	5 18.8	29 16.8	5 27.1
8 T	17 2 1.1	16 21.0	19 8.7	12 14.9	27 20.3	0♌32.0	8 34.4	25 18.2	16 3.2	5 22.3	29 16.7	5 28.3
9 W	17 5 57.6	17 18.4	19 5.6	24 2.7	27 35.8	1 35.8	9 18.3	25 30.0	16 11.0	5 25.8	29 16.7	5 29.5
10 T	17 9 54.1	18 15.8	19 2.4	5♍55.9	27 55.7	2 39.4	10 2.2	25 41.8	16 18.8	5 29.2	29 16.6	5 30.8
11 F	17 13 50.7	19 13.1	18 59.2	17 59.8	28 20.0	3 42.7	10 46.0	25 53.7	16 26.6	5 32.7	29 16.6	5 32.0
12 S	17 17 47.3	20 10.5	18 56.0	0♎19.7	28 48.7	4 45.7	11 29.8	26 5.6	16 34.4	5 36.1	29D16.7	5 33.3
13 S	17 21 43.9	21 7.8	18 52.9	13 0.5	29 21.7	5 48.5	12 13.4	26 17.6	16 42.2	5 39.5	29 16.7	5 34.6
14 M	17 25 40.4	22 5.1	18 49.7	26 6.2	29 59.0	6 51.0	12 57.1	26 29.7	16 50.0	5 42.9	29 16.8	5 35.9
15 T	17 29 36.9	23 2.4	18 46.5	9♏39.4	0♊40.3	7 53.2	13 40.7	26 41.8	16 57.8	5 46.4	29 16.9	5 37.3
16 W	17 33 33.5	23 59.7	18 43.3	23 40.2	1 25.8	8 55.1	14 24.2	26 53.9	17 5.5	5 49.7	29 17.1	5 38.6
17 T	17 37 30.1	24 57.0	18 40.2	8♐ 5.9	2 15.2	9 56.7	15 7.6	27 6.1	17 13.3	5 53.1	29 17.3	5 40.0
18 F	17 41 26.6	25 54.2	18 37.0	22 51.2	3 8.6	10 57.9	15 51.0	27 18.4	17 21.0	5 56.5	29 17.5	5 41.4
19 S	17 45 23.2	26 51.5	18 33.8	7♑48.2	4 5.8	11 58.9	16 34.3	27 30.7	17 28.8	5 59.8	29 17.7	5 42.8
20 S	17 49 19.8	27 48.7	18 30.6	22 48.0	5 6.8	12 59.5	17 17.5	27 43.0	17 36.5	6 3.2	29 18.0	5 44.2
21 M	17 53 16.3	28 46.0	18 27.5	7♒42.2	6 11.6	13 59.7	18 0.7	27 55.4	17 44.2	6 6.5	29 18.3	5 45.6
22 T	17 57 12.8	29 43.2	18 24.3	22 23.7	7 20.0	14 59.6	18 43.8	28 7.8	17 51.9	6 9.8	29 18.7	5 47.0
23 W	18 1 9.4	0♋40.4	18 21.1	6♓47.9	8 32.0	15 59.2	19 26.8	28 20.3	17 59.6	6 13.0	29 19.1	5 48.5
24 T	18 5 6.0	1 37.7	18 17.9	20 52.4	9 47.6	16 58.3	20 9.8	28 32.8	18 7.2	6 16.3	29 19.5	5 50.0
25 F	18 9 2.6	2 34.9	18 14.7	4♈36.7	11 6.7	17 57.1	20 52.7	28 45.4	18 14.9	6 19.6	29 19.9	5 51.5
26 S	18 12 59.1	3 32.1	18 11.6	18 1.8	12 29.4	18 55.5	21 35.5	28 58.0	18 22.5	6 22.8	29 20.4	5 53.0
27 S	18 16 55.6	4 29.4	18 8.4	1♉ 9.2	13 55.5	19 53.5	22 18.2	29 10.7	18 30.1	6 26.0	29 20.9	5 54.5
28 M	18 20 52.2	5 26.6	18 5.2	14 0.8	15 24.9	20 51.1	23 0.8	29 23.4	18 37.7	6 29.2	29 21.4	5 56.0
29 T	18 24 48.8	6 23.8	18 2.0	26 38.5	16 57.8	21 48.2	23 43.3	29 36.1	18 45.3	6 32.3	29 22.0	5 57.5
30 W	18 28 45.3	7 21.1	17 58.9	9♊ 3.9	18 34.0	22 44.9	24 25.8	29 48.9	18 52.9	6 35.5	29 22.6	5 59.1

DECLINATION

DAY	SIDEREAL TIME	☉	☊	☽	☿	♀	♂	♃	♄	♅	♆	♇
1 T	16 34 25.2	21N54.1	14N58.2	12N 5.4	16N19.0	23N54.7	0S16.5	21N44.6	21N15.9	21N 1.0	1N32.4	23N52.7
4 F	16 46 14.8	22 18.1	15 1.2	19 16.2	15 48.2	23 17.6	0N35.2	21 38.7	21 18.7	21 2.9	1 32.6	23 51.7
7 M	16 58 4.5	22 38.6	15 4.1	18 34.7	15 36.7	22 35.8	1 26.7	21 32.6	21 21.4	21 4.8	1 32.7	23 50.7
10 T	17 9 54.1	22 55.6	15 7.1	10 49.9	15 44.0	21 49.4	2 17.8	21 26.3	21 24.0	21 6.6	1 32.7	23 49.7
13 S	17 21 43.9	23 8.9	15 10.1	1S15.3	16 8.4	20 58.9	3 8.4	21 19.7	21 26.5	21 8.5	1 32.5	23 48.6
16 W	17 33 33.5	23 18.5	15 13.0	13 46.2	16 47.5	20 4.5	3 58.6	21 12.9	21 28.9	21 10.3	1 32.3	23 47.6
19 S	17 45 23.2	23 24.4	15 16.0	19 58.5	17 38.3	19 6.6	4 48.2	21 5.9	21 31.2	21 12.1	1 31.9	23 46.5
22 T	17 57 12.8	23 26.7	15 18.9	14 31.3	18 37.5	18 5.5	5 37.1	20 58.7	21 33.5	21 13.8	1 31.4	23 45.4
25 F	18 9 2.6	23 25.2	15 21.8	1 40.8	19 41.7	17 1.7	6 25.3	20 51.2	21 35.7	21 15.5	1 30.8	23 44.2
28 M	18 20 52.2	23 20.0	15 24.8	11N 7.2	20 46.9	15 55.4	7 12.8	20 43.6	21 37.7	21 17.2	1 30.1	23 43.1

LONGITUDE

DAY	EPHEMERIS SIDEREAL TIME h m s	☉ ° ′	☊ ° ′	☽ ° ′	☿ ° ′	♀ ° ′	♂ ° ′	♃ ° ′	♄ ° ′	♅ ° ′	♆ ° ′	♇ ° ′
1 T	18 32 41.9	8♋18.3	17♋55.7	21✕18.6	20✕13.5	23♋41.2	25♈8.2	0♊1.7	19✕0.4	6✕38.6	29♍23.3	6♋0.6
2 F	18 36 38.4	9 15.5	17 52.5	3♈23.9	21 56.1	24 36.9	25 50.4	0 14.5	19 7.9	6 41.7	29 23.9	6 2.2
3 S	18 40 35.0	10 12.7	17 49.3	15 21.4	23 41.9	25 32.2	26 32.6	0 27.4	19 15.4	6 44.8	29 24.6	6 3.8
4 S	18 44 31.5	11 10.0	17 46.2	27 12.8	25 30.7	26 26.9	27 14.7	0 40.3	19 22.8	6 47.8	29 25.3	6 5.4
5 M	18 48 28.1	12 7.2	17 43.0	9♊0.4	27 22.4	27 21.1	27 56.6	0 53.2	19 30.2	6 50.9	29 26.1	6 7.0
6 T	18 52 24.7	13 4.4	17 39.8	20 46.8	29 16.9	28 14.8	28 38.5	1 6.1	19 37.6	6 53.9	29 26.9	6 8.6
7 W	18 56 21.2	14 1.6	17 36.6	2♋35.2	1♋14.0	29 7.9	29 20.2	1 19.1	19 45.0	6 56.8	29 27.7	6 10.2
8 T	19 0 17.7	14 58.9	17 33.4	14 29.5	3 13.4	0♌0.4	0♉1.9	1 32.1	19 52.3	6 59.8	29 28.6	6 11.9
9 F	19 4 14.3	15 56.1	17 30.3	26 34.0	5 15.0	0 52.3	0 43.5	1 45.2	19 59.6	7 2.7	29 29.4	6 13.5
10 S	19 8 10.9	16 53.3	17 27.1	8♎53.3	7 18.6	1 43.5	1 24.9	1 58.2	20 6.9	7 5.6	29 30.4	6 15.2
11 S	19 12 7.4	17 50.5	17 23.9	21 31.9	9 23.7	2 34.1	2 6.2	2 11.3	20 14.1	7 8.5	29 31.3	6 16.8
12 M	19 16 4.0	18 47.7	17 20.7	4♏34.0	11 30.3	3 24.0	2 47.4	2 24.4	20 21.3	7 11.3	29 32.3	6 18.5
13 T	19 20 0.5	19 44.9	17 17.6	18 2.8	13 37.9	4 13.2	3 28.5	2 37.5	20 28.5	7 14.1	29 33.3	6 20.1
14 W	19 23 57.1	20 42.1	17 14.4	1✗59.6	15 46.3	5 1.6	4 9.5	2 50.6	20 35.6	7 16.9	29 34.3	6 21.8
15 T	19 27 53.7	21 39.3	17 11.2	16 23.4	17 55.1	5 49.3	4 50.4	3 3.8	20 42.7	7 19.6	29 35.4	6 23.5
16 F	19 31 50.2	22 36.5	17 8.0	1♑0.4	20 4.0	6 36.1	5 31.1	3 16.9	20 49.8	7 22.4	29 36.4	6 25.2
17 S	19 35 46.8	23 33.8	17 4.8	16 13.8	22 12.9	7 22.1	6 11.8	3 30.1	20 56.8	7 25.0	29 37.6	6 26.9
18 S	19 39 43.3	24 31.0	17 1.7	1♒24.9	24 21.3	8 7.3	6 52.3	3 43.3	21 3.7	7 27.7	29 38.7	6 28.6
19 M	19 43 39.9	25 28.2	16 58.5	16 34.1	26 29.2	8 51.6	7 32.7	3 56.5	21 10.7	7 30.3	29 39.9	6 30.3
20 T	19 47 36.4	26 25.5	16 55.3	1✕32.4	28 36.3	9 34.9	8 13.0	4 9.7	21 17.6	7 32.9	29 41.1	6 32.0
21 W	19 51 33.0	27 22.7	16 52.1	16 12.7	0♌42.3	10 17.3	8 53.1	4 23.0	21 24.4	7 35.5	29 42.3	6 33.7
22 T	19 55 29.6	28 20.0	16 49.0	0♈30.3	2 47.2	10 58.7	9 33.1	4 36.2	21 31.2	7 38.0	29 43.5	6 35.4
23 F	19 59 26.1	29 17.3	16 45.8	14 23.2	4 50.9	11 39.0	10 13.0	4 49.5	21 37.9	7 40.5	29 44.8	6 37.2
24 S	20 3 22.7	0♌14.5	16 42.6	27 51.5	6 53.1	12 18.3	10 52.8	5 2.7	21 44.6	7 42.9	29 46.1	6 38.9
25 S	20 7 19.2	1 11.8	16 39.4	10♉56.8	8 53.9	12 56.5	11 32.4	5 16.0	21 51.3	7 45.3	29 47.5	6 40.6
26 M	20 11 15.8	2 9.2	16 36.3	23 42.0	10 53.1	13 33.6	12 11.9	5 29.3	21 57.9	7 47.7	29 48.8	6 42.3
27 T	20 15 12.4	3 6.5	16 33.1	6✕10.1	12 50.8	14 9.4	12 51.2	5 42.5	22 4.5	7 50.0	29 50.2	6 44.1
28 W	20 19 8.9	4 3.9	16 29.9	18 24.4	14 46.9	14 44.0	13 30.4	5 55.8	22 11.0	7 52.4	29 51.6	6 45.8
29 T	20 23 5.5	5 1.2	16 26.7	0♋28.0	16 41.3	15 17.3	14 9.4	6 9.1	22 17.4	7 54.6	29 53.1	6 47.6
30 F	20 27 2.0	5 58.6	16 23.5	12 23.7	18 34.1	15 49.3	14 48.3	6 22.4	22 23.8	7 56.8	29 54.5	6 49.3
31 S	20 30 58.6	6 56.0	16 20.4	24 14.2	20 25.2	16 19.9	15 27.0	6 35.7	22 30.2	7 59.0	29 56.0	6 51.0

DECLINATION

1 T	18 32 41.9	23N11.1	15N27.7	18N55.2	21N48.8	14N47.0	7N59.4	20N35.7	21N39.7	21N18.8	1N29.3	23N41.9
4 S	18 44 31.5	22 58.5	15 30.6	16 56.2	23 22.4	13 37.0	8 45.1	20 27.6	21 41.6	21 20.4	1 28.4	23 40.7
7 W	18 56 21.2	22 42.4	15 33.5	11 56.2	23 22.5	12 25.7	9 29.8	20 19.3	21 43.4	21 21.9	1 27.3	23 39.5
10 S	19 8 10.9	22 22.7	15 36.4	0 18.6	23 43.7	11 13.4	10 13.5	20 10.7	21 45.0	21 23.4	1 26.2	23 38.3
13 T	19 20 0.5	21 59.5	15 39.3	12S10.4	23 42.3	10 0.7	10 56.1	20 2.1	21 46.6	21 24.8	1 24.9	23 37.1
16 F	19 31 50.2	21 32.9	15 42.2	19 43.9	23 16.2	8 48.0	11 37.5	19 53.2	21 48.1	21 26.2	1 23.5	23 35.9
19 M	19 43 39.9	21 3.0	15 45.1	15 55.6	22 26.2	7 35.7	12 17.9	19 44.1	21 49.5	21 27.5	1 22.1	23 34.7
22 T	19 55 29.6	20 30.0	15 48.0	3 11.7	21 14.9	6 24.3	12 57.0	19 34.9	21 50.8	21 28.8	1 20.5	23 33.6
25 S	20 7 19.2	19 53.8	15 50.9	10N 8.4	19 46.6	5 14.4	13 34.9	19 25.5	21 52.1	21 30.0	1 18.9	23 32.4
28 W	20 19 8.9	19 14.6	15 53.7	18 29.7	18 3.8	4 6.4	14 11.5	19 16.0	21 53.2	21 31.1	1 17.2	23 31.2
31 S	20 30 58.6	18 32.6	15 56.6	19 20.7	16 11.6	3 1.0	14 46.8	19 6.3	21 54.2	21 32.2	1 15.3	23 30.1

LONGITUDE

DAY	EPHEMERIS SIDEREAL TIME h m s	☉ ° ′	☊ ° ′	☽ ° ′	☿ ° ′	♀ ° ′	♂ ° ′	♃ ° ′	♄ ° ′	♅ ° ′	♆ ° ′	♇ ° ′
1 S	20 34 55.1	7♌53.4	16♋17.2	6♋1.8	22♌14.7	16♍49.1	16♉5.5	6♊49.0	22✕36.4	8✕1.2	29♍57.5	6♋52.8
2 M	20 38 51.7	8 50.9	16 14.0	17 48.8	24 2.5	17 16.7	16 43.9	7 2.3	22 42.7	8 3.3	29 59.0	6 54.5
3 T	20 42 48.2	9 48.3	16 10.8	29 37.5	25 48.7	17 42.8	17 22.1	7 15.5	22 48.8	8 5.4	0♎0.6	6 56.2
4 W	20 46 44.8	10 45.7	16 7.7	11♌30.5	27 33.2	18 7.3	18 0.1	7 28.8	22 55.0	8 7.4	0 2.2	6 58.0
5 T	20 50 41.3	11 43.2	16 4.5	23 30.3	29 16.1	18 30.1	18 38.0	7 42.1	23 1.0	8 9.4	0 3.8	6 59.7
6 F	20 54 37.9	12 40.7	16 1.3	5♍40.1	0♍57.4	18 51.2	19 15.7	7 55.3	23 7.0	8 11.3	0 5.4	7 1.4
7 S	20 58 34.5	13 38.2	15 58.1	18 3.1	2 37.1	19 10.5	19 53.2	8 8.6	23 12.9	8 13.2	0 7.1	7 3.2
8 S	21 2 31.0	14 35.7	15 55.0	0♏55.0	4 15.1	19 27.9	20 30.5	8 21.8	23 18.8	8 15.1	0 8.7	7 4.9
9 M	21 6 27.5	15 33.2	15 51.8	13 42.3	5 51.6	19 43.4	21 7.6	8 35.0	23 24.6	8 16.9	0 10.4	7 6.6
10 T	21 10 24.1	16 30.8	15 48.7	27 6.5	7 26.5	19 56.9	21 44.5	8 48.3	23 30.3	8 18.7	0 12.1	7 8.3
11 W	21 14 20.7	17 28.3	15 45.4	10♐52.2	8 59.7	20 8.4	22 21.3	9 1.5	23 36.0	8 20.4	0 13.9	7 10.1
12 T	21 18 17.2	18 25.9	15 42.2	25 1.4	10 31.0	20 17.8	22 57.9	9 14.6	23 41.6	8 22.1	0 15.6	7 11.8
13 F	21 22 13.7	19 23.4	15 39.1	9♑40.6	12 1.5	20 25.0	23 34.2	9 27.8	23 47.1	8 23.7	0 17.4	7 13.5
14 S	21 26 10.3	20 21.0	15 35.9	24 35.5	13 29.0	20 30.0	24 10.4	9 41.0	23 52.6	8 25.3	0 19.2	7 15.2
15 S	21 30 6.9	21 18.6	15 32.7	9♒42.5	14 56.7	20 32.7	24 46.3	9 54.1	23 57.9	8 26.9	0 21.0	7 16.9
16 M	21 34 3.5	22 16.3	15 29.5	24 53.1	16 21.9	20 33.2	25 21.9	10 7.2	24 3.3	8 28.4	0 22.8	7 18.6
17 T	21 37 60.0	23 13.9	15 26.4	9✕57.8	17 45.4	20R31.3	25 57.6	10 20.3	24 8.5	8 29.8	0 24.7	7 20.2
18 W	21 41 56.5	24 11.6	15 23.2	24 48.1	19 7.2	20 27.0	26 33.0	10 33.4	24 13.7	8 31.2	0 26.5	7 21.9
19 T	21 45 53.1	25 9.3	15 19.9	9♈16.9	20 27.3	20 20.4	27 8.1	10 46.4	24 18.8	8 32.6	0 28.4	7 23.6
20 F	21 49 49.7	26 7.0	15 16.8	23 20.1	21 45.6	20 11.4	27 43.0	10 59.5	24 23.8	8 33.9	0 30.3	7 25.3
21 S	21 53 46.2	27 4.8	15 13.6	6♉56.0	23 2.0	20 0.0	28 17.7	11 12.5	24 28.7	8 35.2	0 32.2	7 26.9
22 S	21 57 42.8	28 2.6	15 10.5	20 5.5	24 16.6	19 46.3	28 52.1	11 25.5	24 33.6	8 36.4	0 34.2	7 28.6
23 M	22 1 39.3	29 0.4	15 7.3	2✕53.3	25 29.3	19 30.2	29 26.3	11 38.4	24 38.4	8 37.6	0 36.1	7 30.2
24 T	22 5 35.9	29 58.2	15 4.1	15 16.6	26 39.9	19 11.9	0♊0.2	11 51.4	24 43.1	8 38.7	0 38.1	7 31.8
25 W	22 9 32.4	0♍56.1	15 0.9	27 21.1	27 48.4	18 51.3	0 33.9	12 4.3	24 47.7	8 39.8	0 40.1	7 33.5
26 T	22 13 29.0	1 54.0	14 57.8	9♋24.0	28 54.8	18 28.5	1 7.4	12 17.1	24 52.3	8 40.9	0 42.1	7 35.1
27 F	22 17 25.5	2 51.9	14 54.6	21 14.6	29 58.8	18 3.7	1 40.6	12 30.0	24 56.8	8 41.8	0 44.1	7 36.7
28 S	22 21 22.0	3 49.8	14 51.4	3♌1.8	0♎59.5	17 36.9	2 13.5	12 42.8	25 1.1	8 42.8	0 46.1	7 38.3
29 S	22 25 18.6	4 47.8	14 48.3	14 48.3	1 59.6	17 8.2	2 46.1	12 55.5	25 5.4	8 43.6	0 48.2	7 39.8
30 M	22 29 15.2	5 45.8	14 45.0	26 38.5	2 56.0	16 37.8	3 18.5	13 8.3	25 9.6	8 44.5	0 50.2	7 41.4
31 T	22 33 11.7	6 43.8	14 41.9	8♍33.4	3 49.5	16 5.9	3 50.6	13 21.0	25 13.8	8 45.3	0 52.3	7 43.0

DECLINATION

1 S	20 34 55.1	18N18.0	15N57.5	17N53.3	15N32.5	2N39.9	14N58.3	19N 3.0	21N54.6	21N32.6	1N14.7	23N29.7
4 W	20 46 44.8	17 32.3	16 0.4	9 2.3	13 31.8	1 39.0	15 31.8	18 53.1	21 55.5	21 33.6	1 12.8	23 28.5
7 S	20 58 34.5	16 44.1	16 3.2	2S44.7	11 27.5	0 42.6	16 3.9	18 43.2	21 56.3	21 34.5	1 10.8	23 27.4
10 T	21 10 24.1	15 53.5	16 6.0	16 24.7	9 21.7	0S 8.5	16 34.7	18 33.1	21 57.1	21 35.4	1 8.7	23 26.3
13 F	21 22 13.7	15 0.5	16 8.9	19 57.6	7 16.2	0 53.5	17 4.4	18 22.9	21 57.8	21 36.2	1 6.5	23 25.3
16 M	21 34 3.5	14 5.5	16 11.7	14 0.1	5 12.2	1 30.5	17 32.9	18 12.6	21 58.4	21 36.9	1 4.3	23 24.2
19 T	21 45 53.1	13 8.4	16 14.5	0 13.7	3 11.4	1 59.2	18 0.2	18 2.2	21 58.9	21 37.6	1 2.0	23 23.2
22 S	21 57 42.8	12 9.4	16 17.3	12N41.0	1 15.0	2 18.1	18 23.9	17 51.8	21 59.4	21 38.2	0 59.7	23 22.2
25 W	22 9 32.4	11 8.7	16 20.1	19 27.5	0S35.5	2 26.4	18 47.8	17 41.3	21 59.8	21 38.8	0 57.3	23 21.3
28 S	22 21 22.0	10 6.4	16 22.9	18 0.0	2 18.5	2 23.5	19 10.4	17 30.8	22 0.2	21 39.2	0 54.9	23 20.4
31 T	22 33 11.7	9 2.6	16 25.7	10 14.5	3 51.8	2 9.3	19 31.6	17 20.2	22 0.5	21 39.6	0 52.4	23 19.6

SEPTEMBER 1943

DAY	EPHEMERIS SIDEREAL TIME	☉	☊	☽	☿	♀	♂	♃	♄	♅	♆	♇
	h m s	° '	° '	° '	° '	° '	° '	° '	° '	° '	° '	° '
						LONGITUDE						
1 W	22 37 8.3	7♍41.9	14♌38.7	20♍35.5	4♎40.1	15♍32.6	4♊22.4	13♌33.6	25♊17.8	8♊46.0	0♎54.4	7♌44.5
2 T	22 41 4.8	8 40.0	14 35.5	2♎46.6	5 27.4	14R58.1	4 53.8	13 46.2	25 21.7	8 46.7	0 56.4	7 46.1
3 F	22 45 1.4	9 38.1	14 32.3	15 8.3	6 11.3	14 22.7	5 25.0	13 58.8	25 25.6	8 47.3	0 58.5	7 47.6
4 S	22 48 58.0	10 36.2	14 29.2	27 42.2	6 51.6	13 46.4	5 55.9	14 11.4	25 29.4	8 47.9	1 0.7	7 49.1
5 S	22 52 54.5	11 34.4	14 26.0	10♏30.0	7 28.0	13 9.7	6 26.5	14 23.8	25 33.0	8 48.4	1 2.8	7 50.6
6 M	22 56 51.0	12 32.6	14 22.8	23 33.6	8 0.1	12 32.6	6 56.7	14 36.3	25 36.6	8 48.9	1 4.9	7 52.1
7 T	23 0 47.6	13 30.8	14 19.6	6♐54.5	8 27.9	11 55.5	7 26.6	14 48.7	25 40.1	8 49.3	1 7.0	7 53.5
8 W	23 4 44.2	14 29.0	14 16.4	20 34.4	8 50.9	11 18.5	7 56.2	15 1.0	25 43.5	8 49.7	1 9.2	7 55.0
9 T	23 8 40.7	15 27.3	14 13.3	4♑34.1	9 8.8	10 42.0	8 25.5	15 13.3	25 46.8	8 50.0	1 11.4	7 56.4
10 F	23 12 37.3	16 25.6	14 10.1	18 53.0	9 21.3	10 6.1	8 54.4	15 25.6	25 50.0	8 50.3	1 13.5	7 57.9
11 S	23 16 33.8	17 23.9	14 6.9	3♒29.2	9 28.1	9 31.0	9 23.0	15 37.8	25 53.1	8 50.5	1 15.7	7 59.3
12 S	23 20 30.4	18 22.2	14 3.7	18 18.7	9 29.0	8 57.1	9 51.2	15 49.9	25 56.1	8 50.7	1 17.9	8 0.6
13 M	23 24 26.9	19 20.6	14 0.6	3♓15.3	9R23.5	8 24.5	10 19.0	16 2.0	25 59.0	8 50.8	1 20.1	8 2.0
14 T	23 28 23.5	20 19.0	13 57.4	18 11.2	9 11.5	7 53.4	10 46.5	16 14.0	26 1.8	8 50.9	1 22.3	8 3.4
15 W	23 32 20.0	21 17.4	13 54.2	2♈58.2	8 52.7	7 24.0	11 13.6	16 26.0	26 4.5	8 50.9	1 24.5	8 4.7
16 T	23 36 16.6	22 15.9	13 51.0	17 28.5	8 27.1	6 56.4	11 40.3	16 37.9	26 7.1	8R50.9	1 26.7	8 6.1
17 F	23 40 13.1	23 14.4	13 47.8	1♉36.1	7 54.7	6 30.8	12 6.7	16 49.8	26 9.6	8 50.8	1 28.9	8 7.4
18 S	23 44 9.7	24 12.9	13 44.7	15 17.6	7 15.6	6 7.4	12 32.6	17 1.6	26 12.0	8 50.7	1 31.1	8 8.7
19 S	23 48 6.2	25 11.5	13 41.5	28 32.0	6 30.0	5 46.1	12 58.1	17 13.3	26 14.3	8 50.5	1 33.3	8 9.9
20 M	23 52 2.8	26 10.1	13 38.3	11♊21.1	5 38.6	5 27.1	13 23.2	17 24.9	26 16.5	8 50.2	1 35.5	8 11.2
21 T	23 55 59.3	27 8.7	13 35.1	23 48.0	4 42.1	5 10.4	13 47.8	17 36.5	26 18.6	8 49.9	1 37.8	8 12.4
22 W	23 59 55.9	28 7.4	13 31.9	5♋57.3	3 41.3	4 56.2	14 12.1	17 48.1	26 20.6	8 49.6	1 40.0	8 13.7
23 T	0 3 52.5	29 6.1	13 28.8	17 54.0	2 37.5	4 44.3	14 35.8	17 59.6	26 22.5	8 49.2	1 42.2	8 14.9
24 F	0 7 49.0	0♎ 4.8	13 25.6	29 43.2	1 32.0	4 35.0	14 59.1	18 11.0	26 24.3	8 48.8	1 44.4	8 16.0
25 S	0 11 45.6	1 3.6	13 22.4	11♌29.9	0 26.5	4 28.0	15 21.9	18 22.3	26 25.9	8 48.3	1 46.7	8 17.2
26 S	0 15 42.1	2 2.4	13 19.2	23 18.6	29♍22.4	4 23.5	15 44.3	18 33.5	26 27.5	8 47.7	1 48.9	8 18.3
27 M	0 19 38.7	3 1.3	13 16.1	5♍13.1	28 21.6	4 21.4	16 6.1	18 44.7	26 28.9	8 47.1	1 51.1	8 19.5
28 T	0 23 35.2	4 0.2	13 12.9	17 16.5	27 25.7	4D21.6	16 27.4	18 55.8	26 30.3	8 46.5	1 53.4	8 20.6
29 W	0 27 31.8	4 59.1	13 9.7	29 30.9	26 36.1	4 24.3	16 48.2	19 6.8	26 31.5	8 45.8	1 55.6	8 21.6
30 T	0 31 28.3	5 58.1	13 6.5	11♎57.6	25 54.2	4 29.2	17 8.5	19 17.8	26 32.7	8 45.1	1 57.8	8 22.7

DAY	SIDEREAL TIME	☉	☊	☽	☿	♀	♂	♃	♄	♅	♆	♇
						DECLINATION						
1 W	22 37 8.3	8N41.0	16N26.6	6N28.8	4S20.4	2S 2.1	19N38.4	17N16.7	22N 0.6	21N39.7	0N51.6	23N19.3
4 S	22 48 58.0	7 35.6	16 29.4	6S 0.3	5 36.9	1 33.8	19 57.9	17 6.2	22 0.8	21 40.1	0 49.0	23 18.5
7 T	23 0 47.6	6 29.0	16 32.2	16 39.4	6 36.8	0 56.7	20 16.3	16 55.6	22 1.0	21 40.3	0 46.5	23 17.7
10 F	23 12 37.3	5 21.5	16 34.9	19 46.7	7 15.5	0 12.8	20 33.4	16 45.1	22 1.1	21 40.4	0 43.9	23 17.0
13 M	23 24 26.9	4 13.2	16 37.7	11 47.3	7 27.6	0N35.3	20 49.5	16 34.7	22 1.2	21 40.5	0 41.3	23 16.4
16 T	23 36 16.6	3 4.2	16 40.4	2N37.4	7 7.3	1 24.8	21 4.5	16 24.3	22 1.2	21 40.6	0 38.6	23 15.8
19 S	23 48 6.2	1 54.7	16 43.2	14 54.9	6 10.2	2 13.3	21 18.5	16 14.0	22 1.2	21 40.5	0 36.0	23 15.2
22 W	23 59 55.9	0 44.8	16 45.9	20 2.0	4 37.2	2 58.5	21 31.6	16 3.7	22 1.2	21 40.4	0 33.4	23 14.7
25 S	0 11 45.6	0S25.3	16 48.6	17 1.1	2 38.5	3 38.8	21 43.9	15 53.6	22 1.1	21 40.2	0 30.7	23 14.3
28 T	0 23 35.2	1 35.5	16 51.3	7 33.1	0 34.4	4 13.1	21 55.4	15 43.6	22 1.0	21 39.9	0 28.1	23 13.9

OCTOBER 1943

DAY	SIDEREAL TIME	☉	☊	☽	☿	♀	♂	♃	♄	♅	♆	♇
						LONGITUDE						
1 F	0 35 24.9	6♎57.0	13♌ 3.3	24♎37.2	25♍21.1	4♍36.4	17♊28.2	19♌28.6	26♊33.7	8♊44.3	2♎ 0.1	8♌23.7
2 S	0 39 21.4	7 56.1	13 0.2	7♏29.7	24R57.6	4 45.8	17 47.4	19 39.4	26 34.6	8R43.4	2 2.3	8 24.7
3 S	0 43 18.0	8 55.1	12 57.0	20 34.8	24 44.2	4 57.3	18 6.0	19 50.1	26 35.4	8 42.6	2 4.5	8 25.7
4 M	0 47 14.5	9 54.2	12 53.8	3♐52.1	24 41.3	5 10.9	18 24.0	20 0.7	26 36.1	8 41.6	2 6.7	8 26.7
5 T	0 51 11.1	10 53.3	12 50.6	17 21.2	24D49.0	5 26.6	18 41.5	20 11.2	26 36.7	8 40.6	2 8.9	8 27.6
6 W	0 55 7.6	11 52.5	12 47.5	1♑ 2.4	25 6.9	5 44.3	18 58.3	20 21.6	26 37.1	8 39.6	2 11.1	8 28.6
7 T	0 59 4.2	12 51.7	12 44.3	14 55.7	25 34.8	6 3.8	19 14.6	20 31.9	26 37.5	8 38.5	2 13.3	8 29.5
8 F	1 3 0.7	13 50.9	12 41.1	29 1.0	26 12.1	6 25.3	19 30.2	20 42.2	26 37.7	8 37.4	2 15.5	8 30.3
9 S	1 6 57.3	14 50.1	12 37.9	13♒17.8	26 58.2	6 48.5	19 45.2	20 52.3	26 37.9	8 36.2	2 17.7	8 31.2
10 S	1 10 53.8	15 49.4	12 34.7	27 44.2	27 52.4	7 13.5	19 59.5	21 2.3	26 37.9	8 35.0	2 19.9	8 32.0
11 M	1 14 50.4	16 48.7	12 31.6	12♓16.9	28 54.0	7 40.2	20 13.3	21 12.3	26R37.8	8 33.8	2 22.1	8 32.8
12 T	1 18 47.0	17 48.0	12 28.4	26 50.9	0♎ 2.1	8 8.5	20 26.3	21 22.1	26 37.6	8 32.5	2 24.3	8 33.6
13 W	1 22 43.5	18 47.3	12 25.2	11♈20.0	1 16.0	8 38.5	20 38.7	21 31.9	26 37.3	8 31.1	2 26.4	8 34.4
14 T	1 26 40.0	19 46.7	12 22.0	25 37.6	2 35.0	9 9.9	20 50.4	21 41.5	26 36.9	8 29.7	2 28.6	8 35.1
15 F	1 30 36.6	20 46.1	12 18.8	9♉37.8	3 58.3	9 42.8	21 1.3	21 51.0	26 36.3	8 28.3	2 30.7	8 35.8
16 S	1 34 33.2	21 45.6	12 15.7	23 16.0	5 25.4	10 17.2	21 11.6	22 0.5	26 35.7	8 26.8	2 32.9	8 36.5
17 S	1 38 29.7	22 45.1	12 12.5	6♊30.2	6 55.6	10 52.9	21 21.1	22 9.8	26 35.0	8 25.3	2 35.0	8 37.2
18 M	1 42 26.3	23 44.6	12 9.3	19 20.4	8 28.5	11 29.9	21 29.9	22 19.0	26 34.1	8 23.7	2 37.1	8 37.8
19 T	1 46 22.8	24 44.2	12 6.1	1♋48.9	10 3.4	12 8.3	21 37.9	22 28.1	26 33.1	8 22.1	2 39.2	8 38.4
20 W	1 50 19.4	25 43.8	12 3.0	13 59.4	11 40.0	12 47.8	21 45.2	22 37.1	26 32.0	8 20.5	2 41.3	8 39.0
21 T	1 54 15.9	26 43.5	11 59.8	25 56.7	13 18.1	13 28.5	21 51.7	22 46.0	26 30.9	8 18.8	2 43.4	8 39.5
22 F	1 58 12.5	27 43.1	11 56.6	7♌46.3	14 57.1	14 10.4	21 57.3	22 54.7	26 29.6	8 17.1	2 45.5	8 40.1
23 S	2 2 9.0	28 42.9	11 53.4	19 33.7	16 36.9	14 53.4	22 2.2	23 3.4	26 28.2	8 15.4	2 47.5	8 40.6
24 S	2 6 5.6	29 42.6	11 50.3	1♍24.2	18 17.3	15 37.4	22 6.2	23 11.9	26 26.6	8 13.6	2 49.5	8 41.0
25 M	2 10 2.1	0♏42.4	11 47.1	13 22.8	19 58.0	16 22.4	22 9.4	23 20.3	26 25.0	8 11.7	2 51.6	8 41.5
26 T	2 13 58.7	1 42.3	11 43.9	25 33.5	21 38.9	17 8.5	22 11.7	23 28.5	26 23.3	8 9.9	2 53.6	8 41.9
27 W	2 17 55.3	2 42.1	11 40.7	7♎59.2	23 19.9	17 55.4	22 13.2	23 36.7	26 21.5	8 8.0	2 55.6	8 42.3
28 T	2 21 51.8	3 42.0	11 37.5	20 41.6	25 0.8	18 43.2	22 13.8	23 44.7	26 19.5	8 6.0	2 57.6	8 42.7
29 F	2 25 48.3	4 42.0	11 34.4	3♏41.1	26 41.6	19 31.9	22R13.6	23 52.6	26 17.5	8 4.1	2 59.5	8 43.0
30 S	2 29 44.9	5 41.9	11 31.2	16 56.4	28 22.2	20 21.5	22 12.5	24 0.3	26 15.4	8 2.1	3 1.5	8 43.4
31 S	2 33 41.5	6 41.9	11 28.0	0♐25.6	0♏ 2.5	21 11.8	22 10.5	24 7.9	26 13.1	8 0.0	3 3.4	8 43.7

DAY	SIDEREAL TIME	☉	☊	☽	☿	♀	♂	♃	♄	♅	♆	♇
						DECLINATION						
1 F	0 35 24.9	2S45.6	16N54.1	5S 4.6	1N10.7	4N40.8	22N 6.3	15N33.8	22N 0.9	21N39.6	0N25.4	23N13.6
4 M	0 47 14.5	3 55.4	16 56.8	16 12.4	2 17.8	5 1.4	22 16.5	15 24.2	22 0.7	21 39.2	0 22.8	23 13.4
7 T	0 59 4.2	5 4.8	16 59.5	20 7.8	2 38.4	5 14.9	22 26.3	15 14.7	22 0.6	21 38.7	0 20.2	23 13.2
10 S	1 10 53.8	6 13.7	17 2.1	13 23.5	2 13.7	5 21.2	22 35.6	15 5.5	22 0.4	21 38.2	0 17.7	23 13.1
13 W	1 22 43.5	7 21.8	17 4.8	0N33.2	1 11.1	5 20.5	22 44.6	14 56.5	22 0.2	21 37.6	0 15.1	23 13.1
16 S	1 34 33.2	8 28.9	17 7.5	13 46.6	0S19.5	5 13.1	22 53.3	14 47.7	21 59.9	21 36.9	0 12.6	23 13.1
19 T	1 46 22.8	9 35.0	17 10.2	20 5.8	2 8.7	4 59.1	23 1.8	14 39.3	21 59.7	21 36.2	0 10.2	23 13.2
22 F	1 58 12.5	10 39.9	17 12.8	17 53.5	4 8.8	4 39.0	23 10.1	14 31.1	21 59.4	21 35.4	0 7.8	23 13.3
25 M	2 10 2.1	11 43.3	17 15.5	8 54.4	6 13.9	4 13.1	23 18.3	14 23.2	21 59.2	21 34.6	0 5.4	23 13.6
28 T	2 21 51.8	12 45.2	17 18.1	3S45.7	8 19.9	3 41.7	23 26.4	14 15.7	21 58.9	21 33.7	0 3.1	23 13.9
31 S	2 33 41.5	13 45.3	17 20.7	15 36.1	10 23.9	3 5.3	23 34.3	14 8.6	21 58.6	21 32.8	0 0.9	23 14.2

NOVEMBER 1943

LONGITUDE

DAY	EPHEMERIS SIDEREAL TIME h m s	☉ ° ′	☊ ° ′	☽ ° ′	☿ ° ′	♀ ° ′	♂ ° ′	♃ ° ′	♄ ° ′	♅ ° ′	♆ ° ′	♇ ° ′
1 M	2 37 38.0	7♏42.0	11♌24.8	14♐ 5.9	1♏42.5	22♍ 3.0	22♊ 7.6	24♌15.4	26♊10.8	7♊58.0	3♎ 5.4	8♌43.9
2 T	2 41 34.6	8 42.0	11 21.7	27 54.6	3 22.2	22 54.8	22R 3.8	24 22.7	26R 8.3	7R55.9	3 7.3	8 44.2
3 W	2 45 31.1	9 42.1	11 18.5	11♑49.4	5 1.5	23 47.4	21 59.1	24 29.9	26 5.8	7 53.7	3 9.1	8 44.4
4 T	2 49 27.7	10 42.2	11 15.3	25 48.7	6 40.4	24 40.6	21 53.5	24 37.0	26 3.1	7 51.6	3 11.0	8 44.5
5 F	2 53 24.2	11 42.3	11 12.1	9♒51.6	8 19.0	25 34.6	21 47.1	24 43.9	26 0.4	7 49.4	3 12.8	8 44.7
6 S	2 57 20.8	12 42.5	11 8.9	23 57.4	9 57.2	26 29.2	21 39.8	24 50.6	25 57.6	7 47.2	3 14.7	8 44.8
7 S	3 1 17.3	13 42.7	11 5.8	8♓ 5.4	11 34.9	27 24.4	21 31.6	24 57.3	25 54.6	7 45.0	3 16.5	8 44.9
8 M	3 5 13.9	14 42.9	11 2.6	22 14.2	13 12.3	28 20.2	21 22.5	25 3.7	25 51.6	7 42.7	3 18.3	8 45.0
9 T	3 9 10.4	15 43.1	10 59.4	6♈21.6	14 49.3	29 16.6	21 12.6	25 10.0	25 48.5	7 40.4	3 20.0	8 45.0
10 W	3 13 7.0	16 43.4	10 56.2	20 24.2	16 25.9	0♎13.6	21 1.8	25 16.2	25 45.3	7 38.1	3 21.8	8 45.1
11 T	3 17 3.6	17 43.7	10 53.1	4♉17.8	18 2.2	1 11.1	20 50.2	25 22.2	25 42.0	7 35.8	3 23.5	8R45.1
12 F	3 21 0.1	18 44.0	10 49.9	17 58.2	19 38.1	2 9.2	20 37.8	25 28.1	25 38.7	7 33.5	3 25.2	8 45.0
13 S	3 24 56.7	19 44.3	10 46.7	1♊21.9	21 13.8	3 7.7	20 24.5	25 33.8	25 35.2	7 31.1	3 26.9	8 45.0
14 S	3 28 53.2	20 44.7	10 43.5	14 26.4	22 49.0	4 6.8	20 10.4	25 39.3	25 31.7	7 28.7	3 28.5	8 44.9
15 M	3 32 49.8	21 45.1	10 40.4	27 11.2	24 24.0	5 6.4	19 55.6	25 44.7	25 28.1	7 26.3	3 30.2	8 44.8
16 T	3 36 46.3	22 45.5	10 37.2	9♋37.1	25 58.8	6 6.4	19 40.0	25 49.9	25 24.4	7 23.9	3 31.8	8 44.6
17 W	3 40 42.9	23 46.0	10 34.0	21 46.9	27 33.2	7 6.9	19 23.6	25 55.0	25 20.6	7 21.5	3 33.3	8 44.4
18 T	3 44 39.4	24 46.5	10 30.8	3♌44.2	29 7.4	8 7.8	19 6.6	25 59.9	25 16.8	7 19.0	3 34.9	8 44.2
19 F	3 48 36.0	25 47.0	10 27.6	15 34.0	0♐41.4	9 9.2	18 48.8	26 4.6	25 12.9	7 16.6	3 36.4	8 44.0
20 S	3 52 32.6	26 47.6	10 24.5	27 21.6	2 15.2	10 10.9	18 30.4	26 9.1	25 8.9	7 14.1	3 37.9	8 43.8
21 S	3 56 29.1	27 48.2	10 21.3	9♍12.5	3 48.7	11 13.1	18 11.3	26 13.5	25 4.8	7 11.6	3 39.4	8 43.5
22 M	4 0 25.7	28 48.8	10 18.1	21 12.3	5 22.1	12 15.6	17 51.7	26 17.7	25 0.7	7 9.1	3 40.9	8 43.2
23 T	4 4 22.2	29 49.4	10 14.9	3♎25.9	6 55.3	13 18.5	17 31.5	26 21.7	24 56.5	7 6.6	3 42.3	8 42.9
24 W	4 8 18.8	0♐50.1	10 11.8	15 57.3	8 28.3	14 21.8	17 10.8	26 25.6	24 52.3	7 4.1	3 43.7	8 42.5
25 T	4 12 15.4	1 50.8	10 8.6	28 49.5	10 1.2	15 25.4	16 49.7	26 29.3	24 48.0	7 1.6	3 45.1	8 42.1
26 F	4 16 11.9	2 51.5	10 5.4	12♏ 3.5	11 33.9	16 29.3	16 28.1	26 32.8	24 43.6	6 59.1	3 46.4	8 41.7
27 S	4 20 8.4	3 52.2	10 2.2	25 38.4	13 6.5	17 33.6	16 6.1	26 36.1	24 39.2	6 56.6	3 47.8	8 41.3
28 S	4 24 5.0	4 53.0	9 59.0	9♐31.5	14 39.0	18 38.2	15 43.8	26 39.2	24 34.7	6 54.0	3 49.1	8 40.8
29 M	4 28 1.6	5 53.8	9 55.9	23 38.5	16 11.3	19 43.0	15 21.2	26 42.2	24 30.2	6 51.5	3 50.3	8 40.3
30 T	4 31 58.1	6 54.6	9 52.7	7♑54.3	17 43.5	20 48.2	14 58.4	26 44.9	24 25.6	6 49.0	3 51.6	8 39.8

DECLINATION

DAY	EPHEMERIS SIDEREAL TIME h m s	☉	☊	☽	☿	♀	♂	♃	♄	♅	♆	♇
1 M	2 37 38.0	14S 4.9	17N21.6	18S17.7	11S 4.4	2N52.1	23N36.9	14N 6.3	21N58.5	21N32.5	0N 0.1	23N14.4
4 T	2 49 27.7	15 2.3	17 24.2	19 39.6	13 2.7	2 9.7	23 44.6	13 59.7	21 58.2	21 31.5	0S 2.0	23 14.8
7 S	3 1 17.3	15 57.5	17 26.9	10 38.9	14 55.3	1 23.1	23 52.0	13 53.5	21 57.8	21 30.4	0 4.1	23 15.3
10 W	3 13 7.0	16 50.3	17 29.5	3N37.2	16 41.2	0 32.7	23 59.0	13 47.7	21 57.5	21 29.3	0 6.1	23 15.9
13 S	3 24 56.7	17 40.5	17 32.1	15 51.2	18 19.5	0S21.0	24 5.5	13 42.4	21 57.1	21 28.2	0 8.0	23 16.6
16 T	3 36 46.3	18 28.0	17 34.7	20 33.3	19 49.7	1 17.7	24 11.3	13 37.6	21 56.7	21 27.0	0 9.8	23 17.3
19 F	3 48 36.0	19 12.5	17 37.3	16 39.6	21 11.1	2 17.0	24 16.4	13 33.3	21 56.3	21 25.9	0 11.6	23 18.1
22 M	4 0 25.7	19 53.9	17 39.8	6 34.4	22 23.1	3 18.4	24 20.4	13 29.5	21 55.9	21 24.7	0 13.2	23 18.9
25 T	4 12 15.4	20 32.1	17 42.4	6S24.8	23 25.1	4 21.7	24 23.4	13 26.2	21 55.5	21 23.4	0 14.8	23 19.8
28 S	4 24 5.0	21 6.9	17 45.0	17 34.7	24 16.4	5 26.4	24 25.1	13 23.5	21 55.1	21 22.2	0 16.2	23 20.8

DECEMBER 1943

LONGITUDE

DAY	EPHEMERIS SIDEREAL TIME h m s	☉ ° ′	☊ ° ′	☽ ° ′	☿ ° ′	♀ ° ′	♂ ° ′	♃ ° ′	♄ ° ′	♅ ° ′	♆ ° ′	♇ ° ′
1 W	4 35 54.7	7♐55.4	9♌49.5	22♑13.7	19♐15.5	21♎53.6	14♊35.5	26♌47.5	24♊21.0	6♊46.4	3♎52.8	8♌39.3
2 T	4 39 51.2	8 56.2	9 46.3	6♒32.4	20 47.4	22 59.3	14R12.4	26 49.9	24R16.4	6R43.9	3 53.9	8R38.7
3 F	4 43 47.8	9 57.1	9 43.2	20 47.4	22 19.1	24 5.2	13 49.3	26 52.1	24 11.7	6 41.4	3 55.1	8 38.1
4 S	4 47 44.4	10 58.0	9 40.0	4♓56.5	23 50.6	25 11.5	13 26.1	26 54.1	24 6.9	6 38.9	3 56.2	8 37.5
5 S	4 51 40.9	11 58.8	9 36.8	18 58.6	25 21.9	26 17.9	13 3.0	26 55.9	24 2.2	6 36.3	3 57.3	8 36.9
6 M	4 55 37.4	12 59.7	9 33.6	2♈53.2	26 52.9	27 24.6	12 40.0	26 57.6	23 57.4	6 33.8	3 58.3	8 36.2
7 T	4 59 34.0	14 0.6	9 30.5	16 39.5	28 23.7	28 31.5	12 17.1	26 59.0	23 52.6	6 31.3	3 59.4	8 35.5
8 W	5 3 30.6	15 1.6	9 27.3	0♉16.7	29 54.1	29 38.7	11 54.4	27 0.3	23 47.7	6 28.8	4 0.4	8 34.8
9 T	5 7 27.2	16 2.5	9 24.1	13 43.4	1♑24.0	0♏46.1	11 32.0	27 1.3	23 42.9	6 26.3	4 1.3	8 34.1
10 F	5 11 23.7	17 3.4	9 20.9	26 58.2	2 53.5	1 53.7	11 9.8	27 2.2	23 38.0	6 23.9	4 2.3	8 33.3
11 S	5 15 20.2	18 4.4	9 17.7	9♊59.6	4 22.4	3 1.5	10 48.0	27 2.8	23 33.1	6 21.4	4 3.2	8 32.5
12 S	5 19 16.8	19 5.4	9 14.6	22 46.4	5 50.6	4 9.5	10 26.5	27 3.3	23 28.1	6 18.9	4 4.0	8 31.7
13 M	5 23 13.4	20 6.4	9 11.4	5♋18.5	7 18.0	5 17.7	10 5.5	27 3.6	23 23.2	6 16.5	4 4.9	8 30.9
14 T	5 27 9.9	21 7.4	9 8.2	17 36.2	8 44.4	6 26.1	9 44.9	27 3.7	23 18.3	6 14.1	4 5.7	8 30.1
15 W	5 31 6.5	22 8.4	9 5.0	29 41.5	10 9.6	7 34.7	9 24.8	27R 3.6	23 13.3	6 11.7	4 6.4	8 29.2
16 T	5 35 3.0	23 9.4	9 1.9	11♌36.8	11 33.5	8 43.4	9 5.2	27 3.3	23 8.4	6 9.3	4 7.2	8 28.3
17 F	5 38 59.6	24 10.4	8 58.7	23 25.9	12 55.7	9 52.4	8 46.1	27 2.8	23 3.4	6 6.9	4 7.9	8 27.4
18 S	5 42 56.2	25 11.5	8 55.5	5♍13.1	14 16.1	11 1.5	8 27.7	27 2.1	22 58.5	6 4.5	4 8.6	8 26.5
19 S	5 46 52.7	26 12.6	8 52.3	17 3.4	15 34.2	12 10.8	8 9.9	27 1.2	22 53.5	6 2.2	4 9.2	8 25.6
20 M	5 50 49.3	27 13.7	8 49.2	29 1.8	16 49.6	13 20.2	7 52.7	27 0.1	22 48.6	5 59.9	4 9.8	8 24.6
21 T	5 54 45.8	28 14.8	8 46.0	11♎13.8	18 2.0	14 29.8	7 36.2	26 58.8	22 43.7	5 57.6	4 10.4	8 23.6
22 W	5 58 42.4	29 15.9	8 42.8	23 44.1	19 10.7	15 39.6	7 20.5	26 57.3	22 38.8	5 55.3	4 10.9	8 22.6
23 T	6 2 39.0	0♑17.0	8 39.6	6♏36.7	20 15.3	16 49.5	7 5.4	26 55.6	22 33.9	5 53.1	4 11.4	8 21.6
24 F	6 6 35.5	1 18.1	8 36.4	19 54.2	21 15.1	17 59.5	6 51.1	26 53.8	22 29.0	5 50.9	4 11.9	8 20.5
25 S	6 10 32.0	2 19.3	8 33.3	3♐37.2	22 9.3	19 9.7	6 37.5	26 51.7	22 24.2	5 48.7	4 12.3	8 19.5
26 S	6 14 28.6	3 20.5	8 30.1	17 44.1	22 57.1	20 20.0	6 24.7	26 49.4	22 19.4	5 46.5	4 12.7	8 18.4
27 M	6 18 25.2	4 21.6	8 26.9	2♑10.8	23 37.8	21 30.4	6 12.8	26 47.0	22 14.6	5 44.4	4 13.1	8 17.3
28 T	6 22 21.7	5 22.8	8 23.7	16 51.2	24 10.3	22 41.0	6 1.6	26 44.3	22 9.8	5 42.2	4 13.4	8 16.2
29 W	6 26 18.3	6 24.0	8 20.6	1♒37.9	24 33.9	23 51.6	5 51.2	26 41.5	22 5.1	5 40.2	4 13.7	8 15.1
30 T	6 30 14.8	7 25.1	8 17.4	16 23.8	24 47.5	25 2.4	5 41.7	26 38.5	22 0.4	5 38.1	4 14.0	8 13.9
31 F	6 34 11.4	8 26.3	8 14.2	1♓ 2.3	24 50.5	26 13.2	5 33.0	26 35.2	21 55.7	5 36.1	4 14.2	8 12.8

DECLINATION

DAY	EPHEMERIS SIDEREAL TIME h m s	☉	☊	☽	☿	♀	♂	♃	♄	♅	♆	♇
1 W	4 35 54.7	21S38.1	17N47.5	20S11.8	24S56.4	6S32.1	24N25.6	13N21.3	21N54.6	21N20.9	0S17.6	23N21.8
4 S	4 47 44.4	22 5.6	17 50.1	11 49.4	25 24.6	7 38.4	24 24.9	13 19.8	21 54.2	21 19.7	0 18.8	23 22.8
7 T	4 59 34.0	22 29.2	17 52.6	2N 9.8	25 40.2	8 44.8	24 23.1	13 18.8	21 53.7	21 18.4	0 19.9	23 23.9
10 F	5 11 23.7	22 48.9	17 55.1	14 46.8	25 42.9	9 51.1	24 20.3	13 18.4	21 53.2	21 17.2	0 20.9	23 25.1
13 M	5 23 13.4	23 4.5	17 57.7	20 35.5	25 32.4	10 56.9	24 16.7	13 18.6	21 52.8	21 16.0	0 21.8	23 26.3
16 T	5 35 3.0	23 16.1	18 0.2	17 39.9	25 8.8	12 1.7	24 12.6	13 19.5	21 52.3	21 14.8	0 22.6	23 27.5
19 S	5 46 52.7	23 23.4	18 2.7	8 9.6	24 32.7	13 5.2	24 8.1	13 20.9	21 51.8	21 13.6	0 23.2	23 28.7
22 W	5 58 42.4	23 26.6	18 5.2	4S31.4	23 45.7	14 6.9	24 3.6	13 22.9	21 51.4	21 12.4	0 23.8	23 30.0
25 S	6 10 32.0	23 25.5	18 7.7	16 18.4	22 50.7	15 6.6	23 59.2	13 25.6	21 50.9	21 11.3	0 24.2	23 31.4
28 T	6 22 21.7	23 20.1	18 10.1	20 35.6	21 52.5	16 3.7	23 55.2	13 28.8	21 50.5	21 10.2	0 24.5	23 32.7
31 F	6 34 11.4	23 10.6	18 12.6	13 6.4	20 57.4	16 57.9	23 51.9	13 32.6	21 50.0	21 9.1	0 24.6	23 34.1

JANUARY 1944

LONGITUDE

DAY	EPHEMERIS SIDEREAL TIME h m s	☉ ° '	☊ ° '	☽ ° '	☿ ° '	♀ ° '	♂ ° '	♃ ° '	♄ ° '	♅ ° '	♆ ° '	♇ ° '
1 S	6 38 8.0	9♑27.5	8♌11.0	15♓28.7	24♑42.1	27♏24.2	5♊25.1	26♌31.8	21♊51.1	5♊34.1	4♎14.4	8♌11.6
2 S	6 42 4.5	10 28.7	8 7.9	29 40.0	24R21.9	28 35.3	5R18.1	26R28.3	21R46.6	5R32.2	4 14.5	8R10.4
3 M	6 46 1.1	11 29.8	8 4.7	13♈34.6	23 49.8	29 46.5	5 11.9	26 24.5	21 42.1	5 30.2	4 14.7	8 9.2
4 T	6 49 57.6	12 31.0	8 1.5	27 12.5	23 6.2	0♐57.7	5 6.5	26 20.6	21 37.6	5 28.4	4 14.7	8 8.0
5 W	6 53 54.2	13 32.1	7 58.3	10♉34.1	22 11.8	2 9.1	5 2.0	26 16.4	21 33.2	5 26.5	4 14.8	8 6.8
6 T	6 57 50.7	14 33.3	7 55.2	23 40.5	21 8.0	3 20.5	4 58.2	26 12.2	21 28.8	5 24.7	4 14.8	8 5.5
7 F	7 1 47.3	15 34.4	7 52.0	6♊32.7	19 56.5	4 32.1	4 55.3	26 7.7	21 24.5	5 22.9	4R14.8	8 4.3
8 S	7 5 43.8	16 35.5	7 48.8	19 11.7	18 39.5	5 43.7	4 53.2	26 3.1	21 20.3	5 21.2	4 14.8	8 3.0
9 S	7 9 40.4	17 36.7	7 45.6	1♋38.7	17 19.6	6 55.4	4 51.9	25 58.3	21 16.1	5 19.5	4 14.7	8 1.7
10 M	7 13 37.0	18 37.8	7 42.5	13 54.6	15 59.3	8 7.2	4 51.4	25 53.3	21 12.0	5 17.9	4 14.6	8 0.5
11 T	7 17 33.5	19 38.9	7 39.3	26 0.8	14 41.2	9 19.0	4D51.6	25 48.2	21 8.0	5 16.3	4 14.4	7 59.2
12 W	7 21 30.1	20 40.0	7 36.1	7♌58.9	13 27.6	10 31.0	4 52.6	25 42.9	21 4.0	5 14.7	4 14.2	7 57.9
13 T	7 25 26.6	21 41.2	7 32.9	19 50.7	12 20.3	11 43.0	4 54.4	25 37.5	21 0.1	5 13.2	4 14.0	7 56.5
14 F	7 29 23.2	22 42.3	7 29.7	1♍38.9	11 20.8	12 55.1	4 56.9	25 31.9	20 56.3	5 11.7	4 13.8	7 55.2
15 S	7 33 19.8	23 43.4	7 26.6	13 26.5	10 30.2	14 7.3	5 0.1	25 26.2	20 52.5	5 10.2	4 13.5	7 53.9
16 S	7 37 16.3	24 44.5	7 23.4	25 17.3	9 49.0	15 19.5	5 4.1	25 20.3	20 48.9	5 8.8	4 13.2	7 52.6
17 M	7 41 12.9	25 45.6	7 20.2	7♎15.3	9 17.5	16 31.8	5 8.7	25 14.3	20 45.3	5 7.5	4 12.8	7 51.2
18 T	7 45 9.4	26 46.7	7 17.0	19 25.0	8 55.5	17 44.2	5 14.1	25 8.1	20 41.8	5 6.2	4 12.4	7 49.9
19 W	7 49 6.0	27 47.8	7 13.9	1♏51.1	8 42.7	18 56.6	5 20.1	25 1.9	20 38.3	5 4.9	4 12.0	7 48.5
20 T	7 53 2.5	28 48.9	7 10.7	14 37.9	8 38.8	20 9.1	5 26.8	24 55.4	20 35.0	5 3.7	4 11.5	7 47.2
21 F	7 56 59.1	29 49.9	7 7.5	27 49.2	8D43.1	21 21.6	5 34.2	24 48.9	20 31.7	5 2.5	4 11.1	7 45.8
22 S	8 0 55.6	0♒51.0	7 4.3	11♐27.2	8 55.0	22 34.2	5 42.3	24 42.2	20 28.5	5 1.4	4 10.5	7 44.4
23 S	8 4 52.2	1 52.1	7 1.1	25 32.4	9 14.0	23 46.9	5 51.0	24 35.5	20 25.5	5 0.3	4 10.0	7 43.0
24 M	8 8 48.8	2 53.1	6 58.0	10♑ 2.8	9 39.5	24 59.6	6 0.3	24 28.6	20 22.5	4 59.3	4 9.4	7 41.7
25 T	8 12 45.3	3 54.2	6 54.8	24 53.6	10 10.9	26 12.4	6 10.2	24 21.6	20 19.6	4 58.3	4 8.8	7 40.3
26 W	8 16 41.9	4 55.2	6 51.6	9♒57.4	10 47.6	27 25.2	6 20.7	24 14.5	20 16.8	4 57.4	4 8.2	7 38.9
27 T	8 20 38.4	5 56.2	6 48.4	25 5.5	11 29.1	28 38.0	6 31.9	24 7.3	20 14.1	4 56.5	4 7.5	7 37.5
28 F	8 24 35.0	6 57.2	6 45.3	10♓ 8.6	12 15.0	29 50.9	6 43.6	24 0.0	20 11.5	4 55.7	4 6.8	7 36.1
29 S	8 28 31.6	7 58.2	6 42.1	24 58.4	13 5.0	1♑ 3.8	6 55.9	23 52.7	20 9.0	4 54.9	4 6.0	7 34.8
30 S	8 32 28.1	8 59.2	6 38.9	9♈28.8	13 58.5	2 16.8	7 8.7	23 45.2	20 6.6	4 54.2	4 5.3	7 33.4
31 M	8 36 24.6	10 0.1	6 35.7	23 35.9	14 55.3	3 29.7	7 22.1	23 37.7	20 4.3	4 53.5	4 4.5	7 32.0

DECLINATION

DAY	EPHEMERIS SIDEREAL TIME h m s	☉ ° '	☊ ° '	☽ ° '	☿ ° '	♀ ° '	♂ ° '	♃ ° '	♄ ° '	♅ ° '	♆ ° '	♇ ° '
1 S	6 38 8.0	23S 6.5	18N13.4	8S44.1	20S41.0	17S15.3	23N50.9	13N34.0	21N49.9	21N 8.8	0S24.6	23N34.5
4 T	6 49 57.6	22 51.3	18 15.9	5N39.1	20 0.7	18 5.2	23 48.6	13 38.5	21 49.5	21 7.8	0 24.6	23 35.9
7 F	7 1 47.3	22 32.2	18 18.4	16 54.3	19 36.1	18 51.3	23 47.1	13 43.5	21 49.2	21 6.9	0 24.5	23 37.3
10 M	7 13 37.0	22 9.0	18 20.8	20 40.7	19 27.1	19 33.3	23 46.6	13 49.1	21 48.9	21 6.0	0 24.3	23 38.7
13 T	7 25 26.6	21 41.9	18 23.3	16 0.4	19 31.1	20 11.1	23 47.1	13 55.1	21 48.6	21 5.2	0 23.9	23 40.1
16 S	7 37 16.3	21 11.0	18 25.7	5 31.0	19 45.6	20 44.1	23 48.5	14 1.5	21 48.4	21 4.5	0 23.4	23 41.4
19 W	7 49 6.0	20 36.4	18 28.1	7S 9.8	20 7.4	21 12.3	23 50.8	14 8.2	21 48.2	21 3.9	0 22.8	23 42.8
22 S	8 0 55.6	19 58.4	18 30.5	17 50.3	20 32.6	21 35.2	23 53.9	14 15.4	21 48.1	21 3.3	0 22.1	23 44.2
25 T	8 12 45.3	19 16.9	18 32.9	20 4.7	20 57.4	21 52.8	23 57.7	14 22.8	21 48.1	21 2.7	0 21.3	23 45.5
28 F	8 24 35.0	18 32.3	18 35.3	10 28.2	21 18.5	22 4.9	24 2.3	14 30.5	21 48.1	21 2.3	0 20.3	23 46.9
31 M	8 36 24.6	17 44.7	18 37.7	4N21.8	21 33.5	22 11.2	24 7.5	14 38.3	21 48.2	21 2.0	0 19.3	23 48.2

FEBRUARY 1944

LONGITUDE

DAY	EPHEMERIS SIDEREAL TIME h m s	☉ ° '	☊ ° '	☽ ° '	☿ ° '	♀ ° '	♂ ° '	♃ ° '	♄ ° '	♅ ° '	♆ ° '	♇ ° '
1 T	8 40 21.2	11♒ 1.0	6♌32.5	7♉18.6	15♑55.0	4♑42.8	7♊36.0	23♌30.1	20♊ 2.1	4♊52.9	4♎ 3.6	7♌30.6
2 W	8 44 17.8	12 1.9	6 29.4	20 37.7	16 57.5	5 55.8	7 50.5	23R22.5	19R60.0	4R52.3	4R 2.8	7R29.2
3 T	8 48 14.3	13 2.8	6 26.2	3♊35.3	18 2.5	7 8.9	8 5.4	23 14.8	19 58.0	4 51.8	4 1.9	7 27.8
4 F	8 52 10.9	14 3.7	6 23.0	16 14.4	19 9.8	8 22.1	8 20.8	23 7.1	19 56.1	4 51.3	4 1.0	7 26.5
5 S	8 56 7.4	15 4.5	6 19.8	28 38.1	20 19.1	9 35.2	8 36.7	22 59.3	19 54.3	4 50.9	4 0.1	7 25.1
6 S	9 0 4.0	16 5.3	6 16.7	10♋49.6	21 30.4	10 48.4	8 53.1	22 51.4	19 52.6	4 50.6	3 59.1	7 23.7
7 M	9 4 0.5	17 6.1	6 13.5	22 51.8	22 43.5	12 1.6	9 10.0	22 43.6	19 51.1	4 50.2	3 58.1	7 22.4
8 T	9 7 57.1	18 6.9	6 10.3	4♌47.4	23 58.3	13 14.9	9 27.2	22 35.7	19 49.6	4 50.0	3 57.1	7 21.0
9 W	9 11 53.7	19 7.6	6 7.1	16 38.6	25 14.6	14 28.1	9 44.9	22 27.8	19 48.3	4 49.8	3 56.0	7 19.7
10 T	9 15 50.2	20 8.3	6 4.0	28 27.4	26 32.4	15 41.4	10 3.1	22 19.8	19 47.1	4 49.6	3 55.0	7 18.3
11 F	9 19 46.7	21 9.0	6 0.8	10♍16.1	27 51.6	16 54.8	10 21.6	22 11.9	19 45.9	4 49.5	3 53.9	7 17.0
12 S	9 23 43.3	22 9.7	5 57.6	22 6.7	29 12.1	18 8.1	10 40.5	22 3.9	19 44.9	4 49.5	3 52.7	7 15.6
13 S	9 27 39.9	23 10.4	5 54.4	4♎ 1.5	0♒33.9	19 21.5	10 59.9	21 56.0	19 44.0	4D49.5	3 51.6	7 14.3
14 M	9 31 36.4	24 11.0	5 51.2	16 3.3	1 56.8	20 34.9	11 19.6	21 48.1	19 43.2	4 49.6	3 50.4	7 13.0
15 T	9 35 33.0	25 11.6	5 48.1	28 15.1	3 21.0	21 48.4	11 39.7	21 40.1	19 42.5	4 49.7	3 49.2	7 11.7
16 W	9 39 29.5	26 12.2	5 44.9	10♏40.4	4 46.2	23 1.9	12 0.1	21 32.2	19 42.0	4 49.8	3 48.0	7 10.4
17 T	9 43 26.1	27 12.8	5 41.7	23 22.9	6 12.6	24 15.3	12 20.9	21 24.3	19 41.5	4 50.1	3 46.8	7 9.1
18 F	9 47 22.6	28 13.4	5 38.5	6♐26.2	7 40.0	25 28.9	12 42.1	21 16.5	19 41.2	4 50.3	3 45.5	7 7.8
19 S	9 51 19.2	29 13.9	5 35.4	19 53.3	9 8.4	26 42.4	13 3.6	21 8.6	19 40.9	4 50.7	3 44.2	7 6.5
20 S	9 55 15.7	0♓14.4	5 32.2	3♑46.4	10 37.8	27 55.9	13 25.4	21 0.8	19 40.8	4 51.0	3 42.9	7 5.3
21 M	9 59 12.3	1 14.9	5 29.0	18 5.7	12 8.3	29 9.5	13 47.5	20 53.1	19D40.8	4 51.5	3 41.6	7 4.0
22 T	10 3 8.9	2 15.4	5 25.8	2♒49.1	13 39.8	0♒23.1	14 10.0	20 45.4	19 40.9	4 52.0	3 40.3	7 2.8
23 W	10 7 5.4	3 15.8	5 22.7	17 51.4	15 12.2	1 36.7	14 32.8	20 37.8	19 41.2	4 52.5	3 38.9	7 1.6
24 T	10 11 2.0	4 16.2	5 19.5	3♓ 4.9	16 45.7	2 50.3	14 55.9	20 30.2	19 41.5	4 53.1	3 37.5	7 0.4
25 F	10 14 58.5	5 16.6	5 16.3	18 19.7	18 20.1	4 4.0	15 19.3	20 22.7	19 42.0	4 53.7	3 36.1	6 59.2
26 S	10 18 55.1	6 17.0	5 13.1	3♈25.5	19 55.5	5 17.6	15 43.0	20 15.3	19 42.5	4 54.4	3 34.7	6 58.0
27 S	10 22 51.6	7 17.3	5 9.9	18 13.2	21 31.9	6 31.3	16 6.9	20 8.0	19 43.2	4 55.2	3 33.3	6 56.8
28 M	10 26 48.2	8 17.6	5 6.8	2♉36.0	23 9.3	7 44.9	16 31.2	20 0.7	19 44.0	4 56.0	3 31.8	6 55.7
29 T	10 30 44.7	9 17.9	5 3.6	16 30.7	24 47.8	8 58.6	16 55.7	19 53.5	19 44.9	4 56.8	3 30.3	6 54.5

DECLINATION

DAY	EPHEMERIS SIDEREAL TIME h m s	☉ ° '	☊ ° '	☽ ° '	☿ ° '	♀ ° '	♂ ° '	♃ ° '	♄ ° '	♅ ° '	♆ ° '	♇ ° '
1 T	8 40 21.2	17S28.2	18N38.5	8N56.3	21S36.7	22S12.0	24N 9.4	14N41.0	21N48.2	21N 1.9	0S18.9	23N48.6
4 F	8 52 10.9	16 36.8	18 40.9	18 39.5	21 40.8	22 10.6	24 15.2	14 49.0	21 48.4	21 1.6	0 17.7	23 49.9
7 M	9 4 0.5	15 42.8	18 43.3	20 14.6	21 35.2	22 3.4	24 21.4	14 57.1	21 48.7	21 1.5	0 16.5	23 51.1
10 T	9 15 50.2	14 46.4	18 45.6	13 50.6	21 19.3	21 50.3	24 27.9	15 5.2	21 49.0	21 1.4	0 15.1	23 52.3
13 S	9 27 39.9	13 47.8	18 48.0	2 28.3	20 52.4	21 31.5	24 34.5	15 13.2	21 49.4	21 1.4	0 13.6	23 53.4
16 W	9 39 29.5	12 47.2	18 50.3	10S 2.1	20 14.3	21 6.9	24 41.1	15 21.2	21 49.9	21 1.5	0 12.1	23 54.5
19 S	9 51 19.2	11 44.6	18 52.7	19 14.1	19 24.6	20 36.7	24 47.7	15 29.0	21 50.5	21 1.7	0 10.5	23 55.6
22 T	10 3 8.9	10 40.4	18 55.0	19 11.4	18 23.3	20 1.0	24 54.1	15 36.6	21 51.2	21 2.0	0 8.8	23 56.6
25 F	10 14 58.5	9 34.7	18 57.3	7 49.4	17 10.1	19 20.1	25 0.3	15 43.9	21 51.9	21 2.3	0 7.1	23 57.6
28 M	10 26 48.2	8 27.7	18 59.6	7N29.0	15 45.2	18 34.2	25 6.2	15 51.0	21 52.7	21 2.8	0 5.3	23 58.5

DAY	EPHEMERIS SIDEREAL TIME h m s	☉ ° ′	☊ ° ′	☽ ° ′	☿ ° ′	♀ ° ′	♂ ° ′	♃ ° ′	♄ ° ′	♅ ° ′	♆ ° ′	♇ ° ′
							LONGITUDE					
1 W	10 34 41.3	10♓18.1	5♌0.4	29♍56.7	26⟋27.2	10≏12.3	17♓20.5	19♌R46.5	19♓45.9	4♓57.7	3≏28.8	6♌53.4
2 T	10 38 37.8	11 18.3	4 57.2	12♏56.1	28 7.7	11 26.0	17 45.5	19R39.5	19 47.1	4 58.7	3R27.4	6R52.3
3 F	10 42 34.4	12 18.5	4 54.0	25 32.5	29 49.2	12 39.7	18 10.8	19 32.6	19 48.3	4 59.7	3 25.8	6 51.2
4 S	10 46 30.9	13 18.6	4 50.9	7♏50.3	1♏31.8	13 53.4	18 36.3	19 25.9	19 49.7	5 0.8	3 24.3	6 50.1
5 S	10 50 27.5	14 18.7	4 47.7	19 54.2	3 15.4	15 7.1	19 2.1	19 19.3	19 51.1	5 1.9	3 22.8	6 49.1
6 M	10 54 24.0	15 18.7	4 44.5	1♌48.8	5 0.1	16 20.8	19 28.1	19 12.7	19 52.7	5 3.1	3 21.2	6 48.0
7 T	10 58 20.6	16 18.8	4 41.3	13 38.0	6 46.0	17 34.5	19 54.3	19 6.3	19 54.4	5 4.3	3 19.7	6 47.0
8 W	11 2 17.2	17 18.7	4 38.2	25 25.4	8 32.9	18 48.2	20 20.7	19 0.1	19 56.2	5 5.5	3 18.1	6 46.0
9 T	11 6 13.7	18 18.7	4 35.0	7♍13.8	10 21.0	20 2.0	20 47.3	18 53.9	19 58.1	5 6.8	3 16.5	6 45.0
10 F	11 10 10.2	19 18.6	4 31.8	19 5.4	12 10.2	21 15.7	21 14.2	18 47.9	20 0.1	5 8.2	3 14.9	6 44.1
11 S	11 14 6.8	20 18.5	4 28.6	1≏2.2	14 0.5	22 29.5	21 41.2	18 42.1	20 2.2	5 9.6	3 13.3	6 43.1
12 S	11 18 3.4	21 18.4	4 25.4	13 5.6	15 52.0	23 43.2	22 8.5	18 36.3	20 4.4	5 11.1	3 11.7	6 42.2
13 M	11 21 59.9	22 18.2	4 22.3	25 17.0	17 44.6	24 57.0	22 35.9	18 30.8	20 6.7	5 12.6	3 10.1	6 41.3
14 T	11 25 56.5	23 18.0	4 19.1	7♏37.9	19 38.3	26 10.8	23 3.5	18 25.3	20 9.2	5 14.1	3 8.5	6 40.4
15 W	11 29 53.0	24 17.8	4 15.9	20 10.2	21 33.1	27 24.6	23 31.3	18 20.0	20 11.7	5 15.7	3 6.8	6 39.5
16 T	11 33 49.6	25 17.5	4 12.7	2⟋56.1	23 29.0	28 38.4	23 59.3	18 14.9	20 14.3	5 17.4	3 5.2	6 38.7
17 F	11 37 46.1	26 17.2	4 9.6	15 58.0	25 26.0	29 52.2	24 27.4	18 9.9	20 17.1	5 19.0	3 3.6	6 37.9
18 S	11 41 42.7	27 16.9	4 6.4	29 18.6	27 23.9	1♏6.0	24 55.8	18 5.1	20 19.9	5 20.8	3 1.9	6 37.1
19 S	11 45 39.2	28 16.6	4 3.2	13♑0.1	29 22.7	2 19.8	25 24.3	18 0.4	20 22.9	5 22.6	3 0.3	6 36.3
20 M	11 49 35.8	29 16.2	4 0.0	27 4.1	1♈22.3	3 33.6	25 52.9	17 55.9	20 25.9	5 24.4	2 58.6	6 35.5
21 T	11 53 32.3	0♈15.8	3 56.8	11⟋30.4	3 22.6	4 47.4	26 21.8	17 51.6	20 29.0	5 26.3	2 57.0	6 34.8
22 W	11 57 28.9	1 15.3	3 53.7	26 16.5	5 23.4	6 1.2	26 50.7	17 47.5	20 32.3	5 28.2	2 55.3	6 34.1
23 T	12 1 25.4	2 14.9	3 50.5	11♒17.2	7 24.7	7 15.0	27 19.9	17 43.5	20 35.6	5 30.1	2 53.6	6 33.4
24 F	12 5 22.0	3 14.4	3 47.3	26 24.4	9 26.1	8 28.8	27 49.2	17 39.7	20 39.1	5 32.1	2 52.0	6 32.7
25 S	12 9 18.5	4 13.9	3 44.1	11♓28.6	11 27.5	9 42.7	28 18.6	17 36.0	20 42.6	5 34.2	2 50.3	6 32.1
26 S	12 13 15.1	5 13.3	3 41.0	26 19.7	13 28.6	10 56.5	28 48.3	17 32.6	20 46.2	5 36.3	2 48.7	6 31.5
27 M	12 17 11.6	6 12.7	3 37.8	10♈49.4	15 29.0	12 10.3	29 18.0	17 29.3	20 50.0	5 38.4	2 47.0	6 30.9
28 T	12 21 8.2	7 12.0	3 34.6	24 52.3	17 28.6	13 24.1	29 47.9	17 26.2	20 53.8	5 40.6	2 45.4	6 30.3
29 W	12 25 4.7	8 11.4	3 31.4	8♉25.9	19 26.9	14 37.9	0♈17.9	17 23.3	20 57.7	5 42.8	2 43.7	6 29.8
30 T	12 29 1.3	9 10.7	3 28.2	21 31.2	21 23.5	15 51.7	0 48.1	17 20.6	21 1.7	5 45.1	2 42.1	6 29.2
31 F	12 32 57.9	10 9.9	3 25.1	4♊11.0	23 18.1	17 5.5	1 18.4	17 18.0	21 5.8	5 47.4	2 40.4	6 28.7
							DECLINATION					
1 W	10 34 41.3	7S42.4	19N 1.2	15N28.1	14S42.1	18S 0.1	25N 9.9	15N55.6	21S53.3	21N 3.1	0S 4.1	23N59.0
4 S	10 46 30.9	6 33.7	19 3.5	20 43.7	12 57.4	17 7.0	25 15.0	16 2.1	21 54.3	21 3.7	0 2.2	23 59.8
7 T	10 58 20.6	5 24.1	19 5.8	17 22.1	11 1.0	16 8.9	25 19.6	16 8.2	21 55.3	21 4.4	0 0.3	24 0.6
10 F	11 10 10.2	4 13.9	19 8.0	7 33.0	8 53.2	15 6.6	25 23.5	16 13.9	21 56.3	21 5.1	0N 1.7	24 1.3
13 M	11 21 59.9	3 3.3	19 10.3	5S 5.0	6 34.3	14 0.5	25 26.7	16 19.1	21 57.5	21 6.0	0 3.6	24 1.9
16 T	11 33 49.6	1 52.3	19 12.6	16 16.9	4 4.9	12 51.0	25 29.2	16 23.9	21 58.7	21 6.9	0 5.6	24 2.4
19 S	11 45 39.2	0 41.2	19 14.8	20 51.7	1 26.3	11 38.3	25 30.9	16 28.3	21 59.9	21 7.8	0 7.6	24 2.9
22 W	11 57 28.9	0N30.0	19 17.1	14 28.9	1N19.6	10 22.6	25 31.7	16 32.1	22 1.2	21 8.9	0 9.6	24 3.4
25 S	12 9 18.5	1 40.9	19 19.3	6 0.5	4 9.7	9 4.5	25 31.5	16 35.4	22 2.5	21 10.0	0 11.6	24 3.7
28 T	12 21 8.2	2 51.5	19 21.5	14 21.8	6 59.6	7 44.1	25 30.4	16 38.2	22 3.9	21 11.1	0 13.6	24 4.0
31 F	12 32 57.9	4 1.6	19 23.8	20 48.9	9 43.7	6 21.8	25 28.2	16 40.4	22 5.2	21 12.3	0 15.6	24 4.2

DAY	EPHEMERIS SIDEREAL TIME h m s	☉ ° ′	☊ ° ′	☽ ° ′	☿ ° ′	♀ ° ′	♂ ° ′	♃ ° ′	♄ ° ′	♅ ° ′	♆ ° ′	♇ ° ′
							LONGITUDE					
1 S	12 36 54.4	11♈9.1	3♌21.9	16♋29.9	25♈10.2	18⟋19.3	1♏48.8	17♌15.7	21♓10.0	5♓49.7	2≏38.8	6♌28.3
2 S	12 40 50.9	12 8.3	3 18.8	28 33.2	26 59.6	19 33.1	2 19.3	17R13.5	21 14.3	5 52.1	2R37.1	6R27.8
3 M	12 44 47.5	13 7.4	3 15.5	10♌26.2	28 45.7	20 46.9	2 49.9	17 11.5	21 18.6	5 54.5	2 35.5	6 27.4
4 T	12 48 44.0	14 6.5	3 12.3	22 14.0	0♉28.2	22 0.7	3 20.7	17 9.7	21 23.1	5 56.9	2 33.9	6 27.0
5 W	12 52 40.6	15 5.6	3 9.2	4♍1.2	2 6.8	23 14.5	3 51.6	17 8.1	21 27.6	5 59.4	2 32.3	6 26.6
6 T	12 56 37.2	16 4.6	3 6.0	15 48.2	3 41.1	24 28.3	4 22.6	17 6.7	21 32.2	6 1.9	2 30.7	6 26.3
7 F	13 0 33.7	17 3.6	3 2.8	27 48.6	5 10.9	25 42.0	4 53.7	17 5.5	21 36.9	6 4.5	2 29.1	6 26.0
8 S	13 4 30.3	18 2.5	2 59.6	9≏58.8	6 35.7	26 55.8	5 24.9	17 4.4	21 41.7	6 7.1	2 27.5	6 25.7
9 S	13 8 26.8	19 1.4	2 56.5	22 8.9	7 55.5	28 9.6	5 56.2	17 3.6	21 46.5	6 9.7	2 25.9	6 25.4
10 M	13 12 23.4	20 0.3	2 53.3	4♏34.6	9 10.0	29 23.4	6 27.6	17 2.9	21 51.5	6 12.3	2 24.4	6 25.2
11 T	13 16 19.9	20 59.2	2 50.1	17 11.1	10 19.0	0♏37.1	6 59.2	17 2.4	21 56.5	6 15.0	2 22.8	6 25.0
12 W	13 20 16.5	21 58.0	2 46.9	29 58.6	11 22.3	1 50.9	7 30.8	17 2.1	22 1.6	6 17.7	2 21.3	6 24.8
13 T	13 24 13.0	22 56.8	2 43.7	12⟋57.6	12 19.8	3 4.7	8 2.5	17 2.0	22 6.8	6 20.5	2 19.7	6 24.6
14 F	13 28 9.6	23 55.5	2 40.6	26 8.9	13 11.4	4 18.4	8 34.3	17D 2.1	22 12.0	6 23.3	2 18.2	6 24.5
15 S	13 32 6.1	24 54.3	2 37.4	9♒33.4	13 56.9	5 32.2	9 6.2	17 2.4	22 17.3	6 26.1	2 16.7	6 24.4
16 S	13 36 2.7	25 52.9	2 34.2	23 12.6	14 36.4	6 46.0	9 38.2	17 2.8	22 22.7	6 29.0	2 15.2	6 24.3
17 M	13 39 59.2	26 51.6	2 31.0	7♓0.6	15 9.8	7 59.7	10 10.2	17 3.5	22 28.2	6 31.8	2 13.7	6 24.2
18 T	13 43 55.8	27 50.3	2 27.9	21 19.0	15 37.0	9 13.5	10 42.4	17 4.3	22 33.7	6 34.7	2 12.3	6 24.2
19 W	13 47 52.4	28 49.0	2 24.7	5♈45.7	15 58.0	10 27.2	11 14.7	17 5.3	22 39.3	6 37.7	2 10.8	6D24.2
20 T	13 51 48.9	29 47.5	2 21.5	20 24.6	16 13.0	11 41.0	11 47.0	17 6.5	22 45.0	6 40.6	2 9.4	6 24.2
21 F	13 55 45.4	0♉46.0	2 18.3	5♉10.0	16 21.9	12 54.8	12 19.5	17 7.9	22 50.8	6 43.6	2 8.0	6 24.3
22 S	13 59 42.0	1 44.6	2 15.1	19 56.2	16 24.9	14 8.5	12 52.0	17 9.4	22 56.6	6 46.6	2 6.6	6 24.4
23 S	14 3 38.6	2 43.1	2 12.0	4♊33.4	16R22.2	15 22.2	13 24.6	17 11.2	23 2.5	6 49.7	2 5.2	6 24.5
24 M	14 7 35.1	3 41.5	2 8.8	18 54.5	16 14.0	16 36.0	13 57.3	17 13.1	23 8.4	6 52.8	2 3.8	6 24.6
25 T	14 11 31.7	4 40.0	2 5.6	2♋53.0	16 0.5	17 49.7	14 30.1	17 15.2	23 14.4	6 55.8	2 2.5	6 24.8
26 W	14 15 28.2	5 38.4	2 2.4	16 26.6	15 42.1	19 3.4	15 2.9	17 17.5	23 20.5	6 59.0	2 1.2	6 25.0
27 T	14 19 24.8	6 36.8	1 59.3	29 33.7	15 19.3	20 17.2	15 35.8	17 20.0	23 26.6	7 2.1	1 59.9	6 25.2
28 F	14 23 21.3	7 35.1	1 56.1	12♌16.2	14 52.4	21 30.9	16 8.8	17 22.6	23 32.8	7 5.3	1 58.6	6 25.4
29 S	14 27 17.9	8 33.4	1 52.9	24 37.8	14 22.1	22 44.6	16 41.9	17 25.5	23 39.1	7 8.4	1 57.3	6 25.7
30 S	14 31 14.4	9 31.7	1 49.7	6♍43.2	13 48.9	23 58.3	17 15.1	17 28.5	23 45.4	7 11.7	1 56.1	6 26.0
							DECLINATION					
1 S	12 36 54.4	4N24.8	19N24.5	20N52.2	10N36.0	5S54.0	25N27.3	16N41.1	22N 5.7	21N12.8	0N16.2	24N 4.3
4 T	12 48 44.0	5 33.9	19 26.7	15 34.7	13 2.6	4 29.6	25 23.7	16 42.6	22 7.1	21 14.1	0 18.1	24 4.5
7 F	13 0 33.7	6 42.2	19 28.9	4 35.8	15 9.7	3 4.1	25 19.0	16 43.7	22 8.5	21 15.4	0 20.0	24 4.5
10 M	13 12 23.4	7 49.4	19 31.1	8S19.5	16 53.5	1 37.7	25 13.2	16 44.2	22 10.0	21 16.8	0 21.9	24 4.4
13 W	13 24 13.0	8 55.4	19 33.3	18 32.2	18 1.6	0 10.7	25 6.3	16 44.1	22 11.5	21 18.2	0 23.7	24 4.4
16 S	13 36 2.7	10 0.1	19 35.5	20 37.3	18 2.9	1N16.5	24 58.1	16 43.6	22 12.9	21 19.7	0 25.5	24 4.3
19 W	13 47 52.4	11 3.3	19 37.6	11 57.3	16 26.7	2 43.7	24 48.7	16 43.6	22 14.3	21 21.2	0 27.2	24 4.0
22 S	13 59 42.0	12 5.0	19 39.8	3N15.5	18 23.0	4 10.5	24 38.2	16 40.9	22 15.8	21 22.8	0 28.8	24 3.8
25 T	14 11 31.7	13 4.8	19 41.9	16 31.5	17 58.9	5 36.6	24 26.4	16 38.9	22 17.2	21 24.4	0 30.4	24 3.4
28 F	14 23 21.3	14 2.7	19 44.0	21 13.4	17 1.7	7 1.7	24 13.3	16 36.3	22 18.5	21 26.0	0 31.9	24 3.0

MAY 1944

LONGITUDE

DAY	EPHEMERIS SIDEREAL TIME h m s	☉ ° ′	☊ ° ′	☽ ° ′	☿ ° ′	♀ ° ′	♂ ° ′	♃ ° ′	♄ ° ′	♅ ° ′	♆ ° ′	♇ ° ′
1 M	14 35 11.0	10♉29.9	1♌46.5	18♌37.9	13♉13.4	25♈12.0	17♋48.3	17♌31.6	23♊51.7	7♊14.9	1♎54.9	6♌26.3
2 T	14 39 7.5	11 28.1	1 43.4	0♍27.2	12R36.3	26 25.7	18 21.6	17 35.0	23 58.2	7 18.1	1R53.7	6 26.6
3 W	14 43 4.1	12 26.3	1 40.2	12 16.4	11 58.3	27 39.4	18 54.9	17 38.5	24 4.6	7 21.4	1 52.5	6 27.0
4 T	14 47 0.7	13 24.4	1 37.0	24 10.2	11 20.0	28 53.0	19 28.3	17 42.2	24 11.2	7 24.7	1 51.3	6 27.4
5 F	14 50 57.2	14 22.5	1 33.8	6♎12.4	10 42.3	0♉6.7	20 1.8	17 46.0	24 17.7	7 28.0	1 50.2	6 27.8
6 S	14 54 53.7	15 20.6	1 30.7	18 26.1	10 5.6	1 20.3	20 35.3	17 50.0	24 24.4	7 31.3	1 49.1	6 28.3
7 S	14 58 50.3	16 18.6	1 27.5	0♏53.2	9 30.6	2 34.0	21 8.9	17 54.2	24 31.1	7 34.6	1 48.0	6 28.7
8 M	15 2 46.9	17 16.6	1 24.3	13 34.3	8 58.0	3 47.7	21 42.6	17 58.6	24 37.8	7 38.0	1 47.0	6 29.2
9 T	15 6 43.4	18 14.6	1 21.1	26 29.4	8 28.1	5 1.3	22 16.3	18 3.1	24 44.6	7 41.3	1 45.9	6 29.8
10 W	15 10 40.0	19 12.6	1 18.0	9♐37.5	8 1.5	6 15.0	22 50.1	18 7.7	24 51.4	7 44.7	1 44.9	6 30.3
11 T	15 14 36.5	20 10.5	1 14.8	22 57.3	7 38.6	7 28.6	23 23.9	18 12.5	24 58.2	7 48.1	1 44.0	6 30.9
12 F	15 18 33.1	21 8.4	1 11.6	6♑27.7	7 19.5	8 42.3	23 57.8	18 17.5	25 5.2	7 51.5	1 43.0	6 31.5
13 S	15 22 29.6	22 6.3	1 8.4	20 7.7	7 4.7	9 55.9	24 31.8	18 22.6	25 12.1	7 54.9	1 42.1	6 32.1
14 S	15 26 26.2	23 4.2	1 5.2	3♒56.8	6 54.2	11 9.6	25 5.8	18 27.9	25 19.1	7 58.3	1 41.2	6 32.8
15 M	15 30 22.8	24 2.0	1 2.1	17 54.5	6 48.2	12 23.2	25 39.8	18 33.3	25 26.2	8 1.8	1 40.3	6 33.4
16 T	15 34 19.3	24 59.9	0 58.9	2♓0.7	6 46.7	13 36.9	26 14.0	18 38.9	25 33.2	8 5.2	1 39.4	6 34.1
17 W	15 38 15.9	25 57.7	0 55.7	16 14.4	6D49.9	14 50.5	26 48.2	18 44.7	25 40.4	8 8.7	1 38.6	6 34.9
18 T	15 42 12.4	26 55.5	0 52.5	0♈33.7	6 57.6	16 4.2	27 22.4	18 50.5	25 47.5	8 12.2	1 37.8	6 35.6
19 F	15 46 9.0	27 53.3	0 49.4	14 55.3	7 9.9	17 17.8	27 56.7	18 56.6	25 54.7	8 15.7	1 37.1	6 36.4
20 S	15 50 5.5	28 51.0	0 46.2	29 14.9	7 26.7	18 31.4	28 31.0	19 2.7	26 1.9	8 19.1	1 36.3	6 37.2
21 S	15 54 2.1	29 48.7	0 43.0	13♉27.0	7 47.8	19 45.1	29 5.4	19 9.1	26 9.2	8 22.6	1 35.6	6 38.0
22 M	15 57 58.7	0♊46.5	0 39.8	27 26.3	8 13.3	20 58.8	29 39.9	19 15.5	26 16.5	8 26.1	1 35.0	6 38.8
23 T	16 1 55.2	1 44.2	0 36.7	11♊8.4	8 43.0	22 12.4	0♌14.4	19 22.1	26 23.8	8 29.7	1 34.3	6 39.7
24 W	16 5 51.7	2 41.8	0 33.5	24 30.1	9 16.8	23 26.0	0 49.0	19 28.8	26 31.2	8 33.2	1 33.7	6 40.6
25 T	16 9 48.3	3 39.5	0 30.3	7♋30.2	9 54.5	24 39.7	1 23.6	19 35.7	26 38.6	8 36.7	1 33.1	6 41.5
26 F	16 13 44.9	4 37.1	0 27.1	20 9.6	10 36.1	25 53.3	1 58.2	19 42.7	26 46.0	8 40.2	1 32.5	6 42.4
27 S	16 17 41.4	5 34.7	0 23.9	2♌30.6	11 21.5	27 7.0	2 33.0	19 49.9	26 53.5	8 43.7	1 32.0	6 43.4
28 S	16 21 38.0	6 32.3	0 20.8	14 36.8	12 10.5	28 20.6	3 7.7	19 57.1	27 1.0	8 47.3	1 31.5	6 44.4
29 M	16 25 34.5	7 29.8	0 17.6	26 32.9	13 3.0	29 34.2	3 42.5	20 4.5	27 8.5	8 50.8	1 31.1	6 45.4
30 T	16 29 31.1	8 27.4	0 14.4	8♍23.8	13 59.0	0♊47.8	4 17.4	20 12.0	27 16.0	8 54.3	1 30.6	6 46.4
31 W	16 33 27.6	9 24.9	0 11.2	20 14.9	14 58.3	2 1.5	4 52.3	20 19.7	27 23.5	8 57.8	1 30.2	6 47.5

DECLINATION

DAY	h m s	☉	☊	☽	☿	♀	♂	♃	♄	♅	♆	♇
1 M	14 35 11.0	14N58.5	19N46.2	16N40.1	16N46.5	8N25.5	23N59.0	16N33.2	22N19.9	21N27.6	0N33.3	24N 2.6
4 T	14 47 0.7	15 52.0	19 48.3	6 0.3	15 23.6	9 47.6	23 43.5	16 29.7	22 21.2	21 29.2	0 34.7	24 2.1
7 S	14 58 50.3	16 43.2	19 50.4	7S 4.6	14 0.1	11 7.8	23 26.7	16 25.7	22 22.5	21 30.9	0 35.9	24 1.5
10 W	15 10 40.0	17 31.9	19 52.5	18 2.9	12 45.3	12 25.6	23 8.7	16 21.2	22 23.7	21 32.6	0 37.1	24 0.9
13 S	15 22 29.6	18 17.9	19 54.6	21 4.7	11 46.6	13 40.9	22 49.5	16 16.3	22 24.9	21 34.2	0 38.1	24 0.2
16 T	15 34 19.3	19 1.2	19 56.7	13 17.0	11 8.4	14 53.2	22 29.0	16 10.9	22 26.0	21 35.9	0 39.1	23 59.5
19 F	15 46 9.0	19 41.6	19 58.7	1N21.5	10 52.0	16 2.2	22 7.3	16 5.1	22 27.1	21 37.6	0 39.9	23 58.7
22 M	15 57 58.7	20 19.0	20 0.8	15 13.8	10 57.1	17 7.7	21 44.5	15 58.9	22 28.1	21 39.3	0 40.7	23 57.8
25 T	16 9 48.3	20 53.3	20 2.9	21 21.7	11 21.6	18 9.3	21 20.4	15 52.3	22 29.0	21 41.0	0 41.3	23 57.0
28 S	16 21 38.0	21 24.4	20 4.9	17 47.0	12 3.5	19 6.6	20 55.1	15 45.3	22 29.9	21 42.6	0 41.8	23 56.1
31 W	16 33 27.6	21 52.1	20 6.9	7 33.3	12 59.9	19 59.4	20 28.7	15 37.9	22 30.7	21 44.3	0 42.3	23 55.1

JUNE 1944

LONGITUDE

DAY	h m s	☉	☊	☽	☿	♀	♂	♃	♄	♅	♆	♇
1 T	16 37 24.2	10♊22.4	0♌8.1	2♎11.0	16♉0.9	3♊15.1	5♌27.3	20♌27.5	27♊31.1	9♊1.4	1♎29.9	6♌48.5
2 F	16 41 20.8	11 19.8	0 4.9	14 16.7	17 6.7	4 28.7	6 2.2	20 35.4	27 38.7	9 4.9	1R29.5	6 49.6
3 S	16 45 17.3	12 17.3	0 1.7	26 36.0	18 15.7	5 42.3	6 37.3	20 43.4	27 46.3	9 8.4	1 29.2	6 50.7
4 S	16 49 13.8	13 14.7	29♋58.5	9♏11.6	19 27.7	6 56.0	7 12.4	20 51.5	27 53.9	9 11.9	1 28.9	6 51.8
5 M	16 53 10.4	14 12.1	29 55.4	22 5.1	20 42.7	8 9.6	7 47.5	20 59.8	28 1.6	9 15.5	1 28.7	6 53.0
6 T	16 57 7.0	15 9.5	29 52.2	5♐16.7	22 0.8	9 23.2	8 22.6	21 8.1	28 9.3	9 19.0	1 28.5	6 54.2
7 W	17 1 3.5	16 6.9	29 49.0	18 45.4	23 21.7	10 36.8	8 57.8	21 16.6	28 17.0	9 22.5	1 28.3	6 55.3
8 T	17 5 0.1	17 4.3	29 45.8	2♑28.8	24 45.6	11 50.5	9 33.1	21 25.2	28 24.7	9 26.0	1 28.1	6 56.5
9 F	17 8 56.6	18 1.6	29 42.6	16 24.1	26 12.3	13 4.1	10 8.4	21 33.9	28 32.4	9 29.5	1 28.0	6 57.8
10 S	17 12 53.2	18 59.0	29 39.5	0♒28.0	27 41.9	14 17.7	10 43.7	21 42.7	28 40.1	9 33.0	1 27.9	6 59.0
11 S	17 16 49.8	19 56.3	29 36.3	14 37.4	29 14.3	15 31.4	11 19.1	21 51.6	28 47.8	9 36.5	1 27.9	7 0.3
12 M	17 20 46.3	20 53.6	29 33.1	28 49.7	0♊49.6	16 45.0	11 54.5	22 0.6	28 55.6	9 39.9	1 27.8	7 1.6
13 T	17 24 42.9	21 50.9	29 29.9	13♓2.6	2 27.6	17 58.7	12 30.0	22 9.8	29 3.4	9 43.4	1D27.8	7 2.8
14 W	17 28 39.4	22 48.3	29 26.8	27 14.1	4 8.4	19 12.3	13 5.5	22 19.0	29 11.1	9 46.9	1 27.9	7 4.2
15 T	17 32 36.0	23 45.6	29 23.6	11♈22.4	5 52.0	20 26.0	13 41.0	22 28.3	29 18.9	9 50.3	1 28.0	7 5.5
16 F	17 36 32.5	24 42.9	29 20.4	25 25.2	7 38.3	21 39.7	14 16.6	22 37.8	29 26.7	9 53.8	1 28.1	7 6.9
17 S	17 40 29.1	25 40.2	29 17.2	9♉20.5	9 27.2	22 53.4	14 52.2	22 47.3	29 34.5	9 57.2	1 28.2	7 8.2
18 S	17 44 25.7	26 37.5	29 14.0	23 5.6	11 18.8	24 7.0	15 27.9	22 56.9	29 42.3	10 0.6	1 28.4	7 9.6
19 M	17 48 22.2	27 34.7	29 10.9	6♊38.3	13 12.9	25 20.7	16 3.6	23 6.6	29 50.1	10 4.0	1 28.6	7 11.0
20 T	17 52 18.8	28 32.0	29 7.7	19 56.5	15 9.4	26 34.4	16 39.4	23 16.5	29 57.9	10 7.4	1 28.8	7 12.4
21 W	17 56 15.3	29 29.3	29 4.5	2♋58.6	17 8.3	27 48.1	17 15.2	23 26.4	0♋5.7	10 10.8	1 29.1	7 13.8
22 T	18 0 11.9	0♋26.6	29 1.3	15 44.3	19 9.4	29 1.8	17 51.0	23 36.4	0 13.5	10 14.2	1 29.4	7 15.3
23 F	18 4 8.5	1 23.8	28 58.2	28 14.0	21 12.6	0♋15.5	18 26.9	23 46.5	0 21.3	10 17.6	1 29.7	7 16.7
24 S	18 8 5.0	2 21.1	28 55.0	10♌29.4	23 17.6	1 29.3	19 2.9	23 56.6	0 29.1	10 20.9	1 30.1	7 18.2
25 S	18 12 1.6	3 18.3	28 51.8	22 33.1	25 24.2	2 43.0	19 38.8	24 6.9	0 37.0	10 24.2	1 30.5	7 19.7
26 M	18 15 58.1	4 15.5	28 48.6	4♍28.4	27 32.2	3 56.7	20 14.8	24 17.2	0 44.8	10 27.5	1 30.9	7 21.2
27 T	18 19 54.7	5 12.8	28 45.5	16 19.6	29 41.3	5 10.4	20 50.9	24 27.7	0 52.5	10 30.8	1 31.4	7 22.7
28 W	18 23 51.2	6 10.0	28 42.3	28 11.0	1♋51.3	6 24.2	21 27.0	24 38.2	1 0.3	10 34.1	1 31.9	7 24.2
29 T	18 27 47.8	7 7.2	28 39.1	10♎7.5	4 1.9	7 37.9	22 3.1	24 48.8	1 8.1	10 37.3	1 32.4	7 25.8
30 F	18 31 44.4	8 4.4	28 35.9	22 13.7	6 12.8	8 51.6	22 39.3	24 59.5	1 15.9	10 40.6	1 32.9	7 27.3

DECLINATION

DAY	h m s	☉	☊	☽	☿	♀	♂	♃	♄	♅	♆	♇
1 T	16 37 24.2	22N 0.6	20N 7.6	3N20.7	13N21.5	20N15.9	20N19.7	15N35.3	22N31.0	21N44.8	0N42.4	23N54.8
4 S	16 49 13.8	22 23.7	20♋ 9.6	9S46.3	14 33.3	21 2.1	19 51.8	15 27.4	22 31.7	21 46.5	0 42.6	23 53.8
7 W	17 1 3.5	22 43.3	20 11.6	19 41.7	15 53.6	21 43.2	19 22.8	15 19.1	22 32.3	21 48.1	0 42.8	23 52.7
10 S	17 12 53.2	22 59.3	20 13.6	20 15.6	17 19.4	22 18.8	18 52.7	15 10.5	22 32.9	21 49.7	0 42.8	23 51.6
13 T	17 24 42.9	23 11.7	20 15.6	10 3.1	18 47.6	22 48.7	18 21.6	15 1.5	22 33.4	21 51.3	0 42.7	23 50.5
16 F	17 36 32.5	23 20.4	20 17.6	4N59.8	20 14.6	23 12.7	17 49.4	14 52.2	22 33.8	21 52.9	0 42.5	23 49.4
19 M	17 48 22.2	23 25.4	20 19.6	17 24.9	21 35.9	23 30.7	17 16.3	14 42.5	22 34.1	21 54.4	0 42.2	23 48.2
22 T	18 0 11.9	23 26.7	20 21.6	21 25.9	22 46.6	23 42.4	16 42.1	14 32.5	22 34.3	21 55.9	0 41.8	23 47.1
25 S	18 12 1.6	23 24.2	20 23.5	16 5.0	23 41.3	23 47.9	16 7.1	14 22.2	22 34.5	21 57.4	0 41.3	23 45.9
28 W	18 23 51.2	23 18.1	20 25.5	4 54.9	24 15.0	23 47.0	15 31.1	14 11.6	22 34.6	21 58.8	0 40.6	23 44.6

JULY 1944

DAY	EPHEMERIS SIDEREAL TIME h m s	☉ ° ′	☊ ° ′	☽ ° ′	☿ ° ′	♀ ° ′	♂ ° ′	♃ ° ′	♄ ° ′	♅ ° ′	♆ ° ′	♇ ° ′
						LONGITUDE						
1 S	18 35 40.9	9♋ 1.6	28♋32.8	4♏34.2	8♋23.6	10♋ 5.4	23♌15.4	25♌10.2	1♋23.7	10♊43.8	1♎33.5	7♌28.9
2 S	18 39 37.4	9 58.8	28 29.6	17 12.6	10 34.2	11 19.1	23 51.7	25 21.0	1 31.4	10 47.0	1 34.1	7 30.5
3 M	18 43 34.0	10 56.0	28 26.4	0♐11.8	12 44.3	12 32.9	24 28.0	25 31.9	1 39.2	10 50.1	1 34.8	7 32.1
4 T	18 47 30.6	11 53.1	28 23.2	13 33.1	14 53.6	13 46.6	25 4.3	25 42.9	1 46.9	10 53.3	1 35.5	7 33.7
5 W	18 51 27.2	12 50.3	28 20.1	27 16.4	17 1.9	15 0.4	25 40.6	25 53.9	1 54.6	10 56.4	1 36.2	7 35.3
6 T	18 55 23.7	13 47.5	28 16.9	11♑19.4	19 9.1	16 14.1	26 17.0	26 5.0	2 2.3	10 59.5	1 36.9	7 36.9
7 F	18 59 20.2	14 44.7	28 13.7	25 38.5	21 15.0	17 27.9	26 53.4	26 16.2	2 10.0	11 2.6	1 37.7	7 38.5
8 S	19 3 16.8	15 41.9	28 10.5	10♒ 8.7	23 19.4	18 41.7	27 29.9	26 27.5	2 17.7	11 5.6	1 38.5	7 40.2
9 S	19 7 13.4	16 39.0	28 7.3	24 44.2	25 22.3	19 55.5	28 6.4	26 38.8	2 25.4	11 8.7	1 39.4	7 41.8
10 M	19 11 9.9	17 36.2	28 4.2	9♓19.4	27 23.6	21 9.3	28 42.9	26 50.1	2 33.0	11 11.7	1 40.2	7 43.5
11 T	19 15 6.5	18 33.4	28 1.0	23 49.1	29 23.1	22 23.1	29 19.5	27 1.6	2 40.6	11 14.6	1 41.1	7 45.1
12 W	19 19 3.0	19 30.6	27 57.8	8♈ 9.2	1♌20.9	23 36.9	29 56.1	27 13.1	2 48.2	11 17.6	1 42.0	7 46.8
13 T	19 22 59.6	20 27.9	27 54.6	22 17.0	3 16.8	24 50.7	0♍32.7	27 24.6	2 55.8	11 20.5	1 43.0	7 48.5
14 F	19 26 56.1	21 25.1	27 51.5	6♉10.7	5 11.0	26 4.5	1 9.4	27 36.3	3 3.4	11 23.4	1 44.0	7 50.2
15 S	19 30 52.7	22 22.3	27 48.3	19 49.4	7 3.3	27 18.4	1 46.1	27 47.9	3 10.9	11 26.3	1 45.0	7 51.8
16 S	19 34 49.3	23 19.6	27 45.1	3♊13.1	8 53.7	28 32.2	2 22.9	27 59.7	3 18.4	11 29.1	1 46.0	7 53.5
17 M	19 38 45.8	24 16.8	27 41.9	16 21.9	10 42.3	29 46.1	2 59.7	28 11.5	3 25.9	11 31.9	1 47.1	7 55.3
18 T	19 42 42.4	25 14.1	27 38.8	29 16.4	12 29.1	0♌59.9	3 36.6	28 23.3	3 33.4	11 34.7	1 48.2	7 57.0
19 W	19 46 38.9	26 11.4	27 35.6	11♋57.3	14 14.0	2 13.8	4 13.5	28 35.2	3 40.8	11 37.5	1 49.3	7 58.7
20 T	19 50 35.5	27 8.7	27 32.4	24 25.5	15 57.1	3 27.7	4 50.4	28 47.2	3 48.2	11 40.2	1 50.5	8 0.4
21 F	19 54 32.1	28 5.9	27 29.2	6♌42.2	17 38.3	4 41.6	5 27.4	28 59.2	3 55.6	11 42.9	1 51.7	8 2.1
22 S	19 58 28.6	29 3.2	27 26.0	18 48.8	19 17.6	5 55.5	6 4.4	29 11.2	4 2.9	11 45.5	1 52.9	8 3.9
23 S	20 2 25.2	0♌ 0.6	27 22.9	0♍47.3	20 55.2	7 9.4	6 41.4	29 23.3	4 10.3	11 48.2	1 54.1	8 5.6
24 M	20 6 21.7	0 57.9	27 19.7	12 40.2	22 30.9	8 23.3	7 18.5	29 35.5	4 17.5	11 50.8	1 55.4	8 7.3
25 T	20 10 18.3	1 55.2	27 16.5	24 30.4	24 4.8	9 37.2	7 55.7	29 47.7	4 24.8	11 53.3	1 56.7	8 9.1
26 W	20 14 14.8	2 52.5	27 13.3	6♎21.4	25 36.8	10 51.1	8 32.8	29 59.9	4 32.0	11 55.8	1 58.0	8 10.8
27 T	20 18 11.4	3 49.9	27 10.2	18 17.2	27 6.9	12 5.0	9 10.0	0♍12.2	4 39.2	11 58.3	1 59.4	8 12.6
28 F	20 22 8.0	4 47.2	27 7.0	0♏22.0	28 35.2	13 18.9	9 47.3	0 24.5	4 46.3	12 0.8	2 0.7	8 14.3
29 S	20 26 4.5	5 44.6	27 3.8	12 40.3	0♍ 1.6	14 32.8	10 24.6	0 36.9	4 53.4	12 3.2	2 2.1	8 16.1
30 S	20 30 1.0	6 42.0	27 0.6	25 16.3	1 26.1	15 46.8	11 1.9	0 49.3	5 0.5	12 5.5	2 3.6	8 17.8
31 M	20 33 57.6	7 39.3	26 57.4	8♐13.8	2 48.6	17 0.7	11 39.2	1 1.7	5 7.5	12 7.9	2 5.0	8 19.6
						DECLINATION						
1 S	18 35 40.9	23N 8.3	20N27.4	8S 7.5	24N24.6	23N39.8	14N54.2	14N 0.7	22N34.6	22N 0.2	0N39.8	23N43.4
4 T	18 47 30.6	22 54.8	20 29.3	18 47.2	24 9.0	23 26.3	14 16.4	13 49.6	22 34.5	22 1.6	0 38.9	23 42.2
7 F	18 59 20.2	22 37.8	20 31.3	20 50.2	23 29.6	23 6.5	13 37.9	13 38.2	22 34.3	22 2.9	0 37.9	23 40.9
10 M	19 11 9.9	22 17.2	20 33.2	11 19.8	22 29.4	22 40.6	12 58.5	13 26.5	22 34.1	22 4.2	0 36.8	23 39.6
13 T	19 22 59.6	21 53.2	20 35.1	3N47.5	21 12.1	22 8.7	12 18.4	13 14.5	22 33.8	22 5.4	0 35.6	23 38.4
16 S	19 34 49.3	21 25.8	20 37.0	16 34.7	19 41.5	21 30.9	11 37.6	13 2.4	22 33.5	22 6.6	0 34.3	23 37.1
19 W	19 46 38.9	20 55.1	20 38.9	21 28.6	18 1.0	20 47.6	10 56.1	12 50.0	22 33.0	22 7.8	0 32.9	23 35.9
22 S	19 58 28.6	20 21.2	20 40.7	17 0.3	16 13.5	19 58.9	10 13.9	12 37.3	22 32.5	22 8.9	0 31.4	23 34.6
25 T	20 10 18.3	19 44.3	20 42.6	6 14.8	14 21.6	19 5.1	9 31.1	12 24.5	22 32.0	22 9.9	0 29.8	23 33.4
28 F	20 22 8.0	19 4.4	20 44.4	6S39.3	12 27.5	18 6.5	8 47.7	12 11.5	22 31.4	22 11.0	0 28.1	23 32.1
31 M	20 33 57.6	18 21.6	20 46.3	17 43.0	10 33.2	17 3.3	8 3.7	11 58.3	22 30.7	22 11.9	0 26.3	23 30.9

AUGUST 1944

DAY	EPHEMERIS SIDEREAL TIME h m s	☉ ° ′	☊ ° ′	☽ ° ′	☿ ° ′	♀ ° ′	♂ ° ′	♃ ° ′	♄ ° ′	♅ ° ′	♆ ° ′	♇ ° ′
						LONGITUDE						
1 T	20 37 54.2	8♌36.7	26♋54.3	21♐35.8	4♍ 9.2	18♌14.6	12♍16.6	1♍14.2	5♋14.5	12♊10.2	2♎ 6.5	8♌21.3
2 W	20 41 50.8	9 34.1	26 51.1	5♑23.4	5 27.7	19 28.5	12 54.1	1 26.7	5 21.4	12 12.4	2 8.0	8 23.1
3 T	20 45 47.3	10 31.5	26 47.9	19 36.1	6 44.1	20 42.5	13 31.5	1 39.2	5 28.3	12 14.7	2 9.5	8 24.8
4 F	20 49 43.8	11 28.9	26 44.7	4♒10.5	7 58.5	21 56.4	14 9.0	1 51.8	5 35.1	12 16.8	2 11.0	8 26.6
5 S	20 53 40.4	12 26.4	26 41.6	19 1.3	9 10.6	23 10.3	14 46.6	2 4.4	5 42.0	12 19.0	2 12.6	8 28.3
6 S	20 57 37.0	13 23.8	26 38.4	4♓ 0.7	10 20.5	24 24.3	15 24.2	2 17.0	5 48.7	12 21.1	2 14.2	8 30.1
7 M	21 1 33.5	14 21.3	26 35.2	19 0.4	11 28.1	25 38.2	16 1.8	2 29.7	5 55.4	12 23.2	2 15.8	8 31.8
8 T	21 5 30.0	15 18.8	26 32.0	3♈51.8	12 33.2	26 52.1	16 39.4	2 42.4	6 2.1	12 25.2	2 17.5	8 33.6
9 W	21 9 26.6	16 16.3	26 28.8	18 28.3	13 35.8	28 6.1	17 17.1	2 55.1	6 8.7	12 27.2	2 19.1	8 35.3
10 T	21 13 23.2	17 13.9	26 25.7	2♉45.0	14 35.8	29 20.0	17 54.9	3 7.9	6 15.3	12 29.1	2 20.8	8 37.0
11 F	21 17 19.7	18 11.4	26 22.5	16 39.6	15 33.0	0♍34.0	18 32.7	3 20.6	6 21.8	12 31.0	2 22.5	8 38.8
12 S	21 21 16.3	19 9.0	26 19.3	0♊11.9	16 27.3	1 48.0	19 10.5	3 33.4	6 28.2	12 32.9	2 24.2	8 40.5
13 S	21 25 12.8	20 6.6	26 16.1	13 23.2	17 18.6	3 1.9	19 48.3	3 46.3	6 34.6	12 34.7	2 26.0	8 42.2
14 M	21 29 9.4	21 4.3	26 13.0	26 15.8	18 6.7	4 15.9	20 26.3	3 59.1	6 41.0	12 36.4	2 27.7	8 43.9
15 T	21 33 5.9	22 1.9	26 9.8	8♋52.4	18 51.5	5 29.9	21 4.2	4 12.0	6 47.3	12 38.2	2 29.5	8 45.7
16 W	21 37 2.5	22 59.6	26 6.6	21 15.8	19 32.7	6 43.9	21 42.2	4 24.9	6 53.5	12 39.8	2 31.3	8 47.4
17 T	21 40 59.0	23 57.3	26 3.4	3♌28.5	20 10.1	7 57.8	22 20.2	4 37.8	6 59.7	12 41.5	2 33.1	8 49.1
18 F	21 44 55.6	24 55.1	26 0.3	15 32.7	20 43.6	9 11.8	22 58.3	4 50.7	7 5.8	12 43.1	2 35.0	8 50.8
19 S	21 48 52.1	25 52.8	25 57.1	27 30.6	21 12.8	10 25.8	23 36.5	5 3.6	7 11.9	12 44.6	2 36.8	8 52.5
20 S	21 52 48.7	26 50.6	25 53.9	9♍24.0	21 37.7	11 39.8	24 14.6	5 16.6	7 17.9	12 46.1	2 38.7	8 54.2
21 M	21 56 45.3	27 48.4	25 50.7	21 14.7	21 57.9	12 53.8	24 52.8	5 29.5	7 23.8	12 47.6	2 40.6	8 55.8
22 T	22 0 41.8	28 46.2	25 47.5	3♎ 4.7	22 13.2	14 7.7	25 31.1	5 42.5	7 29.7	12 49.0	2 42.5	8 57.5
23 W	22 4 38.3	29 44.1	25 44.4	14 56.6	22 23.3	15 21.7	26 9.4	5 55.5	7 35.5	12 50.3	2 44.4	8 59.2
24 T	22 8 34.9	0♍41.9	25 41.2	26 53.1	22 28.0	16 35.7	26 47.7	6 8.5	7 41.2	12 51.6	2 46.4	9 0.8
25 F	22 12 31.5	1 39.8	25 38.0	8♏57.4	22R27.1	17 49.7	27 26.1	6 21.5	7 46.9	12 52.9	2 48.4	9 2.5
26 S	22 16 28.1	2 37.7	25 34.8	21 13.5	22 20.5	19 3.7	28 4.5	6 34.5	7 52.5	12 54.1	2 50.3	9 4.1
27 S	22 20 24.6	3 35.7	25 31.7	3♐45.4	22 7.8	20 17.6	28 42.9	6 47.5	7 58.0	12 55.3	2 52.3	9 5.7
28 M	22 24 21.1	4 33.6	25 28.5	16 37.2	21 49.1	21 31.6	29 21.4	7 0.6	8 3.5	12 56.4	2 54.3	9 7.3
29 T	22 28 17.7	5 31.6	25 25.3	29 52.8	21 24.4	22 45.5	29 60.0	7 13.6	8 8.9	12 57.4	2 56.3	9 8.9
30 W	22 32 14.3	6 29.6	25 22.1	13♑35.1	20 53.6	23 59.5	0♎38.5	7 26.6	8 14.2	12 58.5	2 58.4	9 10.5
31 T	22 36 10.8	7 27.6	25 18.9	27 45.0	20 17.1	25 13.4	1 17.2	7 39.6	8 19.4	12 59.4	3 0.4	9 12.1
						DECLINATION						
1 T	20 37 54.2	18N 6.8	20N46.9	20S 4.1	9N55.4	16N41.3	7N48.9	11N53.8	22N30.5	22N12.2	0N25.7	23N30.5
4 F	20 49 43.8	17 20.5	20 48.7	19 47.9	8 3.7	15 32.7	7 4.3	11 40.4	22 29.7	22 13.1	0 23.8	23 29.3
7 M	21 1 33.5	16 31.7	20 50.6	8 8.1	6 16.0	14 20.2	6 19.2	11 26.8	22 29.0	22 14.0	0 21.9	23 28.1
10 T	21 13 23.2	15 40.5	20 52.4	7N30.3	4 34.4	13 4.2	5 33.7	11 13.1	22 28.1	22 14.8	0 19.8	23 27.0
13 S	21 25 12.8	14 47.0	20 54.2	18 46.3	3 1.1	11 45.2	4 47.7	10 59.2	22 27.3	22 15.5	0 17.7	23 25.9
16 W	21 37 2.5	13 51.4	20 56.0	21 11.3	1 38.6	10 23.2	4 1.4	10 45.2	22 26.4	22 16.2	0 15.5	23 24.8
19 S	21 48 52.1	12 53.8	20 57.7	14 47.4	0 30.3	8 58.8	3 14.8	10 31.1	22 25.5	22 16.8	0 13.2	23 23.7
22 T	22 0 41.8	11 54.3	20 59.5	3 7.5	0S19.9	7 32.3	2 27.8	10 16.9	22 24.6	22 17.4	0 10.9	23 22.7
25 F	22 12 31.5	10 53.2	21 1.3	9S40.0	0 47.5	6 3.9	1 40.6	10 2.6	22 23.7	22 17.9	0 8.6	23 21.7
28 M	22 24 21.1	9 50.5	21 3.0	19 25.0	0 47.7	4 34.0	0 53.3	9 48.2	22 22.7	22 18.4	0 6.2	23 20.8
31 T	22 36 10.8	8 46.4	21 4.8	20 40.5	0 16.4	3 3.0	0 5.7	9 33.8	22 21.8	22 18.8	0 3.7	23 19.9

SEPTEMBER 1944

DAY	EPHEMERIS SIDEREAL TIME	☉	☊	☽	☿	♀	♂	♃	♄	♅	♆	♇
	h m s	° ′	° ′	° ′	° ′	° ′	° ′	° ′	° ′	° ′	° ′	° ′
						LONGITUDE						
1 F	22 40 7.3	8♍25.6	25♋15.8	12♒21.2	19♍35.1	26♍27.4	1♎55.8	7♍52.7	8♋24.6	13♊ 0.3	3♎ 2.5	9♌13.7
2 S	22 44 3.9	9 23.7	25 12.6	27 19.3	18R48.1	27 41.3	2 34.5	8 5.7	8 29.7	13 1.2	3 4.6	9 15.2
3 S	22 48 0.5	10 21.8	25 9.4	12♓31.6	17 56.8	28 55.2	3 13.2	8 18.7	8 34.7	13 2.0	3 6.6	9 16.8
4 M	22 51 57.0	11 19.9	25 6.2	27 48.2	17 1.9	0♎ 9.1	3 52.0	8 31.7	8 39.6	13 2.8	3 8.7	9 18.3
5 T	22 55 53.6	12 18.1	25 3.1	12♈58.4	16 4.5	1 23.0	4 30.8	8 44.7	8 44.5	13 3.5	3 10.8	9 19.8
6 W	22 59 50.1	13 16.3	24 59.9	27 52.3	15 5.6	2 36.9	5 9.7	8 57.7	8 49.3	13 4.2	3 13.0	9 21.3
7 T	23 3 46.6	14 14.5	24 56.7	12♉22.7	14 6.5	3 50.9	5 48.6	9 10.8	8 54.0	13 4.8	3 15.1	9 22.8
8 F	23 7 43.2	15 12.7	24 53.5	26 25.8	13 8.5	5 4.8	6 27.6	9 23.8	8 58.6	13 5.4	3 17.2	9 24.3
9 S	23 11 39.8	16 11.0	24 50.3	10♊ 0.8	12 12.9	6 18.7	7 6.6	9 36.7	9 3.2	13 5.9	3 19.4	9 25.8
10 S	23 15 36.3	17 9.3	24 47.2	23 9.5	11 21.1	7 32.5	7 45.6	9 49.7	9 7.6	13 6.4	3 21.5	9 27.2
11 M	23 19 32.8	18 7.7	24 44.0	5♋55.3	10 34.3	8 46.4	8 24.7	10 2.7	9 12.0	13 6.8	3 23.7	9 28.7
12 T	23 23 29.4	19 6.1	24 40.8	18 22.3	9 53.8	10 0.3	9 3.9	10 15.6	9 16.3	13 7.1	3 25.9	9 30.1
13 W	23 27 26.0	20 4.5	24 37.6	0♌35.0	9 20.5	11 14.2	9 43.1	10 28.6	9 20.5	13 7.4	3 28.0	9 31.5
14 T	23 31 22.6	21 3.0	24 34.5	12 37.4	8 55.2	12 28.1	10 22.3	10 41.5	9 24.6	13 7.7	3 30.2	9 32.9
15 F	23 35 19.1	22 1.5	24 31.3	24 33.0	8 38.7	13 42.0	11 1.6	10 54.4	9 28.6	13 7.9	3 32.4	9 34.2
16 S	23 39 15.6	22 60.0	24 28.1	6♍24.8	8 31.3	14 55.8	11 40.9	11 7.3	9 32.5	13 8.1	3 34.6	9 35.6
17 S	23 43 12.2	23 58.5	24 24.9	18 15.1	8D33.5	16 9.7	12 20.3	11 20.2	9 36.4	13 8.2	3 36.8	9 36.9
18 M	23 47 8.8	24 57.1	24 21.7	0♎ 5.8	8 45.2	17 23.6	12 59.7	11 33.1	9 40.1	13 8.2	3 39.0	9 38.2
19 T	23 51 5.3	25 55.8	24 18.6	11 58.4	9 6.4	18 37.4	13 39.2	11 45.9	9 43.8	13 8.2	3 41.2	9 39.6
20 W	23 55 1.8	26 54.4	24 15.4	23 54.4	9 36.9	19 51.3	14 18.7	11 58.7	9 47.3	13R 8.2	3 43.5	9 40.8
21 T	23 58 58.4	27 53.1	24 12.2	5♏55.6	10 16.3	21 5.1	14 58.2	12 11.5	9 50.8	13 8.1	3 45.7	9 42.1
22 F	0 2 55.0	28 51.8	24 9.0	18 4.1	11 4.3	22 18.9	15 37.8	12 24.3	9 54.1	13 7.9	3 47.9	9 43.3
23 S	0 6 51.5	29 50.6	24 5.9	0♐22.4	12 0.3	23 32.7	16 17.5	12 37.0	9 57.4	13 7.7	3 50.1	9 44.6
24 S	0 10 48.1	0♎49.3	24 2.7	12 53.8	13 3.6	24 46.5	16 57.2	12 49.7	10 0.6	13 7.4	3 52.4	9 45.8
25 M	0 14 44.6	1 48.1	23 59.5	25 41.8	14 13.7	26 0.3	17 36.9	13 2.4	10 3.7	13 7.1	3 54.6	9 47.0
26 T	0 18 41.2	2 47.0	23 56.3	8♑50.4	15 29.9	27 14.1	18 16.7	13 15.0	10 6.6	13 6.8	3 56.8	9 48.1
27 W	0 22 37.7	3 45.8	23 53.1	22 22.9	16 51.5	28 27.9	18 56.5	13 27.6	10 9.5	13 6.4	3 59.1	9 49.3
28 T	0 26 34.3	4 44.7	23 50.0	6♒21.8	18 17.9	29 41.6	19 36.4	13 40.2	10 12.3	13 5.9	4 1.3	9 50.4
29 F	0 30 30.8	5 43.6	23 46.8	20 47.5	19 48.3	0♏55.4	20 16.3	13 52.7	10 15.0	13 5.4	4 3.5	9 51.5
30 S	0 34 27.4	6 42.6	23 43.6	5♓37.4	21 22.3	2 9.1	20 56.3	14 5.3	10 17.5	13 4.8	4 5.8	9 52.6
						DECLINATION						
1 F	22 40 7.3	8N24.7	21N 5.4	18S24.5	0N 1.3	2N32.4	0S10.2	9N29.0	22N21.5	22N18.9	0N 2.9	23N19.6
4 M	22 51 57.0	7 19.0	21 7.1	4 59.9	1 14.8	1 0.3	0 57.8	9 14.5	22 20.6	22 19.2	0 0.4	23 18.7
7 T	23 3 46.6	6 12.2	21 8.8	10N50.6	2 52.2	0S32.2	1 45.6	8 60.0	22 19.6	22 19.5	0S 2.2	23 17.9
10 S	23 15 36.3	5 4.5	21 10.5	20 26.6	4 38.9	2 4.9	2 33.4	8 45.5	22 18.8	22 19.7	0 4.8	23 17.2
13 W	23 27 26.0	3 55.9	21 12.2	20 23.3	6 16.8	3 37.3	3 21.1	8 30.9	22 17.9	22 19.9	0 7.4	23 16.5
16 S	23 39 15.6	2 46.8	21 13.9	12 12.4	7 29.6	5 9.2	4 8.8	8 16.4	22 17.1	22 20.0	0N.0.0	23 15.9
19 T	23 51 5.3	1 37.1	21 15.6	0S12.8	8 6.7	6 40.2	4 56.4	8 2.0	22 16.3	22 20.0	0S12.6	23 15.3
22 F	0 2 55.0	0 27.1	21 17.3	12 44.0	8 3.9	8 10.0	5 43.8	7 47.5	22 15.5	22 20.0	0 15.3	23 14.8
25 M	0 14 44.6	0S43.0	21 18.9	20 53.1	7 22.8	9 38.3	6 31.0	7 33.2	22 14.8	22 19.9	0 17.9	23 14.3
28 T	0 26 34.3	1 53.2	21 20.6	19 38.9	6 8.7	11 4.6	7 18.0	7 18.9	22 14.2	22 19.8	0 20.5	23 13.9

OCTOBER 1944

DAY	EPHEMERIS SIDEREAL TIME	☉	☊	☽	☿	♀	♂	♃	♄	♅	♆	♇
						LONGITUDE						
1 S	0 38 23.9	7♎41.5	23♋40.4	20♓45.9	22♍59.2	3♏22.8	21♎36.3	14♍17.7	10♋20.0	13♊ 4.2	4♎ 8.0	9♌53.6
2 M	0 42 20.5	8 40.6	23 37.3	6♈ 3.7	24 38.5	4 36.5	22 16.3	14 30.2	10 22.4	13R 3.5	4 10.2	9 54.7
3 T	0 46 17.1	9 39.6	23 34.1	21 19.7	26 19.8	5 50.2	22 56.4	14 42.6	10 24.7	13 2.8	4 12.4	9 55.7
4 W	0 50 13.6	10 38.7	23 30.9	6♉22.8	28 2.6	7 3.9	23 36.5	14 54.9	10 26.8	13 2.1	4 14.7	9 56.7
5 T	0 54 10.1	11 37.8	23 27.7	21 3.7	29 46.6	8 17.6	24 16.7	15 7.2	10 28.9	13 1.3	4 16.9	9 57.7
6 F	0 58 6.7	12 36.9	23 24.5	5♊16.5	1♎31.4	9 31.2	24 57.0	15 19.5	10 30.8	13 0.4	4 19.1	9 58.6
7 S	1 2 3.3	13 36.1	23 21.4	18 59.0	3 16.8	10 44.9	25 37.3	15 31.7	10 32.7	12 59.5	4 21.3	9 59.6
8 S	1 5 59.8	14 35.4	23 18.2	2♋12.2	5 2.6	11 58.5	26 17.6	15 43.9	10 34.4	12 58.5	4 23.5	10 0.5
9 M	1 9 56.4	15 34.6	23 15.0	14 59.4	6 48.5	13 12.1	26 58.0	15 56.0	10 36.0	12 57.5	4 25.7	10 1.3
10 T	1 13 52.9	16 33.9	23 11.8	27 25.1	8 34.4	14 25.7	27 38.4	16 8.1	10 37.6	12 56.5	4 27.9	10 2.2
11 W	1 17 49.5	17 33.3	23 8.6	9♌34.6	10 20.1	15 39.3	28 18.9	16 20.1	10 39.0	12 55.4	4 30.1	10 3.0
12 T	1 21 46.0	18 32.7	23 5.5	21 33.0	12 5.6	16 52.9	28 59.5	16 32.1	10 40.3	12 54.2	4 32.3	10 3.8
13 F	1 25 42.6	19 32.1	23 2.3	3♍24.8	13 50.7	18 6.5	29 40.0	16 44.0	10 41.5	12 53.0	4 34.5	10 4.6
14 S	1 29 39.1	20 31.5	22 59.1	15 14.2	15 35.3	19 20.1	0♏20.7	16 55.9	10 42.6	12 51.8	4 36.6	10 5.4
15 S	1 33 35.7	21 31.0	22 55.9	27 4.3	17 19.5	20 33.7	1 1.4	17 7.7	10 43.5	12 50.5	4 38.8	10 6.1
16 M	1 37 32.2	22 30.6	22 52.8	8♎57.5	19 3.2	21 47.2	1 42.1	17 19.5	10 44.4	12 49.2	4 40.9	10 6.8
17 T	1 41 28.8	23 30.1	22 49.6	20 55.6	20 46.3	23 0.8	2 22.9	17 31.2	10 45.1	12 47.8	4 43.1	10 7.5
18 W	1 45 25.3	24 29.7	22 46.4	2♏59.7	22 28.8	24 14.3	3 3.7	17 42.8	10 45.8	12 46.4	4 45.2	10 8.2
19 T	1 49 21.9	25 29.4	22 43.2	15 10.8	24 10.8	25 27.8	3 44.6	17 54.3	10 46.3	12 44.9	4 47.3	10 8.8
20 F	1 53 18.4	26 29.0	22 40.0	27 29.9	25 52.1	26 41.3	4 25.5	18 5.9	10 46.7	12 43.4	4 49.4	10 9.4
21 S	1 57 15.0	27 28.7	22 36.9	9♐58.2	27 32.8	27 54.8	5 6.5	18 17.3	10 47.0	12 41.9	4 51.5	10 10.0
22 S	2 1 11.6	28 28.4	22 33.7	22 37.3	29 13.0	29 8.3	5 47.6	18 28.7	10 47.2	12 40.3	4 53.6	10 10.6
23 M	2 5 8.1	29 28.2	22 30.5	5♑29.6	0♏52.5	0♐21.7	6 28.6	18 40.0	10 47.3	12 38.7	4 55.7	10 11.1
24 T	2 9 4.7	0♏28.0	22 27.3	18 37.9	2 31.4	1 35.1	7 9.7	18 51.2	10R47.2	12 37.0	4 57.8	10 11.6
25 W	2 13 1.2	1 27.8	22 24.2	2♒ 5.0	4 9.8	2 48.5	7 50.9	19 2.3	10 47.1	12 35.3	4 59.8	10 12.1
26 T	2 16 57.8	2 27.6	22 21.0	15 53.2	5 47.6	4 1.9	8 32.1	19 13.4	10 46.8	12 33.6	5 1.9	10 12.5
27 F	2 20 54.3	3 27.5	22 17.8	0♓ 3.9	7 24.9	5 15.3	9 13.4	19 24.4	10 46.5	12 31.8	5 3.9	10 12.9
28 S	2 24 50.9	4 27.4	22 14.6	14 36.1	9 1.6	6 28.7	9 54.7	19 35.4	10 46.0	12 30.0	5 5.9	10 13.3
29 S	2 28 47.4	5 27.3	22 11.4	29 26.3	10 37.9	7 42.0	10 36.1	19 46.2	10 45.4	12 28.1	5 7.9	10 13.7
30 M	2 32 44.0	6 27.3	22 8.3	14♈27.8	12 13.6	8 55.3	11 17.5	19 57.0	10 44.7	12 26.2	5 9.9	10 14.1
31 T	2 36 40.5	7 27.2	22 5.1	29 31.6	13 48.8	10 8.6	11 58.9	20 7.7	10 43.9	12 24.3	5 11.8	10 14.4
						DECLINATION						
1 S	0 38 23.9	3S 3.2	21N22.2	7S29.6	4N29.3	12S28.8	8S 4.6	7N 4.7	22N13.6	22N19.6	0S23.2	23N13.6
4 W	0 50 13.6	4 12.9	21 23.9	9N 0.5	2 32.1	13 50.3	8 50.9	6 50.7	22 13.1	22 19.4	0 25.8	23 13.3
7 S	1 2 3.3	5 22.2	21 25.5	20 6.1	0 23.9	15 9.0	9 36.7	6 36.7	22 12.6	22 19.0	0 28.4	23 13.1
10 T	1 13 52.9	6 30.8	21 27.1	20 59.0	1S49.8	16 24.3	10 22.1	6 22.9	22 12.2	22 18.7	0 31.0	23 13.0
13 F	1 25 42.6	7 38.7	21 28.7	13 14.6	4 5.2	17 36.1	11 6.9	6 9.3	22 11.9	22 18.3	0 33.5	23 12.9
16 M	1 37 32.2	8 45.7	21 30.3	0 53.7	6 19.5	18 43.9	11 51.1	5 55.9	22 11.7	22 17.8	0 36.0	23 12.9
19 T	1 49 21.9	9 51.5	21 31.9	11S58.7	8 30.6	19 47.4	12 34.7	5 42.6	22 11.6	22 17.3	0 38.5	23 13.0
22 S	2 1 11.6	10 56.1	21 33.4	20 45.8	10 37.4	20 46.3	13 17.6	5 29.6	22 11.5	22 16.7	0 40.9	23 13.2
25 W	2 13 1.2	11 59.2	21 35.0	20 33.4	12 38.7	21 40.1	13 59.7	5 16.8	22 11.5	22 16.1	0 43.3	23 13.4
28 S	2 24 50.9	13 0.6	21 36.5	9 45.2	14 33.7	22 28.7	14 40.9	5 4.3	22 11.7	22 15.4	0 45.6	23 13.7
31 T	2 36 40.5	14 0.1	21 38.1	6N39.2	16 21.8	23 11.7	15 21.3	4 52.0	22 11.9	22 14.7	0 47.9	23 14.1

NOVEMBER 1944

LONGITUDE

DAY	EPHEMERIS SIDEREAL TIME	☉	☊	☽	☿	♀	♂	♃	♄	♅	♆	♇
	h m s	° ′	° ′	° ′	° ′	° ′	° ′	° ′	° ′	° ′	° ′	° ′
1 W	2 40 37.1	8♏27.2	22♋ 1.9	14♉27.7	15♏23.6	11♐21.8	12♏40.4	20♍18.3	10♋42.9	12♊22.4	5♎13.8	10♌14.7
2 T	2 44 33.6	9 27.3	21 58.7	29 6.7	16 58.0	12 35.1	13 22.0	20 28.8	10R41.9	12R20.4	5 15.7	10 14.9
3 F	2 48 30.2	10 27.4	21 55.6	13♊21.7	18 31.9	13 48.3	14 3.6	20 39.2	10 40.7	12 18.4	5 17.6	10 15.2
4 S	2 52 26.8	11 27.5	21 52.4	27 8.8	20 5.4	15 1.5	14 45.3	20 49.6	10 39.5	12 16.3	5 19.5	10 15.4
5 S	2 56 23.3	12 27.6	21 49.2	10♋27.4	21 38.5	16 14.7	15 27.0	20 59.8	10 38.1	12 14.2	5 21.4	10 15.5
6 M	3 0 19.9	13 27.8	21 46.0	23 19.6	23 11.3	17 27.8	16 8.7	21 10.0	10 36.7	12 12.1	5 23.2	10 15.7
7 T	3 4 16.4	14 28.0	21 42.8	5♌49.1	24 43.6	18 40.9	16 50.5	21 20.1	10 35.1	12 10.0	5 25.0	10 15.8
8 W	3 8 13.0	15 28.2	21 39.7	18 0.9	26 15.6	19 54.0	17 32.4	21 30.0	10 33.4	12 7.8	5 26.9	10 15.9
9 T	3 12 9.5	16 28.5	21 36.5	0♍ 0.3	27 47.2	21 7.1	18 14.3	21 39.9	10 31.6	12 5.6	5 28.7	10 16.0
10 F	3 16 6.1	17 28.8	21 33.3	11 52.5	29 18.5	22 20.2	18 56.3	21 49.7	10 29.7	12 3.4	5 30.4	10 16.0
11 S	3 20 2.6	18 29.2	21 30.1	23 42.4	0♐49.5	23 33.2	19 38.3	21 59.4	10 27.7	12 1.1	5 32.2	10 16.0
12 S	3 23 59.2	19 29.6	21 27.0	5♎34.1	2 20.0	24 46.2	20 20.4	22 9.0	10 25.6	11 58.8	5 33.9	10R16.0
13 M	3 27 55.8	20 30.0	21 23.8	17 31.0	3 50.3	25 59.2	21 2.5	22 18.5	10 23.4	11 56.5	5 35.6	10 16.0
14 T	3 31 52.3	21 30.4	21 20.6	29 35.7	5 20.2	27 12.2	21 44.7	22 27.8	10 21.0	11 54.2	5 37.3	10 15.9
15 W	3 35 48.9	22 30.9	21 17.4	11♏49.8	6 49.7	28 25.1	22 26.9	22 37.1	10 18.6	11 51.9	5 39.0	10 15.8
16 T	3 39 45.4	23 31.4	21 14.3	24 14.2	8 18.8	29 38.0	23 9.2	22 46.2	10 16.1	11 49.5	5 40.6	10 15.7
17 F	3 43 42.0	24 31.9	21 11.1	6♐49.2	9 47.5	0♑50.9	23 51.5	22 55.3	10 13.5	11 47.1	5 42.2	10 15.6
18 S	3 47 38.5	25 32.4	21 7.9	19 35.0	11 15.8	2 3.7	24 33.9	23 4.2	10 10.8	11 44.7	5 43.8	10 15.4
19 S	3 51 35.1	26 33.0	21 4.7	2♑31.8	12 43.6	3 16.6	25 16.3	23 13.0	10 8.0	11 42.3	5 45.4	10 15.2
20 M	3 55 31.6	27 33.6	21 1.5	15 39.8	14 10.9	4 29.3	25 58.8	23 21.7	10 5.1	11 39.9	5 46.9	10 14.9
21 T	3 59 28.2	28 34.2	20 58.4	28 59.8	15 37.7	5 42.1	26 41.3	23 30.3	10 2.1	11 37.4	5 48.5	10 14.7
22 W	4 3 24.8	29 34.8	20 55.2	12♒32.9	17 3.8	6 54.8	27 23.8	23 38.7	9 59.0	11 35.0	5 50.0	10 14.4
23 T	4 7 21.3	0♐35.5	20 52.0	26 20.1	18 29.3	8 7.4	28 6.5	23 47.1	9 55.8	11 32.5	5 51.4	10 14.1
24 F	4 11 17.9	1 36.1	20 48.8	10♓21.8	19 53.9	9 20.0	28 49.1	23 55.3	9 52.5	11 30.0	5 52.9	10 13.8
25 S	4 15 14.4	2 36.8	20 45.7	24 37.5	21 17.7	10 32.6	29 31.8	24 3.4	9 49.2	11 27.5	5 54.3	10 13.4
26 S	4 19 11.0	3 37.5	20 42.5	9♈ 5.0	22 40.4	11 45.1	0♐14.6	24 11.3	9 45.7	11 25.0	5 55.7	10 13.0
27 M	4 23 7.5	4 38.3	20 39.3	23 40.5	24 2.0	12 57.6	0 57.4	24 19.1	9 42.2	11 22.5	5 57.0	10 12.6
28 T	4 27 4.1	5 39.0	20 36.1	8♉17.9	25 22.3	14 10.0	1 40.2	24 26.8	9 38.6	11 20.0	5 58.4	10 12.1
29 W	4 31 0.7	6 39.8	20 33.0	22 50.6	26 41.1	15 22.4	2 23.1	24 34.4	9 35.0	11 17.5	5 59.7	10 11.7
30 T	4 34 57.2	7 40.5	20 29.8	7♊11.4	27 58.1	16 34.7	3 6.1	24 41.8	9 31.2	11 14.9	6 1.0	10 11.2

DECLINATION

DAY	EPHEMERIS SIDEREAL TIME	☉	☊	☽	☿	♀	♂	♃	♄	♅	♆	♇
1 W	2 40 37.1	14S19.6	21N38.6	11N45.8	16S56.1	23S24.8	15S34.5	4N48.0	22N12.0	22N14.5	0S48.6	23N14.2
4 S	2 52 26.8	15 16.4	21 40.1	21 22.3	18 34.1	23 59.9	16 13.5	4 36.2	22 12.3	22 13.7	0 50.8	23 14.7
7 T	3 4 16.4	16 11.0	21 41.6	20 5.5	20 3.7	24 28.8	16 51.5	4 24.6	22 12.7	22 12.9	0 52.9	23 15.2
10 F	3 16 6.1	17 3.2	21 43.1	10 45.5	21 24.6	24 51.5	17 28.3	4 13.5	22 13.2	22 12.1	0 55.0	23 15.8
13 M	3 27 55.8	17 52.7	21 44.6	2S12.3	22 35.9	25 7.6	18 3.9	4 2.6	22 13.7	22 11.2	0 56.9	23 16.5
16 T	3 39 45.4	18 39.5	21 46.1	14 46.1	23 37.3	25 17.0	18 38.3	3 52.2	22 14.4	22 10.3	0 58.8	23 17.2
19 S	3 51 35.1	19 23.3	21 47.6	21 55.3	24 27.8	25 19.8	19 11.3	3 42.2	22 15.1	22 9.3	1 0.5	23 18.0
22 W	4 3 24.8	20 4.0	21 49.0	18 58.5	25 7.0	25 15.9	19 42.9	3 32.6	22 15.9	22 8.4	1 2.2	23 18.9
25 S	4 15 14.4	20 41.3	21 50.5	6 25.0	25 34.2	25 5.3	20 13.0	3 23.4	22 16.7	22 7.4	1 3.8	23 19.8
28 T	4 27 4.1	21 15.2	21 51.9	9N40.3	25 48.9	24 48.1	20 41.5	3 14.7	22 17.6	22 6.4	1 5.3	23 20.8

DECEMBER 1944

LONGITUDE

DAY	EPHEMERIS SIDEREAL TIME	☉	☊	☽	☿	♀	♂	♃	♄	♅	♆	♇
1 F	4 38 53.8	8♐41.3	20♋26.6	21♊14.5	29♐13.2	17♑46.9	3♐49.1	24♍49.1	9♋27.4	11♊12.4	6♎ 2.2	10♌10.6
2 S	4 42 50.3	9 42.1	20 23.4	4♋55.7	0♑26.0	18 59.1	4 32.1	24 56.3	9R23.5	11R 9.8	6 3.4	10R10.1
3 S	4 46 46.9	10 43.0	20 20.3	18 13.1	1 36.1	20 11.3	5 15.2	25 3.3	9 19.5	11 7.3	6 4.6	10 9.5
4 M	4 50 43.4	11 43.8	20 17.1	1♌ 7.2	2 43.3	21 23.3	5 58.4	25 10.1	9 15.4	11 4.8	6 5.8	10 8.9
5 T	4 54 40.0	12 44.7	20 13.9	13 40.3	3 46.9	22 35.4	6 41.6	25 16.9	9 11.3	11 2.2	6 6.9	10 8.3
6 W	4 58 36.6	13 45.6	20 10.7	25 55.8	4 46.6	23 47.3	7 24.8	25 23.4	9 7.2	10 59.7	6 8.0	10 7.7
7 T	5 2 33.1	14 46.5	20 7.5	7♍58.4	5 41.6	24 59.2	8 8.1	25 29.9	9 2.9	10 57.2	6 9.1	10 7.0
8 F	5 6 29.7	15 47.5	20 4.4	19 52.9	6 31.5	26 11.1	8 51.5	25 36.2	8 58.6	10 54.6	6 10.1	10 6.3
9 S	5 10 26.2	16 48.5	20 1.2	1♎44.3	7 15.4	27 22.9	9 34.9	25 42.3	8 54.3	10 52.1	6 11.1	10 5.6
10 S	5 14 22.8	17 49.4	19 58.0	13 37.5	7 52.6	28 34.6	10 18.3	25 48.3	8 49.8	10 49.6	6 12.1	10 4.8
11 M	5 18 19.3	18 50.4	19 54.8	25 36.8	8 22.2	29 46.2	11 1.8	25 54.1	8 45.4	10 47.1	6 13.0	10 4.1
12 T	5 22 15.9	19 51.5	19 51.7	7♏45.9	8 43.4	0♒57.8	11 45.4	25 59.8	8 40.9	10 44.6	6 14.0	10 3.3
13 W	5 26 12.5	20 52.5	19 48.5	20 7.6	8 55.3	2 9.3	12 29.0	26 5.3	8 36.3	10 42.1	6 14.8	10 2.5
14 T	5 30 9.0	21 53.5	19 45.3	2♐43.8	8 57.0	3 20.7	13 12.6	26 10.7	8 31.7	10 39.6	6 15.7	10 1.7
15 F	5 34 5.6	22 54.6	19 42.1	15 35.2	8R47.9	4 32.0	13 56.3	26 15.8	8 27.0	10 37.1	6 16.5	10 0.8
16 S	5 38 2.1	23 55.7	19 38.9	28 41.6	8 27.4	5 43.3	14 40.0	26 20.9	8 22.3	10 34.6	6 17.3	9 59.9
17 S	5 41 58.7	24 56.8	19 35.8	12♑ 2.2	7 55.3	6 54.5	15 23.8	26 25.7	8 17.6	10 32.2	6 18.0	9 59.0
18 M	5 45 55.3	25 57.9	19 32.6	25 35.4	7 11.7	8 5.6	16 7.7	26 30.4	8 12.8	10 29.8	6 18.8	9 58.1
19 T	5 49 51.8	26 59.0	19 29.4	9♒19.4	6 17.1	9 16.6	16 51.6	26 35.0	8 8.0	10 27.4	6 19.4	9 57.2
20 W	5 53 48.4	28 0.1	19 26.2	23 12.5	5 12.7	10 27.5	17 35.5	26 39.3	8 3.2	10 25.0	6 20.1	9 56.2
21 T	5 57 44.9	29 1.2	19 23.1	7♓13.0	4 0.2	11 38.3	18 19.4	26 43.5	7 58.4	10 22.6	6 20.7	9 55.2
22 F	6 1 41.5	0♑ 2.3	19 19.9	21 19.2	2 41.8	12 49.0	19 3.5	26 47.5	7 53.5	10 20.2	6 21.3	9 54.2
23 S	6 5 38.0	1 3.5	19 16.7	5♈29.5	1 19.9	13 59.5	19 47.5	26 51.3	7 48.6	10 17.9	6 21.8	9 53.2
24 S	6 9 34.6	2 4.6	19 13.5	19 41.8	29♐57.4	15 10.0	20 31.6	26 55.0	7 43.7	10 15.6	6 22.4	9 52.2
25 M	6 13 31.2	3 5.7	19 10.4	3♉53.7	28 37.0	16 20.3	21 15.8	26 58.5	7 38.8	10 13.3	6 22.8	9 51.1
26 T	6 17 27.7	4 6.8	19 7.2	18 2.4	27 21.2	17 30.6	21 60.0	27 1.8	7 33.8	10 11.0	6 23.3	9 50.1
27 W	6 21 24.3	5 7.9	19 4.0	2♊ 4.4	26 12.3	18 40.7	22 44.2	27 4.9	7 28.9	10 8.8	6 23.7	9 49.0
28 T	6 25 20.8	6 9.1	19 0.8	15 56.4	25 11.8	19 50.6	23 28.5	27 7.9	7 23.9	10 6.6	6 24.1	9 47.9
29 F	6 29 17.4	7 10.2	18 57.7	29 35.2	24 20.9	21 0.5	24 12.8	27 10.6	7 19.0	10 4.4	6 24.4	9 46.8
30 S	6 33 13.9	8 11.3	18 54.5	12♋58.2	23 40.3	22 10.2	24 57.2	27 13.2	7 14.0	10 2.2	6 24.7	9 45.6
31 S	6 37 10.5	9 12.5	18 51.3	26 3.8	23 10.2	23 19.7	25 41.6	27 15.6	7 9.1	10 0.1	6 25.0	9 44.5

DECLINATION

DAY	EPHEMERIS SIDEREAL TIME	☉	☊	☽	☿	♀	♂	♃	♄	♅	♆	♇
1 F	4 38 53.8	21S45.4	21N53.4	20N45.4	25S50.8	24S24.4	21S 8.4	3N 6.5	22N18.6	22N 5.4	1S 6.7	23N21.9
4 M	4 50 43.4	22 11.9	21 54.8	20 59.5	25 40.0	23 54.4	21 33.6	2 58.8	22 19.6	22 4.3	1 8.0	23 23.0
7 T	5 2 33.1	22 34.6	21 56.2	12 13.8	25 17.1	23 18.3	21 57.1	2 51.6	22 20.6	22 3.3	1 9.1	23 24.1
10 S	5 14 22.8	22 53.2	21 57.6	0S35.9	24 43.4	22 36.3	22 18.7	2 45.0	22 21.7	22 2.3	1 10.2	23 25.3
13 W	5 26 12.5	23 7.9	21 59.0	13 29.4	24 1.3	21 48.7	22 38.5	2 38.9	22 22.8	22 1.2	1 11.1	23 26.5
16 S	5 38 2.1	23 18.4	22 0.4	21 39.8	23 13.3	20 55.8	22 56.3	2 33.5	22 23.9	22 0.2	1 11.9	23 27.8
19 T	5 49 51.8	23 24.7	22 1.7	19 44.0	22 22.3	19 57.9	23 12.1	2 28.6	22 25.0	21 59.2	1 12.6	23 29.1
22 F	6 1 41.5	23 26.7	22 3.1	7 44.6	21 31.5	18 55.4	23 25.8	2 24.3	22 26.2	21 58.2	1 13.2	23 30.4
25 M	6 13 31.2	23 24.6	22 4.5	8N 2.5	20 47.2	17 48.5	23 37.4	2 20.7	22 27.3	21 57.2	1 13.7	23 31.8
28 T	6 25 20.8	23 18.2	22 5.8	19 53.1	20 17.6	16 37.7	23 46.8	2 17.7	22 28.5	21 56.3	1 14.0	23 33.2
31 S	6 37 10.5	23 7.5	22 7.1	21 38.2	20 8.2	15 23.3	23 54.1	2 15.4	22 29.6	21 55.4	1 14.2	23 34.6

JANUARY 1945

DAY	EPHEMERIS SIDEREAL TIME	☉	☊	☽	☿	♀	♂	♃	♄	♅	♆	♇
	h m s	° ′	° ′	° ′	° ′	° ′	° ′	° ′	° ′	° ′	° ′	° ′
						LONGITUDE						
1 M	6 41 7.1	10♑13.6	18♋48.1	8♌51.6	22♐50.5	24♒29.1	26♐26.0	27♍17.8	7♋ 4.1	9♊58.0	6♎25.3	9♌43.3
2 T	6 45 3.6	11 14.7	18 44.9	21 22.6	22R40.8	25 38.4	27 10.5	27 19.9	6R59.2	9R55.9	6 25.5	9R42.1
3 W	6 49 0.2	12 15.9	18 41.8	3♍38.8	22 40.5	26 47.5	27 55.1	27 21.7	6 54.2	9 53.9	6 25.6	9 40.9
4 T	6 52 56.7	13 17.0	18 38.6	15 43.0	22D49.0	27 56.4	28 39.7	27 23.4	6 49.3	9 51.9	6 25.8	9 39.7
5 F	6 56 53.3	14 18.2	18 35.4	27 39.2	23 5.7	29 5.2	29 24.3	27 24.9	6 44.4	9 49.9	6 25.9	9 38.5
6 S	7 0 49.9	15 19.3	18 32.2	9♎31.6	23 29.6	0♓13.8	0♑ 9.0	27 26.1	6 39.6	9 48.0	6 26.0	9 37.3
7 S	7 4 46.4	16 20.5	18 29.1	21 24.9	24 0.3	1 22.3	0 53.7	27 27.2	6 34.7	9 46.1	6 26.0	9 36.0
8 M	7 8 42.9	17 21.6	18 25.9	3♏23.9	24 36.9	2 30.6	1 38.5	27 28.1	6 29.9	9 44.2	6R26.0	9 34.7
9 T	7 12 39.5	18 22.8	18 22.7	15 33.1	25 19.0	3 38.7	2 23.3	27 28.8	6 25.1	9 42.4	6 26.0	9 33.5
10 W	7 16 36.1	19 24.0	18 19.5	27 56.7	26 5.9	4 46.6	3 8.2	27 29.4	6 20.3	9 40.6	6 25.9	9 32.2
11 T	7 20 32.6	20 25.1	18 16.4	10♐38.0	26 57.1	5 54.3	3 53.1	27 29.7	6 15.5	9 38.8	6 25.8	9 30.9
12 F	7 24 29.2	21 26.3	18 13.2	23 39.3	27 52.2	7 1.8	4 38.0	27 29.8	6 10.8	9 37.1	6 25.7	9 29.6
13 S	7 28 25.7	22 27.4	18 10.0	7♑ 1.3	28 50.7	8 9.1	5 23.0	27R29.7	6 6.2	9 35.4	6 25.5	9 28.3
14 S	7 32 22.3	23 28.6	18 6.8	20 43.5	29 52.4	9 16.3	6 8.0	27 29.5	6 1.6	9 33.8	6 25.3	9 26.9
15 M	7 36 18.9	24 29.7	18 3.7	4♒43.4	0♑56.8	10 23.2	6 53.1	27 29.0	5 57.0	9 32.2	6 25.1	9 25.6
16 T	7 40 15.4	25 30.8	18 0.5	18 57.0	2 3.7	11 29.8	7 38.2	27 28.4	5 52.4	9 30.6	6 24.8	9 24.3
17 W	7 44 12.0	26 32.0	17 57.3	3♓19.7	3 12.9	12 36.3	8 23.3	27 27.5	5 48.0	9 29.1	6 24.5	9 22.9
18 T	7 48 8.5	27 33.1	17 54.1	17 46.1	4 24.2	13 42.5	9 8.5	27 26.5	5 43.5	9 27.7	6 24.1	9 21.6
19 F	7 52 5.1	28 34.2	17 50.9	2♈11.4	5 37.3	14 48.4	9 53.7	27 25.3	5 39.2	9 26.2	6 23.8	9 20.2
20 S	7 56 1.7	29 35.2	17 47.8	16 31.1	6 52.1	15 54.1	10 39.0	27 23.9	5 34.9	9 24.9	6 23.4	9 18.8
21 S	7 59 58.2	0♒36.3	17 44.6	0♉42.3	8 8.4	16 59.5	11 24.3	27 22.2	5 30.6	9 23.5	6 22.9	9 17.5
22 M	8 3 54.7	1 37.3	17 41.4	14 42.8	9 26.2	18 4.6	12 9.6	27 20.4	5 26.4	9 22.2	6 22.4	9 16.1
23 T	8 7 51.3	2 38.4	17 38.2	28 31.5	10 45.3	19 9.5	12 54.9	27 18.5	5 22.3	9 21.0	6 21.9	9 14.7
24 W	8 11 47.9	3 39.4	17 35.1	12♊ 7.9	12 5.6	20 14.0	13 40.3	27 16.3	5 18.2	9 19.8	6 21.4	9 13.3
25 T	8 15 44.4	4 40.4	17 31.9	25 31.9	13 27.0	21 18.3	14 25.8	27 13.9	5 14.2	9 18.7	6 20.8	9 12.0
26 F	8 19 41.0	5 41.4	17 28.7	8♋43.2	14 49.6	22 22.2	15 11.2	27 11.4	5 10.3	9 17.6	6 20.2	9 10.6
27 S	8 23 37.5	6 42.3	17 25.5	21 42.1	16 13.1	23 25.7	15 56.7	27 8.7	5 6.5	9 16.5	6 19.6	9 9.2
28 S	8 27 34.1	7 43.3	17 22.4	4♌28.3	17 37.6	24 29.0	16 42.3	27 5.7	5 2.7	9 15.5	6 19.0	9 7.8
29 M	8 31 30.7	8 44.2	17 19.2	17 2.3	19 3.1	25 31.9	17 27.8	27 2.6	4 59.0	9 14.6	6 18.3	9 6.4
30 T	8 35 27.2	9 45.1	17 16.0	29 24.6	20 29.4	26 34.4	18 13.4	26 59.4	4 55.4	9 13.7	6 17.5	9 5.0
31 W	8 39 23.7	10 46.0	17 12.8	11♍36.1	21 56.7	27 36.5	18 59.1	26 55.9	4 51.9	9 12.8	6 16.8	9 3.6
						DECLINATION						
1 M	6 41 7.1	23S 3.1	22N 7.6	19N50.1	20S 9.5	14S57.8	23S56.0	2N14.8	22N30.0	21N55.1	1S14.3	23N35.1
4 T	6 52 56.7	22 46.9	22 8.9	9 44.1	20 24.1	13 39.2	24 0.2	2 13.4	22 31.1	21 54.2	1 14.3	23 36.5
7 S	7 4 46.4	22 26.7	22 10.2	3S27.2	20 50.1	12 17.8	24 2.2	2 12.6	22 32.2	21 53.4	1 14.3	23 38.0
10 W	7 16 36.1	22 2.5	22 11.5	15 43.5	21 21.1	10 54.0	24 1.9	2 12.5	22 33.2	21 52.6	1 14.1	23 39.4
13 S	7 28 25.7	21 34.4	22 12.8	22 12.7	21 52.2	9 28.3	23 59.3	2 13.2	22 34.3	21 51.9	1 13.8	23 40.8
16 T	7 40 15.4	21 2.6	22 14.0	17 41.9	22 19.7	8 0.8	23 54.3	2 14.5	22 35.3	21 51.2	1 13.3	23 42.3
19 F	7 52 5.1	20 27.2	22 15.3	3 46.7	22 41.0	6 32.0	23 47.1	2 16.5	22 36.3	21 50.5	1 12.8	23 43.7
22 M	8 3 54.7	19 48.2	22 16.5	11N43.9	22 54.2	5 2.2	23 37.5	2 19.1	22 37.2	21 50.0	1 12.1	23 45.1
25 T	8 15 44.4	19 6.0	22 17.8	21 19.0	22 58.1	3 31.8	23 25.5	2 22.5	22 38.1	21 49.5	1 11.3	23 46.5
28 S	8 27 34.1	18 20.6	22 19.0	20 33.6	22 51.8	2 1.1	23 11.3	2 26.5	22 39.0	21 49.0	1 10.4	23 47.9
31 W	8 39 23.7	17 32.3	22 20.2	11 5.7	22 34.4	0 30.5	22 54.8	2 31.1	22 39.9	21 48.7	1 9.5	23 49.3

FEBRUARY 1945

DAY	EPHEMERIS SIDEREAL TIME	☉	☊	☽	☿	♀	♂	♃	♄	♅	♆	♇
						LONGITUDE						
1 T	8 43 20.3	11♒46.9	17♋ 9.6	23♍38.6	23♑24.7	28♓38.3	19♑44.7	26♍52.3	4♋48.4	9♊12.0	6♎16.0	9♌ 2.2
2 F	8 47 16.9	12 47.8	17 6.5	5♎34.4	24 53.6	29 39.7	20 30.5	26R48.5	4R45.1	9R11.3	6R15.2	9R 0.8
3 S	8 51 13.4	13 48.6	17 3.3	17 26.6	26 23.3	0♈40.6	21 16.2	26 44.5	4 41.8	9 10.5	6 14.4	8 59.4
4 S	8 55 10.0	14 49.5	17 0.1	29 19.0	27 53.8	1 41.2	22 2.0	26 40.3	4 38.6	9 9.9	6 13.5	8 58.0
5 M	8 59 6.5	15 50.3	16 56.9	11♏16.0	29 25.1	2 41.3	22 47.8	26 36.0	4 35.5	9 9.3	6 12.6	8 56.7
6 T	9 3 3.1	16 51.1	16 53.8	23 22.2	0♒57.2	3 40.9	23 33.6	26 31.5	4 32.5	9 8.7	6 11.7	8 55.3
7 W	9 6 59.7	17 51.9	16 50.6	5♐42.4	2 30.0	4 40.1	24 19.5	26 26.9	4 29.6	9 8.3	6 10.7	8 53.9
8 T	9 10 56.2	18 52.7	16 47.4	18 21.3	4 3.7	5 38.8	25 5.4	26 22.1	4 26.7	9 7.8	6 9.7	8 52.5
9 F	9 14 52.8	19 53.4	16 44.2	1♑22.7	5 38.1	6 37.0	25 51.4	26 17.1	4 24.0	9 7.4	6 8.7	8 51.2
10 S	9 18 49.3	20 54.2	16 41.0	14 49.4	7 13.4	7 34.7	26 37.3	26 12.0	4 21.4	9 7.1	6 7.7	8 49.8
11 S	9 22 45.9	21 54.9	16 37.9	28 42.1	8 49.5	8 31.9	27 23.3	26 6.7	4 18.8	9 6.8	6 6.6	8 48.5
12 M	9 26 42.4	22 55.6	16 34.7	12♒59.3	10 26.4	9 28.5	28 9.4	26 1.3	4 16.4	9 6.6	6 5.5	8 47.1
13 T	9 30 39.0	23 56.3	16 31.5	27 36.6	12 4.1	10 24.6	28 55.4	25 55.7	4 14.1	9 6.4	6 4.4	8 45.8
14 W	9 34 35.5	24 56.9	16 28.3	12♓27.3	13 42.7	11 20.0	29 41.5	25 50.0	4 11.8	9 6.3	6 3.3	8 44.4
15 T	9 38 32.1	25 57.6	16 25.2	27 23.0	15 22.1	12 14.8	0♒27.6	25 44.1	4 9.7	9 6.2	6 2.1	8 43.1
16 F	9 42 28.6	26 58.2	16 22.0	12♈14.9	17 2.4	13 9.1	1 13.7	25 38.1	4 7.7	9 6.2	6 1.0	8 41.8
17 S	9 46 25.2	27 58.7	16 18.8	26 55.5	18 43.5	14 2.6	1 59.9	25 32.0	4 5.8	9D 6.2	5 59.7	8 40.5
18 S	9 50 21.7	28 59.3	16 15.6	11♉19.0	20 25.6	14 55.4	2 46.1	25 25.8	4 3.9	9 6.3	5 58.5	8 39.2
19 M	9 54 18.3	29 59.8	16 12.4	25 22.6	22 8.6	15 47.5	3 32.3	25 19.4	4 2.2	9 6.4	5 57.3	8 37.9
20 T	9 58 14.8	1♓ 0.3	16 9.3	9♊ 5.6	23 52.5	16 38.9	4 18.5	25 12.9	4 0.7	9 6.6	5 56.0	8 36.6
21 W	10 2 11.4	2 0.7	16 6.1	22 29.0	25 37.3	17 29.5	5 4.7	25 6.3	3 59.2	9 6.9	5 54.7	8 35.4
22 T	10 6 8.0	3 1.1	16 2.9	5♋34.8	27 23.1	18 19.3	5 51.0	24 59.6	3 57.8	9 7.2	5 53.4	8 34.1
23 F	10 10 4.5	4 1.5	15 59.7	18 25.4	29 9.8	19 8.2	6 37.3	24 52.8	3 56.5	9 7.5	5 52.0	8 32.9
24 S	10 14 1.0	5 1.9	15 56.6	1♌ 3.3	0♓57.5	19 56.3	7 23.6	24 45.9	3 55.4	9 7.9	5 50.7	8 31.6
25 S	10 17 57.6	6 2.2	15 53.4	13 30.5	2 46.2	20 43.4	8 9.9	24 38.9	3 54.3	9 8.4	5 49.3	8 30.4
26 M	10 21 54.2	7 2.5	15 50.2	25 48.7	4 35.8	21 29.7	8 56.3	24 31.8	3 53.4	9 8.9	5 47.9	8 29.2
27 T	10 25 50.7	8 2.8	15 47.0	7♍59.0	6 26.4	22 14.9	9 42.6	24 24.7	3 52.6	9 9.5	5 46.5	8 28.1
28 W	10 29 47.3	9 3.0	15 43.9	20 2.6	8 17.9	22 59.1	10 29.0	24 17.4	3 51.8	9 10.1	5 45.1	8 26.9
						DECLINATION						
1 T	8 43 20.3	17S15.5	22N20.6	6N53.5	22S26.2	0S 0.3	22S48.8	2N32.7	22N40.2	21N48.5	1S 9.1	23N49.7
4 S	8 55 10.0	16 23.5	22 21.8	6S26.0	21 53.5	1N29.7	22 29.2	2 38.2	22 41.0	21 48.3	1 8.0	23 51.0
7 W	9 6 59.7	15 28.9	22 23.0	17 47.4	21 9.0	2 58.8	22 7.5	2 44.2	22 41.8	21 48.0	1 6.8	23 52.3
10 S	9 18 49.3	14 31.9	22 24.2	22 19.3	20 12.3	4 26.9	21 43.6	2 50.7	22 42.5	21 47.9	1 5.4	23 53.5
13 T	9 30 39.0	13 32.7	22 25.4	15 24.5	19 3.2	5 53.4	21 17.5	2 57.8	22 43.2	21 47.8	1 4.0	23 54.7
16 F	9 42 28.6	12 31.6	22 26.6	0N 6.4	17 41.7	7 18.1	20 49.4	3 5.3	22 43.9	21 47.8	1 2.5	23 55.9
19 M	9 54 18.3	11 28.6	22 27.7	15 8.4	16 7.6	8 40.6	20 19.3	3 13.3	22 44.6	21 47.9	1 1.0	23 57.0
22 T	10 6 8.0	10 24.0	22 28.9	22 15.0	14 21.1	10 0.5	19 47.2	3 21.6	22 45.2	21 48.0	0 59.3	23 58.0
25 S	10 17 57.6	9 18.0	22 30.0	18 55.4	12 22.0	11 17.5	19 13.2	3 30.2	22 45.8	21 48.3	0 57.6	23 59.0
28 W	10 29 47.3	8 10.7	22 31.1	8 6.6	10 10.9	12 31.1	18 37.4	3 39.1	22 46.4	21 48.6	0 55.9	23 ·60.0

MARCH 1945

LONGITUDE

DAY	EPHEMERIS SIDEREAL TIME h m s	☉ ° ′	☊ ° ′	☽ ° ′	☿ ° ′	♀ ° ′	♂ ° ′	♃ ° ′	♄ ° ′	♅ ° ′	♆ ° ′	♇ ° ′
1 T	10 33 43.8	10♓ 3.2	15♋40.7	2♎ 0.7	10♓10.3	23♈42.3	11♒15.4	24♍10.1	3♋51.2	9♊10.8	5♎43.6	8♌25.7
2 F	10 37 40.4	11 3.4	15 37.5	13 54.7	12 3.6	24 24.3	12 1.8	24R 2.7	3R50.7	9 11.5	5R42.2	8R24.6
3 S	10 41 36.9	12 3.5	15 34.3	25 46.5	13 57.8	25 5.3	12 48.3	23 55.2	3 50.4	9 12.3	5 40.7	8 23.5
4 S	10 45 33.5	13 3.7	15 31.1	7♏38.8	15 52.6	25 45.1	13 34.8	23 47.7	3 50.1	9 13.1	5 39.2	8 22.3
5 M	10 49 30.0	14 3.8	15 28.0	19 34.8	17 48.2	26 23.6	14 21.2	23 40.1	3 49.9	9 14.0	5 37.7	8 21.3
6 T	10 53 26.6	15 3.8	15 24.8	1♐38.6	19 44.3	27 0.9	15 7.7	23 32.5	3 49.9	9 14.9	5 36.2	8 20.2
7 W	10 57 23.2	16 3.9	15 21.6	13 54.8	21 40.9	27 36.8	15 54.3	23 24.9	3D50.0	9 15.9	5 34.7	8 19.1
8 T	11 1 19.7	17 3.9	15 18.4	26 28.2	23 37.8	28 11.4	16 40.8	23 17.2	3 50.1	9 17.0	5 33.1	8 18.1
9 F	11 5 16.3	18 3.9	15 15.2	9♑23.7	25 34.8	28 44.6	17 27.3	23 9.4	3 50.4	9 18.0	5 31.6	8 17.1
10 S	11 9 12.8	19 3.8	15 12.1	22 45.3	27 31.7	29 16.3	18 13.9	23 1.7	3 50.8	9 19.2	5 30.0	8 16.0
11 S	11 13 9.4	20 3.8	15 8.9	6♒35.7	29 28.3	29 46.5	19 0.5	22 53.9	3 51.3	9 20.4	5 28.4	8 15.1
12 M	11 17 5.9	21 3.7	15 5.7	20 55.2	1♈24.2	0♉15.1	19 47.1	22 46.1	3 52.0	9 21.6	5 26.9	8 14.1
13 T	11 21 2.5	22 3.6	15 2.5	5♓40.8	3 19.2	0 42.1	20 33.7	22 38.3	3 52.7	9 22.9	5 25.3	8 13.2
14 W	11 24 59.0	23 3.4	14 59.4	20 46.0	5 12.8	1 7.4	21 20.3	22 30.4	3 53.6	9 24.2	5 23.6	8 12.2
15 T	11 28 55.6	24 3.2	14 56.2	6♈ 1.1	7 4.7	1 30.9	22 6.9	22 22.6	3 54.5	9 25.6	5 22.0	8 11.3
16 F	11 32 52.1	25 3.0	14 53.0	21 15.1	8 54.5	1 52.6	22 53.5	22 14.8	3 55.6	9 27.1	5 20.4	8 10.4
17 S	11 36 48.7	26 2.8	14 49.8	6♉17.1	10 41.7	2 12.4	23 40.2	22 7.1	3 56.8	9 28.5	5 18.8	8 9.6
18 S	11 40 45.2	27 2.5	14 46.7	20 58.9	12 25.9	2 30.2	24 26.8	21 59.3	3 58.1	9 30.1	5 17.2	8 8.7
19 M	11 44 41.8	28 2.1	14 43.5	5♊15.2	14 6.6	2 46.0	25 13.4	21 51.5	3 59.5	9 31.7	5 15.5	8 7.9
20 T	11 48 38.3	29 1.8	14 40.3	19 4.5	15 43.3	2 59.7	26 0.1	21 43.8	4 1.0	9 33.3	5 13.9	8 7.1
21 W	11 52 34.9	0♈ 1.3	14 37.1	2♋27.8	17 15.5	3 11.2	26 46.7	21 36.2	4 2.7	9 35.0	5 12.2	8 6.3
22 T	11 56 31.4	1 0.9	14 33.9	15 28.2	18 42.9	3 20.6	27 33.4	21 28.5	4 4.4	9 36.7	5 10.6	8 5.6
23 F	12 0 28.0	2 0.4	14 30.8	28 9.3	20 4.9	3 27.6	28 20.0	21 20.9	4 6.3	9 38.4	5 8.9	8 4.8
24 S	12 4 24.5	2 59.9	14 27.6	10♌35.3	21 21.3	3 32.3	29 6.7	21 13.4	4 8.2	9 40.3	5 7.3	8 4.1
25 S	12 8 21.1	3 59.3	14 24.4	22 49.8	22 31.6	3 34.7	29 53.4	21 5.9	4 10.3	9 42.1	5 5.6	8 3.4
26 M	12 12 17.7	4 58.7	14 21.2	4♍56.0	23 35.5	3R34.6	0♓40.0	20 58.5	4 12.4	9 44.0	5 4.0	8 2.8
27 T	12 16 14.2	5 58.1	14 18.0	16 56.4	24 32.9	3 32.1	1 26.7	20 51.2	4 14.7	9 46.0	5 2.3	8 2.1
28 W	12 20 10.8	6 57.4	14 14.9	28 52.8	25 23.3	3 27.1	2 13.3	20 43.9	4 17.1	9 47.9	5 0.7	8 1.5
29 T	12 24 7.3	7 56.7	14 11.7	10♎46.7	26 6.7	3 19.6	2 60.0	20 36.7	4 19.6	9 50.0	4 59.0	8 0.9
30 F	12 28 3.9	8 56.0	14 8.5	22 39.4	26 42.9	3 9.7	3 46.7	20 29.6	4 22.1	9 52.0	4 57.3	8 0.4
31 S	12 32 0.4	9 55.2	14 5.3	4♏32.2	27 11.8	2 57.2	4 33.3	20 22.6	4 24.8	9 54.2	4 55.7	7 59.8

DECLINATION

DAY	SIDEREAL TIME	☉	☊	☽	☿	♀	♂	♃	♄	♅	♆	♇
1 T	10 33 43.8	7S48.1	22N31.5	3N42.4	9S24.6	12N54.7	18S25.1	3N42.2	22N46.6	21N48.7	0S55.3	24N 0.3
4 S	10 45 33.5	6 39.4	22 32.6	9S34.3	6 58.4	14 3.1	17 46.9	3 51.3	22 47.1	21 49.1	0 53.4	24 1.1
7 W	10 57 23.2	5 29.9	22 33.7	19 45.3	4 22.5	15 6.9	17 7.1	4 0.7	22 47.6	21 49.5	0 51.6	24 1.9
10 S	11 9 12.8	4 19.7	22 34.8	22 4.9	1 39.3	16 5.8	16 25.7	4 10.1	22 48.1	21 50.0	0 49.7	24 2.6
13 T	11 21 2.5	3 9.1	22 35.8	13 0.1	1N 7.5	16 59.0	15 42.9	4 19.5	22 48.5	21 50.6	0 47.7	24 3.3
16 F	11 32 52.1	1 58.1	22 36.9	3N38.5	3 52.6	17 45.8	14 58.6	4 28.8	22 48.9	21 51.3	0 45.8	24 3.9
19 M	11 44 41.8	0 46.9	22 37.9	17 58.6	6 29.3	18 25.4	14 12.9	4 38.1	22 49.2	21 52.0	0 43.8	24 4.4
22 T	11 56 31.4	0N24.2	22 39.0	22 33.7	8 50.4	18 56.8	13 26.1	4 47.2	22 49.6	21 52.8	0 41.8	24 4.9
25 S	12 8 21.1	1 35.2	22 40.0	16 48.7	10 49.4	19 18.7	12 38.0	4 56.0	22 49.9	21 53.6	0 39.8	24 5.3
28 W	12 20 10.8	2 45.8	22 41.0	4 51.2	12 20.7	19 30.1	11 48.9	5 4.6	22 50.1	21 54.5	0 37.8	24 5.6
31 S	12 32 0.4	3 55.8	22 42.0	8S37.6	13 20.5	19 29.7	10 58.8	5 12.8	22 50.3	21 55.5	0 35.8	24 5.8

APRIL 1945

LONGITUDE

DAY	SIDEREAL TIME	☉	☊	☽	☿	♀	♂	♃	♄	♅	♆	♇
1 S	12 35 57.0	10♈54.4	14♋ 2.2	16♏26.9	27♈33.4	2♉42.3	5♓20.0	20♍15.6	4♋27.6	9♊56.3	4♎54.1	7♌59.3
2 M	12 39 53.5	11 53.6	13 59.0	28 25.7	27 47.6	2R24.9	6 6.6	20R 8.8	4 30.5	9 58.5	4R52.4	7R58.8
3 T	12 43 50.1	12 52.7	13 55.8	10♐31.5	27 54.7	2 5.2	6 53.3	20 2.1	4 33.5	10 0.7	4 50.8	7 58.4
4 W	12 47 46.6	13 51.8	13 52.6	22 48.0	27 54.8	1 43.1	7 40.0	19 55.4	4 36.6	10 3.0	4 49.1	7 57.9
5 T	12 51 43.2	14 50.9	13 49.4	5♑19.4	27R48.0	1 18.9	8 26.6	19 48.9	4 39.7	10 5.3	4 47.5	7 57.5
6 F	12 55 39.7	15 50.0	13 46.3	18 10.2	27 34.7	0 52.5	9 13.3	19 42.5	4 43.0	10 7.7	4 45.9	7 57.1
7 S	12 59 36.3	16 49.0	13 43.1	1♒24.8	27 15.3	0 24.2	9 59.9	19 36.2	4 46.4	10 10.1	4 44.3	7 56.8
8 S	13 3 32.8	17 47.9	13 39.9	15 6.7	26 50.3	29♈54.0	10 46.5	19 30.0	4 49.9	10 12.5	4 42.7	7 56.4
9 M	13 7 29.4	18 46.9	13 36.7	29 17.5	26 20.3	29 22.2	11 33.2	19 23.9	4 53.4	10 15.0	4 41.1	7 56.1
10 T	13 11 25.9	19 45.8	13 33.6	13♓56.1	25 45.9	28 48.8	12 19.8	19 18.0	4 57.1	10 17.5	4 39.5	7 55.8
11 W	13 15 22.5	20 44.7	13 30.4	28 57.8	25 7.9	28 14.2	13 6.4	19 12.2	5 0.8	10 20.0	4 37.9	7 55.6
12 T	13 19 19.0	21 43.6	13 27.2	14♈14.3	24 27.0	27 38.5	13 53.0	19 6.6	5 4.7	10 22.6	4 36.3	7 55.3
13 F	13 23 15.6	22 42.4	13 24.0	29 34.5	23 44.0	27 1.9	14 39.6	19 1.1	5 8.6	10 25.2	4 34.8	7 55.1
14 S	13 27 12.2	23 41.2	13 20.8	14♉46.7	22 59.8	26 24.6	15 26.1	18 55.7	5 12.7	10 27.9	4 33.2	7 54.9
15 S	13 31 8.7	24 40.0	13 17.7	29 40.7	22 15.3	25 47.0	16 12.7	18 50.5	5 16.8	10 30.6	4 31.7	7 54.8
16 M	13 35 5.3	25 38.7	13 14.5	14♊ 9.4	21 31.2	25 9.2	16 59.2	18 45.4	5 21.0	10 33.3	4 30.2	7 54.6
17 T	13 39 1.8	26 37.4	13 11.3	28 9.1	20 48.5	24 31.5	17 45.8	18 40.4	5 25.3	10 36.0	4 28.6	7 54.5
18 W	13 42 58.4	27 36.1	13 8.1	11♋40.0	20 7.7	23 54.1	18 32.3	18 35.7	5 29.7	10 38.8	4 27.1	7 54.5
19 T	13 46 54.9	28 34.7	13 5.0	24 44.2	19 29.5	23 17.4	19 18.7	18 31.1	5 34.1	10 41.6	4 25.7	7 54.4
20 F	13 50 51.5	29 33.3	13 1.8	7♌25.8	18 54.6	22 41.4	20 5.2	18 26.6	5 38.7	10 44.4	4 24.2	7 54.4
21 S	13 54 48.0	0♉31.8	12 58.6	19 49.2	18 23.4	22 6.5	20 51.6	18 22.3	5 43.3	10 47.3	4 22.7	7D54.4
22 S	13 58 44.6	1 30.3	12 55.4	1♍59.1	17 56.4	21 32.8	21 38.1	18 18.2	5 48.0	10 50.2	4 21.3	7 54.4
23 M	14 2 41.1	2 28.8	12 52.2	13 59.8	17 33.8	21 0.6	22 24.5	18 14.2	5 52.8	10 53.1	4 19.9	7 54.5
24 T	14 6 37.7	3 27.3	12 49.1	25 54.9	17 15.8	20 30.0	23 10.9	18 10.4	5 57.7	10 56.1	4 18.5	7 54.6
25 W	14 10 34.3	4 25.7	12 45.9	7♎47.3	17 2.7	20 1.3	23 57.2	18 6.8	6 2.7	10 59.1	4 17.1	7 54.7
26 T	14 14 30.8	5 24.0	12 42.7	19 39.4	16 54.5	19 34.5	24 43.6	18 3.4	6 7.7	11 2.1	4 15.7	7 54.9
27 F	14 18 27.3	6 22.4	12 39.5	1♏33.0	16 51.3	19 9.7	25 29.9	18 0.1	6 12.8	11 5.1	4 14.4	7 55.0
28 S	14 22 23.9	7 20.7	12 36.4	13 29.5	16D53.0	18 47.2	26 16.2	17 57.0	6 18.0	11 8.2	4 13.1	7 55.2
29 S	14 26 20.5	8 19.0	12 33.2	25 30.2	16 59.6	18 27.0	27 2.5	17 54.0	6 23.2	11 11.3	4 11.7	7 55.4
30 M	14 30 17.0	9 17.2	12 30.0	7♐36.7	17 11.0	18 9.0	27 48.7	17 51.3	6 28.6	11 14.4	4 10.5	7 55.7

DECLINATION

DAY	SIDEREAL TIME	☉	☊	☽	☿	♀	♂	♃	♄	♅	♆	♇
1 S	12 35 57.0	4N19.1	22N42.4	12S43.1	13N33.0	19N26.8	10S41.9	5N15.5	22N50.4	21N55.8	0S35.2	24N 5.9
4 W	12 47 46.6	5 28.2	22 43.4	21 28.3	13 47.1	19 9.4	9 50.7	5 23.2	22 50.5	21 56.8	0 33.2	24 6.0
7 S	12 59 36.3	6 36.6	22 44.3	21 22.0	13 26.6	18 38.6	8 58.6	5 30.5	22 50.6	21 57.9	0 31.3	24 6.1
10 T	13 11 25.9	7 43.9	22 45.3	10 21.4	12 34.5	17 54.9	8 5.8	5 37.3	22 50.7	21 59.0	0 29.4	24 6.1
13 F	13 23 15.6	8 50.1	22 46.3	6N50.0	11 17.9	16 59.5	7 12.4	5 43.6	22 50.7	22 0.1	0 27.6	24 6.1
16 M	13 35 5.3	9 55.0	22 47.2	20 8.3	9 47.6	15 54.9	6 18.5	5 49.4	22 50.6	22 1.3	0 25.8	24 5.9
19 T	13 46 54.9	10 58.3	22 48.2	22 15.5	8 15.9	14 44.1	5 24.2	5 54.6	22 50.5	22 2.5	0 24.0	24 5.7
22 S	13 58 44.6	12 0.1	22 49.1	14 22.1	6 54.1	13 30.9	4 29.6	5 59.2	22 50.3	22 3.8	0 22.3	24 5.5
25 W	14 10 34.3	12 60.0	22 50.0	1 31.2	5 50.2	12 18.8	3 34.7	6 3.1	22 50.1	22 5.0	0 20.7	24 5.1
28 S	14 22 23.9	13 58.0	22 50.9	11S49.3	5 8.4	11 11.3	2 39.6	6 6.5	22 49.8	22 6.3	0 19.2	24 4.7

MAY 1945

LONGITUDE

DAY	EPHEMERIS SIDEREAL TIME h m s	☉ ° ′	☊ ° ′	☽ ° ′	☿ ° ′	♀ ° ′	♂ ° ′	♃ ° ′	♄ ° ′	♅ ° ′	♆ ° ′	♇ ° ′
1 T	14 34 13.6	10♉15.4	12♋26.8	19♐50.9	17♈27.1	17♈53.5	28♓34.9	17♍48.7	6♋34.0	11♊17.5	4♎ 9.2	7♌56.0
2 W	14 38 10.1	11 13.6	12 23.6	2♑15.1	17 47.7	17R40.5	29 21.1	17R46.3	6 39.4	11 20.7	4R 7.9	7 56.3
3 T	14 42 6.7	12 11.8	12 20.5	14 52.4	18 12.8	17 29.8	0♈ 7.3	17 44.1	6 45.0	11 23.8	4 6.7	7 56.6
4 F	14 46 3.2	13 10.0	12 17.3	27 45.9	18 42.1	17 21.7	0 53.5	17 42.0	6 50.6	11 27.0	4 5.5	7 56.9
5 S	14 49 59.8	14 8.1	12 14.1	10♒59.2	19 15.5	17 15.9	1 39.6	17 40.1	6 56.3	11 30.3	4 4.3	7 57.3
6 S	14 53 56.3	15 6.2	12 10.9	24 35.2	19 52.9	17 12.6	2 25.7	17 38.5	7 2.0	11 33.5	4 3.1	7 57.7
7 M	14 57 52.9	16 4.3	12 7.8	8♓35.7	20 34.1	17 11.8	3 11.8	17 37.0	7 7.8	11 36.8	4 2.0	7 58.2
8 T	15 1 49.5	17 2.3	12 4.6	23 0.6	21 18.9	17D13.2	3 57.8	17 35.6	7 13.7	11 40.0	4 0.9	7 58.6
9 W	15 5 46.0	18 0.4	12 1.4	7♈46.8	22 7.3	17 17.0	4 43.8	17 34.5	7 19.7	11 43.3	3 59.8	7 59.1
10 T	15 9 42.6	18 58.4	11 58.2	22 48.4	22 59.1	17 23.0	5 29.8	17 33.5	7 25.7	11 46.7	3 58.7	7 59.6
11 F	15 13 39.1	19 56.3	11 55.0	7♉56.6	23 54.1	17 31.3	6 15.7	17 32.7	7 31.7	11 50.0	3 57.7	8 0.1
12 S	15 17 35.7	20 54.3	11 51.9	23 1.5	24 52.3	17 41.7	7 1.6	17 32.2	7 37.9	11 53.3	3 56.7	8 0.7
13 S	15 21 32.2	21 52.3	11 48.7	7♊53.3	25 53.5	17 54.2	7 47.5	17 31.8	7 44.1	11 56.7	3 55.7	8 1.3
14 M	15 25 28.8	22 50.2	11 45.5	22 24.1	26 57.7	18 8.7	8 33.3	17 31.5	7 50.3	12 0.1	3 54.7	8 1.9
15 T	15 29 25.3	23 48.0	11 42.3	6♋29.0	28 4.6	18 25.1	9 19.1	17 31.5	7 56.6	12 3.5	3 53.8	8 2.6
16 W	15 33 21.9	24 45.9	11 39.2	20 6.3	29 14.4	18 43.5	10 4.8	17D31.6	8 3.0	12 6.9	3 52.9	8 3.2
17 T	15 37 18.4	25 43.7	11 36.0	3♌16.7	0♉26.9	19 3.7	10 50.5	17 32.0	8 9.4	12 10.3	3 52.0	8 3.9
18 F	15 41 15.0	26 41.5	11 32.8	16 3.2	1 41.9	19 25.7	11 36.2	17 32.5	8 15.9	12 13.8	3 51.1	8 4.6
19 S	15 45 11.6	27 39.3	11 29.6	28 29.7	2 59.6	19 49.3	12 21.8	17 33.2	8 22.4	12 17.2	3 50.3	8 5.4
20 S	15 49 8.1	28 37.0	11 26.5	10♍40.9	4 19.8	20 14.7	13 7.4	17 34.0	8 29.0	12 20.7	3 49.5	8 6.1
21 M	15 53 4.7	29 34.7	11 23.3	22 41.4	5 42.4	20 41.6	13 53.0	17 35.1	8 35.6	12 24.1	3 48.7	8 6.9
22 T	15 57 1.2	0♊32.4	11 20.1	4♎35.6	7 7.5	21 10.1	14 38.4	17 36.3	8 42.3	12 27.6	3 48.0	8 7.7
23 W	16 0 57.8	1 30.1	11 16.9	16 27.5	8 35.1	21 40.0	15 23.9	17 37.7	8 49.0	12 31.1	3 47.2	8 8.5
24 T	16 4 54.3	2 27.7	11 13.7	28 20.3	10 5.0	22 11.4	16 9.3	17 39.3	8 55.8	12 34.6	3 46.6	8 9.4
25 F	16 8 50.9	3 25.4	11 10.6	10♏16.7	11 37.3	22 44.2	16 54.7	17 41.1	9 2.6	12 38.1	3 45.9	8 10.3
26 S	16 12 47.4	4 23.0	11 7.4	22 19.0	13 12.0	23 18.3	17 40.0	17 43.0	9 9.4	12 41.6	3 45.3	8 11.2
27 S	16 16 44.0	5 20.5	11 4.2	4♐28.8	14 49.1	23 53.7	18 25.3	17 45.1	9 16.3	12 45.1	3 44.7	8 12.1
28 M	16 20 40.6	6 18.1	11 1.0	16 47.3	16 28.5	24 30.3	19 10.5	17 47.4	9 23.3	12 48.6	3 44.1	8 13.1
29 T	16 24 37.1	7 15.6	10 57.9	29 15.7	18 10.3	25 8.1	19 55.7	17 49.9	9 30.3	12 52.1	3 43.6	8 14.0
30 W	16 28 33.6	8 13.1	10 54.7	11♑55.4	19 54.4	25 47.0	20 40.8	17 52.5	9 37.3	12 55.7	3 43.0	8 15.0
31 T	16 32 30.2	9 10.6	10 51.5	24 47.6	21 40.9	26 27.0	21 25.9	17 55.3	9 44.4	12 59.2	3 42.6	8 16.0

DECLINATION

DAY	EPHEMERIS SIDEREAL TIME h m s	☉	☊	☽	☿	♀	♂	♃	♄	♅	♆	♇
1 T	14 34 13.6	14N54.0	22N51.8	21S14.5	4N50.0	10N11.0	1S44.4	6N 9.2	22N49.4	22N 7.7	0S17.7	24N 4.3
4 F	14 46 3.2	15 47.7	22 52.7	22 4.9	4 54.0	9 19.7	0 49.2	6 11.2	22 48.9	22 9.0	0 16.3	24 3.7
7 M	14 57 52.9	16 39.1	22 53.5	12 21.5	5 18.5	8 38.4	0N 5.9	6 12.6	22 48.4	22 10.3	0 15.0	24 3.2
10 T	15 9 42.6	17 28.0	22 54.4	4N14.3	6 1.3	8 7.3	1 0.8	6 13.4	22 47.8	22 11.7	0 13.7	24 2.5
13 S	15 21 32.2	18 14.3	22 55.2	18 55.7	7 0.1	7 46.2	1 55.6	6 13.5	22 47.1	22 13.1	0 12.6	24 1.8
16 W	15 33 21.9	18 57.9	22 56.1	22 50.1	8 12.7	7 34.7	2 49.9	6 12.9	22 46.3	22 14.5	0 11.6	24 1.1
19 S	15 45 11.6	19 38.5	22 56.9	15 37.5	9 37.0	7 32.0	3 43.9	6 11.7	22 45.5	22 15.8	0 10.7	24 0.2
22 T	15 57 1.2	20 16.2	22 57.7	2 53.4	11 10.9	7 37.3	4 37.4	6 9.9	22 44.6	22 17.2	0 9.8	23 59.4
25 F	16 8 50.9	20 50.7	22 58.5	10S40.7	12 52.4	7 49.9	5 30.4	6 7.4	22 43.6	22 18.6	0 9.1	23 58.5
28 M	16 20 40.6	21 22.0	22 59.3	20 47.9	14 39.3	8 8.9	6 22.7	6 4.4	22 42.5	22 20.0	0 8.5	23 57.5
31 T	16 32 30.2	21 49.9	23 0.1	22 32.6	16 29.0	8 33.6	7 14.3	6 0.7	22 41.3	22 21.3	0 8.0	23 56.5

JUNE 1945

LONGITUDE

DAY	EPHEMERIS SIDEREAL TIME h m s	☉ ° ′	☊ ° ′	☽ ° ′	☿ ° ′	♀ ° ′	♂ ° ′	♃ ° ′	♄ ° ′	♅ ° ′	♆ ° ′	♇ ° ′
1 F	16 36 26.8	10♊ 8.1	10♋48.3	7♒53.8	23♉29.6	27♈ 8.1	22♈10.9	17♍58.3	9♋51.5	13♊ 2.7	3♎42.1	8♌17.1
2 S	16 40 23.4	11 5.6	10 45.2	21 15.7	25 20.7	27 50.2	22 55.9	18 1.4	9 58.6	13 6.3	3R41.7	8 18.1
3 S	16 44 19.9	12 3.1	10 42.0	4♓54.5	27 14.1	28 33.3	23 40.9	18 4.7	10 5.8	13 9.8	3 41.3	8 19.2
4 M	16 48 16.4	13 0.5	10 38.8	18 51.0	29 9.7	29 17.3	24 25.8	18 8.2	10 13.0	13 13.4	3 40.9	8 20.3
5 T	16 52 13.0	13 58.0	10 35.6	3♈ 4.5	1♊ 7.5	0♉ 2.2	25 10.6	18 11.8	10 20.3	13 16.9	3 40.6	8 21.4
6 W	16 56 9.6	14 55.4	10 32.5	17 33.1	3 7.4	0 47.9	25 55.4	18 15.6	10 27.5	13 20.4	3 40.3	8 22.6
7 T	17 0 6.2	15 52.8	10 29.3	2♉12.7	5 9.3	1 34.5	26 40.1	18 19.6	10 34.9	13 24.0	3 40.1	8 23.7
8 F	17 4 2.7	16 50.2	10 26.1	16 57.6	7 13.1	2 21.9	27 24.8	18 23.7	10 42.2	13 27.5	3 39.8	8 24.9
9 S	17 7 59.2	17 47.6	10 22.9	1♊40.8	9 18.7	3 10.1	28 9.4	18 28.0	10 49.6	13 31.0	3 39.6	8 26.1
10 S	17 11 55.8	18 45.0	10 19.7	16 15.2	11 25.8	3 58.9	28 54.0	18 32.4	10 57.0	13 34.6	3 39.5	8 27.3
11 M	17 15 52.3	19 42.4	10 16.6	0♋34.1	13 34.4	4 48.5	29 38.5	18 37.0	11 4.4	13 38.1	3 39.3	8 28.6
12 T	17 19 48.9	20 39.8	10 13.4	14 32.8	15 44.2	5 38.8	0♉22.9	18 41.8	11 11.9	13 41.6	3 39.2	8 29.8
13 W	17 23 45.5	21 37.1	10 10.2	28 8.5	17 54.9	6 29.6	1 7.3	18 46.7	11 19.4	13 45.2	3 39.2	8 31.1
14 T	17 27 42.0	22 34.4	10 7.0	11♌20.5	20 6.2	7 21.2	1 51.6	18 51.7	11 26.9	13 48.7	3 39.1	8 32.4
15 F	17 31 38.6	23 31.8	10 3.9	24 10.1	22 18.1	8 13.3	2 35.9	18 57.0	11 34.5	13 52.2	3 39.1	8 33.7
16 S	17 35 35.1	24 29.1	10 0.7	6♍40.0	24 30.0	9 6.0	3 20.1	19 2.3	11 42.0	13 55.7	3D39.1	8 35.0
17 S	17 39 31.7	25 26.4	9 57.5	18 54.1	26 41.8	9 59.3	4 4.2	19 7.8	11 49.6	13 59.2	3 39.2	8 36.4
18 M	17 43 28.3	26 23.6	9 54.3	0♎56.5	28 53.2	10 53.1	4 48.3	19 13.5	11 57.2	14 2.6	3 39.3	8 37.8
19 T	17 47 24.8	27 20.9	9 51.2	12 51.9	1♋ 3.9	11 47.4	5 32.3	19 19.3	12 4.8	14 6.1	3 39.4	8 39.1
20 W	17 51 21.4	28 18.2	9 48.0	24 44.7	3 13.8	12 42.2	6 16.2	19 25.2	12 12.5	14 9.6	3 39.6	8 40.5
21 T	17 55 17.9	29 15.4	9 44.8	6♏39.1	5 22.5	13 37.6	7 0.1	19 31.3	12 20.1	14 13.0	3 39.8	8 42.0
22 F	17 59 14.5	0♋12.6	9 41.6	18 38.8	7 29.9	14 33.4	7 43.9	19 37.6	12 27.8	14 16.5	3 40.0	8 43.4
23 S	18 3 11.1	1 9.9	9 38.4	0♐47.1	9 35.8	15 29.6	8 27.6	19 43.9	12 35.5	14 19.9	3 40.2	8 44.8
24 S	18 7 7.6	2 7.1	9 35.3	13 6.4	11 40.1	16 26.3	9 11.3	19 50.4	12 43.2	14 23.3	3 40.5	8 46.3
25 M	18 11 4.2	3 4.3	9 32.1	25 38.5	13 42.7	17 23.5	9 54.9	19 57.1	12 50.9	14 26.7	3 40.8	8 47.8
26 T	18 15 0.7	4 1.5	9 28.9	8♑24.4	15 43.4	18 21.0	10 38.4	20 3.8	12 58.6	14 30.1	3 41.2	8 49.2
27 W	18 18 57.2	4 58.7	9 25.7	21 24.7	17 42.2	19 19.0	11 21.9	20 10.7	13 6.4	14 33.5	3 41.6	8 50.7
28 T	18 22 53.8	5 55.9	9 22.6	4♒39.2	19 39.0	20 17.3	12 5.3	20 17.8	13 14.1	14 36.8	3 42.0	8 52.3
29 F	18 26 50.4	6 53.1	9 19.4	18 7.2	21 33.8	21 16.1	12 48.6	20 24.9	13 21.9	14 40.2	3 42.4	8 53.8
30 S	18 30 47.0	7 50.3	9 16.2	1♓48.0	23 26.6	22 15.2	13 31.8	20 32.2	13 29.6	14 43.5	3 42.9	8 55.3

DECLINATION

DAY	EPHEMERIS SIDEREAL TIME h m s	☉	☊	☽	☿	♀	♂	♃	♄	♅	♆	♇
1 F	16 36 26.8	21N58.5	23N 0.4	20S42.8	17N 5.7	8N43.0	7N31.3	5N59.3	22N40.9	22N21.8	0S 7.8	23N56.2
4 M	16 48 16.4	22 21.9	23 1.1	8 55.0	18 54.1	9 14.0	8 21.9	5 54.8	22 39.6	22 23.1	0 7.5	23 55.1
7 T	17 0 6.2	22 41.8	23 1.9	7N42.8	20 36.7	9 49.0	9 11.6	5 49.8	22 38.2	22 24.5	0 7.2	23 54.0
10 S	17 11 55.8	22 58.1	23 2.6	20 41.9	22 8.5	10 27.2	10 0.4	5 44.2	22 36.7	22 25.8	0 7.1	23 52.9
13 W	17 23 45.5	23 10.8	23 3.4	22 13.0	23 24.1	11 8.0	10 48.2	5 38.0	22 35.1	22 27.1	0 7.1	23 51.8
16 S	17 35 35.1	23 19.9	23 4.1	13 11.4	24 18.7	11 50.8	11 34.9	5 31.3	22 33.5	22 28.4	0 7.2	23 50.6
19 T	17 47 24.8	23 25.2	23 4.8	0S14.3	24 48.8	12 35.0	12 20.5	5 24.1	22 31.7	22 29.7	0 7.4	23 49.4
22 F	17 59 14.5	23 26.7	23 5.5	13 27.5	24 53.7	13 20.1	13 4.8	5 16.4	22 29.9	22 30.9	0 7.8	23 48.1
25 M	18 11 4.2	23 24.6	23 6.2	22 8.3	24 34.5	14 5.7	13 48.0	5 8.2	22 28.0	22 32.1	0 8.2	23 46.9
28 T	18 22 53.8	23 18.8	23 6.9	21 19.0	23 54.2	14 51.2	14 29.8	4 59.6	22 26.0	22 33.3	0 8.8	23 45.6

JULY 1945

DAY	EPHEMERIS SIDEREAL TIME	☉	☊	☽	☿	♀	♂	♃	♄	♅	♆	♇
	h m s	° ′	° ′	° ′	° ′	° ′	° ′	° ′	° ′	° ′	° ′	° ′
LONGITUDE												
1 S	18 34 43.5	8♋47.5	9♋13.0	15♓40.3	25♋17.3	23♉14.7	14♉15.0	20♍39.6	13♋37.4	14♊46.8	3♎43.4	8♌56.9
2 M	18 38 40.0	9 44.7	9 9.9	29 42.6	27 5.9	24 14.5	14 58.1	20 47.1	13 45.2	14 50.1	3 43.9	8 58.5
3 T	18 42 36.6	10 41.9	9 6.7	13♈53.2	28 52.5	25 14.6	15 41.2	20 54.8	13 53.0	14 53.4	3 44.5	9 0.0
4 W	18 46 33.2	11 39.1	9 3.5	28 9.8	0♌36.9	26 15.1	16 24.2	21 2.6	14 0.8	14 56.7	3 45.1	9 1.6
5 T	18 50 29.8	12 36.3	9 0.3	12♉29.6	2 19.3	27 15.9	17 7.1	21 10.5	14 8.6	14 59.9	3 45.8	9 3.2
6 F	18 54 26.3	13 33.5	8 57.2	26 49.4	3 59.5	28 17.0	17 49.9	21 18.5	14 16.4	15 3.1	3 46.4	9 4.8
7 S	18 58 22.8	14 30.7	8 54.0	11♊ 5.3	5 37.7	29 18.4	18 32.6	21 26.6	14 24.2	15 6.3	3 47.1	9 6.5
8 S	19 2 19.4	15 27.9	8 50.8	25 13.4	7 13.7	0♊20.1	19 15.3	21 34.9	14 31.9	15 9.5	3 47.8	9 8.1
9 M	19 6 16.0	16 25.2	8 47.6	9♋ 9.9	8 47.7	1 22.0	19 57.9	21 43.2	14 39.8	15 12.7	3 48.6	9 9.8
10 T	19 10 12.5	17 22.4	8 44.5	22 51.3	10 19.5	2 24.2	20 40.4	21 51.7	14 47.5	15 15.8	3 49.4	9 11.4
11 W	19 14 9.1	18 19.7	8 41.3	6♌15.4	11 49.2	3 26.7	21 22.8	22 0.3	14 55.3	15 18.9	3 50.2	9 13.1
12 T	19 18 5.6	19 16.9	8 38.1	19 20.7	13 16.7	4 29.4	22 5.1	22 9.0	15 3.1	15 22.0	3 51.1	9 14.7
13 F	19 22 2.2	20 14.1	8 34.9	2♍ 7.5	14 42.0	5 32.4	22 47.4	22 17.8	15 10.9	15 25.0	3 51.9	9 16.4
14 S	19 25 58.7	21 11.4	8 31.7	14 37.0	16 5.1	6 35.6	23 29.5	22 26.7	15 18.7	15 28.1	3 52.9	9 18.1
15 S	19 29 55.3	22 8.6	8 28.6	26 51.7	17 26.0	7 39.1	24 11.6	22 35.8	15 26.4	15 31.1	3 53.8	9 19.8
16 M	19 33 51.9	23 5.9	8 25.4	8♎54.9	18 44.6	8 42.7	24 53.6	22 44.9	15 34.2	15 34.1	3 54.8	9 21.5
17 T	19 37 48.4	24 3.1	8 22.2	20 50.8	20 0.8	9 46.6	25 35.5	22 54.1	15 41.9	15 37.0	3 55.8	9 23.2
18 W	19 41 45.0	25 0.4	8 19.0	2♏43.8	21 14.7	10 50.7	26 17.3	23 3.4	15 49.7	15 40.0	3 56.8	9 24.9
19 T	19 45 41.5	25 57.6	8 15.9	14 38.7	22 26.1	11 55.0	26 59.0	23 12.8	15 57.4	15 42.9	3 57.9	9 26.7
20 F	19 49 38.1	26 54.9	8 12.7	26 39.8	23 35.0	12 59.5	27 40.6	23 22.4	16 5.1	15 45.7	3 58.9	9 28.4
21 S	19 53 34.7	27 52.1	8 9.5	8♐51.6	24 41.2	14 4.2	28 22.1	23 32.0	16 12.8	15 48.6	4 0.0	9 30.1
22 S	19 57 31.2	28 49.4	8 6.3	21 17.7	25 44.8	15 9.2	29 3.6	23 41.7	16 20.5	15 51.4	4 1.2	9 31.9
23 M	20 1 27.8	29 46.7	8 3.2	4♑ 1.0	26 45.6	16 14.3	29 45.0	23 51.5	16 28.2	15 54.2	4 2.4	9 33.6
24 T	20 5 24.3	0♌43.9	7 60.0	17 3.1	27 43.5	17 19.6	0♊26.2	24 1.4	16 35.8	15 56.9	4 3.6	9 35.3
25 W	20 9 20.9	1 41.2	7 56.8	0♒24.4	28 38.3	18 25.1	1 7.4	24 11.3	16 43.4	15 59.6	4 4.8	9 37.1
26 T	20 13 17.4	2 38.5	7 53.6	14 3.8	29 30.0	19 30.7	1 48.5	24 21.4	16 51.0	16 2.3	4 6.0	9 38.8
27 F	20 17 14.0	3 35.8	7 50.4	27 58.9	0♍18.5	20 36.6	2 29.5	24 31.5	16 58.6	16 5.0	4 7.3	9 40.6
28 S	20 21 10.6	4 33.2	7 47.3	12♓ 6.0	1 3.5	21 42.6	3 10.4	24 41.8	17 6.2	16 7.6	4 8.6	9 42.4
29 S	20 25 7.1	5 30.5	7 44.1	26 21.0	1 44.9	22 48.9	3 51.2	24 52.1	17 13.8	16 10.2	4 10.0	9 44.1
30 M	20 29 3.6	6 27.9	7 40.9	10♈39.4	2 22.6	23 55.2	4 31.9	25 2.5	17 21.3	16 12.7	4 11.3	9 45.9
31 T	20 33 0.2	7 25.3	7 37.7	24 57.4	2 56.4	25 1.8	5 12.5	25 13.0	17 28.8	16 15.3	4 12.7	9 47.6
DECLINATION												
1 S	18 34 43.5	23N 9.2	23N 7.5	10S 6.9	22N56.1	15N36.2	15N10.3	4N50.4	22N24.0	22N34.5	0S 9.5	23N44.3
4 W	18 46 33.2	22 56.1	23 8.2	6N 9.2	21 43.8	16 20.3	15 49.4	4 40.9	22 21.8	22 35.6	0 10.3	23 43.0
7 S	18 58 22.8	22 39.3	23 8.8	19 38.6	20 20.7	17 3.0	16 27.1	4 31.0	22 19.6	22 36.7	0 11.2	23 41.7
10 T	19 10 12.5	22 19.0	23 9.5	22 44.5	18 49.9	17 43.8	17 3.3	4 20.6	22 17.4	22 37.8	0 12.2	23 40.4
13 F	19 22 2.2	21 55.3	23 10.1	14 38.9	17 14.0	18 22.5	17 37.9	4 9.8	22 15.0	22 38.8	0 13.3	23 39.0
16 M	19 33 51.9	21 28.1	23 10.7	1 18.3	15 35.4	18 58.7	18 11.0	3 58.7	22 12.6	22 39.8	0 14.5	23 37.7
19 T	19 45 41.5	20 57.7	23 11.3	12S 8.2	13 56.6	19 31.9	18 42.5	3 47.3	22 10.1	22 40.8	0 15.9	23 36.4
22 S	19 57 31.2	20 24.1	23 11.9	21 32.9	12 19.9	20 1.9	19 12.4	3 35.4	22 7.6	22 41.7	0 17.3	23 35.1
25 W	20 9 20.9	19 47.4	23 12.5	21 55.7	10 47.6	20 28.3	19 40.6	3 23.3	22 5.1	22 42.6	0 18.8	23 33.7
28 S	20 21 10.6	19 7.7	23 13.0	11 19.6	9 22.3	20 50.8	20 7.2	3 10.9	22 2.4	22 43.5	0 20.4	23 32.4
31 T	20 33 0.2	18 25.3	23 13.6	4N59.6	8 7.0	21 9.3	20 32.1	2 58.2	21 59.8	22 44.3	0 22.2	23 31.2

AUGUST 1945

DAY	EPHEMERIS SIDEREAL TIME	☉	☊	☽	☿	♀	♂	♃	♄	♅	♆	♇
LONGITUDE												
1 W	20 36 56.8	8♌22.7	7♋34.6	9♉11.7	3♍26.1	26♊ 8.5	5♊53.0	25♍23.5	17♋36.3	16♊17.8	4♎14.1	9♌49.4
2 T	20 40 53.4	9 20.1	7 31.4	23 20.0	3 51.5	27 15.4	6 33.4	25 34.2	17 43.7	16 20.2	4 15.6	9 51.2
3 F	20 44 49.9	10 17.5	7 28.2	7♊20.6	4 12.5	28 22.4	7 13.7	25 44.9	17 51.1	16 22.6	4 17.0	9 52.9
4 S	20 48 46.4	11 15.0	7 25.0	21 12.2	4 28.8	29 29.6	7 53.9	25 55.7	17 58.5	16 25.0	4 18.5	9 54.7
5 S	20 52 43.0	12 12.4	7 21.8	4♋53.8	4 40.3	0♋37.0	8 34.0	26 6.5	18 5.9	16 27.3	4 20.0	9 56.5
6 M	20 56 39.6	13 9.9	7 18.7	18 24.5	4 46.7	1 44.5	9 14.0	26 17.5	18 13.2	16 29.6	4 21.5	9 58.3
7 T	21 0 36.1	14 7.5	7 15.5	1♌43.0	4 48.0	2 52.1	9 53.9	26 28.5	18 20.5	16 31.9	4 23.1	10 0.0
8 W	21 4 32.7	15 5.0	7 12.3	14 48.5	4R44.1	3 59.9	10 33.7	26 39.6	18 27.8	16 34.1	4 24.7	10 1.8
9 T	21 8 29.2	16 2.5	7 9.1	27 40.0	4 34.7	5 7.8	11 13.3	26 50.7	18 35.0	16 36.3	4 26.3	10 3.5
10 F	21 12 25.8	17 0.1	7 6.0	10♍17.4	4 20.0	6 15.8	11 52.9	27 1.9	18 42.3	16 38.4	4 27.9	10 5.3
11 S	21 16 22.3	17 57.7	7 2.8	22 41.1	3 59.9	7 24.0	12 32.3	27 13.2	18 49.4	16 40.5	4 29.6	10 7.1
12 S	21 20 18.9	18 55.3	6 59.6	4♎52.5	3 34.5	8 32.3	13 11.6	27 24.6	18 56.6	16 42.6	4 31.2	10 8.8
13 M	21 24 15.4	19 52.9	6 56.4	16 53.9	3 3.9	9 40.7	13 50.8	27 36.0	19 3.6	16 44.6	4 32.9	10 10.6
14 T	21 28 11.9	20 50.6	6 53.2	28 48.3	2 28.5	10 49.3	14 29.9	27 47.5	19 10.7	16 46.6	4 34.6	10 12.3
15 W	21 32 8.5	21 48.2	6 50.1	10♏39.9	1 48.7	11 58.0	15 8.8	27 59.0	19 17.7	16 48.5	4 36.4	10 14.0
16 T	21 36 5.1	22 45.9	6 46.9	22 33.1	1 4.9	13 6.8	15 47.7	28 10.6	19 24.7	16 50.4	4 38.1	10 15.8
17 F	21 40 1.7	23 43.6	6 43.7	4♐32.9	0 17.8	14 15.7	16 26.4	28 22.3	19 31.6	16 52.3	4 39.9	10 17.5
18 S	21 43 58.2	24 41.3	6 40.5	16 44.3	29♌28.2	15 24.7	17 5.0	28 34.0	19 38.5	16 54.1	4 41.7	10 19.2
19 S	21 47 54.7	25 39.0	6 37.4	29 12.1	28 36.7	16 33.9	17 43.4	28 45.7	19 45.3	16 55.8	4 43.5	10 20.9
20 M	21 51 51.3	26 36.7	6 34.2	12♑ 0.4	27 44.5	17 43.1	18 21.8	28 57.5	19 52.1	16 57.6	4 45.3	10 22.7
21 T	21 55 47.9	27 34.5	6 31.0	25 12.1	26 52.5	18 52.5	19 0.0	29 9.4	19 58.9	16 59.2	4 47.2	10 24.4
22 W	21 59 44.4	28 32.3	6 27.8	8♒48.6	26 1.8	20 2.0	19 38.1	29 21.3	20 5.6	17 0.9	4 49.1	10 26.1
23 T	22 3 41.0	29 30.1	6 24.7	22 48.8	25 13.4	21 11.7	20 16.1	29 33.3	20 12.2	17 2.4	4 50.9	10 27.7
24 F	22 7 37.5	0♍27.9	6 21.5	7♓ 9.1	24 28.5	22 21.4	20 53.9	29 45.3	20 18.8	17 4.0	4 52.9	10 29.4
25 S	22 11 34.1	1 25.8	6 18.3	21 44.0	23 47.9	23 31.2	21 31.6	29 57.4	20 25.3	17 5.5	4 54.8	10 31.1
26 S	22 15 30.7	2 23.6	6 15.1	6♈26.1	23 12.5	24 41.2	22 9.2	0♎ 9.5	20 31.8	17 6.9	4 56.7	10 32.8
27 M	22 19 27.2	3 21.5	6 11.9	21 7.9	22 43.4	25 51.3	22 46.7	0 21.6	20 38.3	17 8.3	4 58.7	10 34.4
28 T	22 23 23.7	4 19.5	6 8.8	5♉42.7	22 21.0	27 1.4	23 24.0	0 33.8	20 44.7	17 9.6	5 0.6	10 36.1
29 W	22 27 20.3	5 17.4	6 5.6	20 5.4	22 6.0	28 11.7	24 1.2	0 46.1	20 51.0	17 10.9	5 2.6	10 37.7
30 T	22 31 16.8	6 15.4	6 2.4	4♊13.2	21 58.9	29 22.1	24 38.2	0 58.4	20 57.3	17 12.2	5 4.6	10 39.3
31 F	22 35 13.4	7 13.5	5 59.2	18 5.0	22D 0.0	0♌32.6	25 15.1	1 10.7	21 3.5	17 13.4	5 6.6	10 40.9
DECLINATION												
1 W	20 36 56.8	18N10.5	23N13.8	10N17.3	7N44.6	21N14.5	20N40.0	2N53.9	21N58.9	22N44.5	0S22.7	23N30.7
4 S	20 48 46.4	17 24.4	23 14.3	21 34.2	6 47.8	21 27.0	21 2.7	2 40.8	21 56.2	22 45.3	0 24.6	23 29.5
7 T	21 0 36.1	16 35.7	23 14.8	21 45.0	6 9.1	21 34.9	21 23.6	2 27.4	21 53.5	22 46.0	0 26.5	23 28.2
10 F	21 12 25.8	15 44.7	23 15.3	11 54.9	5 52.7	21 38.0	21 42.9	2 13.9	21 50.8	22 46.7	0 28.5	23 27.0
13 M	21 24 15.4	14 51.3	23 15.9	1S55.9	6 1.6	21 36.1	22 0.5	2 0.1	21 48.0	22 47.4	0 30.5	23 25.8
16 T	21 36 5.1	13 55.9	23 16.3	14 50.5	6 37.0	21 29.1	22 16.4	1 46.0	21 45.3	22 48.0	0 32.7	23 24.7
19 S	21 47 54.7	12 58.4	23 16.8	22 38.0	7 36.5	21 17.0	22 30.7	1 31.8	21 42.5	22 48.5	0 34.9	23 23.5
22 W	21 59 44.4	11 59.2	23 17.3	20 35.0	8 52.9	20 59.7	22 43.3	1 17.4	21 39.8	22 49.0	0 37.1	23 22.4
25 S	22 11 34.1	10 58.2	23 17.8	7 46.4	10 15.4	20 37.2	22 54.4	1 2.9	21 37.0	22 49.5	0 39.4	23 21.4
28 T	22 23 23.7	9 55.6	23 18.2	9N11.5	11 31.8	20 9.6	23 3.9	0 48.2	21 34.3	22 50.0	0 41.8	23 20.4
31 F	22 35 13.4	8 51.6	23 18.6	21 13.7	12 31.2	19 36.9	23 11.8	0 33.4	21 31.7	22 50.3	0 44.2	23 19.4

SEPTEMBER 1945

DAY	EPHEMERIS SIDEREAL TIME h m s	☉ ° ′	☊ ° ′	☽ ° ′	☿ ° ′	♀ ° ′	♂ ° ′	♃ ° ′	♄ ° ′	♅ ° ′	♆ ° ′	♇ ° ′
						LONGITUDE						
1 S	22 39 10.0	8♍11.5	5♋56.1	1♋41.1	22♌ 9.5	1♌43.2	25♊51.8	1♎23.1	21♋ 9.7	17♊14.6	5♎ 8.7	10♌42.5
2 S	22 43 6.5	9 9.6	5 52.9	15 2.9	22 27.4	2 53.9	26 28.5	1 35.5	21 15.8	17 15.7	5 10.7	10 44.1
3 M	22 47 3.0	10 7.8	5 49.7	28 11.5	22 53.8	4 4.7	27 4.9	1 47.9	21 21.8	17 16.7	5 12.7	10 45.7
4 T	22 50 59.6	11 5.9	5 46.5	11♌ 8.1	23 28.5	5 15.6	27 41.2	2 0.4	21 27.8	17 17.7	5 14.8	10 47.3
5 W	22 54 56.2	12 4.1	5 43.3	23 53.5	24 11.4	6 26.6	28 17.4	2 12.9	21 33.7	17 18.7	5 16.9	10 48.9
6 T	22 58 52.7	13 2.3	5 40.2	6♍28.1	25 2.1	7 37.7	28 53.4	2 25.5	21 39.5	17 19.6	5 19.0	10 50.4
7 F	23 2 49.3	14 0.6	5 37.0	18 52.4	26 0.3	8 48.9	29 29.2	2 38.1	21 45.3	17 20.5	5 21.1	10 51.9
8 S	23 6 45.8	14 58.9	5 33.8	1♎ 6.6	27 5.6	10 0.2	0♋ 4.8	2 50.7	21 51.0	17 21.3	5 23.2	10 53.4
9 S	23 10 42.4	15 57.2	5 30.6	13 11.6	28 17.6	11 11.5	0 40.3	3 3.3	21 56.7	17 22.0	5 25.3	10 55.0
10 M	23 14 39.0	16 55.5	5 27.5	25 8.8	29 35.6	12 23.0	1 15.7	3 16.0	22 2.3	17 22.7	5 27.5	10 56.4
11 T	23 18 35.5	17 53.9	5 24.3	7♏ 0.5	0♍59.2	13 34.5	1 50.8	3 28.7	22 7.8	17 23.4	5 29.6	10 57.9
12 W	23 22 32.0	18 52.3	5 21.1	18 49.9	2 27.8	14 46.1	2 25.8	3 41.4	22 13.2	17 24.0	5 31.8	10 59.4
13 T	23 26 28.6	19 50.7	5 17.9	0♐40.7	4 0.8	15 57.9	3 0.6	3 54.1	22 18.6	17 24.5	5 33.9	11 0.8
14 F	23 30 25.2	20 49.1	5 14.7	12 37.7	5 37.7	17 9.6	3 35.3	4 6.9	22 23.9	17 25.0	5 36.1	11 2.3
15 S	23 34 21.7	21 47.6	5 11.6	24 45.9	7 17.9	18 21.5	4 9.7	4 19.7	22 29.1	17 25.5	5 38.3	11 3.7
16 S	23 38 18.2	22 46.1	5 8.4	7♑10.7	9 0.8	19 33.4	4 44.0	4 32.5	22 34.2	17 25.9	5 40.4	11 5.1
17 M	23 42 14.8	23 44.6	5 5.2	19 57.2	10 46.1	20 45.5	5 18.1	4 45.3	22 39.3	17 26.2	5 42.6	11 6.4
18 T	23 46 11.4	24 43.2	5 2.0	3♒ 9.7	12 33.3	21 57.6	5 52.0	4 58.2	22 44.3	17 26.5	5 44.8	11 7.8
19 W	23 50 7.9	25 41.7	4 58.9	16 50.6	14 21.8	23 9.8	6 25.7	5 11.1	22 49.2	17 26.8	5 47.0	11 9.1
20 T	23 54 4.5	26 40.3	4 55.7	1♓ 0.4	16 11.4	24 22.0	6 59.3	5 23.9	22 54.0	17 26.9	5 49.2	11 10.5
21 F	23 58 1.0	27 39.0	4 52.5	15 35.8	18 1.8	25 34.4	7 32.6	5 36.8	22 58.8	17 27.1	5 51.5	11 11.8
22 S	0 1 57.6	28 37.7	4 49.3	0♈30.7	19 52.5	26 46.8	8 5.7	5 49.7	23 3.4	17 27.2	5 53.7	11 13.1
23 S	0 5 54.2	29 36.4	4 46.1	15 36.1	21 43.5	27 59.3	8 38.7	6 2.7	23 8.0	17 27.2	5 55.9	11 14.3
24 M	0 9 50.7	0♎35.1	4 43.0	0♉41.7	23 34.5	29 11.9	9 11.4	6 15.6	23 12.5	17R27.2	5 58.1	11 15.6
25 T	0 13 47.3	1 33.9	4 39.8	15 37.8	25 25.2	0♍24.5	9 44.0	6 28.5	23 16.9	17 27.1	6 0.3	11 16.8
26 W	0 17 43.8	2 32.7	4 36.6	0♊17.0	27 15.6	1 37.3	10 16.3	6 41.5	23 21.3	17 27.0	6 2.6	11 18.0
27 T	0 21 40.4	3 31.5	4 33.4	14 34.7	29 5.6	2 50.1	10 48.4	6 54.4	23 25.5	17 26.8	6 4.8	11 19.2
28 F	0 25 36.9	4 30.4	4 30.3	28 29.4	0♎55.0	4 2.9	11 20.3	7 7.4	23 29.7	17 26.6	6 7.0	11 20.4
29 S	0 29 33.5	5 29.3	4 27.1	12♋ 1.9	2 43.8	5 15.9	11 52.0	7 20.4	23 33.8	17 26.3	6 9.3	11 21.6
30 S	0 33 30.0	6 28.3	4 23.9	25 14.3	4 31.9	6 28.9	12 23.5	7 33.4	23 37.7	17 26.0	6 11.5	11 22.7

DAY	EPHEMERIS SIDEREAL TIME h m s	☉ ° ′	☊ ° ′	☽ ° ′	☿ ° ′	♀ ° ′	♂ ° ′	♃ ° ′	♄ ° ′	♅ ° ′	♆ ° ′	♇ ° ′
						DECLINATION						
1 S	22 39 10.0	8N30.0	23N18.8	22N55.6	12N45.8	19N24.9	23N14.1	0N28.4	21N30.8	22N50.5	0S45.0	23N19.1
4 T	22 50 59.6	7 24.3	23 19.2	20 9.1	13 10.6	18 45.6	23 20.1	0 13.4	21 28.2	22 50.8	0 47.5	23 18.2
7 F	23 2 49.3	6 17.6	23 19.6	8 48.3	13 4.3	18 1.5	23 24.7	0S 1.7	21 25.6	22 51.1	0 50.0	23 17.3
10 M	23 14 39.0	5 9.9	23 20.0	5S18.0	12 26.0	17 12.8	23 27.9	0 16.9	21 23.1	22 51.3	0 52.6	23 16.5
13 T	23 26 28.6	4 1.4	23 20.4	17 26.6	11 17.5	16 19.6	23 29.8	0 32.1	21 20.7	22 51.5	0 55.2	23 15.8
16 S	23 38 18.2	2 52.3	23 20.8	23 22.0	9 43.4	15 22.3	23 30.5	0 47.4	21 18.4	22 51.7	0 57.8	23 15.1
19 W	23 50 7.9	1 42.7	23 21.2	18 56.6	7 49.6	14 21.0	23 30.0	1 2.8	21 16.1	22 51.8	1 0.4	23 14.4
22 S	0 1 57.6	0 32.8	23 21.5	4 22.3	5 42.1	13 15.9	23 28.4	1 18.1	21 13.9	22 51.9	1 3.0	23 13.9
25 T	0 13 47.3	0S37.4	23 21.8	12N53.1	3 26.3	12 7.4	23 25.8	1 33.5	21 11.9	22 51.9	1 5.6	23 13.4
28 F	0 25 36.9	1 47.5	23 22.2	22 53.7	1 6.4	10 55.6	23 22.3	1 48.9	21 9.9	22 51.9	1 8.3	23 12.9

OCTOBER 1945

DAY	EPHEMERIS SIDEREAL TIME h m s	☉ ° ′	☊ ° ′	☽ ° ′	☿ ° ′	♀ ° ′	♂ ° ′	♃ ° ′	♄ ° ′	♅ ° ′	♆ ° ′	♇ ° ′
						LONGITUDE						
1 M	0 37 26.6	7♎27.3	4♋20.7	8♌ 9.5	6♎19.2	7♍42.0	12♋54.7	7♎46.3	23♋41.6	17♊25.6	6♎13.7	11♌23.8
2 T	0 41 23.1	8 26.3	4 17.5	20 50.5	8 5.8	8 55.2	13 25.7	7 59.3	23 45.4	17R25.2	6 16.0	11 24.9
3 W	0 45 19.7	9 25.4	4 14.4	3♍19.7	9 51.7	10 8.4	13 56.4	8 12.3	23 49.1	17 24.7	6 18.2	11 26.0
4 T	0 49 16.2	10 24.5	4 11.2	15 39.1	11 36.7	11 21.7	14 26.9	8 25.3	23 52.7	17 24.2	6 20.4	11 27.0
5 F	0 53 12.8	11 23.7	4 8.0	27 50.3	13 20.9	12 35.1	14 57.1	8 38.3	23 56.2	17 23.6	6 22.7	11 28.0
6 S	0 57 9.3	12 22.9	4 4.8	9♎54.3	15 4.3	13 48.5	15 27.1	8 51.3	23 59.7	17 23.0	6 24.9	11 29.0
7 S	1 1 5.9	13 22.1	4 1.7	21 52.3	16 46.9	15 2.0	15 56.8	9 4.2	24 3.0	17 22.3	6 27.1	11 30.0
8 M	1 5 2.5	14 21.3	3 58.5	3♏45.2	18 28.7	16 15.5	16 26.3	9 17.2	24 6.2	17 21.5	6 29.3	11 31.0
9 T	1 8 59.0	15 20.6	3 55.3	15 34.9	20 9.7	17 29.1	16 55.5	9 30.2	24 9.3	17 20.8	6 31.5	11 31.9
10 W	1 12 55.5	16 19.9	3 52.1	27 23.4	21 49.9	18 42.7	17 24.4	9 43.1	24 12.4	17 19.9	6 33.7	11 32.8
11 T	1 16 52.1	17 19.3	3 48.9	9♐13.9	23 29.4	19 56.4	17 53.0	9 56.0	24 15.3	17 19.0	6 36.0	11 33.7
12 F	1 20 48.7	18 18.7	3 45.8	21 10.1	25 8.1	21 10.2	18 21.3	10 9.0	24 18.1	17 18.1	6 38.2	11 34.6
13 S	1 24 45.2	19 18.1	3 42.6	3♑16.3	26 46.1	22 24.0	18 49.4	10 21.9	24 20.8	17 17.1	6 40.4	11 35.4
14 S	1 28 41.8	20 17.5	3 39.4	15 37.7	28 23.4	23 37.8	19 17.1	10 34.8	24 23.5	17 16.1	6 42.5	11 36.2
15 M	1 32 38.3	21 17.0	3 36.2	28 19.3	0♏ 0.0	24 51.7	19 44.5	10 47.7	24 26.0	17 15.0	6 44.7	11 37.0
16 T	1 36 34.9	22 16.5	3 33.0	11♒26.0	1 35.9	26 5.7	20 11.7	11 0.6	24 28.4	17 13.9	6 46.9	11 37.8
17 W	1 40 31.4	23 16.0	3 29.9	25 1.5	3 11.2	27 19.7	20 38.5	11 13.4	24 30.7	17 12.7	6 49.1	11 38.5
18 T	1 44 28.0	24 15.6	3 26.7	9♓ 7.3	4 45.8	28 33.8	21 5.0	11 26.2	24 32.9	17 11.5	6 51.2	11 39.2
19 F	1 48 24.5	25 15.1	3 23.5	23 42.1	6 19.8	29 47.9	21 31.2	11 39.0	24 35.0	17 10.3	6 53.3	11 39.9
20 S	1 52 21.1	26 14.8	3 20.3	8♈41.1	7 53.2	1♎ 2.0	21 57.0	11 51.8	24 37.0	17 8.9	6 55.5	11 40.5
21 S	1 56 17.7	27 14.4	3 17.2	23 55.7	9 26.0	2 16.2	22 22.6	12 4.6	24 38.9	17 7.6	6 57.6	11 41.2
22 M	2 0 14.2	28 14.1	3 14.0	9♉15.1	10 58.2	3 30.4	22 47.7	12 17.4	24 40.7	17 6.2	6 59.7	11 41.8
23 T	2 4 10.7	29 13.8	3 10.8	24 27.9	12 29.8	4 44.7	23 12.6	12 30.1	24 42.3	17 4.8	7 1.8	11 42.4
24 W	2 8 7.3	0♏13.5	3 7.6	9♊24.3	14 0.9	5 59.0	23 37.0	12 42.8	24 43.9	17 3.3	7 3.9	11 42.9
25 T	2 12 3.8	1 13.3	3 4.4	23 57.4	15 31.4	7 13.4	24 1.1	12 55.4	24 45.4	17 1.8	7 6.0	11 43.5
26 F	2 16 0.4	2 13.2	3 1.3	8♋ 3.8	17 1.3	8 27.9	24 24.9	13 8.1	24 46.7	17 0.2	7 8.1	11 44.0
27 S	2 19 57.0	3 13.0	2 58.1	21 43.3	18 30.7	9 42.3	24 48.2	13 20.7	24 47.9	16 58.6	7 10.1	11 44.5
28 S	2 23 53.5	4 12.9	2 54.9	4♌57.6	19 59.4	10 56.8	25 11.2	13 33.2	24 49.1	16 57.0	7 12.2	11 44.9
29 M	2 27 50.1	5 12.8	2 51.7	17 50.2	21 27.7	12 11.4	25 33.7	13 45.8	24 50.1	16 55.3	7 14.2	11 45.3
30 T	2 31 46.6	6 12.8	2 48.6	0♍24.7	22 55.3	13 26.0	25 55.9	13 58.3	24 51.0	16 53.5	7 16.2	11 45.7
31 W	2 35 43.2	7 12.8	2 45.4	12 45.0	24 22.3	14 40.6	26 17.6	14 10.8	24 51.8	16 51.8	7 18.2	11 46.1

DAY	EPHEMERIS SIDEREAL TIME h m s	☉ ° ′	☊ ° ′	☽ ° ′	☿ ° ′	♀ ° ′	♂ ° ′	♃ ° ′	♄ ° ′	♅ ° ′	♆ ° ′	♇ ° ′
						DECLINATION						
1 M	0 37 26.6	2S57.5	23N22.5	20N55.0	1S14.4	9N40.9	23N17.9	2S 4.2	21N 8.1	22N51.8	1S10.9	23N12.5
4 T	0 49 16.2	4 7.3	23 22.8	10 1.5	3 33.9	8 23.7	23 12.9	2 19.6	21 6.4	22 51.7	1 13.5	23 12.2
7 S	1 1 5.9	5 16.7	23 23.1	4S 7.0	5 50.5	7 4.0	23 7.2	2 34.8	21 4.8	22 51.6	1 16.1	23 12.0
10 W	1 12 55.5	6 25.4	23 23.4	16 43.5	8 3.0	5 42.4	23 0.9	2 50.1	21 3.4	22 51.4	1 18.7	23 11.8
13 S	1 24 45.2	7 33.4	23 23.7	23 26.6	10 10.5	4 19.0	22 54.3	3 5.2	21 2.1	22 51.1	1 21.3	23 11.7
16 T	1 36 34.9	8 40.5	23 23.9	20 23.7	12 12.4	2 54.3	22 47.3	3 20.2	21 1.0	22 50.9	1 23.8	23 11.7
19 F	1 48 24.5	9 46.4	23 24.2	7 4.9	14 8.0	1 28.6	22 40.2	3 35.2	21 0.0	22 50.5	1 26.3	23 11.8
22 M	2 0 14.2	10 51.0	23 24.4	10N45.3	15 56.7	0 2.0	22 32.9	3 50.0	20 59.2	22 50.2	1 28.8	23 11.9
25 T	2 12 3.8	11 54.2	23 24.6	22 36.6	17 38.1	1S24.9	22 25.8	4 4.7	20 58.6	22 49.8	1 31.2	23 12.1
28 S	2 23 53.5	12 55.7	23 24.8	21 44.5	19 11.6	2 52.0	22 18.8	4 19.2	20 58.2	22 49.4	1 33.5	23 12.4
31 W	2 35 43.2	13 55.4	23 25.1	11 13.6	20 36.5	4 18.8	22 12.2	4 33.5	20 57.9	22 48.9	1 35.8	23 12.7

NOVEMBER 1945

LONGITUDE

DAY	EPHEMERIS SIDEREAL TIME	☉	☊	☽	☿	♀	♂	♃	♄	♅	♆	♇
	h m s	° ′	° ′	° ′	° ′	° ′	° ′	° ′	° ′	° ′	° ′	° ′
1 T	2 39 39.7	8♏12.9	2♋42.2	24♍54.4	25♏48.7	15♎55.3	26♋38.9	14♎23.2	24♋52.4	16♊50.0	7♎20.2	11♌46.4
2 F	2 43 36.3	9 12.9	2 39.0	6♎56.0	27 14.5	17 10.0	26 59.8	14 35.6	24 53.0	16R48.1	7 22.2	11 46.8
3 S	2 47 32.8	10 13.0	2 35.9	18 52.1	28 39.5	18 24.7	27 20.2	14 47.9	24 53.5	16 46.3	7 24.1	11 47.0
4 S	2 51 29.4	11 13.2	2 32.7	0♏44.5	0♐ 3.8	19 39.5	27 40.1	15 0.3	24 53.8	16 44.3	7 26.1	11 47.3
5 M	2 55 26.0	12 13.4	2 29.5	12 35.0	1 27.4	20 54.3	27 59.6	15 12.5	24 54.0	16 42.4	7 28.0	11 47.5
6 T	2 59 22.5	13 13.6	2 26.3	24 25.1	2 50.1	22 9.1	28 18.6	15 24.8	24 54.1	16 40.4	7 29.9	11 47.7
7 W	3 3 19.1	14 13.8	2 23.1	6♐16.5	4 11.9	23 23.9	28 37.1	15 36.9	24R54.1	16 38.4	7 31.8	11 47.9
8 T	3 7 15.6	15 14.1	2 20.0	18 11.3	5 32.6	24 38.8	28 55.1	15 49.1	24 54.0	16 36.4	7 33.6	11 48.1
9 F	3 11 12.2	16 14.3	2 16.8	0♑12.3	6 52.3	25 53.7	29 12.6	16 1.1	24 53.8	16 34.3	7 35.5	11 48.2
10 S	3 15 8.7	17 14.7	2 13.6	12 22.5	8 10.8	27 8.7	29 29.6	16 13.2	24 53.5	16 32.2	7 37.3	11 48.3
11 S	3 19 5.3	18 15.0	2 10.4	24 45.8	9 28.0	28 23.6	29 46.0	16 25.1	24 53.0	16 30.0	7 39.1	11 48.3
12 M	3 23 1.8	19 15.3	2 7.3	7♒26.4	10 43.6	29 38.6	0♌ 2.0	16 37.1	24 52.4	16 27.9	7 40.9	11 48.4
13 T	3 26 58.4	20 15.7	2 4.1	20 28.2	11 57.6	0♏53.6	0 17.3	16 48.9	24 51.8	16 25.7	7 42.6	11 48.4
14 W	3 30 55.0	21 16.1	2 0.9	3♓55.0	13 9.7	2 8.6	0 32.1	17 0.7	24 51.0	16 23.5	7 44.4	11R48.4
15 T	3 34 51.5	22 16.6	1 57.7	17 49.1	14 19.6	3 23.7	0 46.4	17 12.5	24 50.1	16 21.2	7 46.1	11 48.3
16 F	3 38 48.1	23 17.0	1 54.5	2♈10.5	15 27.2	4 38.7	1 0.1	17 24.2	24 49.1	16 18.9	7 47.8	11 48.3
17 S	3 42 44.6	24 17.5	1 51.4	16 56.6	16 32.1	5 53.8	1 13.1	17 35.8	24 47.9	16 16.6	7 49.5	11 48.2
18 S	3 46 41.2	25 18.0	1 48.2	2♉ 1.4	17 33.9	7 8.9	1 25.6	17 47.4	24 46.7	16 14.3	7 51.1	11 48.0
19 M	3 50 37.7	26 18.5	1 45.0	17 16.0	18 32.2	8 24.1	1 37.5	17 58.9	24 45.4	16 12.0	7 52.8	11 47.9
20 T	3 54 34.3	27 19.0	1 41.8	2♊30.1	19 26.7	9 39.2	1 48.7	18 10.3	24 43.9	16 9.6	7 54.4	11 47.7
21 W	3 58 30.8	28 19.6	1 38.7	17 33.4	20 16.7	10 54.4	1 59.3	18 21.6	24 42.4	16 7.2	7 55.9	11 47.5
22 T	4 2 27.4	29 20.2	1 35.5	2♋17.2	21 1.7	12 9.5	2 9.3	18 32.9	24 40.7	16 4.9	7 57.5	11 47.2
23 F	4 6 24.0	0♐20.8	1 32.3	16 36.0	21 41.0	13 24.8	2 18.6	18 44.2	24 38.9	16 2.4	7 59.0	11 47.0
24 S	4 10 20.5	1 21.5	1 29.1	0♌27.1	22 14.0	14 40.0	2 27.2	18 55.3	24 37.1	16 0.0	8 0.5	11 46.7
25 S	4 14 17.1	2 22.1	1 26.0	13 50.7	22 40.0	15 55.2	2 35.1	19 6.4	24 35.1	15 57.6	8 2.0	11 46.4
26 M	4 18 13.6	3 22.8	1 22.8	26 49.2	22 58.0	17 10.5	2 42.3	19 17.4	24 33.0	15 55.1	8 3.5	11 46.0
27 T	4 22 10.2	4 23.6	1 19.6	9♍26.0	23 7.4	18 25.8	2 48.9	19 28.3	24 30.8	15 52.6	8 4.9	11 45.7
28 W	4 26 6.8	5 24.3	1 16.4	21 45.3	23R 7.3	19 41.1	2 54.6	19 39.2	24 28.5	15 50.1	8 6.3	11 45.3
29 T	4 30 3.3	6 25.1	1 13.3	3♎51.4	22 57.1	20 56.4	2 59.7	19 50.0	24 26.1	15 47.6	8 7.7	11 44.8
30 F	4 33 59.9	7 25.9	1 10.1	15 48.4	22 36.1	22 11.7	3 4.0	20 0.7	24 23.6	15 45.1	8 9.0	11 44.4

DECLINATION

DAY	EPHEMERIS SIDEREAL TIME	☉	☊	☽	☿	♀	♂	♃	♄	♅	♆	♇
1 T	2 39 39.7	14S14.9	23N25.1	6N40.0	21S 2.8	4S47.7	22N10.1	4S38.3	20N57.9	22N48.7	1S36.6	23N12.8
4 S	2 51 29.4	15 12.0	23 25.3	7S34.4	22 15.3	6 13.7	22 4.1	4 52.4	20 57.9	22 48.2	1 38.8	23 13.3
7 W	3 3 19.1	16 6.8	23 25.5	19 15.8	23 17.7	7 38.6	21 58.7	5 6.3	20 58.1	22 47.6	1 41.0	23 13.8
10 S	3 15 8.7	16 59.2	23 25.6	23 55.3	24 9.2	9 2.2	21 54.2	5 20.0	20 58.4	22 47.0	1 43.1	23 14.4
13 T	3 26 58.4	17 49.0	23 25.8	18 25.6	24 49.0	10 24.0	21 50.6	5 33.4	20 59.0	22 46.4	1 45.1	23 15.1
16 F	3 38 48.1	18 36.0	23 25.9	3 53.4	25 16.2	11 43.7	21 48.1	5 46.6	20 59.7	22 45.8	1 47.0	23 15.8
19 M	3 50 37.7	19 20.0	23 26.1	13N35.0	25 30.0	13 1.0	21 46.8	5 59.5	21 0.6	22 45.1	1 48.8	23 16.6
22 T	4 2 27.4	20 0.9	23 26.2	23 37.0	25 29.4	14 15.4	21 46.9	6 12.1	21 1.7	22 44.4	1 50.6	23 17.5
25 S	4 14 17.1	20 38.4	23 26.3	20 8.1	25 13.5	15 26.7	21 48.4	6 24.5	21 2.9	22 43.6	1 52.2	23 18.4
28 W	4 26 6.8	21 12.6	23 26.4	8 1.8	24 41.1	16 34.4	21 51.5	6 36.5	21 4.4	22 42.9	1 53.8	23 19.4

DECEMBER 1945

LONGITUDE

DAY	EPHEMERIS SIDEREAL TIME	☉	☊	☽	☿	♀	♂	♃	♄	♅	♆	♇
1 S	4 37 56.4	8♐26.7	1♋ 6.9	27♎40.2	22♐ 4.1	23♏27.0	3♌ 7.5	20♎11.3	24♋21.0	15♊42.6	8♎10.3	11♌43.9
2 S	4 41 53.0	9 27.6	1 3.7	9♏29.9	21R21.1	24 42.4	3 10.2	20 21.8	24R18.3	15R40.1	8 11.6	11R43.4
3 M	4 45 49.5	10 28.5	1 0.5	21 20.2	20 27.4	25 57.7	3 12.2	20 32.2	24 15.6	15 37.5	8 12.9	11 42.9
4 T	4 49 46.1	11 29.4	0 57.4	3♐13.4	19 24.0	27 13.1	3 13.4	20 42.6	24 12.7	15 35.0	8 14.1	11 42.3
5 W	4 53 42.7	12 30.3	0 54.2	15 11.4	18 12.4	28 28.5	3 13.7	20 52.8	24 9.7	15 32.5	8 15.3	11 41.7
6 T	4 57 39.2	13 31.2	0 51.0	27 16.0	16 54.4	29 43.9	3R13.3	21 3.0	24 6.6	15 29.9	8 16.5	11 41.1
7 F	5 1 35.8	14 32.2	0 47.8	9♑28.8	15 32.5	0♐59.3	3 12.0	21 13.0	24 3.5	15 27.4	8 17.6	11 40.5
8 S	5 5 32.3	15 33.1	0 44.7	21 51.6	14 9.6	2 14.7	3 9.9	21 23.0	24 0.2	15 24.8	8 18.8	11 39.8
9 S	5 9 28.9	16 34.1	0 41.5	4♒26.5	12 48.3	3 30.1	3 7.0	21 32.9	23 56.9	15 22.3	8 19.8	11 39.2
10 M	5 13 25.4	17 35.1	0 38.3	17 15.8	11 31.4	4 45.5	3 3.2	21 42.6	23 53.5	15 19.7	8 20.9	11 38.5
11 T	5 17 22.0	18 36.1	0 35.1	0♓21.7	10 21.2	6 1.0	2 58.6	21 52.3	23 50.0	15 17.2	8 21.9	11 37.7
12 W	5 21 18.6	19 37.1	0 32.0	13 46.4	9 19.7	7 16.4	2 53.2	22 1.9	23 46.4	15 14.6	8 22.9	11 37.0
13 T	5 25 15.1	20 38.1	0 28.8	27 31.4	8 28.2	8 31.8	2 46.9	22 11.3	23 42.7	15 12.1	8 23.9	11 36.2
14 F	5 29 11.7	21 39.1	0 25.6	11♈37.2	7 47.6	9 47.3	2 39.8	22 20.7	23 39.0	15 9.5	8 24.8	11 35.4
15 S	5 33 8.2	22 40.1	0 22.4	26 2.5	7 18.1	11 2.7	2 31.8	22 29.9	23 35.1	15 7.0	8 25.7	11 34.6
16 S	5 37 4.8	23 41.2	0 19.2	10♉44.2	6 59.7	12 18.1	2 23.0	22 39.0	23 31.3	15 4.5	8 26.5	11 33.8
17 M	5 41 1.4	24 42.2	0 16.1	25 36.8	6 52.0	13 33.6	2 13.4	22 48.1	23 27.3	15 2.0	8 27.4	11 32.9
18 T	5 44 57.9	25 43.2	0 12.9	10♊33.1	6D54.4	14 49.0	2 3.0	22 57.0	23 23.3	14 59.5	8 28.2	11 32.0
19 W	5 48 54.5	26 44.3	0 9.7	25 24.9	7 6.2	16 4.5	1 51.7	23 5.7	23 19.2	14 57.0	8 28.9	11 31.1
20 T	5 52 51.0	27 45.4	0 6.5	10♋ 4.5	7 26.6	17 19.9	1 39.6	23 14.4	23 15.0	14 54.5	8 29.7	11 30.2
21 F	5 56 47.6	28 46.4	0 3.4	24 25.2	7 54.7	18 35.4	1 26.7	23 23.0	23 10.8	14 52.1	8 30.4	11 29.2
22 S	6 0 44.1	29 47.5	0 0.2	8♌22.5	8 29.9	19 50.8	1 13.1	23 31.4	23 6.5	14 49.6	8 31.0	11 28.3
23 S	6 4 40.7	0♑48.6	29♊57.0	21 54.3	9 11.3	21 6.3	0 58.6	23 39.7	23 2.2	14 47.2	8 31.7	11 27.3
24 M	6 8 37.3	1 49.7	29 53.8	5♍ 0.8	9 58.2	22 21.8	0 43.4	23 47.9	22 57.8	14 44.8	8 32.3	11 26.3
25 T	6 12 33.8	2 50.9	29 50.7	17 44.0	10 50.1	23 37.3	0 27.4	23 56.0	22 53.3	14 42.4	8 32.8	11 25.2
26 W	6 16 30.4	3 52.0	29 47.5	0♎ 7.5	11 46.3	24 52.7	0 10.7	24 3.9	22 48.8	14 40.0	8 33.4	11 24.2
27 T	6 20 26.9	4 53.1	29 44.3	12 15.4	12 46.3	26 8.2	29♋53.3	24 11.7	22 44.3	14 37.7	8 33.9	11 23.1
28 F	6 24 23.5	5 54.3	29 41.1	24 12.4	13 49.7	27 23.7	29 35.2	24 19.4	22 39.7	14 35.4	8 34.3	11 22.1
29 S	6 28 20.0	6 55.4	29 38.0	6♏ 3.2	14 56.2	28 39.2	29 16.4	24 27.0	22 35.0	14 33.0	8 34.8	11 21.0
30 S	6 32 16.6	7 56.6	29 34.8	17 52.3	16 5.2	29 54.7	28 57.0	24 34.4	22 30.3	14 30.8	8 35.2	11 19.8
31 M	6 36 13.2	8 57.8	29 31.6	29 43.8	17 16.6	1♑10.2	28 37.0	24 41.6	22 25.6	14 28.5	8 35.5	11 18.7

DECLINATION

DAY	EPHEMERIS SIDEREAL TIME	☉	☊	☽	☿	♀	♂	♃	♄	♅	♆	♇
1 S	4 37 56.4	21S43.2	23N26.5	6S18.2	23S50.6	17S38.3	21N56.4	6S48.2	21N 6.0	22N42.1	1S55.3	23N20.5
4 T	4 49 46.1	22 0.0	23 26.6	18 28.9	22 41.9	18 37.9	22 2.9	6 59.6	21 7.7	22 41.3	1 56.6	23 21.6
7 F	5 1 35.8	22 33.0	23 26.6	23 59.1	21 20.4	19 32.9	22 11.3	7 10.6	21 9.6	22 40.5	1 57.9	23 22.7
10 M	5 13 25.4	22 52.0	23 26.7	19 22.1	20 1.4	20 23.0	22 21.5	7 21.2	21 11.6	22 39.7	1 59.0	23 24.0
13 T	5 25 15.1	23 6.9	23 26.7	5 49.8	19 3.9	21 7.9	22 33.5	7 31.4	21 13.7	22 38.9	2 0.0	23 25.2
16 S	5 37 4.8	23 17.7	23 26.7	11N14.2	18 38.4	21 47.2	22 47.2	7 41.2	21 16.0	22 38.1	2 0.9	23 26.5
19 W	5 48 54.5	23 24.4	23 26.8	22 56.9	18 43.5	22 20.8	23 2.4	7 50.6	21 18.3	22 37.3	2 1.7	23 27.9
22 S	6 0 44.1	23 26.8	23 26.8	21 21.4	19 10.9	22 48.3	23 18.9	7 59.6	21 20.8	22 36.5	2 2.4	23 29.2
25 T	6 12 33.8	23 24.9	23 26.8	9 36.6	19 51.6	23 9.7	23 36.5	8 8.1	21 23.3	22 35.7	2 2.9	23 30.7
28 F	6 24 23.5	23 18.9	23 26.8	4S53.7	20 38.2	23 24.7	23 54.9	8 16.2	21 25.8	22 34.9	2 3.4	23 32.1
31 M	6 36 13.2	23 8.6	23 26.7	17 29.3	21 25.2	23 33.2	24 13.8	8 23.8	21 28.4	22 34.2	2 3.7	23 33.5

JANUARY 1946

DAY	EPHEMERIS SIDEREAL TIME	☉	☊	☽	☿	♀	♂	♃	♄	♅	♆	♇
	h m s	° ′	° ′	° ′	° ′	° ′	° ′	° ′	° ′	° ′	° ′	° ′
						LONGITUDE						
1 T	6 40 9.7	9♑58.9	29♊28.4	11♐41.1	18♐30.1	2♑25.7	28♋16.4	24♎48.8	22♋20.9	14♊26.3	8♎35.8	11♌17.6
2 W	6 44 6.3	11 0.1	29 25.2	23 47.2	19 45.5	3 41.2	27R55.3	24 55.8	22R16.1	14R24.0	8 36.1	11R16.4
3 T	6 48 2.8	12 1.3	29 22.1	6♑ 4.1	21 2.4	4 56.7	27 33.7	25 2.6	22 11.3	14 21.9	8 36.4	11 15.2
4 F	6 51 59.4	13 2.5	29 18.9	18 33.3	22 20.9	6 12.2	27 11.6	25 9.3	22 6.4	14 19.7	8 36.6	11 14.0
5 S	6 55 56.0	14 3.6	29 15.7	1♒15.7	23 40.7	7 27.7	26 49.2	25 15.9	22 1.6	14 17.6	8 36.8	11 12.8
6 S	6 59 52.5	15 4.8	29 12.5	14 11.6	25 1.7	8 43.2	26 26.4	25 22.3	21 56.7	14 15.5	8 37.0	11 11.6
7 M	7 3 49.1	16 6.0	29 9.4	27 21.0	26 23.7	9 58.6	26 3.2	25 28.5	21 51.8	14 13.4	8 37.1	11 10.4
8 T	7 7 45.6	17 7.1	29 6.2	10♓43.6	27 46.8	11 14.1	25 39.8	25 34.6	21 46.8	14 11.4	8 37.2	11 9.1
9 W	7 11 42.2	18 8.3	29 3.0	24 18.9	29 10.8	12 29.6	25 16.2	25 40.6	21 41.9	14 9.4	8 37.2	11 7.8
10 T	7 15 38.7	19 9.5	28 59.8	8♈ 6.5	0♑35.6	13 45.1	24 52.4	25 46.4	21 37.0	14 7.4	8 37.2	11 6.6
11 F	7 19 35.3	20 10.6	28 56.7	22 5.8	2 1.2	15 0.5	24 28.4	25 52.0	21 32.0	14 5.5	8R37.2	11 5.3
12 S	7 23 31.9	21 11.7	28 53.5	6♉15.5	3 27.6	16 16.0	24 4.4	25 57.5	21 27.1	14 3.6	8 37.1	11 4.0
13 S	7 27 28.4	22 12.8	28 50.3	20 34.2	4 54.6	17 31.4	23 40.4	26 2.8	21 22.1	14 1.8	8 37.1	11 2.7
14 M	7 31 25.0	23 13.9	28 47.1	4♊59.1	6 22.3	18 46.9	23 16.4	26 8.0	21 17.2	13 59.9	8 36.9	11 1.4
15 T	7 35 21.5	24 15.0	28 44.0	19 26.7	7 50.7	20 2.3	22 52.4	26 13.0	21 12.2	13 58.2	8 36.8	11 0.0
16 W	7 39 18.1	25 16.1	28 40.8	3♋52.4	9 19.7	21 17.7	22 28.6	26 17.9	21 7.3	13 56.4	8 36.6	10 58.7
17 T	7 43 14.6	26 17.2	28 37.6	18 11.2	10 49.3	22 33.2	22 4.9	26 22.5	21 2.4	13 54.7	8 36.4	10 57.4
18 F	7 47 11.2	27 18.3	28 34.4	2♌17.8	12 19.5	23 48.6	21 41.4	26 27.0	20 57.5	13 53.1	8 36.1	10 56.0
19 S	7 51 7.8	28 19.3	28 31.2	16 7.6	13 50.3	25 4.0	21 18.2	26 31.4	20 52.6	13 51.4	8 35.8	10 54.7
20 S	7 55 4.3	29 20.4	28 28.1	29 37.4	15 21.6	26 19.4	20 55.3	26 35.6	20 47.7	13 49.9	8 35.5	10 53.3
21 M	7 59 0.9	0♒21.4	28 24.9	12♍45.6	16 53.6	27 34.8	20 32.7	26 39.6	20 42.9	13 48.3	8 35.1	10 51.9
22 T	8 2 57.4	1 22.4	28 21.7	25 32.3	18 26.1	28 50.2	20 10.4	26 43.4	20 38.0	13 46.8	8 34.7	10 50.6
23 W	8 6 54.0	2 23.5	28 18.5	7♎59.5	19 59.3	0♒ 5.6	19 48.6	26 47.1	20 33.2	13 45.4	8 34.3	10 49.2
24 T	8 10 50.5	3 24.5	28 15.4	20 10.3	21 33.0	1 21.0	19 27.2	26 50.5	20 28.5	13 44.0	8 33.9	10 47.8
25 F	8 14 47.1	4 25.5	28 12.2	2♏ 8.9	23 7.4	2 36.4	19 6.3	26 53.9	20 23.8	13 42.6	8 33.4	10 46.4
26 S	8 18 43.6	5 26.5	28 9.0	14 0.3	24 42.3	3 51.8	18 45.9	26 57.0	20 19.0	13 41.3	8 32.9	10 45.0
27 S	8 22 40.2	6 27.5	28 5.8	25 49.5	26 17.9	5 7.2	18 26.1	26 59.9	20 14.4	13 40.0	8 32.3	10 43.6
28 M	8 26 36.7	7 28.4	28 2.6	7♐41.7	27 54.1	6 22.6	18 6.9	27 2.7	20 9.8	13 38.8	8 31.7	10 42.2
29 T	8 30 33.3	8 29.4	27 59.5	19 41.7	29 31.0	7 37.9	17 48.2	27 5.3	20 5.2	13 37.6	8 31.1	10 40.8
30 W	8 34 29.9	9 30.4	27 56.3	1♑53.6	1♒ 8.6	8 53.3	17 30.3	27 7.7	20 0.7	13 36.5	8 30.5	10 39.4
31 T	8 38 26.4	10 31.3	27 53.1	14 20.8	2 46.8	10 8.6	17 12.9	27 9.9	19 56.2	13 35.4	8 29.8	10 38.0
						DECLINATION						
1 T	6 40 9.7	23S 4.2	23N26.7	20S32.6	21S40.2	23S34.6	24N20.1	8S26.2	21N29.3	22N33.9	2S 3.8	23N34.0
4 F	6 51 59.4	22 48.4	23 26.7	23 49.7	22 22.1	23 34.3	24 38.9	8 33.1	21 32.0	22 33.2	2 3.9	23 35.5
7 M	7 3 49.1	22 28.5	23 26.6	16 33.6	22 57.2	23 27.5	24 57.2	8 39.5	21 34.6	22 32.5	2 3.9	23 37.0
10 T	7 15 38.7	22 4.6	23 26.5	1 34.0	23 23.9	23 14.2	25 14.6	8 45.4	21 37.3	22 31.8	2 3.8	23 38.5
13 S	7 27 28.4	21 36.9	23 26.5	14N41.0	23 41.1	22 54.4	25 30.8	8 50.7	21 39.9	22 31.2	2 3.6	23 40.0
16 W	7 39 18.1	21 5.3	23 26.4	23 45.4	23 47.7	22 28.2	25 45.4	8 55.5	21 42.6	22 30.6	2 3.3	23 41.5
19 S	7 51 7.8	20 30.2	23 26.3	19 36.8	23 43.2	21 55.9	25 58.2	8 59.7	21 45.2	22 30.0	2 2.8	23 43.0
22 T	8 2 57.4	19 51.6	23 26.2	6 32.4	23 27.0	21 17.6	26 9.1	9 3.4	21 47.7	22 29.5	2 2.3	23 44.5
25 F	8 14 47.1	19 9.6	23 26.0	8S 6.2	22 58.6	20 33.6	26 18.0	9 6.5	21 50.2	22 29.0	2 1.6	23 45.9
28 M	8 26 36.7	18 24.5	23 25.9	19 41.6	22 17.7	19 44.1	26 25.0	9 9.0	21 52.6	22 28.6	2 0.8	23 47.4
31 T	8 38 26.4	17 36.3	23 25.8	23 59.9	21 23.9	18 49.4	26 30.1	9 11.0	21 54.9	22 28.2	1 59.9	23 48.8

FEBRUARY 1946

DAY	EPHEMERIS SIDEREAL TIME	☉	☊	☽	☿	♀	♂	♃	♄	♅	♆	♇
						LONGITUDE						
1 F	8 42 23.0	11♒32.2	27♊49.9	27♑ 5.5	4♒25.7	11♒24.0	16♋56.3	27♎11.9	19♋51.7	13♊34.4	8♎29.1	10♌36.6
2 S	8 46 19.5	12 33.1	27 46.8	10♒ 8.4	6 5.3	12 39.3	16R40.4	27 13.8	19R47.4	13R33.4	8R28.3	10R35.2
3 S	8 50 16.1	13 34.0	27 43.6	23 29.0	7 45.6	13 54.7	16 25.2	27 15.5	19 43.1	13 32.5	8 27.6	10 33.8
4 M	8 54 12.7	14 34.9	27 40.4	7♓ 5.4	9 26.7	15 10.0	16 10.8	27 16.9	19 38.8	13 31.6	8 26.8	10 32.4
5 T	8 58 9.2	15 35.7	27 37.2	20 54.5	11 8.5	16 25.3	15 57.1	27 18.2	19 34.6	13 30.8	8 25.9	10 31.0
6 W	9 2 5.8	16 36.6	27 34.1	4♈52.9	12 51.1	17 40.6	15 44.3	27 19.3	19 30.5	13 30.0	8 25.1	10 29.6
7 T	9 6 2.3	17 37.4	27 30.9	18 57.2	14 34.5	18 55.9	15 32.2	27 20.2	19 26.4	13 29.3	8 24.2	10 28.2
8 F	9 9 58.9	18 38.1	27 27.7	3♉ 4.3	16 18.6	20 11.1	15 20.9	27 20.9	19 22.4	13 28.6	8 23.3	10 26.8
9 S	9 13 55.4	19 38.9	27 24.5	17 12.1	18 3.5	21 26.4	15 10.4	27 21.5	19 18.5	13 28.0	8 22.3	10 25.5
10 S	9 17 52.0	20 39.6	27 21.3	1♊18.9	19 49.2	22 41.6	15 0.7	27 21.8	19 14.6	13 27.4	8 21.4	10 24.1
11 M	9 21 48.5	21 40.3	27 18.2	15 23.8	21 35.6	23 56.8	14 51.8	27 22.0	19 10.8	13 26.9	8 20.4	10 22.7
12 T	9 25 45.1	22 41.0	27 15.0	29 25.5	23 22.9	25 12.1	14 43.7	27R21.9	19 7.2	13 26.4	8 19.4	10 21.3
13 W	9 29 41.7	23 41.6	27 11.8	13♋22.7	25 10.9	26 27.2	14 36.5	27 21.7	19 3.5	13 26.0	8 18.3	10 20.0
14 T	9 33 38.2	24 42.2	27 8.6	27 13.4	26 59.6	27 42.4	14 30.0	27 21.3	18 60.0	13 25.6	8 17.2	10 18.6
15 F	9 37 34.7	25 42.8	27 5.5	10♌55.1	28 49.0	28 57.6	14 24.3	27 20.7	18 56.5	13 25.3	8 16.1	10 17.3
16 S	9 41 31.3	26 43.4	27 2.3	24 24.9	0♓39.1	0♓12.7	14 19.4	27 19.9	18 53.1	13 25.0	8 15.0	10 15.9
17 S	9 45 27.9	27 43.9	26 59.1	7♍40.3	2 29.7	1 27.9	14 15.3	27 18.9	18 49.9	13 24.8	8 13.9	10 14.6
18 M	9 49 24.4	28 44.4	26 55.9	20 39.4	4 20.9	2 43.0	14 12.0	27 17.8	18 46.7	13 24.7	8 12.7	10 13.3
19 T	9 53 21.0	29 44.9	26 52.8	3♎21.2	6 12.5	3 58.1	14 9.5	27 16.4	18 43.5	13 24.6	8 11.5	10 12.0
20 W	9 57 17.5	0♓45.4	26 49.6	15 46.5	8 4.4	5 13.2	14 7.7	27 14.9	18 40.5	13 24.5	8 10.3	10 10.7
21 T	10 1 14.1	1 45.8	26 46.4	27 56.9	9 56.5	6 28.3	14 6.7	27 13.1	18 37.6	13D24.6	8 9.0	10 9.4
22 F	10 5 10.6	2 46.3	26 43.2	9♏55.8	11 48.6	7 43.3	14 6.4	27 11.2	18 34.7	13 24.6	8 7.8	10 8.1
23 S	10 9 7.2	3 46.7	26 40.0	21 47.1	13 40.4	8 58.4	14D 6.8	27 9.1	18 32.0	13 24.7	8 6.5	10 6.8
24 S	10 13 3.7	4 47.0	26 36.9	3♐35.9	15 31.8	10 13.4	14 8.0	27 6.8	18 29.3	13 24.9	8 5.2	10 5.6
25 M	10 17 0.3	5 47.4	26 33.7	15 27.5	17 22.5	11 28.4	14 9.9	27 4.4	18 26.8	13 25.1	8 3.9	10 4.3
26 T	10 20 56.9	6 47.7	26 30.5	27 27.5	19 12.1	12 43.4	14 12.6	27 1.7	18 24.3	13 25.4	8 2.5	10 3.1
27 W	10 24 53.4	7 48.0	26 27.3	9♑41.0	21 0.3	13 58.4	14 15.9	26 58.9	18 22.0	13 25.7	8 1.2	10 1.9
28 T	10 28 50.0	8 48.3	26 24.2	22 12.8	22 46.7	15 13.4	14 19.9	26 55.9	18 19.7	13 26.1	7 59.8	10 0.7
						DECLINATION						
1 F	8 42 23.0	17S19.7	23N25.7	23S 6.2	21S 3.1	18S30.1	26N31.3	9S11.5	21N55.6	22N28.1	1S59.5	23N49.2
4 M	8 54 12.7	16 27.8	23 25.6	13 19.6	19 51.9	17 29.0	26 34.0	9 12.6	21 57.9	22 27.7	1 58.5	23 50.6
7 T	9 6 2.3	15 33.4	23 25.4	2N58.1	18 27.5	16 23.4	26 35.0	9 13.1	21 60.0	22 27.5	1 57.4	23 52.0
10 S	9 17 52.0	14 36.6	23 25.2	18 7.1	16 49.8	15 13.8	26 34.6	9 13.0	22 2.0	22 27.3	1 56.1	23 53.3
13 W	9 29 41.7	13 37.6	23 25.0	24 4.2	14 58.9	14 0.3	26 33.0	9 12.3	22 3.8	22 27.1	1 54.8	23 54.5
16 S	9 41 31.3	12 36.6	23 24.8	17 21.4	12 55.3	12 43.5	26 30.1	9 11.0	22 5.6	22 27.0	1 53.4	23 55.7
19 T	9 53 21.0	11 33.8	23 24.6	3 17.4	10 39.7	11 23.6	26 26.3	9 9.1	22 7.3	22 27.0	1 51.9	23 56.9
22 F	10 5 10.6	10 29.4	23 24.4	11S14.3	8 13.8	10 1.0	26 21.5	9 6.6	22 8.8	22 27.0	1 50.3	23 58.0
25 M	10 17 0.3	9 23.5	23 24.1	21 36.4	5 40.1	8 35.9	26 15.9	9 3.5	22 10.2	22 27.1	1 48.7	23 59.0
28 T	10 28 50.0	8 16.3	23 23.9	23 43.0	3 2.9	7 8.9	26 9.6	8 59.9	22 11.5	22 27.3	1 47.0	24 0.0

MARCH 1946

LONGITUDE

DAY	EPHEMERIS SIDEREAL TIME h m s	☉ ° ′	☊ ° ′	☽ ° ′	☿ ° ′	♀ ° ′	♂ ° ′	♃ ° ′	♄ ° ′	♅ ° ′	♆ ° ′	♇ ° ′
1 F	10 32 46.5	9♓48.5	26♊21.0	5♒ 6.2	24♓30.9	16♓28.3	14♋24.6	26♎52.7	18♋17.5	13♊26.5	7♎58.4	9♌59.5
2 S	10 36 43.1	10 48.8	26 17.8	18 23.3	26 12.3	17 43.3	14 30.0	26R49.3	18R15.5	13 27.0	7R57.0	9R58.3
3 S	10 40 39.6	11 49.0	26 14.6	2♓ 3.6	27 50.4	18 58.2	14 36.0	26 45.8	18 13.5	13 27.6	7 55.5	9 57.2
4 M	10 44 36.2	12 49.1	26 11.4	16 4.7	29 24.7	20 13.1	14 42.7	26 42.0	18 11.7	13 28.2	7 54.1	9 56.0
5 T	10 48 32.7	13 49.3	26 8.3	0♈21.7	0♈54.7	21 28.0	14 50.0	26 38.1	18 10.0	13 28.8	7 52.6	9 54.9
6 W	10 52 29.3	14 49.4	26 5.1	14 48.5	2 19.7	22 42.9	14 58.0	26 34.1	18 8.3	13 29.5	7 51.1	9 53.8
7 T	10 56 25.8	15 49.4	26 1.9	29 18.6	3 39.2	23 57.7	15 6.5	26 29.9	18 6.8	13 30.3	7 49.6	9 52.7
8 F	11 0 22.4	16 49.5	25 58.7	13♉45.9	4 52.7	25 12.5	15 15.7	26 25.5	18 5.4	13 31.1	7 48.1	9 51.6
9 S	11 4 19.0	17 49.5	25 55.6	28 6.0	5 59.6	26 27.3	15 25.5	26 20.9	18 4.1	13 31.9	7 46.6	9 50.5
10 S	11 8 15.5	18 49.4	25 52.4	12♊16.2	6 59.4	27 42.1	15 35.8	26 16.2	18 2.9	13 32.8	7 45.1	9 49.5
11 M	11 12 12.0	19 49.4	25 49.2	26 15.3	7 51.8	28 56.9	15 46.7	26 11.4	18 1.8	13 33.8	7 43.5	9 48.5
12 T	11 16 8.6	20 49.3	25 46.0	10♋ 3.3	8 36.3	0♈11.6	15 58.2	26 6.4	18 0.8	13 34.8	7 41.9	9 47.5
13 W	11 20 5.2	21 49.1	25 42.8	23 40.6	9 12.6	1 26.3	16 10.2	26 1.2	17 60.0	13 35.9	7 40.4	9 46.5
14 T	11 24 1.7	22 48.9	25 39.7	7♌ 7.6	9 40.6	2 41.0	16 22.7	25 55.9	17 59.2	13 37.0	7 38.8	9 45.5
15 F	11 27 58.3	23 48.7	25 36.5	20 24.4	10 0.0	3 55.6	16 35.7	25 50.4	17 58.5	13 38.2	7 37.2	9 44.6
16 S	11 31 54.8	24 48.4	25 33.3	3♍30.4	10 10.9	5 10.2	16 49.3	25 44.9	17 58.0	13 39.4	7 35.6	9 43.6
17 S	11 35 51.4	25 48.2	25 30.1	16 24.9	10 13.3	6 24.8	17 3.3	25 39.1	17 57.6	13 40.6	7 34.0	9 42.7
18 M	11 39 47.9	26 47.8	25 27.0	29 7.2	10R 7.4	7 39.4	17 17.8	25 33.3	17 57.3	13 42.0	7 32.4	9 41.8
19 T	11 43 44.5	27 47.5	25 23.8	11♎36.7	9 53.5	8 54.0	17 32.8	25 27.3	17 57.1	13 43.3	7 30.8	9 41.0
20 W	11 47 41.0	28 47.1	25 20.6	23 53.5	9 32.0	10 8.5	17 48.2	25 21.2	17 57.0	13 44.7	7 29.1	9 40.1
21 T	11 51 37.6	29 46.7	25 17.4	5♏59.0	9 3.6	11 23.0	18 4.1	25 15.0	17D57.0	13 46.2	7 27.5	9 39.3
22 F	11 55 34.1	0♈46.2	25 14.2	17 55.0	8 28.9	12 37.5	18 20.4	25 8.7	17 57.1	13 47.7	7 25.9	9 38.5
23 S	11 59 30.7	1 45.7	25 11.1	29 44.9	7 48.8	13 51.9	18 37.1	25 2.2	17 57.4	13 49.3	7 24.2	9 37.7
24 S	12 3 27.2	2 45.2	25 7.9	11♐32.7	7 4.2	15 6.4	18 54.3	24 55.6	17 57.7	13 50.9	7 22.6	9 37.0
25 M	12 7 23.8	3 44.7	25 4.7	23 23.1	6 16.1	16 20.8	19 11.8	24 49.0	17 58.2	13 52.5	7 20.9	9 36.2
26 T	12 11 20.3	4 44.1	25 1.5	5♑21.7	5 25.5	17 35.1	19 29.8	24 42.2	17 58.8	13 54.2	7 19.3	9 35.5
27 W	12 15 16.9	5 43.5	24 58.4	17 33.7	4 33.7	18 49.5	19 48.2	24 35.4	17 59.4	13 56.0	7 17.6	9 34.9
28 T	12 19 13.5	6 42.9	24 55.2	0♒ 4.7	3 41.6	20 3.8	20 6.9	24 28.4	18 0.2	13 57.7	7 16.0	9 34.2
29 F	12 23 10.0	7 42.2	24 52.0	12 59.1	2 50.2	21 18.2	20 26.0	24 21.4	18 1.1	13 59.6	7 14.3	9 33.6
30 S	12 27 6.5	8 41.5	24 48.8	26 20.2	2 0.7	22 32.4	20 45.5	24 14.3	18 2.2	14 1.5	7 12.7	9 32.9
31 S	12 31 3.1	9 40.8	24 45.6	10♓ 8.9	1 13.8	23 46.7	21 5.4	24 7.1	18 3.3	14 3.4	7 11.0	9 32.4

DECLINATION

DAY	EPHEMERIS SIDEREAL TIME h m s	☉ ° ′	☊ ° ′	☽ ° ′	☿ ° ′	♀ ° ′	♂ ° ′	♃ ° ′	♄ ° ′	♅ ° ′	♆ ° ′	♇ ° ′
1 F	10 32 46.5	7S53.6	23N23.8	22S 0.2	2S10.8	6S39.5	26N 7.4	8S58.5	22N11.9	22N27.3	1S46.4	24N 0.3
4 M	10 44 36.2	6 45.0	23 23.5	10 2.0	0N21.4	5 10.2	26 0.1	8 54.2	22 13.0	22 27.6	1 44.6	24 1.3
7 T	10 56 25.8	5 35.5	23 23.2	7N17.3	2 40.3	3 39.7	25 52.2	8 49.2	22 13.9	22 27.8	1 42.8	24 2.1
10 S	11 8 15.5	4 25.4	23 22.9	21 4.7	4 37.3	2 8.3	25 43.7	8 43.8	22 14.7	22 28.2	1 40.9	24 2.9
13 W	11 20 5.2	3 14.8	23 22.6	23 40.6	6 4.4	0 36.3	25 34.5	8 37.9	22 15.4	22 28.6	1 39.0	24 3.6
16 S	11 31 54.8	2 3.8	23 22.3	14 32.4	6 54.9	0N55.9	25 24.6	8 31.6	22 16.0	22 29.0	1 37.0	24 4.2
19 T	11 43 44.5	0 52.7	23 22.0	0S10.9	7 5.1	2 28.0	25 14.1	8 24.8	22 16.4	22 29.5	1 35.1	24 4.8
22 F	11 55 34.1	0N18.4	23 21.7	14 17.6	6 35.3	3 59.7	25 2.9	8 17.7	22 16.7	22 30.1	1 33.1	24 5.3
25 M	12 7 23.8	1 29.3	23 21.3	23 11.8	5 31.2	5 30.6	24 51.0	8 10.2	22 16.8	22 30.7	1 31.1	24 5.7
28 T	12 19 13.5	2 40.0	23 20.9	23 1.7	4 4.2	7 0.5	24 38.4	8 2.5	22 16.8	22 31.3	1 29.1	24 6.1
31 S	12 31 3.1	3 50.2	23 20.6	12 17.1	2 28.9	8 29.0	24 25.0	7 54.4	22 16.7	22 32.0	1 27.2	24 6.3

APRIL 1946

LONGITUDE

DAY	EPHEMERIS SIDEREAL TIME h m s	☉ ° ′	☊ ° ′	☽ ° ′	☿ ° ′	♀ ° ′	♂ ° ′	♃ ° ′	♄ ° ′	♅ ° ′	♆ ° ′	♇ ° ′
1 M	12 34 59.7	10♈40.0	24♊42.5	24♓23.6	0♈30.3	25♈ 0.9	21♋25.6	23♎59.8	18♋ 4.5	14♊ 5.3	7♎ 9.4	9♌31.8
2 T	12 38 56.2	11 39.2	24 39.3	8♈59.4	29♓50.8	26 15.1	21 46.1	23R52.5	18 5.9	14 7.4	7R 7.7	9R31.3
3 W	12 42 52.8	12 38.4	24 36.1	23 49.3	29 15.9	27 29.3	22 7.0	23 45.1	18 7.3	14 9.4	7 6.1	9 30.7
4 T	12 46 49.3	13 37.6	24 32.9	8♉44.3	28 46.0	28 43.5	22 28.2	23 37.6	18 8.9	14 11.5	7 4.4	9 30.3
5 F	12 50 45.9	14 36.7	24 29.8	23 35.8	28 21.3	29 57.6	22 49.8	23 30.1	18 10.5	14 13.7	7 2.8	9 29.8
6 S	12 54 42.4	15 35.7	24 26.6	8♊16.6	28 2.0	1♉11.7	23 11.7	23 22.6	18 12.3	14 15.8	7 1.1	9 29.4
7 S	12 58 39.0	16 34.8	24 23.4	22 41.7	27 48.1	2 25.8	23 33.8	23 15.0	18 14.2	14 18.1	6 59.5	9 28.9
8 M	13 2 35.5	17 33.8	24 20.2	6♋48.6	27 39.9	3 39.8	23 56.3	23 7.4	18 16.2	14 20.3	6 57.9	9 28.6
9 T	13 6 32.1	18 32.7	24 17.0	20 36.8	27 37.0	4 53.8	24 19.1	22 59.8	18 18.3	14 22.6	6 56.3	9 28.2
10 W	13 10 28.6	19 31.7	24 13.9	4♌ 7.2	27D39.6	6 7.8	24 42.2	22 52.1	18 20.5	14 25.0	6 54.7	9 27.9
11 T	13 14 25.2	20 30.5	24 10.7	17 21.4	27 47.4	7 21.7	25 5.5	22 44.4	18 22.8	14 27.3	6 53.1	9 27.6
12 F	13 18 21.7	21 29.4	24 7.5	0♍21.2	28 0.2	8 35.6	25 29.1	22 36.8	18 25.2	14 29.8	6 51.5	9 27.3
13 S	13 22 18.3	22 28.2	24 4.3	13 8.2	28 18.0	9 49.5	25 53.0	22 29.1	18 27.7	14 32.2	6 49.9	9 27.0
14 S	13 26 14.8	23 26.9	24 1.1	25 43.6	28 40.4	11 3.3	26 17.1	22 21.4	18 30.3	14 34.7	6 48.3	9 26.8
15 M	13 30 11.4	24 25.7	23 58.0	8♎ 8.2	29 7.4	12 17.1	26 41.5	22 13.7	18 33.0	14 37.2	6 46.8	9 26.6
16 T	13 34 8.0	25 24.4	23 54.8	20 23.0	29 38.7	13 30.9	27 6.2	22 6.0	18 35.8	14 39.8	6 45.2	9 26.4
17 W	13 38 4.5	26 23.0	23 51.6	2♏28.7	0♈14.1	14 44.7	27 31.0	21 58.4	18 38.8	14 42.4	6 43.7	9 26.3
18 T	13 42 1.1	27 21.7	23 48.4	14 26.6	0 53.4	15 58.4	27 56.2	21 50.7	18 41.8	14 45.0	6 42.1	9 26.2
19 F	13 45 57.6	28 20.3	23 45.3	26 18.4	1 36.4	17 12.0	28 21.5	21 43.1	18 44.9	14 47.7	6 40.6	9 26.1
20 S	13 49 54.2	29 18.9	23 42.1	8♐ 6.4	2 23.1	18 25.7	28 47.1	21 35.5	18 48.1	14 50.4	6 39.1	9 26.0
21 S	13 53 50.7	0♉17.4	23 38.9	19 53.9	3 13.1	19 39.3	29 12.9	21 28.0	18 51.4	14 53.1	6 37.6	9 26.0
22 M	13 57 47.3	1 15.9	23 35.7	1♑44.7	4 6.3	20 52.9	29 38.9	21 20.4	18 54.7	14 55.9	6 36.2	9 25.9
23 T	14 1 43.8	2 14.4	23 32.5	13 43.2	5 2.7	22 6.4	0♌ 5.1	21 13.0	18 58.2	14 58.7	6 34.7	9D26.0
24 W	14 5 40.4	3 12.9	23 29.4	25 54.3	6 2.1	23 20.0	0 31.6	21 5.6	19 1.8	15 1.5	6 33.3	9 26.0
25 T	14 9 37.0	4 11.3	23 26.2	8♒23.1	7 4.2	24 33.5	0 58.2	20 58.2	19 5.5	15 4.4	6 31.8	9 26.1
26 F	14 13 33.5	5 9.7	23 23.0	21 14.3	8 9.1	25 46.9	1 25.0	20 50.9	19 9.2	15 7.3	6 30.4	9 26.2
27 S	14 17 30.0	6 8.1	23 19.8	4♓31.9	9 16.7	27 0.3	1 52.1	20 43.7	19 13.1	15 10.2	6 29.0	9 26.3
28 S	14 21 26.6	7 6.4	23 16.7	18 18.1	10 26.7	28 13.8	2 19.3	20 36.5	19 17.0	15 13.1	6 27.6	9 26.4
29 M	14 25 23.2	8 4.8	23 13.5	2♈32.7	11 39.3	29 27.1	2 46.8	20 29.4	19 21.1	15 16.1	6 26.3	9 26.6
30 T	14 29 19.7	9 3.1	23 10.3	17 12.5	12 54.2	0♊40.5	3 14.4	20 22.4	19 25.2	15 19.1	6 25.0	9 26.8

DECLINATION

DAY	EPHEMERIS SIDEREAL TIME h m s	☉ ° ′	☊ ° ′	☽ ° ′	☿ ° ′	♀ ° ′	♂ ° ′	♃ ° ′	♄ ° ′	♅ ° ′	♆ ° ′	♇ ° ′
1 M	12 34 59.7	4N13.4	23N20.4	6S50.6	1N57.9	8N58.1	24N20.3	7S51.7	22N16.6	22N32.2	1S26.5	24N 6.4
4 T	12 46 49.3	5 22.7	23 20.1	11N 3.4	0 32.8	10 24.2	24 5.8	7 43.5	22 16.3	22 33.0	1 24.6	24 6.6
7 S	12 58 39.0	6 31.2	23 19.7	23 12.4	0S33.9	11 48.1	23 50.5	7 35.0	22 15.9	22 33.8	1 22.6	24 6.7
10 W	13 10 28.6	7 38.6	23 19.3	22 28.5	1 18.1	13 9.5	23 34.4	7 26.6	22 15.3	22 34.6	1 20.7	24 6.7
13 S	13 22 18.3	8 44.8	23 18.8	11 14.3	1 39.1	14 28.0	23 17.3	7 18.1	22 14.6	22 35.5	1 18.8	24 6.7
16 T	13 34 8.0	9 49.8	23 18.4	3S48.6	1 37.8	15 43.3	22 59.4	7 9.6	22 13.7	22 36.3	1 17.0	24 6.5
19 F	13 45 57.6	10 53.2	23 18.0	17 10.7	1 16.1	16 55.1	22 40.6	7 1.2	22 12.8	22 37.3	1 15.2	24 6.3
22 M	13 57 47.3	11 55.1	23 17.5	24 19.3	0 36.0	18 3.0	22 20.8	6 53.0	22 11.6	22 38.2	1 13.5	24 6.1
25 T	14 9 37.0	12 55.2	23 17.0	21 47.2	0N20.4	19 6.7	22 0.1	6 44.9	22 10.4	22 39.2	1 11.8	24 5.7
28 S	14 21 26.6	13 53.4	23 16.6	9 21.5	1 31.4	20 5.8	21 38.4	6 37.1	22 9.0	22 40.2	1 10.2	24 5.3

MAY 1946

LONGITUDE

DAY	EPHEMERIS SIDEREAL TIME	☉	☊	☽	☿	♀	♂	♃	♄	♅	♆	♇
	h m s	° ′	° ′	° ′	° ′	° ′	° ′	° ′	° ′	° ′	° ′	° ′
1 W	14 33 16.3	10♉ 1.3	23♊ 7.1	2♉11.1	14♈11.3	1♊53.8	3♌42.2	20♎15.5	19♋29.4	15♊22.1	6♎23.6	9♌27.0
2 T	14 37 12.8	10 59.6	23 3.9	17 19.9	15 30.8	3 7.1	4 10.2	20R 8.7	19 33.7	15 25.2	6R22.3	9 27.3
3 F	14 41 9.4	11 57.8	23 0.8	2♊28.8	16 52.4	4 20.3	4 38.4	20 2.0	19 38.1	15 28.3	6 21.0	9 27.6
4 S	14 45 5.9	12 56.0	22 57.6	17 28.6	18 16.2	5 33.5	5 6.8	19 55.3	19 42.6	15 31.4	6 19.8	9 27.9
5 S	14 49 2.5	13 54.2	22 54.4	2♋11.8	19 42.1	6 46.7	5 35.3	19 48.8	19 47.1	15 34.5	6 18.6	9 28.2
6 M	14 52 59.0	14 52.3	22 51.2	16 33.5	21 10.1	7 59.8	6 4.0	19 42.4	19 51.7	15 37.6	6 17.3	9 28.6
7 T	14 56 55.6	15 50.4	22 48.1	0♌31.6	22 40.1	9 12.9	6 32.9	19 36.1	19 56.5	15 40.8	6 16.1	9 29.0
8 W	15 0 52.2	16 48.4	22 44.9	14 6.2	24 12.2	10 26.0	7 1.9	19 29.9	20 1.2	15 44.0	6 15.0	9 29.4
9 T	15 4 48.7	17 46.4	22 41.7	27 18.8	25 46.3	11 39.0	7 31.1	19 23.8	20 6.1	15 47.2	6 13.8	9 29.8
10 F	15 8 45.3	18 44.4	22 38.5	10♍11.9	27 22.4	12 52.0	8 0.4	19 17.9	20 11.1	15 50.5	6 12.7	9 30.3
11 S	15 12 41.8	19 42.4	22 35.4	22 48.4	29 0.6	14 4.9	8 29.9	19 12.1	20 16.1	15 53.7	6 11.6	9 30.8
12 S	15 16 38.4	20 40.3	22 32.2	5♎11.2	0♉40.7	15 17.8	8 59.5	19 6.4	20 21.2	15 57.0	6 10.5	9 31.3
13 M	15 20 34.9	21 38.2	22 29.0	17 22.8	2 22.9	16 30.7	9 29.3	19 0.8	20 26.4	16 0.3	6 9.5	9 31.9
14 T	15 24 31.5	22 36.1	22 25.8	29 25.6	4 7.0	17 43.5	9 59.2	18 55.4	20 31.6	16 3.6	6 8.4	9 32.5
15 W	15 28 28.0	23 34.0	22 22.6	11♏21.7	5 53.2	18 56.3	10 29.2	18 50.1	20 36.9	16 7.0	6 7.4	9 33.1
16 T	15 32 24.6	24 31.8	22 19.5	23 13.1	7 41.4	20 9.1	10 59.4	18 45.0	20 42.3	16 10.3	6 6.5	9 33.7
17 F	15 36 21.1	25 29.6	22 16.3	5♐ 1.8	9 31.6	21 21.8	11 29.7	18 40.0	20 47.8	16 13.7	6 5.5	9 34.3
18 S	15 40 17.7	26 27.4	22 13.1	16 49.8	11 23.9	22 34.4	12 0.2	18 35.1	20 53.3	16 17.1	6 4.6	9 35.0
19 S	15 44 14.3	27 25.1	22 9.9	28 39.8	13 18.1	23 47.1	12 30.7	18 30.5	20 58.9	16 20.5	6 3.7	9 35.7
20 M	15 48 10.8	28 22.9	22 6.8	10♑34.4	15 14.3	24 59.7	13 1.4	18 25.9	21 4.6	16 23.9	6 2.8	9 36.4
21 T	15 52 7.4	29 20.6	22 3.6	22 37.1	17 12.4	26 12.2	13 32.3	18 21.5	21 10.3	16 27.3	6 2.0	9 37.2
22 W	15 56 3.9	0♊18.3	22 0.4	4♒51.5	19 12.5	27 24.7	14 3.2	18 17.3	21 16.1	16 30.7	6 1.1	9 37.9
23 T	16 0 0.5	1 16.0	21 57.2	17 21.6	21 14.4	28 37.2	14 34.3	18 13.2	21 22.0	16 34.2	6 0.4	9 38.7
24 F	16 3 57.0	2 13.6	21 54.1	0♓11.3	23 18.0	29 49.6	15 5.5	18 9.3	21 27.9	16 37.6	5 59.6	9 39.6
25 S	16 7 53.6	3 11.3	21 50.9	13 24.3	25 23.4	1♋ 2.0	15 36.8	18 5.6	21 33.9	16 41.1	5 58.9	9 40.4
26 S	16 11 50.2	4 8.9	21 47.7	27 3.0	27 30.2	2 14.4	16 8.3	18 2.0	21 39.9	16 44.6	5 58.2	9 41.3
27 M	16 15 46.7	5 6.5	21 44.5	11♈ 8.5	29 38.4	3 26.7	16 39.8	17 58.6	21 46.0	16 48.1	5 57.5	9 42.2
28 T	16 19 43.3	6 4.1	21 41.4	25 39.3	1♊47.9	4 39.0	17 11.5	17 55.3	21 52.2	16 51.6	5 56.8	9 43.1
29 W	16 23 39.8	7 1.7	21 38.2	10♉31.2	3 58.4	5 51.2	17 43.5	17 52.2	21 58.4	16 55.1	5 56.2	9 44.0
30 T	16 27 36.4	7 59.3	21 35.0	25 37.5	6 9.6	7 3.4	18 15.2	17 49.3	22 4.7	16 58.6	5 55.6	9 45.0
31 F	16 31 32.9	8 56.8	21 31.8	10♊49.2	8 21.4	8 15.5	18 47.2	17 46.6	22 11.0	17 2.1	5 55.1	9 46.0

DECLINATION

DAY	EPHEMERIS SIDEREAL TIME	☉	☊	☽	☿	♀	♂	♃	♄	♅	♆	♇
1 W	14 33 16.3	14N49.5	23N16.1	8N33.5	2N55.3	21N 0.2	21N15.8	6S29.6	22N 7.5	22N41.2	1S 8.7	24N 4.9
4 S	14 45 5.9	15 43.5	23 15.6	22 30.8	4 30.5	21 49.5	20 52.1	6 22.4	22 5.9	22 42.2	1 7.3	24 4.3
7 T	14 56 55.6	16 35.1	23 15.1	23 15.7	6 15.5	22 33.3	20 27.6	6 15.6	22 4.1	22 43.2	1 5.9	24 3.7
10 F	15 8 45.3	17 24.3	23 14.5	12 28.3	8 9.1	23 11.5	20 2.0	6 9.2	22 2.2	22 44.3	1 4.6	24 3.1
13 M	15 20 34.9	18 10.8	23 14.0	2S30.3	10 9.6	23 43.9	19 35.4	6 3.3	22 0.1	22 45.3	1 3.4	24 2.4
16 T	15 32 24.6	18 54.5	23 13.4	16 13.7	12 15.1	24 10.1	19 7.9	5 57.8	21 58.0	22 46.4	1 2.3	24 1.6
19 S	15 44 14.3	19 35.4	23 12.9	24 9.5	14 23.6	24 30.2	18 39.4	5 52.9	21 55.7	22 47.5	1 1.3	24 0.7
22 W	15 56 3.9	20 13.2	23 12.3	22 36.6	16 31.9	24 43.9	18 10.0	5 48.5	21 53.3	22 48.5	1 0.4	23 59.9
25 S	16 7 53.6	20 48.0	23 11.7	11 20.8	18 36.3	24 51.1	17 39.6	5 44.7	21 50.7	22 49.6	0 59.6	23 58.9
28 T	16 19 43.3	21 19.6	23 11.2	5N52.8	20 32.0	24 52.0	17 8.3	5 41.5	21 48.0	22 50.7	0 58.9	23 57.9
31 F	16 31 32.9	21 47.9	23 10.5	21 10.0	22 13.5	24 46.3	16 36.1	5 38.9	21 45.2	22 51.7	0 58.3	23 56.9

JUNE 1946

LONGITUDE

DAY	EPHEMERIS SIDEREAL TIME	☉	☊	☽	☿	♀	♂	♃	♄	♅	♆	♇
1 S	16 35 29.5	9♊54.3	21♊28.6	25♊56.8	10♊33.4	9♋27.7	19♌19.3	17♎44.1	22♋17.4	17♊ 5.7	5♎54.6	9♌47.0
2 S	16 39 26.1	10 51.9	21 25.5	10♋51.3	12 45.5	10 39.7	19 51.6	17R41.7	22 23.9	17 9.2	5R54.1	9 48.0
3 M	16 43 22.6	11 49.3	21 22.3	25 25.8	14 57.2	11 51.7	20 23.9	17 39.5	22 30.4	17 12.7	5 53.6	9 49.0
4 T	16 47 19.1	12 46.8	21 19.1	9♌35.8	17 8.5	13 3.7	20 56.4	17 37.5	22 36.9	17 16.3	5 53.2	9 50.1
5 W	16 51 15.7	13 44.3	21 15.9	23 19.6	19 18.9	14 15.6	21 28.9	17 35.6	22 43.5	17 19.8	5 52.8	9 51.2
6 T	16 55 12.3	14 41.7	21 12.8	6♍37.5	21 28.3	15 27.5	22 1.6	17 34.0	22 50.2	17 23.4	5 52.4	9 52.3
7 F	16 59 8.9	15 39.1	21 9.6	19 31.8	23 36.3	16 39.3	22 34.3	17 32.5	22 56.9	17 26.9	5 52.1	9 53.5
8 S	17 3 5.4	16 36.5	21 6.4	2♎ 5.8	25 42.9	17 51.1	23 7.1	17 31.2	23 3.6	17 30.5	5 51.7	9 54.6
9 S	17 7 1.9	17 33.9	21 3.2	14 23.2	27 47.8	19 2.8	23 40.1	17 30.1	23 10.4	17 34.0	5 51.5	9 55.8
10 M	17 10 58.5	18 31.2	21 0.1	26 28.0	29 50.8	20 14.5	24 13.1	17 29.1	23 17.2	17 37.6	5 51.2	9 57.0
11 T	17 14 55.1	19 28.6	20 56.9	8♏23.9	1♋51.9	21 26.1	24 46.2	17 28.4	23 24.1	17 41.1	5 51.0	9 58.2
12 W	17 18 51.6	20 25.9	20 53.7	20 14.4	3 50.9	22 37.6	25 19.5	17 27.8	23 31.0	17 44.7	5 50.8	9 59.4
13 T	17 22 48.2	21 23.2	20 50.5	2♐ 2.5	5 47.8	23 49.1	25 52.8	17 27.4	23 38.0	17 48.2	5 50.7	10 0.7
14 F	17 26 44.7	22 20.5	20 47.3	13 50.9	7 42.4	25 0.6	26 26.1	17 27.2	23 45.0	17 51.8	5 50.6	10 2.0
15 S	17 30 41.3	23 17.8	20 44.2	25 42.2	9 34.8	26 11.9	26 59.6	17 27.1	23 52.0	17 55.3	5 50.5	10 3.3
16 S	17 34 37.8	24 15.1	20 41.0	7♑38.4	11 24.8	27 23.3	27 33.2	17D27.3	23 59.1	17 58.9	5 50.4	10 4.6
17 M	17 38 34.4	25 12.4	20 37.8	19 41.8	13 12.4	28 34.5	28 6.8	17 27.6	24 6.2	18 2.4	5 50.4	10 5.9
18 T	17 42 31.0	26 9.6	20 34.6	1♒54.5	14 57.7	29 45.7	28 40.6	17 28.1	24 13.3	18 5.9	5D50.4	10 7.2
19 W	17 46 27.5	27 6.9	20 31.5	14 18.8	16 40.6	0♌56.9	29 14.4	17 28.7	24 20.5	18 9.4	5 50.4	10 8.6
20 T	17 50 24.1	28 4.2	20 28.3	26 57.0	18 21.1	2 8.0	29 48.3	17 29.6	24 27.7	18 13.0	5 50.5	10 10.0
21 F	17 54 20.7	29 1.4	20 25.1	9♓51.5	19 59.2	3 19.0	0♍22.3	17 30.6	24 35.0	18 16.5	5 50.6	10 11.4
22 S	17 58 17.2	29 58.6	20 21.9	23 4.6	21 34.8	4 30.0	0 56.4	17 31.8	24 42.3	18 20.0	5 50.8	10 12.8
23 S	18 2 13.8	0♋55.9	20 18.8	6♈38.3	23 8.0	5 40.9	1 30.5	17 33.2	24 49.6	18 23.5	5 50.9	10 14.2
24 M	18 6 10.3	1 53.1	20 15.6	20 33.5	24 38.7	6 51.7	2 4.8	17 34.8	24 56.9	18 27.0	5 51.1	10 15.7
25 T	18 10 6.9	2 50.4	20 12.4	4♉50.0	26 7.0	8 2.5	2 39.1	17 36.5	25 4.3	18 30.4	5 51.4	10 17.1
26 W	18 14 3.5	3 47.6	20 9.2	19 25.7	27 32.8	9 13.3	3 13.5	17 38.4	25 11.7	18 33.9	5 51.6	10 18.6
27 T	18 18 0.0	4 44.8	20 6.1	4♊16.2	28 56.0	10 23.9	3 48.0	17 40.5	25 19.2	18 37.3	5 51.9	10 20.1
28 F	18 21 56.5	5 42.1	20 2.9	19 15.4	0♌16.7	11 34.5	4 22.6	17 42.7	25 26.6	18 40.8	5 52.3	10 21.6
29 S	18 25 53.1	6 39.3	19 59.7	4♋15.3	1 34.8	12 45.1	4 57.2	17 45.2	25 34.1	18 44.2	5 52.6	10 23.1
30 S	18 29 49.7	7 36.6	19 56.5	19 7.8	2 50.2	13 55.6	5 32.0	17 47.8	25 41.6	18 47.6	5 53.0	10 24.6

DECLINATION

DAY	EPHEMERIS SIDEREAL TIME	☉	☊	☽	☿	♀	♂	♃	♄	♅	♆	♇
1 S	16 35 29.5	21N56.5	23N10.3	23N51.7	22N43.3	24N43.0	16N25.2	5S38.1	21N44.3	22N52.1	0S58.1	23N56.5
4 T	16 47 19.1	22 20.2	23 9.7	21 41.5	23 58.1	24 28.9	15 51.8	5 36.3	21 41.3	22 53.1	0 57.7	23 55.5
7 F	16 59 8.9	22 40.4	23 9.1	9 0.5	24 48.9	24 8.4	15 17.4	5 35.2	21 38.3	22 54.1	0 57.4	23 54.3
10 M	17 10 58.5	22 57.0	23 8.5	6S11.9	25 14.9	23 41.9	14 42.3	5 34.6	21 35.1	22 55.2	0 57.1	23 53.2
13 T	17 22 48.2	23 10.0	23 7.8	18 54.2	25 17.1	23 9.4	14 6.3	5 34.7	21 31.8	22 56.2	0 57.0	23 51.9
16 S	17 34 37.8	23 19.3	23 7.1	24 45.6	24 58.1	22 31.2	13 29.4	5 35.4	21 28.4	22 57.2	0 57.1	23 50.7
19 W	17 46 27.5	23 24.9	23 6.5	20 36.7	24 21.1	21 47.4	12 51.8	5 36.7	21 24.9	22 58.1	0 57.2	23 49.4
22 S	17 58 17.2	23 26.8	23 5.8	7 35.8	23 29.6	20 58.5	12 13.5	5 38.6	21 21.2	22 59.1	0 57.4	23 48.2
25 T	18 10 6.9	23 25.0	23 5.1	9N33.1	22 26.7	20 4.5	11 34.4	5 41.2	21 17.5	23 0.0	0 57.8	23 46.8
28 F	18 21 56.5	23 19.4	23 4.4	22 52.2	21 15.6	19 6.0	10 54.5	5 44.3	21 13.7	23 0.9	0 58.3	23 45.5

JULY 1946

DAY	EPHEMERIS SIDEREAL TIME	☉	☊	☽	☿	♀	♂	♃	♄	♅	♆	♇
	h m s	° ′	° ′	° ′	° ′	° ′	° ′	° ′	° ′	° ′	° ′	° ′
						LONGITUDE						
1 M	18 33 46.2	8♋33.8	19♓53.4	3♌44.8	4♌ 2.9	15♌ 6.0	6♍ 6.8	17♎50.6	25♋49.1	18♊51.0	5♎53.5	10♌26.2
2 T	18 37 42.8	9 31.0	19 50.2	18 0.4	5 12.9	16 16.3	6 41.7	17 53.5	25 56.7	18 54.4	5 53.9	10 27.7
3 W	18 41 39.3	10 28.2	19 47.0	1♍50.7	6 20.0	17 26.5	7 16.7	17 56.6	26 4.3	18 57.8	5 54.4	10 29.3
4 T	18 45 35.9	11 25.5	19 43.8	15 14.6	7 24.1	18 36.7	7 51.7	17 59.9	26 11.8	19 1.1	5 54.9	10 30.9
5 F	18 49 32.5	12 22.7	19 40.6	28 13.1	8 25.3	19 46.8	8 26.8	18 3.4	26 19.5	19 4.5	5 55.5	10 32.5
6 S	18 53 29.0	13 19.9	19 37.5	10♎48.9	9 23.4	20 56.8	9 2.0	18 7.0	26 27.1	19 7.8	5 56.1	10 34.1
7 S	18 57 25.6	14 17.1	19 34.3	23 6.0	10 18.2	22 6.8	9 37.3	18 10.7	26 34.7	19 11.1	5 56.7	10 35.7
8 M	19 1 22.1	15 14.3	19 31.1	5♏ 8.9	11 9.8	23 16.6	10 12.6	18 14.7	26 42.4	19 14.4	5 57.4	10 37.4
9 T	19 5 18.7	16 11.5	19 27.9	17 2.3	11 57.9	24 26.4	10 48.1	18 18.8	26 50.1	19 17.7	5 58.0	10 39.0
10 W	19 9 15.2	17 8.7	19 24.8	28 50.9	12 42.4	25 36.1	11 23.5	18 23.0	26 57.7	19 20.9	5 58.8	10 40.7
11 T	19 13 11.8	18 5.9	19 21.6	10♐38.8	13 23.2	26 45.7	11 59.1	18 27.5	27 5.4	19 24.1	5 59.5	10 42.3
12 F	19 17 8.3	19 3.1	19 18.4	22 29.8	14 0.2	27 55.2	12 34.7	18 32.0	27 13.1	19 27.3	6 0.3	10 44.0
13 S	19 21 4.9	20 0.3	19 15.2	4♑27.0	14 33.2	29 4.6	13 10.4	18 36.8	27 20.8	19 30.5	6 1.1	10 45.7
14 S	19 25 1.5	20 57.5	19 12.1	16 32.8	15 2.1	0♍13.9	13 46.1	18 41.6	27 28.6	19 33.7	6 1.9	10 47.3
15 M	19 28 58.0	21 54.7	19 8.9	28 49.2	15 26.7	1 23.1	14 22.0	18 46.7	27 36.3	19 36.8	6 2.8	10 49.0
16 T	19 32 54.6	22 51.9	19 5.7	11♒17.5	15 47.0	2 32.2	14 57.9	18 51.9	27 44.0	19 39.9	6 3.7	10 50.7
17 W	19 36 51.2	23 49.1	19 2.5	23 58.4	16 2.6	3 41.2	15 33.8	18 57.2	27 51.8	19 43.0	6 4.6	10 52.4
18 T	19 40 47.7	24 46.3	18 59.3	6♓52.6	16 13.6	4 50.1	16 9.8	19 2.7	27 59.5	19 46.1	6 5.6	10 54.2
19 F	19 44 44.3	25 43.6	18 56.2	20 0.4	16 19.9	5 58.9	16 45.9	19 8.3	28 7.3	19 49.1	6 6.5	10 55.9
20 S	19 48 40.8	26 40.8	18 53.0	3♈22.3	16 21.3	7 7.6	17 22.1	19 14.1	28 15.1	19 52.1	6 7.6	10 57.6
21 S	19 52 37.4	27 38.1	18 49.8	16 58.4	16R17.8	8 16.3	17 58.3	19 20.0	28 22.8	19 55.1	6 8.6	10 59.4
22 M	19 56 34.0	28 35.4	18 46.6	0♉49.1	16 9.3	9 24.8	18 34.6	19 26.0	28 30.6	19 58.1	6 9.7	11 1.1
23 T	20 0 30.5	29 32.7	18 43.5	14 54.2	15 56.0	10 33.1	19 11.0	19 32.2	28 38.3	20 1.0	6 10.8	11 2.9
24 W	20 4 27.1	0♌30.0	18 40.3	29 12.6	15 37.8	11 41.4	19 47.5	19 38.6	28 46.1	20 3.9	6 11.9	11 4.6
25 T	20 8 23.6	1 27.3	18 37.1	13♊42.4	15 15.0	12 49.6	20 24.0	19 45.1	28 53.9	20 6.8	6 13.0	11 6.4
26 F	20 12 20.1	2 24.6	18 33.9	28 19.8	14 47.8	13 57.7	21 0.6	19 51.7	29 1.6	20 9.7	6 14.2	11 8.1
27 S	20 16 16.7	3 22.0	18 30.8	12♋59.9	14 16.4	15 5.6	21 37.2	19 58.4	29 9.4	20 12.5	6 15.4	11 9.9
28 S	20 20 13.3	4 19.4	18 27.6	27 36.3	13 41.3	16 13.5	22 13.9	20 5.3	29 17.1	20 15.3	6 16.7	11 11.7
29 M	20 24 9.9	5 16.7	18 24.4	12♌ 2.3	13 2.8	17 21.2	22 50.7	20 12.4	29 24.9	20 18.0	6 18.0	11 13.4
30 T	20 28 6.4	6 14.1	18 21.2	26 11.8	12 21.6	18 28.8	23 27.6	20 19.5	29 32.6	20 20.7	6 19.2	11 15.2
31 W	20 32 2.9	7 11.5	18 18.0	10♍ 0.0	11 38.3	19 36.2	24 4.5	20 26.8	29 40.3	20 23.4	6 20.6	11 17.0
						DECLINATION						
1 M	18 33 46.2	23N10.2	23N 3.7	22N48.8	19N59.0	18N 3.0	10N14.0	5S48.0	21N 9.8	23N 1.8	0S58.9	23N44.2
4 T	18 45 35.9	22 57.3	23 2.9	10 38.4	18 39.7	16 56.1	9 32.8	5 52.3	21 5.8	23 2.7	0 59.6	23 42.8
7 S	18 57 25.6	22 40.8	23 2.2	4S51.4	17 20.4	15 45.4	8 50.9	5 57.1	21 1.7	23 3.5	1 0.4	23 41.4
10 W	19 9 15.2	22 20.8	23 1.5	18 0.0	16 3.9	14 31.3	8 8.5	6 2.5	20 57.5	23 4.4	1 1.3	23 40.0
13 S	19 21 4.9	21 57.3	23 0.7	24 37.1	14 53.1	13 14.2	7 25.5	6 8.4	20 53.3	23 5.2	1 2.3	23 38.6
16 T	19 32 54.6	21 30.5	22 59.9	21 16.1	13 51.0	11 54.3	6 41.9	6 14.9	20 48.9	23 5.9	1 3.5	23 37.2
19 F	19 44 44.3	21 0.3	22 59.1	8 43.7	13 0.8	10 32.0	5 57.9	6 21.8	20 44.6	23 6.7	1 4.7	23 35.8
22 M	19 56 34.0	20 27.0	22 58.3	8N 3.9	12 25.7	9 7.5	5 13.4	6 29.1	20 40.1	23 7.4	1 6.1	23 34.5
25 T	20 8 23.6	19 50.5	22 57.5	21 52.2	12 8.6	7 41.3	4 28.4	6 37.0	20 35.6	23 8.1	1 7.5	23 33.1
28 S	20 20 13.3	19 11.1	22 56.7	23 43.6	12 11.1	6 13.5	3 43.0	6 45.2	20 31.1	23 8.7	1 9.0	23 31.7
31 W	20 32 2.9	18 28.8	22 55.9	12 30.1	12 33.1	4 44.5	2 57.2	6 53.9	20 26.5	23 9.4	1 10.7	23 30.3

AUGUST 1946

DAY	EPHEMERIS SIDEREAL TIME	☉	☊	☽	☿	♀	♂	♃	♄	♅	♆	♇
						LONGITUDE						
1 T	20 35 59.5	8♌ 8.9	18♓14.9	23♍24.3	10♌53.6	20♍43.5	24♍41.5	20♎34.2	29♋48.0	20♊26.1	6♎21.9	11♌18.8
2 F	20 39 56.1	9 6.4	18 11.7	6♎24.3	10R 8.3	21 50.7	25 18.6	20 41.7	29 55.7	20 28.7	6 23.3	11 20.6
3 S	20 43 52.7	10 3.8	18 8.5	19 1.7	9 23.2	22 57.8	25 55.7	20 49.4	0♌ 3.4	20 31.3	6 24.7	11 22.3
4 S	20 47 49.2	11 1.3	18 5.3	1♏19.7	8 39.0	24 4.7	26 32.9	20 57.2	0 11.1	20 33.9	6 26.1	11 24.1
5 M	20 51 45.7	11 58.7	18 2.2	13 22.7	7 56.7	25 11.4	27 10.1	21 5.1	0 18.8	20 36.4	6 27.6	11 25.9
6 T	20 55 42.3	12 56.2	17 59.0	25 15.9	7 17.1	26 18.0	27 47.4	21 13.1	0 26.4	20 38.9	6 29.0	11 27.7
7 W	20 59 38.9	13 53.7	17 55.8	7♐ 4.5	6 41.0	27 24.5	28 24.8	21 21.3	0 34.1	20 41.3	6 30.5	11 29.5
8 T	21 3 35.4	14 51.2	17 52.6	18 53.6	6 9.0	28 30.7	29 2.2	21 29.5	0 41.7	20 43.7	6 32.1	11 31.2
9 F	21 7 31.9	15 48.7	17 49.5	0♑48.0	5 41.9	29 36.8	29 39.7	21 37.9	0 49.3	20 46.1	6 33.6	11 33.0
10 S	21 11 28.5	16 46.2	17 46.3	12 51.6	5 20.3	0♎42.8	0♎17.3	21 46.4	0 56.8	20 48.4	6 35.2	11 34.8
11 S	21 15 25.0	17 43.7	17 43.1	25 7.8	5 4.6	1 48.5	0 54.9	21 55.0	1 4.4	20 50.7	6 36.8	11 36.6
12 M	21 19 21.6	18 41.3	17 39.9	7♒38.6	4 55.3	2 54.1	1 32.6	22 3.7	1 11.9	20 53.0	6 38.4	11 38.4
13 T	21 23 18.2	19 38.9	17 36.7	20 25.1	4 52.8	3 59.5	2 10.3	22 12.6	1 19.4	20 55.2	6 40.0	11 40.1
14 W	21 27 14.7	20 36.5	17 33.6	3♓27.1	4D57.2	5 4.7	2 48.1	22 21.5	1 26.9	20 57.4	6 41.7	11 41.9
15 T	21 31 11.2	21 34.1	17 30.4	16 43.6	5 8.8	6 9.8	3 26.0	22 30.5	1 34.4	20 59.5	6 43.4	11 43.6
16 F	21 35 7.8	22 31.7	17 27.2	0♈12.8	5 27.6	7 14.6	4 3.9	22 39.7	1 41.9	21 1.6	6 45.1	11 45.4
17 S	21 39 4.4	23 29.4	17 24.0	13 52.6	5 53.8	8 19.2	4 41.9	22 48.9	1 49.3	21 3.7	6 46.8	11 47.2
18 S	21 43 1.0	24 27.1	17 20.9	27 41.4	6 27.3	9 23.7	5 20.0	22 58.3	1 56.7	21 5.7	6 48.5	11 48.9
19 M	21 46 57.5	25 24.8	17 17.7	11♉37.5	7 8.0	10 27.9	5 58.1	23 7.7	2 4.0	21 7.7	6 50.3	11 50.6
20 T	21 50 54.0	26 22.5	17 14.5	25 39.9	7 55.8	11 31.9	6 36.3	23 17.2	2 11.3	21 9.6	6 52.1	11 52.4
21 W	21 54 50.6	27 20.3	17 11.3	9♊47.7	8 50.5	12 35.7	7 14.6	23 26.9	2 18.6	21 11.5	6 53.9	11 54.1
22 T	21 58 47.2	28 18.1	17 8.2	24 0.0	9 52.0	13 39.2	7 52.9	23 36.6	2 25.9	21 13.4	6 55.7	11 55.9
23 F	22 2 43.7	29 16.0	17 5.0	8♋15.2	10 59.9	14 42.6	8 31.3	23 46.5	2 33.2	21 15.2	6 57.5	11 57.6
24 S	22 6 40.3	0♍13.8	17 1.8	22 30.6	12 14.0	15 45.7	9 9.7	23 56.4	2 40.4	21 16.9	6 59.4	11 59.3
25 S	22 10 36.8	1 11.7	16 58.6	6♌42.7	13 33.8	16 48.5	9 48.2	24 6.4	2 47.5	21 18.6	7 1.3	12 1.0
26 M	22 14 33.4	2 9.6	16 55.4	20 47.1	14 59.1	17 51.2	10 26.8	24 16.5	2 54.7	21 20.3	7 3.2	12 2.7
27 T	22 18 29.9	3 7.6	16 52.3	4♍38.9	16 29.4	18 53.5	11 5.4	24 26.8	3 1.7	21 21.9	7 5.1	12 4.4
28 W	22 22 26.5	4 5.5	16 49.1	18 14.2	18 4.3	19 55.6	11 44.2	24 37.0	3 8.8	21 23.5	7 7.0	12 6.1
29 T	22 26 23.0	5 3.5	16 45.9	1♎29.9	19 43.2	20 57.4	12 22.9	24 47.4	3 15.8	21 25.0	7 9.0	12 7.7
30 F	22 30 19.6	6 1.5	16 42.7	14 24.9	21 25.8	21 59.0	13 1.8	24 57.9	3 22.8	21 26.5	7 10.9	12 9.4
31 S	22 34 16.1	6 59.6	16 39.6	26 59.6	23 11.5	23 0.2	13 40.7	25 8.4	3 29.7	21 28.0	7 12.9	12 11.0
						DECLINATION						
1 T	20 35 59.5	18N14.1	22N55.6	7N19.2	12N44.3	4N14.6	2N41.9	6S56.9	20N24.9	23N 9.6	1S11.2	23N29.9
4 S	20 47 49.2	17 28.2	22 54.8	8S20.7	13 27.7	2 44.4	1 55.7	7 6.1	20 20.3	23 10.2	1 13.0	23 28.6
7 W	20 59 38.9	16 39.7	22 53.9	20 24.7	14 20.7	1 13.6	1 9.2	7 15.7	20 15.7	23 10.7	1 14.8	23 27.2
10 S	21 11 28.5	15 48.9	22 53.0	24 51.1	15 16.5	0S17.4	0 22.5	7 25.7	20 11.0	23 11.2	1 16.8	23 26.0
13 T	21 23 18.2	14 55.8	22 52.2	18 54.2	16 8.2	1 48.3	0S24.4	7 36.0	20 6.3	23 11.7	1 18.7	23 24.7
16 F	21 35 7.8	14 0.5	22 51.3	4 27.7	16 49.5	3 18.9	1 11.5	7 46.6	20 1.6	23 12.2	1 20.8	23 23.5
19 M	21 46 57.5	13 3.2	22 50.4	12N26.3	17 14.8	4 49.0	1 58.7	7 57.5	19 57.0	23 12.7	1 23.0	23 22.3
22 T	21 58 47.2	12 4.1	22 49.5	23 49.1	17 19.4	6 18.3	2 45.9	8 8.6	19 52.3	23 13.1	1 25.2	23 21.1
25 S	22 10 36.8	11 3.2	22 48.6	22 15.7	16 59.4	7 46.4	3 33.3	8 20.1	19 47.7	23 13.5	1 27.4	23 20.0
28 W	22 22 26.5	10 0.7	22 47.6	9 16.2	16 13.0	9 13.2	4 20.6	8 31.8	19 43.1	23 13.8	1 29.7	23 18.9
31 S	22 34 16.1	8 56.8	22 46.7	6S47.8	15 0.5	10 38.4	5 7.8	8 43.7	19 38.5	23 14.1	1 32.1	23 17.9

SEPTEMBER 1946

DAY	EPHEMERIS SIDEREAL TIME	☉	☊	☽	☿	♀	♂	♃	♄	♅	♆	♇
	h m s	° ′	° ′	° ′	° ′	° ′	° ′	° ′	° ′	° ′	° ′	° ′
						LONGITUDE						
1 S	22 38 12.7	7♍57.6	16♊36.4	9♏16.4	24♌59.9	24♎ 1.1	14♎19.6	25♎19.1	3♌36.6	21♊29.4	7♎14.9	12♌12.7
2 M	22 42 9.2	8 55.7	16 33.2	21 18.8	26 50.5	25 1.7	14 58.6	25 29.8	3 43.5	21 30.7	7 16.9	12 14.3
3 T	22 46 5.8	9 53.8	16 30.0	3♐11.7	28 42.9	26 2.0	15 37.7	25 40.6	3 50.3	21 32.0	7 18.9	12 15.9
4 W	22 50 2.4	10 52.0	16 26.8	15 0.2	0♍36.7	27 2.0	16 16.9	25 51.5	3 57.0	21 33.2	7 21.0	12 17.5
5 T	22 53 58.9	11 50.1	16 23.7	26 49.8	2 31.4	28 1.6	16 56.1	26 2.4	4 3.7	21 34.4	7 23.0	12 19.1
6 F	22 57 55.5	12 48.3	16 20.5	8♑46.0	4 26.9	29 0.8	17 35.3	26 13.4	4 10.4	21 35.6	7 25.1	12 20.7
7 S	23 1 52.0	13 46.5	16 17.3	20 53.7	6 22.6	29 59.7	18 14.6	26 24.5	4 17.0	21 36.7	7 27.1	12 22.3
8 S	23 5 48.5	14 44.7	16 14.1	3♒17.0	8 18.5	0♏58.1	18 54.0	26 35.7	4 23.5	21 37.7	7 29.2	12 23.8
9 M	23 9 45.1	15 43.0	16 11.0	15 59.2	10 14.3	1 56.2	19 33.5	26 46.9	4 30.0	21 38.7	7 31.3	12 25.4
10 T	23 13 41.7	16 41.3	16 7.8	29 1.5	12 9.7	2 53.9	20 13.0	26 58.2	4 36.5	21 39.7	7 33.4	12 26.9
11 W	23 17 38.3	17 39.6	16 4.6	12♓23.8	14 4.7	3 51.1	20 52.6	27 9.6	4 42.9	21 40.6	7 35.6	12 28.4
12 T	23 21 34.8	18 37.9	16 1.4	26 4.0	15 59.0	4 47.8	21 32.2	27 21.0	4 49.2	21 41.4	7 37.7	12 29.9
13 F	23 25 31.3	19 36.3	15 58.2	9♈58.8	17 52.7	5 44.2	22 11.9	27 32.5	4 55.5	21 42.2	7 39.8	12 31.4
14 S	23 29 27.9	20 34.7	15 55.1	24 3.7	19 45.5	6 40.0	22 51.6	27 44.1	5 1.7	21 42.9	7 42.0	12 32.9
15 S	23 33 24.5	21 33.2	15 51.9	8♉14.4	21 37.5	7 35.3	23 31.4	27 55.7	5 7.9	21 43.6	7 44.1	12 34.3
16 M	23 37 21.0	22 31.6	15 48.7	22 26.9	23 28.5	8 30.2	24 11.3	28 7.4	5 14.0	21 44.3	7 46.3	12 35.8
17 T	23 41 17.5	23 30.2	15 45.5	6♊38.3	25 18.6	9 24.5	24 51.3	28 19.1	5 20.1	21 44.9	7 48.5	12 37.2
18 W	23 45 14.1	24 28.7	15 42.4	20 46.9	27 7.7	10 18.3	25 31.3	28 31.0	5 26.1	21 45.4	7 50.7	12 38.6
19 T	23 49 10.7	25 27.3	15 39.2	4♋51.5	28 55.9	11 11.5	26 11.3	28 42.8	5 32.0	21 45.9	7 52.8	12 40.0
20 F	23 53 7.2	26 25.9	15 36.0	18 51.4	0♎43.0	12 4.1	26 51.5	28 54.8	5 37.9	21 46.3	7 55.0	12 41.3
21 S	23 57 3.7	27 24.6	15 32.8	2♌45.8	2 29.1	12 56.2	27 31.7	29 6.7	5 43.6	21 46.7	7 57.2	12 42.7
22 S	0 1 0.3	28 23.3	15 29.6	16 33.4	4 14.2	13 47.6	28 11.9	29 18.8	5 49.4	21 47.1	7 59.4	12 44.0
23 M	0 4 56.9	29 22.0	15 26.5	0♍12.2	5 58.3	14 38.4	28 52.2	29 30.9	5 55.1	21 47.3	8 1.7	12 45.4
24 T	0 8 53.5	0♎20.8	15 23.3	13 40.0	7 41.5	15 28.5	29 32.6	29 43.0	6 0.7	21 47.6	8 3.9	12 46.7
25 W	0 12 50.0	1 19.6	15 20.1	26 54.4	9 23.6	16 17.9	0♏13.1	29 55.2	6 6.2	21 47.7	8 6.1	12 47.9
26 T	0 16 46.5	2 18.4	15 16.9	9♎53.5	11 4.8	17 6.6	0 53.6	0♏ 7.4	6 11.6	21 47.9	8 8.3	12 49.2
27 F	0 20 43.1	3 17.3	15 13.7	22 36.2	12 45.1	17 54.5	1 34.2	0 19.7	6 17.0	21 47.9	8 10.5	12 50.4
28 S	0 24 39.7	4 16.2	15 10.6	5♏ 2.7	14 24.5	18 41.6	2 14.8	0 32.1	6 22.3	21 47.9	8 12.8	12 51.7
29 S	0 28 36.2	5 15.1	15 7.4	17 14.4	16 2.9	19 27.9	2 55.5	0 44.4	6 27.6	21R47.9	8 15.0	12 52.9
30 M	0 32 32.8	6 14.1	15 4.2	29 14.0	17 40.5	20 13.4	3 36.3	0 56.9	6 32.7	21 47.8	8 17.2	12 54.0
						DECLINATION						
1 S	22 38 12.7	8N35.2	22N46.4	11S39.5	14N31.0	11S 6.4	5S23.6	8S47.7	19N37.0	23N14.2	1S32.9	23N17.5
4 W	22 50 2.4	7 29.6	22 45.4	22 26.2	12 48.7	12 29.0	6 10.7	8 59.9	19 32.5	23 14.5	1 35.4	23 16.5
7 S	23 1 52.0	6 23.0	22 44.4	24 37.0	10 49.7	13 49.3	6 57.6	9 12.3	19 28.1	23 14.8	1 37.8	23 15.6
10 T	23 13 41.7	5 15.4	22 43.5	16 17.6	8 38.9	15 7.1	7 44.2	9 24.8	19 23.7	23 15.0	1 40.4	23 14.8
13 F	23 25 31.3	4 7.0	22 42.5	0 15.2	6 20.9	16 22.2	8 30.6	9 37.5	19 19.5	23 15.2	1 42.9	23 13.9
16 M	23 37 21.0	2 58.0	22 41.5	16N28.7	3 59.2	17 34.2	9 16.7	9 50.3	19 15.3	23 15.4	1 45.5	23 13.2
19 T	23 49 10.7	1 48.4	22 40.5	25 2.4	1 36.6	18 43.0	10 2.3	10 3.2	19 11.3	23 15.5	1 48.1	23 12.5
22 S	0 1 0.3	0 38.5	22 39.4	20 5.2	0S45.1	19 48.2	10 47.5	10 16.3	19 7.3	23 15.6	1 50.7	23 11.9
25 W	0 12 50.0	0S31.7	22 38.4	5 44.1	3 4.3	20 49.8	11 32.3	10 29.4	19 3.5	23 15.7	1 53.3	23 11.3
28 S	0 24 39.7	1 41.9	22 37.4	10S11.8	5 20.0	21 47.4	12 16.4	10 42.6	18 59.8	23 15.8	1 55.9	23 10.8

OCTOBER 1946

DAY	EPHEMERIS SIDEREAL TIME	☉	☊	☽	☿	♀	♂	♃	♄	♅	♆	♇
						LONGITUDE						
1 T	0 36 29.3	7♎13.1	15♊ 1.0	11♐ 5.1	19♎17.2	20♏57.9	4♏17.1	1♏ 9.3	6♌37.8	21♊47.7	8♎19.5	12♌55.2
2 W	0 40 25.9	8 12.1	14 57.9	22 52.5	20 53.0	21 41.5	4 58.0	1 21.8	6 42.8	21R47.5	8 21.7	12 56.3
3 T	0 44 22.4	9 11.2	14 54.7	4♑41.3	22 28.0	22 24.2	5 39.0	1 34.4	6 47.7	21 47.2	8 23.9	12 57.5
4 F	0 48 19.0	10 10.3	14 51.5	16 36.8	24 2.2	23 5.8	6 20.0	1 47.0	6 52.6	21 47.0	8 26.2	12 58.6
5 S	0 52 15.5	11 9.4	14 48.3	28 44.5	25 35.5	23 46.4	7 1.0	1 59.6	6 57.3	21 46.6	8 28.4	12 59.6
6 S	0 56 12.1	12 8.5	14 45.1	11♒ 9.5	27 8.1	24 25.8	7 42.2	2 12.2	7 2.0	21 46.2	8 30.6	13 0.7
7 M	1 0 8.6	13 7.7	14 42.0	23 55.8	28 39.8	25 4.2	8 23.4	2 24.9	7 6.6	21 45.8	8 32.9	13 1.7
8 T	1 4 5.2	14 6.9	14 38.8	7♓ 5.9	0♏10.8	25 41.3	9 4.6	2 37.6	7 11.1	21 45.3	8 35.1	13 2.7
9 W	1 8 1.7	15 6.1	14 35.6	20 40.7	1 41.0	26 17.2	9 45.9	2 50.4	7 15.6	21 44.7	8 37.3	13 3.7
10 T	1 11 58.3	16 5.4	14 32.4	4♈38.5	3 10.4	26 51.8	10 27.3	3 3.1	7 19.9	21 44.1	8 39.5	13 4.7
11 F	1 15 54.8	17 4.7	14 29.3	18 55.5	4 39.0	27 25.0	11 8.7	3 16.0	7 24.2	21 43.4	8 41.7	13 5.6
12 S	1 19 51.4	18 4.0	14 26.1	3♉25.9	6 6.8	27 56.9	11 50.2	3 28.8	7 28.4	21 42.7	8 44.0	13 6.5
13 S	1 23 48.0	19 3.4	14 22.9	18 2.9	7 33.8	28 27.3	12 31.8	3 41.7	7 32.5	21 42.0	8 46.2	13 7.4
14 M	1 27 44.5	20 2.8	14 19.7	2♊40.0	8 60.0	28 56.2	13 13.4	3 54.6	7 36.4	21 41.2	8 48.4	13 8.3
15 T	1 31 41.0	21 2.3	14 16.5	17 11.4	10 25.3	29 23.5	13 55.1	4 7.5	7 40.3	21 40.3	8 50.6	13 9.1
16 W	1 35 37.6	22 1.7	14 13.4	1♋33.2	11 49.8	29 49.2	14 36.8	4 20.4	7 44.2	21 39.4	8 52.8	13 9.9
17 T	1 39 34.2	23 1.3	14 10.2	15 43.0	13 13.4	0♐13.2	15 18.6	4 33.4	7 47.9	21 38.5	8 54.9	13 10.7
18 F	1 43 30.7	24 0.8	14 7.0	29 39.6	14 36.2	0 35.6	16 0.5	4 46.3	7 51.5	21 37.5	8 57.1	13 11.5
19 S	1 47 27.3	25 0.4	14 3.8	13♌22.8	15 57.9	0 56.1	16 42.4	4 59.3	7 55.0	21 36.4	8 59.3	13 12.2
20 S	1 51 23.8	26 0.1	14 0.7	26 52.9	17 18.6	1 14.7	17 24.4	5 12.4	7 58.5	21 35.3	9 1.4	13 12.9
21 M	1 55 20.4	26 59.7	13 57.5	10♍10.1	18 38.3	1 31.5	18 6.5	5 25.4	8 1.8	21 34.2	9 3.6	13 13.6
22 T	1 59 17.0	27 59.4	13 54.3	23 14.6	19 56.8	1 46.2	18 48.6	5 38.5	8 5.1	21 33.0	9 5.7	13 14.3
23 W	2 3 13.5	28 59.2	13 51.1	6♎ 6.3	21 14.1	1 59.0	19 30.8	5 51.5	8 8.2	21 31.8	9 7.9	13 14.9
24 T	2 7 10.0	29 59.0	13 47.9	18 45.2	22 30.0	2 9.6	20 13.0	6 4.6	8 11.3	21 30.5	9 10.0	13 15.6
25 F	2 11 6.6	0♏58.8	13 44.8	1♏11.5	23 44.6	2 18.1	20 55.3	6 17.7	8 14.2	21 29.2	9 12.1	13 16.1
26 S	2 15 3.2	1 58.6	13 41.6	13 25.8	24 57.5	2 24.3	21 37.7	6 30.8	8 17.0	21 27.8	9 14.2	13 16.7
27 S	2 18 59.7	2 58.5	13 38.4	25 29.3	26 8.8	2 28.3	22 20.1	6 43.9	8 19.8	21 26.4	9 16.3	13 17.2
28 M	2 22 56.3	3 58.4	13 35.2	7♐24.1	27 18.2	2 29.9	23 2.6	6 57.0	8 22.4	21 24.9	9 18.4	13 17.7
29 T	2 26 52.8	4 58.4	13 32.1	19 12.8	28 25.5	2R29.2	23 45.1	7 10.2	8 24.9	21 23.4	9 20.4	13 18.2
30 W	2 30 49.4	5 58.3	13 28.9	0♑59.0	29 30.5	2 26.1	24 27.8	7 23.3	8 27.4	21 21.9	9 22.5	13 18.7
31 T	2 34 45.9	6 58.3	13 25.7	12 46.8	0♐33.0	2 20.6	25 10.4	7 36.5	8 29.7	21 20.3	9 24.5	13 19.1
						DECLINATION						
1 T	0 36 29.3	2S51.9	22N36.3	21S51.3	7S31.4	22S40.8	12S59.9	10S55.8	18N56.3	23N15.8	1S58.5	23N10.4
4 F	0 48 19.0	4 1.8	22 35.2	25 8.7	9 37.7	23 29.8	13 42.7	11 9.1	18 52.9	23 15.8	2 1.2	23 10.0
7 M	1 0 8.6	5 11.1	22 34.1	18 3.5	11 38.3	24 14.0	14 24.7	11 22.4	18 49.7	23 15.8	2 3.8	23 9.7
10 T	1 11 58.3	6 19.9	22 33.1	2 30.4	13 32.8	24 53.1	15 5.9	11 35.7	18 46.7	23 15.7	2 6.4	23 9.5
13 S	1 23 48.0	7 27.9	22 32.0	15N 8.1	15 20.4	25 27.0	15 46.1	11 49.0	18 43.9	23 15.6	2 8.9	23 9.4
16 W	1 35 37.6	8 35.0	22 30.8	25 4.8	17 0.6	25 55.1	16 25.4	12 2.2	18 41.3	23 15.5	2 11.5	23 9.3
19 S	1 47 27.3	9 41.0	22 29.7	21 5.7	18 32.7	26 17.0	17 3.6	12 15.5	18 38.8	23 15.3	2 14.0	23 9.3
22 T	1 59 17.0	10 45.8	22 28.6	7 19.3	19 56.0	26 32.4	17 40.7	12 28.6	18 36.6	23 15.1	2 16.5	23 9.4
25 F	2 11 6.6	11 49.1	22 27.4	8S42.2	21 9.5	26 40.4	18 16.6	12 41.7	18 34.7	23 14.9	2 18.9	23 9.6
28 M	2 22 56.3	12 50.8	22 26.3	21 7.7	22 12.1	26 40.5	18 51.3	12 54.8	18 32.9	23 14.7	2 21.3	23 9.9
31 T	2 34 45.9	13 50.7	22 25.1	25 29.1	23 2.6	26 31.7	19 24.5	13 7.7	18 31.4	23 14.4	2 23.7	23 10.2

NOVEMBER 1946

DAY	EPHEMERIS SIDEREAL TIME h m s	☉ ° ′	☊ ° ′	☽ ° ′	☿ ° ′	♀ ° ′	♂ ° ′	♃ ° ′	♄ ° ′	♅ ° ′	♆ ° ′	♇ ° ′
						LONGITUDE						
1 F	2 38 42.5	7♏58.4	13♊22.5	24♑40.9	1♐32.6	2♐12.6	25♏53.2	7♏49.6	8♌31.9	21♊18.6	9♎26.6	13♌19.5
2 S	2 42 39.0	8 58.4	13 19.4	6♒46.4	2 29.1	2R 2.2	26 35.9	8 2.7	8 34.0	21R17.0	9 28.6	13 19.9
3 S	2 46 35.6	9 58.5	13 16.2	19 8.4	3 22.0	1 49.3	27 18.8	8 15.9	8 36.0	21 15.3	9 30.5	13 20.2
4 M	2 50 32.1	10 58.6	13 13.0	1♓51.5	4 11.1	1 34.0	28 1.7	8 29.0	8 37.9	21 13.5	9 32.5	13 20.5
5 T	2 54 28.7	11 58.7	13 9.8	14 59.4	4 55.7	1 16.4	28 44.6	8 42.1	8 39.7	21 11.7	9 34.5	13 20.8
6 W	2 58 25.3	12 58.9	13 6.6	28 34.4	5 35.5	0 56.4	29 27.7	8 55.3	8 41.4	21 9.9	9 36.4	13 21.1
7 T	3 2 21.8	13 59.1	13 3.5	12♈36.6	6 9.7	0 34.1	0♐10.7	9 8.4	8 43.0	21 8.0	9 38.3	13 21.3
8 F	3 6 18.4	14 59.3	13 0.3	27 3.3	6 38.0	0 9.8	0 53.9	9 21.5	8 44.4	21 6.1	9 40.3	13 21.5
9 S	3 10 14.9	15 59.5	12 57.1	11♉49.4	6 59.4	29♏43.3	1 37.1	9 34.6	8 45.8	21 4.2	9 42.1	13 21.7
10 S	3 14 11.5	16 59.8	12 53.9	26 47.4	7 13.5	29 15.0	2 20.3	9 47.7	8 47.1	21 2.2	9 44.0	13 21.8
11 M	3 18 8.0	18 0.1	12 50.8	11♊48.7	7 19.5	28 44.9	3 3.6	10 0.8	8 48.2	21 0.2	9 45.9	13 21.9
12 T	3 22 4.6	19 0.4	12 47.6	26 44.9	7R16.7	28 13.3	3 47.0	10 13.9	8 49.2	20 58.2	9 47.7	13 22.0
13 W	3 26 1.2	20 0.8	12 44.4	11♋28.8	7 4.5	27 40.3	4 30.4	10 26.9	8 50.1	20 56.1	9 49.5	13 22.1
14 T	3 29 57.7	21 1.2	12 41.2	25 55.2	6 42.3	27 6.2	5 13.9	10 40.0	8 50.9	20 54.1	9 51.3	13 22.1
15 F	3 33 54.3	22 1.6	12 38.1	10♌ 1.2	6 10.0	26 31.1	5 57.4	10 53.0	8 51.6	20 51.9	9 53.1	13 22.1
16 S	3 37 50.8	23 2.0	12 34.9	23 46.1	5 27.4	25 55.3	6 41.0	11 6.1	8 52.2	20 49.8	9 54.8	13R22.1
17 S	3 41 47.4	24 2.5	12 31.7	7♍10.3	4 34.8	25 19.1	7 24.7	11 19.1	8 52.7	20 47.6	9 56.6	13 22.1
18 M	3 45 43.9	25 3.0	12 28.5	20 15.5	3 33.0	24 42.7	8 8.4	11 32.0	8 53.0	20 45.4	9 58.3	13 22.0
19 T	3 49 40.5	26 3.6	12 25.3	3♎ 3.9	2 23.2	24 6.3	8 52.2	11 45.0	8 53.3	20 43.1	9 60.0	13 21.9
20 W	3 53 37.1	27 4.2	12 22.2	15 37.4	1 7.1	23 30.2	9 36.0	11 58.0	8 53.4	20 40.9	10 1.6	13 21.8
21 T	3 57 33.6	28 4.8	12 19.0	27 58.4	29♏47.0	22 54.6	10 19.9	12 10.9	8 53.4	20 38.6	10 3.3	13 21.6
22 F	4 1 30.2	29 5.4	12 15.8	10♏ 8.9	28 25.3	22 19.9	11 3.9	12 23.8	8R53.3	20 36.3	10 4.9	13 21.4
23 S	4 5 26.7	0♐ 6.1	12 12.6	22 10.6	27 4.8	21 46.1	11 47.9	12 36.6	8 53.1	20 33.9	10 6.5	13 21.2
24 S	4 9 23.3	1 6.7	12 9.5	4♐ 5.5	25 48.2	21 13.6	12 32.0	12 49.5	8 52.7	20 31.6	10 8.0	13 20.9
25 M	4 13 19.9	2 7.4	12 6.3	15 55.5	24 37.9	20 42.4	13 16.1	13 2.3	8 52.3	20 29.2	10 9.6	13 20.7
26 T	4 17 16.4	3 8.2	12 3.1	27 42.6	23 36.0	20 12.9	14 0.3	13 15.1	8 51.7	20 26.8	10 11.1	13 20.4
27 W	4 21 13.0	4 8.9	11 59.9	9♑29.5	22 44.1	19 45.2	14 44.5	13 27.8	8 51.1	20 24.4	10 12.6	13 20.0
28 T	4 25 9.5	5 9.7	11 56.8	21 19.0	22 3.2	19 19.4	15 28.8	13 40.5	8 50.3	20 21.9	10 14.1	13 19.7
29 F	4 29 6.1	6 10.5	11 53.6	3♒14.5	21 33.8	18 55.6	16 13.1	13 53.2	8 49.4	20 19.5	10 15.5	13 19.3
30 S	4 33 2.6	7 11.3	11 50.4	15 19.9	21 15.9	18 34.0	16 57.5	14 5.8	8 48.4	20 17.0	10 16.9	13 18.9
						DECLINATION						
1 F	2 38 42.5	14S10.3	22N24.7	24S40.3	23S16.4	26S26.7	19S35.3	13S12.0	18N31.0	23N14.3	2S24.4	23N10.3
4 M	2 50 32.1	15 7.5	22 23.6	15 36.8	23 47.9	26 4.8	20 6.6	13 24.7	18 29.8	23 14.0	2 26.7	23 10.7
7 T	3 2 21.8	16 2.5	22 22.4	0N50.1	24 2.4	25 32.3	20 36.5	13 37.4	18 28.9	23 13.7	2 28.9	23 11.2
10 S	3 14 11.5	16 55.0	22 21.2	18 7.0	23 56.6	24 49.1	21 4.6	13 49.9	18 28.2	23 13.4	2 31.0	23 11.8
13 W	3 26 1.2	17 45.0	22 20.0	25 32.9	23 26.2	23 55.8	21 31.2	14 2.2	18 27.8	23 13.0	2 33.1	23 12.5
16 S	3 37 50.8	18 32.2	22 18.7	18 19.4	22 26.5	22 53.8	21 55.9	14 14.4	18 27.7	23 12.6	2 35.0	23 13.2
19 T	3 49 40.5	19 16.5	22 17.5	3 17.5	20 56.7	21 45.7	22 18.8	14 26.4	18 27.8	23 12.2	2 36.9	23 14.0
22 F	4 1 30.2	19 57.7	22 16.3	12S14.0	19 7.1	20 34.7	22 39.9	14 38.3	18 28.3	23 11.7	2 38.8	23 14.9
25 M	4 13 19.9	20 35.6	22 15.0	23 5.5	17 21.5	19 24.1	22 58.9	14 49.9	18 28.9	23 11.3	2 40.5	23 15.8
28 T	4 25 9.5	21 10.0	22 13.7	25 5.9	16 6.3	18 17.2	23 15.9	15 1.3	18 29.9	23 10.8	2 42.1	23 16.8

DECEMBER 1946

DAY	EPHEMERIS SIDEREAL TIME h m s	☉ ° ′	☊ ° ′	☽ ° ′	☿ ° ′	♀ ° ′	♂ ° ′	♃ ° ′	♄ ° ′	♅ ° ′	♆ ° ′	♇ ° ′
						LONGITUDE						
1 S	4 36 59.2	8♐12.1	11♊47.2	27♒39.4	21♏ 9.4	18♏14.7	17♐42.0	14♏18.4	8♌47.3	20♊14.5	10♎18.3	13♌18.5
2 M	4 40 55.7	9 12.9	11 44.0	10♓17.2	21D13.6	17R57.7	18 26.5	14 31.0	8R46.1	20R12.1	10 19.7	13R18.0
3 T	4 44 52.3	10 13.8	11 40.9	23 17.4	21 27.7	17 43.2	19 11.0	14 43.5	8 44.7	20 9.6	10 21.0	13 17.5
4 W	4 48 48.9	11 14.6	11 37.7	6♈43.1	21 51.1	17 31.0	19 55.6	14 56.0	8 43.3	20 7.0	10 22.3	13 17.0
5 T	4 52 45.4	12 15.5	11 34.5	20 36.1	22 22.6	17 21.4	20 40.3	15 8.4	8 41.7	20 4.5	10 23.6	13 16.5
6 F	4 56 42.0	13 16.4	11 31.3	4♉56.3	23 1.6	17 14.2	21 25.0	15 20.8	8 40.1	20 2.0	10 24.8	13 15.9
7 S	5 0 38.5	14 17.3	11 28.2	19 40.7	23 47.2	17 9.5	22 9.7	15 33.1	8 38.3	19 59.4	10 26.0	13 15.3
8 S	5 4 35.1	15 18.2	11 25.0	4♊43.6	24 38.6	17 7.3	22 54.5	15 45.4	8 36.5	19 56.9	10 27.2	13 14.7
9 M	5 8 31.7	16 19.1	11 21.8	19 56.7	25 35.1	17D 7.5	23 39.4	15 57.7	8 34.5	19 54.4	10 28.4	13 14.1
10 T	5 12 28.2	17 20.1	11 18.6	5♋10.3	26 36.1	17 10.2	24 24.3	16 9.9	8 32.4	19 51.8	10 29.5	13 13.4
11 W	5 16 24.8	18 21.0	11 15.5	20 14.6	27 40.9	17 15.3	25 9.2	16 22.0	8 30.2	19 49.2	10 30.6	13 12.7
12 T	5 20 21.3	19 22.0	11 12.3	5♌ 1.3	28 49.2	17 22.7	25 54.2	16 34.1	8 28.0	19 46.7	10 31.6	13 12.0
13 F	5 24 17.9	20 23.0	11 9.1	19 24.6	0♐ 0.4	17 32.5	26 39.3	16 46.1	8 25.6	19 44.1	10 32.7	13 11.3
14 S	5 28 14.5	21 24.0	11 5.9	3♍21.4	1 14.2	17 44.4	27 24.4	16 58.1	8 23.1	19 41.6	10 33.7	13 10.5
15 S	5 32 11.0	22 25.0	11 2.8	16 51.2	2 30.2	17 58.6	28 9.6	17 10.0	8 20.5	19 39.0	10 34.7	13 9.7
16 M	5 36 7.6	23 26.1	10 59.6	29 55.9	3 48.1	18 14.9	28 54.8	17 21.8	8 17.8	19 36.5	10 35.6	13 8.9
17 T	5 40 4.1	24 27.2	10 56.4	12♎38.5	5 7.8	18 33.2	29 40.0	17 33.6	8 15.1	19 33.9	10 36.5	13 8.1
18 W	5 44 0.7	25 28.2	10 53.2	25 2.8	6 28.9	18 53.5	0♑25.4	17 45.4	8 12.2	19 31.4	10 37.4	13 7.3
19 T	5 47 57.2	26 29.3	10 50.0	7♏12.7	7 51.3	19 15.8	1 10.7	17 57.0	8 9.2	19 28.8	10 38.2	13 6.4
20 F	5 51 53.8	27 30.4	10 46.9	19 12.2	9 14.8	19 39.8	1 56.1	18 8.6	8 6.2	19 26.3	10 39.0	13 5.5
21 S	5 55 50.3	28 31.6	10 43.7	1♐ 4.7	10 39.3	20 5.7	2 41.6	18 20.2	8 3.0	19 23.8	10 39.8	13 4.6
22 S	5 59 46.9	29 32.7	10 40.5	12 53.2	12 4.7	20 33.3	3 27.1	18 31.6	7 59.8	19 21.3	10 40.6	13 3.6
23 M	6 3 43.5	0♑33.8	10 37.3	24 40.3	13 30.9	21 2.6	4 12.6	18 43.0	7 56.5	19 18.8	10 41.3	13 2.7
24 T	6 7 40.0	1 35.0	10 34.2	6♑28.4	14 57.8	21 33.4	4 58.2	18 54.3	7 53.1	19 16.3	10 42.0	13 1.7
25 W	6 11 36.6	2 36.1	10 31.0	18 19.3	16 25.3	22 5.8	5 43.9	19 5.6	7 49.6	19 13.8	10 42.6	13 0.7
26 T	6 15 33.1	3 37.3	10 27.8	0♒15.0	17 53.3	22 39.7	6 29.5	19 16.7	7 46.0	19 11.3	10 43.2	12 59.7
27 F	6 19 29.7	4 38.4	10 24.6	12 17.6	19 21.9	23 14.9	7 15.3	19 27.8	7 42.4	19 8.9	10 43.8	12 58.7
28 S	6 23 26.3	5 39.6	10 21.5	24 29.3	20 51.0	23 51.6	8 1.0	19 38.8	7 38.6	19 6.5	10 44.4	12 57.6
29 S	6 27 22.8	6 40.8	10 18.3	6♓52.6	22 20.5	24 29.5	8 46.8	19 49.7	7 34.8	19 4.0	10 44.9	12 56.5
30 M	6 31 19.4	7 41.9	10 15.1	19 30.6	23 50.4	25 8.7	9 32.7	20 0.6	7 30.9	19 1.6	10 45.3	12 55.4
31 T	6 35 15.9	8 43.1	10 11.9	2♈26.1	25 20.7	25 49.1	10 18.6	20 11.3	7 27.0	18 59.3	10 45.8	12 54.3
						DECLINATION						
1 S	4 36 59.2	21S40.9	22N12.5	17S 6.8	15S34.0	17S17.0	23S30.9	15S12.5	18N31.1	23N10.3	2S43.6	23N17.9
4 W	4 48 48.9	22 8.0	22 11.2	1 44.9	15 41.4	16 25.3	23 43.6	15 23.5	18 32.6	23 9.7	2 45.1	23 19.0
7 S	5 0 38.5	22 31.3	22 9.9	15N44.2	16 18.0	15 43.3	23 54.2	15 34.2	18 34.3	23 9.2	2 46.4	23 20.2
10 T	5 12 28.2	22 50.6	22 8.6	25 27.3	17 12.6	15 11.4	24 2.5	15 44.7	18 36.3	23 8.6	2 47.6	23 21.4
13 F	5 24 17.9	23 5.9	22 7.3	19 39.1	18 16.3	14 49.6	24 8.5	15 54.9	18 38.5	23 8.1	2 48.7	23 22.7
16 M	5 36 7.6	23 17.0	22 5.9	4 38.4	19 22.8	14 37.3	24 12.2	16 4.9	18 40.9	23 7.5	2 49.7	23 24.0
19 T	5 47 57.2	23 24.0	22 4.6	11S 4.9	20 27.7	14 33.4	24 13.5	16 14.6	18 43.6	23 7.0	2 50.6	23 25.4
22 S	5 59 46.9	23 26.8	22 3.2	22 27.1	21 27.8	14 37.1	24 12.4	16 24.0	18 46.5	23 6.4	2 51.3	23 26.8
25 W	6 11 36.6	23 25.3	22 1.9	25 18.1	22 21.2	14 47.2	24 8.9	16 33.1	18 49.5	23 5.8	2 52.0	23 28.3
28 S	6 23 26.3	23 19.6	22 0.5	18 4.9	23 6.1	15 2.7	24 3.0	16 41.9	18 52.7	23 5.2	2 52.5	23 29.8
31 T	6 35 15.9	23 9.6	21 59.1	3 31.1	23 41.6	15 22.6	23 54.7	16 50.4	18 56.1	23 4.7	2 52.9	23 31.3

JANUARY 1947

LONGITUDE

DAY	EPHEMERIS SIDEREAL TIME h m s	☉ ° ′	☊ ° ′	☽ ° ′	☿ ° ′	♀ ° ′	♂ ° ′	♃ ° ′	♄ ° ′	♅ ° ′	♆ ° ′	♇ ° ′
1 W	6 39 12.5	9♑44.2	10♊ 8.8	15♈42.3	26♐51.5	26♏30.7	11♑ 4.5	20♏22.0	7♌23.0	18♊56.9	10♎46.2	12♌53.2
2 T	6 43 9.1	10 45.4	10 5.6	29 21.7	28 22.6	27 13.3	11 50.5	20 32.6	7R18.9	18R54.6	10 46.6	12R52.1
3 F	6 47 5.6	11 46.5	10 2.4	13♉25.6	29 54.1	27 57.1	12 36.5	20 43.0	7 14.7	18 52.3	10 46.9	12 50.9
4 S	6 51 2.2	12 47.7	9 59.2	27 53.7	1♑25.9	28 41.9	13 22.5	20 53.4	7 10.5	18 50.0	10 47.2	12 49.7
5 S	6 54 58.7	13 48.8	9 56.0	12♊43.2	2 58.2	29 27.7	14 8.6	21 3.7	7 6.3	18 47.8	10 47.5	12 48.5
6 M	6 58 55.3	14 50.0	9 52.9	27 48.3	4 30.8	0♐14.4	14 54.7	21 13.9	7 1.9	18 45.5	10 47.7	12 47.3
7 T	7 2 51.8	15 51.1	9 49.7	13♋ 0.9	6 3.8	1 2.1	15 40.9	21 24.0	6 57.6	18 43.3	10 47.9	12 46.1
8 W	7 6 48.4	16 52.2	9 46.5	28 11.0	7 37.2	1 50.7	16 27.1	21 34.1	6 53.1	18 41.1	10 48.1	12 44.9
9 T	7 10 45.0	17 53.3	9 43.3	13♌ 8.7	9 11.0	2 40.1	17 13.3	21 44.0	6 48.6	18 39.0	10 48.2	12 43.6
10 F	7 14 41.5	18 54.5	9 40.2	27 45.4	10 45.2	3 30.4	17 59.6	21 53.8	6 44.1	18 36.9	10 48.3	12 42.4
11 S	7 18 38.1	19 55.6	9 37.0	11♍55.4	12 19.8	4 21.4	18 45.9	22 3.5	6 39.5	18 34.8	10 48.4	12 41.1
12 S	7 22 34.6	20 56.7	9 33.8	25 36.1	13 54.9	5 13.2	19 32.2	22 13.1	6 34.9	18 32.7	10 48.4	12 39.8
13 M	7 26 31.2	21 57.8	9 30.6	8♎48.0	15 30.4	6 5.8	20 18.6	22 22.6	6 30.3	18 30.7	10R48.4	12 38.5
14 T	7 30 27.7	22 59.0	9 27.5	21 33.8	17 6.5	6 59.0	21 5.0	22 32.0	6 25.6	18 28.7	10 48.4	12 37.2
15 W	7 34 24.3	24 0.1	9 24.3	3♏57.7	18 42.9	7 52.9	21 51.5	22 41.3	6 20.8	18 26.8	10 48.3	12 35.9
16 T	7 38 20.9	25 1.2	9 21.1	16 4.7	20 19.9	8 47.5	22 38.0	22 50.5	6 16.1	18 24.9	10 48.2	12 34.6
17 F	7 42 17.4	26 2.3	9 17.9	27 59.9	21 57.4	9 42.6	23 24.5	22 59.5	6 11.3	18 23.0	10 48.1	12 33.2
18 S	7 46 14.0	27 3.4	9 14.7	9♐48.3	23 35.4	10 38.4	24 11.1	23 8.4	6 6.5	18 21.1	10 47.9	12 31.9
19 S	7 50 10.5	28 4.5	9 11.6	21 34.1	25 14.0	11 34.8	24 57.6	23 17.3	6 1.6	18 19.3	10 47.7	12 30.5
20 M	7 54 7.1	29 5.6	9 8.4	3♑21.3	26 53.1	12 31.7	25 44.3	23 26.0	5 56.8	18 17.6	10 47.4	12 29.2
21 T	7 58 3.7	0♒ 6.7	9 5.2	15 12.7	28 32.8	13 29.1	26 30.9	23 34.6	5 51.9	18 15.8	10 47.1	12 27.8
22 W	8 2 0.2	1 7.8	9 2.0	27 10.6	0♒13.1	14 27.0	27 17.6	23 43.0	5 47.0	18 14.1	10 46.8	12 26.4
23 T	8 5 56.8	2 8.9	8 58.9	9♒16.7	1 53.9	15 25.4	28 4.3	23 51.4	5 42.1	18 12.5	10 46.5	12 25.1
24 F	8 9 53.3	3 9.9	8 55.7	21 32.1	3 35.4	16 24.3	28 51.0	23 59.6	5 37.1	18 10.9	10 46.1	12 23.7
25 S	8 13 49.9	4 10.9	8 52.5	3♓57.5	5 17.4	17 23.6	29 37.8	24 7.6	5 32.2	18 9.3	10 45.7	12 22.3
26 S	8 17 46.4	5 12.0	8 49.3	16 33.8	7 0.0	18 23.4	0♒24.6	24 15.6	5 27.3	18 7.8	10 45.3	12 20.9
27 M	8 21 43.0	6 13.0	8 46.2	29 21.9	8 43.2	19 23.5	1 11.4	24 23.4	5 22.4	18 6.3	10 44.8	12 19.5
28 T	8 25 39.5	7 14.0	8 43.0	12♈23.1	10 27.0	20 24.1	1 58.2	24 31.1	5 17.4	18 4.9	10 44.3	12 18.1
29 W	8 29 36.1	8 14.9	8 39.8	25 39.1	12 11.4	21 25.1	2 45.1	24 38.6	5 12.5	18 3.5	10 43.7	12 16.7
30 T	8 33 32.7	9 15.9	8 36.6	9♉11.5	13 56.3	22 26.4	3 32.0	24 46.1	5 7.6	18 2.2	10 43.2	12 15.3
31 F	8 37 29.2	10 16.8	8 33.5	23 2.1	15 41.7	23 28.1	4 18.9	24 53.3	5 2.7	18 0.9	10 42.6	12 13.9

DECLINATION

DAY	EPHEMERIS SIDEREAL TIME h m s	☉	☊	☽	☿	♀	♂	♃	♄	♅	♆	♇
1 W	6 39 12.5	23S 5.4	21N58.7	2N11.1	23S51.2	15S30.0	23S51.4	16S53.2	18N57.3	23N 4.5	2S53.0	23N31.8
4 S	6 51 2.2	22 49.9	21 57.3	18 30.0	24 12.6	15 54.2	23 39.8	17 1.3	19 0.8	23 3.9	2 53.3	23 33.3
7 T	7 2 51.8	22 30.3	21 55.9	25 31.7	24 22.8	16 20.8	23 25.8	17 9.0	19 4.5	23 3.4	2 53.4	23 34.8
10 F	7 14 41.5	22 6.7	21 54.5	16 59.1	24 21.0	16 48.8	23 9.5	17 16.5	19 8.3	23 2.9	2 53.4	23 36.4
13 M	7 26 31.2	21 39.3	21 53.0	0 43.6	24 6.8	17 17.5	22 50.8	17 23.6	19 12.1	23 2.4	2 53.2	23 37.9
16 T	7 38 20.9	21 8.1	21 51.6	14S33.7	23 39.8	17 46.3	22 29.8	17 30.4	19 16.0	23 1.9	2 53.0	23 39.5
19 S	7 50 10.5	20 33.2	21 50.2	24 7.6	22 59.6	18 14.4	22 6.5	17 36.8	19 19.9	23 1.4	2 52.6	23 41.0
22 W	8 2 0.2	19 54.8	21 48.7	24 22.1	22 5.8	18 41.2	21 40.9	17 42.9	19 23.9	23 1.0	2 52.2	23 42.6
25 S	8 13 49.9	19 13.1	21 47.2	14 46.2	20 58.3	19 6.2	21 13.2	17 48.7	19 27.8	23 0.6	2 51.6	23 44.1
28 T	8 25 39.5	18 28.2	21 45.8	0N56.1	19 36.9	19 28.9	20 43.3	17 54.1	19 31.8	23 0.2	2 50.9	23 45.6
31 F	8 37 29.2	17 40.3	21 44.3	17 6.8	18 1.8	19 48.9	20 11.3	17 59.1	19 35.6	22 59.9	2 50.0	23 47.1

FEBRUARY 1947

LONGITUDE

DAY	EPHEMERIS SIDEREAL TIME h m s	☉ ° ′	☊ ° ′	☽ ° ′	☿ ° ′	♀ ° ′	♂ ° ′	♃ ° ′	♄ ° ′	♅ ° ′	♆ ° ′	♇ ° ′
1 S	8 41 25.8	11♒17.7	8♊30.3	7♊11.6	17♒27.5	24♐30.1	5♒ 5.8	25♏ 0.4	4♌57.8	17♊59.6	10♎41.9	12♌12.4
2 S	8 45 22.3	12 18.6	8 27.1	21 39.4	19 13.8	25 32.5	5 52.7	25 7.4	4R52.9	17R58.4	10R41.3	12R11.0
3 M	8 49 18.9	13 19.4	8 23.9	6♋22.6	21 0.4	26 35.2	6 39.7	25 14.3	4 48.1	17 57.3	10 40.6	12 9.6
4 T	8 53 15.5	14 20.3	8 20.7	21 16.0	22 47.2	27 38.3	7 26.7	25 21.0	4 43.3	17 56.2	10 39.9	12 8.2
5 W	8 57 12.0	15 21.1	8 17.6	6♌12.0	24 34.1	28 41.6	8 13.6	25 27.5	4 38.5	17 55.1	10 39.1	12 6.8
6 T	9 1 8.5	16 21.9	8 14.4	21 1.8	26 21.0	29 45.2	9 0.7	25 34.0	4 33.7	17 54.1	10 38.3	12 5.4
7 F	9 5 5.1	17 22.7	8 11.2	5♍36.6	28 7.8	0♑49.1	9 47.7	25 40.2	4 28.9	17 53.1	10 37.5	12 4.0
8 S	9 9 1.7	18 23.4	8 8.0	19 49.3	29 54.1	1 53.3	10 34.7	25 46.3	4 24.2	17 52.2	10 36.6	12 2.6
9 S	9 12 58.2	19 24.2	8 4.9	3♎35.5	1♓39.9	2 57.8	11 21.8	25 52.3	4 19.6	17 51.4	10 35.8	12 1.2
10 M	9 16 54.8	20 24.9	8 1.7	16 53.6	3 24.8	4 2.5	12 8.9	25 58.1	4 14.9	17 50.6	10 34.9	11 59.8
11 T	9 20 51.3	21 25.6	7 58.5	29 45.0	5 8.5	5 7.5	12 56.0	26 3.7	4 10.3	17 49.8	10 33.9	11 58.4
12 W	9 24 47.9	22 26.3	7 55.3	12♏13.1	6 50.6	6 12.8	13 43.1	26 9.2	4 5.8	17 49.1	10 33.0	11 57.0
13 T	9 28 44.4	23 26.9	7 52.2	24 22.5	8 30.8	7 18.2	14 30.3	26 14.6	4 1.3	17 48.4	10 32.0	11 55.6
14 F	9 32 41.0	24 27.6	7 49.0	6♐18.8	10 8.5	8 23.9	15 17.4	26 19.7	3 56.8	17 47.8	10 31.0	11 54.3
15 S	9 36 37.5	25 28.2	7 45.8	18 7.5	11 43.3	9 29.8	16 4.6	26 24.7	3 52.4	17 47.3	10 30.0	11 52.9
16 S	9 40 34.1	26 28.8	7 42.6	29 54.0	13 14.6	10 36.0	16 51.8	26 29.6	3 48.0	17 46.8	10 28.9	11 51.5
17 M	9 44 30.7	27 29.4	7 39.4	11♑43.1	14 41.8	11 42.3	17 39.0	26 34.3	3 43.7	17 46.3	10 27.8	11 50.2
18 T	9 48 27.2	28 30.0	7 36.3	23 38.9	16 4.2	12 48.8	18 26.2	26 38.8	3 39.5	17 45.9	10 26.7	11 48.8
19 W	9 52 23.8	29 30.5	7 33.1	5♒44.6	17 21.2	13 55.5	19 13.4	26 43.1	3 35.3	17 45.6	10 25.6	11 47.5
20 T	9 56 20.3	0♓31.0	7 29.9	18 2.2	18 32.1	15 2.4	20 0.6	26 47.3	3 31.2	17 45.3	10 24.4	11 46.2
21 F	10 0 16.9	1 31.5	7 26.7	0♓32.7	19 36.3	16 9.4	20 47.9	26 51.3	3 27.1	17 45.1	10 23.2	11 44.8
22 S	10 4 13.4	2 32.0	7 23.6	13 16.4	20 33.0	17 16.7	21 35.1	26 55.1	3 23.1	17 44.9	10 22.0	11 43.5
23 S	10 8 10.0	3 32.4	7 20.4	26 12.5	21 21.7	18 24.1	22 22.3	26 58.7	3 19.2	17 44.8	10 20.8	11 42.2
24 M	10 12 6.5	4 32.8	7 17.2	9♈20.2	22 1.8	19 31.6	23 9.6	27 2.2	3 15.3	17 44.7	10 19.5	11 41.0
25 T	10 16 3.1	5 33.2	7 14.0	22 38.7	22 32.8	20 39.3	23 56.8	27 5.5	3 11.6	17 44.7	10 18.2	11 39.7
26 W	10 19 59.6	6 33.5	7 10.8	6♉ 7.4	22 54.4	21 47.1	24 44.1	27 8.6	3 7.9	17D44.7	10 17.0	11 38.4
27 T	10 23 56.2	7 33.8	7 7.7	19 46.3	23 6.4	22 55.1	25 31.4	27 11.6	3 4.3	17 44.8	10 15.6	11 37.2
28 F	10 27 52.8	8 34.1	7 4.5	3♊35.8	23 8.6	24 3.2	26 18.6	27 14.3	3 0.7	17 44.9	10 14.3	11 35.9

DECLINATION

DAY	EPHEMERIS SIDEREAL TIME h m s	☉	☊	☽	☿	♀	♂	♃	♄	♅	♆	♇
1 S	8 41 25.8	17S23.7	21N43.8	21N17.4	17S27.1	19S54.9	20S 0.2	18S 0.7	19N36.9	22N59.8	2S49.7	23N47.6
4 T	8 53 15.5	16 32.1	21 42.3	25 5.5	15 34.4	20 10.5	19 25.6	18 5.3	19 40.7	22 59.5	2 48.8	23 49.0
7 F	9 5 5.1	15 37.9	21 40.8	14 8.0	13 29.7	20 22.6	18 49.1	18 9.5	19 44.4	22 59.2	2 47.7	23 50.4
10 M	9 16 54.8	14 41.3	21 39.2	2S57.9	11 15.3	20 30.6	18 10.8	18 13.3	19 48.0	22 59.0	2 46.6	23 51.8
13 T	9 28 44.4	13 42.5	21 37.7	17 39.7	8 54.8	20 34.5	17 30.7	18 16.8	19 51.5	22 58.8	2 45.3	23 53.1
16 S	9 40 34.1	12 41.6	21 36.2	25 17.3	6 33.7	20 33.9	16 49.0	18 19.9	19 54.8	22 58.7	2 44.0	23 54.3
19 W	9 52 23.8	11 38.9	21 34.6	22 56.5	4 20.1	20 28.7	16 5.6	18 22.6	19 58.0	22 58.6	2 42.6	23 55.6
22 S	10 4 13.4	10 34.5	21 33.1	11 9.8	2 23.8	20 18.7	15 20.8	18 25.0	20 1.1	22 58.5	2 41.1	23 56.7
25 T	10 16 3.1	9 28.7	21 31.5	5N33.0	0 55.2	20 3.9	14 34.5	18 27.0	20 4.0	22 58.5	2 39.5	23 57.8
28 F	10 27 52.8	8 21.6	21 29.9	20 35.8	0 3.8	19 44.2	13 46.9	18 28.6	20 6.6	22 58.6	2 37.8	23 58.9

MARCH 1947

LONGITUDE

DAY	EPHEMERIS SIDEREAL TIME h m s	☉ ° ′	☊ ° ′	☽ ° ′	☿ ° ′	♀ ° ′	♂ ° ′	♃ ° ′	♄ ° ′	♅ ° ′	♆ ° ′	♇ ° ′
1 S	10 31 49.3	9♓34.4	7♊ 1.3	17♊36.2	23♓ 1.1	25♑11.4	27♒ 5.9	27♏16.9	2♌57.2	17♊45.1	10♎12.9	11♌34.7
2 S	10 35 45.9	10 34.6	6 58.1	1♋47.5	22R44.3	26 19.8	27 53.1	27 19.3	2R53.9	17 45.4	10R11.6	11R33.5
3 M	10 39 42.4	11 34.7	6 55.0	16 8.4	22 18.6	27 28.3	28 40.4	27 21.5	2 50.6	17 45.7	10 10.2	11 32.3
4 T	10 43 39.0	12 34.9	6 51.8	0♌36.0	21 44.6	28 36.9	29 27.6	27 23.6	2 47.4	17 46.0	10 8.8	11 31.1
5 W	10 47 35.5	13 35.0	6 48.6	15 5.9	21 3.2	29 45.7	0♓14.9	27 25.4	2 44.3	17 46.4	10 7.3	11 30.0
6 T	10 51 32.1	14 35.1	6 45.4	29 32.0	20 15.6	0♒54.5	1 2.1	27 27.1	2 41.2	17 46.9	10 5.9	11 28.8
7 F	10 55 28.6	15 35.1	6 42.2	13♍47.8	19 22.8	2 3.5	1 49.4	27 28.6	2 38.3	17 47.4	10 4.4	11 27.7
8 S	10 59 25.2	16 35.1	6 39.1	27 47.1	18 26.2	3 12.6	2 36.6	27 29.9	2 35.4	17 48.0	10 3.0	11 26.6
9 S	11 3 21.8	17 35.1	6 35.9	11♎25.5	17 27.2	4 21.8	3 23.9	27 31.0	2 32.7	17 48.6	10 1.5	11 25.5
10 M	11 7 18.3	18 35.0	6 32.7	24 40.5	16 27.3	5 31.1	4 11.1	27 31.9	2 30.0	17 49.3	9 60.0	11 24.4
11 T	11 11 14.8	19 34.9	6 29.5	7♏32.0	15 27.7	6 40.5	4 58.3	27 32.6	2 27.5	17 50.0	9 58.5	11 23.3
12 W	11 15 11.4	20 34.8	6 26.4	20 1.9	14 29.7	7 50.0	5 45.6	27 33.2	2 25.0	17 50.8	9 56.9	11 22.3
13 T	11 19 8.0	21 34.7	6 23.2	2♐14.0	13 34.5	8 59.6	6 32.8	27 33.6	2 22.6	17 51.6	9 55.4	11 21.3
14 F	11 23 4.5	22 34.5	6 20.0	14 12.7	12 43.2	10 9.3	7 20.0	27 33.8	2 20.4	17 52.5	9 53.9	11 20.2
15 S	11 27 1.1	23 34.3	6 16.8	26 3.6	11 56.4	11 19.1	8 7.2	27R33.7	2 18.2	17 53.4	9 52.3	11 19.3
16 S	11 30 57.6	24 34.1	6 13.6	7♑52.0	11 14.8	12 29.0	8 54.4	27 33.5	2 16.1	17 54.4	9 50.7	11 18.3
17 M	11 34 54.2	25 33.9	6 10.5	19 43.4	10 39.0	13 38.9	9 41.6	27 33.2	2 14.1	17 55.4	9 49.1	11 17.3
18 T	11 38 50.7	26 33.6	6 7.3	1♒42.6	10 9.2	14 49.0	10 28.8	27 32.6	2 12.3	17 56.5	9 47.5	11 16.4
19 W	11 42 47.3	27 33.3	6 4.1	13 53.9	9 45.7	15 59.1	11 16.0	27 31.8	2 10.5	17 57.7	9 45.9	11 15.5
20 T	11 46 43.8	28 32.9	6 0.9	26 20.3	9 28.4	17 9.3	12 3.1	27 30.9	2 8.8	17 58.8	9 44.3	11 14.6
21 F	11 50 40.4	29 32.6	5 57.8	9♓ 3.5	9 17.3	18 19.6	12 50.3	27 29.7	2 7.3	18 0.1	9 42.7	11 13.7
22 S	11 54 36.9	0♈32.2	5 54.6	22 4.1	9 12.3	19 29.9	13 37.4	27 28.4	2 5.9	18 1.4	9 41.1	11 12.9
23 S	11 58 33.5	1 31.7	5 51.4	5♈21.1	9D13.3	20 40.3	14 24.5	27 26.9	2 4.5	18 2.7	9 39.4	11 12.1
24 M	12 2 30.0	2 31.3	5 48.2	18 52.4	9 20.0	21 50.8	15 11.6	27 25.2	2 3.3	18 4.1	9 37.8	11 11.3
25 T	12 6 26.6	3 30.7	5 45.0	2♉35.4	9 32.2	23 1.3	15 58.7	27 23.3	2 2.2	18 5.5	9 36.2	11 10.5
26 W	12 10 23.1	4 30.2	5 41.9	16 27.3	9 49.6	24 11.9	16 45.8	27 21.2	2 1.1	18 7.0	9 34.5	11 9.8
27 T	12 14 19.7	5 29.6	5 38.7	0♊25.6	10 12.0	25 22.6	17 32.8	27 19.0	2 0.2	18 8.6	9 32.9	11 9.0
28 F	12 18 16.3	6 29.0	5 35.5	14 28.3	10 39.2	26 33.3	18 19.9	27 16.5	1 59.4	18 10.2	9 31.2	11 8.3
29 S	12 22 12.8	7 28.4	5 32.3	28 34.0	11 10.8	27 44.0	19 6.9	27 13.9	1 58.8	18 11.8	9 29.6	11 7.6
30 S	12 26 9.3	8 27.7	5 29.1	12♋41.6	11 46.6	28 54.8	19 53.9	27 11.1	1 58.2	18 13.5	9 27.9	11 7.0
31 M	12 30 5.9	9 26.9	5 26.0	26 50.1	12 26.4	0♓ 5.7	20 40.8	27 8.1	1 57.7	18 15.2	9 26.3	11 6.3

DECLINATION

DAY	EPHEMERIS SIDEREAL TIME h m s	☉	☊	☽	☿	♀	♂	♃	♄	♅	♆	♇
1 S	10 31 49.3	7S59.0	21N29.4	23N48.4	0N 3.9	19S36.5	13S30.8	18S29.0	20N 7.5	22N58.6	2S37.3	23N59.2
4 T	10 43 39.0	6 50.4	21 27.8	23 59.4	0S 2.3	19 10.3	12 41.6	18 30.1	20 9.9	22 58.7	2 35.5	24 0.2
7 F	10 55 28.6	5 41.1	21 26.2	10 57.2	0 49.1	18 39.4	11 51.3	18 30.8	20 12.2	22 58.8	2 33.8	24 1.1
10 M	11 7 18.3	4 31.0	21 24.6	6S29.2	2 5.7	18 3.7	11 0.1	18 31.2	20 14.2	22 59.0	2 31.9	24 1.9
13 T	11 19 8.0	3 20.4	21 22.9	20 20.0	3 36.1	17 23.3	10 7.8	18 31.2	20 16.0	22 59.2	2 30.1	24 2.7
16 S	11 30 57.6	2 9.5	21 21.3	25 55.7	5 4.1	16 38.5	9 14.8	18 30.8	20 17.6	22 59.5	2 28.2	24 3.4
19 W	11 42 47.3	0 58.4	21 19.7	21 9.8	6 18.2	15 49.5	8 21.0	18 30.1	20 19.0	22 59.8	2 26.2	24 4.0
22 S	11 54 36.9	0N12.8	21 18.0	7 34.3	7 12.4	14 56.3	7 26.5	18 28.9	20 20.1	23 0.2	2 24.3	24 4.5
25 T	12 6 26.6	1 23.8	21 16.3	9N52.1	7 44.7	13 59.3	6 31.5	18 27.4	20 21.1	23 0.6	2 22.3	24 5.0
28 F	12 18 16.3	2 34.5	21 14.7	23 27.4	7 55.7	12 58.7	5 36.0	18 25.6	20 21.8	23 1.0	2 20.3	24 5.4
31 M	12 30 5.9	3 44.7	21 13.0	24 47.3	7 46.8	11 54.7	4 40.2	18 23.4	20 22.2	23 1.4	2 18.4	24 5.7

APRIL 1947

LONGITUDE

DAY	EPHEMERIS SIDEREAL TIME h m s	☉ ° ′	☊ ° ′	☽ ° ′	☿ ° ′	♀ ° ′	♂ ° ′	♃ ° ′	♄ ° ′	♅ ° ′	♆ ° ′	♇ ° ′
1 T	12 34 2.5	10♈26.2	5♊22.8	10♌57.6	13♓ 9.9	1♓16.6	21♓27.8	27♏ 5.0	1♌57.4	18♊17.0	9♎24.6	11♌ 5.7
2 W	12 37 59.0	11 25.3	5 19.6	25 1.9	13 57.0	2 27.6	22 14.7	27R 1.7	1R57.1	18 18.8	9R23.0	11R 5.2
3 T	12 41 55.6	12 24.5	5 16.4	8♍60.0	14 47.5	3 38.6	23 1.6	26 58.2	1 57.0	18 20.6	9 21.3	11 4.6
4 F	12 45 52.1	13 23.6	5 13.3	22 48.2	15 41.1	4 49.7	23 48.4	26 54.5	1 56.9	18 22.5	9 19.7	11 4.1
5 S	12 49 48.7	14 22.7	5 10.1	6♎23.1	16 37.8	6 0.8	24 35.3	26 50.7	1D57.0	18 24.5	9 18.0	11 3.5
6 S	12 53 45.2	15 21.7	5 6.9	19 41.9	17 37.3	7 11.9	25 22.1	26 46.7	1 57.2	18 26.5	9 16.4	11 3.1
7 M	12 57 41.8	16 20.7	5 3.7	2♏42.8	18 39.6	8 23.1	26 8.9	26 42.6	1 57.5	18 28.5	9 14.7	11 2.6
8 T	13 1 38.3	17 19.7	5 0.6	15 25.5	19 44.4	9 34.4	26 55.7	26 38.2	1 57.9	18 30.6	9 13.1	11 2.2
9 W	13 5 34.9	18 18.6	4 57.4	27 50.9	20 51.7	10 45.7	27 42.4	26 33.8	1 58.4	18 32.7	9 11.5	11 1.8
10 T	13 9 31.5	19 17.6	4 54.2	10♐ 1.4	22 1.4	11 57.0	28 29.1	26 29.1	1 59.1	18 34.9	9 9.9	11 1.4
11 F	13 13 28.0	20 16.5	4 51.0	22 0.5	23 13.4	13 8.4	29 15.8	26 24.3	1 59.8	18 37.1	9 8.2	11 1.0
12 S	13 17 24.5	21 15.3	4 47.8	3♑52.5	24 27.6	14 19.8	0♈ 2.5	26 19.4	2 0.7	18 39.3	9 6.6	11 0.7
13 S	13 21 21.1	22 14.1	4 44.7	15 42.3	25 43.9	15 31.3	0 49.1	26 14.3	2 1.6	18 41.6	9 5.0	11 0.4
14 M	13 25 17.6	23 12.9	4 41.5	27 34.9	27 2.3	16 42.8	1 35.7	26 9.1	2 2.7	18 43.9	9 3.4	11 0.1
15 T	13 29 14.2	24 11.7	4 38.3	9♒35.4	28 22.6	17 54.3	2 22.3	26 3.7	2 3.8	18 46.3	9 1.8	10 59.9
16 W	13 33 10.8	25 10.4	4 35.1	21 48.6	29 44.9	19 5.9	3 8.9	25 58.2	2 5.1	18 48.7	9 0.3	10 59.6
17 T	13 37 7.3	26 9.1	4 32.0	4♓18.5	1♈ 9.1	20 17.5	3 55.4	25 52.5	2 6.5	18 51.1	8 58.7	10 59.4
18 F	13 41 3.9	27 7.8	4 28.8	17 8.1	2 35.1	21 29.2	4 41.9	25 46.8	2 8.0	18 53.6	8 57.1	10 59.3
19 S	13 45 0.4	28 6.5	4 25.6	0♈18.9	4 3.0	22 40.8	5 28.4	25 40.8	2 9.6	18 56.1	8 55.6	10 59.1
20 S	13 48 57.0	29 5.1	4 22.4	13 50.9	5 32.7	23 52.6	6 14.8	25 34.8	2 11.3	18 58.6	8 54.1	10 59.0
21 M	13 52 53.5	0♉ 3.7	4 19.2	27 42.1	7 4.1	25 4.3	7 1.2	25 28.7	2 13.1	19 1.2	8 52.5	10 58.9
22 T	13 56 50.1	1 2.3	4 16.1	11♉49.2	8 37.3	26 16.0	7 47.5	25 22.4	2 15.0	19 3.8	8 51.0	10 58.9
23 W	14 0 46.6	2 0.8	4 12.9	26 7.5	10 12.3	27 27.8	8 33.8	25 16.0	2 17.0	19 6.5	8 49.5	10 58.8
24 T	14 4 43.2	2 59.3	4 9.7	10♊32.1	11 49.0	28 39.6	9 20.1	25 9.5	2 19.2	19 9.2	8 48.1	10 58.8
25 F	14 8 39.8	3 57.7	4 6.5	24 58.2	13 27.4	29 51.5	10 6.4	25 2.9	2 21.4	19 11.9	8 46.6	10D58.9
26 S	14 12 36.3	4 56.2	4 3.4	9♋21.6	15 7.6	1♈ 3.3	10 52.6	24 56.2	2 23.7	19 14.7	8 45.1	10 58.9
27 S	14 16 32.9	5 54.5	4 0.2	23 38.9	16 49.5	2 15.2	11 38.7	24 49.4	2 26.2	19 17.4	8 43.7	10 59.0
28 M	14 20 29.4	6 52.9	3 57.0	7♌47.9	18 33.1	3 27.1	12 24.8	24 42.5	2 28.7	19 20.3	8 42.3	10 59.1
29 T	14 24 26.0	7 51.2	3 53.8	21 46.9	20 18.5	4 39.0	13 10.9	24 35.6	2 31.3	19 23.1	8 40.9	10 59.2
30 W	14 28 22.5	8 49.5	3 50.7	5♍34.6	22 5.7	5 51.0	13 57.0	24 28.5	2 34.1	19 26.0	8 39.5	10 59.4

DECLINATION

DAY	EPHEMERIS SIDEREAL TIME h m s	☉	☊	☽	☿	♀	♂	♃	♄	♅	♆	♇
1 T	12 34 2.5	4N 8.0	21N12.4	22N 0.1	7S39.7	11S32.7	4S21.5	18S22.5	20N22.3	23N 1.6	2S17.7	24N 5.8
4 F	12 45 52.1	5 17.3	21 10.7	7 17.4	7 6.9	10 24.7	3 25.4	18 19.9	20 22.5	23 2.1	2 15.8	24 6.0
7 M	12 57 41.8	6 25.8	21 9.0	9S57.3	6 18.1	9 13.9	2 29.0	18 16.9	20 22.5	23 2.6	2 13.8	24 6.1
10 T	13 9 31.5	7 33.3	21 7.3	22 33.9	5 14.8	8 0.6	1 32.6	18 13.6	20 22.2	23 3.2	2 11.9	24 6.1
13 S	13 21 21.1	8 39.6	21 5.5	25 59.9	3 58.2	6 45.2	0 36.2	18 9.9	20 21.7	23 3.8	2 10.0	24 6.1
16 W	13 33 10.8	9 44.7	21 3.8	19 2.6	2 29.4	5 27.8	0N20.2	18 6.0	20 20.9	23 4.4	2 8.2	24 6.0
19 S	13 45 0.4	10 48.3	21 2.0	4 6.1	0 49.4	4 8.8	1 16.4	18 1.8	20 20.0	23 5.0	2 6.4	24 5.8
22 T	13 56 50.1	11 50.3	21 0.3	13N36.6	1N 0.8	2 48.6	2 12.3	17 57.3	20 18.8	23 5.7	2 4.6	24 5.6
25 F	14 8 39.8	12 50.6	20 58.5	25 19.9	3 0.2	1 27.2	3 7.9	17 52.6	20 17.4	23 6.3	2 2.9	24 5.2
28 M	14 20 29.4	13 49.0	20 56.7	22 54.5	5 7.9	0 5.2	4 3.0	17 47.7	20 15.8	23 7.0	2 1.2	24 4.8

MAY 1947

DAY	EPHEMERIS SIDEREAL TIME	☉	☊	☽	☿	♀	♂	♃	♄	♅	♆	♇
	h m s	° ′	° ′	° ′	° ′	° ′	° ′	° ′	° ′	° ′	° ′	° ′
						LONGITUDE						
1 T	14 32 19.1	9♉47.7	3♊47.5	19♍10.1	23♈54.6	7♈ 2.9	14♈42.9	24♏21.4	2♌36.9	19♊28.9	8♎38.1	10♌59.6
2 F	14 36 15.6	10 46.0	3 44.3	2♎32.8	25 45.3	8 14.9	15 28.9	24R14.2	2 39.8	19 31.8	8R36.8	10 59.8
3 S	14 40 12.2	11 44.1	3 41.1	15 41.9	27 37.7	9 26.9	16 14.8	24 7.0	2 42.8	19 34.8	8 35.5	11 0.0
4 S	14 44 8.8	12 42.3	3 37.9	28 37.1	29 31.9	10 39.0	17 0.7	23 59.7	2 45.9	19 37.8	8 34.2	11 0.3
5 M	14 48 5.3	13 40.4	3 34.8	11♏18.3	1♉27.9	11 51.0	17 46.5	23 52.3	2 49.2	19 40.8	8 32.9	11 0.6
6 T	14 52 1.9	14 38.5	3 31.6	23 46.0	3 25.6	13 3.1	18 32.3	23 44.9	2 52.5	19 43.9	8 31.6	11 0.9
7 W	14 55 58.4	15 36.6	3 28.4	6♐ 1.3	5 25.0	14 15.2	19 18.0	23 37.4	2 55.9	19 46.9	8 30.4	11 1.2
8 T	14 59 55.0	16 34.6	3 25.2	18 5.9	7 26.2	15 27.3	20 3.7	23 29.9	2 59.4	19 50.0	8 29.1	11 1.6
9 F	15 3 51.5	17 32.6	3 22.1	0♑ 2.4	9 28.9	16 39.4	20 49.4	23 22.4	3 2.9	19 53.2	8 27.9	11 2.0
10 S	15 7 48.1	18 30.6	3 18.9	11 53.8	11 33.2	17 51.6	21 35.0	23 14.8	3 6.6	19 56.3	8 26.8	11 2.4
11 S	15 11 44.6	19 28.6	3 15.7	23 43.8	13 38.9	19 3.8	22 20.6	23 7.2	3 10.4	19 59.5	8 25.6	11 2.9
12 M	15 15 41.2	20 26.5	3 12.5	5♒36.7	15 46.0	20 16.0	23 6.1	22 59.6	3 14.2	20 2.7	8 24.5	11 3.4
13 T	15 19 37.7	21 24.5	3 9.3	17 37.0	17 54.3	21 28.2	23 51.6	22 52.0	3 18.2	20 5.9	8 23.3	11 3.9
14 W	15 23 34.3	22 22.4	3 6.2	29 49.4	20 3.6	22 40.5	24 37.0	22 44.3	3 22.2	20 9.1	8 22.3	11 4.4
15 T	15 27 30.9	23 20.3	3 3.0	12♓18.2	22 13.8	23 52.7	25 22.4	22 36.7	3 26.3	20 12.4	8 21.2	11 5.0
16 F	15 31 27.4	24 18.1	2 59.8	25 7.4	24 24.5	25 5.0	26 7.7	22 29.0	3 30.5	20 15.6	8 20.1	11 5.5
17 S	15 35 24.0	25 16.0	2 56.6	8♈19.8	26 35.7	26 17.3	26 53.0	22 21.4	3 34.8	20 18.9	8 19.1	11 6.1
18 S	15 39 20.5	26 13.8	2 53.5	21 56.9	28 47.0	27 29.7	27 38.3	22 13.8	3 39.2	20 22.3	8 18.1	11 6.8
19 M	15 43 17.1	27 11.6	2 50.3	5♉58.0	0♊58.2	28 42.0	28 23.5	22 6.2	3 43.6	20 25.6	8 17.2	11 7.4
20 T	15 47 13.6	28 9.4	2 47.1	20 20.6	3 8.9	29 54.3	29 8.6	21 58.6	3 48.2	20 28.9	8 16.2	11 8.1
21 W	15 51 10.2	29 7.1	2 43.9	4♊59.6	5 18.9	1♉ 6.7	29 53.7	21 51.0	3 52.8	20 32.3	8 15.3	11 8.8
22 T	15 55 6.8	0♊ 4.9	2 40.8	19 48.6	7 28.0	2 19.1	0♉38.8	21 43.5	3 57.5	20 35.7	8 14.4	11 9.6
23 F	15 59 3.3	1 2.6	2 37.6	4♋40.2	9 35.8	3 31.5	1 23.8	21 36.0	4 2.3	20 39.1	8 13.6	11 10.3
24 S	16 2 59.8	2 0.3	2 34.4	19 27.1	11 42.0	4 43.9	2 8.7	21 28.6	4 7.1	20 42.5	8 12.8	11 11.1
25 S	16 6 56.4	2 57.9	2 31.2	4♌ 2.9	13 46.6	5 56.3	2 53.6	21 21.2	4 12.1	20 45.9	8 12.0	11 11.9
26 M	16 10 53.0	3 55.5	2 28.0	18 23.0	15 49.2	7 8.8	3 38.4	21 13.8	4 17.1	20 49.4	8 11.2	11 12.8
27 T	16 14 49.5	4 53.2	2 24.9	2♍24.7	17 49.8	8 21.2	4 23.2	21 6.6	4 22.1	20 52.8	8 10.4	11 13.6
28 W	16 18 46.1	5 50.8	2 21.7	16 6.9	19 48.1	9 33.7	5 7.9	20 59.4	4 27.3	20 56.3	8 9.7	11 14.5
29 T	16 22 42.6	6 48.3	2 18.5	29 30.1	21 44.0	10 46.2	5 52.6	20 52.2	4 32.5	20 59.8	8 9.0	11 15.4
30 F	16 26 39.2	7 45.9	2 15.3	12♎35.3	23 37.4	11 58.7	6 37.2	20 45.2	4 37.8	21 3.3	8 8.4	11 16.3
31 S	16 30 35.8	8 43.4	2 12.2	25 24.5	25 28.2	13 11.2	7 21.7	20 38.2	4 43.2	21 6.8	8 7.8	11 17.3

DAY	EPHEMERIS SIDEREAL TIME	☉	☊	☽	☿	♀	♂	♃	♄	♅	♆	♇
						DECLINATION						
1 T	14 32 19.1	14N45.3	20N55.0	8N54.4	7N22.6	1N17.2	4N57.7	17S42.6	20N14.0	23N 7.7	1S59.7	24N 4.4
4 S	14 44 8.8	15 39.4	20 53.2	8S14.4	9 42.9	2 39.8	5 51.7	17 37.4	20 12.0	23 8.5	1 58.2	24 3.8
7 W	14 55 58.4	16 31.2	20 51.3	21 38.2	12 6.6	4 2.2	6 45.2	17 32.0	20 9.8	23 9.2	1 56.7	24 3.2
10 S	15 7 48.1	17 20.5	20 49.5	26 15.1	14 30.8	5 24.2	7 37.9	17 26.6	20 7.4	23 9.9	1 55.4	24 2.5
13 T	15 19 37.7	18 7.2	20 47.7	20 24.6	16 51.8	6 45.4	8 29.8	17 21.0	20 4.7	23 10.6	1 54.1	24 1.8
16 F	15 31 27.4	18 51.2	20 45.9	6 25.0	19 4.6	8 5.5	9 20.8	17 15.5	20 1.9	23 11.4	1 53.0	24 1.0
19 M	15 43 17.1	19 32.3	20 44.0	11N16.6	21 3.8	9 24.3	10 10.9	17 9.9	19 58.9	23 12.1	1 51.9	24 0.2
22 T	15 55 6.8	20 10.5	20 42.2	24 37.5	22 44.2	10 41.4	11 0.0	17 4.5	19 55.7	23 12.9	1 50.9	23 59.2
25 S	16 6 56.4	20 45.5	20 40.3	23 45.9	24 2.2	11 56.5	11 48.0	16 59.1	19 52.3	23 13.6	1 50.0	23 58.3
28 W	16 18 46.1	21 17.3	20 38.4	10 12.8	24 56.3	13 9.2	12 34.9	16 53.8	19 48.8	23 14.3	1 49.2	23 57.2
31 S	16 30 35.8	21 45.8	20 36.5	6S50.9	25 26.8	14 19.4	13 20.5	16 48.7	19 45.0	23 15.1	1 48.6	23 56.2

JUNE 1947

DAY	EPHEMERIS SIDEREAL TIME	☉	☊	☽	☿	♀	♂	♃	♄	♅	♆	♇
						LONGITUDE						
1 S	16 34 32.3	9♊40.9	2♊ 9.0	7♏59.5	27♊16.4	14♉23.7	8♉ 6.2	20♏31.3	4♌48.6	21♊10.3	8♎ 7.2	11♌18.3
2 M	16 38 28.9	10 38.3	2 5.8	20 22.2	29 1.9	15 36.2	8 50.7	20R24.5	4 54.1	21 13.8	8R 6.6	11 19.3
3 T	16 42 25.4	11 35.8	2 2.6	2♐34.6	0♋44.7	16 48.8	9 35.1	20 17.8	4 59.7	21 17.3	8 6.0	11 20.3
4 W	16 46 22.0	12 33.2	1 59.5	14 38.5	2 24.6	18 1.3	10 19.4	20 11.1	5 5.4	21 20.8	8 5.5	11 21.3
5 T	16 50 18.5	13 30.7	1 56.3	26 35.8	4 1.8	19 13.9	11 3.7	20 4.6	5 11.1	21 24.4	8 5.1	11 22.4
6 F	16 54 15.1	14 28.1	1 53.1	8♑28.4	5 36.2	20 26.5	11 47.9	19 58.2	5 16.8	21 27.9	8 4.6	11 23.5
7 S	16 58 11.7	15 25.5	1 49.9	20 18.7	7 7.7	21 39.1	12 32.0	19 51.9	5 22.7	21 31.5	8 4.2	11 24.6
8 S	17 2 8.2	16 22.8	1 46.8	2♒ 9.2	8 36.3	22 51.8	13 16.2	19 45.7	5 28.5	21 35.0	8 3.8	11 25.7
9 M	17 6 4.7	17 20.2	1 43.6	14 3.2	10 2.0	24 4.4	14 0.2	19 39.6	5 34.5	21 38.6	8 3.4	11 26.8
10 T	17 10 1.3	18 17.6	1 40.4	26 4.0	11 24.8	25 17.1	14 44.2	19 33.6	5 40.5	21 42.1	8 3.1	11 28.0
11 W	17 13 57.9	19 14.9	1 37.2	8♓15.5	12 44.6	26 29.8	15 28.1	19 27.8	5 46.6	21 45.7	8 2.8	11 29.2
12 T	17 17 54.5	20 12.3	1 34.1	20 41.8	14 1.4	27 42.5	16 12.0	19 22.1	5 52.7	21 49.2	8 2.6	11 30.4
13 F	17 21 51.0	21 9.6	1 30.9	3♈27.1	15 15.1	28 55.3	16 55.9	19 16.5	5 58.9	21 52.8	8 2.3	11 31.6
14 S	17 25 47.5	22 6.9	1 27.7	16 35.0	16 25.7	0♊ 8.0	17 39.6	19 11.0	6 5.1	21 56.4	8 2.1	11 32.9
15 S	17 29 44.1	23 4.3	1 24.5	0♉ 8.2	17 33.1	1 20.8	18 23.3	19 5.7	6 11.4	21 59.9	8 2.0	11 34.2
16 M	17 33 40.7	24 1.6	1 21.3	14 8.0	18 37.3	2 33.6	19 7.0	19 0.6	6 17.8	22 3.5	8 1.8	11 35.4
17 T	17 37 37.3	24 58.9	1 18.2	28 33.4	19 38.2	3 46.4	19 50.6	18 55.5	6 24.2	22 7.1	8 1.7	11 36.8
18 W	17 41 33.8	25 56.2	1 15.0	13♊20.8	20 35.6	4 59.3	20 34.1	18 50.6	6 30.7	22 10.6	8 1.7	11 38.1
19 T	17 45 30.4	26 53.5	1 11.8	28 23.7	21 29.6	6 12.1	21 17.6	18 45.9	6 37.2	22 14.2	8 1.6	11 39.4
20 F	17 49 26.9	27 50.8	1 8.6	13♋33.5	22 20.0	7 25.0	22 1.0	18 41.3	6 43.7	22 17.8	8 1.6	11 40.8
21 S	17 53 23.5	28 48.1	1 5.5	28 40.6	23 6.7	8 37.9	22 44.3	18 36.9	6 50.4	22 21.3	8D 1.6	11 42.2
22 S	17 57 20.0	29 45.3	1 2.3	13♌35.6	23 49.6	9 50.8	23 27.6	18 32.6	6 57.0	22 24.9	8 1.7	11 43.6
23 M	18 1 16.6	0♋42.6	0 59.1	28 11.3	24 28.6	11 3.7	24 10.8	18 28.5	7 3.7	22 28.4	8 1.8	11 45.0
24 T	18 5 13.2	1 39.8	0 55.9	12♍23.0	25 3.6	12 16.6	24 54.0	18 24.6	7 10.5	22 31.9	8 1.9	11 46.4
25 W	18 9 9.7	2 37.1	0 52.8	26 8.7	25 34.5	13 29.5	25 37.1	18 20.8	7 17.3	22 35.5	8 2.1	11 47.8
26 T	18 13 6.3	3 34.3	0 49.6	9♎29.2	26 1.1	14 42.5	26 20.1	18 17.2	7 24.1	22 39.0	8 2.3	11 49.3
27 F	18 17 2.8	4 31.5	0 46.4	22 26.8	26 23.4	15 55.5	27 3.0	18 13.8	7 31.0	22 42.5	8 2.5	11 50.8
28 S	18 20 59.4	5 28.7	0 43.2	5♏ 4.7	26 41.2	17 8.5	27 45.9	18 10.5	7 37.9	22 46.0	8 2.7	11 52.3
29 S	18 24 56.0	6 25.9	0 40.0	17 26.8	26 54.5	18 21.5	28 28.7	18 7.4	7 44.8	22 49.5	8 3.0	11 53.8
30 M	18 28 52.5	7 23.1	0 36.9	29 36.7	27 3.2	19 34.5	29 11.5	18 4.4	7 51.8	22 53.0	8 3.3	11 55.3

DAY	EPHEMERIS SIDEREAL TIME	☉	☊	☽	☿	♀	♂	♃	♄	♅	♆	♇
						DECLINATION						
1 S	16 34 32.3	21N54.6	20N35.9	12S 5.4	25N32.1	14N42.1	13N35.5	16S47.0	19N43.8	23N15.3	1S48.4	23N55.8
4 W	16 46 22.0	22 18.5	20 34.0	23 39.7	25 34.6	15 48.2	14 19.4	16 42.2	19 39.8	23 16.0	1 47.8	23 54.7
7 S	16 58 11.7	22 39.0	20 32.1	25 46.4	25 19.3	16 51.0	15 2.0	16 37.6	19 35.7	23 16.7	1 47.4	23 53.5
10 T	17 10 1.3	22 55.9	20 30.2	17 44.9	24 49.3	17 50.0	15 43.3	16 33.2	19 31.4	23 17.4	1 47.1	23 52.3
13 F	17 21 51.0	23 9.1	20 28.3	2 46.1	24 7.8	18 45.1	16 23.0	16 29.2	19 27.0	23 18.1	1 46.9	23 51.0
16 M	17 33 40.7	23 18.7	20 26.3	14N30.2	23 17.7	19 35.9	17 1.3	16 25.5	19 22.4	23 18.8	1 46.9	23 49.8
19 T	17 45 30.4	23 24.6	20 24.4	25 44.0	22 21.8	20 22.2	17 38.0	16 22.1	19 17.6	23 19.5	1 46.9	23 48.4
22 S	17 57 20.0	23 26.8	20 22.4	21 29.1	21 23.0	21 3.5	18 13.2	16 19.2	19 12.7	23 20.1	1 47.0	23 47.1
25 W	18 9 9.7	23 25.3	20 20.5	5 54.8	20 23.9	21 39.7	18 46.6	16 16.6	19 7.7	23 20.7	1 47.3	23 45.7
28 S	18 20 59.4	23 20.0	20 18.5	10S58.2	19 27.5	22 10.6	19 18.4	16 14.4	19 2.6	23 21.4	1 47.7	23 44.3

JULY 1947

LONGITUDE

DAY	EPHEMERIS SIDEREAL TIME	☉	☊	☽	☿	♀	♂	♃	♄	♅	♆	♇
	h m s	° ′	° ′	° ′	° ′	° ′	° ′	° ′	° ′	° ′	° ′	° ′
1 T	18 32 49.1	8♋20.3	0♊33.7	11♐37.7	27♋ 7.3	20♊47.6	29♉54.2	18♏ 1.7	7♌58.9	22♊56.5	8♎ 3.7	11♌56.8
2 W	18 36 45.6	9 17.5	0 30.5	23 32.7	27R 6.7	22 0.7	0♊36.8	17R59.1	8 5.9	22 59.9	8 4.1	11 58.4
3 T	18 40 42.2	10 14.7	0 27.3	5♑24.4	27 1.5	23 13.8	1 19.4	17 56.7	8 13.0	23 3.4	8 4.5	11 59.9
4 F	18 44 38.7	11 11.8	0 24.2	17 14.7	26 51.8	24 26.9	2 1.9	17 54.4	8 20.2	23 6.8	8 4.9	12 1.5
5 S	18 48 35.3	12 9.0	0 21.0	29 5.6	26 37.6	25 40.0	2 44.3	17 52.4	8 27.4	23 10.2	8 5.4	12 3.1
6 S	18 52 31.9	13 6.2	0 17.8	10♒58.9	26 19.2	26 53.2	3 26.7	17 50.5	8 34.6	23 13.6	8 5.9	12 4.7
7 M	18 56 28.4	14 3.4	0 14.6	22 56.6	25 56.6	28 6.4	4 9.0	17 48.8	8 41.8	23 17.0	8 6.4	12 6.3
8 T	19 0 24.9	15 0.6	0 11.5	5♓ 1.2	25 30.4	29 19.6	4 51.2	17 47.2	8 49.1	23 20.4	8 7.0	12 7.9
9 W	19 4 21.5	15 57.8	0 8.3	17 15.2	25 0.7	0♋32.8	5 33.4	17 45.9	8 56.4	23 23.8	8 7.6	12 9.6
10 T	19 8 18.1	16 55.0	0 5.1	29 41.8	24 28.0	1 46.1	6 15.5	17 44.7	9 3.7	23 27.1	8 8.3	12 11.2
11 F	19 12 14.7	17 52.2	0 1.9	12♈24.6	23 52.9	2 59.3	6 57.6	17 43.7	9 11.0	23 30.4	8 8.9	12 12.9
12 S	19 16 11.2	18 49.4	29♉58.7	25 27.2	23 15.7	4 12.6	7 39.6	17 42.9	9 18.4	23 33.8	8 9.6	12 14.5
13 S	19 20 7.7	19 46.6	29 55.6	8♉53.0	22 37.3	5 26.0	8 21.5	17 42.3	9 25.8	23 37.1	8 10.3	12 16.2
14 M	19 24 4.3	20 43.8	29 52.4	22 44.3	21 58.1	6 39.3	9 3.3	17 41.9	9 33.3	23 40.3	8 11.1	12 17.9
15 T	19 28 0.9	21 41.1	29 49.2	7♊ 1.9	21 18.8	7 52.7	9 45.1	17 41.6	9 40.7	23 43.6	8 11.9	12 19.6
16 W	19 31 57.4	22 38.3	29 46.0	21 44.1	20 40.2	9 6.1	10 26.8	17 41.5	9 48.2	23 46.8	8 12.7	12 21.3
17 T	19 35 54.0	23 35.6	29 42.9	6♋46.0	20 2.9	10 19.6	11 8.5	17D41.6	9 55.7	23 50.0	8 13.6	12 23.0
18 F	19 39 50.5	24 32.8	29 39.7	21 59.8	19 27.6	11 33.0	11 50.0	17 41.9	10 3.2	23 53.2	8 14.4	12 24.7
19 S	19 43 47.1	25 30.1	29 36.5	7♌15.2	18 54.9	12 46.5	12 31.5	17 42.4	10 10.8	23 56.4	8 15.4	12 26.4
20 S	19 47 43.7	26 27.4	29 33.3	22 21.5	18 25.4	13 60.0	13 13.0	17 43.0	10 18.3	23 59.5	8 16.3	12 28.2
21 M	19 51 40.2	27 24.7	29 30.2	7♍ 9.0	17 59.7	15 13.5	13 54.3	17 43.9	10 25.9	24 2.7	8 17.3	12 29.9
22 T	19 55 36.8	28 22.0	29 27.0	21 31.0	17 38.3	16 27.0	14 35.6	17 44.9	10 33.5	24 5.8	8 18.3	12 31.7
23 W	19 59 33.3	29 19.3	29 23.8	5♎24.2	17 21.6	17 40.6	15 16.8	17 46.1	10 41.1	24 8.8	8 19.3	12 33.4
24 T	20 3 29.9	0♌16.6	29 20.6	18 48.4	17 10.0	18 54.2	15 57.9	17 47.5	10 48.8	24 11.9	8 20.4	12 35.2
25 F	20 7 26.5	1 13.9	29 17.5	1♏45.9	17 3.7	20 7.8	16 39.0	17 49.0	10 56.4	24 14.9	8 21.4	12 37.0
26 S	20 11 23.0	2 11.2	29 14.3	14 20.7	17 3.1	21 21.4	17 20.0	17 50.7	11 4.0	24 17.9	8 22.6	12 38.7
27 S	20 15 19.6	3 8.5	29 11.1	26 37.5	17D 8.4	22 35.1	18 0.9	17 52.6	11 11.7	24 20.9	8 23.7	12 40.5
28 M	20 19 16.1	4 5.8	29 7.9	8♐41.2	17 19.6	23 48.7	18 41.7	17 54.7	11 19.4	24 23.8	8 24.9	12 42.3
29 T	20 23 12.7	5 3.1	29 4.8	20 36.4	17 37.0	25 2.4	19 22.5	17 57.0	11 27.0	24 26.7	8 26.1	12 44.1
30 W	20 27 9.2	6 0.5	29 1.6	2♑27.0	18 0.5	26 16.1	20 3.2	17 59.4	11 34.7	24 29.6	8 27.3	12 45.8
31 T	20 31 5.8	6 57.8	28 58.4	14 16.4	18 30.2	27 29.8	20 43.8	18 2.0	11 42.4	24 32.4	8 28.5	12 47.6

DECLINATION

DAY	EPHEMERIS SIDEREAL TIME	☉	☊	☽	☿	♀	♂	♃	♄	♅	♆	♇
1 T	18 32 49.1	23N11.1	20N16.5	23S 1.6	18N36.4	22N35.9	19N48.5	16S12.7	18N57.3	23N22.0	1S48.2	23N42.9
4 F	18 44 38.7	22 58.5	20 14.5	25 58.2	17 53.4	22 55.5	20 16.8	16 11.4	18 51.9	23 22.5	1 48.8	23 41.5
7 M	18 56 28.4	22 42.3	20 12.5	18 40.3	17 20.9	23 9.1	20 43.4	16 10.6	18 46.4	23 23.1	1 49.5	23 40.0
10 T	19 8 18.1	22 22.6	20 10.5	4 16.9	17 0.6	23 16.7	21 8.2	16 10.2	18 40.8	23 23.6	1 50.4	23 38.6
13 S	19 20 7.7	21 59.4	20 8.5	12N35.3	16 53.5	23 18.2	21 31.1	16 10.2	18 35.1	23 24.1	1 51.3	23 37.1
16 W	19 31 57.4	21 32.8	20 6.5	24 58.1	16 59.5	23 13.6	21 52.3	16 10.7	18 29.2	23 24.6	1 52.4	23 35.7
19 S	19 43 47.1	21 2.8	20 4.4	22 58.1	17 17.2	23 2.8	22 11.5	16 11.7	18 23.3	23 25.1	1 53.5	23 34.2
22 T	19 55 36.8	20 29.7	20 2.4	7 44.5	17 44.4	22 45.9	22 28.9	16 13.1	18 17.4	23 25.6	1 54.8	23 32.8
25 F	20 7 26.5	19 53.5	20 0.3	9S46.4	18 17.9	22 23.0	22 44.5	16 15.0	18 11.3	23 26.0	1 56.1	23 31.3
28 M	20 19 16.1	19 14.3	19 58.3	22 27.7	18 54.1	21 54.2	22 58.2	16 17.3	18 5.2	23 26.4	1 57.6	23 29.9
31 T	20 31 5.8	18 32.3	19 56.2	26 9.8	19 28.7	21 19.6	23 10.0	16 20.1	17 59.0	23 26.9	1 59.2	23 28.4

AUGUST 1947

LONGITUDE

DAY	EPHEMERIS SIDEREAL TIME	☉	☊	☽	☿	♀	♂	♃	♄	♅	♆	♇
1 F	20 35 2.3	7♌55.2	28♉55.2	26♑ 7.2	19♋ 6.0	28♋43.6	21♊24.4	18♏ 4.8	11♌50.1	24♊35.3	8♎29.8	12♌49.4
2 S	20 38 58.9	8 52.6	28 52.0	8♒ 1.6	19 48.1	29 57.4	22 4.8	18 7.8	11 57.8	24 38.1	8 31.1	12 51.2
3 S	20 42 55.5	9 50.0	28 48.9	20 1.0	20 36.2	1♌11.2	22 45.2	18 10.9	12 5.5	24 40.8	8 32.5	12 53.0
4 M	20 46 52.0	10 47.4	28 45.7	2♓ 6.8	21 30.3	2 25.0	23 25.6	18 14.2	12 13.2	24 43.5	8 33.8	12 54.8
5 T	20 50 48.5	11 44.8	28 42.5	14 20.1	22 30.3	3 38.9	24 5.8	18 17.7	12 20.9	24 46.2	8 35.2	12 56.6
6 W	20 54 45.1	12 42.3	28 39.3	26 42.4	23 36.1	4 52.7	24 46.0	18 21.3	12 28.6	24 48.9	8 36.6	12 58.4
7 T	20 58 41.7	13 39.7	28 36.2	9♈15.6	24 47.5	6 6.6	25 26.1	18 25.1	12 36.3	24 51.5	8 38.1	13 0.2
8 F	21 2 38.3	14 37.2	28 33.0	22 2.0	26 4.4	7 20.6	26 6.1	18 29.1	12 44.1	24 54.1	8 39.5	13 2.0
9 S	21 6 34.8	15 34.7	28 29.8	5♉ 4.4	27 26.4	8 34.5	26 46.1	18 33.2	12 51.8	24 56.7	8 41.0	13 3.8
10 S	21 10 31.3	16 32.3	28 26.6	18 25.6	28 53.5	9 48.5	27 25.9	18 37.5	12 59.5	24 59.2	8 42.5	13 5.6
11 M	21 14 27.9	17 29.8	28 23.4	2♊ 8.4	0♌25.3	11 2.5	28 5.8	18 41.9	13 7.2	25 1.7	8 44.0	13 7.4
12 T	21 18 24.5	18 27.4	28 20.3	16 14.2	2 1.6	12 16.5	28 45.5	18 46.5	13 14.9	25 4.2	8 45.6	13 9.2
13 W	21 22 21.0	19 25.0	28 17.1	0♋42.8	3 42.0	13 30.6	29 25.1	18 51.3	13 22.5	25 6.6	8 47.2	13 11.0
14 T	21 26 17.6	20 22.6	28 13.9	15 31.2	5 26.0	14 44.6	0♋ 4.7	18 56.2	13 30.2	25 9.0	8 48.8	13 12.8
15 F	21 30 14.1	21 20.3	28 10.7	0♌33.6	7 13.5	15 58.7	0 44.2	19 1.3	13 37.9	25 11.3	8 50.4	13 14.5
16 S	21 34 10.7	22 17.9	28 7.6	15 41.4	9 3.9	17 12.9	1 23.6	19 6.5	13 45.6	25 13.6	8 52.1	13 16.3
17 S	21 38 7.2	23 15.6	28 4.4	0♍44.2	10 57.0	18 27.0	2 2.9	19 11.9	13 53.2	25 15.9	8 53.7	13 18.1
18 M	21 42 3.8	24 13.3	28 1.2	15 32.2	12 52.1	19 41.2	2 42.1	19 17.5	14 0.8	25 18.1	8 55.4	13 19.9
19 T	21 46 0.3	25 11.1	27 58.0	29 57.4	14 49.0	20 55.4	3 21.3	19 23.2	14 8.5	25 20.3	8 57.1	13 21.6
20 W	21 49 56.9	26 8.8	27 54.9	13♎55.0	16 47.3	22 9.6	4 0.4	19 29.0	14 16.1	25 22.4	8 58.9	13 23.4
21 T	21 53 53.5	27 6.6	27 51.7	27 23.5	18 46.6	23 23.8	4 39.3	19 35.1	14 23.7	25 24.5	9 0.6	13 25.2
22 F	21 57 50.0	28 4.4	27 48.5	10♏24.3	20 46.6	24 38.0	5 18.2	19 41.2	14 31.3	25 26.6	9 2.4	13 26.9
23 S	22 1 46.6	29 2.2	27 45.3	23 0.9	22 46.9	25 52.3	5 57.0	19 47.5	14 38.8	25 28.6	9 4.2	13 28.7
24 S	22 5 43.1	0♍ 0.0	27 42.1	5♐18.1	24 47.2	27 6.5	6 35.8	19 53.9	14 46.4	25 30.5	9 6.0	13 30.4
25 M	22 9 39.6	0 57.9	27 39.0	17 21.0	26 47.5	28 20.8	7 14.4	20 0.5	14 53.9	25 32.5	9 7.9	13 32.1
26 T	22 13 36.2	1 55.8	27 35.8	29 15.0	28 47.3	29 35.1	7 52.9	20 7.2	15 1.4	25 34.4	9 9.7	13 33.9
27 W	22 17 32.8	2 53.7	27 32.6	11♑ 5.0	0♍46.5	0♍49.5	8 31.4	20 14.1	15 8.9	25 36.2	9 11.6	13 35.6
28 T	22 21 29.4	3 51.6	27 29.4	22 55.1	2 45.1	2 3.8	9 9.8	20 21.1	15 16.3	25 38.0	9 13.5	13 37.3
29 F	22 25 25.9	4 49.5	27 26.3	4♒48.8	4 42.8	3 18.1	9 48.1	20 28.2	15 23.8	25 39.8	9 15.4	13 39.0
30 S	22 29 22.4	5 47.5	27 23.1	16 48.9	6 39.5	4 32.5	10 26.3	20 35.5	15 31.2	25 41.5	9 17.3	13 40.7
31 S	22 33 19.0	6 45.5	27 19.9	28 57.0	8 35.3	5 46.9	11 4.4	20 42.9	15 38.6	25 43.1	9 19.2	13 42.4

DECLINATION

DAY	EPHEMERIS SIDEREAL TIME	☉	☊	☽	☿	♀	♂	♃	♄	♅	♆	♇
1 F	20 35 2.3	18N17.6	19N55.5	25S 1.7	19N39.2	21N 6.8	23N13.5	16S21.1	17N56.9	23N27.0	1S59.7	23N28.0
4 M	20 46 52.0	17 32.0	19 53.4	15 24.3	20 4.6	20 24.8	23 22.9	16 24.4	17 50.7	23 27.4	2 1.4	23 26.6
7 T	20 58 41.7	16 43.8	19 51.3	0N 7.3	20 17.4	19 37.5	23 30.5	16 28.1	17 44.4	23 27.7	2 3.1	23 25.2
10 S	21 10 31.3	15 53.1	19 49.2	16 25.0	20 12.7	18 45.1	23 36.2	16 32.2	17 38.1	23 28.0	2 5.0	23 23.8
13 W	21 22 21.0	15 0.2	19 47.1	26 5.5	19 46.3	17 47.9	23 40.2	16 36.7	17 31.8	23 28.4	2 6.9	23 22.5
16 S	21 34 10.7	14 5.0	19 45.0	20 47.6	18 56.0	16 46.2	23 42.4	16 41.5	17 25.4	23 28.7	2 8.9	23 21.2
19 T	21 46 0.3	13 7.9	19 42.8	3 55.8	17 41.9	15 40.3	23 42.8	16 46.7	17 19.0	23 29.0	2 11.0	23 19.9
22 F	21 57 50.0	12 8.8	19 40.7	13S30.2	16 6.4	14 30.5	23 41.6	16 52.2	17 12.7	23 29.2	2 13.1	23 18.7
25 M	22 9 39.6	11 8.1	19 38.5	24 31.2	14 13.8	13 17.1	23 38.8	16 58.0	17 6.3	23 29.5	2 15.3	23 17.5
28 T	22 21 29.4	10 5.8	19 36.4	25 33.9	12 8.4	12 0.4	23 34.3	17 4.1	17 0.0	23 29.7	2 17.6	23 16.3
31 S	22 33 19.0	9 2.0	19 34.2	16 31.3	9 54.6	10 40.7	23 28.3	17 10.5	16 53.7	23 29.9	2 19.9	23 15.2

SEPTEMBER 1947

LONGITUDE

DAY	EPHEMERIS SIDEREAL TIME	☉	☊	☽	☿	♀	♂	♃	♄	♅	♆	♇
	h m s	° ′	° ′	° ′	° ′	° ′	° ′	° ′	° ′	° ′	° ′	° ′
1 M	22 37 15.6	7♍43.5	27♉16.7	11♓14.2	10♍29.9	7♍ 1.3	11♋42.4	20♏50.4	15♌45.9	25♊44.8	9♎21.2	13♌44.0
2 T	22 41 12.1	8 41.5	27 13.5	23 41.2	12 23.4	8 15.7	12 20.3	20 58.1	15 53.2	25 46.3	9 23.2	13 45.7
3 W	22 45 8.7	9 39.6	27 10.4	6♈18.3	14 15.8	9 30.2	12 58.2	21 5.9	16 0.5	25 47.8	9 25.1	13 47.4
4 T	22 49 5.2	10 37.7	27 7.2	19 5.9	16 7.0	10 44.6	13 35.9	21 13.8	16 7.8	25 49.3	9 27.1	13 49.0
5 F	22 53 1.8	11 35.8	27 4.0	2♉ 4.9	17 57.0	11 59.1	14 13.6	21 21.8	16 15.0	25 50.8	9 29.2	13 50.6
6 S	22 56 58.3	12 34.0	27 0.8	15 16.3	19 45.8	13 13.6	14 51.1	21 30.0	16 22.2	25 52.1	9 31.2	13 52.3
7 S	23 0 54.9	13 32.2	26 57.7	28 41.7	21 33.4	14 28.1	15 28.6	21 38.3	16 29.4	25 53.5	9 33.2	13 53.9
8 M	23 4 51.4	14 30.4	26 54.5	12♊22.7	23 19.8	15 42.6	16 6.0	21 46.7	16 36.6	25 54.8	9 35.3	13 55.5
9 T	23 8 48.0	15 28.7	26 51.3	26 20.5	25 5.1	16 57.2	16 43.3	21 55.2	16 43.7	25 56.0	9 37.4	13 57.0
10 W	23 12 44.5	16 27.0	26 48.1	10♋35.2	26 49.2	18 11.7	17 20.5	22 3.9	16 50.7	25 57.2	9 39.4	13 58.6
11 T	23 16 41.1	17 25.3	26 44.9	25 5.1	28 32.1	19 26.3	17 57.6	22 12.6	16 57.8	25 58.3	9 41.5	14 0.2
12 F	23 20 37.6	18 23.7	26 41.8	9♌46.5	0♎14.0	20 40.9	18 34.6	22 21.5	17 4.7	25 59.4	9 43.6	14 1.7
13 S	23 24 34.2	19 22.1	26 38.6	24 33.2	1 54.7	21 55.5	19 11.5	22 30.5	17 11.7	26 0.5	9 45.7	14 3.2
14 S	23 28 30.7	20 20.6	26 35.4	9♍17.4	3 34.3	23 10.1	19 48.3	22 39.6	17 18.6	26 1.5	9 47.9	14 4.7
15 M	23 32 27.3	21 19.0	26 32.2	23 51.1	5 12.8	24 24.8	20 24.9	22 48.9	17 25.5	26 2.4	9 50.0	14 6.2
16 T	23 36 23.9	22 17.5	26 29.1	8♎ 7.0	6 50.3	25 39.4	21 1.5	22 58.2	17 32.3	26 3.3	9 52.1	14 7.7
17 W	23 40 20.4	23 16.1	26 25.9	21 59.8	8 26.7	26 54.1	21 38.0	23 7.6	17 39.1	26 4.1	9 54.3	14 9.2
18 T	23 44 16.9	24 14.6	26 22.7	5♏27.1	10 2.0	28 8.7	22 14.3	23 17.2	17 45.8	26 4.9	9 56.5	14 10.6
19 F	23 48 13.5	25 13.2	26 19.5	18 29.0	11 36.4	29 23.4	22 50.6	23 26.8	17 52.5	26 5.6	9 58.6	14 12.1
20 S	23 52 10.1	26 11.8	26 16.3	1♐ 7.8	13 9.7	0♎38.1	23 26.7	23 36.6	17 59.1	26 6.3	10 0.8	14 13.5
21 S	23 56 6.6	27 10.5	26 13.2	13 27.1	14 42.0	1 52.8	24 2.8	23 46.4	18 5.7	26 7.0	10 3.0	14 14.9
22 M	0 0 3.2	28 9.1	26 10.0	25 31.9	16 13.2	3 7.5	24 38.7	23 56.4	18 12.2	26 7.5	10 5.2	14 16.3
23 T	0 3 59.8	29 7.9	26 6.8	7♑27.3	17 43.5	4 22.2	25 14.5	24 6.4	18 18.7	26 8.1	10 7.4	14 17.6
24 W	0 7 56.3	0♎ 6.6	26 3.6	19 18.5	19 12.8	5 36.9	25 50.2	24 16.6	18 25.2	26 8.5	10 9.6	14 19.0
25 T	0 11 52.9	1 5.3	26 0.5	1♒10.3	20 41.0	6 51.6	26 25.7	24 26.8	18 31.5	26 9.0	10 11.8	14 20.3
26 F	0 15 49.4	2 4.1	25 57.3	13 7.2	22 8.3	8 6.4	27 1.2	24 37.2	18 37.9	26 9.3	10 14.0	14 21.6
27 S	0 19 46.0	3 3.0	25 54.1	25 12.5	23 34.5	9 21.1	27 36.5	24 47.6	18 44.1	26 9.6	10 16.2	14 22.9
28 S	0 23 42.5	4 1.8	25 50.9	7♓28.9	24 59.7	10 35.8	28 11.8	24 58.1	18 50.3	26 9.9	10 18.5	14 24.2
29 M	0 27 39.1	5 0.7	25 47.7	19 58.1	26 23.8	11 50.6	28 46.9	25 8.7	18 56.5	26 10.1	10 20.7	14 25.4
30 T	0 31 35.6	5 59.6	25 44.6	2♈40.7	27 46.7	13 5.3	29 21.8	25 19.4	19 2.6	26 10.3	10 22.9	14 26.7

DECLINATION

DAY	EPHEMERIS SIDEREAL TIME	☉	☊	☽	☿	♀	♂	♃	♄	♅	♆	♇
1 M	22 37 15.6	8N40.5	19N33.5	11S49.9	9N 8.8	10N13.6	23N25.9	17S12.7	16N51.7	23N30.0	2S20.7	23N14.9
4 T	22 49 5.2	7 35.0	19 31.3	4N39.5	6 49.0	8 50.5	23 17.9	17 19.4	16 45.4	23 30.2	2 23.1	23 13.8
7 S	23 0 54.9	6 28.5	19 29.1	20 5.3	4 27.7	7 25.2	23 8.4	17 26.3	16 39.3	23 30.3	2 25.5	23 12.8
10 W	23 12 44.5	5 21.0	19 26.9	26 33.3	2 6.8	5 58.1	22 57.6	17 33.5	16 33.2	23 30.5	2 28.0	23 11.9
13 S	23 24 34.2	4 12.6	19 24.7	18 5.4	0S12.4	4 29.4	22 45.4	17 40.8	16 27.2	23 30.7	2 30.5	23 11.0
16 T	23 36 23.9	3 3.6	19 22.5	0 11.9	2 28.7	2 59.4	22 31.9	17 48.4	16 21.3	23 30.8	2 33.1	23 10.2
19 F	23 48 13.5	1 54.0	19 20.3	16S45.8	4 41.3	1 28.6	22 17.3	17 56.1	16 15.4	23 30.9	2 35.6	23 9.4
22 M	0 0 3.2	0 44.1	19 18.1	25 57.5	6 49.4	0S 2.8	22 1.6	18 3.9	16 9.7	23 31.0	2 38.2	23 8.7
25 T	0 11 52.9	0S26.0	19 15.8	24 27.4	8 52.4	1 34.3	21 44.8	18 11.9	16 4.2	23 31.1	2 40.8	23 8.1
28 S	0 23 42.5	1 36.2	19 13.6	13 22.7	10 49.5	3 5.8	21 27.0	18 19.9	15 58.7	23 31.2	2 43.4	23 7.6

OCTOBER 1947

LONGITUDE

DAY	EPHEMERIS SIDEREAL TIME	☉	☊	☽	☿	♀	♂	♃	♄	♅	♆	♇
1 W	0 35 32.2	6♎58.5	25♉41.4	15♈36.6	29♎ 8.6	14♎20.1	29♋56.7	25♏30.2	19♌ 8.6	26♊10.4	10♎25.1	14♌27.9
2 T	0 39 28.7	7 57.5	25 38.2	28 45.2	0♏29.3	15 34.8	0♌31.4	25 41.1	19 14.6	26 10.4	10 27.4	14 29.1
3 F	0 43 25.3	8 56.6	25 35.0	12♉ 5.4	1 48.9	16 49.6	1 6.1	25 52.0	19 20.5	26 10.5	10 29.6	14 30.2
4 S	0 47 21.9	9 55.6	25 31.9	25 36.5	3 7.1	18 4.4	1 40.6	26 3.0	19 26.3	26R10.4	10 31.8	14 31.4
5 S	0 51 18.4	10 54.7	25 28.7	9♊17.7	4 24.0	19 19.2	2 14.9	26 14.2	19 32.1	26 10.3	10 34.1	14 32.5
6 M	0 55 14.9	11 53.8	25 25.5	23 8.5	5 39.6	20 34.0	2 49.2	26 25.3	19 37.8	26 10.1	10 36.3	14 33.6
7 T	0 59 11.5	12 53.0	25 22.3	7♋ 8.5	6 53.6	21 48.8	3 23.3	26 36.6	19 43.5	26 9.9	10 38.5	14 34.7
8 W	1 3 8.1	13 52.2	25 19.1	21 16.9	8 6.1	23 3.6	3 57.2	26 48.0	19 49.0	26 9.7	10 40.8	14 35.7
9 T	1 7 4.6	14 51.5	25 16.0	5♌32.2	9 16.9	24 18.4	4 31.1	26 59.4	19 54.5	26 9.4	10 43.0	14 36.8
10 F	1 11 1.2	15 50.8	25 12.8	19 51.9	10 25.9	25 33.2	5 4.8	27 10.9	19 60.0	26 9.0	10 45.2	14 37.8
11 S	1 14 57.7	16 50.1	25 9.6	4♍12.4	11 33.0	26 48.0	5 38.3	27 22.5	20 5.3	26 8.6	10 47.5	14 38.8
12 S	1 18 54.3	17 49.4	25 6.4	18 29.1	12 37.9	28 2.9	6 11.7	27 34.1	20 10.6	26 8.1	10 49.7	14 39.8
13 M	1 22 50.8	18 48.8	25 3.3	2♎37.0	13 40.6	29 17.7	6 45.0	27 45.8	20 15.9	26 7.6	10 51.9	14 40.7
14 T	1 26 47.4	19 48.3	25 0.1	16 31.2	14 40.7	0♏32.6	7 18.1	27 57.6	20 21.0	26 7.0	10 54.1	14 41.6
15 W	1 30 43.9	20 47.8	24 56.9	0♏ 7.9	15 38.1	1 47.4	7 51.0	28 9.5	20 26.1	26 6.4	10 56.3	14 42.5
16 T	1 34 40.5	21 47.3	24 53.7	13 24.7	16 32.5	3 2.3	8 23.8	28 21.4	20 31.0	26 5.7	10 58.5	14 43.4
17 F	1 38 37.1	22 46.8	24 50.5	26 21.0	17 23.6	4 17.1	8 56.5	28 33.4	20 36.0	26 5.0	11 0.7	14 44.2
18 S	1 42 33.6	23 46.4	24 47.4	8♐57.8	18 11.0	5 32.0	9 28.9	28 45.4	20 40.8	26 4.3	11 2.9	14 45.1
19 S	1 46 30.1	24 46.0	24 44.2	21 17.4	18 54.4	6 46.8	10 1.2	28 57.5	20 45.5	26 3.4	11 5.1	14 45.8
20 M	1 50 26.7	25 45.6	24 41.0	3♑23.4	19 33.4	8 1.7	10 33.4	29 9.7	20 50.2	26 2.5	11 7.3	14 46.6
21 T	1 54 23.2	26 45.2	24 37.8	15 20.1	20 7.5	9 16.5	11 5.4	29 21.9	20 54.8	26 1.6	11 9.5	14 47.4
22 W	1 58 19.8	27 44.9	24 34.7	27 12.3	20 36.3	10 31.4	11 37.2	29 34.2	20 59.3	26 0.7	11 11.6	14 48.1
23 T	2 2 16.4	28 44.7	24 31.5	9♒ 4.9	20 59.1	11 46.2	12 8.8	29 46.5	21 3.7	25 59.6	11 13.8	14 48.8
24 F	2 6 12.9	29 44.4	24 28.3	21 2.7	21 15.5	13 1.1	12 40.3	29 58.9	21 8.0	25 58.6	11 16.0	14 49.4
25 S	2 10 9.5	0♏44.2	24 25.1	3♓10.0	21 24.8	14 15.9	13 11.6	0♐11.3	21 12.3	25 57.4	11 18.1	14 50.1
26 S	2 14 6.0	1 44.0	24 21.9	15 30.7	21 26.6	15 30.8	13 42.7	0 23.8	21 16.4	25 56.3	11 20.2	14 50.7
27 M	2 18 2.6	2 43.8	24 18.8	28 7.5	21R20.1	16 45.6	14 13.6	0 36.4	21 20.5	25 55.1	11 22.3	14 51.3
28 T	2 21 59.1	3 43.7	24 15.6	11♈ 2.2	21 5.0	18 0.5	14 44.3	0 49.0	21 24.4	25 53.8	11 24.4	14 51.8
29 W	2 25 55.7	4 43.6	24 12.4	24 15.1	20 40.8	19 15.3	15 14.9	1 1.6	21 28.3	25 52.5	11 26.5	14 52.4
30 T	2 29 52.2	5 43.5	24 9.2	7♉45.4	20 7.3	20 30.1	15 45.3	1 14.3	21 32.1	25 51.2	11 28.6	14 52.9
31 F	2 33 48.8	6 43.4	24 6.1	21 31.2	19 24.4	21 45.0	16 15.4	1 27.0	21 35.8	25 49.8	11 30.7	14 53.4

DECLINATION

DAY	EPHEMERIS SIDEREAL TIME	☉	☊	☽	☿	♀	♂	♃	♄	♅	♆	♇
1 W	0 35 32.2	2S46.2	19N11.3	3N11.3	12S40.1	4S36.8	21N 8.3	18S28.1	15N53.4	23N31.2	2S46.0	23N 7.1
4 S	0 47 21.9	3 56.0	19 9.0	19 18.0	14 23.3	6 7.0	20 48.7	18 36.3	15 48.3	23 31.3	2 48.6	23 6.7
7 T	0 59 11.5	5 5.4	19 6.8	26 46.9	15 58.4	7 36.2	20 28.4	18 44.5	15 43.3	23 31.3	2 51.2	23 6.3
10 F	1 11 1.2	6 14.2	19 4.5	19 45.0	17 24.1	9 3.8	20 7.4	18 52.8	15 38.6	23 31.3	2 53.8	23 6.1
13 M	1 22 50.8	7 22.4	19 2.2	2 40.0	18 39.0	10 29.7	19 45.7	19 1.2	15 34.0	23 31.4	2 56.4	23 5.9
16 T	1 34 40.5	8 29.6	18 59.9	14S59.2	19 41.2	11 53.4	19 23.6	19 9.5	15 29.6	23 31.3	2 59.0	23 5.8
19 S	1 46 30.1	9 35.7	18 57.6	25 35.2	20 28.3	13 14.6	19 1.0	19 17.8	15 25.5	23 31.3	3 1.5	23 5.8
22 W	1 58 19.8	10 40.6	18 55.2	25 19.2	20 56.6	14 32.9	18 38.1	19 26.1	15 21.5	23 31.3	3 4.0	23 5.8
25 S	2 10 9.5	11 44.0	18 52.9	15 9.4	21 1.5	15 48.0	18 14.9	19 34.3	15 17.9	23 31.2	3 6.5	23 6.0
28 T	2 21 59.1	12 45.9	18 50.6	1N 6.3	20 36.8	16 59.4	17 51.5	19 42.5	15 14.4	23 31.2	3 8.9	23 6.2
31 F	2 33 48.8	13 45.9	18 48.2	17 58.9	19 36.3	18 6.9	17 28.0	19 50.6	15 11.3	23 31.1	3 11.2	23 6.5

NOVEMBER 1947

LONGITUDE

DAY	EPHEMERIS SIDEREAL TIME h m s	☉ ° ′	☊ ° ′	☽ ° ′	☿ ° ′	♀ ° ′	♂ ° ′	♃ ° ′	♄ ° ′	♅ ° ′	♆ ° ′	♇ ° ′
1 S	2 37 45.4	7♏43.4	24♉ 2.9	5♊29.5	18♏32.6	22♏59.8	16♌45.4	1♐39.8	21♌39.4	25♊48.3	11♎32.7	14♌53.8
2 S	2 41 41.9	8 43.5	23 59.7	19 37.0	17R32.3	24 14.7	17 15.2	1 52.6	21 42.9	25R46.9	11 34.8	14 54.2
3 M	2 45 38.5	9 43.5	23 56.5	3♋50.0	16 24.8	25 29.5	17 44.8	2 5.4	21 46.3	25 45.3	11 36.8	14 54.6
4 T	2 49 35.0	10 43.6	23 53.4	18 5.4	15 11.5	26 44.3	18 14.1	2 18.3	21 49.7	25 43.8	11 38.8	14 55.0
5 W	2 53 31.6	11 43.7	23 50.2	2♌20.1	13 54.3	27 59.2	18 43.3	2 31.3	21 52.9	25 42.2	11 40.8	14 55.4
6 T	2 57 28.2	12 43.9	23 47.0	16 31.7	12 35.4	29 14.0	19 12.2	2 44.3	21 56.0	25 40.5	11 42.8	14 55.7
7 F	3 1 24.7	13 44.1	23 43.8	0♍37.9	11 17.5	0♐28.9	19 40.9	2 57.3	21 59.0	25 38.8	11 44.8	14 56.0
8 S	3 5 21.2	14 44.3	23 40.6	14 36.9	10 2.9	1 43.7	20 9.4	3 10.3	22 2.0	25 37.1	11 46.7	14 56.2
9 S	3 9 17.8	15 44.6	23 37.5	28 26.8	8 54.1	2 58.6	20 37.7	3 23.4	22 4.8	25 35.3	11 48.6	14 56.4
10 M	3 13 14.4	16 44.9	23 34.3	12♎ 5.9	7 53.2	4 13.4	21 5.7	3 36.5	22 7.5	25 33.5	11 50.6	14 56.6
11 T	3 17 10.9	17 45.2	23 31.1	25 32.5	7 1.7	5 28.3	21 33.5	3 49.6	22 10.1	25 31.7	11 52.5	14 56.8
12 W	3 21 7.5	18 45.6	23 27.9	8♏45.3	6 21.1	6 43.1	22 1.0	4 2.8	22 12.6	25 29.8	11 54.4	14 57.0
13 T	3 25 4.0	19 46.0	23 24.8	21 43.5	5 51.8	7 58.0	22 28.2	4 16.0	22 15.0	25 27.9	11 56.2	14 57.1
14 F	3 29 0.6	20 46.4	23 21.6	4♐26.6	5 34.4	9 12.8	22 55.2	4 29.2	22 17.4	25 25.9	11 58.1	14 57.2
15 S	3 32 57.2	21 46.9	23 18.4	16 55.2	5 28.4	10 27.7	23 22.0	4 42.5	22 19.6	25 23.9	11 59.9	14 57.2
16 S	3 36 53.7	22 47.3	23 15.2	29 10.7	5D33.7	11 42.5	23 48.5	4 55.7	22 21.6	25 21.9	12 1.7	14 57.3
17 M	3 40 50.3	23 47.8	23 12.1	11♑15.1	5 49.4	12 57.4	24 14.7	5 9.0	22 23.6	25 19.9	12 3.5	14 57.3
18 T	3 44 46.8	24 48.3	23 8.9	23 11.6	6 14.8	14 12.2	24 40.6	5 22.4	22 25.5	25 17.8	12 5.2	14R57.2
19 W	3 48 43.4	25 48.9	23 5.7	5♒ 3.6	6 49.0	15 27.0	25 6.2	5 35.7	22 27.3	25 15.7	12 7.0	14 57.2
20 T	3 52 39.9	26 49.4	23 2.5	16 55.4	7 31.1	16 41.9	25 31.6	5 49.0	22 28.9	25 13.5	12 8.7	14 57.1
21 F	3 56 36.5	27 50.0	22 59.3	28 51.7	8 20.3	17 56.7	25 56.6	6 2.4	22 30.5	25 11.3	12 10.4	14 57.0
22 S	4 0 33.0	28 50.6	22 56.2	10♓56.9	9 15.6	19 11.5	26 21.3	6 15.8	22 31.9	25 9.1	12 12.0	14 56.9
23 S	4 4 29.6	29 51.3	22 53.0	23 15.9	10 16.4	20 26.3	26 45.8	6 29.2	22 33.2	25 6.9	12 13.7	14 56.7
24 M	4 8 26.2	0♐51.9	22 49.8	5♈52.7	11 21.8	21 41.1	27 9.9	6 42.6	22 34.5	25 4.6	12 15.3	14 56.5
25 T	4 12 22.7	1 52.6	22 46.6	18 50.6	12 31.4	22 55.9	27 33.7	6 56.0	22 35.6	25 2.4	12 16.9	14 56.3
26 W	4 16 19.3	2 53.2	22 43.5	2♉11.6	13 44.4	24 10.7	27 57.2	7 9.5	22 36.6	25 0.0	12 18.5	14 56.0
27 T	4 20 15.8	3 53.9	22 40.3	15 56.2	15 0.4	25 25.4	28 20.4	7 22.9	22 37.5	24 57.7	12 20.1	14 55.8
28 F	4 24 12.4	4 54.7	22 37.1	0♊ 2.6	16 19.0	26 40.2	28 43.2	7 36.3	22 38.2	24 55.4	12 21.6	14 55.5
29 S	4 28 9.0	5 55.4	22 33.9	14 27.1	17 39.8	27 55.0	29 5.7	7 49.8	22 38.9	24 53.0	12 23.1	14 55.1
30 S	4 32 5.5	6 56.2	22 30.8	29 4.1	19 2.4	29 9.7	29 27.8	8 3.3	22 39.5	24 50.6	12 24.6	14 54.8

DECLINATION

DAY	EPHEMERIS SIDEREAL TIME h m s	☉ ° ′	☊ ° ′	☽ ° ′	☿ ° ′	♀ ° ′	♂ ° ′	♃ ° ′	♄ ° ′	♅ ° ′	♆ ° ′	♇ ° ′
1 S	2 37 45.4	14S 5.5	18N47.4	22N18.8	19S 7.5	18S28.5	17N20.1	19S53.3	15N10.3	23N31.1	3S12.0	23N 6.6
4 T	2 49 35.0	15 2.8	18 45.1	26 29.4	17 18.3	19 30.2	16 56.6	20 1.3	15 7.5	23 31.0	3 14.3	23 7.0
7 F	3 1 24.7	15 58.0	18 42.7	16 8.5	15 9.1	20 27.1	16 33.3	20 9.2	15 5.0	23 30.9	3 16.5	23 7.5
10 M	3 13 14.4	16 50.8	18 40.3	1S34.1	13 9.8	21 18.9	16 10.1	20 17.0	15 2.8	23 30.7	3 18.7	23 8.0
13 T	3 25 4.0	17 41.1	18 38.0	18 3.1	11 48.6	22 5.3	15 47.3	20 24.6	15 0.9	23 30.6	3 20.8	23 8.7
16 S	3 36 53.7	18 28.5	18 35.6	26 32.4	11 17.3	22 46.0	15 24.8	20 32.2	14 59.3	23 30.4	3 22.8	23 9.4
19 W	3 48 43.4	19 13.1	18 33.2	23 52.3	11 31.4	23 20.7	15 3.0	20 39.5	14 58.0	23 30.2	3 24.8	23 10.2
22 S	4 0 33.0	19 54.5	18 30.8	12 7.3	12 19.2	23 49.2	14 41.7	20 46.8	14 57.0	23 30.0	3 26.7	23 11.1
25 T	4 12 22.7	20 32.7	18 28.4	4N36.2	13 28.3	24 11.3	14 21.2	20 53.8	14 56.4	23 29.8	3 28.4	23 12.0
28 F	4 24 12.4	21 7.4	18 25.9	20 45.5	14 49.2	24 26.8	14 1.5	21 0.7	14 56.1	23 29.6	3 30.1	23 13.0

DECEMBER 1947

LONGITUDE

DAY	EPHEMERIS SIDEREAL TIME h m s	☉ ° ′	☊ ° ′	☽ ° ′	☿ ° ′	♀ ° ′	♂ ° ′	♃ ° ′	♄ ° ′	♅ ° ′	♆ ° ′	♇ ° ′
1 M	4 36 2.1	7♐57.0	22♉27.6	13♋46.8	20♏26.6	0♑24.5	29♌49.6	8♐16.7	22♌39.9	24♊48.2	12♎26.0	14♌54.4
2 T	4 39 58.6	8 57.8	22 24.4	28 28.3	21 52.2	1 39.2	0♍11.0	8 30.2	22 40.2	24R45.7	12 27.4	14R54.0
3 W	4 43 55.2	9 58.6	22 21.2	13♌ 2.2	23 18.8	2 53.9	0 32.1	8 43.7	22 40.5	24 43.3	12 28.8	14 53.5
4 T	4 47 51.7	10 59.5	22 18.1	27 23.8	24 46.5	4 8.7	0 52.7	8 57.1	22 40.6	24 40.8	12 30.2	14 53.1
5 F	4 51 48.3	12 0.3	22 14.9	11♍29.9	26 14.9	5 23.4	1 13.0	9 10.6	22R40.6	24 38.4	12 31.6	14 52.6
6 S	4 55 44.8	13 1.2	22 11.7	25 19.3	27 44.0	6 38.1	1 32.8	9 24.1	22 40.4	24 35.9	12 32.9	14 52.1
7 S	4 59 41.4	14 2.2	22 8.5	8♎52.0	29 13.7	7 52.8	1 52.3	9 37.5	22 40.2	24 33.4	12 34.2	14 51.5
8 M	5 3 38.0	15 3.1	22 5.3	22 8.7	0♐43.9	9 7.5	2 11.3	9 51.0	22 39.9	24 30.9	12 35.4	14 51.0
9 T	5 7 34.5	16 4.1	22 2.2	5♏10.8	2 14.5	10 22.2	2 29.9	10 4.4	22 39.4	24 28.3	12 36.6	14 50.4
10 W	5 11 31.1	17 5.1	21 59.0	17 59.7	3 45.5	11 36.9	2 48.0	10 17.9	22 38.8	24 25.8	12 37.8	14 49.7
11 T	5 15 27.6	18 6.1	21 55.8	0♐36.6	5 16.8	12 51.5	3 5.7	10 31.3	22 38.1	24 23.2	12 39.0	14 49.1
12 F	5 19 24.2	19 7.1	21 52.6	13 2.7	6 48.3	14 6.2	3 22.9	10 44.7	22 37.3	24 20.7	12 40.1	14 48.4
13 S	5 23 20.8	20 8.1	21 49.5	25 19.0	8 20.0	15 20.9	3 39.7	10 58.2	22 36.4	24 18.1	12 41.3	14 47.7
14 S	5 27 17.3	21 9.2	21 46.3	7♑26.5	9 52.0	16 35.5	3 56.0	11 11.6	22 35.4	24 15.6	12 42.3	14 47.0
15 M	5 31 13.9	22 10.2	21 43.1	19 26.6	11 24.2	17 50.2	4 11.8	11 24.9	22 34.3	24 13.0	12 43.4	14 46.3
16 T	5 35 10.4	23 11.3	21 39.9	1♒21.2	12 56.5	19 4.8	4 27.0	11 38.3	22 33.1	24 10.4	12 44.4	14 45.5
17 W	5 39 7.0	24 12.4	21 36.8	13 12.4	14 29.0	20 19.4	4 41.8	11 51.7	22 31.7	24 7.9	12 45.4	14 44.7
18 T	5 43 3.6	25 13.5	21 33.6	25 3.4	16 1.7	21 34.0	4 56.1	12 5.0	22 30.3	24 5.3	12 46.3	14 43.9
19 F	5 47 0.1	26 14.6	21 30.4	6♓57.7	17 34.5	22 48.5	5 9.8	12 18.3	22 28.7	24 2.7	12 47.3	14 43.0
20 S	5 50 56.7	27 15.7	21 27.2	18 59.5	19 7.5	24 3.1	5 23.0	12 31.6	22 27.0	24 0.2	12 48.2	14 42.2
21 S	5 54 53.2	28 16.8	21 24.1	1♈13.5	20 40.7	25 17.6	5 35.6	12 44.8	22 25.2	23 57.6	12 49.0	14 41.3
22 M	5 58 49.8	29 17.9	21 20.9	13 44.3	22 14.0	26 32.1	5 47.7	12 58.1	22 23.4	23 55.0	12 49.8	14 40.4
23 T	6 2 46.4	0♑19.0	21 17.7	26 36.7	23 47.5	27 46.6	5 59.2	13 11.3	22 21.4	23 52.5	12 50.6	14 39.5
24 W	6 6 42.9	1 20.1	21 14.5	9♉54.4	25 21.2	29 1.1	6 10.1	13 24.5	22 19.3	23 50.0	12 51.4	14 38.5
25 T	6 10 39.5	2 21.2	21 11.3	23 39.7	26 55.2	0♒15.5	6 20.4	13 37.6	22 17.1	23 47.4	12 52.1	14 37.6
26 F	6 14 36.0	3 22.3	21 8.2	7♊52.8	28 29.3	1 29.9	6 30.1	13 50.7	22 14.8	23 44.9	12 52.8	14 36.6
27 S	6 18 32.6	4 23.4	21 5.0	22 31.1	0♑ 3.7	2 44.3	6 39.3	14 3.8	22 12.4	23 42.4	12 53.5	14 35.6
28 S	6 22 29.2	5 24.6	21 1.8	7♋28.6	1 38.3	3 58.7	6 47.8	14 16.9	22 9.9	23 39.9	12 54.1	14 34.5
29 M	6 26 25.7	6 25.7	20 58.6	22 36.7	3 13.2	5 13.1	6 55.6	14 29.9	22 7.4	23 37.4	12 54.7	14 33.5
30 T	6 30 22.2	7 26.8	20 55.5	7♌45.3	4 48.4	6 27.4	7 2.8	14 42.9	22 4.7	23 34.9	12 55.2	14 32.4
31 W	6 34 18.8	8 28.0	20 52.3	22 44.5	6 23.9	7 41.7	7 9.4	14 55.8	22 1.9	23 32.4	12 55.8	14 31.3

DECLINATION

DAY	EPHEMERIS SIDEREAL TIME h m s	☉ ° ′	☊ ° ′	☽ ° ′	☿ ° ′	♀ ° ′	♂ ° ′	♃ ° ′	♄ ° ′	♅ ° ′	♆ ° ′	♇ ° ′
1 M	4 36 2.1	21S38.5	18N23.5	26N46.2	16S14.7	24S35.6	13N42.8	21S 7.4	14N56.1	23N29.3	3S31.7	23N14.1
4 T	4 47 51.7	22 5.9	18 21.1	17 18.0	17 40.2	24 37.7	13 25.2	21 13.9	14 56.5	23 29.1	3 33.2	23 15.2
7 S	4 59 41.4	22 29.5	18 18.6	0S 7.5	19 2.2	24 33.0	13 8.7	21 20.2	14 57.2	23 28.8	3 34.6	23 16.4
10 W	5 11 31.1	22 49.2	18 16.2	16 43.3	20 18.4	24 21.5	12 53.6	21 26.3	14 58.2	23 28.5	3 35.9	23 17.7
13 S	5 23 20.8	23 4.8	18 13.7	26 7.9	21 27.3	24 3.3	12 40.0	21 32.3	14 59.6	23 28.2	3 37.1	23 19.0
16 T	5 35 10.4	23 16.3	18 11.2	24 34.4	22 27.7	23 38.5	12 27.9	21 37.9	15 1.2	23 27.9	3 38.2	23 20.3
19 F	5 47 0.1	23 23.7	18 8.7	13 38.0	23 18.5	23 7.3	12 17.6	21 43.4	15 3.2	23 27.6	3 39.1	23 21.7
22 M	5 58 49.8	23 26.7	18 6.3	2N23.9	23 58.9	22 29.9	12 9.2	21 48.7	15 5.5	23 27.3	3 40.0	23 23.2
25 T	6 10 39.5	23 25.6	18 3.8	18 45.7	24 28.3	21 46.5	12 2.7	21 53.7	15 8.1	23 27.0	3 40.7	23 24.7
28 S	6 22 29.2	23 20.2	18 1.3	26 51.4	24 46.1	20 57.4	11 58.3	21 58.5	15 11.0	23 26.6	3 41.3	23 26.2
31 W	6 34 18.8	23 10.6	17 58.7	18 47.0	24 51.6	20 2.9	11 56.1	22 3.1	15 14.2	23 26.3	3 41.8	23 27.7

JANUARY 1948

DAY	EPHEMERIS SIDEREAL TIME	☉	☊	☽	☿	♀	♂	♃	♄	♅	♆	♇
	h m s	° ′	° ′	° ′	° ′	° ′	° ′	° ′	° ′	° ′	° ′	° ′
						LONGITUDE						
1 T	6 38 15.4	9♑29.1	20♉49.1	7♍26.0	7♑59.7	8♒55.9	7♍15.2	15♐ 8.7	21♌59.0	23♊30.0	12♎56.3	14♌30.2
2 F	6 42 12.0	10 30.3	20 45.9	21 44.7	9 35.8	10 10.2	7 20.4	15 21.6	21R56.1	23R27.6	12 56.7	14R29.1
3 S	6 46 8.5	11 31.4	20 42.8	5♎38.4	11 12.3	11 24.4	7 24.9	15 34.4	21 53.0	23 25.2	12 57.1	14 28.0
4 S	6 50 5.0	12 32.6	20 39.6	19 7.5	12 49.1	12 38.6	7 28.7	15 47.2	21 49.9	23 22.8	12 57.5	14 26.8
5 M	6 54 1.6	13 33.7	20 36.4	2♏14.4	14 26.3	13 52.7	7 31.7	15 59.9	21 46.6	23 20.4	12 57.9	14 25.7
6 T	6 57 58.2	14 34.9	20 33.2	15 2.3	16 3.8	15 6.9	7 34.0	16 12.6	21 43.3	23 18.1	12 58.2	14 24.5
7 W	7 1 54.7	15 36.1	20 30.1	27 34.7	17 41.8	16 21.0	7 35.6	16 25.3	21 39.9	23 15.7	12 58.5	14 23.3
8 T	7 5 51.3	16 37.3	20 26.9	9♐55.0	19 20.1	17 35.1	7 36.4	16 37.9	21 36.4	23 13.4	12 58.8	14 22.1
9 F	7 9 47.8	17 38.4	20 23.7	22 6.0	20 58.9	18 49.1	7 36.5	16 50.4	21 32.9	23 11.1	12 59.0	14 20.8
10 S	7 13 44.4	18 39.6	20 20.5	4♑10.0	22 38.0	20 3.1	7R35.7	17 2.9	21 29.2	23 8.9	12 59.2	14 19.6
11 S	7 17 41.0	19 40.8	20 17.3	16 8.9	24 17.6	21 17.1	7 34.2	17 15.4	21 25.5	23 6.7	12 59.3	14 18.3
12 M	7 21 37.5	20 42.0	20 14.2	28 3.9	25 57.5	22 31.0	7 32.0	17 27.8	21 21.7	23 4.5	12 59.4	14 17.1
13 T	7 25 34.1	21 43.1	20 11.0	9♒56.4	27 37.8	23 44.9	7 28.9	17 40.1	21 17.9	23 2.3	12 59.5	14 15.8
14 W	7 29 30.6	22 44.3	20 7.8	21 47.8	29 18.4	24 58.8	7 25.0	17 52.4	21 13.9	23 0.1	12 59.5	14 14.5
15 T	7 33 27.2	23 45.4	20 4.6	3♓39.9	0♒59.4	26 12.6	7 20.3	18 4.6	21 9.9	22 58.0	12 59.5	14 13.2
16 F	7 37 23.8	24 46.5	20 1.5	15 35.2	2 40.7	27 26.4	7 14.9	18 16.7	21 5.8	22 56.0	12R59.5	14 11.9
17 S	7 41 20.3	25 47.7	19 58.3	27 36.6	4 22.2	28 40.1	7 8.6	18 28.8	21 1.7	22 53.9	12 59.5	14 10.5
18 S	7 45 16.8	26 48.8	19 55.1	9♈48.0	6 3.9	29 53.8	7 1.5	18 40.8	20 57.5	22 51.9	12 59.4	14 9.2
19 M	7 49 13.4	27 49.9	19 51.9	22 13.7	7 45.7	1♓ 7.4	6 53.6	18 52.8	20 53.3	22 49.9	12 59.2	14 7.8
20 T	7 53 10.0	28 50.9	19 48.8	4♉58.4	9 27.6	2 21.0	6 44.9	19 4.7	20 49.0	22 48.0	12 59.1	14 6.5
21 W	7 57 6.6	29 52.0	19 45.6	18 6.8	11 9.3	3 34.5	6 35.4	19 16.5	20 44.6	22 46.1	12 58.9	14 5.1
22 T	8 1 3.1	0♒53.1	19 42.4	1♊42.6	12 50.8	4 48.0	6 25.1	19 28.2	20 40.2	22 44.2	12 58.7	14 3.8
23 F	8 4 59.6	1 54.1	19 39.2	15 48.0	14 32.0	6 1.4	6 14.1	19 39.9	20 35.7	22 42.4	12 58.4	14 2.4
24 S	8 8 56.2	2 55.1	19 36.0	0♋22.4	16 12.5	7 14.8	6 2.2	19 51.5	20 31.2	22 40.6	12 58.1	14 1.0
25 S	8 12 52.8	3 56.1	19 32.9	15 21.8	17 52.2	8 28.1	5 49.6	20 3.0	20 26.7	22 38.8	12 57.8	13 59.6
26 M	8 16 49.3	4 57.1	19 29.7	0♌38.3	19 30.9	9 41.3	5 36.2	20 14.5	20 22.1	22 37.1	12 57.4	13 58.2
27 T	8 20 45.9	5 58.1	19 26.5	16 1.2	21 8.1	10 54.5	5 22.1	20 25.8	20 17.4	22 35.4	12 57.0	13 56.8
28 W	8 24 42.4	6 59.0	19 23.3	1♍18.2	22 43.6	12 7.6	5 7.2	20 37.1	20 12.8	22 33.8	12 56.6	13 55.4
29 T	8 28 39.0	7 60.0	19 20.2	16 18.6	24 16.9	13 20.6	4 51.6	20 48.3	20 8.1	22 32.2	12 56.1	13 54.0
30 F	8 32 35.6	9 0.9	19 17.0	0♎54.2	25 47.6	14 33.6	4 35.3	20 59.5	20 3.3	22 30.7	12 55.6	13 52.6
31 S	8 36 32.1	10 1.8	19 13.8	15 0.9	27 15.1	15 46.5	4 18.3	21 10.5	19 58.6	22 29.2	12 55.1	13 51.2
						DECLINATION						
1 T	6 38 15.4	23S 6.5	17N57.9	13N22.7	24S50.6	19S43.6	11N55.9	22S 4.6	15N15.3	23N26.2	3S41.9	23N28.2
4 S	6 50 5.0	22 51.3	17 55.4	4S53.4	24 39.0	18 42.4	11 56.8	22 8.9	15 18.8	23 25.9	3 42.3	23 29.8
7 W	7 1 54.7	22 32.1	17 52.9	20 5.4	24 14.1	17 36.5	12 0.2	22 12.9	15 22.5	23 25.5	3 42.5	23 31.4
10 S	7 13 44.4	22 8.9	17 50.3	26 47.4	23 35.4	16 26.3	12 6.2	22 16.8	15 26.4	23 25.2	3 42.6	23 33.0
13 T	7 25 34.1	21 41.7	17 47.8	22 31.4	22 42.6	15 12.1	12 14.7	22 20.4	15 30.6	23 24.9	3 42.6	23 34.6
16 F	7 37 23.8	21 10.8	17 45.2	9 55.0	21 35.8	13 54.3	12 25.8	22 23.8	15 34.9	23 24.6	3 42.4	23 36.2
19 M	7 49 13.4	20 36.2	17 42.7	6N24.5	20 15.0	12 33.3	12 39.5	22 26.9	15 39.4	23 24.2	3 42.1	23 37.8
22 T	8 1 3.1	19 58.1	17 40.1	21 27.3	18 40.9	11 9.3	12 55.6	22 29.9	15 44.0	23 24.0	3 41.8	23 39.4
25 S	8 12 52.8	19 16.6	17 37.5	26 38.8	16 54.9	9 42.9	13 13.9	22 32.6	15 48.7	23 23.7	3 41.2	23 41.0
28 W	8 24 42.4	18 32.0	17 34.9	15 36.2	14 59.4	8 14.2	13 34.4	22 35.2	15 53.5	23 23.4	3 40.6	23 42.5
31 S	8 36 32.1	17 44.3	17 32.3	3S16.6	12 58.8	6 43.8	13 56.7	22 37.5	15 58.4	23 23.2	3 39.9	23 44.1

FEBRUARY 1948

DAY	EPHEMERIS SIDEREAL TIME	☉	☊	☽	☿	♀	♂	♃	♄	♅	♆	♇
						LONGITUDE						
1 S	8 40 28.7	11♒ 2.7	19♉10.6	28♎37.9	28♒38.8	16♓59.4	4♍ 0.7	21♐21.4	19♌53.8	22♊27.7	12♎54.5	13♌49.7
2 M	8 44 25.2	12 3.6	19 7.5	11♏47.4	29 58.1	18 12.2	3R42.3	21 32.3	19R49.0	22R26.3	12R54.0	13R48.3
3 T	8 48 21.8	13 4.5	19 4.3	24 33.2	1♓12.3	19 24.9	3 23.4	21 43.1	19 44.1	22 24.9	12 53.3	13 46.9
4 W	8 52 18.4	14 5.4	19 1.1	7♐ 0.0	2 20.6	20 37.5	3 3.9	21 53.8	19 39.3	22 23.6	12 52.7	13 45.5
5 T	8 56 14.9	15 6.2	18 57.9	19 12.5	3 22.2	21 50.1	2 43.7	22 4.4	19 34.4	22 22.3	12 52.0	13 44.1
6 F	9 0 11.4	16 7.1	18 54.7	1♑14.9	4 16.4	23 2.6	2 23.1	22 14.9	19 29.5	22 21.1	12 51.3	13 42.6
7 S	9 4 8.0	17 7.9	18 51.6	13 11.0	5 2.4	24 15.0	2 1.9	22 25.3	19 24.7	22 19.9	12 50.5	13 41.2
8 S	9 8 4.6	18 8.7	18 48.4	25 3.8	5 39.5	25 27.4	1 40.3	22 35.6	19 19.8	22 18.7	12 49.8	13 39.8
9 M	9 12 1.1	19 9.5	18 45.2	6♒55.3	6 6.9	26 39.7	1 18.2	22 45.8	19 14.9	22 17.7	12 49.0	13 38.4
10 T	9 15 57.7	20 10.3	18 42.0	18 47.3	6 24.3	27 51.9	0 55.8	22 55.9	19 10.0	22 16.6	12 48.1	13 37.0
11 W	9 19 54.2	21 11.0	18 38.9	0♓41.1	6 31.1	29 4.0	0 33.0	23 5.9	19 5.1	22 15.6	12 47.3	13 35.6
12 T	9 23 50.8	22 11.7	18 35.7	12 37.8	6R27.2	0♈16.0	0 9.9	23 15.8	19 0.2	22 14.7	12 46.4	13 34.2
13 F	9 27 47.3	23 12.4	18 32.5	24 38.8	6 12.6	1 27.9	29♌46.6	23 25.6	18 55.3	22 13.8	12 45.5	13 32.8
14 S	9 31 43.9	24 13.1	18 29.3	6♈46.1	5 47.6	2 39.8	29 23.0	23 35.2	18 50.5	22 12.9	12 44.5	13 31.4
15 S	9 35 40.4	25 13.7	18 26.2	19 2.0	5 12.7	3 51.5	28 59.3	23 44.8	18 45.6	22 12.2	12 43.6	13 30.0
16 M	9 39 37.0	26 14.4	18 23.0	1♉29.8	4 29.0	5 3.2	28 35.5	23 54.2	18 40.8	22 11.4	12 42.6	13 28.6
17 T	9 43 33.6	27 14.9	18 19.8	14 13.2	3 37.4	6 14.7	28 11.6	24 3.6	18 36.0	22 10.7	12 41.5	13 27.2
18 W	9 47 30.1	28 15.5	18 16.6	27 16.2	2 39.5	7 26.2	27 47.6	24 12.8	18 31.2	22 10.1	12 40.5	13 25.9
19 T	9 51 26.7	29 16.0	18 13.4	10♊42.6	1 36.7	8 37.5	27 23.7	24 21.9	18 26.4	22 9.5	12 39.4	13 24.5
20 F	9 55 23.2	0♓16.5	18 10.3	24 35.2	0 30.8	9 48.7	26 59.8	24 30.9	18 21.7	22 9.0	12 38.3	13 23.1
21 S	9 59 19.8	1 17.0	18 7.1	8♋55.1	29♒23.6	10 59.8	26 36.1	24 39.8	18 17.0	22 8.5	12 37.2	13 21.8
22 S	10 3 16.3	2 17.4	18 3.9	23 40.3	28 16.7	12 10.8	26 12.5	24 48.5	18 12.3	22 8.1	12 36.0	13 20.5
23 M	10 7 12.9	3 17.8	18 0.7	8♌45.3	27 11.9	13 21.7	25 49.1	24 57.1	18 7.7	22 7.7	12 34.9	13 19.2
24 T	10 11 9.4	4 18.2	17 57.6	24 1.4	26 10.4	14 32.5	25 26.0	25 5.6	18 3.0	22 7.4	12 33.7	13 17.8
25 W	10 15 6.0	5 18.5	17 54.4	9♍17.5	25 13.5	15 43.1	25 3.1	25 14.0	17 58.5	22 7.1	12 32.4	13 16.5
26 T	10 19 2.5	6 18.8	17 51.2	24 22.3	24 22.2	16 53.6	24 40.6	25 22.2	17 54.0	22 6.9	12 31.2	13 15.2
27 F	10 22 59.1	7 19.1	17 48.0	9♎ 6.3	23 37.1	18 4.0	24 18.4	25 30.4	17 49.5	22 6.8	12 29.9	13 14.0
28 S	10 26 55.7	8 19.4	17 44.9	23 23.3	22 58.8	19 14.3	23 56.6	25 38.3	17 45.1	22 6.7	12 28.7	13 12.7
29 S	10 30 52.2	9 19.6	17 41.7	7♏10.5	22 27.6	20 24.4	23 35.3	25 46.2	17 40.7	22 6.6	12 27.3	13 11.4
						DECLINATION						
1 S	8 40 28.7	17S27.8	17N31.5	9S18.3	12S18.5	6S13.3	14N 4.5	22S38.3	16N 0.0	23N23.1	3S39.6	23N44.6
4 W	8 52 18.4	16 36.4	17 28.9	22 58.7	10 21.9	4 40.9	14 28.7	22 40.4	16 4.9	23 22.8	3 38.8	23 46.1
7 S	9 4 8.0	15 42.4	17 26.3	26 49.1	8 39.7	3 7.5	14 54.0	22 42.3	16 9.8	23 22.6	3 37.8	23 47.6
10 T	9 15 57.7	14 45.9	17 23.6	19 55.6	7 23.5	1 33.3	15 19.8	22 44.0	16 14.7	23 22.5	3 36.7	23 49.0
13 F	9 27 47.3	13 47.2	17 21.0	5 48.4	6 43.9	0N 1.2	15 45.6	22 45.6	16 19.6	23 22.3	3 35.6	23 50.4
16 M	9 39 37.0	12 46.5	17 18.4	10N41.1	6 46.4	1 35.8	16 11.0	22 47.0	16 24.3	23 22.2	3 34.3	23 51.7
19 T	9 51 26.7	11 44.0	17 15.7	24 1.4	7 28.0	3 10.2	16 35.5	22 48.2	16 29.0	23 22.1	3 32.9	23 53.0
22 S	10 3 16.3	10 39.7	17 13.1	25 54.2	8 36.5	4 43.9	16 58.5	22 49.4	16 33.6	23 22.0	3 31.5	23 54.2
25 W	10 15 6.0	9 34.1	17 10.4	12 23.3	9 55.1	6 16.7	17 19.8	22 50.3	16 38.0	23 21.9	3 30.0	23 55.4
28 S	10 26 55.7	8 27.1	17 7.8	7S14.5	11 9.1	7 48.3	17 39.0	22 51.2	16 42.2	23 21.9	3 28.4	23 56.5

MARCH 1948

LONGITUDE

DAY	EPHEMERIS SIDEREAL TIME	☉	☊	☽	☿	♀	♂	♃	♄	♅	♆	♇
	h m s	° ′	° ′	° ′	° ′	° ′	° ′	° ′	° ′	° ′	° ′	° ′
1 M	10 34 48.8	10♓19.8	17♉38.5	20♏28.7	22♒ 3.5	21♈34.4	23♌14.4	25♐53.9	17♌36.4	22♊ 6.6	12♎26.0	13♌10.2
2 T	10 38 45.3	11 20.0	17 35.3	3♐20.6	21R46.4	22 44.2	22R54.0	26 1.5	17R32.1	22D 6.7	12R24.7	13R 9.0
3 W	10 42 41.9	12 20.2	17 32.1	15 50.6	21 36.4	23 53.9	22 34.1	26 8.9	17 27.9	22 6.8	12 23.3	13 7.7
4 T	10 46 38.4	13 20.3	17 29.0	28 3.7	21 33.1	25 3.5	22 14.8	26 16.2	17 23.7	22 6.9	12 21.9	13 6.5
5 F	10 50 35.0	14 20.4	17 25.8	10♑ 4.9	21D36.2	26 13.0	21 56.1	26 23.4	17 19.6	22 7.1	12 20.5	13 5.4
6 S	10 54 31.5	15 20.5	17 22.6	21 58.9	21 45.4	27 22.3	21 38.0	26 30.4	17 15.6	22 7.4	12 19.1	13 4.2
7 S	10 58 28.1	16 20.6	17 19.4	3♒49.6	22 0.5	28 31.4	21 20.6	26 37.3	17 11.7	22 7.7	12 17.7	13 3.0
8 M	11 2 24.6	17 20.6	17 16.3	15 40.5	22 21.0	29 40.4	21 3.8	26 44.0	17 7.8	22 8.1	12 16.2	13 1.9
9 T	11 6 21.2	18 20.6	17 13.1	27 34.0	22 46.6	0♉49.2	20 47.7	26 50.6	17 3.9	22 8.5	12 14.8	13 0.8
10 W	11 10 17.7	19 20.6	17 9.9	9♓32.2	23 17.1	1 57.9	20 32.3	26 57.0	17 0.2	22 9.0	12 13.3	12 59.7
11 T	11 14 14.3	20 20.5	17 6.7	21 36.4	23 52.0	3 6.4	20 17.6	27 3.3	16 56.5	22 9.6	12 11.8	12 58.6
12 F	11 18 10.9	21 20.4	17 3.5	3♈47.6	24 31.1	4 14.8	20 3.7	27 9.4	16 52.9	22 10.2	12 10.3	12 57.5
13 S	11 22 7.4	22 20.3	17 0.4	16 7.1	25 14.1	5 22.9	19 50.6	27 15.3	16 49.4	22 10.8	12 8.7	12 56.5
14 S	11 26 4.0	23 20.1	16 57.2	28 35.8	26 0.7	6 30.9	19 38.2	27 21.1	16 45.9	22 11.5	12 7.2	12 55.4
15 M	11 30 0.5	24 19.9	16 54.0	11♉15.7	26 50.8	7 38.7	19 26.6	27 26.8	16 42.6	22 12.2	12 5.7	12 54.4
16 T	11 33 57.1	25 19.7	16 50.8	24 8.6	27 44.1	8 46.3	19 15.7	27 32.3	16 39.3	22 13.1	12 4.1	12 53.4
17 W	11 37 53.6	26 19.4	16 47.7	7♊17.0	28 40.4	9 53.8	19 5.7	27 37.6	16 36.1	22 13.9	12 2.5	12 52.5
18 T	11 41 50.2	27 19.1	16 44.5	20 43.3	29 39.5	11 1.0	18 56.4	27 42.8	16 33.0	22 14.8	12 1.0	12 51.5
19 F	11 45 46.7	28 18.7	16 41.3	4♋29.4	0♓41.3	12 8.0	18 48.0	27 47.8	16 30.0	22 15.8	11 59.4	12 50.6
20 S	11 49 43.3	29 18.3	16 38.1	18 36.4	1 45.6	13 14.8	18 40.3	27 52.6	16 27.1	22 16.8	11 57.8	12 49.7
21 S	11 53 39.8	0♈17.9	16 34.9	3♌ 3.1	2 52.3	14 21.4	18 33.4	27 57.2	16 24.2	22 17.8	11 56.2	12 48.8
22 M	11 57 36.4	1 17.4	16 31.8	17 46.3	4 1.2	15 27.7	18 27.3	28 1.7	16 21.5	22 19.0	11 54.5	12 47.9
23 T	12 1 33.0	2 16.9	16 28.6	2♍40.0	5 12.3	16 33.9	18 22.0	28 6.1	16 18.8	22 20.1	11 52.9	12 47.1
24 W	12 5 29.5	3 16.4	16 25.4	17 36.3	6 25.5	17 39.7	18 17.5	28 10.2	16 16.3	22 21.3	11 51.3	12 46.3
25 T	12 9 26.0	4 15.8	16 22.2	2♎26.4	7 40.6	18 45.4	18 13.7	28 14.2	16 13.8	22 22.6	11 49.7	12 45.5
26 F	12 13 22.6	5 15.2	16 19.1	17 1.9	8 57.7	19 50.8	18 10.7	28 18.0	16 11.4	22 23.9	11 48.0	12 44.7
27 S	12 17 19.2	6 14.6	16 15.9	1♏16.2	10 16.5	20 55.9	18 8.5	28 21.7	16 9.2	22 25.3	11 46.4	12 43.9
28 S	12 21 15.7	7 13.9	16 12.7	15 5.6	11 37.2	22 0.8	18 7.0	28 25.1	16 7.0	22 26.7	11 44.8	12 43.2
29 M	12 25 12.3	8 13.2	16 9.5	28 28.6	12 59.6	23 5.4	18 6.2	28 28.4	16 4.9	22 28.1	11 43.1	12 42.5
30 T	12 29 8.8	9 12.5	16 6.3	11♐26.6	14 23.6	24 9.8	18 6.2	28 31.6	16 3.0	22 29.7	11 41.5	12 41.8
31 W	12 33 5.4	10 11.7	16 3.2	24 2.4	15 49.3	25 13.9	18D 7.0	28 34.5	16 1.1	22 31.2	11 39.8	12 41.2

DECLINATION

DAY	EPHEMERIS SIDEREAL TIME	☉	☊	☽	☿	♀	♂	♃	♄	♅	♆	♇
1 M	10 34 48.8	7S41.8	17N 6.0	18S13.2	11S51.2	8N48.6	17N50.5	22S51.7	16N45.0	23N21.9	3S27.3	23N57.2
4 T	10 46 38.4	6 33.1	17 3.3	26 48.5	12 39.8	10 17.5	18 5.8	22 52.4	16 49.0	23 21.9	3 25.6	23 58.2
7 S	10 58 28.1	5 23.5	17 0.6	24 6.3	13 0.0	11 44.3	18 18.4	22 53.0	16 52.7	23 22.0	3 23.9	23 59.1
10 W	11 10 17.7	4 13.2	16 57.9	12 17.0	13 22.0	13 8.9	18 28.4	22 53.5	16 56.3	23 22.1	3 22.1	24 0.0
13 S	11 22 7.4	3 2.5	16 55.2	4N 3.1	13 16.8	14 30.9	18 35.7	22 53.9	16 59.6	23 22.2	3 20.3	24 0.8
16 T	11 33 57.1	1 51.4	16 52.5	19 36.0	12 55.6	15 49.9	18 40.4	22 54.3	17 2.6	23 22.3	3 18.4	24 1.5
19 F	11 45 46.7	0 40.3	16 49.8	27 16.7	12 19.5	17 5.8	18 42.6	22 54.6	17 5.4	23 22.5	3 16.5	24 2.1
22 M	11 57 36.4	0N30.8	16 47.1	20 23.5	11 29.5	18 18.1	18 42.2	22 54.8	17 8.0	23 22.7	3 14.6	24 2.7
25 T	12 9 26.0	1 41.7	16 44.4	2 12.6	10 26.4	19 26.7	18 39.6	22 55.0	17 10.2	23 22.9	3 12.6	24 3.2
28 S	12 21 15.7	2 52.3	16 41.6	16S25.2	9 10.9	20 31.4	18 34.8	22 55.2	17 12.2	23 23.1	3 10.7	24 3.6
31 W	12 33 5.4	4 2.3	16 38.9	26 37.4	7 43.6	21 31.8	18 27.9	22 55.3	17 13.9	23 23.4	3 8.7	24 3.9

APRIL 1948

LONGITUDE

DAY	EPHEMERIS SIDEREAL TIME	☉	☊	☽	☿	♀	♂	♃	♄	♅	♆	♇
1 T	12 37 1.9	11♈10.9	15♉60.0	6♑20.2	17♓16.6	26♉17.7	18♌ 8.4	28♐37.3	15♌59.3	22♊32.8	11♎38.2	12♌40.5
2 F	12 40 58.5	12 10.1	15 56.8	18 24.6	18 45.5	27 21.2	18 10.5	28 39.8	15R57.6	22 34.5	11R36.5	12R39.9
3 S	12 44 55.0	13 9.2	15 53.6	0♒20.3	20 16.0	28 24.4	18 13.4	28 42.2	15 56.1	22 36.2	11 34.8	12 39.3
4 S	12 48 51.6	14 8.3	15 50.4	12 12.2	21 47.9	29 27.3	18 16.9	28 44.4	15 54.6	22 37.9	11 33.2	12 38.8
5 M	12 52 48.1	15 7.4	15 47.3	24 4.4	23 21.5	0♊29.9	18 21.1	28 46.5	15 53.3	22 39.7	11 31.6	12 38.2
6 T	12 56 44.7	16 6.5	15 44.1	6♓ 0.6	24 56.5	1 32.1	18 26.0	28 48.3	15 52.0	22 41.5	11 29.9	12 37.7
7 W	13 0 41.3	17 5.5	15 40.9	18 3.7	26 33.0	2 34.1	18 31.6	28 50.0	15 50.9	22 43.4	11 28.3	12 37.3
8 T	13 4 37.8	18 4.5	15 37.7	0♈16.1	28 11.1	3 35.6	18 37.8	28 51.4	15 49.8	22 45.3	11 26.6	12 36.8
9 F	13 8 34.3	19 3.4	15 34.6	12 39.3	29 50.6	4 36.9	18 44.6	28 52.7	15 48.9	22 47.3	11 25.0	12 36.4
10 S	13 12 30.9	20 2.4	15 31.4	25 14.3	1♈31.7	5 37.7	18 52.1	28 53.8	15 48.1	22 49.3	11 23.4	12 36.0
11 S	13 16 27.5	21 1.3	15 28.2	8♉ 1.7	3 14.3	6 38.2	19 0.2	28 54.7	15 47.4	22 51.4	11 21.7	12 35.6
12 M	13 20 24.0	22 0.1	15 25.0	21 1.7	4 58.4	7 38.3	19 8.9	28 55.4	15 46.7	22 53.5	11 20.1	12 35.2
13 T	13 24 20.6	22 58.9	15 21.9	4♊14.5	6 44.1	8 38.0	19 18.2	28 56.0	15 46.2	22 55.6	11 18.5	12 34.9
14 W	13 28 17.1	23 57.7	15 18.7	17 40.3	8 31.3	9 37.3	19 28.1	28 56.3	15 45.9	22 57.8	11 16.9	12 34.6
15 T	13 32 13.7	24 56.5	15 15.5	1♋19.1	10 20.0	10 36.1	19 38.6	28 56.5	15 45.6	23 0.0	11 15.3	12 34.3
16 F	13 36 10.2	25 55.2	15 12.3	15 10.9	12 10.3	11 34.5	19 49.6	28R56.4	15 45.4	23 2.3	11 13.7	12 34.1
17 S	13 40 6.8	26 53.8	15 9.1	29 14.9	14 2.2	12 32.5	20 1.2	28 56.2	15 45.3	23 4.6	11 12.1	12 33.9
18 S	13 44 3.3	27 52.5	15 6.0	13♌29.8	15 55.7	13 29.9	20 13.3	28 55.8	15D45.4	23 6.9	11 10.5	12 33.7
19 M	13 47 59.9	28 51.1	15 2.8	27 53.1	17 50.7	14 26.9	20 26.0	28 55.2	15 45.5	23 9.3	11 9.0	12 33.5
20 T	13 51 56.5	29 49.6	14 59.6	12♍21.3	19 47.3	15 23.3	20 39.2	28 54.4	15 45.8	23 11.7	11 7.4	12 33.4
21 W	13 55 53.0	0♉48.2	14 56.4	26 49.6	21 45.4	16 19.2	20 52.8	28 53.4	15 46.2	23 14.2	11 5.9	12 33.3
22 T	13 59 49.5	1 46.6	14 53.3	11♎12.7	23 45.0	17 14.6	21 7.0	28 52.3	15 46.6	23 16.7	11 4.4	12 33.2
23 F	14 3 46.1	2 45.1	14 50.1	25 25.2	25 46.1	18 9.4	21 21.7	28 50.9	15 47.2	23 19.2	11 2.9	12 33.1
24 S	14 7 42.7	3 43.5	14 46.9	9♏22.4	27 48.7	19 3.6	21 36.8	28 49.4	15 47.9	23 21.8	11 1.4	12 33.1
25 S	14 11 39.2	4 41.9	14 43.7	23 1.0	29 52.6	19 57.2	21 52.4	28 47.7	15 48.7	23 24.4	10 59.9	12D33.1
26 M	14 15 35.8	5 40.3	14 40.5	6♐18.9	1♉57.8	20 50.1	22 8.4	28 45.8	15 49.6	23 27.0	10 58.4	12 33.1
27 T	14 19 32.3	6 38.6	14 37.4	19 16.0	4 4.1	21 42.5	22 24.9	28 43.7	15 50.6	23 29.7	10 57.0	12 33.2
28 W	14 23 28.9	7 36.9	14 34.2	1♑53.6	6 11.5	22 34.1	22 41.8	28 41.5	15 51.7	23 32.4	10 55.5	12 33.3
29 T	14 27 25.4	8 35.2	14 31.0	14 14.3	8 19.7	23 25.1	22 59.1	28 39.0	15 52.9	23 35.2	10 54.1	12 33.4
30 F	14 31 22.0	9 33.5	14 27.8	26 21.6	10 28.6	24 15.3	23 16.8	28 36.4	15 54.3	23 37.9	10 52.7	12 33.5

DECLINATION

DAY	EPHEMERIS SIDEREAL TIME	☉	☊	☽	☿	♀	♂	♃	♄	♅	♆	♇
1 T	12 37 1.9	4N25.5	16N38.0	27S22.9	7S12.0	21N51.0	18N25.1	22S55.4	17N14.4	23N23.5	3S 8.1	24N 4.0
4 S	12 48 51.6	5 34.7	16 35.2	22 7.6	5 30.0	22 45.5	18 15.7	22 55.5	17 15.8	23 23.8	3 6.1	24 4.2
7 W	13 0 41.3	6 43.0	16 32.4	8 42.4	3 37.5	23 35.4	18 4.4	22 55.6	17 16.8	23 24.1	3 4.2	24 4.3
10 S	13 12 30.9	7 50.2	16 29.7	8N11.4	1 35.2	24 20.4	17 51.4	22 55.6	17 17.5	23 24.4	3 2.3	24 4.4
13 T	13 24 20.6	8 56.3	16 26.9	22 46.8	0N36.3	25 0.6	17 36.8	22 55.7	17 17.9	23 24.8	3 0.4	24 4.3
16 F	13 36 10.2	10 1.0	16 24.1	27 9.3	2 56.2	25 35.9	17 20.6	22 55.8	17 18.1	23 25.1	2 58.5	24 4.2
19 M	13 47 59.9	11 4.2	16 21.3	16 60.0	5 23.3	26 6.0	17 2.9	22 55.8	17 17.9	23 25.5	2 56.7	24 4.0
22 T	13 59 49.5	12 5.8	16 18.5	1S48.3	7 56.1	26 31.2	16 43.8	22 55.9	17 17.4	23 25.9	2 54.9	24 3.8
25 S	14 11 39.2	13 5.5	16 15.7	19 19.9	10 32.3	26 51.3	16 23.4	22 55.9	17 16.7	23 26.3	2 53.2	24 3.4
28 W	14 23 28.9	14 3.4	16 12.9	27 21.1	13 8.7	27 6.5	16 1.6	22 56.0	17 15.6	23 26.7	2 51.5	24 3.0

MAY 1948

DAY	EPHEMERIS SIDEREAL TIME	☉	☊	☽	☿	♀	♂	♃	♄	♅	♆	♇
	h m s	° ′	° ′	° ′	° ′	° ′	° ′	° ′	° ′	° ′	° ′	° ′
						LONGITUDE						
1 S	14 35 18.6	10♉31.7	14♉24.7	8♒19.8	12♉38.0	25♊ 4.8	23♌35.0	28♐33.6	15♌55.7	23♊40.7	10♎51.3	12♌33.7
2 S	14 39 15.1	11 29.9	14 21.5	20 13.4	14 47.6	25 53.6	23 53.5	28R30.6	15 57.2	23 43.6	10R49.9	12 33.9
3 M	14 43 11.7	12 28.1	14 18.3	2♓ 6.9	16 57.1	26 41.5	24 12.5	28 27.5	15 58.9	23 46.4	10 48.6	12 34.1
4 T	14 47 8.2	13 26.3	14 15.1	14 4.9	19 6.4	27 28.7	24 31.8	28 24.2	16 0.6	23 49.3	10 47.2	12 34.3
5 W	14 51 4.8	14 24.4	14 12.0	26 11.3	21 15.0	28 14.9	24 51.5	28 20.7	16 2.5	23 52.3	10 45.9	12 34.6
6 T	14 55 1.3	15 22.5	14 8.8	8♈29.8	23 22.7	29 0.3	25 11.6	28 17.0	16 4.4	23 55.2	10 44.6	12 34.9
7 F	14 58 57.9	16 20.6	14 5.6	21 2.9	25 29.2	29 44.8	25 32.1	28 13.1	16 6.5	23 58.2	10 43.3	12 35.2
8 S	15 2 54.5	17 18.7	14 2.4	3♉52.5	27 34.2	0♋28.3	25 52.9	28 9.1	16 8.6	24 1.2	10 42.1	12 35.6
9 S	15 6 51.0	18 16.7	13 59.2	16 59.1	29 37.4	1 10.8	26 14.0	28 4.9	16 10.9	24 4.3	10 40.9	12 36.0
10 M	15 10 47.6	19 14.7	13 56.1	0♊22.4	1♊38.6	1 52.3	26 35.5	28 0.6	16 13.2	24 7.3	10 39.6	12 36.4
11 T	15 14 44.1	20 12.7	13 52.9	14 1.0	3 37.6	2 32.7	26 57.4	27 56.1	16 15.7	24 10.4	10 38.4	12 36.8
12 W	15 18 40.7	21 10.6	13 49.7	27 52.7	5 34.1	3 12.0	27 19.5	27 51.4	16 18.2	24 13.5	10 37.3	12 37.3
13 T	15 22 37.2	22 8.5	13 46.5	11♋54.6	7 28.0	3 50.2	27 42.0	27 46.6	16 20.9	24 16.7	10 36.1	12 37.8
14 F	15 26 33.8	23 6.4	13 43.4	26 3.6	9 19.1	4 27.1	28 4.8	27 41.7	16 23.6	24 19.8	10 35.0	12 38.3
15 S	15 30 30.3	24 4.3	13 40.2	10♌16.8	11 7.3	5 2.8	28 27.9	27 36.6	16 26.5	24 23.0	10 33.9	12 38.8
16 S	15 34 26.9	25 2.1	13 37.0	24 31.1	12 52.4	5 37.2	28 51.3	27 31.3	16 29.4	24 26.2	10 32.8	12 39.4
17 M	15 38 23.4	25 59.9	13 33.8	8♍44.1	14 34.4	6 10.2	29 15.1	27 25.9	16 32.5	24 29.5	10 31.8	12 40.0
18 T	15 42 20.0	26 57.7	13 30.7	22 53.2	16 13.1	6 41.8	29 39.1	27 20.4	16 35.6	24 32.7	10 30.8	12 40.6
19 W	15 46 16.6	27 55.5	13 27.5	6♎56.4	17 48.6	7 11.9	0♍ 3.3	27 14.7	16 38.8	24 36.0	10 29.8	12 41.3
20 T	15 50 13.1	28 53.2	13 24.3	20 51.3	19 20.8	7 40.5	0 27.9	27 8.9	16 42.2	24 39.3	10 28.8	12 41.9
21 F	15 54 9.7	29 50.9	13 21.1	4♏35.9	20 49.6	8 7.5	0 52.7	27 3.0	16 45.6	24 42.6	10 27.8	12 42.6
22 S	15 58 6.2	0♊48.6	13 17.9	18 8.3	22 15.0	8 32.9	1 17.8	26 57.0	16 49.1	24 45.9	10 26.9	12 43.4
23 S	16 2 2.8	1 46.2	13 14.8	1♐26.8	23 36.9	8 56.6	1 43.1	26 50.8	16 52.7	24 49.3	10 26.0	12 44.1
24 M	16 5 59.3	2 43.8	13 11.6	14 30.1	24 55.3	9 18.6	2 8.7	26 44.5	16 56.3	24 52.6	10 25.1	12 44.9
25 T	16 9 55.9	3 41.4	13 8.4	27 17.7	26 10.1	9 38.7	2 34.5	26 38.1	17 0.1	24 56.0	10 24.3	12 45.7
26 W	16 13 52.4	4 39.0	13 5.2	9♑50.2	27 21.3	9 57.0	3 0.6	26 31.6	17 4.0	24 59.4	10 23.5	12 46.5
27 T	16 17 49.0	5 36.6	13 2.1	22 8.8	28 28.9	10 13.3	3 26.9	26 25.0	17 7.9	25 2.8	10 22.7	12 47.3
28 F	16 21 45.6	6 34.2	12 58.9	4♒15.8	29 32.8	10 27.7	3 53.5	26 18.3	17 11.9	25 6.3	10 21.9	12 48.2
29 S	16 25 42.1	7 31.7	12 55.7	16 14.2	0♋32.8	10 40.0	4 20.2	26 11.5	17 16.0	25 9.7	10 21.2	12 49.1
30 S	16 29 38.7	8 29.2	12 52.5	28 7.9	1 29.0	10 50.2	4 47.2	26 4.6	17 20.2	25 13.1	10 20.5	12 50.0
31 M	16 33 35.2	9 26.7	12 49.4	10♓ 1.4	2 21.3	10 58.3	5 14.5	25 57.6	17 24.5	25 16.6	10 19.8	12 50.9
						DECLINATION						
1 S	14 35 18.6	14N59.1	16N10.1	23S15.3	15N40.9	27N17.0	15N38.7	22S56.0	17N14.3	23N27.1	2S50.0	24N 2.5
4 T	14 47 8.2	15 52.7	16 7.3	10 29.1	18 3.8	27 22.9	15 14.5	22 56.0	17 12.7	23 27.5	2 48.4	24 1.9
7 F	14 58 57.9	16 43.9	16 4.4	6N17.8	20 11.7	27 24.4	14 49.2	22 56.0	17 10.8	23 27.9	2 47.0	24 1.3
10 M	15 10 47.6	17 32.6	16 1.6	21 41.2	22 0.2	27 21.7	14 22.7	22 56.0	17 8.6	23 28.3	2 45.6	24 0.6
13 T	15 22 37.2	18 18.6	15 58.8	27 21.7	23 26.4	27 15.2	13 55.0	22 56.0	17 6.2	23 28.8	2 44.3	23 59.8
16 S	15 34 26.9	19 1.9	15 55.9	18 14.0	24 29.7	27 5.0	13 26.3	22 55.9	17 3.5	23 29.2	2 43.1	23 59.0
19 W	15 46 16.6	19 42.3	15 53.1	0 10.2	25 11.0	26 51.5	12 56.6	22 55.8	17 0.5	23 29.6	2 42.0	23 58.1
22 S	15 58 6.2	20 19.6	15 50.2	17S35.8	25 32.2	26 35.0	12 25.9	22 55.6	16 57.3	23 30.0	2 41.0	23 57.1
25 T	16 9 55.9	20 53.8	15 47.3	27 1.1	25 35.8	26 15.8	11 54.1	22 55.4	16 53.8	23 30.4	2 40.0	23 56.1
28 F	16 21 45.6	21 24.8	15 44.4	24 12.4	25 24.6	25 54.1	11 21.5	22 55.2	16 50.1	23 30.8	2 39.2	23 55.1
31 M	16 33 35.2	21 52.5	15 41.5	12 9.4	25 1.1	25 30.1	10 47.9	22 54.8	16 46.1	23 31.2	2 38.5	23 53.9

JUNE 1948

DAY	EPHEMERIS SIDEREAL TIME	☉	☊	☽	☿	♀	♂	♃	♄	♅	♆	♇
						LONGITUDE						
1 T	16 37 31.8	10♊24.3	12♉46.2	21♓59.1	3♋ 9.6	11♋ 4.2	5♍41.9	25♐50.6	17♌28.9	25♊20.1	10♎19.2	12♌51.9
2 W	16 41 28.3	11 21.7	12 43.0	4♈ 6.0	3 53.8	11 7.8	6 9.6	25R43.5	17 33.3	25 23.6	10R18.6	12 52.9
3 T	16 45 24.9	12 19.2	12 39.8	16 26.5	4 33.8	11 9.2	6 37.5	25 36.2	17 37.8	25 27.1	10 18.0	12 53.9
4 F	16 49 21.5	13 16.7	12 36.6	29 4.5	5 9.6	11R 8.2	7 5.6	25 29.0	17 42.4	25 30.6	10 17.4	12 54.9
5 S	16 53 18.0	14 14.1	12 33.5	12♉ 3.3	5 41.1	11 4.8	7 33.9	25 21.6	17 47.1	25 34.1	10 16.9	12 56.0
6 S	16 57 14.6	15 11.6	12 30.3	25 24.2	6 8.2	10 59.1	8 2.4	25 14.2	17 51.9	25 37.7	10 16.4	12 57.1
7 M	17 1 11.1	16 9.0	12 27.1	9♊ 7.4	6 30.8	10 51.0	8 31.1	25 6.8	17 56.7	25 41.2	10 16.0	12 58.2
8 T	17 5 7.7	17 6.4	12 23.9	23 10.6	6 48.9	10 40.5	9 0.0	24 59.3	18 1.6	25 44.7	10 15.5	12 59.3
9 W	17 9 4.3	18 3.8	12 20.8	7♋29.9	7 2.4	10 27.6	9 29.1	24 51.8	18 6.6	25 48.3	10 15.1	13 0.4
10 T	17 13 0.8	19 1.2	12 17.6	21 59.6	7 11.4	10 12.4	9 58.4	24 44.2	18 11.7	25 51.9	10 14.7	13 1.6
11 F	17 16 57.4	19 58.5	12 14.4	6♌33.4	7 15.8	9 54.7	10 27.9	24 36.6	18 16.8	25 55.4	10 14.4	13 2.8
12 S	17 20 53.9	20 55.9	12 11.2	21 5.2	7R15.6	9 34.8	10 57.6	24 29.0	18 22.0	25 59.0	10 14.1	13 4.0
13 S	17 24 50.5	21 53.2	12 8.1	5♍29.7	7 11.0	9 12.6	11 27.4	24 21.3	18 27.3	26 2.5	10 13.8	13 5.2
14 M	17 28 47.1	22 50.5	12 4.9	19 43.5	7 2.0	8 48.2	11 57.5	24 13.7	18 32.7	26 6.1	10 13.6	13 6.4
15 T	17 32 43.6	23 47.8	12 1.7	3♎44.4	6 48.8	8 21.8	12 27.7	24 6.0	18 38.1	26 9.7	10 13.4	13 7.7
16 W	17 36 40.2	24 45.1	11 58.5	17 31.6	6 31.7	7 53.4	12 58.1	23 58.4	18 43.6	26 13.3	10 13.2	13 9.0
17 T	17 40 36.7	25 42.4	11 55.4	1♏ 5.3	6 10.8	7 23.2	13 28.6	23 50.7	18 49.1	26 16.9	10 13.0	13 10.3
18 F	17 44 33.2	26 39.7	11 52.2	14 25.9	5 46.5	6 51.3	13 59.3	23 43.0	18 54.7	26 20.4	10 12.9	13 11.6
19 S	17 48 29.8	27 36.9	11 49.0	27 34.2	5 19.2	6 18.0	14 30.2	23 35.4	19 0.4	26 24.0	10 12.8	13 12.9
2u S	17 52 26.4	28 34.1	11 45.8	10♐30.5	4 49.3	5 43.4	15 1.2	23 27.8	19 6.1	26 27.6	10 12.8	13 14.3
21 M	17 56 23.0	29 31.4	11 42.7	23 15.2	4 17.3	5 7.7	15 32.4	23 20.2	19 11.9	26 31.2	10 12.8	13 15.7
22 T	18 0 19.5	0♋28.6	11 39.5	5♑48.4	3 43.7	4 31.2	16 3.7	23 12.6	19 17.8	26 34.7	10D12.8	13 17.1
23 W	18 4 16.1	1 25.8	11 36.3	18 10.6	3 9.1	3 54.1	16 35.2	23 5.1	19 23.7	26 38.3	10 12.8	13 18.5
24 T	18 8 12.6	2 23.0	11 33.1	0♒22.5	2 34.0	3 16.5	17 6.8	22 57.6	19 29.7	26 41.9	10 12.9	13 19.9
25 F	18 12 9.2	3 20.2	11 29.9	12 25.4	1 59.1	2 38.9	17 38.6	22 50.2	19 35.7	26 45.4	10 13.0	13 21.4
26 S	18 16 5.8	4 17.4	11 26.8	24 21.6	1 25.0	2 1.3	18 10.5	22 42.8	19 41.8	26 49.0	10 13.1	13 22.8
27 S	18 20 2.3	5 14.6	11 23.6	6♓13.9	0 52.2	1 24.1	18 42.6	22 35.4	19 48.0	26 52.6	10 13.3	13 24.3
28 M	18 23 58.9	6 11.8	11 20.4	18 5.9	0 21.4	0 47.5	19 14.8	22 28.1	19 54.2	26 56.1	10 13.5	13 25.8
29 T	18 27 55.4	7 9.0	11 17.2	0♈ 1.9	29♊53.0	0 11.8	19 47.2	22 20.9	20 0.4	26 59.6	10 13.7	13 27.3
30 W	18 31 52.0	8 6.2	11 14.1	12 6.8	29 27.6	29♊37.0	20 19.7	22 13.8	20 6.7	27 3.2	10 14.0	13 28.8
						DECLINATION						
1 T	16 37 31.8	22N 1.0	15N40.6	6S57.6	24N50.9	25N21.6	10N36.5	22S54.7	16N44.8	23N31.4	2S38.3	23N53.5
4 F	16 49 21.5	22 24.1	15 37.7	9N54.1	24 14.9	24 54.7	10 1.8	22 54.3	16 40.5	23 31.7	2 37.7	23 52.4
7 M	17 1 11.1	22 43.6	15 34.8	24 1.5	23 32.4	24 25.7	9 26.2	22 53.9	16 36.0	23 32.1	2 37.3	23 51.1
10 T	17 13 0.8	22 59.6	15 31.9	26 24.0	22 45.5	23 54.5	8 49.7	22 53.4	16 31.3	23 32.5	2 36.9	23 49.9
13 S	17 24 50.5	23 12.0	15 29.0	13 57.4	21 56.6	23 21.2	8 12.5	22 52.8	16 26.4	23 32.8	2 36.7	23 48.6
16 W	17 36 40.2	23 20.6	15 26.0	4S47.4	21 8.0	22 45.9	7 34.5	22 52.2	16 21.3	23 33.2	2 36.5	23 47.2
19 S	17 48 29.8	23 25.6	15 23.1	20 51.1	20 22.5	22 8.8	6 55.7	22 51.5	16 16.0	23 33.5	2 36.5	23 45.8
22 T	18 0 19.5	23 26.8	15 20.2	27 23.2	19 42.8	21 30.6	6 16.3	22 50.8	16 10.5	23 33.8	2 36.6	23 44.4
25 F	18 12 9.2	23 24.3	15 17.2	21 58.3	19 11.6	20 52.2	5 36.2	22 50.0	16 4.8	23 34.1	2 36.8	23 43.0
28 M	18 23 58.9	23 18.1	15 14.3	8 31.9	18 51.4	20 14.9	4 55.5	22 49.3	15 58.9	23 34.4	2 37.2	23 41.5

JULY 1948

DAY	EPHEMERIS SIDEREAL TIME	☉	☊	☽	☿	♀	♂	♃	♄	♅	♆	♇
	h m s	° ′	° ′	° ′	° ′	° ′	° ′	° ′	° ′	° ′	° ′	° ′
						LONGITUDE						
1 T	18 35 48.5	9♋ 3.4	11♉10.9	24♈25.7	29♊ 5.5	29♊ 3.6	20♍52.3	22♐ 6.7	20♌13.1	27♊ 6.7	10♎14.3	13♌30.3
2 F	18 39 45.1	10 0.7	11 7.7	7♉ 3.3	28R47.3	28R31.5	21 25.1	21R59.7	20 19.5	27 10.2	10 14.6	13 31.9
3 S	18 43 41.7	10 57.9	11 4.5	20 4.1	28 33.1	28 1.1	21 58.0	21 52.8	20 26.0	27 13.7	10 15.0	13 33.4
4 S	18 47 38.3	11 55.1	11 1.4	3♊30.9	28 23.4	27 32.5	22 31.1	21 46.0	20 32.5	27 17.2	10 15.4	13 35.0
5 M	18 51 34.8	12 52.3	10 58.2	17 24.9	28 18.4	27 5.7	23 4.3	21 39.2	20 39.1	27 20.7	10 15.8	13 36.6
6 T	18 55 31.3	13 49.5	10 55.0	1♋44.4	28 18.2	26 41.0	23 37.6	21 32.6	20 45.7	27 24.2	10 16.3	13 38.2
7 W	18 59 27.9	14 46.7	10 51.8	16 24.9	28D23.0	26 18.3	24 11.0	21 26.1	20 52.3	27 27.6	10 16.8	13 39.8
8 T	19 3 24.5	15 44.0	10 48.7	1♌18.9	28 32.9	25 57.9	24 44.6	21 19.7	20 59.0	27 31.1	10 17.3	13 41.5
9 F	19 7 21.0	16 41.2	10 45.5	16 17.6	28 48.0	25 39.8	25 18.4	21 13.4	21 5.8	27 34.5	10 17.9	13 43.1
10 S	19 11 17.6	17 38.4	10 42.3	1♍11.7	29 8.2	25 23.9	25 52.2	21 7.2	21 12.6	27 38.0	10 18.4	13 44.8
11 S	19 15 14.1	18 35.7	10 39.1	15 53.4	29 33.7	25 10.4	26 26.2	21 1.1	21 19.4	27 41.4	10 19.1	13 46.4
12 M	19 19 10.7	19 32.9	10 35.9	0♎17.1	0♋ 4.4	24 59.3	27 0.3	20 55.1	21 26.3	27 44.8	10 19.7	13 48.1
13 T	19 23 7.2	20 30.1	10 32.8	14 20.4	0 40.3	24 50.5	27 34.5	20 49.3	21 33.2	27 48.1	10 20.4	13 49.8
14 W	19 27 3.8	21 27.3	10 29.6	28 2.7	1 21.4	24 44.1	28 8.8	20 43.6	21 40.1	27 51.5	10 21.1	13 51.5
15 T	19 31 0.4	22 24.6	10 26.4	11♏25.5	2 7.6	24 40.1	28 43.3	20 38.1	21 47.1	27 54.8	10 21.8	13 53.2
16 F	19 34 56.9	23 21.8	10 23.2	24 31.1	2 58.9	24 38.4	29 17.8	20 32.7	21 54.1	27 58.1	10 22.6	13 54.9
17 S	19 38 53.5	24 19.0	10 20.1	7♐21.8	3 55.2	24D39.1	29 52.5	20 27.4	22 1.2	28 1.5	10 23.4	13 56.6
18 S	19 42 50.0	25 16.2	10 16.9	20 0.1	4 56.5	24 42.0	0♎27.3	20 22.3	22 8.3	28 4.7	10 24.3	13 58.3
19 M	19 46 46.6	26 13.5	10 13.7	2♑27.9	6 2.7	24 47.1	1 2.2	20 17.3	22 15.4	28 8.0	10 25.1	14 0.1
20 T	19 50 43.2	27 10.7	10 10.5	14 46.5	7 13.6	24 54.5	1 37.2	20 12.4	22 22.6	28 11.2	10 26.0	14 1.8
21 W	19 54 39.7	28 8.0	10 7.4	26 57.1	8 29.4	25 4.0	2 12.3	20 7.8	22 29.8	28 14.5	10 26.9	14 3.6
22 T	19 58 36.3	29 5.2	10 4.2	9♒ 0.7	9 49.7	25 15.6	2 47.6	20 3.2	22 37.0	28 17.7	10 27.9	14 5.3
23 F	20 2 32.8	0♌ 2.5	10 1.0	20 58.3	11 14.6	25 29.2	3 22.9	19 58.9	22 44.2	28 20.8	10 28.9	14 7.1
24 S	20 6 29.4	0 59.8	9 57.8	2♓51.4	12 43.8	25 44.9	3 58.4	19 54.7	22 51.5	28 24.0	10 29.9	14 8.9
25 S	20 10 25.9	1 57.1	9 54.7	14 42.0	14 17.3	26 2.4	4 33.9	19 50.6	22 58.8	28 27.1	10 30.9	14 10.6
26 M	20 14 22.5	2 54.4	9 51.5	26 33.1	15 54.9	26 21.8	5 9.6	19 46.7	23 6.1	28 30.2	10 32.0	14 12.4
27 T	20 18 19.0	3 51.7	9 48.3	8♈28.2	17 36.3	26 43.0	5 45.4	19 43.0	23 13.5	28 33.3	10 33.1	14 14.2
28 W	20 22 15.6	4 49.0	9 45.1	20 31.5	19 21.4	27 6.0	6 21.2	19 39.4	23 20.9	28 36.4	10 34.2	14 16.0
29 T	20 26 12.2	5 46.4	9 41.9	2♉47.9	21 9.8	27 30.6	6 57.2	19 36.1	23 28.3	28 39.4	10 35.4	14 17.8
30 F	20 30 8.7	6 43.8	9 38.8	15 22.4	23 1.3	27 56.9	7 33.3	19 32.9	23 35.7	28 42.4	10 36.6	14 19.6
31 S	20 34 5.3	7 41.1	9 35.6	28 20.0	24 55.6	28 24.7	8 9.5	19 29.8	23 43.1	28 45.4	10 37.8	14 21.4
						DECLINATION						
1 T	18 35 48.5	23N 8.3	15N11.3	7N59.9	18N43.9	19N40.1	4N14.2	22S48.5	15N52.9	23N34.7	2S37.6	23N40.1
4 S	18 47 38.3	22 54.8	15 8.4	22 39.9	18 49.3	19 9.0	3 32.3	22 47.7	15 46.7	23 34.9	2 38.2	23 38.6
7 W	18 59 27.9	22 37.7	15 5.4	26 57.7	19 6.7	18 42.6	2 49.9	22 47.0	15 40.4	23 35.2	2 38.8	23 37.1
10 S	19 11 17.6	22 17.1	15 2.4	15 30.0	19 33.8	18 21.6	2 6.9	22 46.2	15 33.9	23 35.4	2 39.6	23 35.5
13 T	19 23 7.2	21 53.0	14 59.5	3S31.3	20 7.7	18 6.1	1 23.6	22 45.5	15 27.3	23 35.6	2 40.5	23 34.0
16 F	19 34 56.9	21 25.5	14 56.5	20 0.9	20 44.5	17 56.2	0 39.8	22 44.9	15 20.6	23 35.8	2 41.5	23 32.5
19 M	19 46 46.6	20 54.8	14 53.5	27 20.6	21 19.8	17 51.2	0S 4.4	22 44.3	15 13.7	23 36.0	2 42.6	23 31.0
22 T	19 58 36.3	20 20.9	14 50.5	22 49.6	21 48.8	17 50.6	0 48.9	22 43.8	15 6.7	23 36.2	2 43.8	23 29.4
25 S	20 10 25.9	19 43.9	14 47.5	9 49.9	22 6.2	17 53.7	1 33.6	22 43.3	14 59.6	23 36.3	2 45.1	23 27.9
28 W	20 22 15.6	19 4.0	14 44.5	6N28.5	22 6.8	17 59.6	2 18.6	22 43.0	14 52.5	23 36.5	2 46.5	23 26.4
31 S	20 34 5.3	18 21.3	14 41.5	21 21.6	21 46.3	18 7.5	3 3.9	22 42.8	14 45.2	23 36.6	2 48.0	23 24.9

AUGUST 1948

DAY	EPHEMERIS SIDEREAL TIME	☉	☊	☽	☿	♀	♂	♃	♄	♅	♆	♇
						LONGITUDE						
1 S	20 38 1.9	8♌38.6	9♉32.4	11♊44.7	26♋52.4	28♊54.1	8♎45.8	19♐27.0	23♌50.6	28♊48.3	10♎39.0	14♌23.2
2 M	20 41 58.4	9 36.0	9 29.2	25 38.8	28 51.3	29 24.9	9 22.2	19R24.3	23 58.1	28 51.2	10 40.3	14 25.0
3 T	20 45 54.9	10 33.4	9 26.1	10♋ 2.0	0♌51.9	29 57.1	9 58.7	19 21.8	24 5.6	28 54.1	10 41.6	14 26.8
4 W	20 49 51.5	11 30.9	9 22.9	24 50.6	2 54.0	0♋30.6	10 35.3	19 19.4	24 13.1	28 57.0	10 42.9	14 28.6
5 T	20 53 48.1	12 28.4	9 19.7	9♌57.4	4 57.1	1 5.5	11 12.0	19 17.3	24 20.6	28 59.8	10 44.3	14 30.4
6 F	20 57 44.6	13 25.9	9 16.5	25 12.4	7 0.9	1 41.5	11 48.9	19 15.4	24 28.2	29 2.6	10 45.6	14 32.2
7 S	21 1 41.2	14 23.4	9 13.4	10♍24.4	9 5.1	2 18.8	12 25.8	19 13.6	24 35.8	29 5.4	10 47.0	14 34.1
8 S	21 5 37.7	15 20.9	9 10.2	25 23.2	11 9.4	2 57.2	13 2.8	19 12.0	24 43.3	29 8.1	10 48.5	14 35.9
9 M	21 9 34.3	16 18.5	9 7.0	10♎ 1.2	13 13.5	3 36.7	13 39.9	19 10.6	24 50.9	29 10.8	10 49.9	14 37.7
10 T	21 13 30.8	17 16.0	9 3.8	24 14.1	15 17.3	4 17.3	14 17.1	19 9.4	24 58.5	29 13.5	10 51.4	14 39.5
11 W	21 17 27.4	18 13.6	9 0.6	8♏ 1.0	17 20.5	4 58.9	14 54.4	19 8.3	25 6.1	29 16.1	10 52.9	14 41.3
12 T	21 21 24.0	19 11.2	8 57.5	21 23.2	19 22.9	5 41.5	15 31.8	19 7.5	25 13.8	29 18.7	10 54.4	14 43.1
13 F	21 25 20.5	20 8.8	8 54.3	4♐23.6	21 24.3	6 25.1	16 9.3	19 6.8	25 21.4	29 21.3	10 56.0	14 44.9
14 S	21 29 17.0	21 6.4	8 51.1	17 5.8	23 24.7	7 9.5	16 46.9	19 6.4	25 29.0	29 23.8	10 57.5	14 46.7
15 S	21 33 13.6	22 4.0	8 47.9	29 33.3	25 24.0	7 54.9	17 24.6	19 6.1	25 36.6	29 26.3	10 59.1	14 48.5
16 M	21 37 10.2	23 1.7	8 44.8	11♑49.5	27 22.1	8 41.1	18 2.3	19 6.0	25 44.3	29 28.8	11 0.7	14 50.3
17 T	21 41 6.8	23 59.4	8 41.6	23 57.2	29 18.9	9 28.2	18 40.2	19D 6.1	25 51.9	29 31.2	11 2.4	14 52.1
18 W	21 45 3.3	24 57.1	8 38.4	5♒58.5	1♍14.4	10 16.0	19 18.2	19 6.4	25 59.6	29 33.6	11 4.0	14 53.9
19 T	21 48 59.8	25 54.8	8 35.2	17 55.0	3 8.5	11 4.7	19 56.2	19 6.8	26 7.2	29 35.9	11 5.7	14 55.7
20 F	21 52 56.4	26 52.5	8 32.0	29 48.4	5 1.3	11 54.1	20 34.3	19 7.5	26 14.9	29 38.2	11 7.4	14 57.5
21 S	21 56 53.0	27 50.3	8 28.9	11♓39.9	6 52.7	12 44.2	21 12.5	19 8.3	26 22.5	29 40.5	11 9.1	14 59.3
22 S	22 0 49.5	28 48.0	8 25.7	23 31.2	8 42.7	13 35.0	21 50.9	19 9.3	26 30.1	29 42.7	11 10.9	15 1.1
23 M	22 4 46.0	29 45.8	8 22.5	5♈24.4	10 31.3	14 26.5	22 29.2	19 10.5	26 37.8	29 44.9	11 12.6	15 2.8
24 T	22 8 42.6	0♍43.7	8 19.3	17 22.1	12 18.6	15 18.6	23 7.7	19 11.9	26 45.4	29 47.0	11 14.4	15 4.6
25 W	22 12 39.2	1 41.6	8 16.2	29 27.6	14 4.6	16 11.4	23 46.3	19 13.5	26 53.0	29 49.1	11 16.2	15 6.3
26 T	22 16 35.7	2 39.4	8 13.0	11♉45.0	15 49.2	17 4.8	24 25.0	19 15.3	27 0.7	29 51.2	11 18.1	15 8.1
27 F	22 20 32.3	3 37.4	8 9.8	24 18.5	17 32.4	17 58.8	25 3.7	19 17.2	27 8.3	29 53.2	11 19.9	15 9.8
28 S	22 24 28.8	4 35.3	8 6.6	7♊12.8	19 14.4	18 53.3	25 42.6	19 19.3	27 15.9	29 55.2	11 21.8	15 11.6
29 S	22 28 25.4	5 33.3	8 3.4	20 32.0	20 55.0	19 48.4	26 21.5	19 21.6	27 23.5	29 57.1	11 23.6	15 13.3
30 M	22 32 21.9	6 31.3	8 0.3	4♋19.0	22 34.4	20 44.1	27 0.5	19 24.1	27 31.1	29 59.0	11 25.5	15 15.0
31 T	22 36 18.5	7 29.4	7 57.1	18 34.8	24 12.6	21 40.3	27 39.6	19 26.8	27 38.7	0♋ 0.8	11 27.5	15 16.7
						DECLINATION						
1 S	20 38 1.9	18N 6.4	14N40.4	24N50.8	21N34.3	18N10.4	3S19.0	22S42.7	14N42.8	23N36.6	2S48.5	23N24.4
4 W	20 49 51.5	17 20.1	14 37.4	25 55.9	20 42.4	18 19.7	4 4.4	22 42.6	14 35.4	23 36.8	2 50.2	23 22.9
7 S	21 1 41.2	16 31.2	14 34.4	11 37.3	19 27.6	18 29.1	4 49.9	22 42.7	14 28.0	23 36.9	2 51.9	23 21.5
10 T	21 13 30.8	15 39.9	14 31.3	8S14.0	17 52.9	18 38.1	5 35.5	22 42.9	14 20.5	23 37.0	2 53.7	23 20.1
13 F	21 25 20.5	14 46.4	14 28.3	23 11.2	16 2.5	18 46.0	6 21.1	22 43.2	14 12.9	23 37.1	2 55.6	23 18.7
16 M	21 37 10.2	13 50.8	14 25.3	27 23.9	14 0.5	18 52.3	7 6.6	22 43.6	14 5.4	23 37.1	2 57.5	23 17.3
19 T	21 48 59.8	12 53.2	14 22.2	20 9.6	11 50.7	18 56.5	7 52.0	22 44.2	13 57.8	23 37.2	2 59.6	23 16.0
22 S	22 0 49.5	11 53.7	14 19.1	5 46.5	9 36.1	18 58.1	8 37.2	22 44.9	13 50.2	23 37.3	3 1.7	23 14.7
25 W	22 12 39.2	10 52.6	14 16.1	10N39.6	7 19.2	18 56.7	9 22.2	22 45.7	13 42.6	23 37.3	3 3.8	23 13.4
28 S	22 24 28.8	9 49.9	14 13.0	24 3.2	5 1.9	18 52.1	10 6.9	22 46.7	13 35.0	23 37.4	3 6.1	23 12.2
31 T	22 36 18.5	8 45.8	14 9.9	26 56.3	2 45.5	18 43.8	10 51.3	22 47.8	13 27.3	23 37.5	3 8.3	23 11.0

SEPTEMBER 1948

DAY	EPHEMERIS SIDEREAL TIME	☉	☊	☽	☿	♀	♂	♃	♄	♅	♆	♇
	h m s	° ′	° ′	° ′	° ′	° ′	° ′	° ′	° ′	° ′	° ′	° ′
						LONGITUDE						
1 W	22 40 15.1	8♍27.4	7♉53.9	3♌17.2	25♍49.4	22♋36.9	28♎18.8	19♐29.6	27♌46.2	0♋ 2.6	11♎29.4	15♌18.4
2 T	22 44 11.6	9 25.5	7 50.7	18 20.6	27 25.0	23 34.0	28 58.1	19 32.6	27 53.8	0 4.4	11 31.3	15 20.1
3 F	22 48 8.1	10 23.7	7 47.6	3♍36.2	28 59.4	24 31.7	29 37.5	19 35.8	28 1.3	0 6.1	11 33.3	15 21.8
4 S	22 52 4.7	11 21.8	7 44.4	18 53.2	0♎32.5	25 29.7	0♏17.0	19 39.2	28 8.9	0 7.8	11 35.3	15 23.4
5 S	22 56 1.3	12 20.0	7 41.2	4♎ 0.6	2 4.4	26 28.2	0 56.5	19 42.8	28 16.4	0 9.4	11 37.3	15 25.1
6 M	22 59 57.8	13 18.3	7 38.0	18 49.2	3 35.1	27 27.1	1 36.2	19 46.5	28 23.9	0 10.9	11 39.3	15 26.8
7 T	23 3 54.4	14 16.5	7 34.9	3♏12.9	5 4.6	28 26.4	2 15.9	19 50.4	28 31.3	0 12.5	11 41.3	15 28.4
8 W	23 7 50.9	15 14.8	7 31.7	17 9.0	6 32.8	29 26.1	2 55.7	19 54.5	28 38.8	0 13.9	11 43.3	15 30.0
9 T	23 11 47.5	16 13.1	7 28.5	0♐37.6	7 59.8	0♌26.2	3 35.6	19 58.8	28 46.2	0 15.4	11 45.4	15 31.6
10 F	23 15 44.1	17 11.4	7 25.3	13 41.0	9 25.5	1 26.7	4 15.6	20 3.2	28 53.6	0 16.7	11 47.5	15 33.2
11 S	23 19 40.6	18 9.7	7 22.1	26 22.9	10 49.9	2 27.5	4 55.6	20 7.8	29 1.0	0 18.1	11 49.5	15 34.8
12 S	23 23 37.1	19 8.1	7 19.0	8♑47.3	12 13.0	3 28.7	5 35.8	20 12.5	29 8.3	0 19.3	11 51.6	15 36.4
13 M	23 27 33.7	20 6.5	7 15.8	20 58.5	13 34.8	4 30.3	6 16.0	20 17.4	29 15.7	0 20.6	11 53.7	15 37.9
14 T	23 31 30.3	21 5.0	7 12.6	3♒ 0.3	14 55.2	5 32.2	6 56.3	20 22.5	29 23.0	0 21.8	11 55.8	15 39.5
15 W	23 35 26.8	22 3.4	7 9.4	14 56.1	16 14.2	6 34.4	7 36.7	20 27.8	29 30.3	0 22.9	11 58.0	15 41.0
16 T	23 39 23.3	23 1.9	7 6.3	26 48.6	17 31.7	7 36.9	8 17.1	20 33.2	29 37.5	0 24.0	12 0.1	15 42.5
17 F	23 43 19.9	24 0.4	7 3.1	8♓40.3	18 47.7	8 39.8	8 57.7	20 38.7	29 44.7	0 25.0	12 2.2	15 44.0
18 S	23 47 16.5	24 59.0	6 59.9	20 32.9	20 2.1	9 43.0	9 38.3	20 44.5	29 51.9	0 26.0	12 4.4	15 45.5
19 S	23 51 13.0	25 57.5	6 56.7	2♈28.3	21 14.9	10 46.5	10 19.0	20 50.4	29 59.1	0 26.9	12 6.5	15 46.9
20 M	23 55 9.6	26 56.2	6 53.5	14 28.0	22 25.9	11 50.2	10 59.8	20 56.4	0♍ 6.2	0 27.8	12 8.7	15 48.4
21 T	23 59 6.1	27 54.8	6 50.4	26 34.0	23 35.1	12 54.3	11 40.6	21 2.6	0 13.3	0 28.6	12 10.9	15 49.8
22 W	0 3 2.7	28 53.5	6 47.2	8♉48.4	24 42.3	13 58.6	12 21.5	21 8.9	0 20.3	0 29.4	12 13.1	15 51.2
23 T	0 6 59.3	29 52.2	6 44.0	21 14.0	25 47.5	15 3.2	13 2.6	21 15.4	0 27.3	0 30.1	12 15.2	15 52.6
24 F	0 10 55.8	0♎50.9	6 40.8	3♊53.6	26 50.4	16 8.1	13 43.7	21 22.1	0 34.3	0 30.8	12 17.4	15 54.0
25 S	0 14 52.4	1 49.7	6 37.7	16 50.4	27 50.9	17 13.3	14 24.8	21 28.8	0 41.2	0 31.4	12 19.6	15 55.3
26 S	0 18 48.9	2 48.6	6 34.5	0♋ 7.7	28 48.9	18 18.7	15 6.1	21 35.8	0 48.1	0 32.0	12 21.8	15 56.7
27 M	0 22 45.5	3 47.4	6 31.3	13 47.8	29 44.1	19 24.3	15 47.4	21 42.9	0 55.0	0 32.5	12 24.1	15 58.0
28 T	0 26 42.0	4 46.3	6 28.1	27 51.8	0♏36.3	20 30.2	16 28.8	21 50.1	1 1.8	0 33.0	12 26.3	15 59.3
29 W	0 30 38.6	5 45.3	6 24.9	12♌18.8	1 25.3	21 36.4	17 10.3	21 57.5	1 8.6	0 33.4	12 28.5	16 0.6
30 T	0 34 35.1	6 44.3	6 21.8	27 5.4	2 10.8	22 42.7	17 51.9	22 5.0	1 15.3	0 33.8	12 30.7	16 1.8
						DECLINATION						
1 W	22 40 15.1	8N24.1	14N 8.9	24N21.4	2N 0.5	18N40.2	11S 6.0	22S48.2	13N24.8	23N37.5	3S 9.1	23N10.7
4 S	22 52 4.7	7 18.3	14 5.8	7 51.2	0S12.8	18 26.8	11 49.9	22 49.4	13 17.2	23 37.5	3 11.5	23 9.6
7 T	23 3 54.4	6 11.5	14 2.7	12S20.5	2 22.6	18 9.3	12 33.2	22 50.7	13 9.7	23 37.6	3 13.9	23 8.5
10 F	23 15 44.1	5 3.7	13 59.6	25 33.6	4 28.0	17 47.6	13 16.0	22 52.1	13 2.2	23 37.6	3 16.3	23 7.5
13 M	23 27 33.7	3 55.2	13 56.5	26 42.5	6 28.1	17 21.8	13 58.2	22 53.6	12 54.8	23 37.7	3 18.8	23 6.6
16 T	23 39 23.3	2 46.0	13 53.4	17 5.0	8 22.1	16 51.6	14 39.7	22 55.2	12 47.5	23 37.7	3 21.3	23 5.7
19 S	23 51 13.0	1 36.4	13 50.3	1 35.7	10 9.0	16 17.1	15 20.4	22 56.8	12 40.3	23 37.8	3 23.8	23 4.9
22 W	0 3 2.7	0 26.5	13 47.1	14N44.7	11 47.3	15 38.4	16 0.2	22 58.5	12 33.1	23 37.8	3 26.4	23 4.2
25 S	0 14 52.4	0S43.7	13 44.0	26 14.4	13 15.8	14 55.5	16 39.2	23 0.2	12 26.1	23 37.9	3 29.0	23 3.5
28 T	0 26 42.0	1 53.8	13 40.9	25 39.6	14 32.2	14 8.4	17 17.1	23 2.0	12 19.1	23 37.9	3 31.6	23 2.9

OCTOBER 1948

DAY	EPHEMERIS SIDEREAL TIME	☉	☊	☽	☿	♀	♂	♃	♄	♅	♆	♇
						LONGITUDE						
1 F	0 38 31.7	7♎43.3	6♉18.6	12♍ 5.3	2♏52.5	23♌49.3	18♏33.6	22♐12.6	1♍22.0	0♋34.1	12♎33.0	16♌ 3.1
2 S	0 42 28.3	8 42.3	6 15.4	27 10.3	3 30.0	24 56.1	19 15.3	22 20.4	1 28.6	0 34.3	12 35.2	16 4.3
3 S	0 46 24.8	9 41.4	6 12.2	12♎10.9	4 3.0	26 3.1	19 57.1	22 28.3	1 35.2	0 34.5	12 37.4	16 5.5
4 M	0 50 21.4	10 40.5	6 9.1	26 58.3	4 31.0	27 10.4	20 39.0	22 36.4	1 41.7	0 34.7	12 39.7	16 6.7
5 T	0 54 17.9	11 39.7	6 5.9	11♏25.4	4 53.7	28 17.8	21 21.0	22 44.6	1 48.2	0 34.8	12 41.9	16 7.8
6 W	0 58 14.4	12 38.9	6 2.7	25 27.8	5 10.6	29 25.4	22 3.0	22 52.9	1 54.7	0 34.8	12 44.1	16 8.9
7 T	1 2 11.0	13 38.1	5 59.5	9♐ 3.6	5 21.3	0♍33.2	22 45.1	23 1.4	2 1.0	0R34.8	12 46.4	16 10.1
8 F	1 6 7.6	14 37.4	5 56.4	22 13.6	5 25.2	1 41.2	23 27.3	23 10.0	2 7.4	0 34.7	12 48.6	16 11.2
9 S	1 10 4.1	15 36.6	5 53.2	5♑ 0.2	5R21.9	2 49.3	24 9.6	23 18.7	2 13.6	0 34.6	12 50.8	16 12.2
10 S	1 14 0.7	16 35.9	5 50.0	17 27.1	5 10.9	3 57.7	24 51.9	23 27.5	2 19.8	0 34.4	12 53.1	16 13.3
11 M	1 17 57.2	17 35.3	5 46.8	29 38.6	4 52.0	5 6.2	25 34.4	23 36.4	2 26.0	0 34.2	12 55.3	16 14.3
12 T	1 21 53.8	18 34.6	5 43.6	11♒39.0	4 24.9	6 14.9	26 16.8	23 45.5	2 32.1	0 34.0	12 57.5	16 15.3
13 W	1 25 50.3	19 34.0	5 40.5	23 32.9	3 49.4	7 23.8	26 59.4	23 54.7	2 38.1	0 33.6	12 59.8	16 16.3
14 T	1 29 46.9	20 33.5	5 37.3	5♓24.1	3 5.6	8 32.8	27 42.0	24 4.0	2 44.1	0 33.2	13 2.0	16 17.2
15 F	1 33 43.4	21 32.9	5 34.1	17 16.0	2 13.9	9 42.0	28 24.7	24 13.5	2 50.0	0 32.8	13 4.2	16 18.1
16 S	1 37 40.0	22 32.4	5 30.9	29 11.8	1 15.0	10 51.3	29 7.5	24 23.0	2 55.9	0 32.3	13 6.4	16 19.0
17 S	1 41 36.6	23 31.9	5 27.7	11♈13.6	0 9.8	12 0.8	29 50.3	24 32.7	3 1.7	0 31.8	13 8.6	16 19.9
18 M	1 45 33.1	24 31.5	5 24.6	23 23.6	28♎59.7	13 10.5	0♐33.3	24 42.4	3 7.4	0 31.2	13 10.8	16 20.8
19 T	1 49 29.6	25 31.1	5 21.4	5♉43.1	27 46.3	14 20.3	1 16.2	24 52.3	3 13.0	0 30.6	13 13.0	16 21.6
20 W	1 53 26.2	26 30.7	5 18.2	18 13.6	26 31.7	15 30.3	1 59.3	25 2.3	3 18.6	0 29.9	13 15.2	16 22.4
21 T	1 57 22.8	27 30.4	5 15.0	0♊56.0	25 18.0	16 40.4	2 42.4	25 12.4	3 24.2	0 29.1	13 17.4	16 23.2
22 F	2 1 19.3	28 30.1	5 11.9	13 51.6	24 7.4	17 50.7	3 25.6	25 22.6	3 29.6	0 28.4	13 19.6	16 23.9
23 S	2 5 15.9	29 29.8	5 8.7	27 1.5	23 2.0	19 1.1	4 8.9	25 32.9	3 35.0	0 27.5	13 21.7	16 24.6
24 S	2 9 12.4	0♏29.6	5 5.5	10♋26.5	22 3.9	20 11.6	4 52.2	25 43.3	3 40.3	0 26.6	13 23.9	16 25.3
25 M	2 13 9.0	1 29.4	5 2.3	24 7.3	21 14.7	21 22.3	5 35.6	25 53.8	3 45.5	0 25.7	13 26.0	16 26.0
26 T	2 17 5.6	2 29.2	4 59.2	8♌ 4.3	20 35.6	22 33.1	6 19.1	26 4.4	3 50.7	0 24.7	13 28.2	16 26.6
27 W	2 21 2.1	3 29.1	4 56.0	22 16.5	20 7.5	23 44.1	7 2.6	26 15.1	3 55.8	0 23.7	13 30.3	16 27.3
28 T	2 24 58.7	4 29.0	4 52.8	6♍41.9	19 50.8	24 55.1	7 46.2	26 25.9	4 0.8	0 22.6	13 32.4	16 27.9
29 F	2 28 55.2	5 29.0	4 49.6	21 17.0	19 45.6	26 6.3	8 29.9	26 36.8	4 5.7	0 21.4	13 34.6	16 28.4
30 S	2 32 51.8	6 29.0	4 46.4	5♎56.9	19D51.7	27 17.6	9 13.7	26 47.8	4 10.6	0 20.3	13 36.7	16 29.0
31 S	2 36 48.3	7 29.0	4 43.3	20 35.4	20 8.5	28 29.0	9 57.5	26 58.8	4 15.4	0 19.0	13 38.7	16 29.5
						DECLINATION						
1 F	0 38 31.7	3S 3.9	13N37.7	10N53.1	15S33.9	13N17.4	17S54.0	23S 3.7	12N12.3	23N38.0	3S34.2	23N 2.4
4 M	0 50 21.4	4 13.6	13 34.6	9S42.7	16 17.1	12 22.6	18 29.7	23 5.5	12 5.7	23 38.0	3 36.8	23 2.0
7 T	1 2 11.0	5 23.0	13 31.4	24 43.6	16 36.8	11 24.2	19 4.2	23 7.2	11 59.2	23 38.1	3 39.4	23 1.6
10 S	1 14 0.7	6 31.6	13 28.3	27 16.7	16 26.5	10 22.5	19 37.4	23 9.0	11 52.9	23 38.1	3 41.9	23 1.3
13 W	1 25 50.3	7 39.5	13 25.1	18 22.8	15 39.5	9 17.6	20 9.2	23 10.6	11 46.8	23 38.2	3 44.5	23 1.1
16 S	1 37 40.0	8 46.4	13 21.9	3 8.8	14 11.9	8 9.7	20 39.5	23 12.2	11 40.9	23 38.3	3 47.1	23 1.0
19 T	1 49 29.6	9 52.2	13 18.7	13N30.3	12 9.5	6 59.2	21 8.3	23 13.8	11 35.2	23 38.3	3 49.6	23 1.0
22 F	2 1 19.3	10 56.7	13 15.6	25 46.5	9 53.0	5 46.3	21 35.4	23 15.3	11 29.7	23 38.4	3 52.1	23 1.0
25 M	2 13 9.0	11 59.8	13 12.4	26 24.3	7 53.4	4 31.2	22 0.8	23 16.6	11 24.4	23 38.5	3 54.5	23 1.1
28 T	2 24 58.7	13 1.2	13 9.2	13 13.9	6 36.4	3 14.2	22 24.4	23 17.9	11 19.4	23 38.5	3 57.0	23 1.3
31 S	2 36 48.3	14 0.8	13 6.0	6S49.6	6 11.7	1 55.7	22 46.2	23 19.1	11 14.6	23 38.6	3 59.3	23 1.6

NOVEMBER 1948

LONGITUDE

DAY	EPHEMERIS SIDEREAL TIME h m s	☉ ° ′	☊ ° ′	☽ ° ′	☿ ° ′	♀ ° ′	♂ ° ′	♃ ° ′	♄ ° ′	♅ ° ′	♆ ° ′	♇ ° ′
1 M	2 40 44.9	8♏29.0	4♉40.1	5♏ 6.2	20♎35.3	29♍40.6	10♐41.4	27♐10.0	4♍20.1	0♋17.8	13♎40.8	16♌29.9
2 T	2 44 41.4	9 29.1	4 36.9	19 23.1	21 11.4	0♎52.2	11 25.4	27 21.3	4 24.7	0R16.4	13 42.9	16 30.4
3 W	2 48 38.0	10 29.3	4 33.7	3♐21.4	21 55.9	2 3.9	12 9.4	27 32.6	4 29.2	0 15.1	13 44.9	16 30.8
4 T	2 52 34.5	11 29.4	4 30.6	16 57.7	22 47.9	3 15.8	12 53.5	27 44.1	4 33.6	0 13.6	13 47.0	16 31.2
5 F	2 56 31.1	12 29.6	4 27.4	0♑10.9	23 46.5	4 27.7	13 37.7	27 55.6	4 38.0	0 12.2	13 49.0	16 31.6
6 S	3 0 27.7	13 29.8	4 24.2	13 1.7	24 50.9	5 39.7	14 21.9	28 7.2	4 42.3	0 10.7	13 51.0	16 31.9
7 S	3 4 24.2	14 30.0	4 21.0	25 32.4	26 0.5	6 51.8	15 6.2	28 18.8	4 46.4	0 9.1	13 53.0	16 32.2
8 M	3 8 20.8	15 30.3	4 17.8	7♒46.4	27 14.3	8 4.1	15 50.5	28 30.6	4 50.5	0 7.6	13 55.0	16 32.5
9 T	3 12 17.3	16 30.6	4 14.7	19 48.0	28 31.9	9 16.4	16 35.0	28 42.4	4 54.5	0 5.9	13 56.9	16 32.8
10 W	3 16 13.9	17 30.9	4 11.5	1♓41.8	29 52.7	10 28.8	17 19.4	28 54.4	4 58.4	0 4.3	13 58.9	16 33.0
11 T	3 20 10.4	18 31.2	4 8.3	13 32.7	1♏16.1	11 41.3	18 4.0	29 6.3	5 2.3	0 2.5	14 0.8	16 33.2
12 F	3 24 7.0	19 31.5	4 5.1	25 25.2	2 41.8	12 53.8	18 48.5	29 18.4	5 6.0	0 0.8	14 2.7	16 33.4
13 S	3 28 3.5	20 31.9	4 2.0	7♈23.6	4 9.3	14 6.5	19 33.2	29 30.5	5 9.6	29♊59.0	14 4.6	16 33.5
14 S	3 32 0.1	21 32.3	3 58.8	19 31.4	5 38.3	15 19.2	20 17.9	29 42.7	5 13.2	29 57.2	14 6.5	16 33.7
15 M	3 35 56.7	22 32.7	3 55.6	1♉51.7	7 8.6	16 32.0	21 2.7	29 55.0	5 16.6	29 55.3	14 8.3	16 33.8
16 T	3 39 53.2	23 33.2	3 52.4	14 26.3	8 40.0	17 44.9	21 47.5	0♑ 7.3	5 20.0	29 53.4	14 10.1	16 33.8
17 W	3 43 49.8	24 33.7	3 49.3	27 16.3	10 12.1	18 57.9	22 32.4	0 19.7	5 23.2	29 51.5	14 11.9	16 33.8
18 T	3 47 46.3	25 34.2	3 46.1	10♊21.9	11 44.9	20 10.9	23 17.3	0 32.2	5 26.4	29 49.5	14 13.7	16 33.8
19 F	3 51 42.9	26 34.7	3 42.9	23 42.1	13 18.2	21 24.0	24 2.4	0 44.7	5 29.4	29 47.5	14 15.5	16R33.8
20 S	3 55 39.5	27 35.3	3 39.7	7♋15.7	14 51.9	22 37.2	24 47.4	0 57.3	5 32.4	29 45.5	14 17.3	16 33.8
21 S	3 59 36.0	28 35.8	3 36.5	21 0.6	16 25.8	23 50.5	25 32.5	1 9.9	5 35.3	29 43.4	14 19.0	16 33.7
22 M	4 3 32.6	29 36.5	3 33.4	4♌54.9	18 0.0	25 3.8	26 17.7	1 22.6	5 38.0	29 41.3	14 20.7	16 33.6
23 T	4 7 29.1	0♐37.1	3 30.2	18 56.4	19 34.4	26 17.2	27 2.9	1 35.4	5 40.7	29 39.2	14 22.4	16 33.4
24 W	4 11 25.7	1 37.8	3 27.0	3♍ 3.5	21 8.8	27 30.7	27 48.2	1 48.2	5 43.2	29 37.0	14 24.0	16 33.3
25 T	4 15 22.2	2 38.5	3 23.8	17 14.2	22 43.3	28 44.2	28 33.6	2 1.1	5 45.7	29 34.8	14 25.7	16 33.1
26 F	4 19 18.8	3 39.2	3 20.7	1♎26.9	24 17.8	29 57.8	29 19.0	2 14.0	5 48.0	29 32.6	14 27.3	16 32.8
27 S	4 23 15.3	4 40.0	3 17.5	15 39.3	25 52.3	1♏11.5	0♑ 4.5	2 27.0	5 50.3	29 30.3	14 28.9	16 32.6
28 S	4 27 11.9	5 40.7	3 14.3	29 48.9	27 26.8	2 25.2	0 50.0	2 40.0	5 52.4	29 28.1	14 30.4	16 32.3
29 M	4 31 8.5	6 41.6	3 11.1	13♏52.5	29 1.3	3 38.9	1 35.5	2 53.1	5 54.5	29 25.8	14 32.0	16 32.0
30 T	4 35 5.0	7 42.4	3 8.0	27 46.6	0♐35.7	4 52.8	2 21.2	3 6.2	5 56.4	29 23.4	14 33.5	16 31.7

DECLINATION

DAY	SIDEREAL TIME	☉	☊	☽	☿	♀	♂	♃	♄	♅	♆	♇
1 M	2 40 44.9	14S20.2	13N 4.9	13S14.5	6S14.5	1N29.3	22S53.0	23S19.4	11N13.1	23N38.6	4S 0.1	23N 1.7
4 T	2 52 34.5	15 17.1	13 1.7	26 20.0	6 50.5	0 9.2	23 12.1	23 20.4	11 8.7	23 38.7	4 2.4	23 2.1
7 S	3 4 24.2	16 11.7	12 58.5	26 9.5	7 58.3	1S11.7	23 29.2	23 21.3	11 4.6	23 38.7	4 4.7	23 2.6
10 W	3 16 13.9	17 3.9	12 55.3	15 16.4	9 26.2	2 33.1	23 44.2	23 22.0	11 0.8	23 38.8	4 6.8	23 3.2
13 S	3 28 3.5	17 53.4	12 52.1	0N41.4	11 5.0	3 54.6	23 57.0	23 22.5	10 57.3	23 38.8	4 9.0	23 3.8
16 T	3 39 53.2	18 40.1	12 48.8	17 0.3	12 48.4	5 16.0	24 7.6	23 22.9	10 54.1	23 38.9	4 11.0	23 4.6
19 F	3 51 42.9	19 23.8	12 45.6	27 14.5	14 31.8	6 36.8	24 15.9	23 23.1	10 51.3	23 38.9	4 13.0	23 5.4
22 M	4 3 32.6	20 4.4	12 42.4	24 6.9	16 12.1	7 56.9	24 21.9	23 23.1	10 48.7	23 39.0	4 14.9	23 6.3
25 T	4 15 22.2	20 41.8	12 39.1	8 35.6	17 47.2	9 15.8	24 25.5	23 22.9	10 46.6	23 39.0	4 16.7	23 7.2
28 S	4 27 11.9	21 15.6	12 35.9	10S59.5	19 15.7	10 33.2	24 26.7	23 22.5	10 44.7	23 39.0	4 18.4	23 8.2

DECEMBER 1948

LONGITUDE

DAY	SIDEREAL TIME	☉	☊	☽	☿	♀	♂	♃	♄	♅	♆	♇
1 W	4 39 1.6	8♐43.2	3♉ 4.8	11♐27.9	2♐10.0	6♏ 6.6	3♑ 6.8	3♑19.4	5♍58.2	29♊21.1	14♎35.0	16♌31.3
2 T	4 42 58.1	9 44.1	3 1.6	24 53.3	3 44.4	7 20.5	3 52.6	3 32.6	5 59.9	29R18.7	14 36.4	16R30.9
3 F	4 46 54.7	10 45.0	2 58.4	8♑ 0.8	5 18.6	8 34.5	4 38.4	3 45.9	6 1.5	29 16.3	14 37.9	16 30.5
4 S	4 50 51.3	11 45.9	2 55.3	20 49.7	6 52.9	9 48.5	5 24.2	3 59.2	6 3.0	29 13.9	14 39.3	16 30.1
5 S	4 54 47.8	12 46.8	2 52.1	3♒20.5	8 27.0	11 2.5	6 10.1	4 12.5	6 4.4	29 11.5	14 40.7	16 29.6
6 M	4 58 44.4	13 47.7	2 48.9	15 35.4	10 1.2	12 16.6	6 56.0	4 25.9	6 5.6	29 9.0	14 42.0	16 29.1
7 T	5 2 40.9	14 48.7	2 45.7	27 37.6	11 35.4	13 30.7	7 42.0	4 39.3	6 6.8	29 6.6	14 43.3	16 28.6
8 W	5 6 37.5	15 49.6	2 42.6	9♓31.4	13 9.5	14 44.9	8 28.0	4 52.8	6 7.9	29 4.1	14 44.6	16 28.0
9 T	5 10 34.1	16 50.6	2 39.4	21 21.5	14 43.7	15 59.1	9 14.1	5 6.3	6 8.8	29 1.6	14 45.9	16 27.4
10 F	5 14 30.6	17 51.6	2 36.2	3♈13.1	16 17.9	17 13.3	10 0.2	5 19.8	6 9.6	28 59.1	14 47.2	16 26.8
11 S	5 18 27.2	18 52.5	2 33.0	15 11.4	17 52.1	18 27.6	10 46.3	5 33.3	6 10.3	28 56.6	14 48.4	16 26.2
12 S	5 22 23.7	19 53.5	2 29.8	27 21.4	19 26.5	19 41.9	11 32.5	5 46.9	6 10.9	28 54.0	14 49.5	16 25.5
13 M	5 26 20.3	20 54.6	2 26.7	9♉47.3	21 0.8	20 56.2	12 18.8	6 0.5	6 11.4	28 51.5	14 50.7	16 24.9
14 T	5 30 16.9	21 55.6	2 23.5	22 32.4	22 35.3	22 10.6	13 5.0	6 14.2	6 11.8	28 49.0	14 51.8	16 24.2
15 W	5 34 13.4	22 56.6	2 20.3	5♊38.6	24 9.9	23 25.0	13 51.4	6 27.8	6 12.1	28 46.4	14 52.9	16 23.4
16 T	5 38 10.0	23 57.6	2 17.1	19 6.1	25 44.6	24 39.4	14 37.7	6 41.5	6 12.2	28 43.8	14 54.0	16 22.7
17 F	5 42 6.5	24 58.7	2 14.0	2♋53.0	27 19.4	25 53.9	15 24.1	6 55.2	6 12.3	28 41.3	14 55.0	16 21.9
18 S	5 46 3.1	25 59.7	2 10.8	16 55.7	28 54.4	27 8.4	16 10.6	7 9.0	6R12.2	28 38.7	14 56.0	16 21.1
19 S	5 49 59.6	27 0.8	2 7.6	1♌ 9.4	0♑29.6	28 22.9	16 57.0	7 22.7	6 12.1	28 36.1	14 57.0	16 20.3
20 M	5 53 56.2	28 1.9	2 4.4	15 28.7	2 4.9	29 37.5	17 43.5	7 36.5	6 11.8	28 33.6	14 57.9	16 19.4
21 T	5 57 52.7	29 3.0	2 1.3	29 48.5	3 40.4	0♐52.0	18 30.1	7 50.3	6 11.4	28 31.0	14 58.8	16 18.6
22 W	6 1 49.3	0♑ 4.1	1 58.1	14♍ 4.7	5 16.1	2 6.7	19 16.7	8 4.1	6 10.9	28 28.4	14 59.7	16 17.7
23 T	6 5 45.9	1 5.2	1 54.9	28 14.6	6 52.0	3 21.3	20 3.3	8 17.9	6 10.3	28 25.8	15 0.5	16 16.8
24 F	6 9 42.4	2 6.4	1 51.7	12♎16.7	8 28.0	4 36.0	20 50.0	8 31.7	6 9.5	28 23.3	15 1.3	16 15.8
25 S	6 13 39.0	3 7.5	1 48.6	26 10.5	10 4.3	5 50.6	21 36.7	8 45.6	6 8.7	28 20.7	15 2.1	16 14.9
26 S	6 17 35.5	4 8.6	1 45.4	9♏55.8	11 40.8	7 5.3	22 23.5	8 59.5	6 7.7	28 18.1	15 2.8	16 13.9
27 M	6 21 32.1	5 9.8	1 42.2	23 32.4	13 17.4	8 20.1	23 10.3	9 13.3	6 6.7	28 15.6	15 3.5	16 12.9
28 T	6 25 28.7	6 11.0	1 39.0	6♐59.8	14 54.2	9 34.8	23 57.1	9 27.2	6 5.5	28 13.0	15 4.2	16 11.9
29 W	6 29 25.2	7 12.2	1 35.8	20 16.8	16 31.2	10 49.6	24 43.9	9 41.1	6 4.2	28 10.5	15 4.9	16 10.8
30 T	6 33 21.8	8 13.3	1 32.7	3♑22.3	18 8.2	12 4.4	25 30.8	9 55.0	6 2.8	28 8.0	15 5.5	16 9.8
31 F	6 37 18.4	9 14.5	1 29.5	16 14.8	19 45.3	13 19.2	26 17.7	10 8.9	6 1.3	28 5.4	15 6.0	16 8.7

DECLINATION

DAY	SIDEREAL TIME	☉	☊	☽	☿	♀	♂	♃	♄	♅	♆	♇
1 W	4 39 1.6	21S45.9	12N32.6	25S15.1	20S36.2	11S48.6	24S25.5	23S21.9	10N43.3	23N39.0	4S20.0	23N 9.3
4 S	4 50 51.3	22 12.4	12 29.4	26 48.1	21 48.0	13 1.9	24 21.8	23 21.1	10 42.2	23 39.0	4 21.5	23 10.5
7 T	5 2 40.9	22 35.0	12 26.1	16 44.9	22 50.2	14 12.4	24 15.7	23 20.1	10 41.4	23 39.0	4 23.0	23 11.7
10 F	5 14 30.6	22 53.6	12 22.8	1 9.5	23 42.2	15 20.0	24 7.0	23 18.8	10 41.1	23 39.0	4 24.3	23 13.0
13 M	5 26 20.3	23 8.2	12 19.6	15N14.2	24 23.2	16 24.3	23 56.0	23 17.4	10 41.1	23 39.0	4 25.5	23 14.4
16 T	5 38 10.0	23 18.6	12 16.3	26 37.1	24 52.8	17 24.9	23 42.4	23 15.7	10 41.5	23 38.9	4 26.6	23 15.8
19 S	5 49 59.6	23 24.8	12 13.0	24 52.1	25 10.1	18 21.5	23 26.5	23 13.8	10 42.2	23 38.9	4 27.6	23 17.2
22 W	6 1 49.3	23 26.9	12 9.7	9 49.6	25 14.8	19 13.7	23 8.1	23 11.7	10 43.3	23 38.8	4 28.5	23 18.7
25 S	6 13 39.0	23 24.7	12 6.4	9S31.7	25 6.3	20 1.2	22 47.3	23 9.4	10 44.8	23 38.8	4 29.3	23 20.2
28 T	6 25 28.7	23 18.2	12 3.1	24 16.5	24 44.2	20 43.8	22 24.2	23 6.8	10 46.7	23 38.7	4 30.0	23 21.8
31 F	6 37 18.4	23 7.6	11 59.8	27 15.2	24 8.1	21 21.0	21 58.8	23 4.0	10 48.9	23 38.6	4 30.5	23 23.4

JANUARY 1949

DAY	EPHEMERIS SIDEREAL TIME	☉	☊	☽	☿	♀	♂	♃	♄	♅	♆	♇
	h m s	° ′	° ′	° ′	° ′	° ′	° ′	° ′	° ′	° ′	° ′	° ′
						LONGITUDE						
1 S	6 41 14.9	10♑15.7	1♉26.3	28♑53.4	21♑22.4	14♐34.0	27♑ 4.7	10♑22.8	5♍59.7	28♊ 2.9	15♎ 6.6	16♌ 7.6
2 S	6 45 11.5	11 16.9	1 23.1	11♒17.9	22 59.5	15 48.8	27 51.7	10 36.7	5R58.0	28R 0.4	15 7.1	16R 6.5
3 M	6 49 8.0	12 18.1	1 20.0	23 29.3	24 36.4	17 3.7	28 38.7	10 50.6	5 56.2	27 57.9	15 7.5	16 5.4
4 T	6 53 4.6	13 19.3	1 16.8	5♓29.6	26 13.2	18 18.5	29 25.7	11 4.6	5 54.3	27 55.5	15 8.0	16 4.2
5 W	6 57 1.2	14 20.4	1 13.6	17 21.9	27 49.6	19 33.4	0♒12.8	11 18.5	5 52.3	27 53.0	15 8.4	16 3.1
6 T	7 0 57.7	15 21.6	1 10.4	29 10.4	29 25.5	20 48.3	0 59.8	11 32.4	5 50.2	27 50.6	15 8.8	16 1.9
7 F	7 4 54.3	16 22.8	1 7.3	10♈59.8	1♒ 0.7	22 3.1	1 46.9	11 46.3	5 47.9	27 48.2	15 9.1	16 0.7
8 S	7 8 50.8	17 23.9	1 4.1	22 55.6	2 35.2	23 18.0	2 34.1	12 0.1	5 45.6	27 45.8	15 9.4	15 59.5
9 S	7 12 47.4	18 25.1	1 0.9	5♉ 3.4	4 8.6	24 32.9	3 21.2	12 14.0	5 43.2	27 43.4	15 9.7	15 58.2
10 M	7 16 43.9	19 26.2	0 57.7	17 28.5	5 40.6	25 47.8	4 8.4	12 27.9	5 40.7	27 41.1	15 9.9	15 57.0
11 T	7 20 40.5	20 27.4	0 54.6	0♊15.7	7 11.0	27 2.7	4 55.6	12 41.8	5 38.1	27 38.8	15 10.1	15 55.8
12 W	7 24 37.1	21 28.5	0 51.4	13 28.2	8 39.4	28 17.7	5 42.8	12 55.6	5 35.4	27 36.5	15 10.2	15 54.5
13 T	7 28 33.6	22 29.6	0 48.2	27 7.6	10 5.3	29 32.6	6 30.0	13 9.4	5 32.6	27 34.2	15 10.4	15 53.2
14 F	7 32 30.2	23 30.7	0 45.0	11♋12.6	11 28.4	0♑47.5	7 17.3	13 23.3	5 29.7	27 32.0	15 10.5	15 51.9
15 S	7 36 26.7	24 31.8	0 41.8	25 39.2	12 47.9	2 2.5	8 4.5	13 37.1	5 26.7	27 29.7	15 10.5	15 50.6
16 S	7 40 23.3	25 32.9	0 38.7	10♌20.6	14 3.4	3 17.4	8 51.8	13 50.9	5 23.6	27 27.5	15 10.6	15 49.3
17 M	7 44 19.8	26 34.0	0 35.5	25 8.7	15 14.2	4 32.4	9 39.1	14 4.6	5 20.5	27 25.4	15R 10.5	15 48.0
18 T	7 48 16.4	27 35.0	0 32.3	9♍55.0	16 19.4	5 47.3	10 26.4	14 18.4	5 17.2	27 23.2	15 10.5	15 46.6
19 W	7 52 13.0	28 36.1	0 29.1	24 32.4	17 18.3	7 2.3	11 13.7	14 32.1	5 13.9	27 21.1	15 10.4	15 45.3
20 T	7 56 9.5	29 37.2	0 26.0	8♎55.9	18 10.1	8 17.3	12 1.1	14 45.8	5 10.5	27 19.1	15 10.3	15 43.9
21 F	8 0 6.1	0♒38.2	0 22.8	23 3.0	18 53.9	9 32.3	12 48.5	14 59.5	5 7.0	27 17.0	15 10.2	15 42.6
22 S	8 4 2.6	1 39.3	0 19.6	6♏53.1	19 28.7	10 47.2	13 35.8	15 13.1	5 3.5	27 15.0	15 10.0	15 41.2
23 S	8 7 59.2	2 40.3	0 16.4	20 27.1	19 54.0	12 2.2	14 23.2	15 26.8	4 59.8	27 13.1	15 9.8	15 39.8
24 M	8 11 55.8	3 41.4	0 13.3	3♐46.7	20 8.8	13 17.3	15 10.6	15 40.4	4 56.1	27 11.1	15 9.5	15 38.4
25 T	8 15 52.3	4 42.4	0 10.1	16 53.3	20 12.6	14 32.3	15 58.1	15 54.0	4 52.3	27 9.2	15 9.2	15 37.0
26 W	8 19 48.9	5 43.4	0 6.9	29 48.3	20R 5.0	15 47.3	16 45.5	16 7.5	4 48.5	27 7.4	15 8.9	15 35.6
27 T	8 23 45.4	6 44.4	0 3.7	12♑32.4	19 46.0	17 2.3	17 32.9	16 21.0	4 44.5	27 5.5	15 8.6	15 34.2
28 F	8 27 42.0	7 45.4	0 0.5	25 6.1	19 15.8	18 17.3	18 20.4	16 34.5	4 40.5	27 3.8	15 8.2	15 32.8
29 S	8 31 38.5	8 46.4	29♈57.4	7♒29.5	18 34.9	19 32.3	19 7.8	16 48.0	4 36.5	27 2.0	15 7.8	15 31.4
30 S	8 35 35.1	9 47.3	29 54.2	19 42.9	17 44.3	20 47.3	19 55.3	17 1.4	4 32.3	27 0.3	15 7.3	15 30.0
31 M	8 39 31.6	10 48.3	29 51.0	1♓46.8	16 45.4	22 2.3	20 42.7	17 14.7	4 28.2	26 58.7	15 6.8	15 28.5
						DECLINATION						
1 S	6 41 14.9	23S 3.1	11N58.7	25S17.9	23S52.9	21S32.2	21S49.8	23S 3.0	10N49.7	23N38.6	4S30.6	23N23.9
4 T	6 53 4.6	22 46.9	11 55.4	13 24.1	22 58.2	22 2.1	21 21.4	22 60.0	10 52.4	23 38.5	4 31.0	23 25.5
7 F	7 4 54.3	22 26.6	11 52.1	2N42.5	21 49.9	22 26.0	20 50.8	22 56.7	10 55.3	23 38.4	4 31.3	23 27.2
10 M	7 16 43.9	22 2.3	11 48.8	18 22.7	20 29.5	22 44.0	20 18.1	22 53.2	10 58.7	23 38.3	4 31.4	23 28.8
13 T	7 28 33.6	21 34.2	11 45.5	27 33.9	18 59.1	22 55.8	19 43.5	22 49.5	11 2.3	23 38.2	4 31.5	23 30.5
16 S	7 40 23.3	21 2.4	11 42.1	22 23.9	17 23.1	23 1.3	19 6.8	22 45.6	11 6.1	23 38.1	4 31.4	23 32.2
19 W	7 52 13.0	20 26.9	11 38.8	4 52.3	15 48.0	23 0.5	18 28.3	22 41.5	11 10.3	23 37.9	4 31.1	23 33.8
22 S	8 4 2.6	19 47.9	11 35.4	14S21.9	14 23.1	22 53.4	17 48.0	22 37.3	11 14.7	23 37.8	4 30.8	23 35.5
25 T	8 15 52.3	19 5.7	11 32.1	26 26.4	13 19.4	22 40.0	17 5.9	22 32.9	11 19.3	23 37.7	4 30.4	23 37.1
28 F	8 27 42.0	18 20.2	11 28.8	26 0.9	12 47.1	22 20.4	16 22.2	22 28.3	11 24.1	23 37.6	4 29.8	23 38.7
31 M	8 39 31.6	17 31.8	11 25.4	14 46.5	12 50.6	21 54.6	15 37.0	22 23.5	11 29.1	23 37.5	4 29.1	23 40.3

FEBRUARY 1949

DAY	EPHEMERIS SIDEREAL TIME	☉	☊	☽	☿	♀	♂	♃	♄	♅	♆	♇
						LONGITUDE						
1 T	8 43 28.2	11♒49.2	29♈47.8	13♓42.6	15♒39.9	23♑17.4	21♒30.2	17♑28.1	4♍23.9	26♊57.0	15♎ 6.3	15♌27.1
2 W	8 47 24.8	12 50.1	29 44.7	25 32.4	14R29.6	24 32.4	22 17.7	17 41.4	4R19.6	26R55.5	15R 5.8	15R25.7
3 T	8 51 21.3	13 51.0	29 41.5	7♈19.4	13 16.7	25 47.4	23 5.2	17 54.6	4 15.3	26 53.9	15 5.2	15 24.3
4 F	8 55 17.9	14 51.8	29 38.3	19 7.4	12 3.3	27 2.4	23 52.6	18 7.8	4 10.9	26 52.4	15 4.6	15 22.8
5 S	8 59 14.4	15 52.7	29 35.1	1♉ 1.1	10 51.4	28 17.4	24 40.1	18 21.0	4 6.4	26 51.0	15 4.0	15 21.4
6 S	9 3 11.0	16 53.5	29 32.0	13 5.8	9 42.8	29 32.4	25 27.6	18 34.1	4 1.9	26 49.6	15 3.3	15 20.0
7 M	9 7 7.5	17 54.3	29 28.8	25 26.9	8 39.1	0♒47.3	26 15.1	18 47.1	3 57.4	26 48.2	15 2.6	15 18.5
8 T	9 11 4.1	18 55.1	29 25.6	8♊ 9.8	7 41.6	2 2.3	27 2.5	19 0.2	3 52.9	26 46.9	15 1.9	15 17.1
9 W	9 15 0.6	19 55.8	29 22.4	21 19.0	6 51.1	3 17.3	27 50.0	19 13.1	3 48.2	26 45.7	15 1.1	15 15.7
10 T	9 18 57.2	20 56.5	29 19.2	4♋57.4	6 8.2	4 32.3	28 37.4	19 26.0	3 43.6	26 44.4	15 0.3	15 14.3
11 F	9 22 53.8	21 57.2	29 16.1	19 5.4	5 33.4	5 47.2	29 24.9	19 38.9	3 38.9	26 43.3	14 59.5	15 12.8
12 S	9 26 50.3	22 57.8	29 12.9	3♌40.4	5 6.6	7 2.2	0♓12.4	19 51.7	3 34.2	26 42.2	14 58.7	15 11.4
13 S	9 30 46.9	23 58.5	29 9.7	18 36.2	4 47.9	8 17.1	0 59.8	20 4.4	3 29.5	26 41.1	14 57.8	15 10.0
14 M	9 34 43.4	24 59.1	29 6.5	3♍43.8	4 36.9	9 32.1	1 47.2	20 17.1	3 24.8	26 40.1	14 56.9	15 8.6
15 T	9 38 40.0	25 59.7	29 3.4	18 53.0	4 33.4	10 47.0	2 34.6	20 29.7	3 20.0	26 39.1	14 55.9	15 7.2
16 W	9 42 36.5	27 0.2	29 0.2	3♎53.9	4D37.0	12 2.0	3 22.1	20 42.3	3 15.2	26 38.2	14 55.0	15 5.8
17 T	9 46 33.1	28 0.8	28 57.0	18 38.6	4 47.3	13 16.9	4 9.5	20 54.8	3 10.4	26 37.3	14 54.0	15 4.4
18 F	9 50 29.7	29 1.3	28 53.8	3♏ 2.0	5 3.7	14 31.9	4 56.9	21 7.2	3 5.6	26 36.5	14 53.0	15 3.0
19 S	9 54 26.2	0♓ 1.8	28 50.7	17 2.2	5 26.0	15 46.8	5 44.3	21 19.6	3 0.8	26 35.7	14 51.9	15 1.7
20 S	9 58 22.8	1 2.3	28 47.5	0♐39.4	5 53.7	17 1.7	6 31.7	21 31.9	2 55.9	26 35.0	14 50.9	15 0.3
21 M	10 2 19.3	2 2.7	28 44.3	13 55.5	6 26.3	18 16.7	7 19.0	21 44.2	2 51.1	26 34.3	14 49.8	14 58.9
22 T	10 6 15.9	3 3.2	28 41.1	26 53.1	7 3.5	19 31.6	8 6.4	21 56.4	2 46.2	26 33.7	14 48.7	14 57.6
23 W	10 10 12.4	4 3.6	28 37.9	9♑35.1	7 45.0	20 46.5	8 53.8	22 8.5	2 41.4	26 33.1	14 47.5	14 56.2
24 T	10 14 9.0	5 4.0	28 34.8	22 4.1	8 30.4	22 1.4	9 41.1	22 20.5	2 36.5	26 32.6	14 46.4	14 54.9
25 F	10 18 5.5	6 4.3	28 31.6	4♒22.2	9 19.4	23 16.3	10 28.4	22 32.5	2 31.7	26 32.2	14 45.2	14 53.6
26 S	10 22 2.1	7 4.7	28 28.4	16 31.4	10 11.8	24 31.2	11 15.8	22 44.3	2 26.9	26 31.8	14 44.0	14 52.3
27 S	10 25 58.7	8 5.0	28 25.2	28 33.1	11 7.3	25 46.1	12 3.1	22 56.1	2 22.1	26 31.4	14 42.7	14 51.0
28 M	10 29 55.2	9 5.3	28 22.1	10♓28.7	12 5.7	27 1.0	12 50.3	23 7.9	2 17.3	26 31.1	14 41.5	14 49.7
						DECLINATION						
1 T	8 43 28.2	17S15.0	11N24.3	9S41.4	12S59.2	21S44.7	15S21.6	22S21.9	11N30.9	23N37.5	4S28.9	23N40.8
4 F	8 55 17.9	16 22.9	11 20.9	6N43.6	13 41.4	21 11.0	14 34.5	22 17.0	11 36.1	23 37.4	4 28.1	23 42.4
7 M	9 7 7.5	15 28.3	11 17.6	21 22.1	14 37.3	20 31.6	13 46.1	22 12.0	11 41.4	23 37.3	4 27.2	23 43.9
10 T	9 18 57.2	14 31.2	11 14.2	27 59.8	15 34.0	19 46.8	12 56.4	22 6.8	11 46.8	23 37.2	4 26.1	23 45.4
13 S	9 30 46.9	13 32.1	11 10.8	19 44.7	16 23.2	18 56.7	12 5.7	22 1.5	11 52.3	23 37.1	4 25.0	23 46.8
16 W	9 42 36.5	12 30.9	11 7.4	0 19.0	17 1.0	18 1.7	11 13.9	21 56.2	11 57.8	23 37.0	4 23.8	23 48.2
19 S	9 54 26.2	11 27.9	11 4.1	18S34.7	17 25.8	17 2.1	10 21.1	21 50.8	12 3.3	23 37.0	4 22.5	23 49.5
22 T	10 6 15.9	10 23.3	11 0.7	27 48.8	17 37.2	15 58.1	9 27.5	21 45.3	12 8.8	23 36.9	4 21.1	23 50.8
25 F	10 18 5.5	9 17.3	10 57.3	24 5.0	17 35.5	14 50.2	8 33.2	21 39.8	12 14.3	23 36.9	4 19.7	23 52.0
28 M	10 29 55.2	8 9.9	10 53.9	11 3.4	17 20.7	13 38.5	7 38.2	21 34.2	12 19.7	23 36.8	4 18.1	23 53.2

MARCH 1949

LONGITUDE

DAY	EPHEMERIS SIDEREAL TIME h m s	☉ ° ′	☊ ° ′	☽ ° ′	☿ ° ′	♀ ° ′	♂ ° ′	♃ ° ′	♄ ° ′	♅ ° ′	♆ ° ′	♇ ° ′
1 T	10 33 51.7	10♓ 5.5	28♈18.9	22♓19.6	13♒ 6.7	28♒15.9	13♓37.6	23♑19.5	2♍12.5	26♊30.9	14♎40.2	14♌48.4
2 W	10 37 48.3	11 5.7	28 15.7	4♈ 7.6	14 10.3	29 30.7	14 24.8	23 31.1	2R 7.7	26R30.7	14R38.9	14R47.1
3 T	10 41 44.9	12 5.9	28 12.5	15 55.0	15 16.2	0♓45.6	15 12.1	23 42.6	2 3.0	26 30.5	14 37.6	14 45.9
4 F	10 45 41.4	13 6.1	28 9.4	27 44.7	16 24.4	2 0.4	15 59.3	23 53.9	1 58.2	26 30.5	14 36.3	14 44.7
5 S	10 49 38.0	14 6.2	28 6.2	9♉40.2	17 34.6	3 15.3	16 46.5	24 5.3	1 53.6	26 30.4	14 34.9	14 43.4
6 S	10 53 34.5	15 6.3	28 3.0	21 45.7	18 46.8	4 30.1	17 33.6	24 16.5	1 48.9	26D30.4	14 33.5	14 42.2
7 M	10 57 31.1	16 6.3	27 59.8	4♊ 5.7	20 0.8	5 44.9	18 20.7	24 27.6	1 44.3	26 30.5	14 32.1	14 41.0
8 T	11 1 27.6	17 6.4	27 56.6	16 44.9	21 16.7	6 59.7	19 7.9	24 38.6	1 39.7	26 30.7	14 30.7	14 39.9
9 W	11 5 24.2	18 6.3	27 53.5	29 47.9	22 34.2	8 14.4	19 54.9	24 49.6	1 35.1	26 30.8	14 29.3	14 38.7
10 T	11 9 20.7	19 6.3	27 50.3	13♋18.1	23 53.4	9 29.2	20 42.0	25 0.4	1 30.6	26 31.1	14 27.9	14 37.6
11 F	11 13 17.3	20 6.2	27 47.1	27 17.3	25 14.1	10 44.0	21 29.0	25 11.2	1 26.2	26 31.4	14 26.4	14 36.5
12 S	11 17 13.8	21 6.1	27 43.9	11♌44.7	26 36.4	11 58.7	22 16.0	25 21.8	1 21.7	26 31.7	14 24.9	14 35.3
13 S	11 21 10.4	22 5.9	27 40.8	26 36.4	28 0.1	13 13.4	23 3.0	25 32.4	1 17.4	26 32.1	14 23.4	14 34.3
14 M	11 25 7.0	23 5.7	27 37.6	11♍45.3	29 25.3	14 28.1	23 50.0	25 42.8	1 13.0	26 32.6	14 21.9	14 33.2
15 T	11 29 3.5	24 5.5	27 34.4	27 1.7	0♓51.8	15 42.8	24 36.9	25 53.2	1 8.8	26 33.1	14 20.4	14 32.1
16 W	11 33 0.1	25 5.2	27 31.2	12♎15.2	2 19.8	16 57.5	25 23.8	26 3.4	1 4.6	26 33.6	14 18.9	14 31.1
17 T	11 36 56.6	26 4.9	27 28.0	27 15.9	3 49.1	18 12.2	26 10.6	26 13.6	1 0.4	26 34.3	14 17.4	14 30.1
18 F	11 40 53.2	27 4.6	27 24.9	11♏56.5	5 19.7	19 26.9	26 57.5	26 23.6	0 56.3	26 34.9	14 15.8	14 29.1
19 S	11 44 49.7	28 4.2	27 21.7	26 12.3	6 51.7	20 41.5	27 44.3	26 33.5	0 52.3	26 35.6	14 14.2	14 28.1
20 S	11 48 46.3	29 3.8	27 18.5	10♐ 1.5	8 25.0	21 56.2	28 31.0	26 43.3	0 48.3	26 36.4	14 12.7	14 27.2
21 M	11 52 42.8	0♈ 3.4	27 15.3	23 24.8	9 59.6	23 10.8	29 17.8	26 53.0	0 44.4	26 37.2	14 11.1	14 26.2
22 T	11 56 39.4	1 2.9	27 12.2	6♑24.5	11 35.5	24 25.4	0♈ 4.5	27 2.6	0 40.5	26 38.1	14 9.5	14 25.3
23 W	12 0 36.0	2 2.5	27 9.0	19 3.9	13 12.7	25 40.0	0 51.2	27 12.1	0 36.8	26 39.0	14 7.9	14 24.4
24 T	12 4 32.5	3 2.0	27 5.8	1♒26.6	14 51.2	26 54.6	1 37.8	27 21.5	0 33.0	26 40.0	14 6.3	14 23.6
25 F	12 8 29.0	4 1.4	27 2.6	13 36.4	16 31.0	28 9.2	2 24.5	27 30.7	0 29.4	26 41.0	14 4.7	14 22.7
26 S	12 12 25.6	5 0.9	26 59.4	25 36.6	18 12.1	29 23.8	3 11.0	27 39.8	0 25.8	26 42.1	14 3.0	14 21.9
27 S	12 16 22.2	6 0.3	26 56.3	7♓30.2	19 54.6	0♈38.4	3 57.6	27 48.8	0 22.4	26 43.3	14 1.4	14 21.1
28 M	12 20 18.7	6 59.6	26 53.1	19 19.9	21 38.4	1 52.9	4 44.1	27 57.7	0 19.0	26 44.4	13 59.8	14 20.3
29 T	12 24 15.3	7 59.0	26 49.9	1♈ 7.9	23 23.6	3 7.5	5 30.6	28 6.5	0 15.6	26 45.7	13 58.1	14 19.6
30 W	12 28 11.8	8 58.3	26 46.7	12 56.5	25 10.1	4 22.0	6 17.0	28 15.1	0 12.4	26 47.0	13 56.5	14 18.8
31 T	12 32 8.4	9 57.6	26 43.6	24 47.7	26 58.0	5 36.5	7 3.5	28 23.6	0 9.2	26 48.3	13 54.9	14 18.1

DECLINATION

DAY	EPHEMERIS SIDEREAL TIME h m s	☉	☊	☽	☿	♀	♂	♃	♄	♅	♆	♇
1 T	10 33 51.7	7S47.2	10N52.8	5S41.6	17S12.9	13S13.9	7S19.7	21S32.4	12N21.4	23N36.8	4S17.6	23N53.6
4 F	10 45 41.4	6 38.5	10 49.4	10N48.1	16 41.1	11 57.8	6 24.0	21 26.8	12 26.7	23 36.8	4 16.0	23 54.6
7 M	10 57 31.1	5 29.0	10 45.9	24 6.2	15 57.0	10 38.9	5 27.8	21 21.3	12 31.8	23 36.8	4 14.3	23 55.6
10 T	11 9 20.7	4 18.8	10 42.5	27 49.1	15 0.8	9 17.4	4 31.3	21 15.8	12 36.7	23 36.8	4 12.5	23 56.5
13 S	11 21 10.4	3 8.1	10 39.1	16 51.4	13 52.7	7 53.7	3 34.5	21 10.3	12 41.5	23 36.8	4 10.7	23 57.4
16 W	11 33 0.1	1 57.2	10 35.7	3S42.6	12 33.1	6 28.1	2 37.6	21 4.9	12 46.1	23 36.9	4 8.9	23 58.1
19 S	11 44 49.7	0 46.1	10 32.3	21 53.0	11 2.1	5 1.0	1 40.6	20 59.6	12 50.4	23 36.9	4 7.1	23 58.8
22 T	11 56 39.4	0N25.0	10 28.8	28 13.7	9 20.1	3 32.6	0 43.5	20 54.4	12 54.6	23 37.0	4 5.2	23 59.4
25 F	12 8 29.0	1 36.0	10 25.4	21 31.5	7 27.4	2 3.2	0N13.4	20 49.3	12 58.4	23 37.0	4 3.2	23 60.0
28 M	12 20 18.7	2 46.6	10 22.0	7 5.6	5 24.1	0 33.3	1 10.2	20 44.3	13 2.0	23 37.1	4 1.3	24 0.4
31 T	12 32 8.4	3 56.8	10 18.5	9N32.2	3 10.9	0N56.8	2 6.7	20 39.5	13 5.3	23 37.2	3 59.4	24 0.8

APRIL 1949

LONGITUDE

DAY	EPHEMERIS SIDEREAL TIME h m s	☉ ° ′	☊ ° ′	☽ ° ′	☿ ° ′	♀ ° ′	♂ ° ′	♃ ° ′	♄ ° ′	♅ ° ′	♆ ° ′	♇ ° ′
1 F	12 36 4.9	10♈56.8	26♈40.4	6♉43.6	28♓47.2	6♈51.0	7♈49.8	28♑31.9	0♍ 6.2	26♊49.7	13♎53.2	14♌17.5
2 S	12 40 1.5	11 56.0	26 37.2	18 46.8	0♈37.9	8 5.5	8 36.2	28 40.2	0R 3.2	26 51.1	13R51.6	14R16.8
3 S	12 43 58.0	12 55.1	26 34.0	0♊59.9	2R29.9	9 20.0	9 22.5	28 48.3	0 0.3	26 52.6	13 49.9	14 16.2
4 M	12 47 54.6	13 54.3	26 30.8	13 26.1	4D23.3	10 34.4	10 8.7	28 56.2	29♌57.5	26 54.1	13 48.3	14 15.6
5 T	12 51 51.1	14 53.4	26 27.7	26 8.5	6 18.2	11 48.8	10 54.9	29 4.1	29 54.8	26 55.7	13 46.6	14 15.0
6 W	12 55 47.7	15 52.4	26 24.5	9♋10.3	8 14.4	13 3.3	11 41.1	29 11.7	29 52.1	26 57.3	13 45.0	14 14.4
7 T	12 59 44.2	16 51.4	26 21.3	22 34.5	10 12.0	14 17.6	12 27.2	29 19.3	29 49.6	26 59.0	13 43.3	14 13.9
8 F	13 3 40.8	17 50.4	26 18.1	6♌22.9	12 10.9	15 32.0	13 13.3	29 26.7	29 47.1	27 0.7	13 41.7	14 13.4
9 S	13 7 37.3	18 49.3	26 14.9	20 35.7	14 11.1	16 46.4	13 59.3	29 33.9	29 44.8	27 2.5	13 40.0	14 12.9
10 S	13 11 33.9	19 48.2	26 11.8	5♍11.2	16 12.6	18 0.7	14 45.3	29 41.0	29 42.6	27 4.3	13 38.4	14 12.4
11 M	13 15 30.5	20 47.1	26 8.6	20 4.8	18 15.2	19 15.0	15 31.3	29 48.0	29 40.4	27 6.2	13 36.7	14 12.0
12 T	13 19 27.0	21 45.9	26 5.4	5♎ 9.9	20 19.0	20 29.3	16 17.2	29 54.8	29 38.4	27 8.1	13 35.1	14 11.6
13 W	13 23 23.6	22 44.7	26 2.2	20 17.9	22 23.7	21 43.6	17 3.0	0♒ 1.5	29 36.4	27 10.0	13 33.5	14 11.2
14 T	13 27 20.1	23 43.4	25 59.1	5♏19.5	24 29.2	22 57.9	17 48.9	0 8.0	29 34.5	27 12.0	13 31.9	14 10.9
15 F	13 31 16.7	24 42.1	25 55.9	20 6.3	26 35.5	24 12.2	18 34.6	0 14.4	29 32.8	27 14.0	13 30.2	14 10.6
16 S	13 35 13.2	25 40.8	25 52.7	4♐31.7	28 42.2	25 26.4	19 20.4	0 20.6	29 31.1	27 16.1	13 28.6	14 10.3
17 S	13 39 9.8	26 39.5	25 49.5	18 31.6	0♉49.2	26 40.6	20 6.1	0 26.7	29 29.6	27 18.2	13 27.0	14 10.0
18 M	13 43 6.3	27 38.1	25 46.4	2♑ 4.6	2 56.2	27 54.9	20 51.7	0 32.6	29 28.1	27 20.4	13 25.4	14 9.8
19 T	13 47 2.9	28 36.7	25 43.2	15 11.6	5 2.9	29 9.1	21 37.3	0 38.3	29 26.8	27 22.6	13 23.9	14 9.6
20 W	13 50 59.5	29 35.3	25 40.0	27 55.0	7 9.1	0♉23.3	22 22.9	0 43.9	29 25.5	27 24.8	13 22.3	14 9.4
21 T	13 54 56.0	0♉33.9	25 36.8	10♒18.6	9 14.5	1 37.4	23 8.4	0 49.3	29 24.4	27 27.1	13 20.7	14 9.2
22 F	13 58 52.5	1 32.4	25 33.6	22 26.7	11 18.7	2 51.6	23 53.8	0 54.6	29 23.3	27 29.4	13 19.2	14 9.1
23 S	14 2 49.1	2 30.9	25 30.5	4♓23.8	13 21.4	4 5.8	24 39.3	0 59.7	29 22.4	27 31.8	13 17.6	14 9.0
24 S	14 6 45.7	3 29.3	25 27.3	16 14.1	15 22.3	5 19.9	25 24.6	1 4.6	29 21.6	27 34.2	13 16.1	14 8.9
25 M	14 10 42.2	4 27.8	25 24.1	28 1.5	17 21.1	6 34.0	26 10.0	1 9.4	29 20.8	27 36.6	13 14.6	14 8.8
26 T	14 14 38.8	5 26.2	25 20.9	9♈49.6	19 17.5	7 48.1	26 55.2	1 13.9	29 20.2	27 39.1	13 13.1	14 8.8
27 W	14 18 35.3	6 24.6	25 17.8	21 41.5	21 11.2	9 2.2	27 40.5	1 18.3	29 19.7	27 41.6	13 11.6	14 8.8
28 T	14 22 31.9	7 22.9	25 14.6	3♉39.6	23 1.9	10 16.3	28 25.7	1 22.6	29 19.3	27 44.2	13 10.1	14D 8.8
29 F	14 26 28.4	8 21.2	25 11.4	15 45.9	24 49.5	11 30.4	29 10.8	1 26.7	29 19.0	27 46.8	13 8.6	14 8.9
30 S	14 30 25.0	9 19.5	25 8.2	28 2.3	26 33.8	12 44.5	29 55.9	1 30.6	29 18.8	27 49.4	13 7.2	14 9.0

DECLINATION

DAY	EPHEMERIS SIDEREAL TIME h m s	☉	☊	☽	☿	♀	♂	♃	♄	♅	♆	♇
1 F	12 36 4.9	4N20.0	10N17.4	14N43.8	2S24.4	1N26.9	2N25.4	20S38.0	13N 6.4	23N37.2	3S58.7	24N 0.9
4 M	12 47 54.6	5 29.2	10 13.9	26 18.6	0N 1.2	2 56.9	3 21.5	20 33.4	13 9.3	23 37.3	3 56.8	24 1.1
7 T	12 59 44.2	6 37.6	10 10.5	26 45.8	2 35.0	4 26.4	4 17.1	20 29.1	13 11.8	23 37.4	3 54.9	24 1.3
10 S	13 11 33.9	7 44.9	10 7.0	13 24.6	5 15.3	5 55.1	5 12.1	20 24.9	13 14.1	23 37.6	3 53.0	24 1.3
13 W	13 23 23.6	8 51.0	10 3.6	7S28.6	7 59.9	7 22.6	6 6.6	20 21.0	13 16.1	23 37.7	3 51.1	24 1.3
16 S	13 35 13.2	9 55.8	10 0.1	24 19.5	10 45.3	8 48.6	7 0.3	20 17.4	13 17.7	23 37.8	3 49.2	24 1.2
19 T	13 47 2.9	10 59.1	9 56.6	27 45.3	13 26.9	10 12.8	7 53.4	20 14.0	13 18.9	23 37.9	3 47.4	24 1.1
22 F	13 58 52.5	12 0.8	9 53.2	18 30.1	15 59.2	11 35.0	8 45.6	20 11.0	13 19.9	23 38.1	3 45.6	24 0.8
25 M	14 10 42.2	13 0.8	9 49.7	3 2.6	18 16.9	12 54.6	9 36.9	20 8.2	13 20.5	23 38.2	3 43.8	24 0.5
28 T	14 22 31.9	13 58.8	9 46.2	13N25.9	20 15.3	14 11.5	10 27.3	20 5.8	13 20.7	23 38.3	3 42.1	24 0.1

MAY 1949

DAY	EPHEMERIS SIDEREAL TIME	☉	☊	☽	☿	♀	♂	♃	♄	♅	♆	♇
	h m s	° ′	° ′	° ′	° ′	° ′	° ′	° ′	° ′	° ′	° ′	° ′
						LONGITUDE						
1 S	14 34 21.6	10♉17.8	25♈ 5.1	10♊30.2	28♉14.5	13♉58.5	0♉40.9	1♒34.3	29♌18.7	27♊52.0	13♎ 5.8	14♌ 9.1
2 M	14 38 18.1	11 16.0	25 1.9	23 10.9	29 51.5	15 12.5	1 25.9	1 37.8	29D18.7	27 54.7	13R 4.3	14 9.3
3 T	14 42 14.7	12 14.2	24 58.7	6♋ 5.8	1♊24.7	16 26.5	2 10.8	1 41.2	29 18.8	27 57.5	13 2.9	14 9.4
4 W	14 46 11.2	13 12.4	24 55.5	19 16.1	2 54.1	17 40.5	2 55.7	1 44.4	29 19.1	28 0.2	13 1.6	14 9.6
5 T	14 50 7.8	14 10.5	24 52.3	2♌42.9	4 19.4	18 54.5	3 40.5	1 47.4	29 19.4	28 3.0	13 0.2	14 9.9
6 F	14 54 4.3	15 8.6	24 49.2	16 27.0	5 40.6	20 8.4	4 25.3	1 50.2	29 19.9	28 5.8	12 58.9	14 10.1
7 S	14 58 0.9	16 6.7	24 46.0	0♍28.4	6 57.6	21 22.4	5 10.0	1 52.8	29 20.4	28 8.7	12 57.5	14 10.4
8 S	15 1 57.4	17 4.7	24 42.8	14 46.5	8 10.5	22 36.3	5 54.7	1 55.3	29 21.1	28 11.6	12 56.2	14 10.7
9 M	15 5 54.0	18 2.7	24 39.6	29 19.0	9 18.9	23 50.2	6 39.3	1 57.6	29 21.8	28 14.5	12 55.0	14 11.0
10 T	15 9 50.6	19 0.7	24 36.5	14♎ 1.8	10 23.1	25 4.1	7 23.9	1 59.6	29 22.7	28 17.4	12 53.7	14 11.4
11 W	15 13 47.1	19 58.6	24 33.3	28 49.7	11 22.7	26 18.0	8 8.4	2 1.6	29 23.7	28 20.4	12 52.4	14 11.8
12 T	15 17 43.7	20 56.5	24 30.1	13♏35.8	12 17.9	27 31.8	8 52.8	2 3.3	29 24.8	28 23.4	12 51.2	14 12.2
13 F	15 21 40.2	21 54.4	24 26.9	28 12.9	13 8.5	28 45.7	9 37.2	2 4.8	29 25.9	28 26.4	12 50.0	14 12.7
14 S	15 25 36.8	22 52.3	24 23.8	12♐34.4	13 54.5	29 59.5	10 21.6	2 6.2	29 27.2	28 29.5	12 48.8	14 13.1
15 S	15 29 33.3	23 50.1	24 20.6	26 35.1	14 35.8	1♊13.3	11 5.9	2 7.3	29 28.6	28 32.6	12 47.7	14 13.6
16 M	15 33 29.9	24 47.9	24 17.4	10♑11.6	15 12.3	2 27.1	11 50.1	2 8.3	29 30.1	28 35.7	12 46.5	14 14.1
17 T	15 37 26.4	25 45.7	24 14.2	23 23.1	15 44.1	3 40.9	12 34.3	2 9.1	29 31.7	28 38.8	12 45.4	14 14.7
18 W	15 41 23.0	26 43.5	24 11.0	6♒10.7	16 11.0	4 54.7	13 18.5	2 9.7	29 33.4	28 42.0	12 44.4	14 15.3
19 T	15 45 19.6	27 41.3	24 7.9	18 37.3	16 33.1	6 8.4	14 2.6	2 10.1	29 35.2	28 45.1	12 43.3	14 15.9
20 F	15 49 16.1	28 39.0	24 4.7	0♓47.0	16 50.3	7 22.2	14 46.6	2 10.3	29 37.1	28 48.3	12 42.3	14 16.5
21 S	15 53 12.7	29 36.7	24 1.5	12 44.3	17 2.7	8 35.9	15 30.6	2 10.3	29 39.1	28 51.6	12 41.2	14 17.2
22 S	15 57 9.2	0♊34.4	23 58.3	24 34.5	17 10.2	9 49.6	16 14.5	2R10.1	29 41.2	28 54.8	12 40.2	14 17.8
23 M	16 1 5.8	1 32.1	23 55.2	6♈22.3	17 13.0	11 3.4	16 58.4	2 9.8	29 43.4	28 58.1	12 39.3	14 18.6
24 T	16 5 2.3	2 29.8	23 52.0	18 12.5	17R11.1	12 17.1	17 42.3	2 9.2	29 45.7	29 1.4	12 38.4	14 19.3
25 W	16 8 58.9	3 27.4	23 48.8	0♉ 9.0	17 4.7	13 30.8	18 26.0	2 8.5	29 48.1	29 4.7	12 37.4	14 20.0
26 T	16 12 55.4	4 25.1	23 45.6	12 15.3	16 53.9	14 44.5	19 9.8	2 7.6	29 50.5	29 8.0	12 36.6	14 20.8
27 F	16 16 52.0	5 22.7	23 42.5	24 33.9	16 39.1	15 58.1	19 53.4	2 6.5	29 53.1	29 11.4	12 35.7	14 21.6
28 S	16 20 48.6	6 20.3	23 39.3	7♊ 6.5	16 20.4	17 11.8	20 37.1	2 5.1	29 55.8	29 14.7	12 34.9	14 22.5
29 S	16 24 45.1	7 17.9	23 36.1	19 53.7	15 58.2	18 25.5	21 20.6	2 3.6	29 58.6	29 18.1	12 34.1	14 23.3
30 M	16 28 41.7	8 15.4	23 32.9	2♋55.5	15 32.9	19 39.1	22 4.1	2 2.0	0♍ 1.5	29 21.5	12 33.3	14 24.2
31 T	16 32 38.2	9 13.0	23 29.7	16 11.1	15 5.0	20 52.7	22 47.6	2 0.1	0 4.5	29 24.9	12 32.6	14 25.1

						DECLINATION						
1 S	14 34 21.6	14N54.8	9N42.7	25N42.8	21N52.1	15N25.2	11N16.7	20S 3.7	13N20.6	23N38.5	3S40.5	23N59.6
4 W	14 46 11.2	15 48.5	9 39.2	27 14.3	23 6.3	16 35.5	12 4.9	20 1.9	13 20.2	23 38.6	3 38.9	23 59.0
7 S	14 58 0.9	16 39.9	9 35.7	15 20.6	23 58.7	17 41.9	12 52.0	20 0.5	13 19.4	23 38.7	3 37.4	23 58.4
10 T	15 9 50.6	17 28.8	9 32.3	4S33.9	24 30.6	18 44.2	13 37.8	19 59.5	13 18.2	23 38.8	3 36.0	23 57.7
13 F	15 21 40.2	18 15.0	9 28.8	22 31.8	24 43.9	19 42.0	14 22.4	19 58.9	13 16.8	23 39.0	3 34.7	23 56.9
16 M	15 33 29.9	18 58.5	9 25.3	28 4.8	24 40.2	20 35.1	15 5.6	19 58.6	13 15.0	23 39.1	3 33.4	23 56.0
19 T	15 45 19.6	19 39.1	9 21.7	19 48.0	24 21.2	21 23.1	15 47.5	19 58.7	13 12.9	23 39.2	3 32.2	23 55.1
22 S	15 57 9.2	20 16.7	9 18.2	4 36.0	23 48.5	22 5.9	16 27.9	19 59.2	13 10.5	23 39.3	3 31.1	23 54.1
25 W	16 8 58.9	20 51.2	9 14.7	11N56.6	23 4.1	22 43.0	17 6.8	20 0.1	13 7.7	23 39.4	3 30.1	23 53.1
28 S	16 20 48.6	21 22.5	9 11.2	24 54.7	22 10.1	23 14.3	17 44.1	20 1.4	13 4.7	23 39.4	3 29.2	23 52.0
31 T	16 32 38.2	21 50.4	9 7.7	27 30.7	21 10.2	23 39.5	18 19.9	20 3.1	13 1.3	23 39.5	3 28.5	23 50.9

JUNE 1949

						LONGITUDE						
1 W	16 36 34.8	10♊10.5	23♈26.6	29♋39.4	14♊34.8	22♊ 6.4	23♉31.0	1♒58.0	0♍ 7.5	29♊28.4	12♎31.8	14♌26.0
2 T	16 40 31.4	11 8.0	23 23.4	13♌19.2	14R 3.0	23 20.0	24 14.3	1R55.8	0 10.7	29 31.8	12R31.2	14 27.0
3 F	16 44 27.9	12 5.4	23 20.2	27 9.4	13 30.0	24 33.5	24 57.6	1 53.3	0 13.9	29 35.3	12 30.5	14 28.0
4 S	16 48 24.5	13 2.9	23 17.0	11♍ 8.9	12 56.5	25 47.1	25 40.8	1 50.7	0 17.3	29 38.7	12 29.9	14 29.0
5 S	16 52 21.0	14 0.3	23 13.9	25 16.9	12 23.0	27 0.7	26 24.0	1 47.9	0 20.7	29 42.2	12 29.3	14 30.0
6 M	16 56 17.6	14 57.7	23 10.7	9♎32.0	11 50.1	28 14.2	27 7.1	1 45.0	0 24.2	29 45.7	12 28.7	14 31.0
7 T	17 0 14.2	15 55.1	23 7.5	23 52.4	11 18.4	29 27.7	27 50.1	1 41.8	0 27.8	29 49.2	12 28.2	14 32.1
8 W	17 4 10.7	16 52.5	23 4.3	8♏15.3	10 48.3	0♋41.2	28 33.1	1 38.5	0 31.5	29 52.7	12 27.7	14 33.2
9 T	17 8 7.2	17 49.9	23 1.2	22 36.9	10 20.5	1 54.7	29 16.0	1 35.0	0 35.3	29 56.3	12 27.2	14 34.3
10 F	17 12 3.8	18 47.2	22 58.0	6♐52.4	9 55.3	3 8.2	29 58.9	1 31.3	0 39.2	29 59.8	12 26.7	14 35.4
11 S	17 16 0.4	19 44.5	22 54.8	20 56.9	9 33.2	4 21.7	0♊41.8	1 27.5	0 43.1	0♋ 3.3	12 26.3	14 36.6
12 S	17 19 57.0	20 41.9	22 51.6	4♑45.6	9 14.6	5 35.1	1 24.5	1 23.5	0 47.2	0 6.9	12 25.9	14 37.8
13 M	17 23 53.5	21 39.2	22 48.5	18 14.9	8 59.7	6 48.6	2 7.2	1 19.3	0 51.3	0 10.4	12 25.6	14 39.0
14 T	17 27 50.0	22 36.5	22 45.3	1♒22.9	8 48.8	8 2.0	2 49.9	1 14.9	0 55.5	0 14.0	12 25.2	14 40.2
15 W	17 31 46.6	23 33.7	22 42.1	14 9.5	8 42.2	9 15.4	3 32.5	1 10.4	0 59.8	0 17.6	12 25.0	14 41.4
16 T	17 35 43.2	24 31.0	22 38.9	26 36.3	8 40.0	10 28.8	4 15.1	1 5.8	1 4.1	0 21.2	12 24.7	14 42.7
17 F	17 39 39.7	25 28.3	22 35.7	8♓46.5	8D42.2	11 42.2	4 57.6	1 0.9	1 8.6	0 24.7	12 24.5	14 43.9
18 S	17 43 36.3	26 25.6	22 32.6	20 44.4	8 49.1	12 55.6	5 40.0	0 56.0	1 13.1	0 28.3	12 24.3	14 45.2
19 S	17 47 32.8	27 22.8	22 29.4	2♈35.0	9 0.6	14 8.9	6 22.4	0 50.8	1 17.7	0 31.9	12 24.1	14 46.6
20 M	17 51 29.4	28 20.1	22 26.2	14 23.7	9 16.7	15 22.3	7 4.8	0 45.6	1 22.4	0 35.5	12 24.0	14 47.9
21 T	17 55 26.0	29 17.4	22 23.0	26 15.7	9 37.5	16 35.7	7 47.0	0 40.1	1 27.1	0 39.1	12 23.9	14 49.2
22 W	17 59 22.5	0♋14.6	22 19.9	8♉16.1	10 2.9	17 49.0	8 29.3	0 34.6	1 32.0	0 42.7	12 23.8	14 50.6
23 T	18 3 19.1	1 11.9	22 16.7	20 29.2	10 32.8	19 2.3	9 11.4	0 28.8	1 36.8	0 46.3	12 23.7	14 52.0
24 F	18 7 15.6	2 9.1	22 13.5	2♊58.4	11 7.3	20 15.6	9 53.6	0 23.0	1 41.8	0 49.9	12 23.7	14 53.4
25 S	18 11 12.2	3 6.4	22 10.3	15 46.0	11 46.3	21 29.0	10 35.6	0 17.0	1 46.9	0 53.5	12D23.8	14 54.8
26 S	18 15 8.8	4 3.6	22 7.2	28 52.6	12 29.7	22 42.3	11 17.6	0 10.9	1 52.0	0 57.1	12 23.8	14 56.3
27 M	18 19 5.3	5 0.8	22 4.0	12♋17.2	13 17.4	23 55.5	11 59.6	0 4.7	1 57.2	1 0.7	12 23.9	14 57.7
28 T	18 23 1.9	5 58.1	22 0.8	25 57.6	14 9.4	25 8.8	12 41.5	29♑58.4	2 2.4	1 4.2	12 24.0	14 59.2
29 W	18 26 58.5	6 55.3	21 57.6	9♌50.4	15 5.6	26 22.0	13 23.3	29 51.9	2 7.8	1 7.8	12 24.2	15 0.7
30 T	18 30 55.0	7 52.5	21 54.5	23 51.9	16 6.0	27 35.3	14 5.1	29 45.3	2 13.2	1 11.4	12 24.4	15 2.2

						DECLINATION						
1 W	16 36 34.8	21N59.0	9N 6.5	25N13.9	20N49.6	23N46.6	18N31.4	20S 3.8	13N 0.1	23N39.5	3S28.2	23N50.5
4 S	16 48 24.5	22 22.4	9 3.0	10 39.4	19 48.9	24 3.6	19 4.9	20 5.9	12 56.4	23 39.6	3 27.6	23 49.2
7 T	17 0 14.2	22 42.2	8 59.5	9S12.7	18 53.9	24 14.2	19 36.8	20 8.5	12 52.3	23 39.6	3 27.0	23 48.0
10 F	17 12 3.8	22 58.5	8 55.9	24 52.0	18 10.0	24 18.4	20 6.8	20 11.4	12 48.0	23 39.6	3 26.6	23 46.7
13 M	17 23 53.5	23 11.1	8 52.4	27 12.9	17 41.0	24 16.1	20 35.2	20 14.6	12 43.5	23 39.6	3 26.3	23 45.3
16 T	17 35 43.2	23 20.1	8 48.9	16 39.8	17 29.0	24 7.4	21 1.7	20 18.1	12 38.6	23 39.6	3 26.0	23 43.9
19 S	17 47 32.8	23 25.3	8 45.3	0 38.7	17 34.0	23 52.2	21 26.3	20 21.9	12 33.5	23 39.6	3 25.9	23 42.5
22 W	17 59 22.5	23 26.9	8 41.8	15N29.8	17 54.6	23 30.8	21 49.2	20 26.0	12 28.2	23 39.6	3 25.9	23 41.0
25 S	18 11 12.2	23 24.7	8 38.2	26 40.2	18 28.4	23 3.2	22 10.1	20 30.2	12 22.6	23 39.6	3 26.1	23 39.5
28 T	18 23 1.9	23 18.8	8 34.7	25 53.4	19 12.1	22 29.5	22 29.2	20 34.8	12 16.8	23 39.5	3 26.3	23 38.0

JULY 1949

DAY	EPHEMERIS SIDEREAL TIME	☉	☊	☽	☿	♀	♂	♃	♄	♅	♆	♇
	h m s	° ′	° ′	° ′	° ′	° ′	° ′	° ′	° ′	° ′	° ′	° ′
						LONGITUDE						
1 F	18 34 51.6	8♋49.8	21♈51.3	7♍58.4	17♊10.5	28♋48.5	14♊46.8	29♑38.6	2♍18.6	1♋15.0	12♎24.6	15♌ 3.7
2 S	18 38 48.1	9 47.0	21 48.1	22 7.0	18 19.0	0♌ 1.7	15 28.5	29R31.9	2 24.2	1 18.5	12 24.8	15 5.3
3 S	18 42 44.6	10 44.2	21 44.9	6♎15.7	19 31.5	1 14.9	16 10.1	29 25.0	2 29.7	1 22.1	12 25.1	15 6.8
4 M	18 46 41.2	11 41.4	21 41.8	20 23.2	20 48.0	2 28.1	16 51.7	29 18.0	2 35.4	1 25.7	12 25.5	15 8.4
5 T	18 50 37.8	12 38.6	21 38.6	4♏28.4	22 8.4	3 41.2	17 33.2	29 11.0	2 41.1	1 29.2	12 25.8	15 10.0
6 W	18 54 34.4	13 35.8	21 35.4	18 30.4	23 32.6	4 54.3	18 14.6	29 3.8	2 46.9	1 32.7	12 26.2	15 11.6
7 T	18 58 30.9	14 32.9	21 32.2	2♐27.6	25 0.7	6 7.4	18 56.0	28 56.6	2 52.7	1 36.3	12 26.6	15 13.2
8 F	19 2 27.4	15 30.1	21 29.0	16 17.9	26 32.4	7 20.5	19 37.3	28 49.3	2 58.6	1 39.8	12 27.0	15 14.8
9 S	19 6 24.0	16 27.3	21 25.9	29 58.5	28 7.8	8 33.6	20 18.6	28 42.0	3 4.6	1 43.3	12 27.5	15 16.4
10 S	19 10 20.6	17 24.5	21 22.7	13♑26.5	29 46.8	9 46.7	20 59.8	28 34.6	3 10.6	1 46.8	12 28.0	15 18.1
11 M	19 14 17.2	18 21.7	21 19.5	26 39.3	1♋29.2	10 59.7	21 40.9	28 27.1	3 16.7	1 50.3	12 28.6	15 19.7
12 T	19 18 13.7	19 18.9	21 16.3	9♒35.2	3 14.9	12 12.7	22 22.0	28 19.6	3 22.8	1 53.7	12 29.1	15 21.4
13 W	19 22 10.2	20 16.1	21 13.2	22 13.6	5 3.9	13 25.7	23 3.1	28 12.0	3 28.9	1 57.2	12 29.7	15 23.0
14 T	19 26 6.8	21 13.3	21 10.0	4♓35.4	6 55.8	14 38.7	23 44.1	28 4.4	3 35.2	2 0.6	12 30.4	15 24.7
15 F	19 30 3.4	22 10.5	21 6.8	16 42.8	8 50.6	15 51.6	24 25.0	27 56.7	3 41.5	2 4.1	12 31.0	15 26.4
16 S	19 33 59.9	23 7.7	21 3.6	28 39.3	10 48.0	17 4.6	25 5.9	27 49.1	3 47.8	2 7.5	12 31.7	15 28.1
17 S	19 37 56.5	24 4.9	21 0.5	10♈29.2	12 47.6	18 17.5	25 46.7	27 41.3	3 54.2	2 10.9	12 32.5	15 29.9
18 M	19 41 53.1	25 2.2	20 57.3	22 17.7	14 49.4	19 30.4	26 27.5	27 33.6	4 0.6	2 14.3	12 33.2	15 31.6
19 T	19 45 49.6	25 59.5	20 54.1	4♉10.0	16 52.8	20 43.3	27 8.3	27 25.9	4 7.1	2 17.7	12 34.0	15 33.3
20 W	19 49 46.2	26 56.7	20 50.9	16 11.8	18 57.7	21 56.2	27 48.9	27 18.1	4 13.6	2 21.0	12 34.8	15 35.1
21 T	19 53 42.7	27 54.0	20 47.8	28 28.0	21 3.8	23 9.0	28 29.5	27 10.4	4 20.2	2 24.3	12 35.7	15 36.8
22 F	19 57 39.3	28 51.3	20 44.6	11♊ 3.1	23 10.6	24 21.9	29 10.1	27 2.6	4 26.8	2 27.7	12 36.6	15 38.6
23 S	20 1 35.9	29 48.6	20 41.4	24 0.2	25 17.9	25 34.7	29 50.6	26 54.9	4 33.4	2 31.0	12 37.5	15 40.4
24 S	20 5 32.4	0♌45.9	20 38.2	7♋20.7	27 25.4	26 47.5	0♋31.1	26 47.1	4 40.1	2 34.2	12 38.4	15 42.1
25 M	20 9 28.9	1 43.3	20 35.0	21 3.9	29 32.9	28 0.3	1 11.5	26 39.4	4 46.9	2 37.5	12 39.4	15 43.9
26 T	20 13 25.5	2 40.6	20 31.9	5♌ 6.8	1♌39.9	29 13.0	1 51.8	26 31.7	4 53.7	2 40.7	12 40.4	15 45.7
27 W	20 17 22.1	3 37.9	20 28.7	19 24.7	3 46.4	0♍25.7	2 32.1	26 24.0	5 0.5	2 43.9	12 41.4	15 47.5
28 T	20 21 18.6	4 35.3	20 25.5	3♍51.5	5 52.2	1 38.5	3 12.3	26 16.4	5 7.4	2 47.1	12 42.5	15 49.3
29 F	20 25 15.2	5 32.7	20 22.3	18 21.1	7 57.0	2 51.1	3 52.5	26 8.8	5 14.3	2 50.3	12 43.6	15 51.1
30 S	20 29 11.8	6 30.1	20 19.2	2♎48.1	10 0.6	4 3.8	4 32.6	26 1.3	5 21.2	2 53.4	12 44.7	15 52.9
31 S	20 33 8.3	7 27.5	20 16.0	17 8.5	12 3.1	5 16.4	5 12.7	25 53.8	5 28.2	2 56.5	12 45.8	15 54.7
						DECLINATION						
1 F	18 34 51.6	23N 9.2	8N31.1	11N51.1	20N 2.4	21N50.1	22N46.3	20S39.4	12N10.8	23N39.5	3S26.7	23N36.5
4 M	18 46 41.2	22 56.0	8 27.5	7S49.1	20 55.2	21 5.1	23 1.5	20 44.3	12 4.6	23 39.4	3 27.1	23 34.9
7 T	18 58 30.9	22 39.2	8 24.0	23 51.4	21 46.1	20 14.8	23 14.8	20 49.2	11 58.1	23 39.3	3 27.7	23 33.4
10 S	19 10 20.6	22 18.9	8 20.4	27 41.9	22 30.2	19 19.5	23 26.2	20 54.2	11 51.5	23 39.2	3 28.4	23 31.8
13 W	19 22 10.2	21 55.1	8 16.8	18 9.9	23 2.2	18 19.4	23 35.6	20 59.2	11 44.7	23 39.1	3 29.2	23 30.2
16 S	19 33 59.9	21 27.9	8 13.3	2 16.8	23 16.9	17 14.9	23 43.1	21 4.2	11 37.7	23 39.0	3 30.1	23 28.6
19 T	19 45 49.6	20 57.5	8 9.7	14N 1.3	23 9.9	16 6.2	23 48.8	21 9.2	11 30.6	23 38.8	3 31.1	23 27.0
22 F	19 57 39.3	20 23.8	8 6.1	25 57.4	22 38.9	14 53.8	23 52.5	21 14.2	11 23.3	23 38.7	3 32.2	23 25.4
25 M	20 9 28.9	19 47.1	8 2.5	26 45.2	21 44.0	13 37.9	23 54.3	21 19.1	11 15.8	23 38.5	3 33.4	23 23.8
28 T	20 21 18.6	19 7.4	7 58.9	13 27.5	20 27.6	12 18.8	23 54.3	21 23.8	11 8.3	23 38.4	3 34.8	23 22.2
31 S	20 33 8.3	18 24.8	7 55.3	6S32.9	18 53.4	10 56.8	23 52.5	21 28.4	11 0.5	23 38.2	3 36.2	23 20.7

AUGUST 1949

DAY	EPHEMERIS SIDEREAL TIME	☉	☊	☽	☿	♀	♂	♃	♄	♅	♆	♇
						LONGITUDE						
1 M	20 37 4.8	8♌24.9	20♈12.8	1♏19.8	14♌ 4.2	6♍29.0	5♋52.7	25♑46.4	5♍35.2	2♋59.6	12♎47.0	15♌56.5
2 T	20 41 1.4	9 22.3	20 9.6	15 20.8	16 4.0	7 41.6	6 32.6	25R39.0	5 42.2	3 2.7	12 48.2	15 58.4
3 W	20 44 58.0	10 19.7	20 6.5	29 11.2	18 2.3	8 54.2	7 12.5	25 31.8	5 49.3	3 5.7	12 49.4	16 0.2
4 T	20 48 54.5	11 17.1	20 3.3	12♐50.7	19 59.1	10 6.7	7 52.3	25 24.6	5 56.4	3 8.7	12 50.7	16 2.0
5 F	20 52 51.1	12 14.6	20 0.1	26 19.3	21 54.4	11 19.2	8 32.1	25 17.4	6 3.6	3 11.7	12 51.9	16 3.8
6 S	20 56 47.6	13 12.0	19 56.9	9♑36.6	23 48.2	12 31.6	9 11.8	25 10.4	6 10.7	3 14.7	12 53.2	16 5.6
7 S	21 0 44.2	14 9.5	19 53.7	22 41.7	25 40.4	13 44.0	9 51.4	25 3.4	6 17.9	3 17.6	12 54.6	16 7.5
8 M	21 4 40.8	15 7.0	19 50.6	5♒34.0	27 31.0	14 56.4	10 31.0	24 56.5	6 25.1	3 20.5	12 55.9	16 9.3
9 T	21 8 37.3	16 4.5	19 47.4	18 12.7	29 20.1	16 8.8	11 10.6	24 49.8	6 32.4	3 23.4	12 57.3	16 11.1
10 W	21 12 33.9	17 2.0	19 44.2	0♓38.0	1♍ 7.6	17 21.1	11 50.1	24 43.1	6 39.7	3 26.2	12 58.7	16 13.0
11 T	21 16 30.4	17 59.6	19 41.0	12 50.6	2 53.7	18 33.4	12 29.5	24 36.6	6 47.0	3 29.0	13 0.2	16 14.8
12 F	21 20 27.0	18 57.1	19 37.9	24 52.0	4 38.1	19 45.7	13 8.9	24 30.1	6 54.3	3 31.8	13 1.6	16 16.6
13 S	21 24 23.5	19 54.7	19 34.7	6♈45.0	6 21.1	20 57.9	13 48.2	24 23.8	7 1.6	3 34.5	13 3.1	16 18.5
14 S	21 28 20.1	20 52.3	19 31.5	18 33.1	8 2.6	22 10.1	14 27.5	24 17.6	7 9.0	3 37.2	13 4.6	16 20.3
15 M	21 32 16.6	21 49.9	19 28.3	0♉20.5	9 42.6	23 22.3	15 6.7	24 11.5	7 16.4	3 39.9	13 6.2	16 22.1
16 T	21 36 13.2	22 47.6	19 25.2	12 12.1	11 21.1	24 34.4	15 45.9	24 5.5	7 23.8	3 42.5	13 7.7	16 23.9
17 W	21 40 9.8	23 45.3	19 22.0	24 13.2	12 58.1	25 46.6	16 25.0	23 59.7	7 31.2	3 45.2	13 9.3	16 25.8
18 T	21 44 6.3	24 43.0	19 18.8	6♊28.9	14 33.7	26 58.6	17 4.0	23 54.0	7 38.7	3 47.7	13 10.9	16 27.6
19 F	21 48 2.9	25 40.7	19 15.6	19 4.2	16 7.8	28 10.7	17 43.0	23 48.4	7 46.1	3 50.2	13 12.5	16 29.4
20 S	21 51 59.4	26 38.5	19 12.4	2♋ 3.2	17 40.5	29 22.7	18 22.0	23 43.0	7 53.6	3 52.7	13 14.2	16 31.2
21 S	21 55 56.0	27 36.3	19 9.3	15 28.4	19 11.7	0♎34.7	19 0.9	23 37.7	8 1.1	3 55.2	13 15.9	16 33.0
22 M	21 59 52.5	28 34.1	19 6.1	29 20.1	20 41.4	1 46.6	19 39.7	23 32.6	8 8.6	3 57.6	13 17.6	16 34.8
23 T	22 3 49.1	29 31.9	19 2.9	13♌36.2	22 9.7	2 58.5	20 18.5	23 27.7	8 16.1	4 0.0	13 19.3	16 36.6
24 W	22 7 45.6	0♍29.8	18 59.7	28 11.9	23 36.5	4 10.4	20 57.2	23 22.8	8 23.6	4 2.4	13 21.0	16 38.4
25 T	22 11 42.2	1 27.7	18 56.6	13♍ 0.3	25 1.8	5 22.3	21 35.8	23 18.2	8 31.1	4 4.7	13 22.8	16 40.2
26 F	22 15 38.7	2 25.6	18 53.4	27 53.3	26 25.6	6 34.1	22 14.4	23 13.7	8 38.7	4 6.9	13 24.5	16 42.0
27 S	22 19 35.3	3 23.6	18 50.2	12♎42.9	27 47.8	7 45.8	22 53.0	23 9.4	8 46.2	4 9.2	13 26.3	16 43.7
28 S	22 23 31.9	4 21.5	18 47.0	27 22.7	29 8.4	8 57.6	23 31.4	23 5.3	8 53.8	4 11.4	13 28.1	16 45.5
29 M	22 27 28.4	5 19.5	18 43.8	11♏47.8	0♎27.4	10 9.3	24 9.9	23 1.3	9 1.4	4 13.5	13 30.0	16 47.2
30 T	22 31 25.0	6 17.5	18 40.7	25 55.7	1 44.8	11 20.9	24 48.2	22 57.5	9 8.9	4 15.6	13 31.8	16 49.0
31 W	22 35 21.5	7 15.6	18 37.5	9♐45.5	3 0.4	12 32.5	25 26.5	22 53.9	9 16.5	4 17.7	13 33.7	16 50.7
						DECLINATION						
1 M	20 37 4.8	18N10.0	7N54.2	12S55.4	18N18.8	10N29.0	23N51.5	21S29.9	10N57.9	23N38.2	3S36.7	23N20.1
4 T	20 48 54.5	17 23.9	7 50.6	26 23.1	16 27.2	9 3.8	23 47.3	21 34.3	10 50.1	23 38.0	3 38.2	23 18.6
7 S	21 0 44.2	16 35.2	7 47.0	26 30.3	14 26.8	7 36.6	23 41.3	21 38.4	10 42.1	23 37.8	3 39.8	23 17.1
10 W	21 12 33.9	15 44.2	7 43.4	14 45.9	12 20.6	6 7.6	23 33.6	21 42.4	10 34.1	23 37.7	3 41.6	23 15.6
13 S	21 24 23.5	14 50.9	7 39.8	1N45.0	10 11.1	4 37.2	23 24.3	21 46.1	10 25.9	23 37.5	3 43.4	23 14.1
16 T	21 36 13.2	13 55.4	7 36.2	17 29.8	8 0.3	3 5.7	23 13.3	21 49.5	10 17.7	23 37.3	3 45.2	23 12.6
19 F	21 48 2.9	12 57.9	7 32.5	27 28.2	5 49.7	1 33.3	23 0.7	21 52.7	10 9.4	23 37.2	3 47.2	23 11.2
22 M	21 59 52.5	11 58.6	7 28.9	25 12.5	3 40.7	0 0.4	22 46.5	21 55.6	10 1.1	23 37.0	3 49.2	23 9.9
25 T	22 11 42.2	10 57.5	7 25.3	9 22.3	1 34.5	1S32.7	22 30.9	21 58.3	9 52.8	23 36.9	3 51.3	23 8.5
28 S	22 23 31.9	9 54.9	7 21.7	11S23.0	0S27.7	3 5.6	22 13.8	22 0.6	9 44.4	23 36.7	3 53.5	23 7.2
31 W	22 35 21.5	8 50.9	7 18.1	25 58.9	2 24.7	4 38.2	21 55.3	22 2.7	9 35.9	23 36.6	3 55.7	23 6.0

SEPTEMBER 1949

DAY	EPHEMERIS SIDEREAL TIME	☉	☊	☽	☿	♀	♂	♃	♄	♅	♆	♇
	h m s	° ′	° ′	° ′	° ′	° ′	° ′	° ′	° ′	° ′	° ′	° ′
LONGITUDE												
1 T	22 39 18.1	8♍13.6	18♈34.3	23♐17.5	4♎14.2	13♎44.1	26♋ 4.7	22♑50.4	9♍24.1	4♋19.7	13♎35.6	16♌52.5
2 F	22 43 14.6	9 11.7	18 31.1	6♑32.8	5 26.1	14 55.6	26 42.9	22R47.1	9 31.6	4 21.6	13 37.5	16 54.2
3 S	22 47 11.2	10 9.8	18 28.0	19 32.7	6 36.1	16 7.0	27 21.0	22 44.1	9 39.2	4 23.6	13 39.4	16 55.9
4 S	22 51 7.8	11 7.9	18 24.8	2♒18.7	7 44.1	17 18.4	27 59.0	22 41.2	9 46.8	4 25.5	13 41.4	16 57.6
5 M	22 55 4.3	12 6.0	18 21.6	14 51.9	8 49.9	18 29.8	28 37.0	22 38.4	9 54.4	4 27.3	13 43.3	16 59.3
6 T	22 59 0.8	13 4.2	18 18.4	27 13.4	9 53.5	19 41.1	29 15.0	22 35.9	10 1.9	4 29.1	13 45.3	17 1.0
7 W	23 2 57.4	14 2.4	18 15.2	9♓24.5	10 54.7	20 52.4	29 52.8	22 33.5	10 9.5	4 30.9	13 47.3	17 2.6
8 T	23 6 53.9	15 0.6	18 12.1	21 26.5	11 53.4	22 3.6	0♌30.6	22 31.4	10 17.0	4 32.6	13 49.3	17 4.3
9 F	23 10 50.5	15 58.9	18 8.9	3♈21.1	12 49.4	23 14.7	1 8.4	22 29.4	10 24.6	4 34.2	13 51.3	17 6.0
10 S	23 14 47.1	16 57.2	18 5.7	15 10.4	13 42.5	24 25.8	1 46.1	22 27.6	10 32.1	4 35.9	13 53.3	17 7.6
11 S	23 18 43.6	17 55.5	18 2.5	26 57.2	14 32.6	25 36.9	2 23.7	22 26.0	10 39.7	4 37.4	13 55.4	17 9.2
12 M	23 22 40.2	18 53.9	17 59.4	8♉44.7	15 19.4	26 47.9	3 1.3	22 24.6	10 47.2	4 38.9	13 57.4	17 10.8
13 T	23 26 36.7	19 52.3	17 56.2	20 36.7	16 2.7	27 58.9	3 38.8	22 23.4	10 54.7	4 40.4	13 59.5	17 12.4
14 W	23 30 33.3	20 50.7	17 53.0	2♊37.7	16 42.2	29 9.8	4 16.2	22 22.4	11 2.2	4 41.8	14 1.6	17 14.0
15 T	23 34 29.8	21 49.2	17 49.8	14 52.1	17 17.6	0♏20.6	4 53.6	22 21.6	11 9.7	4 43.2	14 3.7	17 15.6
16 F	23 38 26.4	22 47.6	17 46.6	27 24.7	17 48.8	1 31.4	5 30.9	22 20.9	11 17.2	4 44.5	14 5.8	17 17.1
17 S	23 42 23.0	23 46.2	17 43.5	10♋19.9	18 15.2	2 42.1	6 8.2	22 20.5	11 24.7	4 45.8	14 7.9	17 18.7
18 S	23 46 19.5	24 44.8	17 40.3	23 40.8	18 36.6	3 52.8	6 45.4	22 20.2	11 32.1	4 47.1	14 10.0	17 20.2
19 M	23 50 16.1	25 43.4	17 37.1	7♌29.4	18 52.7	5 3.5	7 22.5	22 20.2	11 39.5	4 48.2	14 12.2	17 21.7
20 T	23 54 12.6	26 42.0	17 33.9	21 45.1	19 3.0	6 14.0	7 59.6	22D20.3	11 47.0	4 49.4	14 14.3	17 23.2
21 W	23 58 9.1	27 40.7	17 30.8	6♍24.9	19 7.1	7 24.6	8 36.6	22 20.7	11 54.4	4 50.4	14 16.5	17 24.6
22 T	0 2 5.7	28 39.4	17 27.6	21 22.6	19R 4.9	8 35.0	9 13.5	22 21.2	12 1.7	4 51.5	14 18.6	17 26.1
23 F	0 6 2.3	29 38.1	17 24.4	6♎30.1	18 55.8	9 45.4	9 50.4	22 21.9	12 9.1	4 52.4	14 20.8	17 27.6
24 S	0 9 58.9	0♎36.9	17 21.2	21 38.1	18 39.6	10 55.8	10 27.2	22 22.9	12 16.4	4 53.4	14 23.0	17 29.0
25 S	0 13 55.4	1 35.7	17 18.1	6♏37.7	18 16.1	12 6.1	11 3.9	22 24.0	12 23.7	4 54.2	14 25.2	17 30.4
26 M	0 17 51.9	2 34.6	17 14.9	21 21.3	17 45.3	13 16.3	11 40.6	22 25.3	12 31.0	4 55.1	14 27.4	17 31.8
27 T	0 21 48.5	3 33.4	17 11.7	5♐43.8	17 7.2	14 26.4	12 17.2	22 26.8	12 38.3	4 55.8	14 29.6	17 33.1
28 W	0 25 45.1	4 32.3	17 8.5	19 42.7	16 22.0	15 36.5	12 53.7	22 28.5	12 45.5	4 56.6	14 31.8	17 34.5
29 T	0 29 41.6	5 31.3	17 5.3	3♑17.4	15 30.1	16 46.5	13 30.1	22 30.4	12 52.7	4 57.2	14 34.0	17 35.8
30 F	0 33 38.2	6 30.2	17 2.2	16 29.5	14 32.3	17 56.4	14 6.5	22 32.5	12 59.9	4 57.8	14 36.2	17 37.1
DECLINATION												
1 T	22 39 18.1	8N29.3	7N16.9	28S 0.3	3S 2.3	5S 8.9	21N48.8	22S 3.3	9N33.1	23N36.5	3S56.5	23N 5.6
4 S	22 51 7.8	7 23.6	7 13.2	24 31.3	4 50.3	6 40.5	21 28.6	22 5.0	9 24.7	23 36.4	3 58.8	23 4.4
7 W	23 2 57.4	6 16.9	7 9.6	10 58.9	6 29.8	8 10.9	21 7.0	22 6.3	9 16.3	23 36.3	4 1.1	23 3.3
10 S	23 14 47.1	5 9.2	7 6.0	5N50.5	7 58.7	9 39.8	20 44.3	22 7.4	9 7.9	23 36.2	4 3.5	23 2.2
13 T	23 26 36.7	4 0.8	7 2.3	20 43.7	9 14.5	11 7.0	20 20.4	22 8.2	8 59.5	23 36.1	4 6.0	23 1.2
16 F	23 38 26.4	2 51.7	6 58.7	28 22.7	10 13.8	12 32.2	19 55.4	22 8.6	8 51.2	23 36.0	4 8.4	23 0.3
19 M	23 50 16.1	1 42.0	6 55.1	23 9.4	10 52.1	13 55.0	19 29.4	22 8.8	8 43.0	23 35.9	4 10.9	22 59.4
22 T	0 2 5.7	0 32.1	6 51.4	5 29.7	11 3.8	15 15.1	19 2.3	22 8.7	8 34.8	23 35.9	4 13.5	22 58.6
25 S	0 13 55.4	0S38.1	6 47.8	15S26.3	10 42.5	16 32.2	18 34.4	22 8.3	8 26.6	23 35.8	4 16.0	22 57.9
28 W	0 25 45.1	1 48.3	6 44.1	27 44.8	9 42.9	17 46.0	18 5.6	22 7.6	8 18.6	23 35.8	4 18.6	22 57.2

OCTOBER 1949

DAY	EPHEMERIS SIDEREAL TIME	☉	☊	☽	☿	♀	♂	♃	♄	♅	♆	♇
LONGITUDE												
1 S	0 37 34.7	7♎29.2	16♈59.0	29♑21.1	13♎29.5	19♏ 6.2	14♌42.8	22♑34.8	13♍ 7.0	4♋58.4	14♎38.4	17♌38.4
2 S	0 41 31.3	8 28.2	16 55.8	11♒55.2	12R23.1	20 16.0	15 19.0	22 37.3	13 14.1	4 58.9	14 40.6	17 39.7
3 M	0 45 27.8	9 27.3	16 52.6	24 14.9	11 14.4	21 25.7	15 55.1	22 39.9	13 21.2	4 59.4	14 42.9	17 40.9
4 T	0 49 24.4	10 26.3	16 49.5	6♓23.1	10 5.2	22 35.2	16 31.2	22 42.8	13 28.3	4 59.8	14 45.1	17 42.2
5 W	0 53 20.9	11 25.4	16 46.3	18 22.7	8 57.3	23 44.7	17 7.2	22 45.8	13 35.3	5 0.1	14 47.3	17 43.4
6 T	0 57 17.5	12 24.6	16 43.1	0♈16.0	7 52.6	24 54.1	17 43.1	22 49.0	13 42.2	5 0.4	14 49.6	17 44.6
7 F	1 1 14.0	13 23.7	16 39.9	12 5.3	6 53.0	26 3.5	18 19.0	22 52.4	13 49.2	5 0.6	14 51.8	17 45.7
8 S	1 5 10.6	14 22.9	16 36.7	23 53.0	6 0.0	27 12.7	18 54.8	22 56.0	13 56.1	5 0.8	14 54.0	17 46.9
9 S	1 9 7.1	15 22.2	16 33.6	5♉41.1	5 15.3	28 21.8	19 30.5	22 59.8	14 2.9	5 1.0	14 56.3	17 48.0
10 M	1 13 3.7	16 21.5	16 30.4	17 32.1	4 39.9	29 30.9	20 6.1	23 3.7	14 9.8	5 1.1	14 58.5	17 49.1
11 T	1 17 0.2	17 20.8	16 27.2	29 28.7	4 14.7	0♐39.8	20 41.6	23 7.9	14 16.5	5 1.1	15 0.7	17 50.2
12 W	1 20 56.8	18 20.1	16 24.0	11♊33.7	4 0.3	1 48.6	21 17.1	23 12.2	14 23.3	5R 1.1	15 3.0	17 51.2
13 T	1 24 53.4	19 19.5	16 20.9	23 50.6	3 56.8	2 57.4	21 52.5	23 16.7	14 30.0	5 1.0	15 5.2	17 52.2
14 F	1 28 49.9	20 18.9	16 17.7	6♋22.8	4D 4.2	4 6.0	22 27.8	23 21.3	14 36.6	5 0.9	15 7.4	17 53.2
15 S	1 32 46.5	21 18.4	16 14.5	19 14.1	4 22.2	5 14.5	23 3.0	23 26.1	14 43.2	5 0.7	15 9.7	17 54.2
16 S	1 36 43.0	22 17.9	16 11.3	2♌27.6	4 50.3	6 22.9	23 38.2	23 31.2	14 49.8	5 0.4	15 11.9	17 55.2
17 M	1 40 39.6	23 17.4	16 8.1	16 6.0	5 27.8	7 31.2	24 13.3	23 36.3	14 56.3	5 0.2	15 14.1	17 56.1
18 T	1 44 36.1	24 17.0	16 5.0	0♍10.2	6 14.0	8 39.4	24 48.3	23 41.7	15 2.7	4 59.8	15 16.3	17 57.0
19 W	1 48 32.7	25 16.6	16 1.8	14 39.4	7 8.1	9 47.5	25 23.2	23 47.2	15 9.1	4 59.4	15 18.5	17 57.9
20 T	1 52 29.2	26 16.3	15 58.6	29 29.9	8 9.3	10 55.4	25 58.0	23 52.9	15 15.5	4 59.0	15 20.7	17 58.8
21 F	1 56 25.8	27 16.0	15 55.4	14♎35.6	9 16.8	12 3.3	26 32.7	23 58.8	15 21.8	4 58.5	15 22.9	17 59.6
22 S	2 0 22.4	28 15.7	15 52.3	29 48.1	10 29.8	13 11.0	27 7.3	24 4.8	15 28.0	4 57.9	15 25.1	18 0.4
23 S	2 4 18.9	29 15.5	15 49.1	14♏57.7	11 47.4	14 18.5	27 41.8	24 11.0	15 34.2	4 57.3	15 27.3	18 1.2
24 M	2 8 15.4	0♏15.2	15 45.9	29 54.9	13 9.2	15 26.0	28 16.3	24 17.3	15 40.4	4 56.7	15 29.5	18 1.9
25 T	2 12 12.0	1 15.1	15 42.7	14♐32.1	14 34.4	16 33.2	28 50.6	24 23.9	15 46.4	4 56.0	15 31.7	18 2.7
26 W	2 16 8.6	2 14.9	15 39.5	28 44.0	16 2.5	17 40.4	29 24.9	24 30.5	15 52.5	4 55.2	15 33.9	18 3.4
27 T	2 20 5.1	3 14.8	15 36.4	12♑28.2	17 32.9	18 47.4	29 59.0	24 37.4	15 58.4	4 54.4	15 36.0	18 4.1
28 F	2 24 1.7	4 14.7	15 33.2	25 45.2	19 5.4	19 54.2	0♍33.0	24 44.3	16 4.3	4 53.6	15 38.2	18 4.7
29 S	2 27 58.2	5 14.6	15 30.0	8♒37.2	20 39.4	21 0.8	1 7.0	24 51.5	16 10.1	4 52.6	15 40.3	18 5.3
30 S	2 31 54.8	6 14.6	15 26.8	21 7.8	22 14.6	22 7.3	1 40.8	24 58.8	16 15.9	4 51.7	15 42.4	18 5.9
31 M	2 35 51.4	7 14.6	15 23.7	3♓21.4	23 50.9	23 13.6	2 14.6	25 6.2	16 21.6	4 50.7	15 44.5	18 6.5
DECLINATION												
1 S	0 37 34.7	2S58.3	6N40.5	25S20.2	8S 5.1	18S56.1	17N36.1	22S 6.6	8N10.7	23N35.8	4S21.1	22N56.7
4 T	0 49 24.4	4 8.1	6 36.8	12 21.2	5 59.5	20 2.3	17 5.8	22 5.3	8 2.9	23 35.8	4 23.7	22 56.2
7 F	1 1 14.0	5 17.4	6 33.2	4N23.5	3 48.9	21 4.2	16 34.8	22 3.7	7 55.2	23 35.8	4 26.3	22 55.7
10 M	1 13 3.7	6 26.1	6 29.5	19 41.0	2 0.6	22 1.6	16 3.2	22 1.8	7 47.6	23 35.9	4 28.9	22 55.4
13 T	1 24 53.4	7 34.0	6 25.8	28 11.0	0 55.2	22 54.1	15 31.0	21 59.6	7 40.2	23 36.0	4 31.4	22 55.1
16 S	1 36 43.0	8 41.0	6 22.2	24 34.6	0 39.8	23 41.6	14 58.4	21 57.2	7 33.0	23 36.1	4 34.0	22 55.0
19 W	1 48 32.7	9 47.0	6 18.5	8 38.2	1 10.5	24 23.8	14 25.2	21 54.4	7 26.0	23 36.2	4 36.5	22 54.9
22 S	2 0 22.4	10 51.6	6 14.8	12S31.9	2 17.4	25 0.4	13 51.8	21 51.4	7 19.1	23 36.3	4 39.0	22 54.9
25 T	2 12 12.0	11 54.8	6 11.2	26 59.7	3 49.6	25 31.4	13 18.0	21 48.0	7 12.4	23 36.4	4 41.5	22 54.9
28 F	2 24 1.7	12 56.4	6 7.5	26 6.9	5 37.4	25 56.5	12 44.0	21 44.4	7 6.0	23 36.6	4 43.9	22 55.1
31 M	2 35 51.4	13 56.1	6 3.8	13 38.8	7 33.3	26 15.6	12 9.8	21 40.5	6 59.8	23 36.7	4 46.3	22 55.4

NOVEMBER 1949

LONGITUDE

DAY	EPHEMERIS SIDEREAL TIME h m s	☉ ° ′	☊ ° ′	☽ ° ′	☿ ° ′	♀ ° ′	♂ ° ′	♃ ° ′	♄ ° ′	♅ ° ′	♆ ° ′	♇ ° ′
1 T	2 39 47.9	8♏14.6	15♈20.5	15♓22.4	25♎27.9	24♐19.7	2♍48.2	25♑13.8	16♍27.2	4♋49.6	15♎46.6	18♌ 7.0
2 W	2 43 44.5	9 14.6	15 17.3	27 15.1	27 5.4	25 25.6	3 21.7	25 21.6	16 32.8	4R48.5	15 48.7	18 7.5
3 T	2 47 41.0	10 14.7	15 14.1	9♈ 3.3	28 43.3	26 31.3	3 55.1	25 29.4	16 38.3	4 47.4	15 50.8	18 8.0
4 F	2 51 37.6	11 14.8	15 10.9	20 50.4	0♏21.5	27 36.8	4 28.5	25 37.5	16 43.7	4 46.2	15 52.9	18 8.5
5 S	2 55 34.1	12 14.9	15 7.8	2♉39.3	1 59.8	28 42.1	5 1.7	25 45.6	16 49.1	4 44.9	15 54.9	18 8.9
6 S	2 59 30.7	13 15.1	15 4.6	14 32.2	3 38.1	29 47.2	5 34.8	25 53.9	16 54.4	4 43.6	15 57.0	18 9.3
7 M	3 3 27.2	14 15.3	15 1.4	26 31.2	5 16.3	0♑52.0	6 7.8	26 2.4	16 59.6	4 42.3	15 59.0	18 9.7
8 T	3 7 23.8	15 15.5	14 58.2	8♊37.9	6 54.5	1 56.6	6 40.7	26 11.0	17 4.7	4 40.9	16 1.0	18 10.0
9 W	3 11 20.4	16 15.7	14 55.1	20 53.8	8 32.5	3 1.0	7 13.4	26 19.7	17 9.8	4 39.5	16 3.0	18 10.3
10 T	3 15 16.9	17 16.0	14 51.9	3♋20.6	10 10.3	4 5.1	7 46.1	26 28.5	17 14.8	4 38.0	16 5.0	18 10.6
11 F	3 19 13.5	18 16.3	14 48.7	16 0.1	11 47.9	5 8.9	8 18.6	26 37.5	17 19.7	4 36.5	16 7.0	18 10.9
12 S	3 23 10.0	19 16.7	14 45.5	28 54.3	13 25.2	6 12.5	8 51.0	26 46.6	17 24.6	4 34.9	16 8.9	18 11.1
13 S	3 27 6.6	20 17.1	14 42.4	12♌ 5.4	15 2.3	7 15.8	9 23.3	26 55.8	17 29.3	4 33.3	16 10.8	18 11.3
14 M	3 31 3.1	21 17.5	14 39.2	25 35.4	16 39.2	8 18.8	9 55.5	27 5.2	17 34.0	4 31.7	16 12.8	18 11.5
15 T	3 34 59.7	22 17.9	14 36.0	9♍25.8	18 15.8	9 21.6	10 27.5	27 14.7	17 38.6	4 30.0	16 14.7	18 11.6
16 W	3 38 56.3	23 18.4	14 32.8	23 37.4	19 52.1	10 24.0	10 59.4	27 24.3	17 43.1	4 28.3	16 16.5	18 11.8
17 T	3 42 52.8	24 18.9	14 29.6	8♎ 8.9	21 28.1	11 26.1	11 31.2	27 34.0	17 47.6	4 26.5	16 18.4	18 11.8
18 F	3 46 49.3	25 19.4	14 26.5	22 57.0	23 4.0	12 27.9	12 2.8	27 43.9	17 51.9	4 24.7	16 20.2	18 11.9
19 S	3 50 45.9	26 20.0	14 23.3	7♏56.1	24 39.5	13 29.4	12 34.3	27 53.9	17 56.2	4 22.8	16 22.1	18 11.9
20 S	3 54 42.5	27 20.6	14 20.1	22 58.2	26 14.9	14 30.5	13 5.7	28 4.0	18 0.3	4 21.0	16 23.9	18 11.9
21 M	3 58 39.0	28 21.2	14 16.9	7♐54.3	27 50.0	15 31.3	13 36.9	28 14.2	18 4.4	4 19.0	16 25.6	18R11.9
22 T	4 2 35.6	29 21.8	14 13.8	22 35.5	29 24.9	16 31.6	14 8.0	28 24.5	18 8.4	4 17.1	16 27.4	18 11.8
23 W	4 6 32.1	0♐22.5	14 10.6	6♑54.6	0♐59.7	17 31.6	14 38.9	28 34.9	18 12.3	4 15.1	16 29.1	18 11.8
24 T	4 10 28.7	1 23.2	14 7.4	20 47.1	2 34.2	18 31.2	15 9.6	28 45.5	18 16.1	4 13.1	16 30.9	18 11.6
25 F	4 14 25.3	2 23.9	14 4.2	4♒11.3	4 8.6	19 30.3	15 40.2	28 56.1	18 19.9	4 11.0	16 32.6	18 11.5
26 S	4 18 21.8	3 24.6	14 1.1	17 8.4	5 42.8	20 29.0	16 10.7	29 6.9	18 23.5	4 8.9	16 34.2	18 11.3
27 S	4 22 18.4	4 25.3	13 57.9	29 41.6	7 17.0	21 27.3	16 41.0	29 17.7	18 27.0	4 6.8	16 35.9	18 11.1
28 M	4 26 14.9	5 26.1	13 54.7	11♓55.4	8 50.9	22 25.0	17 11.1	29 28.7	18 30.5	4 4.6	16 37.5	18 10.9
29 T	4 30 11.5	6 26.9	13 51.5	23 54.9	10 24.8	23 22.2	17 41.1	29 39.8	18 33.8	4 2.5	16 39.1	18 10.6
30 W	4 34 8.1	7 27.7	13 48.4	5♈45.4	11 58.7	24 18.9	18 10.8	29 50.9	18 37.1	4 0.3	16 40.7	18 10.4

DECLINATION

DAY	SIDEREAL TIME	☉	☊	☽	☿	♀	♂	♃	♄	♅	♆	♇
1 T	2 39 47.9	14S15.6	6N 2.6	8S17.4	8S12.8	26S20.6	11N58.3	21S39.1	6N57.8	23N36.8	4S47.1	22N55.5
4 F	2 51 37.6	15 12.6	5 58.9	8N29.7	10 11.7	26 31.8	11 24.0	21 34.7	6 51.9	23 37.0	4 49.4	22 55.8
7 M	3 3 27.2	16 7.3	5 55.2	22 39.1	12 8.8	26 36.9	10 49.6	21 30.1	6 46.3	23 37.2	4 51.7	22 56.3
10 T	3 15 16.9	16 59.7	5 51.5	28 28.8	14 2.0	26 36.0	10 15.2	21 25.2	6 41.0	23 37.4	4 53.9	22 56.8
13 S	3 27 6.6	17 49.4	5 47.9	21 40.0	15 49.6	26 29.3	9 40.8	21 20.0	6 35.9	23 37.6	4 56.0	22 57.5
16 W	3 38 56.3	18 36.4	5 44.2	4 22.0	17 30.6	26 16.8	9 6.6	21 14.4	6 31.1	23 37.9	4 58.1	22 58.2
19 S	3 50 45.9	19 20.4	5 40.5	15S58.9	19 3.9	25 58.9	8 32.6	21 8.6	6 26.7	23 38.1	5 0.1	22 59.0
22 T	4 2 35.6	20 1.3	5 36.8	27 58.1	20 28.8	25 35.6	7 58.8	21 2.5	6 22.5	23 38.3	5 2.0	22 59.8
25 F	4 14 25.3	20 38.9	5 33.1	23 57.3	21 44.7	25 7.2	7 25.4	20 56.1	6 18.7	23 38.6	5 3.9	23 0.8
28 M	4 26 14.9	21 13.0	5 29.4	9 43.7	22 50.9	24 34.2	6 52.4	20 49.3	6 15.2	23 38.8	5 5.7	23 1.8

DECEMBER 1949

LONGITUDE

DAY	SIDEREAL TIME	☉	☊	☽	☿	♀	♂	♃	♄	♅	♆	♇
1 T	4 38 4.6	8♐28.5	13♈45.2	17♈32.1	13♐32.4	25♑15.1	18♍40.5	0♒ 2.2	18♍40.2	3♋58.0	16♎42.2	18♌10.0
2 F	4 42 1.2	9 29.3	13 42.0	29 19.5	15 6.1	26 10.7	19 9.9	0 13.5	18 43.3	3R55.7	16 43.7	18R 9.7
3 S	4 45 57.7	10 30.1	13 38.8	11♉11.6	16 39.7	27 5.7	19 39.2	0 25.0	18 46.2	3 53.5	16 45.2	18 9.3
4 S	4 49 54.3	11 31.0	13 35.7	23 11.4	18 13.3	28 0.1	20 8.3	0 36.5	18 49.1	3 51.2	16 46.7	18 9.0
5 M	4 53 50.9	12 31.8	13 32.5	5♊21.1	19 46.9	28 53.8	20 37.2	0 48.2	18 51.9	3 48.8	16 48.2	18 8.5
6 T	4 57 47.4	13 32.7	13 29.3	17 42.1	21 20.4	29 46.9	21 5.9	0 59.9	18 54.5	3 46.4	16 49.6	18 8.1
7 W	5 1 44.0	14 33.6	13 26.1	0♋14.9	22 53.9	0♒39.3	21 34.5	1 11.7	18 57.1	3 44.1	16 51.0	18 7.6
8 T	5 5 40.5	15 34.6	13 22.9	12 59.6	24 27.4	1 30.9	22 2.8	1 23.6	18 59.5	3 41.7	16 52.3	18 7.1
9 F	5 9 37.1	16 35.5	13 19.8	25 56.1	26 0.9	2 21.9	22 31.0	1 35.6	19 1.9	3 39.2	16 53.7	18 6.6
10 S	5 13 33.7	17 36.4	13 16.6	9♌ 4.1	27 34.4	3 12.0	22 58.9	1 47.6	19 4.1	3 36.8	16 55.0	18 6.0
11 S	5 17 30.2	18 37.4	13 13.4	22 23.9	29 7.8	4 1.3	23 26.7	1 59.8	19 6.3	3 34.3	16 56.3	18 5.4
12 M	5 21 26.7	19 38.4	13 10.2	5♍55.9	0♑41.2	4 49.8	23 54.2	2 12.0	19 8.3	3 31.9	16 57.5	18 4.8
13 T	5 25 23.3	20 39.4	13 7.1	19 40.9	2 14.5	5 37.5	24 21.5	2 24.3	19 10.2	3 29.4	16 58.7	18 4.2
14 W	5 29 19.9	21 40.5	13 3.9	3♎39.5	3 47.8	6 24.2	24 48.7	2 36.7	19 12.1	3 26.9	16 59.9	18 3.5
15 T	5 33 16.4	22 41.5	13 0.7	17 51.8	5 20.9	7 10.0	25 15.5	2 49.1	19 13.8	3 24.4	17 1.1	18 2.8
16 F	5 37 13.0	23 42.6	12 57.5	2♏16.6	6 53.8	7 54.8	25 42.2	3 1.6	19 15.4	3 21.8	17 2.2	18 2.1
17 S	5 41 9.6	24 43.7	12 54.4	16 51.0	8 26.5	8 38.6	26 8.6	3 14.2	19 16.9	3 19.3	17 3.3	18 1.4
18 S	5 45 6.1	25 44.8	12 51.2	1♐30.2	9 58.8	9 21.3	26 34.8	3 26.9	19 18.3	3 16.7	17 4.4	18 0.6
19 M	5 49 2.7	26 45.9	12 48.0	16 7.6	11 30.8	10 2.9	27 0.7	3 39.6	19 19.6	3 14.2	17 5.5	17 59.9
20 T	5 52 59.2	27 47.0	12 44.8	0♑35.8	13 2.3	10 43.4	27 26.4	3 52.4	19 20.7	3 11.6	17 6.5	17 59.0
21 W	5 56 55.8	28 48.1	12 41.7	14 47.7	14 33.2	11 22.6	27 51.8	4 5.3	19 21.8	3 9.0	17 7.4	17 58.2
22 T	6 0 52.4	29 49.3	12 38.5	28 37.9	16 3.4	12 0.7	28 16.9	4 18.3	19 22.8	3 6.5	17 8.4	17 57.4
23 F	6 4 48.9	0♑50.4	12 35.3	12♒ 3.2	17 32.6	12 37.4	28 41.8	4 31.3	19 23.6	3 3.9	17 9.3	17 56.5
24 S	6 8 45.5	1 51.5	12 32.1	25 3.1	19 0.7	13 12.7	29 6.4	4 44.3	19 24.3	3 1.3	17 10.2	17 55.6
25 S	6 12 42.0	2 52.7	12 28.9	7♓39.4	20 27.4	13 46.6	29 30.8	4 57.4	19 25.0	2 58.7	17 11.0	17 54.7
26 M	6 16 38.6	3 53.8	12 25.8	19 55.7	21 52.6	14 19.0	29 54.8	5 10.6	19 25.5	2 56.1	17 11.9	17 53.7
27 T	6 20 35.2	4 55.0	12 22.6	1♈56.8	23 15.7	14 49.9	0♎18.6	5 23.8	19 25.9	2 53.5	17 12.6	17 52.8
28 W	6 24 31.7	5 56.1	12 19.4	13 48.2	24 36.6	15 19.2	0 42.0	5 37.1	19 26.2	2 51.0	17 13.4	17 51.8
29 T	6 28 28.3	6 57.3	12 16.2	25 35.5	25 54.7	15 46.8	1 5.2	5 50.5	19 26.3	2 48.4	17 14.1	17 50.8
30 F	6 32 24.8	7 58.4	12 13.1	7♉24.1	27 9.5	16 12.7	1 28.0	6 3.9	19 26.4	2 45.8	17 14.8	17 49.7
31 S	6 36 21.4	8 59.6	12 9.9	19 19.1	28 20.6	16 36.7	1 50.6	6 17.3	19R26.4	2 43.2	17 15.5	17 48.7

DECLINATION

DAY	SIDEREAL TIME	☉	☊	☽	☿	♀	♂	♃	♄	♅	♆	♇
1 T	4 38 4.6	21S43.6	5N25.7	7N 3.3	23S46.7	23S56.9	6N19.8	20S42.3	6N12.1	23N39.1	5S 7.4	23N 2.9
4 S	4 49 54.3	22 10.3	5 22.0	21 36.3	24 31.6	23 15.5	5 47.7	20 35.0	6 9.3	23 39.3	5 8.9	23 4.1
7 W	5 1 44.0	22 33.3	5 18.3	28 20.9	25 4.9	22 30.7	5 16.2	20 27.4	6 6.9	23 39.6	5 10.4	23 5.3
10 S	5 13 33.7	22 52.2	5 14.6	22 25.8	25 26.0	21 42.9	4 45.4	20 19.5	6 4.9	23 39.8	5 11.8	23 6.6
13 T	5 25 23.3	23 7.1	5 10.9	6 1.5	25 34.4	20 52.4	4 15.2	20 11.3	6 3.2	23 40.1	5 13.1	23 8.0
16 F	5 37 13.0	23 17.9	5 7.2	13S45.0	25 29.6	19 59.9	3 45.8	20 2.8	6 1.9	23 40.3	5 14.3	23 9.4
19 M	5 49 2.7	23 24.5	5 3.5	27 9.3	25 11.2	19 5.8	3 17.3	19 54.1	6 1.1	23 40.5	5 15.4	23 10.9
22 T	6 0 52.4	23 26.9	4 59.8	25 10.8	24 39.3	18 10.8	2 49.7	19 45.1	6 0.5	23 40.7	5 16.4	23 12.4
25 S	6 12 42.0	23 25.0	4 56.0	11 24.1	23 54.3	17 15.4	2 23.2	19 35.8	6 0.4	23 40.9	5 17.2	23 13.9
28 W	6 24 31.7	23 18.9	4 52.3	5N31.8	22 57.6	16 20.4	1 57.7	19 26.2	6 0.7	23 41.1	5 17.9	23 15.5
31 S	6 36 21.4	23 8.6	4 48.6	20 27.2	21 51.5	15 26.6	1 33.3	19 16.4	6 1.4	23 41.3	5 18.6	23 17.2

LUNAR PHASES

1900

Month	Day	Phase	Time	
JAN	1	N	1:52	P
	8	¼	5:40	A
	15	F	7:08	P
	23	¾	11:53	P
	31	N	1:23	A
FEB	6	¼	4:23	P
	14	F	1:51	P
	22	¾	4:45	P
MAR	1	N	11:26	A
	8	¼	5:35	A
	16	F	8:12	A
	24	¾	5:37	A
	30	N	8:31	P
APR	6	¼	8:55	P
	15	F	1:03	A
	22	¾	2:34	P
	29	N	5:24	A
MAY	6	¼	1:39	P
	14	F	3:37	P
	21	¾	8:31	P
	28	N	2:50	P
JUN	5	¼	6:59	A
	13	F	3:39	A
	20	¾	0:58	A
	27	N	1:28	A
JUL	5	¼	0:14	A
	12	F	1:22	P
	19	¾	5:32	A
	26	N	1:43	P
AUG	3	¼	4:46	P
	10	F	9:30	P
	17	¾	11:47	A
	25	N	3:53	A
SEP	2	¼	7:56	A
	9	F	5:06	A
	15	¾	8:58	P
	23	N	7:58	P
OCT	1	¼	9:11	P
	8	F	1:19	P
	15	¾	9:51	A
	23	N	1:28	P
	31	¼	8:18	A
NOV	6	F	11:00	P
	14	¾	2:38	A
	22	N	7:18	A
	29	¼	5:36	P
DEC	6	F	10:39	A
	13	¾	10:43	P
	22	N	0:02	A
	29	¼	1:48	A

1901

Month	Day	Phase	Time	
JAN	5	F	0:14	A
	12	¾	8:39	P
	20	N	2:36	P
	27	¼	9:53	A
FEB	3	F	3:30	P
	11	¾	6:12	P
	19	N	2:46	A
	25	¼	6:39	P
MAR	5	F	8:05	A
	13	¾	1:07	P
	20	N	0:53	P
	27	¼	4:39	A
APR	4	F	1:21	A
	12	¾	3:58	A
	18	N	9:38	P
	25	¼	4:15	P
MAY	3	F	6:19	P
	11	¾	2:39	P
	18	N	5:38	A
	25	¼	5:40	A
JUN	2	F	9:53	A
	9	¾	10:00	P
	16	N	1:33	P
	23	¼	9:00	P
JUL	1	F	11:18	P
	9	¾	3:21	A
	15	N	10:11	P
	23	¼	1:59	P
	31	F	10:34	A
AUG	7	¾	8:03	A
	14	N	8:28	A
	22	¼	7:53	A
	29	F	8:22	P
SEP	5	¾	1:28	P
	12	N	9:19	P
	21	¼	1:34	A
	28	F	5:36	A
OCT	4	¾	8:53	P
	12	N	1:12	P
	20	¼	5:58	P
	27	F	3:07	P
NOV	3	¾	7:25	A
	11	N	7:35	A
	19	¼	8:24	A
	26	F	1:18	A
DEC	2	¾	9:50	P
	11	N	2:54	A
	18	¼	8:36	P
	25	F	0:16	P

1902

Month	Day	Phase	Time	
JAN	1	¾	4:08	P
	9	N	9:15	P
	17	¼	6:39	A
	24	F	0:07	A
	31	¾	1:09	P
FEB	8	N	1:22	P
	15	¼	2:57	P
	22	F	1:04	P
MAR	2	¾	10:40	A
	10	N	2:51	A
	16	¼	10:13	P
	24	F	3:22	A
APR	1	¾	6:25	A
	8	N	1:51	P
	15	¼	5:26	A
	22	F	6:50	P
	30	¾	10:59	P
MAY	7	N	10:46	P
	14	¼	1:40	P
	22	F	10:47	A
	30	¾	0:01	P
JUN	6	N	6:11	A
	12	¼	11:54	P
	21	F	2:17	A
	28	¾	9:53	P
JUL	5	N	0:60	P
	12	¼	0:47	P
	20	F	4:46	P
	28	¾	5:15	A
AUG	3	N	8:18	P
	11	¼	4:25	A
	19	F	6:04	A
	26	¾	11:05	A
SEP	2	N	5:20	A
	9	¼	10:16	P
	17	F	6:24	P
	24	¾	4:32	P
OCT	1	N	5:10	P
	9	¼	5:22	P
	17	F	6:02	A
	23	¾	10:58	P
	31	N	8:14	A
NOV	8	¼	0:31	P
	15	F	5:07	P
	22	¾	7:47	A
	30	N	2:05	A
DEC	8	¼	6:27	A
	15	F	3:48	A
	21	¾	8:01	P
	29	N	9:25	P

1903

Month	Day	Phase	Time	
JAN	6	¼	9:57	P
	13	F	2:18	P
	20	¾	11:50	A
	28	N	4:39	P
FEB	5	¼	10:13	A
	12	F	0:58	A
	19	¾	6:23	A
	27	N	10:20	A
MAR	6	¼	7:14	P
	13	F	0:13	P
	21	¾	2:09	A
	29	N	1:27	A
APR	5	¼	1:52	A
	12	F	0:19	A
	19	¾	9:31	P
	27	N	1:32	P
MAY	4	¼	7:26	A
	11	F	1:19	P
	19	¾	3:19	P
	26	N	10:50	P
JUN	2	¼	1:25	P
	10	F	3:09	A
	18	¾	6:45	A
	25	N	6:11	A
JUL	1	¼	9:02	P
	9	F	5:44	P
	17	¾	7:25	P
	24	N	0:47	P
	31	¼	7:15	A
AUG	8	F	8:55	A
	16	¾	5:23	A
	22	N	7:52	P
	29	¼	8:35	P
SEPT	7	F	0:21	A
	14	¾	1:14	P
	21	N	4:31	A
	28	¼	1:09	P
OCT	6	F	3:24	P
	13	¾	7:57	P
	20	N	3:31	P
	28	¼	8:33	A
NOV	5	F	5:28	A
	12	¾	2:46	A
	19	N	5:11	A
	27	¼	5:37	A
DEC	4	F	6:13	P
	11	¾	10:54	A
	18	N	9:27	P
	27	¼	2:23	A

1904

Month	Day	Phase	Time	
JAN	3	F	5:48	A
	9	¾	9:11	P
	17	N	3:47	P
	25	¼	8:41	P
FEB	1	F	4:34	P
	8	¾	9:57	A
	16	N	11:05	A
	24	¼	11:09	A
MAR	2	F	2:49	A
	9	¾	1:01	A
	17	N	5:40	A
	24	¼	9:37	P
	31	F	0:45	P
APR	7	¾	5:54	P
	15	N	9:53	P
	23	¼	4:55	A
	29	F	10:37	P
MAY	7	¾	11:51	A
	15	N	10:59	A
	22	¼	10:19	A
	29	F	8:55	A
JUN	6	¾	5:53	A
	13	N	9:11	P
	20	¼	3:11	P
	27	F	8:24	P
JUL	5	¾	10:55	P
	13	N	5:28	A
	19	¼	8:49	P
	27	F	9:43	A
AUG	4	¾	2:03	P
	11	N	0:59	P
	18	¼	4:28	A
	26	F	1:03	A
SEP	3	¾	2:59	A
	9	N	8:43	P
	16	¼	3:13	P
	24	F	5:50	P
OCT	2	¾	1:53	P
	9	N	5:25	A
	16	¼	5:55	A
	24	F	10:57	A
	31	¾	11:14	P
NOV	7	N	3:37	P
	15	¼	0:36	A
	23	F	3:13	A
	30	¾	7:39	A
DEC	7	N	3:47	A
	14	¼	10:08	P
	22	F	6:02	P
	29	¾	3:47	P

1905

Month	Day	Phase	Time	
JAN	5	N	6:18	P
	13	¼	8:11	P
	21	F	7:15	A
	28	¾	0:20	A
FEB	4	N	11:07	A
	12	¼	4:21	P
	19	F	6:53	P
	26	¾	10:04	A
MAR	6	N	5:20	A
	14	¼	9:00	A
	21	F	4:56	A
	27	¾	9:36	P
APR	4	N	11:24	P
	12	¼	9:42	P
	19	F	1:38	P
	26	¾	11:14	P
MAY	4	N	3:50	P
	12	¼	6:47	A
	18	F	9:37	P
	26	¾	2:51	P
JUN	3	N	5:57	A
	10	¼	1:05	P
	17	F	5:52	A
	24	¾	7:46	P
JUL	2	N	5:50	P
	9	¼	5:47	P
	16	F	3:32	P
	24	¾	1:09	P
AUG	1	N	4:03	A
	7	¼	10:17	P
	15	F	3:32	A
	23	¾	6:11	A
	30	N	1:14	P
SEP	6	¼	4:09	A
	13	F	6:11	P
	21	¾	10:14	P
	28	N	10:00	P
OCT	5	¼	0:55	P
	13	F	11:04	A
	21	¾	0:51	P
	28	N	6:58	A
NOV	4	¼	1:40	A
	12	F	5:12	A
	20	¾	1:35	A
	26	N	4:48	P
DEC	3	¼	6:38	P
	11	F	11:26	P
	19	¾	0:09	P
	26	N	4:04	A

1906

Month	Day	Phase	Time	
JAN	2	¼	2:53	P
	10	F	4:37	P
	17	¾	8:49	P
	24	N	5:10	P
FEB	1	¼	0:31	P
	9	F	7:46	A
	16	¾	4:23	P
	23	N	7:58	A
MAR	3	¼	9:29	A
	10	F	8:18	P
	17	¾	11:58	A
	24	N	11:53	P
APR	2	¼	4:03	A
	9	F	6:13	A
	15	¾	8:37	P
	23	N	4:07	P
MAY	1	¼	7:07	P
	8	F	2:10	P
	15	¾	7:03	A
	23	N	8:01	A
	31	¼	6:24	A
JUN	6	F	9:12	P
	13	¾	7:35	P
	21	N	11:06	P
	29	¼	2:19	P
JUL	6	F	4:28	A
	13	¾	10:13	A
	21	N	1:00	P
	28	¼	7:57	P
AUG	4	F	1:00	P
	12	¾	2:48	A
	20	N	1:28	A
	27	¼	0:43	A
SEP	2	F	11:37	P
	10	¾	8:54	P
	18	N	0:34	P
	25	¼	6:12	A
OCT	2	F	0:49	P
	10	¾	3:40	P
	17	N	10:43	P
	24	¼	1:50	P
NOV	1	F	4:47	A
	9	¾	9:46	A
	16	N	8:37	A
	23	¼	0:40	A
	30	F	11:08	P
DEC	9	¾	1:46	A
	15	N	6:55	P
	22	¼	3:04	P
	30	F	8:44	P

1907

Month	Day	Phase	Time	
JAN	7	¾	2:48	P
	14	N	5:57	A
	21	¼	8:43	A
	29	F	1:46	P
FEB	6	¾	0:52	A
	12	N	5:44	P
	20	¼	4:36	A
	28	F	6:23	A
MAR	7	¾	8:42	A
	14	N	6:05	A
	22	¼	1:10	A
	29	F	7:45	P
APR	5	¾	3:21	P
	12	N	7:07	P
	20	¼	8:39	P
	28	F	6:05	A
MAY	4	¾	9:54	P
	12	N	9:00	A
	20	¼	1:28	P
	27	F	2:18	P
JUN	3	¾	5:20	A
	10	N	11:51	P
	19	¼	2:55	A
	25	F	9:28	P
JUL	2	¾	2:35	P
	10	N	3:17	P
	18	¼	1:12	P
	25	F	4:30	A
AUG	1	¾	2:26	A
	9	N	6:37	A
	16	¼	9:06	P
	23	F	0:16	P
	30	¾	5:29	P
SEP	7	N	9:04	P
	15	¼	3:41	A
	21	F	9:34	P
	29	¾	11:38	A
OCT	7	N	10:21	A
	14	¼	10:02	A
	21	F	9:17	A
	29	¾	7:52	A
NOV	5	N	10:32	P
	12	¼	5:15	P
	20	F	0:05	A
	28	¾	4:22	A
DEC	5	N	10:23	A
	12	¼	2:17	A
	19	F	5:56	P
	27	¾	11:11	P

1908

Month	Day	Phase	Time	
JAN	3	N	9:44	P
	10	¼	1:53	P
	18	F	1:38	P
	26	¾	3:02	P
FEB	2	N	8:37	A
	9	¼	4:28	A
	17	F	9:06	A
	25	¾	3:25	A
MAR	2	N	6:58	P
	9	¼	9:43	P
	18	F	2:29	A
	25	¾	0:32	P
APR	1	N	5:03	A
	8	¼	4:32	P
	16	F	4:56	P
	23	¾	7:07	P
	30	N	3:34	P
MAY	8	¼	11:24	A
	16	F	4:33	A
	23	¾	0:18	A
	30	N	3:15	A
JUN	7	¼	4:57	A
	14	F	1:56	P
	21	¾	5:27	A
	28	N	4:32	P
JUL	6	¼	8:25	P
	13	F	9:48	P
	20	¾	0:02	P
	28	N	7:18	A
AUG	5	¼	9:41	A
	12	F	4:59	A
	18	¾	9:26	P
	26	N	10:59	P
SEP	3	¼	8:51	P
	10	F	0:24	P
	17	¾	10:34	A
	25	N	3:00	P
OCT	3	¼	6:14	A
	9	F	9:04	P
	17	¾	3:36	A
	25	N	6:47	A
NOV	1	¼	2:17	P
	8	F	7:59	A
	15	¾	11:42	P
	23	N	9:54	P
	30	¼	9:45	P
DEC	7	F	9:45	P
	15	¾	9:13	P
	23	N	11:50	A
	30	¼	5:40	A

1909

Month	Day	Phase	Time	
JAN	6	F	2:13	P
	14	¾	6:12	P
	22	N	0:12	A
	28	¼	3:08	P
FEB	5	F	8:25	A
	13	¾	0:48	P
	20	N	10:53	A
	27	¼	2:50	A
MAR	7	F	2:56	A
	15	¾	3:42	A
	21	N	8:12	P
	28	¼	4:49	P
APR	5	F	8:29	P
	13	¾	2:31	P
	20	N	4:52	A
	27	¼	8:37	A
MAY	5	F	0:08	P
	12	¾	9:46	P
	19	N	1:43	P
	27	¼	1:28	A
JUN	4	F	1:25	A
	11	¾	2:43	A
	17	N	11:29	P
	25	¼	6:44	P
JUL	3	F	0:18	P
	10	¾	6:59	A
	17	N	10:45	A
	25	¼	11:46	A
AUG	1	F	9:15	P
	8	¾	0:11	P
	15	N	11:55	P
	24	¼	3:56	A
	31	F	5:08	A
SEP	6	¾	7:45	P
	14	N	3:09	P
	22	¼	6:32	P
	29	F	1:06	P
OCT	6	¾	6:45	A
	14	N	8:14	A
	22	¼	7:04	A
	28	F	10:08	P
NOV	4	¾	9:38	P
	13	N	2:19	A
	20	¼	5:30	P
	27	F	8:52	A
DEC	4	¾	4:13	P
	12	N	7:59	P
	20	¼	2:18	A
	26	F	9:31	P

LUNAR PHASES

1910

JAN	3	¾	1:27	P
	11	N	11:52	A
	18	¼	10:21	A
	25	F	11:51	A
FEB	2	¾	11:28	A
	10	N	1:14	A
	16	¼	6:33	P
	24	F	3:36	A
MAR	4	¾	7:53	A
	11	N	0:13	P
	18	¼	3:38	A
	25	F	8:21	P
APR	3	¾	0:48	A
	9	N	9:26	P
	16	¼	2:05	P
	24	F	1:24	P
MAY	2	¾	1:30	P
	9	N	5:33	A
	16	¼	2:14	A
	24	F	5:40	A
	31	¾	10:25	P
JUN	7	N	1:17	P
	14	¼	4:20	P
	22	F	8:12	P
	30	¾	4:40	A
JUL	6	N	9:21	P
	14	¼	8:25	A
	22	F	8:38	A
	29	¾	9:35	A
AUG	5	N	6:37	A
	13	¼	2:02	A
	20	F	7:15	P
	27	¾	2:34	P
SEP	3	N	6:06	P
	11	¼	8:11	P
	19	F	4:53	A
	25	¾	8:54	P
OCT	3	N	8:33	A
	11	¼	1:41	P
	18	F	2:25	P
	25	¾	5:49	A
NOV	2	N	1:57	A
	10	¼	5:30	A
	17	F	0:26	A
	23	¾	6:14	P
DEC	1	N	9:11	P
	9	¼	7:06	P
	16	F	11:06	A
	23	¾	10:36	A
	31	N	4:22	P

1911

JAN	8	¼	6:21	A
	14	F	10:27	P
	22	¾	6:22	A
	30	N	9:45	A
FEB	6	¼	3:28	P
	13	F	10:38	A
	21	¾	3:45	A
MAR	1	N	0:32	A
	7	¼	11:02	P
	14	F	11:59	P
	23	¾	0:27	A
	30	N	0:38	P
APR	6	¼	5:55	A
	13	F	2:37	P
	21	¾	6:36	P
	28	N	10:26	P
MAY	5	¼	1:14	P
	13	F	6:10	A
	21	¾	9:23	A
	28	N	6:25	A
JUN	3	¼	10:05	P
	11	F	9:51	P
	19	¾	8:51	P
	26	N	1:20	P
JUL	3	¼	9:21	A
	11	F	0:54	P
	19	¾	5:32	A
	25	N	8:13	P
AUG	1	¼	11:30	P
	10	F	2:55	A
	17	¾	0:11	P
	24	N	4:15	A
	31	¼	4:21	P
SEP	8	F	3:57	P
	15	¾	5:51	P
	22	N	2:38	P
	30	¼	11:08	A
OCT	8	F	4:12	A
	14	¾	11:47	P
	22	N	4:10	A
	30	¼	6:42	A
NOV	6	F	3:49	P
	13	¾	7:20	A
	20	N	8:50	P
	29	¼	1:43	A
DEC	6	F	2:52	A
	12	¾	5:46	P
	20	N	3:41	P
	28	¼	6:48	P

1912

JAN	4	F	1:30	P
	11	¾	7:43	A
	19	N	11:11	A
	27	¼	8:52	A
FEB	2	F	11:59	P
	10	¾	0:51	A
	18	N	5:45	A
	25	¼	7:27	P
MAR	3	F	10:42	A
	10	¾	7:56	P
	18	N	10:09	P
	26	¼	3:02	A
APR	1	F	10:05	P
	9	¾	3:24	P
	17	N	11:41	A
	24	¼	8:48	A
MAY	1	F	10:20	A
	9	¾	9:57	A
	16	N	10:14	P
	23	¼	2:12	P
	30	F	11:30	P
JUN	8	¾	2:36	A
	15	N	6:24	A
	21	¼	8:39	P
	29	F	1:34	P
JUL	7	¾	4:47	P
	14	N	1:14	P
	21	¼	5:19	A
	29	F	4:29	A
AUG	6	¾	4:18	A
	12	N	7:58	P
	19	¼	4:57	P
	27	F	7:59	P
SEP	4	¾	1:24	P
	11	N	3:49	A
	18	¼	7:55	A
	26	F	11:35	A
OCT	3	¾	8:49	P
	10	N	1:41	P
	18	¼	2:07	A
	26	F	2:31	A
NOV	2	¾	3:38	A
	9	N	2:05	A
	16	¼	10:44	P
	24	F	4:13	P
DEC	1	¾	11:06	A
	8	N	5:07	P
	16	¼	8:07	P
	24	F	4:31	A
	30	¾	8:13	P

1913

JAN	7	N	10:29	A
	15	¼	4:02	P
	22	F	3:41	P
	29	¾	7:35	A
FEB	6	N	5:23	A
	14	¼	8:34	A
	21	F	2:04	A
	27	¾	9:16	P
MAR	8	N	0:23	A
	15	¼	8:58	P
	22	F	11:57	A
	29	¾	0:58	P
APR	6	N	5:49	P
	14	¼	5:40	A
	20	F	9:33	P
	28	¾	6:10	A
MAY	6	N	8:25	A
	13	¼	11:45	A
	20	F	7:19	A
	28	¾	0:04	A
JUN	4	N	7:58	P
	11	¼	4:38	P
	18	F	5:54	P
	26	¾	5:41	P
JUL	4	N	5:07	A
	10	¼	9:38	P
	18	F	6:07	A
	26	¾	9:59	A
AUG	2	N	0:59	P
	9	¼	4:04	A
	16	F	8:28	P
	25	¾	0:18	A
	31	N	8:39	P
SEP	7	¼	1:06	P
	15	F	0:47	P
	23	¾	0:31	P
	30	N	4:57	A
OCT	7	¼	1:47	A
	15	F	6:07	A
	22	¾	10:54	P
	29	N	2:30	P
NOV	5	¼	6:35	P
	13	F	11:12	P
	21	¾	7:57	A
	28	N	1:42	A
DEC	5	¼	2:59	P
	13	F	3:01	P
	20	¾	4:16	P
	27	N	2:59	P

1914

JAN	4	¼	1:10	P
	12	F	5:10	A
	19	¾	0:30	A
	26	N	6:35	A
FEB	3	¼	10:33	A
	10	F	5:35	P
	17	¾	9:24	A
	25	N	0:03	A
MAR	5	¼	5:04	A
	12	F	4:19	A
	18	¾	7:40	P
	26	N	6:10	P
APR	3	¼	7:42	P
	10	F	1:29	P
	17	¾	7:53	A
	25	N	11:22	A
MAY	3	¼	6:30	A
	9	F	9:31	P
	16	¾	10:13	P
	25	N	2:35	A
JUN	1	¼	2:04	P
	8	F	5:19	A
	15	¾	2:21	P
	23	N	3:34	P
	30	¼	7:25	P
JUL	7	F	2:00	P
	15	¾	7:32	A
	23	N	2:39	A
	29	¼	11:52	P
AUG	6	F	0:41	A
	14	¾	0:57	A
	21	N	0:27	P
	28	¼	4:53	A
SEP	4	F	2:02	P
	12	¾	5:49	P
	19	N	9:34	P
	26	¼	0:04	P
OCT	4	F	6:00	A
	12	¾	9:34	A
	19	N	6:34	A
	25	¼	10:45	P
NOV	2	F	11:49	P
	10	¾	11:37	P
	17	N	4:03	P
	24	¼	1:39	P
DEC	2	F	6:21	P
	10	¾	11:32	A
	17	N	2:36	A
	24	¼	8:25	A

1915

JAN	1	F	0:21	P
	8	¾	9:13	P
	15	N	2:43	P
	23	¼	5:33	A
	31	F	4:42	A
FEB	7	¾	5:11	A
	14	N	4:32	A
	22	¼	2:59	A
MAR	1	F	6:33	P
	8	¾	0:28	P
	15	N	7:43	P
	23	¼	10:49	P
	31	F	5:38	A
APR	6	¾	8:13	P
	14	N	11:36	A
	22	¼	3:40	P
	29	F	2:20	P
MAY	6	¾	5:23	A
	14	N	3:32	A
	22	¼	4:51	A
	28	F	9:33	P
JUN	4	¾	4:33	P
	12	N	6:58	P
	20	¼	2:25	P
	27	F	4:28	A
JUL	4	¾	5:55	A
	12	N	9:31	A
	19	¼	9:09	P
	26	F	0:12	P
AUG	2	¾	9:28	P
	10	N	10:53	P
	18	¼	2:18	A
	24	F	9:41	P
SEP	1	¾	2:57	P
	9	N	10:53	A
	16	¼	7:22	A
	23	F	9:36	A
OCT	1	¾	9:45	A
	8	N	9:43	P
	15	¼	1:52	P
	23	F	0:16	A
	31	¾	4:41	A
NOV	7	N	7:53	A
	13	¼	11:04	P
	21	F	5:37	P
	29	¾	10:11	P
DEC	6	N	6:04	P
	13	¼	11:39	A
	21	F	0:53	P
	29	¾	0:59	P

1916

JAN	5	N	4:46	A
	12	¼	3:38	A
	20	F	8:30	A
	28	¾	0:36	A
FEB	3	N	4:06	P
	10	¼	10:21	P
	19	F	2:29	A
	26	¾	9:24	A
MAR	4	N	3:58	A
	11	¼	6:34	P
	19	F	5:27	P
	26	¾	4:23	P
APR	2	N	4:22	P
	10	¼	2:36	P
	18	F	5:08	A
	24	¾	10:39	P
MAY	2	N	5:30	A
	10	¼	8:48	A
	17	F	2:12	P
	24	¾	5:17	A
	31	N	7:38	P
JUN	8	¼	11:59	P
	15	F	9:42	P
	22	¾	1:17	P
	30	N	10:44	A
JUL	8	¼	11:56	A
	15	F	4:41	A
	21	¾	11:34	P
	30	N	2:16	A
AUG	6	¼	9:06	P
	13	F	0:01	P
	20	¾	0:53	P
	28	N	5:25	P
SEP	5	¼	4:27	A
	11	F	8:31	P
	19	¾	5:36	A
	27	N	7:35	A
OCT	4	¼	11:01	A
	11	F	7:02	A
	19	¾	1:09	A
	26	N	8:38	P
NOV	2	¼	5:51	P
	9	F	8:19	P
	17	¾	10:01	P
	25	N	8:51	A
DEC	2	¼	1:56	A
	9	F	0:45	P
	17	¾	6:07	P
	24	N	8:32	P
	31	¼	0:08	P

1917

JAN	8	F	7:43	A
	16	¾	11:43	A
	23	N	7:40	A
	30	¼	1:02	A
FEB	7	F	3:29	A
	15	¾	1:54	A
	21	N	6:10	P
	28	¼	4:44	P
MAR	8	F	9:59	P
	16	¾	0:34	P
	23	N	4:06	A
	30	¼	10:37	A
APR	7	F	1:50	P
	14	¾	8:13	P
	21	N	2:02	P
	29	¼	5:23	A
MAY	7	F	2:44	A
	14	¾	1:49	A
	21	N	0:47	A
	28	¼	11:34	P
JUN	5	F	1:07	P
	12	¾	6:39	A
	19	N	1:03	P
	27	¼	4:09	P
JUL	4	F	9:41	P
	11	¾	0:13	P
	19	N	3:01	A
	27	¼	6:41	A
AUG	3	F	5:11	A
	9	¾	7:57	P
	17	N	6:22	P
	25	¼	7:09	P
SEP	1	F	0:29	P
	8	¾	7:06	A
	16	N	10:28	A
	24	¼	5:42	A
	30	F	8:32	P
OCT	7	¾	10:15	P
	16	N	2:42	A
	23	¼	2:38	P
	30	F	6:20	A
NOV	6	¾	5:04	P
	14	N	6:29	P
	21	¼	10:29	P
	28	F	6:42	P
DEC	6	¾	2:14	P
	14	N	9:18	A
	21	¼	6:08	A
	28	F	9:52	A

1918

JAN	5	¾	11:50	A
	12	N	10:36	P
	19	¼	2:38	P
	27	F	3:15	A
FEB	4	¾	7:53	A
	11	N	10:05	A
	18	¼	0:57	A
	25	F	9:35	P
MAR	6	¾	0:44	A
	12	N	7:53	P
	19	¼	1:31	P
	27	F	3:34	P
APR	4	¾	1:34	P
	11	N	4:35	A
	18	¼	4:08	A
	26	F	8:06	A
MAY	3	¾	10:27	P
	10	N	1:01	P
	17	¼	8:15	P
	25	F	10:33	P
JUN	2	¾	4:21	A
	8	N	10:03	P
	16	¼	1:12	P
	24	F	10:39	A
JUL	1	¾	8:44	A
	8	N	8:23	A
	16	¼	6:25	A
	23	F	8:35	P
	30	¾	1:15	P
AUG	6	N	8:30	P
	14	¼	11:17	P
	22	F	5:03	A
	28	¾	7:28	P
SEP	5	N	10:44	A
	13	¼	3:03	P
	20	F	1:02	P
	27	¾	4:39	A
OCT	5	N	3:06	A
	13	¼	5:01	A
	19	F	9:35	P
	26	¾	5:36	P
NOV	3	N	9:02	P
	11	¼	4:47	P
	18	F	7:33	A
	25	¾	10:26	A
DEC	3	N	3:20	P
	11	¼	2:32	A
	17	F	7:18	P
	25	¾	6:31	A

1919

JAN	2	N	8:25	A
	9	¼	10:56	A
	16	F	8:45	A
	24	¾	4:23	A
	31	N	11:08	P
FEB	7	¼	6:53	P
	14	F	11:39	P
	23	¾	1:49	A
MAR	2	N	11:12	A
	9	¼	3:15	A
	16	F	3:42	P
	24	¾	8:35	P
	31	N	9:06	P
APR	7	¼	0:39	P
	15	F	8:26	A
	23	¾	11:22	A
	30	N	5:31	A
MAY	6	¼	11:34	P
	15	F	1:02	A
	22	¾	10:05	P
	29	N	1:13	P
JUN	5	¼	0:23	P
	13	F	4:29	P
	21	¾	5:34	A
	27	N	8:53	P
JUL	5	¼	3:18	A
	13	F	6:03	A
	20	¾	11:04	A
	27	N	5:22	A
AUG	3	¼	8:12	P
	11	F	5:40	P
	18	¾	3:57	P
	25	N	3:38	P
SEP	2	¼	2:23	P
	10	F	3:55	A
	16	¾	9:32	P
	24	N	4:35	A
OCT	2	¼	8:38	A
	9	F	1:39	P
	16	¾	5:05	A
	23	N	8:40	P
NOV	1	¼	1:44	A
	7	F	11:36	P
	14	¾	3:41	P
	22	N	3:21	P
	30	¼	4:48	P
DEC	7	F	10:04	A
	14	¾	6:03	A
	22	N	10:56	A
	30	¼	5:26	A

LUNAR PHASES

1920

JAN	5	F	9:06	P
	13	¾	0:09	A
	21	N	5:28	A
	28	¼	3:39	P
FEB	4	F	8:43	A
	11	¾	8:50	P
	19	N	9:35	P
	26	¼	11:50	P
MAR	4	F	9:13	P
	12	¾	5:58	P
	20	N	10:56	A
	27	¼	6:46	A
APR	3	F	10:55	A
	11	¾	1:25	P
	18	N	9:44	P
	25	¼	1:28	P
MAY	3	F	1:48	A
	11	¾	5:52	A
	18	N	6:26	A
	24	¼	9:08	P
JUN	1	F	5:19	P
	9	¾	6:59	P
	16	N	1:42	P
	23	¼	6:50	A
JUL	1	F	8:42	A
	9	¾	5:06	A
	15	N	8:26	P
	22	¼	7:21	P
	30	F	11:20	P
AUG	7	¾	0:51	P
	14	N	3:44	A
	21	¼	10:53	A
	29	F	1:04	P
SEP	5	¾	7:06	P
	12	N	0:52	P
	20	¼	4:56	A
	28	F	1:57	A
OCT	5	¾	0:54	A
	12	N	0:51	A
	20	¼	0:30	A
	27	F	2:10	P
NOV	3	¾	7:36	A
	10	N	4:06	P
	18	¼	8:13	P
	26	F	1:43	A
DEC	2	¾	4:30	P
	10	N	10:05	A
	18	¼	2:41	P
	25	F	0:39	P

1921

JAN	1	¾	4:30	A
	9	N	5:28	A
	17	¼	6:32	A
	23	F	11:08	P
	30	¾	8:03	P
FEB	8	N	0:38	A
	15	¼	6:54	P
	22	F	9:33	A
MAR	1	¾	2:04	P
	9	N	6:10	P
	17	¼	3:50	A
	23	F	8:20	P
	31	¾	9:14	A
APR	8	N	9:06	A
	15	¼	10:12	A
	22	F	7:50	A
	30	¾	4:10	A
MAY	7	N	9:02	P
	14	¼	3:25	P
	21	F	8:16	P
	29	¾	9:45	P
JUN	6	N	6:15	A
	12	¼	9:00	P
	20	F	9:42	A
	28	¾	1:18	P
JUL	5	N	1:37	P
	12	¼	4:16	A
	20	F	0:09	A
	28	¾	2:21	A
AUG	3	N	8:18	P
	10	¼	2:14	P
	18	F	3:29	P
	26	¾	0:52	P
SEP	2	N	3:34	A
	9	¼	3:30	A
	17	F	7:21	A
	24	¾	9:18	P
OCT	1	N	0:27	P
	8	¼	8:13	P
	16	F	11:00	P
	24	¾	4:32	A
	30	N	11:39	P
NOV	7	¼	3:55	P
	15	F	1:40	P
	22	¾	11:42	A
	29	N	1:26	P
DEC	7	¼	1:20	P
	15	F	2:51	A
	21	¾	7:55	P
	29	N	5:40	A

1922

JAN	6	¼	10:25	A
	13	F	2:37	P
	20	¾	6:01	A
	27	N	11:49	P
FEB	5	¼	4:53	A
	12	F	1:18	A
	18	¾	6:19	P
	26	N	6:49	P
MAR	6	¼	7:22	P
	13	F	11:15	A
	20	¾	8:44	A
	28	N	1:04	P
APR	5	¼	5:46	A
	11	F	8:44	P
	19	¾	0:55	A
	27	N	5:05	A
MAY	4	¼	0:56	P
	11	F	6:07	A
	18	¾	6:18	P
	26	N	6:05	P
JUN	2	¼	6:10	P
	9	F	3:59	P
	17	¾	0:04	P
	25	N	4:20	A
JUL	1	¼	10:53	P
	9	F	3:08	A
	17	¾	5:12	A
	24	N	0:48	P
	31	¼	4:22	A
AUG	7	F	4:20	P
	15	¾	8:47	P
	22	N	8:35	P
	29	¼	11:56	A
SEP	6	F	7:48	A
	14	¾	10:21	A
	21	N	4:39	A
	27	¼	10:41	P
OCT	6	F	0:59	A
	13	¾	9:56	P
	20	N	1:41	P
	27	¼	1:27	P
NOV	4	F	6:37	P
	12	¾	7:53	A
	19	N	0:07	A
	26	¼	8:16	A
DEC	4	F	11:24	A
	11	¾	4:41	P
	18	N	0:21	P
	26	¼	5:54	A

1923

JAN	3	F	2:34	A
	10	¾	0:55	A
	17	N	2:42	A
	25	¼	4:00	A
FEB	1	F	3:54	P
	8	¾	9:17	A
	15	N	7:08	P
	24	¼	0:07	A
MAR	3	F	3:24	A
	9	¾	6:32	P
	17	N	0:52	P
	25	¼	4:42	P
APR	1	F	1:11	P
	8	¾	5:23	A
	16	N	6:29	A
	24	¼	5:21	A
	30	F	9:31	P
MAY	7	¾	6:19	P
	15	N	10:39	P
	23	¼	2:26	P
	30	F	5:08	A
JUN	6	¾	9:20	A
	14	N	0:43	P
	21	¼	8:47	P
	28	F	1:05	P
JUL	6	¾	1:57	A
	14	N	0:46	A
	21	¼	1:33	A
	27	F	10:34	P
AUG	4	¾	7:23	P
	12	N	11:17	A
	19	¼	6:08	A
	26	F	10:30	A
SEP	3	¾	0:48	P
	10	N	8:54	P
	17	¼	0:05	P
	25	F	1:17	A
OCT	3	¾	5:30	A
	10	N	6:06	A
	16	¼	8:54	P
	24	F	6:27	P
NOV	1	¾	8:50	P
	8	N	3:28	P
	15	¼	9:42	A
	23	F	0:59	P
DEC	1	¾	10:10	A
	8	N	1:31	A
	15	¼	2:39	A
	23	F	7:34	A
	30	¾	9:08	P

1924

JAN	6	N	0:49	P
	13	¼	10:45	P
	22	F	0:58	A
	29	¾	5:54	A
FEB	5	N	1:39	A
	12	¼	8:10	P
	20	F	4:08	P
	27	¾	1:16	P
MAR	5	N	3:59	P
	13	¼	4:51	P
	21	F	4:31	A
	27	¾	8:25	P
APR	4	N	7:18	A
	12	¼	11:13	A
	19	F	2:12	P
	26	¾	4:29	A
MAY	3	N	11:01	P
	12	¼	2:15	A
	18	F	9:53	P
	25	¾	2:17	P
JUN	2	N	2:35	P
	10	¼	1:38	P
	17	F	4:42	A
	24	¾	2:17	A
JUL	2	N	5:36	A
	9	¼	9:47	P
	16	F	11:50	A
	23	¾	4:37	P
	31	N	7:43	P
AUG	8	¼	3:42	A
	14	F	8:20	P
	22	¾	9:12	A
	30	N	8:38	A
SEP	6	¼	8:46	A
	13	F	7:01	A
	21	¾	3:36	A
	28	N	8:17	P
OCT	5	¼	2:31	P
	12	F	8:22	P
	20	¾	10:55	P
	28	N	6:58	A
NOV	3	¼	10:19	P
	11	F	0:32	P
	19	¾	5:39	P
	26	N	5:17	P
DEC	3	¼	9:11	A
	11	F	7:05	A
	19	¾	10:12	A
	26	N	3:46	A

1925

JAN	1	¼	11:27	P
	10	F	2:48	A
	17	¾	11:34	P
	24	N	2:46	P
	31	¼	4:44	P
FEB	8	F	9:50	P
	16	¾	9:42	A
	23	N	2:13	A
MAR	2	¼	0:08	P
	10	F	2:22	P
	17	¾	5:22	P
	24	N	2:04	P
APR	1	¼	8:13	A
	9	F	3:34	A
	15	¾	11:41	P
	23	N	2:29	A
MAY	1	¼	3:21	A
	8	F	1:44	P
	15	¾	5:47	A
	22	N	3:49	P
	30	¼	8:05	P
JUN	6	F	9:49	P
	13	¾	0:45	P
	21	N	6:18	A
	29	¼	9:44	A
JUL	6	F	4:55	A
	12	¾	9:35	P
	20	N	9:41	P
	28	¼	8:24	P
AUG	4	F	12:00	P
	11	¾	9:12	A
	19	N	1:16	P
	27	¼	4:47	A
SEP	2	F	7:54	P
	10	¾	0:13	A
	18	N	4:13	A
	25	¼	11:52	A
OCT	2	F	5:24	A
	9	¾	6:35	P
	17	N	6:07	P
	24	¼	6:39	P
	31	F	5:18	P
NOV	8	¾	3:14	P
	16	N	6:59	A
	23	¼	2:06	A
	30	F	8:12	A
DEC	8	¾	0:12	P
	15	N	7:06	P
	22	¼	11:09	A
	30	F	2:03	A

1926

JAN	7	¾	7:23	A
	14	N	6:36	A
	20	¼	10:32	P
	28	F	9:36	P
FEB	5	¾	11:26	P
	12	N	5:21	P
	19	¼	0:37	P
	27	F	4:52	P
MAR	7	¾	11:50	A
	14	N	3:21	A
	21	¼	5:13	A
	29	F	10:01	A
APR	5	¾	8:51	P
	12	N	0:57	P
	19	¼	11:24	P
	28	F	0:18	A
MAY	5	¾	3:14	A
	11	N	10:56	P
	19	¼	5:49	P
	27	F	11:50	A
JUN	3	¾	8:10	A
	10	N	10:09	A
	18	¼	11:15	A
	25	F	9:14	P
JUL	2	¾	1:03	P
	9	N	11:07	P
	18	¼	2:56	A
	25	F	5:14	A
	31	¾	7:26	P
AUG	8	N	1:50	P
	16	¼	4:40	P
	23	F	0:39	P
	30	¾	4:41	A
SEP	7	N	5:46	A
	15	¼	4:28	A
	21	F	8:20	P
	28	¾	5:49	P
OCT	6	N	10:14	P
	14	¼	2:29	P
	21	F	5:16	A
	28	¾	10:58	A
NOV	5	N	2:35	P
	12	¼	11:02	P
	19	F	4:22	P
	27	¾	7:16	A
DEC	5	N	6:13	A
	12	¼	6:48	A
	19	F	6:10	A
	27	¾	5:00	A

1927

JAN	3	N	8:29	P
	10	¼	2:44	P
	17	F	10:28	P
	26	¾	2:06	A
FEB	2	N	8:55	A
	8	¼	11:55	P
	16	F	4:19	P
	24	¾	8:43	P
MAR	3	N	7:26	P
	10	¼	11:04	A
	18	F	10:25	A
	26	¾	11:36	A
APR	2	N	4:25	A
	9	¼	0:22	A
	17	F	3:36	A
	24	¾	10:22	P
MAY	1	N	0:41	P
	8	¼	3:28	P
	16	F	7:04	P
	24	¾	5:35	A
	30	N	9:07	P
JUN	7	¼	7:50	A
	15	F	8:20	A
	22	¾	10:30	A
	29	N	6:33	A
JUL	7	¼	0:53	A
	14	F	7:23	P
	21	¾	2:44	P
	28	N	5:37	P
AUG	5	¼	6:06	P
	13	F	4:38	A
	19	¾	7:55	P
	27	N	6:47	A
SEP	4	¼	10:46	A
	11	F	0:55	P
	18	¾	3:31	A
	25	N	10:12	P
OCT	4	¼	2:03	A
	10	F	9:16	P
	17	¾	2:33	P
	25	N	3:39	P
NOV	2	¼	3:17	P
	9	F	6:37	A
	16	¾	5:29	A
	24	N	10:10	A
DEC	2	¼	2:16	A
	8	F	5:33	P
	16	¾	0:05	A
	24	N	4:14	A
	31	¼	11:23	A

1928

JAN	7	F	6:09	A
	14	¾	9:15	P
	22	N	8:20	P
	29	¼	7:27	P
FEB	5	F	8:12	P
	13	¾	7:06	P
	21	N	9:42	A
	28	¼	3:22	A
MAR	6	F	11:28	A
	14	¾	3:21	P
	21	N	8:30	P
	28	¼	11:55	A
APR	5	F	3:39	A
	13	¾	8:10	A
	20	N	5:25	A
	26	¼	9:43	P
MAY	4	F	8:13	P
	12	¾	8:51	P
	19	N	1:15	P
	26	¼	9:13	A
JUN	3	F	0:15	P
	11	¾	5:52	A
	17	N	8:43	P
	24	¼	10:48	P
JUL	3	F	2:50	A
	10	¾	0:17	P
	17	N	4:36	A
	24	¼	2:39	P
AUG	1	F	3:32	P
	8	¾	5:25	P
	15	N	1:50	P
	23	¼	8:22	A
	31	F	2:35	A
SEP	6	¾	10:36	P
	14	N	1:21	A
	22	¼	2:59	A
	29	F	0:44	P
OCT	6	¾	5:07	A
	13	N	3:57	P
	21	¼	9:07	P
	28	F	10:44	P
NOV	4	¾	2:07	P
	12	N	9:37	A
	20	¼	1:37	P
	27	F	9:06	A
DEC	4	¾	2:33	A
	12	N	5:07	A
	20	¼	3:44	A
	26	F	7:56	P

1929

JAN	2	¾	6:45	P
	11	N	0:29	A
	18	¼	3:16	P
	25	F	7:10	A
FEB	1	¾	2:11	P
	9	N	5:56	P
	17	¼	0:23	A
	23	F	7:00	P
MAR	3	¾	11:10	A
	11	N	8:38	A
	18	¼	7:42	A
	25	F	7:47	A
APR	2	¾	7:30	A
	9	N	8:34	P
	16	¼	2:10	P
	23	F	9:49	P
MAY	2	¾	1:27	A
	9	N	6:08	A
	15	¼	8:57	P
	23	F	0:51	P
	31	¾	4:14	P
JUN	7	N	1:57	P
	14	¼	5:16	A
	22	F	4:16	A
	30	¾	3:55	A
JUL	6	N	8:48	P
	13	¼	4:06	P
	21	F	7:22	P
	29	¾	0:57	P
AUG	5	N	3:41	A
	12	¼	6:03	A
	20	F	9:43	A
	27	¾	8:03	P
SEP	3	N	11:48	A
	10	¼	10:58	P
	18	F	11:17	P
	26	¾	2:08	A
OCT	2	N	10:20	P
	10	¼	6:06	P
	18	F	0:07	P
	25	¾	8:22	A
NOV	1	N	0:02	P
	9	¼	2:11	P
	17	F	0:15	A
	23	¾	4:05	P
DEC	1	N	4:50	A
	9	¼	9:43	A
	16	F	11:39	A
	23	¾	2:28	A
	30	N	11:43	P

LUNAR PHASES

1930

JAN	8	¼	3:12	A
	14	F	10:22	P
	21	¾	4:08	P
	29	N	7:08	P
FEB	6	¼	5:27	P
	13	F	8:39	A
	20	¾	8:46	A
	28	N	1:34	P
MAR	8	¼	4:01	A
	14	F	6:59	P
	22	¾	3:14	A
	30	N	5:47	A
APR	6	¼	11:26	A
	13	F	5:50	A
	20	¾	10:10	P
	28	N	7:10	P
MAY	5	¼	4:54	P
	12	F	5:30	P
	20	¾	4:23	P
	28	N	5:38	A
JUN	3	¼	9:57	P
	11	F	6:13	A
	19	¾	9:02	A
	26	N	1:48	P
JUL	3	¼	4:04	A
	10	F	8:02	P
	18	¾	11:30	P
	25	N	8:43	P
AUG	1	¼	0:27	P
	9	F	10:59	A
	17	¾	11:32	A
	24	N	3:38	A
	30	¼	11:58	P
SEP	8	F	2:49	A
	15	¾	9:14	P
	22	N	11:43	A
	29	¼	2:59	P
OCT	7	F	6:57	P
	15	¾	5:13	A
	21	N	9:49	P
	29	¼	9:23	A
NOV	6	F	10:29	A
	13	¾	0:28	P
	20	N	10:22	A
	28	¼	6:19	A
DEC	6	F	0:41	A
	12	¾	8:08	P
	20	N	1:25	A
	28	¼	4:00	A

1931

JAN	4	F	1:16	P
	11	¾	5:10	A
	18	N	6:37	P
	27	¼	0:07	A
FEB	3	F	0:27	A
	9	¾	4:11	P
	17	N	1:12	P
	25	¼	4:43	P
MAR	4	F	10:37	A
	11	¾	5:16	A
	19	N	7:52	A
	27	¼	5:05	A
APR	2	F	8:07	P
	9	¾	8:16	P
	18	N	1:01	A
	25	¼	1:41	P
MAY	2	F	5:15	A
	9	¾	0:49	P
	17	N	3:29	P
	24	¼	7:40	P
	31	F	2:34	P
JUN	8	¾	6:19	A
	16	N	3:03	A
	23	¼	0:24	A
	30	F	0:48	A
JUL	7	¾	11:53	P
	15	N	0:21	P
	22	¼	5:17	A
	29	F	0:49	P
AUG	6	¾	4:29	P
	13	N	8:28	P
	20	¼	11:37	A
	28	F	3:11	A
SEP	5	¾	7:22	A
	12	N	4:27	A
	18	¼	8:38	P
	26	F	7:46	P
OCT	4	¾	8:16	P
	11	N	1:07	P
	18	¼	9:21	A
	26	F	1:35	P
NOV	3	¾	7:19	A
	9	N	10:56	P
	17	¼	2:15	A
	25	F	7:11	A
DEC	2	¾	4:51	P
	9	N	10:17	A
	16	¼	10:44	P
	24	F	11:25	P

1932

JAN	1	¾	1:24	A
	7	N	11:30	P
	15	¼	8:56	P
	23	F	1:45	P
	30	¾	9:33	A
FEB	6	N	2:46	P
	14	¼	6:17	P
	22	F	2:08	A
	28	¾	6:04	P
MAR	7	N	7:45	A
	15	¼	0:42	P
	22	F	0:38	P
	29	¾	3:45	A
APR	6	N	1:22	A
	14	¼	3:17	A
	20	F	9:28	P
	27	¾	3:15	P
MAY	5	N	6:13	P
	13	¼	2:03	P
	20	F	5:09	A
	27	¾	4:56	A
JUN	4	N	9:17	A
	11	¼	9:40	P
	18	F	0:39	P
	25	¾	8:37	P
JUL	3	N	10:21	P
	11	¼	3:08	A
	17	F	9:07	P
	25	¾	1:43	P
AUG	2	N	9:43	A
	9	¼	7:42	A
	16	F	7:43	A
	24	¾	7:23	A
	31	N	7:56	P
SEP	7	¼	0:50	P
	14	F	9:07	P
	23	¾	0:48	A
	30	N	5:31	A
OCT	6	¼	8:06	P
	14	F	1:19	P
	22	¾	5:15	P
	29	N	2:57	P
NOV	5	¼	6:52	A
	13	F	7:29	A
	21	¾	7:59	A
	28	N	0:44	A
DEC	4	¼	9:46	P
	13	F	2:22	A
	20	¾	8:23	P
	27	N	11:23	A

1933

JAN	3	¼	4:25	P
	11	F	8:37	P
	19	¾	6:16	A
	25	N	11:21	P
FEB	2	¼	1:17	P
	10	F	1:02	P
	17	¾	2:09	P
	24	N	0:45	P
MAR	4	¼	10:24	A
	12	F	2:47	A
	18	¾	9:06	P
	26	N	3:21	A
APR	3	¼	5:58	A
	10	F	1:39	P
	17	¾	4:19	A
	24	N	6:39	P
MAY	2	¼	10:40	P
	9	F	10:05	P
	16	¾	0:51	P
	24	N	10:08	A
JUN	1	¼	11:54	A
	8	F	5:06	A
	14	¾	11:27	P
	23	N	1:23	A
	30	¼	9:41	P
JUL	7	F	11:52	A
	14	¾	0:25	P
	22	N	4:04	P
	30	¼	4:45	A
AUG	5	F	7:33	P
	13	¾	3:51	A
	21	N	5:49	A
	28	¼	10:14	A
SEP	4	F	5:05	A
	11	¾	9:31	P
	19	N	6:22	P
	26	¼	3:37	P
OCT	3	F	5:09	P
	11	¾	4:47	P
	19	N	5:46	A
	25	¼	10:22	P
NOV	2	F	8:00	A
	10	¾	0:19	P
	17	N	4:25	P
	24	¼	7:40	A
DEC	2	F	1:32	A
	10	¾	6:25	A
	17	N	2:54	A
	23	¼	8:10	P
	31	F	8:55	P

1934

JAN	8	¾	9:37	P
	15	N	1:38	P
	22	¼	11:51	A
	30	F	4:33	P
FEB	7	¾	9:23	A
	14	N	0:44	A
	21	¼	6:06	A
MAR	1	F	10:27	A
	8	¾	6:07	P
	15	N	0:09	P
	23	¼	1:46	A
	31	F	1:16	A
APR	7	¾	0:50	A
	13	N	11:58	P
	21	¼	9:22	P
	29	F	0:47	P
MAY	6	¾	6:42	A
	13	N	0:31	P
	21	¼	3:21	P
	28	F	9:42	P
JUN	4	¾	0:54	P
	12	N	2:13	A
	20	¼	6:38	A
	27	F	5:09	A
JUL	3	¾	8:29	P
	11	N	5:07	P
	19	¼	6:54	P
	26	F	0:10	P
AUG	2	¾	6:28	A
	10	N	8:47	A
	18	¼	4:34	A
	24	F	7:38	P
	31	¾	7:41	P
SEP	9	N	0:21	A
	16	¼	0:27	P
	23	F	4:20	A
	30	¾	0:30	P
OCT	8	N	3:06	P
	15	¼	7:30	P
	22	F	3:02	P
	30	¾	8:23	A
NOV	7	N	4:45	A
	14	¼	2:40	A
	21	F	4:27	A
	29	¾	5:40	A
DEC	6	N	5:26	P
	13	¼	10:53	A
	20	F	8:55	P
	29	¾	2:09	A

1935

JAN	5	N	5:21	A
	11	¼	8:56	P
	19	F	3:45	P
	27	¾	8:00	P
FEB	3	N	4:28	P
	10	¼	9:26	A
	18	F	11:18	A
	26	¾	10:15	A
MAR	5	N	2:41	A
	12	¼	0:31	A
	20	F	5:33	A
	27	¾	8:52	P
APR	3	N	0:12	P
	10	¼	5:43	P
	18	F	9:11	P
	26	¾	4:22	A
MAY	2	N	9:37	P
	10	¼	11:55	A
	18	F	9:58	A
	25	¾	9:45	A
JUN	1	N	7:53	A
	9	¼	5:51	A
	16	F	8:21	P
	23	¾	2:22	P
	30	N	7:46	P
JUL	8	¼	10:29	P
	16	F	5:01	A
	22	¾	7:43	P
	30	N	9:34	A
AUG	7	¼	1:24	P
	14	F	0:45	P
	21	¾	3:19	A
	29	N	1:02	A
SEP	6	¼	2:27	A
	12	F	8:19	P
	19	¾	2:24	P
	27	N	5:31	P
OCT	5	¼	1:41	P
	12	F	4:40	A
	19	¾	5:38	A
	27	N	10:17	A
NOV	3	¼	11:13	P
	10	F	2:43	P
	18	¾	0:37	A
	26	N	2:37	A
DEC	3	¼	7:29	A
	10	F	3:11	A
	17	¾	9:59	P
	25	N	5:51	P

1936

JAN	1	¼	3:16	P
	8	F	6:16	P
	16	¾	7:42	P
	24	N	7:19	A
	30	¼	11:37	P
FEB	7	F	11:20	A
	15	¾	3:47	P
	22	N	6:43	P
	29	¼	9:29	A
MAR	8	F	5:15	A
	16	¾	8:36	A
	23	N	4:14	A
	29	¼	9:23	P
APR	6	F	10:48	P
	14	¾	9:22	P
	21	N	0:34	P
	28	¼	11:17	A
MAY	6	F	3:02	P
	14	¾	6:13	A
	20	N	8:36	P
	28	¼	2:47	A
JUN	5	F	5:24	A
	12	¾	0:06	P
	19	N	5:15	A
	26	¼	7:24	P
JUL	4	F	5:36	P
	11	¾	4:29	P
	18	N	3:20	P
	26	¼	0:37	P
AUG	3	F	3:48	A
	9	¾	9:00	P
	17	N	3:22	A
	25	¼	5:50	A
SEP	1	F	0:38	P
	8	¾	3:15	A
	15	N	5:43	P
	23	¼	10:14	P
	30	F	9:02	P
OCT	7	¾	0:29	P
	15	N	10:22	A
	23	¼	0:55	P
	30	F	5:59	A
NOV	6	¾	1:30	A
	14	N	4:43	A
	22	¼	1:20	A
	28	F	4:13	P
DEC	5	¾	6:21	P
	13	N	11:26	P
	21	¼	11:31	A
	28	F	4:01	A

1937

JAN	4	¾	2:23	P
	12	N	4:48	P
	19	¼	8:03	P
	26	F	5:16	P
FEB	3	¾	0:06	P
	11	N	7:35	A
	18	¼	3:51	A
	25	F	7:44	A
MAR	5	¾	9:18	A
	12	N	7:33	P
	19	¼	11:47	A
	26	F	11:13	P
APR	4	¾	3:54	A
	11	N	5:11	A
	17	¼	8:35	P
	25	F	3:25	P
MAY	3	¾	6:38	P
	10	N	1:18	P
	17	¼	6:51	A
	25	F	7:39	A
JUN	2	¾	5:25	A
	8	N	8:44	P
	15	¼	7:04	P
	23	F	11:01	P
JUL	1	¾	1:04	P
	8	N	4:14	A
	15	¼	9:38	A
	23	F	0:47	P
	30	¾	6:48	P
AUG	6	N	0:38	P
	14	¼	2:30	A
	22	F	0:48	A
	28	¾	11:56	P
SEP	4	N	10:55	P
	12	¼	8:58	P
	20	F	11:34	A
	27	¾	5:44	A
OCT	4	N	11:59	A
	12	¼	3:48	P
	19	F	9:49	P
	26	¾	1:27	P
NOV	3	N	4:17	A
	11	¼	9:35	A
	18	F	8:10	A
	25	¾	0:05	A
DEC	2	N	11:12	P
	11	¼	1:14	A
	17	F	6:54	P
	24	¾	2:21	P

1938

JAN	1	N	6:59	P
	9	¼	2:14	P
	16	F	5:54	A
	23	¾	8:10	A
	31	N	1:36	P
FEB	8	¼	0:34	A
	14	F	5:16	P
	22	¾	4:26	A
MAR	2	N	5:41	A
	9	¼	8:36	A
	16	F	5:16	A
	24	¾	1:07	A
	31	N	6:53	P
APR	7	¼	3:11	P
	14	F	6:22	P
	22	¾	8:16	P
	30	N	5:29	A
MAY	6	¼	9:25	P
	14	F	8:40	A
	22	¾	0:37	P
	29	N	2:01	P
JUN	5	¼	4:33	A
	12	F	11:48	P
	21	¾	1:53	A
	27	N	9:11	P
JUL	4	¼	1:48	P
	12	F	3:06	P
	20	¾	0:20	P
	27	N	3:54	A
AUG	3	¼	2:01	A
	11	F	5:58	A
	18	¾	8:31	P
	25	N	11:18	A
SEP	1	¼	5:29	P
	9	F	8:09	P
	17	¾	3:13	A
	23	N	8:35	P
OCT	1	¼	11:46	A
	9	F	9:38	A
	16	¾	9:25	A
	23	N	8:43	A
	31	¼	7:46	A
NOV	7	F	10:25	P
	14	¾	4:21	P
	22	N	0:06	A
	30	¼	4:01	A
DEC	7	F	10:23	A
	14	¾	1:18	A
	21	N	6:08	P
	29	¼	10:54	P

1939

JAN	5	F	9:31	P
	12	¾	1:12	P
	20	N	1:28	P
	28	¼	3:01	P
FEB	4	F	7:56	A
	11	¾	4:13	A
	19	N	8:29	A
	27	¼	3:27	A
MAR	5	F	6:02	P
	12	¾	9:38	P
	21	N	1:51	A
	28	¼	0:17	P
APR	4	F	4:19	A
	11	¾	4:13	P
	19	N	4:36	P
	26	¼	6:26	P
MAY	3	F	3:16	P
	11	¾	10:41	A
	19	N	4:26	A
	25	¼	11:21	P
JUN	2	F	3:12	A
	10	¾	4:08	A
	17	N	1:38	P
	24	¼	4:36	A
JUL	1	F	4:17	P
	9	¾	7:50	P
	16	N	9:04	P
	23	¼	11:35	A
	31	F	6:38	A
AUG	8	¾	9:19	A
	15	N	3:54	A
	21	¼	9:22	P
	29	F	10:10	P
SEP	6	¾	8:26	P
	13	N	11:23	A
	20	¼	10:35	A
	28	F	2:28	P
OCT	6	¾	5:29	A
	12	N	8:31	P
	20	¼	3:26	A
	28	F	6:43	A
NOV	4	¾	1:13	P
	11	N	7:55	A
	18	¼	11:22	P
	26	F	9:56	P
DEC	3	¾	8:41	P
	10	N	9:47	P
	18	¼	9:05	P
	26	F	11:30	A

LUNAR PHASES

1940

Month	Day	Phase	Time	
JAN	2	¾	4:57	A
	9	N	1:54	P
	17	¼	6:22	P
	24	F	11:23	P
	31	¾	2:48	P
FEB	8	N	7:46	A
	16	¼	0:57	P
	23	F	9:56	A
MAR	1	¾	2:36	A
	9	N	2:24	A
	17	¼	3:26	A
	23	F	7:34	P
	30	¾	4:21	P
APR	7	N	8:20	P
	15	¼	1:47	P
	22	F	4:38	A
	29	¾	7:50	A
MAY	7	N	0:08	P
	14	¼	8:52	P
	21	F	1:34	P
	29	¾	0:42	A
JUN	6	N	1:06	A
	13	¼	2:00	A
	19	F	11:03	P
	27	¾	6:14	P
JUL	5	N	11:29	A
	12	¼	6:36	A
	19	F	9:57	A
	27	¾	11:31	A
AUG	3	N	8:10	P
	10	¼	0:01	P
	17	F	11:04	P
	26	¾	3:34	A
SEP	2	N	4:16	A
	8	¼	7:33	P
	16	F	2:42	P
	24	¾	5:48	P
OCT	1	N	0:42	P
	8	¼	6:19	A
	16	F	8:16	A
	24	¾	6:05	A
	30	N	10:04	P
NOV	6	¼	9:09	P
	15	F	2:25	A
	22	¾	4:37	P
	29	N	8:43	A
DEC	6	¼	4:02	P
	14	F	7:39	P
	22	¾	1:46	A
	28	N	8:57	P

1941

Month	Day	Phase	Time	
JAN	5	¼	1:41	P
	13	F	11:05	A
	20	¾	10:03	A
	27	N	11:04	A
FEB	4	¼	11:44	A
	12	F	0:28	A
	18	¾	6:08	P
	26	N	3:03	A
MAR	6	¼	7:44	A
	13	F	11:48	A
	20	¾	2:53	A
	27	N	8:15	P
APR	5	¼	0:13	A
	11	F	9:16	P
	18	¾	1:04	P
	26	N	1:24	P
MAY	4	¼	0:50	P
	11	F	5:16	A
	18	¾	1:18	A
	26	N	5:20	A
JUN	2	¼	9:57	P
	9	F	0:35	P
	16	¾	3:46	P
	24	N	7:23	P
JUL	2	¼	4:25	A
	8	F	8:19	P
	16	¾	8:09	A
	24	N	7:40	A
	31	¼	9:20	A
AUG	7	F	5:40	A
	15	¾	1:41	A
	22	N	6:35	P
	29	¼	2:05	P
SEP	5	F	5:37	P
	13	¾	7:32	P
	21	N	4:40	A
	27	¼	8:10	P
OCT	5	F	8:34	A
	13	¾	0:53	P
	20	N	2:21	P
	27	¼	5:05	A
NOV	4	F	2:01	A
	12	¾	4:55	A
	19	N	0:05	A
	25	¼	5:54	P
DEC	3	F	8:52	P
	11	¾	6:49	P
	18	N	10:19	A
	25	¼	10:45	A

1942

Month	Day	Phase	Time	
JAN	2	F	3:43	P
	10	¾	6:06	A
	16	N	9:33	P
	24	¼	6:37	A
FEB	1	F	9:13	A
	8	¾	2:53	P
	15	N	10:04	A
	23	¼	3:41	A
MAR	3	F	0:21	A
	9	¾	10:02	P
	16	N	11:51	P
	25	¼	0:02	A
APR	1	F	0:33	P
	8	¾	4:44	A
	15	N	2:35	P
	23	¼	6:11	P
	30	F	10:01	P
MAY	7	¾	0:14	P
	15	N	5:46	A
	23	¼	9:12	A
	30	F	5:30	A
JUN	5	¾	9:27	P
	13	N	9:03	P
	21	¼	8:46	P
	28	F	0:10	P
JUL	5	¾	8:59	A
	13	N	0:04	P
	21	¼	5:14	A
	27	F	7:15	P
AUG	3	¾	11:05	P
	12	N	2:29	A
	19	¼	11:32	A
	26	F	3:47	A
SEP	2	¾	3:43	P
	10	N	3:54	P
	17	¼	4:58	P
	24	F	2:35	P
OCT	2	¾	10:28	A
	10	N	4:07	A
	16	¼	10:59	P
	24	F	4:07	A
NOV	1	¾	6:19	A
	8	N	3:20	P
	15	¼	6:58	A
	22	F	8:26	P
DEC	1	¾	1:38	A
	8	N	2:00	A
	14	¼	5:48	P
	22	F	3:04	P
	30	¾	6:38	P

1943

Month	Day	Phase	Time	
JAN	6	N	0:39	P
	13	¼	7:50	A
	21	F	10:49	A
	29	¾	8:14	A
FEB	4	N	11:30	P
	12	¼	0:41	A
	20	F	5:46	A
	27	¾	6:24	P
MAR	6	N	10:35	A
	13	¼	7:31	P
	21	F	10:09	P
	29	¾	1:53	A
APR	4	N	9:54	P
	12	¼	3:05	P
	20	F	11:12	A
	27	¾	7:52	A
MAY	4	N	9:44	A
	12	¼	9:54	A
	19	F	9:14	P
	26	¾	1:35	P
JUN	2	N	10:34	P
	11	¼	2:37	A
	18	F	5:15	A
	24	¾	8:09	P
JUL	2	N	0:45	P
	10	¼	4:30	P
	17	F	0:23	P
	24	¾	4:40	A
AUG	1	N	4:08	A
	9	¼	3:37	A
	15	F	7:35	P
	22	¾	4:05	P
	30	N	8:01	P
SEP	7	¼	0:34	P
	14	F	3:41	A
	21	¾	7:07	A
	29	N	11:31	A
OCT	6	¼	8:11	P
	13	F	1:24	P
	21	¾	1:43	A
	29	N	2:00	A
NOV	5	¼	3:23	A
	12	F	1:28	A
	19	¾	10:44	P
	27	N	3:24	P
DEC	4	¼	11:05	A
	11	F	4:26	P
	19	¾	8:05	P
	27	N	3:51	A

1944

Month	Day	Phase	Time	
JAN	2	¼	8:05	P
	10	F	10:11	A
	18	¾	3:33	P
	25	N	3:25	P
FEB	1	¼	7:09	A
	9	F	5:31	A
	17	¾	7:43	A
	24	N	2:00	A
MAR	1	¼	8:41	P
	10	F	0:29	A
	17	¾	8:06	P
	24	N	11:37	A
	31	¼	0:36	P
APR	8	F	5:23	P
	16	¾	5:00	A
	22	N	8:45	P
	30	¼	6:08	A
MAY	8	F	7:29	A
	15	¾	11:13	A
	22	N	6:14	A
	30	¼	0:08	A
JUN	6	F	6:59	P
	13	¾	3:58	P
	20	N	5:01	P
	28	¼	5:28	P
JUL	6	F	4:28	A
	12	¾	8:40	P
	20	N	5:44	A
	28	¼	9:25	A
AUG	4	F	0:40	P
	11	¾	2:53	A
	18	N	8:26	P
	26	¼	11:40	P
SEP	2	F	8:22	P
	9	¾	0:04	P
	17	N	0:38	P
	25	¼	0:08	P
OCT	2	F	4:23	A
	9	¾	1:13	A
	17	N	5:36	A
	24	¼	10:49	P
	31	F	1:37	P
NOV	7	¾	6:30	P
	15	N	10:31	P
	23	¼	7:54	A
	30	F	0:53	A
DEC	7	¾	2:58	P
	15	N	2:36	P
	22	¼	3:55	P
	29	F	2:39	P

1945

Month	Day	Phase	Time	
JAN	6	¾	0:49	P
	14	N	5:08	A
	20	¼	11:49	P
	28	F	6:42	A
FEB	5	¾	9:57	A
	12	N	5:34	P
	19	¼	8:39	A
	27	F	0:08	A
MAR	7	¾	4:31	A
	14	N	3:52	A
	20	¼	7:13	P
	28	F	5:46	P
APR	5	¾	7:20	P
	12	N	0:31	P
	19	¼	7:48	A
	27	F	10:34	A
MAY	5	¾	6:03	A
	11	N	8:23	P
	18	¼	10:13	P
	27	F	1:50	A
JUN	3	¾	1:16	P
	10	N	4:27	A
	17	¼	2:07	P
	25	F	3:09	P
JUL	2	¾	6:14	P
	9	N	1:36	P
	17	¼	7:02	A
	25	F	2:27	A
	31	¾	10:31	P
AUG	8	N	0:33	A
	16	¼	0:28	A
	23	F	0:04	P
	30	¾	3:46	A
SEP	6	N	1:45	P
	14	¼	5:40	P
	21	F	8:47	P
	28	¾	11:25	A
OCT	6	N	5:24	A
	14	¼	9:39	A
	21	F	5:33	A
	27	¾	10:31	P
NOV	4	N	11:12	P
	12	¼	11:35	P
	19	F	3:14	P
	26	¾	1:29	P
DEC	4	N	6:08	P
	12	¼	11:06	A
	19	F	2:18	A
	26	¾	8:02	A

1946

Month	Day	Phase	Time	
JAN	3	N	0:31	P
	10	¼	8:28	P
	17	F	2:48	P
	25	¾	5:01	A
FEB	2	N	4:44	A
	9	¼	4:29	A
	16	F	4:29	A
	24	¾	2:38	A
MAR	3	N	6:03	P
	10	¼	0:04	P
	17	F	7:12	P
	25	¾	10:39	P
APR	2	N	4:38	A
	8	¼	8:05	P
	16	F	10:48	A
	24	¾	3:20	P
MAY	1	N	1:17	P
	8	¼	5:15	A
	16	F	2:54	A
	24	¾	4:03	A
	30	N	8:51	P
JUN	6	¼	4:08	P
	14	F	6:43	P
	22	¾	1:13	P
	29	N	4:07	A
JUL	6	¼	5:17	A
	14	F	9:24	A
	21	¾	7:53	P
	28	N	11:55	A
AUG	4	¼	8:57	P
	12	F	10:27	P
	20	¾	1:18	A
	26	N	9:09	P
SEP	3	¼	2:50	P
	11	F	10:01	A
	18	¾	6:46	A
	25	N	8:46	A
OCT	3	¼	9:55	A
	10	F	8:42	P
	17	¾	1:29	P
	24	N	11:33	P
NOV	2	¼	4:42	A
	9	F	7:11	A
	15	¾	10:36	P
	23	N	5:25	P
DEC	1	¼	9:49	P
	8	F	5:53	P
	15	¾	10:58	A
	23	N	1:07	P
	31	¼	0:24	P

1947

Month	Day	Phase	Time	
JAN	7	F	4:48	A
	14	¾	2:57	A
	22	N	8:36	A
	30	¼	0:08	A
FEB	5	F	3:52	P
	12	¾	9:59	P
	21	N	2:01	A
	28	¼	9:13	A
MAR	7	F	3:16	A
	14	¾	6:29	P
	22	N	4:35	P
	29	¼	4:16	P
APR	5	F	3:30	P
	13	¾	2:25	P
	21	N	4:20	A
	27	¼	10:19	P
MAY	5	F	4:55	A
	13	¾	8:09	A
	20	N	1:45	P
	27	¼	4:37	A
JUN	3	F	7:28	P
	11	¾	10:59	P
	18	N	9:27	P
	25	¼	0:26	P
JUL	3	F	10:40	A
	11	¾	10:56	A
	18	N	4:16	A
	24	¼	10:55	P
AUG	2	F	1:51	A
	9	¾	8:23	P
	16	N	11:14	A
	23	¼	0:41	P
	31	F	4:35	P
SEP	8	¾	3:58	A
	14	N	7:29	P
	22	¼	5:43	A
	30	F	6:42	A
OCT	7	¾	10:30	A
	14	N	6:11	A
	22	¼	1:12	A
	29	F	8:08	P
NOV	5	¾	5:05	P
	12	N	8:02	P
	20	¼	9:45	P
	28	F	8:46	A
DEC	5	¾	0:56	A
	12	N	0:55	P
	20	¼	5:45	P
	27	F	8:28	P

1948

Month	Day	Phase	Time	
JAN	3	¾	11:14	A
	11	N	7:46	A
	19	¼	11:33	A
	26	F	7:12	A
FEB	2	¾	0:33	A
	10	N	3:03	A
	18	¼	1:56	A
	24	F	5:17	P
MAR	2	¾	4:37	P
	10	N	9:16	P
	18	¼	0:28	P
	25	F	3:11	A
APR	1	¾	10:26	A
	9	N	1:18	P
	16	¼	7:43	P
	23	F	1:30	P
MAY	1	¾	4:50	A
	9	N	2:31	A
	16	¼	0:56	A
	23	F	0:38	A
	30	¾	10:44	P
JUN	7	N	0:57	P
	14	¼	5:41	A
	21	F	0:55	P
	29	¾	3:24	P
JUL	6	N	9:10	P
	13	¼	11:31	A
	21	F	2:32	A
	29	¾	6:13	A
AUG	5	N	4:14	A
	11	¼	7:41	P
	19	F	5:33	P
	27	¾	6:47	P
SEP	3	N	11:22	A
	10	¼	7:06	A
	18	F	9:44	A
	26	¾	5:08	A
OCT	2	N	7:43	P
	9	¼	10:12	P
	18	F	2:25	A
	25	¾	1:43	P
NOV	1	N	6:04	A
	8	¼	4:48	P
	16	F	6:33	P
	23	¾	9:23	P
	30	N	6:46	P
DEC	8	¼	1:59	P
	16	F	9:12	A
	23	¾	5:13	A
	30	N	9:46	A

1949

Month	Day	Phase	Time	
JAN	7	¼	11:53	A
	14	F	10:01	P
	21	¾	2:09	P
	29	N	2:44	A
FEB	6	¼	8:07	A
	13	F	9:09	A
	20	¾	0:44	A
	27	N	8:56	P
MAR	8	¼	0:43	A
	14	F	7:04	P
	21	¾	1:12	P
	29	N	3:12	P
APR	6	¼	1:03	P
	13	F	4:09	A
	20	¾	3:29	A
	28	N	8:04	A
MAY	5	¼	9:34	P
	12	F	0:52	P
	19	¾	7:23	P
	27	N	10:25	P
JUN	4	¼	3:28	A
	10	F	9:47	P
	18	¾	0:31	P
	26	N	10:03	A
JUL	3	¼	8:09	A
	10	F	7:42	A
	18	¾	6:03	A
	25	N	7:34	P
AUG	1	¼	0:59	P
	8	F	7:35	P
	16	¾	11:00	P
	24	N	4:00	A
	30	¼	7:18	P
SEP	7	F	10:01	A
	15	¾	2:30	P
	22	N	0:22	P
	29	¼	4:20	A
OCT	7	F	2:54	A
	15	¾	4:07	A
	21	N	9:24	P
	28	¼	5:06	P
NOV	5	F	9:10	P
	13	¾	3:49	P
	20	N	7:30	A
	27	¼	10:03	A
DEC	5	F	3:15	P
	13	¾	1:49	A
	19	N	6:57	P
	27	¼	6:33	A

DIURNAL PROPORTIONAL LOGARITHMS

	0	1	2	3	4	5	6	7	8	9	10	11
0	∞	1.3802	1.0792	.90309	.77815	.68124	.60206	.53511	.47712	.42597	.38021	.33882
1	3.1584	1.3730	1.0756	.90068	.77635	.67980	.60086	.53408	.47622	.42517	.37949	.33816
2	2.8573	1.3660	1.0720	.89829	.77455	.67836	.59965	.53305	.47532	.42436	.37877	.33750
3	2.6812	1.3590	1.0685	.89591	.77276	.67692	.59846	.53202	.47442	.42356	.37805	.33685
4	2.5563	1.3522	1.0649	.89354	.77097	.67549	.59726	.53100	.47352	.42276	.37733	.33620
5	2.4594	1.3454	1.0615	.89119	.76920	.67406	.59607	.52997	.47262	.42197	.37661	.33554
6	2.3802	1.3388	1.0580	.88885	.76743	.67264	.59488	.52895	.47173	.42117	.37589	.33489
7	2.3133	1.3323	1.0546	.88652	.76567	.67122	.59370	.52793	.47083	.42038	.37517	.33424
8	2.2553	1.3259	1.0512	.88420	.76391	.66981	.59251	.52692	.46994	.41958	.37446	.33359
9	2.2041	1.3195	1.0478	.88190	.76216	.66840	.59134	.52591	.46905	.41879	.37375	.33294
10	2.1584	1.3133	1.0444	.87961	.76042	.66700	.59016	.52489	.46817	.41800	.37303	.33229
11	2.1170	1.3071	1.0411	.87733	.75869	.66560	.58899	.52389	.46728	.41721	.37232	.33164
12	2.0792	1.3010	1.0378	.87506	.75696	.66421	.58782	.52288	.46640	.41642	.37161	.33099
13	2.0444	1.2950	1.0345	.87281	.75524	.66282	.58665	.52187	.46552	.41564	.37090	.33035
14	2.0122	1.2891	1.0313	.87056	.75353	.66143	.58549	.52087	.46464	.41485	.37019	.32970
15	1.9823	1.2833	1.0280	.86833	.75182	.66005	.58433	.51987	.46376	.41407	.36949	.32906
16	1.9542	1.2775	1.0248	.86611	.75012	.65868	.58317	.51888	.46288	.41329	.36878	.32842
17	1.9279	1.2719	1.0216	.86390	.74843	.65730	.58202	.51788	.46201	.41251	.36808	.32777
18	1.9031	1.2663	1.0185	.86170	.74674	.65594	.58087	.51689	.46113	.41173	.36737	.32713
19	1.8796	1.2607	1.0153	.85951	.74506	.65457	.57972	.51590	.46026	.41095	.36667	.32649
20	1.8573	1.2553	1.0122	.85733	.74339	.65321	.57858	.51491	.45939	.41017	.36597	.32585
21	1.8361	1.2499	1.0091	.85517	.74172	.65186	.57744	.51392	.45852	.40940	.36527	.32522
22	1.8159	1.2445	1.0061	.85301	.74006	.65051	.57630	.51294	.45766	.40863	.36457	.32458
23	1.7966	1.2393	1.0030	.85087	.73841	.64916	.57516	.51196	.45679	.40785	.36387	.32394
24	1.7782	1.2341	1.0000	.84873	.73676	.64782	.57403	.51098	.45593	.40708	.36318	.32331
25	1.7604	1.2289	0.9970	.84661	.73512	.64648	.57290	.51000	.45507	.40631	.36248	.32267
26	1.7434	1.2239	0.9940	.84450	.73348	.64514	.57178	.50903	.45421	.40555	.36179	.32204
27	1.7270	1.2188	0.9910	.84239	.73185	.64382	.57065	.50805	.45335	.40478	.36110	.32141
28	1.7112	1.2139	0.9881	.84030	.73023	.64250	.56953	.50708	.45250	.40401	.36040	.32077
29	1.6960	1.2090	0.9852	.83822	.72861	.64117	.56841	.50612	.45165	.40325	.35971	.32014
30	1.6812	1.2041	0.9823	.83614	.72700	.63985	.56730	.50515	.45079	.40249	.35902	.31951
31	1.6670	1.1993	0.9794	.83408	.72539	.63853	.56619	.50419	.44994	.40173	.35833	.31889
32	1.6532	1.1946	0.9765	.83203	.72379	.63722	.56508	.50322	.44909	.40097	.35765	.31826
33	1.6398	1.1899	0.9737	.82998	.72220	.63592	.56397	.50226	.44825	.40021	.35696	.31763
34	1.6269	1.1852	0.9708	.82795	.72061	.63462	.56287	.50131	.44740	.39945	.35627	.31700
35	1.6143	1.1806	0.9680	.82592	.71903	.63332	.56177	.50035	.44656	.39869	.35559	.31638
36	1.6021	1.1761	0.9652	.82391	.71745	.63202	.56067	.49940	.44571	.39794	.35491	.31575
37	1.5902	1.1716	0.9625	.83190	.71588	.63073	.55957	.49845	.44487	.39719	.35422	.31513
38	1.5786	1.1671	0.9597	.81991	.71432	.62945	.55848	.49750	.44403	.39643	.35354	.31451
39	1.5673	1.1627	0.9570	.81792	.71276	.62816	.55739	.49655	.44320	.39568	.35286	.31389
40	1.5563	1.1584	0.9542	.81594	.71120	.62688	.55630	.45960	.44236	.39493	.35218	.31327
41	1.5456	1.1540	0.9515	.81397	.70966	.62561	.55522	.49466	.44153	.39419	.35150	.31265
42	1.5351	1.1498	0.9488	.81201	.70811	.62434	.55414	.49372	.44069	.39344	.35083	.31203
43	1.5249	1.1455	0.9462	.81006	.70658	.62307	.55306	.49278	.43986	.39269	.35015	.31141
44	1.5149	1.1413	0.9435	.80811	.70504	.62180	.55198	.49184	.43903	.39195	.34948	.31079
45	1.5051	1.1372	0.9409	.80618	.70352	.62054	.55091	.49091	.43820	.39121	.34880	.31017
46	1.4956	1.1331	0.9383	.80425	.70200	.61929	.54984	.48998	.43738	.39047	.34813	.30956
47	1.4863	1.1290	0.9356	.80234	.70048	.61803	.54877	.48905	.43655	.38972	.34746	.30894
48	1.4771	1.1249	0.9331	.80043	.69897	.61678	.54770	.48812	.43573	.38899	.34679	.30833
49	1.4682	1.1209	0.9305	.79853	.69746	.61554	.54664	.48719	.43491	.38825	.34612	.30772
50	1.4594	1.1170	0.9279	.79663	.69596	.61429	.54558	.48626	.43409	.38751	.34545	.30710
51	1.4508	1.1130	0.9254	.79475	.69447	.61306	.54452	.48534	.43327	.38678	.34478	.30649
52	1.4424	1.1091	0.9228	.79287	.69298	.61182	.54347	.48442	.43245	.38604	.34412	.30588
53	1.4341	1.1053	0.9203	.79101	.69149	.61059	.54241	.48350	.43164	.38531	.34345	.30527
54	1.4260	1.1015	0.9178	.78915	.69002	.60936	.54136	.48258	.43082	.38458	.34279	.30466
55	1.4180	1.0977	0.9153	.78729	.68854	.60813	.54031	.48167	.43001	.38385	.34212	.30406
56	1.4102	1.0939	0.9129	.78545	.68707	.60691	.53927	.48076	.42920	.38312	.34146	.30345
57	1.4025	1.0902	0.9104	.78361	.68561	.60569	.53823	.47984	.42839	.38239	.34080	.30284
58	1.3949	1.0865	0.9079	.78179	.68415	.60448	.53719	.47893	.42758	.38166	.34014	.30224
59	1.3875	1.0828	0.9055	.77996	.68269	.60327	.53615	.47803	.42677	.38094	.33948	.30163

DIURNAL PROPORTIONAL LOGARITHMS

	12	13	14	15	16	17	18	19	20	21	22	23
0	.30103	.26627	.23408	.20412	.17609	.14976	.12494	.10146	.07918	.05799	.03779	.01848
1	.30043	.26571	.23357	.20364	.17564	.14934	.12454	.10108	.07882	.05765	.03746	.01817
2	.29983	.26516	.23305	.20316	.17519	.14891	.12414	.10070	.07846	.05730	.03713	.01786
3	.29923	.26460	.23254	.20268	.17474	.14849	.12373	.10032	.07810	.05696	.03680	.01754
4	.29862	.26405	.23202	.20219	.17429	.14806	.12333	.09994	.07774	.05662	.03648	.01723
5	.29802	.26349	.23151	.20171	.17384	.14764	.12293	.09956	.07738	.05627	.03615	.01691
6	.29743	.26294	.23099	.20124	.17339	.14722	.12253	.09918	.07702	.05593	.03582	.01660
7	.29683	.26239	.23048	.20076	.17294	.14679	.12213	.09880	.07666	.05559	.03549	.01629
8	.29623	.26184	.22997	.20028	.17249	.14637	.12173	.09842	.07630	.05524	.03517	.01597
9	.29564	.26129	.22946	.19980	.17204	.14595	.12134	.09804	.07594	.05490	.03484	.01566
10	.29504	.26074	.22894	.19932	.17159	.14553	.12094	.09767	.07558	.05456	.03451	.01535
11	.29445	.26019	.22843	.19884	.17114	.14510	.12054	.09729	.07522	.05422	.03418	.01504
12	.29385	.25964	.22792	.19837	.17070	.14468	.12014	.09691	.07486	.05388	.03386	.01472
13	.29326	.25909	.22741	.19789	.17025	.14426	.11974	.09653	.07450	.05353	.03353	.01441
14	.29267	.25854	.22691	.19742	.16980	.14384	.11935	.09616	.07414	.05319	.03321	.01410
15	.29208	.25800	.22640	.19694	.16936	.14342	.11895	.09578	.07379	.05285	.03288	.01379
16	.29149	.25745	.22589	.19647	.16891	.14300	.11855	.09540	.07343	.05251	.03256	.01348
17	.29090	.25690	.22538	.19599	.16847	.14258	.11816	.09503	.07307	.05217	.03223	.01317
18	.29031	.25636	.22488	.19552	.16802	.14217	.11776	.09465	.07272	.05183	.03191	.01286
19	.28972	.25582	.22437	.19505	.16758	.14175	.11737	.09428	.07236	.05149	.03158	.01254
20	.28913	.25527	.22386	.19457	.16714	.14133	.11697	.09390	.07200	.05115	.03126	.01224
21	.28855	.25473	.22336	.19410	.16669	.14091	.11658	.09353	.07165	.05081	.03093	.01193
22	.28796	.25419	.22286	.19363	.16625	.14050	.11618	.09316	.07129	.05048	.03061	.01162
23	.28737	.25365	.22235	.19316	.16581	.14008	.11579	.09278	.07094	.05014	.03029	.01131
24	.28679	.25311	.22185	.19269	.16537	.13966	.11539	.09241	.07058	.04980	.02996	.01100
25	.28621	.25257	.22135	.19222	.16493	.13925	.11500	.09204	.07023	.04946	.02964	.01069
26	.28562	.25203	.22084	.19175	.16449	.13883	.11461	.09166	.06987	.04912	.02932	.01038
27	.28504	.25149	.22034	.19128	.16405	.13842	.11422	.09129	.06952	.04878	.02900	.01007
28	.28446	.25095	.21984	.19082	.16361	.13800	.11382	.09092	.06916	.04845	.02867	.00976
29	.28388	.25041	.21934	.19035	.16317	.13759	.11343	.09055	.06881	.04811	.02835	.00945
30	.28330	.24988	.21884	.18988	.16273	.13717	.11304	.09018	.06846	.04777	.02803	.00914
31	.28272	.24934	.21835	.18941	.16229	.13676	.11265	.08981	.06811	.04744	.02771	.00884
32	.28214	.24881	.21785	.18895	.16185	.13635	.11226	.08943	.06775	.04710	.02739	.00853
33	.28157	.24827	.21735	.18848	.16141	.13594	.11187	.08906	.06740	.04676	.02707	.00822
34	.28099	.24774	.21685	.18802	.16098	.13552	.11148	.08869	.06705	.04643	.02674	.00791
35	.28042	.24721	.21635	.18755	.16054	.13511	.11109	.08832	.06670	.04609	.02642	.00761
36	.27984	.24667	.21586	.18709	.16010	.13470	.11070	.08796	.06634	.04576	.02610	.00730
37	.27927	.24614	.21536	.18662	.15967	.13429	.11031	.08759	.06599	.04542	.02578	.00699
38	.27869	.24561	.21487	.18616	.15923	.13388	.10992	.08722	.06564	.04509	.02546	.00669
39	.27812	.24508	.21437	.18570	.15880	.13347	.10953	.08685	.06529	.04475	.02514	.00638
40	.27755	.24455	.21388	.18524	.15836	.13306	.10915	.08648	.06494	.04442	.02482	.00607
41	.27698	.24402	.21339	.18477	.15793	.13265	.10876	.08611	.06459	.04409	.02451	.00577
42	.27641	.24349	.21289	.18431	.15749	.13224	.10837	.08575	.06424	.04375	.02419	.00546
43	.27584	.24296	.21240	.18385	.15706	.13183	.10798	.08538	.06389	.04342	.02387	.00516
44	.27527	.24244	.21191	.18339	.15663	.13142	.10760	.08501	.06354	.04309	.02355	.00485
45	.27470	.24191	.21142	.18293	.15620	.13101	.10721	.08464	.06319	.04275	.02323	.00455
46	.27413	.24138	.21093	.18247	.15576	.13061	.10683	.08428	.06284	.04242	.02291	.00424
47	.27357	.24086	.21044	.18201	.15533	.13020	.10644	.08391	.06250	.04209	.02259	.00394
48	.27300	.24033	.20995	.18155	.15490	.12979	.10605	.08355	.06215	.04176	.02228	.00363
49	.27244	.23981	.20946	.18110	.15447	.12939	.10567	.08318	.06180	.04142	.02196	.00333
50	.27187	.23928	.20897	.18064	.15404	.12898	.10529	.08282	.06145	.04109	.02164	.00303
51	.27131	.23876	.20849	.18018	.15361	.12857	.10490	.08245	.06111	.04076	.02133	.00272
52	.27075	.23824	.20800	.17973	.15318	.12817	.10452	.08209	.06076	.04043	.02101	.00242
53	.27018	.23772	.20751	.17927	.15275	.12776	.10413	.08172	.06041	.04010	.02069	.00212
54	.26962	.23720	.20703	.17881	.15233	.12736	.10375	.08136	.06007	.03977	.02038	.00181
55	.26906	.23668	.20654	.17836	.15190	.12695	.10337	.08099	.05972	.03944	.02006	.00151
56	.26850	.23616	.20606	.17791	.15147	.12655	.10298	.08063	.05937	.03911	.01975	.00121
57	.26794	.23564	.20557	.17745	.15104	.12615	.10260	.08027	.05903	.03878	.01943	.00091
58	.26738	.23512	.20509	.17700	.15062	.12574	.10222	.07991	.05868	.03845	.01911	.00060
59	.26683	.23460	.20460	.17654	.15019	.12534	.10184	.07954	.05834	.03812	.01880	.00030